CALIFORNIA MIDDLE SCHOOL

Mathematics

Concepts and Skills

COURSE 2

TEACHER'S EDITION

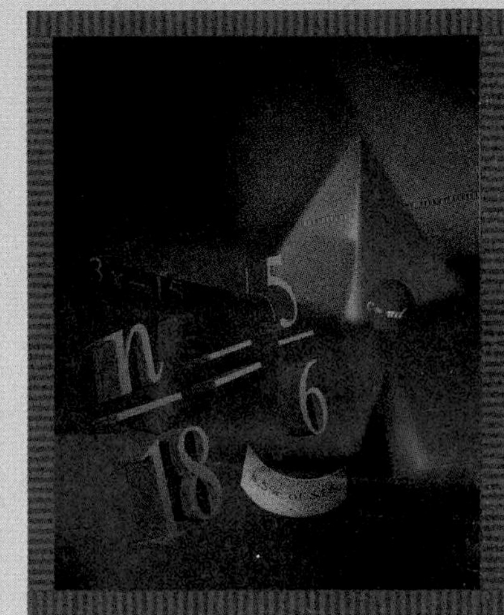

Contents

McDougal Littell
A HOUGHTON MIFFLIN COMPANY
Evanston, Illinois • Boston • Dallas

Mathematics, Concepts and Skills Course 2

This book was written to help students learn the concepts, skills, and reasoning strategies in the Mathematics Content Standards for Grade 7. For quick reference, the key Standards taught in each lesson are listed in the margin.

This book also helps prepare students for assessments in multiple-choice format through the Multiple-Choice Practice in each lesson and at the end of each chapter.

This book has been designed to make learning as easy as possible for students through clear presentation of topics, many easy-to-follow examples, and built-in learning support that includes Student Help notes, pre-chapter Getting Ready pages, and review of basic skills.

ISBN: 0-618-05050-7   6789101112-DWO-100908070605

Internet Web Site: http://www.mcdougallittell.com

About the Authors

RON LARSON is a professor of mathematics at Penn State University at Erie, where he has taught since receiving his Ph.D. in mathematics from the University of Colorado in 1970. He is the author of a broad range of instructional materials for middle school, high school, and college. Dr. Larson has been an innovative writer of multimedia approaches to mathematics, and his Calculus and Precalculus texts are both available in interactive form on the Internet.

LAURIE BOSWELL is a mathematics teacher at Profile Junior-Senior High School in Bethlehem, New Hampshire. A recipient of the 1986 Presidential Award for Excellence in Mathematics Teaching, she is also the 1992 Tandy Technology Scholar and the 1991 recipient of the Richard Balomenos Mathematics Education Service Award presented by the New Hampshire Association of Teachers of Mathematics.

TIMOTHY D. KANOLD is Director of Mathematics and a mathematics teacher at Adlai E. Stevenson High School in Lincolnshire, Illinois. In 1995 he received the Award of Excellence from the Illinois State Board of Education for outstanding contributions to education. A 1986 recipient of the Presidential Award for Excellence in Mathematics Teaching, he served as President of the Council of Presidential Awardees of Mathematics.

LEE STIFF is a professor of mathematics education in the College of Education and Psychology of North Carolina State University at Raleigh and has taught mathematics at the high school and middle school levels. He is the 1992 recipient of the W. W. Rankin Award for Excellence in Mathematics Education presented by the North Carolina Council of Teachers of Mathematics, and a 1995-96 Fulbright Scholar to the Department of Mathematics of the University of Ghana.

All authors contributed to planning the content, organization, and instructional design of the program, and to reviewing and writing the manuscript. Ron Larson played a major role in writing the textbook and in establishing the program philosophy.

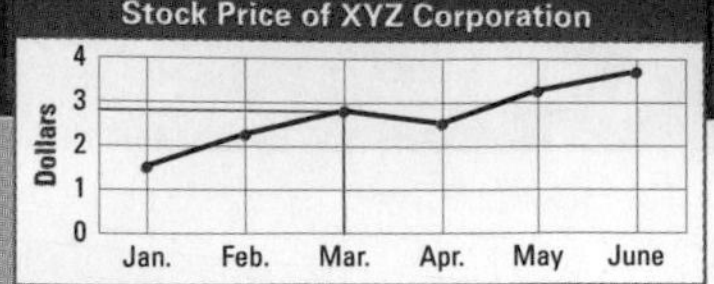

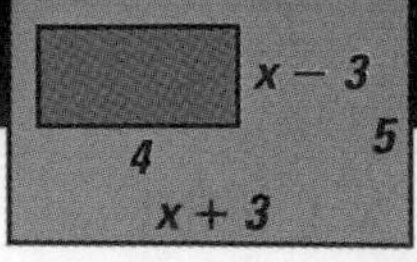

CALIFORNIA REVIEWERS

Mayumi Anderson
Math Department Chair
Ahwahnee Middle School
Fresno, CA

Shakeh Balmanoukian
Mathematics Teacher
Hoover Senior High School
Glendale, CA

Virginia DeBry
Mathematics Teacher
Serrano Middle School
Montclair, CA

Mark Freathy
Mathematics Department Chair
Harriet Eddy Middle School
Elk Grove, CA

Marguerita Gonzalez
Mathematics Teacher
Kastner Intermediate School
Fresno, CA

Charles Petrilla
Mathematics Teacher
Lexington Junior High School
Cypress, CA

Lark Wingert
Mathematics Teacher
Hillview Middle School
Whittier, CA

Mayer Wisotsky
Mathematics Teacher
Will C. Wood Middle School
Sacramento, CA

The California Reviewers read and commented on textbook chapters in pre-publication format. They also provided teaching suggestions for the Teacher's Edition.

CALIFORNIA CONSULTING MATHEMATICIANS

Kurt Kreith
Professor of Mathematics
University of California, Davis

Don Chakerian
Professor of Mathematics
University of California, Davis

The California Consulting Mathematicians prepared the *Mathematical Background Notes* preceding each chapter in the Teacher's Edition of this textbook.

Program Overview

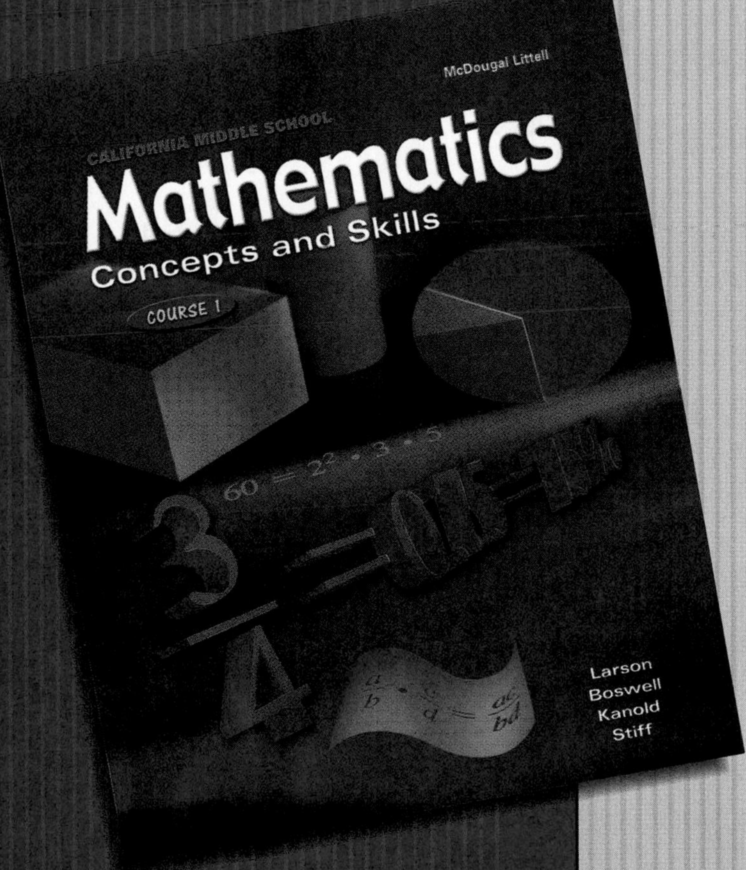

When every student absolutely, positively, needs to meet the Standards

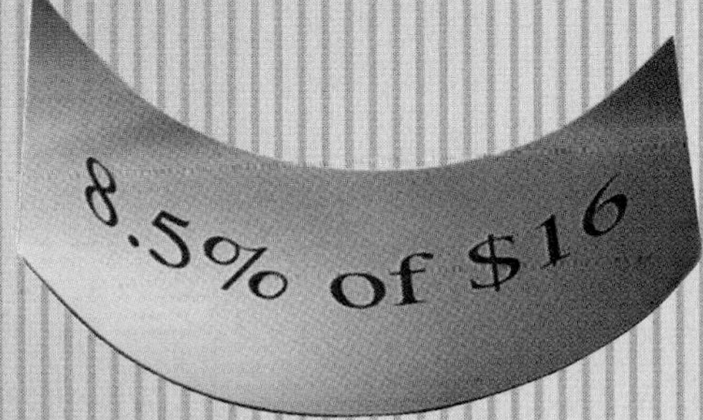

CALIFORNIA MIDDLE SCHOOL

Mathematics

Concepts and Skills

Course 2

gives students:

a. Standards-based curriculum

b. Multiple-Choice practice

c. Built-in student help

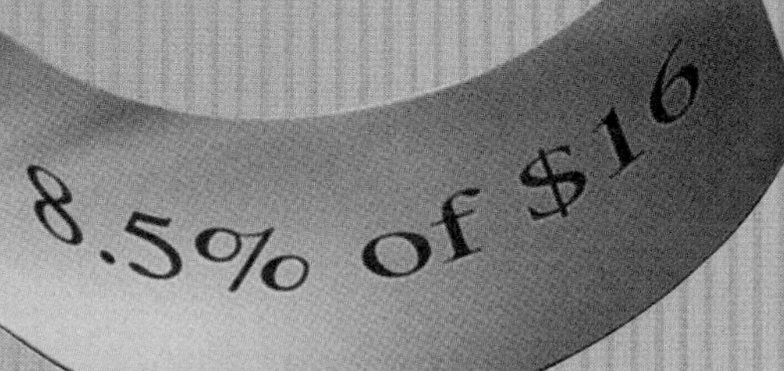

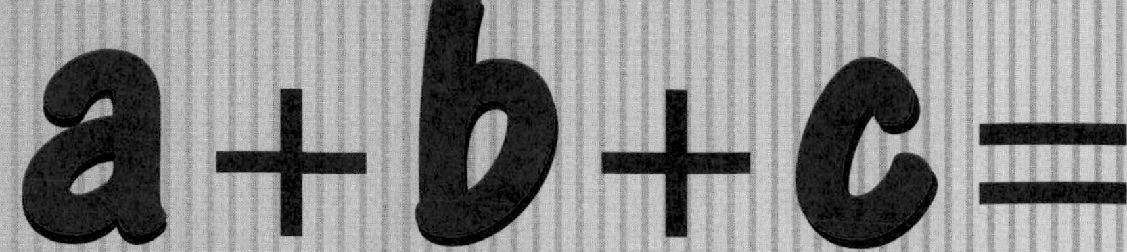

3.3 Using Rules to Add Integers

California Standards

In this lesson you'll:
- Add integers. (NS 1.2)
- Simplify expressions by applying properties of rational numbers and justify the process used. (AF 1.3)

Goal 1 Adding Two Integers

As you saw in Developing Concepts 3.3, page 114, you can follow these rules for adding integers.

Adding Two Integers

1. To add two integers with the *same sign*, add their absolute values and write the common sign.
2. To add two integers with *different signs*, subtract the smaller absolute value from the larger absolute value. Write the sign of the integer with the larger absolute value.
3. The sum of 0 and any integer is that integer.

EXAMPLE 1 Adding Integers with the Same Sign

a. The sum of two positive numbers is positive.

$4 + 5 = 9$ — Add $|4| + |5|$. Use the common sign.

b. The sum of two negative numbers is negative.

$-12 + (-3) = -15$ — Use $|-12| + |-3|$. Use the common sign.

EXAMPLE 2 Adding Integers with Different Signs

a. The sum of 5 and −8 is negative because −8 has a great[er]
value than 5.

$5 + (-8) = -3$ — Subtract $|5|$ from $|-8|$. Use sign of −8.

b. The sum of −5 and 8 is positive because 8 has a greater
value than −5.

$-5 + 8 = 3$ — Subtract $|-5|$...

116 Chapter 3 *Operations with Integers*

California Standards

In this lesson you'll:
- Add integers. (NS 1.2)
- Simplify expressions by applying properties of rational numbers and justify the process used. (AF 1.3)

a = standards-based curriculum

This book was written to help students learn the concepts, skills, and reasoning strategies in the California Standards.

For quick reference, the key Standards taught in each lesson or Developing Concepts are listed in the margin.

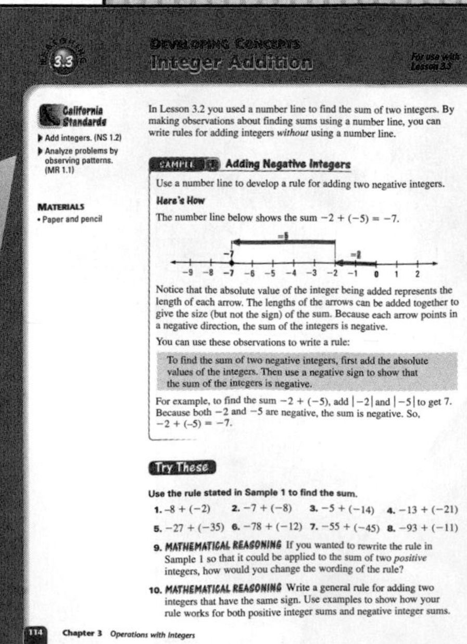

Developing Concepts 3.3

Integer Addition

For use with Lesson 3.3

California Standards
- Add integers. (NS 1.2)
- Analyze problems by observing patterns. (MR 1.1)

Materials
- Paper and pencil

In Lesson 3.2 you used a number line to find the sum of two integers. By making observations about finding sums using a number line, you can write rules for adding integers *without* using a number line.

SAMPLE 1 Adding Negative Integers

Use a number line to develop a rule for adding two negative integers.

Here's How

The number line below shows the sum $-2 + (-5) = -7$.

Notice that the absolute value of the integer being added represents the length of each arrow. The lengths of the arrows can be added together to give the size (but not the sign) of the sum. Because each arrow points in a negative direction, the sum of the integers is negative.

You can use these observations to write a rule:

To find the sum of two negative integers, first add the absolute values of the integers. Then use a negative sign to show that the sum of the integers is negative.

For example, to find the sum $-2 + (-5)$, add $|-2|$ and $|-5|$ to get 7. Because both −2 and −5 are negative, the sum is negative. So, $-2 + (-5) = -7$.

Try These

Use the rule stated in Sample 1 to find the sum.

1. $-8 + (-2)$ 2. $-7 + (-8)$ 3. $-5 + (-14)$ 4. $-13 + (-21)$
5. $-27 + (-35)$ 6. $-78 + (-12)$ 7. $-55 + (-45)$ 8. $-93 + (-11)$
9. **MATHEMATICAL REASONING** If you wanted to rewrite the rule in Sample 1 so that it could be applied to the sum of two *positive* integers, how would you change the wording of the rule?
10. **MATHEMATICAL REASONING** Write a general rule for adding two integers that have the same sign. Use examples to show how your rule works for both positive integer sums and negative integer sums.

114 Chapter 3 *Operations with Integers*

California Standards
- Add integers. (NS 1.2)
- Analyze problems by observing patterns. (MR 1.1)

success!

Course 2 provides a balanced equation for student success.

Multiple-Choice Practice

Test Tip Be careful to avoid careless errors on easy questions.

1. Find the perimeter of the figure. D

Ⓐ $6x + 3$

Ⓑ $9x + 3$

Ⓒ $7 + 3x$

Ⓓ $7x + 3$

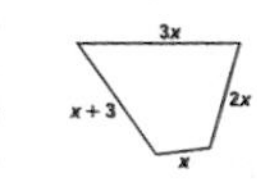

2. Decide which equation represents this verbal statement: *A number subtracted from 8 is 9.* F

Ⓕ $8 - n = 9$ Ⓖ $n - 9 = 8$

Ⓗ $n - 8 = 9$ Ⓙ $9 - n = 8$

3. Which statement does *not* represent the equation $20 + x = 35$? D

Ⓐ The cake needs 35 minutes to bake. It has been in the oven 20 minutes.

Ⓑ You are on the 20th floor. You climb the stairs to the 35th floor.

Ⓒ You have earned \$20. You earn more money for a total of \$35.

Ⓓ You buy a shirt for \$20 and a pair of jeans for \$35.

4. The area of the rectangle below is 63 square inches. Which equation can you use to find its width w? F

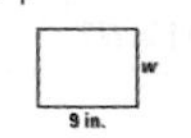

Ⓕ $9w = 63$ Ⓖ $63w = 9$

Ⓗ $\frac{w}{63} = 9$ Ⓙ $\frac{w}{9} = 63$

5. Solve $y - 4.2 = 5.7$. D

Ⓐ 1.5 Ⓑ 1.9 Ⓒ 9.5 Ⓓ 9.9

6. Find the solution of the equation that represents this statement: *A number divided by 6 is 5.* J

Ⓕ $\frac{1}{6}$ Ⓖ $\frac{5}{6}$

Ⓗ 11 Ⓙ 30

7. You save $\frac{1}{3}$ off the original price, or \$18.34, on a pair of shoes. What was the original price? C

Ⓐ \$36.66 Ⓑ \$41.25

Ⓒ \$55.00 Ⓓ \$73.34

8. A walking path around a four-sided city park is 1.5 miles long. Three of the sides have lengths of 0.25 miles, 0.5 miles, and 0.4 miles. How long is the fourth side? H

Ⓕ 0.25 miles Ⓖ 0.3 miles

Ⓗ 0.35 miles Ⓙ 0.45 miles

9. Which is *not* a solution of the inequality $m - 9 \leq 3$? D

Ⓐ 9 Ⓑ 10

Ⓒ 12 Ⓓ 13

10. Solve $3.5p \leq 17.5$. G

Ⓕ $p \leq 3.5$ Ⓖ $p \leq 5$

Ⓗ $p \geq 5$ Ⓙ $p \geq 17.5$

Multiple-Choice Practice 99

b = multiple-choice practice

Multiple-Choice Practice exercises in each lesson and at the end of each chapter help students become comfortable with multiple-choice format.

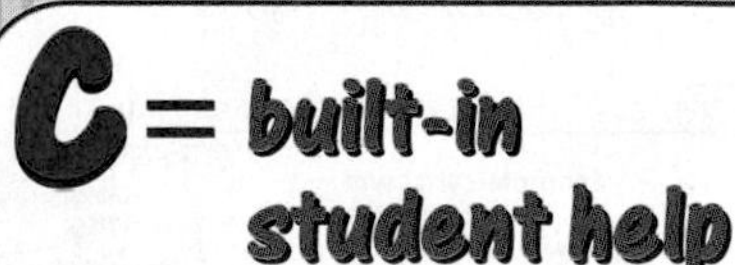

Easy-to-follow examples, readiness pages, and margin notes support students as they learn. See Student Help guide on the next page.

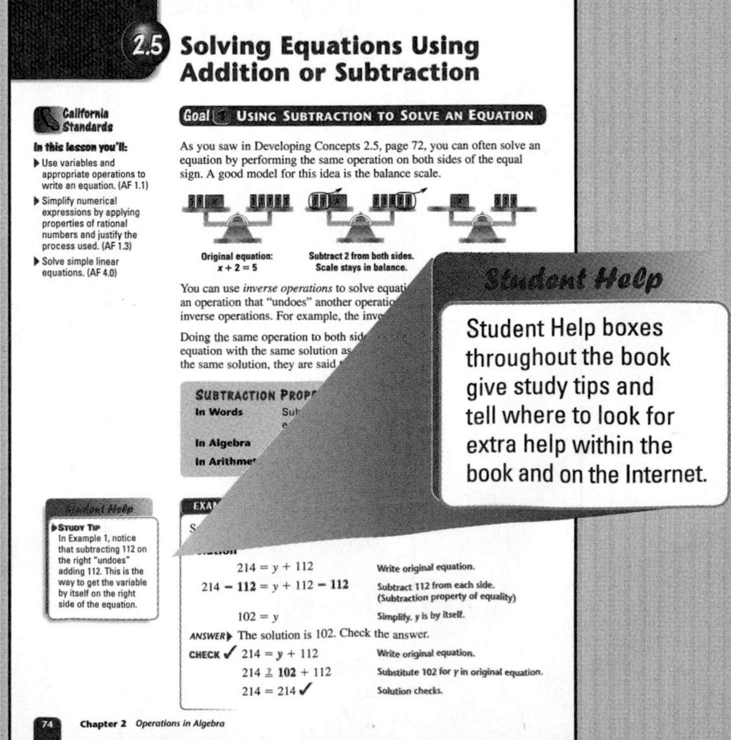

2.5 Solving Equations Using Addition or Subtraction
California Standards
In this lesson you'll:
Use variables and appropriate operations to write an equation. (AF 1.1)
Simplify numerical expressions by applying properties of rational numbers and justify the process used. (AF 1.3)
Solve simple linear equations. (AF 4.0)
Goal 1 Using Subtraction to Solve an Equation
As you saw in Developing Concepts 2.5, page 72, you can often solve an equation by performing the same operation on both sides of the equal sign. A good model for this idea is the balance scale.
Original equation: x + 2 = 5
Subtract 2 from both sides. Scale stays in balance.
Student Help
Study Tip
In Example 1, notice that subtracting 112 on the right "undoes" adding 112. This is the way to get the variable by itself on the right side of the equation.
214 = y + 112 Write original equation.
214 − 112 = y + 112 − 112 Subtract 112 from each side. (Subtraction property of equality)
102 = y Simplify. y is by itself.
ANSWER The solution is 102. Check the answer.
CHECK 214 = y + 112 Write original equation.
214 ≟ 102 + 112 Substitute 102 for y in original equation.
214 = 214 ✓ Solution checks.
74 Chapter 2 Operations in Algebra
Student Help
Student Help boxes throughout the book give study tips and tell where to look for extra help within the book and on the Internet.

A Guide to Student Help

▸ Each chapter begins with Getting Ready

Chapter Preview
gives an overview of what you will be learning.

Words to Know
lists important new words in the chapter.

Readiness Quiz
checks your understanding of words and skills that you will use in the chapter, and tells you where to go for review.

Study Tip
suggests ways to make your studying and learning easier.

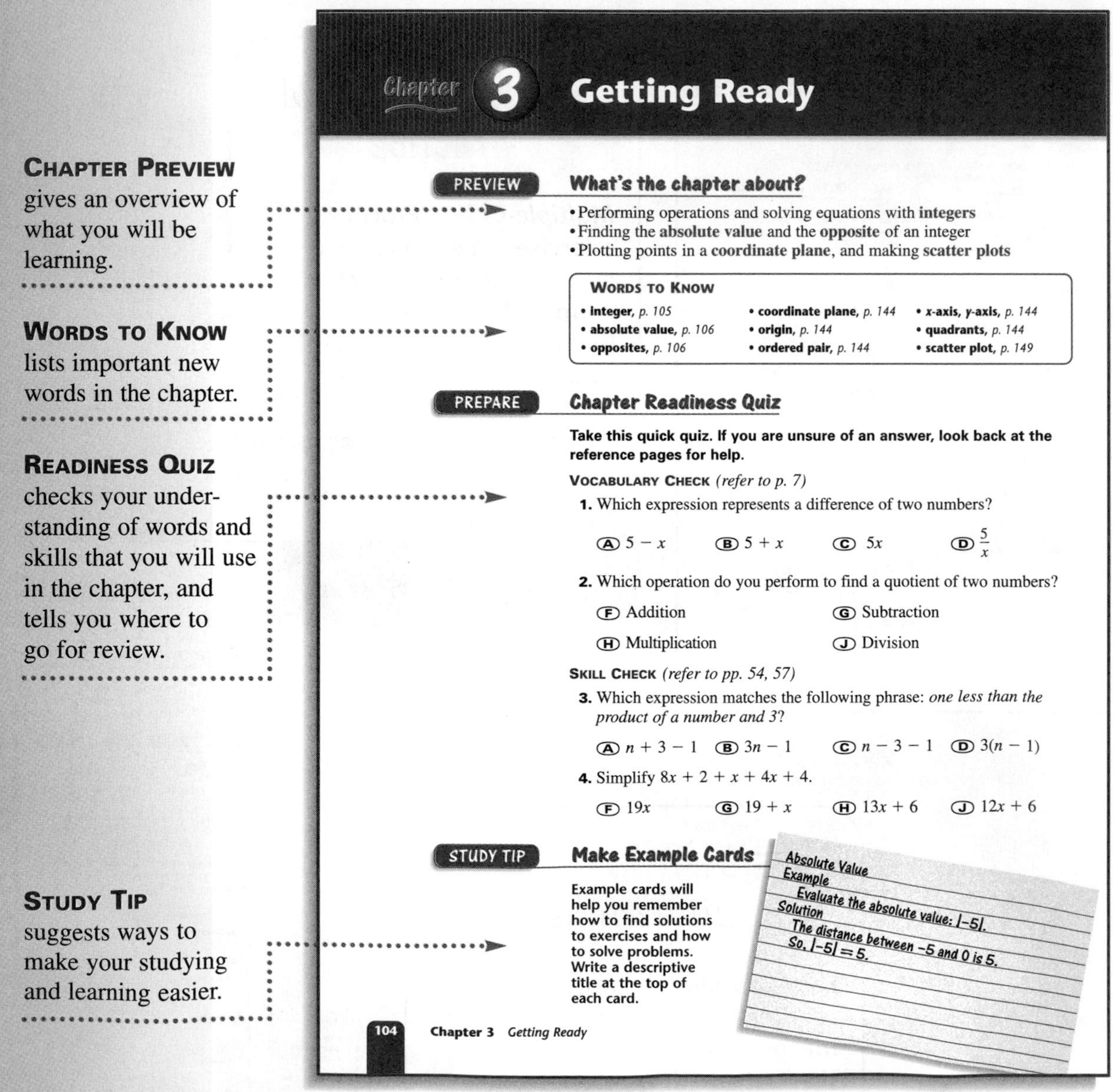

Chapter 3 Getting Ready

PREVIEW **What's the chapter about?**

- Performing operations and solving equations with **integers**
- Finding the **absolute value** and the **opposite** of an integer
- Plotting points in a **coordinate plane**, and making **scatter plots**

Words to Know

- **integer**, *p. 105*
- **absolute value**, *p. 106*
- **opposites**, *p. 106*
- **coordinate plane**, *p. 144*
- **origin**, *p. 144*
- **ordered pair**, *p. 144*
- ***x*-axis, *y*-axis**, *p. 144*
- **quadrants**, *p. 144*
- **scatter plot**, *p. 149*

PREPARE **Chapter Readiness Quiz**

Take this quick quiz. If you are unsure of an answer, look back at the reference pages for help.

Vocabulary Check *(refer to p. 7)*

1. Which expression represents a difference of two numbers?

(A) $5 - x$ (B) $5 + x$ (C) $5x$ (D) $\frac{5}{x}$

2. Which operation do you perform to find a quotient of two numbers?

(F) Addition (G) Subtraction
(H) Multiplication (J) Division

Skill Check *(refer to pp. 54, 57)*

3. Which expression matches the following phrase: *one less than the product of a number and 3*?

(A) $n + 3 - 1$ (B) $3n - 1$ (C) $n - 3 - 1$ (D) $3(n - 1)$

4. Simplify $8x + 2 + x + 4x + 4$.

(F) $19x$ (G) $19 + x$ (H) $13x + 6$ (J) $12x + 6$

STUDY TIP **Make Example Cards**

Example cards will help you remember how to find solutions to exercises and how to solve problems. Write a descriptive title at the top of each card.

Absolute Value
Example
Evaluate the absolute value: |−5|.
Solution
The distance between −5 and 0 is 5.
So, |−5| = 5.

104 **Chapter 3** *Getting Ready*

▸ Student Help notes throughout the book

Skills Review refers you to the pages where you can go for review and practice of topics from earlier courses.

Study Tips help you understand and apply concepts and avoid common errors.

Reading Tips guide you in reading and understanding your textbook.

Student Help

▸ Reading Tip
Remember that like terms have variables raised to the *same* power. For example, $2b$ and b^2 are not like terms.

Student Help

▸ Skills Review
For help with subtracting decimals, see p. 675.

EXAMPLE 2 *Solving an Equation with Decimals*

Solve $z + 4.7 = 10.3$.

Solution

$z + 4.7 = 10.3$	Write original equation.
$z + 4.7 - \mathbf{4.7} = 10.3 - \mathbf{4.7}$	Subtract 4.7 from each side.
$z = 5.6$	Simplify. z is by itself.

The solution is 5.6. Check the answer in the original equation.

Goal 2 Using Addition to Solve an Equation

You can use addition to solve an equation involving subtraction.

Addition Property of Equality

In Words	Adding the same number to each side of an equation produces an equivalent equation.
In Algebra	If $x - a = b$, then $x - a + a = b + a$.
In Arithmetic	If $x - 3 = 7$, then $x - 3 + 3 = 7 + 3$.

Student Help

▸ Study Tip
You can use vertical format for solving an equation. For example,

$$\begin{array}{rcr} x - 31 & = & 14 \\ \underline{+31} & & \underline{+31} \\ x & = & 45 \end{array}$$

EXAMPLE 3 *Using Addition to Solve an Equation*

Solve $x - 31 = 14$.

Solution

$x - 31 = 14$	Write original equation.
$x - 31 + \mathbf{31} = 14 + \mathbf{31}$	Add 31 to each side. (Addition property of equality)
$x = 45$	Simplify. x is by itself.

The solution is 45. Check the answer in the original equation.

EXAMPLE 4 *Solving an Equation with Decimals*

Solve $0.5 = y - 1.25$.

Solution

$0.5 = y - 1.25$	Write original equation.
$0.5 + \mathbf{1.25} = y - 1.25 + \mathbf{1.25}$	Add 1.25 to each side.
$1.75 = y$	Simplify. y is by itself.

The solution is 1.75. Check the answer in the original equation.

2.5 *Solving Equations Using Addition or Subtraction* 75

More Examples indicates that there are more worked-out examples on the Internet.

Student Help

▸ More Examples

More examples are available at www.mcdougallittell.com

Homework Help lets you know when there are suggestions and strategies for solving homework exercises available on the Internet.

Student Help

▸ Homework Help
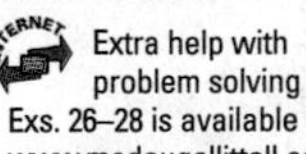
Extra help with problem solving in Exs. 26–28 is available at www.mcdougallittell.com

Other notes included are:

- **Technology Tip**
- **Test Tip**
- **Look Back**
- **More Practice**

Vocabulary Tips explain the meaning and origin of words.

Student Help

▸ Vocabulary Tip
To *factor* an expression means to write the expression as a product of its factors.

TEACHER'S RESOURCE PACKAGE

This package is conveniently organized and includes a variety of materials to help you adapt the program to your teaching style and to the specific needs of your students!

Package Includes:

- Chapter Resource Books (one for each chapter, organized by lesson)
- Practice Workbook (TE)
- Practice Workbook Spanish Edition
- Math Log
- Home and School Connection
- Technology: Using Calculators and Computers
- Assessment Book
- California Standards Key Concepts Book

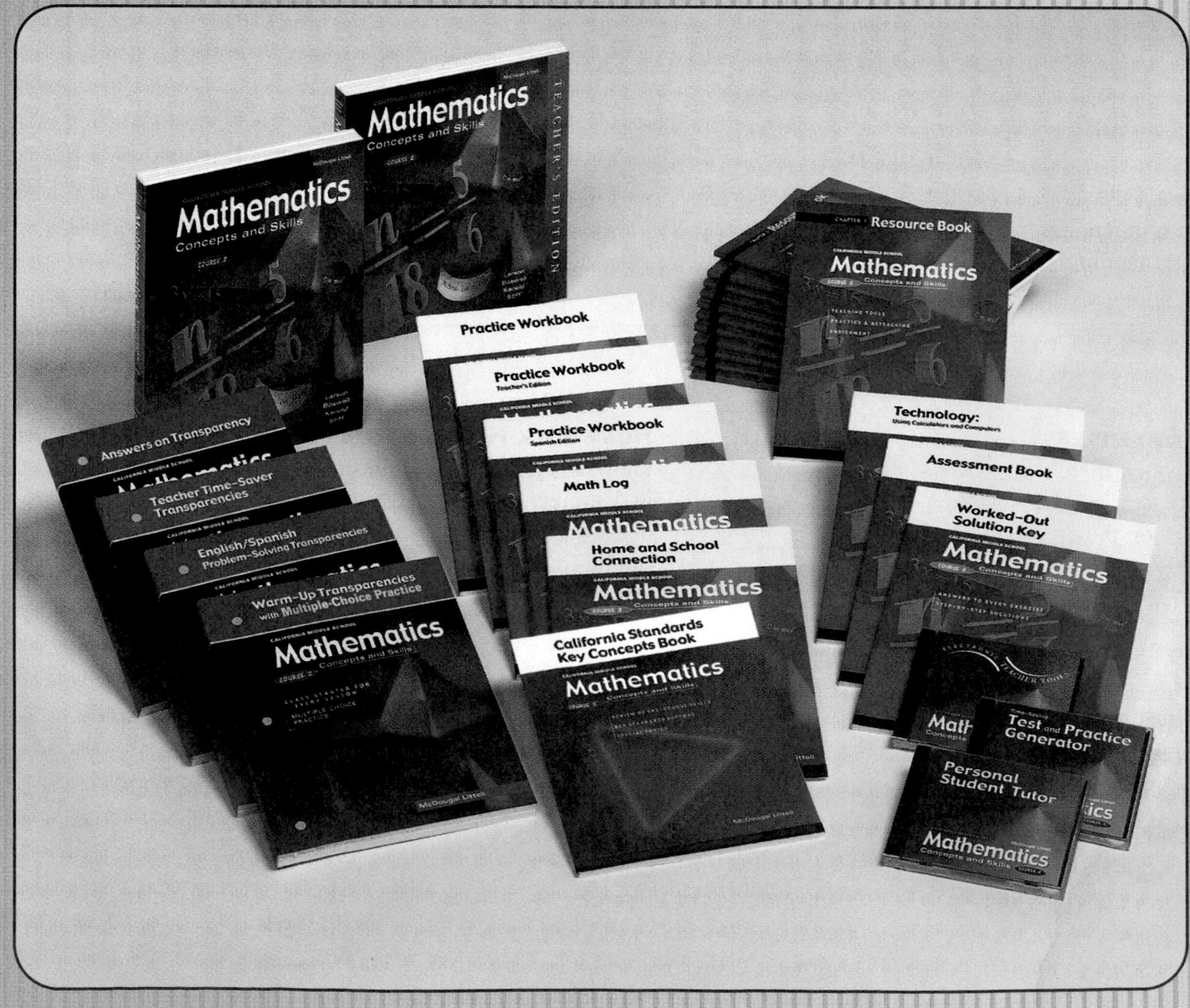

CHAPTER RESOURCE BOOKS

Chapter Resource Books allow you to carry the resources you have for a chapter in one manageable book. The materials in each Chapter Resource Book are organized by lesson so that you can see easily everything you have available.

Chapter Resource Books Include:

- Lesson Plans
- Lesson Plans for Block Scheduling
- Warm-Ups with Multiple-Choice Practice
- Problem of the Day
- Daily Cumulative Review
- Practice Masters
- Reteaching Masters
- Enrichment Masters
- Resource Book Answers

TRANSPARENCY PACKAGES

The transparency packages give you many easy-to-use options for reviewing homework, starting class, and teaching a lesson.

ANSWERS ON TRANSPARENCY

WARM-UP TRANSPARENCIES WITH MULTIPLE-CHOICE PRACTICE

- Class Starter for Every Lesson
- Practice for Multiple-Choice Testing

TEACHER TIME-SAVER TRANSPARENCIES

- Problem-Solving Support
- Focus on Vocabulary
- Teaching Tools

ENGLISH/SPANISH PROBLEM-SOLVING TRANSPARENCIES

- Problem-Solving Examples
- Worked-Out Solutions
- English and Spanish Side-by-Side

WORKBOOKS AND COPY MASTERS

- Practice Workbook (English and Spanish)
- Math Log
- Home and School Connection
- Assessment Book
- Worked-Out Solution Key

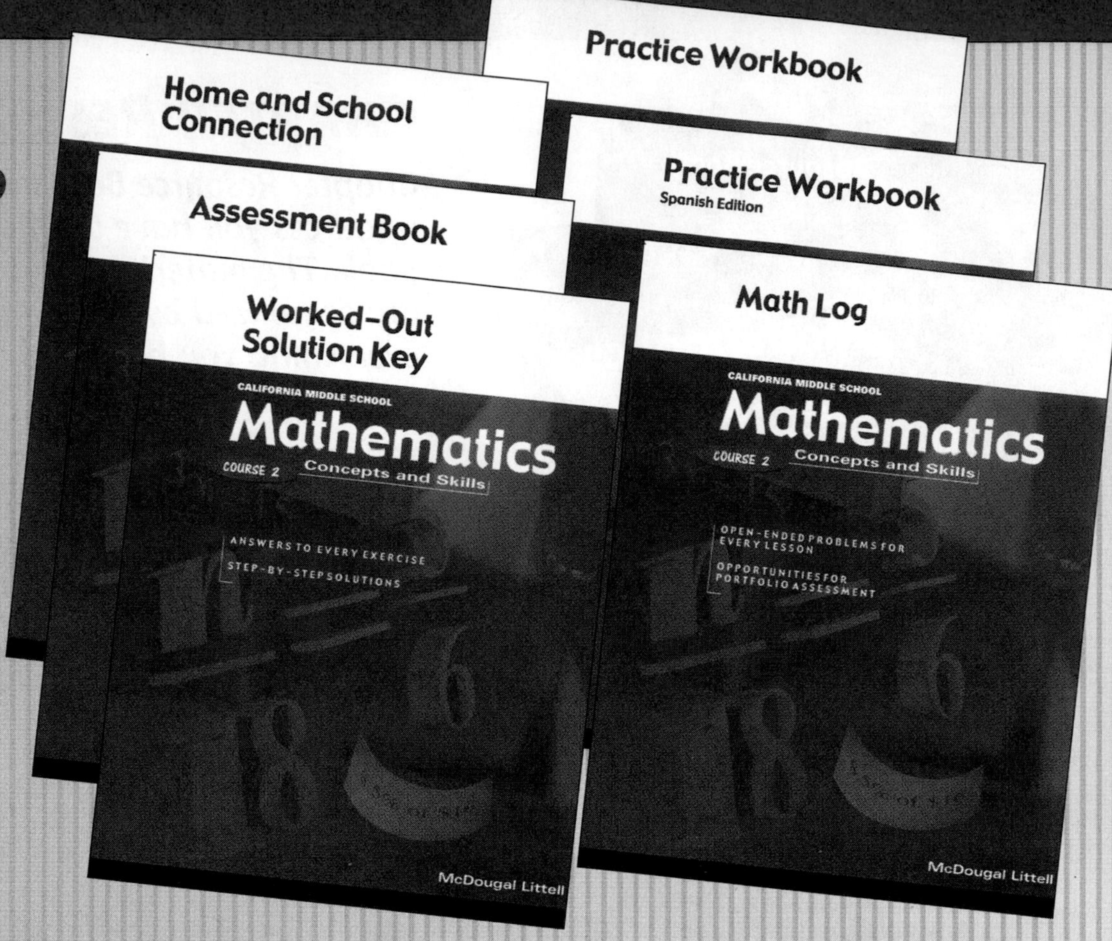

TECHNOLOGY RESOURCES

The technology resources help you with planning, teaching, and assessment and they help your students to build understanding.

- Online Lesson Planner
- Electronic Teacher Tools
- Technology: Using Calculators and Computers
- Time-Saving Test and Practice Generator
- Personal Student Tutor

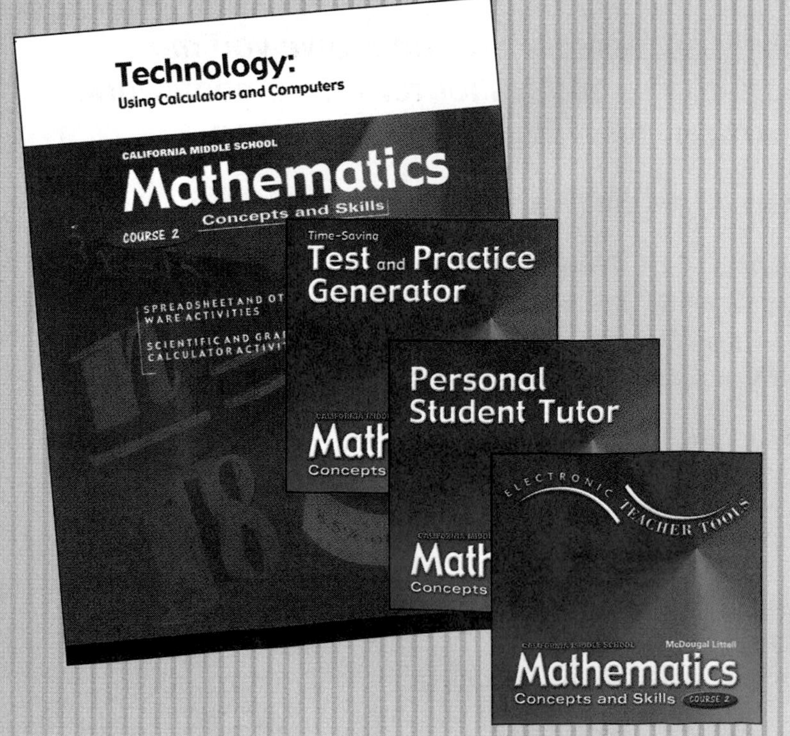

CLASSZONE

ClassZone is the companion Web site to McDougal Littell *Mathematics, Concepts and Skills* that includes Student Help, Application Links, and more. To access ClassZone, go to ***www.mcdougallittell.com.***

California Standards Key Concepts Book

This book reinforces and extends textbook lessons by providing additional instruction and practice on the Key Standards in an appealing, interactive format. Review of pre-course topics is also included.

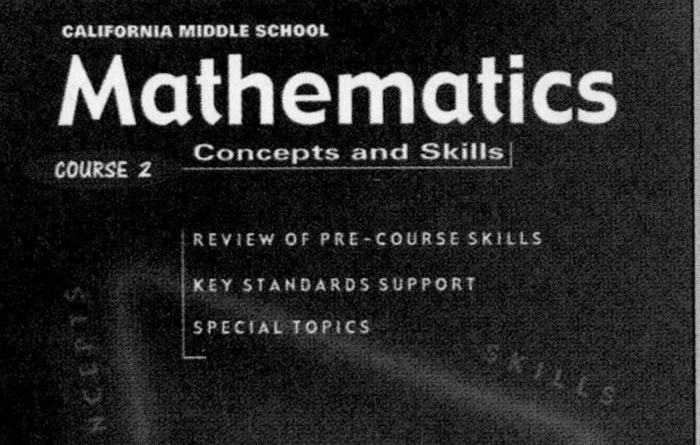

Key Standards pages offer practice in course content for classroom or independent student use.

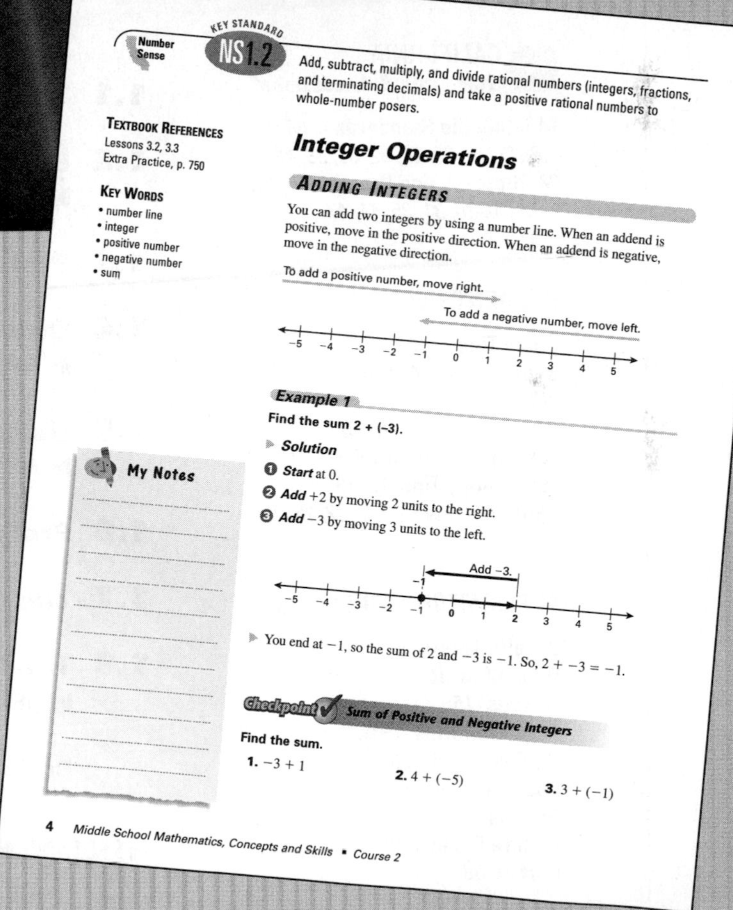

Number Sense — KEY STANDARD NS1.2

Add, subtract, multiply, and divide rational numbers (integers, fractions, and terminating decimals) and take a positive rational numbers to whole-number posers.

Textbook References
Lessons 3.2, 3.3
Extra Practice, p. 750

Key Words
- number line
- integer
- positive number
- negative number
- sum

Integer Operations

Adding Integers

You can add two integers by using a number line. When an addend is positive, move in the positive direction. When an addend is negative, move in the negative direction.

To add a positive number, move right.

To add a negative number, move left.

−5 −4 −3 −2 −1 0 1 2 3 4 5

Example 1

Find the sum 2 + (−3).

Solution

1. **Start** at 0.
2. **Add** +2 by moving 2 units to the right.
3. **Add** −3 by moving 3 units to the left.

Add −3. −1

−5 −4 −3 −2 −1 0 1 2 3 4 5

You end at −1, so the sum of 2 and −3 is −1. So, 2 + −3 = −1.

My Notes

Checkpoint Sum of Positive and Negative Integers

Find the sum.

1. −3 + 1
2. 4 + (−5)
3. 3 + (−1)

4 *Middle School Mathematics, Concepts and Skills* • Course 2

Pre-course review pages help the less-prepared student reach grade level.

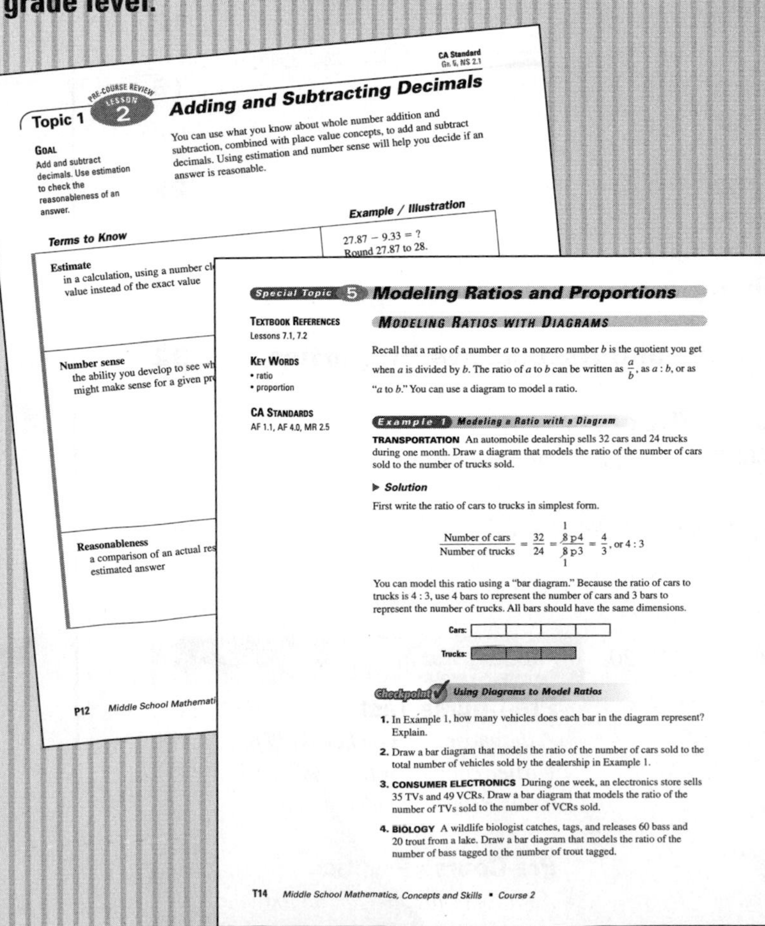

CA Standard Gr. 6, NS 2.1

Topic 1 — Pre-Course Review Lesson 2

Adding and Subtracting Decimals

Goal
Add and subtract decimals. Use estimation to check the reasonableness of an answer.

You can use what you know about whole number addition and subtraction, combined with place value concepts, to add and subtract decimals. Using estimation and number sense will help you decide if an answer is reasonable.

Terms to Know	Example / Illustration
Estimate in a calculation, using a number cl... value instead of the exact value	27.87 − 9.33 = ? Round 27.87 to 28.
Number sense the ability you develop to see wh... might make sense for a given pr...	
Reasonableness a comparison of an actual res... estimated answer	

P12 Middle School Mathemati...

Special Topic 5

Modeling Ratios and Proportions

Modeling Ratios with Diagrams

Textbook References
Lessons 7.1, 7.2

Key Words
- ratio
- proportion

CA Standards
AF 1.1, AF 4.0, MR 2.5

Recall that a ratio of a number a to a nonzero number b is the quotient you get when a is divided by b. The ratio of a to b can be written as $\frac{a}{b}$, as $a : b$, or as "a to b." You can use a diagram to model a ratio.

Example 1 Modeling a Ratio with a Diagram

TRANSPORTATION An automobile dealership sells 32 cars and 24 trucks during one month. Draw a diagram that models the ratio of the number of cars sold to the number of trucks sold.

Solution

First write the ratio of cars to trucks in simplest form.

$$\frac{\text{Number of cars}}{\text{Number of trucks}} = \frac{32}{24} = \frac{8 \cdot 4}{8 \cdot 3} = \frac{4}{3}, \text{ or } 4:3$$

You can model this ratio using a "bar diagram." Because the ratio of cars to trucks is 4 : 3, use 4 bars to represent the number of cars and 3 bars to represent the number of trucks. All bars should have the same dimensions.

Cars:
Trucks:

Checkpoint Using Diagrams to Model Ratios

1. In Example 1, how many vehicles does each bar in the diagram represent? Explain.
2. Draw a bar diagram that models the ratio of the number of cars sold to the total number of vehicles sold by the dealership in Example 1.
3. **CONSUMER ELECTRONICS** During one week, an electronics store sells 35 TVs and 49 VCRs. Draw a bar diagram that models the ratio of the number of TVs sold to the number of VCRs sold.
4. **BIOLOGY** A wildlife biologist catches, tags, and releases 60 bass and 20 trout from a lake. Draw a bar diagram that models the ratio of the number of bass tagged to the number of trout tagged.

T14 *Middle School Mathematics, Concepts and Skills* • Course 2

Special Topics pages help students develop mathematical reasoning skills.

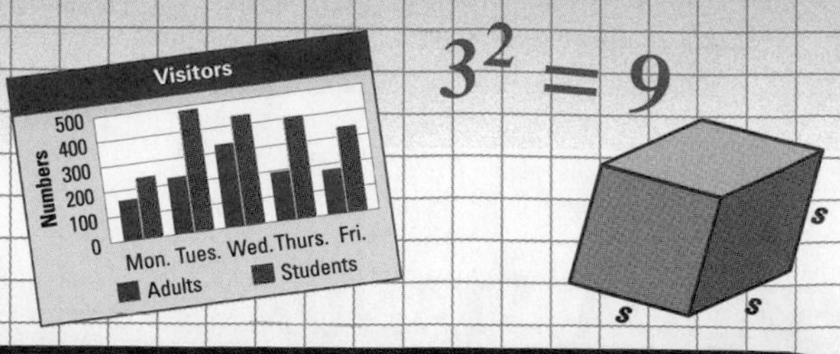

Operations with Numbers

ASSESSMENT

CALIFORNIA Standards & Assessment

STUDENT HELP

APPLICATION HIGHLIGHTS

INTERNET

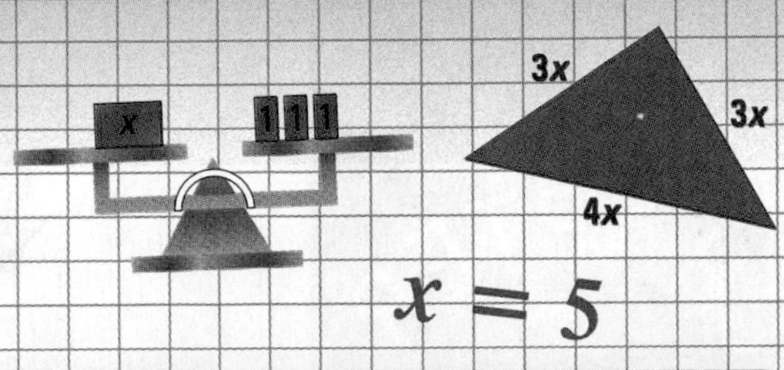

CHAPTER 2

Operations in Algebra

CALIFORNIA Standards & Assessment

Meeting the Standards *50, 53, 57, 61, 66, 72, 74, 78, 80, 85, 90, 100*
Multiple-Choice Practice *56, 60, 65, 70, 77, 84, 89, 93, 99*

STUDENT HELP

Study Tips *53, 62, 66, 74, 75, 85, 87, 90*
Reading Tip *59*
Vocabulary Tip *61*
Test Tips *60, 77, 89, 99*
Skills Review *58, 75*

APPLICATION HIGHLIGHTS

Currency Tables *56*
Wages *60*
Growing Pumpkins *65*
Exploration *69*
Fitness *71*
Mountain Elevation *77*
Basketball *83*
Landscaping *89*
Bicycle Racing *93*

INTERNET

55, 56, 58, 62, 64, 69, 70, 76, 80, 86, 92, 101

ASSESSMENT

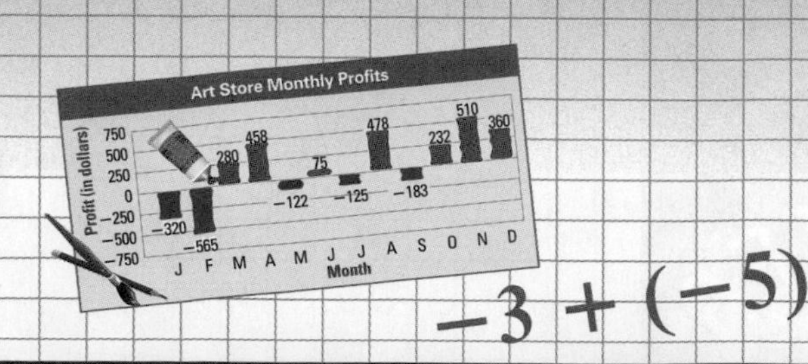

$-3 + (-5)$

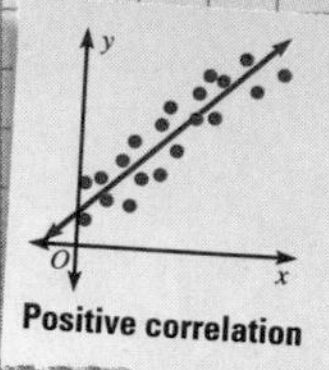

Operations with Integers

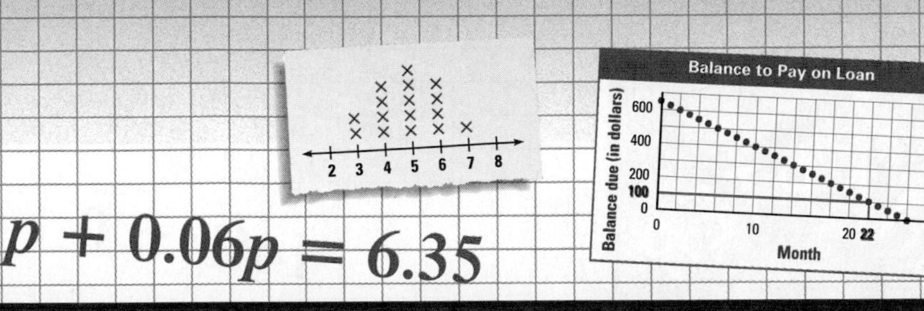

$p + 0.06p = 6.35$

Algebra and Equation Solving

CALIFORNIA
Standards & Assessment

Meeting the Standards *166, 169, 170, 174, 179, 183, 189, 193, 198, 203, 214*
Multiple-Choice Practice *173, 178, 182, 187, 192, 197, 202, 207, 213*

STUDENT HELP

Study Tips *169, 174, 179, 184, 186, 189, 193, 198, 200, 205*
Reading Tip *198*
Vocabulary Tip *196*
Test Tips *173, 178, 213*
Skills Review *199, 203*
Look Back *175, 190*

APPLICATION HIGHLIGHTS

Car Repair *173*
Printing Costs *177*
Depreciation *182*
Pony Express System *184*
Movies *192*
Dance Lessons *196*
Sales Tax *201*
pH Levels *207*

INTERNET

171, 173, 175, 177, 180, 182, 183, 184, 186, 190, 196, 201, 202, 204, 207, 215

Rational Numbers and Percents

CALIFORNIA *Standards & Assessment*

STUDENT HELP

APPLICATION HIGHLIGHTS

INTERNET

ASSESSMENT

CHAPTER 6

Operations with Rational Numbers

ASSESSMENT

CALIFORNIA Standards & Assessment

STUDENT HELP

APPLICATION HIGHLIGHTS

INTERNET

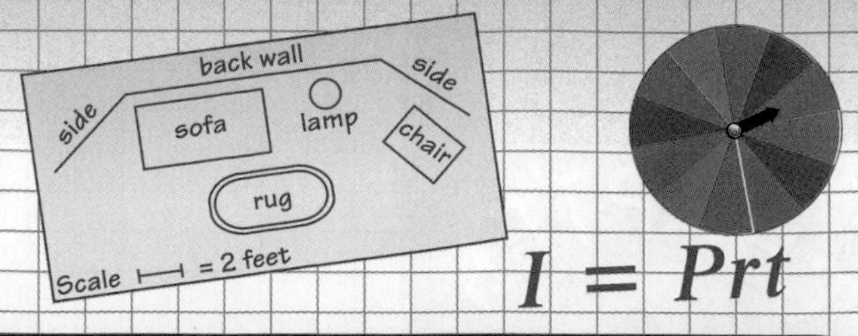

Proportional Reasoning

ASSESSMENT

CALIFORNIA Standards & Assessment

STUDENT HELP

APPLICATION HIGHLIGHTS

INTERNET

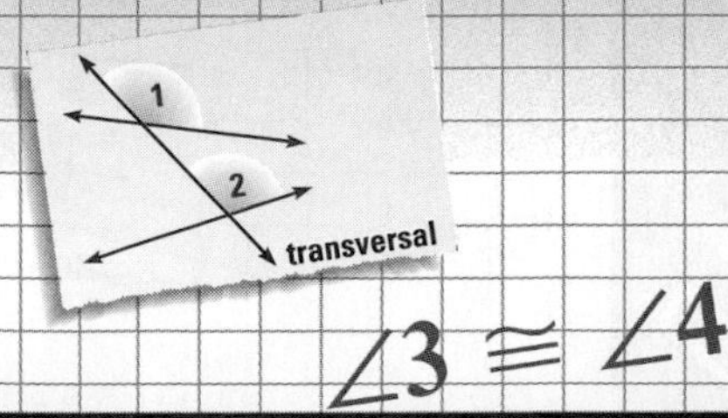

CHAPTER 8

Geometry Concepts

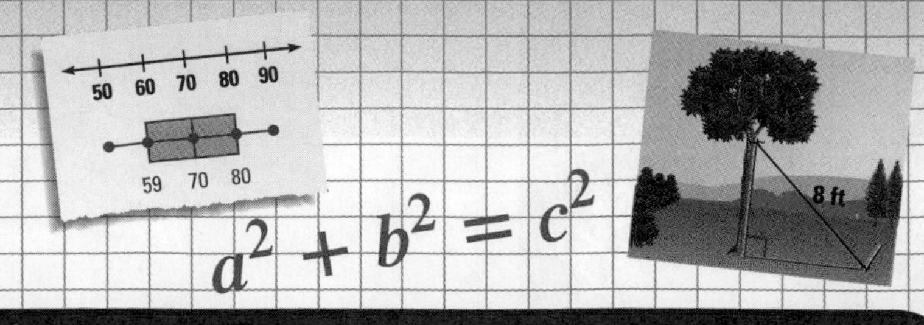

Real Numbers and Solving Inequalities

ASSESSMENT

CALIFORNIA Standards & Assessment

STUDENT HELP

APPLICATION HIGHLIGHTS

INTERNET

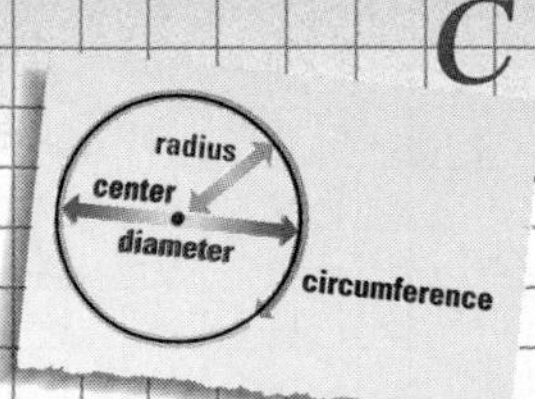

$C = \pi d$

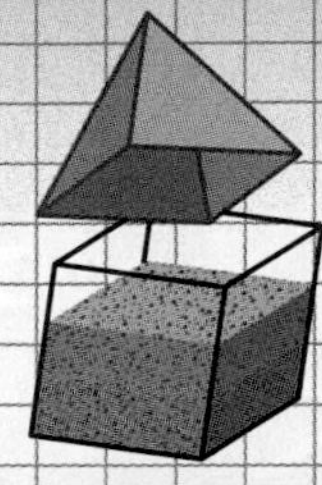

CHAPTER 10

Geometry and Measurement

CALIFORNIA
Standards & Assessment

Meeting the Standards *506, 509, 511, 517, 522, 523, 528, 530, 535, 539, 543, 548, 558*
Multiple-Choice Practice *515, 521, 527, 533, 538, 542, 547, 551, 557*

STUDENT HELP

Study Tips *509, 512, 516, 517*
Reading Tips *511, 523, 525*
Vocabulary Tips *514, 518*
Test Tips *521, 538, 557*
Technology Tip *523*
Skills Review *516*
Look Back *513, 524*

APPLICATION HIGHLIGHTS

Washington, D.C. *515*
Package Design *521*
Canned Goods *524*
Mayan Pyramids *531*
Unit Pricing *536*
Sports *538*
Grain *540*
Planetariums *546*
Nesting Boxes *551*

INTERNET

511, 515, 518, 526, 531, 532, 533, 536, 539, 544, 546, 550, 551, 559

ASSESSMENT

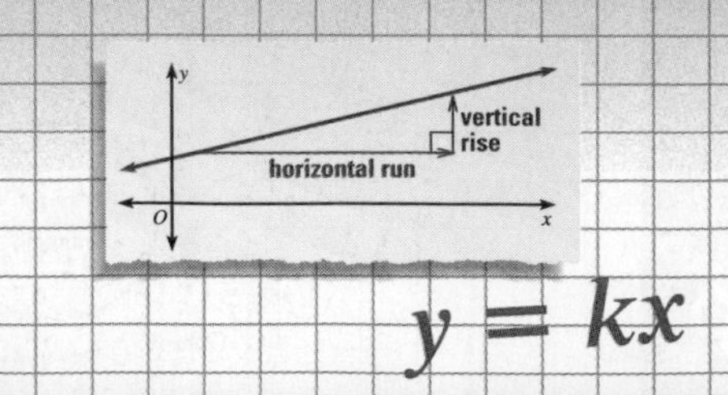

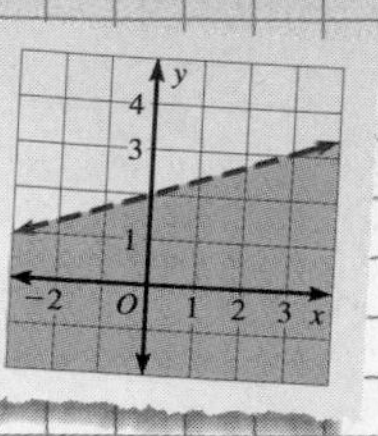

$y = kx$

Graphing Linear Equations and Inequalities

CALIFORNIA
Standards & Assessment

Meeting the Standards *560, 563, 567, 571, 576, 582, 583, 588, 589, 593, 598, 602, 612*
Multiple-Choice Practice *566, 570, 575, 580, 587, 592, 597, 601, 605, 611*

STUDENT HELP

Study Tips *564, 568, 571, 572, 577, 582, 583, 588, 589, 593, 595, 599, 602*
Test Tips *570, 605, 611*
Skills Review *570*

APPLICATION HIGHLIGHTS

Thunderstorms *563*
Web Page Design *570*
On-Line Shopping *575*
Car Wash *579*
Record Rainfall *586*
Acceleration *592*
Banking *596*
Road Race *601*

INTERNET

566, 568, 574, 575, 577, 580, 585, 590, 597, 601, 603, 613

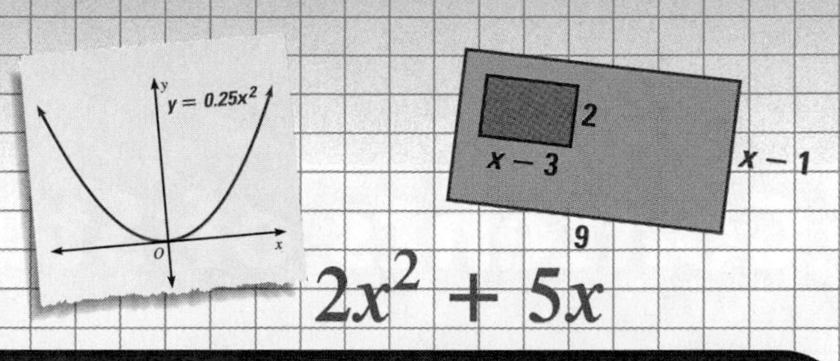

Polynomials

CALIFORNIA *Standards & Assessment*

Meeting the Standards *614, 617, 622, 626, 630, 636, 638, 642, 648, 660, 664*
Multiple-Choice Practice *621, 625, 629, 634, 641, 647, 653, 659*

STUDENT HELP

Study Tips *626, 627, 630, 639, 642, 643, 649, 650*
Reading Tips *617, 648*
Vocabulary Tip *622*
Test Tips *634, 647, 659*
Look Back *621, 631, 652*

APPLICATION HIGHLIGHTS

Planets *621*
Royal Gorge Bridge *625*
Hexadecimal *629*
Geometry *633*
Pay Raise *639*
Brickwork *646*
Parachuting *652*
Skid Lengths *653*

INTERNET

618, 619, 623, 625, 629, 633, 638, 639, 644, 646, 649, 652, 661

Contents of Student Resources

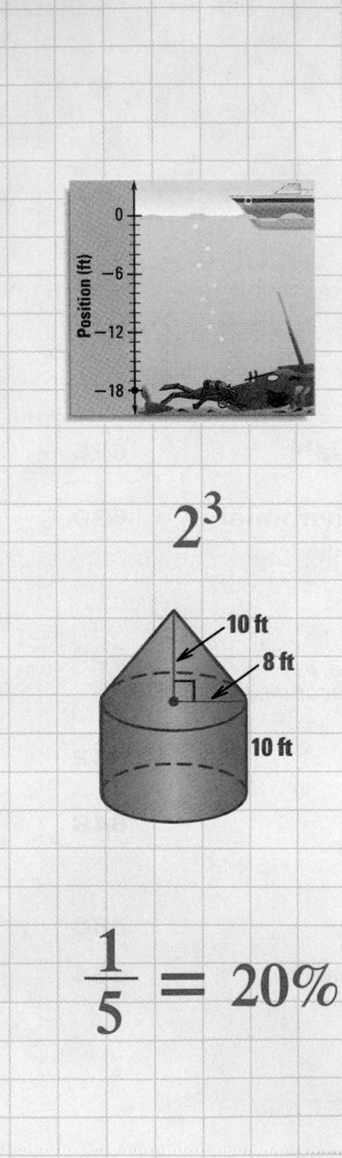

$n \leq 10$

U.S. Farms

Year	Number (in millions)
1990	
1970	
1950	
1930	
1910	
1890	
1870	
1850	

0 1 2 3 4 5 6 7

$A = \ell w$

Pre-Course and Post-Course Assessment

The Pre-Course Test on the next page checks understanding of key skills from earlier courses. If you have difficulty with a question on the Pre-Course Test, go to the indicated Skills Review pages for worked-out examples and to the Pre-Course Practice on pages xxii–xxv for additional practice. The End-of-Course Test on pages 714–716 checks mastery of the key concepts and skills in this course.

California Curriculum Support

Pages T29–T42 will help you coordinate your teaching of California Middle School Mathematics, Course 2 with the California Mathematics Standards for Grade 7. These pages include:

- ***Correlation to the California Standards p. T29***
- ***California Standards Reference Guide p. T39***

Correlation to the California Standards

The chart on pages T29–T37 lists the California Mathematics Standards for Grade 7 and indicates where in the Student Edition and Teacher's Edition of California Middle School Mathematics, Course 2 *these standards are addressed. Note that the Mathematical Reasoning Standards are addressed throughout. Representative examples are given in the correlation.*

Mathematics Grade 7

Correlation to California Standards

NUMBER SENSE

1 Students know the properties of, and compute with, rational numbers expressed in a variety of forms:

	California Standard	Student and Teacher's Edition	California Standards: Key Concepts Book	California Standards: Practice Workbook
1.1	Read, write, and compare rational numbers in scientific notation (positive and negative powers of 10) with approximate numbers using scientific notation.	pp. 309–313		p. 33
1.2	Add, subtract, multiply, and divide rational numbers (integers, fractions, and terminating decimals) and take positive rational numbers to whole-number powers.	pp. 7–11, 114–115, 116–120, 121–122, 123–126, 127–128, 129–133, 135–139, 160, 220–224, 269–272, 278–282, 289–293, 320, 324–325	pp. S3–S21, T1–T2, T3–T7, T8–T11, T12–T14	p. 34
1.3	Convert fractions to decimals and percents and use these representations in estimations, computations, and applications.	pp. 239–243, 244–247, 248–252, 283–287, 324–325, 345–349, 350–354, 365–368		p. 35
1.4	Differentiate between rational and irrational numbers.	pp. 239–243, 453–457, 500	pp. S22–S23	p. 36
1.5	Know that every rational number is either a terminating or repeating decimal and be able to convert terminating decimals into reduced fractions.	pp. 239–243, 453–457	pp. S24–S27	p. 37
1.6	Calculate the percentage of increases and decreases of a quantity.	pp. 361–364		p. 38
1.7	Solve problems that involve discounts, markups, commissions, and profit and compute simple and compound interest.	pp. 140–143, 174–178, 283–287, 356–360, 365–368, 369–373, 480–483	pp. S28–S35	pp. 39–40

Mathematics Grade 7

Correlation to California Standards

NUMBER SENSE

2 Students use exponents, powers, and roots and use exponents in working with fractions:

	California Standard	Student and Teacher's Edition	California Standards: Key Concepts Book	California Standards: Practice Workbook
2.1	Understand negative whole-number exponents. Multiply and divide expressions involving exponents with a common base.	pp. 303–304, 305–308, 320		p. 41
2.2	Add and subtract fractions by using factoring to find common denominators.	pp. 233–237, 269–272, 273–277	pp. S36–S38	pp. 42–43
2.3	Multiply, divide, and simplify rational numbers by using exponent rules.	pp. 299–302, 617–621	pp. S39–S41	p. 44
2.4	Use the inverse relationship between raising to a power and extracting the root of a perfect square integer; for an integer that is not square, determine without a calculator the two integers between which its square root lies and explain why.	pp. 449–452		p. 45
2.5	Understand the meaning of the absolute value of a number; interpret the absolute value as the distance of the number from zero on a number line; and determine the absolute value of real numbers.	pp. 105–109, 145, 469	pp. S42–S43	p. 46

ALGEBRA AND FUNCTIONS

1 Students express quantitative relationships by using algebraic terminology, expressions, equations, inequalities, and graphs:

	California Standard	Student and Teacher's Edition	California Standards: Key Concepts Book	California Standards: Practice Workbook
1.1	Use variables and appropriate operations to write an expression, an equation, an inequality, or a system of equations or inequalities that represents a verbal description (e.g., three less than a number, half as large as area *A*).	pp. 53–56, 66–70, 74–77, 80–84, 85–89, 140–143, 164–165, 174–178, 179–182, 333–337, 476–479, 563–566, 602–605	T14–T17	p. 47

ALGEBRA AND FUNCTIONS

	California Standard	Student and Teacher's Edition	California Standards Key Concepts Book	California Standards Practice Workbook
1.2	**Use the correct order of operations to evaluate algebraic expressions such as $3(2x + 5)^2$.**	pp. 16–20		p. 48
1.3	**Simplify numerical expressions by applying properties of rational numbers (e.g., identity, inverse, distributive, associative, commutative) and justify the process used.**	pp. 7–11, 16–20, 32–35, 36–37, 38–41, 57–60, 74–77, 80–84, 116–120, 123–126, 164–165, 183–187, 273–277, 278–282, 622–625, 626–629, 630–634, 636–637, 638–641, 660	pp. S44–S53	p. 49
1.4	**Use algebraic terminology (e.g., variable, equation, term, coefficient, inequality, expression, constant) correctly.**	pp. 7–11, 57–60, 61–65, 622–625		p. 50
1.5	**Represent quantitative relationships graphically and interpret the meaning of a specific part of a graph in the situation represented by the graph.**	pp. 105–109, 144–148, 571–575, 576–580, 589–592, 598–601, 602–605, 648–653		p. 51
2	**Students interpret and evaluate expressions involving integer powers and simple roots:**			
2.1	**Interpret positive whole-number powers as repeated multiplication and negative whole-number powers as repeated division or multiplication by the multiplicative inverse. Simplify and evaluate expressions that include exponents.**	pp. 12–15, 129–133, 220–224, 225–228, 229–232, 233–237, 303–304, 309–313, 626–629	T8–T11	p. 52
2.2	**Multiply and divide monomials; extend the process of taking powers and extracting roots to monomials when the latter results in a monomial with an integer exponent.**	pp. 299–302, 617–621, 630–634, 638–641, 648–653, 660		p. 53
3	**Students graph and interpret linear and some nonlinear functions:**			
3.1	**Graph functions of the form $y = nx^2$ and $y = nx^3$ and use in solving problems.**	pp. 642–647, 664–665		p. 54
3.2	**Plot the values from the volumes of three-dimensional shapes for various values of the edge lengths (e.g., cubes with varying edge lengths or a triangle prism with a fixed height and an equilateral triangle base of varying lengths).**	pp. 642–647		p. 55

Mathematics Grade 7
Correlation to California Standards

Algebra and Functions

	California Standard	Student and Teacher's Edition	California Standards: Key Concepts Book	California Standards: Practice Workbook
3.3	**Graph linear functions, noting that the vertical change (change in *y*-value) per unit of horizontal change (change in *x*-value) is always the same and know that the ratio ("rise over run") is called the slope of a graph.**	pp. 582, 583–587, 589–592	pp. S54–S60	p. 56
3.4	**Plot the values of quantities who ratios are always the same (e.g., cost to the number of an item, feet to inches, circumference to diameter of a circle). Fit a line to the plot and understand that the slope of the line equals the quantities.**	pp. 149–153, 583–587	pp. S61–S63	p. 57
4	**Students solve simple linear equations and inequalities over the rational numbers:**			
4.1	**Solve two-step linear equations and inequalities in one variable over the rational numbers, interpret the solution or solutions in the context from which they arose, and verify the reasonableness of the results.**	pp. 170–173, 179–182, 189–192, 198–202, 214, 294–298, 350–354, 380, 484–488, 500	pp. S64–S73	p. 58
4.2	**Solve multistep problems involving rate, average speed, distance, and time or a direct variation.**	pp. 22–26, 183–187, 329–332, 470–474, 593–597	pp. S74–S76, T18–T21	p. 59

Measurement and Geometry

	California Standard	Student and Teacher's Edition	California Standards: Key Concepts Book	California Standards: Practice Workbook
1	**Students choose appropriate units of measure and use ratios to convert within and between measurement systems to solve problems:**			
1.1	**Compare weights, capacities, geometric measures, times, and temperatures within and between measurement systems (e.g., miles per hour and feet per second, cubic inches to cubic centimeters).**	pp. 294–298, 329–332, 333–337, 535–538	T18–T21	p. 60

MEASUREMENT AND GEOMETRY

	California Standard	Student and Teacher's Edition	California Standards: Key Concepts Book	California Standards: Practice Workbook
1.2	**Construct and read drawings and models made to scale.**	pp. 338–342, 504–505		p. 61
1.3	**Use measures expressed as rates (e.g., speed, density) and measures expressed as products (e.g., person-days) to solve problems; check the units of the solutions; and use dimensional analysis to check the reasonableness of the answer.**	pp. 85–89, 174–178, 289–293, 305–308	pp. S77–S78	p. 62
2	**Students compute the perimeter, area, and volume of common geometric objects and use the results to find measures of less common objects. They know how perimeter, area, and volume are affected by changes of scale:**			
2.1	**Use formulas routinely for finding the perimeter and area of basic two-dimensional figures and the surface area and volume of basic three-dimensional figures, including rectangles, parallelograms, trapezoids, squares, triangles, circles, prisms, and cylinders.**	pp. 12–15, 22–26, 38–41, 189–192, 417–418, 419–422, 509–510, 511–516, 522, 523–527, 528–529, 530–533, 535–538, 539–542, 543–547, 558, 664–665		pp. 63–65
2.2	**Estimate and compute the area of more complex or irregular two- and three-dimensional figures by breaking the figures down into more basic geometric objects.**	pp. 22–26, 419–422, 504–505, 539–542		p. 66
2.3	**Compute the length of the perimeter, the surface area of the faces, and the volume of a three-dimensional object built from rectangular solids. Understand that when the lengths of all dimensions are multiplied by a scale factor, the surface area is multiplied by the square of the scale factor and the volume is multiplied by the cube of the scale factor.**	pp. 530–533, 543–547, 548–551		p. 67
2.4	**Relate the changes in measurement with a change of scale to the units used (e.g., square inches, cubic feet) and to conversions between units (1 square foot = 144 square inches or [1 ft^2] = [144 in.^{2}], 1 cubic inch is approximately 16.38 cubic centimeters or [1 in.^{3}] = [16.38 cm^3]).**	pp. 548–551		p. 68

Mathematics Grade 7

Correlation to California Standards

Measurement and Geometry

3 Students know the Pythagorean theorem and deepen their understanding of plane and solid geometric shapes by constructing figures that meet given conditions and by identifying attributes of figures:

	California Standard	Student and Teacher's Edition	California Standards: Key Concepts Book	California Standards: Practice Workbook
3.1	**Identify and construct basic elements of geometric figures (e.g., altitudes, midpoints, diagonals, angle bisectors, and perpendicular bisectors; central angles, radii, diameters, and chords of circles) by using a compass and straightedge.**	pp. 385–389, 390–395, 398–403, 404–410, 444, 511–516		p. 69
3.2	**Understand and use coordinate graphs to plot simple figures, determine lengths and areas related to them, and determine their image under translations and reflections.**	pp. 144–148, 423–427, 428–431, 469, 470–474		p. 70
3.3	**Know and understand the Pythagorean theorem and its converse and use it to find the length of the missing side of a right triangle and the lengths of other line segments and, in some situations, empirically verify the Pythagorean theorem by direct measurement.**	pp. 458–459, 460–464, 465–468, 500	pp. S79–S86	p. 71
3.4	**Demonstrate an understanding of conditions that indicate two geometrical figures are congruent and what congruence means about the relationships between the sides and angles of the two figures.**	pp. 385–389, 390–395, 396–397, 398–403, 412–416, 423–427, 428–431	pp. S87–S92	p. 72
3.5	**Construct two-dimensional patterns for three-dimensional models, such as cylinders, prisms, and cones.**	pp. 517–521		p. 73

MEASUREMENT AND GEOMETRY

	California Standard	Student and Teacher's Edition	California Standards: Key Concepts Book	California Standards: Practice Workbook
3.6	**Identify elements of three-dimensional geometric objects (e.g., diagonals of rectangular solids) and describe how two or more objects are related in space (e.g., skew lines, the possible ways three planes might intersect).**	pp. 385–389, 517–521	pp. S93–S99	p. 74

STATISTICS, DATA ANALYSIS, AND PROBABILITY

1 **Students collect, organize, and represent data sets that have one or more variables and identify relationships among variables within a data set by hand and through the use of an electronic spreadsheet software program:**

	California Standard	Student and Teacher's Edition	Key Concepts Book	Practice Workbook
1.1	**Know various forms of display for data sets, including stem-and-leaf plot or box-and-whisker plot; use the forms to display a single set of data or to compare two sets of data.**	pp. 3–6, 203–207, 253–257, 489–493		p. 75
1.2	**Represent two numerical variables on a scatterplot and informally describe how the data points are distributed and any apparent relationship that exists between the two variables (e.g., between time spent on homework and grade level).**	pp. 149–153		p. 76
1.3	**Understand the meaning of, and be able to compute, the minimum, the lower quartile, the median, the upper quartile, and the maximum of a data set.**	pp. 253–257, 489–493	pp. S100–S103	p. 77

MATHEMATICAL REASONING

1 **Students make decisions about how to approach problems:**

	California Standard	Student and Teacher's Edition	Key Concepts Book	Practice Workbook
1.1	**Analyze problems by identifying relationships, distinguishing relevant from irrelevant information, identifying missing information, sequencing and prioritizing information, and observing patterns.**	Occurs throughout. For example, see pp. 27–31, 87–88 (Exs. 1, 3), 114–115, 181 (Exs. 3–5), 239 (Example 2 and text preceding), 303–304, 338 (Example 1 and text preceding), 444, 458–459, 578 (Exs. 4, 5), 639 (text before Example 3; Study Tip), 667.	T1–T2	
1.2	**Formulate and justify mathematical conjectures based on a general description of the mathematical question or problem posed.**	Occurs throughout. For example, see pp. 33 (Example 4), 93 (Ex. 41), 114–115, 121–122, 169 (Ex. 5), 223 (Ex. 77), 271 (Ex. 25), 397 (Exs. 3–6), 459 (Sample 2), 542 (Ex. 25), 578 (Ex. 21), 633 (Ex. 41).		

Mathematics Grade 7

Correlation to California Standards

MATHEMATICAL REASONING

	California Standard	Student and Teacher's Edition	California Standards: Key Concepts Book	California Standards: Practice Workbook
1.3	**Determine when and how to break a problem into simpler parts.**	Occurs throughout. For example, see pp. 13 (Examples 2, 3), 39 (Example 4), 169, 420 (Example 2 and text preceding), 431 (Ex. 20), 504–505, 522 (Sample 1), 536 (Example 3), 540 (Example 3), 558, 631 (Example 3), 670.		
2	**Students use strategies, skills, and concepts in finding solutions:**			
2.1	**Use estimation to verify the reasonableness of calculated results.**	Occurs throughout. For example, see pp. 13 (Example 3), 15 (Exs. 34–37), 49 (Example 2; Exs. 10–21), 86 (Example 2), 88–89 (Exs. 11, 15, 16), 283 (Example 2), 284 (Example 5), 285 (Exs. 35–40), 350 (Study Tip), 449 (Example 2), 527 (Ex. 24), 671 (third Example; Exs. 1–3).		
2.2	**Apply strategies and results from simpler problems to more complex problems.**	Occurs throughout. For example, see pp. 48, 66 (Examples 1, 2), 202 (Ex. 28), 219 (Ex. 3), 270 (Example 4 and text preceding), 373 (Ex. 29), 420 (Examples 2, 3), 493 (Exs. 27, 28), 551 (Exs. 15–17), 599 (Example 2), 625 (Examples; Exs. 44–51), 660.		
2.3	**Estimate unknown quantities graphically and solve for them by using logical reasoning and arithmetic and algebraic techniques.**	Occurs throughout. For example, see pp. 4 (Examples 3, 4; Reading Graphs), 84 (Exs. 52–54), 150 (Example 3), 169, 174–178, 183–187, 193–197, 245 (Example 4), 500, 526 (Ex. 17), 593–597, 648–653.		
2.4	**Make and test conjectures by using both inductive and deductive reasoning.**	Occurs throughout. For example, see pp. 40 (Exs. 30–33), 114–115, 121–122, 127–128, 133 (Ex. 71), 231 (Ex. 43), 277 (Exs. 57, 58), 344 (Ex. 5), 394 (Exs. 42–45), 456 (Exs. 30–34), 545 (Exs. 12–14), 570 (Ex. 41).		

MATHEMATICAL REASONING

	California Standard	Student and Teacher's Edition	California Standards: Key Concepts Book	California Standards: Practice Workbook
2.5	**Use a variety of methods, such as words, numbers, symbols, charts, graphs, tables, diagrams, and models, to explain mathematical reasoning.**	Occurs throughout. For example, see pp. 27–31, 72–73, 141 (Examples 3, 4), 199–200 (text following Example 3), 219, 278 (text before Example 1), 369 (Examples 1, 2), 417–418, 485 (Example 3), 509–510, 574 (Exs. 29–32), 636–637.	T14–T17	
2.6	**Express the solution clearly and logically by using the appropriate mathematical notation and terms and clear language; support solutions with evidence in both verbal and symbolic work.**	Occurs throughout. For example, see pp. 32–35, 79 (Sample 2; Exs. 11–13, 17–19), 164–165, 194, 279 (Example 3), 330 (Examples 3, 4), 380, 398 (Examples 1, 2), 477 (Example 4), 516 (Construction Ex. 3), 586 (Ex. 22), 628 (Ex. 13).		
2.7	**Indicate the relative advantages of exact and approximate solutions to problems and give answers to a specified degree of accuracy.**	Occurs throughout. For example, see pp. 196 (Ex. 16), 198–202, 205 (Example 4), 284 (Example 5), 287 (Exs. 54–56), 449 (Example 2; Technology Tip), 452 (Exs. 37–40, 56, 57), 514 (Exs. 6–14), 579 (Exs. 32, 33), 599 (Example 2), 619 (Example 5), 664 (Ex. 1).		
2.8	**Make precise calculations and check the validity of results from the context of the problem.**	Occurs throughout. For example, see pp. 41 (Exs. 39, 40), 62 (Example 3; Study Tip), 138 (Exs. 57–59), 183 (Example 1), 237 (Ex. 53), 289 (Example 1), 333 (Example 1), 480 (Study Tip), 493 (Ex. 26), 589 (Example 1), 602 (Example 2; Study Tip), 629 (Exs. 16, 17).		
3	**Students determine a solution is complete and move beyond a particular problem by generalizing to other situations:**			
3.1	**Evaluate the reasonableness of the solution in the context of the original situation.**	Occurs throughout. For example, see pp. 23 (text following Example 2), 49 (Example 2), 87 (Example 3), 88–89 (Exs. 8, 11, 14–16), 171 (Example 4), 193–197, 199 (Example 3), 237 (Ex. 53), 290 (Example 4 and text preceding), 343–344, 579 (Ex. 22), 671.		
3.2	**Note the method of deriving the solution and demonstrate a conceptual understanding of the derivation by solving similar problems.**	Occurs throughout. For example, see pp. 25 (Example; Exs. 12–14), 41 (Example; Exs. 41–43), 131 (Example 4), 169, 174 (Example 2; Study Tip), 182 (Ex. 38), 370–371 (Example 3 and text preceding; Exs. 9–15), 395 (Construction Exs. 1–3), 414 (Example 5; Ex. 5), 464 (Construction Exs. 1–5), 522, 601 (Ex. 37).		
3.3	**Develop generalizations of the results obtained and the strategies used and apply them to new problem situations.**	Occurs throughout. For example, see pp. 79 (Ex. 10), 127–128, 186 (Study Tip; Ex. 36), 214 (Brain Teaser), 303 (Sample 1 and text following; Exs. 1–8), 417–418, 469, 522 (Ex. 2), 528–529, 588, 620 (Ex. 45), 641 (Exs. 51, 52).		

California Standards Reference Guide

***For quick reference, the California Mathematics Standards for Grade 7 are listed on pages T40–T42. The Key Standards for Grade 7, as indicated in the* Mathematics Framework for California Public Schools, *are denoted by the symbol* ⬬.**

California Standards Reference Guide

Number Sense

1.0 Students know the properties of, and compute with, rational numbers expressed in a variety of forms:

1.1 Read, write, and compare rational numbers in scientific notation (positive and negative powers of 10) with approximate numbers using scientific notation.

1.2 Add, subtract, multiply, and divide rational numbers (integers, fractions, and terminating decimals) and take positive rational numbers to whole-number powers.

1.3 Convert fractions to decimals and percents and use these representations in estimations, computations, and applications.

1.4 Differentiate between rational and irrational numbers.

1.5 Know that every rational number is either a terminating or repeating decimal and be able to convert terminating decimals into reduced fractions.

1.6 Calculate the percentage of increases and decreases of a quantity.

1.7 Solve problems that involve discounts, markups, commissions, and profit and compute simple and compound interest.

2.0 Students use exponents, powers, and roots and use exponents in working with fractions:

2.1 Understand negative whole-number exponents. Multiply and divide expressions involving exponents with a common base.

2.2 Add and subtract fractions by using factoring to find common denominators.

2.3 Multiply, divide, and simplify rational numbers by using exponent rules.

2.4 Use the inverse relationship between raising to a power and extracting the root of a perfect square integer; for an integer that is not square, determine without a calculator the two integers between which its square root lies and explain why.

2.5 Understand the meaning of the absolute value of a number; interpret the absolute value as the distance of the number from zero on a number line; and determine the absolute value of real numbers.

Algebra and Functions

1.0 Students express quantitative relationships by using algebraic terminology, expressions, equations, inequalities, and graphs:

1.1 Use variables and appropriate operations to write an expression, an equation, an inequality, or a system of equations or inequalities that represents a verbal description (e.g., three less than a number, half as large as area *A*).

1.2 Use the correct order of operations to evaluate algebraic expressions such as $3(2x + 5)^2$.

1.3 Simplify numerical expressions by applying properties of rational numbers (e.g., identity, inverse, distributive, associative, commutative) and justify the process used.

1.4 Use algebraic terminology (e.g., variable, equation, term, coefficient, inequality, expression, constant) correctly.

1.5 Represent quantitative relationships graphically and interpret the meaning of a specific part of a graph in the situation represented by the graph.

2.0 Students interpret and evaluate expressions involving integer powers and simple roots:

2.1 Interpret positive whole-number powers as repeated multiplication and negative whole-number powers as repeated division or multiplication by the multiplicative inverse. Simplify and evaluate expressions that include exponents.

2.2 Multiply and divide monomials; extend the process of taking powers and extracting roots to monomials when the latter results in a monomial with an integer exponent.

3.0 Students graph and interpret linear and some nonlinear functions:

3.1 Graph functions of the form $y = nx^2$ and $y = nx^3$ and use in solving problems.

3.2 Plot the values from the volumes of three-dimensional shapes for various values of the edge lengths (e.g., cubes with varying edge lengths or a triangle prism with a fixed height and an equilateral triangle base of varying lengths).

ALGEBRA AND FUNCTIONS (*CONTINUED*)

3.3 Graph linear functions, noting that the vertical change (change in *y*-value) per unit of horizontal change (change in *x*-value) is always the same and know that the ratio ("rise over run") is called the slope of a graph.

3.4 Plot the values of quantities who ratios are always the same (e.g., cost to the number of an item, feet to inches, circumference to diameter of a circle). Fit a line to the plot and understand that the slope of the line equals the quantities.

4.0 Students solve simple linear equations and inequalities over the rational numbers:

4.1 Solve two-step linear equations and inequalities in one variable over the rational numbers, interpret the solution or solutions in the context from which they arose, and verify the reasonableness of the results.

4.2 Solve multistep problems involving rate, average speed, distance, and time or a direct variation.

MEASUREMENT AND GEOMETRY

1.0 Students choose appropriate units of measure and use ratios to convert within and between measurement systems to solve problems:

1.1 Compare weights, capacities, geometric measures, times, and temperatures within and between measurement systems (e.g., miles per hour and feet per second, cubic inches to cubic centimeters).

1.2 Construct and read drawings and models made to scale.

1.3 Use measures expressed as rates (e.g., speed, density) and measures expressed as products (e.g., person-days) to solve problems; check the units of the solutions; and use dimensional analysis to check the reasonableness of the answer.

2.0 Students compute the perimeter, area, and volume of common geometric objects and use the results to find measures of less common objects. They know how perimeter, area, and volume are affected by changes of scale:

2.1 Use formulas routinely for finding the perimeter and area of basic two-dimensional figures and the surface area and volume of basic three-dimensional figures, including rectangles, parallelograms, trapezoids, squares, triangles, circles, prisms, and cylinders.

2.2 Estimate and compute the area of more complex or irregular two- and three-dimensional figures by breaking the figures down into more basic geometric objects.

2.3 Compute the length of the perimeter, the surface area of the faces, and the volume of a three-dimensional object built from rectangular solids. Understand that when the lengths of all dimensions are multiplied by a scale factor, the surface area is multiplied by the square of the scale factor and the volume is multiplied by the cube of the scale factor.

2.4 Relate the changes in measurement with a change of scale to the units used (e.g., square inches, cubic feet) and to conversions between units (1 square foot = 144 square inches or [1 ft^2] = [144 $in.^2$], 1 cubic inch is approximately 16.38 cubic centimeters or [1 $in.^3$] = 16.38 cm^3]).

3.0 Students know the Pythagorean theorem and deepen their understanding of plane and solid geometric shapes by constructing figures that meet given conditions and by identifying attributes of figures:

3.1 Identify and construct basic elements of geometric figures (e.g., altitudes, midpoints, diagonals, angle bisectors, and perpendicular bisectors; central angles, radii, diameters, and chords of circles) by using a compass and straightedge.

3.2 Understand and use coordinate graphs to plot simple figures, determine lengths and areas related to them, and determine their image under translations and reflections.

3.3 Know and understand the Pythagorean theorem and its converse and use it to find the length of the missing side of a right triangle and the lengths of other line segments and, in some situations, empirically verify the Pythagorean theorem by direct measurement.

(Continued on next page.)

California Standards Reference Guide

Measurement and Geometry (continued)

3.4 Demonstrate an understanding of conditions that indicate two geometrical figures are congruent and what congruence means about the relationships between the sides and angles of the two figures.

3.5 Construct two-dimensional patterns for three-dimensional models, such as cylinders, prisms, and cones.

3.6 Identify elements of three-dimensional geometric objects (e.g., diagonals of rectangular solids) and describe how two or more objects are related in space (e.g., skew lines, the possible ways three planes might intersect).

Statistics, Data Analysis, and Probability

1.0 Students collect, organize, and represent data sets that have one or more variables and identify relationships among variables within a data set by hand and through the use of an electronic spreadsheet software program:

1.1 Know various forms of display for data sets, including stem-and-leaf plot or box-and-whisker plot; use the forms to display a single set of data or to compare two sets of data.

1.2 Represent two numerical variables on a scatterplot and informally describe how the data points are distributed and any apparent relationship that exists between the two variables (e.g., between time spent on homework and grade level).

1.3 Understand the meaning of, and be able to compute, the minimum, the lower quartile, the median, the upper quartile, and the maximum of a data set.

Mathematical Reasoning

1.0 Students make decisions about how to approach problems:

1.1 Analyze problems by identifying relationships, distinguishing relevant from irrelevant information, identifying missing information, sequencing and prioritizing information, and observing patterns.

1.2 Formulate and justify mathematical conjectures based on a general description of the mathematical question or problem posed.

1.3 Determine when and how to break a problem into simpler parts.

2.0 Students use strategies, skills, and concepts in finding solutions:

2.1 Use estimation to verify the reasonableness of calculated results.

2.2 Apply strategies and results from simpler problems to more complex problems.

2.3 Estimate unknown quantities graphically and solve for them by using logical reasoning and arithmetic and algebraic techniques.

2.4 Make and test conjectures by using both inductive and deductive reasoning.

2.5 Use a variety of methods, such as words, numbers, symbols, charts, graphs, tables, diagrams, and models, to explain mathematical reasoning.

2.6 Express the solution clearly and logically by using the appropriate mathematical notation and terms and clear language; support solutions with evidence in both verbal and symbolic work.

2.7 Indicate the relative advantages of exact and approximate solutions to problems and give answers to a specified degree of accuracy.

2.8 Make precise calculations and check the validity of results from the context of the problem.

3.0 Students determine a solution is complete and move beyond a particular problem by generalizing to other situations:

3.1 Evaluate the reasonableness of the solution in the context of the original situation.

3.2 Note the method of deriving the solution and demonstrate a conceptual understanding of the derivation by solving similar problems.

3.3 Develop generalizations of the results obtained and the strategies used and apply them to new problem situations.

Guide to Using the Teacher's Edition

Pages T44–T49 provide an overview of the content and the organization of this Teacher's Edition, as well as a suggested pacing chart for the course.

The following information is included on these pages:

PLANNING THE CHAPTER

Complete planning support preceding each chapter.

- **Regular and block schedules for pacing the course.**

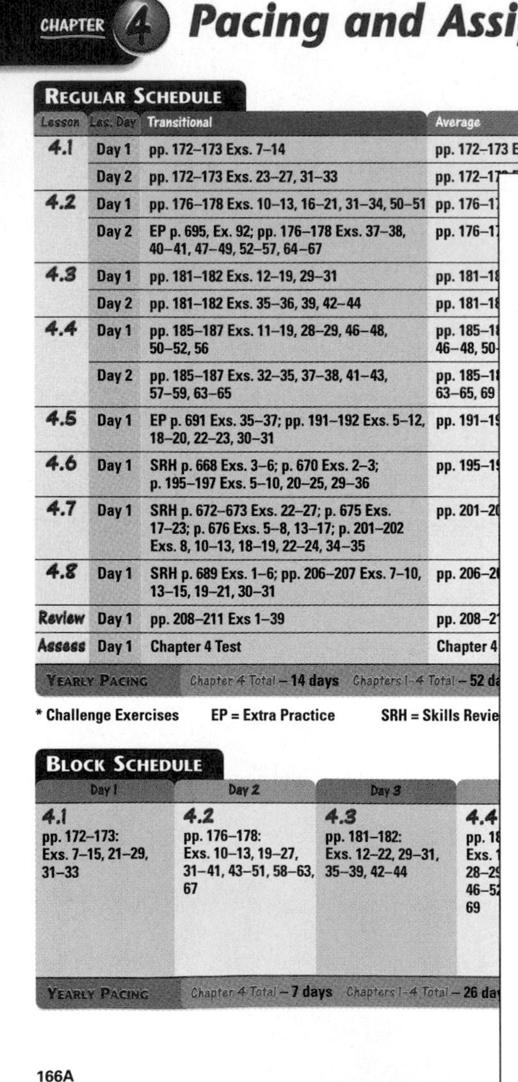

CHAPTER 4 **Pacing and Assignment Guide**

REGULAR SCHEDULE

Lesson	Les. Day	Transitional	Average	Advanced
4.1	Day 1	pp. 172–173 Exs. 7–14	pp. 172–173 Exs. 7–15, 21–22	pp. 172–173 Exs. 12–22
	Day 2	pp. 172–173 Exs. 23–27, 31–33	pp. 172–17	
4.2	Day 1	pp. 176–178 Exs. 10–13, 16–21, 31–34, 50–51	pp. 176–1	
	Day 2	EP p. 695, Ex. 92; pp. 176–178 Exs. 37–38, 40–41, 47–49, 52–57, 64–67	pp. 176–1	
4.3	Day 1	pp. 181–182 Exs. 12–19, 29–31	pp. 181–1	
	Day 2	pp. 181–182 Exs. 35–36, 39, 42–44	pp. 181–1	
4.4	Day 1	pp. 185–187 Exs. 11–19, 28–29, 46–48, 50–52, 56	pp. 185–1 46–48, 50-	
	Day 2	pp. 185–187 Exs. 32–35, 37–38, 41–43, 57–59, 63–65	pp. 185–1 63–65, 69	
4.5	Day 1	EP p. 691 Exs. 35–37; pp. 191–192 Exs. 5–12, 18–20, 22–23, 30–31	pp. 191–1	
4.6	Day 1	SRH p. 668 Exs. 3–6; p. 670 Exs. 2–3; p. 195–197 Exs. 5–10, 20–25, 29–36	pp. 195–1	
4.7	Day 1	SRH p. 672–673 Exs. 22–27; p. 675 Exs. 17–23; p. 676 Exs. 5–8, 13–17; p. 201–202 Exs. 8, 10–13, 18–19, 22–24, 34–35	pp. 201–2	
4.8	Day 1	SRH p. 689 Exs. 1–6; pp. 206–207 Exs. 7–10, 13–15, 19–21, 30–31	pp. 206–2	
Review	Day 1	pp. 208–211 Exs 1–39	pp. 208–2	
Assess	Day 1	Chapter 4 Test	Chapter 4	

YEARLY PACING Chapter 4 Total – 14 days Chapters 1–4 Total – 52 da

* Challenge Exercises EP = Extra Practice SRH = Skills Revie

BLOCK SCHEDULE

Day 1	Day 2	Day 3	
4.1 pp. 172–173: Exs. 7–15, 21–29, 31–33	4.2 pp. 176–178: Exs. 10–13, 19–27, 31–41, 43–51, 58–63, 67	4.3 pp. 181–182: Exs. 12–22, 29–31, 35–39, 42–44	4.4 pp. 18 Exs. 1 28–2 46–5 69

YEARLY PACING Chapter 4 Total – 7 days Chapters 1–4 Total – 26 da

166A

- **A handy guide for integrating resource materials into your lessons.**

Support Materials

CHAPTER RESOURCE BOOK

LESSON SUPPORT	4.1	4.2	4.3	4.4	4.5	4.6	4.7	4.8
Lesson Plans	p. 1	p. 10	p. 19	p. 28	p. 37	p. 46	p. 55	p. 64
Lesson Plans for Block Scheduling	p. 2	p. 11	p. 20	p. 29	p. 38	p. 47	p. 56	p. 65
Warm-Ups with Multiple-Choice Practice	p. 3	p. 12	p. 21	p. 30	p. 39	p. 48	p. 57	p. 66
Problem of the Day	p. 4	p. 13	p. 22	p. 31	p. 40	p. 49	p. 58	p. 67
Daily Cumulative Review	p. 5	p. 14	p. 23	p. 32	p. 41	p. 50	p. 59	p. 68
Practice Masters	p. 6	p. 15	p. 24	p. 33	p. 42	p. 51	p. 60	p. 69
Reteaching Masters	p. 7	p. 16	p. 25	p. 34	p. 43	p. 52	p. 61	p. 70
Enrichment Masters	p. 9	p. 18	p. 27	p. 36	p. 45	p. 54	p. 63	p. 72

TRANSPARENCIES

	4.1	4.2	4.3	4.4	4.5	4.6	4.7	4.8
Warm-Ups with Multiple-Choice Practice	p. 26	p. 27	p. 28	p. 29	p. 30	p. 31	p. 32	p. 33
Teacher Time-Saver Transparencies	✓	✓	✓	✓	✓	✓	✓	✓
English/Spanish Problem Solving	p. 14			p. 15	p. 16	p. 17		p. 18
Answer Transparencies	✓	✓	✓	✓	✓	✓	✓	✓

TECHNOLOGY

- Personal Student Tutor
- Time-Saving Test and Practice Generator
- Electronic Teacher Tools
- Technology: Using Calculators and Computers

ADDITIONAL RESOURCES

- Math Log
- Assessment Book
- Worked-Out Solution Key
- Practice Workbook (English/Spanish)
- Home and School Connection
- California Standards: Key Concepts Book

Correlation to the California Curriculum

Correlations to the California Standards
CA Standards: NS 1.0, NS 1.7, AF 1.1, AF 1.3, AF 4.1, AF 4.2, MG 1.3, MG 2.1, SDP 1.0, SDP 1.1, MR 1.3, MR 2.3, MR 2.8, MR 3.1, MR 3.2

California Curriculum Support

Key Concepts Book
- Pre-Course Review: Topic 1 Working with Decimals
  Topic 5 Measurement
- Key Standards: NS 1.2 Decimal Operations *(Lesson 4.7)*
  AF 4.1 Solving Two-Step Equations *(Lesson 4.1)*
  AF 4.1 Solving Equations with Variables on Both Sides *(Lesson 4.5)*
  MG 1.3 Dimensional Analysis *(Lesson 4.6)*

California Standards Practice Workbook provides practice for each Standard that is covered in this chapter.

166B

• **Strategies for enabling all students to learn mathematics.**

Providing Universal Access

Strategies for Strategic Learners

FOCUS ON KEY CONCEPTS

In this chapter students are presented with three measures of central tendency. None of these concepts is difficult in and of itself, but when the three concepts are presented together, some students can become overwhelmed. Students will be familiar with the concept and the calculation of the mean, but perhaps know the term *average* rather than *mean*. Determining mo
as no calculation is required. Median, while not a di
cept, may be confusing because the method of calcu
median depends on whether the number of data item
even. One strategy teachers can use is to introduce t
concepts over a period of time, with plenty of space
and to avoid introducing problems that require stude
three until each concept has been mastered separate
strategy is to focus on the key concepts. The most co
used measure of central tendency is mean. If teacher
mean and make sure that concept is explored solidly
understood, the concepts of mode and median can b
later, with a minimum of time spent on them.

RETEACH KEY CONCEPTS

Students should understand that in order to solve a
you need to isolate the variable on a side by itself.
four operations you can use to do that, and they w
in detail in Chapter 3. You can:

Add the same number to each side of the equation

Subtract the same number from each side of the eq

Multiply each side of the equation by the same nu
(except 0).

Divide each side of the equation by the same num
(except 0).

When you add or subtract to solve an equation, yo
usually looking for a number that makes a sum of
Example 1 on page 170, when you subtract 8 from
get $3x$ on the left. Students need to remember that
number and its opposite is zero (you can show this
number line).

When you multiply or divide to solve an equation,
often looking for a number that will make a produ
in Example 1, when you divide each side by 3 to g
on the left. A review of Examples 1 and 2 on page
helpful for students who are having difficulty.

Strategies for English Learners

VOCABULARY DEVELOPMENT

In math class, you might review with students the concept of *opposite*, which is a key mathematical concept and a good way for English learners to learn and remember vocabulary. Start with some simple opposites such as *up* and *down*, *high* and *low*, *tall* and *short*, and *in* and *out*, to make sure students have

• **Mathematical background to help you develop students' conceptual understanding and reasoning skills.**

Mathematical Background Notes

The modeling of real-life situations often involves linear equations. While a single equation may be sufficient to model simple situations, more complex problems may call for equating several linear expressions involving several variables. The present chapter continues the study of a single linear equation and thereby sets the stage for the solution of systems.

Lessons 4.1–4.5

These lessons deal mainly with the solution of linear equations whose coefficients are integers. This provides a simple format in which to pose problems and illustrate solution techniques. It also reinforces the arithmetic of integers, as studied in Chapter 3.

Lesson 4.6

The opening problem of this lesson is typical of modeling situations that invite several problem solving strategies, not all of which need be based on the solution of linear equations. In this problem, a logging company has 90 square miles of land cleared of trees. Starting in year 0, it continues to log land at the rate of 15 square miles per year while, at the same time, replanting trees at the rate of 30 square miles per year.

VERBAL REASONING Here students might reason that of the 30 square miles to be replanted each year, 15 are required to cover the land that was logged that year. This means that 15 square miles of replanting are to be applied to the original 90 square miles of logged land. Such reasoning may lead the student directly to the equation

$$90 - 15n = 0.$$

While reasonable and correct, this basis for arriving at $n = 6$ involves verbal reasoning and cannot be viewed as a routine method. However, it provides an alternative basis for arriving at the equation $90 = 15n$ appearing toward the end of Example 2 on page 194.

USING GRAPHS Another method is used in Example 1, where data are visualized in terms of a scatter plot corresponding to

$$30n = 90 + 15n, \text{ where } n = 0, 1, 2, 3, 4, 5, \text{ and } 6.$$

We can think of the above equation in terms of two functions

$$y = 30n$$

and

$$y = 90 + 15n$$

for which we are seeking to achieve equal outputs for the same whole number value of n. By enlarging the domain of the functions involved to include all real numbers x, we can rewrite the problem as

$$30x = 90 + 15x$$

where x is allowed to be any real number. This equation is of the form

$$Ax + B = Cx + D,$$

where A, B, C, and D are given real numbers.

In Chapter 11 students will learn that the graph of a linear equation is a straight line and will give the problem of finding a solution of $Ax + B = Cx + D$ an interesting geometric interpretation. Since the graphs of $y = Ax + B$ and $y = Cx + D$ are straight lines, the solution of $Ax + B = Cx + D$ will correspond to finding the x-coordinate of the intersection of these two lines.

In the case at hand, we would graph $y = 30x$ and $y = 15x + 90$, seeking the point of intersection of the resulting graphs. As in the scatter plot on page 193, different numerical scales are used on the x- and y-axes.

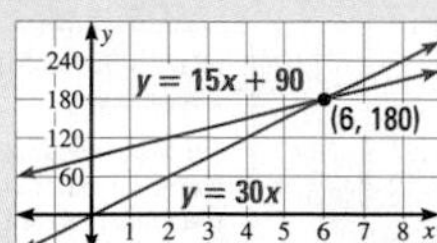

The two lines appear to intersect at the point (6, 180), so we can estimate that $x = 6$ is a solution of $30x = 90 + 15x$. That $x = 6$ is in fact a solution can be verified by direct substitution.

A graphical solution of the equivalent equation $90 - 15x = 0$ can also be provided. Here we would only have to graph the function $y = 90 - 15x$. The solution of this equation is the x-intercept of the function $y = 90 - 15x$, the point at which the graph of this function intersects the line $y = 0$.

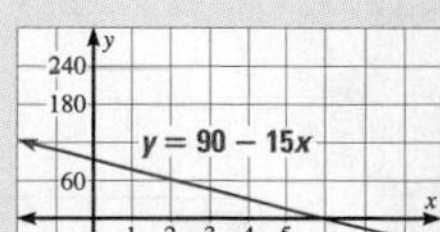

While it is important to be able to recognize that graphing $y = 90 - 15x$ can lead to a solution of the equation $90 - 15x = 0$, this is not an efficient procedure for students to follow. The most efficient way to graph this equation is to *first* find the x-intercept (6, 0) and y-intercept (0, 90) and use these two points to graph the equation. But finding the x-intercept is tantamount to solving the problem!

USING EQUIVALENT PROBLEMS A problem given in verbal form can sometimes be translated into another verbal form that is easier to comprehend and put into algebraic form. For instance, the logging problem

PLANNING THE LESSON

Handy, point-of-use support for each lesson.

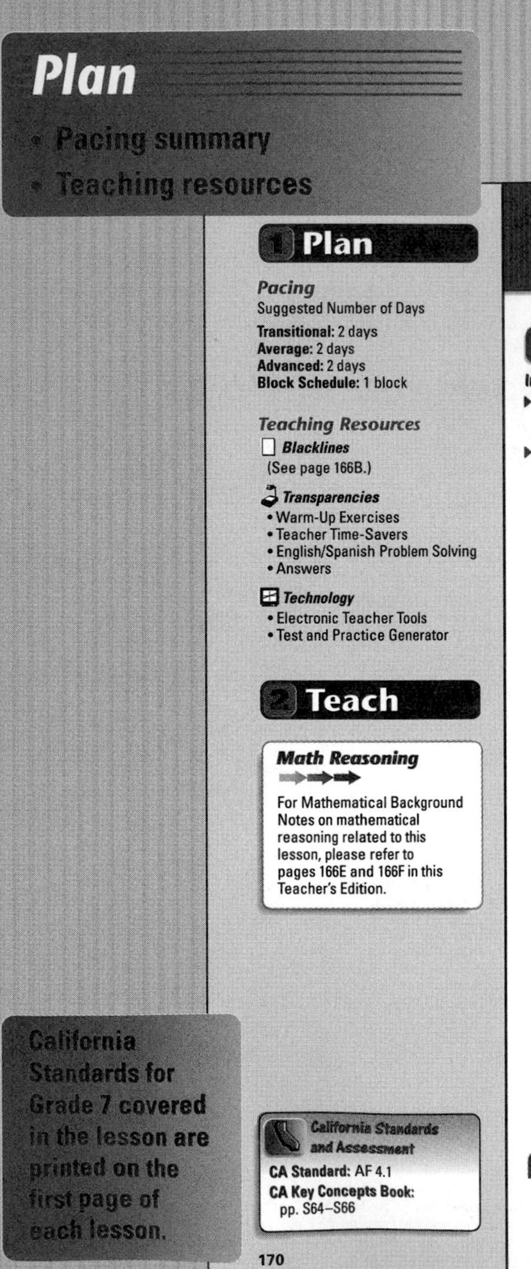

Plan

- Pacing summary
- Teaching resources

1 Plan

Pacing

Suggested Number of Days

Transitional: 2 days
Average: 2 days
Advanced: 2 days
Block Schedule: 1 block

Teaching Resources

Blacklines
(See page 166B.)

Transparencies
- Warm-Up Exercises
- Teacher Time-Savers
- English/Spanish Problem Solving
- Answers

Technology
- Electronic Teacher Tools
- Test and Practice Generator

2 Teach

Math Reasoning

For Mathematical Background Notes on mathematical reasoning related to this lesson, please refer to pages 166E and 166F in this Teacher's Edition.

California Standards for Grade 7 covered in the lesson are printed on the first page of each lesson.

California Standards and Assessment
CA Standard: AF 4.1
CA Key Concepts Book: pp. S64–S66

170

4.1 Solving Two

California Standards

In this l
▶ Solve t equati (AF 4.1
▶ Interpr equati which reaso result.

Goal 1 SOLVING TWO

170

Teach

- Extra Example for each example in the book
- Math Reasoning notes to build conceptual understanding
- Concept Check question at the end of each lesson
- Teaching Tips
- ... AND MORE

Goal 2 V

Link to Sports

TENNIS Tennis associations across the U.S. are trying to get more young people interested in playing tennis. Currently only about 6% of 6- to 12-year-olds play tennis. Community tennis clubs like the one shown can help young people learn the game.

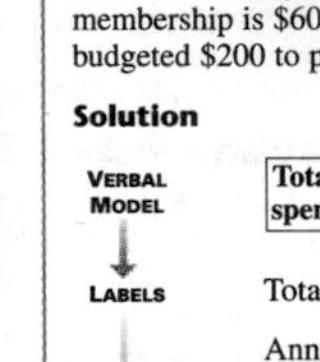

EXAMPLE

TENNIS You are joining a community tennis club. The annual membership is \$60, and a tennis court rents for \$10 per hour. You have budgeted \$200 to play tennis this year. How many hours can you play?

Solution

VERBAL MODEL: Total spent = Annual fee + Hourly rate · Hours of tennis

LABELS:

Total spent = **200**	(dollars)
Annual fee = **60**	(dollars)
Hourly rate = **10**	(dollars per hour)
Number of hours played = n	(hours)

ALGEBRAIC MODEL:

$200 = 60 + 10 \cdot n$	Write algebraic model.
$200 - 60 = 60 + 10n - 60$	Subtract 60 from each side.
$140 = 10n$	Simplify.
$\frac{140}{10} = \frac{10n}{10}$	Divide each side by 10.
$14 = n$	Simplify. n is by itself.

ANSWER ▶ You can play 14 hours of tennis.

When you check a solution involving units of measure, check the units of measure as well as the numbers.

EXAMPLE 4 **Checking Reasonableness of a Solution**

Use unit analysis to check that proper units were used in the solution from Example 3. Place the values and units in the verbal model.

Solution

Total spent = Annual fee + Hourly rate · Hours of tennis

$200 \text{ dollars} \stackrel{?}{=} 60 \text{ dollars} + \frac{10 \text{ dollars}}{\cancel{\text{hour}}} \cdot 14 \cancel{\text{ hours}}$

$200 \text{ dollars} \stackrel{?}{=} 60 \text{ dollars} + 140 \text{ dollars}$

$200 \text{ dollars} = 200 \text{ dollars}$ ✓

Student Help

▶ MORE EXAMPLES
More examples are available at www.mcdougallittell.com

4.1 Solving Two-Step Equations 171

Math Reasoning

Example 2, starting with x, then dividing by 4, then subtracting 12, results in 1. Therefore starting with 1, then adding 12, then multiplying by 4, results in x. That is, $(1 + 12) \cdot 4 = x$, so $x = 52$.

Extra Example 1

Solve $6x - 11 = 13$. 4

Extra Example 2

Solve $\frac{n}{7} + 4 = -3$. −49

Extra Example 3

You and four friends have joined a recreational basketball league. The team membership fee is \$50 plus a \$5 fee per game to pay the referee. If the team's total cost for the league will be \$125, how many games are you scheduled to play? 15 games

Extra Example 4

Use unit analysis to check the reasonableness of the solution of Extra Example 3. Place the values with their units in the verbal model.

125 dollars = 50 dollars + $\frac{5 \text{ dollars}}{\cancel{\text{game}}}$ · 15 ~~games~~

Teaching Tip

Remind students that addition and subtraction are inverse operations and that multiplication and division are inverse operations.

Concept Check

How are inverse operations used when solving a two-step equation? Which inverse operations must be used first? The operations that are the inverses of the ones found in the original equation form the two steps of the solution. An addition or subtraction step is done before a multiplication or division step.

171

Apply

- Assignment Guide
- Extra practice references
- Homework Check exercises

3 Apply

Assignment Guide

TRANSITIONAL
Day 1: SRH p. 689 Exs. 1–6; pp. 206–207 Exs. 7–10, 13–15, 19–21, 30–31

AVERAGE
Day 1: pp. 206–207 Exs. 9–12, 18–21, 24–27, 30–31

ADVANCED
Day 1: pp. 206–207 Exs. 11–12, 18–23, 28, 29*, 30–31; EC: TE p. 166D*

BLOCK SCHEDULE
pp. 206–207 Exs. 9–12, 18–21, 24–27, 30–31 (with 4.7)

Extra Practice

- Student Edition, pp. 696–697
- Chapter 4 Resource Book, p. 69

Homework Check

To quickly check student understanding of key concepts, go over the following exercises:

Transitional: 8, 10, 14, 15, 20, 21
Average: 10, 12, 18, 20, 21, 24
Advanced: 12, 18, 20, 21, 28

Practice and Problem Solving

Student Help
▶ **MORE PRACTICE** Extra practice to help you master skills is on page 697.

Find the mean, median, and mode of the data.

7. 85, 86, 90, 90, 91, 92 **mean = 89; median = 90; mode = 90**

8. 36, 67, 52, 82, 96, 81 **mean = 69; median = 74; no mode**

9. 76, 41, 77, 80, 81 **mean = 71; median = 77; no mode**

10. 105, 109, 100, 99, 156 **mean = 113.8; median = 105; no mode**

11. 9.5, 10.7, 7.8, 8.5, 10.1, 7.0, 6.2, 8.6 **mean ≈ 8.6; median ≈ 8.6; no mode**

12. 52.8, 53.6, 53.9, 54, 54.8, 55.1, 54.5 **mean = 54.1; median = 54; no mode**

21. *Sample answer:* M... median; most empl... earn $30,000.

Link to Science

pH LEVELS Freshwater fish, such as the angelfish shown, can survive in a wide range of pH levels, from 6.0 to 9.0. Saltwater fish are better in a less acidic environment with a pH level of 8.2.

More about aquariums at www.mcdougallittell.com

pH LEVELS In Exercises 22 and 23, use the following information. The pH level of pure water is 7. Lower levels indicate the water is *acidic*. The table shows the pH levels measured in an aquarium over ten days.

Day number	1	2	3	4	5	6	7	8	9	10
pH level each day	7.1	6.9	6.7	6.5	6.3	6.9	6.8	6.5	6.3	6.1

22. Find the mean pH level over these ten days. **6.61**

23. Given that the water in the aquarium tends to become *more acidic*, on which day do you think a chemical was added to change the pH level? Explain your choice. **Day 6; the pH level jumped to 6.9 from 6.3.**

In Exercises 24–27, use the table below. The table shows the number of minutes three people spent walking dogs on eight different days.

Person	Minutes spent walking the dog	Mean	Median	Mode
A	10, 10, 12, 12, 12, 13, 13, 14	?	?	?
B	10, 11, 12, 12, 12, 13, 13, 15	?	?	?
C	10, 11, 11, 12, 14, 15, 35, 40	?	?	?

24. Find the mean, median, and mode for each person.

24.

Person	Mean	Median	Mode
A	12	12	12
B	12.3	12	12
C	18.5	13	11

25. Compare the mean, median, and mode for Person A. **All three measures are the same.**

26. Compare the mean, median, and mode for Person B. **The mean is slightly higher than the median or the mode.**

27. Compare the mean, median, and mode for Person C. Identify the outlier(s) and explain how the outliers affect the mean.

27. The mean is much higher than the median or the mode. Outliers: 35, 40; since they are high compared to the rest of the data, they raise the mean.

28. RAINFALL A city's annual rainfall over the past four years has been 29.86, 28.32, 25.21, and 27.63 inches. What is the amount of rainfall needed this year so that the average over the five years is 28 inches? **28.98**

29. CHALLENGE Make up two lists of five different numbers that have these measures of central tendency: mean = 20, median = 20, mode = 20. *Sample answer:* **19, 20, 20, 20, 21; 15, 20, 20, 20, 25**

Multiple-Choice Practice

In Exercises 30 and 31, use the data 14, 10, 16, 11, 20, 19, 18, 16, 10, and 16.

30. What is the mean of the data? **C**

Ⓐ 10 Ⓑ 14 Ⓒ 15 Ⓓ 19.5

31. The median and mode are the same number. What number are they? **G**

Ⓕ 10 Ⓖ 16 Ⓗ 18 Ⓙ 19.5

Assess

- Mini-Quiz for each lesson
- Assessment resources

4 Assess

Assessment Resources

- Assessment Book (Formal Assessment and Alternative Assessment)
- Test and Practice Generator

Mini-Quiz

1. Find the mean, median, and mode of the data.
   a. 34, 29, 31, 56, 20, 19, 20 **mean: about 29.9; median: 29; mode: 20**
   b. 5, 19, 31, 20, 47, 89, 6, 101 **mean: 39.75; median: 25.5; mode: none**
2. The bar graph below shows the number of times a family ate pizza each month during one year. Find the mean, median, and mode of the data.

Pizza Eating

Number of months (0–5) vs. Number of times per month (0–5)

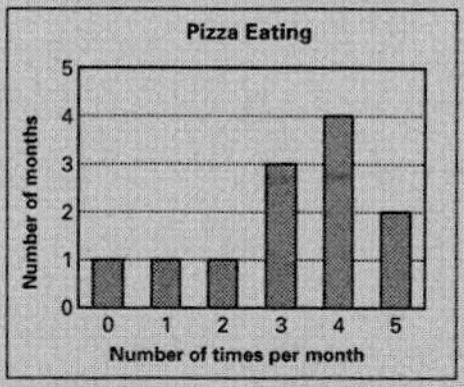

mean: about 3.2; median: 3.5; mode: 4

PACING THE COURSE

The Pacing Chart below shows the number of days allotted for each chapter. The Regular Schedule requires 160 days. The Block Schedule requires 80 days. These time frames include days for review and assessment: 2 days per chapter for the Regular Schedule and 1 day per chapter for the Block Schedule. Semester and trimester divisions are indicated by red and blue, respectively.

	Semester 1						Semester 2					
Chapter	1	2	3	4	5	6	7	8	9	10	11	12
Regular Schedule	10	14	14	14	14	14	12	12	16	16	14	10
Block Schedule	5	7	7	7	7	7	6	6	8	8	7	5
	Trimester 1				Trimester 2				Trimester 3			

Assignments are provided with each lesson for a transitional course, an average course, an advanced course, and a block-schedule course. Each of the four courses covers all twelve chapters.

TRANSITIONAL COURSE

The transitional course is intended for students who enter with below-average mathematical and problem-solving skills. Assignments include:

- spiral review of pre-course and on-level topics through Skills Review Handbook and Extra Practice references
- substantial work with the skills and concepts presented in the lesson
- straightforward applications of these skills and concepts
- test preparation and mixed review exercises

AVERAGE COURSE

The average course is intended for students who enter with typical mathematical and problem-solving skills. Assignments include:

- substantial work with the skills and concepts presented in the lesson
- applications of these skills and concepts
- test preparation and mixed review exercises

ADVANCED COURSE

The advanced course is intended for students who enter with above-average mathematical and problem-solving skills. Assignments include:

- substantial work with the skills and concepts presented in the lesson
- more complex applications and challenge exercises
- test preparation and mixed review exercises

BLOCK-SCHEDULE COURSE

The block-schedule course is intended for schools that use a block schedule. The exercises assigned are comparable to the exercises for the average course.

The Pacing and Assignment Guide for each chapter is located on the interleaved pages preceding the chapter. Part of the Pacing Chart for Chapter 4 is shown here.

The ***Regular-Schedule Chart*** provides pacing for the transitional, average, and advanced courses.

REGULAR SCHEDULE

Lesson	Les. Day	Transitional	Average	Advanced
4.7	Day 1	SRH pp. 672–673 Exs. 22–27, p. 675 Exs. 17–23, p. 676 Exs. 5–8, 13–17; pp. 201–202 Exs. 8, 10–13, 18–19, 22–24, 34–35	pp. 201–202 Exs. 8–13, 16–19, 26–28, 34–35	pp. 201–202 Exs. 12–21, 29–32, 33*, 34–35
4.8	Day 1	SRH p. 689 Exs. 1–6; pp. 206–207 Exs. 7–10, 13–15, 19–21, 30–31	pp. 206–207 Exs. 9–12, 18–21, 24–27, 30–31	pp. 206–207 Exs. 11–12, 18–23, 28, 29*, 30–31; EC: TE p. 166D*
Review	Day 1	pp. 208–211 Exs. 1–39	pp. 208–211 Exs. 1–39	pp. 208–211 Exs. 1–39
Assess	Day 1	Chapter 4 Test	Chapter 4 Test	Chapter 4 Test

YEARLY PACING Chapter 4 Total – 14 days Chapters 1–4 Total – 52 days Remaining

* Challenge Exercises EP = Extra Practice SRH = Skills Review Handbook EC = Extra Challenge

The ***Block-Schedule Chart*** provides pacing for the block-schedule course.

BLOCK SCHEDULE

Day 1	Day 2	Day 3	Day 4	Day 5
4.3 pp. 181–182: Exs. 12–22, 29–31, 35–39, 42–44	**4.4** pp. 185–187: Exs. 11–19, 24–25, 28–29, 32–39, 41–43, 46–52, 56–59, 63–65, 69	**4.5** pp. 191–192: Exs. 7–14, 17–21, 27–28, 30–31 **4.6** pp. 195–197: Exs. 9–15, 20–25, 29–36, 44	**4.7** pp. 201–202: Exs. 8–13, 16–19, 26–28, 34–35 **4.8** pp. 206–207: Exs. 9–12, 18–21, 24–27, 30–31	**Review** pp. 208–211: Exs. 1–39 **Assess** Chapter 4 Test

YEARLY PACING Chapter 4 Total – 7 days Chapters 1–4 Total – 26 days Remaining

An ***Assignment Guide*** for each lesson is provided at the beginning of the exercise set. Assignments are provided for transitional, average, advanced, and block-schedule courses.

Assignment Guide

TRANSITIONAL

Day 1: SRH p. 689 Exs. 1–6; pp. 206–207 Exs. 7–10, 13–15, 19–21, 30–31

AVERAGE

Day 1: pp. 206–207 Exs. 9–12, 18–21, 24–27, 30–31

ADVANCED

Day 1: pp. 206–207 Exs. 11–12, 18–23, 28, 29*, 30–31, EC: TE p. 166D

BLOCK SCHEDULE

pp. 206–207 Exs. 9–12, 18–21, 24–27, 30–31 (with 4.7)

Providing Universal Access

By Catherine Barkett

With careful planning, teachers can help all students reach a level of mathematical competence needed to continue their education in mathematics.

Introduction

In most classrooms, students present a variety of achievement levels, skills, and needs. The goal for all students is the same: We want them to develop sufficient computational, procedural, and problem solving skills to provide a solid foundation for further study in mathematics. In this article we suggest research-based strategies teachers can use to modify curriculum and instruction for special needs students. The basic instructional plan in *Concepts and Skills, Course 2* is designed for students who are achieving at near grade level; but just prior to each chapter we include specific suggestions for students who are achieving above and below grade level, and for students who are not fluent in English (see also the article titled "Adapting Curriculum and Instruction for English Learners").

Teachers may find it helpful to view students as members of four basic groups. (English learners can be found in all four groups.) Teachers do not need to place students in these groups; the categories are suggested so teachers can plan ahead to meet different needs of students. Note on the following chart the use of the term *strategic learners* to emphasize the kind of instruction needed by students achieving below grade level. This term may include some special education pupils but also includes students whose low achievement is the result of inadequate prior schooling or attendance, high mobility rates, or a host of other reasons. The term *strategic learner* was selected because it is a positive term that emphasizes what needs to happen in order for these students to be successful and implies what we believe: students achieving below grade level *can* be successful in mathematics given carefully designed instruction.

Setting the Right Tone

There are three key strategies recommended for teachers as they adapt any program to students' needs:

- Use frequent assessment as a way to determine what each student does or does not know, and use that assessment as the basis for planning.

Four Basic Student Groups

Advanced Group	Grade Level Group	Strategic Group	Intensive Needs Group
Advanced students have already completed some of the grade-level material. They make rapid progress and become bored with repetition. They may or may not have been formally identified as gifted or talented in the area of mathematics. **Suggested Plan** 1. Assess what these students already know. 2. Allow these students to "test out" of chapters or assignments. 3. Substitute challenging assignments for easier ones. 4. Modify instruction so that it is more complex or more in-depth.	Students achieving at grade level may have minor, occasional difficulties but they can be assisted to maintain their progress with extra practice and individual or group assistance on an ad hoc basis. **Suggested Plan** 1. Assess what these students already know. 2. Progress through *Concepts and Skills* at the recommended pace and sequence. 3. On an ad hoc basis, review or provide additional practice as needed.	Strategic learners are not achieving at expected grade level but can, with a carefully designed program that provides targeted assistance. Systematic differentiation such as preteaching, reteaching, and additional instructional time should be planned for these students, as suggested in each chapter. **Suggested Plan** 1. Assess what these students already know. 2. Provide additional scaffolding and the instructional variations suggested in this book. 3. Focus on the key concepts and present material systematically. 4. Vary the kinds of instruction so that students have several opportunities to understand. 5. Provide additional practice homework.	Intensive needs students are those whose performance is two or more standard deviations below the mean on standardized measures. These students will probably already be eligible for special education services. This is a very small percentage of the general population. **Suggested Plan** 1. Assess what these students already know. 2. Determine if these students have an IEP. 3. Refer students for special education testing or child study team discussion; enlist the help of specialists. 4. Carefully consider each student's most appropriate placement in mathematics. 5. Use the specific suggestions for strategic learners.

(Adapted from the Mathematics Framework for California Public Schools, K–12, California department of Education, 1999.)

- Plan modifications of curriculum and instruction ahead of time so that you are ready to differentiate as the need arises.
- Use a variety of grouping strategies to facilitate learning. A combination of whole class instruction and temporary groupings of students, with groups organized around students' needs, will facilitate management of the variety of achievement levels and learning needs in the classroom.

Assessment, planning, and flexible grouping are essential to ensuring that your students have the optimal chance for success. In addition to these three key strategies, general guidelines for establishing a classroom designed to meet students' needs are:

1. Establish an atmosphere where students feel comfortable asking questions and are rewarded for asking about things they don't understand.
2. Maintain the same goals for all students. Allow additional time and practice for students who need it, and provide challenging alternatives for those who are ready to move more quickly.
3. Clearly identify the skill, concept, or standards you are working on and measure progress towards those ends.
4. Have students show their work. It is much easier for teachers to understand where a student gets confused if they have evidence of the student's thought process.
5. Try small modifications in curriculum and instruction before more drastic ones.
6. Don't persist with a strategy that is not working. Try something else.
7. Encourage effort and persistence, and celebrate successes with your students.

Varying Curriculum and Instruction

1. **Time** Most students whose achievement is below grade level will need more time. Students who are not fluent in English will need more time. The contents of this book might be offered over a two-year period, or two periods a day. Perhaps the day can be extended through study hall, regular homework assignments, tutoring, or Saturday, summer, or "off track" catch-up sessions. Advanced students might "test out" of portions of the book and complete the material in half a year, or they may compact two courses into one.
2. **Presentation** Instructing in a variety of ways and taking a single concept and explaining it verbally and visually with concrete and abstract examples provide students multiple opportunities for understanding. Factoring, for example, is a key concept for success in algebra. It can be introduced and practiced in a variety of ways: with tree diagrams, with repeated division by hand and on a calculator, and oral problems or games that require students to factor mentally. If students don't understand factoring when presented one way, they can be retaught using a different approach.
3. **Task parameters** Multi-step problems can be especially difficult for students. These types of problems are just combinations of simpler problems and can be broken down into those simpler steps, with additional help and practice at each step. Confusing elements can be minimized and extraneous material can be eliminated. For advanced students, simpler problems can be eliminated and more challenging ones (as suggested in each chapter) may be substituted.
4. **Methods of assessment** Students learning English may be able to demonstrate on paper what they cannot yet verbalize. Students with physical challenges may be unable to draw a graph but may be able to select the right graph from a series of options or verbally describe the graph so that someone else can draw it. Allow students to demonstrate their knowledge in a variety of ways while helping all students to master the skills and knowledge necessary to exhibit their understanding in standard ways.

Concepts and Skills, Course 2 is organized so that much of the differentiation for special needs students is built into the design of the program. Note that simpler concepts are introduced before more complex ones. Ample practice is provided. Challenge exercises are included throughout the pupil text. Developing Concepts provide students with models for conceptual understanding of the mathematical reasoning behind each key concept. Mathematical reasoning is stressed throughout each chapter. Vocabulary words, examples, and Guided Practice exercises are standard features of each chapter. Each chapter includes Mixed Review exercises so that students recall and use skills and understandings from previous chapters. These features were designed to help you meet the needs of the students in your class.

For Students who have Trouble Paying Attention

Some students in your classroom may be formally identified as having Attention Deficit Hyperactivity Disorder (ADHD) or Attention Deficit Disorder (ADD). Others may exhibit the same learning challenges but may not be formally identified. Whether formally identified or not, students who have trouble paying attention generally share the following characteristics:

- Trouble paying attention is not just occasional. It occurs most or all of the time, across content areas, and is inappropriate for the age of the child.
- Forgetfulness, memory problems, losing things, disorganization
- Restlessness, fidgeting
- Socially inappropriate behavior such as excessive talking, interrupting others, and difficulty waiting their turn

These students may be very bright and capable in mathematics but have a hard time staying focused for long periods of time. They need to be taught strategies for organizing their work and keeping track of where they are. In general, students with attention problems need to be helped to develop coping strategies. The teacher should approach the student in a problem solving mode: "Let's find ways to help you concentrate and organize your work," rather than using one of the following strategies in a punitive way.

1. **Present the work in smaller chunks over smaller time periods** and then gradually increase expectations. If students have trouble completing long tests, for example, break the material into smaller quizzes and increase the length of the quizzes as the year progresses.
2. **Use cumulative review and practice.** Have students periodically review what they learned in previous chapters and provide additional practice if they have forgotten.
3. **Make it more obvious what the student should focus on.** For example, use the test generator to put only four problems on each page; use a large font; or use an index card or piece of cardboard with a hole cut out of the middle to place on the page so that the student can focus on one problem at a time. A pencil, finger, highlighter, or sticky paper can also be used by the student to keep track of which problem he or she is working on.
4. **Have students race against the clock.** For some students, racing against the clock to see how many problems can be completed accurately within a five-minute time period is more motivating than doing the same number of problems at their leisure. The time period can be extended gradually.
5. **Help students develop simple strategies for bringing work to and from class.** A two-pocket folder, where homework goes home in the left pocket and comes back in the right, is a simple way to keep track of assignments.
6. **Allow movement and schedule breaks.**
7. **Minimize distractions by seating students that are easily distracted near the teacher** and away from hallway noise. Tables with several students at a table are more distracting than rows of desks. When students are to work quietly, offer headphones to block out noise. Headphones can be set to play quiet music, "white noise," or can be used just as earplugs to help block out noise.
8. **Graphic organizers** such as Venn diagrams, tree diagrams, lists, outlines, tables, and charts can all provide structures for organizing and remembering information. Mental images, choral responses, or even hand signals can help students remember. Highlighters can be used to make sure that decimal points are lined up. Graph paper is excellent for keeping homework problems neat, even when a graph is not required.
9. **Keep instructions simple and clear, especially at the beginning of the year.** Establish routines (*e.g.*, the week's homework is always due on Thursday; assignments are written in a specific place on the board; the last ten minutes of class is used to make sure everyone understands what homework is expected and how to do it). Students who know the routine find it easier to work independently.

For Students who have Trouble Understanding the Concepts

Success in mathematics, as in music, sports, or other areas, comes for most students only with hard work and persistent effort. Concepts may seem difficult at first, but with repeated teaching and practice virtually all students can master the mathematics they need to graduate from high school, access a variety of jobs, and lay the foundation for further study in mathematics or a related field.

Several strategies can help students make steady progress in mathematics. These include:

1. Focus on key mathematical concepts.
2. Review key concepts and skills from earlier lessons, chapters, or years.
3. Preteach key concepts and vocabulary.
4. Anticipate problem areas.
5. Provide scaffolding (guided practice) for students who need extra help.
6. Think out loud to show hidden steps.
7. Provide a sample problem to which students can return when they get stuck.
8. Break problems into simpler components.
9. Explicitly teach students a variety of problem solving strategies and help them select one that fits the situation.
10. Present concepts in a variety of ways: visually, verbally, concretely, abstractly, etc.
11. Encourage students to draw a picture or use a visual aid such as a number line, graph, or diagram.
12. Provide sufficient practice.

Finally, good teachers are perpetual students themselves. They are always looking for ways to deepen their understanding of mathematics and for good ways to explain and teach mathematics to others.

For Advanced Students

Occasionally students can demonstrate mastery of all the mathematics expected to be learned in a given grade level. Repeating previously learned material for a year is deadly to these students. It can make them dislike mathematics. For these students, moving them up a grade level for math is a simple and cost-effective solution.

Most advanced students, however, are advanced in some areas but not in others. They tend to learn quickly and need more instructional material, as well as more difficult material. The pupil edition, teacher's edition, Web site, and ancillaries to this program provide challenging exercises that can be used when students have demonstrated competence in a particular area. These challenge exercises should be substituted for the easier exercises in a homework assignment or lesson. When they have the time and interest, all students should be encouraged to work the challenge exercises.

General strategies for differentiating the curriculum for advanced learners include:

1. **Vary the pacing.** Allow advanced students some flexibility in how they progress through the course. Students who can demonstrate mastery of the objectives for a given lesson or chapter can be working on challenge exercises. Advanced students may become fascinated with a particular aspect of mathematics and want to spend *more* time on it.
2. **Differentiate in terms of depth.** Encourage advanced students to delve more in depth into mathematics. Looking at the details and the patterns; studying the language of the discipline; and looking at trends, themes, properties, theorems, proofs, and unanswered questions can enrich the curriculum for advanced students.
3. **Differentiate in terms of complexity.** Advanced students may be ready to connect ideas across disciplines in ways characteristic of older students or adults. Encourage them to investigate relationships between mathematics and art, history, science, and music, and to look at the development of mathematics over time.

Using Grouping to Benefit All Students

Grouping advanced learners together for investigations of challenge problems can provide you with time to work more closely with a group of students who need help in a particular area. Alternatively, while students who need more help are working on additional reinforcement activities or practice, you can work with a group of advanced students on a challenge project. Groups can be organized and revised daily, weekly, or by lesson according to how proficient students are with the concepts and skills targeted for that day, week, or lesson. At times you may have only one student who is ready for a challenge problem; at other times the whole class may be ready. Flexible grouping is the key to ensuring that students do not become "tracked." Asking advanced students to report to the whole class on their progress on challenge problems can provide the opportunity for the whole class to engage in more abstract and theoretical thinking.

Adapting Curriculum and Instruction for English Learners

By Olga Bautista and Catherine Barkett

Introduction

English learners come to the classroom with all the variety of English speakers in regard to mathematics achievement. They may be at, behind, or ahead of grade expectations in mathematics. They may be gifted or eligible for special education services. They may have been born in the United States, or they may have arrived in this country very recently. They may speak one or more languages, and they may be literate in one or more languages other than English. They have in common one characteristic: They are all learning English.

With careful planning, teachers can maximize success for English learners in the mathematics classroom. Assessing each student's competencies in mathematics and English will form a basis for program planning.

Getting to know your students

Before school starts, check the cumulative folder on each student in your class to determine which ones are learning English. See if there is recent testing. Two types of testing are most useful: mathematics achievement and reading achievement levels. Use the following chart as a guide to understanding student assessment data:

English Learners

Low Reading Achievement — Low Mathematics Achievement

Who is this student?

Student may be new to the class, school, or country.

Student may have had inadequate schooling.

Student may have moved a lot.

Student may be unmotivated or have test anxiety.

Low reading achievement may be depressing mathematics scores.

Student may have gaps and holes in knowledge.

Student may need special education assistance.

What to do?

Examine cumulative folder for other testing, notes, etc.

Delay any testing for a week or two. Help student feel comfortable in the class during that period of time.

Administer mathematics achievement test and reading test, preferably in an individual setting.

Plan to assess this student at weekly intervals and closely monitor classroom work to determine if progress is being made.

Look at the English Learners suggestions in each chapter.

Low Reading Achievement — High Mathematics Achievement

Who is this student?

Student has had good prior mathematics instruction.

Mathematics is an area where this student can excel.

Math achievement level may actually be higher than scores indicate. (Inability to read affects mathematics achievement as well.)

Word problems will be especially difficult.

What to do?

Mathematics instruction should proceed at normal or near normal pace.

Student should be involved in a systematic English language development program and intensive reading program outside of mathematics class.

Spend part of each class period on mathematics vocabulary study.

Provide a bilingual dictionary and grade-level mathematics text in the home language for home use.

Look at the English Learners suggestions in each chapter for those that are most useful.

High Reading Achievement — Low Mathematics Achievement

Who is this student?

Student may have been designated as an English learner because oral fluency is not at grade level.

Student may be able to use reading ability to improve math scores.

Student may not test well in mathematics.

Most students can make rapid progress in mathematics; a few may have learning difficulties that require the help of a specialist.

What to do?

Assess mathematics achievement in a variety of ways.

Concentrate on developing oral fluency.

Focus on vocabulary specific to mathematics.

High Reading Achievement — High Mathematics Achievement

Who is this student?

May be a student who is ready for re-designation as a fluent English speaker.

May need extra study in academic vocabulary, *i.e.*, the specialized vocabulary of mathematics.

Given systematic instruction, this student should be able to achieve at or above grade level.

What to do?

Scan all of the suggestions for English learners in each chapter and progress through the ones the student needs as quickly as possible.

Monitor carefully to make sure this student continues to progress at a reasonable pace.

Suggestions for Mathematics Teachers of English Learners

1. Allocate additional time for mathematics. Many students will be translating from English to their primary language and back again. The meaning of many words will not be immediately clear. When you ask questions, allow extra time for students to respond. Reading mathematics textbooks and understanding what is asked for in a word problem will be slower.
2. Use students' background knowledge. Some English learners will have developed substantial background in mathematics; others will have very little. Find out what students know and then build on that knowledge.
3. Reduce the amount and sophistication of the English language used. This may be done by reordering the lessons in each chapter to begin with key vocabulary, followed by problems with a minimum of written English, followed by at least one word problem each day. Monitor and simplify the speech you use. Speak more slowly, avoid idioms and slang, be precise and concise, and use short sentences and simple vocabulary. Using hand gestures and pictures as well as words aids communication.
4. Introduce one concept per day. *Concepts and Skills* is organized in this manner. Keeping the focus of each day simple will aid students in understanding the point of the lesson. Focus on key concepts, and use mathematics instructional time well.
5. Use a variety of different methods for getting a point across. Presenting concepts verbally and visually, with concrete examples and in abstract mathematical symbols, and using pictures, graphs, diagrams, and charts will enhance the chance that students will understand at least one of the presentations. As you introduce a new word, rule, or theorem, write it down.
6. Provide opportunities for English learners to interact with their English-speaking peers. Students who are learning a language need to hear native speakers using the language, and they need opportunities to use their new mathematics vocabulary in their speech and in their writing.
7. Provide opportunities for English learners to discuss their understandings with each other, confirm the homework assignments, or ask questions of each other in whatever language they may have in common.
8. Allow English learners to demonstrate what they know in a variety of ways. When students first learn a language, they are usually shy about speaking. They generally understand spoken language before they can reproduce it. Students who have recently arrived from another country with good prior schooling may be able to read in English but not speak it. Allow students to point, nod, gesture, draw a picture, or work math problems without words as they learn English.
9. Extend mathematics instructional time through homework, an extra class period, summer school, or tutoring. Many of the language-related suggestions for English learners in this series can be carried out by the language arts teacher.
10. Keep on hand picture dictionaries, foreign language dictionaries, and drawing materials.

Specific Suggestions

Prior to each chapter you will find suggestions to help you modify curriculum and instruction so that the content is accessible to English learners. Many of the suggestions are well suited for discussion in a language arts class, English as a second language class, or in a tutorial. In these sections we will provide you suggestions and activities designed to (1) teach the vocabulary commonly used in mathematics;
(2) explain mathematical concepts in a variety of ways; and (3) dissect the structure of word problems. Much of the vocabulary study in this book may be review for your students, and in that case, you should feel free to work as quickly as possible through the activities. For those students who need more systematic study, progressing through the activities as indicated will ensure that students have refreshed their understanding of basic terms prior to statewide testing that generally occurs toward the end of each school year. We recommend that if you have English learners in your classroom, you skim all the chapter suggestions for English learners so that you may use them as you need them.

7.

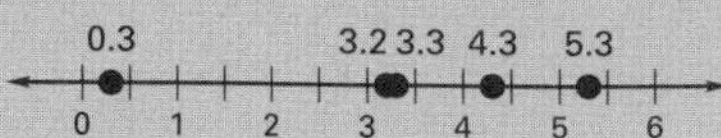

8.

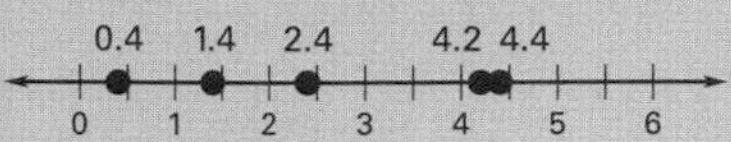

9.

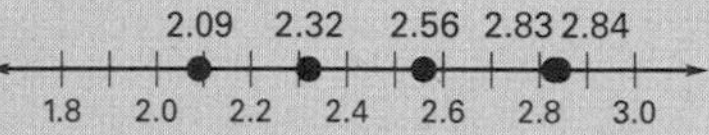

Getting Ready

Pre-Course Test

Number Sense

NUMBER SENSE

PLACE VALUE AND ROUNDING (Skills Review pp. 672–673)

Write the number in standard decimal form.

1. $6 \times 1000 + 3 \times 100 + 5 \times 1$ **6305**

2. Six hundred, twenty four, and thirty-five hundredths **624.35**

Round each decimal to the place value of the underlined digit.

3. 9.5<u>6</u>6 **9.57**

4. 100,234,<u>2</u>22 **100,234,200**

5. 9.<u>7</u>77 **9.8**

6. 56.00<u>9</u>8 **56.010**

USING A NUMBER LINE (Skills Review p. 674)

Graph the numbers on the same number line. Then order the numbers from least to greatest. **7–9. See margin for art.**

7. 3.2, 5.3, 3.3, 0.3, 4.3 **0.3, 3.2, 3.3, 4.3, 5.3**

8. 0.4, 4.4, 4.2, 1.4, 2.4 **0.4, 1.4, 2.4, 4.2, 4.4**

9. 2.32, 2.84, 2.56, 2.83, 2.09 **2.09, 2.32, 2.56, 2.83, 2.84**

ADDING, SUBTRACTING, MULTIPLYING, DIVIDING DECIMALS (Skills Review pp. 675–676)

Perform the indicated operation.

10. $4.9 + 5.5$ **10.4**

11. $102.8 - 22.4$ **80.4**

12. $0.88 + 0.06$ **0.94**

13. $47.77 - 23.08$ **24.69**

14. 12.5×0.017 **0.2125**

15. 7.5×3.03 **22.725**

16. $8.4 \div 0.2$ **42**

17. $0.002 \div 0.01$ **0.2**

FRACTIONS AND PERCENTS (Skills Review p. 677)

Tell what fraction the model represents. Then write the fraction as a percent.

18. $\frac{25}{100}$; 25%

19. 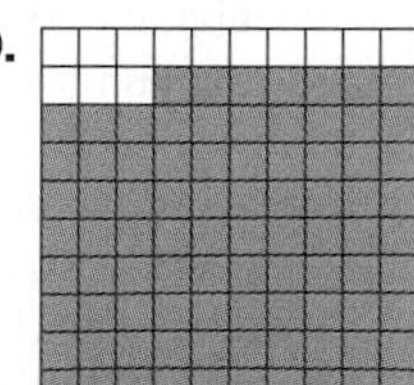 $\frac{87}{100}$; 87%

20. 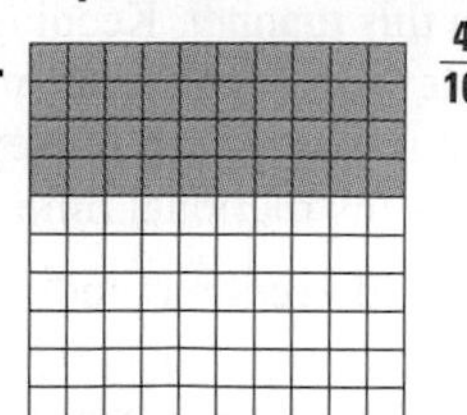 $\frac{40}{100}$; 40%

MIXED NUMBERS AND IMPROPER FRACTIONS (Skills Review p. 678)

Write the improper fractions as mixed numbers. Write the mixed numbers as improper fractions.

21. $\frac{12}{7}$ $1\frac{5}{7}$

22. $\frac{11}{9}$ $1\frac{2}{9}$

23. $\frac{23}{10}$ $2\frac{3}{10}$

24. $8\frac{4}{5}$ $\frac{44}{5}$

25. $19\frac{2}{3}$ $\frac{59}{3}$

26. $1\frac{11}{12}$ $\frac{23}{12}$

ESTIMATING SUMS, DIFFERENCES, PRODUCTS, QUOTIENTS (Skills Review pp. 679–680)

Estimate the sum, difference, product, or quotient.

27. $3825.67 + 221.9$ ***Sample answer:* 4050**

28. $746 - 129$ ***Sample answer:* 620**

29. 535.8×260.3 ***Sample answer:* 150,000**

30. $1702 \div 846$ ***Sample answer:* 2**

Measurement and Geometry — MEASUREMENT AND GEOMETRY

CONVERTING UNITS OF MEASUREMENT (Skills Review p. 681)

31. Write the conversion fraction for converting inches to feet. $\frac{\textbf{1 feet}}{\textbf{12 inches}}$

32. Use the conversion fraction from Exercise 31 to find the number of feet in 122 inches. **$10\frac{1}{6}$ feet**

PERIMETER, AREA, AND VOLUME (Skills Review pp. 682–684)

33. Find the perimeter and area of a square with sides of length 9.2 centimeters. **36.8 cm; 84.64 cm^2**

34. Find the volume of a cube with edges of length 4.4 meters. **85.184 m^3**

Statistics, Data Analysis, & Probability — STATISTICS, DATA ANALYSIS, & PROBABILITY

READING AND DRAWING BAR GRAPHS, LINE GRAPHS, CIRCLE GRAPHS, AND LINE PLOTS (Skills Review pp. 686–689)

In Exercises 35–37, use the bar graph of music preferences shown.

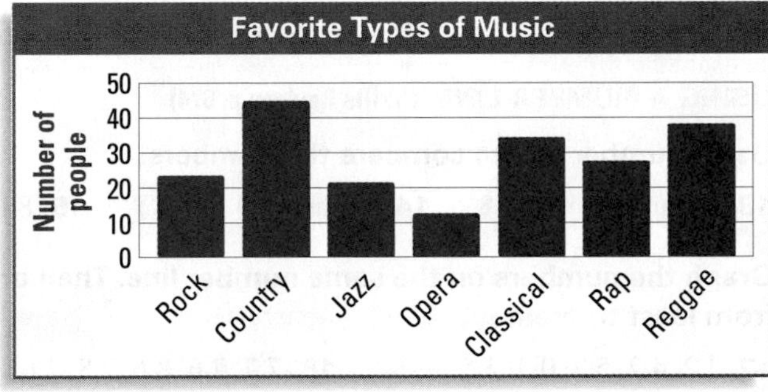

35. About how many people prefer to listen to classical music? **≈ 33 people**

36. About how many more people prefer rock music than prefer opera? **≈ 10 people**

37. Which type of music is about twice as popular as jazz? **country**

In Exercises 38 and 39, use the table of running times shown.

38. Every day for 7 days, Danny ran down the block and timed how long it took. Draw a line graph for the data he collected. **See margin.**

Day	1	2	3	4	5	6	7
Time (in seconds)	158	149	148	145	145	144	143

39. Predict how fast you think Danny would run on Day 8. Explain your prediction. ***Sample answer:* 143 seconds; Danny's running times are starting to level off.**

40. At Ronnie's Used Car Lot, there are 25 red cars, 44 blue cars, 19 white cars, and 12 black cars. Draw a circle graph to represent the data. **See margin.**

In Exercises 41 and 42, use the following information. The test scores in Mr. Huff's mathematics class were:

100, 89, 88, 84, 90, 97, 100, 89, 90, 90, 73, 91, 83,
95, 95, 96, 95, 95, 71, 90, 89, 72, 90

41. Use a line plot to display the data. **See margin.**

42. Describe how the data are distributed. ***Sample answer:* The range of data is 29 and most students scored 89, 90, or 95.**

38.

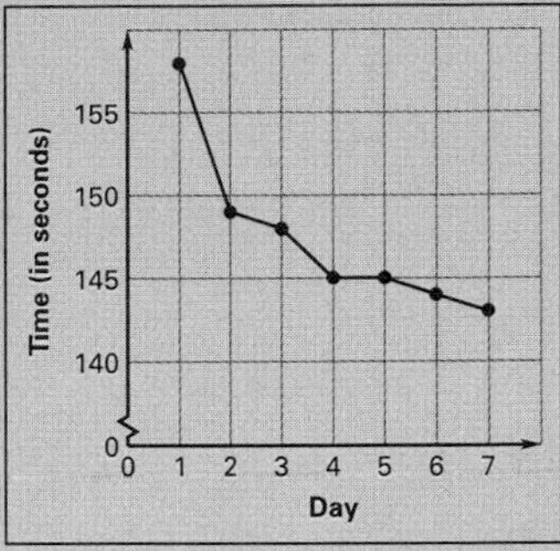

40.

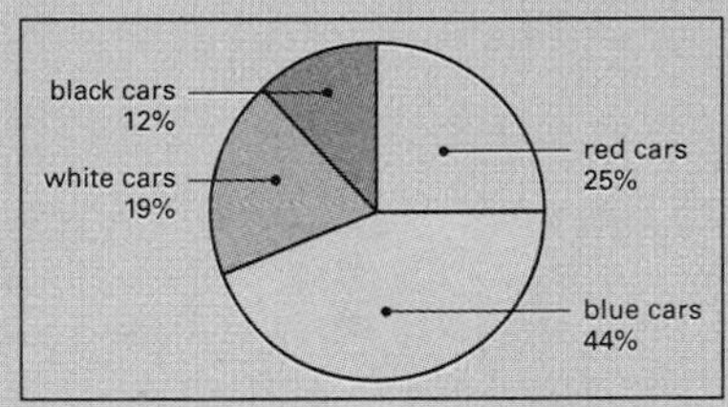

41.

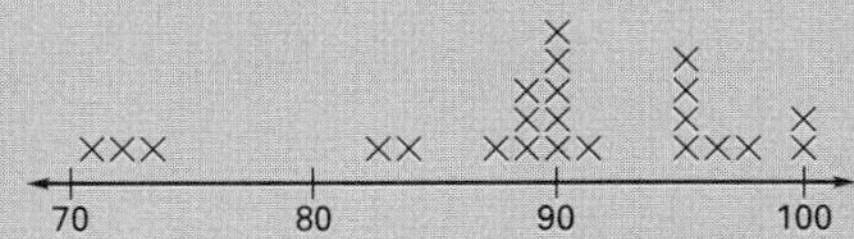

17. 0.3, 2.2, 4.2, 4.5, 5.2

18. 2.6, 7.6, 7.7, 7.8, 8.6

19. 0.3, 0.9, 3.3, 4.3, 5.4

Pre-Course Practice

Number Sense

Place Value and Rounding (Skills Review pp. 672–673)

Write the number in expanded form.

1. 2365 **1. 2 × 1000 + 3 × 100 + 6 × 10 + 5 × 1**
2. 7,000,861 **2. 7 × 1,000,000 + 8 × 100 + 6 × 10 + 1 × 1**
3. 491.3 **3. 4 × 100 + 9 × 10 + 1 × 1 + 3 × 0.1**
4. 11,854 **4. 1 × 10,000 + 1 × 1000 + 8 × 100 + 5 × 10 + 4 × 1**

Write the number in standard decimal form.

5. 5 × 10,000 + 5 × 1000 + 9 × 10 + 8 × 1 **55,098**
6. Two million, seven hundred thousand, seventeen **2,700,017**
7. Five hundred eight and seventeen hundredths **508.17**
8. Seven and sixty-four thousandths **7.064**

Identify the place value of the underlined digit. Then round the decimal to that place.

9. 0.76<u>9</u>49 **thousandths; 0.769**
10. 0.6<u>3</u>14 **hundredths; 0.63**
11. 8.<u>7</u>247 **tenths; 8.7**
12. 41<u>5</u>.782 **ones; 416**

Using a Number Line (Skills Review p. 674)

Use a number line to compare the numbers.

13. 0.8 and 2.8 **0.8 < 2.8**
14. 2.3 and 0.9 **2.3 > 0.9**
15. 8.08 and 8.09 **8.08 < 8.09**
16. 0.18 and 0.17 **0.18 > 0.17**

Graph the numbers on the same number line. Then order the numbers from least to greatest. **17–19. See margin.**

17. 2.2, 4.2, 5.2, 0.3, 4.5
18. 7.7, 7.6, 8.6, 7.8, 2.6
19. 3.3, 4.3, 0.3, 5.4, 0.9

Adding, Subtracting, Multiplying, Dividing Decimals (Skills Review pp. 675–676)

Add or subtract.

20. 3.9 + 4.2 **8.1**
21. 13 + 6.6 **19.6**
22. 2.11 + 5.3 **7.41**
23. 0.77 + 0.05 **0.82**
24. 9.9 − 3.4 **6.5**
25. 103.5 − 23.4 **80.1**
26. 45.66 − 22.09 **23.57**
27. 20 − 2.7 **17.3**

Multiply or divide.

28. 9.6 × 8.5 **81.6**
29. 3.55 × 0.05 **0.1775**
30. 0.00004 × 18 **0.00072**
31. 600,000 × 0.0005 **300**
32. 10.8 ÷ 2.7 **4**
33. 22.568 ÷ 26 **0.868**
34. 0.003 ÷ 0.6 **0.005**
35. 0.00195 ÷ 0.13 **0.015**

Solve the problem.

36. Carol works in a department store and earns $7.60 per hour. Last week she worked 39.5 hours. How much did she earn for the week? **$300.20**

37. Henry bought 3.2 yards of fabric for a total price of $13.92. How much did the fabric cost per yard? **$4.35/yd**

Fractions and Percents (Skills Review p. 677)

Tell what fraction the model represents. Then write two equivalent fractions.

38. 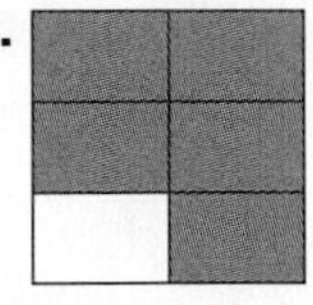 $\frac{5}{6}$, *Sample answer:* $\frac{10}{12}$; $\frac{20}{24}$

39. 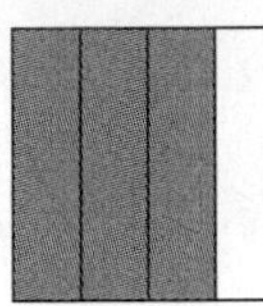 $\frac{3}{4}$, *Sample answer:* $\frac{6}{8}$; $\frac{12}{16}$

40. 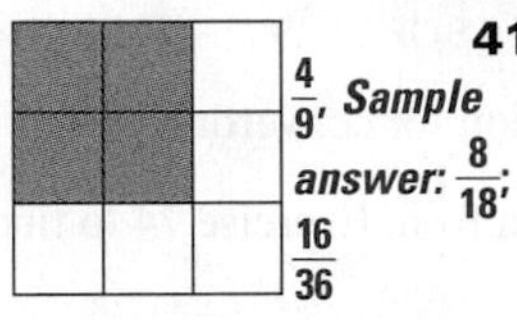 $\frac{4}{9}$, *Sample answer:* $\frac{8}{18}$; $\frac{16}{36}$

41. 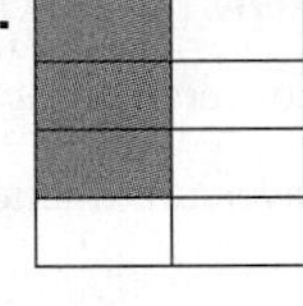 $\frac{3}{8}$, *Sample answer:* $\frac{6}{16}$; $\frac{12}{32}$

Tell what fraction the model represents. Then write the fraction as a percent.

42. 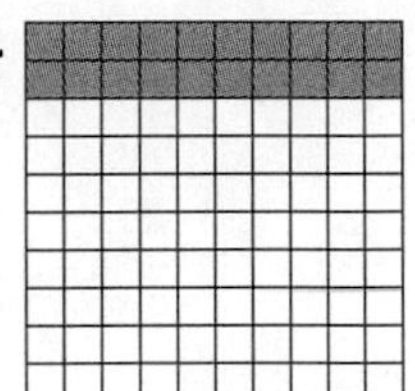 $\frac{20}{100}$, 20%

43. 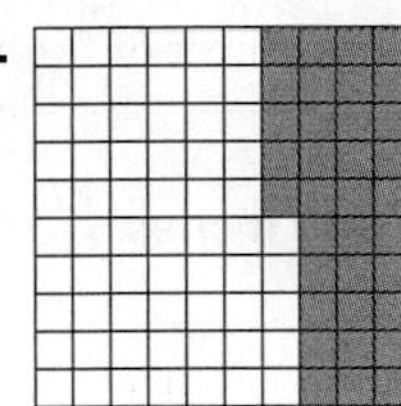 $\frac{35}{100}$, 35%

44. 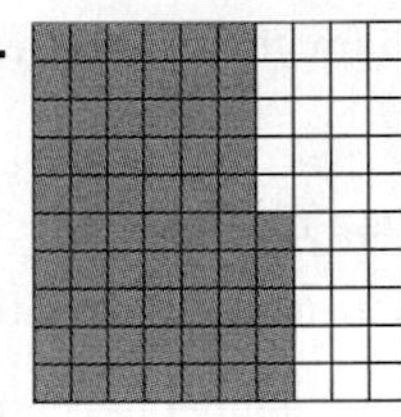 $\frac{65}{100}$, 65%

Mixed Numbers and Improper Fractions (Skills Review p. 678)

Write the improper fraction as a mixed number. Simplify if possible.

45. $\frac{11}{4}$ $2\frac{3}{4}$ **46.** $\frac{12}{8}$ $1\frac{1}{2}$ **47.** $\frac{16}{3}$ $5\frac{1}{3}$ **48.** $\frac{120}{100}$ $1\frac{1}{5}$

49. $\frac{14}{6}$ $2\frac{1}{3}$ **50.** $\frac{31}{6}$ $5\frac{1}{6}$ **51.** $\frac{38}{15}$ $2\frac{8}{15}$ **52.** $\frac{65}{15}$ $4\frac{1}{3}$

Write the mixed number as an improper fraction.

53. $8\frac{2}{3}$ $\frac{26}{3}$ **54.** $5\frac{7}{9}$ $\frac{52}{9}$ **55.** $1\frac{12}{25}$ $\frac{37}{25}$ **56.** $11\frac{3}{7}$ $\frac{80}{7}$

57. $9\frac{4}{9}$ $\frac{85}{9}$ **58.** $6\frac{19}{26}$ $\frac{175}{26}$ **59.** $15\frac{1}{2}$ $\frac{31}{2}$ **60.** $18\frac{4}{5}$ $\frac{94}{5}$

Estimating Sums, Differences, Products, Quotients (Skills Review pp. 679–680)

In Exercises 61–66, estimate the sum or difference. **61–66. Estimates may vary.**

61. $32.8 + 52.9 + 84.3$ **160** **62.** $2359.654 + 943.087$ **3300** **63.** $234{,}932 + 875$ **236,000**

64. $2053 - 1824.036$ **300** **65.** $94{,}326 - 68{,}752$ **25,000** **66.** $4652.357 - 2572.84$ **2100**

67. At the grocery store, you want to buy a bag of oranges for \$1.89, shredded cheese for \$2.49, bread dough for \$3.68, and a gallon of juice for \$3.15. You have \$11.00 with you. Estimate whether you have enough money. Explain your estimate. ***Sample answer:* yes; An estimate might be \$11.00, but this would not be enough money because the real answer is \$11.21.**

Estimate the product or quotient. Tell whether you used *rounding* or *compatible numbers* to find the estimate.

68. 11×241 **2400** **69.** 48×132 **6500** **70.** 706.82×21 **14,000**

71. $542 \div 19$ **27** **72.** $35.824 \div 8.793$ **4** **73.** $5486 \div 113$ **50**

continued on next page

84. 35.2 cm; 77.44 cm^2

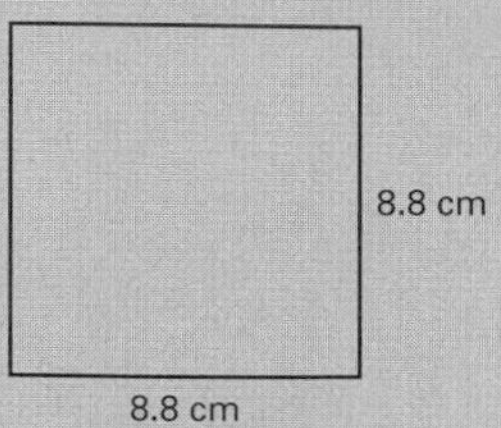

85. 108 mm; 704 mm^2

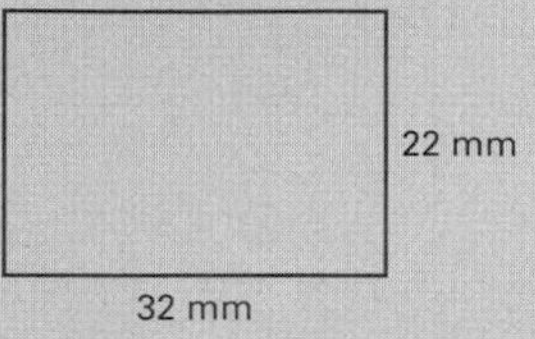

86. 24 in.; 24 in.^{2}

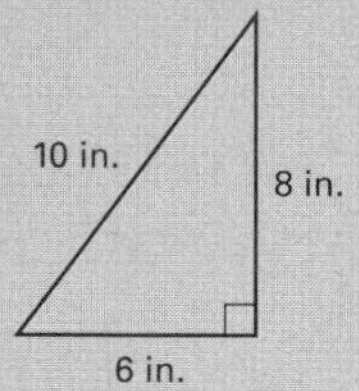

90. 1728 ft^3

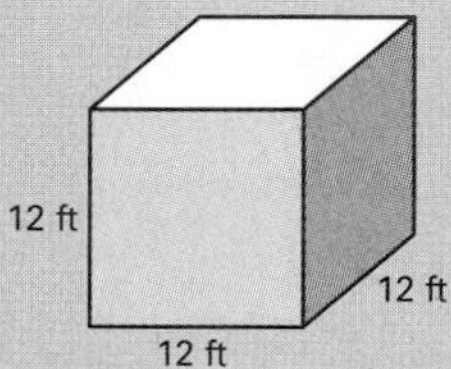

91. 46.656 cm^3

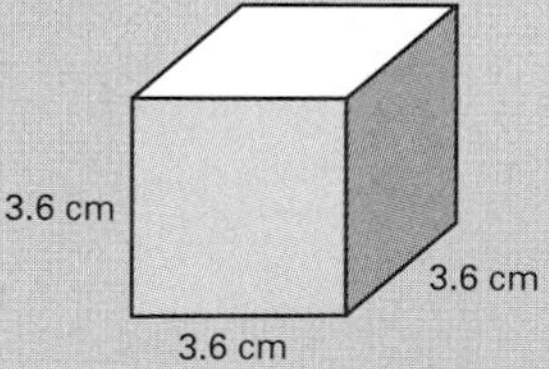

92. 1260 in.^{3}

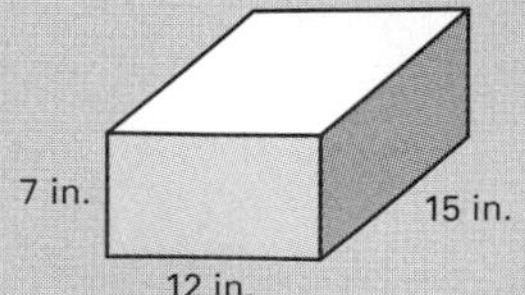

CONVERTING UNITS OF MEASUREMENT (Skills Review p. 681)

74. Write the conversion fraction for converting feet to yards. $\frac{\text{yd}}{3\text{ ft}}$

75. Use the conversion fraction from Exercise 74 to find the number of yards in 614 feet. **$204.\overline{6}$ yd**

76. Write the conversion fraction for converting inches to feet. $\frac{\text{ft}}{12\text{ in.}}$

77. Use the conversion fraction from Exercise 76 to find the number of feet in 420 inches. **35 ft**

In Exercises 78–80, use the fact that 1 centimeter ≈ 0.39 inches.

78. Find the approximate number of centimeters in 12 inches. **30.8 cm**

79. Find the approximate number of centimeters in 1 yard. **92.3 cm**

80. Find the approximate number of inches in 1 meter. **39 in.**

PERIMETER, AREA, AND VOLUME (Skills Review pp. 682–684)

Find the perimeter and area of the figure.

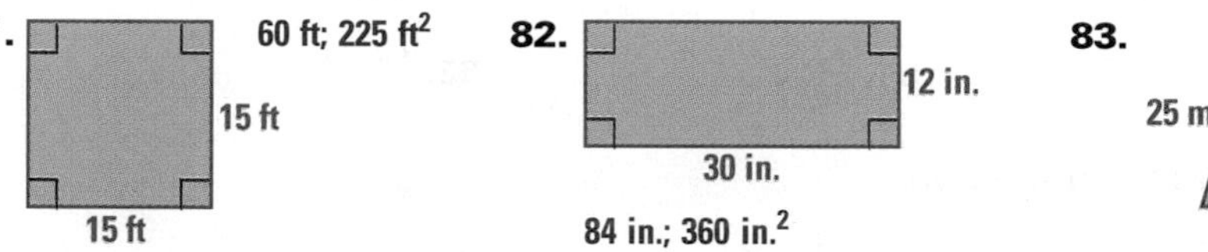

Sketch and label the figure described. Then find the perimeter and area of the figure. **84–86. See margin.**

84. A square with sides of length 8.8 centimeters

85. A rectangle with a length of 32 millimeters and a width of 22 millimeters

86. A right triangle with sides of length 6 inches, 8 inches, and 10 inches

Find the volume of the box.

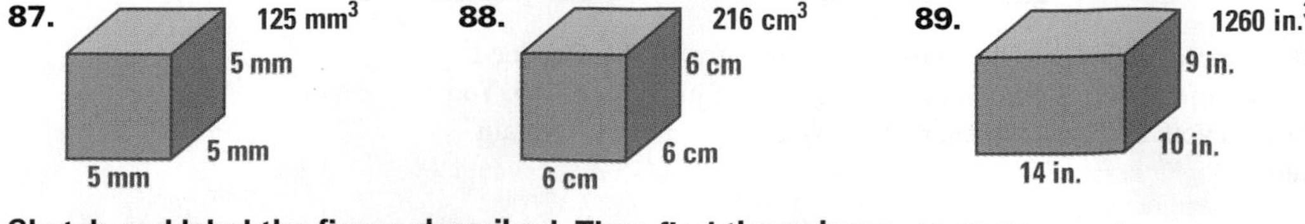

Sketch and label the figure described. Then find the volume. **90–92. See margin.**

90. A cube with edges of length 12 feet

91. A cube with edges of length 3.6 centimeters

92. A box with a length of 15 inches, a width of 12 inches, and a height of 7 inches

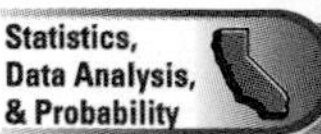

STATISTICS, DATA ANALYSIS, & PROBABILITY

READING AND DRAWING BAR GRAPHS, LINE GRAPHS, CIRCLE GRAPHS, AND LINE PLOTS (Skills Review pp. 686–689)

In Exercises 93 and 94, draw a bar graph to display the data. **93–94. See margin.**

93.

Favorite Color	Frequency
Red	25
Blue	32
Yellow	18
Green	28
Pink	2

94.

School Subject	My Grade
Mathematics	92
Science	88
Social Studies	74
English	91
French	82

In Exercises 95–97, use the line graph at the right. It shows the wind-chill factor for a temperature of 35°F and various wind speeds. At a wind speed of 10 miles per hour, for example, a temperature of 35°F actually feels like 22°F (approximately).

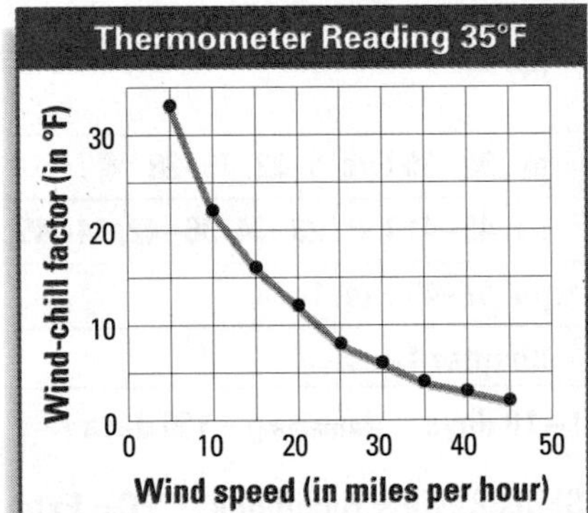

95. Between what two given wind speeds does the wind-chill factor decrease the most? **5 and 10 mi/h**

96. What is the approximate difference (in °F) in wind-chill factors between wind speeds of 20 miles per hour and 25 miles per hour? **about 4°F**

97. Predict the wind-chill factor with a wind speed of 50 miles per hour. **about 1.5°F**

Draw a circle graph to represent the information given. **98–99. See margin.**

98. Favorite sports of Mrs. Sanchez's mathematics class: swimming, 20%; basketball, 25%; tennis, 5%; baseball, 10%; football, 40%

99. Favorite lunches of students in Mr. Chung's mathematics classes: hamburgers, 30 students; pizza, 48 students; hot dogs, 10 students; grilled cheese, 12 students; spaghetti, 19 students

In Exercises 100 and 101, use the following information. In a consumer survey, 25 people were asked how many telephones their family owned. Their responses were:

4, 3, 3, 2, 1, 4, 3, 2, 2, 2, 3, 4, 5, 2, 6, 2, 3, 4, 4, 5, 5, 3, 5, 2, 7

100. Use a line plot to display the results. **See margin.**

101. Describe how the data are distributed. ***Sample answer*: Most families had either 2, 3, or 4 telephones.**

93.

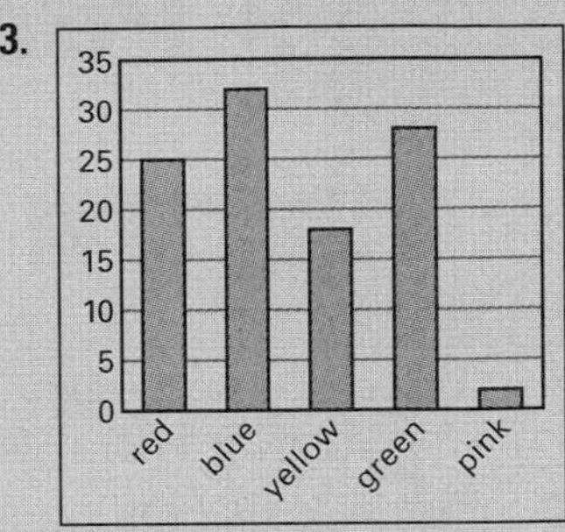

94.

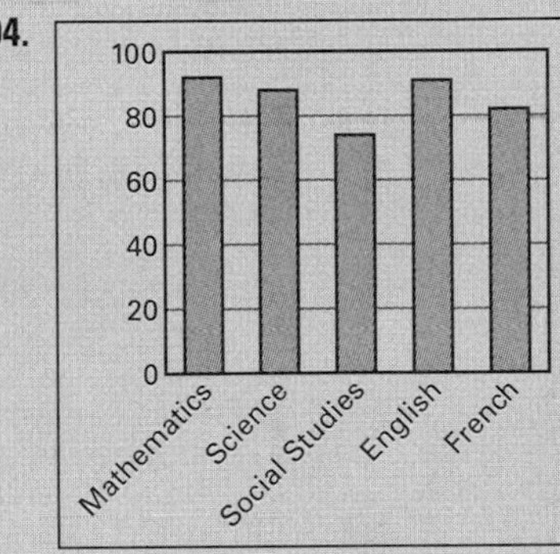

98.

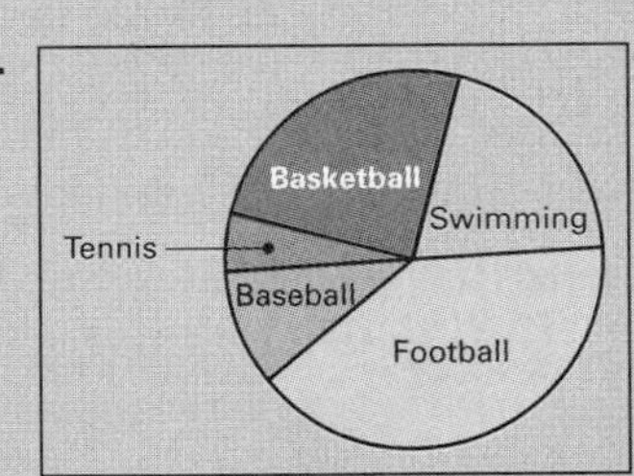

99.

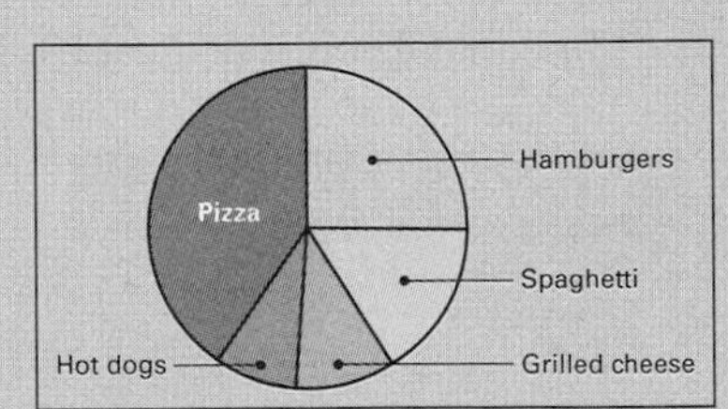

100.

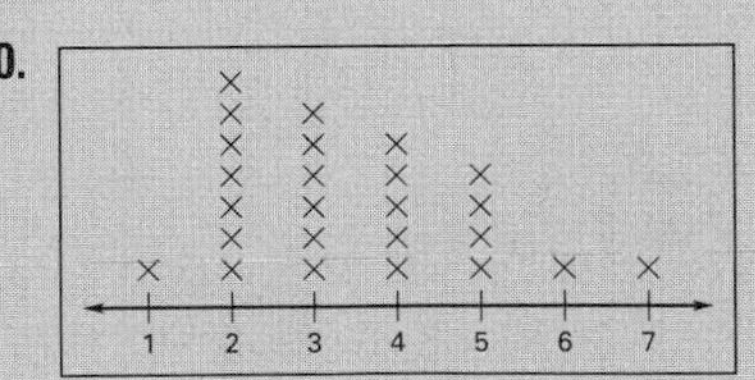

Pacing and Assignment Guide

Regular Schedule

Lesson	Les. Day	Transitional	Average	Advanced
1.1	Day 1	SRH p. 686 Exs. 1–2, p. 687 Exs. 1–2; pp. 5–6 Exs. 3–8, 13–15	pp. 5–6 Exs. 3–9, 11–15	pp. 5–6 Exs. 4–9, 10*, 11–15
1.2	Day 1	SRH p. 675 Exs. 5–12, p. 676 Exs. 5–12; pp. 9–11 Exs. 23–30, 35–38, 48–51, 64–65, 83–91	pp. 9–11 Exs. 26–31, 35–42, 50–53, 58–61, 66–68, 83–85, 89–93	pp. 9–11 Exs. 29–38, 43–47, 54–61, 66–68, 69–71*, 80–85, 92–96
1.3	Day 1	SRH pp. 672–673 Exs. 17–22; pp. 14–15 Exs. 12–16, 20–21, 25–28, 32–35, 41–42, 47–48	pp. 14–15 Exs. 12–15, 21–24, 27–35, 38–39, 42–44, 47–48	pp. 14–15 Exs. 10–15, 22–23, 26–33, 36–40, 43–45, 46*, 47–48
1.4	Day 1	pp. 18–20 Exs. 20–25, 32–34, 38–39, 42–44, 47–48, 53–55, 62–63, 77–81	pp. 18–20 Exs. 22–27, 32–35, 39–44, 47–48, 54–57, 64–65, 77–81	pp. 18–20 Exs. 30–36, 40–44, 47–49, 51*, 52–55, 66–70, 71–74*, 77–81
1.5	Day 1	SRH pp. 682–684 Exs. 4–9; pp. 24–26 Exs. 5–8, 10–11, 24–29, 34–37	pp. 24–26 Exs. 5–8, 10–16, 22*, 24–29, 34–37	pp. 24–26 Exs. 6–16, 22–23*, 24–27, 31–38
1.6	Day 1	SRH p. 667 Exs. 1–4, 7; pp. 29–31 Exs. 10–12, 15–21, 32–36	pp. 29–31 Exs. 10–13, 15–21, 26–28, 32–36	pp. 29–31 Exs. 11–14, 19–28, 29*, 30, 32–36
1.7	Day 1	pp. 34–35 Exs. 9–13, 17–22, 26–28	pp. 34–35 Exs. 9–22, 26–28	pp. 34–35 Exs. 11–18, 21–23, 24*, 25–28
1.8	Day 1	pp. 40–41 Exs. 21–26, 30–33, 36–39, 44–45	pp. 40–41 Exs. 23–34, 36–42, 44–45	pp. 40–41 Exs. 24–34, 35*, 36–38, 40–45
Review	Day 1	pp. 42–45 Exs. 1–38	pp. 42–45 Exs. 1–38	pp. 42–45 Exs. 1–38
Assess	Day 1	Chapter 1 Test	Chapter 1 Test	Chapter 1 Test
Yearly Pacing		Chapter 1 Total – 10 days	Chapter 1 Total – 10 days	Remaining – 150 days

* Challenge Exercises EP = Extra Practice SRH = Skills Review Handbook EC = Extra Challenge

Block Schedule

Day 1	Day 2	Day 3	Day 4	Day 5
1.1 pp. 5–6: Exs. 3–9, 11–15 **1.2** pp. 9–11: Exs. 26–31, 35–42, 50–53, 58–61, 66–68, 83–85, 89–93	**1.3** pp. 14–15: Exs. 12–15, 21–24, 27–35, 38–39, 42–44, 47–48 **1.4** pp. 18–20: Exs. 22–27, 32–35, 39–44, 47–48, 54–57, 64–65, 77–81	**1.5** pp. 24–26: Exs. 5–8, 10–16, 22*, 24–29, 34–37 **1.6** pp. 29–31: Exs. 10–13, 15–21, 26–28, 32–36	**1.7** pp. 34–35: Exs. 9–22, 26–28 **1.8** pp. 40–41: Exs. 23–34, 36–42, 44–45	**Review** pp. 42–45: Exs. 1–38 **Assess** Chapter 1 Test

Yearly Pacing: Chapter 1 Total – 5 days | Chapter 1 Total – 5 days | Remaining – 75 days

Support Materials

Chapter Resource Book

LESSON SUPPORT	1.1	1.2	1.3	1.4	1.5	1.6	1.7	1.8
Lesson Plans	p. 1	p. 10	p. 19	p. 28	p. 37	p. 46	p. 55	p. 64
Lesson Plans for Block Scheduling	p. 2	p. 11	p. 20	p. 29	p. 38	p. 47	p. 56	p. 65
Warm-Ups with Multiple-Choice Practice	p. 3	p. 12	p. 21	p. 30	p. 39	p. 48	p. 57	p. 66
Problem of the Day	p. 4	p. 13	p. 22	p. 31	p. 40	p. 49	p. 58	p. 67
Daily Cumulative Review	p. 5	p. 14	p. 23	p. 32	p. 41	p. 50	p. 59	p. 68
Practice Masters	p. 6	p. 15	p. 24	p. 33	p. 42	p. 51	p. 60	p. 69
Reteaching Masters	p. 7	p. 16	p. 25	p. 34	p. 43	p. 52	p. 61	p. 70
Enrichment Masters	p. 9	p. 18	p. 27	p. 36	p. 45	p. 54	p. 63	p. 72

Transparencies

	1.1	1.2	1.3	1.4	1.5	1.6	1.7	1.8
Warm-Ups with Multiple-Choice Practice	p. 1	p. 2	p. 3	p. 4	p. 5	p. 6	p. 7	p. 8
Teacher Time-Saver Transparencies	✓	✓	✓	✓	✓	✓	✓	✓
English/Spanish Problem Solving	p. 1			p. 2	p. 3			
Answer Transparencies	✓	✓	✓	✓	✓	✓	✓	✓

Technology

- Personal Student Tutor
- Time-Saving Test and Practice Generator
- Electronic Teacher Tools
- Technology: Using Calculators and Computers

Additional Resources

- Math Log
- Assessment Book
- Worked-Out Solution Key
- Practice Workbook (English/Spanish)
- Home and School Connection
- California Standards: Key Concepts Book

Correlation to the California Curriculum

Correlations to the California Standards

CA Standards: NS 1.2, AF 1.0, AF 1.2, AF 1.3, AF 1.4, AF 2.0, AF 2.1, AF 4.2, MG 2.1, MG 2.2, SDP 1.0, SDP 1.1, MR 1.1, MR 2.2, MR 2.5

California Curriculum Support

Key Concepts Book

- Pre-Course Review: Topic 1 Working with Decimals
  Topic 5 Measurement
- Key Standards: NS 1.2 Powers of Rational Numbers *(Lesson 1.3)*
  AF 1.3 Commutative and Associative Properties *(Lesson 1.7)*
  AF 1.3 The Distributive Property *(Lesson 1.8)*
  MG 1.3 Dimensional Analysis *(Lesson 1.5)*
- Special Topics: A Quick Search *(Lesson 1.3)*

California Standards Practice Workbook provides practice for each Standard that is covered in this chapter.

CHAPTER 1

Providing Universal Access

Prior to each chapter, we will outline modifications of curriculum and instruction designed to address the unique needs of English Learners, Advanced Learners, and Strategic Learners. English Learners are those who are not yet fluent in English; Advanced Learners are those whose mathematics achievement is above grade level; and Strategic Learners are those whose mathematics achievement is below grade level (in other words, those who need strategic and sustained assistance in order to be successful in mathematics). Each group of students is different, and you may find your whole class benefits from some of the suggestions. You may also have some students who belong to two groups; for example, English learners who are gifted. Because English Learners and Strategic Learners need increased instructional time in mathematics, most of the activities for both groups would best be done in a second class period, as homework, or in a tutorial. Some of the activities, particularly those involving vocabulary development, would fit nicely into a language arts period. The activities for advanced learners in these pages and throughout the text are meant as substitutes for the easier problems in the text.

Strategies for Strategic Learners

ASSESS FREQUENTLY

You may not be able to determine at the beginning of the year which students will need strategic and ongoing assistance in order to be successful in mathematics. Review students' assessment results from previous years, looking for any which indicate achievement levels that are significantly below grade level in mathematics. Since the start of the school year is an anxious time for many students, you may want to delay any formal testing for two or three weeks. Use that time to informally monitor the progress of all students in the class by circulating around the room as students work, encouraging them to ask questions about things they do not understand, and checking homework. Students who enter seventh grade with weak skills, particularly in the area of fractions, will have difficulty in algebra and beyond. This is the year to ensure that students have the solid foundation they need in order to progress successfully in mathematics. As you identify areas in which students need assistance, use the prior year's instructional resources, the on-line test generator, and ancillaries to this program to provide instruction and additional practice in skills taught in prior years.

Strategies for English Learners

ASSESS FREQUENTLY

Middle school is a time of change for many students. Check any available test results for your English learners. For those students new to your school this year or entering mid-year, review any standardized testing in mathematics and language arts and look for a reading fluency test. For those students who attended your school last year, look for an end-of-year math test as well. Students whose reading scores are significantly below grade level will need regular assistance in vocabulary development and in understanding the structure of the English language. Word problems will present a particular challenge. Look for any support for these students from the language arts teacher, study hall or tutorial assistance, siblings, or relatives. Help English learners develop a study group of classroom peers with whom they can discuss assignments and ask questions.

PRESENT A COURSE OVERVIEW

This course is designed so that students learn foundational skills and understandings before more complex ones. The instructional materials present mathematics in a straightforward way, and extraneous material that might distract or confuse English learners has been eliminated. Pointing out the specific, regular features of the text and giving English learners a brief overview of the course can help them organize their work in mathematics and anticipate and prepare for assignments and tests. Walk through the Table of Contents with students and point out the following regular features in each chapter:

- Getting Ready: Preview of the Chapter including Words to Know and the page numbers on which these words can be found; Chapter Readiness Quiz
- Goals, followed by Examples
- Study Tips
- Student Help boxes
- Links to other subject areas
- Exercises, including State Test Practice

OTHER FEATURES Each of these features is repeated in each chapter. You might also point out the color coding of regular features, the appendices, any available ancillaries, and the help available on the web site. Most search engines on the Internet have a bilingual translator readily available, and students should be encouraged to use bilingual dictionaries.

Strategies for Advanced Learners

ASSESS FREQUENTLY

If you have students for whom the math seems too easy, look for any previous testing information to determine whether students are appropriately placed. If testing is not available or conclusive, administer the end-of-year exam that goes with this series. If a student can complete 80% of the test accurately, find someone (parent, teacher, community mentor, tutor) who can review with this student the mathematics that was difficult so that he or she can quickly progress to the next level. For students who missed more than 20% of the items but showed that certain sections of the mathematics planned for this year have already been mastered, consider an individualized program in class, where the challenge problems in this book and the ancillaries can be substituted for easier problems. Since advanced students tend to move more quickly through the instructional material than other students, peruse the web site with these students to look for additional problems and activities that can supplement their mathematics program. Point out the challenge problems in each chapter. Encourage these students throughout the year to delve more deeply into mathematics content that interests them and to find connections between the mathematics in this course and the content of other courses, such as science, language arts, music, art, and history.

DIFFERENTIATE IN TERMS OF DEPTH

Advanced students at this point may think they have learned all there is to learn about fractions. By the end of seventh grade, all students should be completely comfortable with factoring of numerators and denominators, converting among fractions, decimals, and percents, and using fractional numbers to compute simple and compound interest. To help advanced students think about the abstract nature of fractions, give them the following true/false questions. You might have them discuss the questions in small groups, try the rules out on sample numbers, and see if the group can agree on an answer.

1. All fractions can be rewritten as terminating decimals. (*False. Try* $\frac{1}{3}$*, which is a repeating decimal, and* $\frac{5}{17}$*, which is repeating but may be much more difficult to recognize as such.*)
2. If you divide the numerator of a fraction, or multiply its denominator, you have divided the fraction. (*True*)
3. To divide an integer by a fraction, you can multiply the integer by the denominator of the fraction and divide the product by the numerator. (*True*)
4. To divide an integer by a fraction you can divide the integer by the numerator, and divide the quotient by the denominator. (*False. Instead of dividing the quotient by the denominator, you multiply it.*)
5. The quotient of two fractions having a common denominator is equal to the quotient of their numerators. (*True*)
6. It is not always possible to find a common denominator for a pair of fractions. (*False. You can always multiply the denominators together to get a common denominator that will, by definition, have both denominators as a factor.*)
7. If two fractions have the same numerator, you can compare them by looking at just their denominators. (*True*)
8. If two fractions have the same denominator, you can compare them by looking at just their numerators. (*True*)
9. Multiplying both dividend and divisor by the same nonzero number does not change the value of the quotient. (*True*)
10. There is only one way to divide a fraction by a fraction: Invert the terms of the divisor. Multiply the dividend by the reciprical of the divisor. (*False. This way works, but it is not the only way. Have the students also try rewriting the fractions with a common denominator and dividing the numerator of the dividend by the numerator of the divisor.*)

Mathematical Background Notes

Lesson 1.2

EXPRESSIONS Familiar problems such as $5 + 3 = 8$ and $4 \times 6 = 24$ provide the teacher with an opportunity to review the laws of arithmetic while also reinforcing terminology that is central to algebra (see page 7). Instead of referring to $5 + 3 = 8$ as a *sum* or an *addition problem*, $5 + 3$ is now referred to as a **numerical expression** that the student is asked to evaluate. This terminology sets the stage for considering more elaborate expressions, including:

> **Expressions involving variables, such as $x + 7$ and $2t - 3$.**
> **Expressions involving variables and several operations, such as $5 + a \div b + c$.**
> **Expressions involving variables and exponents, such as $ax^2 + bx + c$.**

The fact that these variables represent real numbers enables us to extend rules that underlie the study of arithmetic to variable expressions. These rules include the commutative, associative, and distributive laws (or CAD laws) to be addressed in Lessons 1.7 and 1.8.

Lesson 1.3

EXPONENTIAL NOTATION Corresponding to a special symbol for repeated addition:

$$5 + 5 + 5 = 3 \times 5 \text{ or } 3 \cdot 5$$

arithmetic and algebra call for a special symbol for repeated multiplication:

$$5 \times 5 \times 5 = 5^3.$$

This lesson reviews this notation with an emphasis on its connection to geometry. The fact that a^2 is the area of a square of side length a leads us to refer to a^2 as "a squared." The fact that a^3 is the volume of a cube of edge length a leads us to refer to a^3 as "a cubed." Figures such as those on page 12 can be used as a the source of enrichment as well as convenient terminology.

In the representations of 1^2, 2^2, 3^2, and 4^2, we have broken the areas into shaded and unshaded unit squares. The number of unshaded squares progresses in the pattern

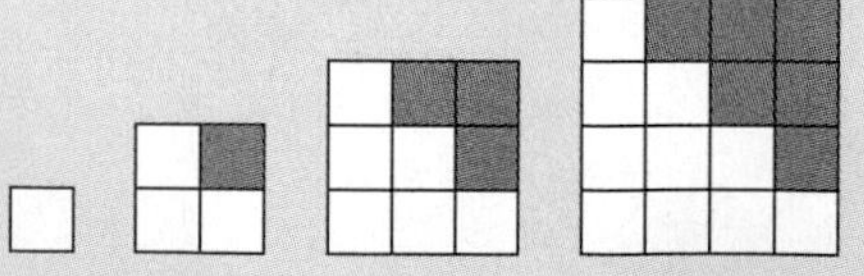

$$T_1 = 1, T_2 = 1 + 2 = 3, T_3 = 1 + 2 + 3 = 6, T_4 = 1 + 2 + 3 + 4 = 10,$$

in which $T_n = 1 + 2 + 3 + \ldots + n$ is called the nth **triangular number.** The number of shaded squares progresses similarly, but the nth square has only T_{n-1} shaded squares. This leads to the interesting relation

$$n^2 = T_{n-1} + T_n.$$

As a variant of this pattern, we can consider the rectangles formed by combining two copies of T_1, T_2, T_3, and so on.

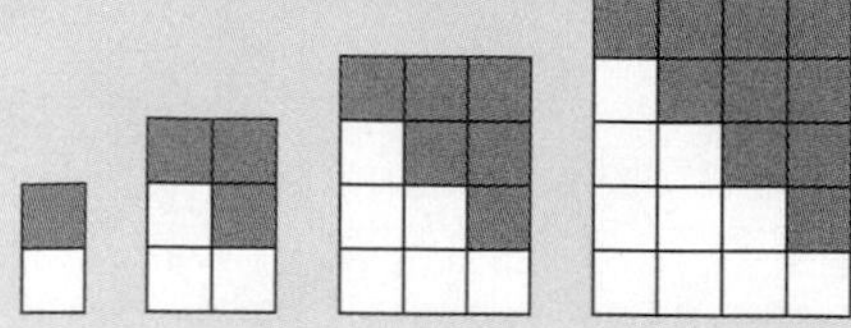

Here we observe that

$$2T_1 = 1 \cdot 2, \quad 2T_2 = 2 \cdot 3, \quad 2T_3 = 3 \cdot 4,$$

and, more generally, that

$$2T_n = n(n + 1).$$

In this way we arrive at a general expression for evaluating

$$T_n = 1 + 2 + 3 + \ldots + n = \frac{n(n+1)}{2}.$$

Lesson 1.4

LEFT-TO-RIGHT RULE Expressions calling for more than one arithmetic operation confront the student with uncertainty about which operation to implement first. Part of this uncertainty is dispelled by the commutative and associative laws of addition and multiplication: **In case an expression involves only additions or only multiplications, the value of the expression does not depend on the order in which these sums or products are performed.** That is, the CAD laws enable us to write

$$2 + 7 + 4 = (2 + 7) + 4 = 2 + (7 + 4) = (7 + 4) + 2 = 7 + (4 + 2)$$

and

$$2 \times 7 \times 4 = (2 \times 7) \times 4 = 2 \times (7 \times 4) = (7 \times 4) \times 2 = 7 \times (4 \times 2).$$

If, however, an expression involves subtraction or division, this is not the case. The value of an expression such as $24 - 8 - 6$ *is* dependent on the order in which the operations are performed. For example,

$$(24 - 8) - 6 \neq 24 - (8 - 6).$$

The *left-to-right rule* displayed on page 16 tells the student that

$$24 - 8 - 6 = (24 - 8) - 6 = 16 - 6 = 10.$$

Here students may be left with the impression that the rules for order of operations constitute a rather arbitrary set of conventions. In fact, however, these rules are dictated by the laws of arithmetic, and the teacher should be prepared to provide the student with an explanation for why a particular rule has been adopted.

To explain the left-to-right rule it is useful to recall that $a - b = a + (-b)$. On this basis,

$$24 - 8 - 6 = 24 + (-8) + (-6)$$

and, because of the associative law of addition,

$$24 + (-8) + (-6) = (24 + (-8)) + (-6) = 16 + (-6) = 10.$$

This procedure corresponds to applying the left-to-right rule, and that is the reason this rule has been adopted. A similar argument applies to $24 \div 8 \div 6 = 24 \times \left(\frac{1}{8}\right) \times \left(\frac{1}{6}\right) = \frac{1}{2}$.

Exponential notation requires an additional order of operations rule, one that calls for the evaluation of powers before performing the other four arithmetic operations (see page 16). As a result,

$$ab^2 = a(b^2) \quad \text{and} \quad a \div b^2 = a \div (b)^2.$$

Again, the reasons for this rule are rooted in the laws of arithmetic. If we were to interpret ax^2 as $(ax)^2$, then for $a = -1$ we would be led to the contradictory result

$$-x^2 = (-1)x^2 = ((-1)x)^2 = (-1)(x)(-1)(x) = (-1)(-1)(x)(x) = x^2.$$

The rule "exponentiation before multiplication" leads to the more satisfactory result

$$-x^2 = (-1)x^2 = (-1)(x^2) = -(x^2).$$

Lesson 1.5

AREAS While this lesson focuses on *using* formulas, it is important to keep in mind the procedures used to justify them. Starting with the fact that the area of a rectangle of height h and base b is $A = bh$, we can derive the formula for the area of a parallelogram. The picture below shows that a parallelogram of height h and base b can be cut into two pieces and then rearranged to form a rectangle of the same height and base.

The area of the parallelogram is the sum of the areas of the two pieces, which is also the area of the rectangle. Therefore the parallelogram has area $A = bh$.

Having found a formula for the area of a parallelogram, we can proceed to triangles. Given a triangle of height h and base b, two copies of the triangle fit together to form a parallelogram of height h and base b.

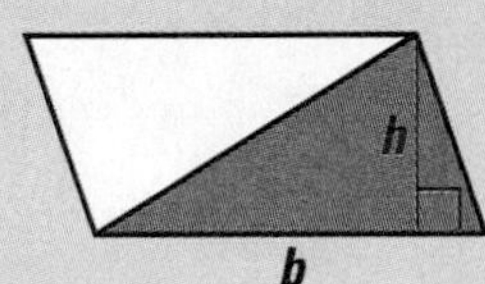

The area of the parallelogram is bh, and this is *twice* the area of the triangle. Therefore the area of the triangle is

$$A = \frac{1}{2}bh.$$

Often there is more than one way to derive an area formula. By way of example, one can also obtain the formula $A = \frac{1}{2}bh$ from the picture below.

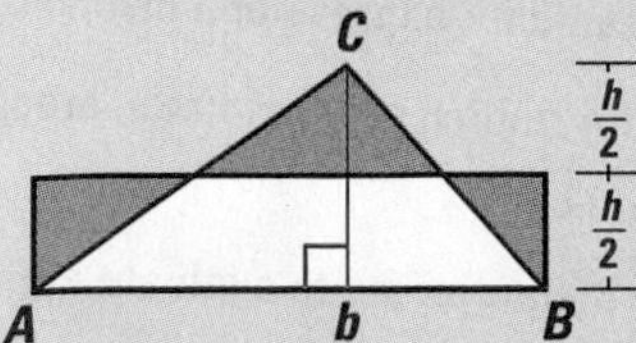

Notice that triangle ABC can be cut into three pieces which can be rearranged into a rectangle with the same base and *half* the height of the triangle.

Lessons 1.7–1.8

CAD LAWS In the context of whole numbers, it is possible to draw pictures that illustrate the essence of the CAD laws. For example, the commutative laws of addition and multiplication can be represented by:

$3 + 5 = 5 + 3$

$3 \times 5 = 5 \times 3$

whereas the associative laws of addition and multiplication are represented by:

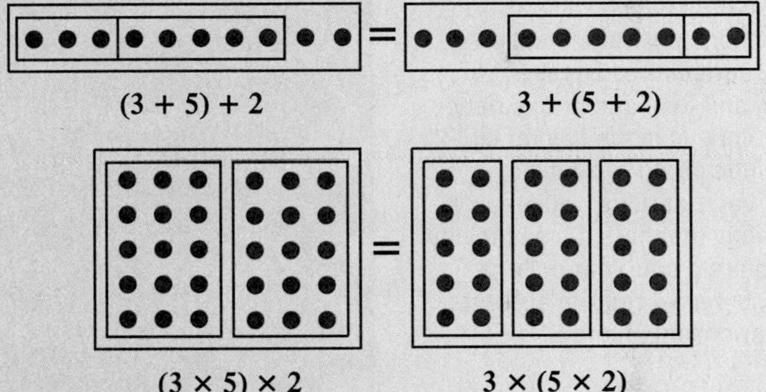

$(3 + 5) + 2$ $\quad$ $3 + (5 + 2)$

$(3 \times 5) \times 2$ $\quad$ $3 \times (5 \times 2)$

The distributive property is similarly illustrated by:

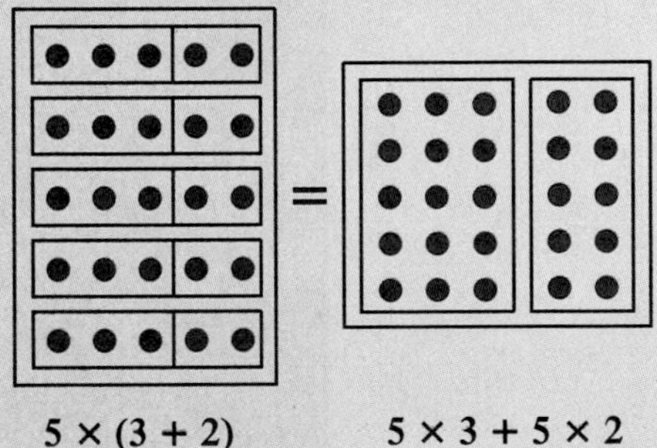

$5 \times (3 + 2)$ $\quad$ $5 \times 3 + 5 \times 2$

In algebra, the student learns to apply these laws to arbitrary real numbers and to variables. Furthermore, they are now to be implemented symbolically without reference to numerical values. Still, when questions arise as to *why* $3(a + 7) = 3a + 21$, the answers are rooted in diagrams such as those given above. The CAD laws guided the transition from whole numbers to integers to real numbers, and they are now to be carried over to the language and symbolism of algebra.

Chapter Overview

Chapter Goals

In this chapter, students will learn problem-solving and reasoning skills. They will:

- Read and interpret tables and graphs.
- Evaluate expressions and formulas.
- Use order of operations and number properties.
- Use the distributive property.

Career Note

Research biologists may work at colleges and universities, in industry, or for the government. They work in varied fields, such as drug development, environmental protection, agriculture, disease prevention, and food and drug safety. Others working in the field of biology include doctors, dentists, nurses, veterinarians, zookeepers, and biology teachers. Some biology jobs require a two-year college degree, but most require at least a four-year college degree.

Operations with Numbers

Why are operations with numbers important?

It is important to understand operations with numbers because, in algebra, you will need to use the same operations with variables. You will use operations with numbers throughout your future studies.

Operations with numbers are necessary for many careers, including biology (page 1) and nutrition (page 27). For example, biologists use operations with numbers as they plan experiments, record observations, and make predictions.

Meeting the California Standards

The skills you'll develop in this chapter will help you meet state standards and prepare for standardized tests. In this chapter you'll:

- **Identify relationships within a data set.** LESSON 1.1
- **Simplify numerical expressions by applying properties and justifying the process used.** LESSONS 1.2, 1.4, 1.7, 1.8
- **Interpret and evaluate expressions involving powers.** LESSON 1.3
- **Use formulas for finding the perimeter, area, and volume of basic figures.** LESSONS 1.3, 1.5, 1.8
- **Use the order of operations to evaluate algebraic expressions.** LESSON 1.4

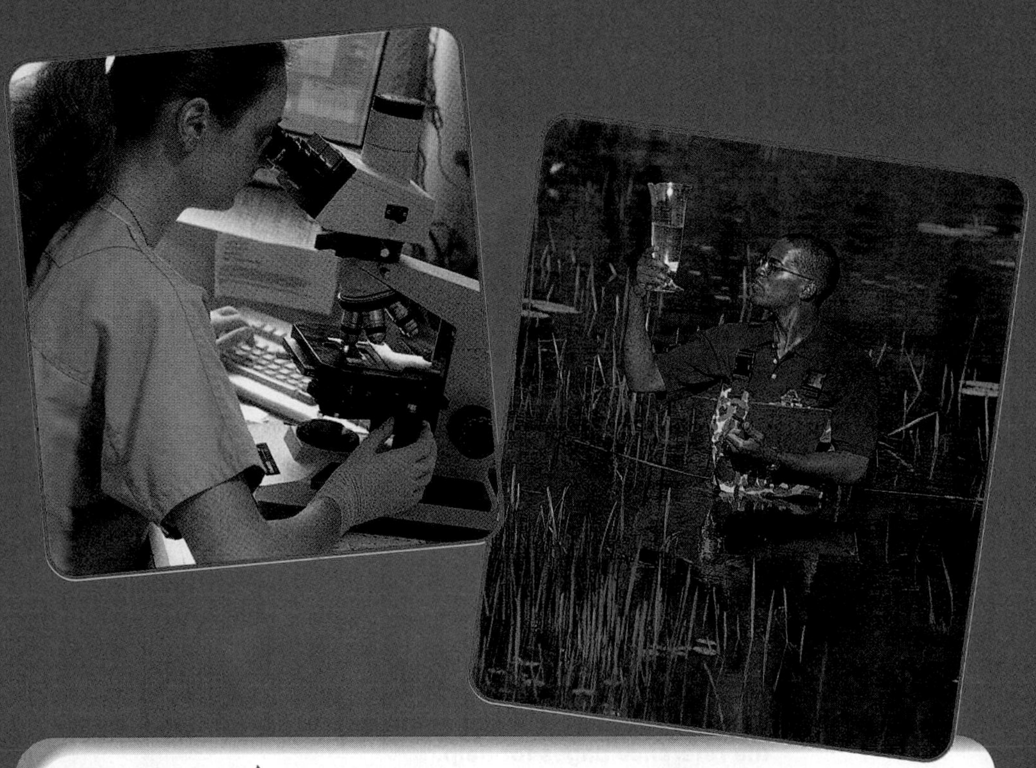

Career Link **BIOLOGIST** A biologist uses operations with numbers when:

- identifying and continuing patterns.
- using data to make conclusions.

Mitosis seen through a microscope

EXERCISES

During *mitosis*, a cell divides to form two new cells. Then each new cell divides again. This pattern continues as shown in the diagram.

1. After one cell divides, how many cells are there? **2**
2. How many cells are there after each of the new cells from Exercise 1 divides? **4**
3. How many cells are there after each of the new cells from Exercise 2 divides? **8**

In Lesson 1.6, you will learn how to describe the pattern above and use it to make predictions about the number of cells at later stages of mitosis.

Projects

A project covering Chapters 1–3 appears on pages 164–165 of the Student Edition. Additional projects for selected lessons in Chapter 1 are available in the *Assessment Book,* pp. 208–209.

Technology

Software

- Electronic Teacher Tools
- Online Lesson Planner
- Personal Student Tutor
- Test and Practice Generator

Internet Connections

- Application and Career Links 15, 25, 27, 30
- Student Help 10, 13, 17, 30, 33, 35, 39, 41, 49

These Internet connections are available at **www.mcdougallittell.com**

Prepare

Diagnostic Tools

The **chapter readiness quiz** can help you diagnose whether students have the following skills needed in Chapter 1:

- Recognize and apply the meaning of the words *sum, difference, product,* and *quotient.*

Reteaching Materials

The following resources are available for students who need additional help with the skills on the chapter readiness quiz:

Personal Student Tutor

Additional Resources

The following resources are provided to help you prepare for the upcoming chapter and customize review materials:

Chapter 1 Resource Book

- Lesson Plans, pp. 1, 10, 19, 28, 37, 46, 55, 64
- Lesson Plans for Block Scheduling, pp. 2, 11, 20, 29, 38, 47, 56, 65

Technology

- Electronic Teacher Tools with Lesson Planning Software
- Test and Practice Generator

Chapter 1 Getting Ready

PREVIEW

What's the chapter about?

- Understanding **tables** and **graphs**
- Evaluating **numerical** and **variable expressions**
- Using the **order of operations** and **number properties**

WORDS TO KNOW

- **numerical expression,** *p. 7*
- **variable,** *p. 8*
- **variable expression,** *p. 8*
- **power,** *p. 12*
- **base,** *p. 12*
- **exponent,** *p. 12*
- **order of operations,** *p. 16*
- **formula,** *p. 22*
- **sequence,** *p. 28*
- **commutative properties,** *p. 32*
- **associative properties,** *p. 32*
- **distributive property,** *p. 38*

PREPARE

Chapter Readiness Quiz

Take this quick quiz. If you are unsure of a Skill Check answer, look at the reference pages for help.

VOCABULARY CHECK

1. Which of the following represents a product? C

Ⓐ $4 + 2$ Ⓑ $4 - 2$ Ⓒ 4×2 Ⓓ $4 \div 2$

2. Which of the following represents a difference? G

Ⓕ $4 + 2$ Ⓖ $4 - 2$ Ⓗ 4×2 Ⓙ $4 \div 2$

SKILL CHECK *(refer to pp. 675, 676)*

3. What is the sum of 4.1 and 8.2? C

Ⓐ 2 Ⓑ 4.1 Ⓒ 12.3 Ⓓ 33.62

4. What is the quotient of 1000 and 0.1? J

Ⓕ 10 Ⓖ 100 Ⓗ 1000 Ⓙ 10,000

Student Help

STUDY TIP
"Student Help" boxes throughout the chapter give you study tips and tell you where to look for extra help in this book and on the Internet.

STUDY TIP

Make Vocabulary Cards

Vocabulary cards will help you remember definitions. Include a sketch whenever possible.

Formula
A formula is an algebraic equation that relates two or more variables. The formula for the area of a square is:
A = s²
s
s

1.1 Tables and Graphs

California Standards

In this lesson you'll:

- Identify relationships within a data set. (SDP 1.0)
- Know various forms of display for data sets. (SDP 1.1)

Goal 1 Using Tables

Numbers or facts that describe something are called **data**. To be useful, numerical data should be organized so you can look for patterns and relationships. One way to organize data is in a table.

EXAMPLE 1 Making and Using a Table

Data for the perimeters of six rectangles are shown below. Make a table to organize the data. Then describe a pattern for the data.

A. Perimeter = 4 **B.** Perimeter = 6 **C.** Perimeter = 8

D. Perimeter = 10 **E.** Perimeter = 12 **F.** Perimeter = 14

Solution

Make a table with two rows. Compare the perimeters to find a pattern.

Rectangle	A	B	C	D	E	F
Perimeter	4	6	8	10	12	14

+2 +2 +2 +2 +2

ANSWER ▶ From the table you can see that the perimeters increase by 2.

Student Help

▶ **Skills Review**
For help with perimeter, see pages 682–684.

EXAMPLE 2 Comparing Data in a Table

Below are winning and losing state high school football championship scores from 1993 to 2000. Look at the difference between the winning and losing scores. Which years have a difference *greater* than 20?

State High School Football Championship Scores

Year	1993	1994	1995	1996	1997	1998	1999	2000
Winning score	55	20	37	52	30	49	27	35
Losing score	10	19	24	17	13	26	17	21

Solution

Subtract the losing score from the winning score year by year. There are three years with differences greater than 20: 1993, 1996, and 1998.

Student Help

▶ **Study Tip**
To record differences between the scores in Example 2, add a fourth row to the table.

1 Plan

Pacing

Suggested Number of Days

Transitional: 1 day
Average: 1 day
Advanced: 1 day
Block Schedule: 0.5 block with 1.2

Teaching Resources

Blacklines
(See page 1B.)

Transparencies

- Warm-Up Exercises
- Teacher Time-Savers
- English/Spanish Problem Solving
- Answers

Technology

- Electronic Teacher Tools
- Test and Practice Generator

2 Teach

Math Reasoning

The strategies in the Mathematical Reasoning Standards are used so often it is not practical to list them with each lesson. Since the Developing Concepts pages focus so strongly on mathematical reasoning, both reasoning and content Standards are listed for these pages.

Extra Examples 1 and 2
See next page.

California Standards and Assessment

CA Standards: SDP 1.0, SDP 1.1

Extra Examples 1 and 2

From 1992 through 1994, the gold production (in millions of troy ounces) of the United States and of Canada, respectively, was:

1992—U.S.: 10.6, Canada: 5.2
1993—U.S.: 10.6, Canada: 4.9
1994—U.S.: 10.5, Canada: 4.7

Organize the data in a table. In what year was the difference in gold production the greatest?

Year	1992	1993	1994
U.S.	10.6	10.6	10.5
Canada	5.2	4.9	4.7

1994

Extra Example 3

The graph shows the number of children and adults attending a movie. On which day was there the greatest difference in the numbers of children and adults?

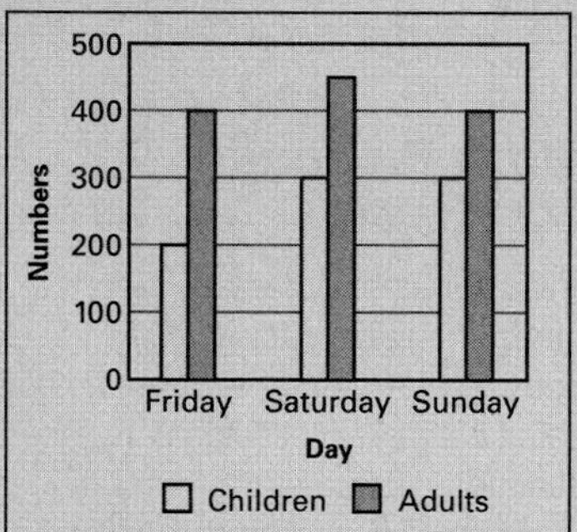

Friday

Extra Example 4

Is the temperature increasing or decreasing? Explain.

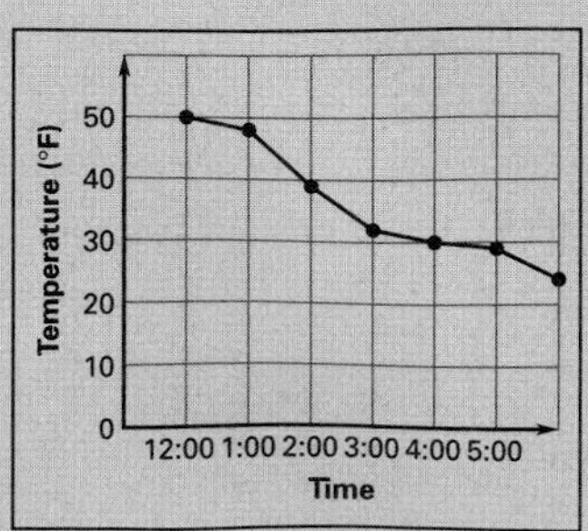

decreasing; the graph falls from left to right.

Goal 2 USING GRAPHS

Another way to present data is to use a graph. A graph presents a picture of the data. You use different types of graphs for different purposes.

You can use a *bar graph* to compare different items. In a **bar graph**, the lengths of the bars represent the data. If there are two sets of data for each item, then you can use a **double bar graph**.

Student Help

▶SKILLS REVIEW
For help with bar graphs and line graphs, see pages 686 and 687.

EXAMPLE 3 Using a Double Bar Graph

The double bar graph shows the average daily high and low temperatures during July in four United States cities. Which city has had the greatest difference between average daily highest and lowest temperatures?

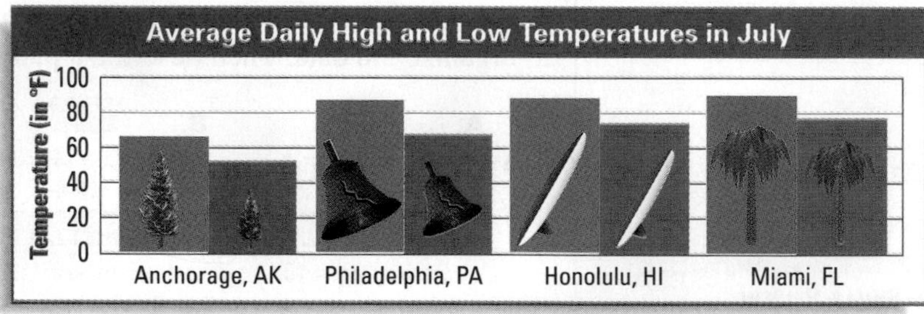

Solution

Compare the difference between the lengths of the bars for each city.

ANSWER ▶ Philadelphia, Pennsylvania, has had the greatest difference between its average daily high and low temperatures in July.

A **line graph** displays data using points connected by line segments. It can sometimes be used to show how a quantity changes over time. To see the *trend*, or how the data change, decide if the segments generally rise or fall.

EXAMPLE 4 Using a Line Graph

The line graph shows how the average price of a stock in a company changed over 6 months. Is the price increasing or decreasing? Explain.

Student Help

▶READING GRAPHS
To approximate data on the line graph, first read across the horizontal scale to find the month, go up to the graph, then read over to the vertical scale to find the price. The price for March is about $2.90.

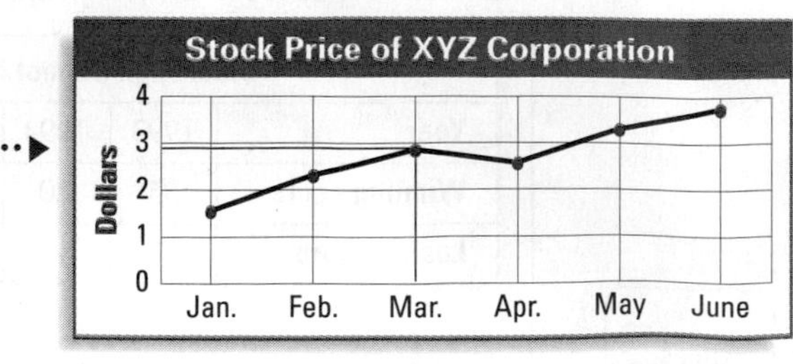

Solution

Prices are generally increasing because most segments rise to the right.

1.1 Exercises

Guided Practice

1. The table below shows the prices that Company A and Company B charge for a soccer trophy. The price depends on the number of letters to be engraved. How would you decide which company to hire? **See margin.**

Number of letters	1	2	3	4	5	6
Company A (in dollars)	4.10	4.20	4.30	4.40	4.50	4.60
Company B (in dollars)	4.30	4.35	4.40	4.45	4.50	4.55

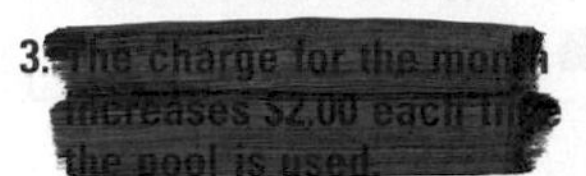

2. You know the total annual population of your town over several years. What type of graph would you use to present the data? Explain.

Practice and Problem Solving

Student Help

▶ **More Practice**
Extra practice to help you master skills is on page 690.

3. **SWIMMING** A fitness club charges a monthly fee of $10. There is also a charge of $2 each time you use the swimming pool. Make a table to show the total cost if you swim 0, 1, 2, 3, 4, 5, 6, 7, or 8 times in one month. Describe any patterns in the data. **See margin.**

4. **MATHEMATICAL REASONING** The table shows the attendance at a musical. Attendance was not taken on Wednesday and Thursday.

Day	Mon.	Tues.	Wed.	Thurs.	Fri.	Sat.	Sun.
Attendance	80	110			200	230	260

If attendance increased at the same rate all week, what was the attendance on Wednesday and Thursday? Justify your answer.

Link to Science

HOT AIR BALLOONS
In 1783 French physicist Jacques Charles (1746–1823) flew 27 miles from Paris in a hot-air balloon. In 1787 he developed the law that relates the expansion of gas with heat, which is discussed in Exercises 5 and 6.

Science Link **In Exercises 5 and 6, use the graph showing how the temperature and volume of a gas under constant pressure are related. (The volume of a gas is the amount of space the gas occupies.)**

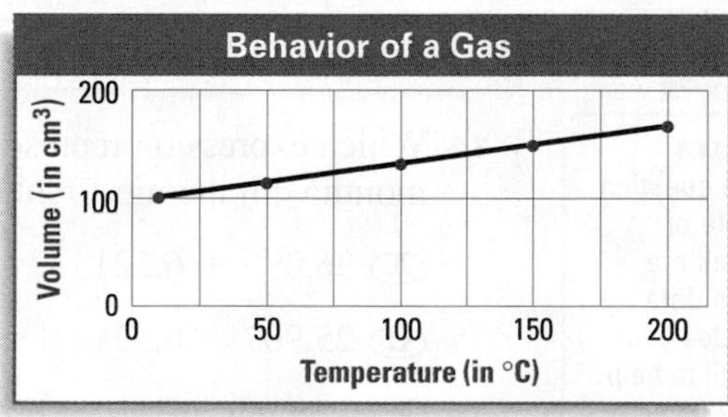

5. What happens to the volume of the gas as the temperature increases?

6. What happens to the volume of the gas as the temperature decreases?

Concept Check

What are some advantages of representing data with a graph, instead of a table? ***Sample answer:*** **One advantage is that a graph often helps you visualize the data better so you can see any differences between the values more clearly.**

3 Apply

Assignment Guide

Transitional
Day 1: SRH p. 686 Exs. 1–2, p. 687, Exs. 1–2, pp. 5–6 Exs. 3–8, 13–15

Average
Day 1: pp. 5–6 Exs. 3–9, 11–15

Advanced
Day 1: pp. 5–6 Exs. 4–9, 10*, 11–15

Block Schedule
pp. 5–6 Exs. 3–9, 11–15 (with 1.2)

Extra Practice

- Student Edition, pp. 690–691
- Chapter 1 Resource Book, p. 6

Homework Check

To quickly check student understanding of key concepts, go over the following exercises:

Transitional: 3, 4, 6, 7, 12
Average: 3, 4, 6, 8, 12
Advanced: 3, 4, 6, 8, 12

3.
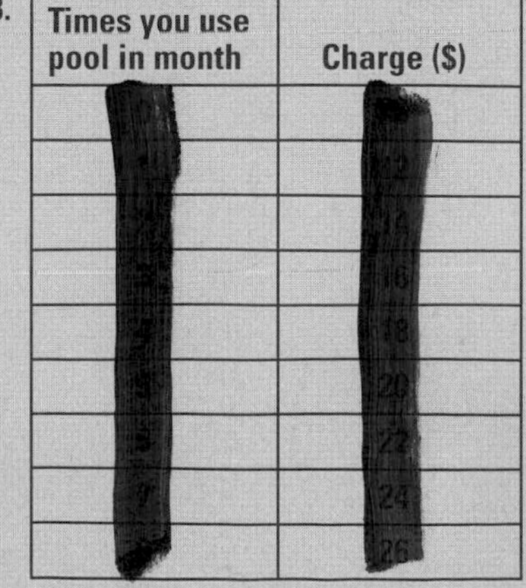

Times you use pool in month	Charge ($)
[illegible]	[illegible]

4 Assess

Assessment Resources

- Assessment Book (Formal Assessment and Alternative Assessment)
- Test and Practice Generator

Mini-Quiz

1. Use a line or bar graph to represent the data in the table.

Year	Sales (millions of dollars)
1990	3.2
1991	6.8
1992	10.2
1993	10.4
1994	11.0

Check students' work.

2. Use your graph from Exercise 1 to write a statement about the data. **Answers may vary. *Sample answer:* Sales are increasing each year.**
3. By how much did the sales increase from 1990 to 1994? **7.8 million dollars**
4. Which one-year period showed the greatest increase in sales? **from 1990 to 1991**

10.

Year	Men's Distance (in feet)	Women's Distance (in feet)
1984	280	220
1988	270	240
1992	290	220
1996	285	215

Link to Sports

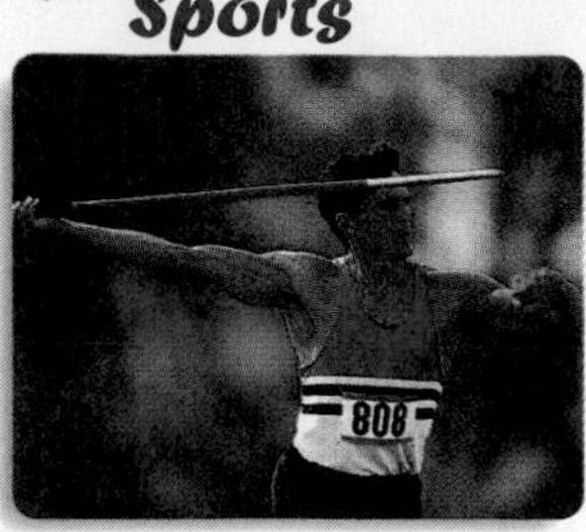

JAVELIN THROW A javelin can be made of metal or wood and has a metal tip that must land with the point hitting the ground first. In the Olympic javelin throw, an athlete runs about 37 yards and hurls the javelin over the shoulder.

10. ***Sample answer:*** **Decide the value by estimating how much of the fifty feet between distances marked is covered.**

JAVELIN THROW **In Exercises 7–10, use the double bar graph below. It shows the winning distances for the javelin throw in the Olympics.**

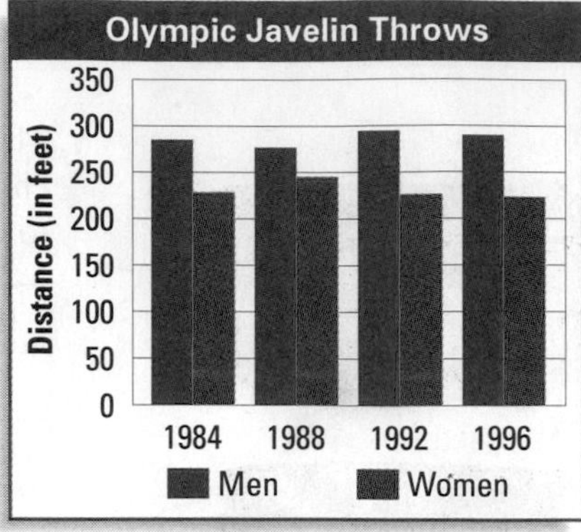

7. About how far was the women's champion throw in 1988?
8. In what year was the difference between the men's and women's throws the least? In what year was this difference greatest?
9. If the graph did not have any numbers on its vertical scale, what could you tell about the distances, using only the lengths of the bars?
10. **CHALLENGE** From the information in the bar graph, make a table. Explain how you decided on the values for the distance.

OLYMPIC MEDALS **In Exercises 11–13, use the table below. It shows the top five medal winning countries at the 1996 Summer Olympics.**

11. Which country's team won 101 medals?
12. As a group, did the five countries win more gold, silver, or bronze medals?
13. Which country won ten fewer bronze medals than gold medals?

1996 Olympic Medals

	Gold	Silver	Bronze
United States	44	32	25
Russia	26	21	16
Germany	20	18	27
China	16	22	12
France	15	7	15

Multiple-Choice Practice

Test Tip A B C D

▶ READING TABLES
Often, when a question involves a table or graph, mistakes are made because data are misread. Use your finger or pencil to help guide your eyes to the correct column or scale.

In Exercises 14 and 15, use the table below. The table shows the number of video rentals per month at Video City for January through June.

Month	January	February	March	April	May	June
Number	12,820	6,521	13,042	25,907	26,095	19,263

14. Which expression represents how many more tapes were rented in the month with the most rentals than in the month with the fewest rentals?

Ⓐ 36,095 + 6,521 Ⓑ 25,907 + 6,521
Ⓒ 25,907 − 6,521 Ⓓ 26,095 − 6,521

15. May rentals are about how many times greater than February rentals?

Ⓕ About 2 times Ⓖ About 3 times
Ⓗ About 4 times Ⓙ Not here

1.2 Expressions and Variables

California Standards

In this lesson you'll:

Add, subtract, multiply, and divide rational numbers. (NS 1.2)

- ▶ Simplify numerical expressions. (AF 1.3)
- ▶ Use algebraic terminology correctly. (AF 1.4)

Goal 1 EVALUATING NUMERICAL EXPRESSIONS

The table shows the four basic operations in arithmetic and algebra.

Operation	Words and Symbols	Verbal Phrases
Addition	$5 + 3 = 8$ (terms: 5, 3; plus: +; sum: 8)	The sum of 5 and 3 is 8. 5 plus 3 is 8.
Subtraction	$8 - 5 = 3$ (minus: −; difference: 3)	The difference of 8 and 5 is 3. 8 minus 5 is 3.
Multiplication	$4 \times 6 = 24$ (factors: 4, 6; times: ×; product: 24)	The product of 4 and 6 is 24. 4 times 6 is 24.
Division	$28 \div 7 = 4$ (dividend: 28; divided by: ÷; divisor: 7; quotient: 4)	The quotient of 28 and 7 is 4. 28 divided by 7 is 4.

Student Help

▶**READING TIP**
Multiplication can be shown by ×, by •, or by parentheses ( ). Division can be shown by ÷ or by a fraction bar.

An expression that represents a particular number is called a **numerical expression**. A numerical expression consists of numbers and operations to be performed on them. For example, in the table above, $5 + 3$, $8 - 5$, 4×6, and $28 \div 7$ are all numerical expressions. Finding the value of an expression is called **evaluating the expression**.

EXAMPLE 1 Evaluating Numerical Expressions

Evaluate the expression. Then describe the result in words.

a. $124 + 82$ **b.** $0.45 - 0.39$ **c.** $6 \cdot 12$ **d.** $\frac{8.1}{0.9}$

Solution

a. $124 + 82 = 206$
The sum of 124 and 82 is 206.

b. $0.45 - 0.39 = 0.06$
The difference of 0.45 and 0.39 is 0.06.

c. $6 \cdot 12 = 72$
The product of 6 and 12 is 72.

d. $\frac{8.1}{0.9} = 8.1 \div 0.9 = 9$
The quotient of 8.1 and 0.9 is 9.

Student Help

▶**SKILLS REVIEW**
For help with decimal operations, see pages 675 and 676.

1 Plan

Pacing
Suggested Number of Days
Transitional: 1 day
Average: 1 day
Advanced: 1 day
Block Schedule: 0.5 block with 1.1

Teaching Resources

Blacklines
(See page 1B.)

Transparencies
- Warm-Up Exercises
- Teacher Time-Savers
- English/Spanish Problem Solving
- Answers

Technology
- Electronic Teacher Tools
- Test and Practice Generator

2 Teach

Math Reasoning

For Mathematical Background Notes on mathematical reasoning related to this lesson, please refer to pages 1E and 1F in this Teacher's Edition.

Extra Example 1
See next page.

California Standards and Assessment

CA Standards: NS 1.2, AF 1.3, AF 1.4

Extra Example 1

Evaluate the expression. Then describe the results in words.

a. 254 + 37 **The sum of 254 and 37 is 291.**

b. 3.84 − 2.69 **The difference of 3.84 and 2.69 is 1.15.**

c. 8 • 11 **The product of 8 and 11 is 88.**

d. $\frac{7.2}{0.8}$ **The quotient of 7.2 and 0.8 is 9.**

Extra Example 2

a. Evaluate $12n$ when $n = 4$. **48**

b. Evaluate $x - y$ when $x = 5.4$ and $y = 2.1$. **3.3**

Extra Example 3

The distance from home to school is *x* miles. The distance between the grocery store and the school is *y* miles. The grocery store lies on the path between home and the school. The distance from home to the grocery store is $x - y$. Find this distance given $x = 515$ yards and $y = 381$ yards. **134 yards**

Math Reasoning

As Example 3 is worded, *x* and *y* are given numbers rather than variables. One could rephrase the problem so it corresponds to Example 2(b). First give the distance from Copiapo to Cuzco as 1150 miles and from Copiapo to Catarpe as 375 miles, and then ask students to evaluate the variable expression $x - y$ when *x* and *y* are the given distances.

Concept Check

Explain how to evaluate a variable expression. ***Sample answer:*** **Substitute a number for each variable and simplify.**

Goal 2 EVALUATING VARIABLE EXPRESSIONS

A **variable** is a letter that is used to represent one or more numbers. The numbers are the **values** of the variable. A **variable expression** consists of numbers and variables and operations to be performed on them.

Student Help

▶ **STUDY TIP**
In this book, the phrase *the difference of a and b* means you start with *a* and subtract *b*, so you write $a - b$. Similarly, the phrase *the quotient of a and b* means you start with *a* and divide by *b*, so you write $\frac{a}{b}$.

Variable Expression	Verbal Phrase
$5n$	The product of 5 and *n*
$3 + x$	The sum of 3 and *x*
$R - C$	The difference of *R* and *C*
$\frac{y}{12}$	The quotient of *y* and 12

To **evaluate a variable expression**, substitute a number for the variable (or variables) and find the value of the resulting numerical expression.

EXAMPLE 2 Evaluating Variable Expressions

a. Evaluate $5n$ when $n = 6$.

b. Evaluate $x + y$ when $x = 2.5$ and $y = 1.4$.

Solution

a. $5n = 5(\mathbf{6})$ Substitute 6 for *n*.

$= 30$ Simplify.

b. $x + y = \mathbf{2.5} + \mathbf{1.4}$ Substitute 2.5 for *x* and 1.4 for *y*.

$= 3.9$ Simplify.

Link to History

ROYAL ROADS The Incas built a road system over 14,000 miles long, from Quito, Ecuador, to southern Chile.

EXAMPLE 3 Using an Expression

HISTORY LINK Suppose the distance along Inca roads from Cuzco, Peru, to Copiapo, Chile, is *x* miles. The distance from Copiapo to Catarpe, Chile, is *y* miles. Then the distance from Catarpe to Cuzco can be represented by the expression $x - y$. Find the approximate distance given *x* is about 1150 miles and *y* is about 375 miles.

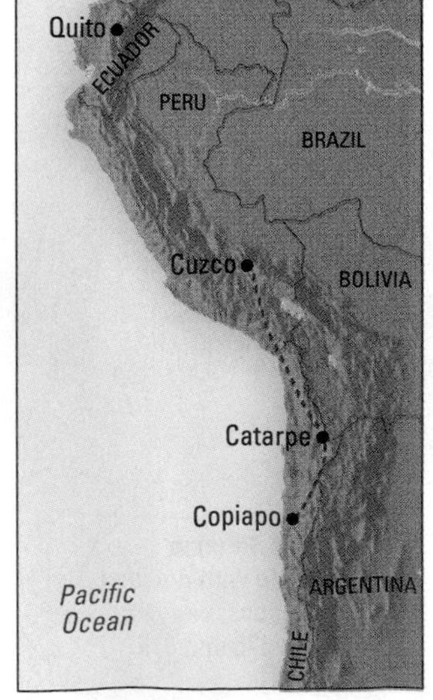

Solution

$x - y = \mathbf{1150} - \mathbf{375}$ Substitute.

$= 775$ Simplify.

ANSWER ▶ The road from Catarpe to Cuzco is about 775 miles long.

1.2 Exercises

Guided Practice

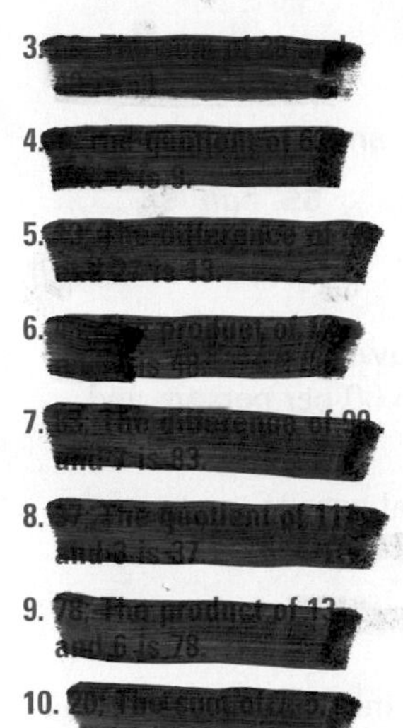

1. Are the parts of the expression 32 • 5.2 called *terms* or *factors*?
2. Are the parts of the expression 112 + 96 called *terms* or *factors*?

Evaluate the expression. Then describe the result in words.

3. 28 + 40 **4.** 63 ÷ 7 **5.** 40 − 27 **6.** 12 • 4

7. 90 − 7 **8.** 111 ÷ 3 **9.** 13 × 6 **10.** 7 + 5 + 8

Write the numerical expression. Then evaluate.

11. The sum of 15 and 33 **12.** The product of 20 and 7

13. The difference of 18 and 9 **14.** The quotient of 360 and 9

Evaluate the variable expression when $n = 3$.

15. $3n$ **16.** $n + 20$ **17.** $n - 2$ **18.** $n + 0$

19. $\frac{n}{1}$ **20.** $\frac{n}{3}$ **21.** $\frac{18}{n}$ **22.** $100 - n$

Practice and Problem Solving

Student Help

▶ More Practice
Extra practice to help you master skills is on page 690.

Evaluate the expression. Then write the result in words.

23. 6 × 8 **24.** 25 ÷ 5 **25.** 33 + 14

26. 9 × 7 **27.** 111 − 56 **28.** 12 − 4

29. 10 + 6 + 4 **30.** 76 ÷ 4 **31.** 5 • 12

32. 27 − 19 **33.** 5.4 + 4.3 **34.** 70 ÷ 35

In Exercises 35–38, match the verbal phrase with the expression.

A. $x + 8$ **B.** $x - 8$ **C.** $\frac{x}{8}$ **D.** $8x$

35. The difference of x and 8 **36.** The product of x and 8

37. The quotient of x and 8 **38.** The sum of x and 8

Write a numerical expression for the phrase. Then evaluate.

39. The sum of 56 and 89 **40.** The product of 19 and 9

41. The quotient of 50 and 10 **42.** The difference of 30 and 21

43. The product of 6 and 5 **44.** The sum of 92 and 8

45. The difference of 200 and 36 **46.** The quotient of 72 and 24

3 Apply

Assignment Guide

Transitional
Day 1: SRH p. 675 Exs. 5–12, p. 676 Exs. 5–12; pp. 9–11 Exs. 23–30, 35–38, 48–51, 64–65, 83–91

Average
Day 1: pp. 9–11 Exs. 26–31, 35–42, 50–53, 58–61, 66–68, 83–85, 89–93

Advanced
Day 1: pp. 9–11 Exs. 29–38, 43–47, 54–61, 66–68, 69–71*, 80–85, 92–96

Block Schedule
pp. 9–11 Exs. 26–31, 35–42, 50–53, 58–61, 66–68, 83–85, 89–93 (with 1.1)

Extra Practice

- Student Edition, pp. 690–691
- Chapter 1 Resource Book, p. 15

Homework Check

To quickly check student understanding of key concepts, go over the following exercises:

Transitional: 26, 28, 38, 50, 64
Average: 26, 40, 50, 58, 66
Advanced: 30, 44, 54, 58, 66

47. Write three different expressions whose value is 99.

ALGEBRA Evaluate the variable expression when $x = 4$.

48. $5 + x$ **49.** $\frac{8.8}{x}$ **50.** $7x$ **51.** $\frac{x}{4}$

52. $x - 2$ **53.** $10x$ **54.** $x + 6$ **55.** $9 - x$

ALGEBRA Evaluate the expression when $a = 2$ and $b = 7$.

56. $b - a$ **57.** $15 - b$ **58.** ab **59.** $5ab$

60. $a + b$ **61.** $b + a$ **62.** $a + b + 1$ **63.** $b + 9 + a$

MOVIE COSTS In Exercises 64 and 65, use the following information. You and 5 friends go to the movies. Tickets cost \$6.00 per person, and each person buys a bag of popcorn for \$2.00.

64. Write a numerical expression that gives the total cost of the movies and popcorn for you and your friends.

65. Evaluate your expression from Exercise 64.

Student Help

▶ **HOMEWORK HELP**

Extra help with problem solving in Exs. 66–68 is available at www.mcdougallittell.com

BOOK CLUB In Exercises 66–68, use the following information. To join a book club, you need to buy 8 books for \$2. Shipping costs are \$4.95 for all 8 books. Later, you must buy 4 more books at \$7 each. These shipments cost \$2.95 for each book.

66. Write and evaluate a numerical expression to represent the total number of books you must purchase if you join the club.

67. Write and evaluate a numerical expression to represent how much you will spend in shipping costs.

68. Write and evaluate a numerical expression to represent the total cost for the books and shipping.

CHALLENGE In Exercises 69–74, the expression has a value of 20. Find the value of the variable in the expression.

69. $5w$ **70.** $45 - t$ **71.** $\frac{y}{4}$

72. $14 + s$ **73.** $p - 8$ **74.** $3n + 2$

75. WRITING Evaluate the expressions in the sequence below when $s = 2$. Then write a description of the pattern.

$$s, 2s, 3s, 4s, 5s, 6s, 7s, 8s, 9s, 10s$$

AGES Write a numerical expression that represents the verbal phrase. Then evaluate the expression.

76. Your age two years ago **77.** Five times your age

78. Your age two years from now **79.** Your age divided by 2

MATHEMATICAL REASONING Find the value for the variable.

80. What value of w makes the expressions $2w$ and $2 + w$ equal?

81. What value of n makes the expressions $3n$ and $n + 6$ equal?

82. What value of d makes the expressions $d - 2$ and $\frac{d}{2}$ equal?

Multiple-Choice Practice

83. If $x = 15$ and $y = 7$, which of the following is true?

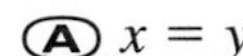

Ⓐ $x = y$ Ⓑ $xy = 35$ Ⓒ $x + 8 = y$ Ⓓ $x + y = 22$

84. What is the value of $x - y$ when $x = 19$ and $y = 11$?

Ⓕ 2 Ⓖ 8 Ⓗ 20 Ⓙ 31

85. What is the value of $9t$ when $t = 7$?

Ⓐ 16 Ⓑ 54 Ⓒ 63 Ⓓ 71

Mixed Review

Estimate the sum, difference, product, or quotient. *(pp. 679, 680)*

86. $983 + 512 + 194$ **87.** $8642 - 2194$ **88.** 38×22

89. 829×11 **90.** $229 \div 6$ **91.** $102.62 \div 4$

HEALTH In Exercises 92 and 93, use the following information. You start an exercise program gradually. The first day you work out for 5 minutes. After that you double your exercise time each day for 1 week. *(1.1)*

92. Make a table to show the amount of time you exercise each day for 1 week.

93. Describe any pattern you see in the data. Is your exercise program reasonable? Explain.

93. The doubling pattern increases by large amounts. No; by day 7 exercise time will be $5\frac{1}{3}$ hours, probably more time than you can spend exercising.

INFORMATION CENTER Use the graph below. It shows the number of visitors each day to a tourist information center. *(1.1)*

94. About how many adults visited the center on Wednesday?

95. On what day did the greatest number of students visit the information center?

96. On what day was the difference between the numbers of adult visitors and student visitors the least? On what day was the difference greatest?

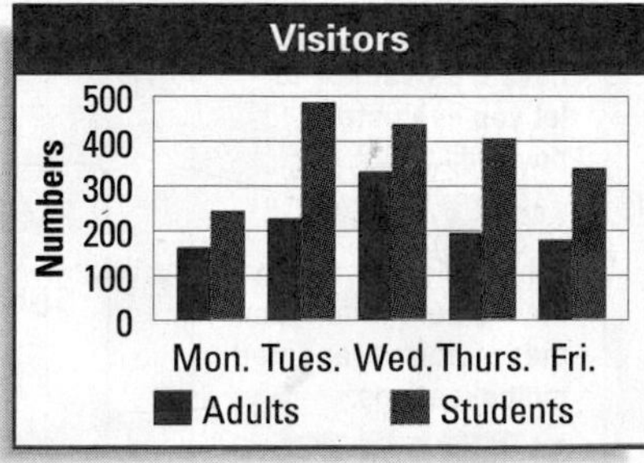

4 Assess

Assessment Resources

- Assessment Book (Formal Assessment and Alternative Assessment)
- Test and Practice Generator

Mini-Quiz

Evaluate the expression. Write the results in words.

1. 6×9
2. $52 \div 4$
3. $65 - 43$
4. Evaluate $\frac{56}{x}$ when $x = 8$.
5. Evaluate $x + y - 3$ when $x = 7$ and $y = 6$.

92.

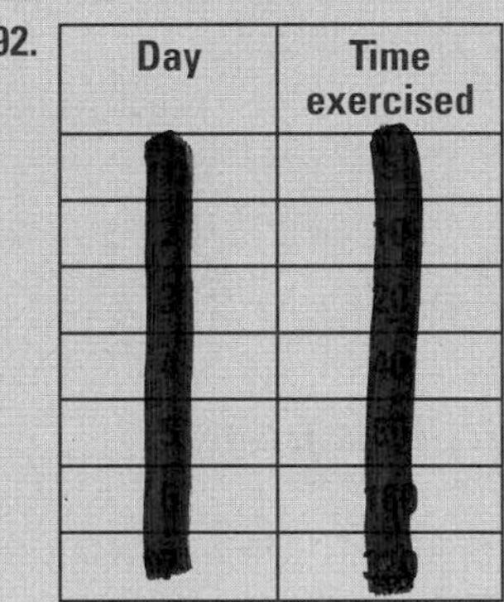

Day	Time exercised

1 Plan

Pacing

Suggested Number of Days

Transitional: 1 day
Average: 1 day
Advanced: 1 day
Block Schedule: 0.5 block with 1.4

Teaching Resources

Blacklines
(See page 1B.)

Transparencies
- Warm-Up Exercises
- Teacher Time-Savers
- English/Spanish Problem Solving
- Answers

Technology
- Electronic Teacher Tools
- Test and Practice Generator

2 Teach

Math Reasoning

For Mathematical Background Notes on mathematical reasoning related to this lesson, please refer to pages 1E and 1F in this Teacher's Edition.

California Standards and Assessment

CA Standards: AF 2.0, AF 2.1, MG 2.1

CA Key Concepts Book: pp. S19, S21, T1–T2

1.3 Powers and Exponents

California Standards

In this lesson you'll:
- Interpret and evaluate expressions involving powers. (AF 2.0)
- Interpret positive whole-number powers as repeated multiplication. (AF 2.1)
- Use formulas for finding the area and volume of basic figures. (MG 2.1)

Goal 1 Evaluating Powers

You can write the areas of the squares below as products or as *powers*.

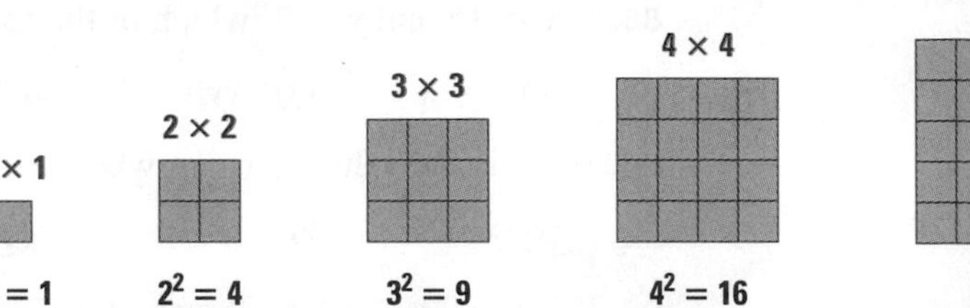

$1^2 = 1$ $2^2 = 4$ $3^2 = 9$ $4^2 = 16$ $5^2 = 25$

A **power** has two parts: a **base** and an **exponent**. In general, if a is any number and m is any positive whole number, then the mth power of a is

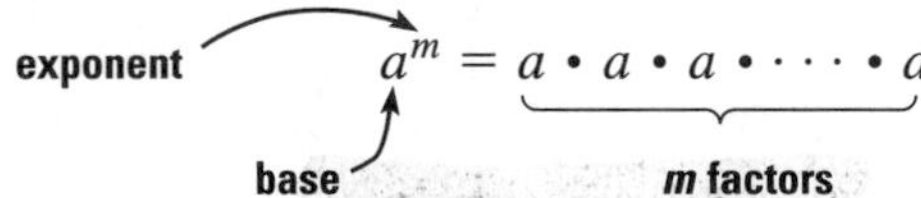

$$a^m = a \cdot a \cdot a \cdot \cdots \cdot a$$

where the exponent m tells you how many times the base a is repeated as a factor. In the power 5^2, the base is 5 and the exponent is 2.

EXAMPLE 1 Reading a Power

State a verbal phrase for the power and write the power using repeated multiplication.

a. 6^2 **b.** 10^3 **c.** x^4

Solution

	Power	Verbal Phrase	Repeated Multiplication
a.	6^2	6 to the second power or 6 squared	$6 \cdot 6$
b.	10^3	10 to the third power or 10 cubed	$10 \cdot 10 \cdot 10$
c.	x^4	x to the fourth power	$x \cdot x \cdot x \cdot x$

EXAMPLE 2 Evaluating a Power

Evaluate x^4 when $x = 5$.

Solution

$x^4 = 5^4$ Substitute 5 for x.

$= 5 \cdot 5 \cdot 5 \cdot 5$ Write power as a product.

$= 625$ Multiply.

Student Help

TECHNOLOGY TIP
Some calculators have a power key to let you evaluate a power like 6.1^3.

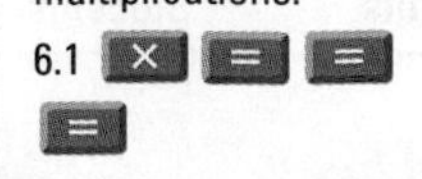

Other calculators may have a built-in function that performs repeated multiplications:

Goal 2 Using Powers to Find Area and Volume

> **Student Help**
> ▶ **VOCABULARY TIP**
> The word *squared* is used to describe raising to the second power because finding the area of a *square* involves a second power. The word *cubed* is used to describe raising to the third power because finding the volume of a *cube* involves a third power. For help with area and volume, see pages 682–684.

Exponents can be used to express the area of a square and the volume of a cube.

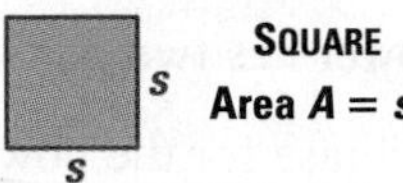

SQUARE
Area $A = s^2$

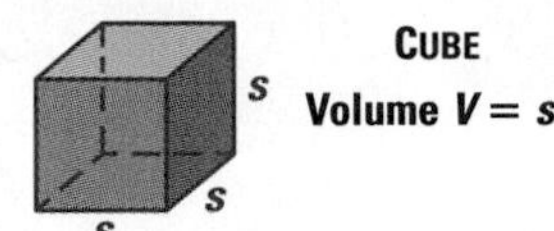

CUBE
Volume $V = s^3$

EXAMPLE 3 Finding the Area of a Square

A baseball diamond is being fertilized. Each bag of fertilizer covers 1200 square feet of grass. About how many bags of fertilizer are needed?

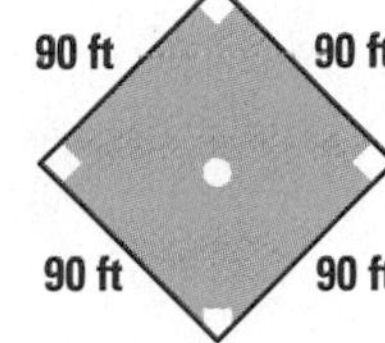

Solution

Find the area of the square field.

$A = s^2$	Area of a square
$= \mathbf{90}^2$	Substitute 90 for *s*.
$= 8100 \text{ ft}^2$	Evaluate power.

Divide the area by the number of square feet that one bag covers.

$8100 \div 1200 = 6.75$

ANSWER ▶ About 7 bags of fertilizer are needed.

EXAMPLE 4 Finding the Volume of a Cube

A 12 inch by 12 inch by 12 inch box is to be filled with small wooden cubes measuring 2 inches by 2 inches by 2 inches. How many cubes fill the box?

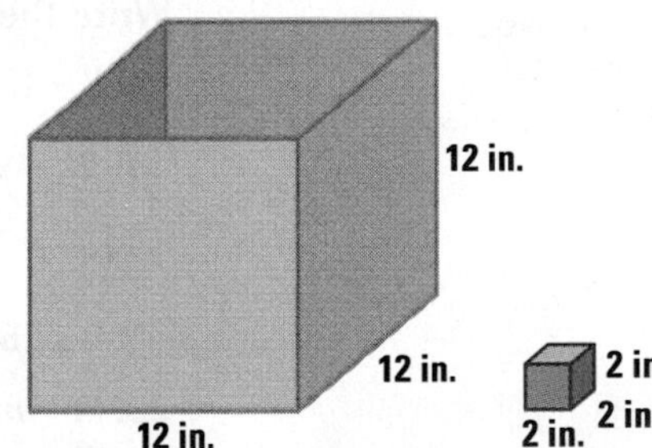

Solution

Find the volume of the box.

$V = s^3 = \mathbf{12}^3 = 1728 \text{ in.}^3$

Find the volume of one wooden cube.

$V = s^3 = \mathbf{2}^3 = 8 \text{ in.}^3$

Divide the volume of the box by the volume of the wooden cube.

$1728 \div 8 = 216$

ANSWER ▶ You can fit 216 cubes inside the box.

> **Student Help**
> ▶ **MORE EXAMPLES**
> More examples are available at www.mcdougallittell.com

Math Reasoning

Repeated multiplication leads to the special notation of exponents, much the same way that repeated addition leads to the special notation of multiplication.

Extra Example 1

State a verbal phrase and meaning for each power.

a. 2^5 **2 to the 5th power; 2 • 2 • 2 • 2 • 2**

b. 3^4 **3 to the 4th power; 3 • 3 • 3 • 3**

c. x^3 ***x*** **to the 3rd power; *x* • *x* • *x***

Extra Example 2

Evaluate x^3 when $x = 6$. **216**

Extra Example 3

The side of a barn is to be painted. The side is square, 20 feet long and 20 feet high. A can of paint covers 225 square feet. Estimate the number of cans needed. **about 2 cans**

Extra Example 4

A box measures 18 inches by 18 inches by 18 inches. It is to be filled with cubes measuring 3 inches by 3 inches by 3 inches. How many cubes fill the box? **216 cubes**

> **Teaching Tip**
> The Technology Tip gives calculator steps for evaluating powers on most scientific calculators. However, if a student is using a graphing calculator, 6.1^3 must be entered as
> 6.1 [^] 3 [ENTER].

Concept Check

Describe how to evaluate a number raised to a power. ***Sample answer:*** **The power tells how many times to multiply the number by itself.**

3 Apply

Assignment Guide

TRANSITIONAL
Day 1: SRH pp. 672–673 Exs. 17–22; pp. 14–15 Exs. 12–16, 20–21, 25–28, 32–35, 41–42, 47–48

AVERAGE
Day 1: pp. 14–15 Exs. 12–15, 21–24, 27–35, 38–39, 42–44, 47–48

ADVANCED
Day 1: pp. 14–15 Exs. 10–15, 22–23, 26–33, 36–40, 43–45, 46*, 47–48

BLOCK SCHEDULE
pp. 14–15 Exs. 12–15, 21–24, 27–35, 38–39, 42–44, 47–48 (with 1.4)

Extra Practice

- Student Edition, pp. 690–691
- Chapter 1 Resource Book, p. 24

Homework Check

To quickly check student understanding of key concepts, go over the following exercises:

Transitional: 12, 14, 26, 32, 42, 44
Average: 12, 14, 22, 28, 42, 44
Advanced: 12, 14, 20, 28, 42, 44

1.3 Exercises

Guided Practice

1. Complete: A power has two parts, a(n) __?__ and a(n) __?__.

2. Write a verbal phrase for the power 3^4.

Rewrite the power as repeated multiplication. Then evaluate.

3. 4^2 **4.** 7^2 **5.** 3^4 **6.** 2^3 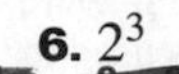

DESIGNING A GARDEN In Exercises 7 and 8, use the following information. You are designing a garden. You want to have a square plot with each side measuring 14 feet.

7. Find the area of the garden. 

8. What would the area be if each side measured 28 feet instead?

9. A toy box is in the shape of a cube, measuring 24 inches by 24 inches by 24 inches. How many wooden cubes measuring 3 inches by 3 inches by 3 inches are needed to fill the box? **512**

Practice and Problem Solving

Student Help

▶MORE PRACTICE
Extra practice to help you master skills is on page 690.

Rewrite the power as repeated multiplication. Then evaluate.

10. 6^2 **11.** 5^3 **12.** 4^4 **13.** 3^3

Write the expression as a power.

14. $8 \cdot 8 \cdot 8 \cdot 8 \cdot 8$ **15.** $3 \cdot 3 \cdot 3 \cdot 3 \cdot 3 \cdot 3 \cdot 3$

16. $97 \cdot 97$ **17.** $10 \cdot 10 \cdot 10 \cdot 10$

18. $35 \cdot 35 \cdot 35$ **19.** $1 \cdot 1 \cdot 1 \cdot 1 \cdot 1$

ALGEBRA Write the expression as a power. Then evaluate.

20. $m \cdot m \cdot m$, when $m = 6$ **21.** $x \cdot x \cdot x \cdot x \cdot x$, when $x = 2$

22. $z \cdot z \cdot z \cdot z$, when $z = 10$ **23.** $n \cdot n$, when $n = 12$

ALGEBRA Evaluate the expression when $m = 3$.

24. m^2 **25.** m^3 **26.** m^4

27. $m \cdot m^2$ **28.** $m^3 \cdot m^2$ **29.** $m^2 \cdot m \cdot m^2$

Student Help

▶READING TIP
Remember: The symbol < is read *is less than* and the symbol > is read *is greater than.*

Complete the statement using <, =, or >.

30. 2^3 ? 3^2 **31.** 2^4 ? 4^2 **32.** 4^3 ? 3^4 **33.** 2^6 ? 6^2

CALCULATOR In Exercises 34–37, round the base to estimate the value of the power. Then use a calculator to check your estimate.

34. 1.9^3 **35.** 9^6 **36.** 0.8^4 **37.** 68^2

38. MATHEMATICAL REASONING Using a calculator, you find that 2^{10} is equal to 1024. Explain how you can find 2^{10} without the calculator. Given this value, how would you find 2^{11} without the calculator?

In Exercises 39–41, find the number that makes the sentence true.

39. $y \cdot y = 9$ **40.** $m \cdot m \cdot m = 512$ **41.** $r \cdot r \cdot r \cdot r = 625$

42. PAINTING A WALL You want to paint an auditorium wall that measures 25 feet by 25 feet. If each can of paint covers 400 square feet, how many cans will be needed to paint the wall?

AIR CONDITIONING In Exercises 43 and 44, use the following information. The square floor of an empty room measures 10 feet by 10 feet. The height of the room is also 10 feet. An air conditioner will cool 50 cubic feet of air in 8 minutes.

43. How long will it take to cool all the air in the room?

44. Think of the air conditioner cooling 100 cubic feet in 16 minutes. How does this help you check your answer in Exercise 43?

45. 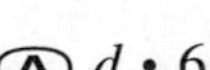 Each column in an abacus represents a power of ten. Complete the place-value table below. Describe a pattern in the powers of ten. Then use the pattern to evaluate 10^{10}.

Power	10^6	10^5	10^4	10^3	10^2	10^1
Number	?	?	?	?	?	10

46. CHALLENGE A box measures 16 inches by 16 inches by 16 inches. Either red or blue cubes can be used to fill the box. Red cubes measure 2 inches by 2 inches by 2 inches. Blue cubes measure 4 inches by 4 inches by 4 inches. To fill the box, do you need twice as many red cubes as blue cubes? Explain your answer. **See margin.**

ABACUS Ancient Egyptians, Hindus, and Chinese used the abacus for counting, adding, and subtracting. The trade routes of the Middle Ages brought the abacus to European merchants.

More about using an abacus available at www.mcdougallittell.com

Multiple-Choice Practice

47. What is another way to write $d \cdot d \cdot d \cdot d \cdot d \cdot d$?

Ⓐ $d \cdot 6$ Ⓑ d^6 Ⓒ $6d$ Ⓓ d cubed

48. Which expression represents the area of a square with sides that measure 7 feet by 7 feet?

Ⓕ $4 \cdot 7$ feet Ⓖ $4 \cdot 7$ square feet

Ⓗ 7^2 feet Ⓙ 7^2 square feet

46. No, you need 8 times as many. The volume of each red cube is 8 cubic inches and the volume of each blue cube is 64 inches.

4 Assess

Assessment Resources

- Assessment Book (Formal Assessment and Alternative Assessment)
- Test and Practice Generator

Mini-Quiz

State a verbal phrase and meaning for each power.

1. 5^4 **5 raised to the fourth power; $5 \cdot 5 \cdot 5 \cdot 5$**
2. x^5 **x raised to the fifth power; $x \cdot x \cdot x \cdot x \cdot x$**
3. Evaluate x^5 when $x = 2$. **32**
4. An entry area in a house is square, 60 inches by 60 inches. Tiles 3 inches by 3 inches are to cover the floor. How many tiles will be needed? **400 tiles**

Math Reasoning

In connection with Exercise 46, could you fill the box using one blue cube and the rest red cubes? Using one red cube and the rest blue cubes? **Yes; no**

45.

Power	Number
[illegible]	[illegible]
[illegible]	[illegible]
[illegible]	[illegible]
[illegible]	[illegible]
[illegible]	[illegible]
[illegible]	[illegible]

The exponent is the number of zeros; 10,000,000,000.

1 Plan

Pacing

Suggested Number of Days

Transitional: 1 day
Average: 1 day
Advanced: 1 day
Block Schedule: 0.5 block with 1.3

Teaching Resources

Blacklines
(See page 1B.)

Transparencies
- Warm-Up Exercises
- Teacher Time-Savers
- English/Spanish Problem Solving
- Answers

Technology
- Electronic Teacher Tools
- Test and Practice Generator

2 Teach

Math Reasoning

For Mathematical Background Notes on mathematical reasoning related to this lesson, please refer to pages 1E and 1F in this Teacher's Edition.

California Standards and Assessment

CA Standards: AF 1.2, AF 1.3

1.4 Order of Operations

California Standards

In this lesson you'll:
- Use the correct order of operations to evaluate algebraic expressions. (AF 1.2)
- Simplify numerical expressions and justify the process used. (AF 1.3)

Goal 1 Using Order of Operations

When you evaluate the expression $4 + 3 \cdot 5$, is the value 35 or 19? Rules for **order of operations** are necessary so that expressions are evaluated in a consistent way by everyone.

ORDER OF OPERATIONS

1. Evaluate expressions inside grouping symbols.
2. Evaluate powers.
3. Multiply and divide from left to right.
4. Add and subtract from left to right.

EXAMPLE 1 Using the Order of Operations

Evaluate. **a.** $2 + 12 \div 3$ **b.** 4×3^2

Solution

a. $2 + \mathbf{12 \div 3} = 2 + \mathbf{4}$ First divide 12 by 3.
$= 6$ Then add 2 and 4.

b. $4 \times \mathbf{3^2} = 4 \times \mathbf{9}$ First evaluate the power 3^2.
$= 36$ Then multiply 4 and 9.

If an expression has more than one multiplication, more than one division, or a combination of multiplications and divisions, perform them in left-to-right order. The same rule applies to additions and subtractions.

EXAMPLE 2 Using the Left-to-Right Rule

Evaluate. **a.** $6 \div 3 \cdot 5$ **b.** $7 - 5 + 8 - 4$

Solution

a. $\mathbf{6 \div 3} \cdot 5 = \mathbf{2} \cdot 5$ Left-to-right rule: Divide 6 by 3.
$= 10$ Then multiply 2 and 5.

b. $\mathbf{7 - 5} + 8 - 4 = \mathbf{2 + 8} - 4$ Left-to-right rule: Subtract 5 from 7.
$= \mathbf{10} - 4$ Then add 2 and 8.
$= 6$ Then subtract 4 from 10.

Goal 2 USING GROUPING SYMBOLS

To change the order of operations or to make an expression clearer, you can use **grouping symbols**. The most common grouping symbols are parentheses ( ), brackets [ ], and fraction bars.

EXAMPLE 3 Evaluating with Grouping Symbols

Evaluate the expression.

a. $(3 + 4) \cdot 2$ **b.** $8 \div (5 \cdot 3 - 7)$

Solution

a. $(\mathbf{3 + 4}) \cdot 2 = \mathbf{7} \cdot 2$ Add inside parentheses.

$= 14$ Multiply.

b. $8 \div (\mathbf{5 \cdot 3} - 7) = 8 \div (\mathbf{15} - 7)$ Multiply inside parentheses.

$= 8 \div \mathbf{8}$ Subtract inside parentheses.

$= 1$ Divide.

EXAMPLE 4 Writing Verbal Phrases

Write a verbal phrase for the expression. Then evaluate the expression.

a. $14 - 6 \cdot 2$ **b.** $(14 - 6) \cdot 2$

Solution

a. The product of 6 and 2, subtracted from 14

$14 - \mathbf{6 \cdot 2} = 14 - \mathbf{12}$ First multiply.

$= 2$ Then subtract.

b. The difference of 14 and 6, multiplied by 2

$(\mathbf{14 - 6}) \cdot 2 = \mathbf{8} \cdot 2$ First evaluate inside parentheses.

$= 16$ Then multiply.

EXAMPLE 5 Evaluating a Variable Expression

Evaluate $2x^2 + 3x - 4$ when $x = 2$.

Solution

$2x^2 + 3x - 4 = 2(2^2) + 3(2) - 4$ Substitute 2 for *x*.

$= 2(4) + 3(2) - 4$ Evaluate power.

$= 8 + 6 - 4$ Multiply.

$= 14 - 4$ Use left-to-right rule.

$= 10$ Subtract.

Student Help

MORE EXAMPLES

More examples are available at www.mcdougallittell.com

Extra Example 1

Evaluate each expression.

a. $16 - 20 \div 2^2$ **11**

b. $3^3 + 4 \times 6$ **51**

Extra Example 2

Evaluate each expression.

a. $64 \div 8 \times 4$ **32**

b. $23 - 8 - 5$ **10**

Extra Example 3

Evaluate each expression.

a. $64 \div (8 \cdot 4)$ **2**

b. $3 + [(18 - 7) \cdot 2]$ **25**

Extra Example 4

Write a verbal phrase for the expression. Then evaluate the expression.

a. $20 - 8 \cdot 2$ **the product of 8 and 2 subtracted from 20; 4**

b. $(20 - 8) \cdot 2$ **the difference of 20 and 8 multiplied by 2; 24**

Extra Example 5

Evaluate $3x^2 - 8x + 1$ when $x = 3$. **4**

Teaching Tip

Avoiding Common Errors
Point out that when an expression contains more than one set of grouping symbols, at each stage of the computation the expression within the innermost grouping symbols is evaluated first.

Concept Check

How do you use the order of operations to simplify an expression? **First simplify expressions within grouping symbols. Next, evaluate powers. Then do multiplications and divisions from left to right. Finally, do additions and subtractions from left to right.**

3 Apply

Assignment Guide

TRANSITIONAL
Day 1: pp. 18–20 Exs. 20–25, 32–34, 38–39, 42–44, 47–48, 53–55, 62–63, 77–81

AVERAGE
Day 1: pp. 18–20 Exs. 22–27, 32–35, 39–44, 47–48, 54–57, 64–65, 77–81

ADVANCED
Day 1: pp. 18–20 Exs. 30–36, 40–44, 47–49, 51*, 52–55, 66–70, 71–74*, 77–81

BLOCK SCHEDULE
pp. 18–20 Exs. 22–27, 32–35, 39–44, 47–48, 54–57, 64–65, 77–81 (with 1.3)

Extra Practice

- Student Edition, pp. 690–691
- Chapter 1 Resource Book, p. 33

Homework Check

To quickly check student understanding of key concepts, go over the following exercises:

Transitional: 22, 34, 38, 42, 54, 62
Average: 24, 34, 40, 48, 54, 64
Advanced: 28, 34, 42, 48, 54, 68

1.4 Exercises

Guided Practice

Evaluate the expression.

1. $18 - 4 \cdot 3$ **2.** $48 \div 6 + 3$ **3.** $(12 + 6) \div 2$

4. $12 + 4^2 - 3$ **5.** $3^2 + (7 - 1)$ **6.** $(9 - 2 + 3) \cdot 6$

In Exercises 7–12, match the expression with the verbal phrase.

7. $4(8 - 7)$ **A.** The difference of 20 and 2, multiplied by 6

8. $6 \cdot 21 \div 3$ **B.** The product of 4 and 8, minus 7

9. $(20 - 2) \cdot 6$ **C.** The difference of 8 and 7, multiplied by 4

10. $6(21 \div 3)$ **D.** The product of 2 and 6, subtracted from 20

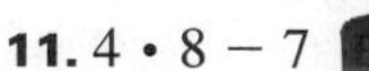

11. $4 \cdot 8 - 7$ **E.** The quotient of 21 and 3, multiplied by 6

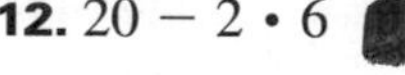

12. $20 - 2 \cdot 6$ **F.** The product of 6 and 21, divided by 3

32.
33.
34.

35.

36.
37.

In Exercises 13–18, evaluate the variable expression when $x = 3$.

13. $\frac{10x}{5}$ **14.** $3x + 9$ **15.** $4x + 7$

16. $19 - 2x$ **17.** $(x + 6) \cdot 5$ **18.** $2x^2 + 3x + 1$

19. ERROR ANALYSIS Describe and correct the error.

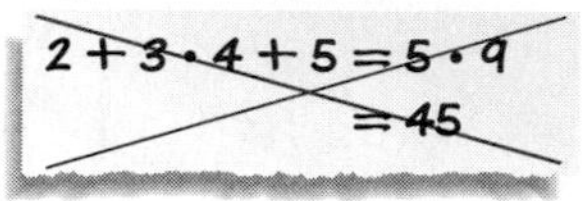

Practice and Problem Solving

Student Help

▶**MORE PRACTICE**
Extra practice to help you master skills is on page 690.

Evaluate the expression.

20. $7 + 12 \div 6$ **21.** $12 - 3 \times 4$

22. $5 \cdot 3 + 2^2$ **23.** $5^2 - 8 \div 2$

24. $(4 \div 2) \times 9 + 11$ **25.** $(21 - 1) \cdot 2 \div 4$

26. $14 - 8 + 4 \cdot 2^3$ **27.** $3^3 - 8 \cdot 3 \div 12$

28. $(9 + 7) \div 4 \times 2$ **29.** $34 - 5(5) + 13$

30. $16 + 4 \cdot 2 - 7$ **31.** $3[16 - (3 + 7) \div 5]$

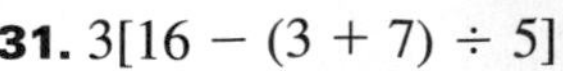

Write a verbal phrase that describes the expression. Then evaluate.

32. $25 - 5 \cdot 2$ **33.** $20 - 16 \div 4$ **34.** $12 \cdot 10 - 3$

35. $(20 - 16) \div 4$ **36.** $(25 - 5) \cdot 2$ **37.** $12(10 - 3)$

38. **TEAM UNIFORMS** There are 20 players on the baseball team. Each player receives a cap, a jersey, and pants. Caps cost \$15, jerseys cost \$75, and pants cost \$60. Write and evaluate an expression for the total cost of the team's outfits.

$\frac{1}{2}$ price Junior Admission
Aquarium
Present this coupon and receive a $\frac{1}{2}$ price Junior Admission (Ages 3–11) with a purchase of a General Admission (Ages 12+)

39. **DISCOUNTS** An aquarium charges a regular general admission price of \$15 and a regular junior admission price of \$6. Three adults, a 4-year-old, an 8-year-old, and a 12-year-old visit the aquarium. They have the discount coupon shown. Write and evaluate an expression for the total cost for their visit.

40. **CLOTHING SALE** A dress store advertises that if you buy one sweater you get a second of lesser or equal value at half price. You buy one sweater that costs \$38 and another that costs \$42. Write and evaluate an expression for the total cost of the sweaters.

Evaluate the expression when $x = 5$ and $y = 8$.

41. $3y + 2x + y$

42. $5x + y - 4 + 2y$

43. $\frac{xy}{10}$

44. $2(x + y) - 19$

45. $5(x - 4) + 5(y - 4)$

46. $x^2 + y^2$

Evaluate the expression when $a = 10$, $b = 5$, and $c = 2$.

47. $a - b \cdot c$

48. $\frac{ab}{c}$

49. $(5 + a) \div b + c$

50. $(b + a + 3 + c) \cdot 3$

51. **CHALLENGE** Write two 2-digit numbers using each of the digits 1, 2, 3, and 4 only once. Then find the sum of the numbers. What are the greatest and the least possible sums that can be made in this way? Justify your answers.

51. $14 + 23 = 37$ The greatest sum is 73 and the least is 37. Letting the two largest numbers represent the number of tens results in the largest sum while letting the two smallest numbers represent the tens results in the smallest sum.

Student Help

▶TECHNOLOGY TIP
Check your calculator to see if it follows the order of operations. Enter 3 [+] 6 [×] 2 [=]. If the display is 15, the calculator uses the correct order of operations. If it displays 18, it does not.

CALCULATOR Evaluate the expression. You may use a calculator if you wish.

52. $3 \cdot 5 + 2 - 1$

53. $4 \cdot 10 - 3 - 2$

54. $29 + 16 \div 8 \cdot 25$

55. $36 + 16 - 50 \div 25$

56. $18 \cdot 3 \div 3^3$

57. $10 + 5^3 - 25$

58. $20 - (3^4 \div 27) \cdot 2$

59. $149 - (2^8 - 40) \div 6$

60. $22 + (34 \cdot 2)^2 \div 8$

61. $85 - (4 \cdot 2)^2 - 3$

MATHEMATICAL REASONING If the given value of the expression is incorrect, insert parentheses to make it correct.

62. $15 + 6 \div 3 = 17$

63. $7 + 2 \div 7 - 4 = 3$

64. $10 - 2 + 1 \times 2 = 10$

65. $6 \times 3 - 2 \times 5 = 8$

66. $6 + 3^2 \div 3 = 5$

67. $8 + 16 \div 2 \times 2 = 6$

67. $(8 + 16) \div (2 \cdot 2) = 6$

4 Assess

Assessment Resources

- Assessment Book (Formal Assessment and Alternative Assessment)
- Test and Practice Generator

Mini-Quiz

1. Simplify the expression without using a calculator.
   a. $2 \cdot 9 + 4 \div 2$ **20**
   b. $11 - 3 \cdot 4 \div 6$ **9**
   c. $(9 + 12) \div 3 + 7$ **14**
2. Decide whether the number sentence is *true* or *false*. If it is false, copy it and insert parentheses to make it true.
   a. $24 \div 6 + 2 \cdot 3 = 9$ **false;** $24 \div (6 + 2) \cdot 3 = 9$
   b. $72 - 6 \div 3 + 4 = 26$ **false;** $(72 - 6) \div 3 + 4 = 26$
   c. $7 + 3^2 - 4 \cdot 3 = 4$ **true**

68. BUYING POWER Prices for school supplies are shown on the sign. You purchase 5 folders, 3 notebooks, and a calculator at the bookstore. Write an expression that represents your total cost. Then evaluate the expression to find your total cost.

BACK TO SCHOOL
SALE
FOLDER $.50
HIGHLIGHTER $1.49
NOTEBOOK $2.25
CALCULATOR $5.99

69. MUSIC In 1995 about \$2 billion worth of recorded country music was sold. Recorded rock music sold about twice that amount. The total amount of *all* recorded music sold was about twice the sum of country and rock. Write an expression that approximates the total amount of all recorded music sold in 1995. Then evaluate the expression. ▶ Source: *The Universal Almanac 1997*

70. CHALLENGE In high school football, a touchdown is worth 6 points, a field goal is worth 3 points, and a safety is worth 2 points. Following a touchdown, a team can try for a 1-point or 2-point conversion. In how many ways can a team score 9 points? Explain your answer.

CHALLENGE Copy the expression. Insert grouping symbols if necessary so that the value of the expression is 25 when $x = 2$ and $y = 5$.

71. $x^2 + 1 \cdot y$ **72.** $1 + y^2 - x - 1$ **73.** $3 \cdot x + y + 4$

74. $x^2 \div y - 1 + 12x$ **75.** $y - x^2 \cdot 5^2$ **76.** $3 \cdot x^3 + y - x^2$

Multiple-Choice Practice

Test Tip Ⓐ Ⓑ Ⓒ Ⓓ

▶ When you prepare for a test, review rules and formulas. The order of operations will be used throughout your study of math. Memorize the order of operations so you will be able to successfully evaluate expressions such as those in Exs. 77–79.

77. What is the value of the expression $8 - 1 \cdot 4 \div 2$?

Ⓐ 2 Ⓑ 6 Ⓒ 14 Ⓓ Not here

78. What is the value of the expression $n + 6 \div 3 - 1$ when $n = 6$?

Ⓕ 3 Ⓖ 6 Ⓗ 7 Ⓙ 9

79. Which expression does *not* have a value of 38?

Ⓐ $(8 + 2) \cdot 3 + 8$ Ⓑ $8 + 2 \cdot 15$

Ⓒ $45 - (15 + 8)$ Ⓓ $(40 - 20) + 2 \cdot 9$

80. You purchase 3 cans of vegetables at \$.89 per can. How much change will you get if you pay with a \$10 bill?

Ⓕ \$.89 Ⓖ \$2.67 Ⓗ \$7.33 Ⓙ \$9.11

81. Which expression represents the product of 6 and a number n?

Ⓐ $6n$ Ⓑ $6 + n$ Ⓒ $6 - n$ Ⓓ $\frac{6}{n}$

Chapter 1 Mid-Chapter Test

Take this test as you would take a test in class. The answers to the exercises are given in the back of the book.

In Exercises 1–3, use the graph of town populations shown.

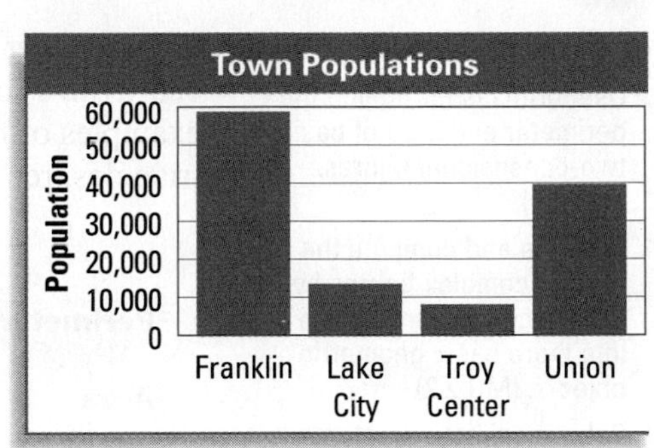

1. Which town has about three times as many residents as Lake City does?

2. Estimate the combined population of Franklin and Union.

3. What is the approximate difference between the populations of Franklin and Troy Center?

Evaluate the expression. Then write the result in words.

4. 19×3 **5.** $27 + 32$ **6.** $59 - 22$ **7.** $60 \div 15$

Evaluate the expression when $z = 3$.

8. $3z$ **9.** $9 - z$ **10.** $\frac{12}{z}$ **11.** $12 + z$

Rewrite the power as repeated multiplication. Then evaluate the product.

12. 8^2 **13.** 2^4 **14.** 3^3 **15.** 1^8

Evaluate the expression when $x = 2$.

16. x^1 **17.** x^5 **18.** $(x + 3)^2$ **19.** $10 - x^2$

In Exercises 20 and 21, you are planting a strawberry garden. The garden is a square plot with sides that measure 21 feet.

20. Find the area of the garden.

21. Each strawberry plant requires an area of 3 square feet. How many strawberry plants should you buy?

Evaluate the expression.

22. $13 - 8 + 5 - 2$ **23.** $14 + 12 - 4 \cdot 2$ **24.** $28 - 21 \div 7$

25. $24 \div 4 \cdot 3$ **26.** $24 \div (4 \cdot 3)$ **27.** $(40 + 15) \div 5$

28. $6 + 9 \div 3 - 1$ **29.** $9 \times (3 + 4) - 7$ **30.** $48 \div [2 \cdot (12 - 4)]$

Determine whether the value of the expression is correct. If it is incorrect, insert parentheses to make it correct.

31. $21 - 10 \times 2 = 22$ **32.** $42 - 10 \times 2 = 22$ **33.** $24 - 20 \div 4 + 6 = 22$

34. $10 \cdot 6 \div 4 + 7 = 22$ **35.** $2^2 \cdot 5 + 6 \div 2 = 22$ **36.** $3^3 - 15 \div 5 + 2 = 22$

Additional Resources

A Mid-Chapter Test and a Mid-Chapter Partner Quiz are available in the *Assessment Book*, pp. 3–4 and p. 210.

1 Plan

Pacing

Suggested Number of Days

Transitional: 1 day
Average: 1 day
Advanced: 1 day
Block Schedule: 0.5 block with 1.6

Teaching Resources

Blacklines
(See page 1B.)

Transparencies
- Warm-Up Exercises
- Teacher Time-Savers
- English/Spanish Problem Solving
- Answers

Technology
- Electronic Teacher Tools
- Test and Practice Generator

2 Teach

Math Reasoning

For Mathematical Background Notes on mathematical reasoning related to this lesson, please refer to pages 1E and 1F in this Teacher's Edition.

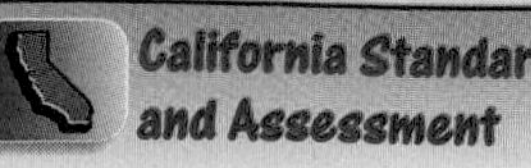

California Standards and Assessment

CA Standards: AF 4.2, MG 2.1, MG 2.2

CA Key Concepts Book: p. S77

1.5 Using Formulas

California Standards

In this lesson you'll:
- Use formulas for finding the perimeter and area of basic two-dimensional figures. (MG 2.1)
- Estimate and compute the area of complex figures by breaking the figures down into more basic geometric objects. (MG 2.2)
- Solve multi-step problems involving speed, distance, and time. (AF 4.2)

Goal 1 Finding Perimeter and Area

A **formula** is an algebraic equation that relates two or more variables. You can write a formula using numbers, operations, and variables. Important examples of formulas are those used to find the perimeter and area of triangles, rectangles, and squares.

	Triangle	Rectangle	Square
Perimeter	$P = a + b + c$	$P = 2w + 2\ell$	$P = 4s$
Area	$A = \frac{1}{2}bh$	$A = \ell w$	$A = s^2$

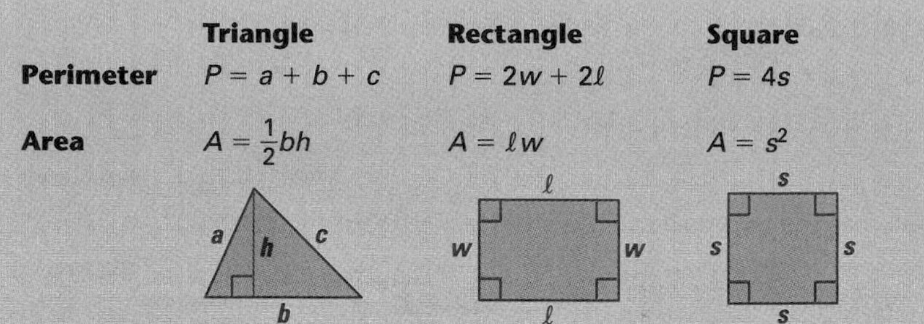

Student Help

Skills Review
For help with perimeter and area, see pages 682–684.

EXAMPLE 1 Finding Perimeter and Area

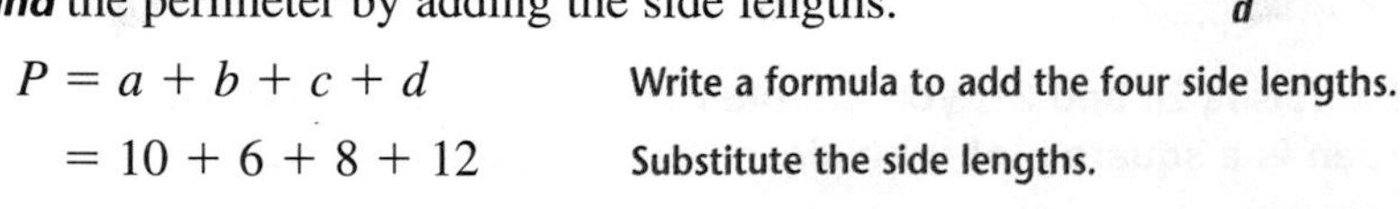

Find the perimeter and area of the figure given that $a = 10$ feet, $b = 6$ feet, $c = 8$ feet, and $d = 12$ feet.

Solution

Find the perimeter by adding the side lengths.

$P = a + b + c + d$ — Write a formula to add the four side lengths.

$= 10 + 6 + 8 + 12$ — Substitute the side lengths.

$= 36$ — Add.

ANSWER ▶ The perimeter of the figure is 36 feet.

Student Help

Reading Tip
Right triangles, squares, and rectangles use the symbol ⌟ to show right angles.

Find the area by dividing the figure into a triangle and a rectangle as shown.

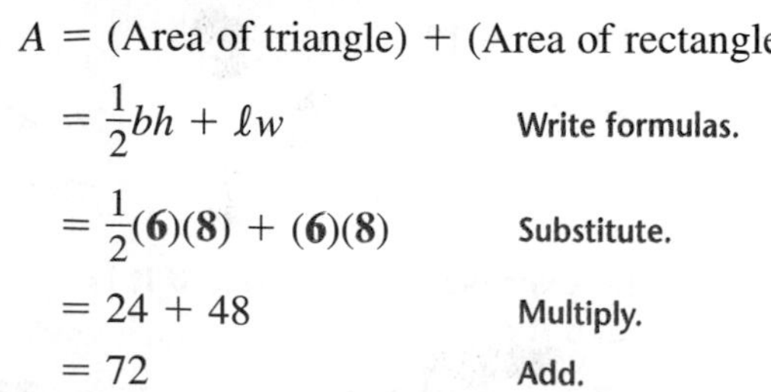

$A = $ (Area of triangle) + (Area of rectangle)

$= \frac{1}{2}bh + \ell w$ — Write formulas.

$= \frac{1}{2}(\mathbf{6})(\mathbf{8}) + (\mathbf{6})(\mathbf{8})$ — Substitute.

$= 24 + 48$ — Multiply.

$= 72$ — Add.

ANSWER ▶ The area of the figure is 72 square feet.

Goal 2 FINDING DISTANCE TRAVELED

You can use a formula involving distance, speed, and time.

DISTANCE TRAVELED

In Words To find the distance d that an object travels, multiply the speed r by the time t.
Distance = speed × time

In Algebra $d = r \cdot t$ or $d = rt$

In Arithmetic If the speed is 30 miles per hour and the time is 3 hours, then the distance is $30 \times 3 = 90$ miles.

EXAMPLE 2 Finding the Distance Traveled

CROSSING TIME ZONES An airplane flies across the United States at 450 miles per hour. It passes over Pittsburgh at about 9:00 A.M. (Eastern Standard Time) and over San Francisco at about 11:00 A.M. (Pacific Standard Time). About how far is San Francisco from Pittsburgh?

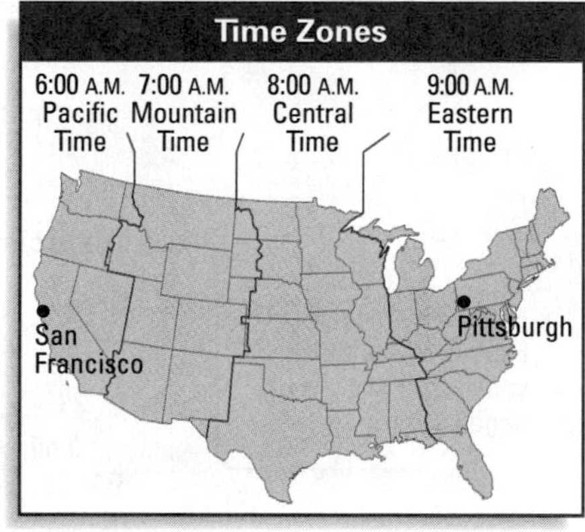

Solution

Find the time in hours. When it is 9:00 A.M. (EST), it is 6:00 A.M. (PST). So, from 6:00 A.M. PST to 11:00 A.M. PST is 5 hours.

Find the distance using the distance formula.

$d = rt$	Write formula.
$= \mathbf{450} \cdot \mathbf{5}$	Substitute 450 for r and 5 for t.
$= 2250$	Simplify.

ANSWER ▶ The distance is about 2250 miles.

You can use *unit analysis* to make sure that the units used in your answer are correct. Notice what happens when you consider only the units without the numbers in Example 2.

$$\frac{\text{miles}}{\cancel{\text{hour}}} \cdot \cancel{\text{hours}} = \text{miles}$$

The result is miles, which agrees with the fact that you are finding distance in Example 2.

Student Help

▶ **READING TIP**
You can write *miles per hour* as mi/h, or as $\frac{\text{miles}}{\text{hour}}$. They both represent division.

Math Reasoning

Once a student knows that the perimeter of any polygon is the sum of the lengths of its sides, there is no need to memorize formulas for perimeter. On the other hand, the area formulas for a rectangle and a triangle should be firmly committed to memory.

Extra Example 1

Find the perimeter and area of the figure.

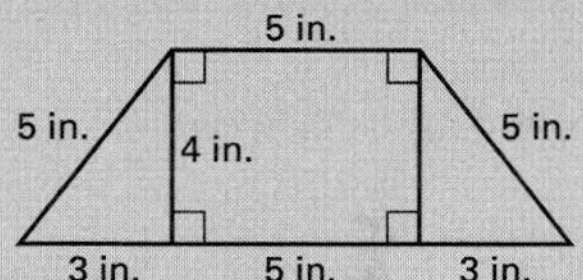

Perimeter: 26 inches
Area: 32 square inches

Extra Example 2

A train travels at an average speed of 85 miles per hour. How far will it travel in 2 hours? **170 miles**

Teaching Tip

Stress that in rate problems, the units for the rate and the time must be "compatible." A rate given in miles per hour must be multiplied by a time given in hours.

Concept Check

Explain how to use a formula to find an unknown quantity. ***Sample answer:*** **Substitute a number for each variable except the one that is unknown. Simplify the resulting equation.**

3 Apply

Assignment Guide

TRANSITIONAL
Day 1: SRH pp. 682–684 Exs. 4–9; pp. 24–26 Exs. 5–8, 10–11, 24–29, 34–37

AVERAGE
Day 1: pp. 24–26 Exs. 5–8, 10–16, 22*, 24–29, 34–37

ADVANCED
Day 1: pp. 24–26 Exs. 6–16, 22–23*, 24–27, 31–38

BLOCK SCHEDULE
pp. 24–26 Exs. 5–8, 10–16, 22*, 24–29, 34–37 (with 1.6)

Extra Practice

- Student Edition, pp. 690–691
- Chapter 1 Resource Book, p. 42

Homework Check

To quickly check student understanding of key concepts, go over the following exercises:

Transitional: 6, 7, 8, 10, 11, 14
Average: 6, 8, 10, 12, 16
Advanced: 6, 8, 10, 12, 16, 22

9.
10 yd, 6 yd, 8 yd; 3 yd, 3 yd

1.5 Exercises

Guided Practice

In Exercises 1 and 2, find the perimeter and area of the figure.

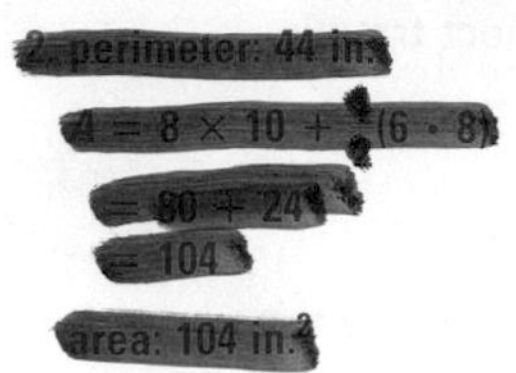

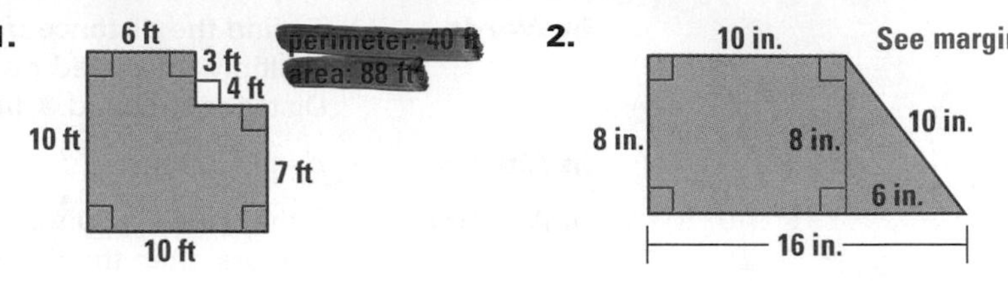

3. A parachutist falls for two minutes at a speed of 1200 feet per minute. How far does the parachutist fall during this time?

4. A rock dropped from the top of a cliff falls at a speed of 4.5 meters per second for 15 seconds. How far did the rock fall during this time?

Practice and Problem Solving

Student Help

▶ MORE PRACTICE
Extra practice to help you master skills is on page 691.

In Exercises 5–8, find the perimeter and area of the figure.

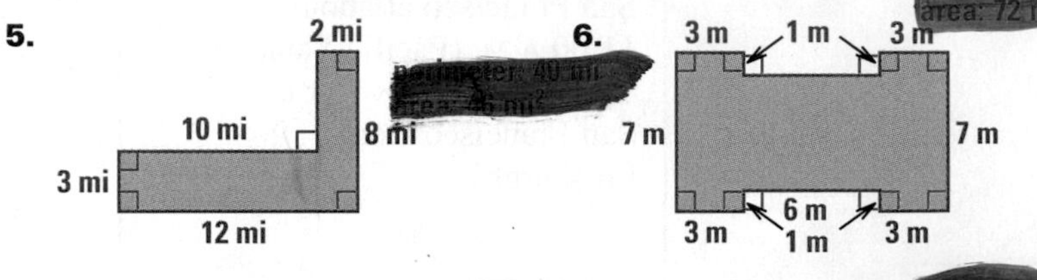

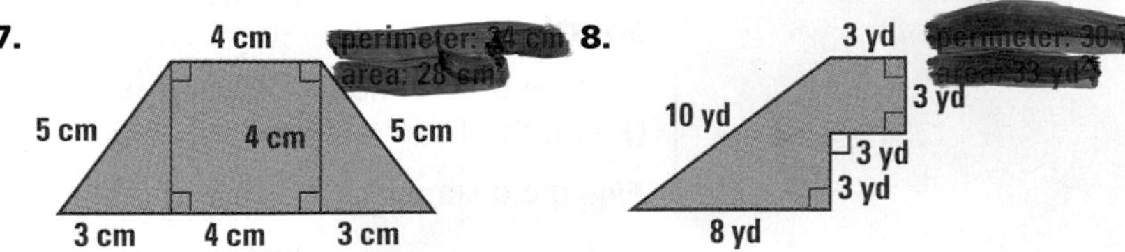

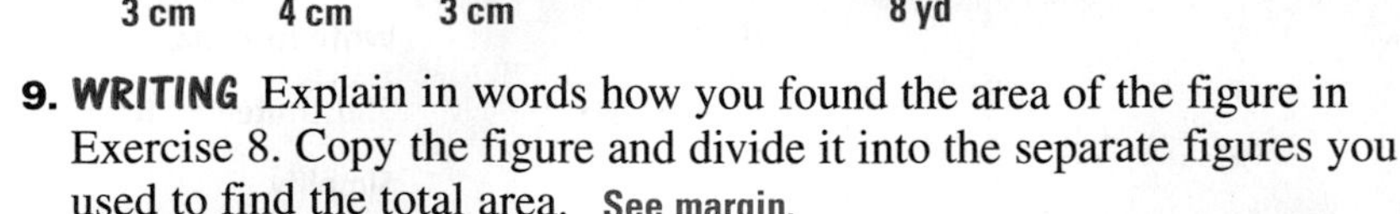

9. WRITING Explain in words how you found the area of the figure in Exercise 8. Copy the figure and divide it into the separate figures you used to find the total area. See margin.

Sample answer: **I divided the figures into a 6, 8, 10 right triangle and a 3 yd square, found the area of each and summed the areas.**

GARDENING Use the diagram of a rectangular tree farm.

10. Fencing is placed around the tree farm to keep out animals. How much fencing is needed?

11. The tree farm needs fertilizing. Each box of fertilizer covers 36 square feet. About how many boxes of fertilizer are needed?

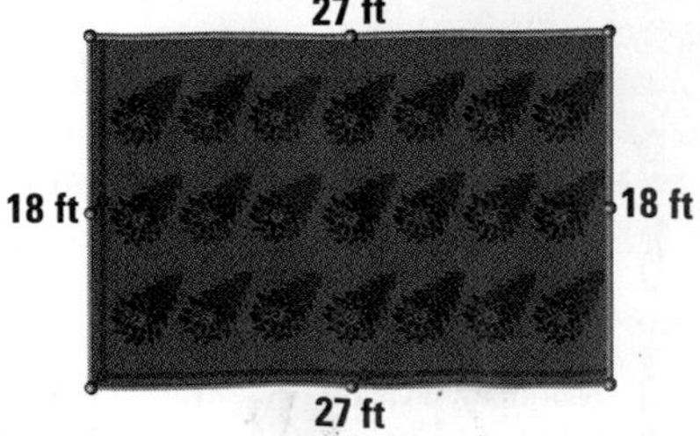

FITNESS In Exercises 12–14, use the following information. On a treadmill, you run at a speed of about 10 feet per second.

EXAMPLE

Find the total distance you run on a treadmill in 45 minutes.

Solution

Because your speed is measured in feet per *second* and your running time is measured in *minutes*, you must express your running time in seconds for the units to be compatible. There are 60 seconds in a minute, so your running time is $45 \cdot 60 = 2700$ seconds.

$d = r \cdot t$	Write formula.
$= \mathbf{10 \cdot 2700}$	Substitute 10 for r and 2700 for t.
$= 27{,}000$	Simplify.

ANSWER ▶ You will run about 27,000 feet in 45 minutes.

Student Help

▶ **SKILLS REVIEW**
For help with converting measures, see pages 681 and 717.

12. There are 5280 feet in a mile. About how many miles do you run in 45 minutes? Round your answer to the nearest hundredth. 5.11 mi

13. About how many miles will you run in 100 minutes? 11.36 mi

14. On Monday and on Tuesday you run for 25 minutes. On Wednesday you run for 15 minutes. About how many miles have you run in all? 7.39 mi

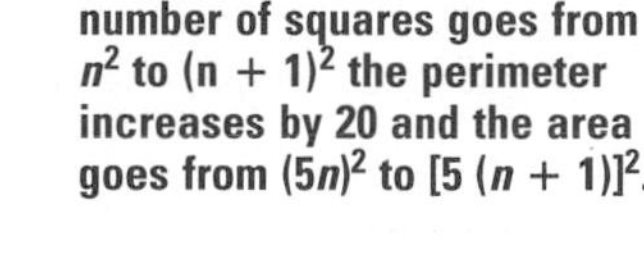

20. *Sample answer:* As the number of squares goes from n^2 to $(n + 1)^2$ the perimeter increases by 20 and the area goes from $(5n)^2$ to $[5(n + 1)]^2$.

Science Link **In Exercises 15 and 16, use the following information.** The *Cassini* spacecraft to Saturn, launched on October 15, 1997, will reach Saturn on July 1, 2004 (2460 days later). The spacecraft will then orbit Saturn until July 1, 2008 (1461 days later).

15. If the spacecraft travels at a speed of 813,000 miles per day, how many miles will it travel in 6 weeks on its trip to Saturn? 34,146,000 mi

16. If the spacecraft orbits Saturn at a speed of 752,900 miles per day, how many miles will it travel while orbiting Saturn? 1,099,986,900 mi

Link to Careers

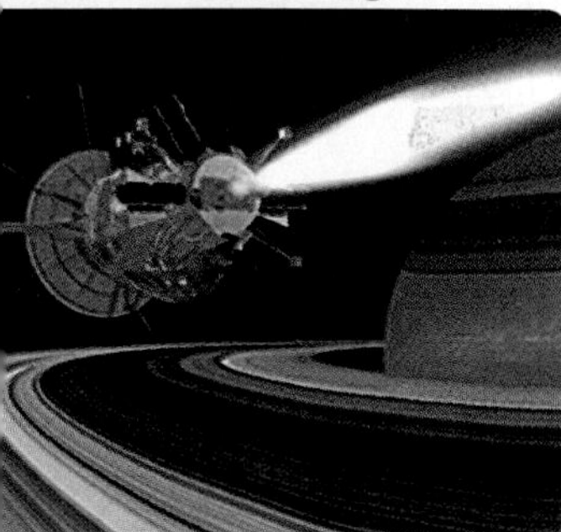

SPACE TRAVEL The *Cassini* spacecraft can reach a speed of 42,511 miles per hour. At that speed, a flight from Los Angeles to Boston would take less than five minutes.

More about space travel available at www.mcdougallittell.com

In Exercises 17–20, suppose you are tiling a floor using square tiles with sides of length 5 inches.

17. Find the perimeter and area of one of the small tiles shown. perimeter: 20 in., area: 25 in.²

18. If you use 4 tiles to make the large square shown, what are the perimeter and area of this square? perimeter: 40 in., area: 100 in.²

19. If you use 9 tiles to make a larger square, what are the perimeter and area of this square? perimeter: 60 in., area: 225 in.²

20. What pattern do you see in the perimeters you found? in the areas? See margin.

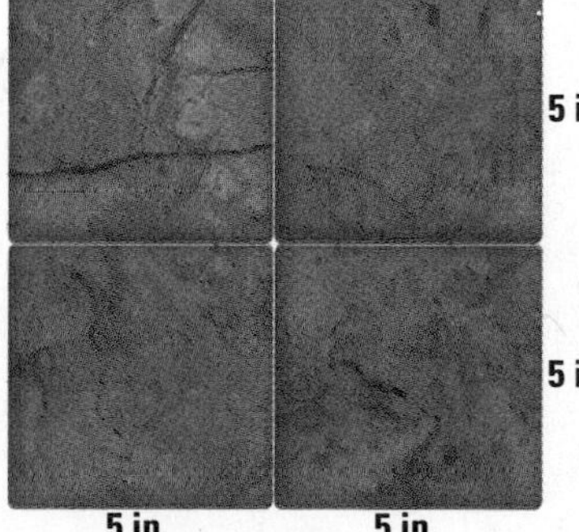

Problem Solving

Exercise 15

Remind students that since the rate is given in miles per day and the time is given in weeks, one must be converted so that the units will correspond. It will be easier to convert weeks to days.

20.

# of squares	Perimeter	Area
1	20	25
4	40	100
9	60	225

Sample answer: **As the number of squares goes from n^2 to $(n + 1)^2$ the perimeter increases by 20 and the area goes from $(5n)^2$ to $[5(n + 1)]^2$.**

4 Assess

Assessment Resources

- Assessment Book (Formal Assessment and Alternative Assessment)
- Test and Practice Generator

Mini-Quiz

1. Find the perimeter of a rectangle with length 5 in. and width 4 in. **18 in.**
2. Find the perimeter and area of the figure shown.

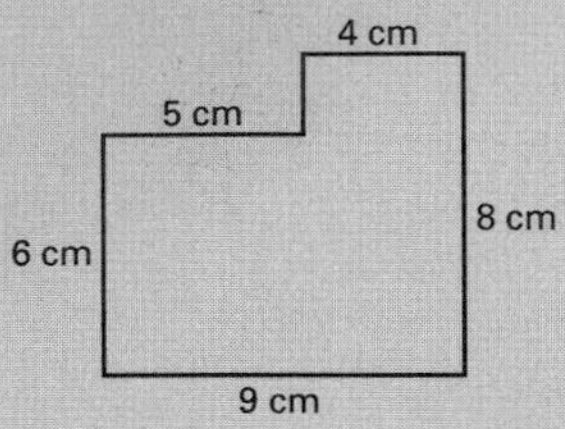

perimeter: 34 cm area: 62 cm^2

3. A car travels at 60 miles per hour. How far can the car travel in 2 hours and 30 minutes? **150 miles**
4. A man who is trying to walk across the country walks 5 hours one day, $4\frac{1}{2}$ hours the next day, and $6\frac{1}{2}$ hours the third day. How far did he walk in these three days if he walks at an average speed of 3 miles per hour? **48 miles**

27.

Distance traveled	Cost in dollars
20	49
40	53
60	57
80	61
100	65
120	69

21. MATHEMATICAL REASONING Find the length of a side of a square whose perimeter and area are the same number. Explain how you obtained your answer. 4; because the area is s^2 and the perimeter is $4s$, so s must equal 4.

22. CHALLENGE The perimeter of a square is 48 inches. Find the area of the square and describe the steps you take. The area is 144 in.^{2} A side must be 12 in. if the perimeter is 48 in.

23. CHALLENGE Write a formula that gives the area of a square in terms of its perimeter. $A = \left(\frac{P}{4}\right)^2$

Multiple-Choice Practice

Test Tip A B C D

▶ To prepare for standardized tests, review basic definitions and formulas for area and perimeter.

24. The base of a triangle is 6 inches. Its height is 4 inches. What is the area of the triangle?

Ⓐ 6 in.^{2} Ⓑ 10 in.^{2} Ⓒ 12 in.^{2} Ⓓ 24 in.^{2}

25. The sides of a square are 10 centimeters long. What is its perimeter?

Ⓕ 10 cm Ⓖ 40 cm Ⓗ 100 cm Ⓙ Not here

26. A car travels 8 hours at 60 miles per hour. Which equation represents the distance traveled?

Ⓐ $d = 60 + 8$ Ⓑ $d = 60 \div 8$

Ⓒ $d = 8 \div 60$ Ⓓ $d = 8 \cdot 60$

Mixed Review

27. A car rental agency charges a flat fee of \$45.00 plus \$.20 per mile that you travel. Make a table to show the total cost for the rental car if you travel 20 miles, 40 miles, 60 miles, 80 miles, 100 miles, or 120 miles. Describe any patterns in the data. *(1.1)* **See margin;** the cost increases \$4 each time the distance increases 20 mi.

Evaluate the expression when $x = 4$. *(1.2, 1.3, 1.4)*

28. $7 - x$ 3 **29.** $2x$ 8 **30.** $x - (5 - x)$ 3

31. x^2 16 **32.** $11x - 10$ 34 **33.** $5(x + 1)$ 25

Solve the problem. *(1.3)*

34. A gallon of paint covers an area of 400 square feet. How many gallons do you need to paint a wall that measures 12 feet by 32 feet? 1 gallon

35. A box is filled with 27 cubes. Each cube measures 2 inches by 2 inches by 2 inches. What is the volume of the box? 216 in.^{3}

Evaluate the expression. *(1.4)*

36. $8 + (2^2 \div 2) - 4$ **37.** $8 + 16 \div 2 \cdot 2$ **38.** $11 - 5 \cdot (8 \div 4)$

39. $18 \div 3^2 \cdot 2$ **40.** $11 - (1 + 8) \div 3$ **41.** $(3^2 + 2^3 + 7) \div 4$

1.6 Problem Solving

California Standards

In this lesson you'll:

- Analyze problems by distinguishing relevant from irrelevant information. (MR 1.1)
- Analyze problems by observing patterns. (MR 1.1)
- Use words, numbers, tables, and diagrams to explain mathematical reasoning. (MR 2.5)

Goal 1 IDENTIFYING RELEVANT INFORMATION

Sometimes problems include numbers, measurements, or other data that are not needed for finding a solution. Information that is not needed is called *irrelevant* information. You may also find that some problems cannot be solved because they do not contain enough information.

EXAMPLE 1 *Identifying Needed Information*

The following table is used by a nutritionist in totaling daily calories.

a. Find the number of calories in two slices of wheat bread.

b. Find the number of calories in one strawberry.

Food	Measure	Grams	Calories	Fat (grams)
Fruits				
Apple, approx. $2\frac{3}{4}$ inch diameter	1	138	80	1
Strawberries, whole	1 cup	149	55	1
Grain Products				
Bread, whole wheat, soft crumb	1 slice	28	67	2.6
Pasta, dry, packaged	8 ounces	227	838	2.7
Vegetables				
Broccoli, raw, crowns and stems	1 pound	454	89.1	1.4
Carrot, raw, approx. $2\frac{7}{8}$ ounces	1 carrot	81	30	0.1

Solution

a. ***Notice*** what data are given. Food type, portion size, total number of grams, calories, and grams of fat are given.

Select the data you need. Look at the *Grain Products* category.

1 slice of wheat bread has 67 Calories.

Solve the problem. You need the number of calories in 2 slices of wheat bread, so multiply 67 by 2.

$67 \cdot 2 = 134$ Calories in 2 slices of wheat bread

Check your result. Two slices at about 70 Calories each is about 140 Calories. Your answer of 134 Calories is reasonable.

b. Find the *Fruits* category. Note that 1 cup of strawberries contains 55 Calories, but the table does not give data on individual strawberries. There is not enough information to find the answer.

Link to Careers

NUTRITIONISTS

Nutritionists who work in hospitals and nursing homes evaluate patients, consult with nurses and doctors, and develop appropriate and nutritional meal plans.

More about nutrition counseling available at www.mcdougallittell.com

1 Plan

Pacing

Suggested Number of Days

Transitional: 1 day
Average: 1 day
Advanced: 1 day
Block Schedule: 0.5 block with 1.5

Teaching Resources

Blacklines
(See page 1B.)

Transparencies
- Warm-Up Exercises
- Teacher Time-Savers
- English/Spanish Problem Solving
- Answers

Technology
- Electronic Teacher Tools
- Test and Practice Generator

2 Teach

Math Reasoning

For Mathematical Background Notes on mathematical reasoning related to this lesson, please refer to pages 1E and 1F in this Teacher's Edition.

Extra Example 1
See next page.

California Standards and Assessment

CA Standards: MR 1.1, MR 2.5

Extra Example 1

The following table shows the number of votes cast for each of the presidential candidates in the 1996 election.

a. Find the number of people who voted for Perot in Alabama and Alaska. **118,482**

b. Find the total number of people who voted for Clinton in all 50 states. **not enough information**

1996 Presidential Election

	Candidate		
State	Clinton	Dole	Perot
AL	662,165	769,044	92,149
AK	80,380	122,746	26,333
AZ	653,288	622,073	112,072
AR	475,171	325,416	69,884
CA	5,119,835	3,828,380	697,847

Extra Example 2

Describe a pattern for each sequence. Use the pattern to write the next three numbers in the sequence.

a. 3, 8, 13, 18, . . .
One pattern is that each number is 5 more than the previous number. The next three numbers are 23, 28, and 33.

b. 1, 2, 4, 8, 16, . . .
One pattern is that each number is twice the previous number. The next three numbers are 32, 64, and 128.

Extra Example 3

A new drug is being tested on bacteria in a petri dish. There are 8,000 bacteria at the beginning of the experiment, and each hour the number of bacteria is halved. If this continues, how many bacteria will be present after 4 hours? 5 hours? **500; 250**

Teaching Tip

Point out that when students identify and extend patterns, the sequence of numbers can often be extended in more than one way.

Goal 2 LOOKING FOR A PATTERN

Student Help

▶ READING TIP
Three dots (. . .) are used at the end of a list to show that each sequence continues without stopping.

An ordered list of numbers is called a **sequence**. Here are some familiar sequences.

Whole numbers: 0, 1, 2, 3, 4, 5, 6, 7, 8, 9, . . .
Even whole numbers: 0, 2, 4, 6, 8, 10, 12, 14, 16, 18, . . .
Odd whole numbers: 1, 3, 5, 7, 9, 11, 13, 15, 17, 19, . . .

EXAMPLE 2 Describing a Number Pattern

Describe the pattern for the sequence. Use the pattern to write the next three numbers you expect to find in the sequence.

a. 4, 8, 12, 16, ?, ?, ?

b. 128, 64, 32, 16, ?, ?, ?

Solution

a. Each number is 4 more than the previous number. Continue the pattern.

4, 8, 12, 16, 20, 24, 28
(+ 4, + 4, + 4)

b. Each number is the previous number divided by 2. Continue the pattern.

128, 64, 32, 16, 8, 4, 2
(÷ 2, ÷ 2, ÷ 2)

Link to Science

FIBONACCI SEQUENCE
The problem about rabbits posed in Example 3 results in the sequence 1, 1, 2, 3, 5, 8, 13, ..., which is called the *Fibonacci sequence.* This sequence appears often in nature. In the head of the sunflower shown above, for example, the number of clockwise spirals and the number of counterclockwise spirals are consecutive terms in the sequence.

EXAMPLE 3 Using a Number Pattern to Solve a Problem

Begin with a pair of newborn rabbits. After two months, the pair begins to produce a new pair of rabbits each month. Each new pair follows this same pattern. If all the rabbits live, how many pairs of rabbits will there be in the eighth month? in the ninth month?

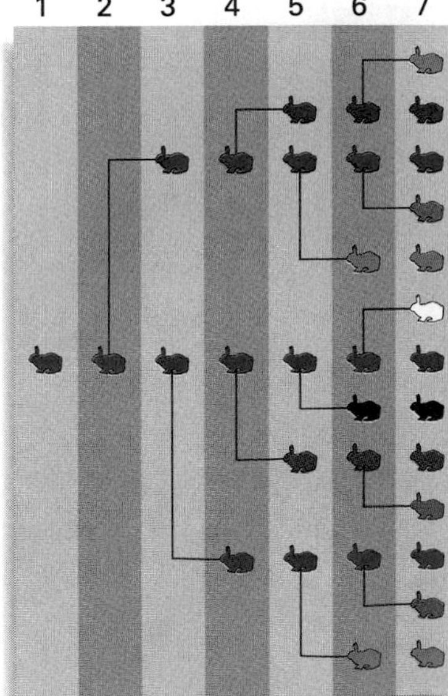

Solution

Draw a diagram. (Seven months are shown. Same color means same pair.)

Make a list of the number of pairs each month. (Read down a column.)

Pairs 1, 1, 2, 3, 5, 8, 13, . . .

Look for a pattern. The number of pairs is the sum of the two previous months' pairs.

Month 8: $13 + 8 = 21$ pairs

Month 9: $21 + 13 = 34$ pairs

1.6 Exercises

Guided Practice

Identify the irrelevant information. Do not solve the problem.

1. **GROCERIES** You buy four boxes of fish sticks on sale at $1.99 per box. The fish sticks regularly sell for $2.49 per box. Lemons are also on sale at two for $1.00. How much money did you save by buying the fish sticks on sale? The price of lemons

2. **EMPLOYEE BENEFITS** A company has 412 employees at 32 branches throughout California and Texas. Each employee receives $500 as a bonus at the end of the year. How much money is spent on year-end bonuses? The number of branches and the location of the employees

Student Help

▶ **SKILLS REVIEW**
For help with problem solving strategies, see pages 667–671.

3. **OFFICE SUPPLIES** A company buys 1500 writing pads and 3000 black pens for office meetings. On Tuesday, 188 writing pads are used. On Wednesday, 234 writing pads are used. There are 1900 pens left on Thursday. How many writing pads are left? The number of pens purchased and the number of pens remaining

Describe the pattern. List the next three numbers you expect to find in the sequence. 4–7. See margin.

4. 50, 47, 44, 41, ? , ? , ?
5. 20, 21, 23, 26, 30, ? , ? , ?
6. 13, 26, 39, 52, ? , ? , ?
7. 100, 10, 1, 0.1, ? , ? , ?

4. Each number is 3 less than the preceding one. 38, 35, 32

5. Start with 20. Add 1, then 2, then 3, and so on. 35, 41, 48

6. Each number is 13 more than the previous number. 65, 78, 91

7. Each number is $\frac{1}{10}$ the number before it. 0.01, 0.001, 0.0001

Describe the missing information that is needed to solve the problem.

8. **GROCERIES** You buy 6 pounds of grapes at $1.19 per pound, a loaf of bread for $1.89, and cheese at $4.39 per pound. How much did you spend? The number of pounds of cheese.

9. **DELIVERIES** One case of ketchup contains 24 bottles. One case of mustard contains 30 bottles. There are 6 cases of ketchup and 8 cases of mustard to be delivered. If one bottle of ketchup weighs 8 ounces, what is the total weight of the delivery? The weight of a bottle of mustard.

Practice and Problem Solving

Identify the irrelevant information. Then solve the problem.

Student Help

▶ **MORE PRACTICE**
Extra practice to help you master skills is on page 691.

10. **SPORTS** A coliseum seats 26,500 people. Twenty football games have been held per year at the coliseum for the past 8 years. Tonight's football tickets cost $20. The game is sold out. How much money is collected for tonight's game? The number of football games and the number of years; $530,000

11. **KITCHENS** A family is remodeling the kitchen in their home. Cabinets cost $1548. Plumbing costs $618. Tiles for the kitchen floor cost $720. Exactly 240 tiles are needed for the floor. What is the price of one floor tile? The cost of the cabinets and of the plumbing; $3.00

Concept Check

Explain how you might find the next term in a sequence of numbers.
Sample answer: **Look for a constant increase or decrease in the pattern, a constant multiple from one term to the next, or another pattern. Then use the pattern to write the next term.**

3 Apply

Assignment Guide

TRANSITIONAL
Day 1: SRH p. 667 Exs. 1–4, 7; pp. 29–31 Exs. 10–12, 15–21, 32–36

AVERAGE
Day 1: pp. 29–31 Exs. 10–13, 15–21, 26–28, 32–36

ADVANCED
Day 1: pp. 29–31 Exs. 11–14, 19–28, 29*, 30, 32–36

BLOCK SCHEDULE
pp. 29–31 Exs. 10–13, 15–21, 26–28, 32–36 (with 1.5)

Extra Practice

- Student Edition, pp. 690–691
- Chapter 1 Resource Book, p. 51

Homework Check

To quickly check student understanding of key concepts, go over the following exercises:

Transitional: 10, 12, 16, 18, 32
Average: 10, 12, 16, 18, 32
Advanced: 10, 14, 20, 22, 32

Problem Solving

Exercises 15–22

Students should be encouraged to go through a mental checklist when identifying patterns.

- Is there a constant number added or subtracted?
- Is there a constant number multiplied or divided?
- Is there another pattern involving addition, subtraction, multiplication, or division?
- Is there a pattern of even or odd numbers?
- Is there a pattern involving powers of numbers?

Math Reasoning

The pattern indicated in Exercise 30 corresponds to the triangular numbers 1, 3, 6, 10, 15, ..., where the nth number in the sequence is given by $1 + 2 + 3 + \ldots + n = \frac{n(n+1)}{2}$. The clerk in Exercise 29 will use the fact that $1 + 2 + 3 + \ldots + 15 = \frac{15 \cdot 16}{2} = 120 = 5 \cdot 24$.

15. Subtract 5 from the preceding number; 60, 55, 50

16. Multiply the preceding number by 3; 162, 486, 1,458

17. Add 9 to the preceding number; 99, 108, 117

18. Subtract 3, then 4, then 5 and so on; 45, 38, 30

19. Add 1 to the numerator and the denominator of the preceding term. $\frac{5}{6}, \frac{6}{7}, \frac{7}{8}$

20. Each fraction's numerator is the next even number from the previous term's and each fraction's denominator is the next odd number from the previous term's. $\frac{10}{11}, \frac{12}{13}, \frac{14}{15}$

21. Each term is the square of one less than the square root of the preceding term; 36, 25, 16

22. Divide the preceding number by 3; 9, 3, 1

Identify the irrelevant information. Describe the missing information that is needed to solve the problem.

12. BUS TRIP There are 125 seventh-graders and 186 eighth-graders going on a class trip to the museum. Each bus will seat 48 students and 5 adults. How many buses are needed? Irrelevant: the grades students are in; Needed: number of adults

13. FAMILY TRIP A family trip covered 320 miles. Half of the distance was traveled during the first day of the trip. During the trip, the car used 24 gallons of gasoline. How many days did the trip take? Irrelevant: gallons of gas used; Needed: distance traveled on subsequent days

14. TYPING Suppose you type 30 words per minute. Your friend types 40 words per minute. How long will it take you to type an essay that is 12 handwritten pages long? Irrelevant: your friend's rate; Needed: the number of words per page

Describe the pattern. List the next three numbers you expect to find in the sequence. 15–22. See margin.

15. 80, 75, 70, 65, ?, ?, ?

16. 2, 6, 18, 54, ?, ?, ?

17. 63, 72, 81, 90, ?, ?, ?

18. 63, 60, 56, 51, ?, ?, ?

19. $\frac{1}{2}, \frac{2}{3}, \frac{3}{4}, \frac{4}{5}$, ?, ?, ?

20. $\frac{2}{3}, \frac{4}{5}, \frac{6}{7}, \frac{8}{9}$, ?, ?, ?

21. 100, 81, 64, 49, ?, ?, ?

22. 729, 243, 81, 27, ?, ?, ?

Link to Science

MITOSIS
A cell magnified 600 times can be seen in the process of mitosis.

More about mitosis available at www.mcdougallittell.com

Chapter Opener Link **In Exercises 23–25, use the following information from page 1.** During *mitosis*, a cell divides to form two new cells. Then each new cell divides again. This pattern continues.

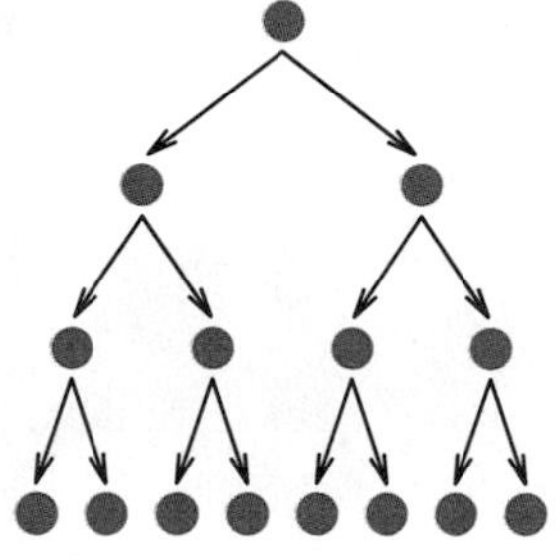

23. Write a sequence to show the number of cells produced at each stage during mitosis. Begin with one cell. 1, 2, 4, 8, 16, 32, ...

24. What is the pattern in the sequence? Each term is 2 times the preceding one.

25. During one stage of mitosis there are 8192 cells. How many cells can be expected at the next stage? Explain how you found your answer. 16,384. I doubled 8192.

MATHEMATICAL REASONING In Exercises 26–28, use the following information. You drive 73 miles along a straight highway from Auburn to Betton, then 38 more miles to Cranford. When you stop to refuel, you realize the car averaged 26 miles per gallon. You want to determine how much farther it is to Dunsville, which is 255 miles from Auburn.

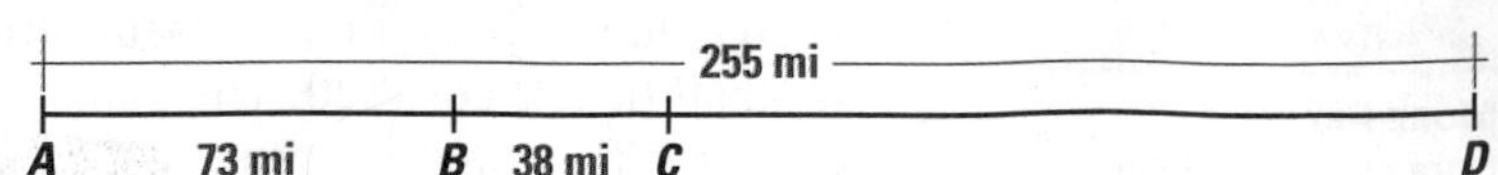

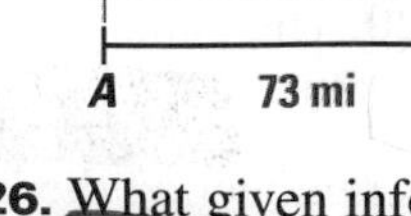

Student Help

▶ HOMEWORK HELP
Extra help with problem solving in Exs. 26–28 is available at www.mcdougallittell.com

26. What given information do you need to solve the problem? The miles driven and the total distance.

27. What steps will you use to solve the problem? Subtract miles driven from total distance.

28. What is the answer? How do you know it is reasonable?

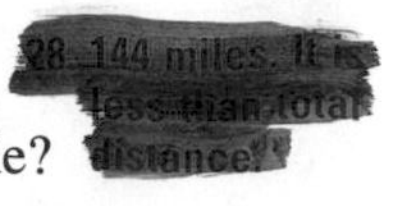

28. 144 miles. It is less than total distance.

29. CHALLENGE A store clerk wants to build a display of soup cans from five cases with 24 cans in each case. The top row of the display will have 1 can of soup, the next row will have 2 cans, the third row will have 3 cans, and so on. To build the display, though, the clerk must start from the bottom row. How many cans will be in the bottom row? How many rows will there be in the display?
15 cans in the bottom row; 15 rows in the display.

Draw the next three figures in the pattern.

30. **See margin.**

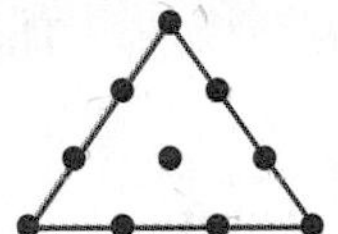

31.

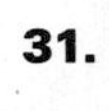
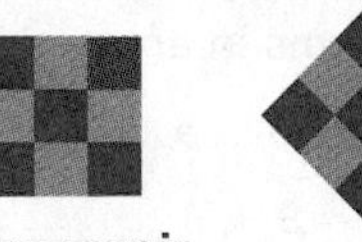

See margin.

32.

See margin.

33. 1 2 3 4 5 9 **See margin.**

Multiple-Choice Practice

In Exercises 34 and 35, use the following information. Last year a school district had 18,596 children enrolled and employed 670 teachers and staff. This year there are 20,132 children enrolled with 725 teachers and staff employed.

34. What was the increase in enrollment from last year to this year?

Ⓐ 1536 Ⓑ 1591 Ⓒ 2536 Ⓓ 2693

35. What information was not needed to solve Exercise 34?

Ⓕ Last year 18,596 children were enrolled.

Ⓖ Last year the district employed 670 teachers and staff.

Ⓗ This year 20,132 children are enrolled.

Ⓙ Not here

36. The seventh row of a theater has 26 seats, the sixth row has 23 seats, and the fifth row has 20 seats. If this pattern continues, how many seats does the first row have?

Ⓐ 5 Ⓑ 8 Ⓒ 11 Ⓓ 14

4 Assess

Assessment Resources

- Assessment Book (Formal Assessment and Alternative Assessment)
- Test and Practice Generator

Mini-Quiz

1. Identify the irrelevant information. Then solve the problem.
   A red car travels at 50 miles per hour for 3 hours. A green car travels at 60 miles per hour for 2 hours. How far did the red car travel? **The information about the green car is irrelevant; 150 miles**
2. Describe a pattern for the sequence. Then list the next three numbers.
   a. 4, 10, 16, 22, ?, ?, ?, . . . **Each number is 6 more than the previous number; 28, 34, 40**
   b. 2, 6, 18, 54, ?, ?, ?, . . . **Each number is 3 times the previous number; 162, 486, 1458**
   c. 95, 93, 90, 86, ?, ?, ?, . . . **The second number is 2 less than the first number, the third number is 3 less than the second number, the fourth number is 4 less than the third number, and so on; 81, 75, 68**

30.

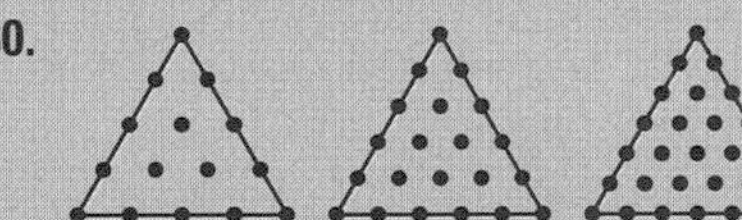

31.

32.

33. 7 8 9

1 Plan

Pacing

Suggested Number of Days

Transitional: 1 day
Average: 1 day
Advanced: 1 day
Block Schedule: 0.5 block with 1.8

Teaching Resources

Blacklines
(See page 1B.)

Transparencies
- Warm-Up Exercises
- Teacher Time-Savers
- English/Spanish Problem Solving
- Answers

Technology
- Electronic Teacher Tools
- Test and Practice Generator

2 Teach

Math Reasoning

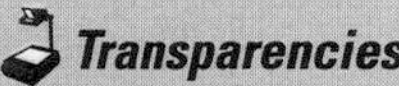

For Mathematical Background Notes on mathematical reasoning related to this lesson, please refer to pages 1E and 1F in this Teacher's Edition.

CA Standard: AF 1.3
CA Key Concepts Book: pp. S44–S47

1.7 The Commutative and Associative Properties

In this lesson you'll:
- Simplify expressions by applying the associative and commutative properties. (AF 1.3)
- Justify the process used to simplify an expression. (AF 1.3)

Goal 1 Using Properties of Operations

The operations of addition and multiplication have special properties.

	Commutative Property of Addition	Commutative Property of Multiplication
In Words	In a sum, you can add terms in any order.	In a product, you can multiply factors in any order.
In Algebra	$a + b = b + a$	$ab = ba$
In Arithmetic	$6 + 9 = 9 + 6$	$4 \cdot 7 = 7 \cdot 4$
	Associative Property of Addition	**Associative Property of Multiplication**
In Words	Changing the grouping of terms will not change the sum.	Changing the grouping of factors will not change the product.
In Algebra	$(a + b) + c = a + (b + c)$	$(ab)c = a(bc)$
In Arithmetic	$(9 + 5) + 6 = 9 + (5 + 6)$	$(5 \cdot 10) \cdot 3 = 5 \cdot (10 \cdot 3)$

Student Help

Vocabulary Tip
In English, *commute* means to change locations and *associate* means to join or group together. In the commutative properties, numbers change position. In the associative properties, numbers are grouped together in different ways.

EXAMPLE 1 Using Commutative Property

Explain why it does not matter which of the two numbers you use as the length when you find the area of a rectangle.

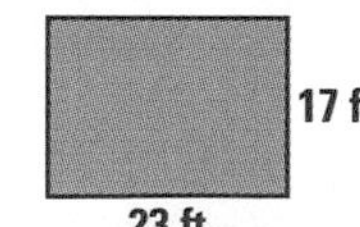

Solution

The area A of a rectangle is the product of its length ℓ and width w. Using the commutative property of multiplication, you can write $A = \ell \cdot w = 23 \cdot 17 = 17 \cdot 23$. The choice of ℓ does not matter.

EXAMPLE 2 Using Associative Property

Show that $(13 + 8) + 25$ is equal to $13 + (8 + 25)$.

Solution

Evaluate each expression separately.

$(\mathbf{13 + 8}) + 25 = \mathbf{21} + 25 = 46$ $\qquad$ $13 + (\mathbf{8 + 25}) = 13 + \mathbf{33} = 46$

Goal 2 JUSTIFYING STEPS

Knowing properties of numbers can help you use mental math to evaluate expressions. When you use a property of numbers to explain why a step in your answer is valid, you are *justifying* the step.

EXAMPLE 3 Justifying an Answer

Use mental math to evaluate $43 + (68 + 57)$. Justify each step.

Solution

To evaluate the expression $43 + (68 + 57)$ using mental math, look for numbers that are easy to add first. Notice that the ones' digits in 43 and 57 are easy to add. So, it is easier to add 43 and 57 than 68 and 57.

$43 + (68 + 57) = 43 + (57 + 68)$	Commutative property of addition
$= (\mathbf{43 + 57}) + 68$	Associative property of addition
$= \mathbf{100} + 68$	Add 43 and 57.
$= 168$	Add 100 and 68.

Addition and multiplication are always commutative and associative. This is not the case with subtraction and division. To show that a statement is not always true, you need to find only one example, called a **counterexample**, to which the statement does not apply.

EXAMPLE 4 Using a Counterexample

Give a counterexample to show that subtraction is not associative.

Solution

You need to find numbers that show that $(a - b) - c$ and $a - (b - c)$ can have different values. Try $a = 10$, $b = 6$, and $c = 1$.

First, find $(a - b) - c$.

$(a - b) - c = (\mathbf{10 - 6}) - 1$	Substitute.
$= \mathbf{4 - 1}$	Subtract 6 from 10.
$= 3$	Subtract 1 from 4.

Second, find $a - (b - c)$.

$a - (b - c) = 10 - (\mathbf{6 - 1})$	Substitute.
$= \mathbf{10 - 5}$	Subtract 1 from 6.
$= 5$	Subtract 5 from 10.

Notice that $(10 - 6) - 1 \neq 10 - (6 - 1)$. This counterexample shows that subtraction is not associative.

Student Help

▶ **MORE EXAMPLES**

INTERNET More examples are available at www.mcdougallittell.com

Extra Example 1

Explain why it doesn't matter which number you use as length when you find the perimeter of the rectangle in Example 1. ***Sample answer:*** **$P = 2\ell + 2w$. Using the commutative property of addition, you can write $P = 2 \cdot 23 + 2 \cdot 17 = 2 \cdot 17 + 2 \cdot 23$.**

Extra Example 2

Show that $(2 \cdot 6) \cdot 3 = 2 \cdot (6 \cdot 3)$. **$(2 \cdot 6) \cdot 3 = 36$ and $2 \cdot (6 \cdot 3) = 36$**

Extra Example 3

Use mental math to evaluate $(29 + 38) + 71$. Justify each step.

$(29 + 38) + 71$	
$= (38 + 29) + 71$	**Commutative property of addition**
$= 38 + (29 + 71)$	**Associative property of addition**
$= 38 + 100$	**Add 29 and 71.**
$= 138$	**Add 38 and 100.**

Extra Example 4

Give a counterexample to show that subtraction is not commutative. ***Sample answer:*** **$12 - 5 = 7$ but $7 - 12 \neq 7$, so subtraction is not commutative.**

Math Reasoning

In connection with Example 4, a correct identity can be established using the distributive law and the fact that $x - y = x + (-1)y$.
$(a - b) - c =$
$(a + (-1)b) + (-1)c =$
$a + ((-1)b + (-1)c) =$
$a + (-1)(b + c) =$
$a - (b + c)$.

Concept Check

Explain how the associative property of addition can be used as an aid in mental math. ***Sample answer:*** **Group the two terms which are easy to add first. Then add the last number to the sum.**

3 Apply

Assignment Guide

TRANSITIONAL
Day 1: pp. 34–35 Exs. 9–13, 17–22, 26–28

AVERAGE
Day 1: pp. 34–35 Exs. 9–22, 26–28

ADVANCED
Day 1: pp. 34–35 Exs. 11–18, 21–23, 24*, 25–28

BLOCK SCHEDULE
pp. 34–35 Exs. 9–22, 26–28 (with 1.8)

Extra Practice

- Student Edition, pp. 690–691
- Chapter 1 Resource Book, p. 60

Homework Check

To quickly check student understanding of key concepts, go over the following exercises:

Transitional: 10, 11, 12, 18, 22
Average: 10, 11, 12, 14, 22
Advanced: 10, 11, 12, 14, 22

Math Reasoning

The CAD laws usually play a role in simplifying calculations. Exercise 13 involves an idea that can be used when multiplying 25 and any multiple of 4. For instance,

$25 \cdot 32 = 25 \cdot (4 \cdot 8) = (25 \cdot 4) \cdot 8 = 100 \cdot 8 = 800.$

In Exercise 25 on page 35, the associative and commutative laws of addition enable us to simplify the computation:

$46 + 15 + 37 + 54 + 85 =$
$(46 + 54) + (15 + 85) + 37 =$
$100 + 100 + 37 = 237.$

1.7 Exercises

Guided Practice

Name the property shown.

1. $3 \cdot (8 \cdot 4) = (3 \cdot 8) \cdot 4$
Associative property of multiplication.

2. $3 \cdot 8 = 8 \cdot 3$
Commutative property of multiplication.

3. $4 + 7 = 7 + 4$
Commutative property of addition.

4. $8 + (9 + 7) = (8 + 9) + 7$
Associative property of addition.

In Exercises 5–8, match the property and the correct numerical expression.

A. $19 \cdot 10 = 10 \cdot 19$

B. $21 + 9 = 9 + 21$

C. $(6 + 9) + 11 = 6 + (9 + 11)$

D. $(25 \cdot 10) \cdot 10 = 25 \cdot (10 \cdot 10)$

5. Associative property of addition **C**

6. Commutative property of addition **B**

7. Associative property of multiplication **D**

8. Commutative property of multiplication **A**

Practice and Problem Solving

Student Help

▶ **MORE PRACTICE**
Extra practice to help you master skills is on page 691.

9. Commutative property of addition.
10. Associative property of multiplication.
11. Commutative property of multiplication.
12. Associative property of addition.

In Exercises 9–12, name the property illustrated. **9–12. See margin.**

9. $3(4 + 9) = 3(9 + 4)$

10. $10 \cdot (11 \cdot 12) = (10 \cdot 11) \cdot 12$

11. $1 \cdot 2 \cdot 3 = 1 \cdot 3 \cdot 2$

12. $\frac{1}{2} + \left(\frac{1}{2} + \frac{3}{4}\right) = \left(\frac{1}{2} + \frac{1}{2}\right) + \frac{3}{4}$

13. Here is one way to evaluate $25 \cdot (78 \cdot 4)$. Justify each step.

$25 \cdot (78 \cdot 4) = 25 \cdot (4 \cdot 78)$ Commutative property of multiplication.
$= (25 \cdot 4) \cdot 78$ Associative property of multiplication.
$= 100 \cdot 78$
$= 7800$

14. Use a counterexample to show that division is not commutative.

MATHEMATICAL REASONING **Use the commutative and associative properties to find the missing number. (Do not evaluate.)**

15. $67 \cdot 81 = 81 \cdot$?

16. $56 +$? $= 72 + 56$

17. $5 \cdot (4 + 7) = (4 + 7) \cdot$?

18. ? $\cdot (35 \cdot 20) = (2 \cdot 35) \cdot 20$

19. $(89 + 67) + 49 =$? $+ (67 + 49)$

20. $(4 + 16) \cdot (13 + 7) = (13 + 7) \cdot (16 +$?$)$

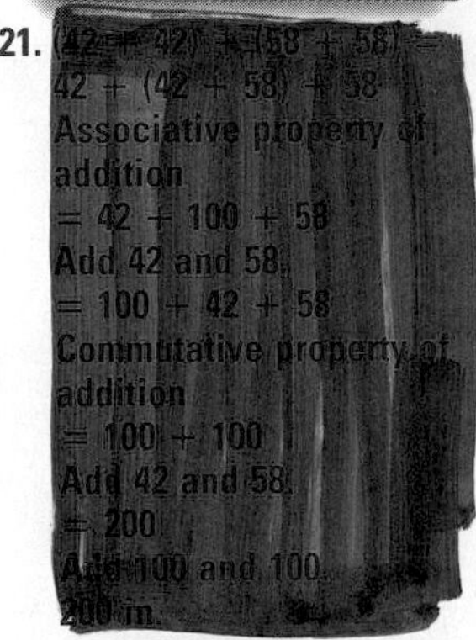

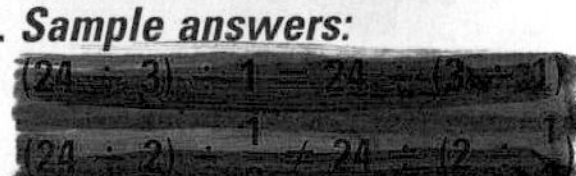

PICTURE FRAMES In Exercises 21–23, use the following information. To frame the oil painting as shown below, a picture framer charges a certain amount for each inch of framing needed.

21. The perimeter of the frame shown can be found by the expression (42 + 42) + (58 + 58). Use the commutative and associative properties of addition to find the perimeter using mental math. Justify each step. **See margin.**

22. The picture framer charges $3.00 for each inch of the perimeter. What is the cost of framing the painting? $600

23. Another oil painting is framed at the same rate of $3.00 per inch. Its total cost is $360. What are three different possible pairs of values for the length and width of the finished frame? **See margin.**

24. CHALLENGE Division is not associative. Sometimes it appears to be associative, though. Give an example in which division appears to be associative. Give a counterexample to show that division is not associative. **See margin.**

25. You need to find the sum of 46, 15, 37, 54, and 85. Explain how the commutative and associative properties of addition can help you find the sum using mental math. Add 46 and 54 to get 100. Add 15 and 85 to get 100. So: 46 + 15 + 37 + 54 + 85 = 237.

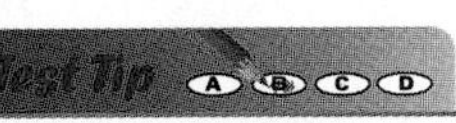

Multiple-Choice Practice

Test Tip Ⓐ Ⓑ Ⓒ Ⓓ

Recall that you can change order in many expressions by a *commutative property.* You can regroup parts of many expressions by an *associative property.*

26. Which property is illustrated below? C

$$150 + 73 + 25 + 22 = (150 + 25) + (73 + 22)$$

Ⓐ Associative property of addition

Ⓑ Commutative property of addition

Ⓒ Both the commutative and associative properties of addition

Ⓓ Neither the commutative nor associative properties of addition

27. Which expression best shows how to use mental math to evaluate 61 + 17 + 39 + 3? J

Ⓕ (61 + 3) + (39 + 17) Ⓖ (17 + 61) + (39 + 3)

Ⓗ 39 + (61 + 3) + 17 Ⓙ (61 + 39) + (17 + 3)

28. Which activities are *not* commutative? B

Ⓐ Putting on your hat and coat Ⓑ Washing and drying clothes

Ⓒ Combing your hair and brushing your teeth Ⓓ Setting the table and reading the mail

4 Assess

Assessment Resources

- Assessment Book (Formal Assessment and Alternative Assessment)
- Test and Practice Generator

Mini-Quiz

Name the property shown.

1. $8 \cdot (5 + 2) = 8 \cdot (2 + 5)$ **Commutative property of addition**
2. $8 \cdot (5 + 2) = (5 + 2) \cdot 8$ **Commutative property of multiplication**
3. $\frac{2}{3} \cdot \left(\frac{1}{2} \cdot \frac{3}{4}\right) = \left(\frac{2}{3} \cdot \frac{1}{2}\right) \cdot \frac{3}{4}$ **Associative property of multiplication**
4. Give a counterexample to show that division is not associative. ***Sample answer:*** **$(20 \div 10) \div 2 = 1$ but $20 \div (10 \div 2) = 4$, and $1 \neq 4$.**

1 Planning the Activity

Purpose and Materials

See the margin of the student page.

▶ LINK TO LESSON

Sample 2 models part (a) of Example 2 in Lesson 1.8. Point this out to students when doing Example 2. Then ask students to model part (c) of Example 2 and part (b) of Example 3.

Math Reasoning

Students use models to explain the mathematical reasoning behind equivalent expressions. They then apply the results to more complex problems.

California Standards and Assessment

CA Standards: AF 1.3, MR 2.5

Equivalent Expressions

For use with Lesson 1.8

California Standards

- ▶ Use models to explain mathematical reasoning. (MR 2.5)
- ▶ Simplify expressions by using the distributive property. (AF 1.3)

MATERIALS

- Algebra tiles

You can use algebra tiles to model variable expressions.

1-TILE

This 1-by-1 square tile has an area of 1 square unit. It represents the number 1.

X-TILE

This 1-by-x rectangular tile has an area of x square units. It represents the variable x.

SAMPLE 1 Modeling Expressions

Use algebra tiles to model the expressions.

a. $3x + 2$ **b.** $2x + 5$ **c.** $x + 11$

Here's How

a. **b.** **c.**

Try These

Write the expression that is modeled by the tiles.

1. $4x + 3$ **2.** $3x + 8$ **3.** $x + 7$

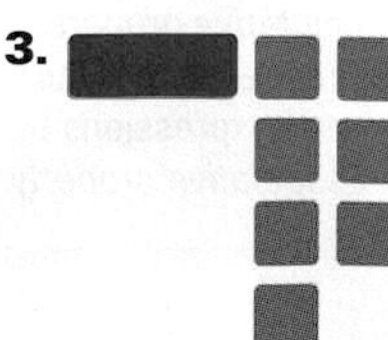

In Exercises 4–9, model the expression with algebra tiles. Make a sketch of your model. 4–9. Check sketches.

4. 8 **5.** $2x$ **6.** $3x + 9$

7. $2x + 5$ **8.** $x + 3$ **9.** $4x + 7$

10. MATHEMATICAL REASONING What expression does each circled group of tiles represent? Explain why the entire model represents the expression $2(x + 1)$.
$x + 1$; *Sample answer:* There are two groups of $x + 1$, so it represents $2(x + 1)$.

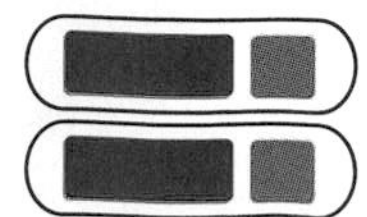

Two variable expressions are *equivalent* if they always have the same values when numbers are substituted for the variables. For instance, $(x + 1 + 1)$ and $(x + 2)$ are equivalent. You can write an *equation* relating the two expressions.

$$x + 1 + 1 = x + 2$$

You can use algebra tiles to discover whether expressions are equivalent.

SAMPLE 2 Modeling Equivalent Expressions

Use algebra tiles to model $2(x + 3)$ and $2x + 6$. Are the expressions equivalent? Explain.

Here's How

1. Model $x + 3$ twice.

$x + 3$

$x + 3$

2. Model $2x + 6$.

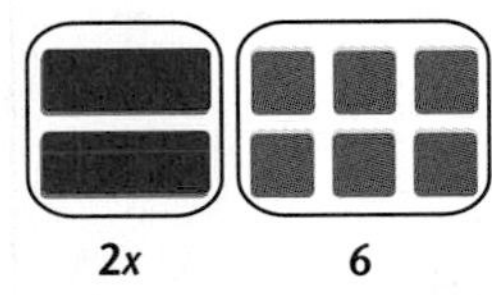

$2x$ 6

Each expression is represented by the same set of tiles: two x-tiles and six 1-tiles. So the expressions are equivalent: $2(x + 3) = 2x + 6$.

Try These

In Exercises 11–14, match the algebra tiles with two expressions. Write an equation relating the two expressions.

A. $4x + 2$ **B.** $6x + 9$ **C.** $3x + 3$ **D.** $2(3x + 1)$

E. $3(2x + 3)$ **F.** $2(2x + 1)$ **G.** $6x + 2$ **H.** $3(x + 1)$

11.   **A, F**

12.  **D, G**

13. 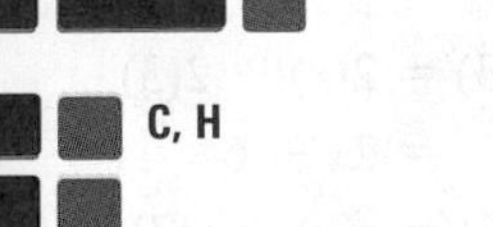 **C, H**

14.  **B, E**

15. MATHEMATICAL REASONING Use the results of Exercises 11–14 to rewrite $4(2x + 3)$ in an equivalent form. Sketch an algebra tile model to confirm your result. **$8x + 12$; Check sketches.**

11. $4x + 2 = 2(2x + 1)$
12. $2(3x + 1) = 6x + 2$
13. $3x + 3 = 3(x + 1)$
14. $6x + 9 = 3(2x + 3)$

2 Managing the Activity

Classroom Management

If a commercial set of algebra tiles is not available, a laminated classroom set can be made. An overhead set of tiles is very useful for demonstration purposes. You may wish to have students work with a partner or in a group for this lab activity.

3 Closing the Activity

★ KEY DISCOVERY

Students use area models to visualize the distributive property and realize that $a(b + c) = ab + ac$.

Activity Assessment

Use Exercises 10 and 15 to assess student understanding.

Plan

Pacing

Suggested Number of Days

Transitional: 1 day
Average: 1 day
Advanced: 1 day
Block Schedule: 0.5 block with 1.7

Teaching Resources

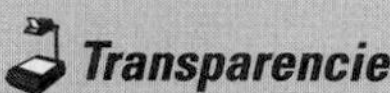

(See page 1B.)

Transparencies

- Warm-Up Exercises
- Teacher Time-Savers
- English/Spanish Problem Solving
- Answers

Technology

- Electronic Teacher Tools
- Test and Practice Generator

Teach

Math Reasoning

For Mathematical Background Notes on mathematical reasoning related to this lesson, please refer to pages 1E and 1F in this Teacher's Edition.

California Standards and Assessment

CA Standards: AF 1.3, MG 2.1
CA Key Concepts Book: pp. S48–S50

1.8 The Distributive Property

California Standards

In this lesson you'll:

- Simplify expressions by applying the distributive property and justify the process used. (AF 1.3)
- Use formulas for finding the area of rectangles. (MG 2.1)

Goal 1 USING THE DISTRIBUTIVE PROPERTY

In Developing Concepts 1.8, page 36, you worked with *equivalent expressions*. **Equivalent numerical expressions** have the same value. You can use the *distributive property* to write equivalent expressions.

DISTRIBUTIVE PROPERTY

In Algebra $a(b + c) = ab + ac$

In Arithmetic $4(3 + 8) = 4(3) + 4(8)$

EXAMPLE 1 Using the Distributive Property

a. Use the distributive property to write an equivalent numerical expression for the expression $8(3 + 5)$.

b. Show that the two expressions in part (a) have the same value.

Solution

a. Use the distributive property to write $\mathbf{8(3 + 5) = 8(3) + 8(5)}$.

b. $\mathbf{8(3 + 5)} = 8(8) = 64$ $\mathbf{8(3) + 8(5)} = 24 + 40 = 64$

The expressions have the same value so they are equivalent.

Equivalent variable expressions always have the same values when numbers are substituted for the variables. You can use the distributive property to write equivalent variable expressions.

EXAMPLE 2 Using the Distributive Property

Write an equivalent expression. Then simplify.

a. $2(x + 3)$ **b.** $x(x + 7)$ **c.** $5x + 9x$

Solution

a. $2(x + 3) = 2(x) + 2(3)$ Distribute the number 2.
$= 2x + 6$ Simplify.

b. $x(x + 7) = x(x) + x(7)$ Distribute the variable x.
$= x^2 + 7x$ Simplify.

c. $5x + 9x = (5 + 9)x$ Use the distributive property.
$= 14x$ Add.

Student Help

STUDY TIP
In part (c) of Example 2, notice that the distributive property is applied in reverse. That is, $ab + ac$ can be rewritten as $a(b + c)$.

The distributive property applies to sums with more than two terms and can also be used with subtraction.

$$a(b + c + d) = ab + ac + ad \qquad a(b - c) = ab - ac$$

EXAMPLE 3 Using the Distributive Property

Write an equivalent expression using the distributive property. Then evaluate or simplify the equivalent expression.

a. $8(2 + 3 + 4)$ **b.** $2(3x - 5)$

Solution

a. $8(2 + 3 + 4) = 8(2) + 8(3) + 8(4)$ **Use distributive property.**

$= 16 + 24 + 32$ **Multiply.**

$= 72$ **Add.**

b. $2(3x - 5) = 2(3x) - 2(5)$ **Use distributive property.**

$= (2 \cdot 3)x - 2(5)$ **Use associative property.**

$= 6x - 10$ **Simplify.**

Student Help

▶READING TIP
The expression $3x$ in part (b) of Example 3 means $3 \cdot x$. So $2(3x) = 2 \cdot (3 \cdot x)$ and you can rewrite the expression as $(2 \cdot 3) \cdot x$ using the associative property.

Goal 2 APPLYING THE DISTRIBUTIVE PROPERTY

You can use the distributive property to solve problems. In Example 4, either of two equivalent expressions can be used to find the total area.

EXAMPLE 4 Applying the Distributive Property

CARPET You are carpeting a bedroom and closet. One square yard of carpet costs $20. What will the total cost be?

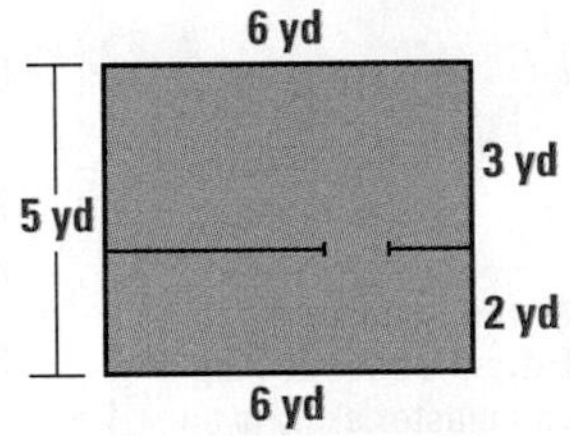

Solution

Find the total area of the room and closet.

Method 1 Think of the region as one large rectangle.

$A = 6(3 + 2)$

$= 6(5)$

$= 30$ square yards

Method 2 Think of the region as two smaller rectangles.

$A = 6 \cdot 3 + 6 \cdot 2$

$= 18 + 12$

$= 30$ square yards

Multiply the cost for a square yard of carpeting by the number of square yards needed.

$$20 \cdot 30 = 600$$

ANSWER ▶ It will cost $600 to carpet the bedroom and closet.

Student Help

▶MORE EXAMPLES
More examples are available at www.mcdougallittell.com

Extra Examples 1 and 2

Use the distributive property to simplify the expression.

a. $6(3) + 6(2)$ **30**

b. $12(x + 4)$ $\mathbf{12x + 48}$

c. $x(5 + 2x)$ $\mathbf{5x + 2x^2}$

d. $6x + 2x$ $\mathbf{8x}$

Extra Example 3

Write an equivalent expression using the distributive property. Then evaluate or simplify.

a. $6(4 + 5 + 7)$ $\mathbf{6 \cdot 4 + 6 \cdot 5 + 6 \cdot 7 = 96}$

b. $4(6x + 11)$ $\mathbf{24x + 44}$

Extra Example 4

You are fertilizing your garden and backyard. One bag of fertilizer covers 400 square feet. How many bags will be needed?

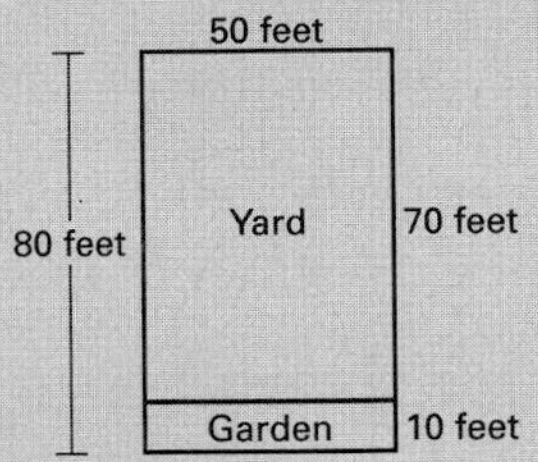

10 bags

Math Reasoning

The fact that the distributive law holds for subtraction, that is, $a(b - c) = ab - ac$, follows from the usual CAD laws and the fact that $x - y = x + (-1)y$:

$a(b - c) = a(b + (-1)c) = ab + a(-1)c = ab + (-1)ac = ab - ac$.

Concept Check

Explain how the distributive property can be used to simplify $3(8) + 3(2) + 6(3) + 6(7)$. ***Sample answer:*** **Rewrite the expression as $3(8 + 2) + 6(3 + 7) = 3(10) + 6(10) = (3 + 6)10 = 9(10) = 90$.**

3 Apply

Assignment Guide

TRANSITIONAL
Day 1: pp. 40–41 Exs. 21–26, 30–33, 36–39, 44–45

AVERAGE
Day 1: pp. 40–41 Exs. 23–34, 36–42, 44–45

ADVANCED
Day 1: pp. 40–41 Exs. 24–34, 35*, 36–38, 40–45

BLOCK SCHEDULE
pp. 40–41 Exs. 23–34, 36–42, 44–45 (with 1.7)

Extra Practice

- Student Edition, pp. 690–691
- Chapter 1 Resource Book, p. 69

Homework Check

To quickly check student understanding of key concepts, go over the following exercises:

Transitional: 22, 24, 32, 36, 38
Average: 24, 28, 32, 36, 38
Advanced: 24, 28, 32, 36, 42

34.

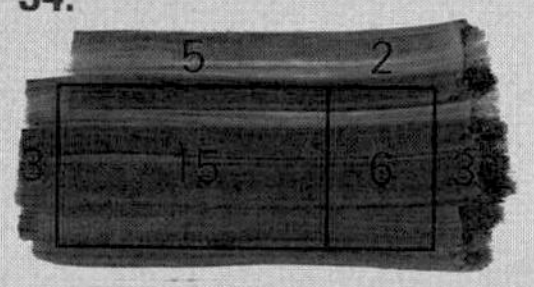

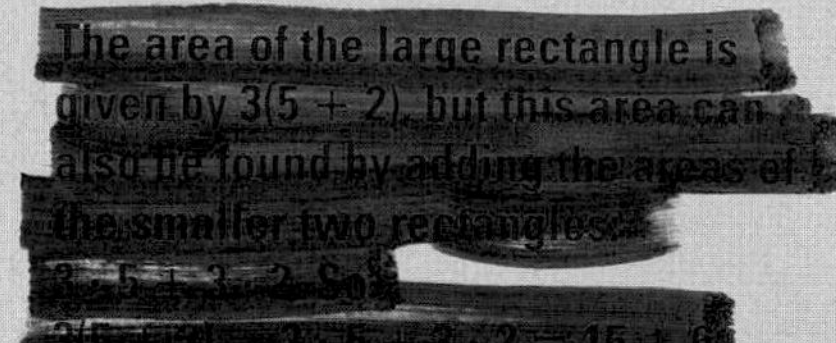

1.8 Exercises

Guided Practice

1. $3(2 + 7) = 3 \cdot 2 + 3 \cdot 7$; $3(9) = 6 + 21$; $27 = 27$
2. $11(10 + 5) = 11 \cdot 10 + 11 \cdot 5$; $11(15) = 110 + 55$; $165 = 165$
3. $17(8.5 - 1.5) = 17(8.5) - 17(1.5)$; $17(7) = 144.5 - 25.5$; $119 = 119$
4. $9(8 - 7) = 9 \cdot 8 - 9 \cdot 7$; $9(1) = 72 - 63$; $9 = 9$

Use the distributive property to write an equivalent numerical expression. Then show that the two expressions have the same value. 1–4. See margin.

1. $3(2 + 7)$ **2.** $11(10 + 5)$ **3.** $17(8.5 - 1.5)$ **4.** $9(8 - 7)$

In Exercises 5–8, tell whether the example illustrates the correct use of the distributive property. If not, rewrite the expression so that it does.

5. $2(3 + 5) = 2(3) + 5$
Incorrect; $2(3 + 5) = 2(3) + 2(5)$

6. $4(y + 7y) = 32y$
Correct

7. $6(4x + 1) = 24x + 1$
Incorrect; $6(4x) + 6(1) = 24x + 6$

8. $2(3a + 6) = 2a + 12$
Incorrect; $2(3a + 6) = 6a + 12$

ALGEBRA In Exercises 9–16, use the distributive property to write an equivalent variable expression. Then simplify. 9–16. See margin.

9. $4(x + 9)$ **10.** $3(5x + 1)$ **11.** $8(4 - q)$ **12.** $2(x - 25)$

13. $32a + 8a$ **14.** $y(7) + y(9)$ **15.** $a(b + 4 + c)$ **16.** $r(s + t)$

9. $4 \cdot x + 4 \cdot 9 = 4x + 36$
10. $3 \cdot 5x + 3 \cdot 1 = 15x + 3$
11. $8 \cdot 4 - 8q = 32 - 8q$
12. $2 \cdot x - 2 \cdot 25 = 2x - 50$
13. $(32 + 8)a = 40a$
14. $y(7 + 9) = 16y$
15. $a \cdot b + a \cdot 4 + a \cdot c = ab + 4a + ac$
16. $rs + rt$

17. Before painting the two green walls a new color, a painter finds the area of the walls. Find the total area in two different ways.
$8 \cdot 10 + 8 \cdot 20 = 240$; $8(10 + 20) = 240$

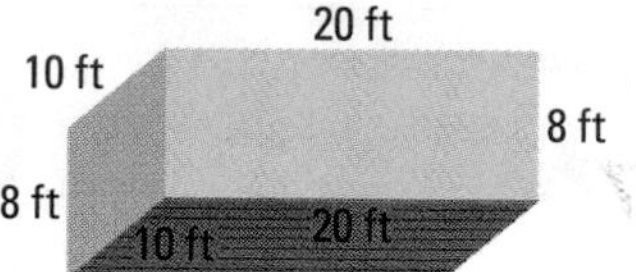

Use the distributive property to evaluate each expression mentally.

18. $4 \cdot 3 + 4 \cdot 7$ 40 **19.** $3.5 \cdot 8 + 3.5 \cdot 12$ 70 **20.** $5 \cdot 13 + 5 \cdot 7$ 100

Practice and Problem Solving

Student Help
▶MORE PRACTICE
Extra practice to help you master skills is on page 691.

Use the distributive property to write an equivalent numerical expression. Then show that the two expressions have the same value. 21–23. See margin.

21. $6(4 + 3)$ **22.** $12(10 - 5)$ **23.** $53 \cdot 6 + 53 \cdot 8$

21. 

22. $12(5) = 12 \cdot 10 - 12 \cdot 5$; $60 = 120 - 60$; $60 = 60$

23. $53 \cdot 6 + 53 \cdot 8 = 53(6 + 8)$; $318 + 424 = 53 \cdot 14$; $742 = 742$

ALGEBRA In Exercises 24–29, use the distributive property to write an equivalent variable expression. Then simplify when possible.

24. $8(x + 6)$ $8x + 48$ **25.** $3(4k - 9)$ $12k - 27$ **26.** $4(15 + r + t)$ $60 + 4r + 4t$

27. $7(c) + 7(3)$ $7c + 21$ **28.** $(8 + 11)s$ $8s + 11s = 19s$ **29.** $m(n + p)$ $mn + mp$

MATHEMATICAL REASONING Find each missing number or expression.

30. $4 \cdot 6 + 4 \cdot 9 = 4(\boxed{?} + 9)$ 6 **31.** $50(x + 9) = \boxed{?} + 450$ 50x

32. $70n = (30 + \boxed{?})n$ 40 **33.** $18 \cdot 5 + 18 \cdot \boxed{?} = 18(5 + n)$ n

34. Show that $3(5 + 2) = 15 + 6$ by drawing a diagram like the one in Example 4. Explain how your diagram models the distributive property. See margin.

35. CHALLENGE Use the associative property of addition and the distributive property to justify that $a(b + c + d) = ab + ac + ad$. **See margin.**

Student Help

▶ **HOMEWORK HELP** Extra help for problem solving in Exs. 36–38 is available at www.mcdougallittell.com

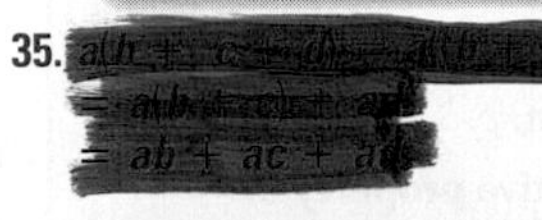

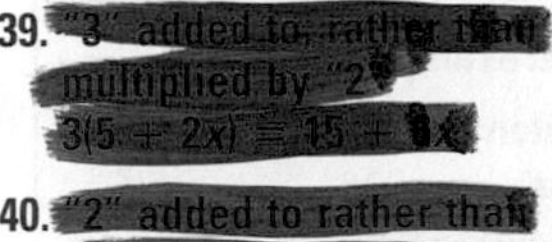

BUSINESS In Exercises 36–38, use the following information. Your small business has three employees. Each month, one employee earns \$1800, the second earns \$1500, and the third earns \$1300.

36. Write an expression for the total the employees earn in a year. $12(1800 + 1500 + 1300)$

37. Write an equivalent expression using the distributive property. $21{,}600 + 18{,}000 + 15{,}600$

38. Evaluate both expressions. Do they have the same value? Explain. 55,200; Equal. Distributive property

ERROR ANALYSIS In Exercises 39 and 40, the distributive property has been used incorrectly. Explain the error. Then write the correct answer.

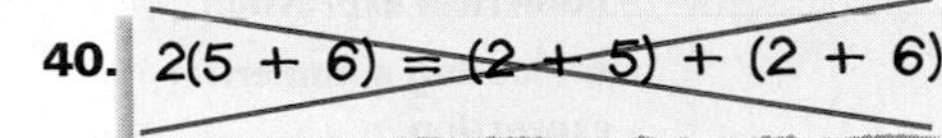

39. $3(5 + 2x) = 15 + 5x$ **40.** $2(5 + 6) = (2 + 5) + (2 + 6)$

39–40. See margin.

In Exercises 41–43, write a numerical expression. Then use the distributive property to evaluate the expression using mental math.

EXAMPLE

You bought four notebooks for \$3.95 each. What was the total cost?

Solution

$4 \cdot \$3.95 = 4(\$4.00 - \$.05)$	**Change \$3.95 to \$4.00 − \$.05.**
$= (4 \cdot \$4) - (4 \cdot \$.05)$	**Use distributive property.**
$= \$16 - \$.20$	**Multiply.**
$= \$15.80$	**Subtract.**

41. One flag costs \$10.50. How much will eight flags cost? $8 \times \$10 + 8 \times \$.50 = \$84$

42. You work for five hours at \$9.20 per hour. How much do you earn? $5 \times \$9 + 5 \times \$.20 = \$46$

43. Each section of a fence is 5.75 meters long. The fence has twelve sections. How long is the fence? $12 \times 6 - 12 \cdot \frac{1}{4}$; $72 - 3 = 69$ m

Multiple-Choice Practice

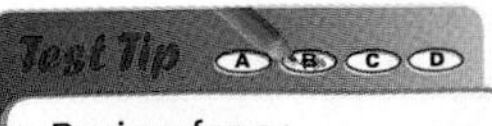

Test Tip

▶ Review for a standardized test at least a week. Several short periods of review are more productive than one or two long periods.

44. A family of four attends a baseball game. Each ticket costs \$9.00. Each person buys a hat for \$7.95 and a T-shirt for \$19.75. Which expression represents the total amount of money spent?

Ⓐ $4 \cdot 9.00 + 7.95 + 19.75$ Ⓑ $4 + (9.00 + 7.95 + 19.75)$

Ⓒ $4(9.00 \cdot 7.95 \cdot 19.75)$ Ⓓ $4(9.00 + 7.95 + 19.75)$

45. Which of the following expressions is equivalent to $3(y + z)$?

Ⓕ $3y + z$ Ⓖ $3yz$ Ⓗ $3y + 3z$ Ⓙ $y + 3z$

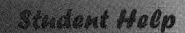

4 Assess

Assessment Resources

- Assessment Book (Formal Assessment and Alternative Assessment)
- Test and Practice Generator

Mini-Quiz

1. Use the distributive property to rewrite the expression.
   a. $4(x + 2)$ $4x + 8$
   b. $3(x + 5)$ $3x + 15$
   c. $9(x + y + 5)$ $9x + 9y + 45$
2. Each week, you baby-sit 3 hours on Monday and 2 hours on Tuesday. You make \$5.00 per hour. Use the distributive property to write two equivalent expressions for the total amount of money you make baby-sitting each week. Then simplify the expressions. $5(3 + 2)$, $5(3) + 5(2)$; 25 dollars

Additional Resources

The following resources are available to help review the material in this chapter:

Technology

- Personal Student Tutor
- Test and Practice Generator

Chapter 1 Chapter Summary and Review

VOCABULARY

- **data,** *p. 3*
- **bar graph,** *p. 4*
- **double bar graph,** *p. 4*
- **line graph,** *p. 4*
- **numerical expression,** *p. 7*
- **evaluating a numerical expression,** *p. 7*
- **variable,** *p. 8*
- **value of a variable,** *p. 8*
- **variable expression,** *p. 8*
- **evaluating a variable expression,** *p. 8*
- **power,** *p. 12*
- **base of a power,** *p. 12*
- **exponent,** *p. 12*
- **order of operations,** *p. 16*
- **grouping symbols,** *p. 17*
- **formula,** *p. 22*
- **sequence,** *p. 28*
- **commutative property of addition,** *p. 32*
- **commutative property of multiplication,** *p. 32*
- **associative property of addition,** *p. 32*
- **associative property of multiplication,** *p. 32*
- **counterexample,** *p. 33*
- **equivalent numerical expressions,** *p. 38*
- **distributive property,** *p. 38*
- **equivalent variable expressions,** *p. 38*

1.1 TABLES AND GRAPHS

Examples on pp. 3–4

Organizing data in tables or graphs helps you to visualize data easily and to find patterns.

EXAMPLE **The table gives the approximate population of Metro City over several years. Use the table to predict the population in 2000.**

Year	1994	1995	1996	1997	1998	1999	2000
Population	240,000	244,000	249,000	255,000	262,000	270,000	?

The yearly population growth is 4000, then 5000, then 6000, and so on. Continuing this pattern gives a year 2000 population prediction of about $270{,}000 + 9000 = 279{,}000$.

Use the double bar graph, which shows the populations in 1980 and 1999 of Arizona, Iowa, Maryland, Washington, and West Virginia.

(Source: U.S. Census Bureau)

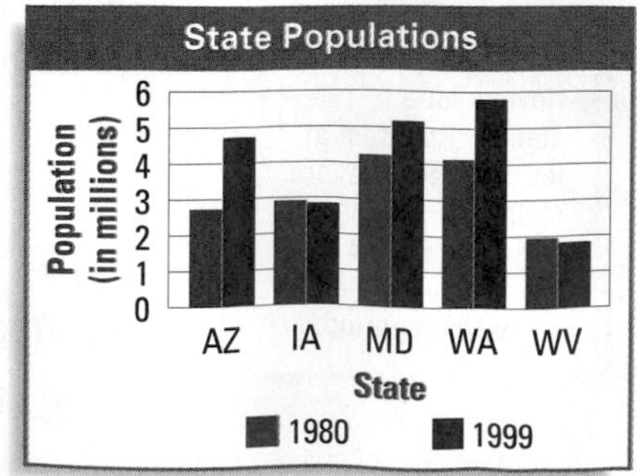

1. In which states did the population increase between 1980 and 1999? **AZ; MD; WA**

2. Which state had the highest population in 1980? **MD**

3. Which state had the highest population in 1999? **WA**

1.2 EXPRESSIONS AND VARIABLES

Examples on pp. 7–8

To evaluate a variable expression, substitute a number for the variable (or variables). Then find the value of the numerical expression that results.

EXAMPLES **Write the expression in words. Then evaluate the expression when $r = 5$.**

a. $3r$ **b.** $9 - r$ **c.** $\frac{16}{r}$

Solution

a. The product of 3 and r

$3r = 3 \cdot 5 = 15$

b. The difference of 9 and r

$9 - r = 9 - 5 = 4$

c. The quotient of 16 and r

$\frac{16}{r} = \frac{16}{5} = 16 \div 5 = 3.2$

Evaluate the expression. Then write the result in words.

4. 9×12 **108; The product of 9 and 12 is 108.**

5. $52 + 13$ **65; The sum of 52 and 13 is 65.**

6. $100 \div 5$ **20; The quotient of 100 and 5 is 20.**

7. $127 - 50$ **77; The difference between 127 and 50 is 77.**

In Exercises 8–11, evaluate the variable expression when $t = 7$.

8. $27 - t$ **20** **9.** $t + 2$ **9** **10.** $16t$ **112** **11.** $\frac{84}{t}$ **12**

12. Evaluate $x + y - 2$ when $x = 3$ and $y = 5$. **6**

13. You order 3 CDs for \$12 each and 2 CDs for \$9 each. Shipping costs \$7. Write and evaluate a numerical expression for the total cost of the CDs. **$3 \cdot 12 + 2 \cdot 9 + 7 = 61$**

1.3 POWERS AND EXPONENTS

Examples on pp. 12–13

EXAMPLES **a. Evaluate b^4 when $b = 3$.** **b. Evaluate $(11 - m)^2$ when $m = 2$.**

a. $b^4 = 3 \cdot 3 \cdot 3 \cdot 3 = 81$ **b.** $(11 - m)^2 = (11 - 2)^2 = 9^2 = 81$

In Exercises 14–19, evaluate the expression. For the variable expressions, find the value when $s = 4$.

14. 9^2 **81** **15.** 10^1 **10** **16.** 2^7 **128**

17. 1^7 **1** **18.** s^3 **64** **19.** $11^2 - s^2$ **105**

20. You can bake a recipe of brownies either in two 8 inch by 8 inch baking pans or in one 12 inch by 12 inch baking pan. Which choice enables you to cut more 2 inch by 2 inch brownies? Explain.

20. One 12-in.-square baking pan; *Sample answer:* The 2 8-in.-square baking pans will give a total of 32 2-in by 2-in. brownies. The 12-in.-square baking pan will give 36 brownies.

21. An ice cube tray makes 12 pieces of ice. Each is a cube 3 centimeters by 3 centimeters by 3 centimeters. Use the volume formula $V = s^3$ to find the total volume of ice cubes in two ice trays. **648 cm³**

1.4 ORDER OF OPERATIONS

Examples on pp. 16–17

When evaluating an expression, use the order of operations from page 16.

EXAMPLE **Evaluate 1 + 18 ÷ (3 + 6) • 5.**

$1 + 18 \div (3 + 6) \cdot 5 = 1 + 18 \div 9 \cdot 5$ Add within parentheses.

$= 1 + 2 \cdot 5$ Left-to-right rule: Divide 18 by 9.

$= 1 + 10$ Then multiply 2 by 5.

$= 11$ Add.

Evaluate the expression.

22. $50 - 20 \times 2 - 1$ **9**
23. $15 - 6 \times 4 \div 8$ **12**
24. $2 + (9 - 6) \div 3$ **3**
25. $12 \times 3^2 - 5$ **103**

1.5 USING FORMULAS

Examples on pp. 22–23

EXAMPLE **Find the perimeter and area of the figure.**

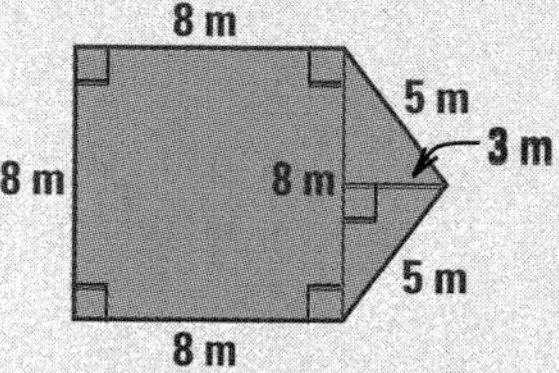

The perimeter is the sum of the side lengths. The area is the sum of the areas of a triangle and a square.

$P = 8 + 8 + 8 + 5 + 5 = 34$ meters

$A = \frac{1}{2}bh + s^2 = \frac{1}{2}(8)(3) + 8^2 = 12 + 64 = 76$ square meters

26. Find the perimeter of a rectangle with length 5 feet and width 3 feet. **16 ft**

27. You drive at a speed of 65 miles per hour for 4 hours. Use the distance formula $d = rt$ to find how far you travel. **260 mi**

1.6 PROBLEM SOLVING

Examples on pp. 27–28

Before solving problems, examine the information given to see what is needed and what is irrelevant. Also, look for a pattern in the given data.

EXAMPLE **Use a pattern to write the next three numbers you expect to find in the sequence 50, 43, 36, 29, ? , ? , ? .**

Each number is 7 less than the previous number. Continue the pattern.

50, 43, 36, 29, 22, 15, 8 (each −7)

Describe the pattern. List the next three numbers you expect to find in the sequence. 28. Each number is $\frac{1}{2}$ the number before it; 12, 6, 3

28. 192, 96, 48, 24, ?, ?, ?

29. 1, 5, 10, 16, ?, ?, ? Add 4, then 5, then 6, and so on; 23, 31, 40

In Exercises 30 and 31, use the following information. You are on a three day hiking trip. The trail is 36 miles long. On the first day you hike 8 miles at 2 miles per hour. On the second day you hike 11 miles at 3 miles per hour.

30. Suppose you want to know how far you will hike on the third day. Identify the given information that is irrelevant to find that distance. The rates at which you hiked on the first two days.

31. Suppose you want to know how long you will hike on the third day. Describe the missing information that is needed to find that time. How fast you will walk on the third day.

1.7 THE COMMUTATIVE AND ASSOCIATIVE PROPERTIES

Examples on pp. 32–33

The commutative and associative properties can help you to rewrite expressions in ways that make them easier to simplify and evaluate.

EXAMPLE **Use the commutative and associative properties to evaluate the expression 25 · (15 · 4). Justify each step.**

$25 \cdot (15 \cdot 4) = 25 \cdot (4 \cdot 15)$	Commutative property of multiplication
$= (25 \cdot 4) \cdot 15$	Associative property of multiplication
$= 100 \cdot 15$	Multiply 25 and 4.
$= 1500$	Multiply 100 and 15.

Use mental math to evaluate the expression. Justify each step. 32–34. See margin.

32. $47 + (19 + 43)$

33. $50 \times (19 \times 40)$

34. $(6 + 58) + (4 + 42)$

1.8 THE DISTRIBUTIVE PROPERTY

Examples on pp. 38–39

For any numbers or variables *a*, *b*, and *c*, $a(b + c) = ab + ac$.

EXAMPLES **a. Rewrite 3(10 − *x*).** **b. Evaluate 10(14) − 10(8).**

a. Distribute the 3.

$$3(10 - x) = 3(10) - 3(x) = 30 - 3x$$

b. Use the distributive property.

$$10(14) - 10(8) = 10(14 - 8) = 10(6) = 60$$

Use the distributive property to write an equivalent expression.

35. $4(x - 2)$ $4x - 8$

36. $7(8 + f + 2)$ $56 + 7f + 14 = 70 + 7f$

37. $14(17) + 14(3)$ $14(17 + 3)$

38. $5x + 7x$ $(5 + 7)x$

32. $47 + (43 + 19)$; Commutative property of addition.
$(47 + 43) + 19$; Associative property of addition
$90 + 19 = 109$;
Add 47 and 43. Then add 90 and 19.

33. $50 \times (40 \times 19)$; Commutative property of multiplication
$(50 \times 40) \times 19$; Associative property of multiplication
$2000 \times 19 = 38{,}000$;
Multiply 50 and 40. Then multiply 2000 and 19.

34. $(58 + 6) + (4 + 42)$; Commutative property of addition
$58 + (6 + 4) + 42$; Associative property of addition
$10 + (58 + 42)$; Commutative and associative properties of addition
$10 + 100 = 110$;
Add 58 and 42. Then add 10 and 100.

Additional Resources

Assessment Book

- Formal Assessment, pp. 7–12
- Alternative Assessment, pp. 193–207

Test and Practice Generator

1.

$21 \times n$	product
21×1	21
21×2	42
21×3	63
21×4	84
21×5	105
21×6	126
21×7	147
21×8	168
21×9	189

2.

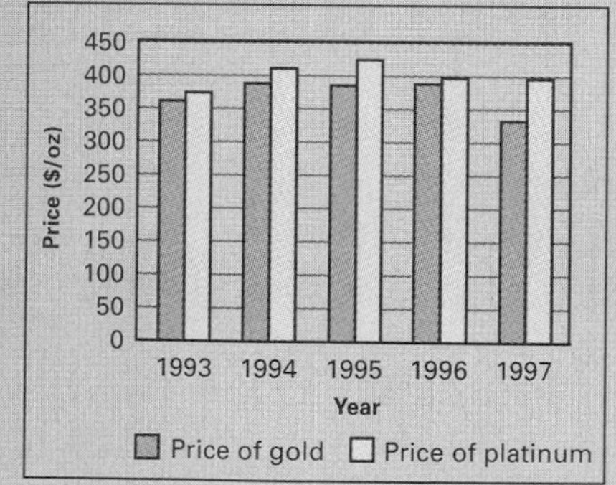

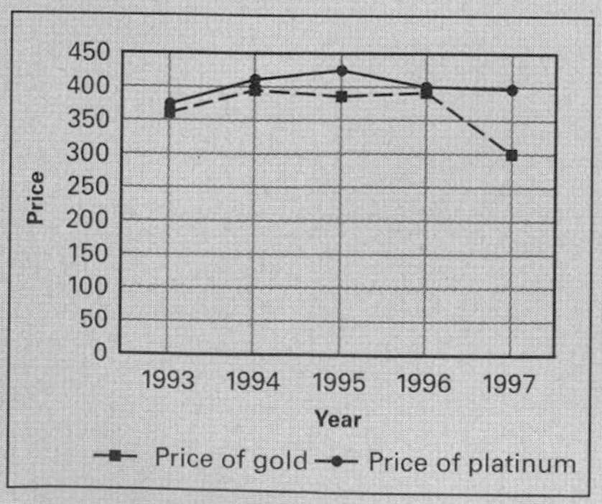

19. Each number is 2 less than the previous number; 7, 5, 3

20. Each number is 2 times the previous number; 48, 96, 192

21. The pattern is $3^2, 4^2, 5^2$, and so on; 49, 64, 81

22. Associative property of addition

23. Commutative property of multiplication

Chapter 1 Chapter Test

1. Find the product of 21 and each of the first 9 counting numbers (1, 2, 3, . . .). Organize the results in a table. Describe any patterns you see in the products. The ones digits are the first 9 counting numbers. The remaining digits are the first 9 even numbers. See margin for table.

2. **PRECIOUS METALS** The average prices of gold and platinum (in dollars per ounce) for the years 1993 through 1997 are shown in the table. Draw a double bar graph and a line graph to represent the data.

Year	1993	1994	1995	1996	1997
Price of gold	361	385	386	389	333
Price of platinum	374	411	425	398	397

See margin.

Evaluate the expression. Then write the result in words.

3. 4×36 144; The product of 4 and 36 is 144.
4. $3 + 95$ 98; The sum of 3 and 95 is 98.
5. $98 \div 7$ 14; The quotient of 98 and 7 is 14.
6. $28 - 9$ 19; The difference between 28 and 9 is 19.

Evaluate the variable expression when $x = 4$.

7. $9x$ 36
8. $14 - x$ 10
9. $\frac{44}{x}$ 11
10. $3 + x^2$ 19

Evaluate the expression.

11. $3 + 5 \times 2 + 4$ 17
12. $10 - 4 + 8 \div 4$ 8
13. $(6 + 2) \times 2 + 3$ 19
14. $3 \times 4 - (8 + 1)$ 3
15. $14 \div (9 - 2) + 5^2$ 27
16. $5 \times (6 - 2) - 2^3 \div 2^2$ 18

Find the perimeter and area of the figure.

17.

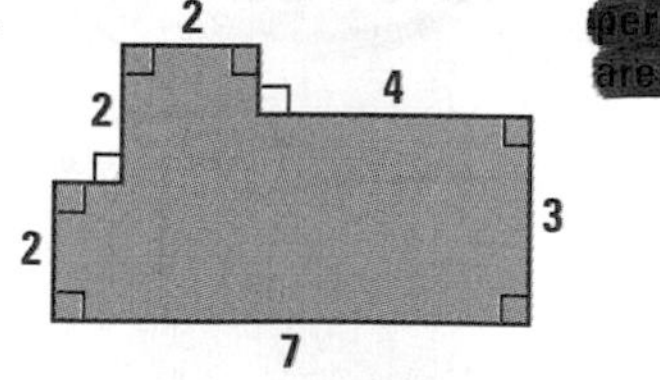

perimeter: 22
area: 22

18.

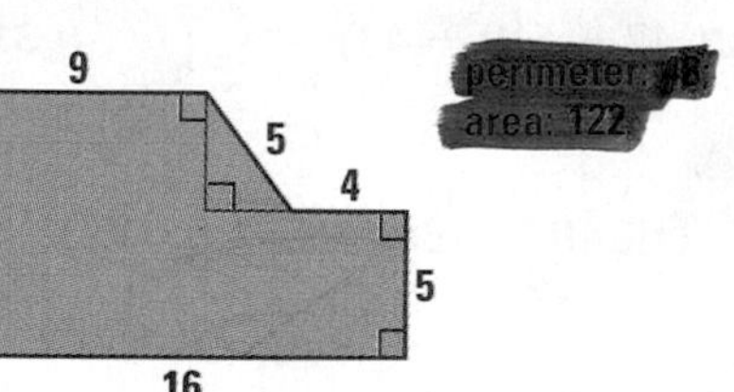

Describe the pattern. List the next three numbers you expect to find in the sequence. 19–21. See margin.

19. 15, 13, 11, 9, ?, ?, ?
20. 3, 6, 12, 24, ?, ?, ?
21. 9, 16, 25, 36, ?, ?, ?

Name the property that justifies the statement. 22–23. See margin.

22. $(37 + 19) + 11 = 37 + (19 + 11)$
23. $0.75(23)(16) = 23(0.75)(16)$

Use the distributive property to write an equivalent expression.

24. $6(x - 3)$ $6x - 18$
25. $17(15) - 17(5)$ $17(15 - 5)$
26. $a(21) - a(13)$  $a(21 - 13)$

Multiple-Choice Practice

Test Tip If you can eliminate one or more wrong answers, you may improve your chances of answering correctly.

1. Which statement describes the pattern in the sequence 1, 3, 5, 7, 9, . . .?

Ⓐ Each number is 1 more than the previous number.

Ⓑ Each number is 2 more than the previous number.

Ⓒ Each number is 3 less than the previous number.

Ⓓ Each number is 3 times the previous number.

2. Evaluate $10 - 2^3 \div 2$.

Ⓕ 1 Ⓖ 6 Ⓗ 8 Ⓙ 10

In Exercises 3 and 4, use the bar graph, which shows the number of boys and girls in your class for four different years.

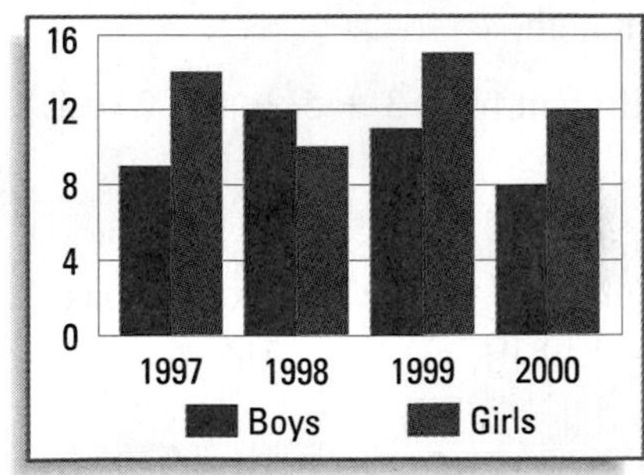

3. When were there more boys than girls?

Ⓐ 1997 Ⓑ 1998

Ⓒ 1999 Ⓓ 2000

4. When was your class the largest?

Ⓕ 1997 Ⓖ 1998

Ⓗ 1999 Ⓙ 2000

5. Which statement illustrates the commutative property of addition?

Ⓐ $(3 + 4) + (5 + 6) = 3 + (4 + 5) + 6$

Ⓑ $3(4 + 5 + 6) = (4 + 5 + 6)3$

Ⓒ $3 + 4 + 5 + 6 = 3 + (4 + 5 + 6)$

Ⓓ $(3 + 4) + (5 + 6) = (5 + 6) + (3 + 4)$

6. The infield of a baseball field is a square with a side length of 90 feet. What is the perimeter of the infield?

Ⓕ 180 ft Ⓖ 360 ft

Ⓗ 1350 ft Ⓙ 8100 ft

7. What is the area of a triangle with base 12 feet and height 4 feet?

Ⓐ 16 ft^2 Ⓑ 24 ft^2

Ⓒ 48 ft^2 Ⓓ 144 ft^2

8. Which expression represents this phrase: *Four times the difference of ten and three*?

Ⓕ $4(10 - 3)$ Ⓖ $4 \times 10 - 3$

Ⓗ $10 - 3 \times 4$ Ⓙ Not here

9. Evaluate $x^2 - 2x$ when $x = 6$.

Ⓐ 0 Ⓑ 24 Ⓒ 28 Ⓓ 48

10. Which statement *incorrectly* shows the distributive property?

Ⓕ $4(x + y + z) = 4x + 4y + 4z$

Ⓖ $3(a + 1) = 3a + 3$

Ⓗ $6(2 - m) = 8 - 6m$

Ⓙ $2(5) + 2(3) = 2(5 + 3)$

Brain games

California Standards

- Express quantitative relationships by using expressions. (AF 1.0)
- Apply strategies and results from simpler problems to more complex problems. (MR 2.2)

Number Jumble

Materials

- Paper and pencil
- Blank cards

Directions

Object of the Game

Play this game in teams of two. Teams earn points by writing *different* expressions. The team with the most points wins.

How to Play

$5 \cdot 3 \cdot (4-2-1) = 15$

$[(5 \cdot 4)-3-2] \div 1 = 15$

STEP 1 Each team writes numerical expressions on blank cards. The numbers 1, 2, 3, 4, and 5 must appear once in each expression. Each expression must have a different whole number value from 1 to 20. Symbols for multiplication, division, addition, subtraction, exponents, and grouping can be used as needed.

STEP 2 Teams compare their expressions with those of other teams. Each team scores one point for every expression that is *not* used by another team. Simple changes in order do not make expressions different enough.

1 + 2 + 3 + 4 + 5 is not different from 3 + 5 + 4 + 2 + 1.

$(5 + 5) \cdot (5 + 5) = 100$

$4 \cdot 4 - (4 + 4) = 8$

Another Way to Play

Teams earn points by using four 5's to write expressions whose value is 100, or by using four 4's to write expressions for each of the numbers from 1 to 10.

Brain Teaser

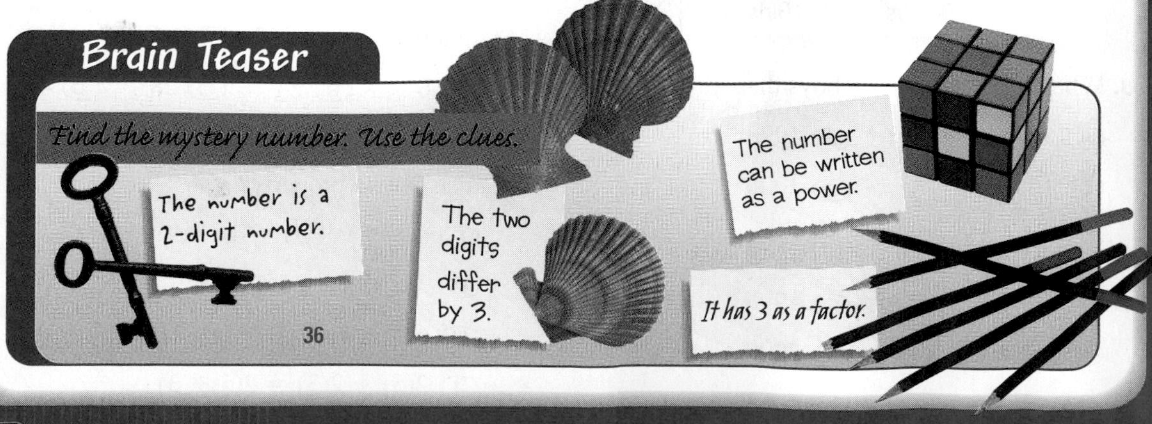

Find the mystery number. Use the clues.
The number is a 2-digit number.
The two digits differ by 3.
The number can be written as a power.
It has 3 as a factor.
36

California Standards and Assessment

CA Standards: AF 1.0, MR 2.2

The basic skills you'll review on this page will help prepare you for the next chapter.

Reviewing the Basics

You may want to use a vertical format to find the difference of two decimals. Remember to line up the decimal points.

EXAMPLE 1 ***Subtracting Decimals***

Subtract 1.25 from 8.1.

Solution

8.10	Write a zero in the hundredths place.
−1.25	Bring down the decimal point, and then subtract as with whole numbers.
6.85	

Try These

Find the difference.

1. 15.5 − 6 **9.5** **2.** 21.67 − 13 **8.67** **3.** 7.4 − 3.3 **4.1**

4. 8 − 6.5 **1.5** **5.** 27 − 13.01 **13.99** **6.** 16.5 − 11.7 **4.8**

7. 25.05 − 17.9 **7.15** **8.** 11.125 − 8.375 **2.75** **9.** 31.1 − 16.01 **15.09**

You can use estimation to check the reasonableness of an answer.

EXAMPLE 2 ***Using Estimation***

Use estimation to verify that 6076 is a reasonable answer for the product of 62 and 98.

Solution

62 is a little more than 60, and 98 is a little less than 100. The product of 62 and 98 will be close to the product of 60 and 100.

ANSWER ▶ The product 62 • 98 is about 60 • 100 = 6000. So, the answer of 6076 is reasonable.

Try These

Estimate the value of the expression. **10–21. Estimates may vary.**

10. 127 − 51 **80** **11.** 323 + 674 **1000** **12.** 24.1 − 15.9 **8**

13. 347 − 198 **150** **14.** 124 + 253 + 376 **800** **15.** 31 • 97 **3000**

16. 19 • 82 **1600** **17.** 0.49 • 41 **20** **18.** 11 • 581 **5800**

19. 749.6 ÷ 24.9 **30** **20.** 0.328 • 1215 **400** **21.** 0.9 • 2.1 • 256 **500**

Student Help

▶ **MORE EXAMPLES**
INTERNET More examples and practice exercises available at www.mcdougallittell.com

Teaching Tip

The Brain Games activity provides a motivating way to review selected content in the chapter. For a more comprehensive review, see the Chapter Summary and Review on pp. 42–45.

Pacing and Assignment Guide

Regular Schedule

Lesson	Les. Day	Transitional	Average	Advanced
2.1	Day 1	pp. 55–56 Exs. 11–14, 16–18, 23–27, 33–34	pp. 55–56 Exs. 11–20, 23–30, 32–34	pp. 55–56 Exs. 13–22, 25–30, 31*, 32–34
2.2	Day 1	SRH p. 686 Exs 3–4; pp. 59–60 Exs. 10–12, 16–20, 26–27, 30–32, 39, 43	pp. 59–60 Exs. 13–15, 18–23, 26–28, 30–32, 36–37, 43	pp. 59–60 Exs. 18–28, 33–37, 40–42*, 43
2.3	Day 1	pp. 63–65 Exs. 12–17, 22–25, 73–83	pp. 63–65 Exs. 12–17, 22–29, 73–83	pp. 63–65 Exs. 15–17, 22–29, 73–83
	Day 2	pp. 63–65 Exs. 18–21, 30–35, 39–40, 43–45, 49–54, 62, 71–72	pp. 63–65 Exs. 30–35, 40–41, 43–45, 49–54, 58–59, 63–65, 71–72	pp. 63–65 Exs. 33–38, 41–42, 46–48, 52–57, 60–61, 66–67*, 71–72
2.4	Day 1	pp. 68–70 Exs. 11–15, 18–19, 21–24	pp. 68–70 Exs. 11–19, 21–26	pp. 68–70 Exs. 11–19, 21–26
	Day 2	pp. 68–70 Exs. 20, 28–32, 39–40	pp. 68–70 Exs. 27–29, 32–35, 37–40	pp. 68–70 Exs. 27, 30–35, 36*, 37–40
2.5	Day 1	SRH p. 679 Exs. 1, 3, 4, 7; pp. 76–77 Exs. 14–20, 34–35, 39–40, 47–49	pp. 76–77 Exs. 14–24, 34–35, 39–40, 47–49	pp. 76–77 Exs. 14–24, 34–35, 39–40, 47–49
	Day 2	SRH p. 679 Exs. 2, 6, 9, 12; pp. 76–77 Exs. 12–13, 25–33, 36–38, 41–46, 50–55, 57–58	pp. 76–77 Exs. 25–33, 36–38, 41–46, 50–55, 57–58	pp. 76–77 Exs. 25–33, 36–38, 41–46, 50–55, 56*, 57–60
2.6	Day 1	SRH p. 680 Exs. 5–8; pp. 82–84 Exs. 10–14, 23–25, 32–34, 42–43, 46–47	pp. 82–84 Exs. 10–16, 23–25, 32–34, 44–48	pp. 82–84 Exs. 12–16, 23–25, 32–34, 44–48
	Day 2	SRH p. 680 Exs. 13–16; pp. 82–84 Exs. 9, 17–20, 26–29, 35–38, 50–60	pp. 82–84 Exs. 9, 17–22, 26–31, 35–41, 50–60	pp. 82–84 Exs. 20–22, 26–31, 35–41, 49*, 50–60
2.7	Day 1	SRH p. 671 Exs. 1–3; pp. 88–89 Exs. 3–8, 15–16, 19–21	pp. 88–89 Exs. 3–8, 12–16, 19–21	pp. 88–89 Exs. 3–5, 9–16 17–18*, 19–21
2.8	Day 1	pp. 92–93 Exs. 11–16, 23–31, 38–40, 44–46, 49–50	pp. 92–93 Exs. 11–16, 23–31, 38–46, 49–50	pp. 92–93 Exs. 13–20, 29–41, 46–47, 48*, 49–50
Review	Day 1	pp. 94–97 Exs. 1–47	pp. 94–97 Exs. 1–47	pp. 94–97 Exs. 1–47
Assess	Day 1	Chapter 2 Test	Chapter 2 Test	Chapter 2 Test

Yearly Pacing Chapter 2 Total – **14 days** Chapters 1–2 Total – **24 days** Remaining – **136 days**

* Challenge Exercises EP = Extra Practice SRH = Skills Review Handbook EC = Extra Challenge

Block Schedule

Day 1	Day 2	Day 3	Day 4	Day 5	Day 6	Day 7
2.1 pp. 55–56: Exs. 11–20, 23–30, 32–34 **2.2** pp. 59–60: Exs. 13–15, 18–23, 26–28, 30–32, 36–37, 43	**2.3** pp. 63–65: Exs. 12–17, 22–35, 40–41, 43–45, 49–54, 58–59, 63–65, 71–83	**2.4** pp. 68–70: Exs. 11–19, 21–29, 32–35, 37–40	**2.5** pp. 76–77: Exs. 14–55, 57–58	**2.6** pp. 82–84: Exs. 9–41, 44–48, 50–60	**2.7** pp. 88–89: Exs. 3–8, 12–16, 19–21 **2.8** pp. 92–93: Exs. 11–16, 23–31, 38–46, 49–50	**Review** pp. 94–97: Exs. 1–47 **Assess** Chapter 2 Test

Yearly Pacing Chapter 2 Total – **7 days** Chapters 1–2 Total – **12 days** Remaining – **68 days**

Support Materials

Chapter Resource Book

LESSON SUPPORT	2.1	2.2	2.3	2.4	2.5	2.6	2.7	2.8
Lesson Plans	p. 1	p. 10	p. 19	p. 28	p. 37	p. 46	p. 55	p. 64
Lesson Plans for Block Scheduling	p. 2	p. 11	p. 20	p. 29	p. 38	p. 47	p. 56	p. 65
Warm-Ups with Multiple-Choice Practice	p. 3	p. 12	p. 21	p. 30	p. 39	p. 48	p. 57	p. 66
Problem of the Day	p. 4	p. 13	p. 22	p. 31	p. 40	p. 49	p. 58	p. 67
Daily Cumulative Review	p. 5	p. 14	p. 23	p. 32	p. 41	p. 50	p. 59	p. 68
Practice Masters	p. 6	p. 15	p. 24	p. 33	p. 42	p. 51	p. 60	p. 69
Reteaching Masters	p. 7	p. 16	p. 25	p. 34	p. 43	p. 52	p. 61	p. 70
Enrichment Masters	p. 9	p. 18	p. 27	p. 36	p. 45	p. 54	p. 63	p. 72

Transparencies

	2.1	2.2	2.3	2.4	2.5	2.6	2.7	2.8
Warm-Ups with Multiple-Choice Practice	p. 9	p. 10	p. 11	p. 12	p. 13	p. 14	p. 15	p. 16
Teacher Time-Saver Transparencies	✓	✓	✓	✓	✓	✓	✓	✓
English/Spanish Problem Solving	p. 4	p. 5		p. 6			p. 7	p. 8
Answer Transparencies	✓	✓	✓	✓	✓	✓	✓	✓

Technology

- Personal Student Tutor
- Time-Saving Test and Practice Generator
- Electronic Teacher Tools
- Technology: Using Calculators and Computers

Additional Resources

- Math Log
- Assessment Book
- Worked-Out Solution Key
- Practice Workbook (English/Spanish)
- Home and School Connection
- California Standards: Key Concepts Book

Correlation to the California Curriculum

Correlations to the California Standards

CA Standards: AF 1.1, AF 1.3, AF 1.4, AF 4.0, MG 1.3, MR 1.1, MR 2.0, MR 2.5

California Curriculum Support

Key Concepts Book

- Pre-Course Review: Topic 1 Working with Decimals
  Topic 5 Measurement
- Key Standards: AF 1.3 The Distributive Property *(Lesson 2.2)*
  AF 1.3 Identity and Inverse Properties *(Lesson 2.2)*
  MG 1.3 Dimensional Analysis *(Lesson 2.7)*

California Standards Practice Workbook provides practice for each Standard that is covered in this chapter.

Providing Universal Access

Strategies for Strategic Learners

PREVIEW KEY CONCEPTS

Students will be introduced this year to the concept of unit or dimensional analysis, which is a way of focusing on the units used in a problem as an aid to problem solving. Understanding unit analysis is a great help to students later in mathematics and in sciences such as chemistry. There are several places in this text where unit analysis is discussed, and students have several opportunities to understand it. It may help students to brainstorm all the possible units of measurement one might use. Their lists should include at least the following:
Time: seconds, minutes, hours, days, weeks, months, years; length or distance: inches, feet, yards, miles, centimeters, meters, kilometers; liquid capacity: ounces, cups, pints, quarts, gallons, milliliters, liters; weight or mass: ounces, pounds, tons, grams, kilograms.

Review with students basic conversions between metric and U.S. customary units. Then do a very simple unit analysis problem:

The perimeter of a rectangle is 42 inches. I have pieces of rope and I will use them to outline the perimeter. Each piece of rope is 2 inches long. How many pieces of rope do I need?

$$\frac{42 \text{ inches}}{2 \text{ inches}} = 21$$

UNIT ANALYSIS In your answer you have eliminated inches because you have divided inches into inches. You have ended up with the number of pieces of rope it would take to outline the perimeter. Have students think about how they started with inches and ended up with an answer that was not expressed in inches. Have students do a number of unit analyses where the numbers are blank, so that they cannot actually perform the calculations. This will force them to focus on the units.

$$\frac{\text{miles}}{\text{hour}} \times \underline{?} = \text{miles}$$

$$\frac{\text{calories}}{\text{banana}} \times \underline{?} = \text{calories}$$

$$\frac{?}{\text{minute}} \times \frac{\text{minutes}}{?} = \frac{\text{pages}}{\text{hour}}$$

Strategies for English Learners

VOCABULARY DEVELOPMENT

You might think about the vocabulary development of English learners as occurring in two strands simultaneously. There are many common English words that are used in mathematics, and there are words and phrases that are specific to the discipline of mathematics. Common English words include not only the thousand most common words in the English language but also words that commonly recur in this textbook. Encourage students to enter new words in their notebooks, along with the following information:

New word
Word in the primary language
Synonym
Opposite
Diagram or picture
A page in the text where the word was found

Parents and older siblings can often be enlisted to help with this activity.

LISTING WORDS Review common words with students, have students practice grouping them by related meanings, and find synonyms and antonyms. This would be an ideal activity for a language arts class or a tutorial program, and it should be done over a period of weeks. These lists can be posted in the classroom, and students can add to the lists as the course progresses:

Verbs	Nouns	Adverbs and phrases	Adjectives and phrases	Pronouns	Prepositions Conjunctions Interjections

VOCABULARY OF TABLES AND GRAPHS Since much of the first chapter relates to using tables and graphs to display and explain information, start with a review of related vocabulary, such as horizontal and vertical axes, bar, column, data, diagram, distance, graph, line, map, pattern, plot, point, relationship, row, scale, and table. If students are familiar with different ways of displaying data, have them name and describe or draw all of the different kinds of tables and graphs with which they are familiar (for example, pictograph, box-and-whisker plot, Venn diagram).

Strategies for Advanced Learners

DIFFERENTIATE INSTRUCTION IN TERMS OF COMPLEXITY

Mathematics is an integral part of the study of other subjects, such as science, economics, and history. Teachers at this grade level may want to work together to develop interesting and more challenging assignments that combine the objectives for other courses into short projects or investigations that can be substituted for easier assignments. These assignments can be a welcome alternative to having advanced students wait until the rest of the class catches up. The assignments should be designed so that students can work relatively independently, with a group, or with the science or history teacher. They can then be used while the mathematics teacher focuses on review or reteaching with the rest of the class.

CROSS-CURRICULAR LINKS The links to other subjects in *Concepts and Skills* suggest areas for students to apply and extend their learning of mathematics. For example, in the link to science on page 60, students learn about the predictability of eruptions of some geysers. The teacher can suggest that a group of students investigate why this occurs. If eruptions are regular, what is the pattern, and what causes the pattern? Do the eruptions have something to do with the buildup of pressure? What could this pressure be caused by? Is heat involved? volume? Suggest that students investigate what geysers are and use graphs to describe their findings about why eruption patterns are predictable. As many states move toward standards-based education, assignments that simultaneously address standards across several subject areas maximize the efficient use of instructional time.

CHAPTER 2 Mathematical Background Notes

Lessons 2.1–2.2

SIMPLIFYING EXPRESSIONS Following the study of variable expressions in Chapter 1, these lessons set the stage for the formulation and solution of algebraic equations. Since we tend to think and communicate with words, an ability to translate verbal phrases into mathematical expressions, and vice versa, is an essential part of algebra.

Once a problem is formulated in algebraic terms, the solution process often calls for simplifying expressions. Here it is important to be able to apply the CAD laws to combine like terms. For example,

$$3x - 7 + 2x = 3x + 2x - 7 = (3 + 2)x - 7 = 5x - 7.$$

By writing the trinomial $3x - 7 + 2x$ without using parentheses, we are making implicit use of the associative law of addition. The rearrangement of terms is justified by the commutative law of addition, while factoring out x from $3x + 2x$ makes use of the distributive law.

The process of simplifying expressions may also involve the identity properties of addition and multiplication, as formulated in the box on page 57. For example, in order to use the distributive law to simplify $3x + x$, students will use the fact that

$$1 \cdot x = x$$

for all numbers x. It is on this basis that we write

$$3x + x = 3x + 1x = (3 + 1)x = 4x.$$

In solving equations by isolating the variable on one side of the equation, we use the fact that

$$0 + x = x$$

for all numbers x. Having internalized this fact, the student will learn to create expressions of the form

$$a + x - a$$

with the knowledge that they can be simplified to

$$a + x - a = a + (-a) + x = (a + (-a)) + x = 0 + x = x.$$

On page 59 variables are used to describe the lengths of the sides of a polygon and the student is asked to simplify the resulting expression for the perimeter. For a triangle such as the one below, one can also ask the student to draw the figure for specific values of x (they are not similar!). This geometric exercise leads to the interesting question: For what values of x is there a triangle with sides of length 4, $x - 2$, and $2x - 5$?

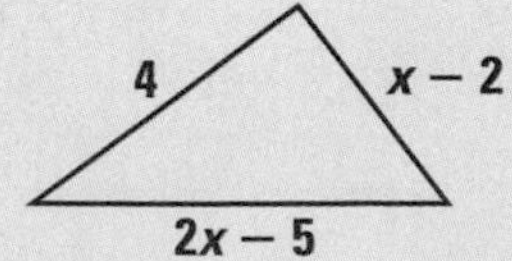

Lessons 2.5–2.6

SOLVING EQUATIONS Having used "mental math" to solve equations in Lesson 2.3, the student is now asked to use the rules of algebra to solve linear equations more methodically. This process calls for transforming a given equation into an **equivalent equation,** whose solutions are the same as the original equation. This is done by means of four properties of equality that assert that performing the same arithmetic operation on *both* sides of the equation produces an equivalent equation.

Using these properties of equality, the student learns to solve equations of the form $Ax + B = C$.

> **Equations of the form $x + B = C$ are solved in a single step by applying the addition or subtraction property of equality.**
>
> **Equations of the form $Ax = C$ ($A \neq 0$) are solved in single step by applying the multiplication or division property of equality.**

These steps enable us to isolate the variable on one side of the equation.

It should be emphasized that the constants and variables in these equations represent real numbers. As such, the transformations to be applied to linear equations (and later to more general equations) depend only on the basic axioms of arithmetic. For example, in transforming $2x - 3 = 5$ to the equivalent equation $x = 4$, as is taught in Lesson 4.1, we could proceed in the following (somewhat tedious) detail.

Recalling that $a - b = a + (-b)$, we have $2x - 3 = 2x + (-3)$, so the equation $2x - 3 = 5$ can be written as $2x + (-3) = 5$. Starting from here,

$$\begin{aligned}
(2x + (-3)) + 3 = 5 + 3 &= 8 && \text{(axioms of equality)}\\
2x + (-3 + 3) &= 8 && \text{(associative law of addition)}\\
2x + 0 &= 8 && \text{(inverse property of addition)}\\
2x &= 8 && \text{(identity property of addition)}\\
\frac{1}{2} \cdot (2x) = \frac{1}{2} \cdot 8 &= 4 && \text{(axioms of equality)}\\
\left(\frac{1}{2} \cdot 2\right)x &= 4 && \text{(associative law of multiplication)}\\
1 \cdot x &= 4 && \text{(inverse property of multiplication)}\\
x &= 4 && \text{(identity property of multiplication)}
\end{aligned}$$

While students should not be asked to provide this degree of algebraic detail, they should be aware that the algebraic procedures they are learning to implement are based on the same axioms that underlie arithmetic. This point, that a mastery of arithmetic is essential preparation for the study of algebra, is emphasized in California's new Standards. Further discussion of this fact and the role of *proof* in algebra instruction can be found in the 1999 *Mathematics Framework for California Public Schools,* pages 154–156.

Lesson 2.8

ORDER PROPERTIES The number line provides a vivid pictorial representation of the order relationships among real numbers. We have $a < b$ if the graph of a lies to the left of the graph of b on the number line. This interpretation of order leads to propositions such as the following. If $a > 0$, then $-a < 0$ and $-a < a$.

While such statements about real numbers may seem obvious when interpreted in terms of the number line, their ultimate justification does not depend on pictures. Rather, deductive reasoning can be used to derive such statements from the axioms that underlie arithmetic. Just as procedures for solving linear equations follow from the laws underlying arithmetic, so do statements such as

"If a is a positive real number, then $-a$ is a negative real number"

follow from the **Axioms of Order** that underlie the present lesson.

These axioms tell us that for each pair a, b of real numbers, exactly one of the following relationships holds: $a < b$, $a = b$, or $a > b$.

Furthermore:

(I) If a, b, and c satisfy $a < b$ and $b < c$, then $a < c$.
(II) If $a < b$, then for all c we have $a + c < b + c$.
(III) If $a < b$ and $c > 0$, then $ac < bc$.

EQUIVALENT INEQUALITIES In Lesson 2.8 the student encounters order properties in a somewhat different form. Closely related to the addition property of equality is the fact that adding the same number to both sides of an inequality results in an **equivalent inequality,** that is, an equality with the same solutions. Here Axiom II and the CAD laws allow us to conclude that if $a + c < b + c$, then $a + c + (-c) < b + c + (-c)$ and therefore $a < b$. In this way we can build on Axiom II to conclude that

$a < b$ if and only if $a + c < b + c$.

It is this consequence of Axiom II that justifies referring to $x - 3 < 5$ and $x < 8$ as *equivalent* inequalities. Replacing c by $(-c)$ in the statement displayed above, we can also conclude that

$a < b$ if and only if $a - c < b - c$.

Analogous rules apply for $>$, $\leq$, and $\geq$.

In the present lesson the student is told that multiplying or dividing both sides of an inequality by the same *positive* number results in an equivalent inequality. For multiplication, this corresponds to Axiom III, while the corresponding statement for division follows from the fact that division by a positive number c is equivalent to multiplying by the positive number $\frac{1}{c}$.

What this lesson leaves for later discussion (see Lesson 9.7) is that multiplying or dividing both sides of an inequality by a *negative* number does *not* result in an equivalent inequality. Instead, following this operation one has to *reverse* the inequality sign to obtain an equivalent inequality. For example, although $2 < 3$, we have

$2 \cdot (-4) > 3 \cdot (-4)$ because $-8 > -12$.

Accordingly, multiplying both sides of $x \leq 3$ by -2 leads to an equivalent inequality $-2x \geq -6$.

To demonstrate this important fact, suppose that $a < b$ and $c < 0$. Then $(-c) > 0$ so Axiom III allows us to write

$(-c)a < (-c)b$ or $-ac < -bc$.

Adding $ac + bc$ to both sides (allowed by Axiom II), we obtain $bc < ac$. This shows that multiplying both sides of an inequality by a negative number *reverses* the inequality.

The fact that division by a negative number also calls for reversing the sign of the inequality is a consequence of the fact that dividing by a negative number c is the same as multiplying by the negative number $\frac{1}{c}$.

It is interesting to note that, so far, we have not used Axiom I. That this axiom is nonetheless an important algebraic tool is indicated by the following problem.

If a and b are positive numbers with $a < b$, show that $a^2 < b^2$.

Since $a > 0$, Axiom III enables us to multiply both sides of $a < b$ by a and to conclude that $a^2 < ab$. Similarly, since $b > 0$ we can multiply both sides of $a < b$ by b to conclude that $ab < b^2$. Then, applying Axiom I to $a^2 < ab$ and $ab < b^2$, we get $a^2 < b^2$. Note that this last inequality might fail if a and b are not both positive.

Chapter Overview

Chapter Goals

In this chapter, students will learn to translate sentences into equations and to solve linear equations. They will:

- Solve equations using mental math.
- Learn a problem solving plan to solve real-life problem situations.
- Solve inequalities.

Career Note

Owners of small floral businesses often do much of the floral arranging themselves. They cut and arrange flowers according to the wishes of the customer. They must not only arrange the flowers, but also make arrangements for delivery, hire employees, coordinate employee work schedules and other management duties, as well as handle the finances of the business. Training for this type of job varies, but classes are offered at vocational schools and colleges on business management and on other skills necessary to own a business. Additional information about small business owners is available at **www.mcdougallittell.com**

Operations in Algebra

Why are operations in algebra important?

To solve real-life problems, you can translate verbal phrases into expressions and equations. Then you can use various operations to solve the problems. Throughout future mathematics courses, you will use algebra to solve problems that are too difficult to solve in your head.

Many people use algebra in their careers, including small business owners (page 51) and farm managers (page 70). For example, business owners can use equations to decide how to charge for their services.

Meeting the California Standards

The skills you'll develop in this chapter will help you meet state standards and prepare for standardized tests. In this chapter you'll:

- **Use variables and appropriate operations to write an expression or equation that represents a verbal description.** LESSONS 2.1, 2.4–2.7
- **Use algebraic terminology correctly.** LESSONS 2.2, 2.3
- **Simplify numerical expressions by applying properties of rational numbers and justifying the process used.** LESSONS 2.2, 2.5, 2.6
- **Solve simple linear equations.** LESSONS 2.3, 2.5, 2.6
- **Solve simple inequalities over the rational numbers.** LESSON 2.8

Career Link **SMALL BUSINESS OWNER** A small business owner uses operations with algebra when:

- deciding whether to charge for services by the hour or by the job.
- calculating the cost of products or services.

EXERCISES

The owner of a flower shop creates centerpieces for special occasions. The flowers cost an average of $12 for each centerpiece.

1. If the owner charges $50 per centerpiece, how much money is left after you subtract the cost of the flowers? This is the *profit*. **$38**
2. If it takes 2 hours to make the centerpiece, what is the profit per hour? Use your answer to Exercise 1. **$19**
3. If it takes 4 hours to make the centerpiece, what is the profit per hour? **$9.50**

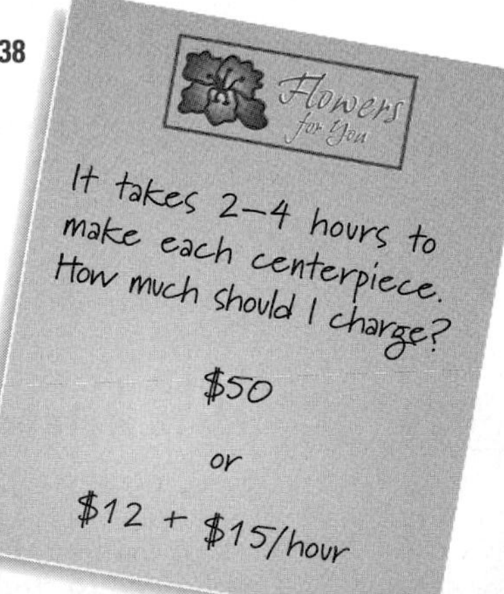

Flowers for You
It takes 2–4 hours to make each centerpiece. How much should I charge?
$50
or
$12 + $15/hour

The flower shop owner can either charge $50 per centerpiece or $15 per hour plus $12 for the cost of the flowers. In Lesson 2.1, you will learn how to tell which method is more profitable.

Projects

A project covering Chapters 1–3 appears on pages 164–165 of the Student Edition. Additional projects for selected lessons in Chapter 2 are available in the *Assessment Book,* pp. 213–214.

Technology

Software

- Electronic Teacher Tools
- Online Lesson Planner
- Personal Student Tutor
- Test and Practice Generator

Internet Connections

- Application and Career Links 56, 64, 69, 70
- Student Help 55, 58, 62, 69, 76, 80, 86, 92, 101

These Internet connections are available at **www.mcdougallittell.com**

Prepare

Diagnostic Tools

The **chapter readiness quiz** can help you diagnose whether students have the following skills needed in Chapter 2:

- Identify the commutative, associative, and distributive properties.
- Apply the correct order of operations to an expression.

Reteaching Materials

The following resources are available for students who need additional help with the skills on the chapter readiness quiz:

Chapter 2 Resource Book

- Reteaching with Practice (Lessons 1.3, 1.4, 1.7, 1.8)

Personal Student Tutor

Additional Resources

The following resources are provided to help you prepare for the upcoming chapter and customize review materials:

Chapter 2 Resource Book

- Lesson Plans, pp. 1, 10, 19, 28, 37, 46, 55, 64
- Lesson Plans for Block Scheduling, pp. 2, 11, 20, 29, 38, 47, 56, 65

Technology

- Electronic Teacher Tools with Lesson Planning Software
- Test and Practice Generator

Chapter 2 Getting Ready

PREVIEW

What's the chapter about?

- Translating **verbal phrases and sentences** into **variable expressions and equations**
- Solving one-step **equations** and **inequalities**
- Using a **general problem solving plan**

WORDS TO KNOW

- **additive identity,** *p. 57*
- **multiplicative identity,** *p. 57*
- **like terms,** *p. 57*
- **coefficient,** *p. 57*
- **constant term,** *p. 57*
- **combining like terms,** *p. 57*
- **conditional equations,** *p. 61*
- **inverse operation,** *p. 74*
- **inequality,** *p. 90*
- **solving an inequality,** *p. 90*

PREPARE

Chapter Readiness Quiz

Take this quick quiz. If you are unsure of an answer, look back at the reference pages for help.

VOCABULARY CHECK *(refer to pp. 32, 33, 38)*

Match the equality with the property it demonstrates.

1. $x + y = y + x$ C

2. $x(y + z) = xy + xz$ E

3. $(x + y) + z = x + (y + z)$ A

4. $(xy)z = x(yz)$ B

5. $x \cdot y = y \cdot x$ D

A. Associative property (addition)

B. Associative property (multiplication)

C. Commutative property (addition)

D. Commutative property (multiplication)

E. Distributive property

SKILL CHECK *(refer to pp. 12, 16)*

6. Which one of the equations is *not* true? D

(A) $3 + 4 \times 8 \div 2 = 19$

(B) $6 \times 3 - (5 + 9) = 4$

(C) $56 \div 8 \times 3 + 3 = 24$

(D) $5^2 - 3^2 \times 2 = 32$

STUDY TIP

Keep a Math Notebook

Keeping a notebook will help you organize all of the information you need to study.

My Math Notebook
- Keep notes and completed homework separate.
- Organize notes and completed homework by date.

2.1 Translating Phrases into Expressions

California Standards

In this lesson you'll:

▶ Use variables and appropriate operations to write an expression that represents a verbal description. (AF 1.1)

Goal 1 TRANSLATING VERBAL PHRASES

To use algebra to solve real-life problems, you may need to translate words, phrases, and sentences into mathematical symbols. To do this, it helps to look for words that indicate operations.

EXAMPLE 1 Translating Addition Phrases

VERBAL PHRASE	VARIABLE EXPRESSION
a. The sum of 5 and a number	$5 + x$
b. Nine more than a number	$n + 9$
c. A number plus 2	$y + 2$

EXAMPLE 2 Translating Subtraction Phrases

VERBAL PHRASE	VARIABLE EXPRESSION
a. The difference of 8 and a number	$8 - n$
b. Ten less than a number	$y - 10$
c. Twelve minus a number	$12 - x$

EXAMPLE 3 Translating Multiplication Phrases

VERBAL PHRASE	VARIABLE EXPRESSION
a. The product of 3 and a number	$3x$
b. Seven times a number	$7y$
c. A number multiplied by 4	$4n$

Student Help

▶ **STUDY TIP**
Subtraction and division are not commutative. For example, *8 less than a number* is written as $y - 8$, not as $8 - y$, and *5 divided by a number* is written as $\frac{5}{x}$, not as $\frac{x}{5}$.

EXAMPLE 4 Translating Division Phrases

VERBAL PHRASE	VARIABLE EXPRESSION
a. The quotient of a number and 3	$\frac{x}{3}$
b. Four divided by a number	$\frac{4}{n}$
c. A number divided by 11	$\frac{y}{11}$

1 Plan

Pacing

Suggested Number of Days

Transitional: 1 day
Average: 1 day
Advanced: 1 day
Block Schedule: 0.5 block with 2.2

Teaching Resources

Blacklines
(See page 50B.)

Transparencies
- Warm-Up Exercises
- Teacher Time-Savers
- English/Spanish Problem Solving
- Answers

Technology
- Electronic Teacher Tools
- Test and Practice Generator

2 Teach

Math Reasoning

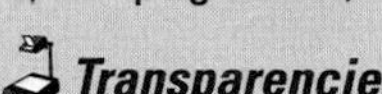

For Mathematical Background Notes on mathematical reasoning related to this lesson, please refer to pages 50E and 50F in this Teacher's Edition.

Extra Examples 1–4
See next page.

California Standards and Assessment

CA Standard: AF 1.1

Extra Example 1

Translate the verbal phrase into an algebraic expression.

a. The sum of a number and 8 $x + 8$

b. Four more than a number $n + 4$

c. Six plus a number $6 + y$

Extra Example 2

Translate the verbal phrase into an algebraic expression.

a. The difference of a number and 15 $n - 15$

b. Three less than a number $y - 3$

Extra Example 3

Translate the verbal phrase into an algebraic expression.

a. The product of a number and 2 $2x$

b. Twelve multiplied by a number $12n$

Extra Example 4

Translate the verbal phrase into an algebraic expression.

a. The quotient of 8 and a number $\frac{8}{x}$

b. Nine divided by a number $\frac{9}{n}$

Extra Example 5

Translate the verbal phrase into an algebraic expression.

a. Two more than 4 times a number $4x + 2$

b. Five times the sum of one number and 3 times another number $5(a + 3b)$

c. Eight times the difference of two numbers $8(x - y)$

Extra Example 6

You are buying some hardback books and some paperback books. Each hardback book costs $28 and each paperback book costs $6. Write an expression for the total cost. Let h be the number of hardback books and p be the number of paperback books. $28h + 6p$

Goal 2 TRANSLATING COMPLICATED VERBAL PHRASES

Some phrases may require more than one operation or variable when you translate them. Also, you may need to use grouping symbols to indicate the correct order of operations.

EXAMPLE 5 Translating Verbal Phrases

VERBAL PHRASE	VARIABLE(S)	EXPRESSION
a. Three more than twice a number	Let x be the number.	$2x + 3$
b. The difference of a number and three times another number	Let m be the first number and n be the second number.	$m - 3n$
c. Twice the sum of two numbers	Let y be one number and z be the other number.	$2(y + z)$

When you are translating verbal phrases that describe real-life situations, you can use the following steps.

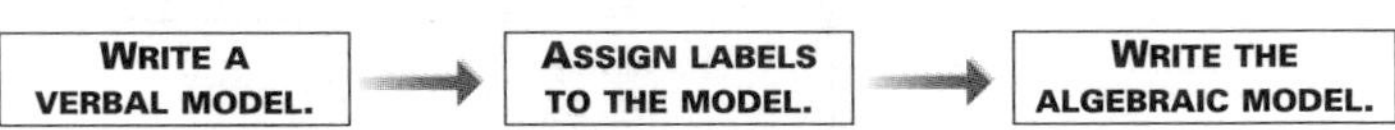

Link to Environment

MUSIC Originally, compact discs were packaged in cardboard longboxes. The longboxes created over 12,000 tons of waste in one year. This prompted manufacturers to package the discs in only their jewel cases.

EXAMPLE 6 Translating Real-Life Phrases

MUSIC You are buying some cassettes and some compact discs. Each cassette costs $12, and each compact disc costs $15. Write an expression for the total cost.

Solution

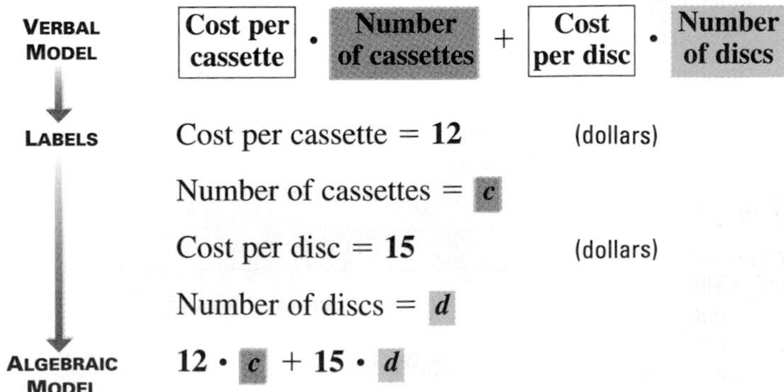

VERBAL MODEL
Cost per cassette • Number of cassettes + Cost per disc • Number of discs
LABELS
Cost per cassette = 12 (dollars)
Number of cassettes = c
Cost per disc = 15 (dollars)
Number of discs = d
ALGEBRAIC MODEL
12 • c + 15 • d

You can use the algebraic model to find the total cost of any combination of cassettes and compact discs. For example, the cost of **1** cassette and **3** compact discs is $12 \cdot \mathbf{1} + 15 \cdot \mathbf{3}$, or $57.

2.1 Exercises

Guided Practice

Match the verbal phrase with its variable expression.

A. $20y$ **B.** $n + 20$ **C.** $6 - m$

D. $2s + 6$ **E.** $x - 6$ **F.** $6 \div x$

1. The sum of a number and 20 **B**
2. Six more than twice a number **D**
3. The difference of 6 and a number **C**
4. Six divided by a number **F**
5. The product of a number and 20 **A**
6. Six less than a number **E**

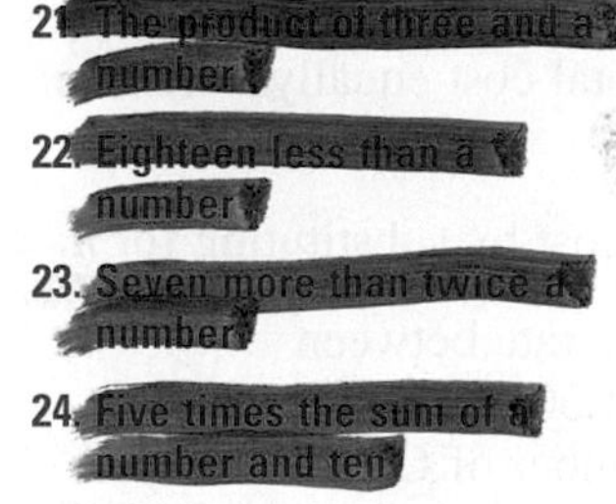

Write the phrase as a variable expression. Tell what the variable represents.

7. The current temperature plus 20 degrees
$t + 20$; t is the current temperature.

8. Five miles per hour under the speed limit
$x - 5$; x is the speed limit.

9. Ten dollars for each ticket, plus a five-dollar service charge
$10t + 5$; t is the number of tickets.

10. Five dollars times the number of people, plus ten dollars
$5p + 10$; p is the number of people.

Practice and Problem Solving

> *Student Help*
> **▶MORE PRACTICE**
> Extra practice to help you master skills is on page 692.

Translate the verbal phrase into a variable expression.

11. Nine more than 10 times a number 

12. Four less than 5 times a number 

13. Eight minus the product of 2 and a number 

14. Eleven times the sum of 6 and a number

15. A number divided by the sum of 2 and another number 

> *Student Help*
> **▶HOMEWORK HELP**
> Extra help with problem solving in Exs. 16–20 is available at www.mcdougallittell.com

Write the verbal phrase as a variable expression. Tell what the variable represents.

16. Four miles more than yesterday

17. Two runs fewer than the other team scored

18. Three times your paycheck plus \$527

19. The number of days divided by 7, plus the number of weeks

20. Four years younger than twice the age of your cousin

Write the variable expression as a word phrase. **21–24. See margin.**

21. $3 \cdot k$ **22.** $v - 18$ **23.** $2r + 7$ **24.** $5(q + 10)$

Concept Check

Why is order not important when writing addition or multiplication expressions? **because of the commutative properties of addition and multiplication**

3 Apply

Assignment Guide

TRANSITIONAL
Day 1: pp. 55–56 Exs. 11–14, 16–18, 23–27, 33–34

AVERAGE
Day 1: pp. 55–56 Exs. 11–20, 23–30, 32–34

ADVANCED
Day 1: pp. 55–56 Exs. 13–22, 25–30, 31*, 32–34

BLOCK SCHEDULE
pp. 55–56 Exs. 11–20, 23–30, 32–34 (with 2.2)

Extra Practice

- Student Edition, pp. 692–693
- Chapter 2 Resource Book, p. 6

Homework Check

To quickly check student understanding of key concepts, go over the following exercises:

Transitional: 14, 16, 20, 22, 26
Average: 14, 18, 20, 24, 28
Advanced: 18, 20, 24, 26, 32

Math Reasoning

Students should be aware that the phrase "the difference of a and b" generally refers to $a - b$ (and not $b - a$). They might tend to subtract the smaller number from the larger. The phrase "the quotient of a and b" refers to $\frac{a}{b}$ (and not $\frac{b}{a}$).

Assess

Assessment Resources

- Assessment Book (Formal Assessment and Alternative Assessment)
- Test and Practice Generator

Mini Quiz

1. Translate the verbal phrase into an algebraic expression.
   - **a.** Three less than 2 times a number $2n - 3$
   - **b.** The product of 5 and the sum of 2 and another number $5(2 + x)$
   - **c.** A number divided by 12 $\frac{b}{12}$
   - **d.** Twice a number $2a$
2. A cable television company charges $46 for installation and $21 per month for basic service. Write an expression to represent the total cost in dollars of *m* months of basic cable service. $46 + 21m$

Math Reasoning

The potential for ambiguity in verbal statements such as that in Exercise 32 is the best reason for using algebraic notation to communicate precisely what is meant. "Two less than 5 times a number" is modeled by $5n - 2$, whereas "two less than 5, times a number" would be modeled by $(5 - 2) \cdot n$.

27. It depends on how long it takes to make each centerpiece. The flat rate is more profitable if the centerpiece takes less than about 2.5 h to make.

31. See Additional Answers beginning on page AA1.

Chapter Opener Link **In Exercises 25–27, look back to the exercises on page 51 and use the following information.** Suppose a florist charges $15 per hour, plus $12 for the cost of the flowers.

25. Write a variable expression that represents the total cost. Let *t* represent the number of hours it takes to make a centerpiece. $15t + 12$

26. What does the centerpiece cost if it takes 2 hours to make? 4 hours? $42; $72

27. Is it more profitable to charge by the hour as in Exercise 26 or to charge a flat rate of $50 for a centerpiece? Explain. **See margin.**

Link to Economics

England Pound
Canada Dollar
Italy Lira
Holland Guilder
Japan Yen
Spain Peseta
Sweden Kroner
Denmark Kroner
Norway Kroner
Belgium Franc
Austria Schilling
Australia Dollar
Israel

CURRENCY TABLES
A currency table shows the exchange rate between the currencies of different countries. The exchange rate between U.S. currency and Canadian currency was used in Exercise 31.

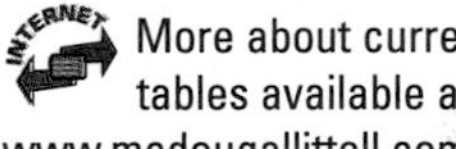
More about currency tables available at www.mcdougallittell.com

TABLE TENNIS **In Exercises 28–30, use the following information.** You and three friends are playing table tennis. The cost to play is $7 for the first hour and $3 for each additional half hour.

28. Write a variable expression that represents the total cost. Let *h* represent the number of additional half hours. $7 + 3h$

29. You and your three friends are sharing the total cost equally. Write an expression that represents *your* cost. $\frac{7 + 3h}{4}$

30. You play for a total of 2.5 hours. Find *your* cost by substituting for *h*.

31. CHALLENGE On April 28, 1999, the exchange rate between U.S. currency and Canadian currency was $1.50 (Canadian) for $1.00 (U.S.). Write an expression for the number of Canadian dollars you can get for *n* U.S. dollars. Then complete the table. $1.5n$

U.S. dollars	1.00	2.00	5.00	10.00	?	?
Canadian dollars	1.50	3.00	?	?	9.00	12.00

▶ Source: U.S. Customs

32. MATHEMATICAL REASONING Choose the correct expression for the verbal phrase *two less than 5 times a number*. Explain your choice.

A. $2 - 5n$ **B.** $5n - 2$ **C.** $2n - 5n$

Multiple-Choice Practice

33. Which verbal phrase translates to the expression $15 - b$? 

Ⓐ Fifteen less than a number

Ⓑ The difference of a number and 15

Ⓒ The difference of 15 and a number

Ⓓ A number minus 15

34. You spend $3.50 for *n* notebooks. Which expression represents the cost of one notebook?

Ⓕ $3.5n$ Ⓖ $\frac{n}{3.5}$ Ⓗ $3.5 - n$ Ⓙ $\frac{3.5}{n}$

2.2 Combining Like Terms

California Standards

In this lesson you'll:

- Simplify numerical expressions by applying properties of rational numbers and justify the process used. (AF 1.3)
- Use algebraic terminology, such as variable, term, coefficient, and constant, correctly. (AF 1.4)

Goal 1 COMBINING LIKE TERMS

You can use properties of addition and multiplication to simplify expressions. Two properties are given below.

	Identity Property of Addition	Identity Property of Multiplication
In Words	The sum of a number and 0 is the number.	The product of a number and 1 is the number.
In Algebra	$a + 0 = a$	$a \cdot 1 = a$
In Arithmetic	$4 + 0 = 4$	$4 \cdot 1 = 4$

When adding 0 to a number, the result is the same as the original number. So, 0 is called the **additive identity**. Similarly, 1 is called the **multiplicative identity**.

Terms in an expression are **like terms** if they have identical variable parts. In a term that is the product of a number and a variable, the numerical part of the term is the **coefficient** of the variable. A term that is a number is called a **constant term**.

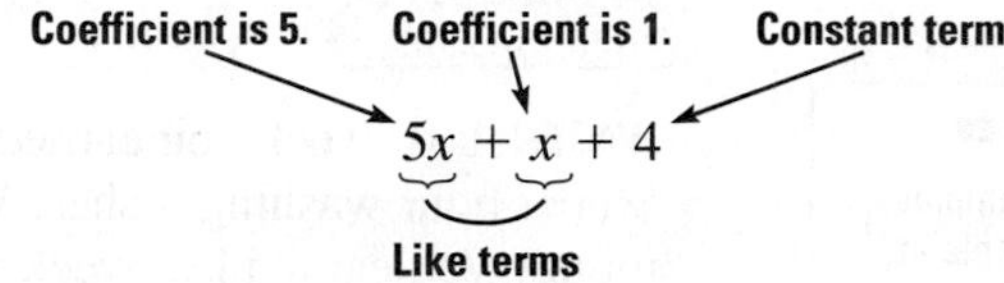

Notice that the coefficient of the second term, x, can be taken to be 1. This is an example of the identity property of multiplication. The process of simplifying expressions with like terms is called **combining like terms**.

EXAMPLE 1 Combining Like Terms

Simplify $b + 2 + 5b$. Justify each step.

Solution

Notice that b and $5b$ are like terms.

$b + 2 + 5b = \mathbf{1b} + 2 + 5b$	Identity property of multiplication
$= 1b + 5b + 2$	Commutative property of addition
$= (1 + 5)b + 2$	Distributive property
$= 6b + 2$	Simplify.

1 Plan

Pacing

Suggested Number of Days

Transitional: 1 day
Average: 1 day
Advanced: 1 day
Block Schedule: 0.5 block with 2.1

Teaching Resources

Blacklines
(See page 50B.)

Transparencies
- Warm-Up Exercises
- Teacher Time-Savers
- English/Spanish Problem Solving
- Answers

Technology
- Electronic Teacher Tools
- Test and Practice Generator

2 Teach

Math Reasoning

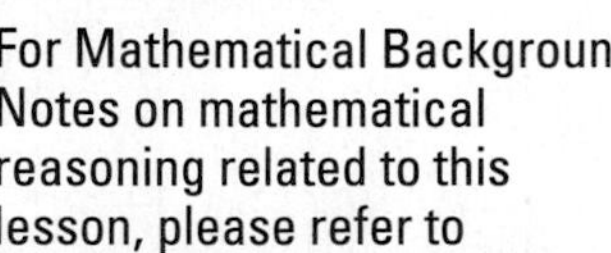

For Mathematical Background Notes on mathematical reasoning related to this lesson, please refer to pages 50E and 50F in this Teacher's Edition.

Extra Example 1
See next page.

California Standards and Assessment

CA Standards: AF 1.3, AF 1.4
CA Key Concepts Book: pp. S48–S53

Extra Example 1

Simplify $7z + 6 + z$. Justify each step.

$7z + 6 + z$	
$= 7z + 6 + 1z$	**Identity property of multiplication**
$= 7z + 1z + 6$	**Commutative property of addition**
$= (7 + 1)z + 6$	**Distributive property**
$= 8z + 6$	**Simplify**

Extra Example 2

Write an expression that represents the perimeter of the triangle. Then evaluate the perimeter when n is 1, 2, 3, 4, and 5. Organize your results in a table and in a bar graph. Describe the pattern.

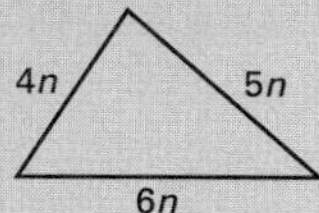

expression: $4n + 5n + 6n = 15n$

n	1	2	3	4	5
Perim.	15	30	45	60	75

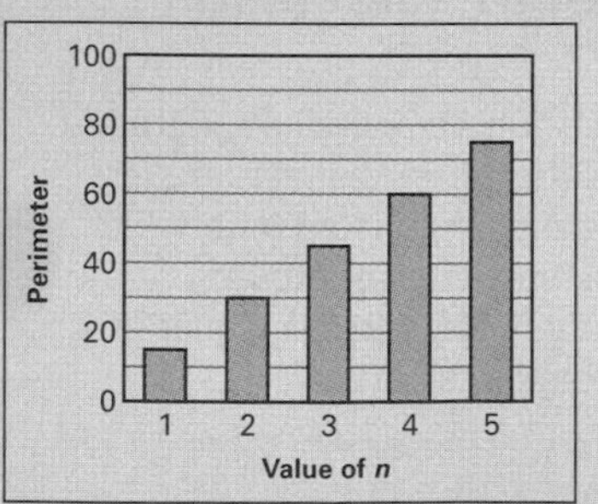

The perimeter increases by 15 each time the value of n increases by 1.

Extra Example 3

On a long trip, your mother drove 50 miles per hour on one highway and 60 miles per hour on another highway. If she drove t hours on each highway, write an expression for the distance she drove. Then find the distance she drove if she was driving for 2 hours at each rate.

$50t + 60t = 110t$; 220 miles

Goal 2 Simplifying Expressions

EXAMPLE 2 Simplifying Before Evaluating

Write an expression that represents the perimeter of the triangle. Then evaluate the expression when x is 1, 2, 3, and 4. Organize your results in a table and in a bar graph. Describe the pattern.

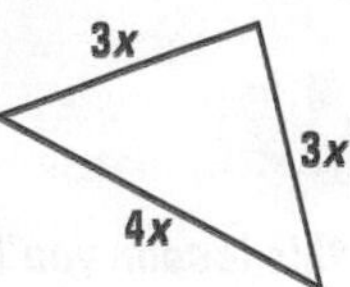

Solution

Perimeter $= 3x + 3x + 4x$ — **Add the side lengths.**

$= 10x$ — **Combine like terms.**

Evaluate the expression $10x$ when x is 1, 2, 3, and 4. The results are organized in the table and in the bar graph.

x	Perimeter
1	10
2	20
3	30
4	40

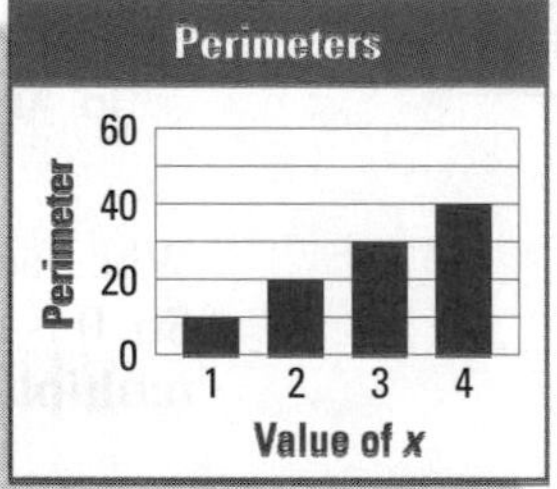

ANSWER ▸ The perimeter increases by 10 each time x increases by 1.

Student Help

▸ SKILLS REVIEW
For help with drawing bar graphs, see p. 686.

Student Help

▸ MORE EXAMPLES

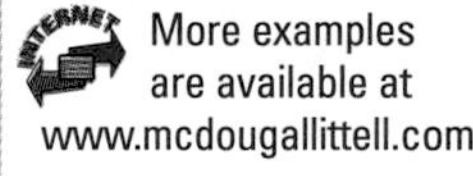

More examples are available at www.mcdougallittell.com

EXAMPLE 3 Writing an Expression

WAGES Last week you earned \$8 per hour delivering groceries and \$6 per hour washing dishes. Write an expression for the amount of money you earned last week if you spent h hours at each job. Then find the amount you earned if you worked for 4 hours at each job.

Solution

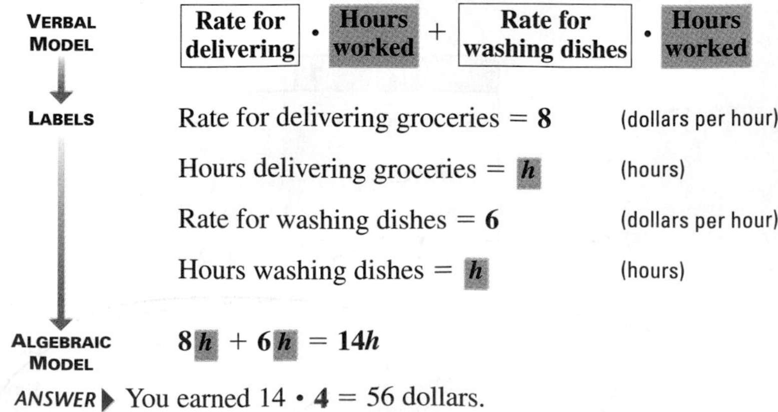

VERBAL MODEL
Rate for delivering · Hours worked + Rate for washing dishes · Hours worked
LABELS
Rate for delivering groceries = 8 (dollars per hour)
Hours delivering groceries = h (hours)
Rate for washing dishes = 6 (dollars per hour)
Hours washing dishes = h (hours)
ALGEBRAIC MODEL
8h + 6h = 14h

ANSWER ▸ You earned $14 \cdot 4 = 56$ dollars.

2.2 Exercises

Guided Practice

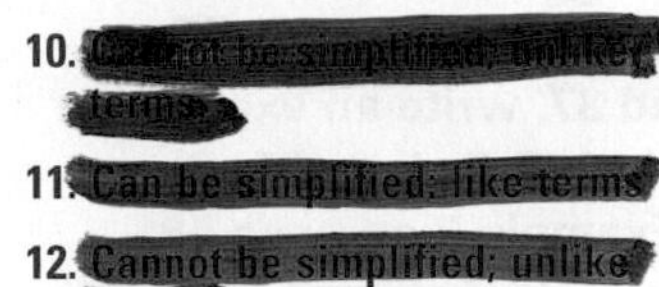

12. Cannot be simplified; unlike terms

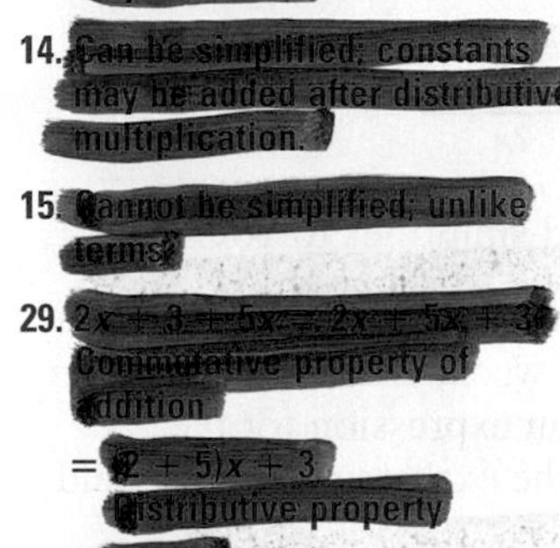

Simplify the expression by combining like terms.

1. $3x + x$ **2.** $3 + 2a + 7$ **3.** $y + 4 + 2x + 3y$

4. $5 + 2(x + 8)$ **5.** $2r^2 + 5r^2$ **6.** $5(a + b) + 2(a + b)$

GEOMETRY In Exercises 7 and 8, write an expression for the perimeter of the figure. Simplify the expression. Then evaluate it when $x = 2$.

7.

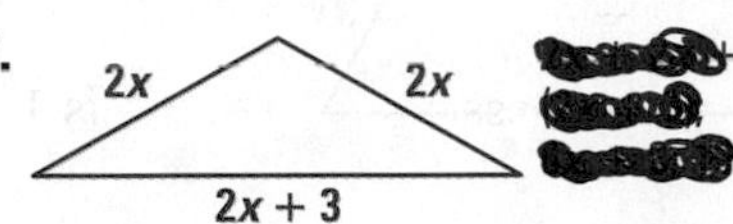

8.

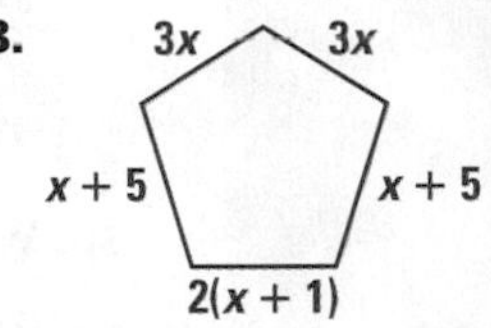

9. SCIENCE PROJECT You are working on a model of an ecosystem for your science project. You estimate that it will take you 3 times as long to build the model as to do your research. Write an expression to find the time it will take to complete your research and your model. where r is the time taken to do research

Practice and Problem Solving

Student Help

▶**MORE PRACTICE** Extra practice to help you master skills is on page 692.

10–15. See margin.

Tell whether the expression can be simplified. Explain why or why not.

10. $2a + 7$ **11.** $3x + x$ **12.** $2r + r^2$

13. $1 + 9p + 4$ **14.** $5 + 2(y + 8)$ **15.** $6m + 6 + 2n$

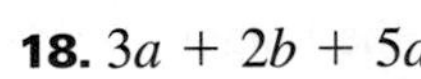

Simplify the expression by combining like terms.

16. $2a + a$ **17.** $5b + 7b + 10$

18. $3a + 2b + 5a$ **19.** $2x + 4y + 3z + 17z$

20. $p + 9q + 9 + 14p$ **21.** $a + 2b + 2a + b + 2c$

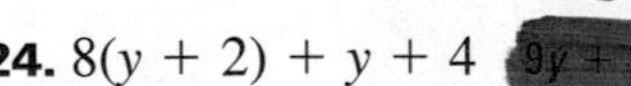

22. $b + b^2 + 2b$ **23.** $x^2 + x^2$

24. $8(y + 2) + y + 4$ **25.** $3(a + b) + 3(b + a)$

Student Help

▶**READING TIP** Remember that like terms have variables raised to the *same* power. For example, $2b$ and b^2 are not like terms.

GEOMETRY In Exercises 26–28, write an expression for the perimeter of the figure. Simplify the expression and evaluate it when $x = 3$.

26. x, x + 3, x + 1, 2x

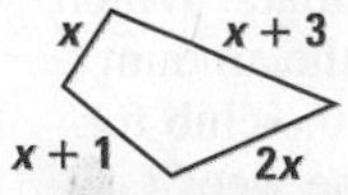

27.

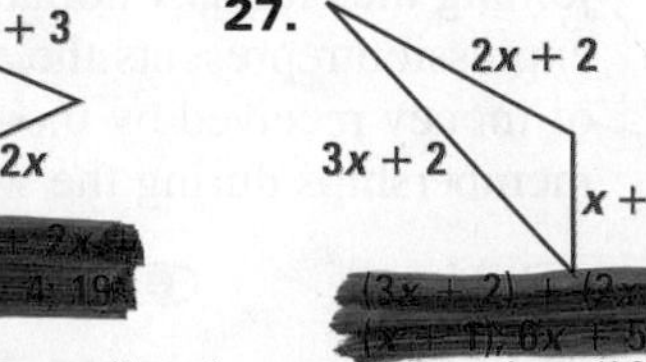

28.

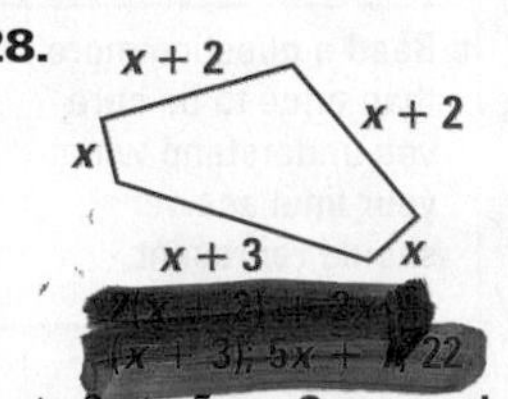

29. WRITING Describe the steps for simplifying $2x + 3 + 5x$. See margin.

Concept Check

How do you determine if an expression is simplified? **The simplified expression will contain no like terms.**

3 Apply

Assignment Guide

TRANSITIONAL
Day 1: SRH p. 686 Exs. 3–4; pp. 59–60 Exs. 10–12, 16–20, 26–27, 30–32, 39, 43

AVERAGE
Day 1: pp. 59–60 Exs. 13–15, 18–23, 26–28, 30–32, 36–37, 43

ADVANCED
Day 1: pp. 59–60 Exs. 18–28, 33–37, 40–42*, 43

BLOCK SCHEDULE
pp. 59–60 Exs. 13–15,18–23, 26–28, 30–32, 36–37, 43 (with 2.1)

Extra Practice

- Student Edition, pp. 692–693
- Chapter 2 Resource Book, p. 15

Homework Check

To quickly check student understanding of key concepts, go over the following exercises:

Transitional: 12, 16, 18, 22, 26, 30, 38
Average: 18, 22, 28, 32, 36
Advanced: 18, 22, 26, 34, 36

Problem Solving

Exercise 22
Point out that b^2 is not a like term for b and $2b$.

Math Reasoning

As a challenge, students could be asked why the triangle in Exercise 7 must have a perimeter greater than 12. **The triangle inequality requires that $2x + 2x > 2x + 3$, so $2x > 3$.**

4 Assess

Assessment Resources

- Assessment Book (Formal Assessment and Alternative Assessment)
- Test and Practice Generator

Mini-Quiz

1. Simplify the expression.
   a. $3b + 6 + 2b$ $5b + 6$
   b. $d + d^2 + 3 + 5d$ $d^2 + 6d + 3$
   c. $2(x + y) + 3(y + x)$ $5x + 5y$
2. A rectangle has side lengths $x + 2$ and $3x + 1$.
   a. Write and simplify an expression for the perimeter of the rectangle. $(x + 2) + (3x + 1) + (x + 2) + (3x + 1) = 8x + 6$
   b. Find the perimeter of the rectangle when x is 1, 2, 3, 4, and 5. Organize your results in a table. Describe the pattern as the value of x increases by 1.

x	Perimeter
1	14
2	22
3	30
4	38
5	46

The perimeter increases by 8 each time the value of x increases by 1.

36. $18x$

x	Perimeter
1	18
2	36
3	54
4	72
5	90

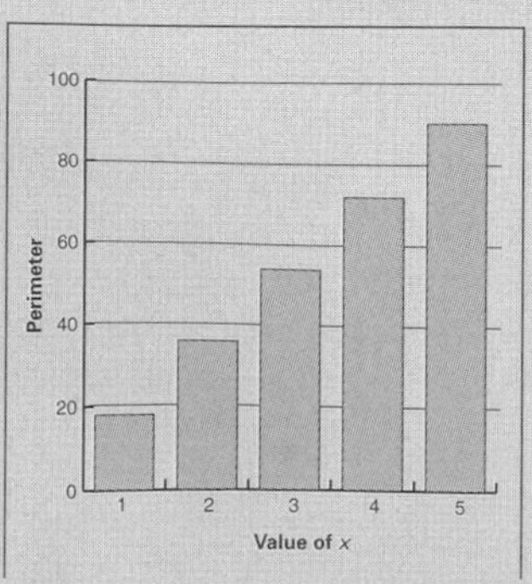

36. $2(3x) + 2(6x)$; perimeter increases by 18 as x increases by 1

Link to Science

GEYSERS The Grand Geyser in Yellowstone National Park is the tallest predictable geyser in the world. It erupts every 7 to 15 hours. A map of Yellowstone is used in Exercises 40–42.

37. $2(2x) + 4(x)$; perimeter increases by 8 as x increases by 1

ALGEBRA **Simplify the expression and justify your steps. Then evaluate the expression when $x = 2$ and $y = 5$.**

30. $2x + 3x + y$ $5x + y$; 15

31. $4(x + y) + x$ $5x + 4y$; 30

32. $5x + 2(2x + y)$ $9x + 2y$; 28

33. $4(x + y) + 7x$ $11x + 4y$; 42

34. $y + 2x^2 + 2y$ $2x^2 + 3y$; 23

35. $6y + x^2 + x^2$ $6y + 2x^2$; 38

MATHEMATICAL REASONING **In Exercises 36 and 37, write an expression for the perimeter. Find the perimeter when x is 1, 2, 3, 4, and 5. Show your results in a table and a bar graph as in Example 2 on page 58. Describe the pattern in the results as the values of x increase by 1.**

36–37. See margin.

36.

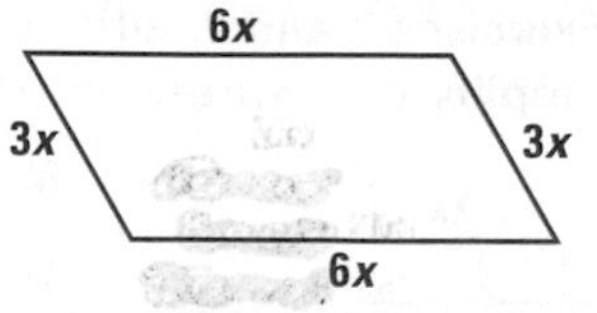

6x
3x
3x
6x

37.

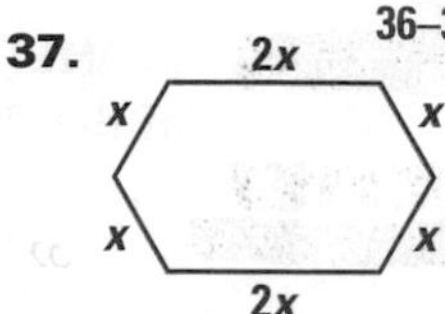

38. Write an expression that has four terms and simplifies to $16x + 5$. For example: $8x + 2 + 8x + 3$

39. WAGES A deli pays cooks d dollars per hour. A cook worked 8 hours the first week of May, 12 hours the second week, 2 hours the third week, and 5 hours the fourth week. Write an expression for the amount the cook earned in May. Evaluate the expression if he is paid \$10 per hour. $8d + 12d + 2d + 5d$, or $27d$; \$270 is the amount paid.

CHALLENGE **The map below shows the routes from the west entrance to the east entrance of Yellowstone National Park.**

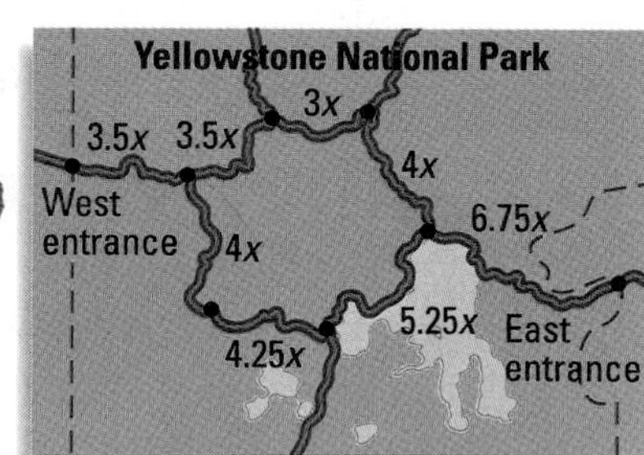

40. Write an expression that represents the shortest distance from the west entrance to the east entrance. $3.5x + 3.5x + 3x + 4x + 6.75x = 20.75x$

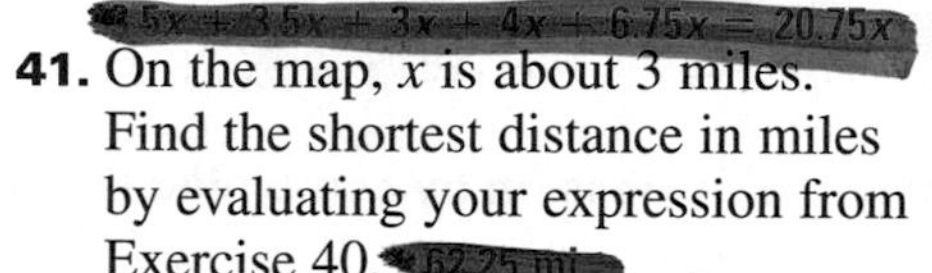

41. On the map, x is about 3 miles. Find the shortest distance in miles by evaluating your expression from Exercise 40. 62.25 mi

42. Write an expression for the longer route and evaluate it to find the distance. $3.5x + 4x + 4.25x + 5.25x + 6.75x = 23.75x$; 71.25 mi

Multiple-Choice Practice

Test Tip A B C D

▶Read a question more than once to be sure you understand what your final answer should represent.

43. The graph shows the number of people who joined a certain health club during one week. The cost of joining the club is x dollars. Which expression represents the amount of money received by the club for memberships during the week? B

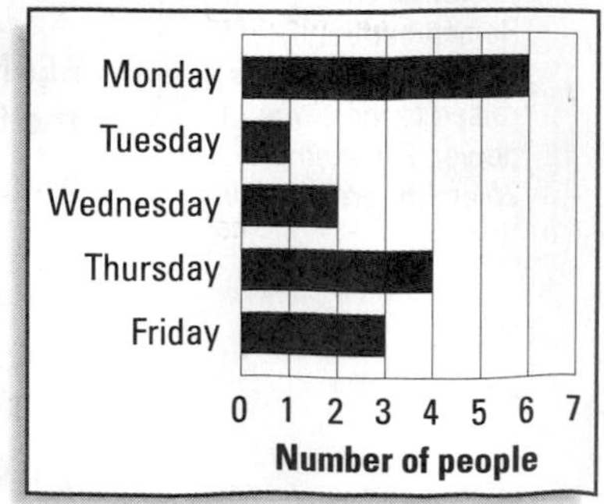

Ⓐ 16 Ⓑ $16x$

Ⓒ $144x$ Ⓓ $16x^5$

2.3 Solving Equations with Mental Math

California Standards

In this lesson you'll:

- Use algebraic terminology correctly. (AF 1.4)
- Solve simple linear equations. (AF 4.0)

Goal 1 Checking Solutions

An **equation** states that two expressions are equal. Some equations, called **conditional equations**, are true for only some values of the variables they contain. Here are two examples:

$x + 1 = 4$ **Conditional equation: true only for $x = 3$**

$3x = 12$ **Conditional equation: true only for $x = 4$**

Finding all values of the variable that make the equation true is called **solving the equation**. The values of the variable are **solutions** of the equation. To check a possible solution, substitute it in the original equation.

EXAMPLE 1 Checking Possible Solutions

Decide whether the value of x is a solution of $4x - 3 = 5$.

a. $x = 2$ **b.** $x = 3$

Solution

a. $4x - 3 = 5$

$4(2) - 3 \stackrel{?}{=} 5$

$8 - 3 \stackrel{?}{=} 5$

$5 = 5$ ✓

2 is a solution.

b. $4x - 3 = 5$

$4(3) - 3 \stackrel{?}{=} 5$

$12 - 3 \stackrel{?}{=} 5$

$9 \neq 5$

3 is *not* a solution.

Some equations, called **identities**, are true for all values of the variables they contain.

EXAMPLE 2 Recognizing an Identity

Is $3z + 9 = 3(z + 3)$ an identity?

Solution

Using the distributive property, rewrite the right side of the equation to obtain an *equivalent* equation.

$3z + 9 = 3(z + 3)$ Original equation

$3z + 9 = 3z + 9$ Use the distributive property.

ANSWER ▶ Because the two sides of the equation are always equal, this equation is true for any value of z. So, it is an identity.

Student Help

▶ **Vocabulary Tip**
You have seen the word *identity* used in two ways. One meaning refers to the additive and multiplicative identities (0 and 1). The other refers to a *variable equation* that is true for all values of the variable.

1 Plan

Pacing

Suggested Number of Days

Transitional: 2 days
Average: 2 days
Advanced: 2 days
Block Schedule: 1 block

Teaching Resources

Blacklines
(See page 50B.)

Transparencies
- Warm-Up Exercises
- Teacher Time-Savers
- English/Spanish Problem Solving
- Answers

Technology
- Electronic Teacher Tools
- Test and Practice Generator

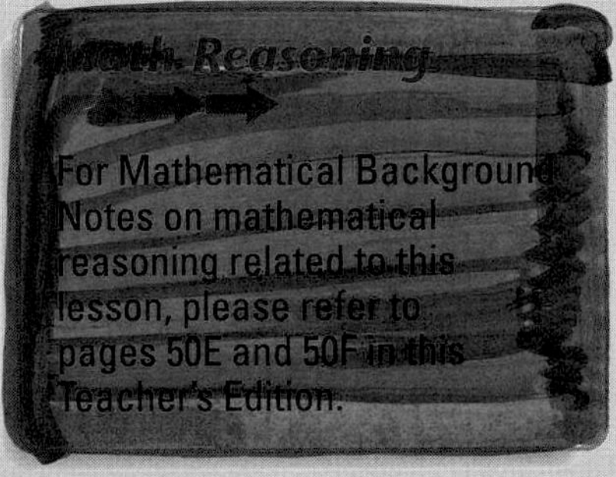

Math Reasoning
For Mathematical Background Notes on mathematical reasoning related to this lesson, please refer to pages 50E and 50F in this Teacher's Edition.

Extra Examples 1 and 2
See next page.

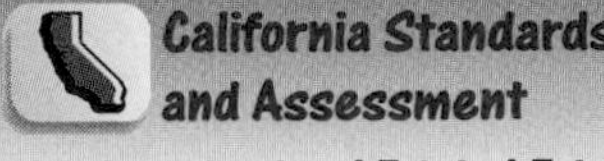

CA Standards: AF 1.4, AF 4.0

Extra Example 1

Decide whether the value of x is a solution of $3x - 5 = 19$.

a. $x = 8$ yes

b. $x = 6$ no

Extra Example 2

Is $4(x + 2) = 2(x + 4) + 2x$ an identity? yes

Extra Example 3

Solve $x - 2 = 7$. $x = 9$

Extra Example 4

Solve $n - 15 = 30$. $n = 45$

Extra Example 5

Solve the equation.

a. $3x = 9$ $x = 3$

b. $\frac{x}{6} = 8$ $x = 48$

Teaching Tip

Encourage students to use parentheses when substituting values for variables, as shown in Example 1. Developing this habit of using parentheses will help students avoid computational errors when negative integers are substituted for variables in Chapter 3.

Concept Check

Determine if the following equation is an identity or a conditional equation. Explain your reasoning.
$7x - 42 + x = 8x + 8 - 50$ identity; *Sample Answer:* Simplifying each side of the equation results in the identity $8x - 42 = 8x - 42$.

Goal 2 SOLVING EQUATIONS WITH MENTAL MATH

As you study algebra, you will learn many techniques for solving equations. Some equations are simple enough that you can solve them mentally. To do this, it helps to *think of the equation as a question.*

Student Help

STUDY TIP
You will learn to be a better problem solver if you develop the habit of *always* checking your solutions.

EXAMPLE 3 Solving an Addition Equation

Solve $x + 4 = 10$.

Solution

EQUATION	STATED AS A QUESTION	SOLUTION
$x + 4 = 10$	What number can you add to 4 to get 10?	$x = 6$

The solution is 6. Check by substituting your solution in the original equation as follows:

CHECK ✓ $x + 4 = 10$ Write original equation.

$6 + 4 \stackrel{?}{=} 10$ Substitute 6 for x.

$10 = 10$ ✓ Solution checks.

EXAMPLE 4 Solving a Subtraction Equation

Solve $n - 12 = 18$.

Solution

EQUATION	STATED AS A QUESTION	SOLUTION
$n - 12 = 18$	From what number can you subtract 12 to get 18?	$n = 30$

The solution is 30. Check by substituting in the original equation.

Student Help

MORE EXAMPLES

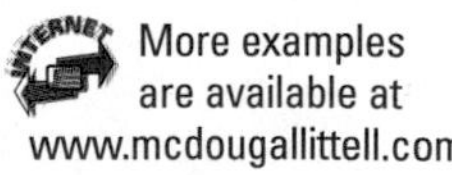

More examples are available at www.mcdougallittell.com

EXAMPLE 5 Solving Multiplication and Division Equations

Solve the equation.

a. $3m = 15$ **b.** $\frac{s}{4} = 5$

Solution

EQUATION	STATED AS A QUESTION	SOLUTION
a. $3m = 15$	What number can you multiply by 3 to get 15?	$m = 5$
b. $\frac{s}{4} = 5$	What number can you divide by 4 to get 5?	$s = 20$

2.3 Exercises

Guided Practice

1. An identity is an equation that is true for all values of the variables it contains, Example: $2(x + 4) = 2x + 8$. A conditional equation is true only for some values of the variables it contains, Example: $3x = 15$ is true only for $x = 5$ and is not true for any other value of x.

12. Identity; equation is true for all values of n.

13. Not an identity; equation only true for $x = \frac{9}{8}$

14. Not an identity; equation only true for $a = 0$

15. Identity; equation is true for all values of b.

16. Not an identity; equation only true for $q = 4$

1. What is the difference between an *identity* and a *conditional equation*? Give an example of each and show why it is either an identity or a conditional equation. **See margin.**

2. Which of the following are solutions of $2 + 4x = 10$? Explain. **C**

A. 0 **B.** 1 **C.** 2 **D.** 3

3. Which of the following are solutions of $2x - 3 = 7$? Explain. **B**

A. 4 **B.** 5 **C.** 6 **D.** 7

Use mental math to solve the equation.

4. $t + 7 = 15$ **8** **5.** $x - 9 = 1$ **10** **6.** $p - 3 = 6$ **9** **7.** $x + 6 = 30$ **24**

8. $z \cdot 3 = 9$ **3** **9.** $\frac{n}{7} = 2$ **14** **10.** $\frac{m}{2} = 4$ **8** **11.** $10 \cdot y = 100$ **10**

Practice and Problem Solving

Student Help

▶ **More Practice**
Extra practice to help you master skills is on page 692.

Decide whether the equation is an identity. Explain your answer. **12–17. See margin.**

12. $2n + 5n = 3n + 4n$ **13.** $9x = 9 + x$ **14.** $5(a - 1) = a - 5$

15. $4(b + 7) = 4b + 28$ **16.** $30 - q = 26$ **17.** $3 + c = 10 + 3$

17. Not an identity; equation only true for $c = 10$

Match the equation with the correct solution.

A. 2 **B.** 3 **C.** 4 **D.** 5

18. $5n - 4 = 21$ **19.** $10 + 2y = 18$ **20.** $5x + 7 = 22$ **21.** $20 = 10z$

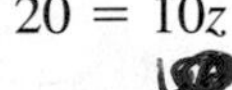

Decide whether the given values of *x* are solutions of the equation. Explain your answer.

22. $x + 12 = 18$; $x = 3, 4, 5$ **23.** $x + 5 = 8$; $x = 3, 4, 5$

24. $3x + 6 = 15$; $x = 1, 2, 3$ **25.** $2x - 9 = 9$; $x = 8, 9, 10$

26. $8 - 4x = 0$; $x = 0, 1, 2$ **27.** $4x + 2 = 14$; $x = 0, 1, 2$

28. $5(x + 1) = 15$; $x = 2, 3, 4$ **29.** $2x - 4.5 = 1.5$; $x = 3, 4, 5$

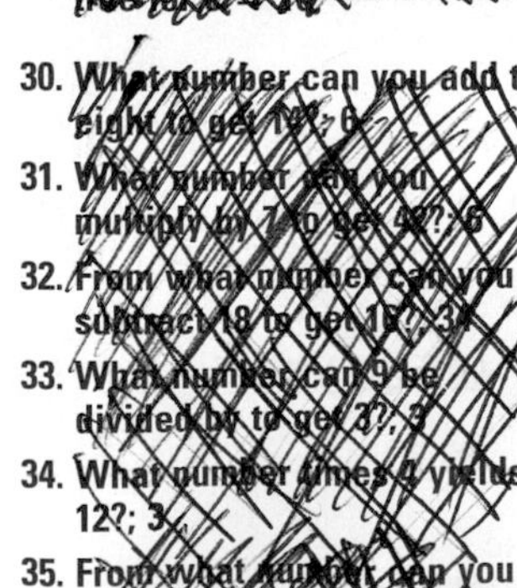

30. What number can you add to eight to get 14?; 6
31. What number can you multiply by 7 to get 42?; 6
32. From what number can you subtract 18 to get 16?; 34
33. What number can 9 be divided by to get 3?; 3
34. What number times 4 yields 12?; 3
35. From what number can you subtract 13 to get 5?; 18
36. What number can 12 be divided by to get 3?; 4
37. What number can you multiply by 4 to get 0?; 0
38. From what number can you subtract 9.8 to get 12?; 21.8

Write the equation as a question. Then solve the equation. **30–38. See margin.**

30. $z + 8 = 14$ **31.** $7y = 42$ **32.** $q - 18 = 16$

33. $\frac{9}{x} = 3$ **34.** $4r = 12$ **35.** $t - 13 = 5$

36. $12 \div n = 3$ **37.** $4d = 0$ **38.** $p - 9.8 = 12$

3 Apply

Assignment Guide

Transitional
Day 1: pp. 63–65 Exs. 12–17, 22–25, 73–83
Day 2: pp. 63–65 Exs. 18–21, 30–35, 39–40, 43–45, 49–54, 62, 71–72

Average
Day 1: pp. 63–65 Exs. 12–17, 22–29, 73–83
Day 2: pp. 63–65 Exs. 30–35, 40–41, 43–45, 49–54, 58–59, 63–65, 71–72

Advanced
Day 1: pp. 63–65 Exs. 15–17, 22–29, 73–83
Day 2: pp. 63–65 Exs. 33–38, 41–42, 46–48, 52–57, 60–61, 66–67*, 71–72

Block Schedule
pp. 63–65 Exs. 12–17, 22–35, 40–41, 43–45, 49–54, 58–59, 63–65, 71–83

Extra Practice

- Student Edition, pp. 692–693
- Chapter 2 Resource Book, p. 24

Homework Check

To quickly check student understanding of key concepts, go over the following exercises:

Transitional: 12, 20, 22, 30, 50, 62
Average: 14, 24, 32, 52, 64
Advanced: 16, 28, 36, 56, 66

Math Reasoning

In Exercises 30–38, observe that phrasing the equation $x + a = b$ as a question is closely related to the definition of subtraction. Asking for the number x that gives b when added to a is the same as asking for $b - a$. Similarly, because of the definition of division, asking for the number x that gives b when multiplied by a is the same as asking for $\frac{b}{a}$, so $x = \frac{b}{a}$ is the solution of the equation $ax = b$.

Find the number that answers the question. Show a check to make sure that your answer is correct.

39. What number can you subtract from 33 to get 24?

40. What number can you add to 7 to get 19?

41. What number can you multiply by 8 to get 56?

42. What number can you divide by 9 to get 5?

Decide whether $r = 4$ is a solution of the equation. If it is not, find the correct solution.

43. $5r = 20$ **44.** $19 - r = 15$ **45.** $24 = 8r$

46. $3r + r = 16$ **47.** $4r = 8$ **48.** $40 - 9r = 4$

Solve the equation using mental math. Check your solution in the original equation.

49. $r + 11 = 14$ **50.** $20 + n = 41$ **51.** $x - 13 = 2$

52. $81 - y = 76$ **53.** $11x = 55$ **54.** $21 = 3m$

55. $\frac{x}{4} = 9$ **56.** $\frac{26}{y} = 2$ **57.** $\frac{z}{5} = 3$

MATHEMATICAL REASONING Determine whether the equations have the same solution. Explain your reasoning.

58. $x - 15 = 8, 15 - x = 8$ **59.** $x + 4 = 17, 4 + x = 17$

60. $x \div 3 = 6, 3x = 54$ **61.** $3x = 12, \frac{x}{12} = 3$

62. BUYING GAS You are taking a trip by automobile with the family of a friend. You have \$75 to help pay for gas. It costs \$15 to fill the tank. Solve the equation $15x = 75$ to find the number of times you can pay to fill the tank.

Link to Science

INDIRECT MEASUREMENT Some things are difficult to measure directly, such as the weight of a pet. Weighing yourself with and without your pet is an example of indirect measurement.

More about indirect measurement at www.mcdougallittell.com

Science Link **In Exercises 63–65, use the following information.** You want to know how much your dog weighs. You hold the dog and step onto the scale. Together, you and the dog weigh 134 pounds. Then you put the dog down and find that your weight is 105 pounds.

63. Write an equation for the weight of the dog.

64. Solve the equation you wrote in Exercise 63.

65. Explain how to check your answer to Exercise 64.

CHALLENGE In Exercises 66 and 67, a five pound bag of oranges costs \$1.98 and contains x oranges.

66. Write an expression for the cost of one orange.

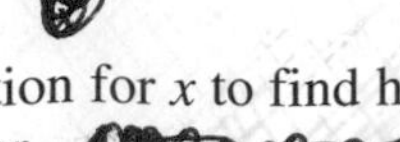

67. Let your expression equal \$.22. Solve the equation for x to find how many oranges are in the bag. Check your answer.

GROWING PUMPKINS Use the graph to write an equation. Then use mental math to solve it.

68. The 1991 winner weighed 209.5 pounds less than the 1994 winner. How much did the 1994 winner weigh?

69. The 1993 winner weighed 106 pounds less than the 1994 winner. How much did the 1993 winner weigh?

70. The 1994 winner weighed 22 pounds more than the 1995 winner. How much did the 1995 winner weigh?

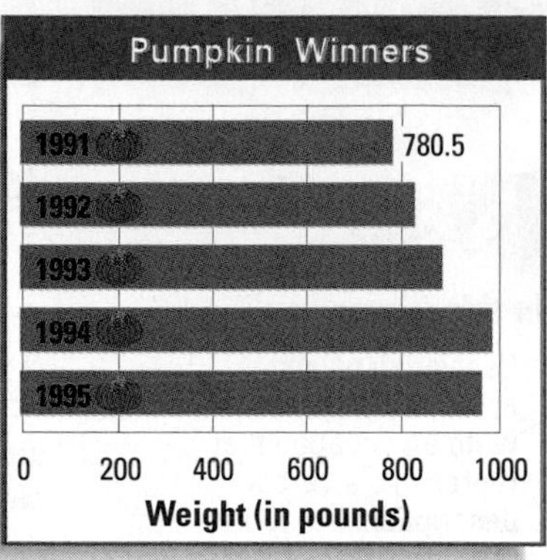

Multiple-Choice Practice

71. What is the solution of the equation $y + 11 = 21$?

Ⓐ 10 Ⓑ 11 Ⓒ 21 Ⓓ 32

72. Which rectangles have the same perimeter for all values of x?

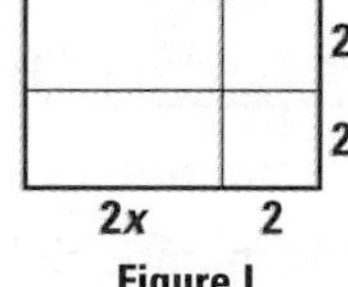

Figure I

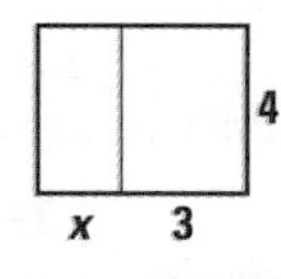

Figure II

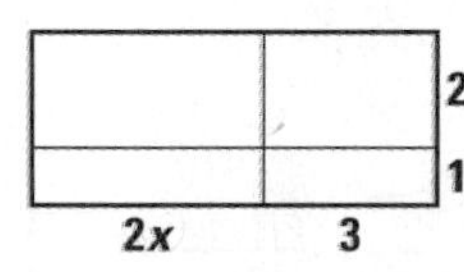

Figure III

Ⓕ I and II only Ⓖ I and III only

Ⓗ II and III only Ⓙ I, II, and III

Mixed Review

Match the equation with the property it illustrates. *(1.7, 1.8)*

73. Associative property of addition — **A.** $x(y) + x(z) = x(y + z)$

74. Commutative property of addition — **B.** $x \cdot y = y \cdot x$

75. Distributive property — **C.** $(xy)z = x(yz)$

76. Associative property of multiplication — **D.** $(x + y) + z = (y + x) + z$

77. Commutative property of multiplication — **E.** $(x + y) + z = x + (y + z)$

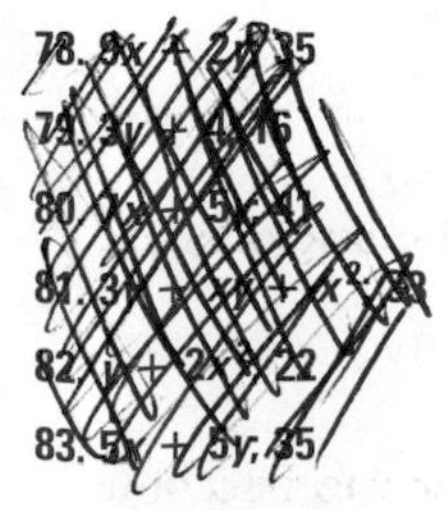

Simplify the expression. Then evaluate when $x = 3$ and $y = 4$. *(2.2)*
78–83. See margin.

78. $3x + 2y + 6x$ **79.** $y + 2(y + 2)$ **80.** $5(x + y) + 2x$

81. $y(3 + x) + x^2$ **82.** $y + x^2 + x^2$ **83.** $3(x + y) + 2(x + y)$

Assess

Assessment Resources

- Assessment Book (Formal Assessment and Alternative Assessment)
- Test and Practice Generator

Mini-Quiz

1. Which of the following are solutions of $5x + 7 = 22$?
   - **a.** $x = 2$ **no**
   - **b.** $x = 3$ **yes**
2. Write the equation as a question. Then solve it mentally.
   - **a.** $8 + x = 11$ **What number can you add to 8 to get 11?; 3**
   - **b.** $\frac{y}{3} = 27$ **What number can you divide by 3 to get 27?; 81**
   - **c.** $6n = 42$ **What number can you multiply by 6 to get 42?; 7**
3. Decide whether the equation is an identity. Explain.
   - **a.** $4x + 12 = 4(x + 3)$ **Yes; the distributive property can be used to show that the expression on the right side of the equation is identical to the expression on the left. So the equation is true for any value of x.**
   - **b.** $2x = 14$ **No; this is a *conditional* equation; it is true only for $x = 7$.**

1 Plan

Pacing

Suggested Number of Days

Transitional: 2 days
Average: 2 days
Advanced: 2 days
Block Schedule: 1 block

Teaching Resources

 ***Blacklines***

(See page 50B.)

Transparencies

- Warm-Up Exercises
- Teacher Time-Savers
- English/Spanish Problem Solving
- Answers

Technology

- Electronic Teacher Tools
- Test and Practice Generator

2 Teach

Math Reasoning

For Mathematical Background Notes on mathematical reasoning related to this lesson, please refer to pages 50E and 50F in this Teacher's Edition.

CA Standard: AF 1.1

2.4 Translating Sentences into Equations

In this lesson you'll:

- Use variables and appropriate operations to write an equation that represents a verbal description. (AF 1.1)

Goal 1 Translating Verbal Sentences

A phrase does not usually have a verb, but a sentence must contain a verb. As you learned in Lesson 2.1, some phrases can be modeled as variable expressions. You will now learn how to write sentences as equations. Here are examples of translating verbal models into certain algebraic models. Notice that the example on the left results in an expression while the example on the right results in an equation.

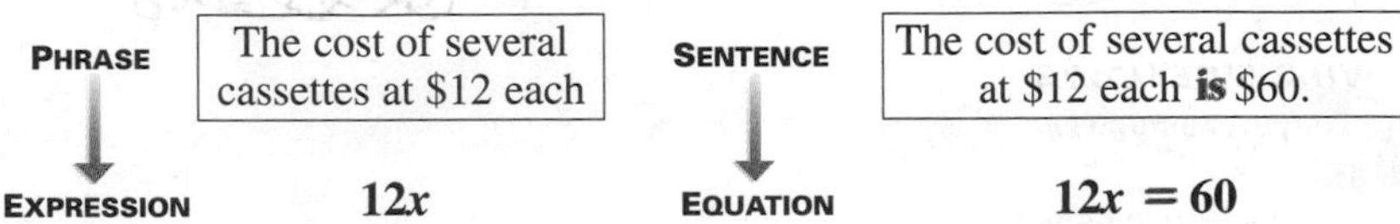

Notice that you evaluate an expression and solve an equation. For instance, the value of the expression $12x$ is 60 when $x = 5$, and the solution of the equation $12x = 60$ is 5.

Student Help

Study Tip
When you translate a sentence into an equation, words like *is*, *is equal to*, and *gives*, can all be translated into an equal sign.

Example 1 Translating Simple Sentences

VERBAL SENTENCE	EQUATION
a. The sum of 5 and a number is 20.	$5 + q = 20$
b. Ten less than a number is 30.	$y - 10 = 30$
c. 35 equals seven times a number.	$35 = 7r$
d. The quotient of a number and 3 is 6.	$\frac{x}{3} = 6$

Example 2 Translating More Complex Sentences

VERBAL SENTENCE	EQUATION
a. The sum of 12 and five times a number is equal to 30.	$12 + 5p = 30$
b. 20 subtracted from the product of 2 and a number is 14.	$2x - 20 = 14$
c. The quotient of 9 and a number added to 30 is 33.	$\frac{9}{n} + 30 = 33$
d. The difference of 15 and three times a number is that number divided by 3.	$15 - 3y = \frac{y}{3}$

Goal 2 MODELING REAL-LIFE SITUATIONS

Link to Transportation

MOVING SIDEWALKS
Large airports often have moving sidewalks to help people save time in getting from one gate to another.

EXAMPLE 3 Writing a Model

MOVING SIDEWALKS A typical moving sidewalk moves at a rate of 2 miles per hour, which is 1 mile per hour less than the walking rate of an average person. Write an equation that relates the sidewalk rate to the walking rate.

Solution

VERBAL MODEL: Sidewalk rate = Walking rate − Difference in rates

LABELS:
Sidewalk rate = **2** (miles per hour)
Walking rate = w (miles per hour)
Difference in rates = **1** (miles per hour)

ALGEBRAIC MODEL: $2 = w - 1$

You can use mental math in Example 3 to find $w = 3$. This means that the average person's walking rate is 3 miles per hour.

EXAMPLE 4 Using an Equation

SHOPPING You have a $25 gift certificate for a bookstore. You want to buy a book that costs $34. How much more money do you need?

Solution

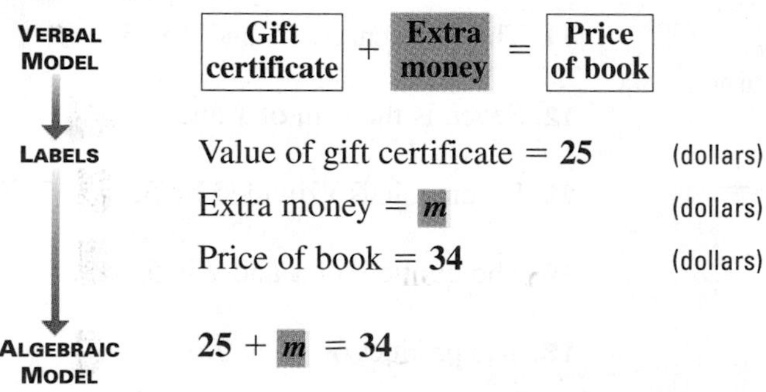

VERBAL MODEL: Gift certificate + Extra money = Price of book

LABELS:
Value of gift certificate = **25** (dollars)
Extra money = m (dollars)
Price of book = **34** (dollars)

ALGEBRAIC MODEL: $25 + m = 34$

ANSWER ▶ Use mental math to find $m = 9$. So, you need another $9 to buy the book.

CHECK ✓ $25 + 9 \stackrel{?}{=} 34$ Substitute 9 for m in original equation.

$34 = 34$ ✓   Solution checks.

Extra Example 1

Translate the verbal sentence into an algebraic equation.

a. Eighteen less than a number is 2. $x - 18 = 2$

b. The quotient of a number and 4 is 9. $\frac{x}{4} = 9$

Extra Example 2

Translate the verbal sentence into an algebraic equation.

a. The sum of three times a number and 6 is 24. $3x + 6 = 24$

b. Four subtracted from the product of 5 and a number is 31. $5x - 4 = 31$

c. The quotient of a number and 6, added to 8 is 10. $\frac{x}{6} + 8 = 10$

d. The difference of two times a number and 21 is that number divided by 2. $2x - 21 = \frac{x}{2}$

Extra Example 3

The price of a movie ticket is $5 for children under age 12, which is $2 less than an adult ticket. Write an equation that relates the price of a child's ticket to the price of an adult ticket. $5 = a - 2$

Extra Example 4

Suppose a company sold $435 million worth of boats in 1995 and $510 million worth in 1996. Find the company's increase in sales.
$435 + b = 510$; $b = 75$; the increase in sales was $75 million.

Concept Check

Explain how to write an equation to represent a verbal sentence.
Sample answer: **Look for key words to represent addition, subtraction, multiplication, or division, and key words to represent equality. Translate the words into symbols and write the equation.**

Apply

Assignment Guide

TRANSITIONAL

Day 1: pp. 68–70 Exs. 11–15, 18–19, 21–24
Day 2: pp. 68–70 Exs. 20, 28–32, 39–40

AVERAGE

Day 1: pp. 68–70 Exs. 11–19, 21–26
Day 2: pp. 68–70 Exs. 27–29, 32–35, 37–40

ADVANCED

Day 1: pp. 68–70 Exs. 11–19, 21–26
Day 2: pp. 68–70 Exs. 27, 30–35, 36*, 37–40

BLOCK SCHEDULE

pp. 68–70 Exs. 11–19, 21–29, 32–35, 37–40

Extra Practice

- Student Edition, pp. 692–693
- Chapter 2 Resource Book, p. 33

Homework Check

To quickly check student understanding of key concepts, go over the following exercises:

Transitional: 12, 20, 22, 28, 30
Average: 16, 20, 24, 28, 32
Advanced: 18, 26, 30, 32, 38

Problem Solving

Exercises 16–19

Point out to students that the English sentence can be interpreted in more than one way, though often only one is accepted as correct. For example, Exercise 17 might be interpreted as either

$$18 + 2x = 30$$
$$\text{or } (18 + 2)x = 30.$$

The second would be correct if a comma were inserted after the 2 in the sentence.

It may help students to think of a "fill in the blank" sentence, such as: The sum of ______ and ______ is ______.

2.4 Exercises

Guided Practice

State whether the quantity is an expression or an equation. Then simplify the expression or solve the the equation.

1. $3 + x = 19$ **equation; 16**
2. $5x - 3x + 6$ **expression; 2x + 6**
3. $2x = 18$ **equation; 9**
4. $\frac{x}{3} = 7$ **equation; 21**

In Exercises 5–8, write an equation that represents the verbal sentence.

5. The number of cars decreased by 20 is 64. **$x - 20 = 64$**

6. The cost of 10 T-shirts at x dollars each is \$77. **$10x = 77$**

7. The number of books divided by 24 students is 3 books per student. **$\frac{x}{24} = 3$**

8. The number of cats increased by 8 kittens is 12. **$x + 8 = 12$**

9. An ad states that the price of computer disks after a \$5.00 rebate is \$13.00. Let p represent the original price. Use the verbal model below to write an equation that relates the original price of the disks to the price you pay. **$13 = p - 5$**

VERBAL MODEL: [Price you pay] = [Original price] − [Rebate amount]

10. Use mental math to solve the equation you wrote for Exercise 9 to find the original price. **\$18**

Practice and Problem Solving

Student Help

▶MORE PRACTICE
Extra practice to help you master skills is on page 692.

Match the sentence with the equation.

11. The difference of x and 7 is 5.

12. Seven is the sum of x and 5. **A**

13. Seven equals x divided by 5. **E**

14. The quotient of x and 7 is 5. **B**

15. The product of x and 7 is 35. **D**

A. $7 = x + 5$

B. $\frac{x}{7} = 5$

C. $x - 7 = 5$

D. $7x = 35$

E. $7 = \frac{x}{5}$

Write an equation that represents the verbal sentence.

16. A number times 38 is 152. **$38x = 152$**

17. The sum of 18 and 2 times a number is 30. **$18 + 2x = 30$**

18. The quotient of 12 and 4 times a number is 1. 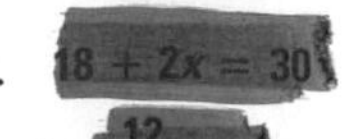

19. The difference of 10 and a number divided by 2 is 3. 

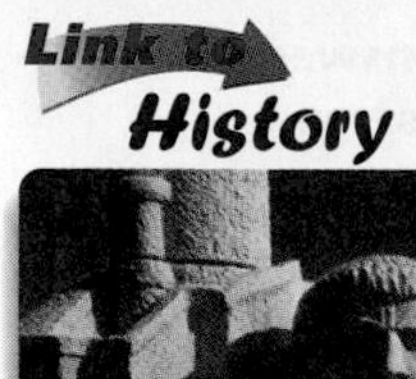

EXPLORATION In 1542, Juan Rodriguez Cabrillo was sent by Spain to explore the Pacific Coast north of Mexico.

More about exploring available at www.mcdougallittell.com

20. **History Link** In 1542, Juan Rodriguez Cabrillo became the first European to sail to what is now California. That was 308 years before California became a state. Choose the equation that models how to find the year y that California became a state. Explain your answer.

A. $y - 308 = 1542$ **B.** $y + 308 = 1542$ **C.** $308 \cdot y = 1542$

In Exercises 21–26, write an equation that represents the verbal sentence.

21. The number of dogs increased by 9 is 20.

22. Sixteen equals the number of tennis shoes decreased by 3. $16 = x - 3$

23. The cost of 3 sweaters at x dollars each is \$90.75. $3x = 90.75$

24. Two hours equals a number of miles divided by 8 miles per hour. $\frac{x}{8} = 2$

25. The cost of a number of compact discs at \$11.99 each is \$35.97.

26. The number of minutes divided by 60 is 6 hours. $\frac{x}{60} = 6$

27. **MATHEMATICAL REASONING** Choose the equation that best represents the following sentence: *The sum of twice your sister's age and 5 is 55.* Explain your choice.

A. $2j + 5 = 55$ **B.** $2(j + 5) = 55$

In Exercises 28 and 29, the price of one television set is \$400. It costs \$150 less than another set.

28. Let x represent the cost of the higher priced television set. Then use the verbal model below to write an equation. $400 = x - 150$

VERBAL MODEL	Lower price	=	Higher price	−	Difference in price

29. Use mental math to solve the equation in Exercise 28 to find the cost of the higher priced television set. Check your solution. \$550

In Exercises 30 and 31, a new go-cart can travel at a top speed of 22 miles per hour. This is three miles per hour faster than an older model of the go-cart.

30. Let y represent the speed of the older model. Then use the verbal model below to write an equation. $22 = y + 3$

VERBAL MODEL	New model's top speed	=	Older model's top speed	+	Difference in speed

31. Use mental math to solve the equation in Exercise 30 to find the speed of the older model. Check your solution. 19 miles per hour

32. **GEOMETRY** Write a variable equation for the area of the rectangle at the right. Then solve the equation to find w. $8w = 24$; 3 cm

Area = 24 cm^2, width w, length 8 cm

Student Help

HOMEWORK HELP Extra help with problem solving in Exs. 28–31 is available at www. mcdougallittell.com

Assess

Assessment Resources

- Assessment Book (Formal Assessment and Alternative Assessment)
- Test and Practice Generator

Mini-Quiz

1. Translate the verbal sentence into an algebraic equation.
   a. The difference of 15 and a number is 3. $15 - x = 3$
   b. The quotient of 8 and a number is 24. $\frac{8}{x} = 24$
   c. The sum of 14 and two times a number is 16. $14 + 2x = 16$
   d. The difference of three times a number and 8 is twice the number. $3x - 8 = 2x$
2. Your uncle sent you a $25 gift certificate for a music store. You decide to use the certificate to buy a double compact disc set that costs $23. Write an equation to show the amount of change you will receive, then solve the equation using mental math. **$23 + x = 25$; you will receive $2 in change.**

Math Reasoning

In Exercise 36, if x is the value of the smaller check and y the value of the larger check, we are given that $y = 2x$ and $x + y = 181 - 100 = 81$, so $3x = 81$ and $x = 27$. This problem can be used to prepare the student for systems of linear equations. In this case, the system is $-2x + y = 0$ and $x + y = 81$.

Link to Careers

FARM MANAGER
Managing a farm requires knowledge of finance, marketing, and economics. An understanding of science and horticulture is also necessary.

More about farm managers available at www.mcdougallittell.com

FARMS In Exercises 33–35, use an algebraic model to answer the questions. Then use the graph below to check your answer.

▶ Source: *The Universal Almanac 1997*

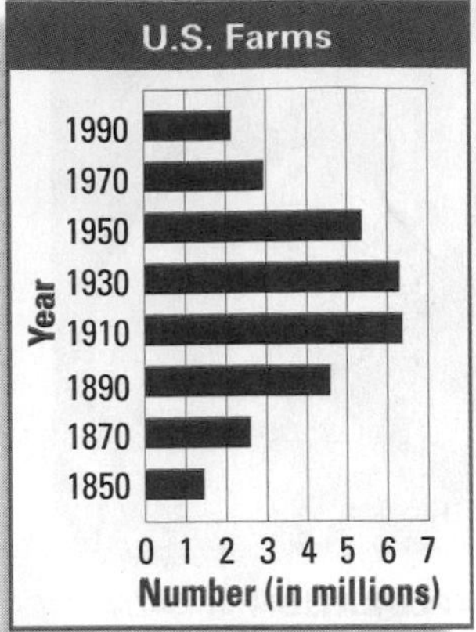

33. The number of farms in 1870 was 2.7 million. The number in 1910 was 3.7 million more than the number in 1870. How many farms were there in 1910? $x = 2.7 + 3.7$; 6.4 million

34. The number of farms in 1950 was two times the number in 1870. How many farms were there in 1950? $x = 2(2.7)$; 5.4 million

35. The number of farms in 1930 divided by the number in 1990 is 3. The number in 1990 was 2.1 million. How many farms were there in 1930? $\frac{x}{2.1} = 3$; 6.3 million

36. CHALLENGE You have two checks; one is twice the amount of the other. After depositing the checks in your savings account, your balance is $181. Before the deposit, your account had a balance of $100. Find the amount of the smaller check. $27

In Exercises 37 and 38, use a verbal model, labels, and an algebraic model to answer the question.

37. You purchase a shirt using a coupon from the newspaper worth $3 off the original price. The clerk tells you the final cost not including tax is $23. What was the original price of the shirt? $x - 3 = 23$; $26

38. One copy machine can make 40 copies per minute. With the help of a second copy machine you can make 72 copies per minute. How many copies per minute can the second machine make? $40 + x = 72$; 32

Multiple-Choice Practice

39. You and a friend are on a canoe trip. The trip is 56 miles long. The first day you travel 18 miles. How many more miles do you have to travel to complete the trip? B

Ⓐ 28 Ⓑ 38 Ⓒ 44 Ⓓ 74

40. Which equation models the situation illustrated at the right? Let q equal the distance across the quarter. J

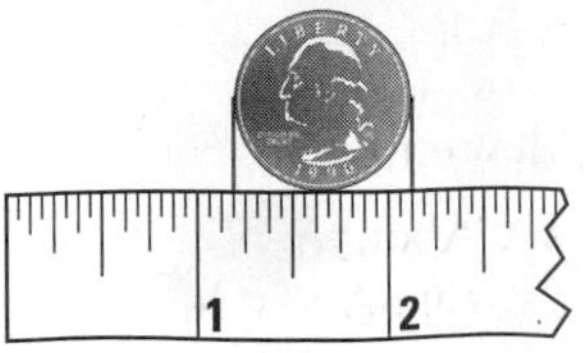

Ⓕ $1\frac{3}{2} + q = 2\frac{1}{2}$ Ⓖ $1\frac{3}{4} + q = 2\frac{1}{4}$

Ⓗ $1\frac{3}{8} + q = 2\frac{1}{8}$ Ⓙ $1\frac{3}{16} + q = 2\frac{1}{8}$

Mid-Chapter Test

Take this test as you would take a test in class. The answers to the exercises are given in the back of the book.

Translate the verbal phrase into a variable expression.

1. Eight less than 9 times a number $9x - 8$

2. Two times a number plus 2 times another number $2x + 2y$

3. A number divided by the sum of 7 and another number  $\frac{x}{7+y}$

In Exercises 4–7, simplify the expression.

4. $2a + 10a$ $12a$ **5.** $2x + 8 + x$ $3x + 8$ **6.** $7(y + 3) + 2y$ $9y + 21$ **7.** $8(4b + b)$ $40b$

8. Simplify $2(3x + 4) + x$. Evaluate when $x = 4$ and when $x = 7$. $7x + 8$; 36, 57

9. Write an expression for the perimeter of the rectangle. Then evaluate the expression when $z = 4$ and when $z = 5$. $2z + 10$; 18, 20

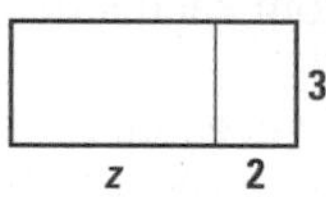

Decide whether the equation is an identity. Explain your reasoning.

10. $7(m + 2) = 3m + 2 + 4m$ Not an identity **11.** $8p + 9p = 10p + 7p$ Identity

Use mental math to solve the equation.

12. $3x = 39$ 13 **13.** $\frac{n}{4} = 20$ 80 **14.** $y + 4 = 7$ 3 **15.** $d - 12 = 8$ 20

Write an equation that represents the verbal sentence. Then solve the equation and check your answer.

16. The amount of people decreased by 12 is 20. $x - 12 = 20$; 32

17. The total cost of n pens at \$.99 each is \$9.90. $0.99n = 9.90$; 10

18. The distance traveled divided by 60 miles per hour is 2 hours. $\frac{x}{60} = 2$; 120

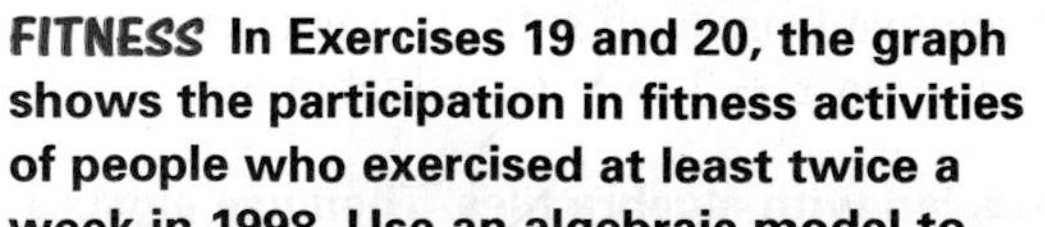

FITNESS In Exercises 19 and 20, the graph shows the participation in fitness activities of people who exercised at least twice a week in 1998. Use an algebraic model to answer the questions. ▶ Source:Fitness Products Council

19. About 6 million more people walk than run. About how many people run? 11 million

20. About 5.3 million fewer people use the treadmill than lift weights. About how many people lift weights? 14.5 million

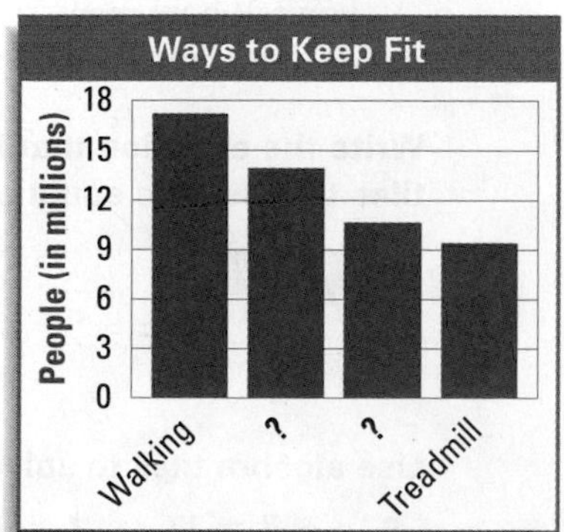

Additional Resources

A Mid-Chapter Test and a Mid-Chapter Partner Quiz are available in the *Assessment Book*, pp. 15–16 and p. 215.

1 Planning the Activity

Purpose and Materials

See the margin of the student page.

LINK TO LESSON

Students may wish to use algebra tile models to visualize some of the exercises on page 76.

Math Reasoning

Students analyze problems by identifying relationships, applying strategies for solving problems, and checking the validity of results.

California Standards and Assessment

CA Standards: AF 4.0, MR 2.5

REASONING 2.5

DEVELOPING CONCEPTS
Addition and Subtraction Equations

For use with Lesson 2.5

California Standards

- Use a variety of methods, such as words, numbers, symbols, diagrams, and models, to explain mathematical reasoning. (MR 2.5)
- Solve simple linear equations over the rational numbers. (AF 4.0)

MATERIALS

- Algebra tiles

Algebra tiles can be used to model and solve an equation.

SAMPLE 1 Using Algebra Tiles

Use algebra tiles to solve the equation $x + 3 = 6$.

Here's How

1. Model the equation with algebra tiles.

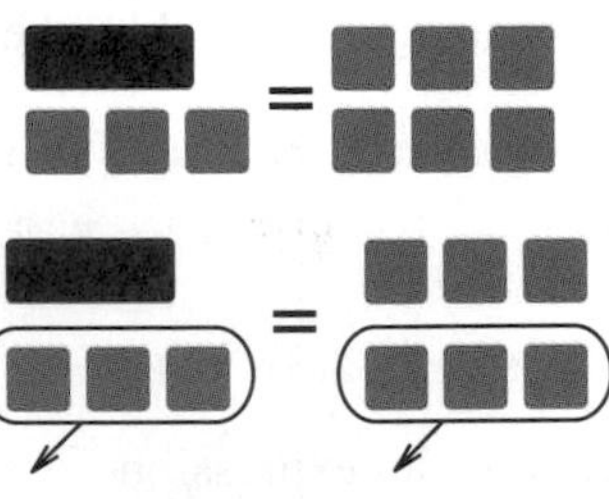

2. To find the value of x, get the x-tile by itself. You can undo the addition of 3 by removing (subtracting) three 1-tiles from each side.

3. The x-tile is equal to three 1-tiles. So, the solution is 3. This solution checks because $3 + 3 = 6$ is true.

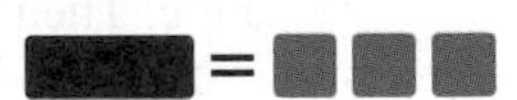

Try These

Write the equation that is modeled with algebra tiles. Describe the step shown to solve the equation. 1–3. See margin.

1. **2.**

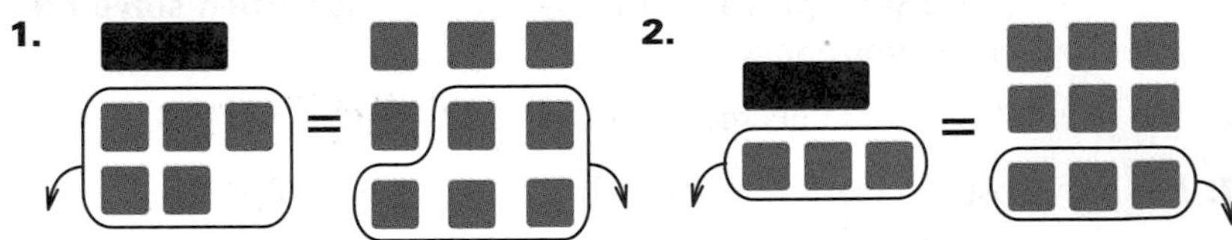

3. When you use algebra tiles to solve an addition equation, how can you tell how many tiles to remove from each side? Use your rule to describe how to solve the equation $x + 2 = 5$ with algebra tiles.

1. $x + 5 = 9$; Five tiles are removed from each side. $x = 4$
2. $x + 3 = 9$; Three tiles are removed from each side. $x = 6$
3. Remove all the 1-tiles from one side of the equation in order to get the x-tile by itself. Then remove the same number from the other side. To solve $x + 2 = 5$, remove two 1-tiles from both sides.

Write the equation that is modeled with algebra tiles. Then use algebra tiles to solve the equation. Make a sketch of your steps. Check sketches.

4. **5.**

4. $x + 5 = 11$; $x = 6$ 5. $x + 2 = 7$; $x = 5$

Use algebra tiles to solve the equation. Make a sketch of your steps. Check sketches.

6. $x + 7 = 11$ 4 **7.** $x + 1 = 8$ 7 **8.** $x + 4 = 14$ 10 **9.** $x + 8 = 8$ 0

In Sample 1 and in Exercises 1–9, you used the "algebra tile rule" which states that you can remove the same number and type of algebra tiles from each side of the equation without changing the solution of the equation. In algebra, this rule can be stated as follows.

SUBTRACTION PROPERTY OF EQUALITY Subtracting the same number from each side of an equation produces a new equation having the same solution as the original.

If $x + a = b$, then $x + a - a = b - a$.

SAMPLE 2 Justifying the Steps of a Solution

The steps shown below can be used to solve the equation that is modeled in Sample 1. Justify the second and third steps.

$x + 3 = 6$	Write original equation.
$x + 3 - 3 = 6 - 3$	?
$x = 3$	?

Here's How

$x + 3 = 6$	Write original equation.
$x + 3 - 3 = 6 - 3$	Subtraction property of equality
$x = 3$	Simplify. *x* is by itself.

Notice that the second step is performed to isolate the variable x.

Try These

10. MATHEMATICAL REASONING Use what you know about the subtraction property of equality to write an addition property of equality. **See margin.**

Justify the steps of the solution. **11–12. See margin.**

11. $x + 5 = 9$
$x + 5 - 5 = 9 - 5$
$x = 4$

12. $x - 3 = 11$
$x - 3 + 3 = 11 + 3$
$x = 14$

Describe the property of equality you can use to isolate the variable.

13. $x + 4 = 12$ **Subtraction property**

14. $y - 5 = 11$ **Addition property**

15. $9 + z = 21$ **Subtraction property**

Solve the equation. Write your steps and justify each step.

16. $p - 2 = 15$ **17**

17. $6 + q = 9$ **3**

18. $r - 9 = 17$ **26**

10. Adding the same number to each side of an equation produces an equation having the same solution as the original.

11. Subtraction property of equality; Simplify. *x* is by itself.

12. Addition property of equality; Simplify. *x* is by itself.

2 Managing the Activity

Classroom Management

If algebra tiles are not available, students could sketch the tile arrangement for each step on graph paper. Ask for volunteers to model solutions at the overhead, encouraging them to verbalize what is going on mathematically as they manipulate the tiles. The underlying concept of equality (balance) should be emphasized.

3 Closing the Activity

★ **KEY DISCOVERY**

To solve an addition equation, the same number is subtracted from each side of the equation.

Activity Assessment

Use Exercises 6–9 and 16–18 to assess student understanding.

1 Plan

Pacing

Suggested Number of Days

Transitional: 2 days
Average: 2 days
Advanced: 2 days
Block Schedule: 1 block

Teaching Resources

Blacklines
(See page 50B.)

Transparencies
- Warm-Up Exercises
- Teacher Time-Savers
- English/Spanish Problem Solving
- Answers

Technology
- Electronic Teacher Tools
- Test and Practice Generator

2 Teach

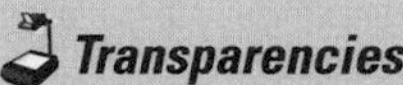

Math Reasoning

For Mathematical Background Notes on mathematical reasoning related to this lesson, please refer to pages 50E and 50F in this Teacher's Edition.

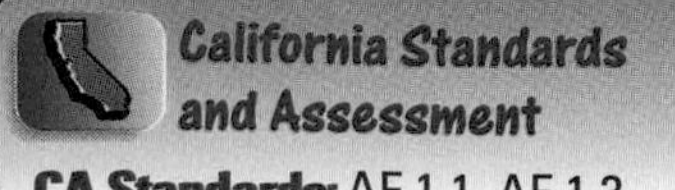

California Standards and Assessment

CA Standards: AF 1.1, AF 1.3, AF 4.0

2.5 Solving Equations Using Addition or Subtraction

California Standards

In this lesson you'll:
- Use variables and appropriate operations to write an equation. (AF 1.1)
- Simplify numerical expressions by applying properties of rational numbers and justify the process used. (AF 1.3)
- Solve simple linear equations. (AF 4.0)

Goal 1 Using Subtraction to Solve an Equation

As you saw in Developing Concepts 2.5, page 72, you can often solve an equation by performing the same operation on both sides of the equal sign. A good model for this idea is the balance scale.

Original equation: $x + 2 = 5$ | **Subtract 2 from both sides.** Scale stays in balance. | **Simplify both sides.** Solution is 3.

You can use *inverse operations* to solve equations. An **inverse operation** is an operation that "undoes" another operation. Addition and subtraction are inverse operations. For example, the inverse of adding 2 is subtracting 2.

Doing the same operation to both sides of an equation results in a new equation with the same solution as the original. When two equations have

Subtraction Property of Equality

In Words	Subtracting the same number from each side of an equation produces an equivalent equation.
In Algebra	If $x + a = b$, then $x + a - a = b - a$.
In Arithmetic	If $x + 7 = 10$, then $x + 7 - 7 = 10 - 7$.

Student Help

Study Tip
In Example 1, notice that subtracting 112 on the right "undoes" adding 112. This is the way to get the variable by itself on the right side of the equation.

Example 1 Using Subtraction to Solve an Equation

Solve $214 = y + 112$.

Solution

$214 = y + 112$	Write original equation.
$214 - \mathbf{112} = y + 112 - \mathbf{112}$	Subtract 112 from each side. (Subtraction property of equality)
$102 = y$	Simplify. y is by itself.

ANSWER ▶ The solution is 102. Check the answer.

CHECK ✓ $214 = y + 112$	Write original equation.
$214 \stackrel{?}{=} \mathbf{102} + 112$	Substitute 102 for y in original equation.
$214 = 214$ ✓	Solution checks.

EXAMPLE 2 Solving an Equation with Decimals

Solve $z + 4.7 = 10.3$.

Solution

$z + 4.7 = 10.3$ Write original equation.

$z + 4.7 - \mathbf{4.7} = 10.3 - \mathbf{4.7}$ Subtract 4.7 from each side.

$z = 5.6$ Simplify. z is by itself.

The solution is 5.6. Check the answer in the original equation.

Student Help

▶ **SKILLS REVIEW**
For help with subtracting decimals, see p. 675.

Goal 2 USING ADDITION TO SOLVE AN EQUATION

You can use addition to solve an equation involving subtraction.

ADDITION PROPERTY OF EQUALITY

In Words Adding the same number to each side of an equation produces an equivalent equation.

In Algebra If $x - a = b$, then $x - a + a = b + a$.

In Arithmetic If $x - 3 = 7$, then $x - 3 + 3 = 7 + 3$.

EXAMPLE 3 Using Addition to Solve an Equation

Solve $x - 31 = 14$.

Solution

$x - 31 = 14$ Write original equation.

$x - 31 + \mathbf{31} = 14 + \mathbf{31}$ Add 31 to each side. (Addition property of equality)

$x = 45$ Simplify. x is by itself.

The solution is 45. Check the answer in the original equation.

Student Help

▶ **STUDY TIP**
You can use a vertical format for solving an equation. For example,

$$\begin{array}{rcr} x - 31 & = & 14 \\ +31 & & +31 \\ \hline x & = & 45 \end{array}$$

EXAMPLE 4 Solving an Equation with Decimals

Solve $0.5 = y - 1.25$.

Solution

$0.5 = y - 1.25$ Write original equation.

$0.5 + \mathbf{1.25} = y - 1.25 + \mathbf{1.25}$ Add 1.25 to each side.

$1.75 = y$ Simplify. y is by itself.

The solution is 1.75. Check the answer in the original equation.

Math Reasoning

When two equations are equivalent, the set of all solutions of one is the same as the set of all solutions of the other. For a linear equation in one variable, the solution set contains only one number.

Extra Example 1

Solve $356 = y + 241$. **115**

Extra Example 2

Solve $z + 2.6 = 8.1$. **5.5**

Extra Example 3

Solve $x - 18 = 21$. **39**

Teaching Tip

Alternate Approach
Some students may prefer to use a vertical format to show the steps of a solution to an equation. In Example 3, they could write the following:

$$\begin{array}{rcr} x - 31 & = & 14 \\ +31 & = & +31 \\ \hline x & = & 45 \end{array}$$

Extra Example 4

Solve $8.5 = y - 4.25$. **12.75**

Concept Check

How do you know whether to use addition or subtraction to solve an equation? **If the equation is an addition equation, subtract an amount equal to the number added to the variable from both sides of the equation and then simplify. If the equation is a subtraction equation, add an amount equal to the number subtracted from the variable to both sides of the equation and then simplify.**

3 Apply

Assignment Guide

TRANSITIONAL

Day 1: SRH p. 679 Exs. 1, 3, 4, 7; pp. 76–77 Exs. 14–20, 34–35, 39–40, 47–49

Day 2: SRH p. 679 Exs. 2, 6, 9, 12; pp. 76–77 Exs. 12–13, 25–33, 36–38, 41–46, 50–55, 57–58

AVERAGE

Day 1: pp. 76–77 Exs. 14–24, 34–35, 39–40, 47–49

Day 2: pp. 76–77 Exs. 25–33, 36–38, 41–46, 50–55, 57–58

ADVANCED

Day 1: pp. 76–77 Exs. 14–24, 34–35, 39–40, 47–49

Day 2: pp. 76–77 Exs. 25–33, 36–38, 41–46, 50–55, 56*, 57–60

BLOCK SCHEDULE

pp. 76–77 Exs. 14–55, 57–58

Extra Practice

- Student Edition, pp. 692–693
- Chapter 2 Resource Book, p. 42

Homework Check

To quickly check student understanding of key concepts, go over the following exercises:

Transitional: 12, 16, 26, 38, 46, 54
Average: 18, 28, 40, 46, 54
Advanced: 24, 32, 42, 46, 54

Problem Solving

Exercises 16–42

Encourage students to show each step of their solution. Stress that they should vertically align the equal signs in their steps.

2.5 Exercises

Guided Practice

Copy and complete the solution.

1. $q - 16 = 29$
$q - 16 + ? = 29 + ?$
$q = ?$
$q - 16 + 16 = 29 + 16$; $q = 45$

2. $r + 37 = 65$
$r + 37 - ? = 65 - ?$
$r = ?$
$r + 37 - 37 = 65 - 37$; $r = 28$

Tell which property of equality you would use to solve the equation.

3. $x + 24 = 38$ **Subtraction property**
4. $y - 16 = 53$ **Addition property**
5. $z + 3.2 = 5.6$ **Subtraction property**
6. $9.1 + j = 10$ **Subtraction property**
7. $m - 18 = 4$ **Addition property**
8. $37 = n - 11$ **Addition property**
9. $a - 13 = 13$ **Addition property**
10. $8.8 = k - 2.1$ **Addition property**
11. $231 + d = 475$ **Subtraction property**

Practice and Problem Solving

> **Student Help**
> **MORE PRACTICE** Extra practice to help you master skills is on page 693.

Copy and complete the solution. Justify each step.

12. $x - 34 = 52$
$x - 34 + ? = 52 + ?$
$x = ?$
$x - 34 + 34 = 52 + 34$; $x = 86$

13. $76 = y - 29$
$76 + ? = y - 29 + ?$
$? = y$
$76 + 29 = y - 29 + 29$; $105 = y$

14. $r + 62 = 111$
$r + 62 - ? = 111 - ?$
$r = ?$
$r + 62 - 62 = 111 - 62$; $r = 49$

15. $279 = t + 194$
$279 - ? = t + 194 - ?$
$? = t$
$279 - 194 = t + 194 - 194$; $85 = t$

Use the subtraction property of equality to solve the equation. Then check your solution.

16. $w + 1 = 14$ 13
17. $q + 0.5 = 8$ 7.5
18. $x + 12 = 22$ 10
19. $14 = m + 0.75$ 13.25
20. $z + 19 = 22$ 3
21. $52 = c + 20.25$ 31.75
22. $y + 7 = 13$ 6
23. $10 = k + 4.2$ 5.8
24. $5.4 = a + 3.3$ 2.1

Use the addition property of equality to solve the equation. Then check your solution.

25. $p - 7 = 3$ 10
26. $s - 15.3 = 4.2$ 19.5
27. $v - 12 = 9$ 21
28. $26 = j - 14.5$ 40.5
29. $f - 16 = 7$ 23
30. $42 = k - 10.7$ 52.7
31. $b - 5 = 6$ 11
32. $a - 18 = 4.2$ 22.2
33. $19.1 = c - 11$ 30.1

> **Student Help**
> **HOMEWORK HELP** Extra help with problem solving in Exs. 34–42 is available at www.mcdougallittell.com

Solve the equation. Justify your steps and check your solution.

34. $n + 17 = 98$ 81
35. $m + 40.5 = 81$ 40.5
36. $x - 61 = 78$ 139
37. $z - 129 = 201.5$ 330.5

38. $356 = y - 219$ 575
39. $142.7 + t = 193$ 50.3
40. $10.3 + q = 14$ 3.7
41. $q - 5.3 = 9.3$ 14.6
42. $0.67 + r = 0.89$ 0.22

In Exercises 43–46, write an equation that represents the statement. Then solve the equation.

43. The sum of x and 45 is 65. **$x + 45 = 65$; 20**

44. The difference of y and 5.8 is 12.2. **$y - 5.8 = 12.2$; 18**

45. The difference of 723 and a number is 317. **$723 - x = 317$; 406**

46. The sum of a number and 137 is 189. **$x + 137 = 189$; 52**

Link to Geography

47. MATHEMATICAL REASONING Your friend says that in order to solve $q + 18.1 = 22$, you should subtract 22 from each side. Do you agree? Explain your reasoning. **No; You must subtract 18.1 from each side to get x by itself.**

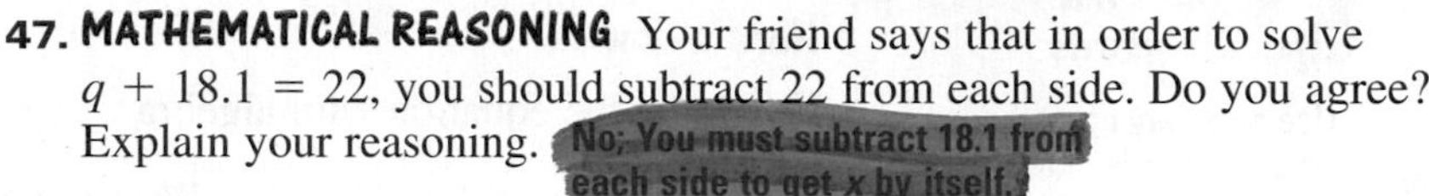

CALCULATOR In Exercises 48–53, estimate the solution. Then use a calculator to solve the equation. Check your answer.

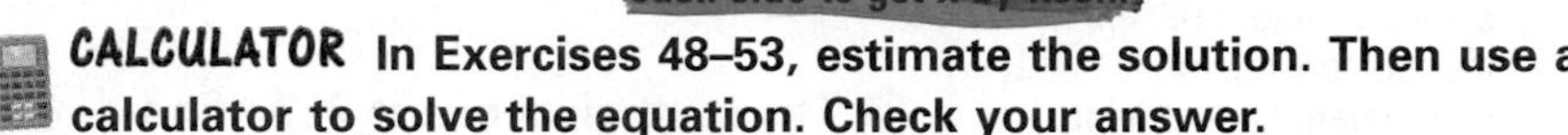

48. $y + 217.46 = 598.07$ **380.61**

49. $952.70 = s + 420.38$ **532.32**

50. $1.397 = x - 1.973$ **3.37**

51. $y - 4.85 = 13.01$ **17.86**

52. $m + 1024 = 9785$ **8761**

53. $826 = p - 2290$ **3116**

ELEVATION In Exercises 54 and 55, use the following information.
You are hiking Whatcom Peak in the Cascade Mountains of Washington. On your second day of hiking, you start at Whatcom Pass and decide to make a campsite at an elevation of 6500 feet.

54. The sum of the elevation at Whatcom Pass and 1300 feet is equal to the elevation at your campsite. Write an equation to find the elevation of Whatcom Pass. Then solve the equation. **$x + 1300 = 6500$; 5200 ft**

55. The difference between the elevation of Whatcom Peak and the elevation at your campsite is 1100 feet. Write an equation to find the elevation of Whatcom Peak. Then solve the equation. **$y - 6500 = 1100$; 7600 ft**

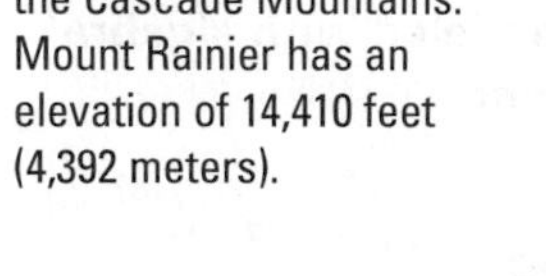

ELEVATION The highest point in Washington is Mount Rainier, which is located in the Cascade Mountains. Mount Rainier has an elevation of 14,410 feet (4,392 meters).

56. CHALLENGE Your school band bought boxes of stationery for \$6 each. They sold the boxes of stationery for \$10 each. After subtracting the amount they paid for the stationery from the amount they collected, their profit was \$2000. Write and solve an equation to find the number of boxes of stationery the band sold. **$x(10 - 6) = 2000$; 500 boxes**

Multiple-Choice Practice

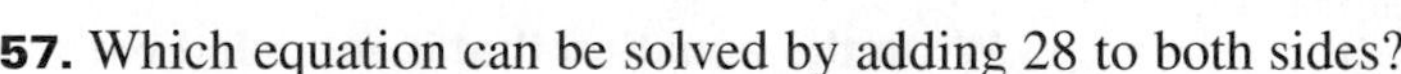

Test Tip A B C D

▶ You may be able to eliminate choices by estimating. For instance, in Exercise 58 you can estimate the answer to be $60 - 20 = 40$ miles. This estimate eliminates choices F and J.

57. Which equation can be solved by adding 28 to both sides? **A**

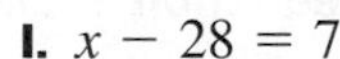

I. $x - 28 = 7$ **II.** $x + 28 = 7$ **III.** $x - 7 = 28$

Ⓐ I only Ⓑ II only Ⓒ I and II Ⓓ I and III

58. You are on a field trip. You have to travel 56 miles to reach your destination. You have traveled 18 miles so far. How much farther do you have to travel? **G**

Ⓕ 28 miles Ⓖ 38 miles Ⓗ 44 miles Ⓙ 74 miles

4 Assess

Assessment Resources

- Assessment Book (Formal Assessment and Alternative Assessment)
- Test and Practice Generator

Mini-Quiz

1. Solve the equation. Then check your solution.
   a. $b + 19 = 23$ **4**
   b. $n - 13 = 40$ **53**
   c. $823 = y + 467$ **356**
   d. $t - 3.87 = 4.55$ **8.42**
2. When buying a pair of basketball shoes for \$47.95, you give the cashier \$60.00. Write and solve an equation to determine the amount of change you should receive. **$47.95 + x = 60.00$; \$12.05**

1 Planning the Activity

Purpose and Materials

See the margin of the student page.

LINK TO LESSON

You may wish to use algebra tiles to demonstrate Example 1 on page 80. Students may wish to use algebra tile models to visualize some of the exercises on page 82.

Math Reasoning

Students analyze problems by identifying relationships, applying strategies for solving problems, and checking the validity of results.

California Standards and Assessment

CA Standards: AF 4.0, MR 2.5

DEVELOPING CONCEPTS
Multiplication and Division Equations

For use with Lesson 2.6

California Standards

- Use a variety of methods, such as words, numbers, symbols, diagrams, and models to explain mathematical reasoning. (MR 2.5)
- Solve simple linear equations over the rational numbers. (AF 4.0)

SAMPLE 1 Using Algebra Tiles

Use algebra tiles to solve the equation $2x = 6$.

Here's How

1. Model the equation with algebra tiles.

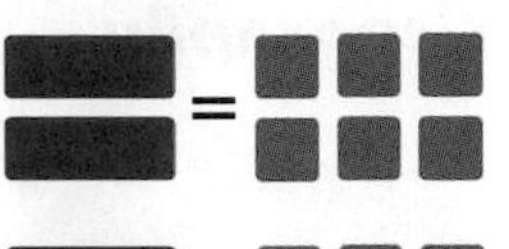

2. The coefficient of x is 2. To find the value of x, get the x-tile by itself by dividing each side into two equally sized groups. Then remove one group of tiles from each side.

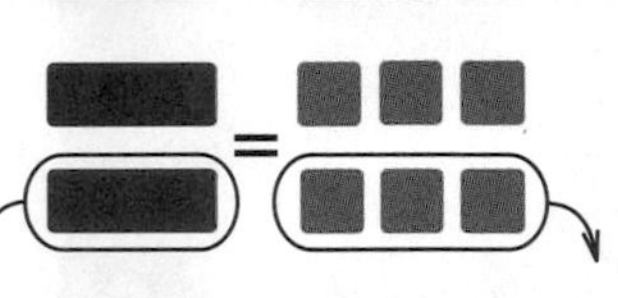

3. The x-tile is equal to three 1-tiles. So, the solution is 3. This solution checks because $2 \cdot 3 = 6$ is true.

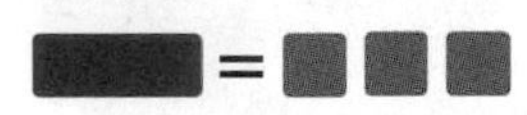

Try These

In Exercises 1 and 2, write the equation that is modeled with algebra tiles. Describe the step shown to solve the equation. **1–3. See margin.**

1. 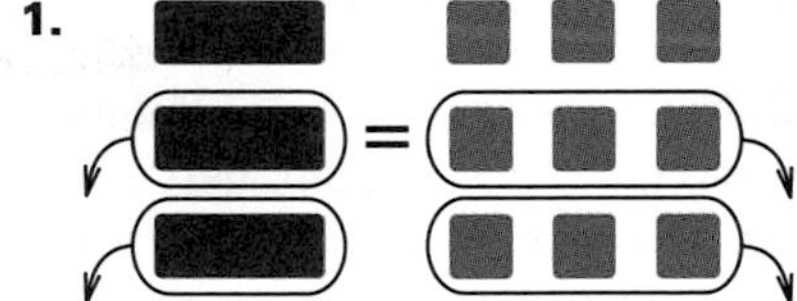

2. 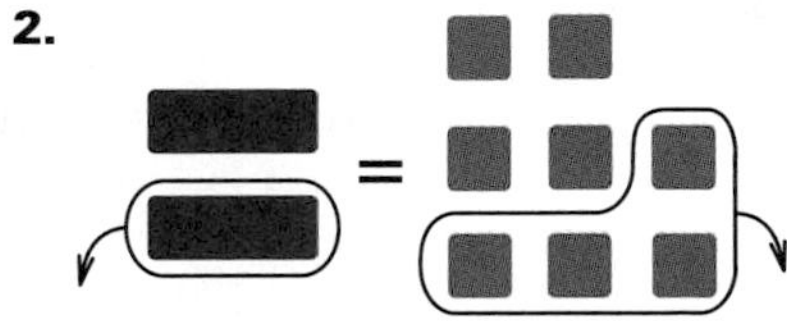

3. When you use algebra tiles to solve a multiplication equation, how can you tell how many tiles to remove from each side? Use your rule to describe how to solve the equation $2x = 10$ with algebra tiles.

1. $3x = 9$; Separate each side into 3 groups of equal tiles. Remove 2 x-tiles from one side to get the x-tile by itself. Remove 2 groups of 1-tiles; $x = 3$.
2. $2x = 8$; Separate each side into two groups of equal tiles. Remove one group from each side to get $x = 4$.
3. Remove all x-tiles but one from one side of the equation. Separate the 1-tiles into as many equal groups as the original number of x-tiles. Remove all but one group. To solve $2x = 10$, divide each side into two groups of equal tiles. Remove one group from each side to get $x = 5$.

Write the equation that is modeled with algebra tiles. Then use algebra tiles to solve the equation. Make a sketch of your steps.

4. **$2x = 4$; $x = 2$**

5. **$3x = 12$; $x = 4$**

Use algebra tiles to solve the equation. Make a sketch of your steps. **Check sketches.**

6. $2x = 10$ **5** **7.** $5x = 15$ **3** **8.** $4x = 12$ **3** **9.** $2x = 12$ **6**

In Sample 1 and in Exercises 1–9, you used the "algebra tile rule" which states that you can divide each side of the equation into the same number of equally sized groups and remove all but one group of tiles from each side. In algebra, this rule can be stated as follows.

DIVISION PROPERTY OF EQUALITY Dividing each side of an equation by the same nonzero number produces an equivalent equation.

If $ax = b$ and $a \neq 0$, then $\frac{ax}{a} = \frac{b}{a}$.

SAMPLE 2 Justifying the Steps of a Solution

Solve $2x = 6$ and justify your steps.

Here's How

$2x = 6$	Write original equation.
$\frac{2x}{2} = \frac{6}{2}$	Division property of equality
$x = 3$	Simplify. x is by itself.

Notice that the second step is performed to isolate the variable x.

Try These

10. MATHEMATICAL REASONING Use what you know about the division property of equality to write a multiplication property of equality in words and in algebra. **Multiplying each side of an equation by the same nonzero number produces an equivalent equation. If $\frac{x}{a} = b$ and $a \neq 0$, then $a \cdot \frac{x}{a} = a \cdot b$.**

Justify the steps of the solution. **11–13. See margin.**

11. $5x = 30$; $\frac{5x}{5} = \frac{30}{5}$; $x = 6$

12. $\frac{x}{7} = 2$; $7 \cdot \frac{x}{7} = 7 \cdot 2$; $x = 14$

13. $\frac{x}{2} = 12$; $2 \cdot \frac{x}{2} = 2 \cdot 12$; $x = 24$

Describe the property of equality you can use to isolate the variable.

14. $\frac{x}{3} = 13$ **Multiplication property**

15. $5y = 45$ **Division property**

16. $\frac{z}{9} = 2$ **Multiplication property**

Solve the equation. Write your steps and justify each step. **17–19. See margin.**

17. $3p = 54$

18. $\frac{q}{2} = 7$

19. $4r = 16$

11. Division property of equality; solution: x is by itself.

12. Multiplication property of equality; solution: x is by itself.

13. Multiplication property of equality; solution: x is by itself.

17. $\frac{3p}{3} = \frac{54}{3}$; $p = 18$

18. $2 \cdot \frac{q}{2} = 2 \cdot 7$; $q = 14$

19. $\frac{4r}{4} = \frac{16}{4}$; $r = 4$

2 Managing the Activity

Classroom Management

If algebra tiles are not available, students could sketch the tile arrangement for each step on graph paper. Ask for volunteers to model solutions at the overhead, encouraging them to verbalize what is going on mathematically as they manipulate the tiles. The underlying concept of equality (balance) should be emphasized.

3 Closing the Activity

★ Key Discovery

In order to solve a multiplication equation, each side of the equation must be divided by the same nonzero number.

Activity Assessment

Use Exercises 6–9 and 17–19 to assess student understanding.

1 Plan

Pacing

Suggested Number of Days

Transitional: 2 days
Average: 2 days
Advanced: 2 days
Block Schedule: 1 block

Teaching Resources

Blacklines
(See page 50B.)

- Warm-Up Exercises
- Teacher Time-Savers
- English/Spanish Problem Solving
- Answers

Technology
- Electronic Teacher Tools
- Test and Practice Generator

2 Teach

Math Reasoning

For Mathematical Background Notes on mathematical reasoning related to this lesson, please refer to pages 50E and 50F in this Teacher's Edition.

CA Standards: AF 1.1, AF 1.3, AF 4.0

2.6 Solving Equations Using Multiplication or Division

In this lesson you'll:
- Use variables and appropriate operations to write an equation. (AF 1.1)
- Simplify numerical expressions by applying properties of rational numbers and justify the process used. (AF 1.3)
- Solve simple linear equations. (AF 4.0)

Goal 1 Using Division to Solve an Equation

As you learned in Developing Concepts 2.6, page 78, division can be used to help solve multiplication equations.

Division Property of Equality

In Words	Dividing each side of an equation by the same nonzero number produces an equivalent equation.
In Algebra	If $ax = b$ and $a \neq 0$, then $\frac{ax}{a} = \frac{b}{a}$.
In Arithmetic	If $3x = 15$, then $\frac{3x}{3} = \frac{15}{3}$.

Example 1 Using Division to Solve an Equation

Solve $5x = 20$.

Solution

$5x = 20$ — Write original equation.

$\frac{5x}{5} = \frac{20}{5}$ — Divide each side by 5. (Division property of equality)

$x = 4$ — Simplify. x is by itself.

ANSWER ▶ The solution is 4. Check the answer.

CHECK ✓ $5(4) \stackrel{?}{=} 20$ — Substitute 4 for x in original equation.

$20 = 20$ ✓ — The solution checks.

Student Help

▶More Examples

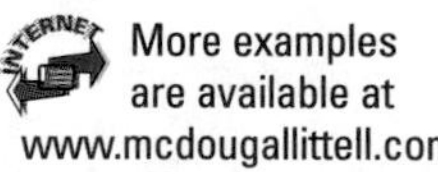

More examples are available at www.mcdougallittell.com

Example 2 Solving an Equation with Decimals

Solve $2.3 = 4.6m$.

Solution

$2.3 = 4.6m$ — Write original equation.

$\frac{2.3}{4.6} = \frac{4.6m}{4.6}$ — Divide each side by 4.6.

$0.5 = m$ — Simplify. m is by itself.

ANSWER ▶ The solution is 0.5. Check this in the original equation.

Goal 2 Using Multiplication to Solve an Equation

In Goal 1, you used division to solve equations involving multiplication. Now you will learn how to use multiplication to solve equations involving division.

Multiplication Property of Equality

In Words Multiplying each side of an equation by the same nonzero number produces an equivalent equation.

In Algebra If $\frac{x}{a} = b$ and $a \neq 0$, then $a \cdot \frac{x}{a} = a \cdot b$.

In Arithmetic If $\frac{x}{4} = 3$, then $4 \cdot \frac{x}{4} = 4 \cdot 3$.

EXAMPLE 3 Using Multiplication to Solve an Equation

Solve $\frac{x}{5} = 12$.

Solution

$\frac{x}{5} = 12$ Write original equation.

$\mathbf{5} \cdot \frac{x}{5} = \mathbf{5} \cdot 12$ Multiply each side by 5. (Multiplication property of equality)

$x = 60$ Simplify. x is by itself.

ANSWER ▶ The solution is 60. Check the answer.

CHECK ✓ $\frac{x}{5} = 12$ Write original equation.

$\frac{60}{5} \stackrel{?}{=} 12$ Substitute 60 for x.

$12 = 12$ ✓ The solution checks.

EXAMPLE 4 Solving an Equation with Decimals

Solve $3.2 = \frac{n}{2}$.

Solution

$3.2 = \frac{n}{2}$ Write original equation.

$\mathbf{2} \cdot 3.2 = \mathbf{2} \cdot \frac{n}{2}$ Multiply each side by 2.

$6.4 = n$ Simplify. n is by itself.

ANSWER ▶ The solution is 6.4. Check this in the original equation.

Math Reasoning

Solving an equation $ax = b$, $a \neq 0$, by dividing both sides of the equation by a is equivalent to solving it by multiplying both sides by $\frac{1}{a}$.

Extra Example 1

Solve $15a = 45$. $a = 3$

Extra Example 2

Solve $4.8 = 6.4x$. $x = 0.75$

Extra Example 3

Solve $\frac{a}{3} = 14$. $a = 42$

Extra Example 4

Solve $1.8 = \frac{x}{3}$. $x = 5.4$

Teaching Tip

Note the use of the fraction bar to indicate division, rather than using "÷." Point out that while the division symbol is used frequently in arithmetic, the fraction bar is used more frequently in algebra.

Concept Check

How do you know whether to use multiplication or division to solve an equation? **In a multiplication equation, identify the number being multiplied times the variable. Then divide both sides of the equation by this number and simplify. In a division equation, identify the number by which the variable is being divided. Then multiply both sides of the equation by this number and simplify.**

3 Apply

Assignment Guide

Transitional

Day 1: SRH p. 680 Exs. 5–8; pp. 82–84 Exs. 10–14, 23–25, 32–34, 42–43, 46–47

Day 2: SRH p. 680 Exs. 13–16; pp. 82–84 Exs. 9, 17–20, 26–29, 35–38, 50–60

Average

Day 1: pp. 82–84 Exs. 10–16, 23–25, 32–34, 44–48

Day 2: pp. 82–84 Exs. 9, 17–22, 26–31, 35–41, 50–60

Advanced

Day 1: pp. 82–84 Exs. 12–16, 23–25, 32–34, 44–48

Day 2: pp. 82–84 Exs. 20–22, 26–31, 35–41, 49*, 50–60

Block Schedule

pp. 82–84 Exs. 9–41, 44–48, 50–60

Extra Practice

- Student Edition, pp. 692–693
- Chapter 2 Resource Book, p. 51

Homework Check

To quickly check student understanding of key concepts, go over the following exercises:

Transitional: 12, 18, 26, 32, 46
Average: 14, 20, 28, 36, 46
Advanced: 16, 22, 30, 38, 46

2.6 Exercises

Guided Practice

Complete the solution.

1. $3a = 21$ **$\frac{3a}{3} = \frac{21}{3}$; $a = 7$**

$\frac{3a}{?} = \frac{21}{?}$

$a = ?$

2. $\frac{b}{3} = 3$ **$3 \cdot \frac{b}{3} = 3 \cdot 3$; $b = 9$**

$? \cdot \frac{b}{3} = ? \cdot 3$

$b = ?$

Decide which property of equality you would use to solve the equation.

3. $6x = 54$ **Division property**

4. $\frac{y}{3} = 12$ **Multiplication property**

5. $\frac{z}{5} = 24$ **Multiplication property**

6. $7p = 42$ **Division property**

7. $\frac{q}{5} = 54$ **Multiplication property**

8. $72 = 4r$ **Division property**

Practice and Problem Solving

Student Help

▶More Practice
Extra practice to help you master skills is on page 693.

Copy and complete solution. Justify each step.

9. $\frac{m}{14} = 5$ 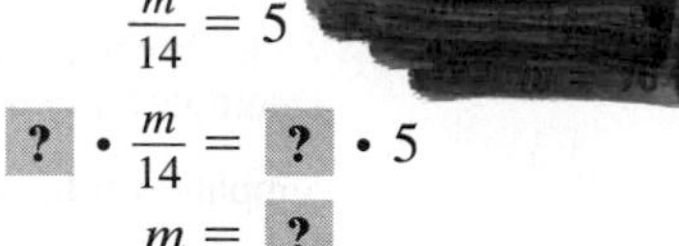

$? \cdot \frac{m}{14} = ? \cdot 5$

$m = ?$

10. $2.2q = 8.8$ 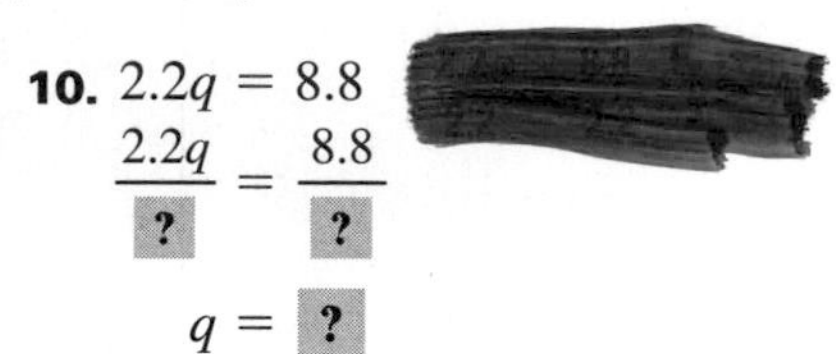

$\frac{2.2q}{?} = \frac{8.8}{?}$

$q = ?$

Use the division property of equality to solve the equation. Then check your solution.

11. $4k = 16$

12. $12y = 144$

13. $56 = 7n$

14. $2w = 50$

15. $10a = 240$

16. $5d = 625$

Use the multiplication property of equality to solve the equation. Then check your solution.

17. $\frac{n}{4} = 25$

18. $\frac{m}{3} = 3$

19. $\frac{b}{20} = 2$

20. $16 = \frac{x}{4}$

21. $\frac{z}{3.2} = 8$

22. $\frac{t}{7.4} = 6$

Solve the equation. Justify your steps and check your solution.

23. $6r = 48$

24. $5u = 100$

25. $5t = 6.5$

26. $\frac{y}{6} = 34$

27. $\frac{d}{3} = 2.1$

28. $72 = 9h$

29. $524 = \frac{a}{1}$

30. $4b = 36$

31. $\frac{x}{3} = 21$

CALCULATOR **In Exercises 32–40, estimate the solution. Then use a calculator to solve the equation. Check your answer.**

32. $456r = 1368$ **33.** $824x = 1648$ **34.** $23d = 966$

35. $55n = 3025$ **36.** $\frac{y}{5.2} = 30$ **37.** $65t = 390$

38. $\frac{b}{9} = 1025$ **39.** $\frac{m}{8} = 624$ **40.** $\frac{v}{136} = 17$

41. MATHEMATICAL REASONING A mail carrier who has a rural delivery route can cover the 105 mile route in seven hours. About how many miles does she travel per hour? Explain what method you used to solve the problem and what units your answer has.

GEOMETRY **Write an equation that relates the length and the width of the rectangle to its area. Then solve the equation to find the missing side length.**

42. Area = 15 ft^2

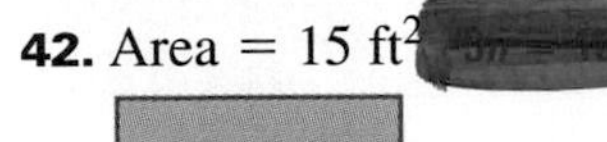

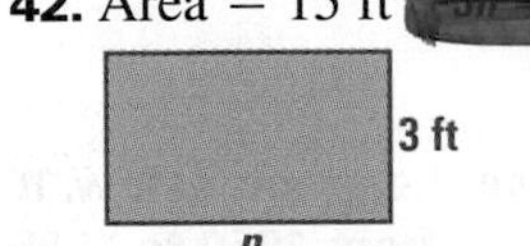

43. Area = 27 cm^2

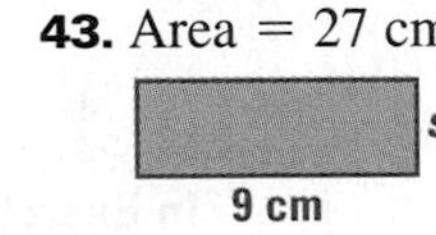

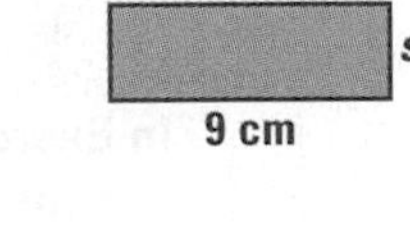

44. Area = 20 m^2

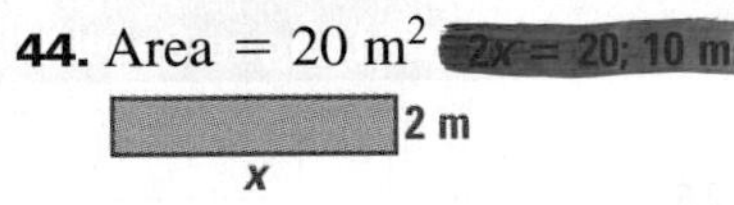

45. Area = 48 km^2

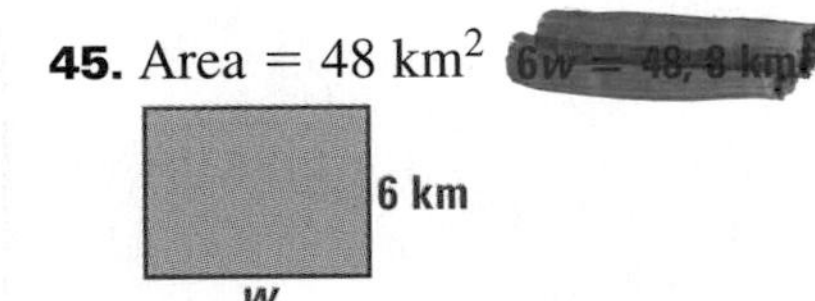

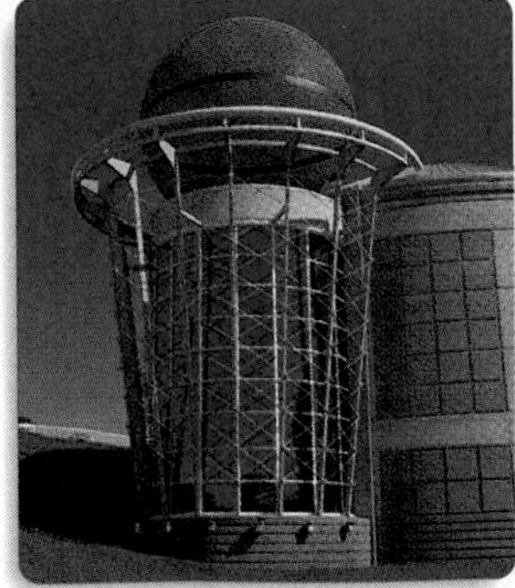

BASKETBALL The 20,000 pound basketball that sits outside the Women's Basketball Hall of Fame in Knoxville, Tennessee, is a scale model of a real basketball.

BASKETBALL **In Exercises 46 and 47, use the diagram of the basketball court at the right. The area of the court is 4700 square feet.**

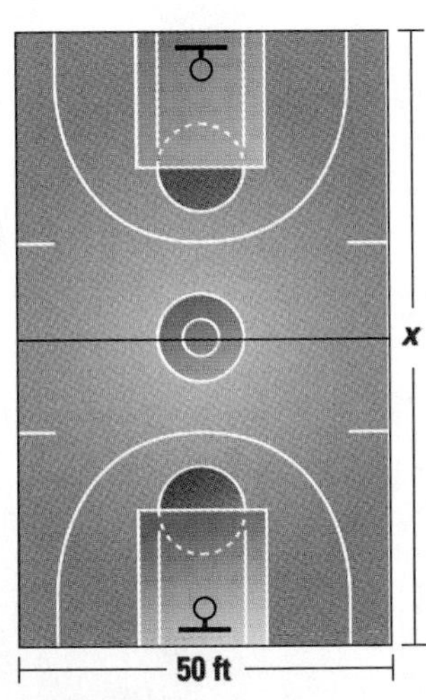

46. Write an equation that relates the area of the court to its length and width.

47. Solve the equation to find the length of the court.

48. You play on a basketball team. You scored 378 points for the season and played in 24 games. Your average points per game multiplied by the number of games played is your total points for the season. Write an equation that represents this sentence and solve the equation to find your average points per game.

49. CHALLENGE The formula for the area A of a triangle is $A = \frac{1}{2}bh$, where b is the length of the base and h is the height. Solve this equation for b.

Math Reasoning

Exercise 49 starts with the formula for the area of a triangle, in terms of its height and the length of its base and obtains from this a formula for the height of a triangle, in terms of its area and the length of its base.

Assess

Assessment Resources

- Assessment Book (Formal Assessment and Alternative Assessment)
- Test and Practice Generator

Mini-Quiz

1. Solve the equation. Check your solution.
   a. $7x = 315$ 45; $7 \cdot 45 = 315$
   b. $\frac{d}{3} = 18$ 54; $\frac{54}{3} = 18$
   c. $8.84 = 5.2p$ 1.7; $5.2 \cdot 1.7 = 8.84$
   d. $\frac{y}{234} = 3$ 702; $\frac{702}{234} = 3$
2. Translate the sentence into an equation. Then solve the equation.
   a. The number of computer disks, *d*, divided by 4 equals 3 computer disks. $\frac{d}{4} = 3$; 12
   b. The product of the number of balls, *b*, and 5 is 250 balls. $5b = 250$; 50
3. Find the length of a rectangle with area 21 cm^2 and width 7 cm. 3 cm

Multiple-Choice Practice

50. You competed in a 3.9 kilometer race. You finished the race in 0.4 hours. Which equation can you solve to find your speed *r*?

Ⓐ $0.4 = \frac{r}{3.9}$ Ⓑ $0.4r = 3.9$

Ⓒ $3.9r = 0.4$ Ⓓ $3.9 = \frac{r}{0.4}$

51. You go in-line skating 5 days per week. Each day you travel the same route. You skate a total of 20.5 miles in 5 days. Which equation can you solve to find the number of miles *x* per day that you skate?

Ⓕ $\frac{x}{5} = 20.5$ Ⓖ $5x = 20.5$

Ⓗ $20.5x = 5$ Ⓙ $\frac{x}{20.5} = 5$

Mixed Review

In Exercises 52–54, use the graph below. It shows the number of Little League baseball players from 1950 to 1995. *(1.1)*

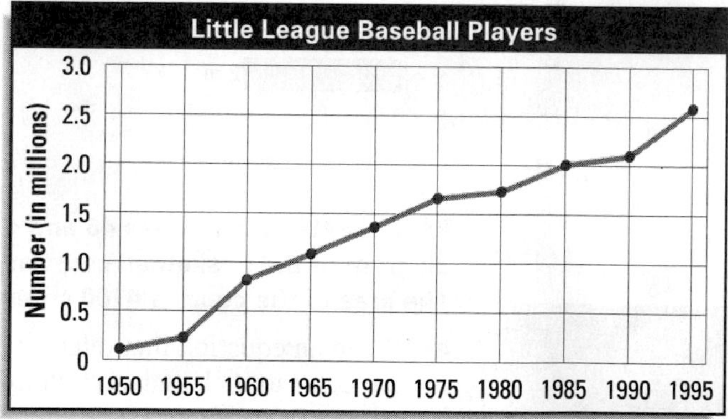

▶ Source: Little League Baseball

52. Estimate the number of players in 1980, 1985, and 1995. 1.75 million; 2 million; 2.6 million

53. Is the number of players increasing or decreasing? How do you know? increasing; graph is rising

54. In which five year interval did the number of players increase the most? 1955–1960

Simplify the expression. Then evaluate it when $r = 4$ and $s = 5$. *(2.2)*

55. $16r + 2 - 12r$ $4r + 2$; 18 **56.** $2r^2 + r + r^2$ $3r^2 + r$; 52 **57.** $3(r + s) - 2r$ $r + 3s$; 19

Write an equation that represents the verbal sentence. *(2.4)*

58. The difference of *x* and 7 is 28. $x - 7 = 28$

59. The sum of 3.1 and *z* is 15.2. $3.1 + z = 15.2$

60. The difference of *a* and 5.01 is 22.7. $a - 5.01 = 22.7$

2.7 A Problem Solving Plan

California Standards

In this lesson you'll:

- ▶ Use variables and appropriate operations to write an equation that represents a verbal description. (AF 1.1)
- ▶ Use measures expressed as rates and measures expressed as products to solve problems and check the units of the solutions. (MG 1.3)
- ▶ Use strategies, skills, and concepts in finding solutions. (MR 2.0)

Goal 1 USING A PROBLEM SOLVING PLAN

In most problem solving situations, you will need to plan how you will solve the problem. Below is a list of steps you can follow.

A GENERAL PROBLEM SOLVING PLAN

1. Decide what you need to know to answer the question. **Write a verbal model** that gives you what you need to know.
2. **Assign values to the labels** in your verbal model. If you don't know the value, use a variable such as *x*.
3. Use the labels to **write an algebraic model** based on your verbal model.
4. **Solve** the algebraic model.
5. **Answer** the original question.
6. **Check** that your answer is reasonable.

EXAMPLE 1 Using a Problem Solving Plan

PHONE RATES The long distance rate at your telephone company is \$.15 per minute all day, every day. This month you paid \$10.95 for long distance calls. How many minutes did you spend on long distance calls?

Solution

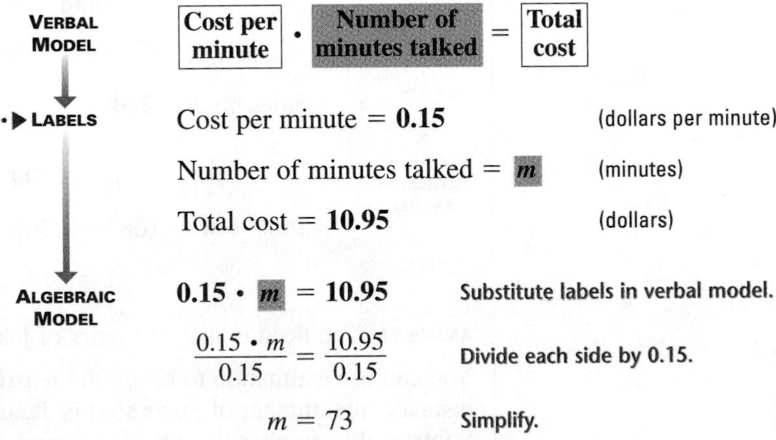

VERBAL MODEL Cost per minute • Number of minutes talked = Total cost

LABELS
Cost per minute = **0.15** (dollars per minute)
Number of minutes talked = m (minutes)
Total cost = **10.95** (dollars)

ALGEBRAIC MODEL

$0.15 \cdot m = 10.95$ Substitute labels in verbal model.

$\frac{0.15 \cdot m}{0.15} = \frac{10.95}{0.15}$ Divide each side by 0.15.

$m = 73$ Simplify.

ANSWER ▶ You spent 73 minutes on long distance calls.

Student Help

▶ **STUDY TIP**
The assigning of labels is the link between the verbal model and the algebraic model. At least one of the labels must be a variable. The other labels are values stated in the problem.

1 Plan

Pacing

Suggested Number of Days

Transitional: 1 day
Average: 1 day
Advanced: 1 day
Block Schedule: 0.5 block with 2.8

Teaching Resources

Blacklines
(See page 50B.)

Transparencies
- Warm-Up Exercises
- Teacher Time-Savers
- English/Spanish Problem Solving
- Answers

Technology
- Electronic Teacher Tools
- Test and Practice Generator

2 Teach

Math Reasoning

For Mathematical Background Notes on mathematical reasoning related to this lesson, please refer to pages 50E and 50F in this Teacher's Edition.

Extra Example 1
See next page.

California Standards and Assessment

CA Standards: AF 1.1, MG 1.3, MR 2.0

CA Key Concepts Book: p. S77

Extra Example 1

The cost of renting a car is \$.29 per mile driven. The total cost to you was \$36.25. How many miles did you drive? **125 miles**

Extra Example 2

You work in a bookstore. Your sales for the first four weeks of this year are \$322, \$297, \$256, and \$283. These sales amounts are 1.2 times higher than for the same four weeks last year. What were your total sales for the first four weeks of last year? **\$965**

Extra Example 3

Your aunt owns a small jewelry business. She makes each piece of jewelry, and has an order for 200 necklaces. She estimates that it will take her 50 hours to make all of the necklaces. How much time does it take her to make each necklace? **0.25 hour or 15 minutes**

Math Reasoning

Unit analysis can help students see if they have made an error in their approach to a problem, but this does not give them information about possible arithmetic errors.

Concept Check

Explain how to use a problem solving plan to solve a problem situation. ***Sample answer:*** **Write a verbal model. Assign values to the labels. Write an algebraic model. Solve the algebraic model and answer the original question. Then check that your answer is reasonable.**

Goal 2 CHECKING THE REASONABLENESS OF SOLUTIONS

You can use estimation to determine whether an answer is reasonable.

Student Help

▶ **MORE EXAMPLES**

INTERNET More examples are available at www.mcdougallittell.com

EXAMPLE 2 *Checking the Reasonableness of a Solution*

SALES You work in a clothing store and are responsible for the jeans department. To meet the projected sales goal, you need to sell 2200 pairs of jeans during the six month period ending June 30th. The number of jeans sold in the first five months of this period are shown in the graph. How many pairs of jeans must be sold in June to meet the goal?

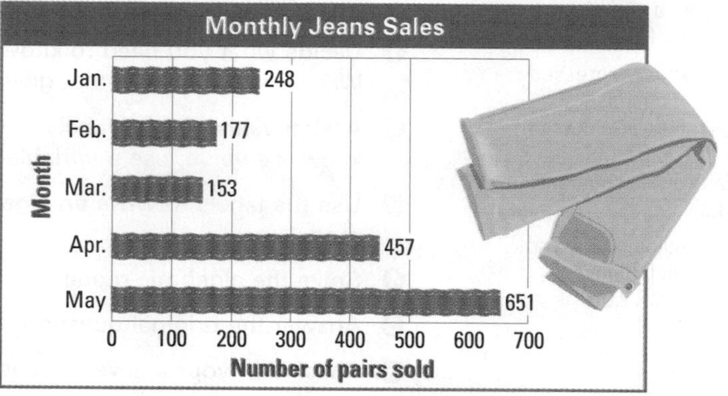

Solution

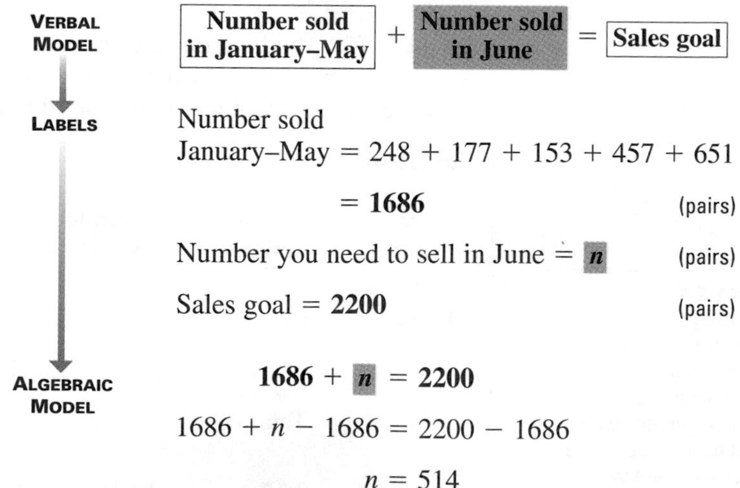

VERBAL MODEL: Number sold in January–May + Number sold in June = Sales goal

LABELS: Number sold January–May $= 248 + 177 + 153 + 457 + 651$

$= \mathbf{1686}$ (pairs)

Number you need to sell in June $= n$ (pairs)

Sales goal $= \mathbf{2200}$ (pairs)

ALGEBRAIC MODEL:

$$\mathbf{1686} + n = \mathbf{2200}$$

$$1686 + n - 1686 = 2200 - 1686$$

$$n = 514$$

ANSWER ▶ You need to sell 514 pairs of jeans in June.

You can use estimation to check the reasonableness of your answer. For instance, the number of jeans sold in January–May was about 1700. Subtract this number from the sales goal of 2200: $2200 - 1700 = 500$.

Your answer is reasonable because 500 and 514 are close.

When you use the operations of addition, subtraction, multiplication, and division in real life, use *unit analysis* to check that your units make sense.

EXAMPLE 3 *Using Unit Analysis*

BUSINESS A person-day is a unit of measure representing one person working for one day. A supervisor estimates that it will take 300 person-days to complete a large order. If 20 workers are available, how many days will it take to complete the order?

Solution

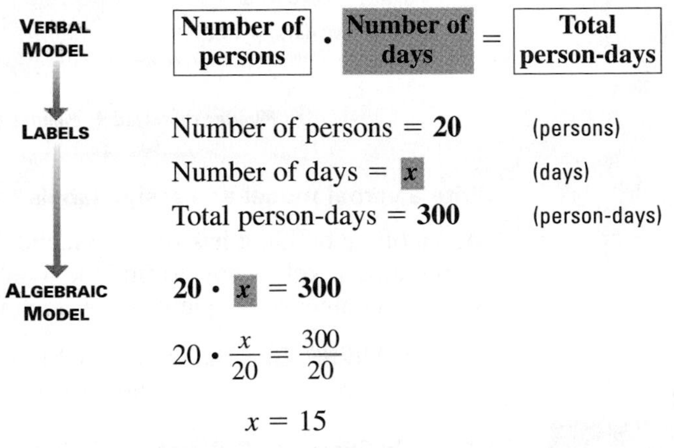

VERBAL MODEL Number of persons • Number of days = Total person-days

LABELS
Number of persons = **20** (persons)
Number of days = x (days)
Total person-days = **300** (person-days)

ALGEBRAIC MODEL

$$20 \cdot x = 300$$

$$20 \cdot \frac{x}{20} = \frac{300}{20}$$

$$x = 15$$

ANSWER ▶ It will take 20 people 15 days to complete the order. Use unit analysis to check your units.

CHECK ✓ Place the values with their units in the verbal model.

20 persons • 15 days $\stackrel{?}{=}$ 300 person-days

300 person-days = 300 person-days ✓

Student Help

▶**STUDY TIP**
Units expressed as products are separated by a hyphen.

2.7 Exercises

Guided Practice

1. Order the steps for a general problem solving plan. D, A, F, B, C, E

A. Assign values to the labels. **B.** Solve the algebraic model.

C. Answer the original question. **D.** Write a verbal model.

E. Check your solution. **F.** Write an algebraic model.

2. WRITING Describe two methods used to check the reasonableness of a solution. Estimation and unit analysis

3 Apply

Assignment Guide

TRANSITIONAL
Day 1: SRH p. 671 Exs. 1–3; pp. 88–89 Exs. 3–8, 15–16, 19–21

AVERAGE
Day 1: pp. 88–89 Exs. 3–8, 12–16, 19–21

ADVANCED
Day 1: pp. 88–89 Exs. 3–5, 9–16, 17–18*, 19–21

BLOCK SCHEDULE
pp. 88–89 Exs. 3–8, 12–16, 19–21 (with 2.8)

Extra Practice

- Student Edition, pp. 692–693
- Chapter 2 Resource Book, p. 60

Homework Check

To quickly check student understanding of key concepts, go over the following exercises:

Transitional: 4, 6, 7, 8, 15, 16
Average: 4, 12, 13, 14, 15, 16
Advanced: 4, 12, 13, 14, 15, 16

Math Reasoning

The speed mentioned in Exercise 5 is the average speed, calculated for the duration of the race.

Problem Solving

Exercise 15

Some students may not have a sense of how large or small the number should be. Ask them questions such as, "On your longest car trip, how long did it take and where did you go?" A map to show the relative distances might be helpful.

5. Rate × Time = Distance; Rate = 9, Time = t, Distance = 26.2

6. Rate per hour × Hours worked = Money earned; Rate = 8.25, Hours worked = x, Money earned = 165

Practice and Problem Solving

Student Help

▶MORE PRACTICE
Extra practice to help you master skills is on page 693.

3. Min exercised + Min needed = Goal for five days; Min exercised = 35 + 60 + 20 + 55 = 170, Min needed = m, Goal for five days = 225; 170 + m = 225; m = 55 min; You need to exercise 55 min on the fifth day; 170 + 55 = 225

4. Number of people who work in building ÷ number of floors = People per floor; Number of people who work = 294; Number of floors = 6; Number of people who work on each floor = x

Sports

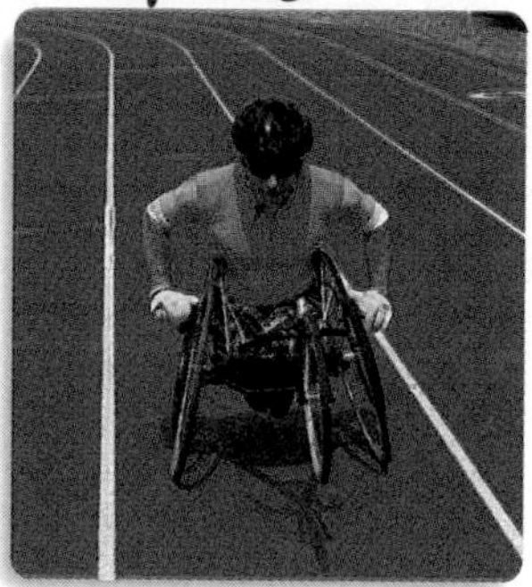

MARATHONS In 1975, Bob Hall became the first wheelchair athlete to win the Boston Marathon. Today, Hall owns a company that makes racing wheelchairs.

9. Distance for two days + Distance on third day = Total distance; Distance for two days = 8.1 + 5.8 = 13.9, Distance on third day = x, Total distance = 18.5

3. EXERCISING You plan to exercise 225 minutes over five days. The first four days you exercise 35 minutes, 60 minutes, 20 minutes, and 55 minutes. Arrange the steps below to find the number of minutes you need to exercise on the fifth day to reach your goal. **See margin.**

170 + m = 225	170 + 55 = 225	m = 55 minutes

Minutes exercised = 35 + 60 + 20 + 55 = 170 Minutes needed = m Goal for five days = 225	You need to exercise 55 minutes on the fifth day.

Minutes exercised + Minutes needed = Goal for five days

Write a verbal model and assign labels to each part.

4. An office building has six floors, and 294 people work in the building. Explain how to find the number of people per floor if the same number of people work on each floor. **See margin.**

5. MARATHONS Bob Hall raced 26.2 miles at a speed of 9 miles per hour. Explain how to find how long it took Hall to finish the race. **See margin.**

WAGES In Exercises 6–8, use the following information. You work after school at a store and are paid $8.25 per hour. Before taxes were taken out, you earned $165 for two weeks of work.

6. Write a verbal model to find the number of hours you worked. Assign labels to each part of the verbal model. **See margin.**

7. Write and solve an algebraic model using the verbal model and labels from Exercise 6. **8.25x = 165; 20 h**

8. Check your solution from Exercise 7 for reasonableness. **160 ÷ 8 = 20; It is reasonable to work 10 hours per week at an after-school job.**

HIKING In Exercises 9–11, use the following information. You are taking a three day hiking trip. The trail is 18.5 miles long. On the first day you hike 8.1 miles and on the second day you hike 5.8 miles.

9. Write a verbal model that relates trail length and number of miles traveled to find number of miles left to travel. Assign labels to each part of the verbal model.

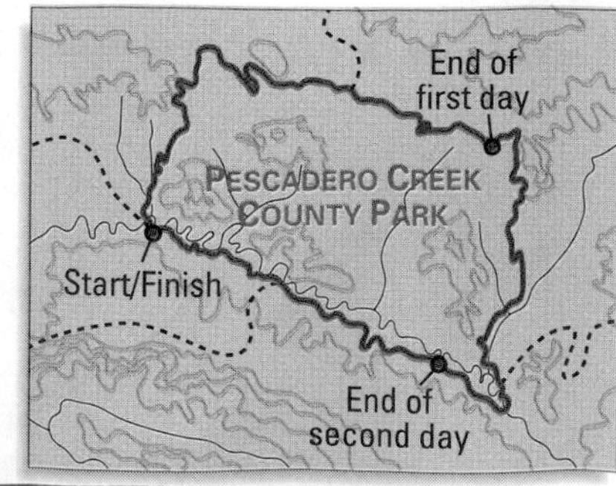

10. Write and solve an algebraic model using the verbal model and labels from Exercise 9. **13.9 + x = 18.5; 4.6 mi**

11. Check your solution from Exercise 10 for reasonableness. **8 + 6 + 5 = 19 and 19 ≈ 18.5**

LANDSCAPING **In Exercises 12–14, use the following information.**
A landscaper estimates that it will take 22 person-hours to build a small stone wall. There are four people working on the wall.

12. Number of persons working · number of hours worked = number of person-hours; number of persons working = 4, number of hours worked = x, number of person-hours = 22

15. This is not reasonable since Washington, DC and Portland, Oregon are more than 3,000 miles apart.

16. This is not reasonable since a desktop of 100 ft^2 would have dimensions of 10 ft by 10 ft, or 20 ft by 5 ft, etc. The desk would be as big as a small room!

12. Write a verbal model to find the number of hours the job will take. Assign labels to each part of the verbal model.

13. Write and solve an algebraic model using the verbal model and labels from Exercise 12. $4x = 22$; 5.5 h

14. Use unit analysis to check the reasonableness of your solution from Exercise 13. 4 persons · 5.5 hours = 22 person-hours

MATHEMATICAL REASONING **Decide whether the answer seems reasonable. Explain.**

15. You are planning a vacation. You estimate that it will take eight hours to drive a car from Washington, D.C., to Portland, Oregon. **See margin.**

16. Your company makes desks for classrooms. You calculate the area of a desktop to be 100 square feet. **See margin.**

CHALLENGE **In Exercises 17 and 18, use the following information.**
Your local electric company charges $.80 per kilowatt-hour. The power consumption of your stereo system is 0.35 kilowatts.

17. Use the verbal model to determine the number of hours you can play your stereo during a month so that the cost of using your stereo is just $6. 21.4 h

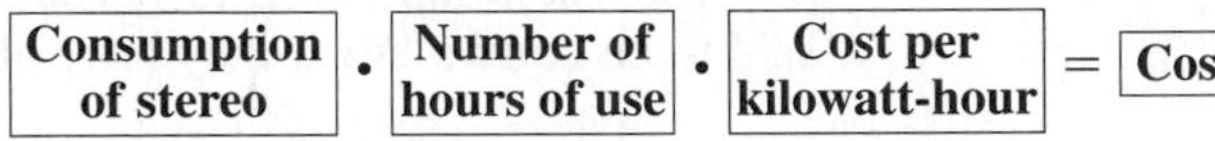

18. Apply unit analysis to the equation in Exercise 17.
0.35 kilowatts × 21.4 h × 0.80 dollars/kilowatt-hour = $6

Multiple-Choice Practice

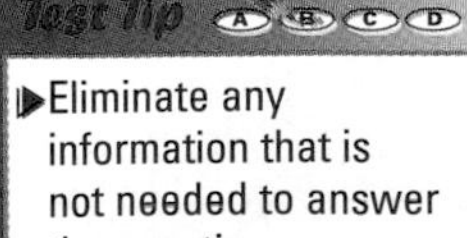

Test Tip Ⓐ Ⓑ Ⓒ Ⓓ

▶Eliminate any information that is not needed to answer the question.

19. Your sister gets the oil in her car changed approximately every 3000 miles. The mileage of the car when she bought it was 52,337. The mileage of her car at the last oil change was 68,452. Which equation models the mileage y at the car's next oil change? D

Ⓐ $68{,}452 - y = 3000$ Ⓑ $52{,}337 - y = 3000$

Ⓒ $52{,}337 + 3000 = y$ Ⓓ $y - 68{,}452 = 3000$

20. You bought a five pound bag of apples for $2.45. There are 12 apples in the bag. What is the *approximate* cost of one apple? G

Ⓕ $.02 Ⓖ $.20 Ⓗ $.45 Ⓙ $2.45

21. It will take about 40 person-hours to build the set for your school play. How many hours will it take for five people to build the set? B

Ⓐ 5 Ⓑ 8 Ⓒ 40 Ⓓ 200

Assess

Assessment Resources

- Assessment Book (Formal Assessment and Alternative Assessment)
- Test and Practice Generator

Mini-Quiz

1. Write an algebraic equation that represents the verbal sentence. Then solve the equation.
   a. The number of batches of muffins you made if one batch makes 9 muffins and you made a total of 72 muffins. **$9x = 72$; 8 batches**
   b. The cost of y pairs of shoes at $22 each is $308. **$22y = 308$; 14 pairs**
   c. The time it takes you to walk 3.3 miles if your average speed is 3 mi/h. **$3t = 3.3$; 1.1 h**
2. Suppose a bill is $47.40 for 6 hours work. Write and solve an equation to find the cost per hour. **$6x = 47.4$; $7.90 per hour**
3. You plan to exercise five days a week and average 50 min per day. So far this week you have exercised 35 min, 65 min, 20 min, and 55 min. How many minutes do you need to exercise on the fifth day in order to reach your goal? **75 minutes**

1 Plan

Pacing

Suggested Number of Days

Transitional: 1 day
Average: 1 day
Advanced: 1 day
Block Schedule: 0.5 block with 2.7

Teaching Resources

Blacklines
(See page 50B.)

Transparencies
- Warm-Up Exercises
- Teacher Time-Savers
- English/Spanish Problem Solving
- Answers

Technology
- Electronic Teacher Tools
- Test and Practice Generator

2 Teach

Math Reasoning

For Mathematical Background Notes on mathematical reasoning related to this lesson, please refer to pages 50E and 50F in this Teacher's Edition.

California Standards and Assessment

CA Standard: AF 4.0

2.8 Solving Inequalities

California Standards

In this lesson you'll:
- Solve simple inequalities over the rational numbers. (AF 4.0)

Goal 1 SOLVING SIMPLE INEQUALITIES

Some modeling situations require inequalities rather than equations. An **inequality** is formed when two expressions are separated by one of the *inequality symbols* >, <, ≤, or ≥.

EXAMPLE 1 Translating Inequalities

VERBAL SENTENCE	INEQUALITY
a. 4 is less than 5.	$4 < 5$
b. n is less than or equal to 10.	$n \leq 10$
c. y plus 2 is greater than 3.	$y + 2 > 3$
d. 6 times x is greater than or equal to 18.	$6x \geq 18$

A **solution** of an inequality is a number that produces a true statement when it is substituted for the variable in the inequality. For example, $x = 7$ is a solution of $x \leq 19$ because $7 \leq 19$ is true. Two inequalities are said to be **equivalent** if they have all the same solutions.

Finding all solutions of an inequality is called **solving the inequality**. When solving an inequality, you can add or subtract the same number from each side, or you can multiply or divide each side by the same *positive* number to produce an equivalent inequality.

Student Help

STUDY TIP
The steps used to solve an inequality are very similar to those used to solve an equation.

EXAMPLE 2 Solving an Inequality

Solve the inequality.

a. $x + 4 \leq 6$ **b.** $3x \geq 12$

Solution

a.

$x + 4 \leq 6$	Write original inequality.
$x + 4 - \mathbf{4} \leq 6 - \mathbf{4}$	Subtract 4 from each side.
$x \leq 2$	Simplify. *x* is by itself.

b.

$3x \geq 12$	Write original inequality.
$\frac{3x}{\mathbf{3}} \geq \frac{12}{\mathbf{3}}$	Divide each side by 3.
$x \geq 4$	Simplify. *x* is by itself.

Goal 2 WRITING AN INEQUALITY

Problems that include the phrases "at least" or "no more than" can be translated as inequalities.

EXAMPLE 3 Write an Inequality

SPORTS In football, the team with the ball must bring the ball at least 10 yards closer to the opponent's end zone within four turns, called *downs*, or else the ball is given to the other team. Your team was given the ball on your 35 yard line. At the end of the third down, the ball is on your 40 yard line. How many more yards must your team gain to keep possession of the ball?

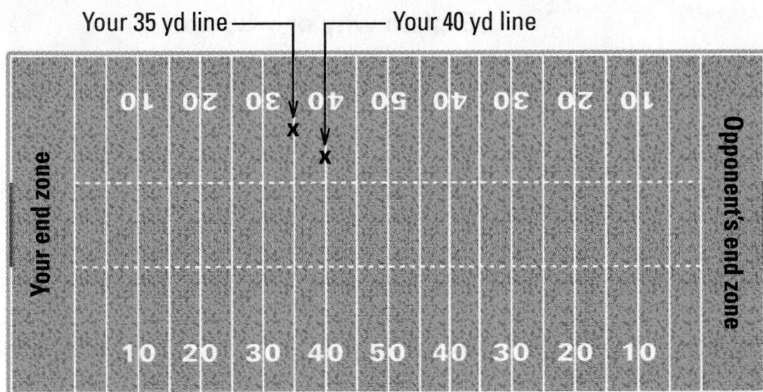

Solution

Going into its fourth down, your team has gained 5 yards. By the end of the fourth down, the team needs to have gained at least 10 yards.

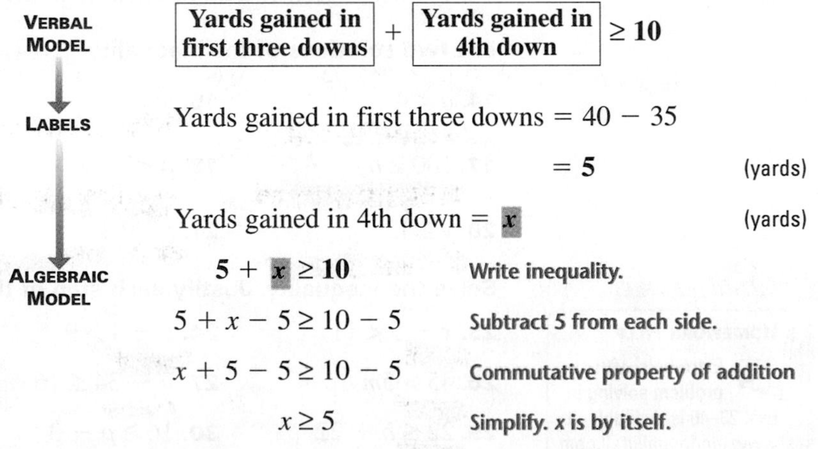

VERBAL MODEL $\boxed{\text{Yards gained in first three downs}} + \boxed{\text{Yards gained in 4th down}} \geq 10$

LABELS Yards gained in first three downs $= 40 - 35$

$= 5$ (yards)

Yards gained in 4th down $= x$ (yards)

ALGEBRAIC MODEL

$5 + x \geq 10$ Write inequality.

$5 + x - 5 \geq 10 - 5$ Subtract 5 from each side.

$x + 5 - 5 \geq 10 - 5$ Commutative property of addition

$x \geq 5$ Simplify. x is by itself.

ANSWER ▶ Your team must gain 5 yards or more in its fourth down.

CHECK ✓ Your team has already gained 5 yards. If they gain at least 5 more yards, they will have gained at least 10 yards. So, the answer is reasonable.

Extra Example 1

Translate the verbal sentence into an algebraic inequality.

a. 10 is less than 20. **$10 < 20$**

b. $x + 4$ is less than or equal to 6. **$x + 4 \leq 6$**

c. $n - 5$ is greater than or equal to 1. **$n - 5 \geq 1$**

d. $9x$ is greater than 27. **$9x > 27$**

Extra Example 2

Solve the inequality.

a. $x + 8 \geq 14$ **$x \geq 6$**

b. $4m \leq 48$ **$m \leq 12$**

Extra Example 3

Your football team begins its first down on its own 33 yard line. After three downs, the team has moved the football to its own 41 yard line. How many additional yards must your team gain on its fourth-down play in order to receive a new first down? **The team must gain at least 2 yards on its fourth-down play.**

Teaching Tip

Avoiding Common Errors
Emphasize that an inequality may have infinitely many solutions. Have students list several solutions to the inequality $x \leq 2$. Point out that not only are 2, 1, and 0 solutions, but values such as 1.77, $\frac{4}{5}$, and $\sqrt{2}$ are also.

Concept Check

How is solving an inequality like solving an equation? ***Sample answer:*** **You can add or subtract the same number from each side of the inequality without changing the solution. You can multiply or divide each side by the same positive number without changing the solution.**

3 Apply

Assignment Guide

TRANSITIONAL
Day 1: pp. 92–93 Exs. 11–16, 23–31, 38–40, 44–46, 49–50

AVERAGE
Day 1: pp. 92–93 Exs. 11–16, 23–31, 38–46, 49–50

ADVANCED
Day 1: pp. 92–93 Exs. 13–20, 29–41, 46–47, 48*, 49–50

BLOCK SCHEDULE
pp. 92–93 Exs. 11–16, 23–31, 38–46, 49–50 (with 2.7)

Extra Practice

- Student Edition, pp. 692–693
- Chapter 2 Resource Book, p. 60

Homework Check

To quickly check student understanding of key concepts, go over the following exercises:

Transitional: 24, 26, 38, 46, 47
Average: 24, 26, 38, 42, 46
Advanced: 30, 32, 34, 38, 46

2.8 Exercises

Guided Practice

1. Write the four inequality symbols and explain their meanings.
$<$ less than; $>$ greater than; $\leq$ less than or equal to; $\geq$ greater than or equal to

MATHEMATICAL REASONING Decide whether the statement is *true* or *false*. Give an example to support your answer.

2. An inequality can have many solutions.
True; If $x < 6$, then x could be equal to 3 or 3.5 or 5, etc.

3. The inequalities $2 < w$ and $w > 2$ are not equivalent.

3. False; These inequalities say the same thing, so they are equivalent. The first says "Two is less than w," and the second says "w is greater than 2."

Decide whether the number is a solution of the inequality $x - 5 < 11$. Explain why or why not.

4. 11 **Yes; $6 < 11$** **5.** 16 **No. $11 = 11$** **6.** 15 **Yes; $10 < 11$** **7.** 30 **No. $25 > 11$**

Describe how to solve the inequality.

8. $x + 4 \leq 7$
Subtract 4 from both sides of the inequality.

9. $3y \geq 10$
Divide both sides of the inequality by 3.

10. $9 < z - 5$
Add 5 to both sides of the inequality.

Practice and Problem Solving

> **Student Help**
> **▶ MORE PRACTICE**
> Extra practice to help you master skills is on page 693.

Write an inequality that represents the sentence. Then solve the inequality.

11. Two times x is less than 42. $2x < 42$; $x < 21$

12. The product of y and 3 is greater than 39. $3y > 39$; $y > 13$

13. Twenty is greater than or equal to m divided by 6. 

List two solutions of the inequality.

14. $q < 4$ 1, 3 among others

15. $m > 4$ 10, 8 among others

16. $45 > b$ 0, 9 among others

17. $100 \geq a$ 100, 80 among others

18. $p < \frac{3}{2}$ $\frac{1}{2}$, 1 among others

19. $z \geq 0$ 3, 1.7, $\frac{1}{2}$ among others

20. $y \geq 12.3$ 12.4, 18 among others

21. $t \leq 0.4$ 0.1, 0 among others

22. $7.7 < n$ 8, 8.2 among others

> **Student Help**
> **▶ HOMEWORK HELP**
> Extra help with problem solving in Exs. 23–40 is available at www.mcdougallittell.com

Solve the inequality. Justify each step of the solution.

23. $x + 5 < 11$ $x < 6$

24. $s - 4 > 9$ $s > 13$

25. $7y \leq 42$ $y \leq 6$

26. $45 > 5m$ $9 > m$

27. $n - 34 \leq 16$ $n \leq 50$

28. $17z \geq 68$ $z \geq 4$

29. $22 \leq b + 22$ $0 \leq b$

30. $16 \geq p - 3$ $19 \geq p$

31. $56 < 14r$ $4 < r$

32. $h + 3.4 > 5.8$ $h > 2.4$

33. $j - 13.7 < 5.4$ $j < 19.1$

34. $8.9k \geq 17.8$ $k \geq 2$

35. $p - 9.9 > 2$ $p > 11.9$

36. $17 > c - 31$ $48 > c$

37. $23 < t + 9$ $14 < t$

38. $\frac{q}{8} \geq 11$ $q \geq 88$

39. $\frac{w}{2} \leq 52$ $w \leq 104$

40. $\frac{a}{2.5} \leq 4.2$ $a \leq 10.5$

Sports

BICYCLE RACING
Some bicycle races are held on oval tracks called velodromes. The track lengths range from 559 feet to 1640 feet.

42. Cyclist A:
6 h 30 min + x < 10 h 40 min
Cyclist B:
6 h 36 min + y < 10 h 40 min
Cyclist C:
6 h 39 min + z < 10 h 40 min

43. Cyclist A: x < 4 h 10 min
Cyclist B: y < 4 h 4 min
Cyclist C: z < 4 h 1 min

41. MATHEMATICAL REASONING Write a true numerical inequality, such as $8 > 3$. Add 5 to each side of your inequality. Is the inequality still true? What general rule does your answer suggest?
An inequality is still true if the same number is added to both sides.

BICYCLE RACING In Exercises 42 and 43, use the following information. A bicycle race covers 228 miles over two days. After the first day, the cyclists have covered 136 miles. The times of the top three finishers are recorded in the table below. The times for the first day will be added to the times for the second day to determine the winner.

Cyclist	Time
Cyclist A	6 h 30 min
Cyclist B	6 h 36 min
Cyclist C	6 h 39 min

42. The record time for this course is 10 hours 40 minutes. For each cyclist write an inequality to determine the time needed on the second day to break the record.
See margin.

43. Solve the inequalities from Exercise 42 using the times listed in the table.
See margin.

ERROR ANALYSIS In Exercises 44 and 45, a student wrote the following steps to solve the inequality. Find the error and correct it.

44.

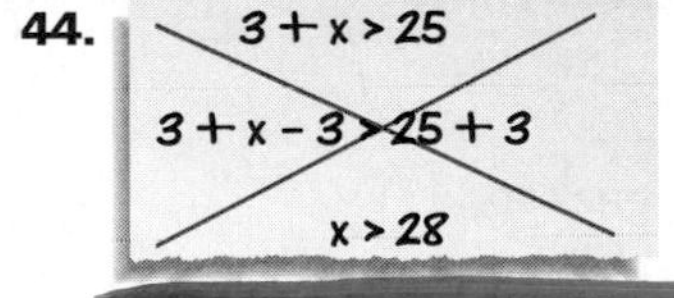

$3 + x > 25$; $3 + x - 3 > 25 - 3$; $x > 22$

45.

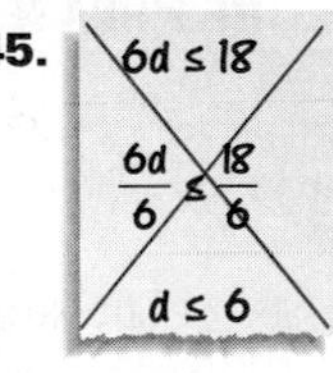

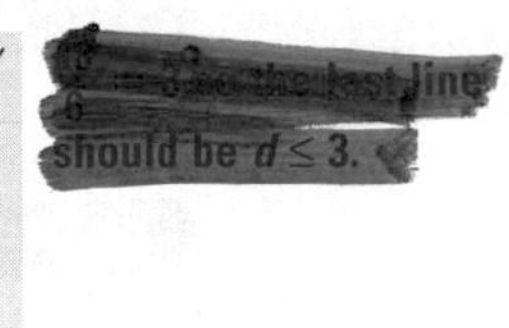

$\frac{6d}{6} \le \frac{18}{6}$ so the last line should be $d \le 3$.

46. FREELANCING You earn \$30 per hour as a freelance computer technician. Your maximum fee per job is \$4500. Write and solve an inequality to determine the number of hours after which you will be working for free. $30t > 4500$; $t > 150$ h

47. MEMBERSHIP To become a member at a local museum, you must donate at least \$50. You have \$37. Write and solve an inequality to determine the additional money you need to become a member.
$37 + x \ge 50$; $x \ge 13$; at least \$13 more

48. CHALLENGE To earn an A in your music class, you must have at least 540 total points. You scored 85, 92, 90, 96, and 86 on the first five exams. Write and solve an inequality to determine how many points you need to score on your last exam to earn an A.
$85 + 92 + 90 + 96 + 86 + x \ge 540$; $x \ge 91$; at least 91 points

Multiple-Choice Practice

49. Which symbol makes the following statement true when $x = 3$?

$6x + 7x \ ? \ 10x + 3x + 1$

Ⓐ = Ⓑ < Ⓒ > Ⓓ ≤

50. If $x = 5$ and $y = 5.01$, which of the following is true?

Ⓕ $x < y$ Ⓖ $x = y$ Ⓗ $y \le x$ Ⓙ $x > y$

4 Assess

Assessment Resources

- Assessment Book (Formal Assessment and Alternative Assessment)
- Test and Practice Generator

Mini-Quiz

1. Solve the inequality.
   a. $23 \ge x + 15$ $8 \ge x$ or $x \le 8$
   b. $c - 5.1 > 12.3$ $c > 17.4$
   c. $17t < 357$ $t < 21$
2. Write an inequality that represents the sentence. Then solve the inequality.
   a. Thirty-two is greater than or equal to y divided by 2.
   $32 \ge \frac{y}{2}$; $64 \ge y$ or $y \le 64$
   b. The difference of d and 9 is less than 19.
   $d - 9 < 19$; $d < 28$
3. In order to become a member at a local museum, you must give a donation of at least \$75 each year. You have \$37. Write and solve an inequality to determine the additional money needed to become a member of the museum. $37 + x \ge 75$; $x \ge 38$; **You need at least \$38 more.**

Additional Resources

The following resources are available to help review the material in this chapter:

Technology

- Personal Student Tutor
- Test and Practice Generator

Chapter 2 Chapter Summary and Review

VOCABULARY

- **additive identity,** *p. 57*
- **multiplicative identity,** *p. 57*
- **like terms,** *p. 57*
- **coefficient,** *p. 57*
- **constant term,** *p. 57*
- **combining like terms,** *p. 57*
- **equation,** *p. 61*
- **conditional equations,** *p. 61*
- **solving an equation,** *p. 61*
- **solution (of an equation),** *p. 61*
- **identity,** *p. 61*
- **inverse operation,** *p. 74*
- **equivalent equations,** *p. 74*
- **inequality,** *p. 90*
- **solution (of an inequality),** *p. 90*
- **equivalent inequalities,** *p. 90*
- **solving an inequality,** *p. 90*

2.1 TRANSLATING PHRASES INTO EXPRESSIONS

Examples on pp. 53–54

EXAMPLES

VERBAL PHRASE	VARIABLE EXPRESSION
The sum of twice a number and 8	$2y + 8$
The quotient of 25 and 5 times a number	$\frac{25}{5p}$

Write the verbal phrase as a variable expression. Tell what the variables represent.

1. \$30 less than your salary **$s - 30$; *s* is your salary**
2. Ten points less than three times the original score **$3s - 10$; *s* is the original score**
3. A down payment of \$60 plus monthly payments of \$27.50 each **$60 + 27.5p$; *p* is the number of monthly payments**

2.2 COMBINING LIKE TERMS

Examples on pp. 57–58

EXAMPLE **Simplify $z + 5y + 3 + y$.**

Notice that $5y$ and y are like terms.

$z + 5y + 3 + y = z + 5y + y + 3$ Commutative property of equality

$= z + 5y + 1y + 3$ Identity property of multiplication

$= z + (5 + 1)y + 3$ Distributive property

$= z + 6y + 3$ Simplify.

Simplify the expression by combining like terms.

4. $8w + 9w$ **$17w$**

5. $3x + 4 + x$ **$4x + 4$**

6. $14 + 7v + v + 2$ **$8v + 16$**

7. $16 + 5b + 3b + 9$ **$8b + 25$**

8. $5a + 6t + 9 + 2a$ **$7a + 6t + 9$**

9. $2x + 3t + x + 2t + y$ **$3x + 5t + y$**

Write an expression for the perimeter of the figure. Simplify the expression and evaluate when $x = 2$.

10. $3 + x$, $3 + x$, $2x$, $2x$, 4

$2(3 + x) + 2(2x) + 4$; $6x + 10$; 22

11.

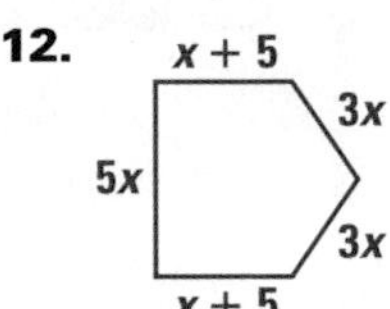

$2(3x + 1) + 6x + 6$; $12x + 8$; 32

12. $x + 5$, $3x$, $5x$, $3x$, $x + 5$

$5x + 2(x + 5) + 2(3x)$; $13x + 10$; 36

2.3 Solving Equations with Mental Math

Examples on pp. 61–62

To solve an equation using mental math, it helps to think of the equation as a question.

EXAMPLE **Solve $\frac{36}{n} = 4$.**

EQUATION	STATED AS A QUESTION	SOLUTION
$\frac{36}{n} = 4$	What number can you divide 36 by to get 4?	$n = 9$

Write the equation as a question. Then solve the equation using mental math. Check your solution in the original equation. **13–20. See margin.**

13. $9 + y = 10$

14. $b - 11 = 11$

15. $q - 6 = 12$

16. $10 + t = 20$

17. $\frac{15}{w} = 5$

18. $\frac{m}{3} = 9$

19. $9r = 36$

20. $2x = 24$

2.4 Translating Sentences into Equations

Examples on pp. 66–67

EXAMPLES

VERBAL SENTENCE	EQUATION
The quotient of twice a number and 5 is 22.	$\frac{2n}{5} = 22$
\$20 more than three times the price is \$95.	$3p + 20 = 95$

Write an equation that represents the verbal sentence.

21. The number of days divided by 7 is 10 weeks. **$\frac{x}{7} = 10$**

22. Twice the number of points plus 100 is 1500. **$2p + 100 = 1500$**

13. What number can you add to 9 to get 10? 1

14. From what number can you subtract 11 to get 11? 22

15. From what number can you subtract 6 to get 12? 18

16. What number can you add to 10 to get 20? 10

17. By what number can you divide 15 to get 5? 3

18. What number can you divide by 3 to get 9? 27

19. What number can you multiply by 9 to get 36? 4

20. What number can you multiply by 2 to get 24? 12

2.5 SOLVING EQUATIONS USING ADDITION OR SUBTRACTION

Examples on pp. 74–75

EXAMPLES **a. Solve $x - 21 = 12$.** **b. Solve $136 = y + 113$.**

a. $x - 21 = 12$

$x - 21 + 21 = 12 + 21$

$x = 33$

b. $136 = y + 113$

$136 - 113 = y + 113 - 113$

$23 = y$

Solve the equation. Justify your steps and check your solution.

23. $x + 9 = 19$ **10**

24. $21 = y - 20$ **41**

25. $m - 54 = 72$ **126**

26. $n + 1.3 = 13.2$ **11.9**

Write an equation that represents the statement. Then solve the equation.

27. The sum of x and 17 is 45. **$x + 17 = 45$; 28**

28. The difference of y and 23 is 97. **$y - 23 = 97$; 120**

29. The difference of z and 32 is 61. **$z - 32 = 61$; 93**

30. The sum of x and 49 is 58. **$x + 49 = 58$; 9**

2.6 SOLVING EQUATIONS USING MULTIPLICATION OR DIVISION

Examples on pp. 80–81

EXAMPLES **a. Solve $6x = 42$.** **b. Solve $11.2 = \frac{y}{3}$.**

a. $6x = 42$

$\frac{6x}{6} = \frac{42}{6}$

$x = 7$

b. $11.2 = \frac{y}{3}$

$3 \cdot 11.2 = 3 \cdot \frac{y}{3}$

$33.6 = y$

Solve the equation. Justify your steps and check your solution.

31. $16 = \frac{y}{3}$ **48**

32. $\frac{r}{7} = 1400$ **9800**

33. $102 = 17y$ **6**

34. $16.5 = 1.5y$ **11**

Write an equation that relates the length and width of the rectangle to the area. Then solve the equation to find the missing side length.

35. Area = 30 in.^{2}

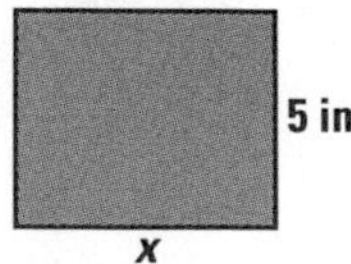

$5x = 30$; 6 in.

36. Area = 28 m^2

$7z = 28$; 4 m

37. Area = 54 ft^2

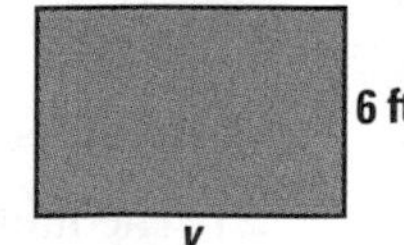

$6y = 54$; 9 ft

2.7 A Problem Solving Plan

Examples on pp. 85–87

EXAMPLE You travel 170 miles in the first 3 hours of a 540 mile trip, and 250 miles in the next 5 hours. Find the distance left to travel.

VERBAL MODEL [Miles traveled] + [Miles left to travel] = [Total miles for trip]

LABELS

Miles traveled = 170 + 250 = **420**

Miles left to travel = t

Total miles for trip = **540**

ALGEBRAIC MODEL

$420 + t = 540$ Substitute labels in verbal model.

$420 + t - 420 = 540 - 420$ Subtract 420 from each side.

$t = 120$ Simplify.

ANSWER ▶ You have 120 miles left to travel.

Write a verbal model, labels, and an algebraic model for each problem situation. Then solve the algebraic model and check your solution. **38–39. See margin.**

38. One twentieth, or 64, of the students in a school have a newspaper route. How many students are in the school?

39. Of your allowance you save $7.50 per week. You want to buy a camera that costs $67.50. How long will it take to buy the camera?

2.8 Solving Inequalities

Examples on pp. 90–91

EXAMPLES **a. Solve $5 + x < 13$.** **b. Solve $3m \geq 18$.**

a. $5 + x < 13$

$5 + x - \mathbf{5} < 13 - \mathbf{5}$

$x < 8$

Any number less than 8 is a solution.

b. $3m \geq 18$

$\frac{3m}{\mathbf{3}} \geq \frac{18}{\mathbf{3}}$

$m \geq 6$

Any number greater than or equal to 6 is a solution.

Solve the inequality.

40. $y - 13 < 3$ $y < 16$ **41.** $z + 13 \leq 16$ $z \leq 3$ **42.** $6k \geq 30$ $k \geq 5$ **43.** $5g < 15$ $g < 3$

44. $\frac{p}{4} < 12$ $p < 48$ **45.** $21 < \frac{w}{0.7}$ $14.7 < w$ **46.** $1.2 \geq 0.2t$ $6 \geq t$ **47.** $2.08 < v + 0.31$ $1.77 < v$

38.

[Fraction] • [Total students] = [Number of students in fraction]

Fraction = $\frac{1}{20}$,
Total students = x,
Number of students in fraction = 64;
$\frac{1}{20} \cdot x = 64$;
$x = 1280$; 1280 students

39.

[Amount of allowance saved per week] × [Number of weeks] = [Cost of camera]

Amount saved per week = 7.50 (dollars);
Number of weeks = n;
Cost of camera = 67.50 (dollars);
$7.50n = 67.50$; $n = 9$;
9 weeks

Additional Resources

Assessment Book

- Formal Assessment, pp. 19–24
- Alternative Assessment, pp. 193–207

Test and Practice Generator

1. $P = 2(x + 2) + 2(2)$
   $= 2x + 8$
   $= 15$
   $A = 2(x + 2)$
   $= 2x + 4$
   $= 11$

5. $P = 2(x) + 2x + 3x$
   $= 7x$

x	1	2	3	4
P	7	14	21	28

P increases by 7 as *x* increases by 1.

6. $P = 2(3x) + 6(x)$
   $= 12x$

x	1	2	3	4
P	12	24	36	48

P increases by 12 as *x* increases by 1.

19. See Additional Answers beginning on page AA1.

20. Cost to operate Store 1 = 3500
    Cost to operate Store 2 = x
    Cost to operate both stores = 8100
    $3500 + x = 8100$
    $3500 - 3500 + x = 8100 - 3500$
    $x = 4600$
    The cost to operate Store 2 is $4600 per week.

Chapter 2 Chapter Test

1. **GEOMETRY** Write an expression for the perimeter and an expression for the area of the rectangle. Then evaluate each expression when $x = 3.5$. **See margin.**

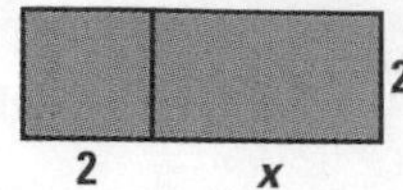

Simplify the expression by combining like terms.

2. $3 + 3a + 6 + 2a$
3. $12p + 4q + 2q + 3p$
4. $3x + 5y + 9x + 10z + 8$

Write and simplify an expression for the perimeter of the figure. Find the perimeter when x is 1, 2, 3, and 4. Organize your results in a table and describe the pattern. **5–6. See margin.**

5.

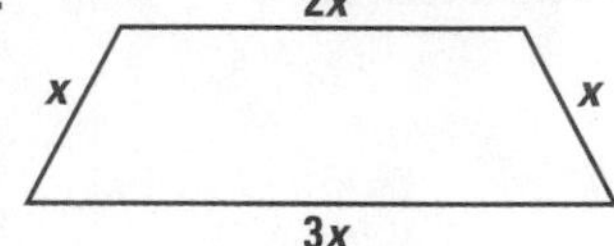

6.

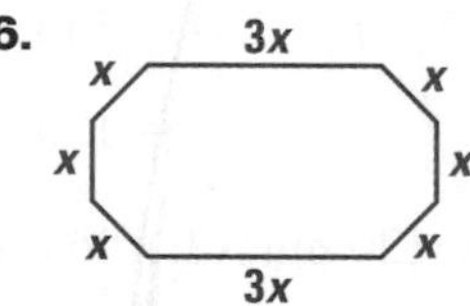

Write an equation that represents the verbal sentence. Then solve the equation using mental math.

7. A number decreased by 14 is 36.
8. The product of a number and 12 is 60.

In Exercises 9–10, you spend $15 on 10 equally priced bottles of juice.

9. Let n represent the cost of one bottle of juice. Write an equation for the total cost of the bottles of juice using n and the number of bottles you bought.
10. Solve the equation to find the cost of one bottle of juice.

Solve the equation. Then check your solution.

11. $3x = 15$
12. $y - 6 = 0$
13. $p + 2 = 9$
14. $16 + z = 31$
15. $\frac{1}{4} = 3q$
16. $9y = 54$
17. $\frac{x}{7} = 6$
18. $r - 19 = 28$

In Exercises 19 and 20, use the following information. You are the manager of two sporting goods stores. The weekly cost to operate Store 1 is $3500, and for both Store 1 and Store 2 is $8100. **19–20. See margin.**

19. Write a verbal model that represents the weekly costs of operating the two stores.
20. Assign labels, and write an equation to determine the weekly cost of operating Store 2. Then solve the equation.

Solve the inequality. Justify each step of the solution.

21. $x - 2 > 4$
22. $10 \geq 3 + y$
23. $20.4 \geq 3.4z$
24. $\frac{s}{14} > 5$

Multiple-Choice Practice

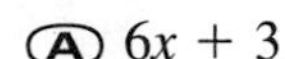

Test Tip Be careful to avoid careless errors on easy questions.

1. Find the perimeter of the figure.

Ⓐ $6x + 3$
Ⓑ $9x + 3$
Ⓒ $7 + 3x$
Ⓓ $7x + 3$

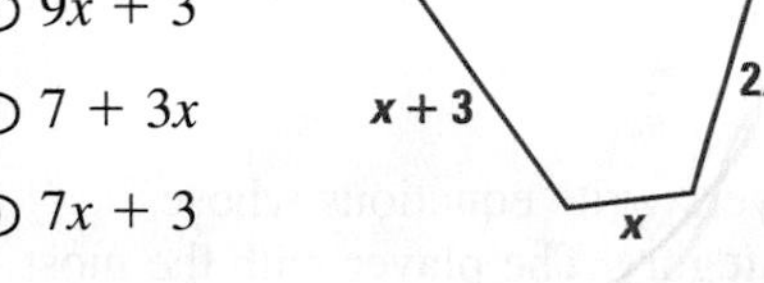

2. Decide which equation represents this verbal statement: *A number subtracted from 8 is 9.*

Ⓕ $8 - n = 9$　　Ⓖ $n - 9 = 8$
Ⓗ $n - 8 = 9$　　Ⓙ $9 - n = 8$

3. Which statement does *not* represent the equation $20 + x = 35$?

Ⓐ The cake needs 35 minutes to bake. It has been in the oven 20 minutes.
Ⓑ You are on the 20th floor. You climb the stairs to the 35th floor.
Ⓒ You have earned \$20. You earn more money for a total of \$35.
Ⓓ You buy a shirt for \$20 and a pair of jeans for \$35.

4. The area of the rectangle below is 63 square inches. Which equation can you use to find its width w?

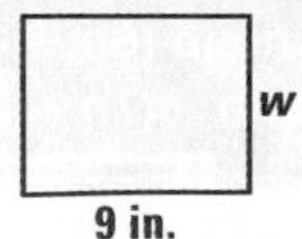

Ⓕ $9w = 63$　　Ⓖ $63w = 9$
Ⓗ $\frac{w}{63} = 9$　　Ⓙ $\frac{w}{9} = 63$

5. Solve $y - 4.2 = 5.7$.

Ⓐ 1.5　Ⓑ 1.9　Ⓒ 9.5　Ⓓ 9.9

6. Find the solution of the equation that represents this statement: *A number divided by 6 is 5.*

Ⓕ $\frac{1}{6}$　　Ⓖ $\frac{5}{6}$
Ⓗ 11　　Ⓙ 30

7. You save $\frac{1}{3}$ off the original price, or \$18.34, on a pair of shoes. What was the original price?

Ⓐ \$36.66　　Ⓑ \$41.25
Ⓒ \$55.00　　Ⓓ \$73.34

8. A walking path around a four-sided city park is 1.5 miles long. Three of the sides have lengths of 0.25 miles, 0.5 miles, and 0.4 miles. How long is the fourth side?

Ⓕ 0.25 miles　　Ⓖ 0.3 miles
Ⓗ 0.35 miles　　Ⓙ 0.45 miles

9. Which is *not* a solution of the inequality $m - 9 \leq 3$?

Ⓐ 9　　Ⓑ 10
Ⓒ 12　　Ⓓ 13

10. Solve $3.5p \leq 17.5$.

Ⓕ $p \leq 3.5$　　Ⓖ $p \leq 5$
Ⓗ $p \geq 5$　　Ⓙ $p \geq 17.5$

Teaching Tip

The Brain Games activity provides a motivating way to review selected content in the chapter. For a more comprehensive review, see the Chapter Summary and Review on pp. 94–97.

Brain games

California Standards

- Solve simple linear equations over the rational numbers. (AF 4.0)
- Analyze problems by identifying relationships. (MR 1.1)

Equation Challenge

Materials

- Spinner with four equal sections
- Timer or watch

Directions

Object of the Game

Play in groups of 3 or 4. Players write equations whose solution matches a chosen category. The player with the most points at the end of the round is the winner.

How to Play

STEP 1 Each group makes a spinner labeled as shown.

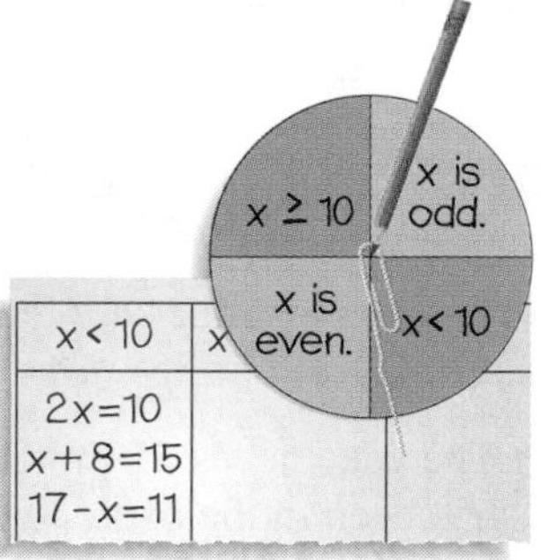

STEP 2 One player in each group spins. Players have one minute to write equations with solutions in the selected category. Each player should record his or her results in a table. Repeat until each player has had a chance to spin.

STEP 3 Players exchange tables with other team members. Players award one point for every correct equation. The player with the most points wins.

Another Way to Play

Instead of writing equations with solutions in the selected category, players write equations with solutions that *do not* fall in the selected category.

Brain Teaser

USE THE SIGNPOST TO ANSWER THE QUESTIONS.

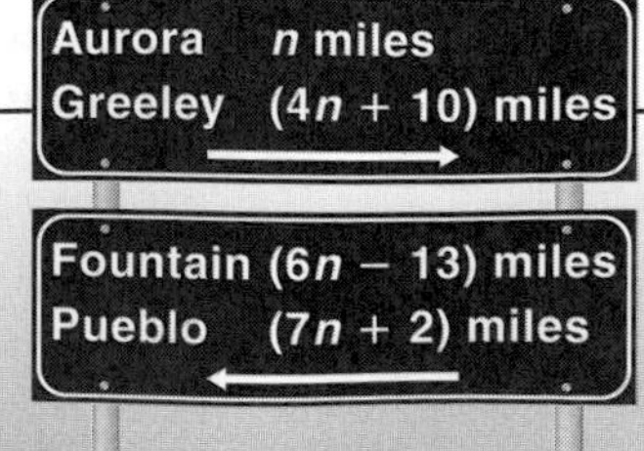

1. Which town is $7n - 13$ miles from Fountain? **Aurora**
2. Which town is $11n + 12$ miles from Pueblo? **Greeley**
3. How many miles is it from Greeley to Fountain? **$(10n - 3)$ mi**
4. If $n = 15$ miles, how many miles is it from Aurora to Pueblo? **122 mi**

California Standards and Assessment

CA Standards: AF 4.0, MR 1.1

The basic skills you'll review on this page will help prepare you for the next chapter.

Reviewing the Basics

EXAMPLE 1 Performing Number Operations

Practice the four number operations—addition, subtraction, multiplication, and division—to develop accuracy.

a. Subtract 2438 from 5025.

b. Multiply 912 by 43.

Solution

a.
```
  5025
- 2438
  2587
```

b.
```
   912
 × 43
  2736
+ 3648
 39216
```

Try These

1. Find the sum of 305 and 463. **768**

2. Find the product of 113 and 45. **5085**

3. Multiply 508 by 76. **38,608**

4. Find the quotient of 1106 and 7. **158**

5. Subtract 167 from 494. **327**

6. Subtract 295 from 1258. **963**

7. Divide 2025 by 25. **81**

8. Find the sum of 93, 37, and 21. **151**

EXAMPLE 2 Using a Number Line

Locate each point on the number line.

a. 8 **b.** 25 **c.** 16

Solution

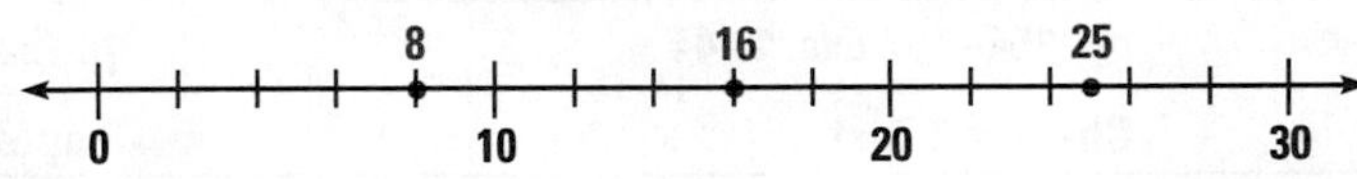

Try These

Copy the number line. Then locate the point on the number line.

9–20. See margin.

0 10 20 30

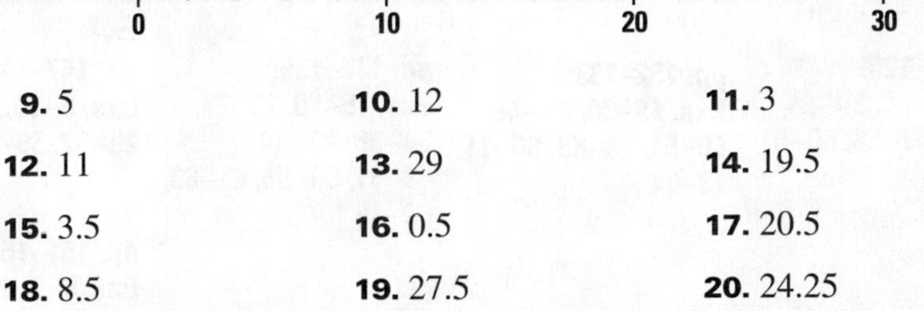

9. 5 **10.** 12 **11.** 3

12. 11 **13.** 29 **14.** 19.5

15. 3.5 **16.** 0.5 **17.** 20.5

18. 8.5 **19.** 27.5 **20.** 24.25

Student Help

▶ MORE EXAMPLES

INTERNET More examples and practice exercises available at www.mcdougallittell.com

Additional Resources

Technology

- Personal Student Tutor
- Test and Practice Generator

9.

10. 0 10 20 30

11. 0 5 10 15 20 25 30

12. 0 10 20 30

13. 0 5 10 15 20 25 30

14. 0 10 20 30

15. 0 5 10 15 20 25 30

16. 0 10 20 30

17. 0 5 10 15 20 25 30

18. 0 10 20 30

19. 0 5 10 15 20 25 30

20.

CHAPTER 3

Pacing and Assignment Guide

Regular Schedule

Lesson	Les. Day	Transitional	Average	Advanced
3.1	Day 1	SRH p. 674 Exs. 7–10; pp. 107–109 Exs. 15–17, 21–23, 32–36, 41–43, 47–48, 57–60, 71–75, 80–86	pp. 107–109 Exs. 18–20, 23–26, 30–36, 43–45, 49–56, 71–75, 83–86	pp. 107–109 Exs. 20, 24–26, 30–38, 43–46, 49–54, 67–69, 70*, 71–73, 85–90
3.2	Day 1	pp. 112–113 Exs. 10–18, 22–23, 26–27, 31–32	pp. 112–113 Exs. 13–28, 31–32	pp. 112–113 Exs. 18–28, 29–30*, 31–32
3.3	Day 1	pp. 119–120 Exs. 14–19, 26–29, 44–46, 53–58	pp. 119–120 Exs. 17–22, 28–31, 44–46, 53–58	pp. 119–120 Exs. 20–25, 30–33, 44–46, 53–56
	Day 2	EP p. 692 Exs. 21–26; pp. 119–120 Exs. 34–35, 38–39, 48, 50–52, 59–64	pp. 119–120 Exs. 34–37, 40–43, 47–48, 50–52, 59–64	pp. 119–120 Exs. 34–43, 47–48, 49*, 50–52, 60–64
3.4	Day 1	pp. 125–126 Exs. 14–19, 23–25, 54–56, 60–61	pp. 125–126 Exs. 14–28, 54–56, 60–61	pp. 125–126 Exs. 20–28, 54–56, 60–61
	Day 2	pp. 125–126 Exs. 29–32, 38–40, 44–46, 50, 57	pp. 125–126 Exs. 30–34, 37–40, 47–53, 57–58	pp. 125–126 Exs. 29–40, 47–53, 57–58, 59*
3.5	Day 1	EP p. 690 Exs. 14–17; pp. 132–133 Exs. 16–25, 38–45, 50–52	pp. 132–133 Exs. 19–30, 38–46, 50–52	pp. 132–133 Exs. 19–24, 31–43, 47–49, 53–55
	Day 2	pp. 132–133 Exs. 56–63, 66–70, 73–74	pp. 132–133 Exs. 56–63, 66–71, 73–74	pp. 132–133 Exs. 56–61, 64–71, 72*, 73–74
3.6	Day 1	pp. 137–139 Exs. 13–18, 27–35, 41–42, 49–51, 54–55, 61–63, 65–68	pp. 137–139 Exs. 15–20, 23–27, 34–36, 43–44, 49–51, 55–58, 61–63, 65–68	Day 1: pp. 137–139 Exs. 19–26, 36–38, 40–44, 52–54, 57–59, 60*, 61–66
3.7	Day 1	pp. 142–143 Exs. 12–15, 24–30, 33–35, 39–40, 48–49	pp. 142–143 Exs. 14–17, 21–28, 33–35, 41–43, 48–49	pp. 142–143 Exs. 15–18, 24–32, 36–42, 44–46, 47*, 48–49
3.8	Day 1	pp. 147–148 Exs. 5–10, 12–15, 26–30, 35–36, 41–42, 45–47	pp. 147–148 Exs. 5–10, 12–15, 26, 29–32, 38–42, 45–47	pp. 147–148 Exs. 8–10, 12–15, 25–26, 31–34, 38–43, 44*, 45–47
3.9	Day 1	pp. 151–153 Exs. 6–11, 14–17, 27–32, 35–37	pp. 151–153 Exs. 6–8, 10–12, 14–15, 19–22, 27–33, 35–38	pp. 151–153 Exs. 10–15, 19–25, 26*, 27–28, 38–40
Review	Day 1	pp. 154–157 Exs. 1–44	pp. 154–157 Exs. 1–44	pp. 154–157 Exs. 1–44
Assess	Day 1	Chapter 3 Test	Chapter 3 Test	Chapter 3 Test

Yearly Pacing Chapter 3 Total – **14 days** Chapters 1–3 Total – **38 days** Remaining – **122 days**

* Challenge Exercises EP = Extra Practice SRH = Skills Review Handbook EC = Extra Challenge

Block Schedule

Day 1	Day 2	Day 3	Day 4	Day 5	Day 6	Day 7
3.1 pp. 107–109: Exs. 18–20, 23–26, 30–36, 43–45, 49–56, 71–75, 83–86 **3.2** pp. 112–113: Exs. 13–28, 31–32	**3.3** pp. 119–120: Exs. 17–22, 28–31, 34–37, 40–48, 50–64	**3.4** pp. 125–126: Exs. 14–28, 30–34, 37–40, 47–58, 60–61	**3.5** pp. 132–133: Exs. 19–30, 38–46, 50–52, 56–63, 66–71, 73–74	**3.6** pp. 137–139: Exs. 15–20, 23–27, 34–36, 43–44, 49–51, 55–58, 61–63, 65–68 **3.7** pp. 142–143: Exs. 14–17, 21–28, 33–35, 41–43, 48–49	**3.8** pp. 147–148: Exs. 5–10, 12–15, 26, 29–32, 36–40, 43–45 **3.9** pp. 151–153: Exs. 6–8, 10–12, 14–15, 19–22, 27–33, 37–39	**Review** pp. 154–157: Exs. 1–44 **Assess** Chapter 3 Test

Yearly Pacing Chapter 3 Total – **7 days** Chapters 1–3 Total – **19 days** Remaining – **61 days**

Support Materials

Chapter Resource Book

LESSON SUPPORT	3.1	3.2	3.3	3.4	3.5	3.6	3.7	3.8	3.9
Lesson Plans	p. 1	p. 10	p. 19	p. 28	p. 37	p. 46	p. 55	p. 64	p. 73
Lesson Plans for Block Scheduling	p. 2	p. 11	p. 20	p. 29	p. 38	p. 47	p. 56	p. 65	p. 74
Warm-Ups with Multiple-Choice Practice	p. 3	p. 12	p. 21	p. 30	p. 39	p. 48	p. 57	p. 66	p. 75
Problem of the Day	p. 4	p. 13	p. 22	p. 31	p. 40	p. 49	p. 58	p. 67	p. 76
Daily Cumulative Review	p. 5	p. 14	p. 23	p. 32	p. 41	p. 50	p. 59	p. 68	p. 77
Practice Masters	p. 6	p. 15	p. 24	p. 33	p. 42	p. 51	p. 60	p. 69	p. 78
Reteaching Masters	p. 7	p. 16	p. 25	p. 34	p. 43	p. 52	p. 61	p. 70	p. 79
Enrichment Masters	p. 9	p. 18	p. 27	p. 36	p. 45	p. 54	p. 63	p. 72	p. 81

Transparencies

	3.1	3.2	3.3	3.4	3.5	3.6	3.7	3.8	3.9
Warm-Ups with Multiple-Choice Practice	p. 17	p. 18	p. 19	p. 20	p. 21	p. 22	p. 23	p. 24	p. 25
Teacher Time-Saver Transparencies	✓	✓	✓	✓	✓	✓	✓	✓	✓
English/Spanish Problem Solving	p. 9	p. 10		p. 11		p. 12		p. 13	
Answer Transparencies	✓	✓	✓	✓	✓	✓	✓	✓	✓

Technology

- Personal Student Tutor
- Time-Saving Test and Practice Generator
- Electronic Teacher Tools
- Technology: Using Calculators and Computers

Additional Resources

- Math Log
- Assessment Book
- Worked-Out Solution Key
- Practice Workbook (English/Spanish)
- Home and School Connection
- California Standards: Key Concepts Book

Correlation to the California Curriculum

Correlations to the California Standards

CA Standards: NS 1.2, NS 1.7, NS 2.5, AF 1.1, AF 1.3, AF 1.5, AF 2.1, AF 3.4, AF 4.0, MG 3.2, SDP 1.0, SDP 1.2, MR 1.1, MR 2.4, MR 2.8

California Curriculum Support

Key Concepts Book

- Pre-Course Review: Topic 1 Working with Decimals
  Topic 5 Measurement
- Key Standards: NS 1.2 Integer Operations *(Lessons 3.2–3.6)*
  NS 2.5 Absolute Value *(Lesson 3.1)*
  AF 1.3 Identity and Inverse Properties *(Lesson 3.3)*
  AF 3.4 Graphing Linear Functions *(Lesson 3.8)*

California Standards Practice Workbook provides practice for each Standard that is covered in this chapter.

Providing Universal Access

Strategies for Strategic Learners

REVIEW PREVIOUSLY LEARNED CONCEPTS

Although students will study geometric concepts later in the year in preparation for more advanced work in this area, the course starts with the assumption that students are familiar with perimeter, area, and volume. Students should be able to use formulas to determine perimeters (or circumferences) and areas of rectangles, triangles, and circles. Students should also be able to use a formula to determine the volume of a cube.

PERIMETER Perimeter is the distance around a two-dimensional figure. Most students are familiar with this concept. They understand that perimeter is measured in units of length and do not find it difficult to understand or calculate perimeter.

AREA In reviewing area, students should understand that area is measured not in linear units such as inches or centimeters, but in square units such as square inches or square centimeters. Students should be reminded that the area of a rectangle is determined by multiplying its length and width ($A = \ell \cdot w$). Since length and width are both given in linear units, their product is given in square units.

VOLUME Students should already be familiar with how to calculate the volume of a rectangular prism by multiplying its length, width, and height ($V = \ell wh$). They will become familiar in this grade with the volumes of other prisms as well as cylinders. Volume can be demonstrated easily to students by filling containers to their maximum capacity with water.

Strategies for English Learners

DISSECT WORD PROBLEMS

Word problems are especially difficult for English learners. Reducing the complexity of the language to avoid specialized vocabulary and idioms allows English learners to focus on the mathematics. The teacher may want to organize lessons for English learners to start first with problems that have few words. Several times a week, however, teachers and students should focus on word problems.

SIGNAL WORDS Fortunately most word problems follow a standard format, and there are clues provided by "signal words," words of high frequency that signal what will follow or what came before. Most word problems also contain numbers, and usually you must do something with the numbers to solve the problems. Analyzing the units in a problem can provide a clue as to the answer that is needed. Chapter 2 starts with a discussion of how to change a verbal description into an expression using appropriate arithmetic and algebraic terminology. English learners can study the techniques that help good problem solvers solve problems, so that they can use these strategies overtly.

With your students examine the structure of a word problem, choosing one from a previous chapter so that students will already be familiar with at least some of the vocabulary. For example, use Exercise 40 from page 19:

> **40. CLOTHING SALE** A dress store advertises that if you buy one sweater you get a second of lesser or equal value at half price. You buy one sweater that costs $38 and another that costs $42. Write and evaluate an expression for the total cost of the sweaters.

Have students look for the following features of word problems and put them in this chart:

Heading (optional) ***CLOTHING SALE***	A word or short phrase at the beginning gives you a clue about something in the problem.
First sentence *A dress store advertises that if you buy one sweater you get a second of lesser or equal value at half price.*	Sometimes the first sentence is a background sentence that provides only context information, but usually it provides at least one numerical fact. In this case, it is the idea that if you buy two sweaters, the second (of equal or lesser value) is half off. Sometimes this first sentence will provide *all* the facts you will need to work with.
Second sentence *You buy one sweater that costs $38 and another that costs $42.*	The second sentence usually gives you at least one more fact or number you will be working with, in this case two prices: *$38* and *$42*.
Third sentence *Write and solve an expression for the total cost of the sweaters.*	The last sentence or group of sentences often contains one of the following phrases: *who*, *what*, *when*, *where*, *why*, *how many*, *how much*, *which*, *how long*, or a command verb like *write*, *evaluate*, *find*, *solve*. The signal word or words (in this case, *write* and *solve*) are usually followed closely by a description of what you are supposed to provide in your answer, in this case, *total cost*.

Have students find other word problems in the text that follow this basic pattern. Look for variations, such as a word problem followed by answers in a multiple choice format.

Strategies for Advanced Learners

PROVIDE WRITING OPPORTUNITIES

Have students make up their own word problems involving products and quotients. Tell students to make the problems as interesting as possible. Advanced students can exchange and critique each other's problems. Selected problems can then be given to the rest of the class as an assignment. It is a positive learning experience for students to see how clear their writing was.

DIFFERENTIATE IN TERMS OF DEPTH

Finding the areas and volumes of unusual or irregular figures often involves seeing a simpler figure, or several simpler figures, embedded in the irregular figures. Have advanced students investigate the following:

1. Can every triangle be divided into two right triangles? (*Yes. Have students try to draw one that can't be.*)

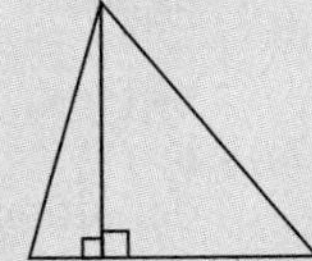

2. Can every square be divided into two isosceles triangles? (*Yes. The sides of a square are equal in length. If a line is drawn from one vertex to the opposite vertex, two of the sides of the square become two of the sides of an isosceles triangle.*)

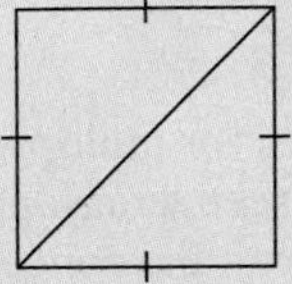

3. If three congruent circles are placed as shown, will their centers always be the vertices of an equilateral triangle? (*Yes. Congruent circles have the same radius.*)

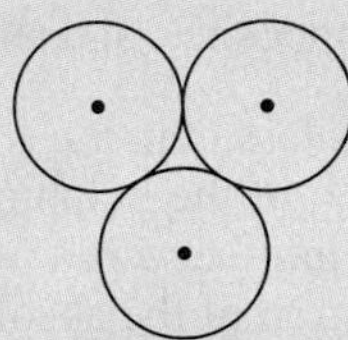

4. Can a circle always be inscribed within a square, and will the diameter of the circle always be equal in length to the length of a side of the square? (*Yes. Have students draw this.*)

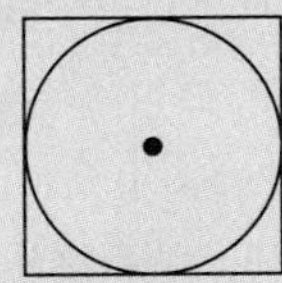

Mathematical Background Notes

Lesson 3.1

NUMBER LINE The real **number line** provides an effective way of making the transition from whole numbers to integers. It also sets the stage for dealing with fractions and decimals, inequalities, opposites, and absolute value.

On a number line the arithmetic notion of a is less than b has a geometric representation as "the graph of a lies to the left of the graph of b" or simply "a lies to the left of b." The opposite of a number a is a number $-a$ which "is the reflection of a about 0." The notion of the absolute value of a, whose arithmetic definition is given by

$$|a| = \begin{cases} a \text{ if } a \geq 0 \\ -a \text{ if } a < 0, \end{cases}$$

has a geometric representation as the distance from a to 0 on the number line. In this way, the number line provides a powerful geometric tool for visualizing and dealing with real numbers.

Lessons 3.2–3.4

ADDING AND SUBTRACTING These lessons begin by using the number line to formulate rules for addition of both positive and negative integers. Using the concept of absolute value, these geometric rules are then put into symbolic form (see page 116). By defining $a - b = a + (-b)$, it becomes possible to extend these symbolic rules to allow for subtraction as well as addition of integers (see page 123).

An alternate way of arriving at these rules is to build on the concept of whole numbers. For very young children the addition problem $5 + 3$ is explained as "combining a heap of five pebbles with a heap of three pebbles." In preparation for other kinds of addition problems, students can now be presented with the *positive* part of the number line, the ray extending to the right of a point denoted as 0. To interpret $5 + 3 = 8$ on this ray, we move five units to the right, and then move three more units to the right. These operations require only the positive part of the number line. So does $5 - 3 = 2$, as represented by "remove three pebbles from five pebbles" or "move five units to the right, and then move three units to the left."

The transition from whole numbers to integers begins with problems such as $3 - 5 = -2$. While it is not physically possible to remove five pebbles from a heap of three pebbles, it *is* geometrically possible to move three units to the right, and then move five units to the left. However, this requires an extension of the number line to the left of 0. It also requires the identification of points to the left of 0 with **negative numbers.**

With the number line so extended, the above rule for subtraction takes the following form:

(*) $\quad a - b = -(b - a).$

This tells us that $3 - 5 = -2$ because

$$3 - 5 = -(5 - 3) = -2.$$

Note that implementing this rule requires only the familiar form of subtraction corresponding to removing three pebbles from a heap of five.

Having extended the number line to include negative numbers, we are also obligated to define $a + b$ for arbitrary integers a and b. Such a definition involves the fact that subtraction is the inverse of addition, that is, that the answer to the subtraction problem

$$a - b = ?$$

is a number c with the property that $c + b = a$. The fact that $a + (-b) + b = a$ leads to $c = a + (-b)$ and to the fundamental rule

(**) $\quad a + (-b) = a - b.$

From here we are guided by the requirement that (**), (*), and the CAD laws must hold for integers as well as the whole numbers. For example,

$5 + (-7) = 5 - 7$	by (**)
$= -(7 - 5)$	by (*)
$= -(2) = -2$	
$-7 + 5 = 5 + (-7)$	commutative law
$= -2$	as above
$-7 + (-5) = -7 - 5$	by (**)
$= -(5 - (-7))$	by (*)
$= -(5 + 7)$	definition of opposites
$= -12$	
$-5 + (-7) = -7 + (-5)$	commutative law
$= -12$	as above

Adding integers on the basis of (*), (**), and the CAD laws can be subtle and require several steps. Rules based on the number line provide students with a practical alternative approach.

Lesson 3.5

MULTIPLYING In extending the rules for multiplication of whole numbers to the multiplication of integers, it seems reasonable to insist that any such definition remain consistent with the concept of multiplication as repeated addition. Since $4a = a + a + a + a$ for any whole number a, we will require that

$$4 \times (-3) = (-3) + (-3) + (-3) + (-3) = -12.$$

Similar reasoning tells us that adding 0 a times leads to

$$a \times 0 = 0 + 0 + \ldots + 0 = 0$$

so that, for any positive integer a,

$$a \times 0 = 0 \times a = 0.$$

The distributive law now enables us to show that $a \times 0 = 0$ for *any* number a. For if we let $b = a \times 0$, then

$$b = a \times 0 = a \times (0 + 0) = a \times 0 + a \times 0 = b + b.$$

Therefore, $0 = b + (-b) = (b + b) + (-b) = b + (b + (-b)) = b + 0 = b = a \times 0$.

The fact that $a \times 0 = 0$ for all integers a can be combined with the distributive property in important ways. Given that

$$a \times (b + c) = a \times b + a \times c$$

is to hold for all integers a, b, and c, it follows that

$$0 = 4 \times 0 = 4 \times (3 + (-3)) = 4 \times 3 + 4 \times (-3).$$

The fact that $4 \times 3 + 4 \times (-3) = 0$ implies that $4 \times (-3)$ is the opposite of 4×3. This again leads to the conclusion that $4 \times (-3) = -12$.

Another important consequence of this line of reasoning is that for any integer a,

$$0 = 0 \times a = (1 + (-1)) \times a = 1 \times a + (-1) \times a = a + (-1) \times a.$$

This shows that $(-1) \times a$ is the opposite of a, that is, for any integer a,

$$(-1) \times a = -a.$$

On this basis, we can conclude that

$$(-4) \times (-3) = (-1) \times (4 \times (-3)) = (-1) \times (-12) = 12.$$

In this way we arrive at the rules on page 129: The product of a positive integer and a negative integer will be negative, whereas the product of two negative integers will be positive.

Lesson 3.6

DIVIDING The solution of a division problem $a \div b$ is a number q with the property that $a = q \times b$. When dealing with integers a and b, it is not always possible to find an *integer* q with this property. However, when $b \neq 0$, the division problem $a \div b$ *does* always have a solution that is the quotient of two integers, that is, a fraction.

To arrive at the rules for dividing integers (see page 135), it is useful to represent division problems in fraction form. Here there is the possibility of confusion between $\frac{a}{b}$ as a way of *posing* the division problem $a \div b$ and $q = \frac{a}{b}$ as the *solution* of the division problem $a \div b$. Having acknowledged this ambiguity, the notation $\frac{a}{b}$ can be very useful in bringing properties of fractions to bear.

The fact that $\frac{a}{b} = a \times \frac{1}{b}$ means that the division problem $a \div b$ can be expressed in the form $a \times \frac{1}{b}$. This notation is consistent with the fact that the solution of a division problem $a \div b$ is a number q with the property that $a = q \times b$. That is,

$$\text{If } q = a \times \frac{1}{b}, \text{ then } q \times b = \left(a \times \frac{1}{b}\right) \times b = a \times \left(\frac{1}{b} \times b\right) = a \times 1 = a.$$

To establish the sign of the quotient of two numbers we recall the corresponding rule for products. Then, noting that $a \div b = q$ is equivalent to $a = q \times b$, we have:

If a and b are of the same sign and $a = q \times b$, then q must be positive.

If a and b are of opposite sign and $a = q \times b$, then q must be negative.

These observations are at the heart of the rules on page 135.

Lesson 3.8

The number line provides a coordinate system in which students learn to associate *right* with plus and *left* with minus. Each point on this number line corresponds to a real number x. Whether the graph of x is to the right or left of 0 is determined by its sign, while its distance from 0 is determined by its absolute value.

COORDINATE PLANE The Cartesian coordinate system confronts the student with *two* number lines and *two* conventions. In addition to the x-axis (which embodies the already familiar horizontal number line) there is a vertical y-axis with which we associate *up* with plus and *down* with minus. Each point in this **coordinate plane** corresponds to a *pair* of numbers (x, y), where the sign of x determines position to the right or left of the y-axis and the sign of y determines position above or below the x-axis. "Coded" into the symbol $(2, -4)$ are two sets of instructions: First move 2 units to the *right* and then move 4 units *down*.

Even for individual points, important geometric concepts arise. In graphing the points $(1, 3)$ and $(1, -3)$ in the first and fourth quadrants, respectively, students may observe that these points are mirror images of each other, with the x-axis serving as the mirror. A mathematical way of saying this is that $(1, 3)$ and $(1, -3)$ are **symmetric about the x-axis.**

This form of symmetry has important geometric consequences. The symmetry of $(1, 3)$ and $(1, -3)$ about the x-axis means that the line $y = 0$ is the **perpendicular bisector** of the line segment connecting $(1, 3)$ and $(1, -3)$. In this way, an important geometric construction (constructing the perpendicular bisector of a line segment) is closely linked to the representation of points in the coordinate plane. It is these kinds of connections between algebra and geometry that make the Cartesian coordinate system such a powerful tool in mathematics.

Bringing the concept of symmetry into Section 3.8 also sets the stage for enrichment. For example, students can be challenged to find an axis of symmetry for the points $(1, 3)$ and $(3, 1)$ (and more generally for (h, k) and (k, h)).

Chapter Overview

Chapter Goals

In this chapter, students will add, subtract, multiply, and divide integers. They will:

- Use number lines to model integer addition and subtraction.
- Solve equations involving integers.
- Use the coordinate plane to graph by point-plotting.
- Make scatter plots.

Career Note

Sportswriters may work in radio, television, newspaper, or in other areas of the media. They must attend sporting events, and interview players and coaches, as well as research the teams or players they are reporting on.

Those interested in careers as sportswriters should be able to write well and meet tight deadlines. A four-year college degree in English or journalism is the normal preparation, along with experience working in the media.

Additional information about sportswriters is available at **www.mcdougallittell.com**

Operations with Integers

Why are operations with integers important?

Integers, which include whole numbers and their opposites, are used to describe signed quantities, such as temperatures above and below 0°, elevations above and below sea level, and gains and losses in value.

Operations with integers are used in many careers, including sports writing (page 103) and paleontology (page 119). For example, sportswriters use integers as they calculate movement on the field in a football game or scores over or under par in a golf game.

Meeting the California Standards

The skills you'll develop in this chapter will help you meet state standards and prepare for standardized tests. In this chapter you'll:

- **Find and interpret the absolute value of a number.** LESSON 3.1
- **Add, subtract, multiply, and divide integers.** LESSONS 3.2–3.6
- **Write an equation that represents a verbal description.** LESSON 3.7
- **Solve simple equations in one variable over the integers.** LESSON 3.7
- **Graph simple figures and determine measures related to them.** LESSON 3.8
- **Represent two variables on a scatter plot.** LESSON 3.9

Career Link **SPORTSWRITER** A sportswriter uses operations with integers when:

- determining a player's score in golf.
- reporting plays in football.

EXERCISES

A sportswriter at a golf tournament uses a table to record the number of times each player hit the ball to get it into the first hole. The first hole is *par 4*, which means that an expert player would be expected to hit the ball 4 times to get it into the hole.

Scores on par 4 hole					
Player	A	B	C	D	E
Number of times player hit ball	7	3	2	5	4
Score	+3	–1	?	?	?

Player A had to hit the ball 7 times. Since the hole is par 4, Player A hit the ball 3 more times than expected; so she is *3 over par* and her score is +3.

Player B had to hit the ball 3 times to get it into the hole. Player B hit the ball one fewer time than expected, so she is *1 under par*. Her score is −1.

1. Is Player C over or under par? Explain. What is Player C's score? **under; −2**

2. Is Player D over or under par? What is Player D's score? **over; +1**

3. Is Player E over or under par? What is Player E's score? **neither; 0**

In Lesson 3.2, you'll learn how to determine players' standings after four rounds of golf.

Projects

A project covering Chapters 1–3 appears on pages 164–165 of the Student Edition. Additional projects for selected lessons in Chapter 3 are available in the *Assessment Book,* pp. 218–219.

Technology

Software

- Electronic Teacher Tools
- Online Lesson Planner
- Personal Student Tutor
- Test and Practice Generator

Internet Connections

- Application and Career Links 111,119,126,131
- Student Help 106, 113, 118, 124, 138, 143, 145, 150, 161

These Internet connections are available at **www.mcdougallittell.com**

Prepare

Diagnostic Tools

The **chapter readiness quiz** can help you diagnose whether students have the following skills needed in Chapter 3:

- Mathematical operations vocabulary.
- Writing mathematical expressions.
- Simplifying expressions.

Reteaching Materials

The following resources are available for students who need additional help with the skills on the chapter readiness quiz:

Chapter 3 Resource Book

- Reteaching with Practice (Lessons 1.2, 2.1, 2.2)

Personal Student Tutor

Additional Resources

The following resources are provided to help you prepare for the upcoming chapter and customize review materials:

Chapter 3 Resource Book

- Lesson Plans, pp. 1, 10, 19, 28, 37, 46, 55, 64, 73
- Lesson Plans for Block Scheduling, pp. 2, 11, 20, 29, 38, 48, 56, 65, 74

Technology

- Electronic Teacher Tools with Lesson Planning Software
- Test and Practice Generator

Chapter 3 Getting Ready

PREVIEW

What's the chapter about?

- Performing operations and solving equations with **integers**
- Finding the **absolute value** and the **opposite** of an integer
- Plotting points in a **coordinate plane**, and making **scatter plots**

WORDS TO KNOW

- **integer,** *p. 105*
- **absolute value,** *p. 106*
- **opposites,** *p. 106*
- **coordinate plane,** *p. 144*
- **origin,** *p. 144*
- **ordered pair,** *p. 144*
- ***x*-axis, *y*-axis,** *p. 144*
- **quadrants,** *p. 144*
- **scatter plot,** *p. 149*

PREPARE

Chapter Readiness Quiz

Take this quick quiz. If you are unsure of an answer, look back at the reference pages for help.

VOCABULARY CHECK *(refer to p. 7)*

1. Which expression represents a difference of two numbers? **A**

(A) $5 - x$ (B) $5 + x$ (C) $5x$ (D) $\frac{5}{x}$

2. Which operation do you perform to find a quotient of two numbers? **J**

(F) Addition (G) Subtraction

(H) Multiplication (J) Division

SKILL CHECK *(refer to pp. 54, 57)*

3. Which expression matches the following phrase: *one less than the product of a number and 3*? **B**

(A) $n + 3 - 1$ (B) $3n - 1$ (C) $n - 3 - 1$ (D) $3(n - 1)$

4. Simplify $8x + 2 + x + 4x + 4$. **H**

(F) $19x$ (G) $19 + x$ (H) $13x + 6$ (J) $12x + 6$

STUDY TIP

Make Example Cards

Example cards will help you remember how to find solutions to exercises and how to solve problems. Write a descriptive title at the top of each card.

Absolute Value
Example
Evaluate the absolute value: |–5|.
Solution
The distance between –5 and 0 is 5.
So, |–5| = 5.

3.1 Integers and Absolute Value

California Standards

In this lesson you'll:

- Represent quantitative relationships graphically and interpret the meaning. (AF 1.5)
- Understand the meaning of the absolute value of a number, interpret it as the distance of the number from zero on a number line, and determine the absolute value of real numbers. (NS 2.5)

Goal 1 GRAPHING AND COMPARING INTEGERS

Many subtraction problems can be solved in terms of whole numbers. But problems such as $5 - 8 =$ **?** require an expanded set of numbers called **integers**.

. . . , −3, −2, −1,	0,	1, 2, 3, . . .
Negative Integers	**Zero**	**Positive Integers**

The integer 0 is neither negative nor positive. You read the integer −3 as "negative 3." It is common for positive integers to be written without the positive sign. You can represent integers on a number line.

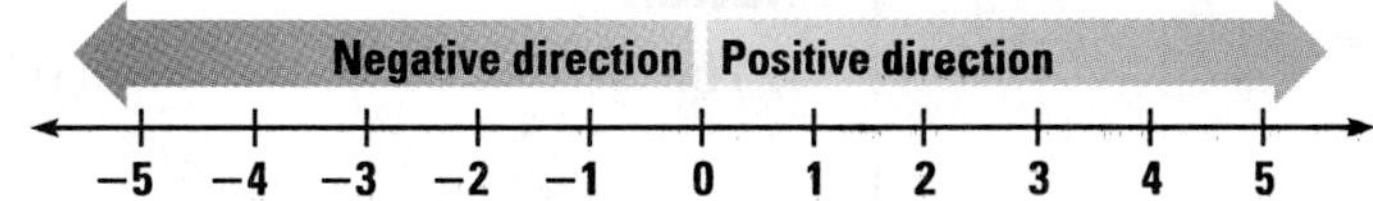

Student Help

READING TIP
Although the negative sign may look like the sign for subtraction, it indicates a direction on a number line, not an operation.

EXAMPLE 1 Graphing Integers on the Number Line

Draw a number line. Graph the integers −6, −2, and 3 by drawing a dot at the point that represents the integer.

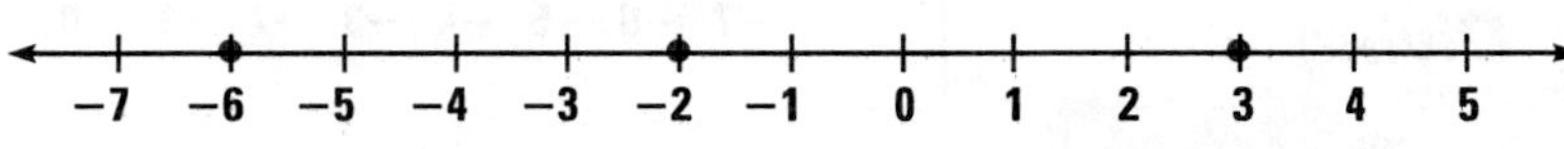

If a and b are integers, then the inequality $a < b$ means that a lies *to the left* of b on a number line. The inequality $a > b$ means that a lies *to the right* of b on a number line.

EXAMPLE 2 Using a Number Line to Order Integers

Order the integers −4, 0, 5, −2, 3, and −3 from least to greatest.

Solution

Begin by graphing the integers on a number line.

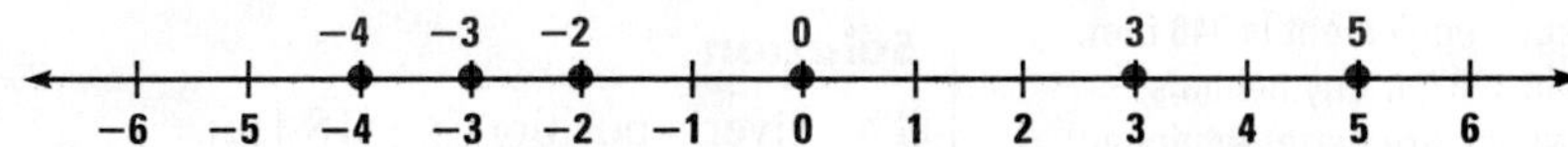

ANSWER ▶ From the number line, you can see that the order is −4, −3, −2, 0, 3, and 5.

1 Plan

Pacing

Suggested Number of Days

Transitional: 1 day
Average: 1 day
Advanced: 1 day
Block Schedule: 0.5 block with 3.2

Teaching Resources

Blacklines
(See page 102B.)

Transparencies
- Warm-Up Exercises
- Teacher Time-Savers
- English/Spanish Problem Solving
- Answers

Technology
- Electronic Teacher Tools
- Test and Practice Generator

2 Teach

Math Reasoning

For Mathematical Background Notes on mathematical reasoning related to this lesson, please refer to pages 102E and 102F in this Teacher's Edition.

Extra Examples 1 and 2
See next page.

California Standards and Assessment

CA Standards: NS 2.5, AF 1.5
CA Key Concepts Book: pp. S42–S43

Math Reasoning

Viewing $-x$ as the opposite of x is consistent with the idea that each is the reflection of the other through the origin 0. This gives a nice geometric interpretation of the relation $-(-x) = x$.

Extra Example 1

Draw a number line. Graph the integers −3, 0, and 1 by drawing a dot at the point that represents the integer.

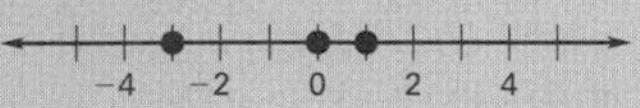

Extra Example 2

Order the integers 4, −2, −5, 0, 2, and −1 from least to greatest.
−5, −2, −1, 0, 2, 4

Extra Example 3

Evaluate the absolute value.

a. $|-9|$ **9** **b.** $|8|$ **8**

Extra Example 4

The graph shows the depth of a whale in feet. Use absolute value to find the distance the whale must travel to reach the surface.

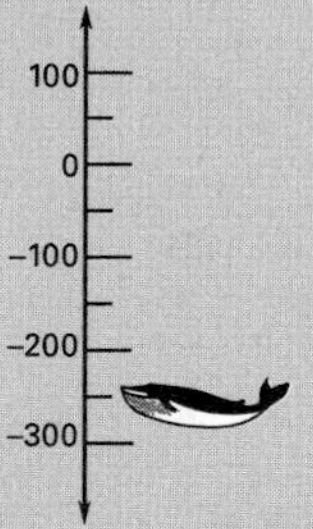

$|-250| = 250$ **feet**

Concept Check

Explain why the absolute value of a number can't be negative. **The absolute value of a number is the distance between the number and 0 on a number line and distance cannot be negative.**

Goal 2 Finding the Absolute Value of a Number

The **absolute value** of a number is the distance between the number and 0 on a number line. Because distance cannot be negative, the absolute value of a number cannot be negative. Absolute values are written with two vertical bars called absolute value signs.

$|7| = 7$ **The absolute value of 7 is 7.**

$|-7| = 7$ **The absolute value of −7 is 7.**

$|0| = 0$ **The absolute value of 0 is 0.**

Student Help

▶ More Examples

More examples are available at www.mcdougallittell.com

Example 3 Evaluating Absolute Values

Evaluate the absolute value.

a. $|-4|$ **b.** $|3|$

Solution

a. The distance between −4 and 0 is 4. So, $|-4| = 4$.

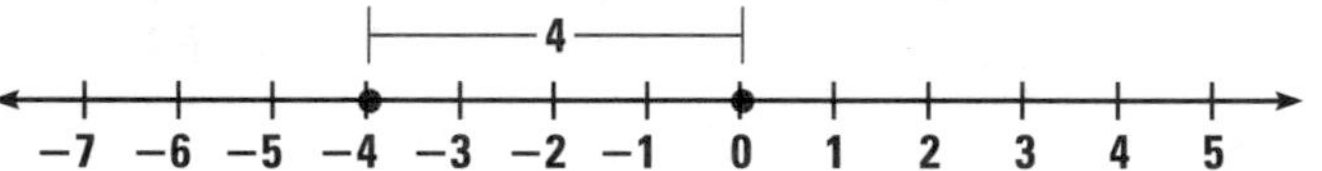

b. The distance between 3 and 0 is 3. So, $|3| = 3$.

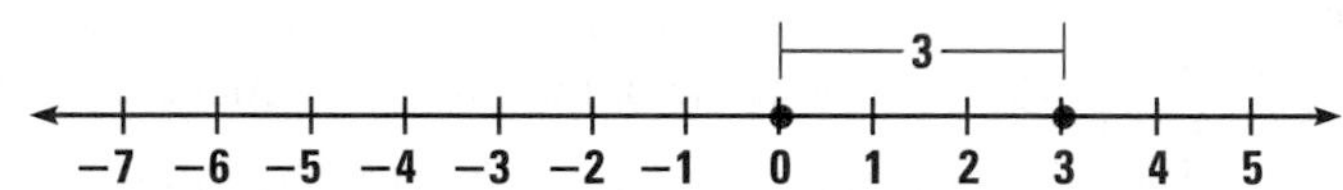

Link to Diving

DIVING A human record for diving without using any special equipment is 246 feet, set in 1997. Many animals, however, are better equipped for diving than humans. Sea lions, for example, have been known to dive as deep as 1233 feet.

Two numbers that have the same absolute value but have different signs are called **opposites**. For example, −7 and 7 are opposites. The negative sign can also be thought of as "the opposite of." Thus, "the opposite of 7" and "negative 7" are the same number.

Example 4 Using Absolute Values in Real Life

The graph shows the position of a diver relative to sea level. Use absolute value to find the diver's distance from the surface.

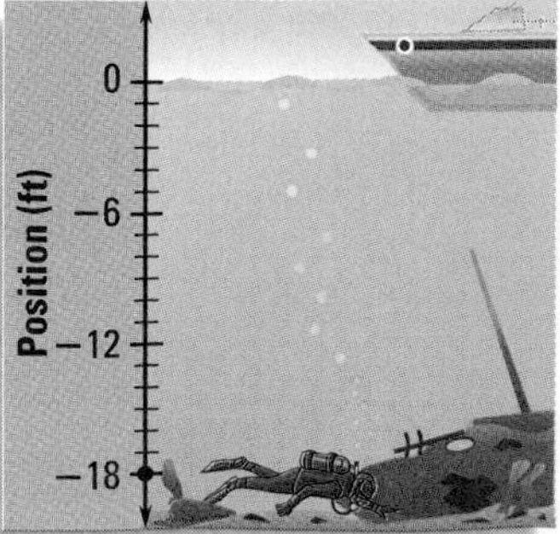

Solution

The diver's position is −18 feet. The diver's distance from the surface is:

$$|-18| = 18 \text{ feet}$$

3.1 Exercises

Guided Practice

In Exercises 1–5, use the following set of numbers.

$-4, -3, -2, -1, 0, 1, 2, 3, 4$

1. Name the integers in the set. **−4, −3, −2, −1, 0, 1, 2, 3, 4**

2. Name the whole numbers. **0, 1, 2, 3, 4**

3. Name the least positive integer. **1**

4. Name the greatest negative integer. **−1**

5. Name the integer that is neither positive nor negative. **0**

> *Student Help*
>
> ▶**Skills Review**
> For help with using a number line, see page 674.

Evaluate the absolute value.

6. $|-3|$ **3** **7.** $|12|$ **12** **8.** $|-15|$ **15** **9.** $|0|$ **0**

In Exercises 10–13, write the opposite of the integer.

10. 1 **−1** **11.** −4 **4** **12.** −3 **3** **13.** 3 **−3**

14. Draw a number line. Graph two different integers that have an absolute value of 2. **See margin.**

Practice and Problem Solving

> *Student Help*
>
> ▶**More Practice**
> Extra practice to help you master skills is on page 694.

Draw a number line and graph the integers. **15–20. See margin.**

15. 0, 4, −3 **16.** −1, 2, −6 **17.** −5, −3, 0

18. −4, 2, 3 **19.** −7, −8, −5 **20.** 0, −2, 7

Order the integers from least to greatest.

21. 0, −6, 5, −3, 4 **−6, −3, 0, 4, 5**

22. −1, −10, 1, −4, −6 **−10, −6, −4, −1, 1**

23. −1, 2, −2, 0, −4 **−4, −2, −1, 0, 2**

24. −9, −11, 11, 1, −7 **−11, −9, −7, 1, 11**

25. 6, 4, −4, −5, −2 **−5, −4, −2, 4, 6**

26. −7, −8, −9, −6, −5 **−9, −8, −7, −6, −5**

Write the integer that represents the situation.

27. 250 feet below sea level **−250** **28.** An elevation of 5050 feet **5050**

29. A gain of 25 yards **25** **30.** A gain of 6 hours **6**

31. 17° below zero **−17** **32.** A profit of $40 **40**

33. A loss of 15 pounds **−15** **34.** A $100 deposit in a savings account **100**

Evaluate the absolute value.

35. $|-11|$ **11** **36.** $|8|$ **8** **37.** $|-2|$ **2** **38.** $|87|$ **87**

3 Apply

Assignment Guide

Transitional
Day 1: SRH p. 674 Exs. 7–10; pp. 107–109 Exs. 15–17, 21–23, 32–36, 41–43, 47–48, 57–60, 71–75, 80–86

Average
Day 1: pp. 107–109 Exs. 18–20, 23–26, 30–36, 43–45, 49–56, 71–75, 83–86

Advanced
Day 1: pp. 107–109 Exs. 20, 24–26, 30–38, 43–46, 49–54, 67–69, 70*, 71–73, 85–90

Block Schedule
pp. 107–109 Exs. 18–20, 23–26, 30–36, 43–45, 49–56, 71–75, 83–86 (with 3.2)

Extra Practice

- Student Edition, pp. 694–695
- Chapter 3 Resource Book, p. 6

Homework Check

To quickly check student understanding of key concepts, go over the following exercises:

Transitional: 16, 22, 36, 50, 58
Average: 18, 24, 36, 50, 54
Advanced: 18, 26, 36, 52, 54

14. 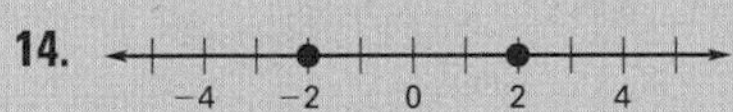

15. 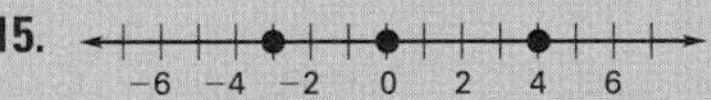

16. −6 −4 −2 0 2 4 6

17. −6 −4 −2 0 2 4 6

18. 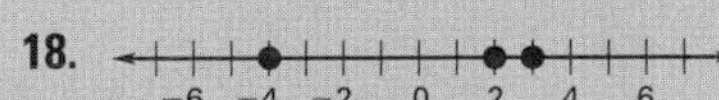

19. 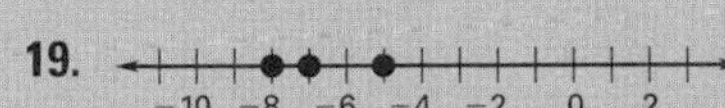

20. 

Math Reasoning

On a number line, the statement in Exercise 70 with "≥" replaced by ">" becomes "If a is to the right of b on the number line, then a is farther from the origin than b."

53.

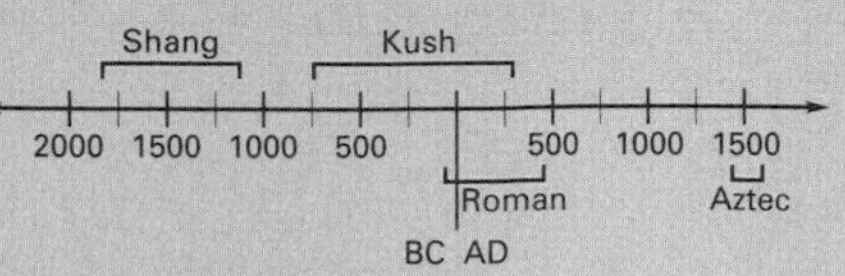

Write the opposite of the integer.

39. 20 **−20** **40.** −32 **32** **41.** −100 **100** **42.** 144 **−144**

Student Help

▶STUDY TIP
In Exercises 43–46, you can rephrase each statement as a verbal sentence. For example, the statement $-x = 2$ means "The opposite of some number x is 2." Then decide which number has 2 as its opposite.

ALGEBRA Find a value or values of x that make the statement true.

43. $|x| = 5$ **−5 or 5** **44.** $|x| = 0$ **0** **45.** $-x = 4$ **−4** **46.** $-x = -3$ **3**

Complete each statement using < or >.

47. 0 **?** 4 **<** **48.** −2 **?** 1 **<** **49.** −3 **?** −5 **>**

50. $|-1|$ **?** −2 **>** **51.** $|2|$ **?** −3 **>** **52.** $|-14|$ **?** $|-13|$ **>**

History Link **In Exercises 53–56, use the table showing the approximate beginning and ending dates of four civilizations from the past.**

Civilization	Begin	End
Kingdom of Kush	750 B.C.	A.D. 300
Shang Dynasty	1766 B.C.	1122 B.C.
Roman Empire	27 B.C.	A.D. 476
Aztec Empire	A.D. 1428	A.D. 1521

53. Copy the time line below. Record the approximate beginning and ending dates of each civilization. **See margin.**

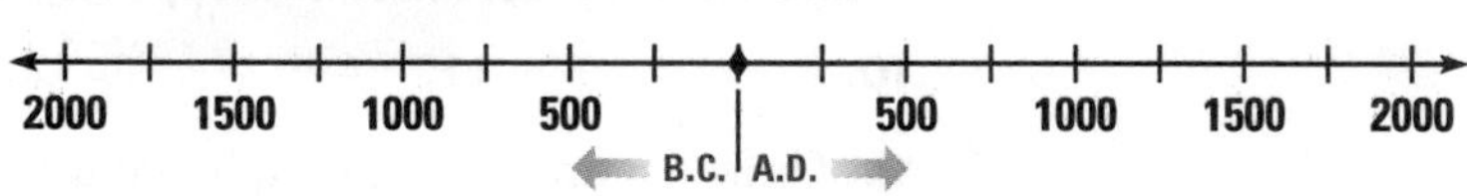

54. Which civilization began and ended before the other civilizations? **Shang Dynasty**

55. Which civilization began and ended after the other civilizations? **Aztec Empire**

56. Which civilization ended during the time of the Roman Empire? **Kingdom of Kush**

CLIMATE Use the number line to estimate the difference in the record low temperatures of the given cities. **57–66. Estimates may vary.**

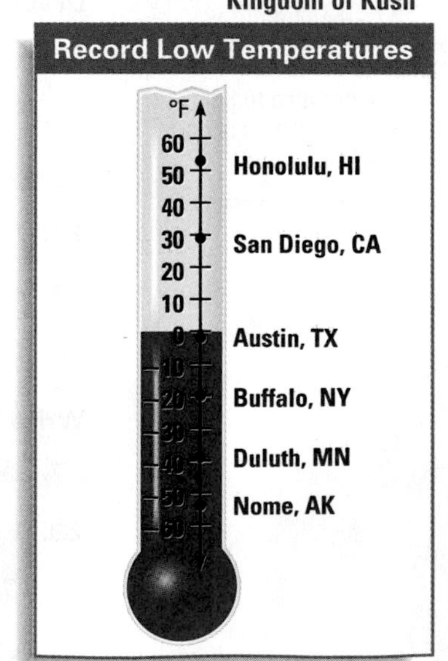

57. Honolulu and Austin **55°F**

58. Honolulu and San Diego **23°F**

59. Buffalo and Austin **18°F**

60. Duluth and Austin **38°F**

61. Duluth and Buffalo **19°F**

62. Nome and Buffalo **34°F**

63. Duluth and San Diego **68°F**

64. Honolulu and Nome **106°F**

65. San Diego and Nome **83°F**

66. Buffalo and San Diego **49°F**

MATHEMATICAL REASONING In Exercises 67–69, decide whether the statement is *true* or *false*. In each case, explain your reasoning.

67. The absolute value of a negative integer is a positive integer. **true**

68. The absolute value of any integer is positive. **false; $|0| = 0$**

69. The absolute value of -6 is less than the absolute value of -4. **false; $6 > 4$**

70. CHALLENGE Decide whether the following statement is true for all integer values of a and b. Explain your reasoning.

If $a \geq b$, then $|a| \geq |b|$. **false; $2 > -4$ but $|2| < |-4|$**

Multiple-Choice Practice

Test Tip

▶ Read a question carefully and completely before you look for the answer. In Exercise 72, you are asked to order the numbers from least to greatest.

71. Which statement is true? **A**

Ⓐ $-6 < 2$ Ⓑ $-4 > -2$ Ⓒ $2 < -10$ Ⓓ $2 < -2$

72. Which list of integers is ordered from least to greatest? **G**

Ⓕ $0, -1, 2, -3$ Ⓖ $-3, -1, 0, 2$

Ⓗ $-1, -3, 0, 2$ Ⓙ $-3, 0, -1, 3$

73. Which statement is true when $x = -2$ and $y = |-2|$? **D**

Ⓐ $x > y$ Ⓑ $x = y$ Ⓒ $|x| < y$ Ⓓ $|x| = y$

Mixed Review

Evaluate the expression when $n = 3$. *(1.4)*

74. $6n - 12$ **6** **75.** $n^2 - 4$ **5** **76.** $13n + 16$ **55**

77. $3n + 7$ **16** **78.** $6(n - 1)$ **12** **79.** $3(8n) - n$ **69**

80. $n^2 + 3$ **12** **81.** $14(n + 2) - 15$ **55** **82.** $21 + 7n - n$ **39**

In Exercises 83 and 84, use the following information. To raise money for a charity, you and a group of friends wash 9 cars on Thursday, 12 cars on Friday, and 16 cars on Saturday. *(2.2)*

83. Write an expression that represents the amount of money you and your friends raise, based on the amount m you charge per car. **$9m + 12m + 16m$**

84. You charge $4.50 to wash a car. How much money do you and your friends raise? **$166.50**

Solve the equation using mental math. Check your solution in the original equation. *(2.3)*

85. $x - 2 = 14$ **16** **86.** $y + 5 = 6$ **1** **87.** $14 + z = 34$ **20**

88. $22 = a - 11$ **33** **89.** $\frac{b}{3} = 6$ **18** **90.** $32 = 16c$ **2**

4 Assess

Assessment Resources

- Assessment Book (Formal Assessment and Alternative Assessment)
- Test and Practice Generator

Mini-Quiz

1. Draw a number line and graph the integers $0, -4, 3$.

2. Order the integers from least to greatest: $2, -4, -10, 5, 1$. **$-10, -4, 1, 2, 5$**

Evaluate the absolute value.

3. $|26|$ **26**

4. $|0|$ **0**

5. $|-15|$ **15**

6. The thermometer shows the temperature in degrees Celsius. Use absolute value to find the number of degrees the temperature must rise to reach the freezing point of 0° Celsius.

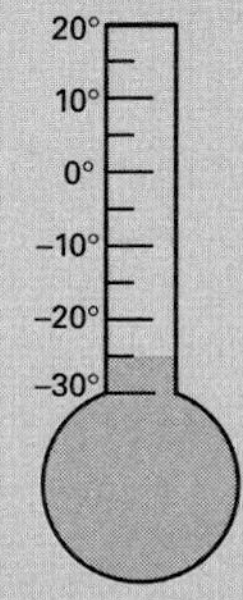

$|-25| = 25°$ Celsius

1 Plan

Pacing

Suggested Number of Days

Transitional: 1 day
Average: 1 day
Advanced: 1 day
Block Schedule: 0.5 block with 3.1

Teaching Resources

Blacklines
(See page 102B.)

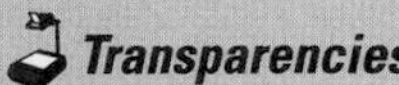

Transparencies
- Warm-Up Exercises
- Teacher Time-Savers
- English/Spanish Problem Solving
- Answers

Technology
- Electronic Teacher Tools
- Test and Practice Generator

2 Teach

Math Reasoning

For Mathematical Background Notes on mathematical reasoning related to this lesson, please refer to pages 102E and 102F in this Teacher's Edition.

California Standards and Assessment

CA Standard: Grade 6, NS 1.2
CA Key Concepts Book: pp. S2, S4, S8

3.2 Using a Number Line to Add Integers

California Standards

In this lesson you'll:

▶ Add positive and negative integers on a number line. (Grade 6, NS 1.2)

Goal 1 Adding Two Integers on the Number Line

You can use a number line to model addition of integers.

Adding Integers on a Number Line

To find the sum of two integers *a* and *b*,

1. Start at 0 and move $|a|$ units to the right if *a* is positive, or to the left if *a* is negative.
2. Then move $|b|$ units to the right if *b* is positive, or to the left if *b* is negative. The sum is the final position on the number line.

EXAMPLE 1 *Using a Number Line to Add Integers*

Use a number line to find the sum.

a. $-3 + (-5)$ **b.** $3 + (-5)$ **c.** $-3 + 5$

Solution

a. Start at 0. Move 3 units to the left. Then move 5 units to the left.

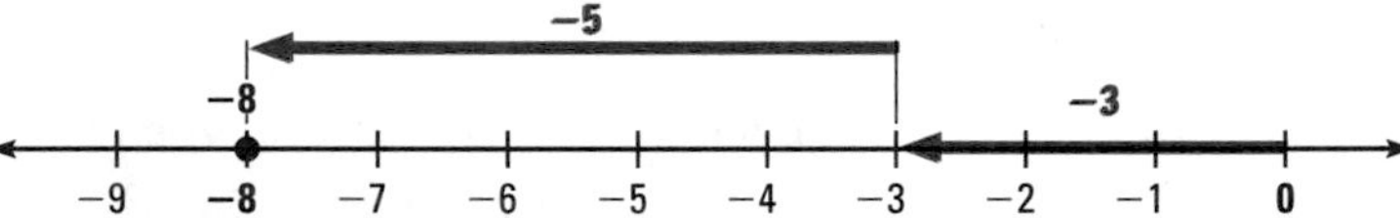

ANSWER ▶ Your final position is −8. So, $-3 + (-5) = -8$.

b. Start at 0. Move 3 units to the right. Then move 5 units to the left.

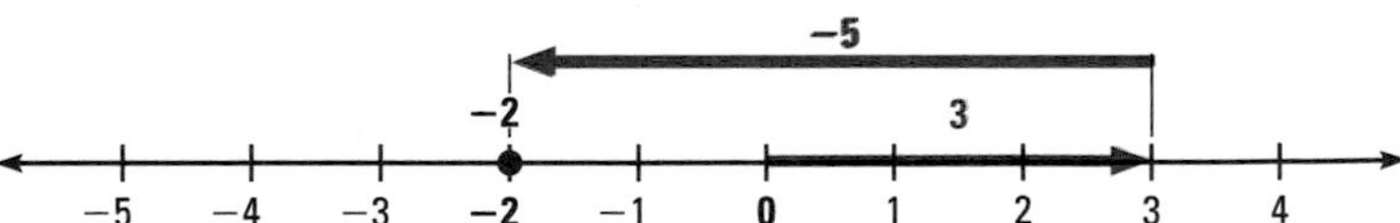

ANSWER ▶ Your final position is −2. So, $3 + (-5) = -2$.

c. Start at 0. Move 3 units to the left. Then move 5 units to the right.

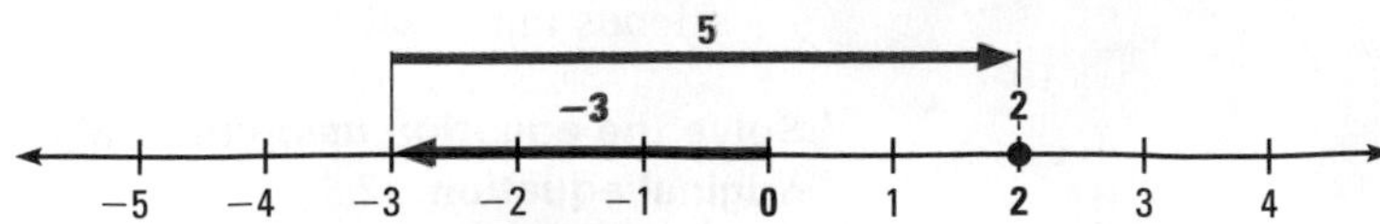

ANSWER ▶ Your final position is 2. So, $-3 + 5 = 2$.

Goal 2 USING INTEGER ADDITION

You can use integer addition in real-life situations when you know the direction and the amount of change in a quantity.

EXAMPLE 2 Using Integer Addition

TEMPERATURE The temperature at 1 P.M. was 20° Fahrenheit. By 7 P.M. it had dropped by 23°. What was the temperature at 7 P.M.?

Solution

Use an expression to model the problem.

Temperature at 1 P.M. + Temperature change

$20 + (-23)$

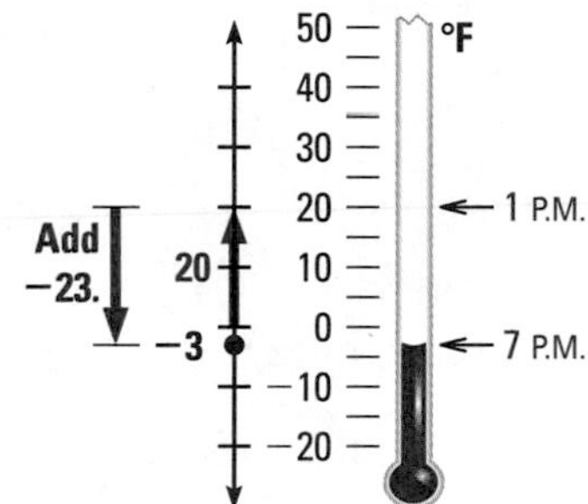

Find the sum by starting at 0. Move 20 units up, in the positive direction. Then move 23 units down, in the negative direction. Your final position is −3.

ANSWER ▶ The temperature at 7 P.M. was −3° Fahrenheit.

EXAMPLE 3 Using Integer Addition to Solve a Problem

FOOTBALL A football team has four chances, called *downs*, to advance the ball. If your team succeeds in advancing the ball ten yards in four downs, it keeps possession of the ball. Here is a record of your team's gains and losses in four downs:

- 1st down: 7 yard gain
- 2nd down: 13 yard loss
- 3rd down: 9 yard gain
- 4th down: 6 yard gain

Does your team keep possession of the ball?

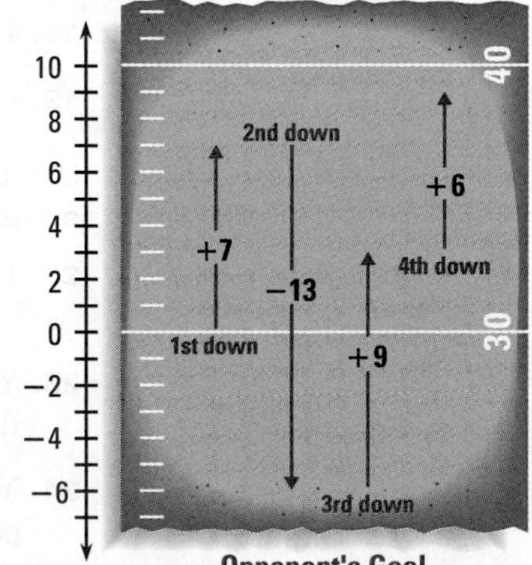

Solution

Follow the arrows in the diagram from left to right to see that the total number of yards gained is:

$7 + (-13) + 9 + 6 = 9$

ANSWER ▶ Your team does not keep possession of the ball.

Link to History

INVENTIONS In the late 1500s, the Italian scientist Galileo Galilei created an early type of thermometer called a *thermoscope*. Galileo is shown in the painting above with such a device, which made use of the fact that air expands when it is heated and contracts when it cools.

INTERNET More about Galileo and thermometers at www.mcdougallittell.com

Extra Example 1

Use a number line to find the sum.

a. $-4 + (-2)$ **−6**

b. $4 + (-2)$ **2**

c. $-4 + 2$ **−2**

Extra Example 2

The temperature at 4 P.M. Tuesday was 14° Fahrenheit. By 6 A.M. Wednesday the temperature had dropped 21°. What was the temperature at 6 A.M.? **−7° Fahrenheit**

Extra Example 3

A football team has 4 downs to advance the ball ten yards. On first down the team gained 3 yards. On second down it lost 12 yards. On third down it lost 1 yard. On fourth down it gained 9 yards. Did the team gain at least 10 yards in 4 downs? **No, since $3 + (-12) + (-1) + 9 = -1$, the team lost 1 yard.**

Concept Check

The following two arrows represent two integers to be added together on a number line. Will the sum be positive or negative? Explain your reasoning.

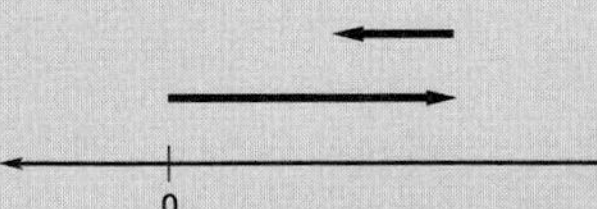

The sum will be positive because the arrow pointing to the right, the positive direction, is longer than the arrow to the left, the negative direction.

3 Apply

Assignment Guide

TRANSITIONAL
Day 1: pp. 112–113 Exs. 10–18, 22–23, 26–27, 31–32
AVERAGE
Day 1: pp. 112–113 Exs. 13–28, 31–32
ADVANCED
Day 1: pp. 112–113 Exs. 18–28, 29–30*, 31–32
BLOCK SCHEDULE
pp. 112–113 Exs. 13–28, 31–32 (with 3.1)

Extra Practice

- Student Edition, pp. 694–695
- Chapter 3 Resource Book, p. 15

Homework Check

To quickly check student understanding of key concepts, go over the following exercises:

Transitional: 10, 14, 16, 22, 24
Average: 14, 16, 18, 24, 26
Advanced: 18, 20, 22, 24, 26

3.2 Exercises

Guided Practice

1. Which sum is represented on the number line below? **C**

A. $-1 + 5$ **B.** $1 + (-5)$ **C.** $-1 + (-5)$ **D.** $1 + 5$

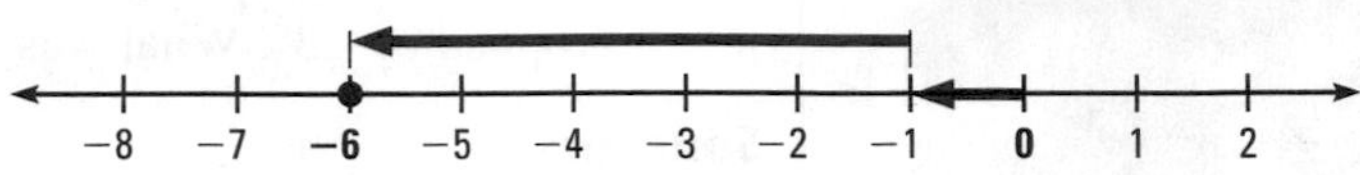

Use a number line to find the sum.

2. $-4 + 3$ **−1** **3.** $2 + (-2)$ **0** **4.** $7 + (-5)$ **2**

5. $-7 + (-5)$ **−12** **6.** $3 + (-2) + 5$ **6** **7.** $9 + (-3) + (-5)$ **1**

Use a number line to solve the problem.

8. TEMPERATURE The temperature at 7 A.M. was $-2°$ Celsius. It had risen 7° by 10 A.M. What was the temperature at 10 A.M.? **5° C**

9. FOOTBALL Your football team started on its own 25 yard line. In the first play, the team lost 6 yards. In the next play, the team gained 14 yards. Did the team gain or lose yards overall in those two plays? On what yard line is the team now? **gain; 33 yd line**

Practice and Problem Solving

Student Help

▶MORE PRACTICE
Extra practice to help you master skills is on page 694.

Use a number line to find the sum.

10. $8 + (-5)$ **3** **11.** $-6 + 7$ **1** **12.** $-8 + (-5)$ **−13**

13. $-7 + 7$ **0** **14.** $-3 + (-9)$ **−12** **15.** $10 + (-6)$ **4**

16. $4 + (-24)$ **−20** **17.** $10 + (-11)$ **−1** **18.** $4 + (-5) + 6$ **5**

19. $-7 + 1 + (-8)$ **−14** **20.** $-12 + 4 + (-8)$ **−16** **21.** $1 + (-12) + (-1)$ **−12**

Use the given information to write a sum of integers. Then use a number line to find the sum and solve the problem.

22. The temperature at 5 A.M. is $-5°$ Fahrenheit. Over the next three hours, it rises by 12°. What is the temperature at 8 A.M.? **7° F**

23. You enter an elevator on the 5th floor. The elevator goes down three floors, then rises seven floors. What floor are you on? **9th**

24. You don't have any money, but your friend's sister owes you \$5. She pays you \$3. How much money does she owe you then? **\$2**

25. A track team's average for the long jump is 15 feet. One athlete jumps 2 feet less than the average. How far did this athlete jump? **13 ft**

Student Help

HOMEWORK HELP

Extra help with problem solving in Exs. 26–27 is available at www.mcdougallittell.com

Chapter Opener Link In **Exercises 26 and 27, use the following information.**

In golf, *par* is the number of strokes in which an expert is expected to complete a hole. A player's score for a hole is given in points above or below par. A player's standing above or below par is calculated after each hole until a *round* of 18 holes is completed. The table shows the standings of five players after each of four rounds of golf.

	Round 1	Round 2	Round 3	Round 4
Player 1	+5	−3	−6	−2
Player 2	−1	−3	−2	+3
Player 3	−4	+2	−3	+2
Player 4	+3	−4	−3	0
Player 5	−2	−6	−7	−3

26. Find each player's standing after four rounds of golf. (That is, find the sum of the standings for each player.) **−6; −3; −3; −4; −18**

27. Which two players were tied after four rounds? **players 2 and 3**

28. MATHEMATICAL REASONING On a number line, show that $4 + (-3)$ is equal to $(-3) + 4$. Which property does this demonstrate? **See margin.**

CHALLENGE Use the bar graph. The graph shows the amounts of money you deposited into your checking account and the amounts you withdrew from the account.

29. −20 + (−15) + 25 + (−30) + 42 + (−45) + 38; −5

29. Write a numerical expression for the sum of the deposits and the withdrawals. Then find the sum.

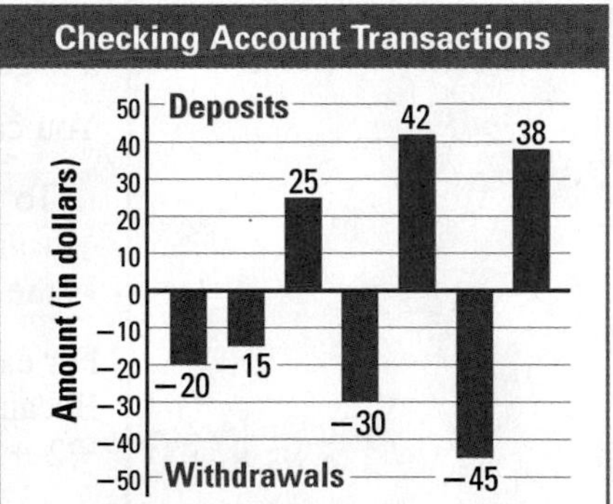

30. Suppose you had \$50 in your checking account before you made your first transaction. Write an expression to show how much money you have in your checking account after your last transaction. Evaluate the expression. **50 + (−5); 45**

Multiple-Choice Practice

31. Which sum is represented on the number line below? **A**

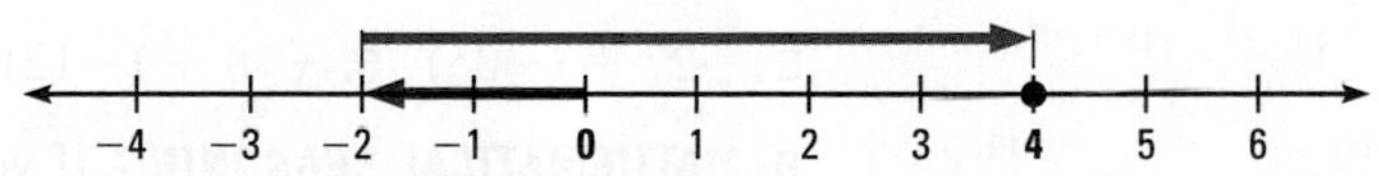

Ⓐ $-2 + 6$ Ⓑ $2 + 6$ Ⓒ $2 + (-6)$ Ⓓ $-2 + (-6)$

32. The current temperature is −2° Fahrenheit. What will the temperature be if the temperature changes by −14° Fahrenheit? **F**

Ⓕ −16°F Ⓖ −12°F Ⓗ 12°F Ⓙ 16°F

4 Assess

Assessment Resources

- Assessment Book (Formal Assessment and Alternative Assessment)
- Test and Practice Generator

Mini-Quiz

Use a number line to find the sum.

1. $-2 + 6$ **4**
2. $5 + (-7) + 2$ **0**
3. The low temperature for today was −3° Celsius, but it rose 10° to reach the high temperature for today. What was today's high temperature? **7° Celsius**
4. Your football team has first down on the opponent's ten yard line and if they can advance the ball 10 yards in 4 downs, they will score a touchdown. On first down they lose 5 yards. On second down they gain 8 yards. On third down they gain 6 yards. On fourth down they gain 2 yards. Did your team score a touchdown on this drive? **Yes, since −5 + 8 + 6 + 2 = 11 yards**

28.

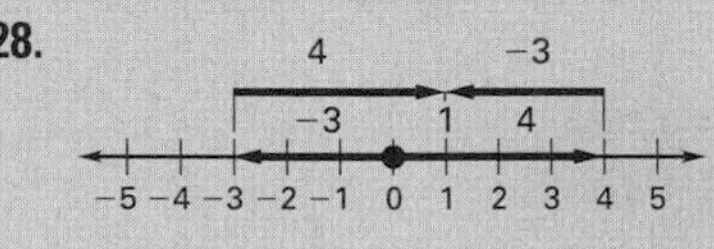

commutative property

Planning the Activity

Purpose and Materials

See the margin of the student page. See also the Activity Support Master in the *Chapter 3 Resource Book.*

LINK TO LESSON

Because students have seen a model for integer addition, they should readily accept the rules presented for integer addition in Lesson 3.3.

Math Reasoning

Students use deductive reasoning to infer rules for adding integers and write accurate rules using precise mathematical terminology.

California Standards and Assessment

CA Standards: NS 1.2, MR 1.1

DEVELOPING CONCEPTS
Integer Addition

For use with Lesson 3.3

California Standards

- Add integers. (NS 1.2)
- Analyze problems by observing patterns. (MR 1.1)

MATERIALS

- Paper and pencil

In Lesson 3.2 you used a number line to find the sum of two integers. By making observations about finding sums using a number line, you can write rules for adding integers *without* using a number line.

SAMPLE 1 Adding Negative Integers

Use a number line to develop a rule for adding two negative integers.

Here's How

The number line below shows the sum $-2 + (-5) = -7$.

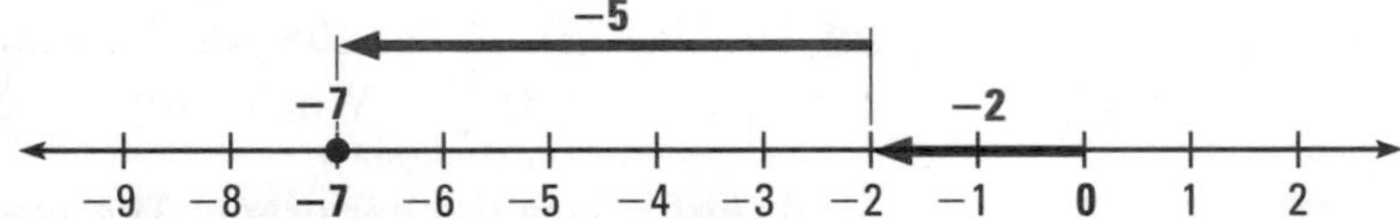

Notice that the absolute value of the integer being added represents the length of each arrow. The lengths of the arrows can be added together to give the size (but not the sign) of the sum. Because each arrow points in a negative direction, the sum of the integers is negative.

You can use these observations to write a rule:

> To find the sum of two negative integers, first add the absolute values of the integers. Then use a negative sign to show that the sum of the integers is negative.

For example, to find the sum $-2 + (-5)$, add $|-2|$ and $|-5|$ to get 7. Because both -2 and -5 are negative, the sum is negative. So, $-2 + (-5) = -7$.

Try These

Use the rule stated in Sample 1 to find the sum.

1. $-8 + (-2)$ **−10**
2. $-7 + (-8)$ **−15**
3. $-5 + (-14)$ **−19**
4. $-13 + (-21)$ **−34**
5. $-27 + (-35)$ **−62**
6. $-78 + (-12)$ **−90**
7. $-55 + (-45)$ **−100**
8. $-93 + (-11)$ **−104**
9. **MATHEMATICAL REASONING** If you wanted to rewrite the rule in Sample 1 so that it could be applied to the sum of two *positive* integers, how would you change the wording of the rule?
10. **MATHEMATICAL REASONING** Write a general rule for adding two integers that have the same sign. Use examples to show how your rule works for both positive integer sums and negative integer sums.

9. ***Sample answer:*** **To find the sum of two positive integers, add the absolute values of the integers and keep the positive sign.**

10. ***Sample answer:*** **To add two integers that have the same sign, add their absolute values and write the common sign.**

SAMPLE 2 Adding Integers with Different Signs

You can use a number line to develop a rule for adding integers with different signs.

Here's How

The number line below shows the sum $-7 + 3 = -4$.

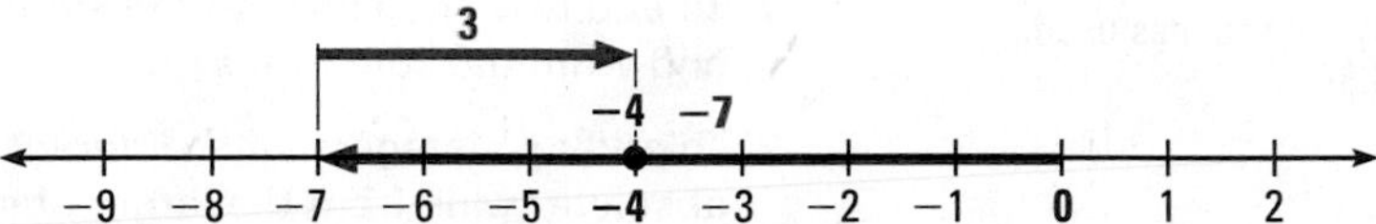

As before, the absolute value of each integer being added represents the length of the corresponding arrow. Because the integers above have different signs, however, the arrows point in different directions.

Notice that the absolute value of the sum of the integers ($|-4|$) is the *difference* between the length of the longer arrow and the length of the shorter arrow. The sign of the sum (negative) is the same as the sign of the integer with the longer arrow.

You can use these observations to write a rule:

> To find the sum of two integers with different signs, find the absolute value of the integers. Then subtract the smaller absolute value from the larger absolute value. Write the sign of the integer with the larger absolute value.

For example, to find the sum $-7 + 3$, subtract the smaller absolute value from the larger absolute value: $|-7| - |3| = 4$. Because $|-7| > |3|$, the sign of the sum is negative. So, $-7 + 3 = -4$.

Try These

11. MATHEMATICAL REASONING Check to see whether the rule in Sample 2 applies to a sum in which the absolute value of the positive integer is greater than the absolute value of the negative integer. Use a number line to support your reasoning.
Sample answer: **$7 + (-3)$; $|7| = 7$ and $|-3| = 3$, so $7 - 3 = 4$.**

Use a rule to find the sum.

12. $7 + (-2)$ **5** **13.** $-9 + 5$ **−4** **14.** $4 + (-1)$ **3** **15.** $-14 + 10$ **−4**

16. $-34 + 35$ **1** **17.** $11 + (-21)$ **−10** **18.** $29 + (-13)$ **16** **19.** $-76 + 5$ **−71**

20. $-81 + 3$ **−78** **21.** $-16 + (-7)$ **−23** **22.** $8 + (-8)$ **0** **23.** $-2 + 118$ **116**

2 Managing the Activity

Classroom Management

After completing Lesson 3.2, students may have already discovered how to add integers without using a number line, but they may not be able to accurately describe the steps they take. As the class goes through this activity, help students use their math vocabulary to accurately describe the steps they take. For example, they may mentally separate the numeral from its sign, but not use the term "absolute value" to describe that step.

3 Closing the Activity

★ KEY DISCOVERY

The sum of two nonzero integers can be less than both integers, greater than both integers, or between the two integers.

Activity Assessment

Use Exercises 8, 12, and 20 to assess student understanding.

1 Plan

Pacing

Suggested Number of Days

Transitional: 2 days
Average: 2 days
Advanced: 2 days
Block Schedule: 1 block

Teaching Resources

Blacklines
(See page 102B.)

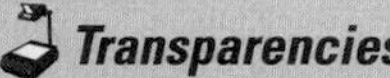

- Warm-Up Exercises
- Teacher Time-Savers
- English/Spanish Problem Solving
- Answers

Technology

- Electronic Teacher Tools
- Test and Practice Generator

2 Teach

Math Reasoning

For Mathematical Background Notes on mathematical reasoning related to this lesson, please refer to pages 102E and 102F in this Teacher's Edition.

California Standards and Assessment

CA Standards: NS 1.2, AF 1.3
CA Key Concepts Book: pp. S3–S4, S8, S51–S53

3.3 Using Rules to Add Integers

California Standards

In this lesson you'll:

- Add integers. (NS 1.2)
- Simplify expressions by applying properties of rational numbers and justify the process used. (AF 1.3)

Goal 1 Adding Two Integers

As you saw in Developing Concepts 3.3, page 114, you can follow these rules for adding integers.

Adding Two Integers

1. To add two integers with the *same sign*, add their absolute values and write the common sign.
2. To add two integers with *different signs*, subtract the smaller absolute value from the larger absolute value. Write the sign of the integer with the larger absolute value.
3. The sum of 0 and any integer is that integer.

EXAMPLE 1 Adding Integers with the Same Sign

a. The sum of two positive numbers is positive.

$$4 + 5 = 9$$

Add $|4| + |5|$.
Use the common sign.

b. The sum of two negative numbers is negative.

$$-12 + (-3) = -15$$

Use $|-12| + |-3|$.
Use the common sign.

EXAMPLE 2 Adding Integers with Different Signs

a. The sum of 5 and -8 is negative because -8 has a greater absolute value than 5.

$$5 + (-8) = -3$$

Subtract $|5|$ from $|-8|$.
Use sign of -8.

b. The sum of -5 and 8 is positive because 8 has a greater absolute value than -5.

$$-5 + 8 = 3$$

Subtract $|-5|$ from $|8|$.
Use sign of 8.

The properties of addition and multiplication you saw in Chapters 1 and 2 also apply to integers. These properties include the commutative, the associative, and the identity properties of addition and multiplication. Another important property is stated below.

INVERSE PROPERTY OF ADDITION

In Words	The sum of an integer and its opposite is 0.
In Algebra	$a + (-a) = 0$
In Arithmetic	$5 + (-5) = 0$ and $-2 + 2 = 0$

Because of the inverse property of addition, two numbers that are opposites are called *additive inverses* of each other. For example, 5 and -5 are additive inverses.

Student Help

▶**STUDY TIP**
When you find the sum of 3 or more integers, you may want to group opposites. Another strategy is to group positive integers and negative integers separately.

EXAMPLE 3 Using Properties of Addition

Find the sum.

a. $3 + (-2) + (-3) = 3 + (-3) + (-2)$ Commutative property
$= 0 + (-2)$ Inverse property of addition
$= -2$ Identity property

b. $-4 + 2 + (-7) + 6 = -4 + (-7) + 2 + 6$ Commutative prop.
$= [-4 + (-7)] + (2 + 6)$ Associative prop.
$= -11 + 8$ Add negative integers. Add positive integers.
$= -3$ Use rules for adding integers.

Student Help

▶**LOOK BACK**
For help simplifying expressions, see pages 57–58.

Goal 2 SIMPLIFYING VARIABLE EXPRESSIONS

In the expression $-5x + 2x + 4$, the numbers -5 and 2 are *coefficients* of x. The terms $-5x$ and $2x$ are *like terms* because their variables are the same. The distributive property allows you to combine like terms by adding their coefficients.

EXAMPLE 4 Simplifying Expressions

Simplify the expression $4n + (-6n) + 3$.

$4n + (-6n) + 3 = [4 + (-6)]n + 3$ Distributive property
$= -2n + 3$ Add coefficients.

Math Reasoning

The addition rules can be mathematically justified using the definition of absolute value and the basic rules of arithmetic. For instance, if $a > 0$ and $b < 0$ and $|a| < |b|$, the second rule tells us that $a + b = -(|b| - |a|)$. To see that this is correct, note that $|b| = -b$ (since $b < 0$) and $|a| = a$ (since $a > 0$), so $-(|b| - |a|) = -(-b - a) = b + a = a + b$.

Extra Example 1

Find the sum.
a. $7 + 6$ **13** **b.** $-5 + (-17)$ **−22**

Extra Example 2

Find the sum.
a. $6 + (-13)$ **−7** **b.** $-6 + 13$ **7**

Extra Example 3

Find the sum.
a. $-5 + 8 + 5$ **8**
b. $6 + (-2) + 3 + (-8)$ **−1**

Extra Example 4

Simplify the expression.
$21w + (-17w) + 6w$ **10w**

Teaching Tip

Students may have difficulty recognizing the application of mathematical properties. Point out how the stated property is used in each step. For example, in step one of Example 3, emphasize that the commutative property is used to change the order of the terms from $3 + (-2) + (-3)$ to $3 + (-3) + (-2)$.

Extra Example 5

Evaluate the expression when $y = 5$.

a. $17y + (-12y) + (-3y)$ **10**

b. $-2y + (-6) + 8y$ **24**

Concept Check

Can the sum of two negative numbers be greater than the sum of a positive number and a negative number? Give an example. **Yes; $-1 + (-1)$ is greater than $1 + (-100)$.**

3 Apply

Assignment Guide

TRANSITIONAL
Day 1: pp. 119–120 Exs. 14–19, 26–29, 44–46, 53–58
Day 2: EP p. 692 Exs. 21–26; pp. 119–120 Exs. 34–35, 38–39, 48, 50–52, 59–64

AVERAGE
Day 1: pp. 119–120 Exs. 17–22, 28–31, 44–46, 53–58
Day 2: pp. 119–120 Exs. 34–37, 40–43, 47–48, 50–52, 59–64

ADVANCED
Day 1: pp. 119–120 Exs. 20–25, 30–33, 44–46, 53–56
Day 2: pp. 119–120 Exs. 34–43, 47–48, 49*, 50–52, 60–64

BLOCK SCHEDULE
pp. 119–120 Exs. 17–22, 28–31, 34–37, 40–48, 50–64

Extra Practice

- Student Edition, pp. 694–695
- Chapter 3 Resource Book, p. 24

Homework Check

To quickly check student understanding of key concepts, go over the following exercises:

Transitional: 18, 28, 36, 40, 44
Average: 18, 30, 36, 42, 46
Advanced: 24, 32, 36, 42, 44

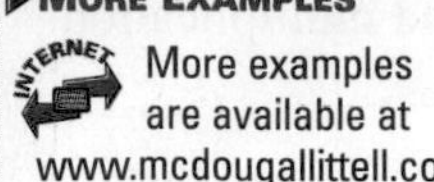

▶ MORE EXAMPLES
More examples are available at www.mcdougallittell.com

EXAMPLE 5 Simplifying before Evaluating

Evaluate the expression when $x = 2$.

a. $-5x + 14x + (-6x)$ **b.** $8x + (-7) + (-5x)$

Solution

For each expression, first simplify to find an equivalent expression. Then evaluate the equivalent expression when $x = 2$.

a. $-5x + 14x + (-6x) = [-5 + 14 + (-6)]x$ **Distributive prop.**
$= 3x$ **Add coefficients.**

ANSWER ▶ When $x = 2$, $3x = 3(2) = 6$.

b. $8x + (-7) + (-5x) = 8x + (-5x) + (-7)$ **Commutative prop.**
$= [8x + (-5x)] + (-7)$ **Associative prop.**
$= [8 + (-5)]x + (-7)$ **Distributive prop.**
$= 3x + (-7)$ **Add coefficients.**

ANSWER ▶ When $x = 2$, $3x + (-7) = 3(2) + (-7) = -1$.

3.3 Exercises

Guided Practice

In Exercises 1–8, find the sum.

1. $9 + 6$ **15** **2.** $-8 + 7$ **−1** **3.** $12 + (-6)$ **6** **4.** $-5 + (-8)$ **−13**

5. $18 + (-18)$ **0** **6.** $9 + 3$ **12** **7.** $-4 + (-6)$ **−10** **8.** $-10 + 11$ **1**

9. Two students used different methods for finding the same sum. Tell what strategy each student is using.

STUDENT 1 $3 + (-2) + 17 + 2 + (-3) = 3 + (-3) + (-2) + 2 + 17$
$= 0 + 0 + 17$
$= 17$

STUDENT 2 $3 + (-2) + 17 + 2 + (-3) = 3 + 17 + 2 + (-2) + (-3)$
$= 22 + (-5)$
$= 17$

9. *Sample answer:* **Student 1 is rearranging the terms to use the inverse property of addition. Student 2 is rearranging the terms to group the positive terms and negative terms.**

10. Identify the like terms in the expression $4 + (-3x) + 5x + (-7)$. Then simplify the expression. **$-3x$ and $5x$ are like terms; 4 and -7 are like terms; $2x - 3$**

Simplify the expression. Then evaluate the expression when $x = 4$.

11. $5x + (-2x) + 7$ **$3x + 7$; 19** **12.** $4x + 6 + (-x)$ **$3x + 6$; 18** **13.** $-3x + 7x + (-2x)$ **$2x$; 8**

Practice and Problem Solving

Student Help

▶**MORE PRACTICE** Extra practice to help you master skills is on page 694.

Find the sum.

14. $11 + 8$ **19** **15.** $-8 + (-2)$ **−10** **16.** $-13 + (-13)$ **−26**

17. $10 + (-10)$ **0** **18.** $-8 + 12$ **4** **19.** $-13 + 7$ **−6**

20. $24 + (-15)$ **9** **21.** $13 + 0$ **13** **22.** $-7 + 0$ **−7**

23. $87 + (-92)$ **−5** **24.** $-53 + 28$ **−25** **25.** $-37 + (-89)$ **−126**

Find the sum.

26. $39 + (-21) + 12$ **30** **27.** $-16 + 23 + 16$ **23**

28. $-172 + 13 + (-4)$ **−163** **29.** $-11 + 17 + (-5) + 6$ **7**

30. $-36 + 49 + (-2) + 15$ **26** **31.** $19 + (-39) + (-51) + 25$ **−46**

32. $13 + (-9) + 12 + (-23)$ **−7** **33.** $-10 + (-4) + 25 + (-8)$ **3**

Simplify the expression.

34. $6x + (-8x) + 9x$ **7x** **35.** $-6x + 3x + (-4x)$ **−7x**

36. $7x + 4x + (-2x)$ **9x** **37.** $2x + (-7x) + (-5x)$ **−10x**

Simplify the expression. Then evaluate the expression when $x = 3$.

38. $-x + 4x + 9$ **3x + 9; 18** **39.** $-2x + 10x + 7x$ **15x; 45**

40. $9x + 13x + (-10x)$ **12x; 36** **41.** $-7x + 8 + 17x$ **10x + 8; 38**

42. $-8x + 10 + 12x$ **4x + 10; 22** **43.** $5x + 3 + (-8) + (-3x)$ **2x − 5; 1**

Link to Careers

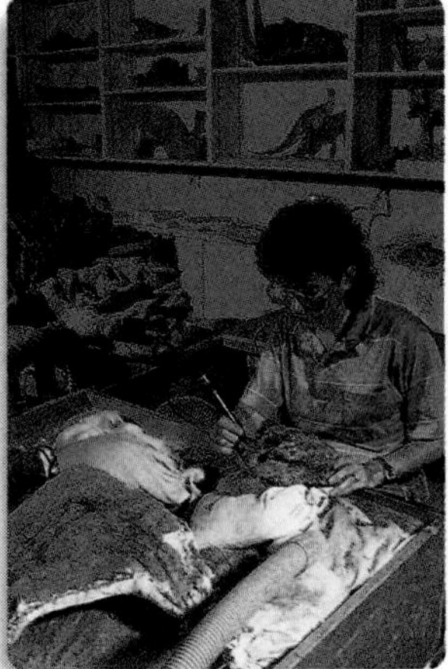

PALEONTOLOGY Paleontologists use fossils to study life forms that existed in prehistoric times. The oldest known dinosaur fossils are about 230 million years old.

More about paleontology available at www.mcdougallittell.com

DINOSAURS In Exercises 44–46, use the time line shown below. The time line shows approximately when three geologic periods began and ended. In each exercise, write a sum that can be used to find a point in time within the period in which the dinosaur lived. Find the sum. Then identify the period in which the dinosaur lived.

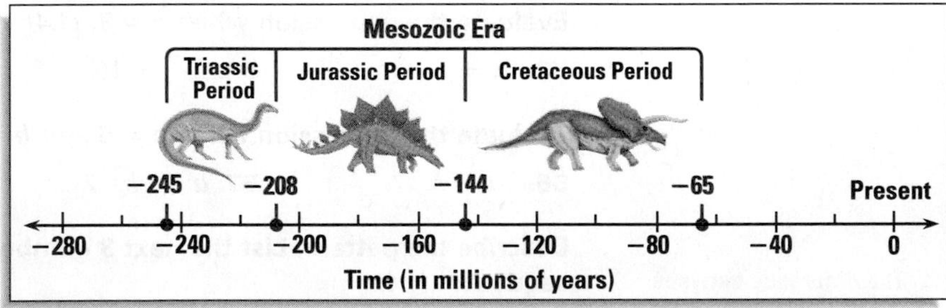

44. Stegosaurus: 90 million years before the end of the Cretaceous Period **−65 + (−90); −155; Jurassic Period**

45. Torosaurus: 142 million years after the beginning of the Jurassic Period **−208 + 142; −66; Cretaceous Period**

46. Plateosaurus: 65 million years before the end of the Jurassic Period **−144 + (−65); −209; Triassic Period**

Assess

Assessment Resources

- Assessment Book (Formal Assessment and Alternative Assessment)
- Test and Practice Generator

Mini-Quiz

Find the sum.

1. $-8 + (-4)$ -12
2. $-7 + 15$ 8
3. $12 + (-4) + (-8) + 4$ 4
4. Simplify the expression $10x + (-2) + (-7x) + 8$. Then evaluate the expression when $x = 5$. $3x + 6$; 36

47. MATHEMATICAL REASONING Give an example that illustrates how each of the following properties applies to integers.
a–d. Sample answers:

a. Commutative property of addition
$3 + (-2) + 7 = 3 + 7 + -2 = 10 + -2 = 8$

b. Associative property of addition
$(3 + 4) + 6 = 3 + (4 + 6) = 3 + 10 = 13$

c. Inverse property of addition $7 + (-7) = (-7) + 7 = 0$

d. Identity property of addition $0 + 14 = 14$

48. *Sample answer:* When the positive integer is greater than the sum of the absolute values of the negative integers, the sum will be positive. When the positive integer is less than the sum of the absolute values of the negative integers, the sum will be negative.

48. MATHEMATICAL REASONING Suppose two integers are negative, and a third integer is positive. When is the sum of the integers positive? When is the sum negative? Explain your reasoning.

49. CHALLENGE The sum of two negative integers is -12. One of the negative integers is two more than the other negative integer. What are the integers? -5 and -7

Multiple-Choice Practice

50. Find the sum $-13 + 15 + (-1)$. C

Ⓐ -29 Ⓑ 2 Ⓒ 1 Ⓓ Not here

51. Which expression does *not* have a value of -3? G

Ⓕ $-2 + (-1)$ Ⓖ $-10 + (-7)$

Ⓗ $-6 + 3$ Ⓙ $3 - 3 - 3$

52. Which expression is equivalent to the expression $5x + 1$? B

Ⓐ $-12x + 7x + 1$ Ⓑ $-4x + 9x + 3 + (-2)$

Ⓒ $-2x + 2 + (-3x) + 3$ Ⓓ $5x + (-4) + (-10x) + 5$

Mixed Review

Evaluate the expression when $x = 3$. *(1.4)*

53. $5x + 3$ 18 **54.** $2x^2 - 16$ 2 **55.** $4x^2 + 3x + 6$ 51

Evaluate the expression when $a = 5$ and $b = 2$. *(1.4)*

56. $2a + b$ 12 **57.** $a^2 - b^2$ 21 **58.** $ab - 6$ 4

Describe the pattern. List the next 3 numbers you expect to find in the sequence. *(1.6)*

59. 503, 490, 477, 464, ?, ?, ? **60.** 10, 12, 15, 19, ?, ?, ?

59. The difference between successive terms is 13; 451, 438, 425.

60. The differences between successive terms are 2, 3, 4, 5, etc.; 24, 30, 37.

Write the variable expression. *(2.1)*

61. The product of 16 and n $16n$ **62.** The quotient of a and 12 $\frac{a}{12}$

63. The difference of x and 16 $x - 16$ **64.** The sum of y and 10 $y + 10$

DEVELOPING CONCEPTS

Integer Subtraction

For use with Lesson 3.4

California Standards

- Subtract integers. (NS 1.2)
- Analyze problems by observing patterns. (MR 1.1)

MATERIALS:

- Paper and pencil

Suppose you want to subtract an integer b from an integer a. You are familiar with finding the difference $a - b$ when a and b are positive and $a > b$. Here, you will write a general rule for subtraction.

SAMPLE 1 Subtracting a Positive Integer

You can use a number line to make some observations and develop a rule about subtracting a positive integer from another positive integer.

Here's How

Let a and b be positive integers. You can use a number line to model the difference $a - b$ when $a > b$ and when $a < b$.

$\boldsymbol{a > b}$ To model the difference $5 - 3$, for example, start at 0. Move 5 units in the positive direction, then 3 units in the negative direction.

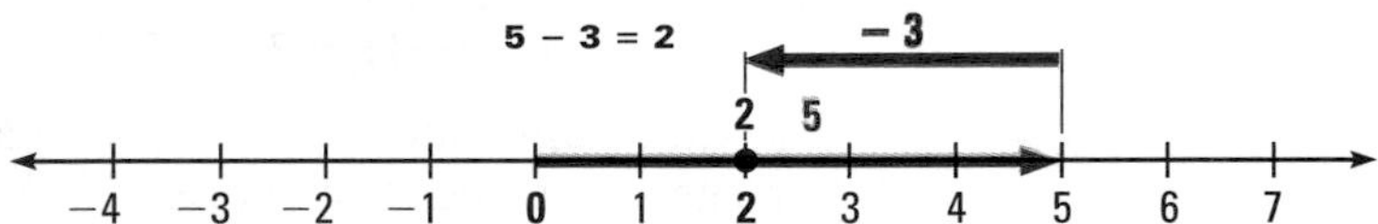

$\boldsymbol{a < b}$ To model the difference $4 - 7$, for example, start at 0. Move 4 units in the positive direction, then 7 units in the negative direction.

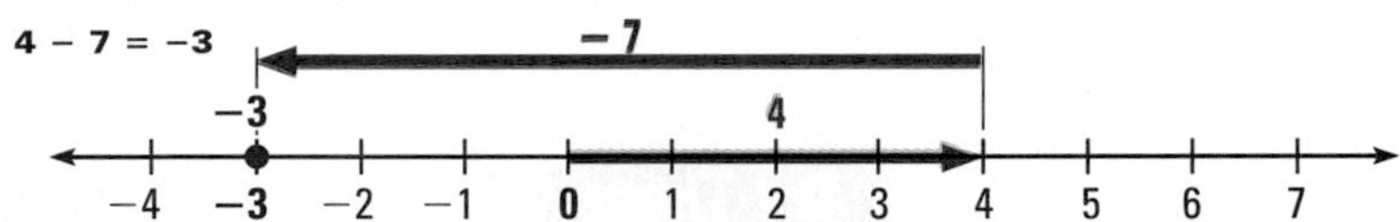

Notice that the number line model for $5 - 3$ can also represent the sum $5 + (-3)$. The model for the difference $4 - 7$ can also model the sum $4 + (-7)$. You can use these observations to write a rule:

> To find the difference of two positive integers a and b, add the opposite of b to a.

Try These

Use the rule stated in Sample 1 to find the difference.

1. $5 - 8$ **−3** **2.** $3 - 9$ **−6** **3.** $7 - 15$ **−8** **4.** $10 - 12$ **−2**

5. MATHEMATICAL REASONING Let a be a negative integer and b be a positive integer. Write a rule for finding the difference $a - b$. Use an example to show how your rule works.

5. *Sample answer:* **Add a and negative b to find $a - b$; $-3 - 7$ becomes $-3 + (-7) = -10$.**

1 Planning the Activity

Purpose and Materials

See the margin of the student page. See also the Activity Support Master in the *Chapter 3 Resource Book.*

LINK TO LESSON

Because students have seen a model for integer subtraction, they should be able to readily accept the algorithm for integer subtraction given in Lesson 3.4.

Math Reasoning

Students use deductive reasoning to infer rules for subtracting integers and write accurate rules using precise mathematical terminology.

2 Managing the Activity

Classroom Management

Begin the pattern recognition activity of Sample 2 by starting the Differences pattern with the whole class. Have students continue the pattern individually for a few minutes. Then work through the Sums pattern with the whole class and have the students compare the two patterns. Have students use the patterns to state a rule for subtracting a negative integer from a positive integer. Compare the rule to the rule for subtracting two positive integers from Sample 1; it is the same. The third case, subtracting a negative integer from a negative integer, is developed in Exercise 10, and again the rule is the same.

California Standards and Assessment

CA Standards: NS 1.2, MR 1.1

Closing the Activity

★ Key Discovery

The result of an integer subtraction problem may be a positive integer, a negative integer, or zero. Students will find it helpful to think about the relationship between the integers involved in order to judge whether their answer makes sense.

Activity Assessment

Use Exercises 4, 8, and 14 to assess student understanding.

SAMPLE 2 Subtracting a Negative Integer

You can use a pattern to write a rule for subtracting a negative integer.

Here's How

Notice that the differences in the list below increase by 1 as you move down the list. So, you can predict that $3 - (-1)$ is 4. The list of sums shows what happens when the rule from Sample 1 (for subtracting a positive integer) is applied to the differences. The pattern suggests that the rule works for subtracting a negative integer.

DIFFERENCES	SUMS
$3 - 3 = 0$	$3 + (-3) = 0$
$3 - 2 = 1$	$3 + (-2) = 1$
$3 - 1 = 2$	$3 + (-1) = 2$
$3 - 0 = 3$	$3 + 0 = 3$
$3 - (-1) = ?$	$3 + 1 = 4$

Based on this pattern, you can write a rule for subtracting a negative integer from a positive integer.

To find the difference of a positive integer a and a negative integer b, add the opposite of b to a.

Try These

Use the rule stated in Sample 2 to find the sum.

6. $3 - (-1)$ **4** **7.** $7 - (-8)$ **15** **8.** $10 - (-1)$ **11** **9.** $9 - (-14)$ **23**

10. *Sample answer:* To find the difference of a negative integer *a* and a negative integer *b*, add the opposite of *b* to *a*.

10. MATHEMATICAL REASONING The sums below show what happens when the rule from Sample 1 is applied to the differences on the left. Copy and complete the lists. Explain your reasoning. Then write a rule for subtracting a negative integer from a negative integer.

DIFFERENCES	SUMS
$-3 - 3 = -6$	$-3 + (-3) = -6$
$-3 - 2 = -5$	$-3 + (-2) = -5$
$-3 - 1 = ?$ **−4**	$-3 + (-1) = ?$ **−4**
$-3 - 0 = ?$ **−3**	$-3 + 0 = ?$ **−3**
$-3 - (-1) = ?$ **−2**	$-3 + 1 = ?$ **−2**

Find the difference by rewriting it as a sum.

11. $-3 - (-2)$ **−1** **12.** $-4 - (-5)$ **1** **13.** $-7 - (-10)$ **3** **14.** $-8 - (-9)$ **1**

3.4 Subtracting Integers

California Standards

In this lesson you'll:

- Subtract integers. (NS 1.2)
- Simplify expressions and use properties of rational numbers to justify the process used. (AF 1.3)

Goal 1 SUBTRACTING INTEGERS

As you saw in Developing Concepts 3.4, page 121, you can express a subtraction problem as an addition problem by using opposites.

SUBTRACTING INTEGERS

In Words To subtract an integer b from an integer a, add the opposite of b to a.

In Algebra $a - b = a + (-b)$

In Arithmetic $3 - 4 = 3 + (-4) = -1$

EXAMPLE 1 *Subtracting Integers*

Find the difference.

a. $5 - 7$ **b.** $-6 - 8$ **c.** $-9 - (-9)$ **d.** $5 - (-1)$

Solution

a. $5 - 7 = 5 + (-7)$ — To subtract 7, add its opposite.
$= -2$ — Use rules for adding integers.

b. $-6 - 8 = -6 + (-8)$ — To subtract 8, add its opposite.
$= -14$ — Use rules for adding integers.

c. $-9 - (-9) = -9 + 9$ — To subtract −9, add its opposite.
$= 0$ — Inverse property of addition

d. $5 - (-1) = 5 + 1$ — To subtract −1, add its opposite.
$= 6$ — Use rules for adding integers.

EXAMPLE 2 *Subtracting More than One Integer*

Evaluate the expression.

a. $-3 - 5 - 2 = -3 + (-5) + (-2)$ — To subtract, add opposites.
$= -10$ — Use rules for adding integers.

b. $-8 - 7 - (-8) = -8 + (-7) + 8$ — To subtract, add opposites.
$= -7$ — Use rules for adding integers.

1 Plan

Pacing

Suggested Number of Days

Transitional: 2 days
Average: 2 days
Advanced: 2 days
Block Schedule: 1 block

Teaching Resources

Blacklines
(See page 102B.)

Transparencies
- Warm-Up Exercises
- Teacher Time-Savers
- English/Spanish Problem Solving
- Answers

Technology
- Electronic Teacher Tools
- Test and Practice Generator

2 Teach

Math Reasoning

For Mathematical Background Notes on mathematical reasoning related to this lesson, please refer to pages 102E and 102F in this Teacher's Edition.

Extra Examples 1 and 2
See next page.

California Standards and Assessment

CA Standards: NS 1.2, AF 1.3

Math Reasoning

The mathematical justification of the rule $a - b = a + (-b)$ is given in the Mathematical Background Notes for Lesson 3.4 on page 102E.

Extra Example 1

Find the difference.

a. $9 - 13$ **−4** **b.** $-10 - 23$ **−33**

c. $-21 - (-7)$ **−14**

d. $6 - (-3)$ **9**

Extra Example 2

Evaluate the expression.

a. $4 - 7 - 10$ **−13**

b. $-2 - 5 - (-9)$ **2**

Extra Example 3

Identify the terms in the expression.

a. $3x - 9$ **3x and −9**

b. $-7n - 14n + 11$ **−7n, −14n, and 11**

Extra Example 4

Simplify $5y - 3y - 12$. Then evaluate the expression when $y = 6$. **2y − 12; 0**

Extra Example 5

A lumber yard cuts boards into segments that are 96 inches long. The actual length of a board may vary from the desired length of 96 inches, and the absolute deviation is expressed by $|96 - l|$ where l is the actual length of the board. Find the absolute deviation when l is 95 inches and when l is 97 inches. **1 in.; 1 in.**

Concept Check

Explain the steps you take to evaluate the expression $-2 + 7 - (-3) - 5 + 1 - 12$. **Answers may vary.** ***Sample answer:*** **Change to equivalent addition statement: $-2 + 7 + 3 + (-5) + 1 + (-12)$. Group positive and negative integers: $-2 + (-5) + (-12) + 7 + 3 + 1$. Add each group to get $-19 + 11$. Add to get -8.**

Goal 2 EVALUATING VARIABLE EXPRESSIONS

The *terms* of a variable expression are separated by addition signs, not by subtraction signs. To identify the terms of an expression involving subtraction, you should rewrite the expression as a sum.

EXAMPLE 3 Identifying Terms

Identify the terms in the expression.

a. $2x - 4$ **b.** $-3x - (-2x) + 5$

Solution

	EXPRESSION	EQUIVALENT SUM	TERMS
a.	$2x - 4$	$2x + (-4)$	$2x$ and -4
b.	$-3x - (-2x) + 5$	$-3x + 2x + 5$	$-3x$, $2x$, and 5

Student Help

▶MORE EXAMPLES

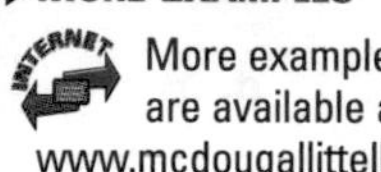

More examples are available at www.mcdougallittell.com

EXAMPLE 4 Simplifying before Evaluating

Simplify $11x - 2x + 3$. Then evaluate the expression when $x = 5$.

Solution

Begin by simplifying the expression.

$11x - 2x + 3 = 11x + (-2x) + 3$ — Use rule for subtraction.

$= [11 + (-2)]x + 3$ — Distributive property

$= 9x + 3$ — Simplify.

ANSWER ▶ When $x = 5$, $9x + 3 = 9(5) + 3 = 48$.

Link to Tools

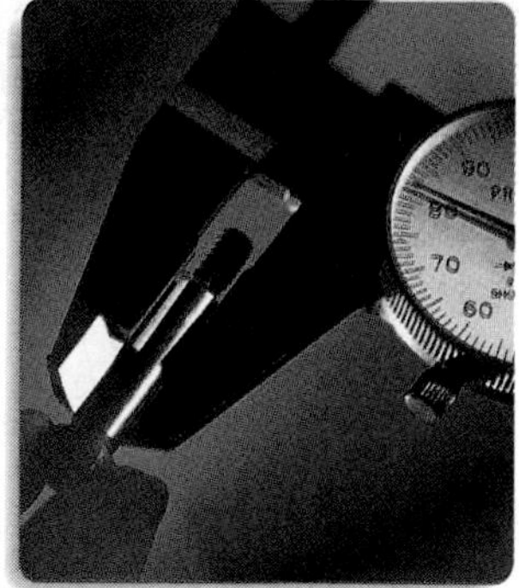

TOLERANCE Tolerance is the amount of acceptable error used in manufacturing. For example, each screw that is made in a factory may be a little shorter or a little longer than a specified length, but only within a given margin of error.

EXAMPLE 5 Subtracting Integers to Solve a Problem

TOOLS A tool manufacturer wants to check the quality of a shipment of screws. Individual screws vary somewhat from an ideal length of 89 millimeters. The expression $|x - 89|$ gives the *absolute deviation* of the actual length x of a screw from the ideal length. Find the absolute deviation when $x = 87$ millimeters and when $x = 92$ millimeters.

Solution

Evaluate the expression $|x - 89|$ when $x = 87$ and when $x = 92$. First evaluate the expression inside the absolute value bars. Then find the absolute value of the result.

$|87 - 89| = |-2| = 2$ — Absolute deviation of 87 mm screw

$|92 - 89| = |3| = 3$ — Absolute deviation of 92 mm screw

3.4 Exercises

Guided Practice

Rewrite the subtraction expression as an addition expression. Then evaluate the expression.

1. $3-(-5)$ **3 + 5; 8**
2. $-4-(-4)$ **−4 + 4; 0**
3. $5-3$ **5 + (−3); 2**
4. $9-12$ **9 + (−12); −3**
5. $-6-(-2)$ **−6 + 2; −4**
6. $-9-5$ **−9 + (−5); −14**
7. $7-(-3)$ **7 + 3; 10**
8. $-2-11$ **−2 + (−11); −13**

Simplify the expression. Then evaluate the expression when $x = 3$.

9. $6x-3x+5$ **3x + 5; 14**
10. $7x-(-2x)-3$ **9x − 3; 24**
11. $10x-3x+4$ **7x + 4; 25**

ERROR ANALYSIS **In Exercises 12 and 13, describe and correct the error.**

12. 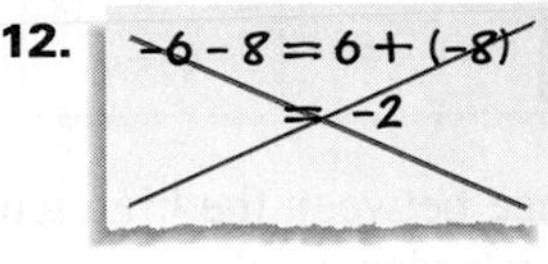

−6 − 8 = −6 + (−8) = −14

13. 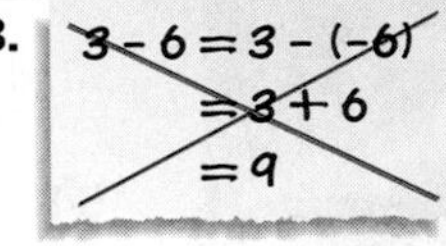

3 − 6 = 3 + (−6) = −3

Practice and Problem Solving

> **Student Help**
> ▶**MORE PRACTICE**
> Extra practice to help you master skills is on page 694.

Find the difference.

14. $19-17$ **2**
15. $5-9$ **−4**
16. $23-(-8)$ **31**
17. $2-(-4)$ **6**
18. $-10-7$ **−17**
19. $-5-(-5)$ **0**
20. $-16-(-8)$ **−8**
21. $-5-5$ **−10**
22. $-3-3$ **−6**

Evaluate the expression.

23. $-6-10-14$ **−30**
24. $-3+9-5$ **1**
25. $4-(-8)-6$ **6**
26. $7-9-(-12)$ **10**
27. $2-11+5$ **−4**
28. $-5-10-(-2)$ **−13**

Evaluate the expression when $a = 5$ and when $a = -5$.

29. $a-1$ **4, −6**
30. $1-a$ **−4, 6**
31. $a-6$ **−1, −11**
32. $6-a$ **1, 11**
33. $|a-2|$ **3, 7**
34. $|2-a|$ **3, 7**
35. $|5-a|$ **0, 10**
36. $|a-5|$ **0, 10**

37. MATHEMATICAL REASONING Is subtraction of integers associative? In other words, is the statement $(a-b)-c = a-(b-c)$ true for all integers a, b, and c? Use examples to explain your reasoning.

Rewrite the expression as a sum. Identify the terms. If possible, simplify the expression.

38. $3x-2x+16$
39. $7x-9x-5$
40. $7a-5b-8$
41. $4-2n+4m$
42. $6r-4s-(-4t)$
43. $-11f-(-3g)-(-9)$

37. Subtraction of integers is not associative.
Sample answer:
(7 − 4) − 2 = 3 − 2 = 1, but
7 − (4 − 2) = 7 − 2 = 5

38. 3x + (−2x) + 16; 3x, −2x, 16; x + 16

39. 7x + (−9x) + (−5); 7x, −9x, −5; −2x − 5

40. 7a + (−5b) + (−8); 7a, −5b, −8; not possible

41. 4 + (−2n) + 4m; 4, −2n, 4m; not possible

42. 6r + (−4s) + 4t; 6r, −4s, 4t; 6r − 4s + 4t

43. −11f + 3g + 9; −11f, 3g, 9; −11f + 3g + 9

3 Apply

Assignment Guide

TRANSITIONAL
Day 1: pp. 125–126 Exs. 14–19, 23–25, 54–56, 60–61
Day 2: pp. 125–126 Exs. 29–32, 38–40, 44–46, 50, 57

AVERAGE
Day 1: pp. 125–126 Exs. 14–28, 54–56, 60–61
Day 2: pp. 125–126 Exs. 30–34, 37–40, 47–53, 57–58

ADVANCED
Day 1: pp. 125–126 Exs. 20–28, 54–56, 60–61
Day 2: pp. 125–126 Exs. 29–40, 47–53, 57–58, 59*

BLOCK SCHEDULE
pp. 125–126 Exs. 14–28, 30–34, 37–40, 47–58, 60–61

Extra Practice

- Student Edition, pp. 694–695
- Chapter 3 Resource Book, p. 33

Homework Check

To quickly check student understanding of key concepts, go over the following exercises:

Transitional: 16, 24, 32, 40, 57
Average: 16, 28, 34, 40, 57
Advanced: 16, 28, 34, 40, 57

4 Assess

Assessment Resources

- Assessment Book (Formal Assessment and Alternative Assessment)
- Test and Practice Generator

Mini-Quiz

Find the difference.

1. $4 - 9$ **−5**
2. $-3 - (-9)$ **6**
3. Evaluate the expression $-5 - 7 - (-10)$. **−2**
4. Identify the terms in the expression $-9x - 5x + 12$. **$-9x$, $-5x$, and 12**
5. Simplify the expression. Then evaluate the expression when $y = 3$. $-13y - (-18y) + 8$ **$5y + 8$; 23**
6. California contains both the highest point and the lowest point in the lower 48 states. Mt. Whitney is the highest point with an elevation of 14,494 feet. Death Valley is the lowest point with an elevation of 282 feet below sea level. What is the difference in elevation between Mt. Whitney and Death Valley? **14,776 feet**

126

Simplify the expression. Then evaluate the expression when $x = 5$.

44. $9x - (-2x)$ **$11x$; 55**
45. $3x - (-3x)$ **$6x$; 30**
46. $-11x - (-15x) - 2$ **$4x - 2$; 18**
47. $9x - 6x - 17$ **$3x - 17$; −2**
48. $8x - 2x + 4$ **$6x + 4$; 34**
49. $-2x - (-3x) + 5$ **$x + 5$; 10**

MATHEMATICAL REASONING Decide whether the statement is true for *all, some,* or *no* values of x. Explain your reasoning.

50. $7x - 2x = 7x + (-2x)$ **true for all values of x**
51. $3(x - 4) = 3x - 12$ **true for all values of x**
52. The opposite of x is 0. **true only for $x = 0$**
53. The opposite of x is negative. **true only for positive values of x**

SOJOURNER In 1997, as part of an unmanned mission to Mars, scientists tested a robotic vehicle called *Sojourner.* Temperature sensors on *Sojourner* helped scientists assess its ability to perform in the extreme Martian temperatures.

More about Mars exploration at www.mcdougallittell.com

Science Link **In Exercises 54–56, use the table, which gives the low and high surface temperatures of four planets.**

	Mercury	Venus	Earth	Mars
Low	−280°F	721°F	−129°F	−220°F
High	800°F	925°F	136°F	68°F

54. Find the difference between the high temperature and the low temperature of each planet. **Mercury: 1080°F; Venus: 204°F; Earth: 265°F; Mars: 288°F**

55. Find the difference between the low temperatures of Earth and Mars. **91°F**

56. Find the difference between the low temperatures of Earth and Venus. **850°F**

57. MANUFACTURING A manufacturer wants each axle created on an assembly line to be 60 inches long. The absolute deviation of the actual length x of an axle from the ideal length is given by the expression $|x - 60|$. Find the absolute deviation of the length of an axle whose actual length is 61 inches. **1 in.**

58. MATHEMATICAL REASONING Evaluate each expression. Then use the results to make a prediction about how the values of $a - b$ and $b - a$ are related. Test your prediction using several other values of a and b.

a. $5 - 3$ **2** **b.** $3 - 5$ **−2** **c.** $-7 - 12$ **−19** **d.** $12 - (-7)$ **19**

$a - b = -(b - a)$

59. CHALLENGE Solve the following problem. Then write and solve a similar problem.

The sum of two integers is 2, and their difference is 6. What are the integers? **4, −2**

Multiple-Choice Practice

60. Which number would you expect to come next in the following sequence: 5, 2, −1, . . .? **A**

Ⓐ −4 Ⓑ −3 Ⓒ −2 Ⓓ 0

61. Find the value of the expression $a - b$ when $a = 2$ and $b = -3$. **J**

Ⓕ −5 Ⓖ −1 Ⓗ 1 Ⓙ 5

Developing Concepts: Integer Multiplication

For use with Lesson 3.5

California Standards

- Multiply integers. (NS 1.2)
- Make and test conjectures by using both inductive and deductive reasoning. (MR 2.4)

Using properties you know, you can develop rules for multiplying integers.

SAMPLE 1 Multiplying a Positive Integer by −1

By looking for a pattern, you can make a conjecture about the product of -1 and a positive integer.

Here's How

In each list below, the products decrease by the same amount as you move down the list. Thus, you can predict that the product of –1 and 3 is –3, and the product of -1 and 2 is -2.

$3 \cdot 3 = 9$	$3 \cdot 2 = 6$
$2 \cdot 3 = 6$	$2 \cdot 2 = 4$
$1 \cdot 3 = 3$	$1 \cdot 2 = 2$
$0 \cdot 3 = 0$	$0 \cdot 2 = 0$
$-1 \cdot 3 = ?$ (Subtract 3.)	$-1 \cdot 2 = ?$ (Subtract 2.)

You can make the following conjecture:

The product of -1 and a positive integer is the opposite of the integer.

Student Help

▶ Vocabulary Tip
A *conjecture* is an unproven statement that is believed might be true.

You can show that the conjecture in Sample 1 is true for *any* integer a (that is, $-1(a) = -a$ for any integer a). Begin with the sum $a + (-1)a$:

$a + (-1)a = 1a + (-1)a$ — Identity property of multiplication

$= [1 + (-1)]a$ — Distributive property

$= 0a$ — Inverse property of addition

$= 0$ — A number multiplied by 0 is 0.

The preceding steps show that $a + (-1)a = 0$. By the inverse property of addition, you can conclude that $(-1)a$ must be the additive inverse of a, which is written as $-a$. So, $(-1)a = -a$.

Try These

Find the product using the fact that $(-1)a = -a$.

1. $(-1)(9)$ −9 **2.** $(-1)(1)$ −1 **3.** $(-1)(-4)$ 4 **4.** $(-1)(-13)$ 13

5. MATHEMATICAL REASONING Simplify the expression $(-1)(-1)a$. Justify the steps you take.

5. $(-1)(-1)(a) = [(-1)(-1)]a$ Associative property
$= (1)a$ The product of -1 and an integer is the opposite of the integer.
$= a$ Identity property

1 Planning the Activity

Purpose and Materials

See the margin of the student page. See also the Activity Support Master in the *Chapter 3 Resource Book.*

▶ Link to Lesson

Using their answers to Exercises 14–17 of this lab, students should readily apply the rules to the problems in Example 1 of Lesson 3.5.

Math Reasoning

Students use deductive reasoning to infer rules for multiplying integers and write accurate rules using precise mathematical terminology.

2 Managing the Activity

Classroom Management

Work through Samples 1 and 2 with the whole class. Have students work through some or all of Exercises 1–13. Then as a class complete the statements in Exercises 14–17; these are the rules for multiplying integers.

California Standards and Assessment

CA Standards: NS 1.2, MR 2.4

3 Closing the Activity

★ **KEY DISCOVERY**

The product of a positive integer and a negative integer is a negative integer, the product of a negative integer and positive integer is a negative integer, and the product of two negative integers is a positive integer.

Activity Assessment

Use Exercises 10–13 to assess student understanding.

SAMPLE 2 Multiplying Integers

You can use the fact that $(-1)a = -a$ to multiply any integers.

Here's How

The rule $(-1)a = -a$ allows you not only to find the product of -1 and an integer but also to rewrite a negative integer as the product of -1 and the integer's opposite. You can use this fact to multiply a negative integer and a positive integer.

$(-3)(2) = [(-1)(3)](2)$ — $(-1)a = -a$
$= (-1)[(3)(2)]$ — Associative property
$= (-1)(6)$ — Multiply positive integers.
$= -6$ — $(-1)a = -a$

You can use similar reasoning to multiply two negative integers.

$(-4)(-7) = (-1)(4)(-1)(7)$ — $(-1)a = -a$
$= (-1)(-1)(4)(7)$ — Commutative property
$= (-1)[(-1)[(4)(7)]]$ — Associative property
$= (-1)[(-1)(28)]$ — Multiply positive integers.
$= (-1)(-28)$ — $(-1)a = -a$
$= 28$ — $(-1)a = -a$

Student Help

▶ **STUDY TIP**
When you see many pairs of grouping symbols (parentheses and brackets), do the operations inside the innermost grouping symbols first.

Try These

Find the product. Explain your steps.

6. $(-8)(20)$ **−160** **7.** $3(-7)$ **−21** **8.** $(-1)(-5)$ **5** **9.** $(-10)(-6)$ **60**

10. $6(-2)$ **−12** **11.** $(-9)(-9)$ **81** **12.** $(-5)(7)$ **−35** **13.** $(-7)(-8)$ **56**

MATHEMATICAL REASONING In Exercises 14–16, complete each statement using *positive* or *negative*. Justify your reasoning.

14. The product of two positive integers is always __?__. **positive**

15. The product of two negative integers is always __?__. **positive**

16. The product of a positive and a negative integer is always __?__. **negative**

17. MATHEMATICAL REASONING Let a and b represent any integers. Under what circumstances is the product $-ab$ positive? Explain your reasoning.

17. ***Sample answer:*** **$-ab$ is positive if the product ab is negative, which means a and b have opposite signs.**

3.5 Multiplying Integers

California Standards

In this lesson you'll:

- Multiply integers and take positive integers to whole number powers. (NS 1.2)
- Interpret whole-number powers as repeated multiplication. (AF 2.1)

Goal 1 MULTIPLYING INTEGERS

In Developing Concepts 3.5, page 127, you saw the following property.

MULTIPLICATIVE PROPERTY OF −1

In Words	The product of −1 and a number is the opposite of the number.
In Algebra	$(-1) \cdot a = -a$
In Arithmetic	$(-1) \cdot 4 = -4$ and $(-1) \cdot (-5) = 5$

The multiplicative property of −1 leads to the following rules for multiplying integers.

MULTIPLYING INTEGERS

Rule	Examples
1. The product of two positive integers is positive.	$4(5) = 20$
2. The product of two negative integers is positive.	$-3(-2) = 6$
3. The product of two integers with different signs is negative.	$-10(10) = -100$ $7(-8) = -56$
4. The product of an integer and 0 is 0.	$0(-2) = 0$

EXAMPLE 1 Multiplying Integers

Find the product.

a. $-7(-8)$ **b.** $-4(11)$ **c.** $3(-5)(-2)$ **d.** $(-9)^2$

Solution

a. $-7(-8) = 56$ The product of two negative integers is positive.

b. $-4(11) = -44$ The product of two integers with different signs is negative.

c. $3(-5)(-2) = -15(-2)$ Multiply two of the integers.

$= 30$ Multiply.

d. $(-9)^2 = (-9)(-9)$ Rewrite as a product.

$= 81$ Multiply.

Student Help

▶ **LOOK BACK**
For help with using exponents, see page 12.

1 Plan

Pacing
Suggested Number of Days

Transitional: 2 days
Average: 2 days
Advanced: 2 days
Block Schedule: 1 block

Teaching Resources

Blacklines
(See page 102B.)

Transparencies
- Warm-Up Exercises
- Teacher Time-Savers
- English/Spanish Problem Solving
- Answers

Technology
- Electronic Teacher Tools
- Test and Practice Generator

2 Teach

Math Reasoning

For Mathematical Background Notes on mathematical reasoning related to this lesson, please refer to pages 102E and 102F in this Teacher's Edition.

Extra Example 1
See next page.

California Standards and Assessment

CA Standards: NS 1.2, AF 2.1
CA Key Concepts Book: pp. S5, S7–S8

Extra Example 1

Find the product.

a. $-3(-4)$ **12** b. $-8(9)$ **−72**
c. $10(-2)(-5)$ **100**
d. $(-6)^2$ **36**

Extra Example 2

Evaluate $-3x + x - 2$ when $x = -4$. **6**

Extra Example 3

Evaluate the expression when $y = -3$.

a. y^3 **−27** b. $-y^3$ **27** c. $y^2 - y$ **12**

Math Reasoning

Since $x^4 = (x \cdot x) \cdot (x \cdot x) = x^2 \cdot x^2$, and since $x^2 \geq 0$, we see that $x^4 \geq 0$ for any number x. Similarly, by pairing factors, we see that $x^n \geq 0$ when n is any even positive integer and x is any number.

Extra Example 4

A boulder falls from the top of a 280 foot tall cliff. The equation $h = -16t^2 + 280$ is used to determine the height h (in feet) of the boulder after t seconds. What is the height of the boulder after 2 seconds? after 4 seconds? Estimate how long it takes the boulder to hit the ground. **216 feet; 24 feet; a little more than 4 seconds**

Concept Check

Is the product of 100 negative numbers always positive, always negative, or sometimes positive and sometimes negative? Explain your reasoning. **Always positive. The product of 100 negative numbers can be expressed as 50 products of pairs of negative numbers. Each of these 50 products will be positive, and the product of the 50 positive numbers will be positive.**

The multiplicative property of -1 and the identity property of multiplication are the reasons why the coefficients -1 and 1 are usually implied rather than written in variable expressions.

EXAMPLE 2 Evaluating an Expression

Evaluate $-n + 5n + 3$ when $n = -7$.

Solution

First simplify the expression.

$-n + 5n + 3 = -1n + 5n + 3$	Coefficient of $-n$ is -1.
$= (-1 + 5)n + 3$	Use distributive property.
$= 4n + 3$	Simplify.

Then evaluate $4n + 3$ when $n = -7$.

$4n + 3 = 4(-7) + 3$	Substitute −7 for n.
$= -28 + 3$	Multiply.
$= -25$	Add.

ANSWER ▶ When $n = -7$, $-n + 5n + 3$ is equal to -25.

Goal 2 USING INTEGER MULTIPLICATION

EXAMPLE 3 Evaluating Expressions with Exponents

Evaluate the expression when $x = -2$.

a. x^4 **b.** $-x^4$ **c.** $x^3 - x$

Solution

a. $x^4 = (-2)^4$	Substitute −2 for x.
$= (-2)(-2)(-2)(-2)$	Rewrite as a product.
$= 16$	Multiply.
b. $-x^4 = -(-2)^4$	Substitute −2 for x.
$= -[(-2)(-2)(-2)(-2)]$	Rewrite as a product.
$= -(16)$	Multiply.
$= -16$	Write opposite of 16.
c. $x^3 - x = (-2)^3 - (-2)$	Substitute −2 for x.
$= (-2)(-2)(-2) - (-2)$	Rewrite as a product.
$= -8 - (-2)$	Multiply.
$= -6$	Use rules for adding integers.

Student Help

▶ **STUDY TIP**
A common error made in problems like the one in part (b) of Example 3 is to think that $-x^4$ means $(-x)^4$. Remember that $-x^4$ means $-1 \cdot x^4$, so you must evaluate the power before multiplying by -1.

Science

PHYSICS When there is no air resistance, a hammer and a feather fall with the same velocity, as astronaut David R. Scott demonstrated on the Apollo 15 mission to the moon. This painting of Scott's experiment was created by astronaut Alan Bean.

More about physics is available at www.mcdougallittell.com

EXAMPLE 4 Evaluating a Formula

A brick falls from the top of a 150 foot tall building. The formula $h = -16t^2 + 150$ is used to model the height h (in feet) of the brick after t seconds. What is the height of the brick after 2 seconds? after 3 seconds? Estimate how long it takes the brick to hit the ground.

Solution

Evaluate the formula when $t = 2$ seconds.

$h = -16t^2 + 150$	Write original equation.
$= -16(\mathbf{2})^2 + 150$	Substitute.
$= -16(4) + 150$	Evaluate power.
$= -64 + 150$	Multiply.
$= 86$	Simplify.

Evaluate the formula when $t = 3$ seconds.

$h = -16t^2 + 150$	Write original equation.
$= -16(\mathbf{3})^2 + 150$	Substitute.
$= -16(9) + 150$	Evaluate power.
$= -144 + 150$	Multiply.
$= 6$	Simplify.

ANSWER ▶ After 2 seconds, the height of the brick is 86 feet. After 3 seconds, its height is 6 feet, which is close to the ground. So, it takes a little more than 3 seconds for the brick to hit the ground.

3.5 Exercises

Guided Practice

Find the product.

1. $4 \cdot 5$ **20** **2.** $-4 \cdot 5$ **−20** **3.** $4(-5)$ **−20**

4. $-4(-5)$ **20** **5.** $-3(8)(2)$ **−48** **6.** $7(-8)(-2)$ **112**

Simplify the expression. Then evaluate the expression when $n = 4$.

7. $n + (-4n) + 5$ **$-3n + 5$; −7** **8.** $-3n + n - 6$ **$-2n - 6$; −14** **9.** $4n - 12 + n - 8n$ **$-3n - 12$; −24**

Evaluate the expression when $x = 3$ and when $x = -3$.

10. $-x^2$ **−9, −9** **11.** $-6x$ **−18, 18** **12.** x^3 **27, −27**

13. $x^2 + 7$ **16, 16** **14.** $-15 - x + 8x$ **6, −36** **15.** $x^2 - x + 2$ **8, 14**

3 Apply

Assignment Guide

TRANSITIONAL
Day 1: EP p. 690 Exs. 14–17; pp. 132–133 Exs. 16–25, 38–45, 50–52
Day 2: pp. 132–133 Exs. 56–63, 66–70, 73–74

AVERAGE
Day 1: pp. 132–133 Exs. 19–30, 38–46, 50–52
Day 2: pp. 132–133 Exs. 56–63, 66–71, 73–74

ADVANCED
Day 1: pp. 132–133 Exs. 19–24, 31–43, 47–49, 53–55
Day 2: pp. 132–133 Exs. 56–61, 64–71, 72*, 73–74

BLOCK SCHEDULE
pp. 132–133 Exs. 19–30, 38–46, 50–52, 56–63, 66–71, 73–74

Extra Practice

- Student Edition, pp. 694–695
- Chapter 3 Resource Book, p. 42

Homework Check

To quickly check student understanding of key concepts, go over the following exercises:

Transitional: 16, 18, 52, 56, 70
Average: 18, 30, 52, 58, 70
Advanced: 20, 34, 54, 58, 70

Math Reasoning

In regards to Exercises 60 and 61, suppose *a, b, c, d, e,* ... are negative numbers. Then ab is a positive number, so $(ab)c$, being the product of a positive number and a negative number, is a negative number. Thus $(abc)d$ is the product of a negative number and a negative number and therefore is positive. From this we see that $(abcd)e$ is the product of a positive number and a negative number and therefore is negative. Continuing in this fashion, we see that the product of an even number of negative numbers is positive and the product of an odd number of negative numbers is negative.

37.

x	−3	−2	−1	0	1	2	3
$4x$	−12	−8	−4	0	4	8	12

As x increases by 1, $4x$ increases by 4. As x decreases by 1, $4x$ decreases by 4.

Practice and Problem Solving

Student Help

▶MORE PRACTICE Extra practice to help you master skills is on page 694.

In Exercises 16–36, find the product.

16. $-4(-6)$ **24** **17.** $-10(-2)$ **20** **18.** $5(-11)$ **−55**

19. $-8(6)$ **−48** **20.** $-7(-9)$ **63** **21.** $-10(-1)$ **10**

22. $-5(-12)$ **60** **23.** $-2(-2)5$ **20** **24.** $(-8)^2$ **64**

25. $-3(2)(-4)$ **24** **26.** $-2(-3)(0)$ **0** **27.** $-1(1)(-2)(2)$ **4**

28. $5(-5)(-1)$ **25** **29.** $3(-7)(-11)$ **231** **30.** $4(3)(-5)(-1)$ **60**

31. $-2(-1)(-3)(6)$ **−36** **32.** $-7(-10)^2$ **−700** **33.** $(-1)(3)(-5)^2$ **−75**

34. $(25)(-4)(-2)$ **200** **35.** $(-8)^3$ **−512** **36.** $-1(-3)^4$ **−81**

37. MATHEMATICAL REASONING Evaluate $4x$ when $x = -3, -2, -1, 0, 1,$ 2 and 3. Use a table to organize your data. Describe the pattern. **See margin.**

MATHEMATICAL REASONING In Exercises 38–43, match the property with an example that illustrates how the property applies to integers.

38. Commutative property of multiplication **E**

39. Associative property of multiplication **D**

40. Commutative property of addition **B**

41. Distributive property **F**

42. Identity property of multiplication **C**

43. Multiplicative property of -1 **A**

A. $-1(-3) = 3$

B. $-2 + 3 = 3 + (-2)$

C. $-7 \cdot 1 = -7$

D. $-5 \cdot (2 \cdot 3) = (-5 \cdot 2) \cdot 3$

E. $5(-3) = -3(5)$

F. $-3(-5 + 6) = -3(-5) + (-3)(6)$

MATHEMATICAL REASONING Simplify the expression. For each step, tell what property you use.

44. $3x - 5 - x$ **$2x - 5$** **45.** $-2x + 7 + 2x$ **7** **46.** $-x + 4x - x$ **$2x$**

47. $6 - 3x + 7 - 2x$ **$-5x + 13$** **48.** $12x - 13x + x$ **0** **49.** $-x - x + 5 - x$ **$-3x + 5$**

Simplify the expression. Then evaluate the expression when $n = -3$.

50. $-5n - 13 + 12n$ **$7n - 13$; −34** **51.** $-n + 8 - 7n$ **$-8n + 8$; 32** **52.** $-n + 11 + 2n - 13$ **$n - 2$; −5**

53. $-3n - 4n + 6$ **$-7n + 6$; 27** **54.** $8n - 16 - 8n + n$ **$n - 16$; −19** **55.** $-2n - 2n - 5n + 4$ **$-9n + 4$; 31**

MATHEMATICAL REASONING Decide whether the expression is positive or negative when the value of x is *not* zero. Explain your reasoning.

56. x^2 **positive** **57.** $2x^2$ **positive** **58.** $-x^2$ **negative** **59.** $-4x^2$ **negative**

Construction

CONSTRUCTION The speed of a hammer dropped from a height of 400 feet increases over time. By the time the hammer hits the ground, it can be traveling at nearly 160 feet per second. This is one of the reasons that construction sites are off limits to pedestrians.

MATHEMATICAL REASONING Answer the question and give an example to support your answer.

60. Is the product of three negative numbers positive or negative? **negative; $(-1)(-1)(-5) = -5$**

61. Is the product of four negative numbers positive or negative? **positive; $(-2)(-1)(-3)(-1) = 6$**

Use the distributive property to write an equivalent expression.

62. $-5(x + 1)$ **$-5x - 5$** **63.** $-5(-7 + x)$ **$35 - 5x$** **64.** $-6(7 + x)$ **$-42 - 6x$** **65.** $-8(-5 + x)$ **$40 - 8x$**

In Exercises 66–69, evaluate the expression when $a = 8$ and $b = -2$.

66. ab **-16** **67.** ab^2 **32** **68.** a^2b **-128** **69.** a^2b^3 **-512**

70. CONSTRUCTION A hammer falls from a platform 400 feet above the ground. The equation $h = -16t^2 + 400$ gives the height h (in feet) of the hammer after t seconds. Find the height of the hammer after 1, 2, 3, 4, and 5 seconds. When does the hammer hit the ground?
384 ft, 336 ft; 256 ft; 144 ft; 0 ft; after 5 sec

71. MATHEMATICAL REASONING To show that $x - y$ and $y - x$ are opposites for all values of x and y, you need to show that $-(y - x)$ is equal to $x - y$. The steps below demonstrate that this statement is true. Supply the missing reasons.

$-(y - x) = -1(y - x)$ **Multiplicative property of −1**

$= -1y - (-1x)$ **a.** ? **Distributive property**

$= -y - (-x)$ **b.** ? **Multiplicative property of −1**

$= -y + x$ **c.** ? **Rule for subtraction**

$= x + (-y)$ **d.** ? **Commutative property of addition**

$= x - y$ **e.** ? **Rule for subtraction**

72. CHALLENGE On a grocery store's "double coupon" day, an item with regular price r costs only $-2c + r$ if you have a coupon with value c.

a. Suppose a bottle of juice costs \$1.29 and you have a \$.25 coupon. Evaluate $-2c + r$ when $r = 1.29$ and $c = 0.25$. **\$.79**

b. What expression can you use to calculate a price on a "triple coupon day?" Find the price of a bottle of juice on such a day. **$-3c + r$; \$.54**

Multiple-Choice Practice

73. Which expression is equal to $-4(-4)$? **C**

Ⓐ -16 Ⓑ -4^2 Ⓒ $(-4)^2$ Ⓓ 8

74. Which expression is *not* equivalent to $5 - x$? **J**

Ⓕ $-2 + 3x - 4x + 7$ Ⓖ $-x + 5$

Ⓗ $3 - 2x + x + 2$ Ⓙ $-5x + 1 + 4x - 6$

4 Assess

Assessment Resources

- Assessment Book (Formal Assessment and Alternative Assessment)
- Test and Practice Generator

Mini-Quiz

Find the product.

1. $11(-7)$ **-77** **2.** $-5(-6)$ **30**

3. $-2(8)(-1)$ **16** **4.** $(-5)^3$ **-125**

5. Evaluate $-8x + 2x - 3$ when $x = -2$. **9**

6. Evaluate $-g^2 + g$ when $g = -10$. **-110**

7. A shingle falls off a roof 70 feet above the ground. The equation $h = -16t^2 + 70$ gives the height of the shingle after t seconds. What is the height of the shingle after 2 seconds? **6 feet**

Additional Resources

A Mid-Chapter Test and a Mid-Chapter Partner Quiz are available in the *Assessment Book*, pp. 27–28 and p. 220.

1. 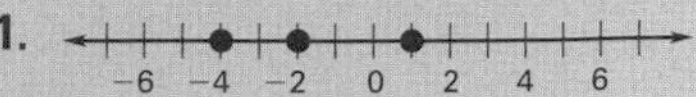

2. 

3. −10 −8 −6 −4 −2 0 2

4. −6 −4 −2 0 2 4 6

21. Lost money; \$194; the sum of the monthly profits for the first 6 months is −\$194.

Chapter 3 Mid-Chapter Test

Take this test as you would take a test in class. The answers to the exercises are given in the back of the book.

Draw a number line and graph the integers. 1–4. See margin.

1. $-2, 1, -4$ **2.** $4, -1, 0$ **3.** $2, -3, -7$ **4.** $5, -6, -5$

Write the opposite and the absolute value of the number.

5. 7 −7, 7 **6.** -5 5, 5 **7.** 42 −42, 42 **8.** -132 132, 132

Order the integers from least to greatest.

9. $-9, 9, -11, 6$ −11, −9, 6, 9 **10.** $0, -1, 1, -5$ −5, −1, 0, 1 **11.** $1, -3, 3, -2$ −3, −2, 1, 3 **12.** $-2, 4, -6, 5$ −6, −2, 4, 5

Use a number line to find the sum.

13. $-4 + 6$ 2 **14.** $-5 + 10$ 5 **15.** $-2 + (-8)$ −10 **16.** $5 + (-6)$ −1

In Exercises 17–20, find the sum or the difference.

17. $5 + (-7)$ −2 **18.** $-8 - 1$ −9 **19.** $-3 + 5$ 2 **20.** $3 - (-7)$ 10

21. *BUSINESS* You own an art supply store whose monthly profits are shown in the graph. A negative monthly profit means the store lost money in that month. From January through June, did the store earn or lose money overall? How much did it earn or lose in that time period? Explain your reasoning. See margin.

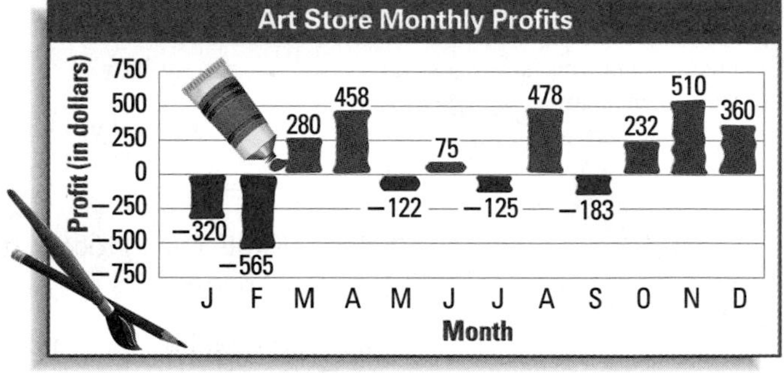

Simplify the expression.

22. $-3x - 12x + 2$ $-15x + 2$ **23.** $-4x + (-9x) - 6$ $-13x - 6$ **24.** $-x + 2x - (-3x)$ $4x$

Simplify the expression. Then evaluate the expression when $a = 6$.

25. $4a + 2a - 6$ $6a - 6$; 30 **26.** $7a - 2 - 3a$ $4a - 2$; 22 **27.** $11 - 5a - 2a$ $11 - 7a$; −31

MATHEMATICAL REASONING Tell whether the statement is *true* or *false*. Explain your reasoning and give an example.

28. The sum of two negative integers is always negative. True; $-1 + (-3) = -4$

29. The absolute value of a negative integer is the opposite of that integer. True; $|-4| = 4$

30. The difference of two negative integers is always negative. False; $-7 - (-8) = 1$

Find the product.

31. $-7(-3)$ 21 **32.** $4(-9)$ −36 **33.** $-2(5)$ −10 **34.** $-3(-2)(-10)$ −60

3.6 Dividing Integers

California Standards

In this lesson you'll:

▶ Divide integers. (NS 1.2)

Goal 1 DIVIDING INTEGERS

The rules for division are related to those for multiplication. This is because multiplication and division are inverse operations. For example, because you know that $5(-6) = -30$, you can write $\frac{-30}{5} = -6$ and $\frac{-30}{-6} = 5$.

DIVIDING INTEGERS

Rule	Examples
1. The quotient of two positive integers is positive.	$\frac{4}{2} = 2$
2. The quotient of two negative integers is positive.	$\frac{-9}{-3} = 3$
3. The quotient of two integers with different signs is negative.	$\frac{10}{-2} = -5$
4. The quotient of 0 and a nonzero integer is 0.	$\frac{0}{-7} = 0$

You cannot divide by zero. For example, $5 \div 0$ is said to be *undefined* because there is no number n such that $0 \cdot n = 5$.

EXAMPLE 1 Evaluating Expressions

a. Evaluate $\frac{15}{x}$ when $x = 5$ and when $x = -3$. Follow the rules for dividing integers.

$\frac{15}{x} = \frac{15}{\mathbf{5}} = 3$ — **Substitute 5 for x. The quotient of two positive integers is positive.**

$\frac{15}{x} = \frac{15}{\mathbf{-3}} = -5$ — **Substitute −3 for x. The quotient of two integers with different signs is negative.**

b. Evaluate $\frac{-24}{x}$ when $x = 4$ and when $x = -6$. Follow the rules for dividing integers.

$\frac{-24}{x} = \frac{-24}{\mathbf{4}} = -6$ — **Substitute 4 for x. The quotient of two integers with different signs is negative.**

$\frac{-24}{x} = \frac{-24}{\mathbf{-6}} = 4$ — **Substitute −6 for x. The quotient of two negative integers is positive.**

Student Help

▶ STUDY TIP
To check your answer to a division problem, you can write a related multiplication problem. To check part (b) of Example 1, you can write $4(-6) = -24$.

1 Plan

Pacing

Suggested Number of Days

Transitional: 1 day
Average: 1 day
Advanced: 1 day
Block Schedule: 0.5 block with 3.7

Teaching Resources

Blacklines
(See page 102B.)

Transparencies
- Warm-Up Exercises
- Teacher Time-Savers
- English/Spanish Problem Solving
- Answers

Technology
- Electronic Teacher Tools
- Test and Practice Generator

2 Teach

Math Reasoning

For Mathematical Background Notes on mathematical reasoning related to this lesson, please refer to pages 102E and 102F in this Teacher's Edition.

Extra Example 1
See next page.

California Standards and Assessment

CA Standard: NS 1.2
CA Key Concepts Book: pp. S6–S8

Math Reasoning

The rules given here for dividing integers are a direct consequence of the rules for multiplication. See the Mathematical Background Notes for Lesson 3.6.

Extra Example 1

a. Evaluate $\frac{36}{x}$ when $x = 6$ and when $x = -4$. Follow the rules for dividing integers. **6; −9**

b. Evaluate $\frac{-28}{x}$ when $x = 7$ and when $x = -14$. Follow the rules for dividing integers. **−4; 2**

Extra Example 2

Collin's math test scores for the first quarter were 78, 86, 92, and 88. Find the mean of these scores. **86**

Extra Example 3

A student is keeping a record of the daily low temperatures in degrees Celsius during the month of October. Her readings for the last two weeks of the month are 5, 4, 4, 1, 7, 2, 2, 0, −1, −2, −1, −2, −3, and −2. What is the average low temperature for these two weeks? **1°C**

Concept Check

Explain how to divide integers. **The rules for dividing integers are similar to those for multiplying integers. If the two integers are the same sign, the quotient is positive. If their signs are different, the quotient is negative. Zero divided by anything is 0, and anything divided by 0 is undefined.**

Goal 2 FINDING THE AVERAGE OF INTEGERS

To find an **average** of a set of integers, you can divide the sum of the integers by the number of integers in the set.

Student Help

▶**STUDY TIP**
A fraction bar can act as a grouping symbol. For example, $\frac{1+2}{4-1}$ equals $(1 + 2) \div (4 - 1)$.

EXAMPLE 2 Averaging Positive Numbers

NEWSPAPERS A newspaper carrier recorded how much money was collected each week for a 4 week period. The amounts were \$126, \$132, \$130, and \$128. Find the average of these amounts.

Solution

$$\begin{aligned}\text{Mean} &= \frac{\text{Sum of amounts}}{\text{Number of amounts}}\\ &= \frac{\$126 + \$132 + \$130 + \$128}{4}\\ &= \frac{\$516}{4}\\ &= \$129\end{aligned}$$

ANSWER ▶ The average of the amounts is \$129.

The order of operations that you learned in Lesson 1.4 applies to negative integers as well as positive ones, as shown in Example 3.

EXAMPLE 3 Averaging Positive and Negative Numbers

NEWSPAPERS The newspaper carrier in Example 2 recorded the number of customers gained or lost each week for 8 weeks.

−5, 2, −4, 3, −6, −2, 0, −4

What was the average gain or loss of customers per week?

Solution

Find the average of the data. Follow the order of operations by simplifying the numerator first.

$$\begin{aligned}\text{Average gain or loss} &= \frac{\text{Sum of gains and losses}}{\text{Number of weeks}}\\ &= \frac{-5 + 2 + (-4) + 3 + (-6) + (-2) + 0 + (-4)}{8}\\ &= \frac{-16}{8}\\ &= -2\end{aligned}$$

ANSWER ▶ On average, the newspaper carrier lost 2 customers each week.

Student Help

▶**TECHNOLOGY TIP**
You may want to use a calculator to add a long list of integers such as those in the numerator of the fraction in Example 3. To enter a negative integer you can use the change sign key: +/−.

3.6 Exercises

Guided Practice

In Exercises 1–4, state whether the quotient is *positive* or *negative*. Then find the quotient.

1. $216 \div 9$ positive; 24

2. $-28 \div 4$ negative; −7

3. $\frac{48}{-6}$ negative; −8

4. $\frac{-522}{-9}$ positive; 58

5. Explain how you could check that the statement $\frac{-6}{-2} = 3$ is true. multiply −2 by 3

MATHEMATICAL REASONING In Exercises 6–9, determine whether the value of $\frac{a}{b}$ is *positive, negative,* or *zero.* Explain your reasoning. See margin.

6. Negative; the quotient of a negative number and a positive number is negative.

7. Positive; the quotient of two negative numbers is positive.

8. Positive; the quotient of two positive numbers is positive.

9. Zero; the quotient of zero and any nonzero number is zero.

6.
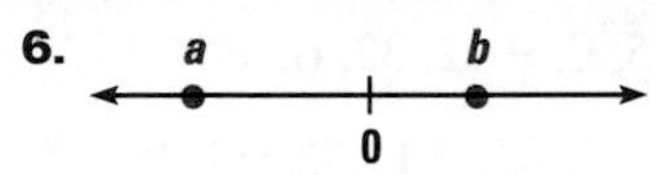

7.
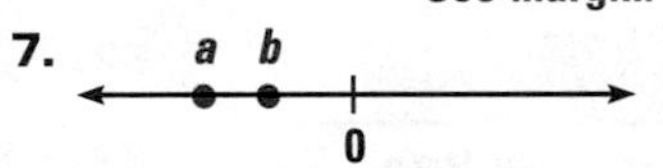

8.
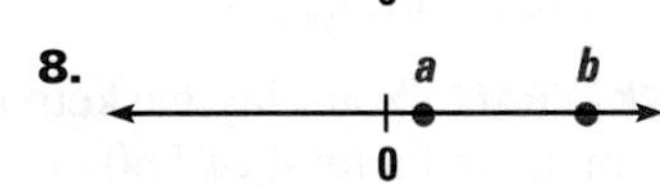

9.
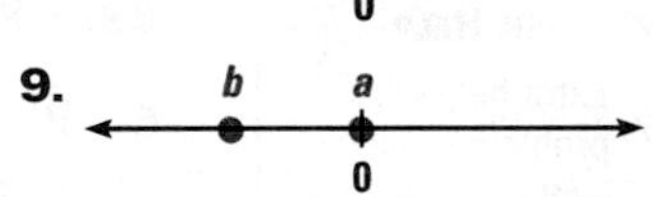

10. Find the average of the integers −8, 6, 5, 7, 12, and 2. 4

Practice and Problem Solving

Student Help

▶MORE PRACTICE
Extra practice to help you master skills is on page 695.

Find the quotient. If the quotient is undefined, explain why.

11. $\frac{54}{2}$ 27

12. $\frac{27}{-3}$ −9

13. $\frac{0}{15}$ 0

14. $\frac{-125}{25}$ −5

15. $\frac{-90}{15}$ −6

16. $\frac{32}{-8}$ −4

17. $\frac{-54}{18}$ −3

18. $\frac{-92}{-46}$ 2

19. $\frac{144}{16}$ 9

20. $\frac{144}{-12}$ −12

21. $\frac{-109}{0}$ Undefined

22. $\frac{-111}{37}$ −3

Evaluate the expression when $x = 3$ and when $x = -12$.

23. $\frac{24}{x}$ 8, −2

24. $\frac{-36}{x}$ −12, 3

25. $\frac{x}{-1}$ −3, 12

26. $\frac{-84}{x}$ −28, 7

27. $\frac{0}{x}$ 0, 0

28. $\frac{-x}{3}$ −1, 4

29. $\frac{-12}{x}$ −4, 1

30. $\frac{48}{-x}$ −16, 4

Evaluate the expression. Follow the order of operations.

31. $(5 - 8) \div 3$ −1

32. $2 \cdot 5 - 7$ 3

33. $18 - 8 \div 4$ 16

34. $\frac{7 - 8 + 1}{2}$ 0

35. $\frac{3 - 5 - 2}{-2}$ 2

36. $\frac{1 - 6 + 20}{-3}$ −5

37. $-2(3 - 9)$ 12

38. $(-3)^2 - 4 + (-8)$ −3

39. $(-8)^2 + 8^2$ 128

3 Apply

Assignment Guide

TRANSITIONAL
Day 1: pp. 137–139 Exs. 13–18, 27–35, 41–42, 49–51, 54–55, 61–63, 65–68

AVERAGE
Day 1: pp. 137–139 Exs. 15–20, 23–27, 34–36, 43–44, 49–51, 55–58, 61–63, 65–68

ADVANCED
Day 1: pp. 137–139 Exs. 19–26, 36–38, 40–44, 52–54, 57–59, 60*, 61–66

BLOCK SCHEDULE
pp. 137–139 Exs. 15–20, 23–27, 34–36, 43–44, 49–51, 55–58, 61–63, 65–68 (with 3.7)

Extra Practice

- Student Edition, pp. 694–695
- Chapter 3 Resource Book, p. 51

Homework Check

To quickly check student understanding of key concepts, go over the following exercises:

Transitional: 14, 24, 34, 50, 56
Average: 18, 26, 36, 50, 56
Advanced: 17, 26, 36, 50, 56

40. Same rules of signs: Multiplication or division of integers with like signs yields a positive result. Multiplication or division of integers with unlike signs yields a negative result.
Example: $\frac{-2}{-1} = 2$; $\frac{-2}{1} = -2$; $\frac{2}{-1} = -2$; $\frac{2}{1} = 2$

40. MATHEMATICAL REASONING Describe how the rules for dividing integers of the same and of different signs are like the rules for multiplying integers. Give examples to illustrate.

Evaluate the expression when $x = 2$, $y = 3$, and $z = 4$.

41. $\frac{x - 2y}{2}$ **−2** **42.** $x^2 - 2z$ **−4** **43.** $\frac{-y - z}{-1}$ **7** **44.** $\frac{2x - z}{x}$ **0**

45. $\frac{-2x}{4}$ **−1** **46.** $\frac{xz}{2}$ **4** **47.** $\frac{2xy}{z}$ **3** **48.** $\frac{-yz}{x}$ **−6**

In Exercises 49–53, find the average of the integers.

49. 22, 19, 21, 20, 18, 22, 25 **21**

50. 3, 3, −4, 6, 2, 1, −2, −1, 2, −4, 5 **1**

51. −8, −4, 0, 1, −6, 1, 2, −3, 2, −5 **−2**

52. −20, −19, 5, 0, −12, 32, 6, −16 **−3**

53. −8, −16, −17, 23, −11, 0, −1, 9 $-\frac{21}{8}$

Student Help

▸ HOMEWORK HELP
INTERNET Extra help with problem solving in Exs. 57–59 is available at www.mcdougallittell.com

54. PLAYING BASKETBALL You play basketball for your school team. Last year, your team scored a total of 560 points in 16 games. Find the average number of points scored per game. **35**

55. TEMPERATURES In one week, the daily high temperatures were −12°F, −6°F, −8°F, 5°F, 3°F, 0°F, and −3°F. Find the average of these daily high temperatures. **−3°F**

56. STOCK MARKET A newspaper reports these changes in the price of a stock during four days: −1, −5, +3, and −9. Find the average daily change. **−3**

Link to Skating

BONNIE BLAIR At the 1994 Olympics, speed skater Bonnie Blair won her fifth gold medal, setting a record for the number of gold medals won by a woman from the United States.

SPEED SKATING In Exercises 57–59, use the following information.
In five trial runs on a 500 meter track, a skater has times of 44.22 seconds, 45.02 seconds, 44.78 seconds, 45.10 seconds, and 44.13 seconds. The table shows how the skater deviated from a team average of 45 seconds in each of the five trials.

Trial Number	Deviation (in hundredths of a second)
1	−78
2	2
3	−22
4	10
5	−87

57. If the deviation for a particular trial is negative, what does that tell you about the skater's time in that trial?
The skater's time was less than the team average.

58. Find the average of the data in the table. What information does the average give you about the skater's performance in the five trials? **−35; On average, the skater is 35 hundredths of a second faster than the team's average.**

59. **CALCULATOR** Find the average of the skater's *actual* times in the five trial runs. Does this average agree with your answer to Exercise 58? Explain.
The skater's average time is 44.65 seconds. Yes; 45 sec − 0.35 sec = 44.65 sec.

60. CHALLENGE The average of four integers is -3. The first three integers are 21, -17, and -5. Write and solve an equation to find the fourth integer. $\frac{21 + (-17) + (-5) + x}{4} = -3$; -11

Multiple-Choice Practice

61. Which of the following statements is *always true*? **D**

Ⓐ The sum of a positive integer and a negative integer is positive.

Ⓑ The difference of two negative integers is negative.

Ⓒ The product of two integers with different signs is positive.

Ⓓ The quotient of two integers with different signs is negative.

62. Which expression can be used to find the average of the integers 6, -4, 3, and 2? **G**

Ⓕ $[6 + (-4) + 3 + 2] \times 4$ Ⓖ $\frac{6 + (-4) + 3 + 2}{4}$

Ⓗ $\frac{6 + 4 + 3 + 2}{4}$ Ⓙ Not here

63. Evaluate $\frac{xz}{y}$ when $x = -4$, $y = -2$, and $z = 6$. **D**

Ⓐ -12 Ⓑ -6 Ⓒ 6 Ⓓ 12

Mixed Review

64. Use the information in the limerick below to write an expression. (*Hint:* A gross is a dozen dozens, and a score is 20.) Then check to determine whether the limerick is true. *(1.4)*
$[12 + 12(12) + 20 + (10-4)] \div 7 + 5(11) = 9^2$; true

A dozen, a gross, and a score,
When added to ten minus four,
Divided by seven,
Plus five times eleven,
Is nine squared and not a bit more.

In Exercises 65 and 66, describe the pattern. List the next three numbers you expect to find in the sequence. *(1.6, 3.5)*

65. 2, -4, 8, -16, ?, ?, ? 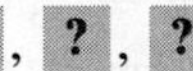 **66.** -1, 3, -9, 27, ?, ?, ?

65. powers of 2 with alternating signs; 32, -64, 128

66. powers of 3 with alternating signs; -81, 243, -729

Solve the equation. Check your solution in the original equation. *(2.5, 2.6)*

67. $x - 5 = 81$ **86** **68.** $y + 13 = 29$ **16** **69.** $\frac{n}{5} = 14$ **70**

70. $\frac{k}{18} = 3$ **54** **71.** $8r = 136$ **17** **72.** $11m = 605$ **55**

4 Assess

Assessment Resources

- Assessment Book (Formal Assessment and Alternative Assessment)
- Test and Practice Generator

Mini-Quiz

1. Evaluate $\frac{60}{y}$ when $y = 12$ and when $y = -20$. **5; -3**
2. Evaluate $\frac{2x - 2}{-2}$ when $x = 3$. **-2**
3. Katie's basketball team has played 5 games this year. Their point totals for the 5 games were 52, 47, 60, 38, and 48. What is the average number of points the team scored per game? **49**
4. A newspaper reports these changes in the price of a stock for one week: -2, -3, 4, 0, 1, -2, -5. Find the average daily change. **-1**

1 Plan

Pacing

Suggested Number of Days

Transitional: 1 day
Average: 1 day
Advanced: 1 day
Block Schedule: 0.5 block with 3.6

Teaching Resources

Blacklines
(See page 102B.)

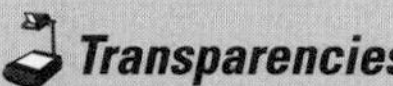

- Warm-Up Exercises
- Teacher Time-Savers
- English/Spanish Problem Solving
- Answers

Technology

- Electronic Teacher Tools
- Test and Practice Generator

2 Teach

Math Reasoning

For Mathematical Background Notes on mathematical reasoning related to this lesson, please refer to pages 102E and 102F in this Teacher's Edition.

CA Standards: NS 1.7, AF 1.1, AF 4.0

3.7 Solving Equations Involving Integers

California Standards

In this lesson you'll:

- Solve simple equations in one variable over the integers. (AF 4.0)
- Solve problems that involve profit. (NS 1.7)
- Use variables and appropriate operations to write an equation that represents a verbal description. (AF 1.1)

Goal 1 SOLVING EQUATIONS

You can use properties of equality to solve equations involving integers.

EXAMPLE 1 *Using Addition and Subtraction*

Solve the equation.

a. $x - 5 = -7$ **b.** $-12 = n + 3$

Solution

a.

$x - 5 = -7$	Write original equation.
$x - 5 + \mathbf{5} = -7 + \mathbf{5}$	Add 5 to each side.
$x = -2$	Simplify. x is by itself.

ANSWER ▶ The solution is -2. Check this in the original equation.

b.

$-12 = n + 3$	Write original equation.
$-12 \mathbf{- 3} = n + 3 \mathbf{- 3}$	Subtract 3 from each side.
$-15 = n$	Simplify. n is by itself.

ANSWER ▶ The solution is -15. Check this in the original equation.

EXAMPLE 2 *Using Multiplication and Division*

Solve the equation.

a. $\frac{m}{-2} = 15$ **b.** $3y = -18$

Solution

a.

$\frac{m}{-2} = 15$	Write original equation.
$\mathbf{-2} \cdot \frac{m}{-2} = \mathbf{-2} \cdot 15$	Multiply each side by -2.
$m = -30$	Simplify. m is by itself.

ANSWER ▶ The solution is -30. Check this in the original equation.

b.

$3y = -18$	Write original equation.
$\frac{3y}{\mathbf{3}} = \frac{-18}{\mathbf{3}}$	Divide each side by 3.
$y = -6$	Simplify. y is by itself.

ANSWER ▶ The solution is -6. Check this in the original equation.

Goal 2 FINDING PROFIT

Student Help

▶ **VOCABULARY TIP**
- If a profit is negative, you have a loss.
- If a profit is zero, you break even.
- If a profit is positive, you earned money.

In business situations, **profit** is the difference between your total income, or revenue, and your total expenses.

Profit = Income − Expenses

EXAMPLE 3 Writing an Equation

SCHOOL DANCE The notebook shows your class's total expenses for a dance it is sponsoring. The class will charge \$6 per ticket. Write an equation for the profit the class will earn based on the number of tickets sold.

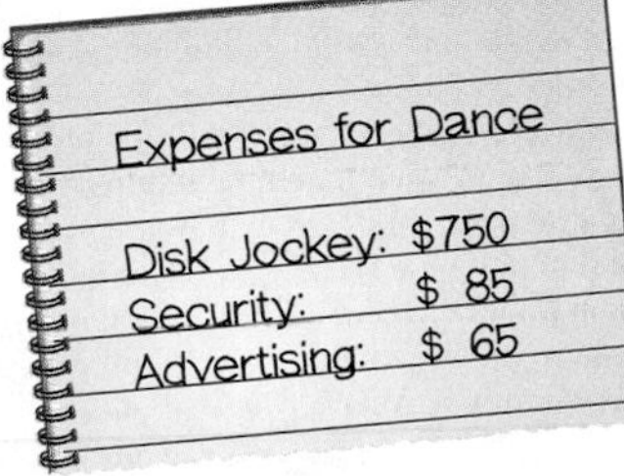

Solution

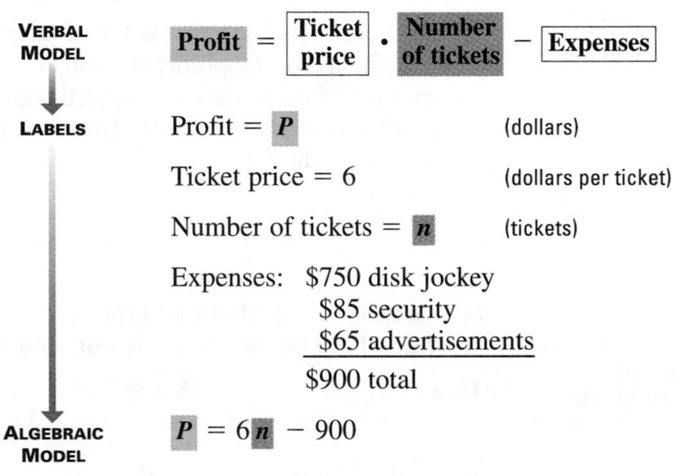

VERBAL MODEL
Profit = Ticket price • Number of tickets − Expenses
LABELS
Profit = P (dollars)
Ticket price = 6 (dollars per ticket)
Number of tickets = n (tickets)
Expenses: $750 disk jockey
$85 security
$65 advertisements
$900 total
ALGEBRAIC MODEL
P = 6n − 900

EXAMPLE 4 Using an Algebraic Model

SCHOOL DANCE In Example 3, what will the class's profit be if 100 tickets are sold? if 150 tickets are sold? if 200 tickets are sold?

Solution

Use the algebraic model $P = 6n - 900$ from Example 3.

100 tickets	150 tickets	200 tickets
$P = 6(100) - 900$	$P = 6(150) - 900$	$P = 6(200) - 900$
$= -\$300$	$= \$0$	$= \$300$

ANSWER ▶ If 100 tickets are sold, the class has a \$300 loss. If 150 tickets are sold, the class breaks even. If 200 tickets are sold, the class earns \$300.

Teaching Tip

Remind students of the general technique for solving equations that was introduced in Chapter 2. Isolate the variable by generating equivalent expressions on each side of the equation, making sure that whatever you do to one side of the equation is also done to the other side.

Extra Example 1

Solve the equation.

a. $y - 6 = -9$ $y = -3$

b. $w + 4 = -6$ $w = -10$

Extra Example 2

Solve the equation.

a. $\frac{n}{-3} = 8$ $n = -24$

b. $5g = -25$ $g = -5$

Extra Example 3

The school band is having a car wash to raise money for new uniforms. Their expenses for the car wash are \$25 for soap and sponges and \$15 for advertising. They will charge \$5 per car. Write an equation for the profit P the band will earn based on the number n of cars washed. **$P = 5n - 40$**

Extra Example 4

Use the expression found in Extra Example 3. What will the band's profit be if 5 cars are washed? if 20 cars are washed? if 50 cars are washed? **−\$15, \$60, \$210**

Concept Check

If a and b are nonzero integers, state the steps you take to solve for x in each equation.

a. $x + a = b$ **Subtract a from both sides to get $x = b - a$.**

b. $x - a = b$ **Add a to both sides to get $x = b + a$.**

c. $ax = b$ **Divide both sides by a to get $x = \frac{b}{a}$.**

d. $\frac{x}{a} = b$ **Multiply both sides by a to get $x = ba$.**

3 Apply

Assignment Guide

TRANSITIONAL
Day 1: pp. 142–143 Exs. 12–15, 24–30, 33–35, 39–40, 48–49
AVERAGE
Day 1: pp. 142–143 Exs. 14–17, 21–28, 33–35, 41–43, 48–49
ADVANCED
Day 1: pp. 142–143 Exs. 15–18, 24–32, 36–42, 44–46, 47*, 48–49
BLOCK SCHEDULE
pp. 142–143 Exs. 14–17, 21–28, 33–35, 41–43, 48–49 (with 3.6)

Extra Practice

- Student Edition, pp. 694–695
- Chapter 3 Resource Book, p. 60

Homework Check

To quickly check student understanding of key concepts, go over the following exercises:

Transitional: 14, 22, 26, 28, 43
Average: 14, 22, 26, 28, 43
Advanced: 16, 24, 26, 28, 46

Problem Solving

Exercise 43
It may help to draw a picture of the balloon with its original height, descent, and resulting height clearly labeled.

Math Reasoning

Problems such as Exercise 47 can be approached using the fact that $|c|$ is either c or $-c$. Therefore if $|x-5| = 4$, then either $x - 5 = 4$ or $-(x - 5) = 4$. The first case gives $x = 9$ and the second gives $-x + 5 = 4$, or $x = 1$.

3.7 Exercises

Guided Practice

In Exercises 1–6, match the equation with one of the solutions below.

A. 9 **B.** -8 **C.** -13

D. 7 **E.** -16 **F.** -12

1. $a + 5 = -8$ C **2.** $t - 9 = -2$ D **3.** $4y = -32$ B

4. $-27 = -3x$ A **5.** $x - 1 = -13$ F **6.** $\frac{p}{2} = -8$ E

In Exercises 7–10, solve the equation. Justify each step.

7. $x - 4 = -8$ **8.** $-6 = y + 8$ **9.** $\frac{a}{-5} = 7$ **10.** $-5b = 35$

7. Addition property; -4
8. Subtraction property; -14
9. Multiplication property; -35
10. Division property; -7

11. Your class is selling pizzas for \$5 each at a school fair. The ingredients for the pizzas are donated by a local restaurant. Your class spends \$55 on posters and advertising. Write an equation for the profit your class will make. Then find the class's profit if 200 pizzas are sold at the fair. $P = 5n - 55$; \$945

Practice and Problem Solving

Student Help
▶MORE PRACTICE
Extra practice to help you master skills is on page 695.

In Exercises 12–20, check whether the value of the variable is a solution of the equation. If it is not, find the solution.

12. $x - 7 = 3$; $x = 10$ yes **13.** $t + 7 = -10$; $t = -17$ yes **14.** $9 = s + 5$; $s = 14$ no; 4

15. $-42 = -14b$; $b = 3$ yes **16.** $\frac{m}{-2} = 12$; $m = -24$ yes **17.** $\frac{n}{-6} = -8$; $n = -48$ no; 48

18. $-32 = 16b$; $b = 2$ no; -2 **19.** $y - 6 = -10$; $y = 4$ no; -4 **20.** $\frac{m}{-2} = 24$; $m = -12$ no; -48

Solve the equation. Check your solution.

21. $x + 2 = 11$ 9 **22.** $y - 9 = 15$ 24 **23.** $-17 = p - 13$ -4

24. $q + 12 = 3$ -9 **25.** $72 = 6z$ 12 **26.** $-15t = 60$ -4

27. $-5 = \frac{s}{-11}$ 55 **28.** $\frac{a}{20} = -4$ -80 **29.** $\frac{f}{-3} = -11$ 33

30. $-22 = -11g$ 2 **31.** $-33h = 99$ -3 **32.** $\frac{b}{-37} = 0$ 0

MATHEMATICAL REASONING **Without solving the equation, predict whether the solution is *positive* or *negative*. Explain your prediction.**

33. $-1088 = y + 129$ **negative** **34.** $m - 364 = 1980$ **positive** **35.** $-486s = 7776$ **negative**

36. $-555t = 8325$ **negative** **37.** $-56 = \frac{p}{-23}$ **positive** **38.** $\frac{q}{67} = -31$ **negative**

Write an equation for the sentence. Then solve the equation and check your solution.

39. -10 is the sum of y and 25. **$-10 = y + 25$; -35**

40. The difference of x and 2 is -4. **$x - 2 = -4$; -2**

41. 51 is the product of a and -3. **$51 = -3a$; -17**

42. The quotient of t and -6 is -14. **$\frac{t}{-6} = -14$; 84**

43. BALLOONING You are in a hot-air balloon at an altitude of x feet. You descend 6891 feet to an altitude of 18,479 feet. Which of the following models can you use to determine your original altitude? Use the model to find your original altitude. **A; 25,370 ft**

A. $x - 6891 = 18,479$ **B.** $18,479 + x = 6891$

Student Help

▶ **HOMEWORK HELP**

Extra help with problem solving in Exs. 44–46 is available at www.mcdougallittell.com

FINDING PROFIT **In Exercises 44–46, use the following information.** Your school is sponsoring a concert. The notebook shows the school's expenses. The school will sell tickets and charge \$5 per person.

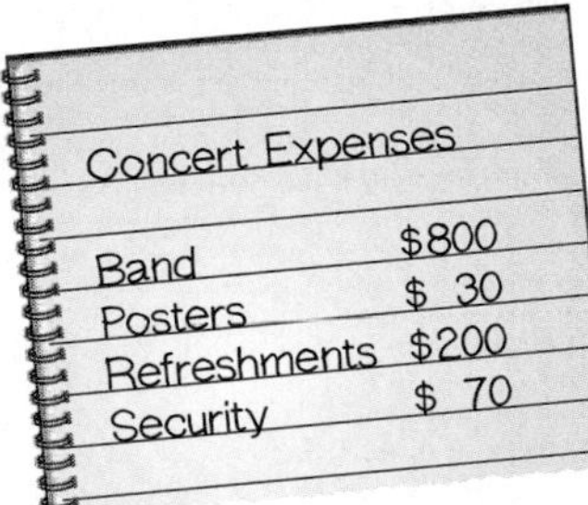

44. Use the verbal model shown below to write an equation for the profit P the school makes based on the number n of tickets sold. **$P = 5n - 1100$**

Profit = Income − Expenses

45. Find the profit the school will make if the following numbers of tickets are sold: 100, 150, 200, 250, 300, and 350. Organize your results in a table. **See margin.**

46. Use your table from Exercise 45 to estimate the number of tickets the school must sell to break even. Then use your equation from Exercise 44 to check your estimate. **220 tickets**

47. CHALLENGE Find all the solutions of the equation $|x - 5| = 4$. **9, 1**

Multiple-Choice Practice

48. What is the solution of the equation $-24 + x = 12$? **C**

Ⓐ -12 Ⓑ 12 Ⓒ 36 Ⓓ 48

49. What is the solution of the equation $-12x = 120$? **F**

Ⓕ -10 Ⓖ -6 Ⓗ 10 Ⓙ Not here

4 Assess

Assessment Resources

- Assessment Book (Formal Assessment and Alternative Assessment)
- Test and Practice Generator

Mini-Quiz

Solve the equation.

1. $w - 8 = 12$ **$w = 20$**
2. $-6 = n + 5$ **$n = -11$**
3. $-48 = -4x$ **$x = 12$**
4. $\frac{d}{10} = -8$ **$d = -80$**
5. Marco is starting a lawn mowing business. He figures that he will have monthly expenses of \$15 for gas and maintenance for his lawn mower plus \$5 for advertising. He plans to charge \$8 for every lawn that he mows. Write an equation for Marco's monthly profit P if he mows n lawns. Then calculate his monthly profit if he mows 2 lawns, 5 lawns, and 10 lawns. **$P = 8n - 20$; $-\$4$; \$20, \$60**

45.

Tickets Sold	Profit
100	−600
150	−350
200	−100
250	150
300	400
350	650

1 Plan

Pacing

Suggested Number of Days

Transitional: 1 day
Average: 1 day
Advanced: 1 day
Block Schedule: 0.5 block with 3.9

Teaching Resources

Blacklines
(See page 102B.)

Transparencies
- Warm-Up Exercises
- Teacher Time-Savers
- English/Spanish Problem Solving
- Answers

Technology
- Electronic Teacher Tools
- Test and Practice Generator

2 Teach

Math Reasoning

For Mathematical Background Notes on mathematical reasoning related to this lesson, please refer to pages 102E and 102F in this Teacher's Edition.

California Standards and Assessment

CA Standards: AF 1.5, MG 3.2
CA Key Concepts Book: pp. S61–S63

3.8 The Coordinate Plane

California Standards

In this lesson you'll:

- Represent quantitative relationships graphically and interpret the meaning of a specific part of a graph. (AF 1.5)
- Understand and use coordinate graphs to plot simple figures and determine lengths and areas related to them. (MG 3.2)

Goal 1 PLOTTING POINTS IN A COORDINATE PLANE

A **coordinate plane** has two number lines, called *axes*, that intersect at a point called the **origin**. The horizontal number line is called the ***x*-axis**. The vertical number line is called the ***y*-axis**. The axes divide the coordinate plane into four **quadrants**, as shown.

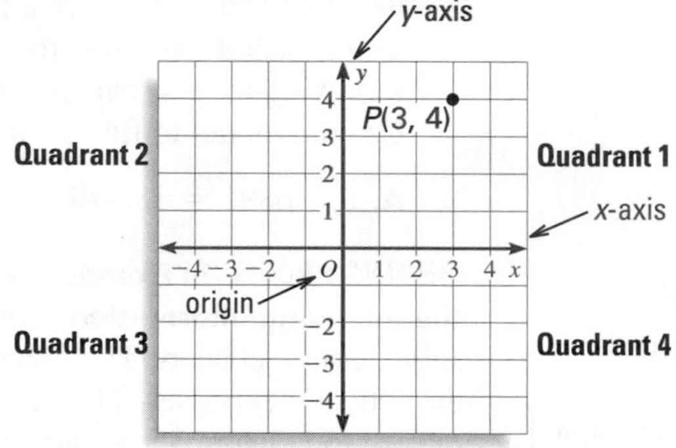

Each point in the coordinate plane can be represented by an **ordered pair** of numbers (x, y). The first number is called the ***x*-coordinate**, and the second number is called the ***y*-coordinate**.

ordered pair ⟶ **(3, 4)**
***x*-coordinate** ↑ ***y*-coordinate** ↑

Point P lies in Quadrant 1 of the coordinate plane shown above. A point on an axis is not considered to be in any quadrant.

EXAMPLE 1 Plotting Points

Plot the points $A(4, 3)$, $B(4, -2)$, $C(-4, -2)$, and $D(-4, 3)$.

Solution

For each point, start at the origin.

To plot $A(4, 3)$, move 4 units right. Then move 3 units up.

To plot $B(4, -2)$, move 4 units right. Then move 2 units down.

Similarly, plot points C and D.

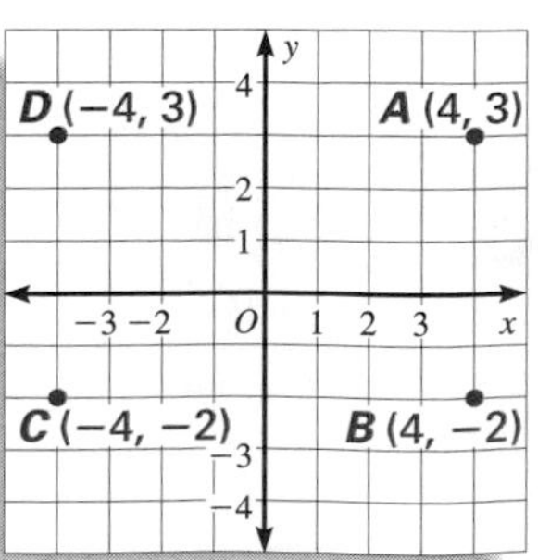

Student Help

▶ **MORE EXAMPLES**

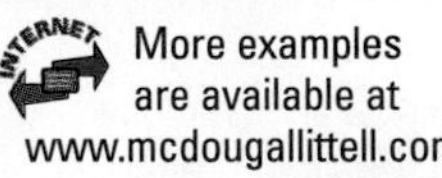

More examples are available at www.mcdougallittell.com

EXAMPLE 2 Finding Segment Lengths

Find the length and the width of the rectangle shown.

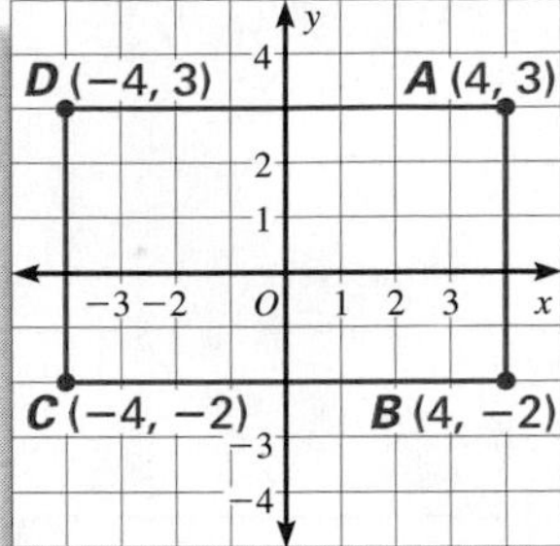

Solution

The length of side $\overline{DA}$ is the length of the rectangle. To find the length of any *horizontal* side in a coordinate plane, find the absolute value of the difference between the *x*-coordinates of the endpoints.

$$\begin{aligned} \text{Length} &= |x\text{-coordinate of } D - x\text{-coordinate of } A| \\ &= |-4 - 4| \\ &= |-8| \\ &= 8 \end{aligned}$$

The length of side $\overline{CD}$ is the width of the rectangle. To find the length of any *vertical* side in the coordinate plane, find the absolute value of the difference between the *y*-coordinates of the endpoints.

$$\begin{aligned} \text{Width} &= |y\text{-coordinate of } C - y\text{-coordinate of } D| \\ &= |-2 - 3| \\ &= |-5| \\ &= 5 \end{aligned}$$

Student Help

▶ **STUDY TIP**

To find the width of the rectangle in Example 2, you can also subtract the *y*-coordinate of *C* from the *y*-coordinate of *D*. The absolute value bars ensure that the result is the same positive number:

$|3 - (-2)| = |5| = 5$

Goal 2 FINDING SOLUTIONS OF EQUATIONS IN *X* AND *Y*

An ordered pair (x, y) is a **solution** of an equation in x and y if substituting the values of x and y into the equation produces a true statement.

EXAMPLE 3 Checking Solutions of Equations in *x* and *y*

Determine whether the ordered pair is a solution of $x + y = 4$.

a. $(-4, 8)$ **b.** $(-3, 6)$ **c.** $(0, 4)$

Solution

Ordered pair	Substitute in $x + y = 4$.	Simplify.	Conclusion
a. $(-4, 8)$	$-4 + 8 \stackrel{?}{=} 4$	$4 = 4$	$(-4, 8)$ is a solution.
b. $(-3, 6)$	$-3 + 6 \stackrel{?}{=} 4$	$3 \neq 4$	$(-3, 6)$ is not a solution.
c. $(0, 4)$	$0 + 4 \stackrel{?}{=} 4$	$4 = 4$	$(0, 4)$ is a solution.

Extra Examples 1 and 2

Plot the points $A(2, 5)$, $B(2, -3)$, $C(-3, -3)$, and $D(-3, 5)$. Connect the points to form a rectangle. Then find length DA and width AB.

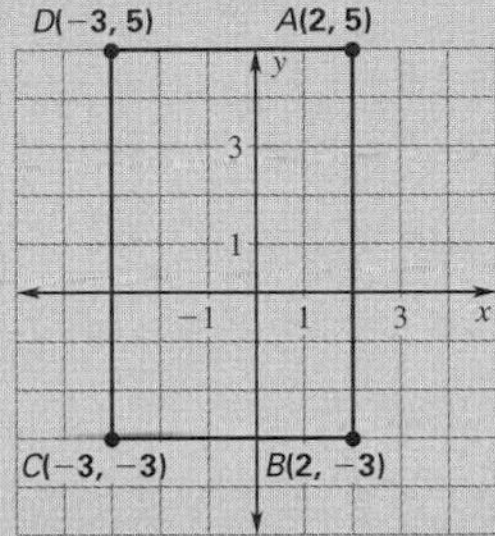

Length $DA = 5$; width $AB = 8$

Extra Example 3

Decide whether the ordered pair is a solution of $x + y = 6$.

a. $(-3, 9)$ **yes**

b. $(10, -4)$ **yes**

c. $(-3, -3)$ **no**

Extra Example 4

Make a table of values for the equation $y = x - 3$. Then plot the corresponding points. What do you notice? **Answers may vary. Sample answer is shown.**

x	*y*	Ordered Pair
−1	−4	(−1, −4)
0	−3	(0, −3)
1	−2	(1, −2)
2	−1	(2, −1)
3	0	(3, 0)
4	1	(4, 1)

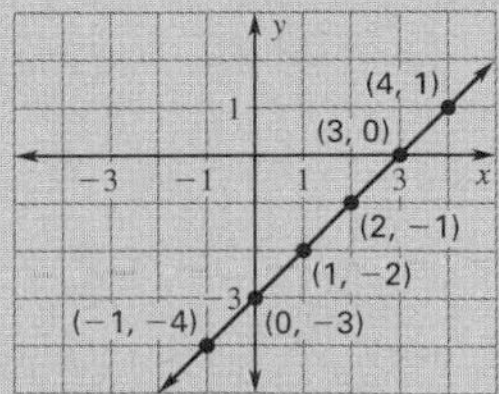

The points lie on a line.

Concept Check
See next page.

Concept Check

Name the quadrant in which each of the following points lies.

a. $(-1, 3)$ **Quadrant 2**
b. $(4, -2)$ **Quadrant 4**
c. $(-7, -7)$ **Quadrant 3**
d. $(6, 8)$ **Quadrant 1**
e. $(1, -100)$ **Quadrant 4**
f. $(-14, 3)$ **Quadrant 2**

3 Apply

Assignment Guide

TRANSITIONAL
Day 1: pp. 147–148 Exs. 5–10, 12–15, 26–30, 35–36, 41–42, 45–47
AVERAGE
Day 1: pp. 147–148 Exs. 5–10, 12–15, 26, 29–32, 38–42, 45–47
ADVANCED
Day 1: pp. 147–148 Exs. 8–10, 12–15, 25–26, 31–34, 38–43, 44*, 45–47
BLOCK SCHEDULE
pp. 147–148 Exs. 5–10, 12–15, 26, 29–32, 36–40, 43–45 (with 3.9)

Extra Practice

- Student Edition, pp. 694–695
- Chapter 3 Resource Book, p. 69

Homework Check

To quickly check student understanding of key concepts, go over the following exercises:

Transitional: 12, 26, 28, 36, 42
Average: 12, 26, 30, 38, 42
Advanced: 14, 26, 32, 38, 42

The solutions of an equation in x and y can be shown in a *table of values*. You can use a table of values to graph the solutions of an equation.

Student Help

STUDY TIP
When you make a table of values, it is a good idea to include enough values to see a pattern when the points are plotted. Choose both negative and positive values of x.

EXAMPLE 4 Using a Table of Values

Make a table of values for the equation $y = x + 2$. Then plot the corresponding points. What do you notice?

Solution

Begin by choosing an x-value, such as $x = -3$. To find a corresponding y-value, substitute -3 for x in the equation and simplify.

$y = x + 2$ Write equation.

$y = -3 + 2$ Substitute for x.

$y = -1$ Simplify.

So, the ordered pair $(-3, -1)$ is a solution. Some other solutions are shown in the table of values at the right.

x	y	Ordered pair
−3	−1	(−3, −1)
−2	0	(−2, 0)
−1	1	(−1, 1)
0	2	(0, 2)
1	3	(1, 3)
2	4	(2, 4)

Plot the points represented by the ordered pairs in the table. All six points appear to lie on a line. If more points were plotted, they would also lie on the line.

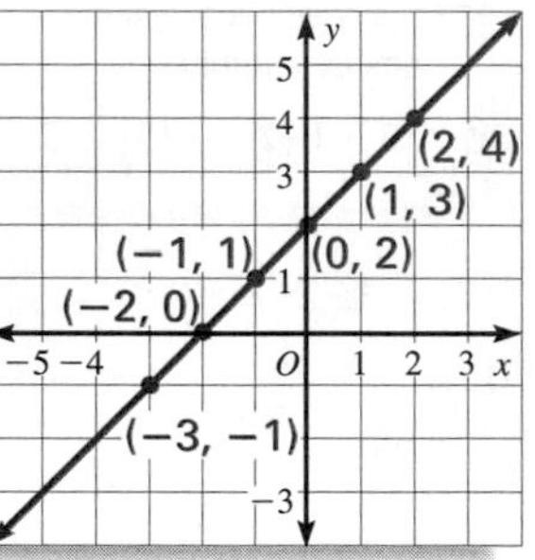

So, you can draw a line through the points that are plotted to represent all the solutions of the equation $y = x + 2$.

3.8 Exercises

Guided Practice

In Exercises 1–3, use the coordinate plane below.

1. Write an ordered pair for each point. Name the quadrant (if any) that contains the point.

1. ***A*(1, 2) Quadrant 1; *B*(−4, 3) Quadrant 2; *C*(1, −3) Quadrant 4; *D*(−3, 0); none *E*(5, 2); Quadrant 1 *F*(−2, −4) Quadrant 3; *G*(5, −3) Quadrant 4; *H*(−5, 5) Quadrant 2**

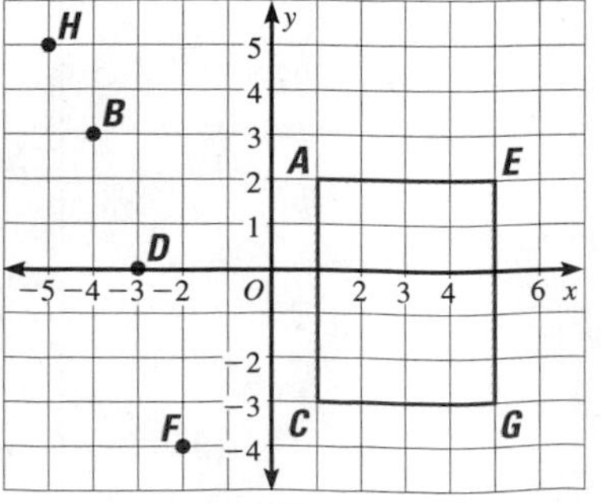

2. Find the length of side $\overline{AC}$. **5**

3. Find the length of side $\overline{AE}$. **4**

4. Show that (7, 10) is a solution of the equation $y = 3 + x$. Then find three other solutions of the equation.

4. **$10 = 3 + 7$; *Sample answers:* (0, 3), (1, 4), (−1, 2)**

Practice and Problem Solving

Student Help

▶More Practice Extra practice to help you master skills is on page 695.

In Exercises 5–10, match the ordered pair with its point in the coordinate plane. Name the quadrant (if any) that contains the point.

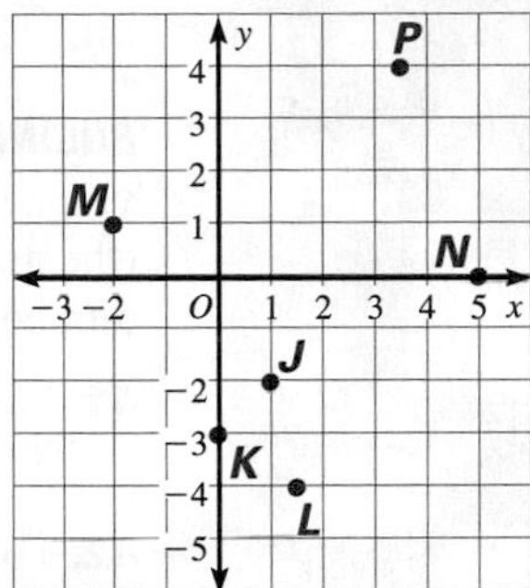

5. $(1, -2)$ **J; Quadrant 4**

6. $(-2, 1)$ **M; Quadrant 2**

7. $(0, -3)$ **K; none**

8. $\left(\frac{3}{2}, -4\right)$ **L; Quadrant 4**

9. $(5, 0)$ **N; none**

10. $\left(\frac{7}{2}, 4\right)$ **P; Quadrant 1**

Plot all the points in the same coordinate plane. Name the quadrant (if any) that contains each point. **11–19. See margin.**

11. $A(3, 7)$ **12.** $B(7, 3)$ **13.** $C(-6, -2)$

14. $D(2, -6)$ **15.** $E(-1, 0)$ **16.** $F(0, 4)$

17. $G(1.5, -5)$ **18.** $H(4.5, 5)$ **19.** $J(0, 2.5)$

In Exercises 20–25, use the coordinate plane below. Name the coordinates of the endpoints of the given side. Then find the length of the side.

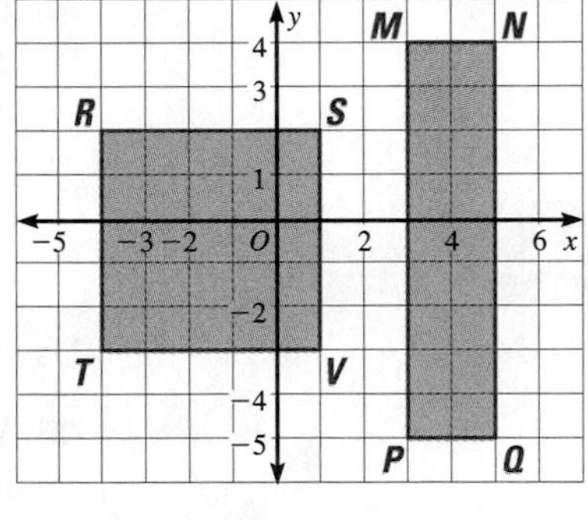

20. Side $\overline{MN}$ **(3, 4), (5, 4); 2**

21. Side $\overline{MP}$ **(3, 4), (3, −5); 9**

22. Side $\overline{PQ}$ **(3, −5), (5, −5); 2**

23. Side $\overline{SV}$ **(1, 2), (1, −3); 5**

24. Side $\overline{RS}$ **(−4, 2), (1, 2) ; 5**

25. Find the perimeter and the area of rectangles *RSVT* and *MNQP*. **See margin.**

25. *RSVT*: perimeter = 20, area = 25; *MNQP*: perimeter = 22, area = 18

26. Plot the points $E(-5, 4)$, $F(2, 4)$, $G(2, -1)$, and $H(-5, -1)$ in a coordinate plane. Connect the points to form a rectangle. Find the perimeter and the area of the rectangle. **See margin.**

Determine whether the ordered pair is a solution of the equation. Then find three other solutions. **27–34. Sample answers are given.**

27. $x + 8 = y$; $(2, 10)$ **solution; (3, 11), (0, 8), (−2, 6)**

28. $y - 5 = x$; $(-8, -3)$ **solution; (−3, 2), (0, 5), (3, 8)**

29. $x + y = 6$; $(8, -2)$ **solution; (2, 4), (−2, 8), (1, 5)**

30. $y + 7 = x$; $(-1, -8)$ **solution; (0, −7), (10, 3), (5, −2)**

31. $y = 2x$; $(1, 2)$ **solution; (0, 0); (−3, −6), (2, 4)**

32. $y = -2x$; $(-3, -6)$ **not a solution; (−1, 2), (1, −2), (6, −12)**

33. $6x - 3 = y$; $(0, -3)$ **See margin.**

34. $xy = 54$; $(-6, -9)$ **See margin.**

Problem Solving

Students may confuse the values of *x* and *y*. One way to remember which is which is that the ordered pair (*x*, *y*) is in alphabetical order—*x* comes first, then *y*. Similarly, the *o* in *over* comes before the *u* in *up*.

11–19.

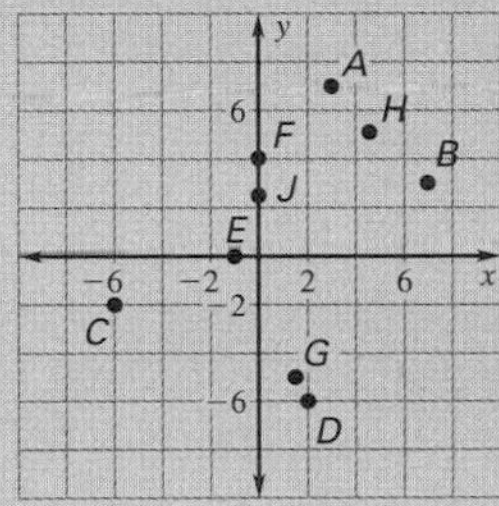

26.

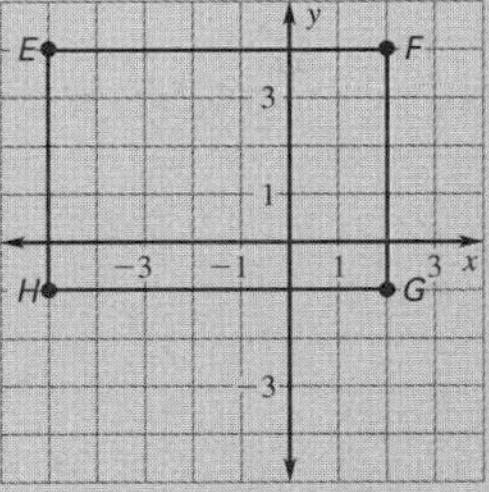

perimeter = 24, area = 35

33. solution; (1, 3), (−1, −9), (2, 9)

34. solution; (3, 18), (6, 9), (−2, −27)

4 Assess

Assessment Resources

- Assessment Book (Formal Assessment and Alternative Assessment)
- Test and Practice Generator

Mini-Quiz

1. Find the lengths AB and AD of the rectangle formed by the points $A(-3, 4)$, $B(4, 4)$, $C(4, -1)$, and $D(-3, -1)$. $AB = 7$; $AD = 5$
2. Make a table of values that shows four solutions of the equation $y = 2x - 3$. Then plot the solutions and draw a line through the points to represent all the solutions of the equation. **For table of values, answers may vary. Sample answer is shown.**

x	y	Ordered Pair
−1	−5	(−1, −5)
0	−3	(0, −3)
1	−1	(1, −1)
2	1	(2, 1)

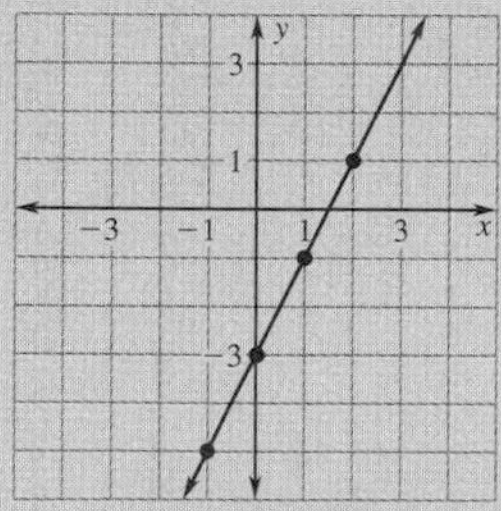

35.

x	0	1	2	3
y	4	3	2	1

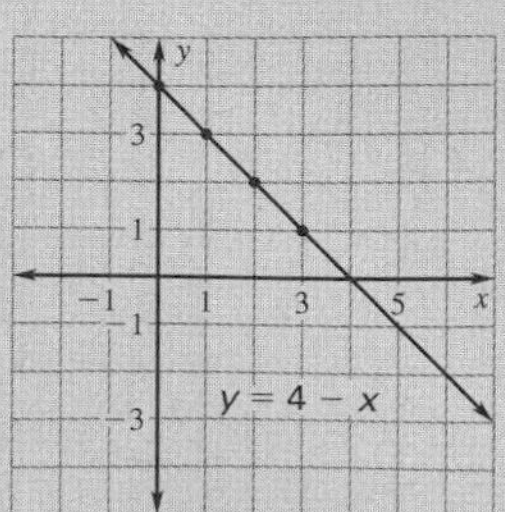

36–41, 44. See Additional Answers beginning on page AA1.

Link to History

JEANS In the late 1800s, pants made of durable cloth became popular among California gold miners. The pants came to be called jeans. The word *jeans* comes from *Gênes*, which is the French name for Genoa, a city in Italy that produced clothing made of denim.

43. Number of pairs sold cannot be negative, a fraction, or a decimal.

Make a table of values that shows four solutions of the equation. Then plot the solutions. Draw a line through the points to represent all the solutions of the equation. 35–40. See margin.

35. $y = 4 - x$ **36.** $y = -5x$ **37.** $2x - y = 1$

38. $-2x + 3 = y$ **39.** $x + y = -2$ **40.** $3x - 1 = y$

BUSINESS In Exercises 41–43, use the following information. Suppose you own a clothing store. You charge $30 for a pair of jeans. Your revenue (the amount of money you make) from selling jeans depends on the number of pairs you sell.

41. Make a table of values that shows your revenue from selling 10, 20, 30, and 40 pairs of jeans. **See margin.**

42. The equation $y = 30x$ can be used to model jeans sales at your store. What real-life quantities do x and y represent? **x: number of jeans sold; y: revenue**

43. MATHEMATICAL REASONING The graph at the right represents solutions of the equation $y = 30x$. Explain why the portion of the graph in Quadrant 3 does not make sense for the real-life situation described above. (*Hint*: Does it make sense for x to be negative?) Does it make sense for x to be a fraction or a decimal? Explain.

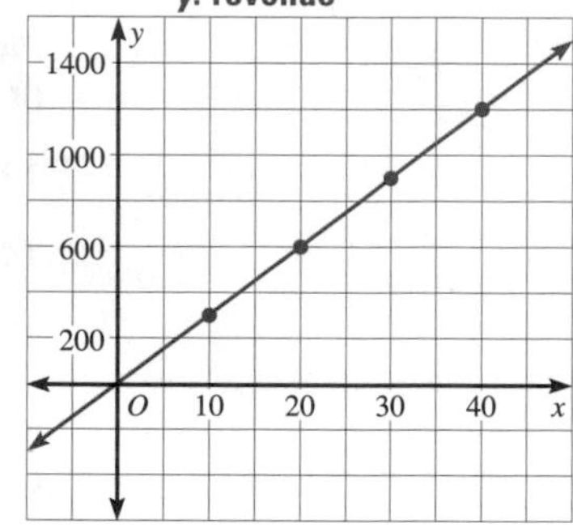

44. CHALLENGE Plot the points $M(-2, -3)$, $N(-2, 5)$, and $Q(4, -3)$ on a coordinate plane. Connect the points to form a right triangle. Find the area of the triangle. **See margin.**

Multiple-Choice Practice

Use the coordinate plane at the right.

45. Which ordered pair describes the location of point D? **C**

Ⓐ (4, 3) Ⓑ (3, −4)

Ⓒ (−4, 3) Ⓓ (−4, −3)

46. What is the length of side $\overline{DA}$? **G**

Ⓕ 4 units Ⓖ 6 units

Ⓗ 7 units Ⓙ Not here

47. Which point is in Quadrant 3? **C**

 A Ⓑ B Ⓒ C  D

3.9 Scatter Plots

California Standards

In this lesson you'll:

- Collect, organize, and represent data sets that have one or more variables and identify relationships among variables within a data set. (SDP 1.0)
- Represent two numerical variables on a scatter plot and informally describe how the data points are distributed and any apparent relationship that exists between the two variables. (SDP 1.2)
- Fit a line to a plot. (AF 3.4)

Goal 1 Drawing Scatter Plots

A **scatter plot** is the graph of a collection of ordered pairs (x, y). If the y-coordinates tend to increase as the x-coordinates increase, then x and y have a **positive correlation**. If the y-coordinates tend to decrease as the x-coordinates increase, then x and y have a **negative correlation**. If no pattern exists between the x-coordinates and the y-coordinates, then x and y have **no obvious correlation.**

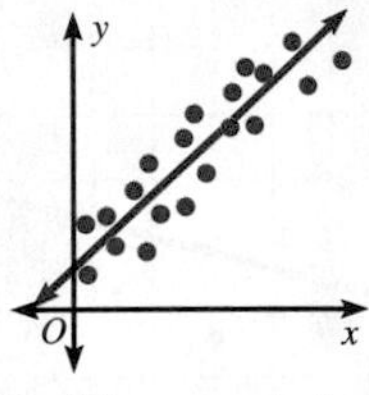

Positive correlation

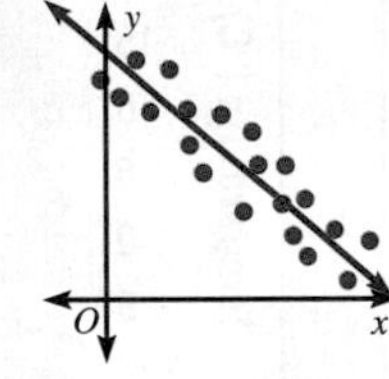

Negative correlation

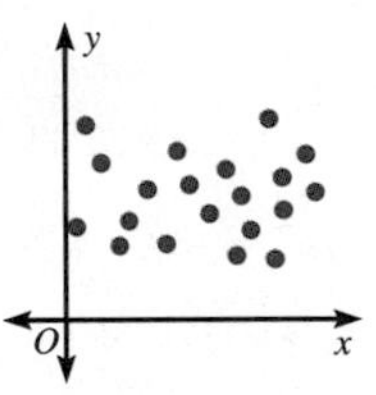

No obvious correlation

If a scatter plot shows a correlation, then you can draw a line that shows the trend in the data. It should come as close as possible to all of the data points. It does not need to pass through any of the data points, however.

Example 1 Drawing a Scatter Plot

The ordered pairs below are measurements taken from 14 students. Each x-coordinate is a student's elbow-to-fingertip distance. Each y-coordinate is the distance around the student's wrist. When the data are plotted in a scatter plot, the data points tend to rise to the right. You can conclude that the data have a positive correlation. A line has been drawn to show the trend in the data.

(32, 12), (42, 16),
(40, 14), (39, 15),
(37, 15), (41, 16),
(43, 17), (38, 14),
(45, 16), (34, 14),
(41, 15), (34, 13),
(35, 13), (37, 14)

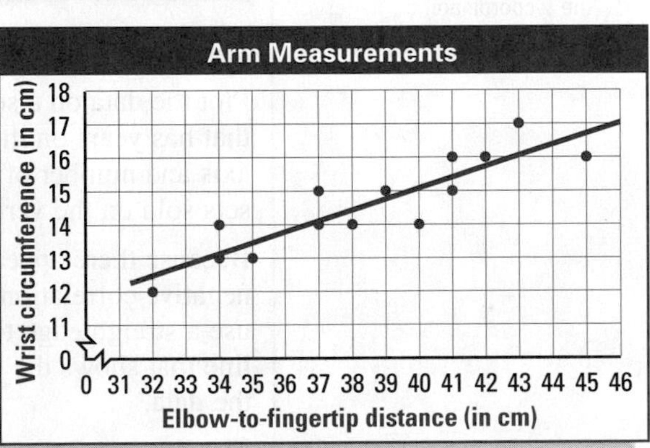

Student Help

Study Tip
When you read a graph, check the scales on the axes carefully. The scatter plot in Example 1 includes a break in the scale on the x-axis and a break in the scale on the y-axis, as indicated by this mark: ⚡.

1 Plan

Pacing

Suggested Number of Days

Transitional: 1 day
Average: 1 day
Advanced: 1 day
Block Schedule: 0.5 block with 3.8

Teaching Resources

Blacklines
(See page 102B.)

Transparencies
- Warm-Up Exercises
- Teacher Time-Savers
- English/Spanish Problem Solving
- Answers

Technology
- Electronic Teacher Tools
- Test and Practice Generator

2 Teach

Math Reasoning

For Mathematical Background Notes on mathematical reasoning related to this lesson, please refer to pages 102E and 102F in this Teacher's Edition.

Extra Example 1
See next page.

California Standards and Assessment

CA Standards: AF 3.4, SDP 1.0, SDP 1.2

Extra Example 1

The table gives the number of hours a baseball team practiced each week and the number of hits they had in games. Draw a scatter plot of the data. What can you conclude?

Number of hours	0	3	5	7	10
Number of hits	2	4	5	8	10

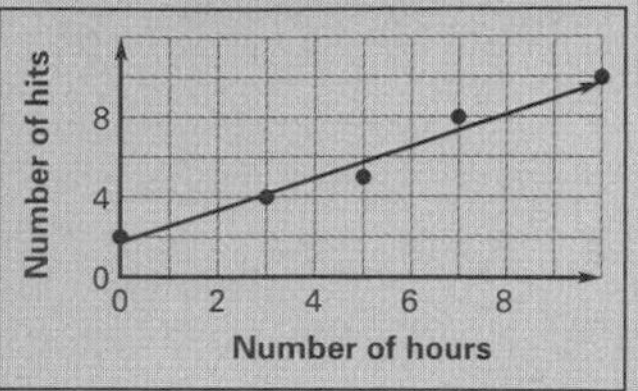

There is a positive correlation. The line approximates the pattern.

Extra Example 2

You want to plan a ski vacation. You use a scatter plot to look at some data from last year. Use the line to check when the snow depth was greater than 24 in.

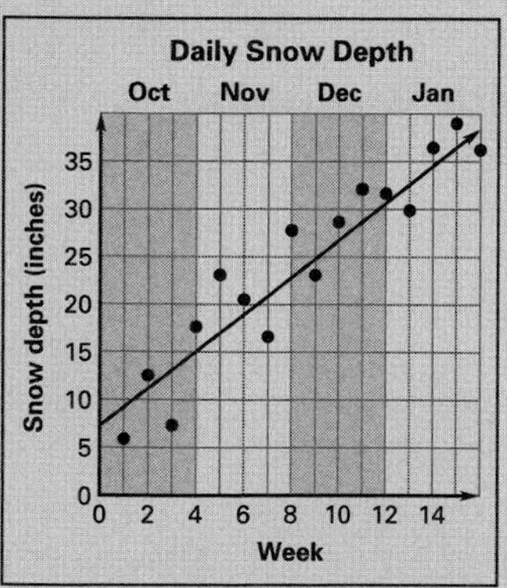

in early December

Extra Example 3

You work in a book store. The numbers of computer books that you have sold in 5 different years are shown in the table. Use a scatter plot to estimate the number of computer books you will sell in 2002.

Year	1996	1997	1998	1999	2000
Books	450	750	700	800	1100

***Sample answer*: about 1200 books**

Goal 2 DESCRIBING RELATIONSHIPS

Student Help

▶ **MORE EXAMPLES**

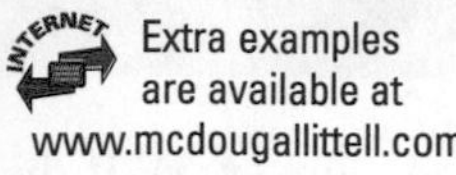

Extra examples are available at www.mcdougallittell.com

EXAMPLE 2 Interpreting a Scatter Plot

You want to plant peas when daily high temperatures rise above 10°C. You use a scatter plot to look at some data from last year. The data have a positive correlation. You can use the line shown to check that by late April of last year, the daily high temperatures had risen above 10°C. So, you may be able to plant in late April of this year.

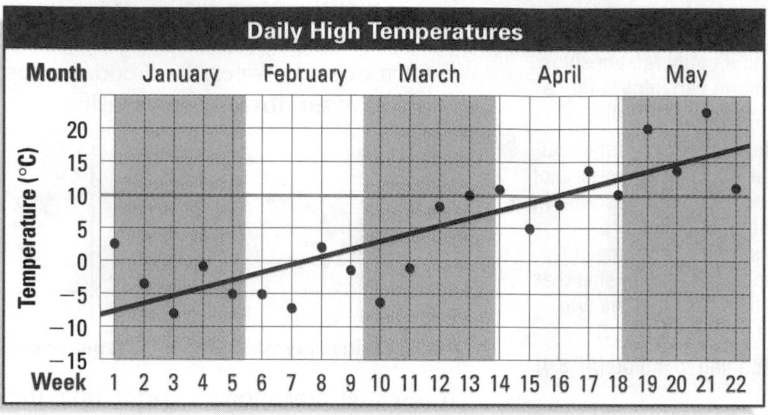

Student Help

▶ **STUDY TIP**

You can write the data in the table in Example 3 as ordered pairs. Each year becomes the x-coordinate, and the corresponding number of TVs sold becomes the y-coordinate.

EXAMPLE 3 Making a Prediction

You manage an appliance store. The number of black and white television sets you have sold in 6 different years are shown in the table. Use a scatter plot to estimate the number of sets you will sell in 2002.

Year	1990	1992	1994	1996	1998	2000
Black and white TVs	67	56	51	40	26	14

Solution

Plot the data on a scatter plot that has years on the horizontal axis and number of television sets sold on the vertical axis.

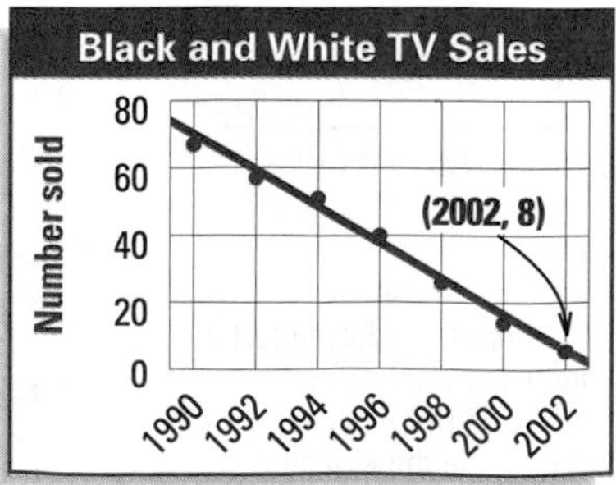

Because there appears to be a negative correlation, you can use a straightedge to draw a line that shows the trend in the data.

The line appears to pass through the point (2002, 8). You can estimate that you will sell about 8 black and white sets in 2002.

3.9 Exercises

Guided Practice

Decide whether the data in the scatter plot have a *positive correlation*, a *negative correlation*, or *no obvious correlation*.

1. negative correlation

2. positive correlation

3.

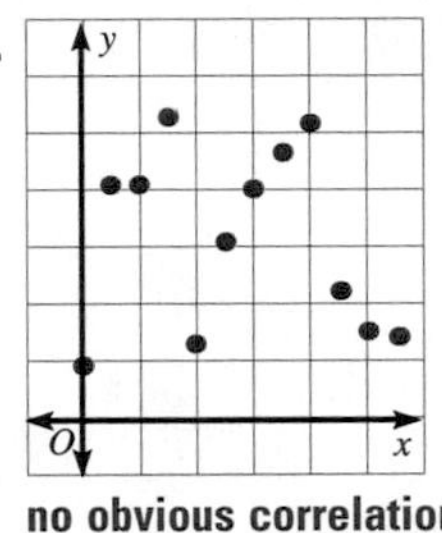

no obvious correlation

In Exercises 4 and 5, refer to Example 3 on page 150.

4. Use the line shown to estimate the number of black and white televisions sold in 1997. ***Sample answer*: about 32**

5. **MATHEMATICAL REASONING** Do you think it is possible that the trend represented by the line will continue until 2010? Explain your answer. **No; the number sold will reach zero before 2010.**

Practice and Problem Solving

Student Help

▶MORE PRACTICE Extra practice to help you master skills is on page 695.

6. no obvious correlation

7. negative correlation

8. positive correlation

Decide whether the data in the scatter plot have a *positive correlation*, a *negative correlation*, or *no obvious correlation*.

6.

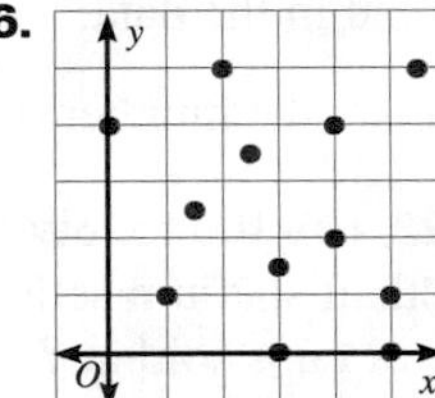

7.

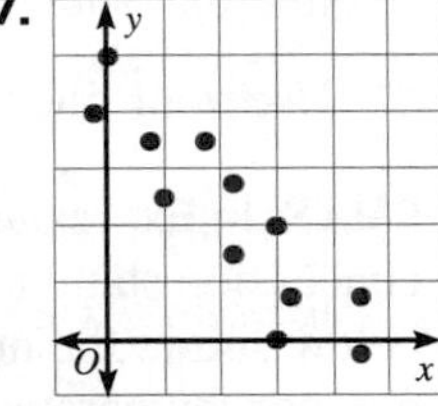

8.

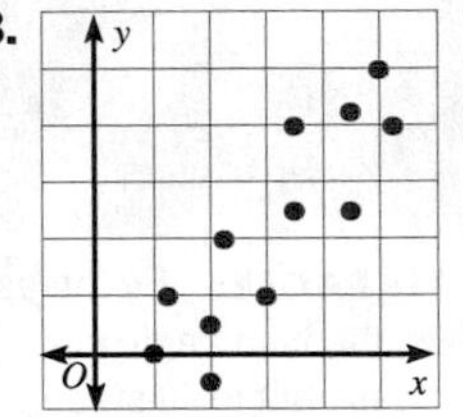

MATHEMATICAL REASONING In Exercises 9–13, decide whether the two quantities have a *positive correlation*, a *negative correlation*, or *no correlation*. Explain your reasoning.

9. The daily high temperature and the number of air conditioners in use on that day **Positive correlation; the higher the temperature, the more air conditioners that will be used.**

10. The age and the value of a family car **Negative correlation; the older the car, the less its value.**

11. A student's height and test scores **No correlation; taller students do not necessarily get better grades.**

12. The height and the age of a pine tree **Positive correlation; the older the tree, the taller it will grow.**

13. The number of pages in a book and the thickness of the book in centimeters **Positive correlation; the greater the number of pages, the thicker the book will be.**

Concept Check

How are the two quantities represented in a scatter plot related if it exhibits a negative correlation? Explain how you can use a line and the value of one quantity to estimate the corresponding value of the other quantity. **As one of the quantities increases, the other decreases. Locate the known value of one quantity on the appropriate axis. Move straight up (or to the right) until you reach the line. Then move straight to the left (or straight down) until you reach the other axis. The corresponding value can be read from this axis.**

3 Apply

Assignment Guide

TRANSITIONAL
Day 1: pp. 151–153 Exs. 6–11, 14–17, 27–32, 35–37

AVERAGE
Day 1: pp. 151–153 Exs. 6–8, 10–12, 14–15, 19–22, 27–33, 35–38

ADVANCED
Day 1: pp. 151–153 Exs. 10–15, 19–25, 26*, 27–28, 38–40

BLOCK SCHEDULE
pp. 151–153 Exs. 6–8, 10–12, 14–15, 19–22, 26–33, 37–39 (with 3.8)

Extra Practice

- Student Edition, pp. 694–695
- Chapter 3 Resource Book, p. 78

Homework Check

To quickly check student understanding of key concepts, go over the following exercises:

Transitional: 6, 8, 10, 14, 16, 18
Average: 6, 8, 10, 14, 20, 22
Advanced: 10, 14, 20, 22

16–17.

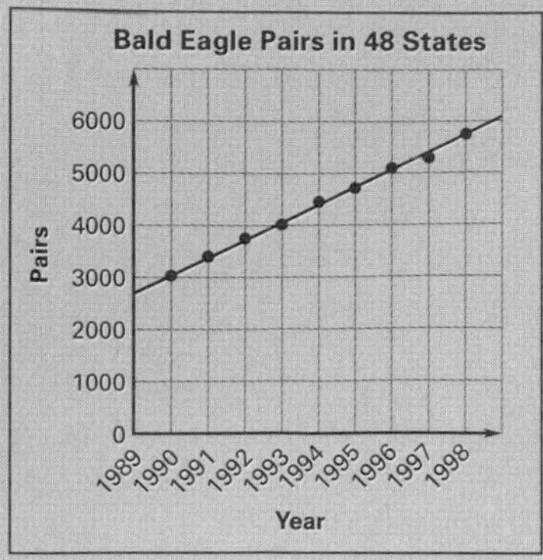

19–20.

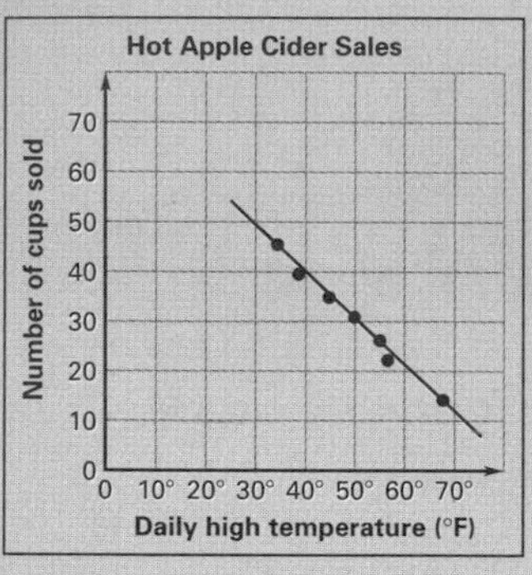

23.

Possible Lengths and Widths for a Rectangle Whose Perimeter is 12 Units					
Length, x	1	2	3	4	5
Width, y	5	4	3	2	1
Perimeter	12	12	12	12	12

24–25.

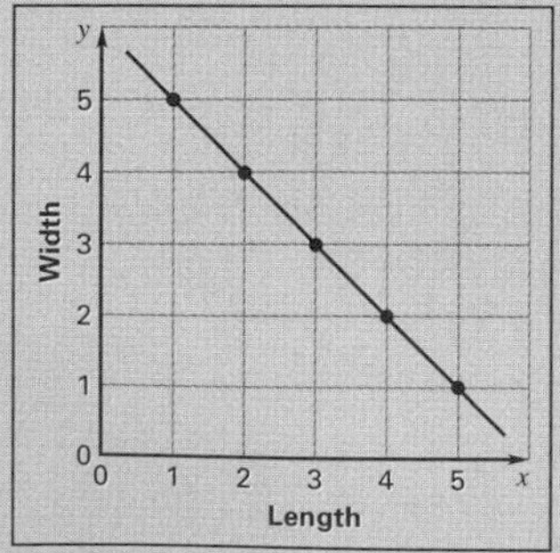

negative correlation

2.5 units

SALAD DRESSING In Exercises 14 and 15, use the scatter plot. It compares the amount of fat (in grams) with the number of calories in 100 grams of different salad dressings.

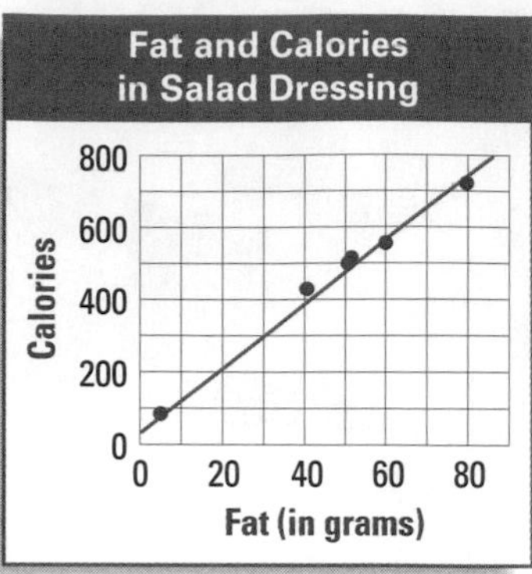

14. There are about 718 Calories in 100 grams of mayonnaise. Find the data point that represents mayonnaise on the scatter plot. Estimate the number of grams of fat in 100 grams of mayonnaise. **80 grams**

15. Decide whether the data have a *positive correlation*, a *negative correlation*, or *no obvious correlation*. **positive correlation**

Link to Science

BALD EAGLES By the early 1960s, the bald eagle was nearly extinct in 48 states, partly because of the pesticide DDT. Once DDT was banned in the United States and the bald eagle became protected by the Endangered Species Act, the number of bald eagle pairs rose dramatically.

Science Link **In Exercises 16–18, use the table below. The table shows the number of bald eagle pairs in 48 states (not including Hawaii and Alaska) for the years 1990 through 1998.** ▶ Source: U.S. Fish & Wildlife Service

Bald Eagle Pairs in 48 States									
Year	1990	1991	1992	1993	1994	1995	1996	1997	1998
Pairs	3035	3399	3749	4015	4449	4712	5094	5295	5748

16. Use the data to make a scatter plot. Put years on the horizontal axis and number of bald eagle pairs on the vertical axis. **See margin.**

17. Use your scatter plot to describe the correlation of the data. Draw a line that shows the trend in the data. **positive correlation**

18. Use your line to estimate the number of bald eagle pairs in 1999. ***Sample answer*: 6100 pairs**

SALES In Exercises 19–22, use the following information. An outdoor concession stand at a football stadium sells hot apple cider. The table below shows the number of cups sold at 7 different games and the average outdoor temperature at each game.

Average temperature at game (°F)	54°	68°	45°	35°	39°	57°	50°
Cups of hot cider sold	26	14	34	46	40	22	31

19. Make a scatter plot of the data. Put daily high temperature on the horizontal axis and the number of cups sold on the vertical axis. **See margin.**

20. Describe the correlation of the data. Draw a line that shows the trend in the data. **negative correlation**

21. Use the line to estimate how many cups will be sold at a game when the average temperature is 75°F. ***Sample answer*: 6 cups**

22. Use the line to estimate the average temperature at a game when 15 cups of cider are sold. ***Sample answer*: 67°F**

GEOMETRY **In Exercises 23–25, use the table below.** **23–25. See margin.**

23. Copy and complete the table.

24. Make a scatter plot of the data. Describe the correlation between the length and the width of a rectangle whose perimeter is 12 units.

Possible Lengths and Widths for a Rectangle Whose Perimeter is 12 Units					
Length, *x*	1	2	3	4	5
Width, *y*	?	?	?	?	?
Perimeter	12	12	12	12	12

25. Draw a line that shows a trend in the data. Use the line to find the width of a rectangle when the length is 3.5 units.

26. CHALLENGE Look back at the data in Exercises 19–22. Let x represent the average outdoor temperature at a game, and y represent the number of cups of hot cider sold. Which of the following equations best describes the relationship between x and y? Explain your thinking. **B; correlation is negative.**

A. $y = x - 78$ **B.** $y = 78 - x$

Multiple-Choice Practice

Use the scatter plot at the right.

27. Describe the correlation shown by the data. **A**

Ⓐ Positive correlation

Ⓑ Negative correlation

Ⓒ No obvious correlation

Ⓓ Not here

College Exam Results

Test score (y: 0, 50, 60, 70, 80, 90); Hours studied (x: 0, 2, 4, 6, 8, 10)

28. Predict the test score of a student who studies 11 hours. **G**

Ⓕ 80 Ⓖ 85 Ⓗ 90 Ⓙ 95

Mixed Review

Evaluate the expression. Follow the order of operations. *(3.3–3.6)*

29. $7^2 + (-5)(8)$ **9**

30. $3(1 - 5) - 11$ **−23**

31. $-12 + 5(-7 - 2)$ **−57**

32. $\frac{3 - 7}{2}$ **−2**

33. $\frac{-5 - 3 - 9 + 1}{-4}$ **4**

34. $\frac{-7 - 24 + 11}{5}$ **−4**

Solve the equation. *(3.7)*

35. $n - 8 = -24$ **−16**

36. $5m = -250$ **−50**

37. $t + 54 = -76$ **−130**

38. $-2x = -48$ **24**

39. $-8x = -8$ **1**

40. $12t = -96$ **−8**

Assessment Resources

- Assessment Book (Formal Assessment and Alternative Assessment)
- Test and Practice Generator

Mini-Quiz

After grading a test, a teacher asked several students how many minutes they had studied.

Minutes studied	15	10	35	25	40	0	60
Grade on test	70	60	80	65	90	50	90

1. Make a scatter plot of the data.

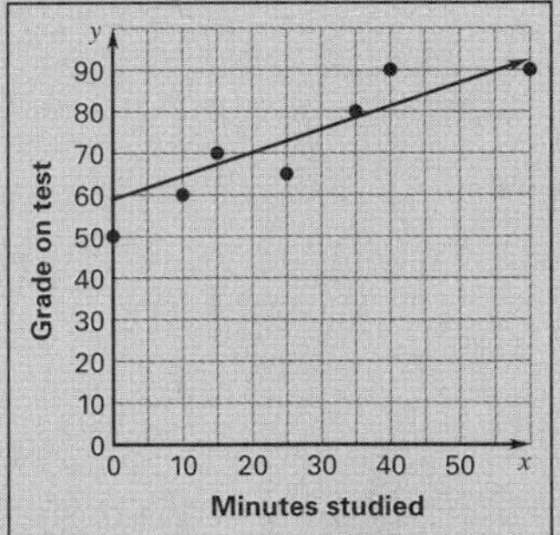

2. Do the number of minutes studied and the grade on the test have a *positive correlation*, a *negative correlation*, or *no correlation*? ***a positive correlation***

3. Draw a line and use it to estimate a student's grade on the test if he or she studied for 20 min. ***Sample answer:*** **70**

Additional Resources

The following resources are available to help review the material in this chapter:

Technology

- Personal Student Tutor
- Test and Practice Generator

Chapter 3 Chapter Summary and Review

VOCABULARY

- **integer,** *p. 105*
- **absolute value,** *p. 106*
- **opposites,** *p. 106*
- **average,** *p. 136*
- **profit,** *p. 141*
- **coordinate plane,** *p. 144*
- ***x*-axis, *y*-axis,** *p. 144*
- **origin,** *p. 144*
- **quadrants,** *p. 144*
- **ordered pair,** *p. 144*
- ***x*-coordinate,** *p. 144*
- ***y*-coordinate,** *p. 144*
- **solution (of an equation in *x* and *y*),** *p. 145*
- **scatter plot,** *p. 149*
- **positive correlation,** *p. 149*
- **negative correlation,** *p. 149*
- **no obvious correlation,** *p. 149*

3.1 INTEGERS AND ABSOLUTE VALUE

Examples on pp. 105–106

The integers are these numbers: . . . , −3, −2, −1, 0, 1, 2, 3, . . .

EXAMPLE **Order the integers 3, 1, −1, 2, −3, and −4 from least to greatest.**

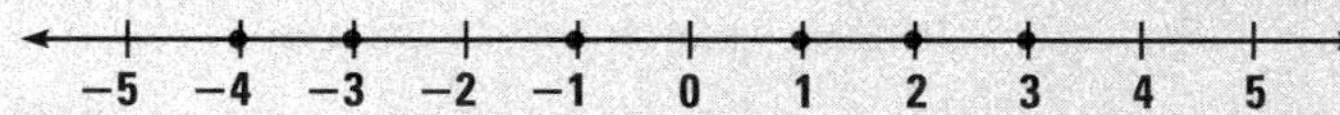

From the number line, you can see that the order is −4, −3, −1, 1, 2, 3. The absolute value of each of these integers is its distance from zero on a number line:

$|-4| = 4$, $|-3| = 3$, $|-1| = 1$, $|1| = 1$, $|2| = 2$, and $|3| = 3$.

1. Order the integers 4, −5, 3, 0, −9, −1, and 5 from least to greatest. **−9, −5, −1, 0, 3, 4, 5**

2. Name two different integers that have an absolute value of 16. **16, −16**

3.2 USING A NUMBER LINE TO ADD INTEGERS

Examples on pp. 110–111

EXAMPLE **Use a number line to find the sum 2 + (−4).**

Start at 0. Move 2 units to the right.
Then move 4 units to the left.

Your final position is −2. So, 2 + (−4) = −2.

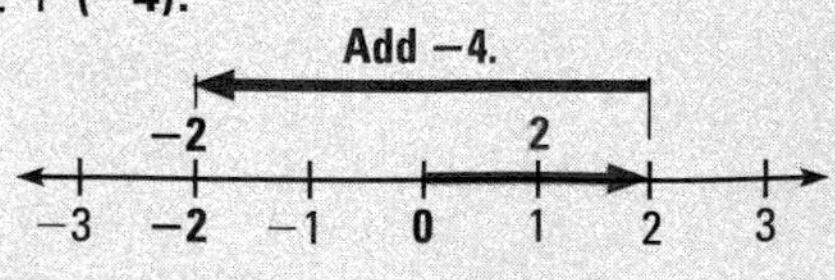

Use a number line to find the sum.

3. −6 + (−3) **−9** **4.** 7 + (−8) **−1** **5.** −7 + 9 **2** **6.** −1 + 5 + (−3) **1**

3.3 USING RULES TO ADD INTEGERS

Examples on pp. 116–118

To add two integers with the same sign, add their absolute values and write the common sign. To add two integers with different signs, subtract the smaller absolute value from the larger absolute value and write the sign of the integer with the larger absolute value.

EXAMPLES

$-3 + -8 = -11$, because $|-3| + |-8| = 11$, and the common sign is $-$.

$2 + (-7) = -5$, because $|-7| - |2| = 5$, and -7 has the greater absolute value.

Find the sum.

7. $-10 + 3$ **−7**

8. $17 + (-16)$ **1**

9. $54 + (-34) + (-14)$ **6**

Simplify the expression. Then evaluate the expression when $x = 5$.

10. $3x + 4x + (-7x)$ **0; 0**

11. $6 + (-2x) + 3x + (-4)$ **$x + 2$; 7**

12. $7x + (-4) + (-4x)$ **$3x - 4$; 11**

3.4 SUBTRACTING INTEGERS

Examples on pp. 123–124

To subtract b from a, add the opposite of b to a: $a - b = a + (-b)$.

EXAMPLE **Simplify $5 + 3x - 7x$.**

$5 + 3x - 7x = 5 + 3x + (-7x)$	**Use rule for subtraction.**
$= 5 + [3 + (-7)]x$	**Distributive property**
$= 5 + (-4x) = 5 - 4x$	**Simplify.**

Find the difference.

13. $-10 - 31$ **−41**

14. $30 - (-12)$ **42**

15. $-11 + (-2) - (-18)$ **5**

Simplify the expression.

16. $-3y - 2y + 5y + 4$ **4**

17. $4y + 5y - 10 - 6y$ **$3y - 10$**

18. $5y + 5 - (-3y) - 15$ **$8y - 10$**

3.5 MULTIPLYING INTEGERS

Examples on pp. 129–131

The product of two positive integers or two negative integers is positive. The product of integers with different signs is negative.

EXAMPLES **a.** $(-13)(3) = -39$ **b.** $(-4)(-9) = 36$

Find the product.

19. $3(-4)$ **−12** **20.** $(-2)(-8)$ **16** **21.** $-3(-5)^3$ **375** **22.** $(-4)(-2)(2)(-1)$ **−16**

Simplify the expression. Then evaluate the expression when $z = -3$.

23. $-5z + 6 - 3z$ **$-8z + 6$; 30** **24.** $4 - 2z + 5 + z$ **$9 - z$; 12** **25.** $-4z + 6z - 7 - 8z$ **$-6z - 7$; 11**

3.6 DIVIDING INTEGERS

Examples on pp. 135–136

The quotient of two positive integers or two negative integers is positive. The quotient of two integers with different signs is negative.

EXAMPLE You can use the rules for division to find the average of a student's quiz scores in a mathematics class where the scores are given as points above or below 90. The student's quiz scores are 4, 1, −9, 7, −4, and −5.

$$\text{Average score} = \frac{\text{Sum of scores}}{\text{Number of quizzes}} = \frac{4 + 1 + (-9) + 7 + (-4) + (-5)}{6} = \frac{-6}{6} = -1$$

The student's average quiz score is −1.

In Exercises 26–29, find the quotient.

26. $\frac{-35}{-7}$ **5** **27.** $\frac{48}{-12}$ **−4** **28.** $\frac{-100}{25}$ **−4** **29.** $\frac{0}{-18}$ **0**

30. A newspaper reports these changes (in cents) in the price of a stock over five days: +45, −103, −27, +86, and −11. Find the average daily change. **−2**

3.7 SOLVING EQUATIONS INVOLVING INTEGERS

Examples on pp. 140–141

EXAMPLES You can solve equations involving integers.

$x + 9 = -6$	Write original equation.	$-5x = -125$	Write original equation.
$x + 9 - 9 = -6 - 9$	Subtract 9 from each side.	$\frac{-5x}{-5} = \frac{-125}{-5}$	Divide each side by −5.
$x = -15$	Simplify. *x* is by itself.	$x = 25$	Simplify. *x* is by itself.

In Exercises 31–34, solve the equation. Check your solution.

31. $-15 = x - 7$ **−8** **32.** $25 + n = 1$ **−24** **33.** $-4t = 68$ **−17** **34.** $-15 = \frac{m}{-4}$ **60**

35. Write and solve an equation for this sentence: *The quotient of a number and −15 is 3.* **$\frac{m}{-15} = 3$; −45**

3.8 THE COORDINATE PLANE

Examples on pp. 144–146

EXAMPLE **Find the length and width of the rectangle.**

Rectangle length $= |x\text{-coordinate of } D - x\text{-coordinate of } C|$
$= |-3 - 3| = |-6| = 6$

Rectangle width $= |y\text{-coordinate of } B - y\text{-coordinate of } C|$
$= |3 - (-2)| = |5| = 5$

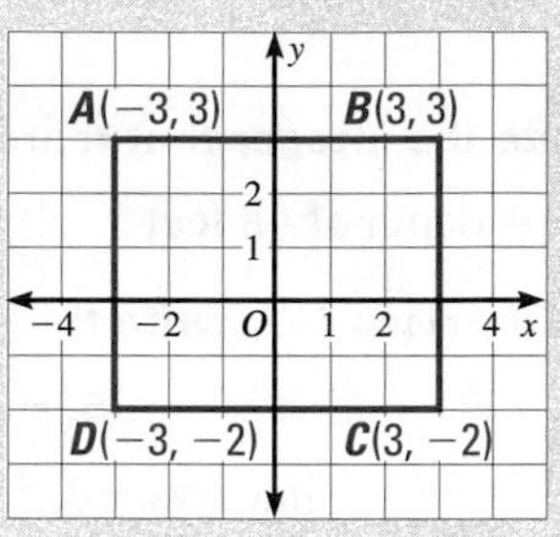

Plot all the points in the same coordinate plane. Name the quadrant (if any) that contains each point. 36–39. See margin.

36. $A(-5, 1)$ **37.** $B(3, -2)$ **38.** $C(4, -2)$ **39.** $D(4, 0)$

Determine whether the ordered pair is a solution of the equation.

40. $x - y = -2; (-3, -1)$ solution

41. $y + 5 = x; (4, 9)$ not a solution

42. $-48 = xy; (-16, 3)$ solution

3.9 SCATTER PLOTS

Examples on pp. 149–150

EXAMPLE You can use a scatter plot to determine whether data have a positive correlation, a negative correlation, or no obvious correlation. The scatter plot shown is based on shot put distances (to the nearest foot) for two throws by 10 athletes. The x- and y-coordinates give the lengths of the first and second throws, respectively. Because the data points tend to rise from left to right, there is a positive correlation between the lengths of the first and second throws. The line shows the trend in the data.

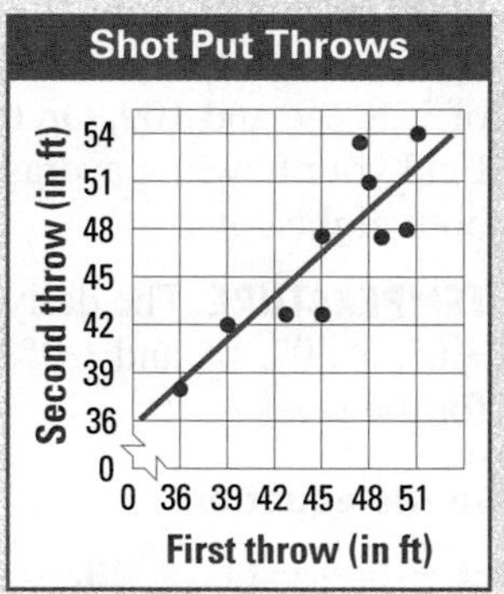

Use the table showing Indiana's yearly population figures.
▶Source: U.S. Census Bureau

Year	1990	1991	1992	1993	1994	1995	1996	1997
Population (millions)	5.54	5.60	5.65	5.70	5.74	5.79	5.83	5.87

43. Draw a scatter plot of the data. Describe the correlation of the data. **See margin.**

44. Draw a line that shows the trend in the data. Predict the 2001 population.
Sample answer: **6.05 million**

36–39.

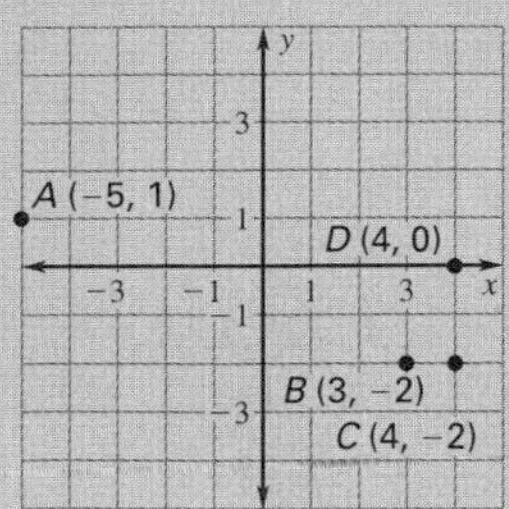

***A*: Quadrant 2;**

***B*: Quadrant 4;**

***C*: Quadrant 4;**

***D*: none**

43–44.

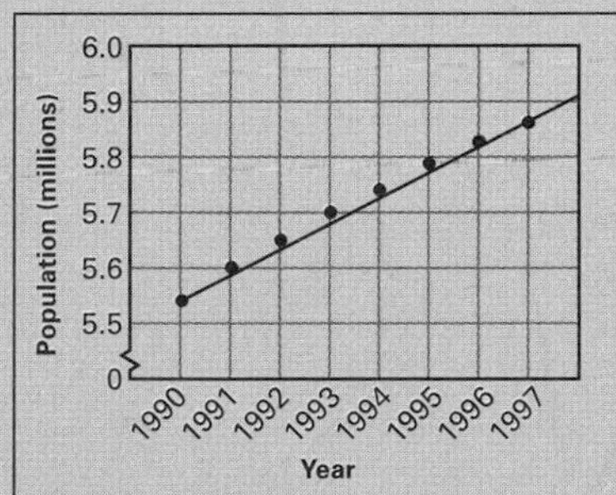

positive correlation

Additional Resources

☐ **Assessment Book**
- Formal Assessment, pp. 31–39
- Alternative Assessment, pp. 193–207

Test and Practice Generator

34.
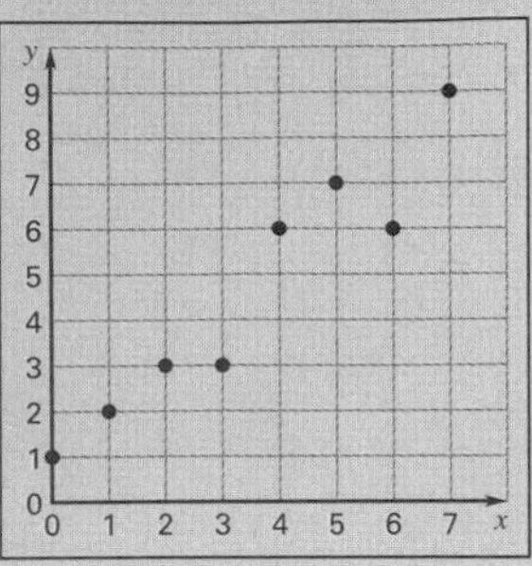

Chapter 3 Chapter Test

Write the integer that represents the situation.

1. A depth of 48 feet **−48** **2.** A rise of 17°F **17** **3.** A loss of \$60 **−60**

In Exercises 4–7, write the opposite and the absolute value of the integer.

4. 120 **−120, 120** **5.** −35 **35, 35** **6.** −54 **54, 54** **7.** 78 **−78, 78**

8. Order the integers −4, 5, −3, 0, 2, and −1 from least to greatest. **−4, −3, −1, 0, 2, 5**

Simplify.

9. $-4 + 8$ **4** **10.** $-6 - (-3)$ **−3** **11.** $2(-5)$ **−10** **12.** $(-4)(-5)$ **20**

13. $\frac{-12}{-6}$ **2** **14.** $19 + (-12)$ **7** **15.** $\frac{36}{-9}$ **−4** **16.** $14 - (-3)$ **17**

Simplify the expression.

17. $-2p + (-3p) + 6 + p$ **−4p + 6** **18.** $4 + 5x - (-7x) - 3$ **12x + 1** **19.** $-3n - 4 - 7n - 11$ **−10n − 15**

In Exercises 20–23, evaluate the expression when $n = -2$.

20. $\frac{-28}{2n}$ **7** **21.** $4n - n^2$ **−12** **22.** $34 - n - \frac{5n}{2}$ **41** **23.** $8 + (-n)^3$ **16**

24. Find the average of the following integers: −7, −5, 3, −4, and −2. **−3**

25. BOWLING Your bowling average is the sum of your scores divided by the number of games bowled. On your first night you bowl games of 128, 99, and 109. On the second night you bowl 117, 101, and 130. Find your bowling average after the first night and your average after both nights. **112; 114**

26. TEMPERATURE The daily low temperatures for a week are −7°, −3°, −6°, 3°, 0°, 1°, and −2°. What was the average daily low temperature for the week? **−2°**

Solve the equation.

27. $x + 6 = -11$ **−17** **28.** $4x = -48$ **−12** **29.** $\frac{x}{-9} = -2$ **18** **30.** $-6 = x - 6$ **0**

In Exercises 31–33, use the coordinate plane shown.

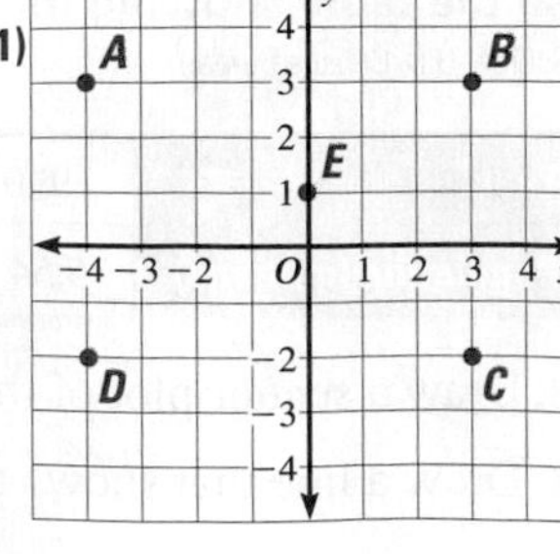

31. Write the coordinates of A, B, C, D, and E. **A(−4, 3), B(3, 3), C(3, −2), D(−4, −2), E(0, 1)**

32. Which point lies in Quadrant 4? **C**

33. Points A, B, C, and D form the four corners of a rectangle. Find the perimeter and the area of the rectangle. **24, 35**

34. Draw a scatter plot of the given data. **See margin.**

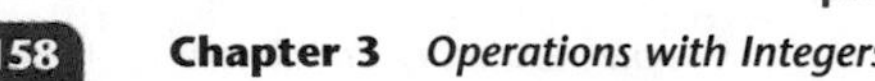
(0, 1), (4, 6), (3, 3), (2, 3), (7, 9), (5, 7) (6, 6), (1, 2)

35. Describe the correlation of the data in Exercise 34. **positive correlation**

Multiple-Choice Practice

Test Tip Think positively during the test. This will help you keep up your confidence and let you focus on each question.

1. Which statement is *false*? **C**

Ⓐ -4 is less than -3.

Ⓑ The opposite of a positive integer is a negative integer.

Ⓒ The absolute value of 10 is greater than the absolute value of -10.

Ⓓ The sum of a number and its opposite is zero.

2. The temperature was -2°F at 5 P.M. The expression $-2 + (-6)$ represents the temperature at 6 P.M. Which statement is *false*? **J**

Ⓕ The temperature fell 6°F between 5 P.M. and 6 P.M.

Ⓖ The temperature was -8°F at 6 P.M.

Ⓗ It was colder at 6 P.M. than at 5 P.M.

Ⓙ The temperature rose 6°F between 5 P.M. and 6 P.M.

3. Which statement about the expression $-14 - (-8)$ is *false*? **C**

Ⓐ The difference is a negative number.

Ⓑ The expression can be rewritten as $-14 + 8$.

Ⓒ The difference is -22.

Ⓓ A verbal phrase for the expression is: *the difference of negative fourteen and negative eight.*

4. Which expression has the greatest value? **J**

Ⓕ $-3(3) - 9$ Ⓖ $-3(-3) - 9$

Ⓗ $-3(3) + 9$ Ⓙ $-3(-3) + 9$

5. Your cousin starts a new business. The monthly profits for the first four months are $-\$45$, $-\$32$, \$70, and $-\$25$. What is the average monthly profit for this period? **B**

Ⓐ $-\$32$ Ⓑ $-\$8$

Ⓒ \$8 Ⓓ \$32

6. Solve the equation $-7x = -84$. **H**

Ⓕ -588 Ⓖ -12

Ⓗ 12 Ⓙ 588

7. If $x - 13 = -17$, then $x = \underline{\ ?\ }$. **B**

Ⓐ -30 Ⓑ -4

Ⓒ 30 Ⓓ Not here

8. Describe the correlation of the data in the scatter plot shown below. **G**

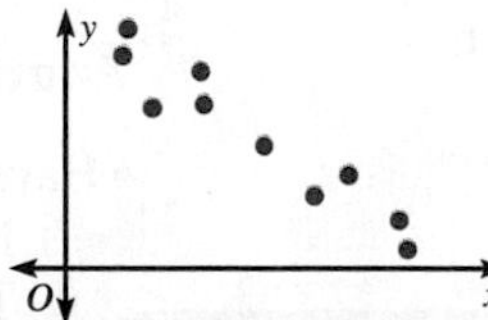

Ⓕ Positive correlation

Ⓖ Negative correlation

Ⓗ No obvious correlation

Ⓙ Not here

Teaching Tip

The Brain Games activity provides a motivating way to review selected content in the chapter. For a more comprehensive review, see the Chapter Summary and Review on pp. 154–157.

Brain games

California Standards

- Add, subtract, multiply, and divide rational numbers. (NS 1.2)
- Make precise calculations and check the validity of the results. (MR 2.8)

Integer Target

Materials

- Coin
- Card stock
- Two different colored markers

Directions

Object of the Game

Divide your group into a red team and a blue team. The first team to reach a target integer on a number line wins.

How to Play

STEP 1 Each team draws a number line from -20 to 20 and makes three decks of cards. Two decks are identical, with the cards being labeled with the integers from -4 to 4. The other cards are labeled with operation symbols: $+$, $-$, and $\cdot$. Shuffle each deck and place the decks face down.

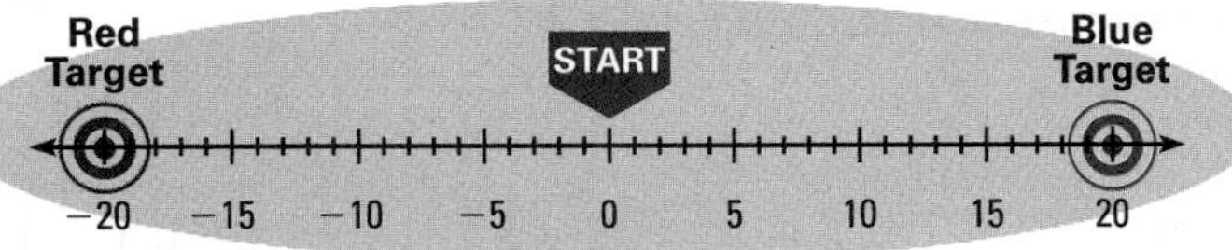

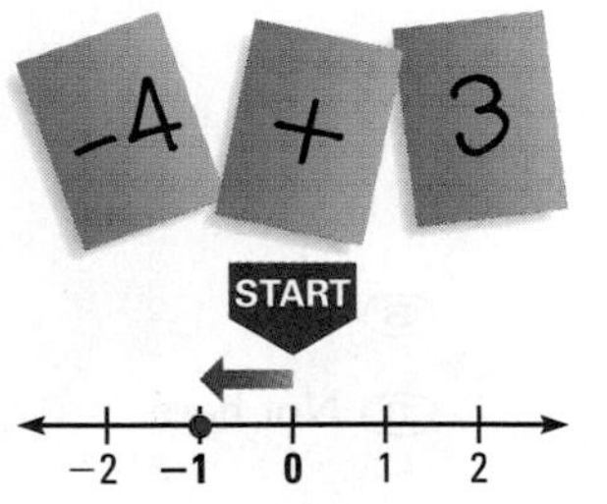

$-4 + 3 = -1$, so your team moves 1 to the left on your first turn. On your next turn, move left or right from -1.

STEP 2 Teams take turns choosing an integer card, an operation card, and an integer card. Use the cards to write an expression. Return the cards to the bottom of the correct decks.

STEP 3 Each team starts at 0 and moves along the number line according to the value of the expression. The team that reaches its target integer first wins.

Another Way to Play

- Have the option of tossing a coin at each turn.
  Heads: Move according to the opposite of the expression.
  Tails: Don't move on that turn and lose your next turn.

Brain Teaser

See margin.

Make a true equation by moving only one toothpick.

You may want to make up some toothpick puzzles of your own.

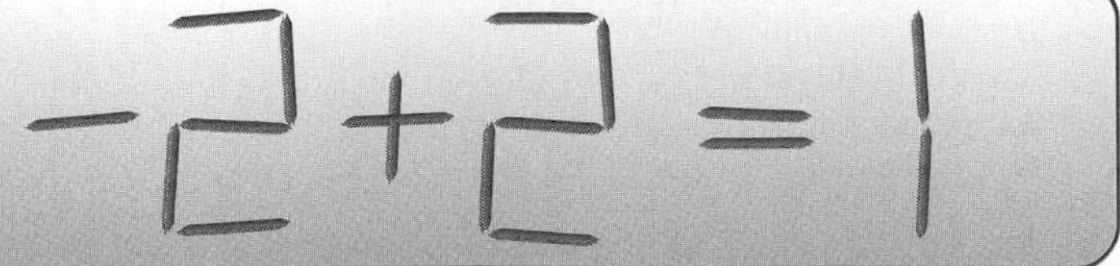

Turn the second 2 into a 3 by moving the lower vertical toothpick to the right. Then $-2 + 3 = 1$.

California Standards and Assessment

CA Standards: NS 1.2, MR 2.8

The basic skills you'll review on this page will help prepare you for the next chapter.

Reviewing the Basics

EXAMPLE 1 Using the Distributive Property

Use the distributive property to write an equivalent expression.

a. $-3(x + 2) = -3(x) + (-3)(2)$ Distributive property

$= -3x + (-6)$ Multiply.

$= -3x - 6$ Rewrite as subtraction.

b. $-5(-4 + x) = -5(-4) + (-5)(x)$ Distributive property

$= 20 + (-5x)$ Multiply.

$= 20 - 5x$ Rewrite as subtraction.

c. $-3x - 5x = -3x + (-5)x$ Use rule for subtraction.

$= [-3 + (-5)]x$ Distributive property

$= -8x$ Simplify.

Try These

Use the distributive property to write an equivalent expression.

1. $3(x + 8)$ **$3x + 24$**
2. $10(s - 5)$ **$10s - 50$**
3. $9(-2 + b)$ **$-18 + 9b$**
4. $-8(-2 + w)$ **$16 - 8w$**
5. $5(8m + 3)$ **$40m + 15$**
6. $-4(7x + 4)$ **$-28x - 16$**
7. $-13x + 12x$ **$(-13 + 12)x = -x$**
8. $15m - 8m$ **$(15 - 8)m = 7m$**
9. $-6t - 11t$ **$(-6 - 11)t = -17t$**

EXAMPLE 2 Evaluating Variable Expressions

Evaluate the expression $\frac{10}{x} + 2y + 3$ when $x = -5$ and $y = -4$.

$\frac{10}{x} + 2y + 3 = \frac{10}{\mathbf{-5}} + 2(\mathbf{-4}) + 3$ Substitute -5 for x and -4 for y.

$= -2 + (-8) + 3$ Simplify.

$= -7$ Use rules for adding integers.

Student Help

▸ **MORE EXAMPLES**
More examples and practice exercises available at www.mcdougallittell.com

Try These

Evaluate the expression when $x = -3$ and $y = 5$.

10. $x + y - 2$ **0**
11. $4x + 1 - 3y$ **-26**
12. $7 - x - 5 + y$ **10**
13. $4x - 5y$ **-37**
14. $-2y - 3x$ **-1**
15. $6xy$ **-90**
16. $20y - \frac{1 - x}{4}$ **99**
17. $\frac{4y}{5} - 2x$ **10**
18. $\frac{2x + 2y}{-4}$ **-1**

Additional Resources

Technology
- Personal Student Tutor
- Test and Practice Generator

Additional Resources

A Cumulative Test for Chapters 1–3 is available in the *Assessment Book*, pp. 40–43.

17. Numerators are sequence of odd numbers and denominators are sequence of even numbers; $\frac{9}{10}, \frac{11}{12}, \frac{13}{14}$.

27.

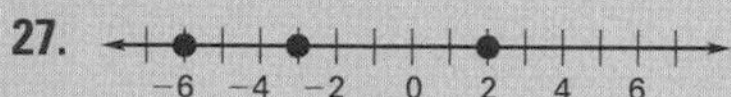

28.

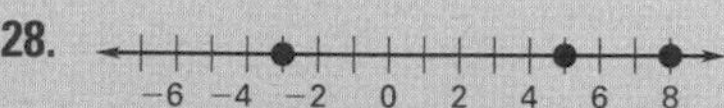

29. −6 −4 −2 0 2 4 6

30.

Chapters 1-3 Cumulative Practice

In Exercises 1–9, evaluate the expression. (1.3, 1.4)

1. 4^3 **64**   **2.** 5^5 **3125**   **3.** 9^3 **729**

4. $3 + 2 \cdot 4$ **11**   **5.** $(3 + 2) \cdot 4$ **20**   **6.** $150 - 60 \div 3 \times 4$ **70**

7. $35 \div (19 - 12) + 4^5$ **1029**   **8.** $14^2 - 84 \div 12 - 157$ **32**   **9.** $3^3 + (14 + 8) \times 12 - 11$ **280**

10. Evaluate the expression $x^2 \cdot (y - 2)$ when $x = 3$ and $y = 5$. **(1.4) 27**

In Exercises 11–13, find the perimeter and area of the figure. (1.5)

11.

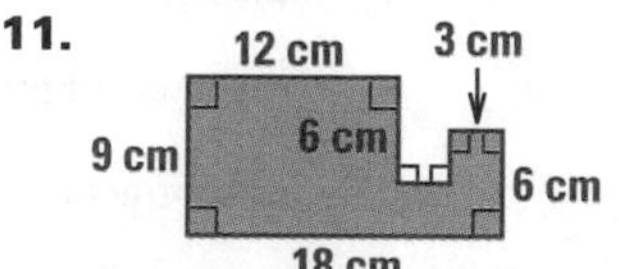

$P = 60$ cm; $A = 135$ cm^2

12.

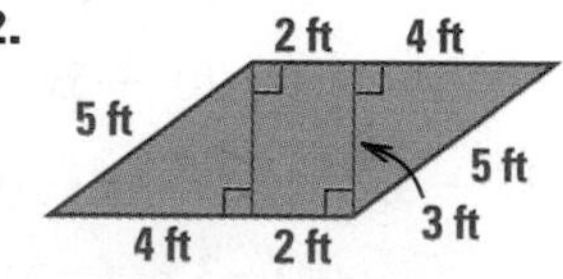

$P = 22$ ft; $A = 18$ ft^2

13.

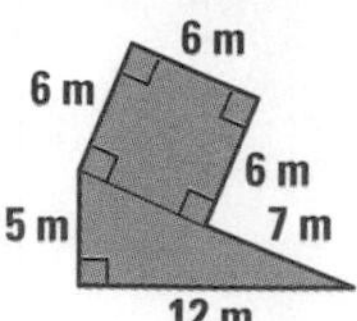

$P = 42$ m ; $A = 66$ m^2

14. BICYCLING You and a friend are riding bicycles. You ride for 80 minutes at a speed of 15 miles per hour. Your friend rides the same amount of time at a speed of 12 miles per hour. How many miles did each of you travel? **(1.5) you: 20 mi, your friend: 16 mi**

Describe the pattern. Then list the next three numbers you expect to find in the sequence. (1.6)

15. 20, 18, 16, 14, ?, ?, ?, . . . **decrease by two; 12, 10, 8**

16. 1, 5, 9, 13, ?, ?, ?, . . . **increase by 4; 17, 21, 25**

17. $\frac{1}{2}, \frac{3}{4}, \frac{5}{6}, \frac{7}{8}$, ?, ?, ?, . . . **See margin.**

18. $\frac{14}{13}, \frac{12}{11}, \frac{10}{9}, \frac{8}{7}$, ?, ?, ?, . . . **Numerator and denominator decrease by two; $\frac{6}{5}, \frac{4}{3}, \frac{2}{1}$**

Name the property shown. (1.7, 1.8)

19. $14 + (27 + 3) = 14 + (3 + 27)$ **commutative property of addition**

20. $4 \cdot 6 + 4 \cdot 8 = 4(6 + 8)$ **distributive property**

21. $(24 \cdot 16) \cdot (4 \cdot 9) = 24 \cdot (16 \cdot 4) \cdot 9$ **associative property of multiplication**

22. $(5 \cdot 9) + (6 \cdot 16) = (6 \cdot 16) + (5 \cdot 9)$ **commutative property of addition**

Write an equation or inequality that represents the sentence. Then solve the equation or inequality. (2.4, 2.5, 2.6, 2.8)

23. The sum of a number and 9 is 33. **$x + 9 = 33$; 24**

24. The difference of a number and 16 is less than or equal to 20. **$x - 16 \leq 20$; $x \leq 36$**

25. The product of 7 and a number is greater than 91. **$7x > 91$; $x > 13$**

26. Three is the quotient of a number and 4. **$3 = \frac{x}{4}$; 12**

Draw a number line and graph the integers. (3.1) 27–30. See margin.

27. −3, −6, 2   **28.** 5, 8, −3   **29.** −4, −1, 5   **30.** 0, −7, 7

Evaluate the expression. (1.4, 3.1–3.6)

31. $|-3|$ **3** **32.** $|-4|$ **4** **33.** $-5 + 12 - 9 - 13$ **−15**

34. $21 - 32 - 1 + 4$ **−8** **35.** $(10)(-11)$ **−110** **36.** $\frac{-144}{-2}$ **72**

37. $(-4)(-6)$ **24** **38.** $2^2 + (3 - 4)^2 \cdot 9$ **13** **39.** $20 - (5 - 8)^3 \div 9$ **23**

Use the distributive property to write an equivalent expression. Then evaluate the expression when $x = -4$. (1.8, 3.5)

40. $5(-2 + x)$ **$-10 + 5x$; −30** **41.** $3(-7 + x)$ **$-21 + 3x$; −33** **42.** $-6(x + 4)$ **$-6x - 24$; 0** **43.** $-9(-1 + x)$ **$9 - 9x$; 45**

Simplify the expression if possible. Then evaluate the expression when $r = -8$ and $t = 2$. (3.2–3.6)

44. $-3r + 5 - 2r + 8r - 7$ **$3r - 2$; −26** **45.** $-7t - 5t + 6 + 2t$ **$-10t + 6$; −14** **46.** $4r - 5t - 10r + 2t + 6$ **$-6r - 3t + 6$; 48**

47. $\frac{3r}{t}$ **−12** **48.** $\frac{t - r}{5}$ **2** **49.** $-5t^2 - r$ **−12**

Solve the equation or inequality. (2.5, 2.6, 2.8, 3.7)

50. $x + 7 = 16$ **9** **51.** $y + 5 = -6$ **−11** **52.** $z - 8 = -16$ **−8** **53.** $a - 8 = 13$ **21**

54. $10b = 100$ **10** **55.** $-9x = 36$ **−4** **56.** $\frac{y}{-12} = 8$ **−96** **57.** $\frac{m}{4} = 16$ **64**

58. $n + 6 < 7$ **$n < 1$** **59.** $p + 4 > 12$ **$p > 8$** **60.** $x - 2 \geq 5$ **$x \geq 7$** **61.** $y - 11 \leq 9$ **$y \leq 20$**

62. $15c > 30$ **$c > 2$** **63.** $26 > 13t$ **$2 > t$** **64.** $\frac{q}{3} \leq 25$ **$q \leq 75$** **65.** $40 \leq \frac{s}{9}$ **$360 \leq s$**

In Exercises 66–69, plot the points in the same coordinate plane. Name the quadrant (if any) that contains each point. (3.8) **See margin for graph.**

66. $A(2, -3)$ **Quadrant 4** **67.** $B(-1, 0)$ **no quadrant** **68.** $C(-4, -5)$ **Quadrant 3** **69.** $D(2, 4)$ **Quadrant 1**

Determine whether the ordered pair is a solution of the equation. Then find three other solutions. (3.8) **70–72. See margin.**

70. $5x - 3 = y$; $(2, 7)$ **71.** $y = 7x$; $(-1, -7)$ **72.** $y + 10 = x$; $(-10, 0)$

In Exercises 73–75, use the following information. The ordered pairs (x, y) below represent data collected from 10 male students. Each x-coordinate gives the height (to the nearest inch) of a student. Each y-coordinate gives the shoe size (to the nearest size) of the student. (3.9) **73–74. See margin.**

(64, 7), (67, 8), (64, 8), (71, 10), (66, 9), (69, 10), (72, 11), (74, 12), (68, 8), (71, 11)

73. Draw a scatter plot of the data.

74. Describe the correlation of the data. Then draw a line that shows the trend in the data.

75. Use your line from Exercise 74 to predict the shoe size of a male student who is 77 inches tall. **12 or 13**

66–69.

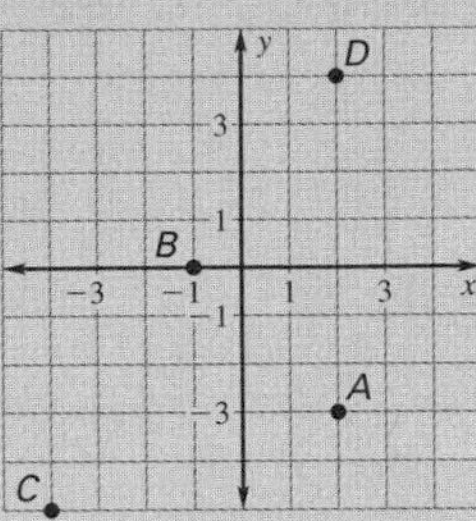

70. solution; *sample answer:* **(0, −3), (−1, −8), (6, 27)**

71. solution; *sample answer:* **(0, 0) (1,7), (2, 14)**

72. not a solution; *sample answer:* **(2, −8), (−2, −12), (5, −5)**

73–74.

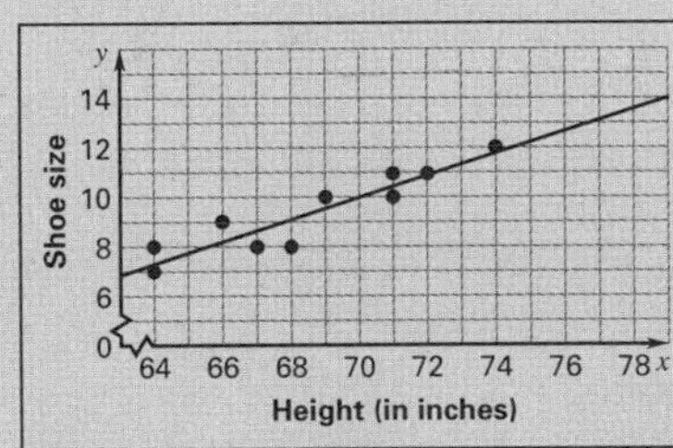

positive correlation

Project Overview

Mathematical Goals

- Use linear equations to model the pressure at a given altitude.
- Evaluate linear equations for one of the variables.
- Make a scatter plot for height and pressure data.

Managing the Project

Classroom Management
Students can work individually or in pairs. If working in pairs, each student should contribute to writing the expression in Exercise 1. In Exercises 2 and 3, students should divide the work and do the calculations individually.

Both of the students should contribute to the poster. One student may draw the map and the other may label the pressures and heights. Both should contribute to the written explanation.

Guiding Students' Work
Students may have difficulty writing the equation in Exercise 1. You may wish to have them review the "Problem Solving Plan" in Lesson 2.7. You may also wish to remind them that the rate of decrease in pressure is $\frac{2 \text{ pounds/in.}^2}{5000 \text{ feet}}$ or 0.0004 pounds per square inch decrease in pressure for every 1 foot increase in altitude. Since pressure decreases by 0.0004 pounds/in.^{2} for a 1 foot increase in altitude, pressure will decrease by $0.0004x$ for an x foot increase in altitude above sea level.

California Standards and Assessment

CA Standards: AF 1.1, AF 1.3, MR 2.6

Chapters 1-3 Project

California Standards

- Use variables and appropriate operations to write an expression that represents a verbal description. (AF 1.1)
- Simplify numerical expressions by applying properties of rational numbers. (AF 1.3)
- Express the solution logically using appropriate notation and terms and clear language. (MR 2.6)

Materials

- Paper
- Colored pencils
- Calculator

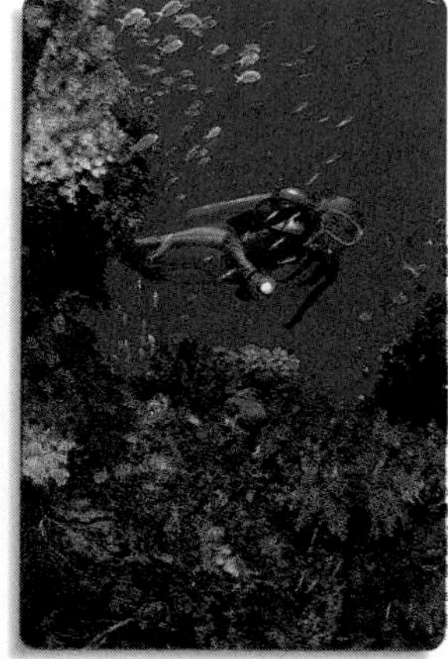

Comparing Pressures

OBJECTIVE **Find the pressures at various places in California.**

Investigation

You may have noticed that your ears pop or hurt when you drive down a steep hill, dive into deep water, or land in an airplane. That happens because the pressure on your ears increases as you go down. One common measure of pressure is pounds per square inch (psi).

1. At sea level, the pressure is about 15 pounds per square inch. As you go up from sea level, the pressure decreases by about 2 pounds per square inch for every 5000 feet you go up. Write an expression to find the pressure when you are x feet above sea level. **$P = 15 - \frac{1}{2500}x$**

2. Use the expression you wrote in Exercise 1 to estimate the pressures at the following places. Copy and complete the table. Give your answers to the nearest pound per square inch. **9, 12, 13, 15, 15, 15**

Location	Position, x, relative to sea level (in feet)	Pressure (in psi)
Top of Mt. Whitney	14,494	?
Top of Yosemite Falls	about 6,500	?
Bottom of Yosemite Falls	about 4,000	?
Redding	557	?
San Diego	40	?
Lowest point in Death Valley	−282	?

3. When you dive into deep water, the pressure increases as you go down under water. You can use the expression $15 - 0.5x$ to find the pressure when you are at x feet relative to sea level. Copy and complete the table, which lists several shipwrecks. **25, 65, 175**

Shipwreck	Position, x, relative to sea level (in feet)	Pressure (in psi)
Melrose (1932)	−20	?
Valiant (1930)	−100	?
City of Rio de Janeiro (1878)	−320	?

PRESENT YOUR RESULTS

Create a poster showing the pressures at various places in or near California.

- Sketch a map of California and nearby ocean. Include the **locations** and **shipwrecks** from Exercises 2 and 3. Next to each of these, write the position relative to sea level and the pressure.
- Write an explanation of how to find pressure above water. Include an explanation of the expression you wrote in Exercise 1.
- Write an explanation of how to find pressure under water.
- Summarize your results. What patterns do you notice?

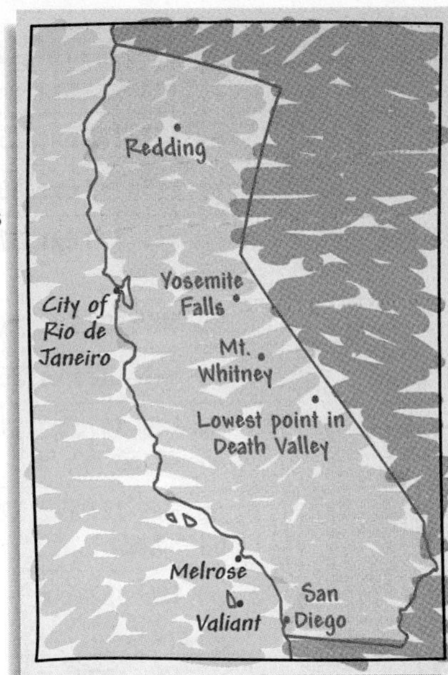

EXTENSION

Materials Colored pencils, graph paper

The expression you wrote in Exercise 1 gives a good estimate for pressures close to sea level but it does not work for all altitudes.

4. Use your expression from Exercise 1 to estimate the pressure at 0 feet, 5000 feet, 10,000 feet, 15,000 feet, 20,000 feet, 25,000 feet, and 30,000 feet. **15, 13, 11, 9, 7, 5, 3**

5. Use the data from Exercise 4 and a colored pencil to draw a scatter plot. Put altitude on the horizontal axis and pressure on the vertical axis. **See margin.**

6. Use a different color to graph the actual pressures from the table below on the scatter plot from Exercise 5. **See margin.**

Actual Pressures							
Altitude (in feet)	0	5,000	10,000	15,000	20,000	25,000	30,000
Pressure (in psi)	14.7	12.23	10.11	8.29	6.75	5.45	4.36

7. What patterns do you notice? Do you think the expression from Exercise 1 gives a good estimate above 30,000 feet? Explain.

7. The estimated pressure is a straight line, while the actual pressures seem to be in a curved line.

Concluding the Project
Students should present their posters to the class and give a brief explanation of how to find the pressure above or below sea level. You can use questions like the following for class discussion:

- Would you feel more pressure at equal distances above water or under water?
- What problems might low pressure or high pressure cause for the human body?

Grading the Project

A well-written project will have the following characteristics:

- Complete and correct solutions to Exercises 1–3.
- A neat and accurate map showing correct heights and pressures.
- A clear and thorough explanation of how to find the pressure both above and below sea level.
- An extension to the project in which students address all four of the extension exercises.

5–6.

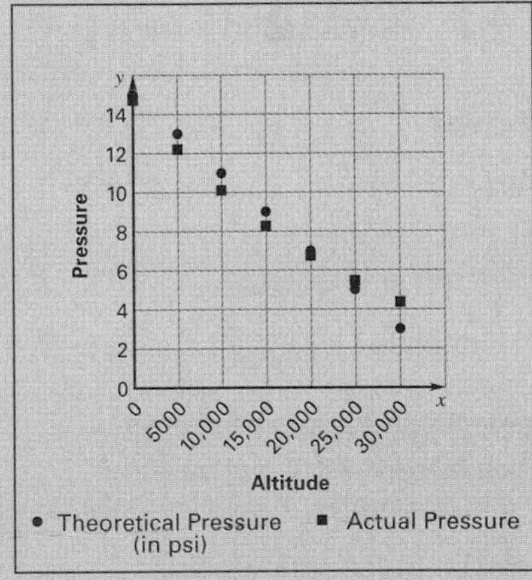

CHAPTER 4 Pacing and Assignment Guide

Regular Schedule

Lesson	Les. Day	Transitional	Average	Advanced
4.1	Day 1	pp. 172–173 Exs. 7–14	pp. 172–173 Exs. 7–15, 21–22	pp. 172–173 Exs. 12–22
	Day 2	pp. 172–173 Exs. 23–27, 31–33	pp. 172–173 Exs. 23–29, 31–33	pp. 172–173 Exs. 23–29, 30*, 31–33
4.2	Day 1	pp. 176–178 Exs. 10–13, 16–21, 31–34, 50–51	pp. 176–178 Exs. 10–13, 19–27, 31–36, 50–51	pp. 176–178 Exs. 12–15, 22–36
	Day 2	EP p. 695 Ex. 92; pp. 176–178 Exs. 37–38, 40–41, 47–49, 52–57, 64–67	pp. 176–178 Exs. 37–41, 43–49, 58–63, 67	pp. 176–178 Exs. 40–41, 42*, 43–49, 58–60, 67
4.3	Day 1	pp. 181–182 Exs. 12–19, 29–31	pp. 181–182 Exs. 12–22, 29–31	pp. 181–182 Exs. 12–19, 29–34
	Day 2	pp. 181–182 Exs. 35–36, 39, 42–44	pp. 181–182 Exs. 35–39, 42–44	pp. 181–182 Exs. 35–40, 41*, 42–44
4.4	Day 1	pp. 185–187 Exs. 11–19, 28–29, 46–48, 50–52, 56	pp. 185–187 Exs. 11–19, 24–25, 28–29, 46–48, 50–52, 56	pp. 185–187 Exs. 11–17, 22–27, 30–31, 46–48, 50–52, 56
	Day 2	pp. 185–187 Exs. 32–35, 37–38, 41–43, 57–59, 63–65	pp. 185–187 Exs. 32–39, 41–43, 57–59, 63–65, 69	pp. 185–187 Exs. 32–39, 40*, 41–43, 57–59, 63–65, 69
4.5	Day 1	EP p. 691 Exs. 35–37; pp. 191–192 Exs. 5–12, 18–20, 22–23, 30–31	pp. 191–192 Exs. 7–14, 17–21, 27–28, 30–31	pp. 191–192 Exs. 13–21, 25–28, 29*, 30–31
4.6	Day 1	SRH p. 668 Exs. 3–6; p. 670 Exs. 2–3; pp. 195–197 Exs. 5–10, 20–25, 29–36	pp. 195–197 Exs. 9–15, 20–25, 29–36, 44	pp. 195–197 Exs. 9–11, 16–18, 19*, 20–25, 29–31, 41–44
4.7	Day 1	SRH pp. 672–673 Exs. 22–27; p. 675 Exs. 17–23; p. 676 Exs. 5–8, 13–17; pp. 201–202 Exs. 8, 10–13, 18–19, 22–24, 34–35	pp. 201–202 Exs. 8–13, 16–19, 26–28, 34–35	pp. 201–202 Exs. 12–21, 29–32, 33*, 34–35
4.8	Day 1	SRH p. 689 Exs. 1–6; pp. 206–207 Exs. 7–10, 13–15, 19–21, 30–31	pp. 206–207 Exs. 9–12, 18–21, 24–27, 30–31	pp. 206–207 Exs. 11–12, 18–23, 28, 29*, 30–31; EC: TE p. 166D*
Review	Day 1	pp. 208–211 Exs 1–39	pp. 208–211 Exs. 1–39	pp. 208–211 Exs. 1–39
Assess	Day 1	Chapter 4 Test	Chapter 4 Test	Chapter 4 Test

Yearly Pacing *Chapter 4 Total* – **14 days** *Chapters 1–4 Total* – **52 days** *Remaining* – **108 days**

* Challenge Exercises EP = Extra Practice SRH = Skills Review Handbook EC = Extra Challenge

Block Schedule

Day 1	Day 2	Day 3	Day 4	Day 5	Day 6	Day 7
4.1 pp. 172–173: Exs. 7–15, 21–29, 31–33	**4.2** pp. 176–178: Exs. 10–13, 19–27, 31–41, 43–51, 58–63, 67	**4.3** pp. 181–182: Exs. 12–22, 29–31, 35–39, 42–44	**4.4** pp. 185–187: Exs. 11–19, 24–25, 28–29, 32–39, 41–43, 46–52, 56–59, 63–65, 69	**4.5** pp. 191–192: Exs. 7–14, 17–21, 27–28, 30–31 **4.6** pp. 195–197: Exs. 9–15, 20–25, 29–36, 44	**4.7** pp. 201–202: Exs. 8–13, 16–19, 26–28, 34–35 **4.8** pp. 206–207: Exs. 9–12, 18–21, 24–27, 30–31	**Review** pp. 208–211: Exs. 1–39 **Assess** Chapter 4 Test

Yearly Pacing *Chapter 4 Total* – **7 days** *Chapters 1–4 Total* – **26 days** *Remaining* – **54 days**

Support Materials

Chapter Resource Book

LESSON SUPPORT	4.1	4.2	4.3	4.4	4.5	4.6	4.7	4.8
Lesson Plans	p. 1	p. 10	p. 19	p. 28	p. 37	p. 46	p. 55	p. 64
Lesson Plans for Block Scheduling	p. 2	p. 11	p. 20	p. 29	p. 38	p. 47	p. 56	p. 65
Warm-Ups with Multiple-Choice Practice	p. 3	p. 12	p. 21	p. 30	p. 39	p. 48	p. 57	p. 66
Problem of the Day	p. 4	p. 13	p. 22	p. 31	p. 40	p. 49	p. 58	p. 67
Daily Cumulative Review	p. 5	p. 14	p. 23	p. 32	p. 41	p. 50	p. 59	p. 68
Practice Masters	p. 6	p. 15	p. 24	p. 33	p. 42	p. 51	p. 60	p. 69
Reteaching Masters	p. 7	p. 16	p. 25	p. 34	p. 43	p. 52	p. 61	p. 70
Enrichment Masters	p. 9	p. 18	p. 27	p. 36	p. 45	p. 54	p. 63	p. 72

Transparencies

	4.1	4.2	4.3	4.4	4.5	4.6	4.7	4.8
Warm-Ups with Multiple-Choice Practice	p. 26	p. 27	p. 28	p. 29	p. 30	p. 31	p. 32	p. 33
Teacher Time-Saver Transparencies	✓	✓	✓	✓	✓	✓	✓	✓
English/Spanish Problem Solving	p. 14			p. 15	p. 16	p. 17		p. 18
Answer Transparencies	✓	✓	✓	✓	✓	✓	✓	✓

Technology

- Personal Student Tutor
- Time-Saving Test and Practice Generator
- Electronic Teacher Tools
- Technology: Using Calculators and Computers

Additional Resources

- Math Log
- Assessment Book
- Worked-Out Solution Key
- Practice Workbook (English/Spanish)
- Home and School Connection
- California Standards: Key Concepts Book

Correlation to the California Curriculum

Correlations to the California Standards
CA Standards: NS 1.0, NS 1.7, AF 1.1, AF 1.3, AF 4.1, AF 4.2, MG 1.3, MG 2.1, SDP 1.0, SDP 1.1, MR 1.3, MR 2.3, MR 2.8, MR 3.1, MR 3.2

California Curriculum Support

Key Concepts Book

- Pre-Course Review: Topic 1 Working with Decimals
  Topic 5 Measurement
- Key Standards: NS 1.2 Decimal Operations *(Lesson 4.7)*
  AF 4.1 Solving Two-Step Equations *(Lesson 4.1)*
  AF 4.1 Solving Equations with Variables on Both Sides *(Lesson 4.5)*
  MG 1.3 Dimensional Analysis *(Lesson 4.6)*

California Standards Practice Workbook provides practice for each Standard that is covered in this chapter.

Providing Universal Access

Strategies for Strategic Learners

FOCUS ON KEY CONCEPTS

In this chapter students are presented with three measures of central tendency. None of these concepts is difficult in and of itself, but when the three concepts are presented together, some students can become overwhelmed. Students will be familiar with the concept and the calculation of the mean, but perhaps know the term *average* rather than *mean*. Determining mode(s) is easy, as no calculation is required. Median, while not a difficult concept, may be confusing because the method of calculating the median depends on whether the number of data items is odd or even. One strategy teachers can use is to introduce these three concepts over a period of time, with plenty of space in between, and to avoid introducing problems that require students to do all three until each concept has been mastered separately. Another strategy is to focus on the key concepts. The most commonly used measure of central tendency is mean. If teachers focus on mean and make sure that concept is explored solidly and is well understood, the concepts of mode and median can be introduced later, with a minimum of time spent on them.

RETEACH KEY CONCEPTS

Students should understand that in order to solve an equation, you need to isolate the variable on a side by itself. You have four operations you can use to do that, and they were explained in detail in Chapter 3. You can:

Add the same number to each side of the equation.

Subtract the same number from each side of the equation.

Multiply each side of the equation by the same number (except 0).

Divide each side of the equation by the same number (except 0).

When you add or subtract to solve an equation, you are usually looking for a number that makes a sum of zero, as in Example 1 on page 170, when you subtract 8 from each side to get $3x$ on the left. Students need to remember that the sum of a number and its opposite is zero (you can show this on a number line).

When you multiply or divide to solve an equation, you are often looking for a number that will make a product of one, as in Example 1, when you divide each side by 3 to get x by itself on the left. A review of Examples 1 and 2 on page 170 may be helpful for students who are having difficulty.

Strategies for English Learners

VOCABULARY DEVELOPMENT

In math class, you might review with students the concept of *opposite*, which is a key mathematical concept and a good way for English learners to learn and remember vocabulary. Start with some simple opposites such as *up* and *down*, *high* and *low*, *tall* and *short*, and *in* and *out*, to make sure students have the concept. Then review the following opposites, which are common and critical to the understanding of mathematics.

Give students one word from each pair and ask them to supply the opposite:

odd : even	plus : minus
add : subtract	positive: negative
multiply : divide	true : false
sum : difference	

MORE OPPOSITES Additional opposites that are discussed in this chapter include profit : loss and depreciate : appreciate. Students can review what opposites would look like on the number line, how absolute value uses opposites (Chapter 3), and how opposites might look on the various charts and graphs introduced in Chapter 1.

KEY WORDS When key words are introduced in each chapter, consider whether each one has an opposite, and, if so, teach it at the same time. Have students keep their lists of opposites in their math journal and encourage students to draw a picture or write an explanation in their primary language to aid in recall.

Strategies for Advanced Learners

DIFFERENTIATE INSTRUCTION IN TERMS OF DEPTH

A theme that runs through all subject areas is patterns. Students encounter patterns in language arts (for example, as spellings change when certain endings are added), in science (as in Chapter 2 with the eruption times of a geyser), and in history (exemplified by the saying "history repeats itself").

PATTERNS Mathematics is full of patterns and students are often fascinated by them. In Chapter 1 students studied patterns and found that representing data on a graph or chart can often suggest a pattern. A common mistake people make, however, is to assume that the pattern they see in a particular set of numbers is the only pattern. Challenge students to make up a series of numbers that could begin at least two patterns. For example, 2, 4, 6, could be the set of all even numbers, in which case the next number would be 8, or it could be a pattern created by this rule: take the last two numbers, add them together for the next number. In the latter case the next number in the pattern is 10. Studying patterns in more depth can help students avoid jumping to conclusions from limited data.

DIFFERENTIATE INSTRUCTION IN TERMS OF COMPLEXITY

Advanced learners may be interested in exploring a relatively new field of mathematics involving patterns. The concept of fractals was introduced by Polish-born Mathematician Benoit Mandelbrot in the 1970s. A fractal is a geometric figure that is self-similar. That is, the appearance of any part of a fractal is similar to the whole fractal. Fractals are widely used in such fields as computer animation, geology, and biology. The figure below shows the first few stages in the formation of one fractal, the *Koch snowflake*.

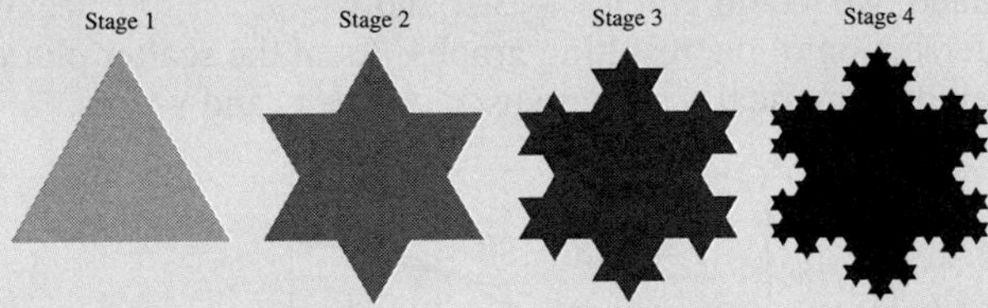

Have advanced learners investigate how the Koch snowflake is formed and how patterns are involved in, for example, the perimeter of the snowflake at each stage. Students may also be interested in studying other common fractals such as the Sierpinski triangle.

Challenge Problem: It would be possible to find the required minimum score in Example 4 on page 205, knowing only the *average* of the scores on the first two tests, since the sum of the first two scores is twice their average. An interesting challenge problem would be the following: If you need an average test score of 85 or more on five tests to receive a B, and you have already scored an average of 83 on the first three tests, what is the minimum average you need on the next two tests to get a B? (*Hint:* The answer 87 is not correct, even though the average of 87 and 83 is 85.) (*Answer: 88*)

Mathematical Background Notes

The modeling of real-life situations often involves linear equations. While a single equation may be sufficient to model simple situations, more complex problems may call for equating several linear expressions involving several variables. The present chapter continues the study of a single linear equation and thereby sets the stage for the solution of systems.

Lessons 4.1–4.5

These lessons deal mainly with the solution of linear equations whose coefficients are integers. This provides a simple format in which to pose problems and illustrate solution techniques. It also reinforces the arithmetic of integers, as studied in Chapter 3.

Lesson 4.6

The opening problem of this lesson is typical of modeling situations that invite several problem solving strategies, not all of which need be based on the solution of linear equations. In this problem, a logging company has 90 square miles of land cleared of trees. Starting in year 0, it continues to log land at the rate of 15 square miles per year while, at the same time, replanting trees at the rate of 30 square miles per year.

VERBAL REASONING Here students might reason that of the 30 square miles to be replanted each year, 15 are required to cover the land that was logged that year. This means that 15 square miles of replanting are to be applied to the original 90 square miles of logged land. Such reasoning may lead the student directly to the equation

$$90 - 15n = 0.$$

While reasonable and correct, this basis for arriving at $n = 6$ involves verbal reasoning and cannot be viewed as a routine method. However, it provides an alternative basis for arriving at the equation $90 = 15n$ appearing toward the end of Example 2 on page 194.

USING GRAPHS Another method is used in Example 1, where data are visualized in terms of a scatter plot corresponding to

$$30n = 90 + 15n, \text{ where } n = 0, 1, 2, 3, 4, 5, \text{ and } 6.$$

We can think of the above equation in terms of two functions

$$y = 30n$$

and

$$y = 90 + 15n$$

for which we are seeking to achieve equal outputs for the same whole number value of n. By enlarging the domain of the functions involved to include all real numbers x, we can rewrite the problem as

$$30x = 90 + 15x$$

where x is allowed to be any real number. This equation is of the form

$$Ax + B = Cx + D,$$

where A, B, C, and D are given real numbers.

In Chapter 11 students will learn that the graph of a linear equation is a straight line and will give the problem of finding a solution of $Ax + B = Cx + D$ an interesting geometric interpretation. Since the graphs of $y = Ax + B$ and $y = Cx + D$ are straight lines, the solution of $Ax + B = Cx + D$ will correspond to finding the x-coordinate of the intersection of these two lines.

In the case at hand, we would graph $y = 30x$ and $y = 15x + 90$, seeking the point of intersection of the resulting graphs. As in the scatter plot on page 193, different numerical scales are used on the x- and y-axes.

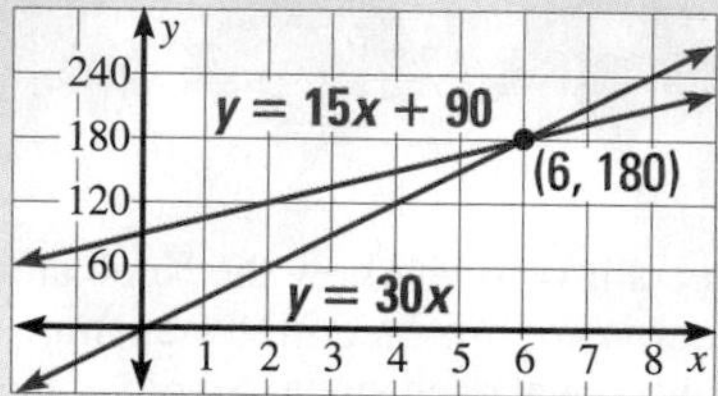

The two lines appear to intersect at the point (6, 180), so we can estimate that $x = 6$ is a solution of $30x = 90 + 15x$. That $x = 6$ is in fact a solution can be verified by direct substitution.

A graphical solution of the equivalent equation $90 - 15x = 0$ can also be provided. Here we would only have to graph the function $y = 90 - 15x$. The solution of this equation is the x-intercept of the function $y = 90 - 15x$, the point at which the graph of this function intersects the line $y = 0$.

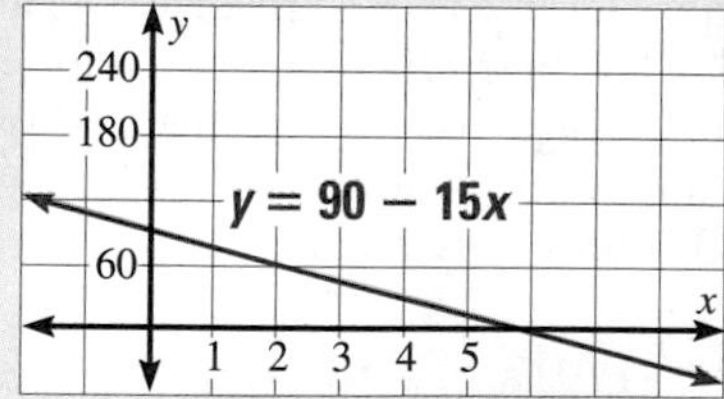

While it is important to be able to recognize that graphing $y = 90 - 15x$ can lead to a solution of the equation $90 - 15x = 0$, this is not an efficient procedure for students to follow. The most efficient way to graph this equation is to *first* find the x-intercept (6, 0) and y-intercept (0, 90) and use these two points to graph the equation. But finding the x-intercept is tantamount to solving the problem!

USING EQUIVALENT PROBLEMS A problem given in verbal form can sometimes be translated into another verbal form that is easier to comprehend and put into algebraic form. For instance, the logging problem considered above is equivalent to that of a tank with a capacity of 90 gallons. Suppose that water flows into the tank at the rate of 30 gallons per hour and, whenever there is water in the tank, it leaks out at a constant rate of 15 gallons per hour. If the tank is empty at time 0, after how many hours will it be full? This formulation is very close to the *reservoir* and *flow* language used in system dynamics, and it may be easier for some students to translate into mathematical form.

Lesson 4.8

DEFINING MEAN Given a data set consisting of n numbers, the **mean** is often defined as the sum of these numbers divided by n. While this is an easy definition to implement and remember, there is an equivalent definition that is often used in probability and statistics.

This alternate definition can be illustrated in terms of a class of eight students whose scores on a test are {60, 80, 50, 100, 60, 90, 80, 80}. One way of computing the mean is to calculate

$$\text{Mean} = \frac{60 + 80 + 50 + 100 + 60 + 90 + 80 + 80}{8} = \frac{600}{8} = 75.$$

An equivalent way is to make a table of values in which the frequency of the various test scores is noted. In so doing, we are defining a function $N(x)$ that assigns an output (the number of students receiving a particular score) to an input (a test score).

x	$N(x)$
50	1
60	2
80	3
90	1
100	1

This table of values provides a basis for describing these particular test results by means of a bar graph or a line plot similar to that used in Example 1 on page 203.

In order to derive the mean from such a table, we need to append two more columns. To the right of $N(x)$ we will enter the value $f(x) = \frac{N(x)}{n}$ for each x. To the right of $f(x)$ we will enter the value of $x \cdot f(x)$ for each x. This leads to the following table.

x	$N(x)$	$f(x) = \frac{N(x)}{n}$	$x \cdot f(x)$
50	1	$\frac{1}{8}$	$\frac{50}{8}$
60	2	$\frac{2}{8}$	$\frac{120}{8}$
80	3	$\frac{3}{8}$	$\frac{240}{8}$
90	1	$\frac{1}{8}$	$\frac{90}{8}$
100	1	$\frac{1}{8}$	$\frac{100}{8}$

Since

$$\text{Mean} = \frac{60 + 80 + 50 + 100 + 60 + 90 + 80 + 80}{8}$$

$$= \frac{50 + (60 + 60) + (80 + 80 + 80) + 90 + 100}{8}$$

$$= \frac{50}{8} + \frac{120}{8} + \frac{240}{8} + \frac{90}{8} + \frac{100}{8},$$

we see that summing the values of $x \cdot f(x)$ provides another way of arriving at Mean = 75. In general, summing the values of $x \cdot f(x)$ in such a representation of a data set provides an alternate way of arriving at the mean.

In this approach to determining the mean, $f(x)$ can be interpreted as a probability. Choosing one of the eight students at random, the probability that this student received a grade x is given by $f(x)$. The fact that such a student is *certain* to have received one of the grades {50, 60, 80, 90, 100} is reflected by the fact that the entries under $f(x)$ sum to 1.

Chapter Overview

Chapter Goals

In this chapter, students will solve many types of linear equations, using multiple steps and involving negative coefficients as well as variables on each side. They will:

- Learn problem solving strategies and unit analysis.
- Solve equations involving decimals.
- Use measures of central tendency: mean, median, and mode.

Career Note

Energy consultants and energy conservation technicians inspect structures and perform tests to help consumers reduce their energy consumption. They give owners advice on ways to save energy, such as caulking windows and insulating hot water heaters. Some energy conservation technicians will do the work of installing the energy-saving devices. A technician usually earns a 2-year degree from a technical college.

Additional information about energy consultants is available at **www.mcdougallittell.com**

Algebra and Equation Solving

Why are algebra and equation solving important?

You have already learned how to solve some simple algebraic equations. In this chapter, you will extend your ability to write and solve equations that require more steps. Such equations typically arise in real-life situations involving comparisons.

Many people use algebra and equation solving in their jobs, including energy consultants (page 167), service managers (page 173), and electrical engineers (page 177). For example, energy consultants solve equations to compare the costs of different kinds of light bulbs.

Meeting the California Standards

The skills you'll develop in this chapter will help you meet state standards and prepare for standardized tests. In this chapter you'll:

- **Solve two-step linear equations with one variable.** Lessons 4.1, 4.3
- **Use unit analysis to check reasonableness of answers.** Lessons 4.2, 4.6
- **Simplify numerical expressions by applying properties.** Lesson 4.4
- **Represent relationships graphically and interpret the graph.** Lesson 4.6
- **Solve two-step linear equations and interpret the solutions.** Lesson 4.7
- **Collect, organize, and represent data sets.** Lesson 4.8

Career Link **ENERGY CONSULTANT** An energy consultant uses algebra to solve equations when:

- deciding how much insulation a building needs.
- comparing the efficiency of different methods of heating.
- comparing the costs of different kinds of light bulbs.

EXERCISES

The light bulbs in the table are equally bright. The verbal model below gives the total cost of using each light bulb for x hours. Assume that the cost of electricity is \$.08 per kilowatt-hour.

Light bulb comparison		
Type of bulb	**Standard**	**Fluorescent**
Cost of bulb (in dollars)	0.75	25.00
Power needed (in kilowatts)	0.075	0.02

[Cost of bulb] + [Cost of electricity] • [Power needed] • x

1. What is the total cost of using a standard light bulb for 100 hours? **\$1.35**
2. Write an expression for the total cost of using a standard light bulb for x hours. **$0.75 + 0.006x$**
3. Write an expression for the total cost of using a fluorescent light bulb for x hours. **$25 + 0.0016x$**

In Lesson 4.5, you'll learn how to find out when the cost of a fluorescent bulb equals the cost of a standard bulb.

Projects

A project covering Chapters 4–6 appears on pages 324–325 of the Student Edition. Additional projects for selected lessons in Chapter 4 are available in the *Assessment Book,* pp. 223–224.

Technology

Software

- Electronic Teacher Tools
- Online Lesson Planner
- Personal Student Tutor
- Test and Practice Generator

Internet Connections

- Application and Career Links 173, 175, 177, 180, 182, 184, 186, 202, 207
- Student Help 171, 177, 180, 183, 190, 196, 201, 204, 215

These Internet connections are available at **www.mcdougallittell.com**

167

Prepare

Diagnostic Tools

The **chapter readiness quiz** can help you diagnose whether students have the following skills needed in Chapter 4:

- Solve linear equations.
- Solve rate problems.
- Calculate an average cost.

Reteaching Materials

The following resources are available for students who need additional help with the skills on the chapter readiness quiz:

Chapter 4 Resource Book

- Reteaching with Practice (Lessons 1.5, 2.3, 3.6, 3.7)

Personal Student Tutor

Additional Resources

The following resources are provided to help you prepare for the upcoming chapter and customize review materials:

Chapter 4 Resource Book

- Lesson Plans, pp. 1, 10, 19, 28, 37, 46, 55, 64
- Lesson Plans for Block Scheduling, pp. 2, 11, 20, 29, 38, 47, 56, 65

Technology

- Electronic Teacher Tools with Lesson Planning Software
- Test and Practice Generator

Chapter 4 Getting Ready

PREVIEW What's the chapter about?

- Solving **two-step** and **multi-step equations**, and equations with **variables on both sides**
- Using **problem solving strategies**
- Finding **measures of central tendency**

WORDS TO KNOW

- **measure of central tendency,** *p. 203*
- **mean,** *p. 203*
- **median,** *p. 203*
- **mode,** *p. 203*
- **outlier,** *p. 204*

PREPARE Chapter Readiness Quiz

Take this quick quiz. If you are unsure of an answer, look back at the reference pages for help.

VOCABULARY CHECK *(refer to pp. 61, 140)*

Match the equation with the correct solution.

A. -8 **B.** -6 **C.** 6 **D.** 8

1. $31 + x = 25$ **B** **2.** $-9x = -72$ **D** **3.** $\frac{x}{2} = -4$ **A** **4.** $10 + x = 16$ **C**

SKILL CHECK *(refer to pp. 23, 136)*

5. Which equation expresses the time it will take to drive a distance of 300 miles at a speed of 60 miles per hour? **C**

Ⓐ $300 = \frac{60}{t}$ Ⓑ $t = \frac{60}{300}$ Ⓒ $300 = 60t$ Ⓓ $300t = 60$

6. You and three friends split the costs for a camping trip evenly. The camper rent is \$132.88. The food is \$156.90. You rent two canoes at \$14.50 each. Which expression shows each person's total expenses? **J**

Ⓕ $132.88 + 156.90 + 14.50$ Ⓖ $132.88 + 156.90 + 2(14.50)$

Ⓗ $\frac{132.88 + 156.90 + 14.50}{4}$ Ⓙ $\frac{132.88 + 156.90 + 2(14.50)}{4}$

STUDY TIP Write a Plan

Writing a plan to solve a problem before you actually solve it will help you to organize your thoughts.

My plan for solving the equation $2x + 3 = 7$:
1. Write the equation.
2. Subtract 3 from each side.
3. Simplify.
4. Divide each side by 2.
5. Simplify.

DEVELOPING CONCEPTS
Inverse Operations

For use with Lesson 4.1

California Standards

- Determine when and how to break a problem into simpler parts. (MR 1.3)
- Note the method of deriving the solution and demonstrate a conceptual understanding of the derivations by solving similar problems. (MR 3.2)

MATERIALS
- Paper and pencil

You can use *box models* to represent and solve equations.

SAMPLE 1 Solving a One-Step Equation

You can use a box model to represent and solve $x + 3 = 5$.

Here's How

$\boxed{x} \xrightarrow{+3} \boxed{5}$ $\boxed{x} \xleftarrow[-3]{} \boxed{5}$ $\boxed{2} \xleftarrow[-3]{} \boxed{5}$

1. Draw a box model to represent the equation $x + 3 = 5$.
2. Subtract 3 from 5 to undo adding 3. The box model now represents the equation $x = 5 - 3$.
3. Since $5 - 3 = 2$, you know $x = 2$. So, the solution is 2.

SAMPLE 2 Solving a Two-Step Equation

You can use a box model to represent and solve $3x - 4 = 11$.

Here's How

Draw a box model to represent $3x - 4 = 11$.

$\boxed{x} \xrightarrow{\times 3} \boxed{?} \xrightarrow{-4} \boxed{11}$

Rewrite the model using inverse operations. To undo subtracting 4, add 4. To undo multiplying by 3, divide by 3. Work from right to left. The box model now represents $x = (11 + 4) \div 3$.

Solve the equation. Because $11 + 4 = 15$ and $15 \div 3 = 5$, you know $x = 5$. So, the solution is 5.

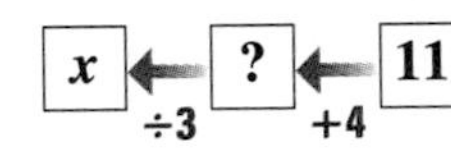

Student Help

STUDY TIP
A *two-step equation* involves two operations being performed on the variable. The equation $3x - 4 = 11$ involves multiplying x by 3 and then subtracting 4.

Try These

In Exercises 1–4, use a box model to represent and solve the equation.
1–4. See margin for models.

1. $2x + 1 = 9$ **$x = 4$**
2. $4x - 1 = 11$ **$x = 3$**
3. $\frac{x}{3} + 2 = 4$ **$x = 6$**
4. $\frac{x}{5} - 3 = 1$ **$x = 20$**
5. **MATHEMATICAL REASONING** Write a general rule for solving a two-step equation *without* using a box model. Give an example.

5. If an equation involves both (1) multiplication or division and (2) addition or subtraction, undo the addition or subtraction first. Then undo the multiplication or division.

1 Planning the Activity

Purpose and Materials
See the margin of the student page.

LINK TO LESSON
Have students use box models to represent Examples 1 and 2.

Math Reasoning
Students analyze a problem and break it into simpler parts to solve the problem.

2 Managing the Activity

Classroom Management
If students are reluctant to use the box models because they already know the solution, remind them that you are trying to develop a technique that will be useful in solving many different types of equations.

3 Closing the Activity

★ KEY DISCOVERY
To solve an equation, inverse operations must be used to reverse the operations of the equation.

Activity Assessment
Use Exercises 1–4 to assess student understanding.

1. $\boxed{x} \xrightarrow{\times 2} \boxed{?} \xrightarrow{+1} \boxed{9}$; $\boxed{x} \xleftarrow[\div 2]{} \boxed{?} \xleftarrow[-1]{} \boxed{9}$; $\boxed{4} \xleftarrow[\div 2]{} \boxed{8} \xleftarrow[-1]{} \boxed{9}$; $x = 4$
2. $\boxed{x} \xrightarrow{\times 4} \boxed{?} \xrightarrow{-1} \boxed{11}$; $\boxed{x} \xleftarrow[\div 4]{} \boxed{?} \xleftarrow[+1]{} \boxed{11}$; $\boxed{3} \xleftarrow[\div 4]{} \boxed{12} \xleftarrow[+1]{} \boxed{11}$; $x = 3$

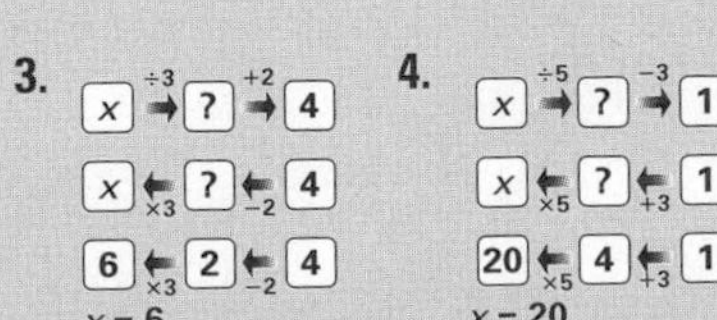

3. $\boxed{x} \xrightarrow{\div 3} \boxed{?} \xrightarrow{+2} \boxed{4}$; $\boxed{x} \xleftarrow[\times 3]{} \boxed{?} \xleftarrow[-2]{} \boxed{4}$; $\boxed{6} \xleftarrow[\times 3]{} \boxed{2} \xleftarrow[-2]{} \boxed{4}$; $x = 6$
4. $\boxed{x} \xrightarrow{\div 5} \boxed{?} \xrightarrow{-3} \boxed{1}$; $\boxed{x} \xleftarrow[\times 5]{} \boxed{?} \xleftarrow[+3]{} \boxed{1}$; $\boxed{20} \xleftarrow[\times 5]{} \boxed{4} \xleftarrow[+3]{} \boxed{1}$; $x = 20$

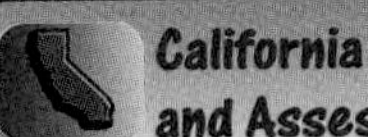

California Standards and Assessment
CA Standards: MR 1.3, MR 3.2

1 Plan

Pacing

Suggested Number of Days

Transitional: 2 days
Average: 2 days
Advanced: 2 days
Block Schedule: 1 block

Teaching Resources

Blacklines
(See page 166B.)

Transparencies
- Warm-Up Exercises
- Teacher Time-Savers
- English/Spanish Problem Solving
- Answers

Technology
- Electronic Teacher Tools
- Test and Practice Generator

2 Teach

Math Reasoning

For Mathematical Background Notes on mathematical reasoning related to this lesson, please refer to pages 166E and 166F in this Teacher's Edition.

California Standards and Assessment

CA Standard: AF 4.1
CA Key Concepts Book: pp. S64–S66

4.1 Solving Two-Step Equations

California Standards

In this lesson you'll:

- Solve two-step linear equations in one variable. (AF 4.1)
- Interpret the solution of an equation in the context in which it arose and verify the reasonableness of the result. (AF 4.1)

Goal 1 Solving Two-Step Equations

As you learned in Developing Concepts 4.1, page 169, solving equations may require using more than one *inverse operation* to write an equivalent equation in which the variable appears alone on one side of the equation.

EXAMPLE 1 *Solving an Equation Using Inverse Operations*

Solve $3x + 8 = 23$.

Solution

$3x + 8 = 23$	Write original equation.
$3x + 8 - \mathbf{8} = 23 - \mathbf{8}$	Subtract 8 from each side.
$3x = 15$	Simplify.
$\frac{3x}{\mathbf{3}} = \frac{15}{\mathbf{3}}$	Divide each side by 3.
$x = 5$	Simplify. x is by itself.

ANSWER ▶ The solution is 5.

CHECK ✓

$3x + 8 = 23$	Write original equation.
$3(\mathbf{5}) + 8 \stackrel{?}{=} 23$	Substitute 5 for x.
$23 = 23$ ✓	The solution checks.

EXAMPLE 2 *Solving an Equation Using Inverse Operations*

Solve $\frac{x}{4} - 12 = 1$.

Solution

$\frac{x}{4} - 12 = 1$	Write original equation.
$\frac{x}{4} - 12 + \mathbf{12} = 1 + \mathbf{12}$	Add 12 to each side.
$\frac{x}{4} = 13$	Simplify.
$\mathbf{4} \cdot \frac{x}{4} = \mathbf{4} \cdot 13$	Multiply each side by 4.
$x = 52$	Simplify. x is by itself.

ANSWER ▶ The solution is 52. Check this in the original equation.

Goal 2 WRITING TWO-STEP EQUATIONS

Link to Sports

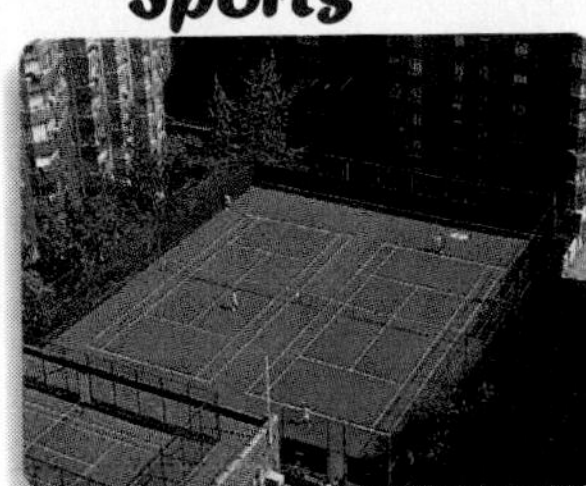

TENNIS Tennis associations across the U.S. are trying to get more young people interested in playing tennis. Currently only about 6% of 6- to 12-year-olds play tennis. Community tennis clubs like the one shown can help young people learn the game.

EXAMPLE 3 Writing a Two-Step Equation

TENNIS You are joining a community tennis club. The annual membership is \$60, and a tennis court rents for \$10 per hour. You have budgeted \$200 to play tennis this year. How many hours can you play?

Solution

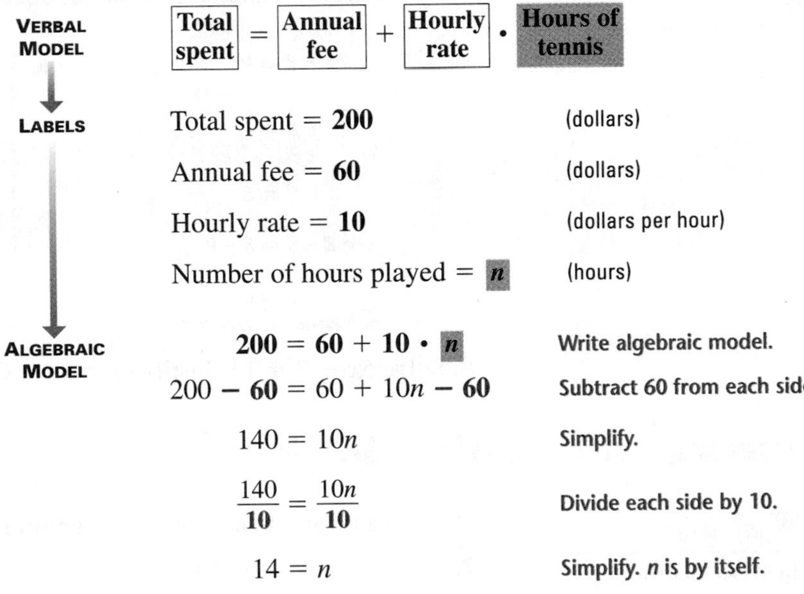

VERBAL MODEL: Total spent = Annual fee + Hourly rate • Hours of tennis

LABELS:

Total spent = **200** (dollars)

Annual fee = **60** (dollars)

Hourly rate = **10** (dollars per hour)

Number of hours played = n (hours)

ALGEBRAIC MODEL:

$200 = 60 + 10 \cdot n$ — Write algebraic model.

$200 - 60 = 60 + 10n - 60$ — Subtract 60 from each side.

$140 = 10n$ — Simplify.

$\frac{140}{10} = \frac{10n}{10}$ — Divide each side by 10.

$14 = n$ — Simplify. n is by itself.

ANSWER ▶ You can play 14 hours of tennis.

When you check a solution involving units of measure, check the units of measure as well as the numbers.

EXAMPLE 4 Checking Reasonableness of a Solution

Use unit analysis to check that proper units were used in the solution from Example 3. Place the values and units in the verbal model.

Solution

Total spent = Annual fee + Hourly rate • Hours of tennis

200 dollars $\stackrel{?}{=}$ 60 dollars + $\frac{10 \text{ dollars}}{\text{hour}}$ • 14 hours

200 dollars $\stackrel{?}{=}$ 60 dollars + 140 dollars

200 dollars = 200 dollars ✓

Student Help

▶ **MORE EXAMPLES**

More examples are available at www.mcdougallittell.com

Math Reasoning

In Example 2, starting with x, then dividing by 4, then subtracting 12, results in 1. Therefore starting with 1, then adding 12, then multiplying by 4, results in x. That is, $(1 + 12) \cdot 4 = x$, so $x = 52$.

Extra Example 1

Solve $6x - 11 = 13$. **4**

Extra Example 2

Solve $\frac{n}{7} + 4 = -3$. **−49**

Extra Example 3

You and four friends have joined a recreational basketball league. The team membership fee is \$50 plus a \$5 fee per game to pay the referee. If the team's total cost for the league will be \$125, how many games are you scheduled to play? **15 games**

Extra Example 4

Use unit analysis to check the reasonableness of the solution of Extra Example 3. Place the values with their units in the verbal model.

125 dollars = 50 dollars + $\frac{5 \text{ dollars}}{\text{game}}$ • 15 games

Teaching Tip

Remind students that addition and subtraction are inverse operations and that multiplication and division are inverse operations.

Concept Check

How are inverse operations used when solving a two-step equation? Which inverse operations must be used first? **The operations that are the inverses of the ones found in the original equation form the two steps of the solution. An addition or subtraction step is done before a multiplication or division step.**

3 Apply

Assignment Guide

TRANSITIONAL
Day 1: pp. 172–173 Exs. 7–14
Day 2: pp. 172–173 Exs. 23–27, 31–33

AVERAGE
Day 1: pp. 172–173 Exs. 7–15, 21–22
Day 2: pp. 172–173 Exs. 23–29, 31–33

ADVANCED
Day 1: pp. 172–173 Exs. 12–22
Day 2: pp. 172–173 Exs. 23–29, 30*, 31–33

BLOCK SCHEDULE
pp. 172–173 Exs. 7–15, 21–29, 31–33

Extra Practice

- Student Edition, pp. 696–697
- Chapter 4 Resource Book, p. 6

Homework Check

To quickly check student understanding of key concepts, go over the following exercises:

Transitional: 10, 12, 18, 24, 26, 28
Average: 12, 14, 22, 24, 28
Advanced: 12, 16, 20, 24, 28

Problem Solving

Exercises 27–30
Remind students to use the six steps of the problem solving plan learned in Lesson 2.7.

4. The "8" should also have been divided by "2."

$$2x + 8 = 16$$
$$\frac{2x}{2} + \frac{8}{2} = \frac{16}{2}$$
$$x + 4 = 8$$
$$x = 8 - 4$$
$$x = 4$$

5. "15" was added to the left side of the equation but should have been added to the right side instead of subtracted.

$$5x - 15 = 25$$
$$5x - 15 + 15 = 25 + 15$$
$$5x = 40$$
$$\frac{5x}{5} = \frac{40}{5}$$
$$x = 8$$

6–8. See Additional Answers beginning on page AA1.

4.1 Exercises

Guided Practice

Describe the first step you would take to solve the equation.

1. $3x - 4 = 2$ **2.** $5x + 3 = 15$ **3.** $-2 = 2 + 4x$

1. Add 4 to each side of the equation.
2. Subtract 3 from each side of the equation.
3. Subtract 2 from each side of the equation.

ERROR ANALYSIS In Exercises 4 and 5, describe and correct the error. **4, 5. See margin.**

4.

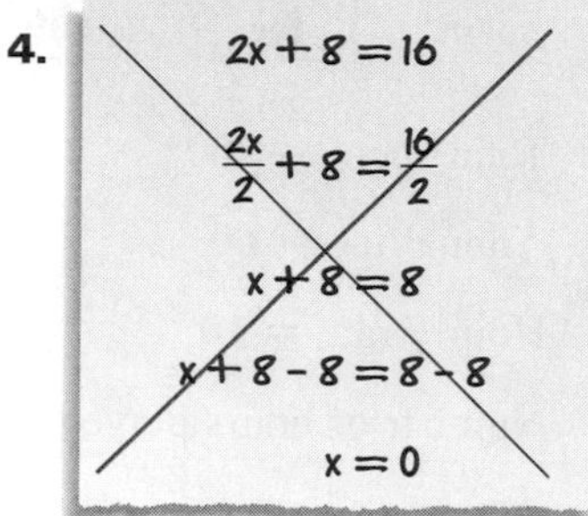

5.

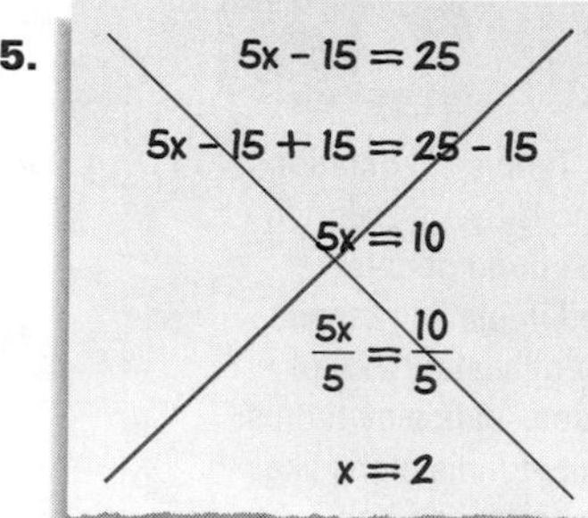

6. Solve $5x - 7 = 13$. Justify each step. Check your solution. **See margin.**

Practice and Problem Solving

> *Student Help*
>
> ▶**MORE PRACTICE**
> Extra practice to help you master skills is on page 696.

In Exercises 7 and 8, complete the solution. Explain your reasoning. **7, 8. See margin.**

7.
$$3x - 13 = 14$$
$$3x - 13 + \underline{\ ?\ } = 14 + \underline{\ ?\ }$$
$$3x = \underline{\ ?\ }$$
$$\frac{3x}{?} = \underline{\ ?\ }$$
$$x = \underline{\ ?\ }$$

8.
$$7x + 15 = 36$$
$$7x + 15 - \underline{\ ?\ } = 36 - \underline{\ ?\ }$$
$$7x = \underline{\ ?\ }$$
$$\frac{7x}{?} = \underline{\ ?\ }$$
$$x = \underline{\ ?\ }$$

Solve the equation. Then check your solution.

9. $3x + 15 = 24$ **$x = 3$** **10.** $4x + 11 = 31$ **$x = 5$** **11.** $20 = 8 + 6p$ **$p = 2$**

12. $14 = 4 + 5q$ **$q = 2$** **13.** $2r - 4 = 22$ **$r = 13$** **14.** $3s - 5 = 31$ **$s = 12$**

15. $3x + 4 = 7$ **$x = 1$** **16.** $4x - 7 = 9$ **$x = 4$** **17.** $5x + 10 = 55$ **$x = 9$**

18. $\frac{t}{3} + 6 = 10$ **$t = 12$** **19.** $21 = 17 + \frac{z}{2}$ **$z = 8$** **20.** $\frac{m}{5} - 3 = 7$ **$m = 50$**

In Exercises 21 and 22, the upper and lower line segments have the same length. Write an equation relating the lengths and solve for x.

21.

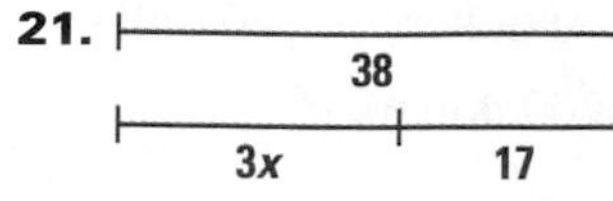

22.

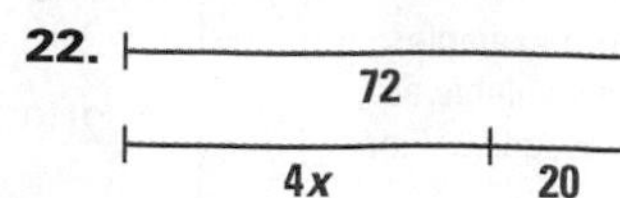

21. $3x + 17 = 38$; $x = 7$
22. $4x + 20 = 72$; $x = 13$

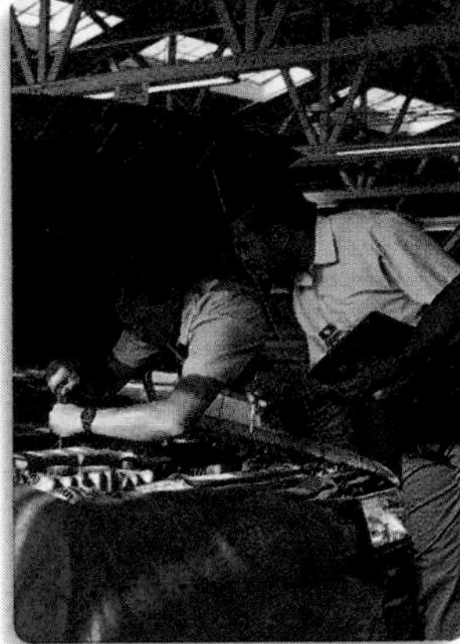

SERVICE MANAGER
Service managers at car repair shops must be organized, friendly, and knowledgeable.

More about car repair available at www.mcdougallittell.com

In Exercises 23–26, write the sentence as an equation. Then solve the equation and check your solution.

23. The sum of three times a number and 7 is 34. **$3x + 7 = 34$; $x = 9$**

24. The difference of eight times a number and 12 is 100. **$8x - 12 = 100$; $x = 14$**

25. The difference of a number divided by 4 and 2 is 5. **$\frac{x}{4} - 2 = 5$; $x = 28$**

26. The sum of a number divided by 2 and 13 is 30. **$\frac{x}{2} + 13 = 30$; 34**

27. PHONE RATES You are at a phone booth and need to make a long-distance call. The call will cost \$.25 for the first minute and \$.15 for each additional minute or part of a minute. You have \$.85 in change. Write an equation to determine how many minutes you can afford. Then solve the equation. **See margin.**

28. CAR REPAIR You take your car to an auto repair shop. The charge for repairs is \$48 per hour for labor plus the cost of parts. Your car needs new parts that cost \$256, and the final bill for the car is \$616. Find how long it took to repair the car. Check whether your solution is reasonable. **See margin.**

29. MATHEMATICAL REASONING The sum of two consecutive integers is 49. Find the two integers. (*Hint:* If x is one integer, the next greater consecutive integer is just one more than x.) Describe the method you used to find the answer. Think of another way to solve the problem. Describe it. **See margin.**

30. CHALLENGE Write and solve an equation to find the width of a rectangle with a perimeter of 30 centimeters and a length of 9 centimeters. **See margin.**

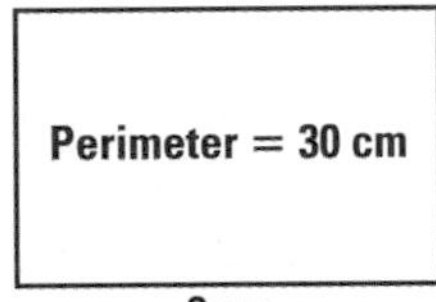

31. What would be the first step in solving the equation $\frac{x}{4} - 7 = 33$? **A**

(A) Add 7 to each side. (B) Subtract 7 from each side.
(C) Add 33 to each side. (D) Divide each side by 4.

32. Which equation is equivalent to the equation $9x - 10 = 35$? **H**

(F) $9x = 25$ (G) $9x = -25$
(H) $9x = 45$ (J) $9x = -45$

Test Tip
▶ In Exercise 32 recall that you can use inverse operations to write equivalent equations.

33. At the fair, you spend \$6 for food, then use the rest of your \$20 to buy ride tickets. You have enough money to buy 56 tickets. How much does each ticket cost? **B**

(A) \$.20 (B) \$.25 (C) \$.35 (D) \$.48

4 Assess

Assessment Resources

- Assessment Book (Formal Assessment and Alternative Assessment)
- Test and Practice Generator

Mini-Quiz

1. Solve the equation. Then check your solution.
   a. $5 = 25 + 4t$ **−5**
   b. $-2y - 4 = 16$ **−10**
   c. $\frac{x}{7} + 9 = 11$ **14**
2. You have saved \$425 to buy a CD player and some CD's. If the player you want costs \$275 and the CD's cost \$15 each, how many CD's can you buy? Write and solve an equation to answer this question. **$275 + 15x = 425$; $x = 10$ CD's**

27. $25 + 15m = 85$
$15m = 60$
$m = 4$
5 min total

28. $48h + 256 = 616$
$48h = 360$
$h = 7.5$
7.5 h

29. $x + (x + 1) = 49$
$x + x + 1 = 49$
$2x = 48$
$x = 24$
24 and 25
***Sample answer*: Guess check and revise**

30. $2(9) + 2w = 30$
$18 + 2w = 30$
$2w = 12$
$w = 6$
6 cm

1 Plan

Pacing

Suggested Number of Days

Transitional: 2 days
Average: 2 days
Advanced: 2 days
Block Schedule: 1 block

Teaching Resources

Blacklines
(See page 166B.)

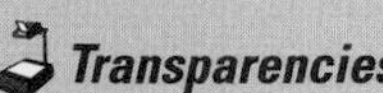

Transparencies
- Warm-Up Exercises
- Teacher Time-Savers
- English/Spanish Problem Solving
- Answers

Technology
- Electronic Teacher Tools
- Test and Practice Generator

2 Teach

Math Reasoning

For Mathematical Background Notes on mathematical reasoning related to this lesson, please refer to pages 166E and 166F in this Teacher's Edition.

California Standards and Assessment

CA Standards: NS 1.7, AF 1.1, MG 1.3

4.2 Solving Multi-Step Equations

California Standards

In this lesson you'll:
- Use variables to write an equation that represents a verbal description. (AF 1.1)
- Solve problems that involve profit. (NS 1.7)
- Use unit analysis to check the reasonableness of an answer. (MG 1.3)

Goal 1 SOLVING MULTI-STEP EQUATIONS

Before you use inverse operations to solve an equation, you should check to see whether one or both sides of the equation can be simplified.

EXAMPLE 1 *Simplifying First*

Solve $2x + 3x - 4 = 11$.

Solution

$2x + 3x - 4 = 11$	Write original equation.
$5x - 4 = 11$	Combine like terms: $2x + 3x = 5x$.
$5x - 4 + \mathbf{4} = 11 + \mathbf{4}$	Add 4 to each side.
$5x = 15$	Simplify.
$\frac{5x}{\mathbf{5}} = \frac{15}{\mathbf{5}}$	Divide each side by 5.
$x = 3$	Simplify. x is by itself.

ANSWER ▶ The solution is 3.

CHECK ✓

$2x + 3x - 4 = 11$	Write original equation.
$2(\mathbf{3}) + 3(\mathbf{3}) - 4 \stackrel{?}{=} 11$	Substitute 3 for x.
$6 + 9 - 4 \stackrel{?}{=} 11$	Simplify.
$11 = 11$ ✓	The solution checks.

As you become more of an expert in solving equations, you may want to perform some steps mentally. Remember to always check your solution.

EXAMPLE 2 *Using an "Expert" Equation Solver Format*

Solve $-13 = 3n + 3 + n$.

Solution

$-13 = 3n + 3 + n$	Write original equation.
$-13 = 4n + 3$	Combine like terms: $3n + n = 4n$.
$-16 = 4n$	Subtract 3 from each side.
$-4 = n$	Divide each side by 4.

ANSWER ▶ The solution is -4. Check this in the original equation.

Student Help

▶ **STUDY TIP**
When some people solve an equation as shown in Example 2, they say they are "skipping steps." Yet, they aren't actually *skipping* steps—they are doing some of the steps mentally.

Goal 2 Writing Multi-Step Equations

Link to Manufacturing

PRINTING YEARBOOKS
Large printing presses can print up to 12,000 sheets of paper per hour.

More about printing available at www.mcdougallittell.com

EXAMPLE 3 Solving Problems Using Multi-Step Equations

MANUFACTURING You are on the yearbook staff at your school. The printer charges \$18 per book, and each yearbook sells for \$30. You also expect to receive \$600 in income from selling advertisement space in the yearbooks. Your goal is to make a profit of \$1500. How many yearbooks must the yearbook staff sell to make this profit?

Solution

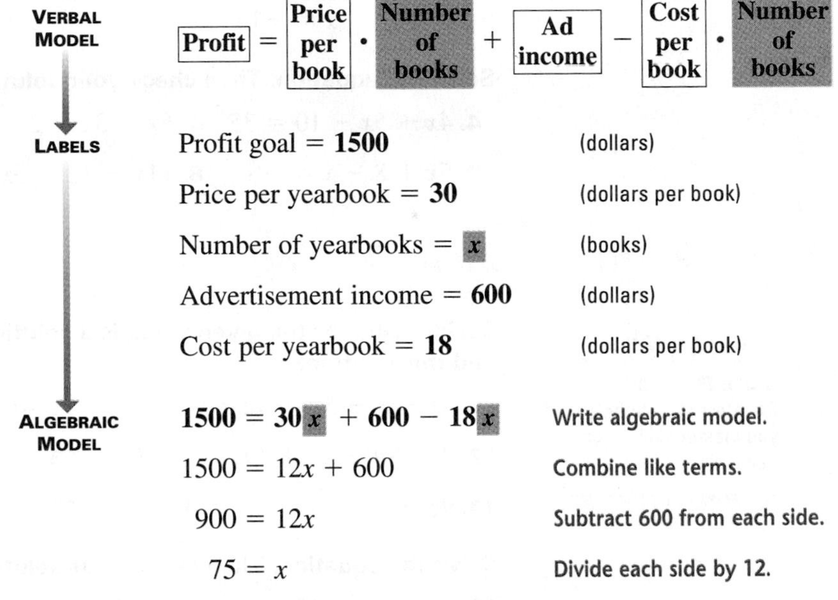

VERBAL MODEL: Profit = Price per book • Number of books + Ad income − Cost per book • Number of books

LABELS:

Profit goal = **1500** (dollars)

Price per yearbook = **30** (dollars per book)

Number of yearbooks = x (books)

Advertisement income = **600** (dollars)

Cost per yearbook = **18** (dollars per book)

ALGEBRAIC MODEL:

$\mathbf{1500 = 30x + 600 - 18x}$ Write algebraic model.

$1500 = 12x + 600$ Combine like terms.

$900 = 12x$ Subtract 600 from each side.

$75 = x$ Divide each side by 12.

ANSWER ▶ The yearbook staff needs to sell 75 yearbooks to make a profit of \$1500.

Student Help

▶ **LOOK BACK**
Recall that the *profit* a business earns is the difference between total income and total expenses. See p. 141.

EXAMPLE 4 Checking Reasonableness of a Solution

Use unit analysis to check the solution from Example 3. Place the values and units in the verbal model.

Solution

Profit = Price per book • Number of books + Ad income − Cost per book • Number of books

$1500 \text{ dollars} \stackrel{?}{=} 30 \frac{\text{dollars}}{\cancel{\text{book}}} \cdot 75 \cancel{\text{books}} + 600 \text{ dollars} - 18 \frac{\text{dollars}}{\cancel{\text{book}}} \cdot 75 \cancel{\text{books}}$

$1500 \text{ dollars} \stackrel{?}{=} 2250 \text{ dollars} + 600 \text{ dollars} - 1350 \text{ dollars}$

$1500 \text{ dollars} = 1500 \text{ dollars}$ ✓

Extra Example 1

Solve $8m - 3m + 3 = 13$. 2

Extra Example 2

Solve $46 = 4x - 4 + 6x$. 5

Teaching Tip

Point out that in Example 3, an alternate approach is to find the profit for each book, \$30 − \$18, and to write the equation as:

Total Profit = Profit per book • Number of books + Ad income

$1500 = 12x + 600$

Extra Example 3

Your school band is having T-shirts printed to help raise money for new uniforms. The silk-screening company charges a base fee of \$250, plus \$7 per shirt. The shirts will be sold for \$12 each. How many T-shirts must the band members sell to make a profit of \$1000?
250 T-shirts

Extra Example 4

Use unit analysis to check the solution of Extra Example 3.

$\$1000 = \frac{\$12}{\cancel{\text{shirt}}} \cdot 250 \cancel{\text{shirts}} - \$250 - \frac{\$7}{\cancel{\text{shirt}}} \cdot 250 \cancel{\text{shirts}}$

Concept Check

What is the difference between solving a multi-step equation and solving a two-step equation? **In a multi-step equation, you must first simplify one or both sides of the equation by combining like terms.**

3 Apply

Assignment Guide

TRANSITIONAL
Day 1: pp. 176–178 Exs. 10–13, 16–21, 31–34, 50–51
Day 2: EP p. 695 Ex. 92; pp. 176–178 Exs. 37–38, 40–41, 47–49, 52–57, 64–67
AVERAGE
Day 1: pp. 176–178 Exs. 10–13, 19–27, 31–36, 50–51
Day 2: pp. 176–178 Exs. 37–41, 43–49, 58–63, 67
ADVANCED
Day 1: pp. 176–178 Exs. 12–15, 22–36
Day 2: pp. 176–178 Exs. 40–41, 42*, 43–49, 58–60, 67
BLOCK SCHEDULE
pp. 176–178 Exs. 10–13, 19–27, 31–41, 43–51, 58–63, 67

Extra Practice

- Student Edition, pp. 696–697
- Chapter 4 Resource Book, p. 15

Homework Check

To quickly check student understanding of key concepts, go over the following exercises:

Transitional: 10, 20, 32, 38, 40
Average: 12, 24, 34, 40, 46
Advanced: 14, 28, 36, 40, 46

4.2 Exercises

Guided Practice

In Exercises 1–3, justify each step of the solution.

1. $3x - x + 8 = -16$
$2x + 8 = -16$
$2x = -24$
$x = -12$

2. $5x - 7 - 3x = 9$
$2x - 7 = 9$
$2x = 16$
$x = 8$

3. $5 = 5x + 11 - 2x$
$5 = 3x + 11$
$-6 = 3x$
$-2 = x$

1. Combine like terms: $3x - x = 2x$, subtract 8 from each side, divide each side by 2.

2. Combine like terms: $5x - 3x = 2x$, add 7 to each side, divide each side by 2.

3. Combine like terms: $5x - 2x = 3x$, subtract 11 from each side, divide each side by 3.

Solve the equation. Then check your solution.

4. $4x + 5x - 10 = 35$ **$x = 5$**
5. $6x - 3x + 2 = -4$ **$x = -2$**
6. $10x + 6 - x = 33$ **$x = 3$**
7. $5x + 8 - x = -8$ **$x = -4$**
8. $11x - 12 - 9x = 2$ **$x = 7$**
9. $12x + 2 - 8x = 6$ **$x = 1$**

Practice and Problem Solving

Student Help
▶MORE PRACTICE
Extra practice to help you master skills is on page 696.

Decide whether the given value is a solution of the equation. If not, find the solution.

10. $4x - x - 5 = -8$; $x = 1$ **$x = -1$**
11. $4t - 2t - 8 = 2$; $t = 5$ **$t = 5$**
12. $2 = 8a - 3a + 17$; $a = -3$ **$a = -3$**
13. $7y - 8 - 4y = 13$; $y = 6$ **$y = 7$**
14. $9z + z - 3 = 17$; $z = 4$ **$z = 2$**
15. $12x + 5 - 3x = 14$; $x = -1$ **$x = 1$**

Solve the equation. Then check your solution.

16. $2a + 3a = 15$ **$a = 3$**
17. $s + 5s - 3s = 21$ **$s = 7$**
18. $22 = 12t + 4t - 5t$ **$t = 2$**
19. $8x + 2x - 4 = 6$ **$x = 1$**
20. $6y - 3y + 4 = 16$ **$y = 4$**
21. $42 = 8a - 2a + 12$ **$a = 5$**
22. $6m - 2m - 8 = 4$ **$m = 3$**
23. $5x - 3x + 12 = 8$ **$x = -2$**
24. $n + 3n + 8 = -8$ **$n = -4$**
25. $4y + 7y - 2y = 81$ **$y = 9$**
26. $5x - x - 3 = 5$ **$x = 2$**
27. $3x - x - 2 = 4$ **$x = 3$**
28. $4x + 6x - 40 = 0$ **$x = 4$**
29. $5x - 8 = -8$ **$x = 0$**
30. $4x + 5x - 10 = 35$ **$x = 5$**

Write an equation that represents the sentence. Then solve the equation.

31. Twice a number increased by -4 is zero. **$2x + (-4) = 0$; $x = 2$**

32. The difference of three times a number and 9 is 6. **$3x - 9 = 6$; $x = 5$**

33. The sum of $3x$ and $2x$ and $7x$ and 6 is 42. **$3x + 2x + 7x + 6 = 42$; $x = 3$**

34. Five subtracted from the difference of $4y$ and y is -29. **$(4y - y) - 5 = -29$; $y = -8$**

35. Fourteen less than the sum of $4x$ and x is equal to 1. **$4x + x - 14 = 1$; $x = 3$**

36. The sum of $4y$ and 18 minus $2y$ is zero. **$4y + 18 - 2y = 0$; $y = -9$**

Student Help

▶ **HOMEWORK HELP**

Extra help with problem solving in Exs. 37–39 is available at www.mcdougallittell.com

PRINTING COSTS In Exercises 37–39, use the following information. Your school's band is making posters to raise money. The printer charges \$2 per poster. At the school fair, you rent a booth for \$30 and you sell each poster for \$5. How many posters must you have printed and then sell to make a profit of \$300? **37–39. See margin.**

37. Write a verbal model using the relationship for profit: *Profit* = *Income* − *Expenses*. Assign labels to your verbal model.

38. Write and solve an algebraic model to find the number of posters your school needs to sell. Check your solution.

39. MATHEMATICAL REASONING The printer has raised the price to \$3 per poster. How does your equation change? Will you make more profit or less profit for the same number of posters? Explain your answer. Find the number of posters your school must now sell at the fair to make a profit of \$300.

BUSINESS In Exercises 40–42, use the following information. You start a business selling bottled fruit juices. You buy them in cases of 12 bottles each from a distributor for \$1 a bottle. You sell each bottle for \$2. The distributor also charges a flat delivery charge of \$15. **40–42. See margin.**

40. Assuming you are able to sell all the bottles you buy, write a verbal model and assign labels to find the number of bottles you must order to make a profit of \$129.

41. Write and solve an algebraic model.

42. CHALLENGE Suppose you buy 20 cases of juice. However, at the end of the day you have made a profit of only \$165. How many bottles of juice do you have left over? **30 bottles**

ELECTRICAL ENGINEER
Engineers are employed by utility companies to maintain electrical and control systems, plan ahead for peak power demands, conduct experiments, evaluate research, and design and oversee work done to overcome power outages.

More about engineering at www.mcdougallittell.com

CALCULATOR For Exercises 43–46, use the following information and the electric bill shown. Electric companies sometimes charge a basic customer service charge in addition to a rate per kilowatt-hour (kW • h) of electricity that you use. **43–44. See margin.**

43. What is the basic service charge? What is the rate per kilowatt-hour?

44. Write a verbal model, assign labels, and write an equation that you can use to calculate the total bill if x kilowatt-hours of electricity are used.

45. If you use 500 kW • h, what will your total bill be? **\$44.38**

46. If you do not want to pay more than \$40.00 for electricity, how many kilowatt-hours of electricity can you use? **about 444 kW•h**

Meter Number	Amount Now Due
894763	\$43.51

ELECTRICITY USED THIS PERIOD	
Previous Meter Reading	4310
Present Meter Reading	4799
kW•h Consumed This Period	489
COST OF ELECTRICITY	
Basic Service Charge	\$5.00
Energy Charge 489 kW•h × \$.078760/kW•h	\$38.51
Total Charges	\$43.51

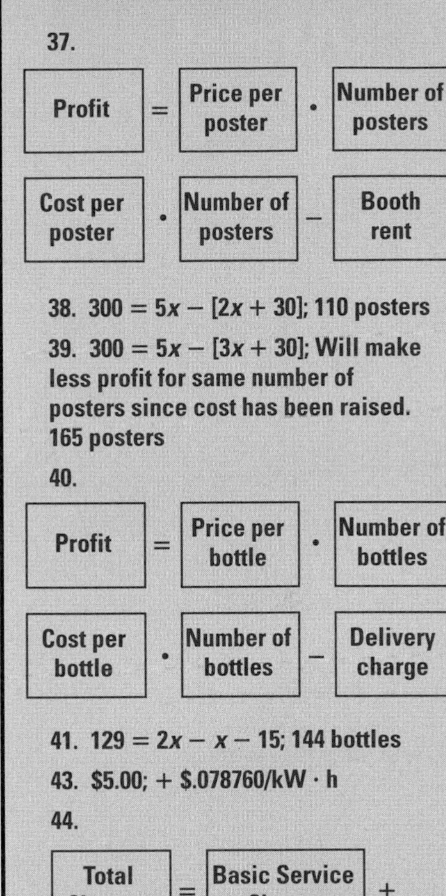

37.
Profit = Price per poster • Number of posters −
Cost per poster • Number of posters − Booth rent
38. 300 = 5x − [2x + 30]; 110 posters
39. 300 = 5x − [3x + 30]; Will make less profit for same number of posters since cost has been raised. 165 posters
40.
Profit = Price per bottle • Number of bottles −
Cost per bottle • Number of bottles − Delivery charge
41. 129 = 2x − x − 15; 144 bottles
43. \$5.00; + \$.078760/kW · h
44.

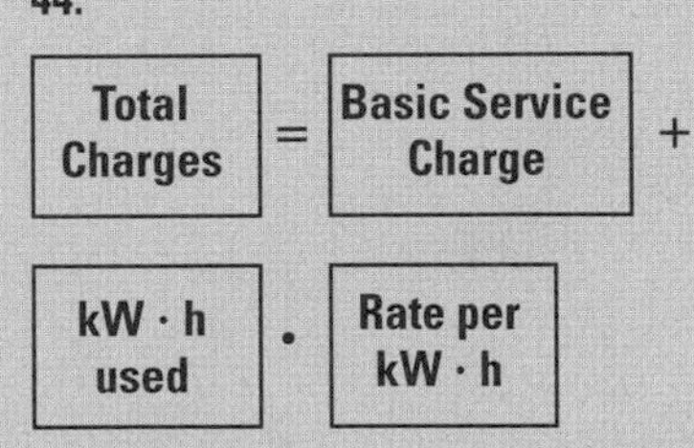

Total charges = $5 + 0.078760x$

4 Assess

Assessment Resources

- Assessment Book (Formal Assessment and Alternative Assessment)
- Test and Practice Generator

Mini-Quiz

1. Solve the equation. Then check your solution.
   a. $32 = 2x + 3x - 8$ **8**
   b. $14 + (3x - 21) = 38$ **15**
   c. $2x - 20 = 4$ **12**
2. You start a T-shirt company with a 12,000 investment for equipment. Each shirt costs you $6 plus $1 for ink. You sell the shirts for $12 each. How many shirts must you sell to earn a profit of $8000? **4000 shirts**

61–66.

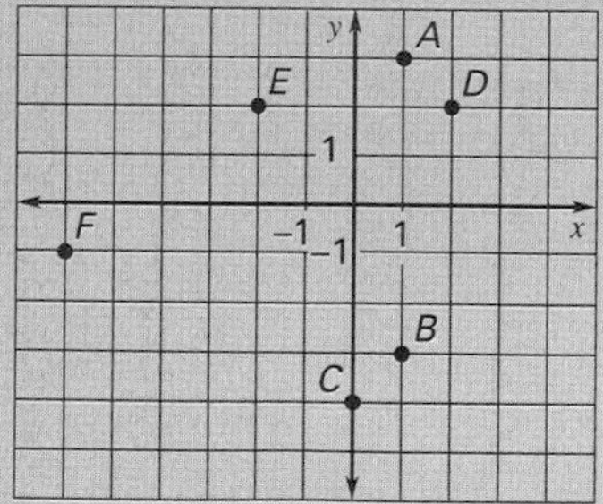

Multiple-Choice Practice

Test Tip A B C D

▶ In Exercise 48, think about a verbal model you could use to represent the problem. Which of the equations listed fits your verbal model?

47. What is the solution of the equation $3x + x + 8 = 4$? **A**

Ⓐ -1 Ⓑ 1 Ⓒ 2 Ⓓ 4

48. On a weekend class gathering at a museum, a teacher brings $50 to pay for museum admission. She buys an adult ticket for $3.50 and 13 student tickets. Three students arrive late so she buys 3 more student tickets. She has $18.50 left. Which equation can you use to find the cost of a student ticket? **H**

Ⓕ $13x + 3x = 50 - 18.50$ Ⓖ $13x + 3.50 + 3x = 50$

Ⓗ $13x + 3.50 + 3x + 18.50 = 50$ Ⓙ $3x = 3.50 + 13x$

49. You are buying carpet to cover a room with area 15 square yards, a hallway with area 6 square yards, and a second room with area 30 square yards. The clerk tells you that your total is $1147.50 before tax. How much did the carpet cost per square yard? **B**

Ⓐ $12.50 Ⓑ $22.50 Ⓒ $42.50 Ⓓ Not here

Mixed Review

50. Find the perimeter and area of the figure. *(1.5)* **60 m; 198 m²**

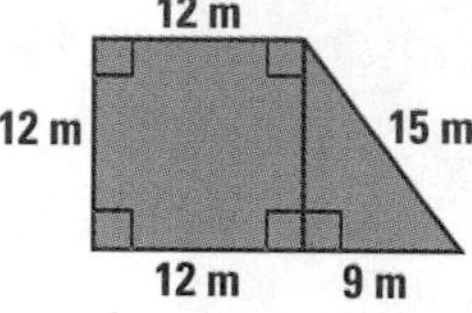

51. Evaluate the expression $6 - 3x$ when $x = -2, -1, 0, 1,$ and 2. Make a table to organize your data. Describe the pattern you see as x increases. *(3.5)* **See margin.**

51.

x	Value
−2	12
−1	9
0	6
1	3
2	0

Value decreases by 3 as x increases by 1.

Solve the equation. Then check your solution. *(3.7, 4.1)*

52. $m + 14 = 23$ **$m = 9$** **53.** $\frac{n}{6} = 6$ **$n = 36$** **54.** $p + 1 = 10$ **$p = 9$**

55. $54 = -9q$ **$q = -6$** **56.** $\frac{r}{-7} = 1$ **$r = -7$** **57.** $s - 9 = 19$ **$s = 28$**

58. $3t - 2 = -11$ **$t = -3$** **59.** $\frac{u}{2} + 3 = 9$ **$u = 12$** **60.** $10 = 28 + 6v$ **$v = -3$**

In Exercises 61–66, plot all the points in the same coordinate plane. Name the quadrant (if any) that contains each point. *(3.8)* **See margin for graph.**

61. $A(1, 3)$ **1** **62.** $B(1, -3)$ **4** **63.** $C(0, -4)$ **none**

64. $D(2, 2)$ **1** **65.** $E(-2, 2)$ **2** **66.** $F(-6, -1)$ **3**

67. You have a summer job running errands for a local business. You earn $5 per day, plus $2 for each errand. Write and solve an equation to find the number of errands you need to run to earn $17 in one day. *(4.1)*

67. $17 = 5 + 2x$; **6 errands**

4.3 Solving Equations Involving Negative Coefficients

California Standards

In this lesson you'll:

- Solve two-step linear equations in one variable. (AF 4.1)
- Write an equation that represents a verbal description. (AF 1.1)

Goal 1 EQUATIONS WITH NEGATIVE COEFFICIENTS

Example 1 shows two methods for solving an equation involving a negative coefficient. You can use whichever method you prefer.

EXAMPLE 1 Handling Negative Coefficients

Solve $8 - x = 3$.

Solution

Method 1 Leave the variable term on the left side.

$8 - x = 3$	Write original equation.
$8 + (-1)x = 3$	Use rule for subtraction.
$8 + (-1)x - \mathbf{8} = 3 - \mathbf{8}$	Subtract 8 from each side.
$(-1)x = -5$	Simplify.
$\frac{(-1)x}{\mathbf{-1}} = \frac{-5}{\mathbf{-1}}$	Divide each side by −1.
$x = 5$	Simplify. *x* is by itself.

Method 2 Move the variable term to the right side.

$8 - x = 3$	Write original equation.
$8 - x + \mathbf{x} = 3 + \mathbf{x}$	Add *x* to each side.
$8 = 3 + x$	Simplify.
$5 = x$	Subtract 3 from each side.

ANSWER ▶ The solution is 5. Check this in the original equation.

Student Help

▶ **STUDY TIP**
In Method 1 of Example 1, the expression $-x$ represents multiplication because $-x = -1 \cdot x$. You should divide by -1 to undo the multiplication.

EXAMPLE 2 Solving a Two-Step Equation

Solve $3 - 2x = 11$.

Solution

$3 - 2x = 11$	Write original equation.
$3 + (-2x) = 11$	Use rule for subtraction.
$-2x = 8$	Subtract 3 from each side.
$x = -4$	Divide each side by −2.

ANSWER ▶ The solution is −4. Check this in the original equation.

1 Plan

Pacing

Suggested Number of Days

Transitional: 2 days
Average: 2 days
Advanced: 2 days
Block Schedule: 1 block

Teaching Resources

Blacklines
(See page 166B.)

Transparencies
- Warm-Up Exercises
- Teacher Time-Savers
- English/Spanish Problem Solving
- Answers

Technology
- Electronic Teacher Tools
- Test and Practice Generator

2 Teach

Math Reasoning

For Mathematical Background Notes on mathematical reasoning related to this lesson, please refer to pages 166E and 166F in this Teacher's Edition.

Extra Examples 1 and 2
See next page.

California Standards and Assessment

CA Standards: AF 1.1, AF 4.1

Math Reasoning

A third method for solving the equation in Example 1 is to begin by multiplying both sides by -1, giving the equivalent equation $-8 + x = -3$.

Extra Example 1

Solve $15 - n = 4$. 11

Extra Example 2

Solve $8 - 3x = 32$. -8

Extra Example 3

Your parents gave you $48 to pay for your school lunches. You have $14 left. Each lunch costs $2. How many lunches have you already bought? 17

Extra Example 4

Use a table and graph to solve the problem in Extra Example 3. Find the value of $48 - 2n$ when $n = 0, 1, 2, 3, \ldots$ and plot the results. Check the value of n when there is $14 left.

Lunches	0	1	2	3
Amount Left	48	46	44	42

Plot the individual points below. Do not draw the line.

(0, 48) (1, 46) (2, 44) (3, 42) (4, 40) (5, 38) (6, 36) (7, 34) (8, 32)
(9, 30) (10, 28) (11, 26) (12, 24) (13, 22) (14, 20) (15, 18) (16, 16)
(17, 14) (18, 12) (19, 10) (20, 8) (21, 6) (22, 4) (23, 2) (24, 0)

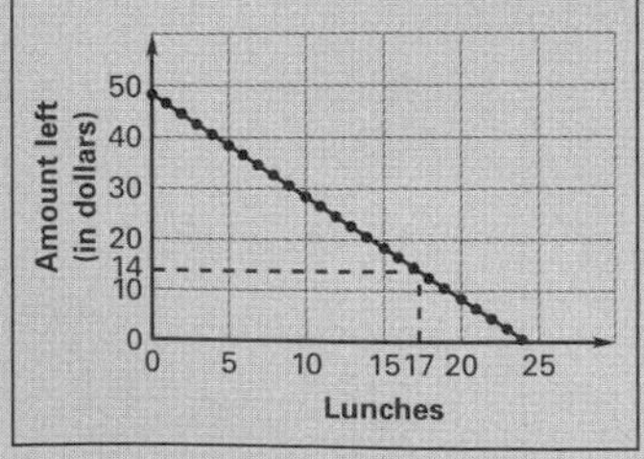

Concept Check

Explain how to solve an equation involving a negative coefficient. ***Sample answer:*** **Isolate the term involving the variable. Divide by the coefficient of the variable.**

Link to History

HISTORY OF BANKING
The early to mid-1800s were known as the Wildcat Period of American banking. There were so many banks issuing bank notes as loans that it was easy for counterfeiters to fool people.

More about banking available at www.mcdougallittell.com

Goal 2 Writing Equations

EXAMPLE 3 Writing a Two-Step Equation

LOANS Suppose you take a $600 loan from a relative. You agree to pay $25 per month. With interest, the total amount to be paid back will be $650. How many months will it take until you owe $100?

Solution

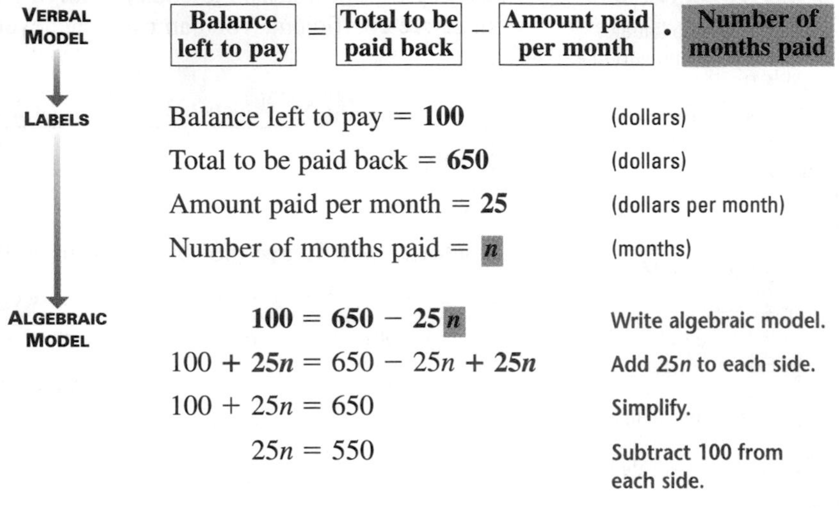

VERBAL MODEL

Balance left to pay = Total to be paid back − Amount paid per month • Number of months paid

LABELS

Balance left to pay = **100** (dollars)

Total to be paid back = **650** (dollars)

Amount paid per month = **25** (dollars per month)

Number of months paid = n (months)

ALGEBRAIC MODEL

$\mathbf{100 = 650 - 25}n$ — Write algebraic model.

$100 + \mathbf{25n} = 650 - 25n + \mathbf{25n}$ — Add $25n$ to each side.

$100 + 25n = 650$ — Simplify.

$25n = 550$ — Subtract 100 from each side.

$n = 22$ — Divide each side by 25.

ANSWER ▶ It will take 22 months until you owe $100.

EXAMPLE 4 Checking the Monthly Balance

You can use a table and a graph to solve the problem in Example 3. Find the value of the expression $650 - 25n$ when $n = 0, 1, 2, 3, \ldots$ and graph the results.

Solution

Month n	Left to pay $650 - 25n$
0	650
1	625
2	600
3	575
4	550

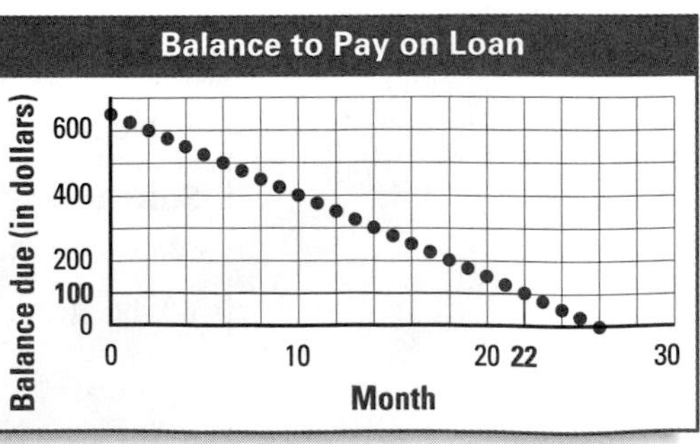

Continue the table to check that you owe $100 after 22 months.

▶ **MORE EXAMPLES**
More examples are available at www.mcdougallittell.com

4.3 Exercises

Guided Practice

1.
$$7 - x = -8$$
$$7 + (-1)x = -8$$
$$7 + (-1)x - 7 = -8 - 7$$
$$\frac{-1x}{-1} = \frac{-15}{-1}$$
$$x = 15$$

2.
$$12 = 6 - 2n$$
$$12 + 2n = 6 - 2n + 2n$$
$$12 + 2n = 6$$
$$12 + 2n - 12 = 6 - 12$$
$$2n = -6$$
$$n = -3$$

In Exercises 1 and 2, copy the equation and complete the solution.
1, 2. See margin.

1. $7 - x = -8$

$7 + \underline{\ ?\ } = -8$

$7 + (-1)x - 7 = -8 - \underline{\ ?\ }$

$\frac{-1x}{-1} = \frac{?}{-1}$

$x = \underline{\ ?\ }$

2. $12 = 6 - 2n$

$12 + 2n = 6 - 2n + \underline{\ ?\ }$

$12 + 2n = \underline{\ ?\ }$

$12 + 2n - \underline{\ ?\ } = 6 - 12$

$2n = \underline{\ ?\ }$

$n = \underline{\ ?\ }$

Describe the first step you would take to solve the equation.

3. $-3x - 6 = -15$ **Add 6 or 3*x* to both sides.**

4. $-48 = -2y + 8$ **Add 2*y* to or subtract 8 from both sides.**

5. $27 = 39 - n$ **Subtract 39 from both sides or add *n* to both sides.**

Solve the equation. Then check your solution.

6. $-2 - x = 14$ **$x = -16$**

7. $21 = 7 - 2m$ **$m = -7$**

8. $-n + 12 = -7$ **$n = 19$**

9. $5 - 3m = -4$ **$m = 3$**

10. $-2k + 13 = 17$ **$k = -2$**

11. $9 - z = 15$ **$z = -6$**

Practice and Problem Solving

Student Help

▶More Practice
Extra practice to help you master skills is on page 696.

12.
$$-5x + 5 = 30$$
$$-5x + 5 - 5 = 30 - 5$$
$$-5x = 25$$
$$\frac{-5x}{-5} = \frac{25}{-5}$$
$$x = -5$$

13.
$$-31 = -4y + 9$$
$$-31 - 9 = -4y + 9 - 9$$
$$-40 = -4y$$
$$\frac{-40}{-4} = \frac{-4y}{-4}$$
$$10 = y$$

Copy and complete the solution. **12, 13. See margin.**

12. $-5x + 5 = 30$

$-5x + 5 - \underline{\ ?\ } = 30 - \underline{\ ?\ }$

$-5x = \underline{\ ?\ }$

$\frac{-5x}{?} = \frac{?}{?}$

$x = \underline{\ ?\ }$

13. $-31 = -4y + 9$

$-31 - \underline{\ ?\ } = -4y + 9 - \underline{\ ?\ }$

$\underline{\ ?\ } = -4y$

$\frac{?}{?} = \frac{-4y}{?}$

$\underline{\ ?\ } = y$

Solve the equation. Then check your solution.

14. $-12t - 7 = -31$ **$t = 2$**

15. $-7x - 16 = 12$ **$x = -4$**

16. $-5r + 15 = 10$ **$r = 1$**

17. $-m - 11 = 1$ **$m = -12$**

18. $3 - x = -2$ **$x = 5$**

19. $-2y + 27 = 39$ **$y = -6$**

20. $-y + 2 = 1$ **$y = 1$**

21. $-3 - 3z = 0$ **$z = -1$**

22. $-2n + 2 = -12$ **$n = 7$**

23. $-11t + 16 = -6$ **$t = 2$**

24. $-2x + 7 = 27$ **$x = -10$**

25. $12 - 2t = -62$ **$t = 37$**

26. $x - 2x = 15$ **$x = -15$**

27. $4 = 19 - x$ **$x = 15$**

28. $52 - x = 19$ **$x = 33$**

29. $8x + 7 - 9x = -3$ **$x = 10$**

30. $4a - 8 - 6a = 4$ **$a = -6$**

31. $9 - 3w + w = 13$ **$w = -2$**

32. $-5 = 7 - p - 2p$ **$p = 4$**

33. $17 = 4y + 8 - 7y$ **$y = -3$**

34. $32 = 92 - 8t - 4t$ **$t = 5$**

3 Apply

Assignment Guide

Transitional
Day 1: pp. 181–182 Exs. 12–19, 29–31
Day 2: pp. 181–182 Exs. 35–36, 39, 42–44

Average
Day 1: pp. 181–182 Exs. 12–22, 29–31
Day 2: pp. 181–182 Exs. 35–39, 42–44

Advanced
Day 1: pp. 181–182 Exs. 12–19, 29–34
Day 2: pp. 181–182 Exs. 35–40, 41*, 42–44

Block Schedule
pp. 181–182 Exs. 12–22, 29–31, 35–39, 42–44

Extra Practice

- Student Edition, pp. 696–697
- Chapter 4 Resource Book, p. 24

Homework Check

To quickly check student understanding of key concepts, go over the following exercises:

Transitional: 12, 14, 20, 30, 36
Average: 16, 20, 30, 36, 39
Advanced: 18, 30, 34, 36, 40

4 Assess

Assessment Resources

- Assessment Book (Formal Assessment and Alternative Assessment)
- Test and Practice Generator

Mini-Quiz

1. Solve the equation. Then check your solution.
   a. $-4 - 8z = 12$ **−2**
   b. $33 = 5 - 7x$ **−4**
   c. $2w + 9 - 5w = 0$ **3**
2. Your parents give you $300 to open a bank account. They let you withdraw $5 a week to use as spending money, but ask you to leave at least $50 in the account. How many weeks can you withdraw money? **50 weeks**

35. [Balance left to pay] = [Total to be paid back] − [Amount paid per week] · [Number of weeks paid]

$0 = 125 - 5n$, $n = 25$; 25 weeks

36.

week n	Left to pay $125 - 5n$
0	125
5	100
10	75
15	50
20	25
25	0

You can substitute the above numbers in the formula to check.

37.

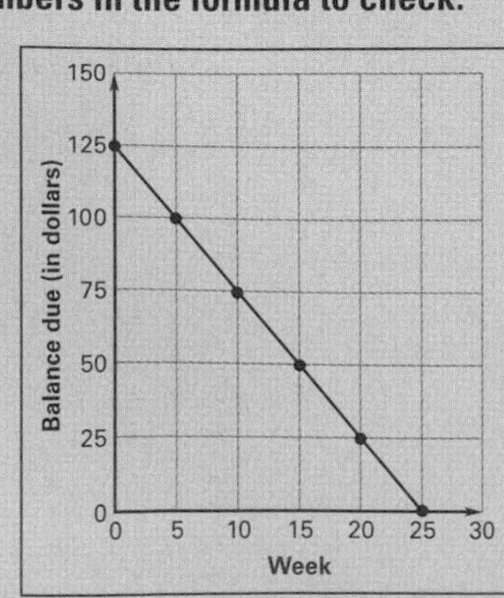

SAVINGS For Exercises 35–38, use the following information. You take $125 out of a savings account. You plan to replace the money by putting back $5 each week until you have replaced all of the money you took out. **35, 36. See margin.**

35. Use a verbal model and an algebraic model like the ones in Example 3 to find out how many weeks it will take to replace all of the money.

36. Make a table that shows the balance you still have left to put back after week n for $n = 0, 5, 10, 15, \ldots$. Explain how this helps you check your solution from Exercise 35.

37. In a coordinate plane, graph the balance you still have left to put back after week n for $n = 0, 5, 10, 15, \ldots$. Explain how this helps you check your solution from Exercise 35. **See margin for graph. You can see that your balance is 0 after 25 weeks.**

38. MATHEMATICAL REASONING Suppose that you find that you are able to replace $25 per week. How will this change the appearance of the graph in Exercise 37? Explain. **The graph will slope downward much more steeply, with repayment completed in 5 weeks.**

Link to History

OIL PIPELINE The Trans-Alaskan Oil Pipeline is about 1300 km long. With a diameter of about 1.2 m, the pipeline can transport 2 million gallons of crude oil per day.

More about oil pipelines available at www.mcdougallittell.com

39. History Link In 1992 about 627,000,000 barrels of crude oil were produced in Alaska. The amount of crude oil produced has decreased by about 33,000,000 barrels each year. In what year were about 429,000,000 barrels of crude oil produced in Alaska? Use the verbal model to assign labels and to write and solve an algebraic model. **See margin.**

[Oil produced (in millions)] = [Oil produced in 1992 (in millions)] − [Change each year (in millions)] · [Number of years since 1992]

40. DEPRECIATION When you buy a car or truck, it tends to lose value (or to *depreciate*) over time. Suppose a truck that originally cost $20,000 depreciates by $2500 each year. After how many years will the truck be worth $7500? **5 yr**

41. CHALLENGE You have $100 to buy school clothes. You buy one pair of jeans and three shirts. The jeans cost $25. You have $24.15 left. How much did each shirt cost? **$16.95**

Multiple-Choice Practice

39. $429 = 627 - 33n$, $n = 6$; in 1998

42. What is the solution of $-2y - 12 = -14$? **C**

Ⓐ −13　Ⓑ −1　Ⓒ 1　Ⓓ 13

43. What is the solution of $10 - x = 16$? **G**

Ⓕ −26　Ⓖ −6　Ⓗ 6　Ⓙ 26

44. Which equation represents this sentence: *The difference of 23 and 2 times a number is 47*? **C**

Ⓐ $(23)(2)x = 47$　Ⓑ $23 + 2 - x = 47$

Ⓒ $23 - 2x = 47$　Ⓓ $23 - 2 + x = 47$

4.4 Solving Equations Using the Distributive Property

California Standards

In this lesson you'll:

- Simplify expressions by applying the distributive property. (AF 1.3)
- Solve multi-step problems involving speed, distance, and time. (AF 4.2)

Goal 1 USING THE DISTRIBUTIVE PROPERTY

You may need to use the distributive property in solving some equations.

EXAMPLE 1 Using the Distributive Property

Solve $5y + 2(y - 3) = 92$.

Solution

$5y + 2(y - 3) = 92$	Write original equation.
$5y + 2y - 6 = 92$	Use distributive property.
$7y - 6 = 92$	Combine like terms.
$7y = 98$	Add 6 to each side.
$y = 14$	Divide each side by 7.

ANSWER ▶ The solution is 14.

CHECK ✓

$5y + 2(y - 3) = 92$	Write original equation.
$5(\mathbf{14}) + 2(\mathbf{14} - 3) \stackrel{?}{=} 92$	Substitute 14 for y.
$5(14) + 2(11) \stackrel{?}{=} 92$	Simplify.
$70 + 22 \stackrel{?}{=} 92$	Simplify.
$92 = 92$ ✓	The solution checks.

EXAMPLE 2 Using the Distributive Property

Solve $13 = 4(3x - 7) + 5$.

Solution

$13 = 4(3x - 7) + 5$	Write original equation.
$13 = 4 \cdot 3x - 4 \cdot 7 + 5$	Use distributive property.
$13 = (4 \cdot 3)x - 4 \cdot 7 + 5$	Use associative property.
$13 = 12x - 28 + 5$	Simplify.
$13 = 12x - 23$	Simplify.
$36 = 12x$	Add 23 to each side.
$3 = x$	Divide each side by 12.

ANSWER ▶ The solution is 3. Check this in the original equation.

Student Help

▶ **MORE EXAMPLES**

More examples are available at www.mcdougallittell.com

1 Plan

Pacing

Suggested Number of Days

Transitional: 2 days
Average: 2 days
Advanced: 2 days
Block Schedule: 1 block

Teaching Resources

Blacklines
(See page 166B.)

Transparencies
- Warm-Up Exercises
- Teacher Time-Savers
- English/Spanish Problem Solving
- Answers

Technology
- Electronic Teacher Tools
- Test and Practice Generator

2 Teach

Math Reasoning

For Mathematical Background Notes on mathematical reasoning related to this lesson, please refer to pages 166E and 166F in this Teacher's Edition.

Extra Examples 1 and 2
See next page.

California Standards and Assessment

CA Standards: AF 1.3, AF 4.2

Math Reasoning

Ask students how the equation in Example 2 could be solved without using the distributive property. (*Hint:* First subtract 5 from both sides.)

Extra Example 1

Solve $14n + 3(n + 5) = 117$. **6**

Extra Example 2

Solve $18 = 3(y + 9)$. **−3**

Extra Example 3

Solve $7 - 4(11 + 3b) = -1$. **−3**

Extra Example 4

Two boats traveling down a river cover a combined distance of 225 miles. Each boat traveled for 3 hours. The second boat traveled 5 miles per hour slower than the first. What was the second boat's speed? **35 miles per hour**

Teaching Tip

In Example 4 and Extra Example 4, remind students that part of the problem solving plan is to solve the equation and *then* answer the question. The solution to the equation may not be the answer to the question, as in these examples.

Concept Check

Explain how the distributive property may be used to solve equations. ***Sample answer:*** **If an equation involves parentheses, distribute the coefficient across the parentheses and then solve as usual.**

Student Help

▶ **STUDY TIP**
When you use the distributive property in Example 3, you can think of $3 - (x - 2)$ as being equivalent to $3 + (-1)(x + (-2))$. Then multiply each term of $x + (-2)$ by -1.

EXAMPLE 3 Solving with Negative Coefficients

Solve $3 - (x - 2) = 4$.

Solution

$3 - (x - 2) = 4$	Write original equation.
$3 - x + 2 = 4$	Use distributive property.
$5 - x = 4$	Combine like terms.
$5 = 4 + x$	Add x to each side.
$1 = x$	Subtract 4 from each side.

ANSWER ▶ The solution is 1. Check this in the original equation.

Goal 2 SOLVING MULTI-STEP PROBLEMS

Solving a multi-step problem often uses the distributive property.

Link to History

PONY EXPRESS SYSTEM
From 1860–1861, a mail delivery system between St. Joseph, Missouri, and Sacramento, California, involved a series of riders in relay. The riders were able to cover the 2000 miles in 10 days. Every 15 miles or so, the riders changed horses.

More about the Pony Express available at www.mcdougallittell.com

EXAMPLE 4 Solving a Multi-Step Rate Problem

PONY EXPRESS Two riders along a Pony Express route covered a combined distance of 300 miles. Each rider rode for two days. The second rider's speed was 10 miles per day faster than the first rider's speed. What were the two riders' speeds?

Solution

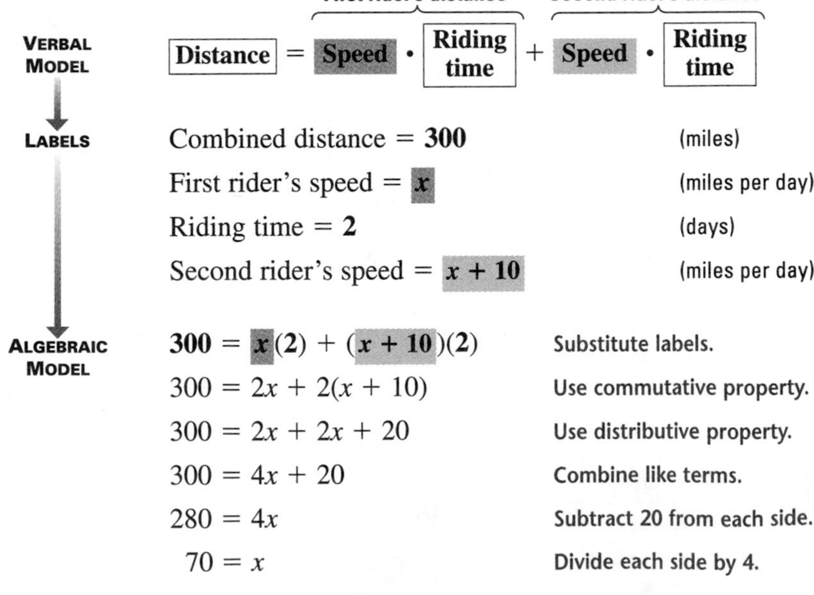

ANSWER ▶ The first rider's speed was 70 miles per day. So, the second rider's speed was $70 + 10 = 80$ miles per day.

4.4 Exercises

Guided Practice

1. The operation of subtraction is the same as adding the opposite of a quantity. The opposite of $(x - 2)$ is $-1(x - 2)$. Subtracting 2 from x is the same as adding -2 to x.

1. Justify the Study Tip on page 184 by explaining why $3 - (x - 2) = 3 + (-1)(x + (-2))$.

Solve the equation. Justify each step.

2. $5(x + 1) = 75$ $5x + 5 = 75$; $x = 14$

3. $5(x - 7) = 5$ $5x - 35 = 5$; $x = 8$

4. $16 = 2(6 + x)$ $16 = 12 + 2x$; $x = 2$

5. $8(x - 2) = -24$ $8x - 16 = -24$; $x = -1$

6. $20 = -5(n + 3)$ $20 = -5n - 15$; $n = -7$

7. $m + 4(m + 1) = 9$ $m + 4m + 4 = 9$; $m = 1$

8. $3(x - 2) + 2x = 14$ $3x - 6 + 2x = 14$; $x = 4$

9. $-1 = 2(2 - t) - 3$ $-1 = 4 - 2t - 3$; $t = 1$

10. $2(x - 4) - 5 = 3$ $2x - 8 - 5 = 3$; $x = 8$

Practice and Problem Solving

Student Help

▸ More Practice
Extra practice to help you master skills is on page 696.

ERROR ANALYSIS In Exercises 11–13, describe and correct the error.
11–13. See margin.

11. 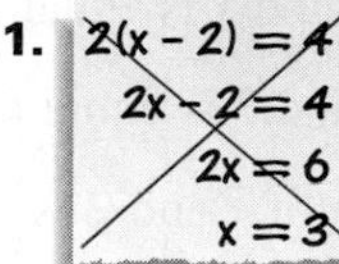

12. 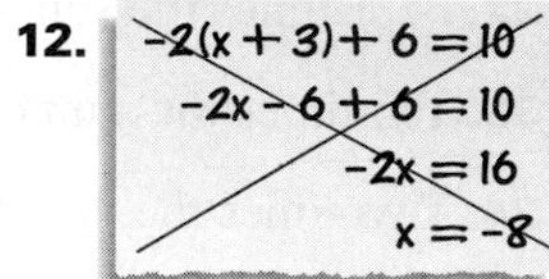

13. 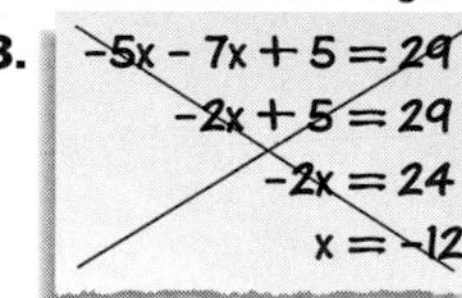

11. The negative 2 was not multiplied by 2.
$2(x - 2) = 4$
$2x - 4 = 4$
$x = 4$

12. The positive six was incorrectly added to the right side.
$-2(x + 3) + 6 = 10$
$-2x - 6 + 6 = 10$
$-2x = 10$
$x = -5$

13. The $-5x$ and $-7x$ were incorrectly added.
$-5x - 7x + 5 = 29$
$-12x = 29 - 5$
$x = -2$

Solve the equation. Then check your solution.

14. $x + 4(x + 6) = -1$ $x = -5$

15. $1 = y + 3(y - 9)$ $y = 7$

16. $3x + 2(x + 8) = 21$ $x = 1$

17. $3(4 - s) + 5s = 8$ $s = -2$

18. $5(2n + 3) - 5 = -70$ $n = -8$

19. $8(4x - 7) = -56$ $x = 0$

20. $2(x + 12) = -8$ $x = -16$

21. $14 = 2(q - 9)$ $q = 16$

22. $-3(y + 4) = 18$ $y = -10$

23. $2 = n - (2n + 3)$ $n = -5$

24. $7r - 5(1 + r) = 5$ $r = 5$

25. $6(2n - 5) = 42$ $n = 6$

26. $4(3p + 2) = -28$ $p = -3$

27. $5x + 2(x + 1) = -40$ $x = -6$

GEOMETRY Write an equation for the area of the rectangle. Then solve for x.

28. Area is 63 square inches.

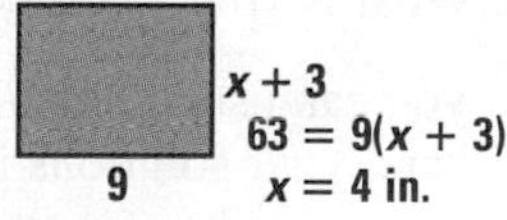

$63 = 9(x + 3)$
$x = 4$ in.

29. Area is 48 square meters.

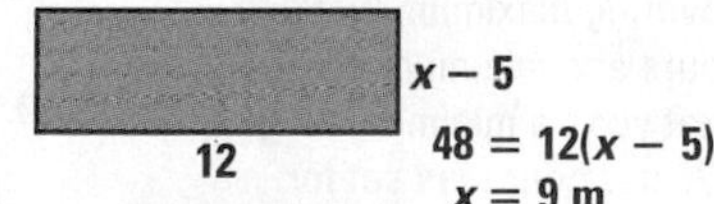

$48 = 12(x - 5)$
$x = 9$ m

30. Area is 45 square feet.

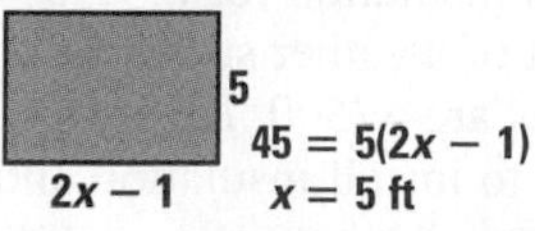

$45 = 5(2x - 1)$
$x = 5$ ft

31. Area is 16 square yards.

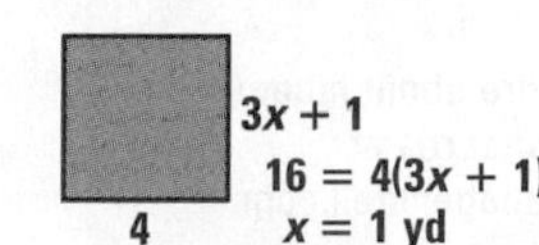

$16 = 4(3x + 1)$
$x = 1$ yd

3 Apply

Assignment Guide

Transitional
Day 1: pp. 185–187 Exs. 11–19, 28–29, 46–48, 50–52, 56
Day 2: pp. 185–187 Exs. 32–35, 37–38, 41–43, 57–59, 63–65

Average
Day 1: pp. 185–187 Exs. 11–19, 24–25, 28–29, 46–48, 50–52, 56
Day 2: pp. 185–187 Exs. 32–39, 41–43, 57–59, 63–65, 69

Advanced
Day 1: pp. 185–187 Exs. 11–17, 22–27, 30–31, 46–48, 50–52, 56
Day 2: pp. 185–187 Exs. 32–39, 40*, 41–43, 57–59, 63–65, 69

Block Schedule
pp. 185–187 Exs. 11–19, 24–25, 28–29, 32–39, 41–43, 46–52, 56–59, 63–65, 69

Extra Practice

- Student Edition, pp. 696–697
- Chapter 4 Resource Book, p. 33

Homework Check

To quickly check student understanding of key concepts, go over the following exercises:

Transitional: 14, 18, 28, 32, 38
Average: 16, 24, 28, 34, 38
Advanced: 16, 26, 30, 34, 38

32. $4(6 + x) = 24; x = 0$

33. $10(n + 3) = 20; n = -1$

34. $2(x - 2) = 22; x = 13$

35. $9(4 - y) = -27; 7 = y$

36. Yes. As long as the properties of real numbers are obeyed, the result will be an equivalent equation.

37. Total earned each week = 142, Total weekday hours = 10, Weekday wage per hour = x, Total Saturday hours = 8, Saturday wage per hour = $x + 2$

38. $142 = 10x + 8(x + 2)$; \$7/hour; \$9/hour

39. $142 \text{ dollars} \stackrel{?}{=} 10\cancel{h} \cdot 7 \frac{\text{dollars}}{\cancel{h}} + 8\cancel{h} \cdot (7 + 2) \frac{\text{dollars}}{\cancel{h}}$; 142 dollars = 70 dollars + 72 dollars

In Exercises 32–35, write and solve an equation for each sentence.

Student Help

▶**Study Tip** For a different approach to solving some equations involving parentheses, as in the Example shown, see Exercise 36.

EXAMPLE

Three times the difference of x and 12 is equal to 21.

Solution

The *difference* is a quantity that must be grouped, so use parentheses to write the equation. Then use the distributive property.

$3(x - 12) = 21$	Write translated equation.
$3x - 36 = 21$	Use distributive property.
$3x - 36 + \mathbf{36} = 21 + \mathbf{36}$	Add 36 to each side.
$3x = 57$	Simplify.
$\frac{3x}{\mathbf{3}} = \frac{57}{\mathbf{3}}$	Divide each side by 3.
$x = 19$	Simplify. x is by itself.

32. Four times the sum of 6 and x is equal to 24. **32–35. See margin.**

33. Ten times the sum of n and 3 is equal to 20.

34. Two times the difference of x and 2 is equal to 22.

35. Nine times the difference of 4 and y is equal to -27.

36. MATHEMATICAL REASONING Suppose you want to solve an equation that involves parentheses, such as $2(x + 3) = 12$. You might use the distributive property and multiply through by 2. Would the results be the same if instead you first divide both sides by 2? Explain. **See margin.**

Link to History

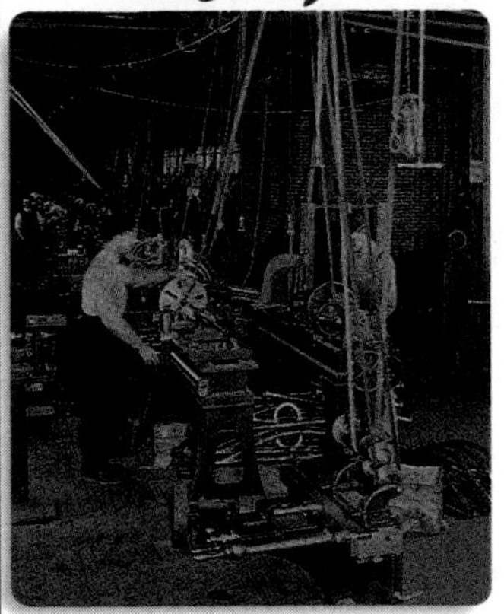

WORKING Before 1938, there were few standards covering maximum working hours and minimum wages. That year, a minimum wage of \$.25 per hour was set for some industries. By 1997 the minimum wage had risen to \$5.15 per hour.

More about labor standards at www.mcdougallittell.com

WORKING In Exercises 37–39, use the following information. You work 2 hours daily after school, Monday through Friday. On Saturdays, you work 8 hours at \$2.00 more per hour than on weekdays. You make \$142 per week. **37–39. See margin.**

37. Use the verbal model below to assign labels for the problem.

Total earned each week	=	Total weekday hours	•	Weekday wage per hour	+	Total Saturday hours	•	Saturday wage per hour

38. Write the algebraic model and solve to find your wage per hour on weekdays. What is your wage per hour on Saturdays?

39. Show how you can use unit analysis to check that the verbal model in Exercise 37 and your solutions in Exercise 38 are correct.

40. CHALLENGE Your cousin installs weather stripping for x dollars per foot and insulation for $(x + 5)$ dollars per foot. This week he installed 480 feet of weather stripping and 2200 feet of insulation. His expenses are \$7500. His profit is \$11,540. Find the prices your cousin charges to install insulation and weather stripping.
He charges \$3/ft to install weather stripping and \$8/ft to install insulation.

Multiple-Choice Practice

41. What is the solution of the equation $50 = 2(3x + 4)$? **A**

Ⓐ 7 Ⓑ 8 Ⓒ 9 Ⓓ 10

42. You earn \$100 each week plus \$2 for each item you sell over 10 items. Last week you earned \$128. Which equation shows how many items you sold? **H**

Ⓕ $100 = 128(x - 10)$ Ⓖ $100 = 128 + 2(x - 10)$

Ⓗ $128 = 100 + 2(x - 10)$ Ⓙ $128 = 100 + 2(x + 10)$

43. Solve for x if the area of the rectangle shown is 39 square units. **C**

Ⓐ 3 Ⓑ 4

Ⓒ 5 Ⓓ 15

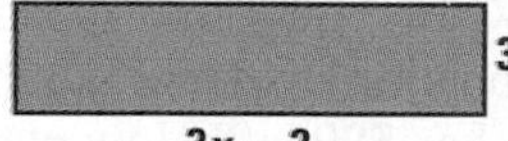

Mixed Review

Evaluate the expression when $a = 4$ and $b = 5$. *(1.2, 1.3, 1.4, 3.4)*

44. $6b - 3$ **27** **45.** $a - 2b$ **−6** **46.** $a \div 2 \cdot b$ **10**

47. $a^2 - b^2$ **−9** **48.** $a^2 - 2b - 3$ **3** **49.** $2a - b + 3a$ **15**

In Exercises 50–55, write an equivalent variable expression. *(1.8)*

50. $4(3 + 2y)$ **12 + 8y** **51.** $4(2x - 3)$ **8x − 12** **52.** $5(3 - x)$ **15 − 5x**

53. $7(2 - z)$ **14 − 7z** **54.** $5(4m + 8)$ **20m + 40** **55.** $6(2 + x - y)$ **12 + 6x − 6y**

56. POSTAGE Your friend is sending out invitations for a party. She spends \$2.64 on stamps to mail the invitations. Each stamp costs \$.33. Write and solve an equation to find the number of invitations your friend is sending. *(2.4, 2.6)* **2.64 = 0.33x; 8 invitations**

Solve the inequality. Then check your solution. *(2.8)*

57. $x + 7 < 12$ **$x < 5$** **58.** $7x \le 49$ **$x \le 7$** **59.** $2x > 4$ **$x > 2$**

60. $5x > 0$ **$x > 0$** **61.** $x - 14 < 16$ **$x < 30$** **62.** $x - 12 \ge 2$ **$x \ge 14$**

In Exercises 63–68, solve the equation. *(4.1–4.3)*

63. $2y - 14 = 0$ **$y = 7$** **64.** $16a + 14 = 110$ **$a = 6$** **65.** $8r + 11r - 5 = 33$ **$r = 2$**

66. $5x - 2x + 5 = -1$ **$x = -2$** **67.** $\frac{m}{3} + 1 = 7$ **$m = 18$** **68.** $2c - 4c - 6 = 18$ **$c = -12$**

69. PROFIT You are selling bracelets at a crafts fair. The materials cost \$10 per bracelet. The rental cost for the booth at the fair is \$25. You decide to sell the bracelets for \$15 each. How many bracelets must you sell to make a profit of \$200? *(4.2)* **45**

4 Assess

Assessment Resources

- Assessment Book (Formal Assessment and Alternative Assessment)
- Test and Practice Generator

Mini-Quiz

1. Solve the equation. Then check your solution.
   - **a.** $2x + 3(x - 2) = 24$ **6**
   - **b.** $5(2s + 3) = 95$ **8**
   - **c.** $6d - 2(d + 3) = -18$ **−3**
2. Two runners cover a total distance of 34 miles. They each run for 2 hours. The second runner runs at an average speed of 1 mile per hour faster than the first runner. How fast does the second runner run?
   - **a.** Write an equation to represent the problem situation. **$34 = 2x + 2(x + 1)$**
   - **b.** Solve the equation and answer the question. **$x = 8$; 9 miles per hour**

Additional Resources

A Mid-Chapter Test and a Mid-Chapter Partner Quiz are available in the *Assessment Book*, pp. 46–47 and p. 225.

Chapter 4 Mid-Chapter Test

Take this test as you would take a test in class. The answers to the exercises are given in the back of the book.

In Exercises 1–8, solve the equation. Check your solution.

1. $2y - 4 = 10$ **y = 7** **2.** $4t + 16 = 0$ **t = −4** **3.** $8 - 2b = 2$ **b = 3** **4.** $7 - 3x = -11$ **x = 6**

5. $\frac{r}{2} + 6 = 8$ **r = 4** **6.** $6m + 5 = -1$ **m = −1** **7.** $20p - 8 = 32$ **p = 2** **8.** $\frac{n}{5} + 9 = 7$ **n = −10**

9. PARKING Your mom spends $15 to park her car in a lot for a day. At the beginning of the month, she had $240 budgeted for parking. She now has $90 left. How many times has she parked her car in the lot so far this month? **10**

Solve the equation. Then check your solution.

10. $9s + 6s - 12s = 24$ **s = 8** **11.** $10t - 7t + t = 24$ **t = 6** **12.** $-5x + 5 + 9x = -31$ **x = −9**

13. $9 = -12 - 3x - 4x$ **x = −3** **14.** $19 + 12p - 17p = -1$ **p = 4** **15.** $-13b + 5b - 4 = 12$ **b = −2**

16. $3(n + 4) + 1 = 28$ **n = 5** **17.** $8 = 4 - 2(x - 2)$ **x = 0** **18.** $-2(3d - 5) + 3 = 55$ **d = −7**

Write an equation that represents the sentence. Then solve the equation and check your solution.

19. The sum of $2x$ and 3 is 21. **$2x + 3 = 21$; $x = 9$** **20.** The difference of $\frac{x}{4}$ and 3 is 1. **$\frac{x}{4} - 3 = 1$; $x = 16$**

21. 17 is the sum of $2x$, x, and 5. **$2x + x + 5 = 17$; $x = 4$** **22.** Two more than the product of 5 and x is 17. **$5x + 2 = 17$; $x = 3$**

TRAVEL In Exercises 23–26, use the following information.
You are in Western Samoa in the Pacific Ocean. In Apia, on Upolu Island, you see the sign at the right. The people of Apia want to add four more cities to the sign, and they ask you for the distances.

23. The distance from Apia to New York City is about the distance to Honolulu plus 64 times the distance to Tagapofu, American Samoa. About how far is it to to Tagapofu? **126 km**

24. The difference of the distance from Apia to London and the distance from Apia to Juneau, Alaska, is about the distance from Apia to Los Angeles. About how far is it to Juneau? **8792 km**

25. Four times the sum of the distance from Apia to Austin, Texas, and the distance from Apia to Nouméa is about 47,000 kilometers. About how far is it to Austin? **9270 km**

26. The distance between Apia and Berlin is about three times the difference of the distance from Apia to Tokyo, Japan, and 900. About how far is it to Tokyo? **7540 km**

4.5 Solving Equations with Variables on Both Sides

California Standards

In this lesson you'll:

- Solve linear equations in one variable. (AF 4.1)
- Use formulas for finding the perimeter of basic two-dimensional figures. (MG 2.1)

Goal 1 Collecting Variables on One Side

Some equations, such as $2x + 3 = 3x + 5$, have variables on both sides of the equal sign. You will need to *collect like variables* on the same side.

EXAMPLE 1 Collecting Like Variables

Solve $2x + 3 = 3x + 5$.

Solution

$2x + 3 = 3x + 5$	Write original equation.
$2x + 3 - \mathbf{2x} = 3x + 5 - \mathbf{2x}$	Subtract 2*x* from each side.
$3 = x + 5$	Simplify.
$3 - \mathbf{5} = x + 5 - \mathbf{5}$	Subtract 5 from each side.
$-2 = x$	Simplify. *x* is by itself.

ANSWER ▶ The solution is -2.

CHECK ✓

$2x + 3 = 3x + 5$	Write original equation.
$2(-2) + 3 \stackrel{?}{=} 3(-2) + 5$	Substitute -2 for *x*.
$-4 + 3 \stackrel{?}{=} -6 + 5$	Simplify.
$-1 = -1$ ✓	The solution checks.

Student Help

STUDY TIP
In Example 1, you could choose to subtract $3x$ from both sides instead. The result would be an equation involving a negative coefficient, $-x + 3 = 5$.

EXAMPLE 2 Using the Distributive Property

Solve $8n - 4 = 3(2n + 8)$.

Solution

$8n - 4 = 3(2n + 8)$	Write original equation.
$8n - 4 = 6n + 24$	Use distributive property.
$8n - 4 - \mathbf{6n} = 6n + 24 - \mathbf{6n}$	Subtract 6*n* from each side.
$2n - 4 = 24$	Simplify.
$2n - 4 + \mathbf{4} = 24 + \mathbf{4}$	Add 4 to each side.
$2n = 28$	Simplify.
$\frac{2n}{2} = \frac{28}{2}$	Divide each side by 2.
$n = 14$	Simplify. *n* is by itself.

ANSWER ▶ The solution is 14. Check this in the original equation.

1 Plan

Pacing

Suggested Number of Days

Transitional: 1 day
Average: 1 day
Advanced: 1 day
Block Schedule: 0.5 block with 4.6

Teaching Resources

Blacklines
(See page 166B.)

Transparencies
- Warm-Up Exercises
- Teacher Time-Savers
- English/Spanish Problem Solving
- Answers

Technology
- Electronic Teacher Tools
- Test and Practice Generator

2 Teach

Math Reasoning

For Mathematical Background Notes on mathematical reasoning related to this lesson, please refer to pages 166E and 166F in this Teacher's Edition.

Extra Examples 1 and 2
See next page.

California Standards and Assessment

CA Standards: AF 4.1, MG 2.1
CA Key Concepts Book: pp. S67–S69

Extra Example 1

Solve $7 + 3x = 7x - 9$. 4

Extra Example 2

Solve $6(3 + 2y) = 5y - 3$. -3

Teaching Tip

Critical Thinking Be sure students understand why the equation $x + 3 = x + 3$ cannot be used in solving for x in Example 3.

Math Reasoning

Using the triangle inequality, one can see that the set of values of x for which the triangle in Example 3 exists is $\frac{1}{3} < x < 7$.

Extra Example 3

Find the value of x so that a triangle with side lengths $2x - 3$, $x + 1$, and $2x - 3$ is equilateral. 4

Extra Example 4

Find the value of x so that the rectangle and triangle have the same perimeter. 3

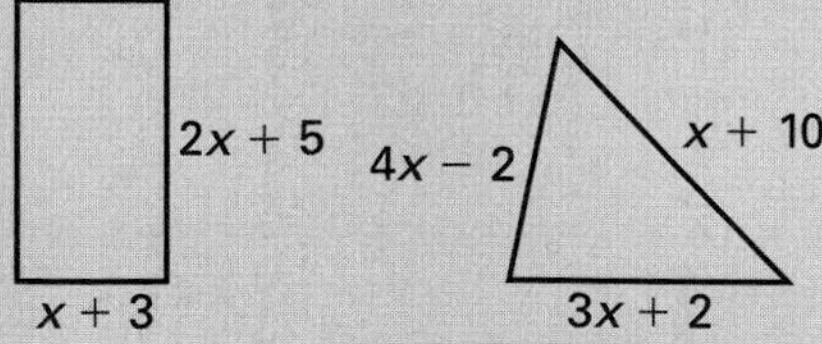

Concept Check

When solving an equation that has variables on both sides, it was suggested that you collect the variables on the side with the term that has the greater variable coefficient. What happens if you collect the variables on the other side? Will you still get the same solution? **The coefficient of the variable term in the resulting equation will be negative, but the solution will still be the same.**

Goal 2 Modeling Problems in Geometry

You can use formulas from geometry to write equations.

EXAMPLE 3 Solving an Equilateral Triangle

A triangle is *equilateral* if its sides all have the same length. Find the value of x so that triangle ABC is equilateral.

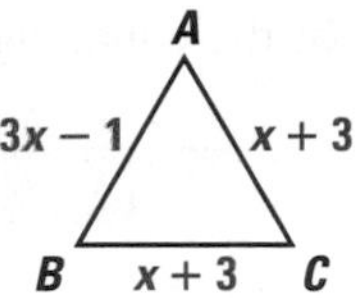

Solution

Length of side AB = **Length of side AC or BC**	**Write verbal model.**
$\mathbf{3x - 1 = x + 3}$	**Write equation.**
$2x - 1 = 3$	**Subtract x from each side.**
$2x = 4$	**Add 1 to each side.**
$x = 2$	**Divide each side by 2.**

When $x = 2$, $\mathbf{3x} - 1 = 3\mathbf{(2)} - 1 = 5$ *and* $\mathbf{x} + 3 = \mathbf{2} + 3 = 5$.

ANSWER ▶ When $x = 2$ units, each side of equilateral triangle ABC has a length of 5 units.

Student Help

▶**Look Back**
For help with perimeter, see page 22.

EXAMPLE 4 Comparing Perimeters

Find the value of x so that the rectangle and the triangle have the same perimeter. What is the perimeter?

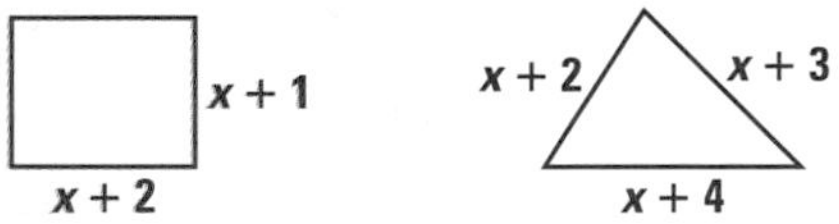

x + 1, x + 2 (rectangle); x + 2, x + 3, x + 4 (triangle)

Solution

Rectangle's perimeter = **Triangle's perimeter**

$$\mathbf{2(x + 1) + 2(x + 2) = (x + 2) + (x + 3) + (x + 4)}$$

$$2x + 2 + 2x + 4 = (x + 2) + (x + 3) + (x + 4)$$

$$4x + 6 = 3x + 9$$

$$x + 6 = 9$$

$$x = 3$$

ANSWER ▶ When $x = 3$ units, each figure has a perimeter of 18 units.

Student Help

▶**More Examples**

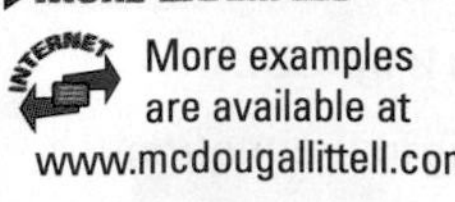

More examples are available at www.mcdougallittell.com

4.5 Exercises

Guided Practice

1. Solve the equation $2x - 4 = x$. Justify each step of the solution.
See margin.

Decide on which side of the equation you would collect the variable terms. Explain your decision. Then solve the equation. **2–4. See margin.**

2. $4y + 10 = 6y$ **3.** $x + 14 = 2(x + 6)$ **4.** $-3x + 5 = x + 3$

Practice and Problem Solving

Student Help

▶ **MORE PRACTICE**
Extra practice to help you master skills is on page 697.

Solve the equation. Then check your solution.

5. $7x + 12 = 13x$

6. $10x + 17 = 4x - 1$

7. $5x - 8 = -2x + 6$

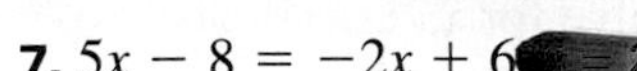

8. $-2x + 6 = -x$

9. $7x = 3(5x - 8)$

10. $9(2x + 10) = 24x$

11. $2(x - 9) = 3(x - 6)$

12. $7t + 12 = 6 + 5t$

13. $5x = -3(x + 4) + 28$

14. $4x = 3(x - 2) + 21$

15. $x + 17 = 2(3x + 1)$

16. $12(2 - x) = 6(1 + x)$

In Exercises 17 and 18, write and solve the equation described.
17, 18. See margin.

17. $3x - 1 = x + 19$
$x = 10$
18. $4x + 17 = 7x + 2$
$x = 5$

17. One less than three times a number is equal to the same number plus 19.

18. The sum of four times a number and 17 is equal to the sum of seven times the same number and 2.

19. GEOMETRY Find the value of x so that the figure is a square.

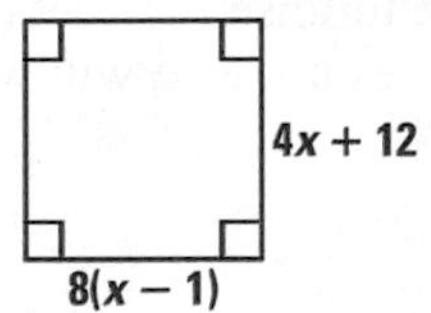

20. GEOMETRY Find the value of x so that the triangle is equilateral.

x + 3 2x – 4
x + 3

21. GEOMETRY Find the value of x so that the rectangle and the triangle have the same perimeter. What is the perimeter?

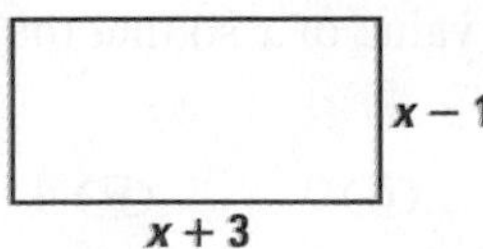

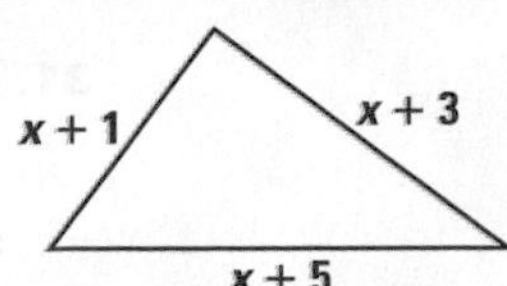

3 Apply

Assignment Guide

TRANSITIONAL
Day 1: EP p. 691 Exs. 35–37; pp. 191–192 Exs. 5–12, 18–20, 22–23, 30–31
AVERAGE
Day 1: pp. 191–192 Exs. 7–14, 17–21, 27–28, 30–31
ADVANCED
Day 1: pp. 191–192 Exs. 13–21, 25–28, 29*, 30–31
BLOCK SCHEDULE
pp. 191–192 Exs. 7–14, 17–21, 27–28, 30–31 (with 4.6)

Extra Practice

- Student Edition, pp. 696–697
- Chapter 4 Resource Book, p. 42

Homework Check

To quickly check student understanding of key concepts, go over the following exercises:

Transitional: 6, 10, 12, 18, 20
Average: 8, 10, 14, 18, 20
Advanced: 14, 18, 20, 26, 28

1. $2x - 4 = x$ **Write original equation.**
$2x - 4 - 2x = x - 2x$ **Subtract 2x from each side.**
$-4 = -x$ **Simplify.**
$-4(-1) = -x(-1)$ **Multiply each side by −1.**
$4 = x$ **Simplify. x is by itself.**

2. Right side, to keep coefficient positive; $5 = y$

3. Right side, to keep coefficient positive; $2 = x$

4. Right side, to keep coefficient positive; $\frac{1}{2} = x$

Problem Solving

Write Equations

In Exercise 24, students should be encouraged to write separate equations for the cost of going to a theater, $C = 7y$, and the cost of renting DVD movies, $D = 360 + 4y$. They may then evaluate each for any number larger than 120. Another question to ask students: How would the problem change if 2 people watch the DVD movies together?

4 Assess

Assessment Resources

- Assessment Book (Formal Assessment and Alternative Assessment)
- Test and Practice Generator

Mini-Quiz

1. Solve the equation. Then check your solution.
   - **a.** $9x + 21 = 16x$ **3**
   - **b.** $5y + 6 = -3y - 10$ **−2**
   - **c.** $4(n + 5) = 3(n - 1)$ **−23**
2. A rectangle has length $4(x - 3)$ and width $x + 6$. Find the value of x if the rectangle is a square. **6**

22. $7y$ = cost at theater; $360 + 4y$ = cost at home

25. $0.75 + 0.006x = 25 + 0.0016x$; $x \approx 5511.4$

MOVIES In Exercises 22–24, use the following information. Suppose the cost of seeing a movie at a theater is $7. Buying a DVD player costs $360 and renting a movie to use on the DVD player is $4.

22. Write expressions to represent the cost of seeing y movies at a theater and renting the same number of movies to use on your DVD player (including the cost of the player). **See margin.**

23. How many movies must you see so that the two costs from Exercise 22 are the same? Write an equation that models the situation and solve for y, the number of movies watched. **$7y = 360 + 4y$; $y = 120$**

24. MATHEMATICAL REASONING Suppose you watch more than the number of movies from Exercise 23. Which will cost less then, going to a theater or renting DVD movies? Explain. **Renting DVD movies. The cost is $4 for DVD vs. $7 at the theater.**

Link to Literature

FABLES A Greek named Aesop is credited with telling many *fables* around 565 B.C. Aesop's fables use animals as characters to tell a story with a moral.

Chapter Opener Link **Look back at the exercises on page 167.**

25. Set the expressions from Exercises 2 and 3 on page 167 equal to each other and solve for x. **See margin.**

26. What does the value of x from Exercise 25 tell you about the standard and the fluorescent light bulbs? **After 5511.4 hours of lighting, the fluorescent bulb becomes the less expensive alternate.**

LITERATURE In Exercises 27–29, use the following information. In one of Aesop's fables, a tortoise and a hare are in a race. The hare is far ahead and is sure it will win, so it takes a nap. When the hare wakes up, it sees the tortoise about to cross the finish line.

27. Suppose the hare runs 600 inches per second and the tortoise runs 3 inches per second. When the hare wakes up, the tortoise is 1000 feet (or 12,000 inches) ahead. Which equation represents when the hare will catch up with the tortoise? (*Hint:* If t represents time in seconds, then $3t$ is the distance in inches the tortoise can travel in t seconds.) **B**

A. $3t = 600t + 12{,}000$ **B.** $600t = 3t + 12{,}000$

C. $3t - 12{,}000 = 600t$ **D.** $600t = 12{,}000$

28. Solve your choice from Exercise 27. Explain what the solution means. **20.1 sec; the time when the hare will catch up with the tortoise**

29. CHALLENGE If the tortoise is 5 feet (or 60 inches) from the finish line when the hare wakes up, who will win the race? Explain. **The tortoise will win the race since he can cover 60 inches in 20.0 seconds.**

Multiple-Choice Practice

30. What is the solution of the equation $4x + 9 = 11x - 33$? **C**

Ⓐ −3 Ⓑ 3 Ⓒ 6 Ⓓ 7

31. Find the value of x so that the figure is a square. **G**

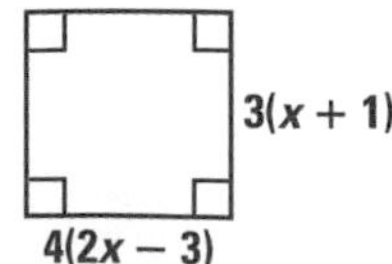

Ⓕ 1 Ⓖ 3 Ⓗ 4 Ⓙ 5

4.6 Problem Solving Strategies

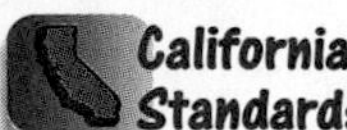

California Standards

In this lesson you'll:

- Estimate unknown quantities graphically and solve for them by using logical reasoning and arithmetic and algebraic techniques. (MR 2.3)
- Evaluate the reasonableness of a solution in the context of the original situation. (MR 3.1)

Goal 1 Using Tables and Graphs

Often there are several ways to solve a real-life problem. It can be helpful to use more than one method and then compare results.

EXAMPLE 1 Using Tables and Graphs

A logging company is making a reforestation plan. The company has 90 square miles of logged land and is logging 15 square miles more each year. The company plants 30 square miles of new trees each year. Predict how long it will take for the logged land to be reforested.

Solution

Method 1 You can use a table and look for a pattern. For the logged land, start with 90 square miles and add 15 square miles each year. For the reforested land, start with 0 square miles and add 30 square miles each year.

Year	0 (now)	1	2	3	4	5	6
Logged land (in square miles)	90	105	120	135	150	165	180
Reforested land (in square miles)	0	30	60	90	120	150	180

From the table you can see that it will take 6 years to reforest all the land that has been logged.

Method 2 You can use a coordinate graph to visualize the same data as in the table and make a prediction.

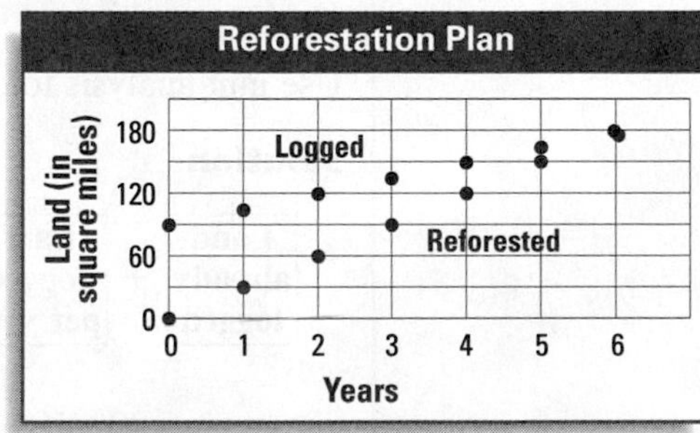

The graph shows that the amount of reforested land steadily approaches the amount of logged land. It also shows that it will take 6 years to reforest the logged land.

Student Help

▶ STUDY TIP
Example 1 lets you compare the data in a table with the same data in a graph.

1 Plan

Pacing

Suggested Number of Days

Transitional: 1 day
Average: 1 day
Advanced: 1 day
Block Schedule: 0.5 block with 4.5

Teaching Resources

Blacklines
(See page 166B.)

Transparencies
- Warm-Up Exercises
- Teacher Time-Savers
- English/Spanish Problem Solving
- Answers

Technology
- Electronic Teacher Tools
- Test and Practice Generator

2 Teach

Math Reasoning

For Mathematical Background Notes on mathematical reasoning related to this lesson, please refer to pages 166E and 166F in this Teacher's Edition.

Extra Example 1
See next page.

California Standards and Assessment

CA Standards: MR 2.3, MR 3.1
CA Key Concepts Book: p. S77

Extra Example 1

A mining company is starting a land reclamation program. Their mine currently covers an area of 21 acres and its size is increasing by 2 acres every year. If 5 acres of the surface mine is filled in and reclaimed each year, when will the entire surface area of the mine be reclaimed? Use a table or a graph to answer the question. **in 7 years**

Year	Mined Acres	Reclaimed Acres
0	21	0
1	23	5
2	25	10
3	27	15
4	29	20
5	31	25
6	33	30
7	35	35

Extra Example 2

Use an equation to solve the problem in Extra Example 1. You need to find the time in years when the entire surface area will be reclaimed. **$21 + 2n = 5n$; $21 = 3n$; $n = 7$; in 7 years**

Extra Example 3

Use unit analysis to check the answer in Extra Example 2. **Substitute in the original equation to be certain the units make sense and the two sides of the equation are equal.** **21 acres + $\frac{2 \text{ acres}}{\cancel{\text{year}}} \cdot 7 \cancel{\text{years}} = \frac{5 \text{ acres}}{\cancel{\text{year}}} \cdot 7 \cancel{\text{years}}$**

Concept Check

Describe some advantages of the *use a table, use a graph,* and *use an equation* strategies shown in this lesson. ***Sample answer:*** **Tables are easy to make and read. Graphs show a visual representation and are easily interpreted to give an estimate of the answer. Using an equation provides a method that results in an exact answer.**

Goal 2 USING A PROBLEM SOLVING PLAN

Using an equation is often an efficient way to solve a problem.

REFORESTATION
Shelterwood cutting is used to promote growth of trees like the Ponderosa pine. As one group of trees is being harvested, another one is being planted.

EXAMPLE 2 *Using an Equation*

Use an equation to solve the problem in Example 1.

Solution

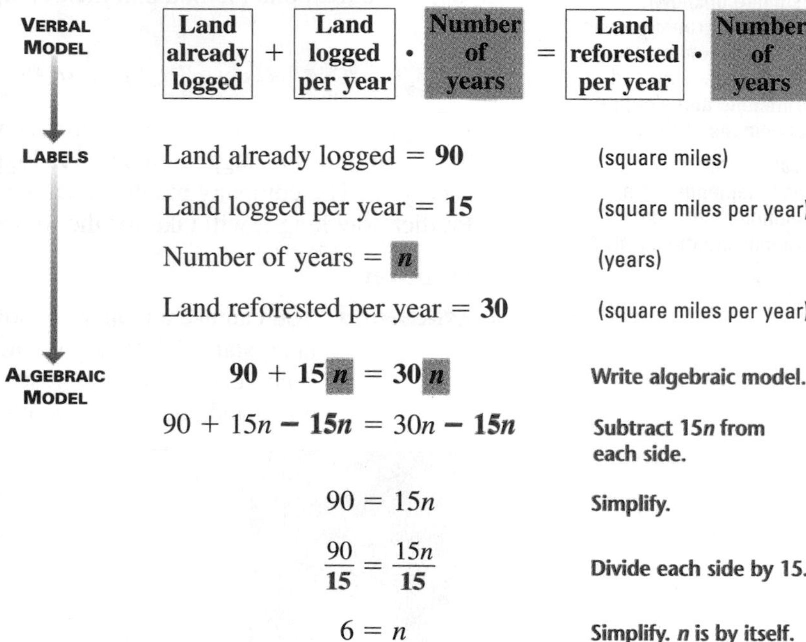

VERBAL MODEL

Land already logged	+	Land logged per year	•	Number of years	=	Land reforested per year	•	Number of years

LABELS

Land already logged = **90** (square miles)

Land logged per year = **15** (square miles per year)

Number of years = ***n*** (years)

Land reforested per year = **30** (square miles per year)

ALGEBRAIC MODEL

$$90 + 15n = 30n \quad \text{Write algebraic model.}$$

$$90 + 15n - 15n = 30n - 15n \quad \text{Subtract } 15n \text{ from each side.}$$

$$90 = 15n \quad \text{Simplify.}$$

$$\frac{90}{15} = \frac{15n}{15} \quad \text{Divide each side by 15.}$$

$$6 = n \quad \text{Simplify. } n \text{ is by itself.}$$

ANSWER ▶ It will take 6 years to reforest all of the logged land. Notice that this agrees with the solution from Example 1.

EXAMPLE 3 *Checking Reasonableness of a Solution*

Use unit analysis to check the solution from Example 2.

Solution

Land already logged	+	Land logged per year	•	Number of years	=	Land reforested per year	•	Number of years

$$90 \text{ mi}^2 + \frac{15 \text{ mi}^2}{\cancel{\text{yr}}} \cdot 6 \cancel{\text{yr}} \stackrel{?}{=} \frac{30 \text{ mi}^2}{\cancel{\text{yr}}} \cdot 6 \cancel{\text{yr}}$$

$$90 \text{ mi}^2 + 90 \text{ mi}^2 \stackrel{?}{=} 180 \text{ mi}^2$$

$$180 \text{ mi}^2 = 180 \text{ mi}^2 \checkmark$$

4.6 Exercises

Guided Practice

PLANT GROWTH In Exercises 1–4, use the illustration and the following information. A cornstalk is 5 inches tall and a weed is 11 inches tall. The cornstalk is growing at a rate of 2 inches per week, and the weed is growing at a rate of 1 inch per week. To determine when the cornstalk and the weed will be the same height, use the verbal model below.

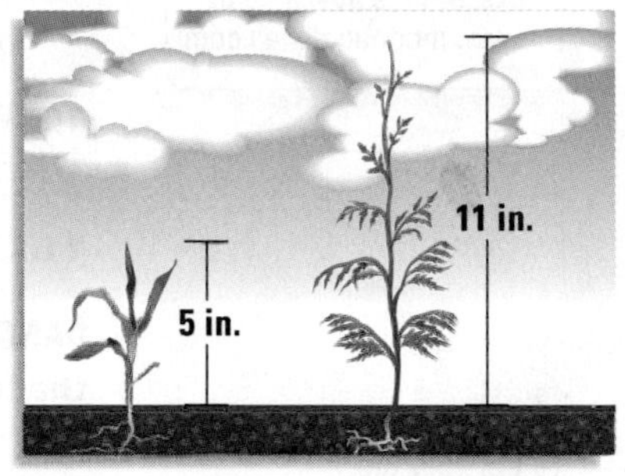

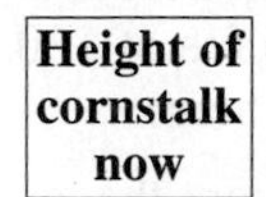
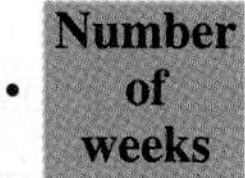
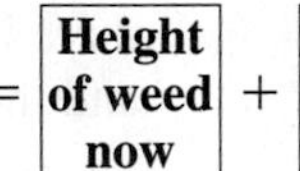

Height of cornstalk now	+	Stalk's rate of growth	•	Number of weeks	=	Height of weed now	+	Weed's rate of growth	•	Number of weeks

1. Height of cornstalk now = 5 in.
   Stalk's rate of growth = 2 in. per wk
   Number of weeks = x
   Height of weed now = 11 in.
   Weed's rate of growth = 1 in. per wk
2. $5 + 2x = 11 + x$
   $x = 6$ weeks
3. 6 weeks from now
4. *Sample answer:* a table of values

1. Assign labels (with units of measure) to each part of the verbal model. **1–4. See margin.**

2. Write and solve an algebraic model.

3. Determine when the cornstalk and the weed will be the same height. Check your solution using unit analysis.

4. What other way can you solve the problem? Use your method to check your solution.

Practice and Problem Solving

Student Help

▶ **MORE PRACTICE**
Extra practice to help you master skills is on page 697.

CDs In Exercises 5–8, use the following information. You want to join a CD club. You decide to compare the cost of buying CDs from the club with the cost of buying CDs from a music store. The CD club has a one-time membership fee of \$50 and then each CD costs \$10. The music store charges \$15 for each CD.

5. Write variable expressions to find the cost of buying CDs from the club (including the membership fee) and from the music store. **club: $50 + 10c$, store: $15c$**

6. Copy and complete the table. **See margin.**

Number of CDs	1	2	3	4	5	6	7	8	9	10
Music store cost (\$)	?	?	?	?	?	?	?	?	?	?
CD club cost (\$)	?	?	?	?	?	?	?	?	?	?

7. Find the number of CDs you must buy for the costs to be the same. **10 CDs**

8. Graph the data from your table in a coordinate plane. Explain how the graph represents your result from Exercise 7. **See margin.**

3 Apply

Assignment Guide

TRANSITIONAL
Day 1: SRH p. 668 Exs. 3–6, p. 670 Exs. 2–3; pp.195–197 Exs. 5–10, 20–25, 29–36

AVERAGE
Day 1: pp. 195–197 Exs. 9–15, 20–25, 29–36, 44

ADVANCED
Day 1: pp. 195–197 Exs. 9–11, 16–18, 19*, 20–25, 29–31, 41–44

BLOCK SCHEDULE
pp. 195–197 Exs. 9–15, 20–25, 29–36, 44 (with 4.5)

Extra Practice

- Student Edition, pp. 696–697
- Chapter 4 Resource Book, p. 51

Homework Check

To quickly check student understanding of key concepts, go over the following exercises:

Transitional: 5, 6, 7, 8, 10
Average: 9, 10, 11, 12, 14
Advanced: 9, 10, 11, 16, 18

6.

Number of CDs	Music Store Cost (\$)	CD Club Cost (\$)
1	15	60
2	30	70
3	45	80
4	60	90
5	75	100
6	90	110
7	105	120
8	120	130
9	135	140
10	150	150

8. See next page for graph.

The graph shows that the costs will be the same if you buy 10 CDs.

8.

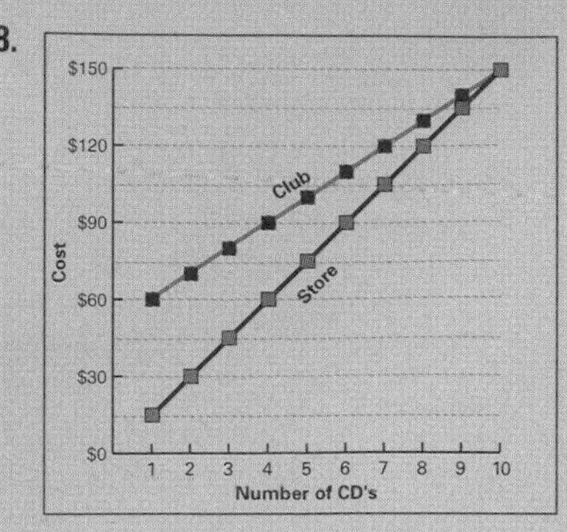

9.

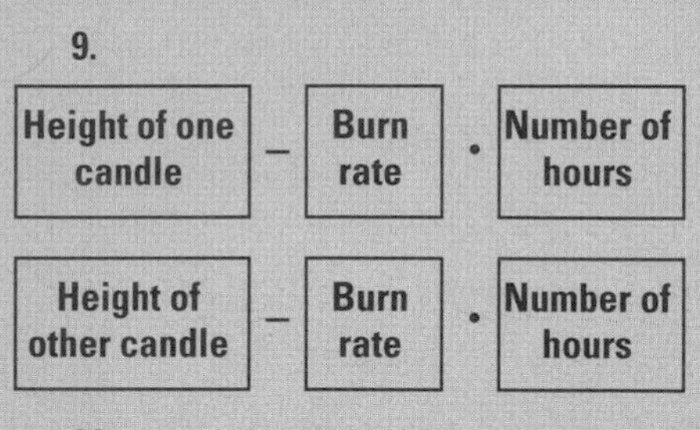

Height of one candle
−
Burn rate
·
Number of hours
=
Height of other candle
−
Burn rate
·
Number of hours

14.

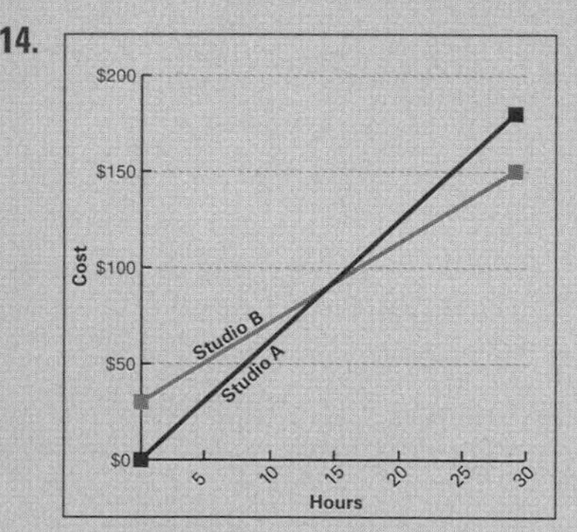

17.

Number of shirts	Revenue	Costs	Profit (loss)
25	850	1950	(1100)
50	1700	2400	(700)
75	2550	2850	(300)
94	3196	3192	4
100	3400	3300	100
200	6800	5100	1700

18.

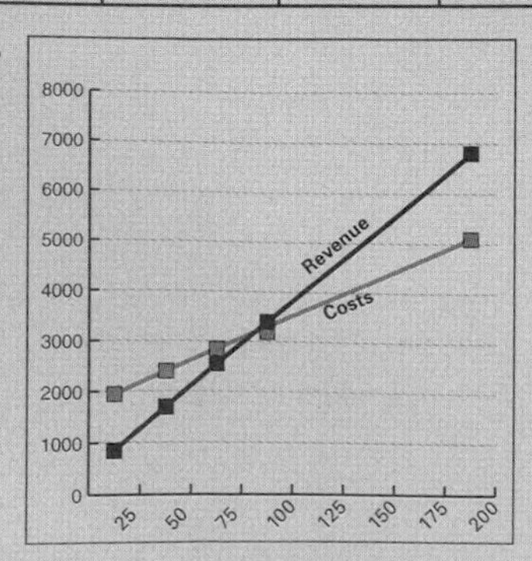

Student Help

▶HOMEWORK HELP

Extra help with problem solving in Exs. 9–11 is available at www.mcdougallittell.com

10. $12 - 3h = 10 - 2h$
$2 = h$

11. $12 \text{ cm} - 3\frac{\text{cm}}{\text{h}} \cdot 2 \text{ h} \stackrel{?}{=}$
$10 \text{ cm} - 2\frac{\text{cm}}{\text{h}} \cdot 2 \text{ h};$
$12 \text{ cm} - 6 \text{ cm} =$
$10 \text{ cm} - 4 \text{ cm}$

12. Studio A: $C = 6h$, Studio B: $C = 30 + 4h$

13. $6h = 30 + 4h$
$h = 15$; 15 h of lessons

16. $34s = 1500 + 18s$
$16s = 1500$
$s = 93.75$; not the answer since you cannot sell part of a shirt; you must sell 94 shirts

BURNING CANDLES **In Exercises 9–11, use the following information.** Suppose you light one candle that is 12 centimeters tall and burns at a rate of 3 centimeters per hour. At the same time, a friend lights a candle that is 10 centimeters tall and burns at a rate of 2 centimeters per hour. **9–11. See margin.**

9. Write a verbal model to find when the heights of the two candles will be the same. Then assign labels to each part of the verbal model.

10. Write and solve an algebraic model to find when the heights of the candles will be the same.

11. Check your answer using unit analysis.

DANCE LESSONS **In Exercises 12–15, use the following information.** You plan to take jazz dance lessons. The poster shows the costs for lessons at Studio A. At Studio B, there is an annual membership fee of $30, and the lessons cost $4.00 per hour. **12–14. See margin.**

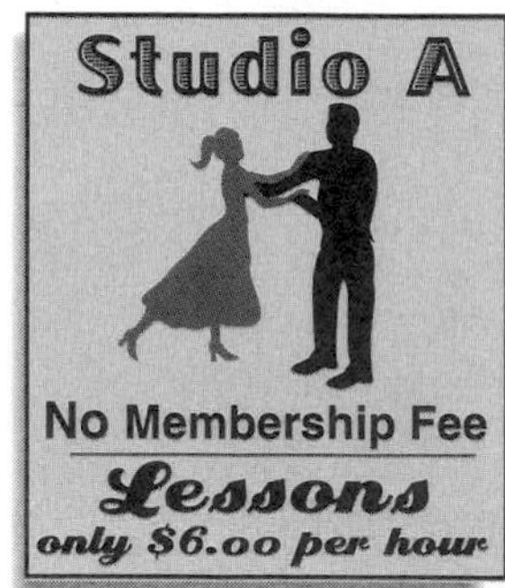

12. Write expressions to represent the cost of each studio. Let x be the number of hours of lessons.

13. Write and solve an algebraic model to decide when the costs of the studios are the same.

14. In the same coordinate plane, graph the costs of lessons at Studio A and lessons at Studio B when x is 5, 10, 15, 20, 25, and 30 hours.

15. MATHEMATICAL REASONING Use your graph to explain the conditions under which you would choose Studio B. **If I plan to take more than 15 hours of lessons in a year.**

Student Help

▶VOCABULARY TIP
Recall that to *break even*, your total income must be equal to your total expenses, so your profit is zero. See page 141.

BUSINESS **In Exercises 16–18, use the following information.** You own a business that sells silk-screened shirts. You want to know how many shirts you must sell to *break even*. Your costs are $1500 for the silk-screen equipment, plus $18 in materials for each shirt. You sell each shirt for $34. **16–18. See margin.**

16. Write and solve an algebraic model to find the number of shirts you must sell to break even. Is the solution of your equation the actual answer to the problem? Explain. How many shirts must you sell?

17. Make a table of data for your costs and income for selling different numbers of shirts. Explain how you can use the table to check your solution from Exercise 16.

18. Graph the data from your table in a coordinate plane. Explain how the graph shows that your solution from Exercise 16 is correct.

19. CHALLENGE You can join the Bestseller Book Club for a membership fee of $100 and then pay $18 for each book you buy. If you buy books from a local bookstore, you pay $26 for each book. Explain how you will decide whether to join the book club. What problem solving method helped you make this decision?

17. The table shows that to break even you must sell about 94 shirts.

18. The graph shows that to break even you must sell just under 100 shirts.

19. Find the breakeven number of books and then decide whether you would be ordering more or fewer than this number.
$100 + 18b = 26b$
If I plan to buy 13 or more books, the club is a better deal.

Multiple-Choice Practice

In Exercises 20 and 21, the table shows the weight of a dozen eggs of different sizes. The egg sizes are listed from largest to smallest. The weights of a dozen eggs from one egg size to the next egg size differ by 3 ounces.

Size	Weight (oz/dozen)
Jumbo	30
Extra Large	27
Large	?
Medium	?
Small	?
Peewee	?

20. Which equation can you solve to find the egg size when the weight of a dozen eggs is 18 ounces? Let s represent the number of size steps smaller than jumbo eggs. **B**

Ⓐ $30 - s = 18$ Ⓑ $30 - 3s = 18$

Ⓒ $30 = 3(s - 18)$ Ⓓ $18s + 30s = 30$

21. What is the weight of a dozen medium eggs? **H**

Ⓕ 15 ounces Ⓖ 18 ounces

Ⓗ 21 ounces Ⓙ 24 ounces

Mixed Review

Translate the verbal phrase into a variable expression. *(2.1)*

22. Seven minus the product of 12 and a number **$7 - 12x$**

23. Four divided by the sum of a number and 9 **$\frac{4}{x+9}$**

Solve the inequality. *(2.8)*

24. $2x \geq 1$ **$x \geq \frac{1}{2}$** **25.** $7y < 28$ **$y < 4$** **26.** $48 < 16z$ **$3 < z$**

27. $3c < 21$ **$c < 7$** **28.** $r + 3 \geq 6$ **$r \geq 3$** **29.** $p - 2 \leq 12$ **$p \leq 14$**

Find the average of the numbers. *(3.6)*

30. 14, 24, 20, 12, 17, 22, 7, 20 **17** **31.** −5, −8, 5, 10, −3, −2, 0, 3 **0**

In Exercises 32–43, solve the equation. *(4.1–4.5)*

32. $4a + 8 = 28$ **5** **33.** $6 - 9x = 42$ **−4** **34.** $4r - 2 = 14$ **4**

35. $12x + 3x = 30$ **2** **36.** $4x - 8x + 3 = 7$ **−1** **37.** $9m + 12 - m = 4$ **−1**

38. $3a = 2 + 2a$ **2** **39.** $14s - 6 = 12s$ **3** **40.** $2p = 12 + 3p$ **−12**

41. $11(x + 5) = 33$ **−2** **42.** $z + 2(4 - z) = 4$ **4** **43.** $4(z - 5) = 3(z - 8)$ **−4**

44. A bicycle repair shop charges $15 per hour for labor plus the cost of parts. A bicycle needs $18.50 worth of new parts, and the final repair bill is $63.50. Write and solve an equation to find how long it took to repair the bicycle. Check that your answer is reasonable. *(4.1)*
$63.50 = 18.50 + 15h$, 3 h

4 Assess

Assessment Resources

- Assessment Book (Formal Assessment and Alternative Assessment)
- Test and Practice Generator

Mini-Quiz

You are given a choice of two salaries at a new job. In option A, you are paid $30,000 per year the first year with an annual raise of $1000. In option B, you are paid $26,000 per year with an annual raise of $1500. After how many years will the two options pay the same salary? Which option should you take if you plan on staying at this job for 7 years?

1. Make a table to model this problem. Use the table to answer the questions.

Year	Option A	Option B
0	$30,000	$26,000
1	$31,000	$27,500
2	$32,000	$29,000
3	$33,000	$30,500
4	$34,000	$32,000
5	$35,000	$33,500
6	$36,000	$35,000
7	$37,000	$36,500
8	$38,000	$38,000

after 8 years; option A

2. Using the problem solving plan, write an equation to model this situation. Solve your equation and answer the questions.
$30,000 + 1000x = 26,000 + 1500x$; $x = 8$; after 8 years; option A

1 Plan

Pacing

Suggested Number of Days

Transitional: 1 day
Average: 1 day
Advanced: 1 day
Block Schedule: 0.5 block with 4.8

Teaching Resources

Blacklines
(See page 166B.)

- Warm-Up Exercises
- Teacher Time-Savers
- English/Spanish Problem Solving
- Answers

Technology

- Electronic Teacher Tools
- Test and Practice Generator

2 Teach

Math Reasoning

For Mathematical Background Notes on mathematical reasoning related to this lesson, please refer to pages 166E and 166F in this Teacher's Edition.

California Standards and Assessment

CA Standards: NS 1.0, AF 4.1
CA Key Concepts Book: pp. S16–S18

4.7 Solving Equations Involving Decimals

In this lesson you'll:

- Compute with rational numbers expressed in a variety of forms. (NS 1.0)
- Solve two-step linear equations and interpret the solutions. (AF 4.1)

Goal 1 Rounding Decimals

When you solve an equation that has decimal coefficients, your results will be different if you round numbers at different steps in the solution.

Student Help

READING TIP The symbol ≈ means "is approximately equal to."

EXAMPLE 1 Rounding Coefficients

In the following solutions, the red numbers are rounded to the nearest hundredth. You may use a calculator to follow the steps and the checks.

Rounding early

$$0.414x - 0.336 = 9.45$$
$$0.41x - 0.34 \approx 9.45$$
$$0.41x \approx 9.79$$
$$x \approx \frac{9.79}{0.41}$$
$$x \approx 23.88$$

Check ✓

$$0.414(23.88) - 0.336 \stackrel{?}{=} 9.45$$
$$9.88632 - 0.336 \stackrel{?}{=} 9.45$$
$$9.55032 \approx 9.45$$

Rounding at final step only

$$0.414x - 0.336 = 9.45$$
$$0.414x = 9.786$$
$$x = \frac{9.786}{0.414}$$
$$x \approx 23.64$$

Check ✓

$$0.414(23.64) - 0.336 \stackrel{?}{=} 9.45$$
$$9.78696 - 0.336 \stackrel{?}{=} 9.45$$
$$9.45096 \approx 9.45$$

Notice that rounding at the final step only gives a better answer.

EXAMPLE 2 Solving an Equation Involving Decimals

Solve $3.6x = 2.8x - 8.6$. Round the solution to the nearest tenth.

Solution

$3.6x = 2.8x - 8.6$	Write original equation.
$3.6x - \mathbf{2.8x} = 2.8x - 8.6 - \mathbf{2.8x}$	Subtract 2.8x from each side.
$0.8x = -8.6$	Simplify.
$\frac{0.8x}{\mathbf{0.8}} = \frac{-8.6}{\mathbf{0.8}}$	Divide each side by 0.8.
$x = -10.75$	Simplify. *x* is by itself.

ANSWER ▶ To the nearest tenth, the solution is about −10.8.

Student Help

STUDY TIP A check of Example 2 using the value −10.8 will show that the answer is not exact. The inaccuracy is called a *round-off error.*

Goal 2 ROUNDING SOLUTIONS TO PROBLEMS

You may need to round a solution due to the circumstances of a problem.

EXAMPLE 3 Finding a Reasonable Solution

PHONE CALLS Suppose you use a local phone service that charges a fee per call plus a cost per minute. A call will cost you \$.01 for the fee and \$.035 per minute. How long can you talk without spending more than \$.75 on the call?

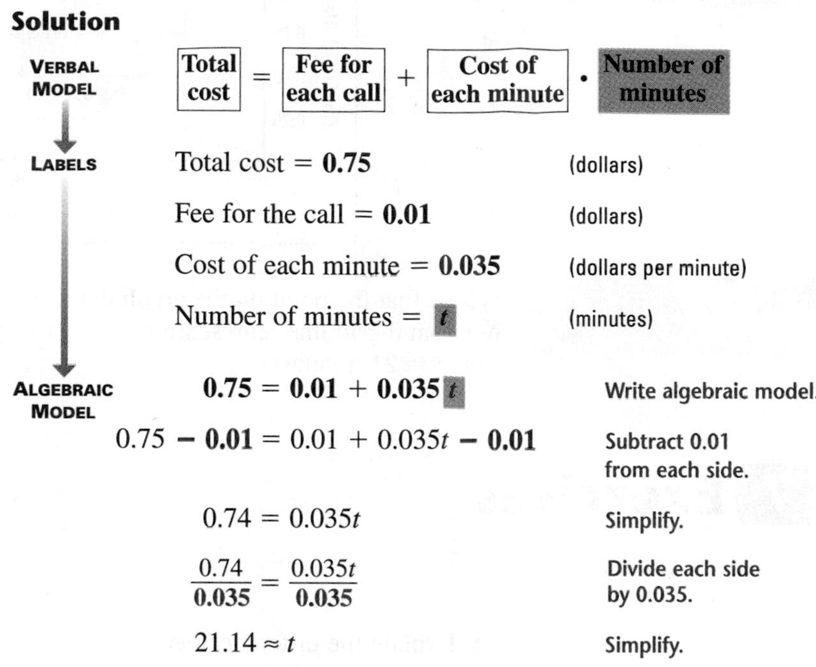

Solution

VERBAL MODEL Total cost = Fee for each call + Cost of each minute • Number of minutes

LABELS

Total cost = **0.75** (dollars)

Fee for the call = **0.01** (dollars)

Cost of each minute = **0.035** (dollars per minute)

Number of minutes = t (minutes)

ALGEBRAIC MODEL

$0.75 = 0.01 + 0.035t$ Write algebraic model.

$0.75 - 0.01 = 0.01 + 0.035t - 0.01$ Subtract 0.01 from each side.

$0.74 = 0.035t$ Simplify.

$\frac{0.74}{0.035} = \frac{0.035t}{0.035}$ Divide each side by 0.035.

$21.14 \approx t$ Simplify.

ANSWER ▶ The solution is about 21.14 minutes. If the charges are based on rounding up to the nearest whole number of minutes, however, you should round down and talk for only 21 minutes.

The following table can help you check the solution from Example 3.

Number of minutes	Calculations	Cost in dollars	
1	0.01 + 0.035 • (1)	\$.045	
2	0.01 + 0.035 • (2)	\$.080	
21	0.01 + 0.035 • (21)	\$.745	← Within your budget
22	0.01 + 0.035 • (22)	\$.780	← Over your budget

Student Help

▶ **SKILLS REVIEW**
For help with place value and rounding and operations with decimals, see pages 672 and 675–676.

Math Reasoning

An equation whose coefficients are given in decimal form is always reducible to an equivalent equation with integer coefficients by multiplying both sides by an appropriate power of 10. For instance, the equation $3.6x = 2.8x - 8.6$ in Example 2 is equivalent to $36x = 28x - 86$, obtained by multiplying both sides by 10. However, the purpose of this lesson is to give students practice with arithmetic operations using decimals and in finding approximate solutions by rounding.

Extra Example 1

Solve $8.217x + 3.946 = 24.12$ by first rounding the decimals to the nearest hundredth and then by rounding only at the final step. **2.45; 2.46**

Extra Example 2

Solve $9.4x + 6.1 = 5.3x$. Round the solution to one decimal place. **−1.5**

Extra Example 3

You have decided to change your long-distance phone company. To call your pen pal, the new company's rates are \$.30 for each call and \$.10 for each minute. How long can you talk on a single call and spend no more than \$5.00? **47 min**

Concept Check

When solving a real-life problem involving decimals, why should you wait until the final step to do any rounding of your results? **Rounding before the last step can lead to a greater rounding error.**

3 Apply

Assignment Guide

TRANSITIONAL
Day 1: SRH pp. 672–673 Exs. 22–27, p. 675 Exs. 17–23, p. 676 Exs. 5–8, 13–17; pp. 201–202 Exs. 8, 10–13, 18–19, 22–24, 34–35
AVERAGE
Day 1: pp. 201–202 Exs. 8–13, 16–19, 26–28, 34–35
ADVANCED
Day 1: pp. 201–202 Exs. 12–21, 29–32, 33*, 34–35
BLOCK SCHEDULE
pp. 201–202 Exs. 8–13, 16–19, 26–28, 34–35 (with 4.8)

Extra Practice

- Student Edition, pp. 696–697
- Chapter 4 Resource Book, p. 60

Homework Check

To quickly check student understanding of key concepts, go over the following exercises:

Transitional: 10, 12, 18, 22, 24
Average: 12, 16, 18, 26, 28
Advanced: 14, 16, 20, 30, 32

Student Help

▶STUDY TIP
To make a graph from the numbers in the table, you will need to round the cost and approximate the point on the graph.

You can also check the solution from Example 3 by graphing $C = 0.01 + 0.035t$ for $t = 1, 2, 3, \ldots$, where C is the cost of the call and t is the number of minutes of the call. The graph shows the cost of local calling with the service described in Example 3.

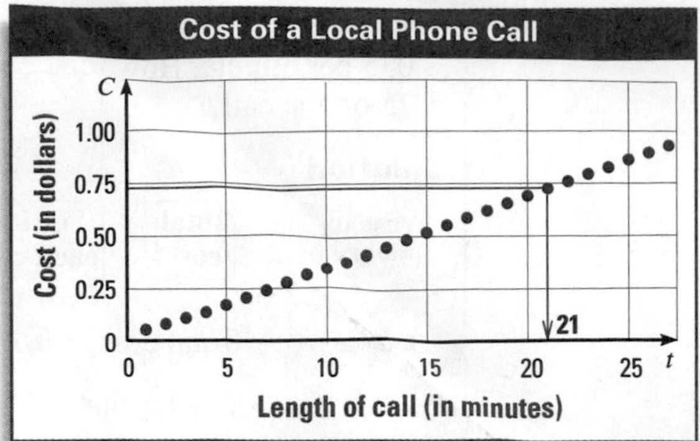

Notice that the point on the graph that is closest to, but still below, the horizontal grid line representing the cost $C = \$.75$ is the point where time $t = 21$ minutes.

4.7 Exercises

Guided Practice

1. Explain the difference between $x = 2.5$ and $x \approx 2.5$.
$x = 2.5$ means "x is exactly 2.5"; $x \approx 2.5$ means "x is approximately 2.5".

Solve the equation. Round your answer to the nearest tenth.

2. $3x + 4.1 = 7.5$ **1.1**

3. $0.3(1.2x + 3.7) = 9.3$ **22.8**

ERROR ANALYSIS **In Exercises 4 and 5, describe and correct the error.**

4. $x \approx 3.7$, rounding error

5. $-15.63 = -2.9x$; $x \approx 5.4$

4.

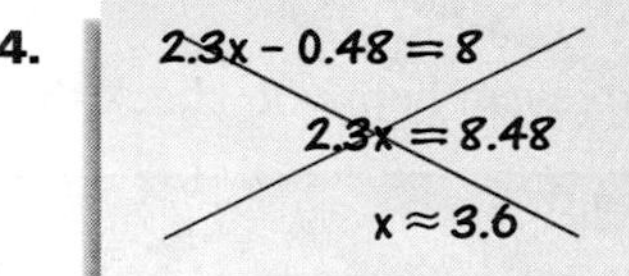

5.

$-14 = 1.63 - 2.9x$
$-15.63 = 2.9x$
$-5.4 \approx x$

6. SALES TAX You purchase an item. The sales tax rate is \$.06 per dollar, and the cost of the item including sales tax is \$6.35. Let p represent the price of the item not including sales tax. Solve the following equation to find the price of the item.

$$p + 0.06p = 6.35$$ **\$5.99**

7. AUTOMOBILE MAINTENANCE You stop at a gas station with \$15 in your pocket. You need to buy a quart of oil for \$1.05, and you want to buy as much gas as you can. The gas you use costs \$1.25 per gallon. How many gallons can you buy? **11.16 gal**

Practice and Problem Solving

Student Help

▶ **More Practice**
Extra practice to help you master skills is on page 697.

CALCULATOR **Copy and complete the steps. You may use a calculator if you wish. Round your answer to the nearest tenth.** 8, 9. See margin.

8. $1.1(2.5x - 3.5) = 11.2$

$\underline{\ ?\ }x - 3.85 = 11.2$

$\underline{\ ?\ }x = \underline{\ ?\ }$

$x \approx \underline{\ ?\ }$

9. $0.2(2.9x - 4.1) = 10.6$

$0.58x - \underline{\ ?\ } = 10.6$

$0.58x = \underline{\ ?\ }$

$x \approx \underline{\ ?\ }$

8. $2.75x - 3.85 = 11.2$
$2.75x = 15.05$
$x \approx 5.5$

9. $0.58x - 0.82 = 10.6$
$0.58x = 11.42$
$x \approx 19.7$

Solve the equation. Round your answer to the nearest tenth.

10. $3x + 12 = 17.2$ **1.7**

11. $13y + 22 = 16.6$ **−0.4**

12. $29t - 17.5 = 86.5$ **3.6**

13. $15.2 - 11x = 108$ **−8.4**

14. $1.3y + 22.1 = 12.9$ **−7.1**

15. $7.4m + 36.4 = 9.5$ **−3.6**

16. $6(4x - 1.2) = 8x + 9.3$ **1.0**

17. $13x - 2.2 = 2(9x + 10)$ **−4.4**

CALCULATOR **In Exercises 18–21, solve the equation. You may use a calculator if you wish. Round your answer to the nearest hundredth.**

18. $0.19t - 1.57 = 0.46t$ **−5.81**

19. $2.43x + 13.71 = 8.12x - 22.54$ **6.37**

20. $0.15(9.85x + 3.70) = 4.65$ **2.77**

21. $-20.23 = 5(2.87 - 1.45x)$ **4.77**

22. SALES TAX You purchase an item. The price of the item (not including sales tax) is \$2.60, and the cost of the item (including sales tax) is \$2.73. Let t represent the sales tax rate per dollar. Solve the following equation to find the sales tax rate. **5%**

$$2.60 + t(2.60) = 2.73$$

Science Link **In Exercises 23–25, use the following information.** Crickets make a chirping sound at night or in deep shade. As the air temperature rises, some crickets chirp faster. You can approximate the air temperature by counting the number of times a particular cricket chirps per minute. Use the equation $T = 0.25n + 39$ where T is the temperature in degrees Fahrenheit (°F) and n is the number of chirps per minute.

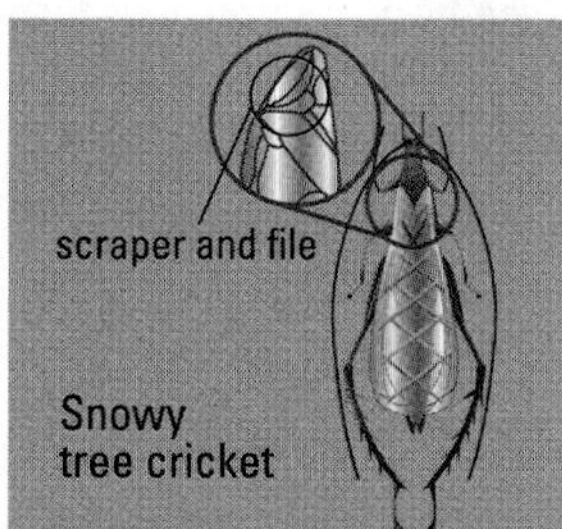

The cricket rubs a vein (file) on one wing against a hard edge (scraper) on the other wing.

Student Help

▶ **Homework Help**
Extra help with problem solving in Exs. 23–25 is available at www.mcdougallittell.com

23. What is the temperature when the cricket chirps 96 times per minute? **63°F**

24. How many times does the cricket chirp per minute at 83°F? **176**

25. If the cricket chirps 24 times in 10 seconds, how many times does it chirp in one minute (60 seconds)? What is the temperature? **144; 75°F**

Problem Solving

Write an Algebraic Model

In Exercises 29–32, students may wish to write an algebraic model. They should be encouraged to think about how the model could be written to represent an additional charge for hours used beyond 5 hours.

4 Assess

Assessment Resources

- Assessment Book (Formal Assessment and Alternative Assessment)
- Test and Practice Generator

Mini-Quiz

1. Solve the equation. Round your answer to two decimal places.
   a. $6.3x - 13.8 = 33.45$ **7.5**
   b. $4(7.7v - 3.1) = 11.8v + 21.5$ **$v \approx 1.78$**
   c. $5.75n + 23.25 = 4.25n + 37.57$ **9.55**
2. An item (including sales tax) costs $13.11. If the tax rate is 0.07, what is the price of the item before the tax? **12.25**

26.

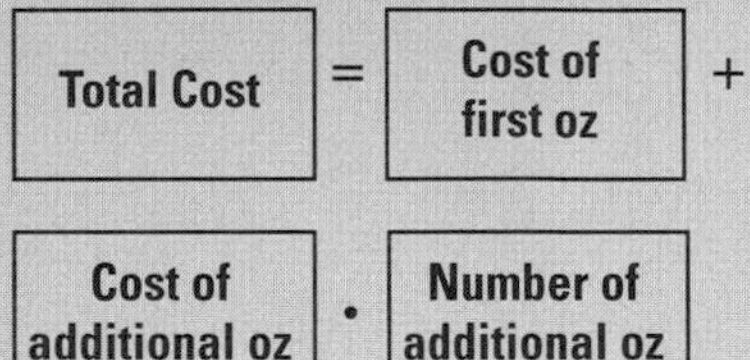

27. $2.00 = 0.33 + 0.22x$
$7.59 \approx x$, **8 oz total**

28.

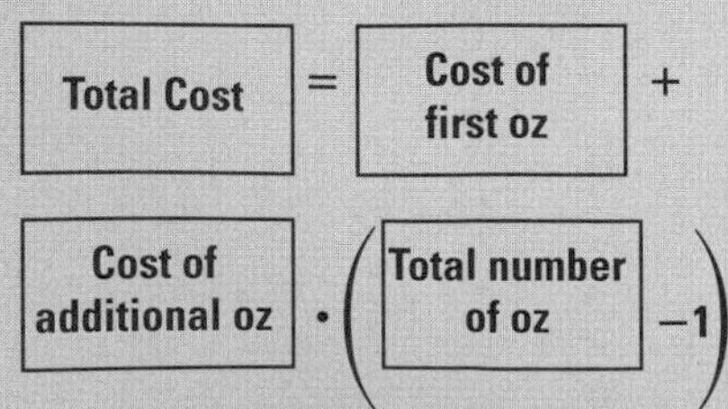

($2.00 = 0.33 + 0.22(x - 1)$)

29, 32. See Additional Answers beginning on page AA1.

Link to History

POSTAGE The stamp shown was first issued at Seneca Falls, New York, on July 19, 1948. The stamp commemorated the first women's rights convention, which was held in Seneca Falls in July, 1848.

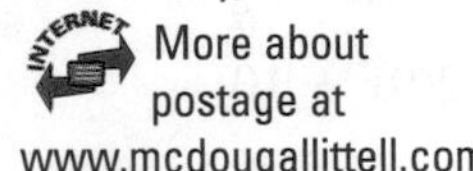

More about postage at www.mcdougallittell.com

POSTAGE In Exercises 26–28, use the following information. You want to mail a package but you have only $2.00 to spend. Postage costs $.33 for the first ounce and $.22 for each additional ounce or part of an ounce. **26–28. See margin.**

26. Write a verbal model to find the maximum your package can weigh. Let x represent the number of additional ounces you can afford.

27. Write and solve an algebraic model.

28. MATHEMATICAL REASONING How would you change the verbal and algebraic models in Exercises 26 and 27 so that x represents the *total* number of ounces you can afford?

INTERNET SERVICE PROVIDERS In Exercises 29–32, use the following information. You are choosing between two Internet service providers that offer an 800 number dial-up service. Provider A charges $24.95 per month for the first five hours of 800 number use and $4.95 for every hour after that. Provider B charges $29.95 per month for the first five hours of 800 number use and $3.95 for every hour after that.

29. Make a table to find how much each company will charge if you are on-line for 1 through 15 hours each month. **See margin.**

30. At what level of use are the companies' charges equal? Which company will charge less if you are on-line for 13 hours each month? **10 h; company B**

31. Under what conditions would you choose Provider B? Explain. **See margin.**

32. Make a graph that shows the charges for both providers. Label the graph and the points on the graph. Label the points that allow you to answer the questions in Exercise 30. **See margin.**

33. CHALLENGE A small business is choosing between two Internet service providers for the office computer system.

Company A: a one-time setup fee of $195, a monthly charge of $99 for 80 hours of use, and $1.50 for every hour after that

Company B: a one-time setup fee of $245, a monthly charge of $159 for 200 hours of use, and $2.50 for every hour after that

Describe a situation in which Company A is preferable to Company B during the first month but Company B is preferable to Company A during the second month.

31. ***Sample answer:*** **Choose Provider B if you plan to use the 800 number dial-up service more than 10 hours per month, since Provider B is cheaper for more than 10 hours of use.**

33. ***Sample answer:*** **Company A is cheaper the first month if the business uses more than 270 hours of Internet time. Company B is cheaper the second month if the business uses less than 320 hours of Internet time. (This assumes the setup fee is considered an expense of the first month only.)**

Multiple-Choice Practice

34. What is the solution of the equation $0.75x + 3.22 = 6.97$? **A**

Ⓐ 5 Ⓑ 6.07 Ⓒ 10.94 Ⓓ 13.59

35. What is the best approximation for the solution of the equation $0.12x - 0.65 = 1.28$? **H**

Ⓕ 0.24 Ⓖ 5.25 Ⓗ 16.08 Ⓙ 16.68

4.8 Measures of Central Tendency

California Standards

In this lesson you'll:

- Collect, organize, and represent data sets that have one or more variables. (SDP 1.0)
- Use various forms to display a single set of data or to compare two sets of data. (SDP 1.1)

Goal 1 FINDING MEASURES OF CENTRAL TENDENCY

Given a set of numerical data, you often seek a single number that is "typical" of the numbers in the set. Such a number is called a **measure of central tendency**. There are three common measures.

- Recall from Lesson 3.6 that the average (also called the **mean**) is the sum of the numbers divided by the number of items in the set.
- The **median** is the middle number when you order the numbers in the set from least to greatest. If there is an even number of items, then the median is the *mean* of the two middle numbers.

6, 8, 8, **9**, 10, 12, 13 — **Median** $= 9$

2, 2, 4, **6**, **8**, 8, 9, 10 — **Median** $= \frac{6+8}{2} = 7$

- The **mode** is the number that occurs most often. The set 2, 5, 7, 8, and 9 has no mode. The set 5, 5, 6, 9, and 9 has two modes: 5 and 9.

Student Help

▶ SKILLS REVIEW
A *line plot* is a number line diagram that shows the frequency of data. Each X represents one data item. For more help with line plots, see page 689.

EXAMPLE 1 Finding Measures of Central Tendency

The line plot shows how many haircuts 16 students had during the past year. Find the mean, median, and mode of the data being represented.

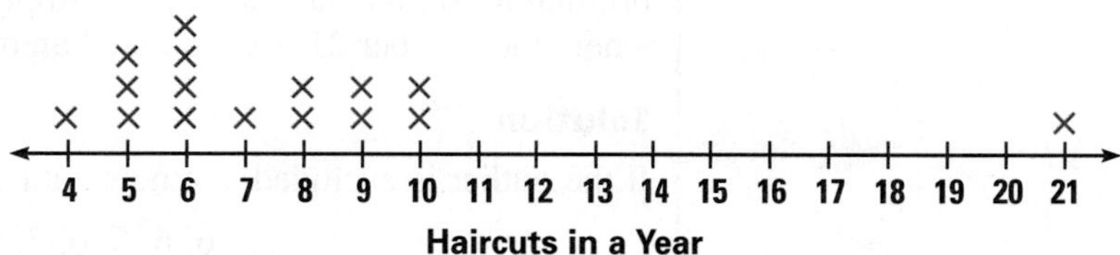

Haircuts in a Year

Solution

The line plot shows that the 16 numbers in the data set are:

4, 5, 5, 5, 6, 6, 6, 6, 7, 8, 8, 9, 9, 10, 10, 21

To find the mean, find the sum of the data and divide by 16.

$$\text{Mean} = \frac{4+5+5+\cdots+10+10+21}{16} = \frac{125}{16} \approx 7.8$$

When you order the data from least to greatest, the middle two numbers are 6 and 7. Find the mean of these numbers to find the median.

$$\text{Median} = \frac{6+7}{2} = 6.5$$

The number occurring most often in the data set is 6. The mode is 6.

1 Plan

Pacing

Suggested Number of Days

Transitional: 1 day
Average: 1 day
Advanced: 1 day
Block Schedule: 0.5 block with 4.7

Teaching Resources

Blacklines
(See page 166B.)

Transparencies
- Warm-Up Exercises
- Teacher Time-Savers
- English/Spanish Problem Solving
- Answers

Technology
- Electronic Teacher Tools
- Test and Practice Generator

2 Teach

Math Reasoning

For Mathematical Background Notes on mathematical reasoning related to this lesson, please refer to pages 166E and 166F in this Teacher's Edition.

Extra Example 1
See next page.

California Standards and Assessment

CA Standards: SDP 1.0, SDP 1.1

Math Reasoning

If all numbers in a given data set are equal to the same number *c*, then the mean, the median, and the mode are also equal to *c*.

Extra Example 1

The line plot shows the number of family members living in 24 students' households. Find the mean, median, and mode of the data. **mean: 5.1; median: 4.5; mode: 4**

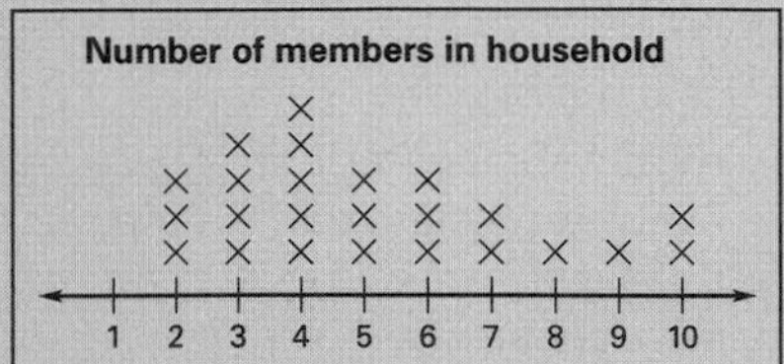

Extra Example 2

What do the measures of central tendency in Extra Example 1 represent? ***Sample answer:*** **The average number of family members is 5.1, the mean. The median is 4.5 and it means that there are the same number of students having less than 4.5 family members as there are students who have more than 4.5 family members. The mode is 4, which means that 4 is the most common number of family members.**

Extra Example 3

The yearly earnings of the employees at a catering business are given below. Which measure of central tendency would you use to describe the typical amount of earnings at the business?

$68,000 $25,000 $12,000
$12,000 $13,000 $25,000

Since no single mode occurs, it would not be a good measure of the earnings. Also, the mean earnings ($25,833) is higher than all but one number. Therefore, the best measure of central tendency would be the median, $19,000.

EXAMPLE 2 Describing the Measures of Central Tendency

What do the measures of central tendency in Example 1 represent?

Solution

The mean of the data is about 7.8, so the average number of haircuts received by the 16 students last year was about 7.8 haircuts.

The median is 6.5, so the number of students who had fewer than 6.5 haircuts equals the number who had more than 6.5 haircuts.

The mode is 6, so more students had 6 haircuts last year than any other number of haircuts.

Goal 2 USING MEASURES OF CENTRAL TENDENCY

The mean, median, and mode of a data set are all numbers that are typical of the data set. Measures of central tendency may be affected by *outliers*, though. An **outlier** is a number in a data set that is much greater or much less than most of the other numbers in the set. You can see by the line plot in Example 1 that the number 21 is an outlier in the set of haircut

EXAMPLE 3 Recalculating Without an Outlier

Because the mean is especially sensitive to outliers, statisticians sometimes recalculate measures of central tendency with an outlier excluded from a data set. They then compare the results with the original mean, median, and mode. Apply this procedure to Example 1, where the number 21 is considered an outlier. What do you notice?

Solution

If the outlier is excluded, the new data set consists of the 15 numbers:

$$4, 5, 5, 5, 6, 6, 6, 6, 7, 8, 8, 9, 9, 10, 10$$

The mean is now $\frac{4 + 5 + \cdots + 10 + 10}{15} = \frac{104}{15} \approx 6.9$.

Because the data set now consists of 15 numbers, there *is* a middle number. The median is now 6.

The mode remains 6.

Excluding the large outlier led to a decrease in two of the three measures of central tendency, with the mean showing the greater decrease (from about 7.8 to about 6.9).

CHECK ✓ If you look at the line plot in Example 1 and ignore the outlier, you would visually estimate the center of data to be between 6 and 7 because the data *cluster* around these numbers. This agrees with the recalculated measures above.

Student Help

▶ MORE EXAMPLES

More examples are available at www.mcdougallittell.com

EXAMPLE 4 Solving a Problem Using Central Tendency

SCIENCE CLASS You need a mean test score of 85.5 points or more on three tests to receive a B for your science grade. So far, you have taken two tests and received an 84 and an 83. What is the minimum score you need on your next test to get a B in science?

Solution

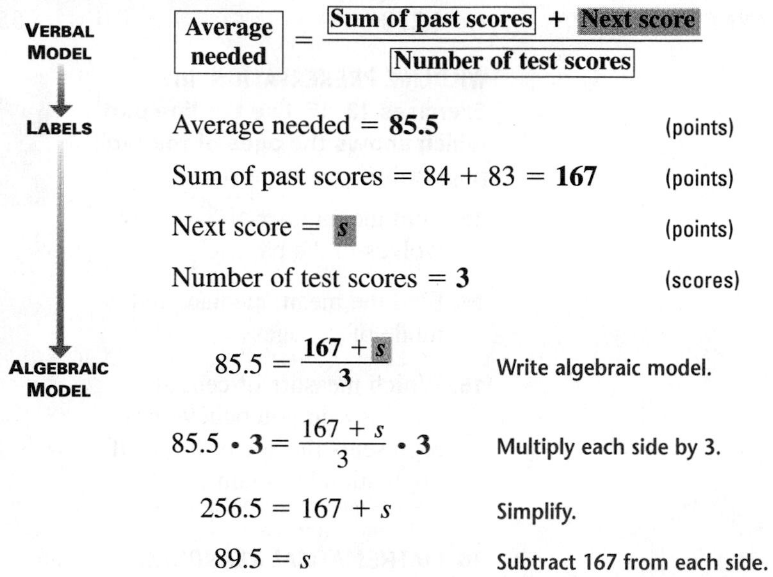

VERBAL MODEL

$$\boxed{\text{Average needed}} = \frac{\boxed{\text{Sum of past scores}} + \boxed{\text{Next score}}}{\boxed{\text{Number of test scores}}}$$

LABELS

Average needed = **85.5** (points)

Sum of past scores = 84 + 83 = **167** (points)

Next score = s (points)

Number of test scores = **3** (scores)

ALGEBRAIC MODEL

$85.5 = \frac{167 + s}{3}$ Write algebraic model.

$85.5 \cdot 3 = \frac{167 + s}{3} \cdot 3$ Multiply each side by 3.

$256.5 = 167 + s$ Simplify.

$89.5 = s$ Subtract 167 from each side.

ANSWER ▶ You need a minimum of 89.5 points to get a grade of B. Scores are usually whole numbers, so you will need to get a 90 or better on the third test to receive a B in science.

Student Help

▶ **STUDY TIP**
Notice that multiplying the mean by the number of data items gives the sum of the data items.

Extra Example 4

You need a mean test score of 90 points or more to receive an A for your math grade. So far, you have taken 5 tests and received these grades: 94, 84, 90, 88, and 91. What is the minimum score you need on your next test to get an A in math? **93 points**

Math Reasoning

The mean, or average, of a set of numbers as used here is the *arithmetic mean.* For two numbers a and b the arithmetic mean is $\frac{a+b}{2}$. Other types of means arise in mathematics. For instance, if a and b are *positive* numbers, their *geometric mean* is defined to be $\sqrt{ab}$. The geometric mean is equal to the arithmetic mean only if $a = b$. Otherwise, if a and b are positive with $a \neq b$, we have $\frac{a+b}{2} > \sqrt{ab}$.

Concept Check

Explain the mean, median, and mode. ***Sample answer:* The mean is the average value. The median is the middle value of the data, and the mode is the data value which occurs most often.**

4.8 Exercises

Guided Practice

Name the measure of central tendency associated with each phrase.

1. Middle **Median** **2.** Most often **Mode** **3.** Average **Mean**

The line plot shows the number of baskets you scored at the last 16 team practices.

4. Order the data from the line plot from least to greatest.
3, 3, 4, 4, 4, 4, 5, 5, 5, 5, 5, 6, 6, 6, 6, 7

5. Find the mean, median, and mode of the data. What does each of these numbers represent?

5. Mean ≈ 4.9; median = 5; mode = 5; mean is the average, median is the middle, mode is the number of baskets scored most often.

6. Are there any outliers? Explain. **No outliers; the data has a narrow range, from 3 to 7.**

2 3 4 5 6 7 8
Baskets Scored

3 Apply

Assignment Guide

TRANSITIONAL
Day 1: SRH p. 689 Exs. 1–6; pp. 206–207 Exs. 7–10, 13–15, 19–21, 30–31

AVERAGE
Day 1: pp. 206–207 Exs. 9–12, 18–21, 24–27, 30–31

ADVANCED
Day 1: pp. 206–207 Exs. 11–12, 18–23, 28, 29*, 30–31; EC: TE p. 166D*

BLOCK SCHEDULE
pp. 206–207 Exs. 9–12, 18–21, 24–27, 30–31 (with 4.7)

Extra Practice

- Student Edition, pp. 696–697
- Chapter 4 Resource Book, p. 69

Homework Check

To quickly check student understanding of key concepts, go over the following exercises:

Transitional: 8, 10, 14, 15, 20, 21
Average: 10, 12, 18, 20, 21, 24
Advanced: 12, 18, 20, 21, 28

Practice and Problem Solving

Student Help

▶**MORE PRACTICE**
Extra practice to help you master skills is on page 697.

Find the mean, median, and mode of the data.

7. 85, 86, 90, 90, 91, 92
mean = 89; median = 90; mode = 90

8. 36, 67, 52, 82, 96, 81
mean = 69; median = 74; no mode

9. 76, 41, 77, 80, 81
mean = 71; median = 77; no mode

10. 105, 109, 100, 99, 156
mean = 113.8; median = 105; no mode

11. 9.5, 10.7, 7.8, 8.5, 10.1, 7.0, 6.2, 8.6 **mean ≈ 8.6; median ≈ 8.6; no mode**

12. 52.8, 53.6, 53.9, 54, 54.8, 55.1, 54.5 **mean = 54.1; median = 54; no mode**

WILDLIFE PRESERVATION In Exercises 13–15, use the line plot, which shows the ages of the wolf population in a state park.

Wolf Ages

Years	1	2	3	4	5	6	7
Number of ×'s	13	8	5	3	3	2	1

13. Find the number of 3-year-old wolves in the park. **5**

14. Find the mean, median, and mode of the ages.
mean ≈ 2.6 yr; median = 2 yr; mode = 1 yr

15. Which measure of central tendency do you believe best represents the age of the wolf population? Explain.
***Sample answer:* Mean, since there are no outliers in this set.**

16. MATHEMATICAL REASONING You have a list of charges of your most recent expenses as follows: \$20, \$22, \$22, \$48, \$56, \$77, \$87. Will adding a \$25 charge to the list change the *median* or the *mean* more? **median**

17. The mean of 5 numbers is 35. Four of the numbers are 6, 6, 7, and 7. Find the fifth number. **149**

18. The data items in a list are 75, 86, 87, 91 and 93. What is the largest integer you can add to the list so that the mean of the six items is less than their median? **101**

In Exercises 19–21, use the spreadsheet. The spreadsheet shows the salaries of all the employees of a small company.

Company Salaries

	A	B	C
1	Position	Number	Annual Salary (\$)
2	President	1	100,000
3	Vice-President	1	60,000
4	Manager	3	40,000
5	Sales Agent	9	30,000

19. Order the 14 salaries from least to greatest.
(thousands) 30, 30, 30, 30, 30, 30, 30, 30, 30, 40, 40, 40, 60, 100

20. Find the mean, median, and mode of the salaries.
Mean = \$39,286; median = \$30,000; mode = \$30,000

21. Which measure of central tendency do you think best represents the salary data? Explain your choice.

21. ***Sample answer:* Mode or median; most employees earn \$30,000.**

Link to Science

pH LEVELS Freshwater fish, such as the angelfish shown, can survive in a wide range of pH levels, from 6.0 to 9.0. Saltwater fish are better in a less acidic environment with a pH level of 8.2.

More about aquariums at www.mcdougallittell.com

pH LEVELS In Exercises 22 and 23, use the following information. The pH level of pure water is 7. Lower levels indicate the water is *acidic*. The table shows the pH levels measured in an aquarium over ten days.

Day number	1	2	3	4	5	6	7	8	9	10
pH level each day	7.1	6.9	6.7	6.5	6.3	6.9	6.8	6.5	6.3	6.1

22. Find the mean pH level over these ten days. **6.61**

23. Given that the water in the aquarium tends to become *more acidic*, on which day do you think a chemical was added to change the pH level? Explain your choice. **Day 6; the pH level jumped to 6.9 from 6.3.**

In Exercises 24–27, use the table below. The table shows the number of minutes three people spent walking dogs on eight different days.

Person	Minutes spent walking the dog	Mean	Median	Mode
A	10, 10, 12, 12, 12, 13, 13, 14	?	?	?
B	10, 11, 12, 12, 12, 13, 13, 15	?	?	?
C	10, 11, 11, 12, 14, 15, 35, 40	?	?	?

24. Find the mean, median, and mode for each person.

25. Compare the mean, median, and mode for Person A. **All three measures are the same.**

26. Compare the mean, median, and mode for Person B. **The mean is slightly higher than the median or the mode.**

27. Compare the mean, median, and mode for Person C. Identify the outlier(s) and explain how the outliers affect the mean.

24.

Person	Mean	Median	Mode
A	12	12	12
B	12.3	12	12
C	18.5	13	11

27. The mean is much higher than the median or the mode. Outliers: 35, 40; since they are high compared to the rest of the data, they raise the mean.

28. RAINFALL A city's annual rainfall over the past four years has been 29.86, 28.32, 25.21, and 27.63 inches. What is the amount of rainfall needed this year so that the average over the five years is 28 inches? **28.98**

29. CHALLENGE Make up two lists of five different numbers that have these measures of central tendency: mean = 20, median = 20, mode = 20. ***Sample answer:* 19, 20, 20, 20, 21; 15, 20, 20, 20, 25**

Multiple-Choice Practice

In Exercises 30 and 31, use the data 14, 10, 16, 11, 20, 19, 18, 16, 10, and 16.

30. What is the mean of the data? **C**

Ⓐ 10 Ⓑ 14 Ⓒ 15 Ⓓ 19.5

31. The median and mode are the same number. What number are they? **G**

Ⓕ 10 Ⓖ 16 Ⓗ 18 Ⓙ 19.5

4 Assess

Assessment Resources

- Assessment Book (Formal Assessment and Alternative Assessment)
- Test and Practice Generator

Mini-Quiz

1. Find the mean, median, and mode of the data.
   a. 34, 29, 31, 56, 20, 19, 20
   mean: about 29.9; median: 29; mode: 20
   b. 5, 19, 31, 20, 47, 89, 6, 101
   mean: 39.75; median: 25.5; mode: none
2. The bar graph below shows the number of times a family ate pizza each month during one year. Find the mean, median, and mode of the data.

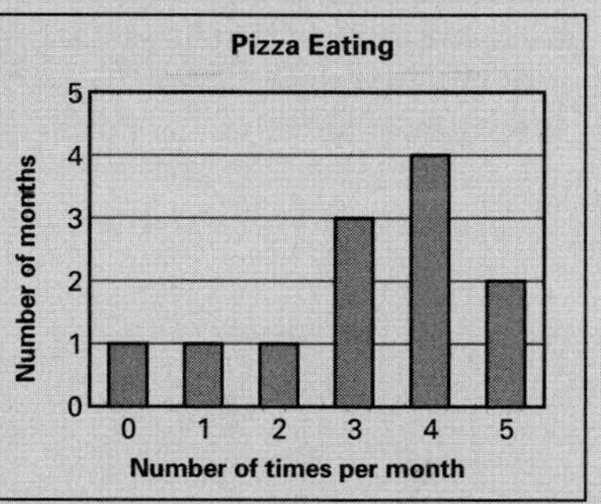

mean: about 3.2; median: 3.5; mode: 4

Additional Resources

The following resources are available to help review the material in this chapter:

Technology
- Personal Student Tutor
- Test and Practice Generator

Chapter 4 Chapter Summary and Review

VOCABULARY

- **measure of central tendency,** *p. 203*
- **mean,** *p. 203*
- **median,** *p. 203*
- **mode,** *p. 203*
- **outlier,** *p. 204*

4.1 SOLVING TWO-STEP EQUATIONS

Examples on pp. 170–171

EXAMPLE **Write this sentence as an equation: *The difference of three times a number and 9 is 0.* Then solve the equation.**

$3x - 9 = 0$ Write translated equation.

$3x = 9$ Add 9 to each side.

$x = 3$ Divide each side by 3.

In Exercises 1–6, solve the equation. Then check your solution.

1. $5x - 4 = 21$ **5**

2. $5x - 8 = -3$ **1**

3. $13 = 3x + 4$ **3**

4. $\frac{x}{3} - 3 = -1$ **6**

5. $\frac{x}{2} + 12 = 20$ **16**

6. $\frac{x}{4} + 5 = 1$ **−16**

7. Write this sentence as an equation: *The difference of a number divided by 4 and −12 is −8.* Then solve the equation and check your solution. $\frac{x}{4} - (-12) = -8, x = -80$

8. You use a \$5 phone card to call a friend. The call is \$.50 for the first minute and \$.15 for each additional minute (or part of a minute). How many minutes can you talk? **31 min**

4.2 SOLVING MULTI-STEP EQUATIONS

Examples on pp. 174–175

EXAMPLE **Solve the equation $5 + 7p - 3p = 29$.**

$5 + 7p - 3p = 29$ Write original equation.

$5 + 4p = 29$ Combine like terms: $7p - 3p = 4p$.

$4p = 24$ Subtract 5 from each side.

$p = 6$ Divide each side by 4.

In Exercises 9–11, solve the equation. Then check your solution.

9. $7x - 4x - 3 = 6$ **3**

10. $8y - 3y - 6 = 19$ **5**

11. $7s - 4s + s - 3 = -7$ **−1**

12. A business owner places a $1400 order for file cabinets. Each cabinet costs $115. There is a $25 shipping fee for the order, plus a special shipping fee of $10 per cabinet. Write and solve an equation to find the number of cabinets ordered. **$1400 = 115x + 25 + 10x$, $x = 11$ cabinets**

4.3 SOLVING EQUATIONS INVOLVING NEGATIVE COEFFICIENTS

Examples on pp. 179–180

EXAMPLE **Solve $-2x + 7 = 5$.**

$-2x + 7 = 5$ Write original equation.

$-2x + 7 - 7 = 5 - 7$ Subtract 7 from each side.

$-2x = -2$ Simplify.

$\frac{-2x}{-2} = \frac{-2}{-2}$ Divide each side by −2.

$x = 1$ Simplify. *x* is by itself.

Or, you can add $2x$ to each side of the original equation to eliminate the term with the negative coefficient and get the equation $7 = 2x + 5$.

Solve the equation. Then check your solution.

13. $10 - x = -5$ **15**

14. $-12 - y = 7$ **−19**

15. $3 = 1 - 2y$ **−1**

16. $2s - 15 - 3s = 1$ **−16**

17. $-a + 5 - 2a = -4$ **3**

18. $2z + 3 - 5z = -9$ **4**

4.4 SOLVING EQUATIONS USING THE DISTRIBUTIVE PROPERTY

Examples on pp. 183–184

EXAMPLE **Solve $3z + 2(z - 10) = 15$.**

$3z + 2(z - 10) = 15$ Write original equation.

$3z + 2z - 20 = 15$ Use distributive property.

$5z - 20 = 15$ Combine like terms.

$5z = 35$ Add 20 to each side.

$z = 7$ Divide each side by 5.

Solve the equation. Then check your solution.

19. $5(t - 9) = 55$ **20**

20. $-2(x + 1) + x = -8$ **6**

21. $11(m - 6) - 17 = 38$ **11**

22. $4(3 - x) + x = 3$ **3**

23. $2x + 2 + 2(x - 1) = 16$ **4**

24. $5(2 - x) + 3x + 3 = 3$ **5**

29.

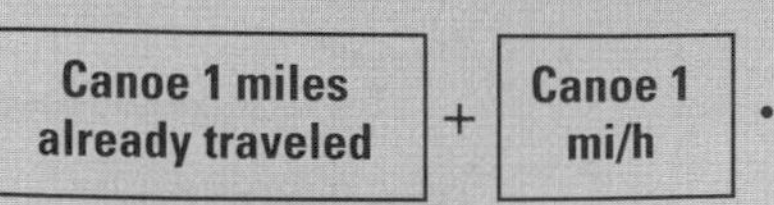

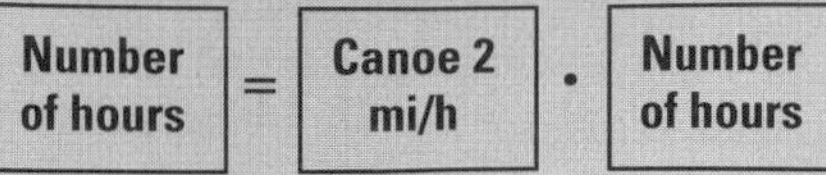

Canoe 1 miles already traveled = 4
Canoe 1 mi/h = 4
Canoe 2 mi/h = 5
Number of hours = n

4.5 SOLVING EQUATIONS WITH VARIABLES ON BOTH SIDES

Examples on pp. 189–190

EXAMPLE **Solve $-18t + 140 = 7(t - 5)$.**

$-18t + 140 = 7(t - 5)$	Write original equation.
$-18t + 140 = 7t - 35$	Use distributive property.
$-18t + 140 + \mathbf{18t} = 7t - 35 + \mathbf{18t}$	Add $18t$ to each side.
$140 = 25t - 35$	Simplify.
$175 = 25t$	Add 35 to each side.
$7 = t$	Divide each side by 25.

In Exercises 25–27, solve the equation. Then check your solution.

25. $2x - 9 = 5x$ **−3** **26.** $-6x - 8 = -7x + 11$ **19** **27.** $6(3 - x) = -2(x + 3)$ **6**

28. GEOMETRY Find the value of x so that the triangle is equilateral (the sides all have the same length). **9**

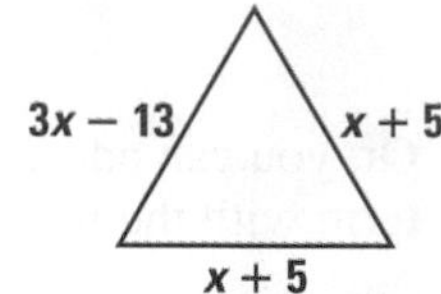

4.6 PROBLEM SOLVING STRATEGIES

Examples on pp. 193–194

EXAMPLE You and your friends go canoeing. One canoe leaves at 11:00 A.M. and goes 4 miles per hour. Your canoe leaves one hour later and goes 5 miles per hour. You can use a table to find when you will catch up to the first canoe.

Time	11:00	12:00	1:00	2:00	3:00	4:00
Canoe 1 distance (in miles)	0	4	8	12	16	20
Canoe 2 distance (in miles)	0	0	5	10	15	20

Your canoe will catch up to the first canoe at 4:00 P.M.

29. Using the formula $d = rt$, write a verbal model to find when the two canoes in the example above will have traveled the same distance. Then assign labels to the verbal model. **See margin.**

30. Write and solve an algebraic model to find when the second canoe will catch up to the first canoe. **$4 + 4n = 5n$; $4 = n$; at 4:00 P.M.**

4.7 SOLVING EQUATIONS INVOLVING DECIMALS

Examples on pp. 198–200

EXAMPLE **Solve $2.51x - 3.06 = 3.54x$. Round your answer to the nearest tenth.**

$$2.51x - 3.06 = 3.54x$$ Write original equation.

$$2.51x - 3.06 - \mathbf{2.51x} = 3.54x - \mathbf{2.51x}$$ Subtract $2.51x$ from each side.

$$-3.06 = 1.03x$$ Simplify.

$$\frac{-3.06}{\mathbf{1.03}} = \frac{1.03x}{\mathbf{1.03}}$$ Divide each side by 1.03.

$$-3.0 \approx x$$ Use a calculator.

If instead you round at the first step, and solve the equation $2.5x - 3.1 = 3.5x$, the solution is about -3.1. This is less accurate than the solution found by rounding at the final step only.

Solve the equation. Round your answer to the nearest hundredth.

31. $4.86y - 3.79 = 19$ **4.69**

32. $0.19 - 1.13x = 12.39$ **−10.80**

33. $1.23x + 14.80 = 8.92x - 4.41$ **2.50**

34. $4(0.28x + 0.56) = 1.61 - 2.37x$ **−0.18**

4.8 MEASURES OF CENTRAL TENDENCY

Examples on pp. 203–205

The three measures of central tendency—the mean, median, and mode—give three different ways to describe a typical number in a set of data.

EXAMPLE **Find the mean, median, and mode of the data 3, 4, 5, 6, 6, and 7.**

Mean $= \frac{3 + 4 + 5 + 6 + 6 + 7}{6} = \frac{31}{6} \approx 5.2$ The sum of the numbers divided by the number of items in the set

Median $= \frac{5 + 6}{2} = \frac{11}{2} = 5.5$ The middle number or the mean of the two middle numbers

Mode $= 6$ The number that occurs most often

In Exercises 35–38, find the mean, median, and mode of the data. Remember to first order the data from least to greatest.

35. 6, 9, 3, 2, 5, 6, 4, 7, 5, 4, 8, 5, 5, 4
mean ≈ 5.21, median = 5, mode = 5

36. 25, 20, 30, 22, 24, 23, 24, 28, 26, 29
mean = 25.1, median = 24.5, mode = 24

37. 41, 44, 47, 40, 48, 49, 41, 45, 46, 42
mean = 44.3, median = 44.5, mode = 41

38. 72, 73, 75, 77, 76, 79, 78, 71, 72, 77
mean = 75, median = 75.5, modes = 72 and 77

39. You have taken five tests in your Spanish class and have received scores of 78, 87, 83, 91, and 85 points. What score do you need to receive on the sixth test so that the average over the six tests is 85 points? **86**

Additional Resources

- **Assessment Book**
  - Formal Assessment, pp. 50–58
  - Alternative Assessment, pp. 193–207
- **Test and Practice Generator**

16.

Minutes	Number of exercises you have solved	Number of exercises your friend has solved
0	0	6
1	2	7
2	4	8
3	6	9
4	8	10
5	10	11
6	12	12
7	14	13
8	16	14

Chapter 4 Chapter Test

Solve the equation. Then check your solution.

1. $4y - 2 = 18$ **5**
2. $3 - 3a = 21$ **−6**
3. $7s - s = 12$ **2**
4. $8x + 4 - 3x = 19$ **3**
5. $12 = 5x + 2 - 7x$ **−5**
6. $12(r - 2) = 36$ **5**
7. $15(2 - t) = 75$ **−3**
8. $-23m - 17 = -15m - 1$ **−2**
9. $p + 2(p - 1) = 2p$ **2**

Solve the equation. Round your answer to the nearest tenth.

10. $5.2x + 10.3 = 3.4x$ **−5.7**
11. $3(3.1 + x) - 2.3x = 17$ **11**
12. $0.1(3.4x - 2.8) = 8.3$ **25.2**

GEOMETRY In Exercises 13 and 14, write an equation for the area of the rectangle. Then solve for *x*.

13. Area is 72 square feet. **12(x − 4) = 72; 10 ft**

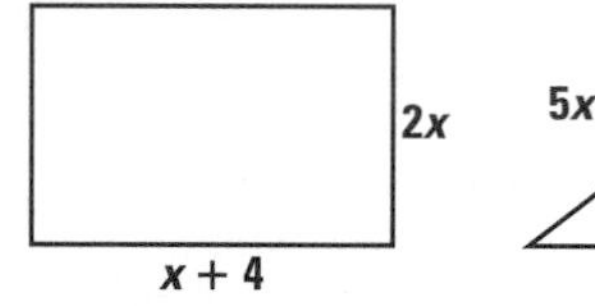

14. Area is 100 square meters. **10(5x − 5) = 100; 3 m**

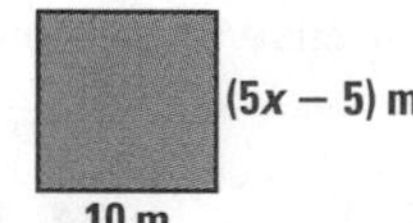

15. GEOMETRY Find the value of x so that the rectangle and the triangle have the same perimeter. What is the perimeter? **x = 2; 20**

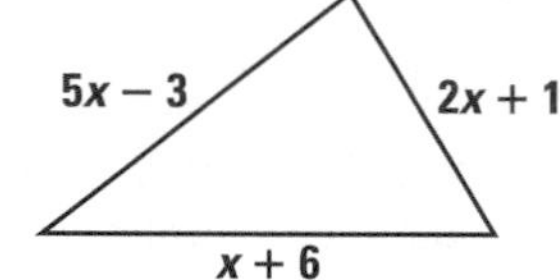

In Exercises 16–18, use the following information. When you started your homework assignment, your friend already had 6 exercises solved. You can solve about 2 exercises per minute. Your friend can solve only 1 exercise per minute.

16. Copy and complete the table. **See margin.**

Minutes	0	1	2	3	4	5	6	7	8
Number of exercises you have solved	0	2	?	?	?	?	?	?	?
Number of exercises your friend has solved	6	7	?	?	?	?	?	?	?

17. Determine how many minutes it will take you to catch up to your friend. **6 min**

18. When you catch up to your friend, how many exercises will you both have solved? **12 exercises**

Find the mean, median, and mode of the data.

19. 77, 84, 93, 93, 99, 99, 99, 102 **mean ≈ 93.3, median = 96, mode = 99**

20. 22, 45, 67, 34, 23, 98, 65, 34, 32, 65, 74 **mean ≈ 50.8, median = 45, modes = 34 and 65**

Multiple-Choice Practice

Test Tip Don't worry about how others are doing; concentrate on your own work.

1. The perimeter of the rectangle is 38 feet. What are its width and length? **C**

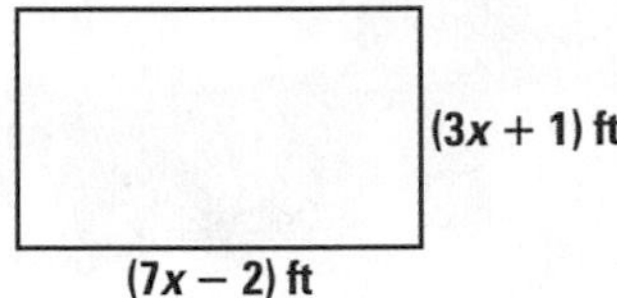

Ⓐ 8 ft by 11 ft Ⓑ 8 ft by 10 ft
Ⓒ 7 ft by 12 ft Ⓓ 6 ft by 13 ft

2. As a food server, you earn $5.50 per hour, plus tips. Last week you earned a total of $288, including $90 in tips. Which equation can be used to find the number of hours you worked? **H**

Ⓕ $5.50p = 288$

Ⓖ $5.50p - 90 = 288$

Ⓗ $5.50p + 90 = 288$

Ⓙ $5.50p - 288 = 90$

3. What is the solution of the equation

$5(1 - x) + 3(1 + x) = 8$? **C**

Ⓐ −8 Ⓑ −3 Ⓒ 0 Ⓓ 8

4. Which is the first incorrect step in this attempt to solve the following equation? **F**

$2y - 4(y - 3) = 10$

Ⓕ **Step 1:** $2y - 4y - 12 = 10$

Ⓖ **Step 2:** $-2y + 12 = 10$

Ⓗ **Step 3:** $-2y = -2$

Ⓙ **Step 4:** $y = 1$

In Exercises 5 and 6, use the following information. You want to join a health club for one year. Club A charges $55 per month and has no initiation fee. Club B costs $45 a month and has an initiation fee of $100.

5. After how many months will the two health clubs cost you the same amount? **C**

Ⓐ 8 months Ⓑ 9 months
Ⓒ 10 months Ⓓ 11 months

6. Which statement is *false*? **H**

Ⓕ Club B is more expensive than Club A for the first 9 months of membership.

Ⓖ Club A costs a total of $330 for one half of a year.

Ⓗ Club A is less expensive for you to join for the year.

Ⓙ Club B costs $145 for 1 month.

7. Which is the best approximation of the solution of the equation

$-2.9n - 4.89 = 1.75(n + 14.5)$? **B**

Ⓐ −17.81 Ⓑ −6.51
Ⓒ −4.55 Ⓓ −4.41

8. The data give ticket prices for several theaters. Which statement is *false*? **H**

$6.00, $6.00, $6.50, $6.25, $2.50, $6.75, $6.50, $3.75, $7.00, $6.25, $6.50, $1.50

Ⓕ Mean ≈ $5.46 Ⓖ Median = $6.25
Ⓗ Mode = $6.00 Ⓙ Mode = $6.50

Teaching Tip

The Brain Games activity provides a motivating way to review selected content in the chapter. For a more comprehensive review, see the Chapter Summary and Review on pp. 208–211.

Brain games

California Standards

- ▶ Solve two-step linear equations. (AF 4.1)
- ▶ Make precise calculations. (MR 2.8)

Equation Tic-Tac-Toe

$5-2x=1.8$	$4(x-3)=4$	$\frac{x}{4}-6=2$
$2x+2(x+1)=-10$	$10-5x=1-2x$	$10+4x+x=$
$\frac{x}{5}+3=7$	$6(x-2)=8(2-x)$	$3x+4(x+3)=-2$

Materials

- Game board
- Markers

Directions

Object of the Game

Play in pairs. The winner is the player who, as a result of solving equations correctly, is the first to complete a row, column, or diagonal, or has the most marks when the game board is filled.

How to Play

STEP 1 On a piece of poster board, make a game board like the one shown. One player is X and the other is O.

STEP 2 Player X chooses an equation and solves it. If the solution is correct, the player places an X in that square. If the solution is incorrect, Player O places an O in the square. Reverse roles. Continue to play until a row, column, or diagonal is completed, or until all the squares are filled.

Another Way to Play

Any player who solves an equation incorrectly does not make a mark on the game board. The other player then takes a turn and can choose any unmarked equation on the game board.

Brain Teaser

Follow the path.

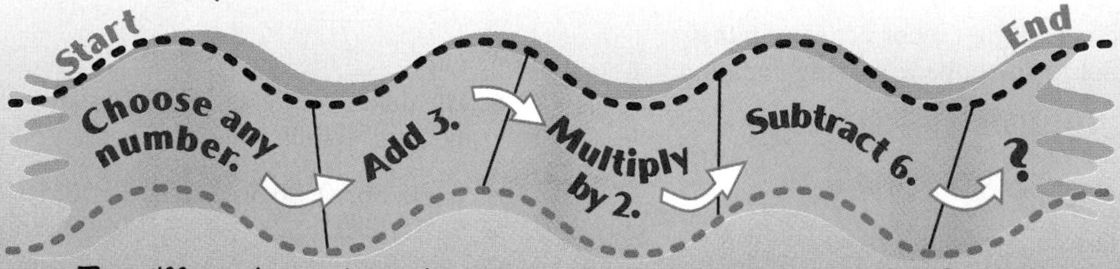

Start
Choose any number.
Add 3.
Multiply by 2.
Subtract 6.
?
End

Try different numbers to start. What happens each time? Explain why this happens. **The end number is twice the original number; $2(n+3)-6=2n$.**

California Standards and Assessment

CA Standards: AF 4.1, MR 2.8

The basic skills you'll review on this page will help prepare you for the next chapter.

Reviewing the Basics

EXAMPLE 1 Using Tables and Graphs

Use the graph and the following information about heating costs.

Heat is often measured in British Thermal Units (BTU). The graph shows typical costs, in dollars per million BTU, to heat a home with different energy sources.

Which energy source costs the most? Which energy source costs the least?

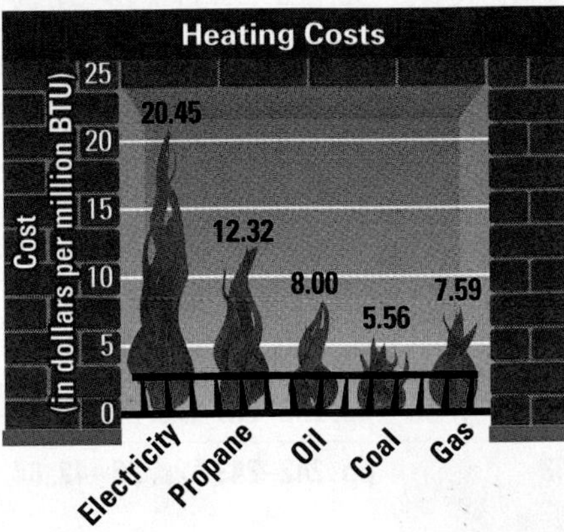

Solution

The longest flame in the graph represents electricity, so electricity costs the most. The shortest flame represents coal, so coal costs the least.

Try These

Use the graph shown in Example 1.

1. How much more would it cost to produce 3 million BTU by using electricity than by using propane? **\$24.39**

2. Make a table to represent the cost in dollars of heating a home with oil to produce 1, 2, 3, 4, 5, 6, 7, or 8 million BTU. **See margin.**

EXAMPLE 2 Working with Powers and Exponents

Write the repeated multiplication as a power.

a. $3 \cdot 3 \cdot 3$ **b.** $x \cdot x \cdot x \cdot x \cdot x$

Solution

a. $3 \cdot 3 \cdot 3 = 3^3$ **b.** $x \cdot x \cdot x \cdot x \cdot x = x^5$

Student Help

▶ **MORE EXAMPLES**

INTERNET More examples and practice exercises available at www.mcdougallittell.com

Try These

Write the expression as a power.

3. $2 \cdot 2 \cdot 2 \cdot 2$ **2^4** **4.** $5 \cdot 5 \cdot 5$ **5^3** **5.** $4 \cdot 4$ **4^2**

6. $(-2) \cdot (-2) \cdot (-2)$ **$(-2)^3$** **7.** $b \cdot b$ **b^2** **8.** $m \cdot m \cdot m \cdot m$ **m^4**

2.

million BTU	Cost in Dollars
1	8
2	16
3	24
4	32
5	40
6	48
7	56
8	64

Pacing and Assignment Guide

Regular Schedule

Lesson	Les. Day	Transitional	Average	Advanced
5.1	Day 1	pp. 223–224 Exs. 26–29, 34–37, 46–49, 70–71	pp. 223–224 Exs. 28–31, 38–41, 46–49, 70–72	pp. 223–224 Exs. 30–33, 42–45, 50–53, 70–72
	Day 2	pp. 223–224 Exs. 54–57, 62–65, 76, 80, 82–88	pp. 223–224 Exs. 54–57, 62–65, 73–75, 77–78, 82–88	pp. 223–224 Exs. 58–61, 66–69, 75–76, 78–79, 81*, 82–88
5.2	Day 1	pp. 227–228 Exs. 15–18, 23–26, 31–33, 40–43, 49–50, 55, 58–59	pp. 227–228 Exs. 19–22, 27–30, 34–36, 40–43, 48–50, 52, 54, 58–59	pp. 227–228 Exs. 19–22, 27–30, 37–39, 44–47, 50–53, 56–57*, 58–59
5.3	Day 1	pp. 231–232 Exs. 20–23, 28–32, 37–39, 47–48, 54–56	pp. 231–232 Exs. 20–23, 30–33, 37–39, 43–49, 54–56	pp. 231–232 Exs. 24–27, 32–36, 40–43, 49–52, 53*, 54–56
5.4	Day 1	pp. 236–237 Exs. 15–20, 23–28, 55–57	pp. 236–237 Exs. 15–30, 55–57	pp. 236–237 Exs. 15–30, 55–57
	Day 2	pp. 236–237 Exs. 31–33, 37–39, 47–48, 51–53	pp. 236–237 Exs. 31–34, 37–39, 43–47, 49–50	pp. 236–237 Exs. 34–36, 40–48, 51–53, 54*
5.5	Day 1	SRH p. 678 Exs. 6–15; pp. 242–243 Exs. 26–30, 32–40, 63, 72–77	pp. 242–243 Exs. 26–42, 64, 66–68, 72–77	pp. 242–243 Exs. 26–42, 64–68, 72–77
	Day 2	pp. 242–243 Exs. 43–48, 51–54, 70–71, 78–81	pp. 242–243 Exs. 43–49, 53–56, 70–71, 78–81	pp. 242–243 Exs. 43–49, 53–56, 69*, 70–71, 78–81
5.6	Day 1	pp. 246–247 Exs. 12–19, 28–30, 32–33, 37–38, 41–42	pp. 246–247 Exs. 16–23, 28–29, 31–34, 41–42	pp. 246–247 Exs. 20–27, 31–39, 40*, 41–42
5.7	Day 1	SRH p. 677 Exs. 1–6; pp. 251–252 Exs. 19–22, 27–30, 35–38, 43–46, 51, 59–60, 65–66, 68–76	pp. 251–252 Exs. 19–22, 31–38, 47–50, 52–53, 60–61, 65–66, 68–76	pp. 251–252 Exs. 23–26, 31–34, 39–42, 47–50, 53–58, 63–64, 67*, 68–76
5.8	Day 1	pp. 255–257 Exs. 7–10, 12, 17–19	pp. 255–257 Exs. 7–12, 17–19	pp. 255–257 Exs. 7–12, 17–19
	Day 2	pp. 255–257 Exs. 13–16, 21	pp. 255–257 Exs. 13–16, 21	pp. 255–257 Exs. 13–16, 20*, 21
Review	Day 1	pp. 258–261 Exs. 1–59	pp. 258–261 Exs. 1–59	pp. 258–261 Exs. 1–59
Assess	Day 1	Chapter 5 Test	Chapter 5 Test	Chapter 5 Test

Yearly Pacing *Chapter 5 Total* – **14 days** *Chapters 1-5 Total* – **66 days** *Remaining* – **94 days**

* Challenge Exercises   EP = Extra Practice   SRH = Skills Review Handbook   EC = Extra Challenge

Block Schedule

Day 1	Day 2	Day 3	Day 4	Day 5	Day 6	Day 7
5.1 pp. 223–224: Exs. 28–31, 38–41, 46–49, 54–57, 62–65, 70–75, 77–78, 82–88	**5.2** pp. 227–228: Exs. 19–22, 27–30, 34–36, 40–43, 48–50, 52, 54, 58–59 **5.3** pp. 231–232: Exs. 20–23, 30–33, 37–39, 43–49, 54–56	**5.4** pp. 236–237: Exs. 15–34, 37–39, 43–47, 49–50, 55–57	**5.5** pp. 242–243: Exs. 26–49, 53–56, 64, 66–68, 70–81	**5.6** pp. 246–247: Exs. 16–23, 28–29, 31–34, 41–42 **5.7** pp. 251–252: Exs. 19–22, 31–38, 47–50, 52–53, 60–61, 65–66, 68–76	**5.8** pp. 255–257: Exs. 7–19, 21	**Review** pp. 258–261: Exs. 1–59 **Assess** Chapter 5 Test

Yearly Pacing *Chapter 5 Total* – **7 days** *Chapters 1-5 Total* – **33 days** *Remaining* – **47 days**

Support Materials

Chapter Resource Book

LESSON SUPPORT	5.1	5.2	5.3	5.4	5.5	5.6	5.7	5.8
Lesson Plans	p. 1	p. 10	p. 19	p. 28	p. 37	p. 46	p. 55	p. 64
Lesson Plans for Block Scheduling	p. 2	p. 11	p. 20	p. 29	p. 38	p. 47	p. 56	p. 65
Warm-Ups with Multiple-Choice Practice	p. 3	p. 12	p. 21	p. 30	p. 39	p. 48	p. 57	p. 66
Problem of the Day	p. 4	p. 13	p. 22	p. 31	p. 40	p. 49	p. 58	p. 67
Daily Cumulative Review	p. 5	p. 14	p. 23	p. 32	p. 41	p. 50	p. 59	p. 68
Practice Masters	p. 6	p. 15	p. 24	p. 33	p. 42	p. 51	p. 60	p. 69
Reteaching Masters	p. 7	p. 16	p. 25	p. 34	p. 43	p. 52	p. 61	p. 70
Enrichment Masters	p. 9	p. 18	p. 27	p. 36	p. 45	p. 54	p. 63	p. 72

Transparencies

	5.1	5.2	5.3	5.4	5.5	5.6	5.7	5.8
Warm-Ups with Multiple-Choice Practice	p. 34	p. 35	p. 36	p. 37	p. 38	p. 39	p. 40	p. 41
Teacher Time-Saver Transparencies	✓	✓	✓	✓	✓	✓	✓	✓
English/Spanish Problem Solving	p. 19		p. 20		p. 21		p. 22	p. 23
Answer Transparencies	✓	✓	✓	✓	✓	✓	✓	✓

Technology

- Personal Student Tutor
- Time-Saving Test and Practice Generator
- Electronic Teacher Tools
- Technology: Using Calculators and Computers

Additional Resources

- Math Log
- Assessment Book
- Worked-Out Solution Key
- Practice Workbook (English/Spanish)
- Home and School Connection
- California Standards: Key Concepts Book

Correlation to the California Curriculum

Correlations to the California Standards

CA Standards: NS 1.0, NS 1.2, NS 1.3, NS 1.4, NS 1.5, NS 2.2, AF 2.1, SDP 1.1, SDP 1.3, MR 1.1, MR 2.5

California Curriculum Support

Key Concepts Book

- Pre-Course Review: Topic 1 Working with Decimals
  Topic 2 Working with Fractions
  Topic 3 Relating Decimals, Fractions, and Percents
  Topic 5 Measurement
- Key Standards: NS 1.5 Rational Numbers and Decimals *(Lesson 5.5)*
- Special Topics: Divisibilty Tests *(Lesson 5.1)*
  The Euclidean Algorithm *(Lesson 5.2)*
  Comparing Fractions *(Lesson 5.4)*

California Standards Practice Workbook provides practice for each Standard that is covered in this chapter.

Strategies for Strategic Learners

DIFFERENTIATE INSTRUCTION IN TERMS OF PACING

The next few chapters are very important for students who are achieving below grade level. A solid understanding of fractions, factoring, ratios, and the Pythagorean theorem are necessary for success in future mathematics courses. Students who are having difficulty keeping up with mathematics classes need additional instructional time at this point. Investigate whether a study hall, additional period, or tutoring are available. Sometimes students have access to an after school support program. Parents or siblings may be available to help. The prior year mathematics text in this series, as well as the web site www.mcdougallittell.com, provide additional problems for practice. Extra time invested at this juncture can keep these students on the path to learning.

PROVIDE CONCRETE EXAMPLES

Look for opportunities in everyday conversation and interactions to reinforce mathematical concepts. Percent, for example, lends itself beautifully to discussions involving money. All students should be familiar with the fact that a dollar is equal to 100 pennies; teachers can build on this understanding by asking students to compute the fraction, percent, and decimal equivalents of coins or stacks of coins. A quarter, for example, is $\frac{25}{100}$ or $\frac{1}{4}$; 25% of a dollar, and 0.25. Be sure to include some stacks of coins that add to more than $1.00, so that students can understand percents greater than 100%. Then have students find the fraction, percent, and decimal equivalents of amounts less than one penny. Extending the discussion of mathematics into everyday life can have the effect of extending the learning time, as students cannot help but be reminded of what they learned in mathematics class every time they pay for something.

USE SCAFFOLDING

Factoring should have been discussed in previous grades and may be review for many students. If students are weak on this concept, you can provide some "stair steps to learning" or scaffolding, by having students fill in missing numbers in factor trees. For example:

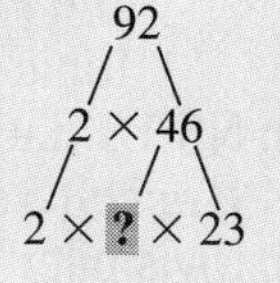

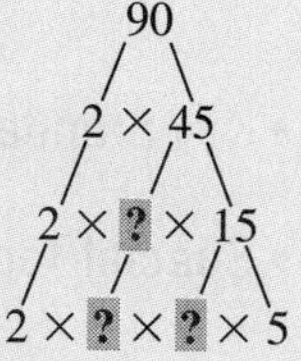

Strategies for English Learners

DISSECT WORD PROBLEMS

Most of the word problems in *Concepts and Skills* follow the basic format discussed earlier. Throughout *Concepts and Skills*, however, and in future mathematics classes and tests, students will be asked to express their thinking in words as well as in mathematical symbols. For example, at the end of a word problem they may be told, "Explain your answer"; "Give an example"; "Explain your thinking"; "Write your findings"; "Justify your ideas"; or "Describe the rule." Some word problems will be open-ended, and students are expected not just to solve the problem and produce the right answer but to discuss how they solved the problem, show their steps, and explain their thinking.

OPEN-ENDED PROBLEMS Open-ended word problems present three challenges for English learners: (1) understanding what is being asked; (2) being able to develop a solution and perform the computations; and (3) finding the right English to explain their thinking. Reassure students that they are not required to write English perfectly. As a general rule, mathematics tests are not scored in terms of English grammar. Furthermore, many open-ended word problems can be explained by showing the mathematical steps that led you to a logical conclusion. Use of the English language can be minimal. Drawing a picture, in many cases, really *can* be worth a thousand words.

MORE PRACTICE Have students practice reading open-ended prompts (such as the ones below) and discussing what is asked for. Then have them respond by using pictures or standard phrases to express their thinking. If students are asked to label their steps, make sure they do so with numerals or using words such as *first*, *second*, *third*, or *finally*. Words that are useful to show conclusions are *thus*, *and so*, and *in conclusion*.

Here is a sample of word problems that ask students to do more than find a right answer:

Page 219, Exercise 2. . . . explain why the next number in the list that has not been crossed out must be prime.

Page 219, Exercise 3. . . . explain why *mp* is *not* a prime number.

Have students work in small groups to brainstorm how these questions could be answered using mathematical explanations and a minimum of English.

Strategies for Advanced Learners

SUBSTITUTE MORE CHALLENGING PROBLEMS

The study of prime numbers has intrigued mathematicians for centuries. While formulas have been found that generate some prime numbers, there is no single formula for producing all prime numbers. Have students investigate the following formulas for generating prime numbers.

- $x^2 + x + 17$ (works for 1, 2 . . . 15, but not for $x = 16$)
- $2^p - 1$, where p is a prime number. Have students find a prime number p less than 20 for which the formula does not produce a prime. (This formula was invented by Marin Mersenne (1588–1648), and the numbers generated by the formula are known as Mersenne numbers.)

See if students can find examples of prime numbers generated by each formula. Students should then find a counterexample for each formula; that is, a value of x or p that does *not* produce a prime number.

PRIME NUMBERS Other mathematicians who have studied prime numbers include Pierre de Fermat, who published his formula in 1640, and Adrien-Marie Legendre, who published his formula in 1778.

In 1742, Christian Goldbach conjectured that every even integer greater than 2 can be written as the sum of two primes, and that every integer greater than 5 can be written as the sum of three primes (see page 223). In 1937 Ivan Vinogradov proved that all sufficiently large odd numbers can be expressed as the sum of three primes.

Mathematical Background Notes

Lesson 5.1

DIVISORS Suppose a and b are given whole numbers. If there is a whole number q such that $b = q \times a$, we say that b is divisible by a and a is called a **divisor** or **factor** of b. Given a whole number b, it is of interest to list *all* divisors of b in increasing order.

Divisors of 12: 1, 2, 3, 4, 6, 12
Divisors of 28: 1, 2, 4, 7, 14, 28
Divisors of 31: 1, 31

Whole numbers with *exactly* two divisors, 1 and the number itself, are called **prime** numbers. Whole numbers with *more* than two divisors are called **composite** numbers.

An important property of composite numbers is that they can be written as the product of numbers smaller than themselves. For example,

$$12 = 2 \times 6 = 3 \times 4 = 2 \times 2 \times 3.$$

When the number has been written as the product of prime factors, the process of breaking it down into smaller factors terminates (we do not include multiplication by 1).

In arriving at a prime factorization, it is instructive to ask some students to compare the result of "chipping away" by always factoring out the smallest prime possible and "splitting asunder" by breaking the number into two large factors. For 126, the process of chipping away corresponds to writing

$$126 = 2 \times 63 = 2 \times 3 \times 21 = 2 \times 3 \times 3 \times 7,$$

while in splitting asunder one might write

$$126 = 9 \times 14 = 3 \times 3 \times 2 \times 7.$$

The fact that both methods lead to the same list of primes is a consequence of the **Fundamental Theorem of Arithmetic.** This important theorem asserts that, aside from the order of the factors, *every whole number greater than one has a unique prime factorization.*

Lessons 5.2–5.3

GCF The meaning of **greatest common factor** (GCF) is best conveyed by a methodical development of *factor*, *common factor,* and then *greatest common factor*. That is, to find the GCF of 36 and 84, one proceeds as follows.

Factors of 36:	1, 2, 3, 4, 6, 9, 12, 18, 36
Factors of 84:	1, 2, 3, 4, 6, 7, 12, 14, 21, 28, 42, 84
Common factors of 36 and 84:	1, 2, 3, 4, 6, 12
GCF of 36 and 84:	12

Once understood, it is of interest to approach GCFs in other ways as well. One important way of arriving at GCFs is through the prime factorizations of the numbers under consideration. For the numbers 36 and 84,

$$36 = 2 \times 2 \times 3 \times 3 \text{ and } 84 = 2 \times 2 \times 3 \times 7.$$

Suppose we now denote the GCF of 36 and 84 by m and try to characterize m in terms of its prime factorization. Since m is a divisor of both 36 and 84, the prime factorization of m will have to appear in the product of primes for both 36 and 84. Furthermore, since m is the *greatest* common factor of 36 and 84, m is the *largest* product of primes *common* to both prime factorizations. In this way we again arrive at the fact that $m = 2 \times 2 \times 3 = 12$.

In Lesson 5.4 an important application of GCFs arises in the simplification of fractions. In order to write $\frac{36}{84}$ in simplest form, we use the GCF of 36 and 84 to write $\frac{36}{84} = \frac{12 \times 3}{12 \times 7} = \frac{3}{7}$.

LCM On the other hand, the **least common multiple** (LCM) of 36 and 84 is the smallest number that is a multiple of both. We could proceed to find this by listing the multiples of each.

multiples of 36: 36, 72, 108, 144, 180, 216, *252,* 288, 324, 360, 396, 432, 468, *504,* 540, . . .
multiples of 84: 84, 168, *252,* 336, 420, *504,* 588, . . .

From these lists we see that the common multiples of 36 and 84 are 252, 504, . . . and that the *least* common multiple (LCM) of 36 and 84 is 252. We have

$$7 \times 36 = 252 = 3 \times 84.$$

Since $7 \times 36 = 3 \times 84$, we also have $14 \times 36 = 6 \times 84$, $21 \times 36 = 9 \times 84$, and so forth. This explains why the common multiples appear in every seventh position in the list for 36 and every third position in the list for 84.

As with the GCF, the prime factorizations of 36 and 84 can be used to find the LCM. Recalling that

$$36 = 2 \times 2 \times 3 \times 3 \quad \text{and} \quad 84 = 2 \times 2 \times 3 \times 7$$

we note that any multiple of 36 must have *at least* two 2s and two 3s in its prime factorization, while any multiple of 84 must have *at least* two 2s, one 3, and one 7 in its prime factorization. The *smallest* number having two 2s, two 3s, and one 7 in its prime factorization is

$$2 \times 2 \times 3 \times 3 \times 7 = 252.$$

In other words, the LCM of 36 and 84 is the *smallest* product of primes containing the prime factorizations of both 36 and 84.

Lesson 5.4

EQUIVALENCE A fundamental relation among fractions is **equivalence.** For any nonzero integer c, the fraction $\frac{a}{b}$ is equivalent to $\frac{ac}{bc}$. At times we start with a fraction $\frac{a}{b}$ and convert it into an equivalent fraction by multiplying numerator and denominator by c. Other times we start with a fraction of the form $\frac{A}{B}$ and divide numerator and denominator by a common factor of A and B. In both cases, the result is an equivalent fraction.

One reason for dividing numerator and denominator by an integer is to **simplify** the fraction. If $\frac{A}{B}$ is not already in simplest form, then dividing A and B by their greatest common factor results in a fraction for which the numerator and denominator have no common factors other than 1.

One way to simplify a fraction $\frac{A}{B}$ is to factor both numerator and denominator into primes. Dividing A and B by the product of the primes common to both factorizations is equivalent to dividing by their greatest common factor. For example, $\frac{24}{42} = \frac{2 \cdot 2 \cdot 2 \cdot 3}{2 \cdot 3 \cdot 7} = \frac{2 \cdot 2}{7} = \frac{4}{7}$.

Our base 10 positional notation provides a convenient way of comparing both whole numbers and decimals. However, the problem of comparing two fractions, such as $\frac{12}{17}$ and $\frac{23}{38}$, is more daunting.

To reduce the comparison of two fractions to an easier problem, we find a pair of equivalent fractions with a common denominator. Instead of trying to compare $\frac{12}{17}$ with $\frac{23}{38}$ directly, one compares $\frac{12 \cdot 38}{17 \cdot 38}$ with $\frac{23 \cdot 17}{38 \cdot 17}$. Now, because $12 \cdot 38 = 456$ is greater than $23 \cdot 17 = 391$, we can conclude that $\frac{12}{17} > \frac{23}{38}$.

These ideas have a general formulation. In order to compare $\frac{a}{b}$ with $\frac{c}{d}$, we place them both over a common denominator bd. Then the original comparison is equivalent to comparing $\frac{ad}{bd}$ with $\frac{bc}{bd}$. For positive fractions this leads to the following results.

$\frac{a}{b} < \frac{c}{d}$ if and only if $ad < bc$.

$\frac{a}{b} > \frac{c}{d}$ if and only if $ad > bc$.

Lessons 5.6–5.7

PERCENT One way of converting a number into a percent is to write it as a fraction of the form $\frac{c}{100}$. The fact that $\frac{1}{4} = \frac{25}{100}$ leads us to conclude that $\frac{1}{4} = 25\%$.

Even when such a fraction fails to exist, this approach can be useful. Although there is no integer c for which $\frac{1}{8} = \frac{c}{100}$, we do have $\frac{1}{8} = \frac{125}{1000}$. On this basis we write

$$\frac{1}{8} = \frac{125}{1000} = \frac{12.5}{100} = 12.5\%.$$

In this example, the fact that there is no integer c for which $\frac{1}{8} = \frac{c}{100}$ resulted in a percent that is not a whole number.

The problem of writing $\frac{1}{3}$ as a percent poses a more difficult situation. Here it can be shown that it is not possible to find positive integers c and n so that $\frac{1}{3} = \frac{c}{10^n}$ and, as a result, that neither $\frac{1}{3}$ nor its percentage equivalent are expressible as terminating decimals. This means that any effort to use terminating decimals to express $\frac{1}{3}$ as a percent will involve an approximation. In this case we could use $\frac{1}{3} \approx 33.3\%$.

These considerations raise the following question.

For what fractions $\frac{a}{b}$ do there exist positive integers c and n such that $\frac{a}{b} = \frac{c}{10^n}$?

Using the Fundamental Theorem of Arithmetic one can establish the following answer.

A fraction $\frac{a}{b}$ in lowest terms is equivalent to a fraction of the form $\frac{c}{10^n}$ if and only if the prime factorization of b consists exclusively of 2s and 5s.

When numbers are written in decimal form, the corresponding result is somewhat easier to establish.

Terminating decimals are exactly those numbers that can be written in the form $\frac{c}{10^n}$.

For instance,

$$\frac{563}{10^4} = 563 \times 10^{-4} = 0.0563$$

whereas

$$3.78093 = 378{,}093 \times 10^{-5} = \frac{378{,}093}{10^5}.$$

In both such cases we are also able to give a terminating decimal representation for the equivalent percent.

$$0.0563 = \frac{563}{10^4} = \frac{5.63}{100} = 5.63\% \quad \text{and}$$

$$3.78093 = \frac{378{,}093}{10^5} = \frac{378.093}{100} = 378.093\%.$$

However, this is not the case for $\frac{1}{3}$, $\frac{1}{90}$, or $\frac{5}{600}$.

Chapter Overview

Chapter Goals

In this chapter, students will learn to identify prime and composite numbers, and to find the greatest common factors and least common multiples of sets of numbers and algebraic expressions. They will:

- Simplify and compare fractions.
- Convert between fractions, terminating or repeating decimals, and percents.
- Make stem-and-leaf plots of data.

Career Note

Market researchers often do work for companies wishing to learn more about the best ways to design and promote their product. Market researchers conduct surveys and analyze statistical data. They prepare charts and reports, and make recommendations so that their clients can make decisions that may affect the future of a product. Market researchers have a strong background in mathematics, statistics, and computer science, and usually hold a master's degree in statistics or in a business-related field.

Additional information on market researchers is available at **www.mcdougallittell.com**

Rational Numbers and Percents

Why are rational numbers and percents important?

Rational numbers and percents often show relationships between two quantities. You will need to use rational numbers and percents as you study probability, proportional reasoning, and statistics.

Rational numbers and percents are used in many careers, including market research (page 217) and cartography (page 247). For example, market researchers use percents to report the results of their research.

Meeting the California Standards

The skills you'll develop in this chapter will help you meet state standards and prepare for standardized tests. In this chapter you'll:

- **Interpret positive whole-number powers as repeated multiplication.** LESSONS 5.1–5.4
- **Use factoring to find common denominators.** LESSON 5.4
- **Recognize terminating and repeating decimals and convert them to fractions.** LESSON 5.5
- **Convert among fractions, decimals, and percents.** LESSONS 5.5–5.7
- **Use stem-and-leaf plots to display and compare data.** LESSON 5.8

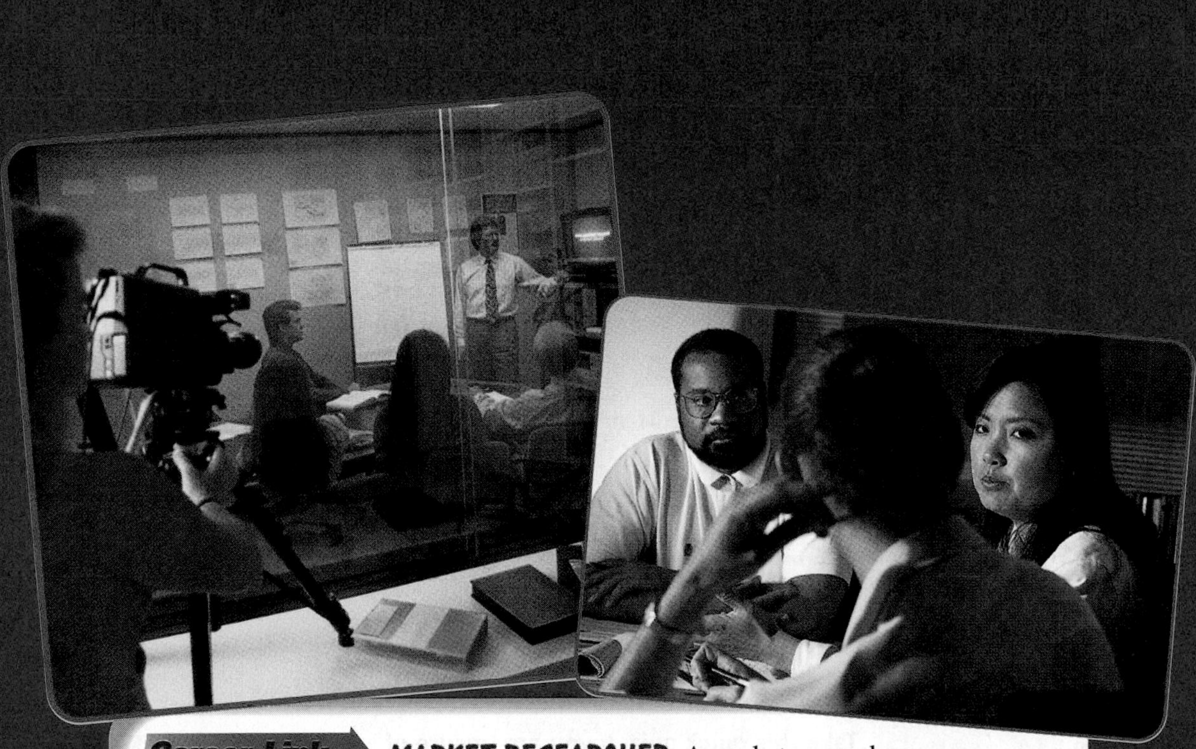

Career Link **MARKET RESEARCHER** A market researcher uses rational numbers and percents when:

- choosing a diverse group of people to interview.
- reporting the results of research.

EXERCISES

A market researcher shows a new product to two different groups of people and asks them whether they agree with various descriptions of the product. The results are shown in the table.

Description	Number who agree	
	Group A (250 people)	Group B (150 people)
Reliable	120	85
Easy to use	225	100
Affordable	105	90

1. Is the product thought to be "reliable" by more than half of the people in Group A? in Group B? **no; yes**

2. Who is more likely to think the product is "easy to use," a person randomly chosen from Group A or a person randomly chosen from Group B? Explain. **Group A**

In Lesson 5.6, you will learn how to write data as percents to make comparisons easier.

Projects

A project covering Chapters 4–6 appears on pages 324–325 of the Student Edition. Additional projects for selected lessons in Chapter 5 are available in the *Assessment Book,* pp. 228–229.

Technology

Software

- Electronic Teacher Tools
- Online Lesson Planner
- Personal Student Tutor
- Test and Practice Generator

Internet Connections

- Application and Career Links 223, 224, 232, 237, 244, 247
- Student Help 221, 228, 229, 235, 240, 245, 251, 254, 265

These Internet connections are available at **www.mcdougallittell.com**

Prepare

Diagnostic Tools

The **chapter readiness quiz** can help you diagnose whether students have the following skills needed in Chapter 5:

- Identify and evaluate exponential expressions.
- Understand the meaning of equivalent expressions.
- Apply multiplication properties to negative integers.

Reteaching Materials

The following resources are available for students who need additional help with the skills on the chapter readiness quiz:

Chapter 5 Resource Book

- Reteaching with Practice (Lessons 1.3, 1.8, 3.3, 3.5)

Personal Student Tutor

Additional Resources

The following resources are provided to help you prepare for the upcoming chapter and customize review materials:

Chapter 5 Resource Book

- Lesson Plans, pp. 1, 10, 19, 28, 37, 46, 55, 64
- Lesson Plans for Block Scheduling, pp. 2, 11, 20, 29, 38, 47, 56, 65

Technology

- Electronic Teacher Tools with Lesson Planning Software
- Test and Practice Generator

Chapter 5 Getting Ready

PREVIEW

What's the chapter about?

- Using **prime factorization** to find the **greatest common factors** and **least common multiples** of numbers and variable expressions
- Converting among **fractions, decimals,** and **percents**
- Using **stem-and-leaf** plots

WORDS TO KNOW

- **prime number,** *p. 220*
- **prime factorization,** *p. 220*
- **greatest common factor (GCF),** *p. 225*
- **least common multiple (LCM),** *p. 229*
- **simplest form (of a fraction),** *p. 233*
- **stem-and-leaf plot,** *p. 253*

PREPARE

Chapter Readiness Quiz

Take this quick quiz. If you are unsure of an answer, look back at the reference pages for help.

VOCABULARY CHECK *(refer to pp. 12, 38)*

1. In the expression a^m, m is called __?__. B

Ⓐ a base Ⓑ an exponent Ⓒ a factor Ⓓ a power

2. Variable expressions that always have the same value when numbers are substituted for the variables are __?__. H

Ⓕ identities Ⓖ inverses Ⓗ equivalent Ⓙ data

SKILL CHECK *(refer to pp. 12, 116, 129–130)*

3. Simplify the expression $-2^3 + (-3)^4$. C

Ⓐ -89 Ⓑ -73 Ⓒ 73 Ⓓ 89

4. Which statement is *false*? G

Ⓕ $2(2)(-3) = -12$ Ⓖ $3(-3)(4)(-4) = -144$

Ⓗ $(-3)(4)(5) = -60$ Ⓙ $(-1)(-2)(-3) = -6$

STUDY TIP

Make Up a Test

Making up a test will help you to better understand the concepts you have studied. Solve each problem you write.

Chapter 5 Test
Find all the factors of the number.
1. 20 2. 35
Factor the variable expression.
3. $9a^2b$ 4. $-72m^3n^2$

DEVELOPING CONCEPTS
Prime Numbers

For use with Lesson 5.1

California Standards

- Analyze problems by observing patterns. (MR 1.1)
- Use words and numbers to explain mathematical reasoning. (MR 2.5)

MATERIALS:
- Paper and pencil

The Greek mathematician Eratosthenes, who lived about 2200 years ago, developed an easy method for finding *prime* numbers, which are numbers that have only themselves and 1 as their whole number factors. His method involves crossing out multiples of numbers known to be prime from a list of whole numbers starting with 2 and ending with any number

SAMPLE 1 Finding Prime Numbers

You can use Eratosthenes' method, called the *sieve of Eratosthenes*, to find all the prime numbers between 2 and 50.

Here's How

1. Make a list of the whole numbers from 2 to 50. Since the only factors of 2 are 2 and 1, 2 is prime. Cross out all multiples of 2 (except for 2) from the list.

2, 3, ~~4~~, 5, ~~6~~, 7, ~~8~~, 9, ~~10~~, 11, ~~12~~, 13, ~~14~~, 15, ~~16~~, 17, ~~18~~, 19, ~~20~~, 21, ~~22~~, 23, ~~24~~, 25, ~~26~~, 27, ~~28~~, 29, ~~30~~, 31, ~~32~~, 33, ~~34~~, 35, ~~36~~, 37, ~~38~~, 39, ~~40~~, 41, ~~42~~, 43, ~~44~~, 45, ~~46~~, 47, ~~48~~, 49, ~~50~~

2. Go to the next number in the list that has not been crossed out. It will be prime. Cross out all multiples of that number (except for the number itself) from the list.

3. Repeat Step 2 until you reach a prime number for which all multiples have already been crossed out. The remaining numbers in the list are all prime.

2, 3, ~~4~~, 5, ~~6~~, 7, ~~8~~, ~~9~~, ~~10~~, 11, ~~12~~, 13, ~~14~~, ~~15~~, ~~16~~, 17, ~~18~~, 19, ~~20~~, ~~21~~, ~~22~~, 23, ~~24~~, ~~25~~, ~~26~~, ~~27~~, ~~28~~, 29, ~~30~~, 31, ~~32~~, ~~33~~, ~~34~~, ~~35~~, ~~36~~, 37, ~~38~~, ~~39~~, ~~40~~, 41, ~~42~~, 43, ~~44~~, ~~45~~, ~~46~~, 47, ~~48~~, ~~49~~, ~~50~~

Try These

1. Use the sieve of Eratosthenes to find all the prime numbers from 2 to 100.
2, 3, 5, 7, 11, 13, 17, 19, 23, 29, 31, 37, 41, 43, 47, 53, 59, 61, 67, 71, 73, 79, 83, 89, 97
2. **MATHEMATICAL REASONING** In Step 2 of Sample 1, explain why the next number in the list that has not been crossed out must be prime.
3. **MATHEMATICAL REASONING** If p is a prime number and m is any whole number greater than 1, explain why mp is *not* a prime number.

2. If the number is not prime, then it must be the product of two numbers less than itself. It cannot be the product of a number on the list before it and another number, since all of these multiples have been crossed off. Therefore, the next number must be prime.

3. *mp* is not prime because it can be factored into at least two factors, *m* and *p*, neither of which is 1 or the number *mp* itself.

1 Planning the Activity

Purpose and Materials
See the margin of the student page.

LINK TO LESSON
Since the students now have a list of the prime numbers less than 100, they will be able to easily verify the factor trees shown in Examples 1 and 2.

Math Reasoning
Students identify relationships between prime and composite numbers, and use words and numbers to explain mathematical reasoning.

2 Managing the Activity

Classroom Management
In order to save time, you may wish to provide students with a list of whole numbers from 2 to 100.

3 Closing the Activity

KEY DISCOVERY
Every prime number has exactly two factors, 1 and the number itself.

Activity Assessment
Use Exercise 1 to assess student understanding.

California Standards and Assessment

CA Standards: MR 1.1, MR 2.5

1 Plan

Pacing

Suggested Number of Days

Transitional: 2 days
Average: 2 days
Advanced: 2 days
Block Schedule: 1 block

Teaching Resources

Blacklines
(See page 216B.)

Transparencies
- Warm-Up Exercises
- Teacher Time-Savers
- English/Spanish Problem Solving
- Answers

Technology
- Electronic Teacher Tools
- Test and Practice Generator

2 Teach

Math Reasoning

For Mathematical Background Notes on mathematical reasoning related to this lesson, please refer to pages 216E and 216F in this Teacher's Edition.

California Standards and Assessment

CA Standards: NS 1.2, AF 2.1
CA Key Concepts Book: pp. T3–T7

5.1 Factoring Numbers and Expressions

California Standards

In this lesson you'll:

- Write the prime factorization of a number. (NS 1.2)
- Interpret positive whole-number powers as repeated multiplication. (AF 2.1)

Goal 1 FINDING PRIME FACTORIZATIONS

As you learned in Developing Concepts 5.1, page 219, certain whole numbers are called *prime* numbers. A **prime number** has exactly two factors, itself and 1. A whole number greater than 1 that has factors other than 1 and itself is a **composite number**. The number 1 is neither prime nor composite.

You can use a *factor tree* to express a number as a product of factors that are all prime numbers. This product of prime numbers is called the **prime factorization** of the number.

EXAMPLE 1 Using Factor Trees

You can use a factor tree to find the prime factorization of 30.

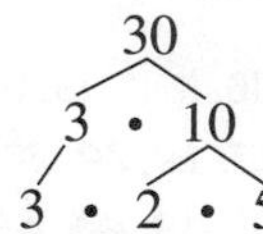

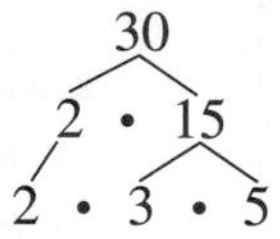

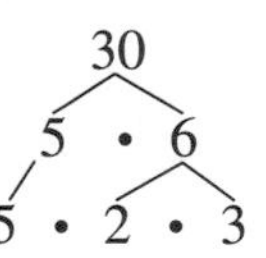

These all result in the same prime factorization: $30 = 2 \cdot 3 \cdot 5$.

Example 1 shows that there is exactly one prime factorization of 30, except for the order of the primes. This is true for all whole numbers greater than 1.

Student Help

▶ VOCABULARY TIP
Because 2, 3, and 5 are factors of 30, you can also say that 30 is *divisible* by 2, 3, and 5, and that 2, 3, and 5 are the prime *divisors* of 30.

EXAMPLE 2 Finding Prime Factorizations

Write the prime factorization of (**a**) 42 and (**b**) 140.

Solution

a.

42	Start with 42.
6 • 7	Factor 42 as 6 • 7.
2 • 3 • 7	Factor 6 as 2 • 3.

ANSWER ▶ The prime factorization of 42 is $2 \cdot 3 \cdot 7$.

b.

140	Start with 140.
10 • 14	Factor 140 as 10 • 14.
2 • 5 • 14	Factor 10 as 2 • 5.
2 • 5 • 2 • 7	Factor 14 as 2 • 7.

ANSWER ▶ The prime factorization of 140 is $2 \cdot 2 \cdot 5 \cdot 7$.

Student Help

▶ MORE EXAMPLES

More examples are available at www.mcdougallittell.com

EXAMPLE 3 Using Exponents in Prime Factorization

Write the prime factorization of (**a**) 40 and (**b**) 225. Use exponents.

Solution

a. $40 = 8 \cdot 5$
$= 2 \cdot 4 \cdot 5$
$= 2 \cdot 2 \cdot 2 \cdot 5$
$= 2^3 \cdot 5$

ANSWER ▶ $40 = 2^3 \cdot 5$

b. $225 = 15 \cdot 15$
$= 3 \cdot 5 \cdot 3 \cdot 5$
$= 3 \cdot 3 \cdot 5 \cdot 5$
$= 3^2 \cdot 5^2$

ANSWER ▶ $225 = 3^2 \cdot 5^2$

EXAMPLE 4 Using Prime Factorization to Find All Factors

Find all the factors of 175.

Solution

The prime factorization of 175 is $5 \cdot 5 \cdot 7$. Make an organized list of single factors, products of pairs of factors, and so on.

Single factors:	5, 7
Products of 2 factors:	$5 \cdot 5 = 25$, $5 \cdot 7 = 35$
Products of 3 factors:	$5 \cdot 5 \cdot 7 = 175$

ANSWER ▶ Including 1, the factors of 175 are 1, 5, 7, 25, 35, and 175.

Goal 2 FACTORING EXPRESSIONS

Student Help

▶ VOCABULARY TIP

To *factor* an expression means to write the expression as a product of its factors.

You can factor an expression like $-6ab^2$ by factoring the coefficient and using the definition of exponent for the variable part of the expression. Negative numbers can be factored using -1 as a factor.

$$-6ab^2 = (-1) \cdot 2 \cdot 3 \cdot a \cdot b \cdot b$$

EXAMPLE 5 Factoring Expressions Completely

Factor the expression completely.

a. $-63a^3$

b. $18x^2y$

Solution

a. $-63a^3 = (-1) \cdot 3 \cdot 3 \cdot 7 \cdot a^3$ — Factor −63.
$= (-1) \cdot 3 \cdot 3 \cdot 7 \cdot a \cdot a \cdot a$ — Write a^3 as $a \cdot a \cdot a$.

b. $18x^2y = 2 \cdot 3 \cdot 3 \cdot x^2 \cdot y$ — Factor 18.
$= 2 \cdot 3 \cdot 3 \cdot x \cdot x \cdot y$ — Write x^2 as $x \cdot x$.

Math Reasoning

The fact that the various factor trees in Example 1 lead to the same prime factorization is a consequence of the Fundamental Theorem of Arithmetic.

Extra Example 1

Write the prime factorization of 165.

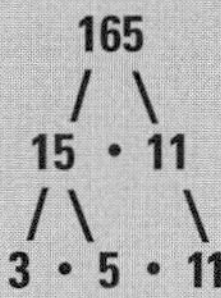

Extra Example 2

Write the prime factorization.

a. 56 **$2 \cdot 2 \cdot 2 \cdot 7$**

b. 60 **$2 \cdot 2 \cdot 3 \cdot 5$**

Extra Example 3

Write the prime factorization. Use exponents.

a. 63 **$3^2 \cdot 7$** **b.** 400 **$2^4 \cdot 5^2$**

Extra Example 4

Find all factors of 105. **1, 3, 5, 7, 15, 21, 35, 105**

Extra Example 5

Factor the expression.

a. $-49b^4$ **$(-1) \cdot 7^2 \cdot b \cdot b \cdot b \cdot b$**

b. $54g^3s^2$

$2 \cdot 3 \cdot 3 \cdot 3 \cdot g \cdot g \cdot g \cdot s \cdot s$

Teaching Tip

In Example 3, part (b), point out that the factored expression $3 \cdot 3 \cdot 5 \cdot 5$ is sometimes called the *expanded form* of the prime factorization of 225 and that the expression $3^2 \cdot 5^2$ is sometimes called the *exponent form* of the factorization.

Before Example 5, mention that writing a number as the product of primes can be thought of as "breaking it down into its simplest parts."

Extra Example 6

Find all factors of $8x^3$. **1, 2, 4, 8, x, $2x$, $4x$, $8x$, x^2, $2x^2$, $4x^2$, $8x^2$, x^3, $2x^3$, $4x^3$, $8x^3$**

Concept Check

What must be true about the numbers in the last row of a factor tree? How do these numbers relate to the original number? ***Sample answer:*** **They must be prime numbers. The product of these numbers is the original number.**

3 Apply

Assignment Guide

TRANSITIONAL

Day 1: pp. 223–224 Exs. 26–29, 34–37, 46–49, 70–71

Day 2: pp. 223–224 Exs. 54–57, 62–65, 76, 80, 82–88

AVERAGE

Day 1: pp. 223–224 Exs. 28–31, 38–41, 46–49, 70–72

Day 2: pp. 223–224 Exs. 54–57, 62–65, 73–75, 77–78, 82–88

ADVANCED

Day 1: pp. 223–224 Exs. 30–33, 42–45, 50–53, 70–72

Day 2: pp. 223–224 Exs. 58–61, 66–69, 75–76, 78–79, 81*, 82–88

BLOCK SCHEDULE

pp. 223–224 Exs. 28–31, 38–41, 46–49, 54–57, 62–65, 70–75, 77–78, 82–88

Extra Practice

- Student Edition, pp. 698–699
- Chapter 5 Resource Book, p. 6

Homework Check

To quickly check student understanding of key concepts, go over the following exercises:

Transitional: 26, 34, 46, 54, 62
Average: 28, 38, 48, 56, 64
Advanced: 30, 42, 50, 58, 66

EXAMPLE 6 Finding All Factors

Find all the factors of $9x^2$.

Solution

The complete factorization of $9x^2$ is $3 \cdot 3 \cdot x \cdot x$. Make an organized list of single factors, products of pairs of factors, and so on.

Single factors:	$3, x$
Products of 2 factors:	$3 \cdot 3 = 9, 3 \cdot x = 3x, x \cdot x = x^2$
Products of 3 factors:	$3 \cdot 3 \cdot x = 9x, 3 \cdot x \cdot x = 3x^2$
Products of 4 factors:	$3 \cdot 3 \cdot x \cdot x = 9x^2$

ANSWER ▶ Including 1, the factors of $9x^2$ are 1, 3, 9, x, $3x$, $9x$, x^2, $3x^2$, and $9x^2$.

5.1 Exercises

Guided Practice

Tell if the statement is *true* or *false*. Explain your reasoning.

1. Thirty-nine is a composite number.
True; 39 is composite since 39 = 3 • 13.

2. Twenty-nine is a prime number.
True; the only factors of 29 are 29 and 1.

3. The prime factorization of 56 is $7 \cdot 8$.
False; 8 can be factored into 2^3, so the prime factorization of 56 is $7 \cdot 2^3$.

4. All the factors of 125 are 1, 5, and 25.
False; 125 is also a factor of 125.

5. 1 is a prime number.
False; 1 is neither prime nor composite.

Use a factor tree to write the prime factorization of the number.

6. 30 **$2 \cdot 3 \cdot 5$** **7.** 66 **$2 \cdot 3 \cdot 11$** **8.** 78 **$2 \cdot 3 \cdot 13$** **9.** 110 **$2 \cdot 5 \cdot 11$**

Write the prime factorization of the number. Use exponents for repeated factors.

10. 18 **$2 \cdot 3^2$** **11.** 24 **$2^3 \cdot 3$** **12.** -72 **$(-1) \cdot 2^3 \cdot 3^2$** **13.** 180 **$2^2 \cdot 3^2 \cdot 5$**

Find all the factors of the number.

14. 19 **1, 19** **15.** 54 **1, 2, 3, 6, 9, 18, 27, 54** **16.** 98 **1, 2, 7, 14, 49, 98** **17.** 130 **1, 2, 5, 10, 13, 26, 65, 130**

ALGEBRA Factor the variable expression completely. **18–21. See margin.**

18. $-14x^2$ **19.** $45y^4$ **20.** $-27r^3s$ **21.** $40n^3$

ALGEBRA Find all the factors of the variable expression. **22–25. See margin.**

22. $20x$ **23.** $44w^2$ **24.** $15x^3$ **25.** $25w^2y$

18. $(-1) \cdot 2 \cdot 7 \cdot x \cdot x$
19. $3 \cdot 3 \cdot 5 \cdot y \cdot y \cdot y \cdot y$
20. $(-1) \cdot 3 \cdot 3 \cdot 3 \cdot r \cdot r \cdot r \cdot s$
21. $2 \cdot 2 \cdot 2 \cdot 5 \cdot n \cdot n \cdot n$
22. 1, 2, 4, 5, 10, 20, x, $2x$, $4x$, $5x$, $10x$, $20x$
23. 1, 2, 4, 11, 22, 44, w, $2w$, $4w$, $11w$, $22w$, $44w$, w^2, $2w^2$, $4w^2$, $11w^2$, $22w^2$, $44w^2$
24. 1, 3, 5, 15, x, $3x$, $5x$, $15x$, x^2, $3x^2$, $5x^2$, $15x^2$, x^3, $3x^3$, $5x^3$, $15x^3$
25. 1, 5, 25, w, $5w$, $25w$, y, $5y$, $25y$, w^2, $5w^2$, $25w^2$, wy, $5wy$, $25wy$, w^2y, $5w^2y$, $25w^2y$

Practice and Problem Solving

Student Help

▶ **MORE PRACTICE** Extra practice to help you master skills is on page 698.

Determine if the number is *prime* or *composite*. Explain your answer. 26–33. See margin.

26. 17 **27.** 9 **28.** 35 **29.** 27

30. 29 **31.** 52 **32.** 1006 **33.** 73

Write the prime factorization of the number. Use exponents for repeated factors.

34. 48 $2^4 \cdot 3$ **35.** 66 $2 \cdot 3 \cdot 11$ **36.** 102 $2 \cdot 3 \cdot 17$ **37.** 144 $2^4 \cdot 3^2$

38. 252 $2^2 \cdot 3^2 \cdot 7$ **39.** 270 $2 \cdot 3^3 \cdot 5$ **40.** 300 $2^2 \cdot 3 \cdot 5^2$ **41.** 880 $2^4 \cdot 5 \cdot 11$

42. 210 $2 \cdot 3 \cdot 5 \cdot 7$ **43.** 178 $2 \cdot 89$ **44.** 150 $2 \cdot 3 \cdot 5^2$ **45.** 266 $2 \cdot 7 \cdot 19$

Find all the factors of the number.

46. 12 1, 2, 3, 4, 6, 12 **47.** 50 1, 2, 5, 10, 25, 50 **48.** 54 1, 2, 3, 6, 9, 18, 27, 54 **49.** 99 1, 3, 9, 11, 33, 99

50. 132 1, 2, 3, 4, 6, 11, 12, 22, 33, 44, 66, 132 **51.** 63 1, 3, 7, 9, 21, 63 **52.** 625 1, 5, 25, 125, 625 **53.** 187 1, 11, 17, 187

Factor the variable expression completely. 54–61. See margin.

54. $8a^3b^2$ **55.** $12p^4q$ **56.** $-45mn^3$ **57.** $-50s^2t^5$

58. $-64m^2n^2$ **59.** $57w^3z^4$ **60.** $81b^7c^2$ **61.** $57p^2q^2$

Find all the factors of the variable expression. 62–69. See margin.

62. $9x$ **63.** $50y$ **64.** $97m^2n^2$ **65.** $87b^2$

66. $15x^3$ **67.** $28z^3$ **68.** $25w^2y$ **69.** $71x^2y^3$

Use mental math to find a number that fits the given description.

70. A number whose factors include 3 and 11 *Sample answer:* 33

71. A three-digit number whose factors include 2 and 7^2 *Sample answers:* 196, 294

72. A number whose factors include 25 and a 2-digit prime number *Sample answers:* 275, 325

73. An expression whose factors include x and an even number *Sample answers:* $2x$, $10x^2$, $20xy$

74. An expression whose factors include -1, 7, and y^2 *Sample answers:* $-7y^2$, $-14y^2x$

75. **History Link** Goldbach's Conjecture states that every even natural number except 2 is the sum of two prime numbers. For example, $24 = 7 + 17$ and $16 = 3 + 13$. Write each even number from 30 to 40 as the sum of two prime numbers. See margin.

76. **LANDSCAPING** You have 96 one-foot-by-one-foot square bricks that you want to lay out in a rectangular shape. If you use all the bricks, how many different rectangles are possible? What are the length and width of each possible rectangle? See margin.

77. **MATHEMATICAL REASONING** A friend tells you that 2 is the only even number that is prime. Do you think your friend is right? Explain. See margin.

Link to History

LEONHARD EULER
Goldbach's Conjecture is known from a 1742 letter from Christian Goldbach to the great mathematician Leonhard Euler.

More about Goldbach's Conjecture available at www.mcdougallittell.com

Math Reasoning

Generalizing Exercise 76, if N is a whole number and we form an $m \times n$ rectangle using N unit squares, then the area of the rectangle is $N = mn$, so m and n are factors of N. Also, regarding Exercise 77, any integer of the form $2n$, with $n > 1$, is not a prime number, since it is the product of two integers, both larger than 1. Since all even integers are of the form $2n$, this shows that the only even prime number is 2.

26. Prime; the only factors are 1 and 17.

27. Composite; 9 can be factored into $3 \cdot 3$.

28. Composite; 35 can be factored into $5 \cdot 7$.

29. Composite; 27 can be factored into $3 \cdot 3 \cdot 3$.

30. Prime; the only factors are 1 and 29.

31. Composite; 52 can be factored into $2 \cdot 2 \cdot 13$.

32. Composite; 1006 can be factored into $2 \cdot 503$.

33. Prime; the only factors are 1 and 73.

54. $2 \cdot 2 \cdot 2 \cdot a \cdot a \cdot a \cdot b \cdot b$

55. $2 \cdot 2 \cdot 3 \cdot p \cdot p \cdot p \cdot p \cdot q$

56. $(-1) \cdot 3 \cdot 3 \cdot 5 \cdot m \cdot n \cdot n \cdot n$

57. $(-1) \cdot 2 \cdot 5 \cdot 5 \cdot s \cdot s \cdot t \cdot t \cdot t \cdot t \cdot t$

58. $(-1) \cdot 2 \cdot 2 \cdot 2 \cdot 2 \cdot 2 \cdot 2 \cdot m \cdot m \cdot n \cdot n$

59. $3 \cdot 19 \cdot w \cdot w \cdot w \cdot z \cdot z \cdot z \cdot z$

60. $3 \cdot 3 \cdot 3 \cdot 3 \cdot b \cdot b \cdot b \cdot b \cdot b \cdot b \cdot b \cdot c \cdot c$

61. $3 \cdot 19 \cdot p \cdot p \cdot q \cdot q$

62. 1, 3, 9, x, $3x$, $9x$

63. 1, 2, 5, 10, 25, 50, y, $2y$, $5y$, $10y$, $25y$, $50y$

64. 1, 97, m, $97m$, n, $97n$, mn, $97mn$, m^2, $97m^2$, n^2, $97n^2$, m^2n, $97m^2n$, mn^2, $97mn^2$, m^2n^2, $97m^2n^2$

65–69, 75–77. See Additional Answers beginning on page AA1.

4 Assess

Assessment Resources

- Assessment Book (Formal Assessment and Alternative Assessment)
- Test and Practice Generator

Mini-Quiz

1. Use a factor tree to write the prime factorization of 50.

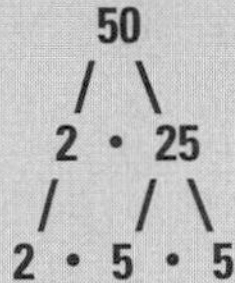

Write the prime factorization of the number. Write your answer in exponent form.

2. 105 $3 \cdot 5 \cdot 7$
3. 153 $3^2 \cdot 17$

Write the expression in expanded form.

4. $9x^2y^3$ $3 \cdot 3 \cdot x \cdot x \cdot y \cdot y \cdot y$
5. $-30ab^3c^2$ $(-1) \cdot 2 \cdot 3 \cdot 5 \cdot a \cdot b \cdot b \cdot b \cdot c \cdot c$

Math Reasoning

The Twin Prime Conjecture states that there exist infinitely many twin prime pairs. Like Goldbach's conjecture, this has neither been proved nor disproved as of this date.

78. No; since the size of each group is the same and is greater than 1, the number of students in the class is divisible by the number of groups and therefore not prime. (Note: This assumes there are at least 2 groups.)

79. 17 and 19, 29 and 31, 41 and 43, 59 and 61, 71 and 73

80. fluorine: composite, $3 \cdot 3$; chlorine: prime; bromine: composite, $5 \cdot 7$; iodine: prime; astatine: composite, $5 \cdot 17$

81. No; Let x be the length of the first side, $x + 1$ the length of the second side, and $x + 2$ the length of the third side. The perimeter is $x + (x + 1) + (x + 2) = 3x + 3$. $3x + 3$ is at least 6 (since $x \geq 1$) and is divisible by 3, and therefore not prime.

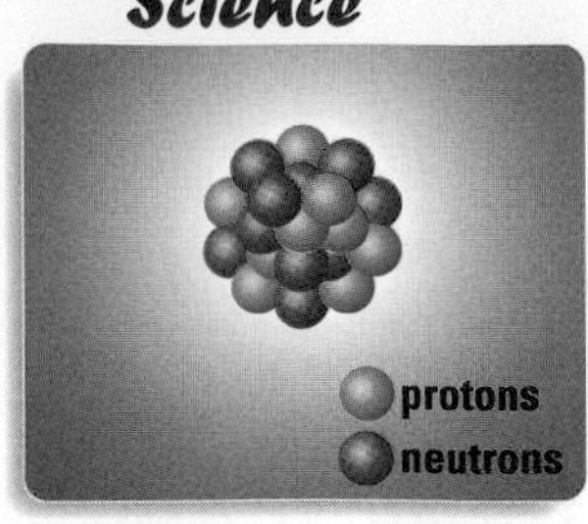

HALOGENS The atomic number of an element tells how many protons are in the nucleus of one atom of the element. The nucleus of a fluorine atom has 9 protons and 10 neutrons.

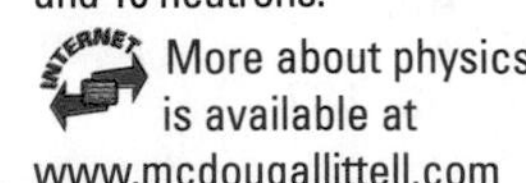
More about physics is available at www.mcdougallittell.com

78. **MATHEMATICAL REASONING** A class is divided into groups, with each group containing more than one student. If each group is the same size, decide if the number of students in the class is prime. Explain. **See margin.**

79. *Twin primes* are pairs of prime numbers whose difference is 2. Examples are 3 and 5, 5 and 7, and 11 and 13. Find the next 5 pairs of twin primes. **See margin.**

80. **Science Link** The table at the right shows the atomic numbers of 5 elements, called halogens, from the periodic table. For each number, tell whether it is *prime*, *composite*, or *neither*. If the number is composite, write its prime factorization. **See margin.**

Halogens	
Element	**Atomic number**
Fluorine	9
Chlorine	17
Bromine	35
Iodine	53
Astatine	85

81. **CHALLENGE** The lengths of the sides of a triangle are consecutive integers. Is it possible for the perimeter of the triangle to be a prime number? Support your answer. **See margin.**

Multiple-Choice Practice

82. Which number is a composite number? **B**

Ⓐ 23 Ⓑ 49 Ⓒ 19 Ⓓ 5

83. Which expression is the prime factorization of 36? **G**

Ⓕ $4 \cdot 9$ Ⓖ $2^2 \cdot 3^2$ Ⓗ $2^3 \cdot 3$ Ⓙ Not here

84. Which list shows all the factors of 84? **C**

Ⓐ 2, 3, 4, 6, 7, 8, 12, 14, 21, 28, 42, 84

Ⓑ 1, 2, 3, 4, 6, 8, 12, 14, 21, 28, 42, 84

Ⓒ 1, 2, 3, 4, 6, 7, 12, 14, 21, 28, 42, 84

Ⓓ 2, 3, 4, 6, 7, 8, 12, 16, 21, 28, 42, 84

Mixed Review

85. **MINIATURE GOLF** With one hole to go in a miniature golf tournament, your score is 3 under par, or -3. On the last hole, you score 2 under par, or -2. Write an expression that represents your final score. Then evaluate the expression. *(3.3)* **$-3 + (-2)$; -5**

Solve the equation. Check your solution. *(3.7)*

86. $x + 2 = -8$ **-10**
87. $5r = -100$ **-20**
88. $-16 = p - 12$ **-4**
89. $y - 2 = -45$ **-43**
90. $\frac{m}{-7} = -8$ **56**
91. $b + 46 = 74$ **28**

5.2 Greatest Common Factor

California Standards

In this lesson you'll:

- Find the greatest common factor of whole numbers. (Grade 6, NS 2.4)
- Interpret positive whole-number powers as repeated multiplication. (AF 2.1)

Goal 1 FINDING COMMON FACTORS

A whole number that is a factor of two or more nonzero whole numbers is called a **common factor** of the numbers. For example, 1, 2, 3, and 6 are common factors of 12 and 18.

The largest common factor of two or more nonzero whole numbers is called the **greatest common factor (GCF)**, sometimes called the *greatest common divisor* (GCD). For example, 6 is the greatest common factor of 12 and 18.

EXAMPLE 1 Using a List to Find the GCF

Find the GCF of 16 and 20.

Solution

With small numbers, you can list all the factors of each number, then compare them.

Factors of 16:	1, 2, 4, 8, 16
Factors of 20:	1, 2, 4, 5, 10, 20
Common factors:	1, 2, 4
Greatest common factor:	4

ANSWER ▶ The GCF of 16 and 20 is 4.

EXAMPLE 2 Using Prime Factorization to Find the GCF

Find the GCF of 180 and 378.

Solution

With large numbers, you can find the GCF by comparing the prime factorization of each number to find the common prime factors.

NUMBER	PRIME FACTORIZATION
180	**2** • 2 • **3** • **3** • 5
378	**2** • **3** • **3** • 3 • 7

The largest product of primes common to both factorizations is 2 • 3 • 3. This product is the greatest common factor:

$$\mathbf{2 \cdot 3 \cdot 3} = 18$$

ANSWER ▶ The GCF of 180 and 378 is 18.

1 Plan

Pacing

Suggested Number of Days

Transitional: 1 day
Average: 1 day
Advanced: 1 day
Block Schedule: 0.5 block with 5.3

Teaching Resources

Blacklines
(See page 216B.)

Transparencies
- Warm-Up Exercises
- Teacher Time-Savers
- English/Spanish Problem Solving
- Answers

Technology
- Electronic Teacher Tools
- Test and Practice Generator

2 Teach

Math Reasoning

For Mathematical Background Notes on mathematical reasoning related to this lesson, please refer to pages 216E and 216F in this Teacher's Edition.

Extra Examples 1 and 2
See next page.

California Standards and Assessment

CA Standards: Grade 6, NS 2.4; AF 2.1
CA Key Concepts Book: pp. T8–T11

Extra Example 1

Find the GCF of 28 and 42. **14**

Extra Example 2

Find the GCF of 297 and 540. **27**

Extra Example 3

Find the GCF of $45x^3y^2$ and $63x^2y^4$. **$9x^2y^2$**

Teaching Tip

Explain to students that if two numbers have a GCF of 1, they are said to be *relatively prime*. If two algebraic expressions have coefficients which are relatively prime, then the coefficient of their GCF is 1.

Extra Example 4

On a piano keyboard, three frequencies for F# (read "F sharp") are 185, 370, and 740. What is the GCF of these frequencies? **185**

Concept Check

Describe two ways to find the greatest common factor of two nonzero whole numbers. **List the factors of both numbers and find the greatest number that is common to both lists, or write the prime factorization of each number and then find the product of the prime factors that are common to both.**

Goal 2 Using Greatest Common Factors

The concept of greatest common factor also applies to variable expressions. For example, the greatest common factor of $18x^2$ and $12x$ is $6x$.

EXAMPLE 3 Finding the GCF of Variable Expressions

Find the GCF of $3x^2y$ and $6xy^3$.

Solution

Write each expression in factored form, as a product of prime numbers and variables with 1 as their exponent.

EXPRESSION	FACTORED FORM
$3x^2y$	$\mathbf{3} \cdot \boldsymbol{x} \cdot x \cdot \boldsymbol{y}$
$6xy^3$	$2 \cdot \mathbf{3} \cdot \boldsymbol{x} \cdot \boldsymbol{y} \cdot y \cdot y$

ANSWER ▶ The GCF is the product of the common factors: $\mathbf{3} \cdot \boldsymbol{x} \cdot \boldsymbol{y} = 3xy$.

EXAMPLE 4 Using the GCF

MUSIC Every musical note has a *frequency*. The frequency is the number of air vibrations per second of the sound wave you hear. Higher-pitched notes have greater frequencies than lower-pitched notes.

a. What is the GCF of the frequencies of the three A notes shown on the piano keyboard below?

b. What is the GCF of the frequencies of the three G notes?

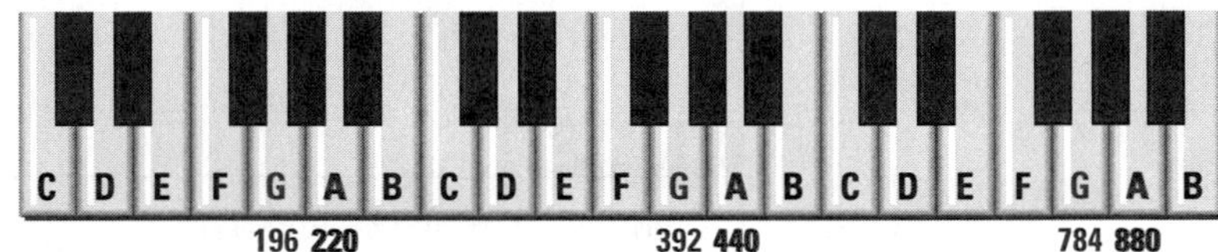

PIANOS When you double the frequency of a musical note, you get the same note with a higher pitch. This distance is called an octave. The modern piano keyboard has 88 keys, with a range of $7\frac{1}{4}$ octaves.

Solution

a. The A notes have frequencies of 220, 440, and 880.

Notice the pattern:
$220 = 220 \cdot 1$
$440 = 220 \cdot 2$
$880 = 220 \cdot 4$

ANSWER ▶ The GCF of the frequencies of the A notes is 220.

b. The G notes have frequencies of 196, 392, and 784.

Notice the pattern:
$196 = 196 \cdot 1$
$392 = 196 \cdot 2$
$784 = 196 \cdot 4$

ANSWER ▶ The GCF of the frequencies of the G notes is 196.

5.2 Exercises

Guided Practice

The factors of two numbers are given. Use the lists to find the common factors. Then find the GCF of the two numbers.

1. Factors of 12: 1, 2, 3, 4, 6, 12
Factors of 18: 1, 2, 3, 6, 9, 18
1, 2, 3, 6; 6

2. Factors of 32: 1, 2, 4, 8, 16, 32
Factors of 16: 1, 2, 4, 8, 16
1, 2, 4, 8, 16; 16

3. Factors of 20: 1, 2, 4, 5, 10, 20
Factors of 35: 1, 5, 7, 35
1, 5; 5

4. Factors of 39: 1, 3, 13, 39
Factors of 25: 1, 5, 25
1; 1

Use the prime factorizations to find the GCF of the two numbers.

5. $12 = 2 \cdot 2 \cdot 3$ **6**
$30 = 2 \cdot 3 \cdot 5$

6. $48 = 2 \cdot 2 \cdot 2 \cdot 2 \cdot 3$ **6**
$54 = 2 \cdot 3 \cdot 3 \cdot 3$

7. $60 = 2 \cdot 2 \cdot 3 \cdot 5$ **10**
$130 = 2 \cdot 5 \cdot 13$

8. $108 = 2 \cdot 2 \cdot 3 \cdot 3 \cdot 3$ **18**
$198 = 2 \cdot 3 \cdot 3 \cdot 11$

ALGEBRA Find the GCF of the variable expressions.

9. $7m$, $14m$ **$7m$**
10. $12r$, $15r^2$ **$3r$**
11. $5xy^2$, $10x^3y$ **$5xy$**
12. $6w^2$, $16w^4$ **$2w^2$**
13. $32xy$, $20xy$ **$4xy$**
14. $45s^2$, $18s^2$ **$9s^2$**

Practice and Problem Solving

> *Student Help*
> **▶ MORE PRACTICE**
> Extra practice to help you master skills is on page 698.

List the factors of each number. Then find the GCF of the numbers.

15. 20, 32 **4**
16. 21, 24 **3**
17. 50, 35 **5**
18. 35, 56 **7**
19. 42, 65 **1**
20. 36, 54 **18**
21. 70, 140 **70**
22. 40, 72 **8**

Write the prime factorization of the numbers. Then find the GCF of the numbers.

23. 120, 210 **30**
24. 54, 144 **18**
25. 68, 136 **68**
26. 84, 350 **14**
27. 91, 187 **1**
28. 81, 132 **3**
29. 252, 270 **18**
30. 36, 60, 96 **12**

ALGEBRA Find the GCF of the variable expressions.

31. x^2y, xy **xy**
32. $2xyz$, $4z^2$ **$2z$**
33. $2y^2z$, $8yz^2$ **$2yz$**
34. $11ac$, $33ab$ **$11a$**
35. $3x^2y^2$, $15x^2y$ **$3x^2y$**
36. $9r^2z$, $21rz$ **$3rz$**
37. $100abc$, $200xyz$ **100**
38. $27m^5n^8$, $9m^8n^5$ **$9m^5n^5$**
39. $42s^3t^4$, $70s^4t^3$ **$14s^3t^3$**

Numbers, such as 8 and 15, are *relatively prime* if their greatest common factor is 1. Tell whether the numbers are relatively prime.
40–47. See margin.

40. 56, 63
41. 64, 81
42. 35, 77
43. 50, 63
44. 12, 45
45. 39, 57
46. 72, 85
47. 200, 441

3 Apply

Assignment Guide

TRANSITIONAL
Day 1: pp. 227–228 Exs. 15–18, 23–26, 31–33, 40–43, 49–50, 55, 58–59

AVERAGE
Day 1: pp. 227–228 Exs. 19–22, 27–30, 34–36, 40–43, 48–50, 52, 54, 58–59

ADVANCED
Day 1: pp. 227–228 Exs. 19–22, 27–30, 37–39, 44–47, 50–53, 56–57*, 58–59

BLOCK SCHEDULE
pp. 227–228 Exs.19–22, 27–30, 34–36, 40–43, 48–50, 52, 54, 58–59 (with 5.3)

Extra Practice

- Student Edition, pp. 698–699
- Chapter 5 Resource Book, p. 15

Homework Check

To quickly check student understanding of key concepts, go over the following exercises:

Transitional: 16, 24, 32, 40, 50
Average: 20, 28, 34, 40, 50
Advanced: 20, 28, 38, 46, 50

Problem Solving

Avoiding Common Errors
In Exercises 9–14 students may recognize the common variables in the expressions, but they may not use the correct exponent in the GCF. Stress that the correct exponent is the smaller of those appearing in the two expressions for a particular common variable.

40. not relatively prime
41. relatively prime
42. not relatively prime
43. relatively prime
44. not relatively prime
45. not relatively prime
46. relatively prime
47. relatively prime

4 Assess

Assessment Resources

- Assessment Book (Formal Assessment and Alternative Assessment)
- Test and Practice Generator

Mini-Quiz

Find the greatest common factor of the numbers or expressions.

1. 45, 70 **5**
2. 225, 360 **45**
3. $12x^2y$, $6xy$ **$6xy$**
4. $18abc^2$, $21a^2bc^3$ **$3abc^2$**
5. Are the numbers 459 and 372 relatively prime? Explain. **No. Both numbers have 3 as a factor.**

Math Reasoning

Note the geometric interpretation of GCF implicit in Exercises 54–57.

48. True; a prime number has only 1 and itself as factors, so two different prime numbers can have only 1 as a common factor. Therefore, 1 is the greatest common factor.

53. No; the greatest common factor is a factor of each number, so it must be less than or equal to each number. *Sample example:* The greatest common factor of 10 and 120 is 10 and any greater factor of 120 could not possibly divide 10 evenly.

Determine if the statement is *true* or *false*. Justify your answer.

48. The greatest common factor of any two prime numbers is 1.
See margin.

49. The number 5 is a common factor of 30, 45, and 60.
True; 5 divides each of the three numbers evenly.

50. The greatest common factor of $2^2 \cdot 3 \cdot 5 \cdot 19$ and $2 \cdot 3^2 \cdot 7 \cdot 19$ is 19.
False; it is $2 \cdot 3 \cdot 19 = 114$.

51. The greatest common factor of $16x^3y^2z$ and $24x^2yz$ is $8x^2y$.
False; it is $8x^2yz$.

52. If 3 and 5 are common factors of a and b, then the GCF of a and b is 15. **False; there could be other common factors not mentioned.**

Link to Arts

WEAVING Mathematical ideas were used to help create the intricate pattern and pleasing shape of this basket.

53. MATHEMATICAL REASONING Is it possible for the greatest common factor of two numbers to be greater than either of the numbers? Explain your answer. Give an example to justify your reasoning.
See margin.

54. WEAVING The reeds below will be used to weave a mat. You need to cut each of the reeds into equal pieces so that all of the resulting pieces are the same length. What is the greatest possible length that can be used for the reeds? **13 cm**

55. SCHOOL BAND The band director wants the 56-member band followed by the 48-member color guard to each march in a rectangular formation. Each row should have the same number of students. Find the greatest number of students that can be in each row. Then find the number of rows for the color guard and the number of rows for the band.
8 students per row; 6 rows for the color guard and 7 rows for the band

CHALLENGE In Exercises 56 and 57, use the following information.
You want to use sections of fence that are all of the same length to enclose the field shown at the right.

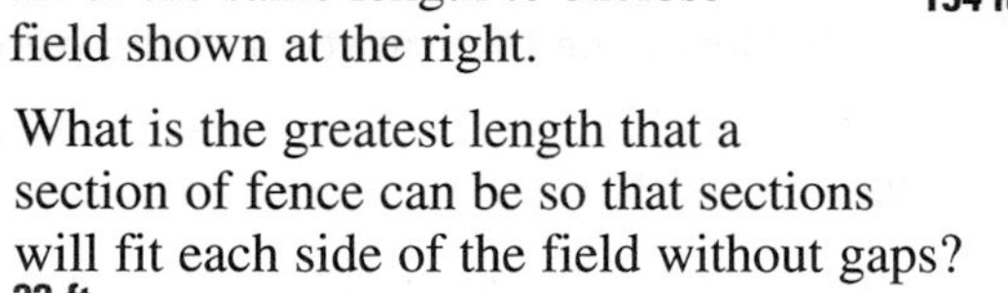

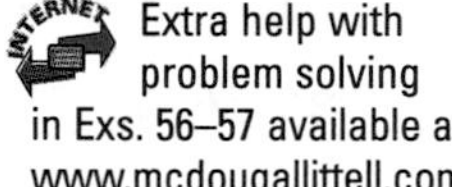

Student Help

▶ HOMEWORK HELP
Extra help with problem solving in Exs. 56–57 available at www.mcdougallittell.com

56. What is the greatest length that a section of fence can be so that sections will fit each side of the field without gaps?
22 ft

57. If you use sections of the greatest length, how many sections are needed to enclose the entire field? Explain your reasoning.
33 sections

Multiple-Choice Practice

58. What is the greatest common factor of 120 and 140? **C**

Ⓐ 4 Ⓑ 10 Ⓒ 20 Ⓓ 40

59. What is the greatest common factor of $84x^2y$ and $96xy^2$? **G**

Ⓕ 12 Ⓖ $12xy$ Ⓗ $12x^2y^2$ Ⓙ $12x^3y^3$

5.3 Least Common Multiple

California Standards

In this lesson you'll:

- Find the least common multiple of whole numbers. (Grade 6, NS 2.4)
- Interpret positive whole-number powers as repeated multiplication. (AF 2.1)

Goal 1 FINDING COMMON MULTIPLES

When you double, triple, or quadruple a number, you are finding *multiples* of the number. A **multiple** is the product of the number and any nonzero whole number. For example, the first three multiples of 16 are as follows:

$$1 \times 16 = 16$$

$$2 \times 16 = 32$$

$$3 \times 16 = 48$$

A **common multiple** is a multiple shared by two or more numbers. Of all the common multiples of two or more numbers, the smallest multiple is the **least common multiple** (LCM).

EXAMPLE 1 Using a List to Find the LCM

To find the LCM of small numbers such as 6 and 9, list the multiples of each number.

NUMBER	MULTIPLES	COMMON MULTIPLES
6	6, 12, 18, 24, 30, 36, . . .	**18**, 36, . . .
9	9, 18, 27, 36, . . .	**18**, 36, . . .

So, the LCM of 6 and 9 is 18.

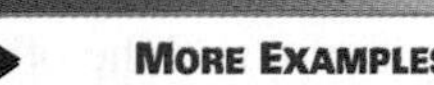

Student Help

MORE EXAMPLES
More examples are available at www.mcdougallittell.com

EXAMPLE 2 Using Prime Factorization to Find the LCM

To find the LCM of large numbers such as 180 and 378, use the prime factorization of each number. The LCM is the smallest product of prime numbers that contains the prime factorization of each number. This is the product of the highest power of each prime number that appears in either factorization.

NUMBER	PRIME FACTORIZATION	USING EXPONENTS
180	$2 \cdot 2 \cdot 3 \cdot 3 \cdot 5$	$\mathbf{2^2} \cdot 3^2 \cdot \mathbf{5}$
378	$2 \cdot 3 \cdot 3 \cdot 3 \cdot 7$	$2 \cdot \mathbf{3^3} \cdot \mathbf{7}$

The highest powers of 2, 3, 5, and 7 appearing in either factorization are $\mathbf{2^2}$, $\mathbf{3^3}$, **5**, and **7**, respectively. So, to find the LCM of 180 and 378, find the product of these highest powers: $2^2 \cdot 3^3 \cdot 5 \cdot 7 = 3780$.

So, the LCM of 180 and 378 is 3780.

1 Plan

Pacing

Suggested Number of Days

Transitional: 1 day
Average: 1 day
Advanced: 1 day
Block Schedule: 0.5 block with 5.2

Teaching Resources

Blacklines
(See page 216B.)

Transparencies
- Warm-Up Exercises
- Teacher Time-Savers
- English/Spanish Problem Solving
- Answers

Technology
- Electronic Teacher Tools
- Test and Practice Generator

2 Teach

Math Reasoning

For Mathematical Background Notes on mathematical reasoning related to this lesson, please refer to pages 216E and 216F in this Teacher's Edition.

Extra Examples 1 and 2
See next page.

California Standards and Assessment

CA Standards: Grade 6, NS 2.4; AF 2.1

Extra Example 1

Find the least common multiple of 12 and 14. **84**

Extra Example 2

Find the LCM of 168 and 462. **1848**

Extra Example 3

Find the LCM of $51n^2p$ and $68np^3$. **$204n^2p^3$**

Extra Example 4

You have a box of tiles, each of which is 6 in. by 8 in. Without overlapping or cutting the tiles, what is the least number of tiles you need to form a square? **12 tiles**

Teaching Tip

Some students may notice that the expanded form of the LCM includes each different prime factor the greater number of times it occurs in either factorization. (The factor 2, which occurs twice in the prime factorization of 180 and once in the prime factorization of 378, is used twice as a factor in computing the LCM, 3780.)

Math Reasoning

To find the LCM of m and n, form the smallest product of prime numbers such that the prime factorization of both m and n appear in the product. For example, with $m = 180$ and $n = 378$ as in Example 2, we see that the product $2 \cdot 2 \cdot 3 \cdot 3 \cdot 3 \cdot 5 \cdot 7$ contains within it both $2 \cdot 2 \cdot 3 \cdot 3 \cdot 5$ and $2 \cdot 3 \cdot 3 \cdot 3 \cdot 7$, and no smaller product of primes has this property.

Concept Check

Describe two ways to find the least common multiple of two non-zero whole numbers. **Write multiples of both numbers and look for the smallest number that is in both lists; write the prime factorization of each number and find the product of the common prime factors and all the factors that are not common.**

Goal 2 Using Least Common Multiples

Finding the LCM of variable expressions is similar to finding the LCM of numbers: find the product of the highest powers of the primes and variables appearing in the factorization of either expression.

Student Help

▶ Study Tip
When writing the LCM of variable expressions, write the numbers first, then the variables.

EXAMPLE 3 Finding the LCM of Variable Expressions

Find the LCM of the variable expressions.

a. $20ab^2$ and $18b$ **b.** $25xy^3$ and $6x^3y^2$

Solution

Write the prime factorization of each coefficient using exponents. Then find the LCM by multiplying the highest power of each factor (including variables) that appears in either expression.

a. $20ab^2 = 2^2 \cdot 5 \cdot a \cdot b^2$

$18b = 2 \cdot 3^2 \cdot b$

ANSWER ▶ LCM $= 2^2 \cdot 3^2 \cdot 5 \cdot a \cdot b^2 = 180ab^2$

b. $25xy^3 = 5^2 \cdot x \cdot y^3$

$6x^3y^2 = 2 \cdot 3 \cdot x^3 \cdot y^2$

ANSWER ▶ LCM $= 2 \cdot 3 \cdot 5^2 \cdot x^3 \cdot y^3 = 150x^3y^3$

EXAMPLE 4 Using the LCM

You have a box of tiles. Each tile measures 4 inches by 6 inches. Without overlapping or cutting the tiles, what is the least number of tiles that will form a square?

Solution

If you use the tiles to form a square and keep all the tiles in the same orientation, one side of the square will be a multiple of 4 and the other side will be a multiple of 6.

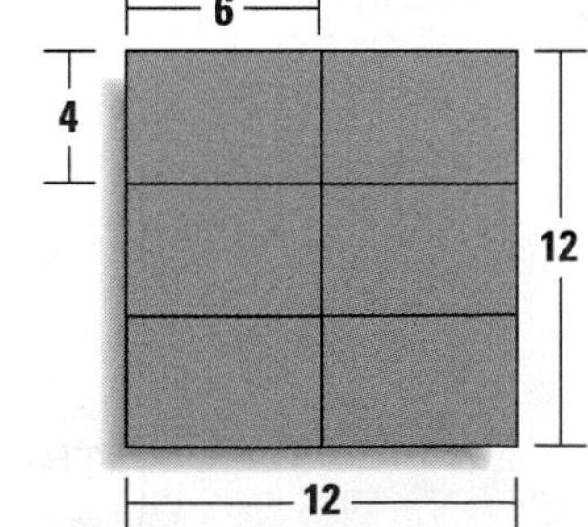

Because the sides of a square are equal in length, the length of a side must be a common multiple of 4 and 6.

Because you want the smallest possible square, the length of a side should be the least common multiple of 4 and 6.

ANSWER ▶ The LCM of 4 and 6 is 12. Arrange the tiles as shown above. The least number of tiles needed to form a square is 6 tiles.

5.3 Exercises

Guided Practice

1. 12, 24, 36, 48, 60, 72, 84, 96, 108

2. 20, 40, 60, 80, 100, 120, 140, 160, 180

3. 32, 64, 96, 128, 160, 192, 224, 256, 288

4. 45, 90, 135, 180, 225, 270, 315, 360, 405

List the first nine multiples of the number. 1–4. See margin.

1. 12 **2.** 20 **3.** 32 **4.** 45

Use the multiples from Exercises 1–4 to find the LCM of the numbers.

5. 12 and 32 **96** **6.** 12 and 20 **60** **7.** 20 and 32 **160** **8.** 20 and 45 **180**

Write the prime factorization of the number.

9. 66 $2 \cdot 3 \cdot 11$ **10.** 90 $2 \cdot 3^2 \cdot 5$ **11.** 165 $3 \cdot 5 \cdot 11$ **12.** 200 $2^3 \cdot 5^2$

Use the answers from Exercises 9–12 to find the LCM of the numbers.

13. 66 and 165 **330** **14.** 90 and 200 **1800** **15.** 66 and 90 **990**

ALGEBRA Find the LCM of the variable expressions.

16. $32x^2, 24x$ $96x^2$ **17.** $12mn, 18m^2n^2$ $36m^2n^2$ **18.** $5abc, 6a^2c$ $30a^2bc$

19. CAFETERIA A cafeteria buys hot dogs in packages of 36 and hot dog rolls in packages of 20. Find the least number of packages of hot dogs and rolls that must be bought to have an equal number of hot dogs and rolls. **5 packages of hot dogs and 9 packages of rolls**

Practice and Problem Solving

Student Help

▶More Practice
Extra practice to help you master skills is on page 698.

List the first few multiples of each number. Then use the lists to find the LCM of the numbers.

20. 3, 7 **21** **21.** 4, 18 **36** **22.** 6, 8 **24** **23.** 3, 9 **9**

24. 8, 10 **40** **25.** 10, 15 **30** **26.** 10, 26 **130** **27.** 4, 22 **44**

Write the prime factorization of the numbers. Then find their LCM.

28. 90, 108 **540** **29.** 7, 8 **56** **30.** 17, 57 **969**

31. 125, 500 **500** **32.** 63, 105 **315** **33.** 160, 432 **4320**

34. 135, 375 **3375** **35.** 225, 324 **8100** **36.** 144, 162 **1296**

ALGEBRA In Exercises 37–42, find the LCM of the variable expressions.

37. $5ab, 7ab^2$ $35ab^2$ **38.** $16x, 32x^4$ $32x^4$ **39.** $7s^2t, 49st^2$ $49s^2t^2$

40. $2x^3y, 3xy^5$ $6x^3y^5$ **41.** $3m^4n^4, 7m^6n^2$ $21m^6n^4$ **42.** $4a^6b^3, 8a^7b^5$ $8a^7b^5$

43. MATHEMATICAL REASONING One number is a multiple of a second number. What is the least common multiple of the numbers? Explain. Use several examples to illustrate your answer.

43. The greater number; The greater number is a multiple of the second number and it is a multiple (· 1) of itself. *Sample example*: LCM of 3 and 15 is 15.

3 Apply

Assignment Guide

Transitional
Day 1: pp. 231–232 Exs. 20–23, 28–32, 37–39, 47–48, 54–56

Average
Day 1: pp. 231–232 Exs. 20–23, 30–33, 37–39, 43–49, 54–56

Advanced
Day 1: pp. 231–232 Exs. 24–27, 32–36, 40–43, 49–52, 53*, 54–56

Block Schedule
pp. 231–232 Exs. 20–23, 30–33, 37–39, 43–49, 54–56 (with 5.2)

Extra Practice

- Student Edition, pp. 698–699
- Chapter 5 Resource Book, p. 24

Homework Check

To quickly check student understanding of key concepts, go over the following exercises:

Transitional: 20, 28, 32, 38, 48
Average: 22, 30, 32, 38, 48
Advanced: 24, 32, 34, 40, 52

Math Reasoning

Exercise 43 can be explained either using the definition of LCM or using the criterion involving prime factorization.

4 Assess

Assessment Resources

- Assessment Book (Formal Assessment and Alternative Assessment)
- Test and Practice Generator

Mini-Quiz

Find the least common multiple of the numbers or expressions.

1. 9, 12 **36**
2. 42, 385 **2310**
3. $12x^2y, 5xy^2$ **$60x^2y^2$**
4. $28a^2b^3, 15a^4b$ **$420a^4b^3$**
5. What is the smallest square that can be made with rectangular tiles that are 12 in. by 18 in.? **a square that is 36 in. by 36 in.**

Math Reasoning

Both Exercise 49 and Example 4 are special cases of the fact that the LCM of m and n is the side of the smallest square that can be tiled with $m \times n$ rectangles.

48. large gear: 27 revolutions, smaller gear: 46 revolutions

49. 14 tiles; These can be placed 7 across and 2 deep to form a 28 in. by 28 in. square.

History

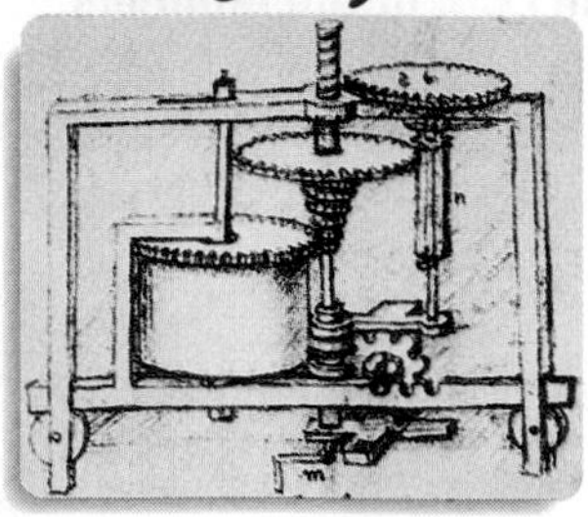

GEARS Leonardo da Vinci's 15th century studies of mechanics included insights that could not be used to advantage until the advent of strong materials that could be shaped with precision.

More about gears available at www.mcdougallittell.com

50. The person did not multiply the common factors by the factors not in common.; 72

51. *Sample answer:* Find the LCM of two of the numbers. Then find the LCM of that number and the third number.

In Exercises 44–46, find a pair of numbers that fits the description.

44–46. Sample answers are given.

44. Two prime numbers whose LCM is 35
5 and 7

45. Two unequal composite numbers whose LCM is 16
4 and 16, 8 and 16

46. Two even numbers less than 10 whose LCM is 12
4 and 6

47. You have enough pens to divide them into 12 equal groups or 20 equal groups. What is the least number of pens you can have?
60 pens

48. GEARS Use the photograph of gears at the right. The large gear has 46 teeth and the small gear has 27 teeth. Find the number of complete revolutions each gear must make for the gears to align again as shown.
See margin.

49. TILES You have a box of 4-inch-by-14-inch tiles. Find the least number of tiles you need to form a square region without overlapping or cutting the tiles. Use a diagram to help explain your answer.
See margin.

50. ERROR ANALYSIS Describe and correct the error shown at the right.
See margin.

$24 = 2 \cdot 3 \cdot 2 \cdot 2$
$36 = 2 \cdot 3 \cdot 2 \cdot 3$
$\text{LCM} = 2 \cdot 3 \cdot 2 = 12$

51. WRITING Explain how you would find the LCM of three different numbers.
See margin.

52. STOPLIGHTS A stoplight turns red every 6 minutes. Another stoplight turns red every 8 minutes. A third stoplight turns red every 10 minutes. At 2:00 P.M., the three stoplights turn red at the same time. Find the next time that all three stoplights turn red at the same time.
4:00 P.M.

53. CHALLENGE You have a tray of muffins. If you try to divide the muffins into groups of 3, one muffin is left over. If you try to divide the muffins into groups of 4, one muffin is left over. If you divide the muffins into groups of 5, there are no muffins left over. What is the least number of muffins that you could have on the tray?
25 muffins

Multiple-Choice Practice

▶ Lightly circle the numbers of questions whose answers you want to check if you complete a test section early and have extra time. Remember to erase the circles later.

54. What is the least common multiple of 20 and 30? **B**

Ⓐ 10 Ⓑ 60 Ⓒ 120 Ⓓ 600

55. What is the least common multiple of $4x^2y$ and $6xy^2$? **G**

Ⓕ $24x^2y^2$ Ⓖ $12x^2y^2$ Ⓗ $12xy$ Ⓙ $2xy$

56. Which of the following is *not* a common multiple of 6 and 8? **A**

Ⓐ 16 Ⓑ 24 Ⓒ 48 Ⓓ 96

5.4 Simplifying and Comparing Fractions

California Standards

In this lesson you'll:

- Use factoring to find common denominators. (NS 2.2)
- Simplify expressions that include exponents. (AF 2.1)

Goal 1 Simplifying a Fraction

The squares below show that $\frac{2}{3}$, $\frac{4}{6}$, and $\frac{8}{12}$ represent the same quantity.

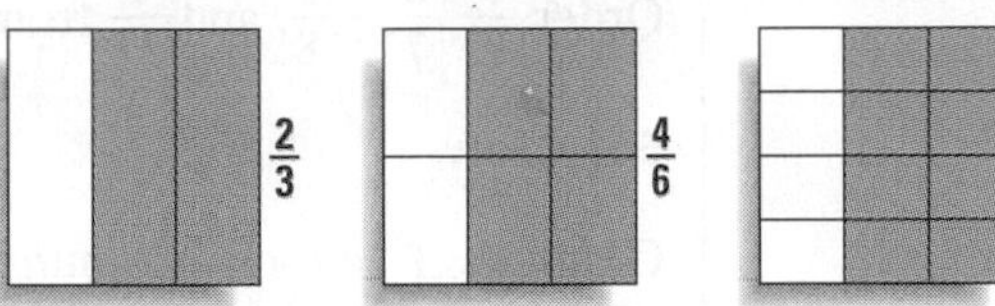

The fraction $\frac{2}{3}$ is in **simplest form** because the only common factor of the numerator and denominator is 1. Writing a fraction in its simplest form is called *simplifying* the fraction. Fractions that have the same simplest form are **equivalent**.

EXAMPLE 1 Simplifying a Fraction

Simplify $\frac{12}{20}$.

Solution

Method 1
Factor the numerator and denominator. Then divide by common prime factors.

$$\frac{12}{20} = \frac{\cancel{2}^{1} \cdot \cancel{2}^{1} \cdot 3}{\cancel{2}_{1} \cdot \cancel{2}_{1} \cdot 5} = \frac{3}{5}$$

Method 2
Divide the numerator and denominator by their GCF. The GCF of 12 and 20 is 4.

$$\frac{12}{20} = \frac{12 \div 4}{20 \div 4} = \frac{3}{5}$$

Method 1 of Example 1 is also useful for simplifying variable expressions.

EXAMPLE 2 Simplifying Variable Expressions

Simplify the expression. **a.** $\frac{4x^2}{6x}$ **b.** $\frac{5x^3}{15x}$

Solution

a. $\frac{4x^2}{6x} = \frac{\cancel{2}^{1} \cdot 2 \cdot x \cdot \cancel{x}^{1}}{\cancel{2}_{1} \cdot 3 \cdot \cancel{x}_{1}} = \frac{2x}{3}$

b. $\frac{5x^3}{15x} = \frac{\cancel{5}^{1} \cdot \cancel{x}^{1} \cdot x \cdot x}{3 \cdot \cancel{5}_{1} \cdot \cancel{x}_{1}} = \frac{x^2}{3}$

1 Plan

Pacing
Suggested Number of Days
Transitional: 2 days
Average: 2 days
Advanced: 2 days
Block Schedule: 1 block

Teaching Resources

Blacklines
(See page 216B.)

Transparencies
- Warm-Up Exercises
- Teacher Time-Savers
- English/Spanish Problem Solving
- Answers

Technology
- Electronic Teacher Tools
- Test and Practice Generator

2 Teach

Math Reasoning

For Mathematical Background Notes on mathematical reasoning related to this lesson, please refer to pages 216E and 216F in this Teacher's Edition.

Extra Examples 1 and 2
See next page.

California Standards and Assessment
CA Standards: NS 2.2, AF 2.1
CA Key Concepts Book: pp. T12–T13

Math Reasoning

Simplifying a fraction can of course be done in several steps. For instance, in Example 1, one can proceed with $\frac{12}{20} = \frac{2 \cdot 6}{2 \cdot 10} = \frac{6}{10} = \frac{2 \cdot 3}{2 \cdot 5} = \frac{3}{5}$.

Extra Example 1

Simplify $\frac{18}{24}$. $\frac{3}{4}$

Extra Example 2

Simplify the expression.

a. $\frac{28n^3}{42n}$ $\frac{2n^2}{3}$

b. $\frac{81x^5}{12x^2}$ $\frac{27x^3}{4}$

Extra Example 3

Order $\frac{11}{20}$, $-\frac{8}{15}$, $\frac{1}{5}$, and $\frac{29}{30}$ from least to greatest. $-\frac{8}{15}, \frac{1}{5}, \frac{11}{20}, \frac{29}{30}$

Extra Example 4

Which fraction is greater, $\frac{5}{11}$ or $\frac{3}{7}$? $\frac{5}{11}$

Extra Example 5

You ate 3 pieces of an apple pie that was cut into 8 equal pieces and your sister ate 2 pieces of a blueberry pie that was cut into 6 equal pieces. The two pies were the same size. Who ate more pie? **You ate more pie.**

Concept Check

How do you know when a fraction is simplified? **The numerator and denominator will have no common factors other than 1.**

234

Goal 2 COMPARING FRACTIONS

To compare fractions with the *same* denominator, compare their numerators. For example, $\frac{5}{7} > \frac{4}{7}$, because 5 (sevenths) > 4 (sevenths).

Use a number line to compare fractions with different denominators.

EXAMPLE 3 Comparing Fractions Using a Number Line

Order $\frac{5}{12}$, $\frac{8}{7}$, $-\frac{3}{8}$, and $\frac{1}{12}$ from least to greatest.

Solution

Graph the fractions on a number line. Negative fractions lie to the left of zero just like negative integers.

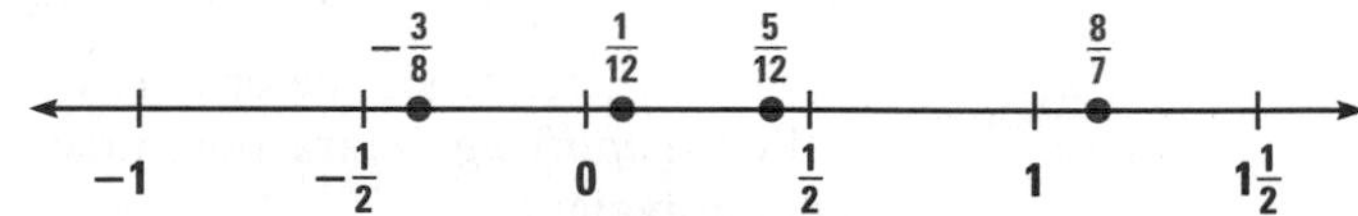

ANSWER ▶ From least to greatest, the order is $-\frac{3}{8}, \frac{1}{12}, \frac{5}{12}, \frac{8}{7}$.

Another way to compare fractions with different denominators is to find equivalent fractions with a common denominator.

EXAMPLE 4 Using Equivalent Fractions

Which fraction is greater, $\frac{7}{12}$ or $\frac{9}{16}$?

Solution

Method 1 Use the product of 12 and 16 to find equivalent fractions.

$\frac{7}{12} = \frac{7 \cdot 16}{12 \cdot 16} = \frac{112}{192}$ **Multiply numerator and denominator by 16.**

$\frac{9}{16} = \frac{9 \cdot 12}{16 \cdot 12} = \frac{108}{192}$ **Multiply numerator and denominator by 12.**

ANSWER ▶ $\frac{112}{192} > \frac{108}{192}$, so $\frac{7}{12} > \frac{9}{16}$.

Method 2 Use the LCM of 12 and 16, which is 48.

$\frac{7}{12} = \frac{7 \cdot 4}{12 \cdot 4} = \frac{28}{48}$ **Multiply numerator and denominator by 4.**

$\frac{9}{16} = \frac{9 \cdot 3}{16 \cdot 3} = \frac{27}{48}$ **Multiply numerator and denominator by 3.**

ANSWER ▶ $\frac{28}{48} > \frac{27}{48}$, so $\frac{7}{12} > \frac{9}{16}$.

MORE EXAMPLES

More examples are available at www.mcdougallittell.com

EXAMPLE 5 Comparing to Solve a Problem

You ate 4 slices of a pizza that was cut into 6 equal slices. Your friend ate 5 slices of a pizza of the same size that was cut into 8 equal pieces. Who ate more pizza?

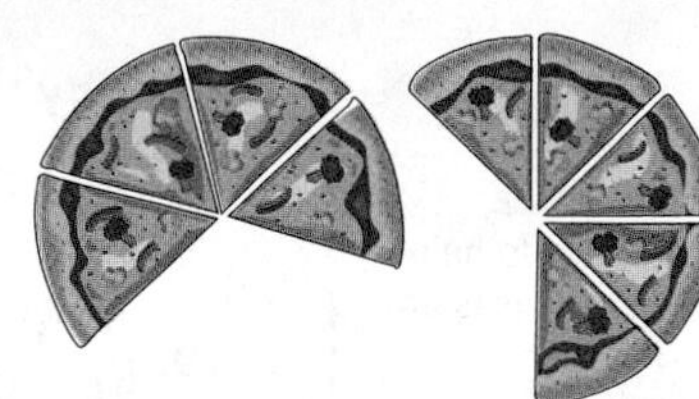

Solution You ate $\frac{4}{6}$ of a pizza, and your friend ate $\frac{5}{8}$ of a pizza. Both fractions are a little more than $\frac{1}{2} = \frac{3}{6} = \frac{4}{8}$. Rewrite each fraction so it has a denominator of 24, the LCM of 6 and 8.

$\frac{4}{6} = \frac{4 \cdot 4}{6 \cdot 4} = \frac{16}{24}$ Multiply numerator and denominator by 4.

$\frac{5}{8} = \frac{5 \cdot 3}{8 \cdot 3} = \frac{15}{24}$ Multiply numerator and denominator by 3.

ANSWER ▶ $\frac{16}{24} > \frac{15}{24}$, so you ate more pizza than your friend.

3 Apply

Assignment Guide

TRANSITIONAL
Day 1: pp. 236–237 Exs. 15–20, 23–28, 55–57
Day 2: pp. 236–237 Exs. 31–33, 37–39, 47–48, 51–53

AVERAGE
Day 1: pp. 236–237 Exs. 15–30, 55–57
Day 2: pp. 236–237 Exs. 31–34, 37–39, 43–47, 49–50

ADVANCED
Day 1: pp. 236–237 Exs. 15–30, 55–57
Day 2: pp. 236–237 Exs. 34–36, 40–48, 51–53, 54*

BLOCK SCHEDULE
pp. 236–237 Exs. 15–34, 37–39, 43–47, 49–50, 55–57

Extra Practice

- Student Edition, pp. 698–699
- Chapter 5 Resource Book, p. 33

Homework Check

To quickly check student understanding of key concepts, go over the following exercises:

Transitional: 16, 24, 32, 38, 48
Average: 18, 26, 32, 38, 50
Advanced: 20, 28, 36, 40, 48

5.4 Exercises

Guided Practice

1. What fraction represents the shaded portion of each figure at the right? Write the fraction in simplest form.

a. 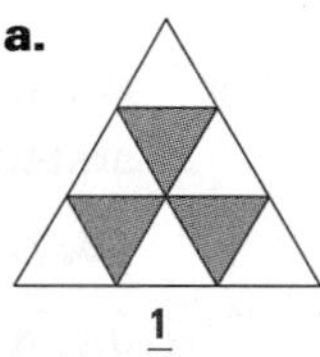 $\frac{1}{3}$

b. 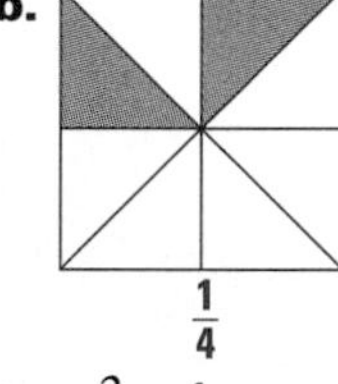 $\frac{1}{4}$

Simplify the fraction.

2. $\frac{4}{10}$ $\frac{2}{5}$ **3.** $-\frac{2}{6}$ $-\frac{1}{3}$ **4.** $\frac{6}{8}$ $\frac{3}{4}$ **5.** $\frac{3}{15}$ $\frac{1}{5}$

In Exercises 6–9, simplify the variable expression.

6. $\frac{42x^3}{56x}$ $\frac{3x^2}{4}$ **7.** $-\frac{30rs}{40x^2}$ $-\frac{3rs}{4x^2}$ **8.** $\frac{12mn^2}{6m^2n^2}$ $\frac{2}{m}$ **9.** $\frac{2xyz}{8wxy}$ $\frac{z}{4w}$

10. Graph $-\frac{15}{18}$, $\frac{3}{7}$, $-\frac{7}{3}$, and $\frac{8}{9}$ on a number line. Then order the fractions from least to greatest. See margin.

Rewrite the fractions as equivalent fractions with a common denominator. Then determine which fraction is greater. 11–14. See margin.

11. $\frac{1}{4}, \frac{1}{5}$ **12.** $-\frac{4}{9}, -\frac{2}{6}$ **13.** $\frac{2}{5}, \frac{3}{7}$ **14.** $\frac{11}{16}, \frac{5}{8}$

10. $-\frac{7}{3}, -\frac{15}{18}, \frac{3}{7}, \frac{8}{9}$

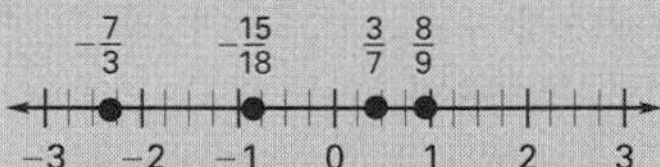

11. $\frac{5}{20}, \frac{4}{20}; \frac{1}{4}$

12. $-\frac{8}{18}, -\frac{6}{18}; -\frac{2}{6}$

13. $\frac{14}{35}, \frac{15}{35}; \frac{3}{7}$

14. $\frac{11}{16}, \frac{10}{16}; \frac{11}{16}$

31. $-\frac{5}{9}, \frac{1}{4}, \frac{8}{10}, \frac{9}{10}$

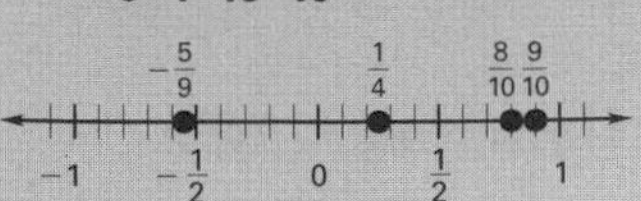

32. $\frac{2}{3}, \frac{9}{12}, \frac{4}{5}, \frac{8}{9}$

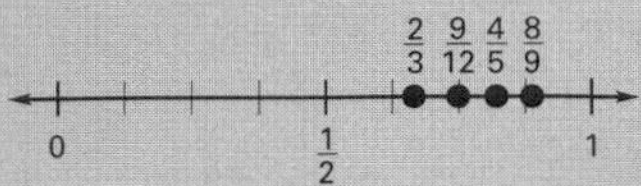

33. $-\frac{1}{3}, -\frac{1}{4}, \frac{1}{10}, \frac{1}{7}$

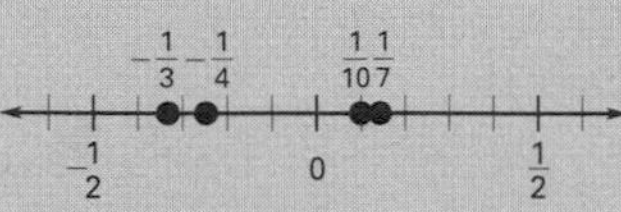

34. $-\frac{7}{3}, -\frac{8}{4}, \frac{3}{4}, \frac{5}{3}$

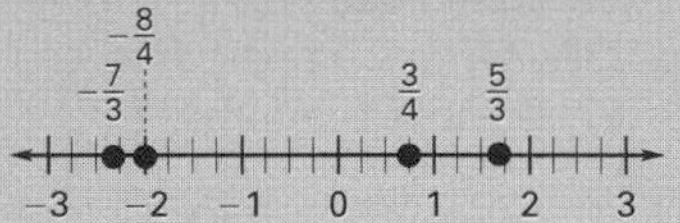

35. $-\frac{7}{8}, -\frac{5}{9}, -\frac{3}{10}, \frac{1}{5}$

$-\frac{7}{8}$ $-\frac{5}{9}$ $-\frac{3}{10}$ $\frac{1}{5}$

−1 0 1

36. $-\frac{12}{16}, -\frac{4}{6}, -\frac{5}{12}, -\frac{3}{9}$

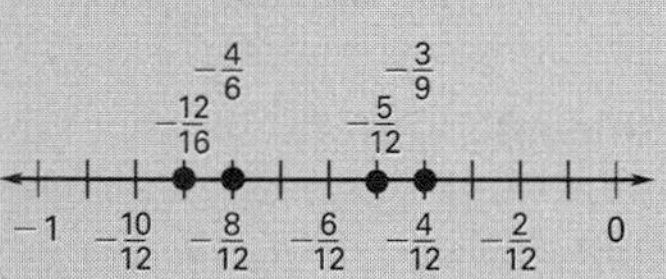

43. False; *Sample answer:* $-\frac{1}{2}$ is graphed halfway between 0 and −1, which is to the left of 0.

46. *Sample answer:* A fraction is in simplest form when the only factor the numerator and denominator have in common is 1. For example, $\frac{2}{3}$ is in simplest form, but $\frac{4}{6}$ is not since 2 is a common factor of 4 and 6.

Practice and Problem Solving

Student Help

▶MORE PRACTICE Extra practice to help you master skills is on page 698.

Simplify the fraction.

15. $\frac{14}{20}$ **$\frac{7}{10}$** 16. $\frac{16}{36}$ **$\frac{4}{9}$** 17. $\frac{9}{42}$ **$\frac{3}{14}$** 18. $\frac{63}{105}$ **$\frac{3}{5}$**

19. $\frac{7}{91}$ **$\frac{1}{13}$** 20. $\frac{18}{30}$ **$\frac{3}{5}$** 21. $\frac{14}{84}$ **$\frac{1}{6}$** 22. $\frac{22}{48}$ **$\frac{11}{24}$**

Simplify the variable expression.

23. $\frac{15g}{50g^3}$ **$\frac{3}{10g^2}$** 24. $\frac{14y^2}{35m^2y}$ **$\frac{2y}{5m^2}$** 25. $\frac{27xy^2}{18x^2y}$ **$\frac{3y}{2x}$** 26. $\frac{32ab^3}{36a^3b^3}$ **$\frac{8}{9a^2}$**

27. $\frac{3x^2y}{9y}$ **$\frac{x^2}{3}$** 28. $\frac{25z^2}{150z^3}$ **$\frac{1}{6z}$** 29. $\frac{22s^3t}{55s^3t^2}$ **$\frac{2}{5t}$** 30. $\frac{15x}{21x^2}$ **$\frac{5}{7x}$**

Graph the fractions on a number line. Then order the fractions from least to greatest. **31–36. See margin.**

31. $\frac{9}{10}, \frac{1}{4}, -\frac{5}{9}, \frac{8}{10}$ 32. $\frac{4}{5}, \frac{2}{3}, \frac{8}{9}, \frac{9}{12}$ 33. $\frac{1}{10}, \frac{1}{7}, -\frac{1}{4}, -\frac{1}{3}$

34. $-\frac{7}{3}, \frac{5}{3}, \frac{3}{4}, -\frac{8}{4}$ 35. $\frac{1}{5}, -\frac{5}{9}, -\frac{7}{8}, -\frac{3}{10}$ 36. $-\frac{3}{9}, -\frac{5}{12}, -\frac{4}{6}, -\frac{12}{16}$

Use <, >, or = to complete the statement.

37. $\frac{7}{8}$? $\frac{8}{9}$ **<** 38. $\frac{1}{12}$? $\frac{1}{13}$ **>** 39. $-\frac{15}{39}$? $-\frac{5}{13}$ **=**

40. $\frac{26}{50}$? $\frac{27}{51}$ **<** 41. $-\frac{9}{16}$? $-\frac{7}{12}$ **>** 42. $\frac{8}{21}$? $\frac{10}{33}$ **>**

MATHEMATICAL REASONING In Exercises 43–45, tell whether the statement is *true* or *false*. Give an example to support your answer.

43. A negative fraction is graphed to the right of zero on a number line. **See margin.**

44. A fraction with a positive denominator twice as great as its positive numerator is equivalent to $\frac{1}{2}$. **true; *Sample answer:* $\frac{2}{4} = \frac{1}{2}$**

45. A fraction with a positive numerator less than its positive denominator is a number greater than 1. **false; *Sample answer:* $\frac{4}{5} < 1$**

46. **MATHEMATICAL REASONING** Explain how you can tell when a fraction is in simplest form. Use an example. **See margin.**

47. **HIKING** You have walked 3 miles of your 11-mile hike. Your friend has walked 5 miles of a 14-mile hike. Who has completed the greater part of his or her hike so far? Explain your answer. **Friend; $\frac{5}{14} > \frac{3}{11}$**

48. **STOCKS** Company A's stock price rose $\frac{3}{4}$ point. Company B's stock price rose $\frac{13}{16}$ point. Which stock price increased more? **Company B**

Link to Visual Arts

PHOTOGRAPHY Besides adjusting shutter speed, a photographer can also control the amount of light to which the film is exposed by adjusting the lens opening of the camera.

More about photography available at www.mcdougallittell.com

53. yes; the graph gives $\frac{4}{21} + \frac{3}{21} = \frac{7}{21} = \frac{1}{3}$.

54. $\frac{8}{15}$; change both fractions to 15ths: $\frac{10}{15}$ and $\frac{6}{15}$. $\frac{8}{15}$ is halfway between them.

PHOTOGRAPHY In Exercises 49 and 50, use the following information. The shutter speed of a camera is the length of time the shutter is open. A slow shutter speed exposes the film for more time than a fast speed.

49. You want to decrease the shutter speed of your camera from $\frac{1}{250}$ of a second. Should you change the speed to $\frac{1}{125}$ of a second or to $\frac{1}{500}$ of a second? Explain your answer. **$\frac{1}{125}$; $\frac{1}{125} > \frac{1}{250}$, so the speed will be slower.**

50. You want to increase the shutter speed of your camera from $\frac{1}{125}$ of a second. Should you change the speed to $\frac{1}{60}$ of a second or to $\frac{1}{500}$ of a second? Explain your answer. **$\frac{1}{500}$; $\frac{1}{500} < \frac{1}{125}$, so the speed will be faster.**

NUTRITION In Exercises 51–53, use the bar graph below. It shows the number of recommended servings for maintaining a balanced diet.

51. Write the servings of meat as a fraction of all servings. Simplify. **$\frac{1}{7}$**

52. Write the combined servings of vegetables and bread as a fraction of all servings. Simplify. **$\frac{4}{7}$**

53. A friend tells you that one third of the food servings should be fruits and vegetables. Compare this to the recommendation given in the graph. Is your friend correct? Explain.

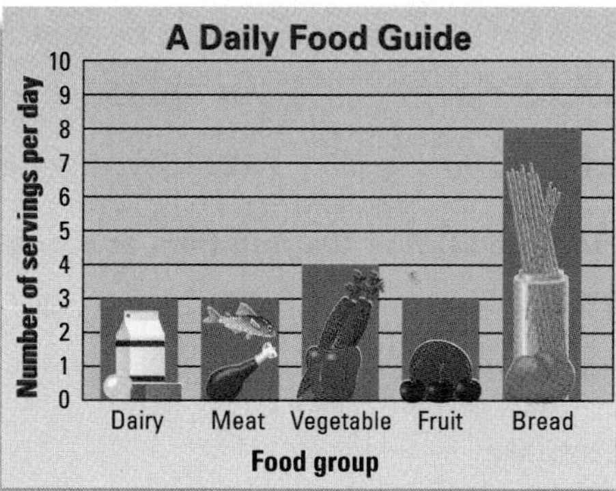

54. CHALLENGE Find a fraction that is exactly halfway between $\frac{2}{3}$ and $\frac{2}{5}$. Explain how you found the fraction.

Multiple-Choice Practice

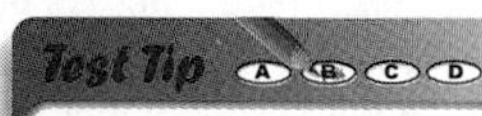

Test Tip

▶ Be alert to the word *not* when used as part of a question in a standardized test. Read questions carefully so you do not miss important words.

55. Which of the following is *not* equivalent to $\frac{7}{8}$? **B**

Ⓐ $\frac{14}{16}$ Ⓑ $\frac{17}{18}$ Ⓒ $\frac{21}{24}$ Ⓓ $\frac{28}{32}$

56. Which group of fractions is correctly ordered from least to greatest? **G**

Ⓕ $\frac{1}{2}, \frac{1}{3}, \frac{1}{4}$ Ⓖ $\frac{2}{9}, \frac{1}{3}, \frac{2}{5}$ Ⓗ $\frac{12}{21}, \frac{4}{9}, \frac{3}{7}$ Ⓙ $\frac{5}{8}, \frac{7}{15}, \frac{1}{2}$

57. To which integer is $-\frac{4}{3}$ closest on a number line? **C**

Ⓐ 1 Ⓑ 0 Ⓒ −1 Ⓓ −2

4 Assess

Assessment Resources

- Assessment Book (Formal Assessment and Alternative Assessment)
- Test and Practice Generator

Mini-Quiz

Simplify the fraction or variable expression.

1. $\frac{8}{36}$ $\frac{2}{9}$
2. $\frac{13}{52}$ $\frac{1}{4}$
3. $\frac{112}{200}$ $\frac{14}{25}$
4. $\frac{15x^3y}{20xy^3}$ $\frac{3x^2}{4y^2}$
5. Which fraction is greater, $\frac{6}{7}$ or $\frac{7}{8}$? $\frac{7}{8}$

Math Reasoning

In Exercise 54, one can use the fact that given *a* and *b* on a number line, their average, $\frac{a+b}{2}$, is halfway between them. Thus $\frac{1}{2}\left(\frac{2}{3} + \frac{2}{5}\right) = \frac{1}{3} + \frac{1}{5} = \frac{8}{15}$ is exactly halfway between $\frac{2}{3}$ and $\frac{2}{5}$. In other words, $\frac{8}{15}$ is the same distance from both $\frac{2}{3}$ and $\frac{2}{5}$. How would you find a fraction whose distance from $\frac{2}{3}$ is three times its distance from $\frac{2}{5}$? (*Hint:* Look at $\frac{6}{15}$ and $\frac{10}{15}$ on a number line. How many $\frac{1}{15}$'s separate them?)

Additional Resources

A Mid-Chapter Test and a Mid-Chapter Partner Quiz are available in the *Assessment Book*, pp. 61–62 and p. 230.

9. 1, 2, 4, 7, 8, 14, 28, 56

10. 1, 2, 3, 4, 5, 6, 10, 12, 15, 20, 30, 60

11. 1, 2, 89, 178

12. 1, 3, 5, 11, 15, 33, 55, 165

13. 1, 2, 5, 10, x, $2x$, $5x$, $10x$, x^2, $2x^2$, $5x^2$, $10x^2$

14. 1, 3, a, b, c, $3a$, $3b$, $3c$, ab, bc, ac, $3ab$, $3ac$, $3bc$, abc, $3abc$

15. 1, 19, x, $19x$, y, $19y$, xy, $19xy$, x^2y, $19x^2y$, x^2, $19x^2$

16. 1, 3, 7, 21, a, $3a$, $7a$, $21a$, b, $3b$, $7b$, $21b$, ab, $3ab$, $7ab$, $21ab$, b^2, $3b^2$, $7b^2$, $21b^2$, ab^2, $3ab^2$, $7ab^2$, $21ab^2$

Chapter 5 Mid-Chapter Test

Take this test as you would take a test in class. The answers to the exercises are given in the back of the book.

Write the prime factorization of the number.

1. 80 $2^4 \cdot 5$ **2.** 44 $2^2 \cdot 11$ **3.** 105 $3 \cdot 5 \cdot 7$ **4.** 132 $2^2 \cdot 3 \cdot 11$

5. 161 $7 \cdot 23$ **6.** 194 $2 \cdot 97$ **7.** 350 $2 \cdot 5^2 \cdot 7$ **8.** 925 $5^2 \cdot 37$

Find all the factors of the number or expression. 9–16. See margin.

9. 56 **10.** 60 **11.** 178 **12.** 165

13. $10x^2$ **14.** $3abc$ **15.** $19x^2y$ **16.** $21ab^2$

Find the GCF of the numbers or expressions.

17. 12, 60 12 **18.** 36, 15 3 **19.** 33, 132 33 **20.** 135, 45, 25 5

21. $3ab$, $9b^2$ $3b$ **22.** $18xy$, $42y^2$ $6y$ **23.** $40a^2b$, $24a^2b^2$ $8a^2b$ **24.** $63x^3y$, $99xy^3$ $9xy$

Find the LCM of the numbers or expressions.

25. 13, 5 65 **26.** 14, 21 42 **27.** 55, 99 495 **28.** 65, 26 130

29. $6x$, $9x^2$ $18x^2$ **30.** $35b$, $7ab$ $35ab$ **31.** $32m$, $64mn^2$ $64mn^2$ **32.** $54x^2y^2$, $18x^3y^2$ $54x^3y^2$

Simplify.

33. $\frac{5}{25}$ $\frac{1}{5}$ **34.** $\frac{45}{306}$ $\frac{5}{34}$ **35.** $\frac{8y^2}{24y}$ $\frac{y}{3}$ **36.** $\frac{27m^2}{90mn}$ $\frac{3m}{10n}$

GEOMETRY In Exercises 37–39, find the least number of the tile shown that you need to form a square without overlapping or cutting tiles. Determine how the length of the square's sides are related to the lengths of the sides of the tile.

37. 10, 6

38. 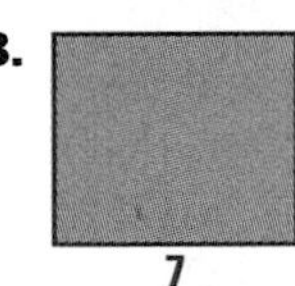

39. 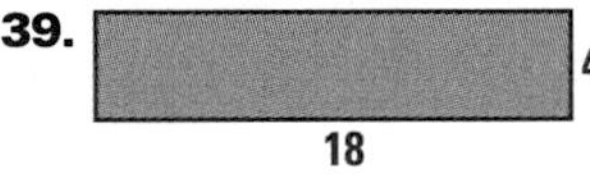

BOXES In Exercises 40 and 41, use the following information. You are stacking boxes. One stack uses boxes 6 inches tall, and the other stack uses boxes 14 inches tall.

40. To make two stacks of the same height, find the least number of boxes of each size.

41. In Exercise 40, is the height of each stack the least common multiple of 6 and 14 or the greatest common factor of 6 and 14? Explain.

37. 15 tiles; place 5 across by 3 deep to form 30 by 30 square. 30 is the LCM of 6 and 10.

38. 42 tiles; place 6 across by 7 deep to form 42 by 42 square. 42 is the LCM of 6 and 7.

39. 18 tiles; place 2 across by 9 deep to form 36 by 36 square. 36 is the LCM of 4 and 18.

40. 7 of the 6 inch boxes, 3 of the 14 inch boxes

41. least common multiple

5.5 Rational Numbers and Decimals

California Standards

In this lesson you'll:

- Recognize rational numbers. (NS 1.4)
- Convert rational numbers from fraction form to decimal form. (NS 1.3)
- Convert rational numbers from terminating and repeating decimal form to fraction form. (NS 1.5)

Goal 1 Identifying Rational Numbers

A number is a **rational number** if it can be written as a fraction, that is, as the quotient $\frac{a}{b}$ of two integers a and b where $b \neq 0$. Some examples of rational numbers are 4, $-\frac{2}{3}$, 0.9, and -1.7.

EXAMPLE 1 Recognizing Rational Numbers

Write the number as a quotient of integers.

a. 4 **b.** 0.5 **c.** -3 **d.** $-\frac{2}{3}$ **e.** $1\frac{1}{4}$

Solution

a. $4 = \frac{4}{1}$ **b.** $0.5 = \frac{1}{2}$ **c.** $-3 = \frac{-3}{1}$ **d.** $-\frac{2}{3} = \frac{-2}{3}$ **e.** $1\frac{1}{4} = \frac{5}{4}$

Student Help

VOCABULARY TIP
Natural (or counting) numbers are: 1, 2, 3, . . .
Whole numbers are: 0, 1, 2, 3, . . .
Integers are: . . . , −2, −1, 0, 1, 2, . . .

A *Venn diagram* is a drawing that uses geometric shapes to indicate relationships among sets.

The Venn diagram at the right illustrates the relationship among the various types of numbers you have used in this book so far.

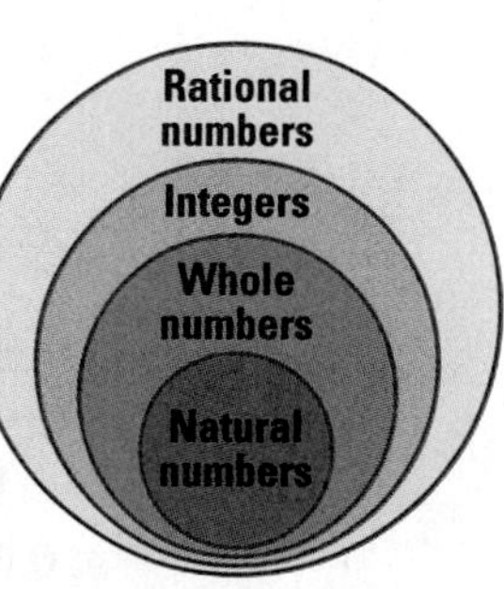

EXAMPLE 2 Identifying Sets to Which Numbers Belong

Identify all sets to which the number belongs.

a. -5 **b.** $\frac{2}{7}$ **c.** 4

Solution

a. The number -5 is an *integer* and a *rational number*.

b. The number $\frac{2}{7}$ is a *rational number*.

c. The number 4 is a *natural number*, a *whole number*, an *integer*, and a *rational number*.

1 Plan

Pacing

Suggested Number of Days

Transitional: 2 days
Average: 2 days
Advanced: 2 days
Block Schedule: 1 block

Teaching Resources

Blacklines
(See page 216B.)

Transparencies
- Warm-Up Exercises
- Teacher Time-Savers
- English/Spanish Problem Solving
- Answers

Technology
- Electronic Teacher Tools
- Test and Practice Generator

2 Teach

Math Reasoning

For Mathematical Background Notes on mathematical reasoning related to this lesson, please refer to pages 216E and 216F in this Teacher's Edition.

Extra Examples 1 and 2
See next page.

California Standards and Assessment

CA Standards: NS 1.3, NS 1.4, NS 1.5
CA Key Concepts Book: pp. S24–S27

Extra Example 1

Write the number as a quotient of integers.

a. 9 $\frac{9}{1}$ b. 0.25 $\frac{1}{4}$

c. -14 $\frac{-14}{1}$ d. $2\frac{5}{8}$ $\frac{21}{8}$

Extra Example 2

Identify all sets to which each of the following numbers belong.

a. $\frac{1}{9}$ **rational number**

b. 0 **whole number, integer, and rational number**

c. -18 **integer and rational number**

Extra Example 3

Write the fraction as a decimal.

a. $\frac{17}{20}$ **0.85**

b. $\frac{9}{11}$ **$0.\overline{81}$**

Extra Example 4

Write the decimal as a fraction. Simplify the fraction if possible.

a. 0.02 $\frac{1}{50}$

b. 0.105 $\frac{21}{200}$

Extra Example 5

Write 0.565656 . . . as a fraction. $\frac{56}{99}$

Teaching Tip

In Example 5, many middle schoolers may find it difficult to accept that the difference of two repeating decimals is a terminating decimal. Work several examples to demonstrate the process and outcome. Stress the importance of multiplying the original repeating decimal by the appropriate power of 10.

Goal 2 WRITING FRACTIONS AND DECIMALS

A fraction $\frac{a}{b}$ can be thought of as a divided by b. It can be written as a decimal by using long division to divide a by b. If the division stops because a remainder is zero, then the decimal form of the number is a **terminating decimal**.

If the long division process does not terminate, then it leads to a digit or group of digits that repeats over and over. In this case, the decimal form of the number is a **repeating decimal**.

Student Help

▶MORE EXAMPLES

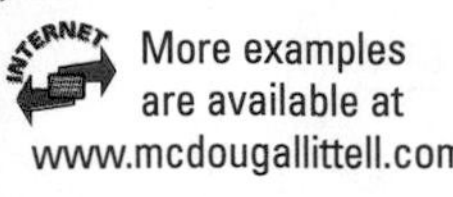

More examples are available at www.mcdougallittell.com

EXAMPLE 3 Writing a Fraction as a Decimal

Write the fraction as a decimal. **a.** $\frac{5}{8}$ **b.** $\frac{3}{11}$

Solution

Divide the numerator by the denominator.

a. $8\overline{)5.000}$ = 0.625

ANSWER ▶ $\frac{5}{8} = 0.625$, a terminating decimal.

b. $11\overline{)3.0000000000}$ = 0.2727272727. . .

ANSWER ▶ $\frac{3}{11} = 0.272727\ldots$, a repeating decimal. Write a repeating decimal with a bar over the digits that repeat: $\frac{3}{11} = 0.\overline{27}$.

EXAMPLE 4 Writing a Terminating Decimal as a Fraction

Write the decimal as a fraction. Simplify the fraction if possible.

a. 0.6 **b.** 0.45

Solution

To write a terminating decimal as a fraction, use the name for the last decimal place in the number as the denominator. The first decimal place is tenths, the second decimal place is hundredths, and so on.

a. $0.6 = \frac{6}{10}$ Write tenths as the denominator.

$= \frac{3}{5}$ Simplify.

b. $0.45 = \frac{45}{100}$ Write hundredths as the denominator.

$= \frac{9}{20}$ Simplify.

EXAMPLE 5 Writing a Repeating Decimal as a Fraction

Write 0.090909. . . as a fraction.

Solution

$x = 0.090909\ldots$	Let x represent the number.
$100x = 9.090909\ldots$	Multiply by 100 because 2 digits repeat.
$100x = 9.090909\ldots$ $-\ (x = 0.090909\ldots)$	Prepare to subtract x from $100x$.
$99x = 9$	Subtract to eliminate repeating decimal.
$x = \frac{9}{99} = \frac{1}{11}$	Divide each side by 99. Simplify.

ANSWER ▶ $0.090909\ldots = \frac{1}{11}$

Student Help

▶ **STUDY TIP**
In Example 5, you multiply by 100 because 0.090909. . . has 2 repeating digits. For 1 repeating digit, multiply by 10. For 3 repeating digits, multiply by 1000.

All rational numbers can be written as either terminating or repeating decimals. Decimals that do not repeat or terminate, such as 0.1010010001. . ., are not rational numbers.

5.5 Exercises

Guided Practice

1. integer, rational; $\frac{-3}{1}$
2. rational; $\frac{13}{5}$
3. natural, whole, integer, rational; $\frac{7}{1}$
4. rational; $\frac{1}{9}$
5. rational; $\frac{97}{20}$
6. rational; $\frac{-84}{5}$
7. rational; $\frac{17}{2}$
8. natural, whole, integer, rational; $\frac{203}{1}$
9. *Sample answer:* You can show that the number can be written in the form $\frac{a}{b}$, where a is an integer and b is an integer not equal to 0. $3 = \frac{3}{1}$, $0.8 = \frac{4}{5}$, $1\frac{1}{2} = \frac{3}{2}$

In Exercises 1–8, use as many words as possible to describe the number: *natural, whole, integer,* or *rational*. Then write the number as a quotient of two integers to show that it is a rational number.

1. -3 **2.** $2\frac{3}{5}$ **3.** 7 **4.** $\frac{1}{9}$

5. 4.85 **6.** -16.8 **7.** 8.5 **8.** 203

9. WRITING Explain how to show that a number is a rational number.

Write the fraction as a decimal.

10. $\frac{3}{4}$ **0.75** **11.** $\frac{5}{6}$ **$0.8\overline{3}$** **12.** $\frac{1}{15}$ **$0.0\overline{6}$** **13.** $\frac{5}{4}$ **1.25**

14. $-\frac{9}{5}$ **−1.8** **15.** $\frac{4}{3}$ **$1.\overline{3}$** **16.** $-\frac{2}{9}$ **$-0.\overline{2}$** **17.** $\frac{1}{12}$ **$0.08\overline{3}$**

Write the terminating decimal as a fraction. Simplify if possible.

18. 0.59 $\frac{59}{100}$ **19.** 0.8 $\frac{4}{5}$ **20.** 0.7777 $\frac{7777}{10,000}$ **21.** 0.375 $\frac{3}{8}$

Write the repeating decimal as a fraction. Simplify if possible.

22. $0.\overline{56}$ $\frac{56}{99}$ **23.** $0.\overline{23}$ $\frac{23}{99}$ **24.** $0.\overline{12}$ $\frac{4}{33}$ **25.** $0.0\overline{6}$ $\frac{1}{15}$

Concept Check

Describe how to write a fraction as a decimal. ***Sample answer:*** **Divide the numerator by the denominator. If the answer is a repeating decimal, indicate the group of digits that repeat by putting a bar over them.**

3 Apply

Assignment Guide

TRANSITIONAL
Day 1: SRH p. 678 Exs. 6–15; pp. 242–243 Exs. 26–30, 32–40, 63, 72–77
Day 2: pp. 242–243 Exs. 43–48, 51–54, 70–71, 78–81

AVERAGE
Day 1: pp. 242–243 Exs. 26–42, 64, 66–68, 72–77
Day 2: pp. 242–243 Exs. 43–49, 53–56, 70–71, 78–81

ADVANCED
Day 1: pp. 242–243 Exs. 26–42, 64–68, 72–77
Day 2: pp. 242–243 Exs. 43–49, 53–56, 69*, 70–71, 78–81

BLOCK SCHEDULE
pp. 242–243 Exs. 26–49, 53–56, 64, 66–68, 70–81

Extra Practice

- Student Edition, pp. 698–699
- Chapter 5 Resource Book, p. 42

Homework Check

To quickly check student understanding of key concepts, go over the following exercises:

Transitional: 28, 36, 44, 48, 54
Average: 28, 38, 46, 48, 54
Advanced: 28, 42, 46, 50, 58

Practice and Problem Solving

Student Help

▶**MORE PRACTICE**
Extra practice to help you master skills is on page 699.

Tell whether the number is a member of the given set.

26. $1\frac{7}{8}$; whole numbers no
27. $\frac{9}{8}$; rational numbers yes
28. -416; integers yes
29. 2.4; rational numbers yes
30. 11; natural numbers yes
31. 3.11; integers no

MATHEMATICAL REASONING Complete the statement using *sometimes, always,* or *never*.

32. A rational number is __?__ an integer. sometimes

33. A whole number is __?__ an integer. always

34. A nonrepeating, nonterminating decimal is __?__ a rational number. never

Write the fraction as a decimal. Use bar notation for repeating decimals.

35. $\frac{7}{20}$ 0.35
36. $\frac{8}{9}$ $0.\overline{8}$
37. $3\frac{3}{25}$ 3.12
38. $-\frac{5}{18}$ $-0.2\overline{7}$
39. $1\frac{7}{9}$ $1.\overline{7}$
40. $-\frac{16}{5}$ -3.2
41. $\frac{11}{12}$ $0.91\overline{6}$
42. $\frac{9}{11}$ $0.\overline{81}$

Write the decimal as a fraction. Simplify if possible.

43. 0.6 $\frac{3}{5}$
44. 0.35 $\frac{7}{20}$
45. -0.84 $-\frac{21}{25}$
46. 0.604 $\frac{151}{250}$
47. 0.517 $\frac{517}{1,000}$
48. $0.\overline{86}$ $\frac{86}{99}$
49. $2.\overline{3}$ $\frac{7}{3}$
50. $-1.\overline{135}$ $-\frac{42}{37}$

Tell whether the decimal form of the fraction is *terminating* or *repeating*.

51. $\frac{3}{5}$ terminating
52. $\frac{11}{20}$ terminating
53. $\frac{9}{11}$ repeating
54. $-\frac{17}{25}$ terminating
55. $\frac{4}{9}$ repeating
56. $-\frac{7}{28}$ terminating
57. $\frac{27}{36}$ terminating
58. $\frac{50}{75}$ repeating

Student Help

▶**STUDY TIP**
Baseball batting averages are rational numbers, written in decimal form. A batting average is a player's number of hits divided by the number of official times at bat.

BASEBALL Write the career batting average of the player as a fraction. Simplify the fraction if possible.

59. Ted Williams, 0.344 $\frac{43}{125}$
60. Roberto Clemente, 0.317 $\frac{317}{1000}$
61. Hank Aaron, 0.305 $\frac{61}{200}$
62. Willie Mays, 0.302 $\frac{151}{500}$

GEOMETRY Express the lengths of the sides of the figures as decimals. Then find the perimeters, expressed as both a decimal and a fraction. 63–65. See margin.

63. 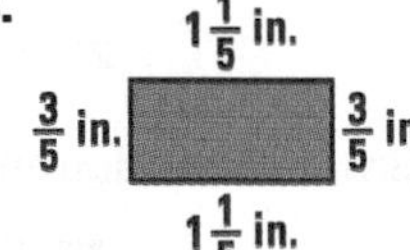

64. 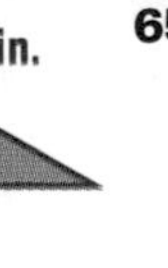

65. 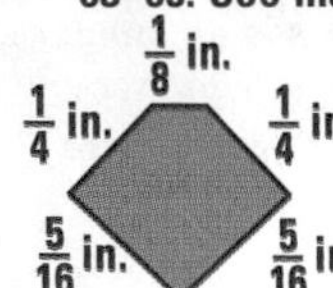

63. 1.2 in., 0.6 in., 1.2 in., 0.6 in.; 3.6 in. ; $3\frac{3}{5}$ in.

64. 0.375 in., 0.625 in., 0.75 in.; 1.75 in.; $1\frac{3}{4}$ in.

65. 0.125 in., 0.25 in., 0.3125 in., 0.3125 in., 0.25 in.; 1.25 in.; $1\frac{1}{4}$ in.

66. $\frac{7}{25} = 0.28$, terminating; $\frac{2}{5} = 0.4$, terminating; $\frac{7}{100} = 0.07$, terminating; $\frac{1}{12} = 0.08\overline{3}$, repeating; $\frac{1}{6} = 0.1\overline{6}$, repeating

68. Decimal form. You would have to change each fraction to an equivalent form with the same denominator before you could compare the values. But with decimals, you can just look to see which decimal has the greatest tenths digit.

69. 0.8631; $\frac{63}{81}$; 0.8631 is closer to 1.

SURVEY In Exercises 66–68, use the table showing the results of a survey about the kind of fruit that students like best.

66. Write each fraction in decimal form. Tell whether the decimal form of the fraction is repeating or terminating.

Favorite Fruit					
Portion of Students	$\frac{7}{25}$	$\frac{2}{5}$	$\frac{7}{100}$	$\frac{1}{12}$	$\frac{1}{6}$

67. Which fruit was chosen most often? banana

68. Is it easier to compare the survey results in fraction form or decimal form? Explain.

69. CHALLENGE Using only the digits 1, 8, 6, and 3, create a decimal that is as close as possible to 1. Then use the same four digits to create a fraction as close as possible to 1. Compare the decimal and fraction. Which is closer to 1? Explain.

Multiple-Choice Practice

70. Which statement is *true*? D

Ⓐ All rational numbers are integers.

Ⓑ All whole numbers are natural numbers.

Ⓒ All integers are whole numbers.

Ⓓ All natural numbers are integers.

71. Which decimal is equivalent to $\frac{7}{20}$? G

Ⓕ 0.27 Ⓖ 0.35 Ⓗ 0.72 Ⓙ 7.2

Mixed Review

Evaluate the expression. *(1.4)*

72. $5 + 3^2$ 14 **73.** $28 - 3 \cdot 4$ 16 **74.** $16 - (10 - 4)$ 10

Solve the inequality. Justify each step of the solution. *(2.8)*

75. $13 > x - 14$ $x < 27$ **76.** $19 + n < 24$ $n < 5$ **77.** $7y \le 105$ $y \le 15$

Solve the equation. Check your solution. *(3.7)*

78. $3x = -27$ −9 **79.** $-8y = 56$ −7 **80.** $-9 + n = -15$ −6

81. TELEPHONE A phone call costs \$.35 for the first minute and \$.08 for each additional minute. You have \$.75 cents. For how many minutes can you talk? Write an equation and solve. *(4.1)* See margin.

4 Assess

Assessment Resources

- Assessment Book (Formal Assessment and Alternative Assessment)
- Test and Practice Generator

Mini-Quiz

1. Write the number as a quotient of integers.
   a. 0.75 $\frac{3}{4}$
   b. $2\frac{2}{3}$ $\frac{8}{3}$
2. Identify all sets to which the number belongs.
   a. −8 integer; rational number
   b. $\frac{2}{5}$ rational number
   c. 13 natural number, whole number, integer, rational number
3. Write the decimal as a fraction. Simplify the result.
   a. 0.48 $\frac{12}{25}$
   b. $0.\overline{421}$ $\frac{421}{999}$

81. $0.35 + 0.08(x - 1) = 0.75$; 6 min

1 Plan

Pacing

Suggested Number of Days

Transitional: 1 day
Average: 1 day
Advanced: 1 day
Block Schedule: 0.5 block with 5.7

Teaching Resources

Blacklines
(See page 216B.)

Transparencies
- Warm-Up Exercises
- Teacher Time-Savers
- English/Spanish Problem Solving
- Answers

Technology
- Electronic Teacher Tools
- Test and Practice Generator

2 Teach

Math Reasoning

For Mathematical Background Notes on mathematical reasoning related to this lesson, please refer to pages 216E and 216F in this Teacher's Edition.

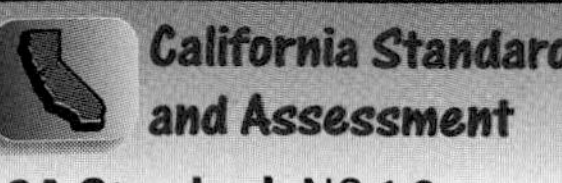
California Standards and Assessment

CA Standard: NS 1.3

5.6 Writing Percents

California Standards

In this lesson you'll:
- Convert fractions to percents. (NS 1.3)
- Convert fractions to percents and use the results in estimations. (NS 1.3)

Goal 1 WRITING PERCENTS

As you learned in Lesson 5.5, rational numbers can be written as decimals or fractions. Another way to write a rational number is as a *percent*. A **percent** is a ratio whose denominator is 100. The symbol % means percent, or per hundred.

DECIMAL	FRACTION	PERCENT	VERBAL PHRASE
0.65	$\frac{65}{100}$	65%	65 percent

EXAMPLE 1 Writing Percents

Write the fraction as a percent.

a. $\frac{3}{20}$ **b.** $\frac{59}{50}$

Solution

To write a fraction as a percent, first find the equivalent fraction with a denominator of 100. Then write the percent.

a. $\frac{3}{20} = \frac{3 \cdot \mathbf{5}}{20 \cdot \mathbf{5}} = \frac{15}{100} = 15\%$ **b.** $\frac{59}{50} = \frac{59 \cdot \mathbf{2}}{50 \cdot \mathbf{2}} = \frac{118}{100} = 118\%$

Link to History

ROSETTA STONE The 1799 discovery of the Rosetta Stone led to the ability to understand hieroglyphics.

More about the Rosetta stone is available at www.mcdougallittell.com

EXAMPLE 2 Writing Percents for a Real-Life Problem

HISTORY LINK In ancient Egyptian writing, called *hieroglyphics*, water is represented by the symbol 〰〰. In the *hieroglyph* below, what percent of the total number of symbols represents water?

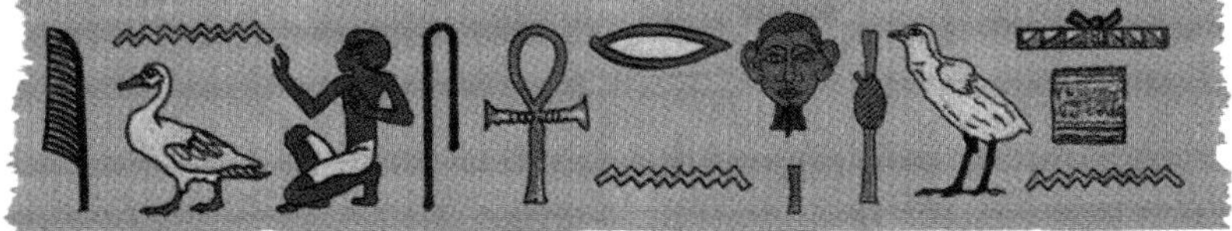

Solution

The hieroglyph contains 15 symbols. Three of the 15 symbols represent water. Write the fraction, then change it to a percent.

$$\frac{3}{15} = \frac{1}{5} = \frac{1 \cdot 20}{5 \cdot 20} = \frac{20}{100} = 20\%$$

ANSWER ▶ So, 20% of the symbols in the hieroglyph represent water.

Goal 2 Using Percents

Student Help

▶ **More Examples**

More examples are available at www.mcdougallittell.com

EXAMPLE 3 Comparing Percents

Which figure has the greatest percent of its area shaded red?

A. 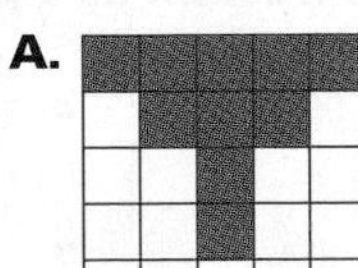 **B.** 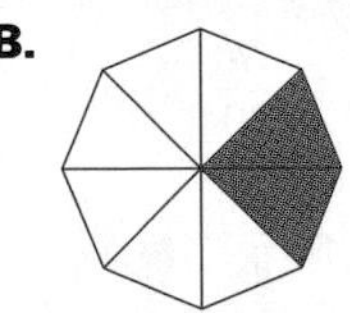 **C.** 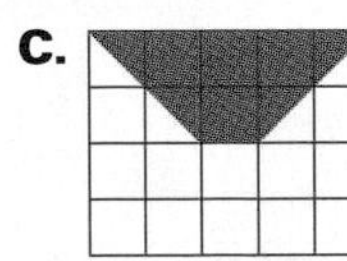

Solution

For each figure, write the fraction that represents the part that is shaded. Then write the fraction as a percent. Compare the percents.

A. $\frac{10}{25} = \frac{10 \cdot 4}{25 \cdot 4} = \frac{40}{100} = 40\%$

B. $\frac{2}{8} = \frac{1}{4} = \frac{1 \cdot 25}{4 \cdot 25} = \frac{25}{100} = 25\%$

C. $\frac{6}{20} = \frac{6 \cdot 5}{20 \cdot 5} = \frac{30}{100} = 30\%$

ANSWER ▶ 40% > 30% > 25%, so Figure A has the greatest percent of its area shaded.

EXAMPLE 4 Estimating with Percents

HISTORY The photograph at the right shows a hieroglyph symbol for the sound "st." Estimate the percent of the area of the photograph that the rabbit's ears represent.

Solution

To estimate the percent, draw a 10-by-10 grid on a tracing of the photograph. Count the number of squares that the ears cover.

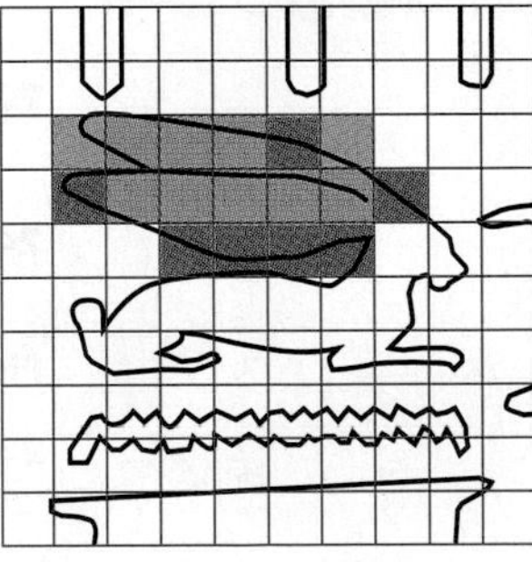

Use fractions of squares to help you estimate.

The ears cover about 8 **full** squares, 7 **half** squares, and 2 **quarter** squares. That is about $8 + 3.5 + 0.5 = 12$ full squares. So, the ears represent about 12% of the photograph.

Math Reasoning

Given a fraction $\frac{a}{b}$, there may be no equivalent fraction with denominator 100. However, we can write $\frac{a}{b} = \frac{p}{100}$ for some number p, and so write $\frac{a}{b} = p\%$. As examples, $\frac{3}{8} = \frac{37.5}{100} = 37.5\%$, and $\frac{7}{3} = 233\frac{1}{3}\%$. It is often convenient to first convert the fraction to a decimal, from which the percent becomes evident. For example, $\frac{3}{125} = 0.024 = \frac{2.4}{100} = 2.4\%$.

Extra Example 1

Write the fraction as a percent.

a. $\frac{3}{25}$ **12%** **b.** $\frac{2}{5}$ **40%**

Extra Example 2

Refer to the ancient Egyptian hieroglyph shown in Example 2. What percent of the symbols represent birds? **about 13%**

Extra Example 3

Which of the following has the greatest percent of its area shaded?

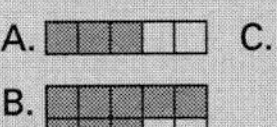

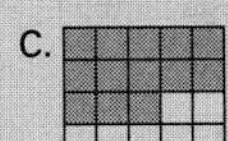

Figure B has the greatest percent (80%) of its area shaded.

Extra Example 4

Refer to the drawing of the ancient Egyptian hieroglyph shown in Example 4. Estimate the percent of the drawing that is occupied by the entire rabbit. **about 21%**

Concept Check

Explain how to write $\frac{13}{25}$ as a percent. ***Sample answer:*** **Multiply the numerator and denominator by 4 to get $\frac{52}{100}$. The numerator 52 is the percent so $\frac{13}{25} = 52\%$.**

3 Apply

Assignment Guide

TRANSITIONAL
Day 1: pp. 246–247 Exs. 12–19, 28–30, 32–33, 37–38, 41–42
AVERAGE
Day 1: pp. 246–247 Exs. 16–23, 28–29, 31–34, 41–42
ADVANCED
Day 1: pp. 246–247 Exs. 20–27, 31–39, 40*, 41–42
BLOCK SCHEDULE
pp. 246–247 Exs. 16–23, 28–29, 31–34, 41–42 (with 5.7)

Extra Practice

- Student Edition, pp. 698–699
- Chapter 5 Resource Book, p. 51

Homework Check

To quickly check student understanding of key concepts, go over the following exercises:

Transitional: 12,18, 28, 32, 38
Average: 20, 22, 28, 34, 38
Advanced: 20, 24, 32, 37, 38

5.6 Exercises

Guided Practice

In Exercises 1–8, write the fraction as a percent.

1. $\frac{7}{20}$ **35%** **2.** $\frac{9}{10}$ **90%** **3.** $\frac{4}{5}$ **80%** **4.** $\frac{7}{50}$ **14%**

5. $\frac{1}{4}$ **25%** **6.** $\frac{12}{16}$ **75%** **7.** $\frac{1}{20}$ **5%** **8.** $\frac{15}{40}$ **37.5%**

9. What percent of the numbers below are integers? **50%**

$\frac{3}{7}$, -4, 39.6, 100, $5\frac{2}{3}$, 0, $-\frac{1}{6}$, 19

10. Find the percent of each figure that is shaded blue. Which figure has the greatest percent of its area shaded blue? **A. 50%, B. 14%, C. 32%; Figure A**

A. 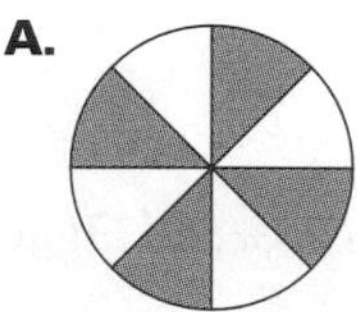

B.

C. 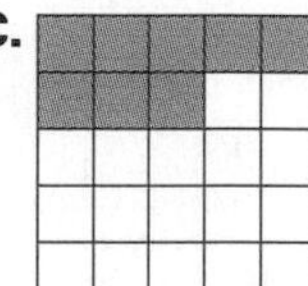

11. Estimate the percent of the 10-by-10 grid that is covered by the blue circle.

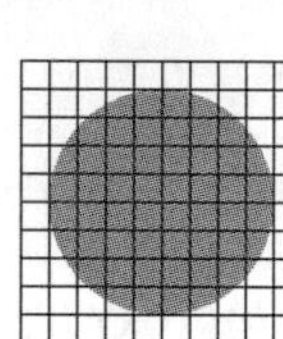

Estimates may vary.
***Sample estimate:* 50%**

Practice and Problem Solving

> ***Student Help***
> **▶MORE PRACTICE**
> Extra practice to help you master skills is on page 699.

Write the fraction as a percent.

12. $\frac{2}{5}$ **40%** **13.** $\frac{19}{20}$ **95%** **14.** $\frac{31}{50}$ **62%** **15.** $\frac{11}{20}$ **55%**

16. $\frac{12}{60}$ **20%** **17.** $\frac{19}{25}$ **76%** **18.** $\frac{8}{40}$ **20%** **19.** $\frac{6}{8}$ **75%**

20. $\frac{13}{50}$ **26%** **21.** $\frac{58}{200}$ **29%** **22.** $\frac{21}{75}$ **28%** **23.** $\frac{95}{500}$ **19%**

24. $\frac{8}{16}$ **50%** **25.** $\frac{25}{125}$ **20%** **26.** $\frac{180}{200}$ **90%** **27.** $\frac{99}{300}$ **33%**

Find the percent of each figure that is shaded blue.

28. 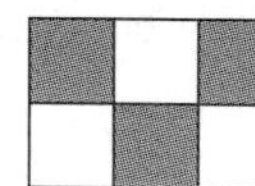 **50%**

29. 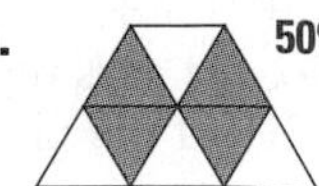 **50%**

30. 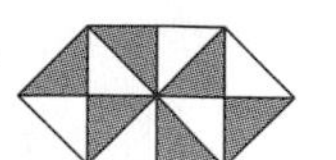 **50%**

35. No; 42% of Group A think the product is affordable, while 60% of Group B think it is affordable.

36. Percents are easier to compare than fractions. It is easier to compare 42% and 60% than it is to compare $\frac{105}{250}$ and $\frac{90}{150}$.

38. *Sample answer:* The whole map is 100%. Find 100% − 67% = 33%.

Careers

CARTOGRAPHERS measure and map areas of Earth's surface.

More about cartographers is available at www.mcdougallittell.com

31. Which figure has the least percent of its area shaded blue? Which figure has the greatest percent of its area shaded blue? **figure C; figure B**

A. 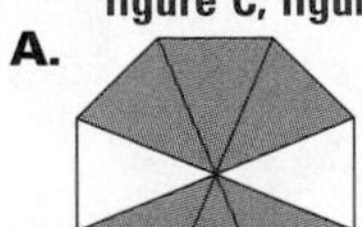 **B.** 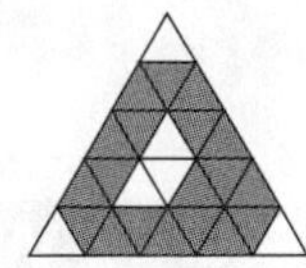 **C.** 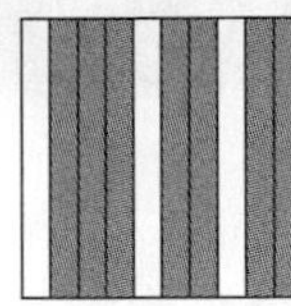

Find the percent of the letters in the word that are the letter A.

32. SACRAMENTO **20%** **33.** CANAL **40%** **34.** ALASKA **50%**

Chapter Opener Link **Look back at page 217.**

35. Is a person randomly chosen from Group A more likely to think that the product is "affordable" than a person randomly chosen from Group B? Use percents to support your answer. **See margin.**

36. Why do you think market researchers use percents to report their research? Give an example to support your answer. **See margin.**

CARTOGRAPHY In Exercises 37 and 38, use the map of Puerto Rico. The blue area indicates water.

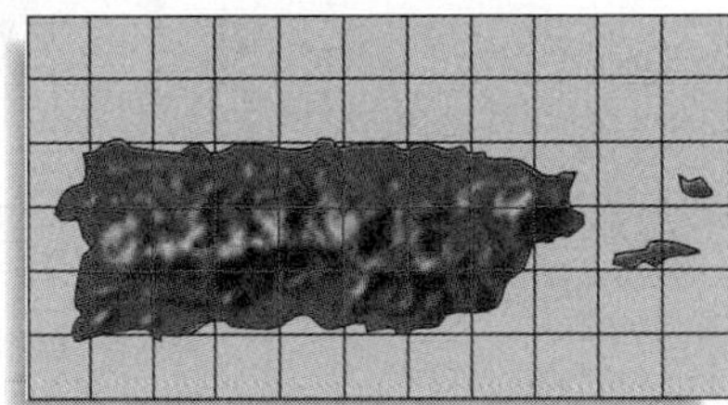

37. Estimate the percent of the map that represents water. ***Sample answer:* 67%**

38. Explain how to use your answer from Exercise 37 to find the percent of the map that is *not* water. **See margin.**

39. MATHEMATICAL REASONING Graph the numbers below on a number line. Explain the method you used. **See margin.**

$$48\%, \frac{7}{10}, 97\%, \frac{3}{4}, 1\%, 26\%$$

40. CHALLENGE A model for 65% is shown.

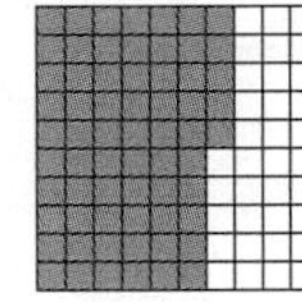

a. Describe a model for 6.5%.

b. Describe a model for 0.65%.

See margin.

Multiple-Choice Practice

40. a. The model would have 1000 squares, of which 65 squares would be shaded.
b. The model would have 10,000 squares, of which 65 squares would be shaded.

41. Which percent is equal to $\frac{3}{5}$? **C**

Ⓐ 40% Ⓑ 50% Ⓒ 60% Ⓓ 70%

42. Which number is *not* equivalent to any of the other numbers? **G**

Ⓕ $\frac{6}{25}$ Ⓖ 6% Ⓗ 24% Ⓙ $\frac{12}{50}$

4 Assess

Assessment Resources

- Assessment Book (Formal Assessment and Alternative Assessment)
- Test and Practice Generator

Mini-Quiz

Write the fraction as a percent.

1. $\frac{7}{20}$ **35%**
2. $\frac{9}{25}$ **36%**
3. $\frac{27}{60}$ **45%**
4. $\frac{160}{400}$ **40%**
5. Find the percent of the figure which is shaded. **75%**

39. ***Sample answer:* I would change all of the numbers to percents.**

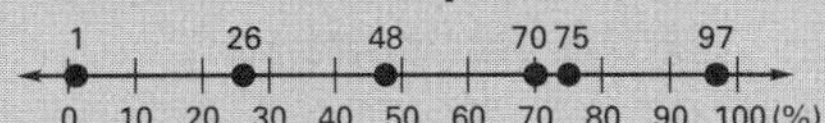

1 Plan

Pacing

Suggested Number of Days

Transitional: 1 day
Average: 1 day
Advanced: 1 day
Block Schedule: 0.5 block with 5.7

Teaching Resources

Blacklines
(See page 216B.)

- Warm-Up Exercises
- Teacher Time-Savers
- English/Spanish Problem Solving
- Answers

Technology

- Electronic Teacher Tools
- Test and Practice Generator

2 Teach

Math Reasoning

For Mathematical Background Notes on mathematical reasoning related to this lesson, please refer to pages 216E and 216F in this Teacher's Edition.

CA Standards: NS 1.0, NS 1.3

5.7 Percents, Decimals, and Fractions

In this lesson you'll:

- Know the properties of and compute with rational numbers in a variety of forms. (NS 1.0)
- Convert fractions to decimals and percents. (NS 1.3)

Goal 1 Writing Percents and Decimals

Percents are written in different forms. Here are four ways to write 35%:

PERCENT FORM	VERBAL FORM	FRACTION FORM	DECIMAL FORM
35%	35 percent	$\frac{35}{100}$ or $\frac{7}{20}$	0.35

You can use the following procedures to convert between percents and decimals. Remember the fact that percent means *per hundred.*

Percents and Decimals

1. To write a percent as a decimal, remove the percent sign from the number and divide the number by 100.
2. To write a decimal as a percent, multiply the decimal by 100%.

Student Help

Study Tip
In Example 1, when you divide by 100, move the decimal point two places to the left: 0.14.

In Example 2, when you multiply by 100, move the decimal point two places to the right: 0.28.

EXAMPLE 1 Writing Percents as Decimals

a. $14\% = \frac{14}{100} = 0.14$

b. $0.5\% = \frac{0.5}{100} = 0.005$

c. $125\% = \frac{125}{100} = 1.25$

d. $33\frac{1}{3}\% \approx \frac{33.3}{100} = 0.333$

Notice that a percent between 0% and 100% converts to a decimal between 0 and 1, and that a percent greater than 100% converts to a decimal greater than 1.

EXAMPLE 2 Writing Decimals as Percents

a. $0.28 = 0.28 \cdot 100\% = 28\%$

b. $0.346 = 0.346 \cdot 100\% = 34.6\%$

c. $1.045 = 1.045 \cdot 100\% = 104.5\%$

d. $0.001 = 0.001 \cdot 100\% = 0.1\%$

Notice that a decimal between 0 and 1 converts to a percent between 0% and 100%, and that a decimal greater than 1 converts to a percent greater than 100%.

Goal 2 WRITING PERCENTS AND FRACTIONS

You can use the following procedures to convert between percents and fractions.

PERCENTS AND FRACTIONS

1. To write a fraction as a percent, first write the fraction as a decimal. Then multiply the decimal by 100%.
2. To write a percent as a fraction, write $n\%$ as $\frac{n}{100}$. Then simplify, if possible.

Student Help

▶**SKILLS REVIEW**
For more help with fractions and percents, see page 677.

EXAMPLE 3 Writing Fractions as Percents

a. $\frac{7}{8} = 0.875$
$= 0.875 \cdot 100\%$
$= 87.5\%$

b. $\frac{2}{3} \approx 0.667$
$= 0.667 \cdot 100\%$
$= 66.7\%$

c. $\frac{12}{5} = 2.4$
$= 2.4 \cdot 100\%$
$= 240\%$

d. $\frac{7}{1000} = 0.007$
$= 0.007 \cdot 100\%$
$= 0.7\%$

EXAMPLE 4 Writing Percents as Fractions

a. $72\% = \frac{72}{100} = \frac{18}{25}$

b. $5\% = \frac{5}{100} = \frac{1}{20}$

c. $140\% = \frac{140}{100} = \frac{7}{5}$

d. $0.3\% = \frac{0.3 \cdot 10}{100 \cdot 10} = \frac{3}{1000}$

EXAMPLE 5 Applying Percents

In a survey, 43% of the people preferred action movies, while $\frac{2}{5}$ of the people preferred comedies. Which was the larger group?

Solution

To compare the percent and the fraction, write each as a decimal.

$43\% = \frac{43}{100} = 0.43$ $\qquad$ $\frac{2}{5} = \frac{2 \cdot 20}{5 \cdot 20} = \frac{40}{100} = 0.4$

ANSWER ▶ Because $0.43 > 0.4$, $43\% > \frac{2}{5}$. So, the group preferring action movies was larger than the group preferring comedies.

Extra Example 1

Rewrite the percent as a decimal.

a. 35% **0.35** **b.** 0.6% **0.006**
c. 300% **3** **d.** $88\frac{1}{3}\%$ **about 0.883**

Extra Example 2

Rewrite the decimal as a percent.

a. 0.375 **37.5%** **b.** 0.98 **98%**
c. 2.105 **210.5%** **d.** 0.0065 **0.65%**

Extra Example 3

Rewrite the fraction as a percent.

a. $\frac{3}{5}$ **60%** **b.** $\frac{11}{8}$ **137.5%**
c. $\frac{1}{6}$ **about 16.67%** **d.** $\frac{13}{4}$ **325%**

Extra Example 4

Rewrite the percent as a fraction.

a. 42% $\frac{21}{50}$ **b.** 185% $\frac{37}{20}$
c. 8% $\frac{2}{25}$ **d.** 2.4% $\frac{3}{125}$

Extra Example 5

During a television ratings period, 35% of households watched a new TV game show, while $\frac{3}{7}$ of the households watched a new TV drama. Which was the larger group? **those watching the drama**

Teaching Tip

In part (a) of Example 2, point out that $100\% = \frac{100}{100}$, so you can think of $0.28 \cdot 100\%$ as $0.28 \cdot \frac{100}{100} = \frac{0.28 \cdot 100}{100} = \frac{28}{100} = 28\%$. However, all of this requires knowledge of fraction multiplication, which is taught in Chapter 6.

Concept Check

Describe in your own words how to change a percent into a decimal and into a fraction. ***Sample answer:*** **To change a percent into a decimal, remove the percent sign and divide by 100. To change a percent into a fraction, write $n\%$ as $\frac{n}{100}$ without a percent sign and simplify, if possible.**

3 Apply

Assignment Guide

TRANSITIONAL
Day 1: SRH p. 677, Exs. 1–6; pp. 251–252 Exs. 19–22, 27–30, 35–38, 43–46, 51, 59–60, 65–66, 68–76

AVERAGE
Day 1: pp. 251–252 Exs. 19–22, 31–38, 47–50, 52–53, 60–61, 65–66, 68–76

ADVANCED
Day 1: pp. 251–252 Exs. 23–26, 31–34, 39–42, 47–50, 53–58, 63–64, 67*, 68–76

BLOCK SCHEDULE
pp. 251–252 Exs. 19–22, 31–38, 47–50, 52–53, 60–61, 65–66, 68–76 (with 5.6)

Extra Practice

- Student Edition, pp. 698–699
- Chapter 5 Resource Book, p. 60

Homework Check

To quickly check student understanding of key concepts, go over the following exercises:

Transitional: 20, 28, 36, 44, 66
Average: 22, 32, 38, 48, 66
Advanced: 24, 34, 40, 50, 58

You can use the table below to convert between fraction, decimal, and percent forms for the common numbers shown. It may be helpful to memorize the equivalent forms of these numbers.

Student Help

▶STUDY TIP
The fractions $\frac{1}{3}$ and $\frac{2}{3}$ are not always rounded in the percent form. They are sometimes written in this form:

$\frac{1}{3} = 33\frac{1}{3}\%$

$\frac{2}{3} = 66\frac{2}{3}\%$

EQUIVALENT FRACTIONS, DECIMALS, AND PERCENTS

$\frac{1}{10} = 0.1 = 10\%$	$\frac{1}{5} = 0.2 = 20\%$	$\frac{1}{8} = 0.125 = 12.5\%$
$\frac{3}{10} = 0.3 = 30\%$	$\frac{2}{5} = 0.4 = 40\%$	$\frac{3}{8} = 0.375 = 37.5\%$
$\frac{7}{10} = 0.7 = 70\%$	$\frac{3}{5} = 0.6 = 60\%$	$\frac{5}{8} = 0.625 = 62.5\%$
$\frac{9}{10} = 0.9 = 90\%$	$\frac{4}{5} = 0.8 = 80\%$	$\frac{7}{8} = 0.875 = 87.5\%$
$\frac{1}{3} \approx 0.333 = 33.3\%$	$\frac{1}{4} = 0.25 = 25\%$	$\frac{1}{2} = 0.5 = 50\%$
$\frac{2}{3} \approx 0.667 = 66.7\%$	$\frac{3}{4} = 0.75 = 75\%$	$1 = 1.00 = 100\%$

5.7 Exercises

Guided Practice

Write the percent as a decimal.

1. 65% **0.65** **2.** 19% **0.19** **3.** 131% **1.31** **4.** 9% **0.09**

Write the decimal as a percent.

5. 0.38 **38%** **6.** 0.2 **20%** **7.** 2.01 **201%** **8.** 0.452 **45.2%**

Write the fraction as a percent.

9. $\frac{17}{20}$ **85%** **10.** $\frac{2}{10}$ **20%** **11.** $\frac{9}{24}$ **37.5%** **12.** $\frac{16}{5}$ **320%**

In Exercises 13–16, write the percent as a fraction. Simplify, if possible.

13. 65% $\frac{13}{20}$ **14.** 2% $\frac{1}{50}$ **15.** 350% $\frac{7}{2}$ **16.** 11% $\frac{11}{100}$

17. MATHEMATICAL REASONING How can you tell if the fraction equivalent of a percent will be greater than 1? How can you tell if the percent equivalent of a fraction will be greater than 100%?

17. The fraction equivalent will be greater than 1 if the percent is greater than 100%. The percent equivalent will be greater than 100% if the numerator is greater than the denominator of the fraction.

18. In the student council election, 35% of the students voted for you and $\frac{2}{5}$ of the students voted for your friend. Who received more votes? How do you know? **Friend; $\frac{2}{5}$ = 40%, and 40% > 35%.**

Practice and Problem Solving

Student Help

▶More Practice
Extra practice to help you master skills is on page 699.

Write the percent as a decimal.

19. 20% 0.2 **20.** 11% 0.11 **21.** 115% 1.15 **22.** 7.2% 0.072

23. 229% 2.29 **24.** 99% 0.99 **25.** 0.3% 0.003 **26.** 342.8% 3.428

Write the decimal as a percent.

27. 0.25 25% **28.** 0.802 80.2% **29.** 0.7 70% **30.** 1.9 190%

31. 0.01 1% **32.** 3.4 340% **33.** 0.009 0.9% **34.** 5.8 580%

Write the fraction as a percent. Round your answer to the nearest tenth if necessary.

35. $\frac{6}{10}$ 60% **36.** $\frac{25}{125}$ 20% **37.** $\frac{3}{16}$ 18.8% **38.** $\frac{11}{4}$ 275%

39. $\frac{12}{18}$ 66.7% **40.** $\frac{18}{24}$ 75% **41.** $\frac{600}{150}$ 400% **42.** $\frac{1}{8}$ 12.5%

Write the percent as a fraction. Simplify, if possible.

43. 52% $\frac{13}{25}$ **44.** 75% $\frac{3}{4}$ **45.** 6% $\frac{3}{50}$ **46.** 8% $\frac{2}{25}$

47. 110% $\frac{11}{10}$ **48.** 33% $\frac{33}{100}$ **49.** 16% $\frac{4}{25}$ **50.** 37.5% $\frac{3}{8}$

CALCULATOR **Estimate the percent. Compare your estimate with the value given by a calculator.**

51. $\frac{45}{144}$ 31.25% **52.** $\frac{52}{650}$ 8% **53.** $\frac{78}{99}$ about 78.8% **54.** $\frac{117}{72}$ 162.5%

Student Help

▶Homework Help
Extra help with problem solving in Exs. 55–58 available at www.mcdougallittell.com

TELEVISION **In Exercises 55–58, use the following information and the table at the right.**
To compare the portion of broadcasting time taken up by commercials on three television channels, you make a table of the amount of time you spent watching each channel and the amount of time taken up by commercials.

Commercial Survey

Channel	Minutes watched	Minutes of commercials
A	95	23
B	140	32
C	29	8

55. For what portion of the time were commercials shown when you watched Channel A? Express your answer as a fraction. $\frac{23}{95}$

56. For what portion of the time were commercials shown when you watched Channel B? Express your answer as a percent. 22.9%

57. For what portion of the time were commercials shown when you watched Channel C? Express your answer as a decimal. 0.2759

58. Which channel used the largest portion of time to show commercials? Explain your reasoning. See margin.

58. Channel C; Expressing the answer for each channel as a percent, the commercial times are 24.21%, 22.86%, and 27.59%. Channel C has the greatest percent of commercial time at 27.59%.

Math Reasoning

In converting a percent to a fraction, after writing $p\% = \frac{p}{100}$ we may still have to multiply numerator and denominator by a power of 10 to obtain the ratio of integers. For instance, in Exercise 50, $37.5\% = \frac{37.5}{100} = \frac{37.5 \times 10}{100 \times 10} = \frac{375}{1000}$.

4 Assess

Assessment Resources

- Assessment Book (Formal Assessment and Alternative Assessment)
- Test and Practice Generator

Mini-Quiz

Rewrite the percent as a decimal and as a fraction in simplest form.

1. 55% **0.55; $\frac{11}{20}$**
2. 3.5% **0.035; $\frac{7}{200}$**
3. 225% **2.25; $\frac{9}{4}$**

Rewrite the fraction as a decimal. Then rewrite the decimal as a percent.

4. $\frac{3}{17}$ **about 0.176; about 17.6%**
5. $\frac{123}{52}$ **about 2.37; about 237%**
6. A circle graph has four parts and three of the parts are labeled 23%, 17%, and 8%. What percent of the graph is represented by the fourth part? Rewrite your answer as a decimal and as a fraction in simplest form. **52%; 0.52; $\frac{13}{25}$**

Problem Solving

Exercises 59–64
Stress that students must find a common form for the three quantities before making the comparison

Tell which of the numbers in the list has the greatest value.

59. $\frac{3}{8}$, 375%, 0.4 **375%** **60.** $\frac{7}{16}$, 0.5, 47% **0.5** **61.** 0.09, $\frac{3}{50}$, 5% **0.09**

62. 11%, $\frac{1}{25}$, 0.333 **0.333** **63.** 83%, $\frac{7}{10}$, 0.572 **83%** **64.** 1.2, $\frac{3}{2}$, 142% **$\frac{3}{2}$**

RUNNING SHOES In Exercises 65–67, use the table. It gives the portion of running shoe buyers who bought one, two, or three or more pairs of running shoes during a one-year period.

Running Shoe Buyers	
Bought 1 pair	74.3%
Bought 2 pairs	0.154
Bought 3+ pairs	$\frac{1}{10}$

▶ Source: Mediamark Research Inc.

65. What fraction of buyers bought 2 pairs of shoes? **$\frac{77}{500}$**

66. What percent of buyers bought 3 or more pairs of shoes? **10%**

67. CHALLENGE About 13.5 million people made at least one running shoe purchase during the year. About how many people bought two or more pairs of running shoes? **3,429,000 people**

Multiple-Choice Practice

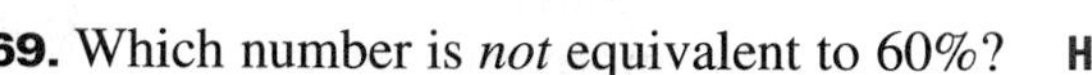

68. What percent of the figure is shaded blue? **D**

Ⓐ $\frac{1}{3}\%$ Ⓑ 30%

Ⓒ 33% Ⓓ $33\frac{1}{3}\%$

69. Which number is *not* equivalent to 60%? **H**

Ⓕ 0.6 Ⓖ $\frac{60}{100}$ Ⓗ 0.06 Ⓙ $\frac{3}{5}$

Mixed Review

Evaluate the expression when $x = 2$ and $y = 7$. *(1.2, 1.3)*

70. $9x - y$ **11** **71.** $2y + x$ **16** **72.** $x^2 + y^2$ **53**

Simplify the expression. *(2.2)*

73. $3n + n$ **4n** **74.** $4(2x + 8)$ **8x + 32** **75.** $5x + 4y + x + 2y$ **6x + 6y**

Write an equation that represents the verbal sentence. *(2.4)*

76. The sum of y and 3.7 is 5.6. **$y + 3.7 = 5.6$**

77. The difference of x and 13 is 24. **$x - 13 = 24$**

78. The result of adding a number and 41 is 138. **$x + 41 = 138$**

5.8 Stem-and-Leaf Plots

California Standards

In this lesson you'll:

- Use a stem-and-leaf plot to display a single set of data or compare two sets of data. (SDP 1.1)
- Understand the meaning of the minimum and maximum of a data set. (SDP 1.3)

Goal 1 Using Stem-and-Leaf Plots

A **stem-and-leaf plot** is a display of data that allows you to see the way the data are distributed. A stem-and-leaf plot can be used to place data in increasing or decreasing order.

EXAMPLE 1 Making a Stem-and-Leaf Plot

You surveyed 20 people at a gym about the number of miles they walk on the gym's treadmills. Your results are shown below.

MILES WALKED: 4.1, 3.5, 5.7, 1.4, 3.9, 3.3, 1.1, 4.5, 3.0, 3.1, 2.9, 5.9, 5.8, 2.3, 7.1, 1.9, 3.1, 3.2, 3.8, 4.3

Use a stem-and-leaf plot to order your data. Describe what the stem-and-leaf plot shows about the distances walked.

Solution

1. The numbers vary from 1.1 to 7.1, so let the *stems* be the ones digits from 1 to 7. Let the *leaves* represent the tenths digits. Use a key to show what the stems and leaves represent.
2. Write the stems first. Then record each distance by writing the leaf, or tenths digit, on the right side of its corresponding stem. For example, for 4.1, write 1 to the right of 4.
3. Rewrite the stem-and-leaf plot so that each line of leaves is in order from least to greatest.

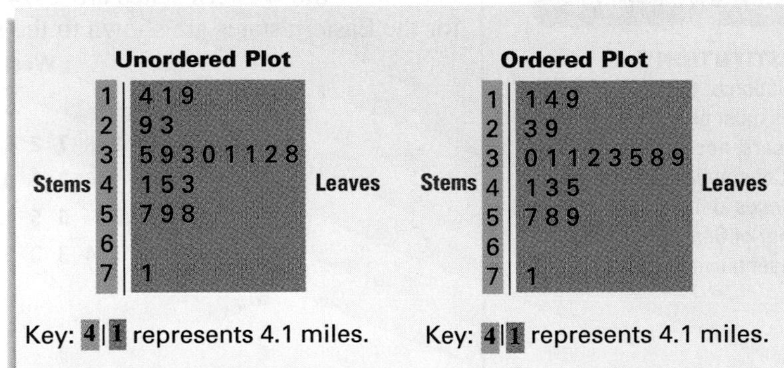

Unordered Plot

Stems	Leaves
1	4 1 9
2	9 3
3	5 9 3 0 1 1 2 8
4	1 5 3
5	7 9 8
6	
7	1

Key: 4 | 1 represents 4.1 miles.

Ordered Plot

Stems	Leaves
1	1 4 9
2	3 9
3	0 1 1 2 3 5 8 9
4	1 3 5
5	7 8 9
6	
7	1

Key: 4 | 1 represents 4.1 miles.

ANSWER ▶ From the ordered stem-and-leaf plot, you can see that the greatest number of people used the treadmill to walk from 3.0 to 3.9 miles, and that the distances range from a minimum of 1.1 miles to a maximum of 7.1 miles.

Student Help

▶ STUDY TIP
A stem-and-leaf plot's key tells what the stems and leaves represent. In the plots at the right, the leaves next to the stem of 4 show the data for the interval 4.0–4.9.

1 Plan

Pacing

Suggested Number of Days

Transitional: 2 days
Average: 2 days
Advanced: 2 days
Block Schedule: 1 block

Teaching Resources

Blacklines
(See page 216B.)

Transparencies
- Warm-Up Exercises
- Teacher Time-Savers
- English/Spanish Problem Solving
- Answers

Technology
- Electronic Teacher Tools
- Test and Practice Generator

2 Teach

Math Reasoning

For Mathematical Background Notes on mathematical reasoning related to this lesson, please refer to pages 216E and 216F in this Teacher's Edition.

Extra Example 1
See next page.

California Standards and Assessment

CA Standards: SDP 1.1, SDP 1.3

Extra Example 1

You surveyed 20 male high school basketball players about their weights. Your results, in pounds, are shown below.

Unordered data: 150, 135, 155, 158, 167, 146, 139, 157, 181, 142, 148, 163, 156, 166, 156, 138, 168, 163, 127, 141
Use a stem-and-leaf plot to order your data. What are the least and greatest weights?

Stem	Leaves
12	7
13	5 8 9
14	1 2 6 8
15	0 5 6 6 7 8
16	3 3 6 7 8
17	
18	1

Ordered data: 127, 135, 138, 139, 141, 142, 146, 148, 150, 155, 156, 156, 157, 158, 163, 163, 166, 167, 168, 181

Key: 18 | 1 represents 181 pounds.
127 lb; 181 lb

Extra Example 2

The scores on the math portion of a standardized test for the students in two 8th-grade classes are given.

Class A: 79, 78, 91, 97, 80, 74, 61, 69, 39, 91, 82, 98, 78, 59, 47, 69, 83, 86, 79, 89, 86, 76

Class B: 95, 88, 69, 79, 90, 49, 72, 75, 81, 88, 85, 55, 63, 63, 99, 68, 88, 90, 58, 93, 77, 82

Use a back-to-back stem-and-leaf plot to compare the two sets of data.

Class A		Class B
9	3	
7	4	9
9	5	5 8
9 9 1	6	3 3 8 9
9 9 8 8 6 4	7	2 5 7 9
9 6 6 3 2 0	8	1 2 5 8 8 8
8 7 1 1	9	0 0 3 5 9

Key: 1 | 9 | 0 represents 91 in class A and 90 in class B.

Teaching Tip

Communicating Mathematics
Point out how the double stem-and-leaf plot in Example 2 makes it easier to see which group of states is more urban when compared to the unordered data sets.

Goal 2 USING BACK-TO-BACK STEM-AND-LEAF PLOTS

You can use a back-to-back stem-and-leaf plot to compare two sets of data. You write the leaves to the left of the stems for one set of data, and to the right of the stems for the other set of data.

Student Help

▶ MORE EXAMPLES

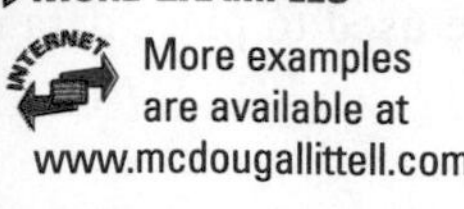

More examples are available at www.mcdougallittell.com

EXAMPLE 2 Making a Back-to-Back Stem-and-Leaf Plot

POPULATION The census data below show the percent of each state's population that is urban (lives in a city). Make a back-to-back stem-and-leaf plot of the data and describe what it suggests.

EAST

AL: 60%	IL: 85%	ME: 45%	NJ: 89%	SC: 55%
CT: 79%	IN: 65%	MI: 71%	NY: 84%	TN: 61%
DE: 73%	KY: 52%	MS: 47%	OH: 74%	VA: 69%
FL: 85%	MA: 84%	NC: 50%	PA: 69%	VT: 32%
GA: 63%	MD: 81%	NH: 51%	RI: 86%	WV: 36%

WEST

AK: 68%	HI: 89%	MN: 70%	NM: 73%	TX: 80%
AR: 54%	IA: 61%	MO: 69%	NV: 88%	UT: 87%
AZ: 88%	ID: 57%	MT: 53%	OK: 68%	WA: 76%
CA: 93%	KS: 69%	ND: 53%	OR: 71%	WI: 66%
CO: 82%	LA: 68%	NE: 66%	SD: 50%	WY: 65%

▶ Source: U.S. Bureau of the Census

Link to History

CONSTITUTION The population of the United States must be counted every ten years, according to the U.S. Constitution. This count, or *census*, determines the number of Congressional representatives from each state.

Solution

Because the data range from 93% to 32%, the stems go from 9 to 3. Leaves for the Western states are shown to the left of the stems. Leaves for the Eastern states are shown to the right of the stems.

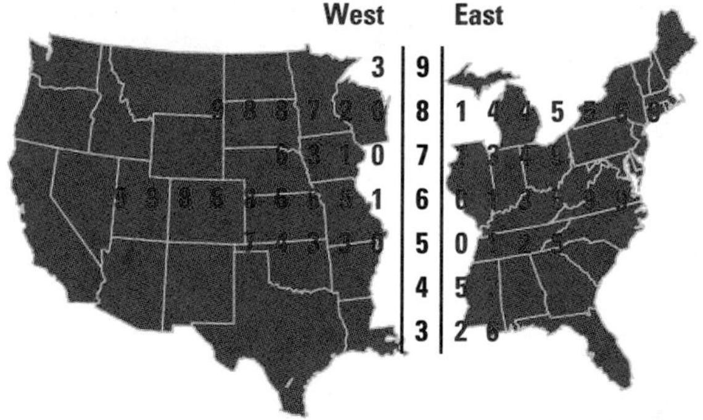

Key: 0 |7| 1 represents 70% Western and 71% Eastern urban populations.

ANSWER ▶ Notice that the higher percents are found to the left side of the stems. This suggests that the Western states tend to have higher percentages of urban populations.

5.8 Exercises

Guided Practice

Write each data set represented in the stem-and-leaf plot as a list ordered from least to greatest.

1.

0	2 2 8
1	0 1 5 5 6 9
2	0 3 5 7
3	1 2 4 4 6

3 | 1 represents 31.

2.

4 2 0	4	3
9 7 3 2	5	2 3 5 8 9
5 5 0	6	1 4 7
8 4 3 1	7	0 3 4 6

8 | 7 | 0 represents 7.8 and 7.0.

TEMPERATURE **In Exercises 3–6, use the list of daily low temperatures in Caribou, Maine, for the month of October, 1998.**

48°, 37°, 37°, 35°, 35°, 30°, 25°, 43°, 41°, 41°, 44°, 45°, 42°, 39°, 40°, 42°, 36°, 45°, 44°, 34°, 34°, 32°, 30°, 37°, 34°, 27°, 19°, 39°, 36°, 34°, 39°

3. Make a stem-and-leaf plot of the temperatures.

4. Which 10-degree interval includes the most temperature values? How does the stem-and-leaf plot help you find the answer? **30°–39°; this line has the most leaves.**

5. What is the minimum temperature? What is the maximum temperature? **19°; 48°**

6. Write two statements that describe the data.

1. 2, 2, 8, 10, 11, 15, 15, 16, 19, 20, 23, 25, 27, 31, 32, 34, 34, 36

2. Left side: 4.0, 4.2, 4.4, 5.2, 5.3, 5.7, 5.9, 6.0, 6.5, 6.5, 7.1, 7.3, 7.4, 7.8

Right side: 4.3, 5.2, 5.3, 5.5, 5.8, 5.9, 6.1, 6.4, 6.7, 7.0, 7.3, 7.4, 7.6

3.

1	9
2	5 7
3	0 0 2 4 4 4 4 5 5 6 6 7 7 7 9 9 9
4	0 1 1 2 2 3 4 4 5 5 8

2 | 5 represents 25°.

6. ***Sample answer:*** **The low temperature was 19° and the high temperature was 48°. Only 3 temperatures were below 30°.**

Practice and Problem Solving

Student Help

▶More Practice
Extra practice to help you master skills is on page 699.

Find the least and greatest number from each stem-and-leaf plot. Then make an ordered list of the data from the stem-and-leaf plot.
7–9. See margin.

7.

2	0 1 1 3
3	5 7 9
4	1 8
5	0 2 3
6	4 6 6 8

6 | 4 represents 64.

8.

8	4 4 5 8
9	0 1
10	1 2 7
11	0 3 8 8 9
12	4 5 6 7

12 | 4 represents 124.

9.

13	5 6
14	3 5 9
15	1 9 9
16	1 2 3 7
17	2 3 4 6 8

17 | 2 represents 17.2.

TEST GRADES **In Exercises 10 and 11, use the list below, which gives the grades of 20 students on a mathematics test.**

93%, 84%, 100%, 92%, 66%, 89%, 78%, 52%, 71%, 85%, 83%, 95%, 81%, 80%, 79%, 67%, 59%, 90%, 85%, 77%

10. Make a stem-and-leaf plot of the data. **See margin.**

11. WRITING Referring to your stem-and-leaf plot, describe how the students did on the test. **See margin.**

7. 20, 68; 20, 21, 21, 23, 35, 37, 39, 41, 48, 50, 52, 53, 64, 66, 66, 68

8. 84, 127; 84, 84, 85, 88, 90, 91, 101, 102, 107, 110, 113, 118, 118, 119, 124, 125, 126, 127

9. 13.5, 17.8; 13.5, 13.6, 14.3, 14.5, 14.9, 15.1, 15.9, 15.9, 16.1, 16.2, 16.3, 16.7, 17.2, 17.3, 17.4, 17.6, 17.8

11. ***Sample answer:*** **The lowest test score was 52% and the highest was 100%. One fourth of the scores were 90% or better.**

Concept Check

Write a list of steps that can be followed when drawing a single or double stem-and-leaf plot. ***Sample answer:*** **1. Decide on the numbers for the stems; they must be consecutive. 2. Draw an unordered plot using these stems. 3. Use the unordered plot to draw an ordered plot. 4. Write a key.**

3 Apply

Assignment Guide

Transitional
Day 1: pp. 255–257 Exs. 7–10, 12, 17–19
Day 2: pp. 255–257 Exs. 13–16, 21

Average
Day 1: pp. 255–257 Exs. 7–12, 17–19
Day 2: pp. 255–257 Exs 13–16, 21

Advanced
Day 1: pp. 255–257 Exs. 7–12, 17–19
Day 2: pp. 255–257 Exs. 13–16, 20*, 21

Block Schedule
pp. 255–257 Exs. 7–19, 21

Extra Practice

- Student Edition, pp. 698–699
- Chapter 5 Resource Book, p. 69

Homework Check

To quickly check student understanding of key concepts, go over the following exercises:

Transitional: 8, 10, 12, 13, 14
Average: 8, 10, 12, 13, 14
Advanced: 8, 10, 12, 13, 14

10.

5	2 9
6	6 7
7	1 7 8 9
8	0 1 3 4 5 5 9
9	0 2 3 5
10	0

Key: 9 | 2 represents 92%.

12.

Stem	Leaves
13	4 9
14	3 5 5 6 8
15	3 3 4 7
16	2 2 2 4 8
17	1 6
18	6

Key: 16 | 2 represents 162.

13.

1980		2000
6	3	
5	4	9
3 3	5	4
6 2	6	4 4 7
6 2	7	1 9
	8	0

Key: 2 | 7 | 1 represents age 72 (in 1980) and age 71 (in 2000).

14. *Sample answer:* Life expectancies tend to be greater in 2000 than in 1980, since the numbers on the right side of the plot represent greater life expectancies.

15. See Additional Answers beginning on page AA1.

16. *Sample answer:* Most western states have a greater percentage of 5-to-17-year-olds than eastern states. The stem-and-leaf plot show the east with most of the data having a stem of 1 while the west has most of the data with a stem of 2.

256

Student Help

▶**STUDY TIP**
A stem in a stem-and-leaf plot can have more than one digit. For example, in Exercise 12, you can use stems from 13 to 18 to represent the first two digits of the three-digit data.

12. AUTO RACING The average winning speeds, in miles per hour, in an auto race for 1980–1999 are given below. Make a stem-and-leaf plot of the winning speeds. **See margin.**

143, 139, 162, 162, 164, 153, 171, 162, 145, 168, 186, 176, 134, 157, 154, 148, 146, 145, 153 ▶Source: Sports Illustrated

LIFE EXPECTANCY In Exercises 13 and 14, use the tables below, which give the life expectancy at birth in eight countries for 1980 and 2000.

Country	1980	2000
Bhutan	45	54
Cambodia	36	49
India	53	64
Indonesia	53	64

Country	1980	2000
Japan	76	80
N. Korea	66	71
Philippines	62	67
Singapore	72	79

▶Source: U.S. Bureau of the Census, International Database

13. Make a back-to-back stem-and-leaf plot to compare the 1980 life expectancies to the 2000 life expectancies. **See margin.**

14. MATHEMATICAL REASONING What conclusion can you make from your back-to-back stem-and-leaf plot? Explain your reasoning. **See margin.**

POPULATION In Exercises 15 and 16, use the tables below, which give the percent of 5-to-17-year-olds in each state for the Eastern and Western parts of the United States in 1997.

EAST

AL: 18%	IL: 19%	ME: 18%	NJ: 18%	SC: 19%
CT: 18%	IN: 19%	MI: 19%	NY: 18%	TN: 18%
DE: 17%	KY: 18%	MS: 20%	OH: 19%	VA: 18%
FL: 17%	MA: 17%	NC: 18%	PA: 18%	VT: 19%
GA: 19%	MD: 18%	NH: 19%	RI: 17%	WV: 17%

WEST

AK: 23%	HI: 18%	MN: 20%	NM: 21%	TX: 20%
AR: 19%	IA: 19%	MO: 19%	NV: 19%	UT: 24%
AZ: 20%	ID: 21%	MT: 20%	OK: 20%	WA: 19%
CA: 19%	KS: 20%	ND: 20%	OR: 18%	WI: 20%
CO: 19%	LA: 20%	NE: 20%	SD: 21%	WY: 21%

▶Source: U.S. Bureau of the Census

15. Make a back-to-back stem-and-leaf plot comparing the data for the two regions. **See margin.**

16. MATHEMATICAL REASONING Write a conclusion based on the stem-and-leaf plot. Explain how the stem-and-leaf plot supports your conclusion. **See margin.**

In Exercises 17–19, use following information. By replacing the leaves of a stem-and-leaf plot with bars whose lengths indicate how many data items are associated with each stem, you can form a *histogram.*

A histogram has a frequency axis so that you can find the lengths of the bars, and the stems are replaced by interval labels.

Student Help

▶**STUDY TIP**
In a histogram there is no space between the bars because there are no gaps in the intervals. Where one interval ends, the next one begins.

EXAMPLE

Make a histogram of the data in Example 1 on page 253.

Solution

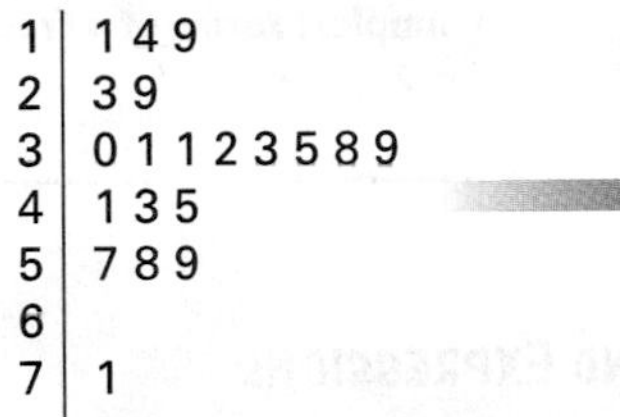

Stem-and-leaf plot

Stem	Leaves
1	1 4 9
2	3 9
3	0 1 1 2 3 5 8 9
4	1 3 5
5	7 8 9
6	
7	1

Key: 4 | 1 represents 4.1 miles.

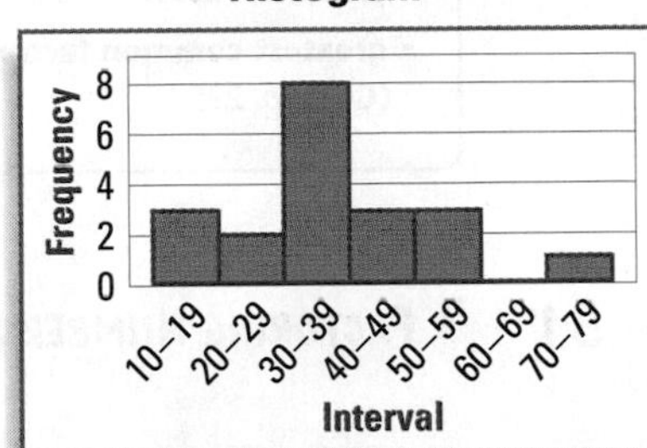

17. Make a stem-and-leaf plot of the following ages of 20 volunteers who cleaned a local park: 9, 14, 21, 15, 16, 8, 32, 13, 27, 11, 10, 16, 21, 39, 9, 25, 31, 7, 12, 18. **See margin.**

18. Use the stem-and-leaf plot from Exercise 17 to make a histogram. **See margin.**

19. How does the shape of the histogram from Exercise 18 compare with the shape of the stem-and-leaf plot from Exercise 17? Explain. **See margin.**

20. CHALLENGE The stem-and-leaf plot compares the heights of plants grown using Fertilizer A to a group grown using Fertilizer B. If Fertilizer A is more effective than Fertilizer B, which side of the data display represents each plant group? Explain your reasoning. **See margin.**

Plant Height (in inches)

Leaves	Stem	Leaves
1 4 9 4	3	7
5 7 1 7 2	4	8 6
3 8 6 1	5	8 7 9 6 9
2 1	6	2 3 8
	7	1 4 0 1

Key: 1 | 3 | 7 represents 31 and 37 inches.

Multiple-Choice Practice

21. What is the greatest value shown in the stem-and-leaf plot? **C**

Stem	Leaves
4	2 9
3	2 3 8
2	5 6
1	9

Key: 2 | 5 represents 25.

Ⓐ 19 Ⓑ 25
Ⓒ 49 Ⓓ 238

4 Assess

Assessment Resources

- Assessment Book (Formal Assessment and Alternative Assessment)
- Test and Practice Generator

Mini-Quiz

1. Use the stem-and-leaf plot to list the data in increasing order.

Stem	Leaves
9	0 3 4 7
10	2 2 3
11	0 1 9
12	8

Key: 12 | 8 represents 128.

90, 93, 94, 97, 102, 102, 103, 110, 111, 119, 128

2. The data below show the number of candles sold in a fundraiser by the students in two different homerooms. Order the data in a back-to-back stem-and-leaf plot.

Homeroom A: 10, 25, 31, 25, 19, 12, 55, 62, 36, 42

Homeroom B: 5, 12, 19, 17, 51, 22, 31, 23, 17, 65

Homeroom A		Homeroom B
	0	5
9 2 0	1	2 7 7 9
5 5	2	2 3
6 1	3	1
2	4	
5	5	1
2	6	5

Key: 5 | 5 | 1 represents 55(A) and 51(B) candles.

17.

Stem	Leaves
0	7 8 9 9
1	0 1 2 3 4 5 6 6 8
2	1 1 5 7
3	1 2 9

Key: 3 | 2 represents 32.

18–20. See Additional Answers beginning on page AA1.

Additional Resources

The following resources are available to help review the material in this chapter:

Technology

- Personal Student Tutor
- Test and Practice Generator

5. $2 \cdot 2 \cdot 3 \cdot 3 \cdot a \cdot a \cdot a$
6. $2 \cdot 2 \cdot 2 \cdot 2 \cdot 3 \cdot c \cdot c \cdot d$
7. $37 \cdot x \cdot y \cdot y \cdot y$
8. $2 \cdot 2 \cdot 2 \cdot 2 \cdot 2 \cdot 2 \cdot m \cdot m \cdot n \cdot n$
9. 1, 2, 4, 19, 38, 76; 1, 2, 3, 4, 6, 8, 9, 12, 18, 24, 36, 72, y, $2y$, $3y$, $4y$, $6y$, $8y$, $9y$, $12y$, $18y$, $24y$, $36y$, $72y$, z, $2z$, $3z$, $4z$, $6z$, $8z$, $9z$, $12z$, $18z$, $24z$, $36z$, $72z$, z^2, $2z^2$, $3z^2$, $4z^2$, $6z^2$, $8z^2$, $9z^2$, $12z^2$, $18z^2$, $24z^2$, $36z^2$, $72z^2$, yz, $2yz$, $3yz$, $4yz$, $6yz$, $8yz$, $9yz$, $12yz$, $18yz$, $24yz$, $36yz$, $72yz$, yz^2, $2yz^2$, $3yz^2$, $4yz^2$, $6yz^2$, $8yz^2$, $9yz^2$, $12yz^2$, $18yz^2$, $24yz^2$, $36yz^2$, $72yz^2$

Chapter 5 Chapter Summary and Review

VOCABULARY

- **prime number,** *p. 220*
- **composite number,** *p. 220*
- **prime factorization,** *p. 220*
- **common factor,** *p. 225*
- **greatest common factor (GCF),** *p. 225*
- **multiple,** *p. 229*
- **common multiple,** *p. 229*
- **least common multiple (LCM),** *p. 229*
- **simplest form (of a fraction),** *p. 233*
- **equivalent (fractions),** *p. 233*
- **rational number,** *p. 239*
- **terminating decimal,** *p. 240*
- **repeating decimal,** *p. 240*
- **percent,** *p. 244*
- **stem-and-leaf plot,** *p. 253*

5.1 Factoring Numbers and Expressions

Examples on pp. 220–222

EXAMPLES

$$48 = 6 \cdot 8 = 2 \cdot 3 \cdot 2 \cdot 2 \cdot 2 = 2^4 \cdot 3$$

$$-36xy^2 = (-1) \cdot 6 \cdot 6 \cdot x \cdot y \cdot y = (-1) \cdot 2 \cdot 3 \cdot 2 \cdot 3 \cdot x \cdot y \cdot y = (-1) \cdot 2^2 \cdot 3^2 \cdot x \cdot y \cdot y$$

Write the prime factorization of the number. Use exponents for repeated multiplication.

1. 72 $2^3 \cdot 3^2$ **2.** 91 $7 \cdot 13$ **3.** 150 $2 \cdot 3 \cdot 5^2$ **4.** 224 $2^5 \cdot 7$

In Exercises 5–8, factor the variable expression completely. **5–8. See margin.**

5. $36a^3$ **6.** $48c^2d$ **7.** $37xy^3$ **8.** $64m^2n^2$

9. Find all the factors of the number 76 and of the expression $72yz^2$. **See margin.**

5.2 Greatest Common Factor

Examples on pp. 225–226

EXAMPLES

a. $300 = \mathbf{2} \cdot 2 \cdot \mathbf{3} \cdot \mathbf{5} \cdot 5$

$630 = \mathbf{2} \cdot \mathbf{3} \cdot 3 \cdot \mathbf{5} \cdot 7$

The GCF of 300 and 630 is $\mathbf{2 \cdot 3 \cdot 5} = 30$.

b. $96x^2 = \mathbf{2} \cdot \mathbf{2} \cdot 2 \cdot 2 \cdot 2 \cdot \mathbf{3} \cdot \boldsymbol{x} \cdot \boldsymbol{x}$

$108x^3 = \mathbf{2} \cdot \mathbf{2} \cdot \mathbf{3} \cdot 3 \cdot 3 \cdot \boldsymbol{x} \cdot \boldsymbol{x} \cdot x$

The GCF of $96x^2$ and $108x^3$ is $\mathbf{2 \cdot 2 \cdot 3} \cdot \boldsymbol{x} \cdot \boldsymbol{x} = 12x^2$.

Find the GCF of the numbers or variable expressions.

10. 30, 45 **15** **11.** 8, 84 **4** **12.** 15, 29 **1** **13.** 160, 195 **5**

14. $14a^3b^2$, $56ab$ **$14ab$** **15.** $12z^4$, $42yz^2$ **$6z^2$** **16.** $8xy$, $24xy$ **$8xy$** **17.** $36m^3n^2$, $63m^2n^3$ **$9m^2n^2$**

5.3 LEAST COMMON MULTIPLE

Examples on pp. 229–230

EXAMPLES The LCM of two numbers is the smallest product of prime numbers that contains the prime factorization of each number. This is the product of the highest power of each prime number that appears in either factorization.

$84 = 2 \cdot 2 \cdot 3 \cdot 7 = \mathbf{2^2} \cdot 3 \cdot \mathbf{7}$

$198 = 2 \cdot 3 \cdot 3 \cdot 11 = 2 \cdot \mathbf{3^2} \cdot \mathbf{11}$

The LCM of 84 and 198 is $\mathbf{2^2} \cdot \mathbf{3^2} \cdot \mathbf{7} \cdot \mathbf{11} = 2772$.

The process is similar for variable expressions.

$14xy^2 = 2 \cdot \mathbf{7} \cdot x \cdot \mathbf{y^2}$

$12x^2y = \mathbf{2^2} \cdot \mathbf{3} \cdot \mathbf{x^2} \cdot y$

The LCM of $14xy^2$ and $12x^2y$ is $\mathbf{2^2} \cdot \mathbf{3} \cdot \mathbf{7} \cdot \mathbf{x^2} \cdot \mathbf{y^2} = 84x^2y^2$.

In Exercises 18–25, find the LCM of the numbers or variable expressions.

18. 12, 15 **60** **19.** 90, 100 **900** **20.** 13, 52 **52** **21.** 34, 68 **68**

22. 6, $7y$ **$42y$** **23.** $12x$, $28y^3$ **$84xy^3$** **24.** $9a^2b$, $33a^2b^2$ **$99a^2b^2$** **25.** $18x^2y^4$, $48x^3y^2$ **$144x^3y^4$**

26. A supermarket gives every 10th customer a coupon and every 25th customer a gift. Which customers will get both a coupon and a gift? **every 50th customer**

5.4 SIMPLIFYING AND COMPARING FRACTIONS

Examples on pp. 233–235

EXAMPLE To simplify a fraction, first factor the numerator and denominator.

$$\frac{32y^2}{12y^3} = \frac{\overset{1}{\cancel{2}} \cdot \overset{1}{\cancel{2}} \cdot 2 \cdot 2 \cdot 2 \cdot \overset{1}{\cancel{y}} \cdot \overset{1}{\cancel{y}}}{\underset{1}{\cancel{2}} \cdot \underset{1}{\cancel{2}} \cdot 3 \cdot \underset{1}{\cancel{y}} \cdot \underset{1}{\cancel{y}} \cdot y} = \frac{8}{3y}$$

In Exercises 27–30, simplify the fraction.

27. $\frac{32}{6}$ $\mathbf{\frac{16}{3}}$ **28.** $\frac{65}{20}$ $\mathbf{\frac{13}{4}}$ **29.** $\frac{200x^2}{14x}$ $\mathbf{\frac{100x}{7}}$ **30.** $\frac{48m}{64m^3}$ $\mathbf{\frac{3}{4m^2}}$

31. Order $\frac{2}{3}$, $\frac{11}{18}$, and $\frac{5}{8}$ from least to greatest. $\mathbf{\frac{11}{18}, \frac{5}{8}, \frac{2}{3}}$

5.5 RATIONAL NUMBERS AND DECIMALS

Examples on pp. 239–241

Integers, fractions, and terminating and repeating decimals are rational numbers. They can be written as the quotient $\frac{a}{b}$ of two integers a and b where $b \neq 0$.

EXAMPLES

a. To write a fraction as a decimal, divide the numerator by the denominator. $\frac{2}{5} = 2 \div 5 = 0.4$

b. To write a terminating decimal as a fraction, use the name of number's last decimal place. $0.42 = 42 \text{ hundredths} = \frac{42}{100} = \frac{21}{50}$

c. To write a repeating decimal as a fraction, multiply the number by a power of ten so that subtracting the original number eliminates the repeating portion.

$$\begin{array}{r} 100x = 42.4242\ldots \\ -\ (x = 0.4242\ldots) \\ \hline 99x = 42 \end{array}$$

So, $0.4242\ldots = \frac{42}{99} = \frac{14}{33}$.

Write the fraction as a decimal.

32. $\frac{13}{16}$ 0.8125 **33.** $\frac{11}{40}$ 0.275 **34.** $\frac{7}{12}$ $0.58\overline{3}$ **35.** $2\frac{1}{11}$ $2.\overline{09}$

Write the decimal as a fraction. Simplify if possible.

36. 0.04 $\frac{1}{25}$ **37.** 0.56 $\frac{14}{25}$ **38.** 0.123 $\frac{123}{1000}$ **39.** $0.\overline{12}$ $\frac{4}{33}$

5.6 WRITING PERCENTS

Examples on pp. 244–245

To write a fraction as a percent, first rewrite the fraction with a denominator of 100.

EXAMPLE **Find the percent of the figure that is shaded blue.**

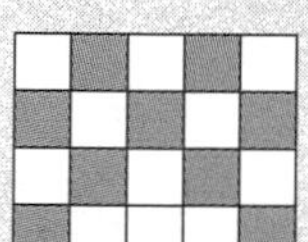

9 of 20 squares are blue: $\frac{9}{20} = \frac{9 \cdot 5}{20 \cdot 5} = \frac{45}{100} = 45\%$

Write the fraction as a percent.

40. $\frac{6}{30}$ 20% **41.** $\frac{55}{220}$ 25% **42.** $\frac{3}{240}$ 1.25% **43.** $\frac{120}{160}$ 75%

Find the percent of the letters in the word that are the letter A.

44. FRACTIONAL 20% **45.** NEBRASKA 25%

46. AREA 50% **47.** CALIFORNIA 20%

5.7 PERCENTS, DECIMALS, AND FRACTIONS

Examples on pp. 248–249

EXAMPLES

a. To write a percent as a decimal, remove the percent sign and divide by 100. $84\% = \frac{84}{100} = 0.84$

b. To write a decimal as a percent, multiply by 100%. $0.49 = 0.49 \cdot 100\% = 49\%$

c. To write a fraction as a percent, write the fraction as a decimal and multiply by 100%. $\frac{3}{8} = 3 \div 8 = 0.375 \cdot 100\% = 37.5\%$

d. To write a percent as a fraction, write $n\%$ as $\frac{n}{100}$. Simplify if possible. $92\% = \frac{92}{100} = \frac{23}{25}$

Write the percent as a decimal and as a fraction. Simplify fractions if possible.

48. 6% **0.06, $\frac{3}{50}$** **49.** 32% **0.32, $\frac{8}{25}$** **50.** 66% **0.66, $\frac{33}{50}$** **51.** 70.5% **0.705, $\frac{141}{200}$**

Write the decimal or fraction as a percent.

52. 0.458 **45.8%** **53.** $\frac{23}{40}$ **57.5%** **54.** $\frac{51}{30}$ **170%** **55.** 3.15 **315%**

5.8 STEM-AND-LEAF PLOTS

Examples on pp. 253–254

EXAMPLE

You can use a stem-and-leaf plot to order the data 72, 43, 42, 56, 86, 65, 79, 43, 55.

Let the tens digits be the **stems** and the ones digits be the **leaves**.

The order of the data from least to greatest is 42, 43, 43, 55, 56, 65, 72, 79, 86.

Stems	Leaves
8	6
7	2 9
6	5
5	5 6
4	2 3 3

Key: 8|6 represents 86.

Make a stem-and-leaf plot and use it to order the data from least to greatest.

56. 5, 26, 48, 24, 32, 58, 51, 34, 26
5, 24, 26, 26, 32, 34, 48, 51, 58

57. 123, 158, 182, 147, 135, 165, 166
123, 135, 147, 158, 165, 166, 182

In Exercises 58 and 59, use the data shown, which give the lengths in centimeters of 20 trout caught during a fish population survey. **58–59. See margin.**

13, 21, 16, 27, 25, 15, 25, 33, 19, 37, 43, 23, 16, 18, 27, 51, 32, 24, 41, 30

58. Make a stem-and-leaf plot of the data.

59. Use your stem-and-leaf plot to describe the sizes of the fish caught.

58.

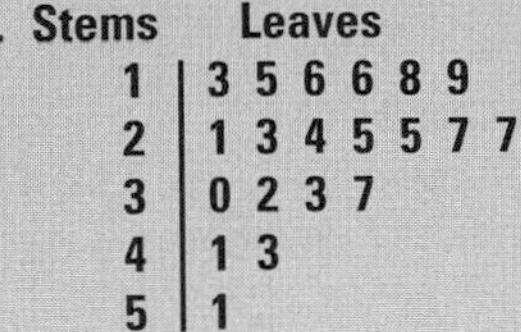

Stems	Leaves
1	3 5 6 6 8 9
2	1 3 4 5 5 7 7
3	0 2 3 7
4	1 3
5	1

Key: 4 | 1 represents 41 cm.

59. ***Sample Answer:*** **13 of the 20 fish were less than 30 centimeters long. The sizes of these smaller fish were fairly evenly distributed from 13 to 27 centimeters.**

Additional Resources

☐ ***Assessment Book***

- Formal Assessment, pp. 65–73
- Alternative Assessment, pp. 193–207

Test and Practice Generator

Chapter 5 Chapter Test

Write the prime factorization of the number. Use exponents for repeated factors.

1. 120 **$2^3 \cdot 3 \cdot 5$** **2.** 124 **$2^2 \cdot 31$** **3.** 125 **5^3** **4.** 222 **$2 \cdot 3 \cdot 37$**

Factor the variable expression completely.

5. $99ab$ **$3 \cdot 3 \cdot 11 \cdot a \cdot b$** **6.** $121x^2$ **$11 \cdot 11 \cdot x \cdot x$** **7.** $67r^2s^2$ **$67 \cdot r \cdot r \cdot s \cdot s$** **8.** $140x^2yz^3$ **$2 \cdot 2 \cdot 5 \cdot 7 \cdot x \cdot x \cdot y \cdot z \cdot z \cdot z$**

Find the GCF of the numbers or variable expressions.

9. 48, 36 **12** **10.** 56, 98 **14** **11.** $26a$, $91a^2b$ **$13a$** **12.** $30mn$, $48m^2n^3$ **$6mn$**

In Exercises 13–16, find the LCM of the numbers or variable expressions.

13. 10, 35 **70** **14.** 5, 18 **90** **15.** $16c^3$, $36cd$ **$144c^3d$** **16.** $22x^2y$, $24x^2y^3$ **$264x^2y^3$**

17. Simplify the fraction $\frac{20}{800}$. **$\frac{1}{40}$** **18.** Which fraction is greater, $\frac{7}{16}$ or $\frac{10}{22}$? **$\frac{10}{22}$**

In Exercises 19–22, write the decimal as a fraction. Simplify if possible.

19. 0.95 **$\frac{19}{20}$** **20.** $0.\overline{78}$ **$\frac{26}{33}$** **21.** 0.66 **$\frac{33}{50}$** **22.** 0.363636. . . **$\frac{4}{11}$**

23. Find the percent of each figure that is shaded blue. Which figure has the greater percent shaded blue? **60%; 62.5%; B**

A.

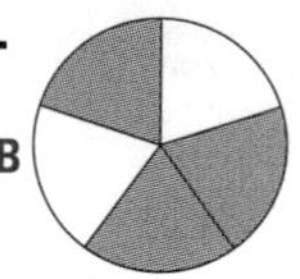

B.

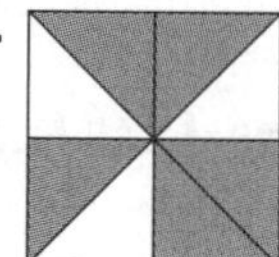

Write the fraction or decimal as a percent.

24. $\frac{10}{25}$ **40%** **25.** 0.365 **36.5%** **26.** 0.98 **98%** **27.** $\frac{87}{150}$ **58%**

Write the percent as a fraction and as a decimal. Simplify fractions if possible.

28. 24.5% **$\frac{49}{200}$; 0.245** **29.** 32% **$\frac{8}{25}$; 0.32** **30.** 87% **$\frac{87}{100}$; 0.87** **31.** 136% **$\frac{34}{25}$; 1.36**

CLOTHING In Exercises 32 and 33, use the following information. A rack of 65 shirts includes 18 T-shirts. Of the 18 T-shirts, 5 are blue and 8 are white.

32. Find the percent of the total number of shirts that are T-shirts. **27.7%**

33. Find the percent of the total number of T-shirts that are blue. **27.8%**

34. Make a stem-and-leaf plot of the data below, which are the heights in feet of 20 trees. Then order the data from least to greatest.

4.5, 5.7, 5.1, 3.9, 6.2, 5.7, 6.9, 7.3, 7.1, 3.2,
4.8, 7.0, 6.5, 5.9, 4.8, 3.6, 7.5, 4.6, 7.7. 4.0

Stem	Leaves
3	**2 6 9**
4	**0 5 6 8 8**
5	**1 7 7 9**
6	**2 5 9**
7	**0 1 3 5 7**

3|2 means 3.2 **3.2, 3.6, 3.9, 4.0, 4.5, 4.6, 4.8, 4.8, 5.1, 5.7, 5.7, 5.9, 6.2, 6.5, 6.9, 7.0, 7.1, 7.3, 7.5, 7.7**

Multiple-Choice Practice

Test Tip Make a mark in your test booklet for unanswered questions so you can find them quickly when you go back.

1. Which of the following is an *incorrect* answer to this question: How many friends can share 20 tokens evenly to play video games if each person gets at least 4 tokens? **D**

Ⓐ 2 Ⓑ 4

Ⓒ 5 Ⓓ 10

2. What is the prime factorization of 126? **H**

Ⓕ $2 \cdot 3 \cdot 21$ Ⓖ $2 \cdot 2 \cdot 3 \cdot 11$

Ⓗ $2 \cdot 3 \cdot 3 \cdot 7$ Ⓙ Not here

3. Which statement is *false*? **B**

Ⓐ Both 8 and 12 are divisible by 2.

Ⓑ The GCF of 8 and 12 is 2.

Ⓒ The LCM of 8 and 12 is 24.

Ⓓ Both 8 and 12 are divisible by 4.

4. A group of people share a rectangular lasagna cut into 18 pieces and a round cake cut into 12 pieces. If everyone is served equal amounts of lasagna and equal amounts of cake, what is the largest number of people the group might contain? **H**

Ⓕ 2 Ⓖ 3

Ⓗ 6 Ⓙ 12

5. Which number is *not* equivalent to $\frac{15}{24}$? **D**

Ⓐ $\frac{10}{16}$ Ⓑ 0.625

Ⓒ $\frac{5}{8}$ Ⓓ $\frac{3}{12}$

6. Two toy cars begin at the starting line of a circular track at the same time. Car 1 goes around the track every 20 seconds, and Car 2 goes around the track every 8 seconds. In how many seconds will the two cars next reach the starting line at the same time? **H**

Ⓕ 4 Ⓖ 24

Ⓗ 40 Ⓙ 160

7. What percent of the figure is shaded? **C**

Ⓐ 35%

Ⓑ 45%

Ⓒ 60%

Ⓓ 90%

8. Which statement is *false*? **G**

Ⓕ $\frac{22}{40} = 55\%$ Ⓖ $\frac{9}{250} = 36\%$

Ⓗ $0.085 = 8.5\%$ Ⓙ $5.46 = 546\%$

9. Which statement about the stem-and-leaf plot shown is *true*? **D**

Stem	Leaves
3	5 8 8
4	0 5 7 9
5	1 1 2 5 9
6	3 4 5 5 7

Key: 6|3 represents 6.3.

Ⓐ The largest data value is 67.

Ⓑ Half the data values are below 5.

Ⓒ The smallest data value is 3.588.

Ⓓ The median of the data values is 5.1.

Teaching Tip

The Brain Games activity provides a motivating way to review selected content in the chapter. For a more comprehensive review, see the Chapter Summary and Review on pp. 258–261.

Brain games

California Standards

- Find the greatest common factor of whole numbers. (Grade 6, NS 2.4)
- Find the least common multiple of whole numbers. (Grade 6, NS 2.4)

GCF-LCM Baseball

Materials

- Two number cubes
- Coin

Directions

Object of the Game

Play in groups of five. Form two teams of two players and choose an umpire. In each round, the two teams find the GCF or LCM of a pair of numbers. The team with the greatest correct answer earns a point. The winner of the game is the team with the most points after seven rounds.

How to Play

STEP 1 Each member of each team rolls the two number cubes and records the results. The two numbers each player records will be used as digits in a two-digit number. Then the umpire tosses the coin. If the coin shows heads, the teams find the GCF of their two numbers. If the coin shows tails, the teams find the LCM of their two numbers.

STEP 2 Each team chooses how to arrange the numbers each player rolled to form two two-digit numbers and then finds the GCF or LCM. Teams may first try out different arrangements of digits to find the one that leads to the greatest GCF or LCM. The umpire checks each team's work and declares the winner of the round.

Another Way to Play

Each team finds the LCM and GCF of its numbers. Each team then adds the LCM and GCF. The team with the greatest sum earns a point.

Brain Teaser

How many days are there in a million seconds?

Use the clues to answer the question. **about 11.57 days**

Clue 1: How many seconds in a minute?

Clue 2: How many minutes in an hour?

Clue 3: How many hours in a day?

California Standards and Assessment

CA Standard: Grade 6, NS 2.4

The basic skills you'll review on this page will help prepare you for the next chapter.

Reviewing the Basics

EXAMPLE 1 Adding and Subtracting Integers

Find the sum or the difference.

a. $4 + (-7)$ **b.** $8 + (-3)$ **c.** $2 - (-5)$

Solution

a. $4 + (-7) = -3$ The sign of 3 is negative because $|-7| > |4|$.

b. $8 + (-3) = 5$ The sign of 5 is positive because $|8| > |-3|$.

c. $2 - (-5) = 2 + 5 = 7$ To subtract, add the opposite.

Try These

Find the sum or the difference.

1. $13 + 9$ **22** **2.** $28 + (-21)$ **7** **3.** $45 - 23$ **22**

4. $19 - (-17)$ **36** **5.** $-43 + (-32)$ **−75** **6.** $-29 - (-11)$ **−18**

EXAMPLE 2 Multiplying Integers

a. $(-2)(-3) = 6$ The product of two numbers with the same sign is positive.

b. $5(-4) = -20$ The product of two numbers with different signs is negative.

Try These

Find the product.

7. $17 \cdot (-5)$ **−85** **8.** $(-24)(-6)$ **144** **9.** $-11 \cdot (9)$ **−99**

10. $(-8) \times (12)$ **−96** **11.** $(-30)(-2)$ **60** **12.** $15(-10)$ **−150**

Student Help

▶ MORE EXAMPLES

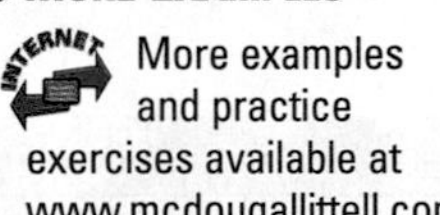

More examples and practice exercises available at www.mcdougallittell.com

EXAMPLE 3 Evaluating Expressions

Evaluate $-5 + 6x$ when $x = -2$.

Solution

$-5 + 6x = -5 + 6(\mathbf{-2})$ Substitute −2 for *x*.

$= -5 + (-12)$ Multiply.

$= -17$ Add.

Try These

13. Evaluate $7 - 3x$ when $x = -3$ and when $x = 5$. **16, −8**

14. Evaluate $-4y + 9$ when $y = 8$ and when $y = -2$. **−23, 17**

Additional Resources

Technology

- Personal Student Tutor
- Test and Practice Generator

Pacing and Assignment Guide

Regular Schedule

Lesson	Les. Day	Transitional	Average	Advanced
6.1	Day 1	pp. 271–272 Exs. 10–21, 26–27, 34–35	pp. 271–272 Exs. 10–24, 28–29, 34–35	pp. 271–272 Exs. 10–24, 30–31, 32–33*, 34–35
6.2	Day 1	EP p. 698 Exs. 35–40; pp. 275–277 Exs. 15–28, 32–34, 39–42, 59–60	pp. 275–277 Exs. 15–16, 20–28, 32–34, 39–40, 43–46, 59–60	pp. 275–277 Exs. 23–31, 35–40, 47–50, 55–58*, 59–60
6.3	Day 1	SRH p. 678 Exs. 1–5, 11–15; pp. 281–282 Exs. 20–30, 32–34, 60–61	pp. 281–282 Exs. 23–36, 48, 50–51, 60–61	pp. 281–282 Exs. 26–39, 48, 50–51, 60–61
	Day 2	pp. 281–282 Exs. 40–47, 52–53, 56, 58–59, 62–63	pp. 281–282 Exs. 40–47, 52–56, 58–59, 62–63	pp. 281–282 Exs. 40–47, 49, 52–56, 57*, 62–63
6.4	Day 1	SRH p. 676 Exs. 1–5; pp. 285–286 Exs. 10–18, 22–28, 35–37, 41	pp. 285–286 Exs. 10–18, 22–25, 29–31, 35–37, 42–43	pp. 285–286 Exs. 12–25, 32–34, 38–40, 42–44
	Day 2	pp. 286–287 Exs. 45–52, 54–56, 60–62	pp. 286–287 Exs. 45–46, 60–62	pp. 286–287 Exs. 45–46, 57–58, 59*, 60–62
6.5	Day 1	pp. 292–293 Exs. 12–23, 28–29, 40–44	pp. 292–293 Exs. 12–29, 40–44	pp. 292–293 Exs. 12–29, 37*, 41–46
	Day 2	pp. 292–293 Exs. 30–35, 38–39, 47–53	pp. 292–293 Exs. 30–36, 38–39, 47–53	pp. 292–293 Exs. 30–36, 38–39, 47–53
6.6	Day 1	pp. 297–298 Exs. 8–15, 18–19, 23–24, 27–28, 31–34, 39–40, 42–44	pp. 297–298 Exs. 8–18, 23–25, 27–29, 31–34, 39–40, 42–44	pp. 297–298 Exs. 11–22, 25–30, 35–40, 41*, 42–44
6.7	Day 1	pp. 301–302 Exs. 10–23, 26–31, 38–39, 49–50	pp. 301–302 Exs. 10–24, 26–34, 38–41, 49–50	pp. 301–302 Exs. 12–28, 35–37, 43–44, 45–46*, 47–50
6.8	Day 1	pp. 307–308 Exs. 14–25, 30–33, 38–41, 48–49, 52–53, 59–60	pp. 307–308 Exs. 18–29, 30–33, 38–41, 46–49, 52–53, 56, 59–60	pp. 307–308 Exs. 18–29, 34–37, 42–45, 50–53, 56–57, 58*, 59–60
6.9	Day 1	pp. 311–313 Exs. 11–14, 23–26, 35–37, 44–45, 50–52, 58–59, 62–63, 69–73, 80–83	pp. 311–313 Exs. 15–18, 27–30, 38–40, 46–47, 50–52, 58–59, 63–64, 69–74, 80–83	pp. 311–313 Exs. 19–22, 31–34, 41–43, 48–49, 53–55, 60, 65–67, 68*, 69–74, 85–87
Review	Day 1	pp. 314–317 Exs. 1–55	pp. 314–317 Exs. 1–55	pp. 314–317 Exs. 1–55
Assess	Day 1	Chapter 6 Test	Chapter 6 Test	Chapter 6 Test

Yearly Pacing Chapter 6 Total – **14 days** Chapters 1–6 Total – **80 days** Remaining – **80 days**

* Challenge Exercises EP = Extra Practice SRH = Skills Review Handbook EC = Extra Challenge

Block Schedule

Day 1	Day 2	Day 3	Day 4	Day 5	Day 6	Day 7
6.1 pp. 271–272: Exs. 10–24, 28–29, 34–35 **6.2** pp. 275–277: Exs. 15–16, 20–28, 32–34, 39–40, 43–46, 59–60	**6.3** pp. 281–282: Exs. 23–36, 40–48, 50–56, 58–63	**6.4** pp. 285–287: Exs. 10–18, 22–25, 29–31, 35–37, 42–43, 45–56, 60–62	**6.5** pp. 292–293: Exs. 12–36, 38–44, 47–53	**6.6** pp. 297–298: Exs. 8–18, 23–25, 27–29, 31–34, 39–40, 42–44 **6.7** pp. 301–302: Exs. 10–24, 26–34, 38–41, 49–50	**6.8** pp. 307–308: Exs. 18–29, 30–33, 38–41, 46–49, 52–53, 56, 59–60 **6.9** pp. 311–313: Exs. 15–18, 27–30, 38–40, 46–47, 50–52, 58–59, 63–64, 69–74, 80–83	**Review** pp. 314–317: Exs. 1–55 **Assess** Chapter 6 Test

Yearly Pacing Chapter 6 Total – **7 days** Chapters 1–6 Total – **40 days** Remaining – **40 days**

Support Materials

Chapter Resource Book

LESSON SUPPORT	6.1	6.2	6.3	6.4	6.5	6.6	6.7	6.8	6.9
Lesson Plans	p. 1	p. 10	p. 19	p. 28	p. 37	p. 46	p. 55	p. 64	p. 73
Lesson Plans for Block Scheduling	p. 2	p. 11	p. 20	p. 29	p. 38	p. 47	p. 56	p. 65	p. 74
Warm-Ups with Multiple-Choice Practice	p. 3	p. 12	p. 21	p. 30	p. 39	p. 48	p. 57	p. 66	p. 75
Problem of the Day	p. 4	p. 13	p. 22	p. 31	p. 40	p. 49	p. 58	p. 67	p. 76
Daily Cumulative Review	p. 5	p. 14	p. 23	p. 32	p. 41	p. 50	p. 59	p. 68	p. 77
Practice Masters	p. 6	p. 15	p. 24	p. 33	p. 42	p. 51	p. 60	p. 69	p. 78
Reteaching Masters	p. 7	p. 16	p. 25	p. 34	p. 43	p. 52	p. 61	p. 70	p. 79
Enrichment Masters	p. 9	p. 18	p. 27	p. 36	p. 45	p. 54	p. 63	p. 72	p. 81

Transparencies

	6.1	6.2	6.3	6.4	6.5	6.6	6.7	6.8	6.9
Warm-Ups with Multiple-Choice Practice	p. 42	p. 43	p. 44	p. 45	p. 46	p. 47	p. 48	p. 49	p. 50
Teacher Time-Saver Transparencies	✓	✓	✓	✓	✓	✓	✓	✓	✓
English/Spanish Problem Solving		p. 24		p. 25	p. 26				p. 27
Answer Transparencies	✓	✓	✓	✓	✓	✓	✓	✓	✓

Technology

- Personal Student Tutor
- Time-Saving Test and Practice Generator
- Electronic Teacher Tools
- Technology: Using Calculators and Computers

Additional Resources

- Math Log
- Assessment Book
- Worked-Out Solution Key
- Practice Workbook (English/Spanish)
- Home and School Connection
- California Standards: Key Concepts Book

Correlation to the California Curriculum

Correlations to the California Standards
CA Standards: NS 1.1, NS 1.2, NS 1.3, NS 1.7, NS 2.1, NS 2.2, NS 2.3, AF 1.3, AF 2.1, AF 2.2, AF 4.1, MG 1.1, MG 1.3, MR 1.1

California Curriculum Support

Key Concepts Book

- Pre-Course Review: Topic 1 Working with Decimals
  Topic 2 Working with Fractions
  Topic 5 Measurement
- Key Standards: NS 1.2 Fraction Operations *(Lessons 6.1–6.3, 6.5)*
  NS 1.2 Powers of Rational Numbers *(Lessons 6.7, 6.8)*
  NS 2.2 Add and Subtract Fractions *(Lessons 6.1, 6.2)*
  NS 2.3 Exponent Rules *(Lesson 6.7)*
  AF 1.3 Identity and Inverse Properties *(Lesson 6.3)*
- Special Topics: Comparing Fractions *(Lessons 6.1–6.3)*

California Standards Practice Workbook provides practice for each Standard that is covered in this chapter.

Providing Universal Access

Strategies for Strategic Learners

REVIEW KEY CONCEPTS

Facility with conversions among fractions, decimals, and percents is an extraordinarily useful skill. Whether students are calculating the sale price of an item, comparing the financial returns on different savings plans, or calculating income taxes, students will benefit from the ability to estimate and the ability to calculate accurately with fractions, decimals, and percents.

ALGORITHMS Many students will have developed solid skills and understand the logic behind the basic algorithms in this area. But others will experience some confusion, will be unsure what algorithm to use, or will be able to apply an algorithm but will not understand why it works. Research indicates that gifted students are often quick to understand mathematical reasoning, but most students need careful explanations of the reasoning and explicit instruction in selecting and applying procedures. Many of us can understand explanations with simple situations for which we can form a mental image, but when numbers become too large, too small, or too unwieldy, we need an algorithm to fall back on.

USING A GRID To provide a review of concepts taught in earlier years and to reinforce the understanding that a number can be written as a fraction, a decimal, and a percent, have students represent numbers on a 10-by-10 grid. Graph paper may be used, or a grid can be drawn on the board.

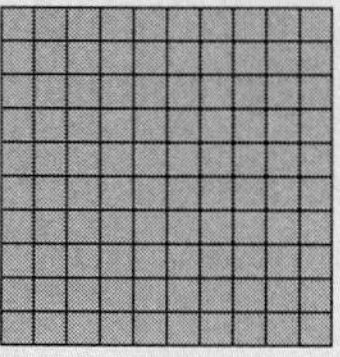

Have students use grids to shade percents such as the following, and then express each percent as a decimal and as a fraction first with 100 as the denominator, and then as a fraction in lowest terms:

1%, 2%, 5%, 10%, 12%, 15%, 20%, 35%, 50%, 60%, 75%, 90%, 100%, 110%, 125%.

Once students are comfortable with this, have them consider the following questions:

1. Which is closer to 1, $\frac{86}{100}$ or $\frac{87}{100}$? $\frac{123}{100}$ or $\frac{124}{100}$?
2. Which is closer to 1, $\frac{103}{100}$ or $\frac{97}{100}$? (*They are equally close to 1. If students have trouble with this, have them locate the numbers on a number line.*)
3. How can you use the grid to find a fraction between $\frac{57}{100}$ and $\frac{58}{100}$? How would you write this fraction as a decimal and as a percent? (*Sample answer: Imagine that each square is cut in half, making 200 rectangles. The first fraction is represented by 114 rectangles and the second by 116 rectangles. The number $\frac{115}{200}$ represented by 115 rectangles, is between $\frac{57}{100}$ and $\frac{58}{100}$. $\frac{115}{200} = 0.575 = 57.5\%$.*)

Once students understand that percent is a way of expressing how many parts out of a hundred, they may find it easier to understand and use the procedures taught in this chapter.

Strategies for English Learners

VOCABULARY STUDY

Greek and Latin roots, prefixes, and suffixes occur repeatedly in mathematical and scientific terms. Students who are familiar with common word parts can apply this knowledge to deciphering new words. This word study could be covered in a few minutes each week during math class or in a more extended way during the language arts period.

GREEK AND LATIN PREFIXES Here are some common prefixes that students will see:

Bi- (from the Latin for *two*)
Co/com/cum- (from the Latin for *with*)
Dis-, di-, dif- (from the Latin for *away from*, *out of*, *apart*)
In- (from the Latin for *in* or *not*, *without*)
Iso- (from the Greek for *equal*)
Mono- (from the Greek for *single* or *alone*)
Multi- (from the Latin for *many*)
Para- (from the Greek for *beside*)
Per- (from the Latin for *through*, or *by means of*)
Poly- (from the Greek for *many*)
Pre- (from the Latin for *before*)
Re- (from the Latin for *again* or *backward*)
Sub- (from the Latin for *under*, *beneath*)
Quad- (from the Latin for *four*)
Tri- (from the Latin for *three*)

WORDS AND PREFIXES Ask students to consider how those prefixes contribute to these words: similar : dissimilar; continuous : discontinuous; order : disorder; solve : dissolve; unite : disunite; bisect, commutative, congruent, coordinate, diagram, diameter, distance, distribute, isosceles, monomial, multiple, multiply, parabola, parallelogram, parallel, parameter, percent, polynomial, polygon, quadrilateral, quadrant, subtract, triangle.

NUMBERS Latin numbers have also influenced English mathematical words. Put these Latin words for cardinal numbers on the board and ask students to think of words that use them:

Unus, una, unum (one)
Duo, duae (two)
Tres, tria (three)
Quattor (four)
Quinque (five)
Sex (six)
Septum (seven)
Octo (eight)
Novem (nine)
Decem (ten)

Spanish speakers will see that many words for numbers in Spanish are very close to the Latin number names.

Strategies for Advanced Learners

DIFFERENTIATE INSTRUCTION IN TERMS OF DEPTH

Sometimes one good problem can provide the opportunity for students to delve into many areas of mathematics. As students progress through mathematics courses, they may find at advanced levels that a single problem can consume a class period, several class periods, or much, much longer. Take any of the challenge problems in this chapter and ask students to find several ways to solve the problem. As they generate different methods for solving the problem, ask them to consider what method is simplest. Help students understand that looking at a problem from a variety of ways can help them select the simplest method for solution. Students can generate a variety of problem solving strategies and can list these in their notebooks. Remind them to look not only at what changes in a problem, but what remains the same. The answers to a multiple-choice problem can provide clues; sometimes it is much easier to work backward from the answer. Using a diagram, graph, or table can help organize or represent information in a way that leads to a solution.

CHAPTER 6 Mathematical Background Notes

As discussed in Chapter 5, equivalent fractions represent the same number. For example, for any nonzero whole number k we have

$$\frac{3 \cdot k}{5 \cdot k} = \frac{3}{5}.$$

Given two fractions $\frac{a}{b}$ and $\frac{c}{d}$, it is possible to find fractions that represent the same two numbers but have a common denominator. For instance, given $\frac{8}{11}$ and $\frac{7}{9}$, we have $\frac{8}{11} = \frac{72}{99}$ and $\frac{7}{9} = \frac{77}{99}$. In this form, we can easily compare the sizes of these two numbers. Since $72 < 77$, we have

$$\frac{72}{99} < \frac{77}{99} \text{ and } \frac{8}{11} < \frac{7}{9}.$$

The use of such representations with common denominators enables us to extend the basic arithmetic operations to fractions in such a way that the CAD laws are satisfied. Doing so for both positive and negative fractions leads to the entire set of **rational numbers.**

Lessons 6.1–6.2

ADDING AND SUBTRACTING The addition and subtraction of fractions relies heavily on the concept of equivalence. The fact that $\frac{2}{7} + \frac{3}{7} = \frac{5}{7}$ reflects the fact that we are combining two and three numbers of the same denomination. This corresponds to the most basic concept of mathematics, that of "combining heaps" when the heaps contain objects of the same kind.

The problem $\frac{3}{4} + \frac{1}{6}$ poses a different kind of challenge. Here we must convert $\frac{3}{4}$ and $\frac{1}{6}$ into fractions of the same denomination before doing the addition. This can be done either in the form

$$\frac{3}{4} + \frac{1}{6} = \frac{3 \cdot 6}{4 \cdot 6} + \frac{1 \cdot 4}{6 \cdot 4} = \frac{18}{24} + \frac{4}{24} = \frac{22}{24} = \frac{11}{12}$$

or in the form

$$\frac{3}{4} + \frac{1}{6} = \frac{3 \cdot 3}{4 \cdot 3} + \frac{1 \cdot 2}{6 \cdot 2} = \frac{9}{12} + \frac{2}{12} = \frac{11}{12}.$$

In the first case we were using the obvious common denominator $4 \times 6 = 24$. This corresponds to the general rule for adding two fractions,

$$\frac{a}{b} + \frac{c}{d} = \frac{ad}{bd} + \frac{bc}{bd} = \frac{ad + bc}{bd}.$$

In the second case it was possible to simplify the addition process by using the *least* common denominator, which is the least common multiple of 4 and 6, as studied in Lesson 6.2.

While it is good to encourage students to look for a least common denominator, this should not be made a blanket requirement. There are situations in which finding the least common multiple of b and d is far more difficult than using the rule $\frac{a}{b} + \frac{c}{d} = \frac{ad + bc}{bd}$. By way of example, the general rule readily gives the answer

$$\frac{5}{153} + \frac{1}{6} = \frac{183}{918}.$$

Although it is instructive to find the least common multiple of 153 and 6:

Multiples of 153: 153, *306*, 459, 612, 765, 918, . . .
Multiples of 6: 6, 12, 18, 24, . . . , 294, 300, *306*, 312, . . .

and then use this fact to write

$$\frac{5}{153} + \frac{1}{6} = \frac{5 \cdot 2}{153 \cdot 2} + \frac{1 \cdot 51}{6 \cdot 51} = \frac{10}{306} + \frac{51}{306} = \frac{61}{306},$$

it is not clear that this should be made a requirement in all cases.

Addition or subtraction involving three or more fractions can also be carried out by first converting all the fractions to a form with a common denominator, as in Example 2 on page 274. However, such calculations can also be done one step at a time, using the rules for two fractions at each stage. For example,

$$\frac{1}{2} - \frac{3}{8} + \frac{3}{4} = \left(\frac{1}{2} - \frac{3}{8}\right) + \frac{3}{4} = \left(\frac{4}{8} - \frac{3}{8}\right) + \frac{3}{4} = \frac{1}{8} + \frac{3}{4} = \frac{1}{8} + \frac{6}{8} = \frac{7}{8}.$$

Lesson 6.3

MULTIPLYING The multiplication rule for fractions

$$\frac{a}{b} \cdot \frac{c}{d} = \frac{ac}{bd}$$

can be justified algebraically on the grounds that it is consistent with the CAD laws. It is, however, preferable to provide the student with a geometric model for multiplication, one that convincingly conveys the above rule. Such a model can be based on the familiar formula *Area* = *base* × *height* for the area of a rectangle.

$A = \frac{a}{b} \cdot \frac{c}{d}$ height $= \frac{c}{d}$

base $= \frac{a}{b}$

If this formula is to hold when the base and height assume fractional values $\frac{a}{b}$ and $\frac{c}{d}$, then the calculation of area by the formula Area = base × height must correspond to the multiplication of fractions.

To explain why $\frac{2}{3} \cdot \frac{3}{5} = \frac{2 \cdot 3}{3 \cdot 5} = \frac{6}{15}$, we consider a unit square whose base is divided into 3 equal segments of length $\frac{1}{3}$ and whose height is divided into 5 equal segments of length $\frac{1}{5}$. The resulting grid divides the unit square into $3 \cdot 5$ congruent rectangles.

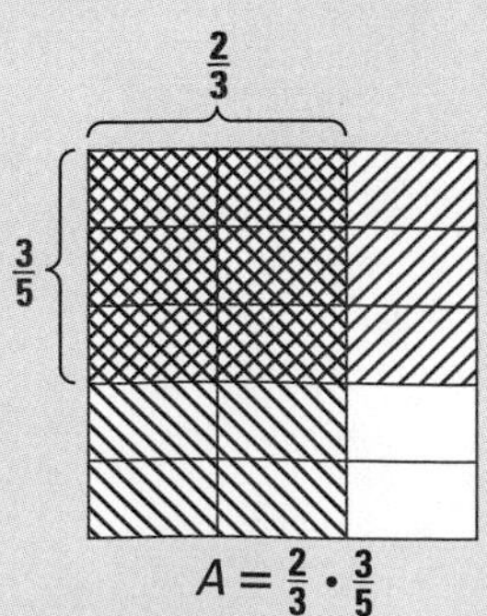

Since these rectangles all have the same area and the sum of their areas is 1 (the area of the unit square), we conclude that each rectangle has area $\frac{1}{15}$. In the picture above we see that a $\frac{2}{3}$ by $\frac{3}{5}$ rectangle consists of $2 \cdot 3$ such rectangles, so it has area $6 \times \frac{1}{15} = \frac{6}{15}$. Thus we are led to the area of the shaded rectangle as $\frac{2}{3} \cdot \frac{3}{5} = \frac{6}{15}$. Since $\frac{6}{15} = \frac{2 \cdot 3}{3 \cdot 5}$, we have $\frac{2}{3} \cdot \frac{3}{5} = \frac{2 \cdot 3}{3 \cdot 5}$. In the general case, this argument leads to

$$\frac{a}{b} \cdot \frac{c}{d} = \frac{a \cdot c}{b \cdot d}$$

for positive integers a, b, c, d.

Lesson 6.5

DIVIDING Having arrived at the rule $\frac{a}{b} \times \frac{c}{d} = \frac{ac}{bd}$ for multiplying fractions, it remains to develop the corresponding rule for $\frac{a}{b} \div \frac{c}{d}$. Our answer will be guided by the laws of arithmetic that we seek to extend from whole numbers and integers to fractions.

If A and B are integers, then $A \div B$ is a number C with the property that $A = B \times C$. That is, $12 \div 3 = 4$ because $12 = 3 \times 4$. The "acid test" for whether or not $527 \div 17 = 31$ is not the long division algorithm, rather it is whether or not $527 = 17 \times 31$.

Suppose now that $A = \frac{a}{b}$ and $B = \frac{c}{d}$ and that we are seeking the answer to $A \div B = \frac{a}{b} \div \frac{c}{d}$. If we can find a fraction C for which $\frac{a}{b} = \frac{c}{d} \times C$, then C is *the* solution to the division problem $\frac{a}{b} \div \frac{c}{d}$.

This is the basis for the rule $\frac{a}{b} \div \frac{c}{d} = \frac{a}{b} \times \frac{d}{c}$ that is sometimes taught as "'Tis not yours to question why, just invert and multiply." But for those willing to question and ask *why,* the justification of this rule lies in the fact that $C = \frac{a}{b} \times \frac{d}{c}$ has the crucial property $\frac{a}{b} = \frac{c}{d} \times C$. By the commutative and associative laws of multiplication,

$$\frac{c}{d} \times C = \frac{c}{d} \times \left(\frac{a}{b} \times \frac{d}{c}\right) = \frac{c}{d} \times \left(\frac{d}{c} \times \frac{a}{b}\right) = \left(\frac{c}{d} \times \frac{d}{c}\right) \times \frac{a}{b} = \frac{a}{b}.$$

Since this is a rather abstract argument, presenting students an explanation based on equivalent fractions may be preferable. Because $\frac{a}{b}$ is equivalent to $\frac{ad}{bd}$ and $\frac{c}{d}$ is equivalent to $\frac{bc}{bd}$, it is reasonable to define $\frac{a}{b} \div \frac{c}{d} = \frac{ad}{bd} \div \frac{bc}{bd} = \frac{ad}{bc}$. This result can be remembered by the "invert and multiply rule"

$$\frac{a}{b} \div \frac{c}{d} = \frac{a}{b} \times \frac{d}{c}.$$

Lessons 6.7–6.8

ZERO AND NEGATIVE EXPONENTS These lessons provide the student with the basic multiplication rules for powers having the same base. Here the associative law of multiplication underlies the multiplication property stated on page 299. For example,

$$a^2 \cdot a^3 = (a \cdot a) \cdot (a \cdot a \cdot a) = a \cdot a \cdot a \cdot a \cdot a = a^5,$$

where we have used the associative law to remove parentheses.

Having defined a^n for positive integer values of n, there arises the question of whether meaning can be ascribed to a^0 and a^{-n}. Developing Concepts on pages 303–304 uses patterns to arrive at the following definitions.

If $a \neq 0$ and n is a positive integer, then $a^0 = 1$ and $a^{-n} = \frac{1}{a^n}$.

It is important for the student to understand that these definitions also follow from the multiplication rule and the laws of arithmetic. If we are to reconcile zero exponents with the multiplication properties of exponents we must have

$$a^n \cdot a^0 = a^{n+0} = a^n.$$

This shows that a^0 will have to play the role of multiplicative identity, and this in turn requires that $a^0 = 1$. In this calculation, the fact that 0 is the identity element under addition has translated into the requirement that a^0 be the identity element under multiplication.

Similar considerations underlie the definition of a^{-n} for positive integer values of n. If we are to allow for negative integer values of n, then the multiplication property will demand that

$$a^n \cdot a^{-n} = a^{n+(-n)} = a^0 = 1.$$

This shows that a^{-n} will have to play the role of multiplicative inverse of a^n, and it is this requirement that leads us to define $a^{-n} = \frac{1}{a^n}$. Again, the fact that $-n$ is the additive inverse of n has translated into a requirement that a^{-n} be the multiplicative inverse of a^n.

In Lesson 6.7 the student learns to relate these considerations to the division property of exponents. In the expression $\frac{4^5}{4^3} = \frac{4 \cdot 4 \cdot 4 \cdot 4 \cdot 4}{4 \cdot 4 \cdot 4}$ it is possible to cancel 4^3 to obtain 4^2. It is this property of fractions that underlies the property $a^m \div a^n = a^{m-n}$.

One can also arrive at this definition using the division rule $b \div a = b \cdot \frac{1}{a}$. Applying this rule to a^m and a^n, one obtains

$$a^m \div a^n = a^m \cdot \frac{1}{a^n} = a^m \cdot a^{-n}.$$

In order to reconcile negative exponents with the multiplication property, it will be necessary to define $a^m \div a^n = a^{m-n}$.

Chapter Overview

Chapter Goals

In this chapter, students will add, subtract, multiply, and divide fractions, with like or unlike denominators. They will:

- Multiply with percents.
- Use properties of exponents to simplify exponential expressions.
- Use scientific notation.

Career Note

Registered nurses observe patient's symptoms and assist physicians. They administer medication and assist in the convalescence of the patient, as well as give instruction to patients and families on proper care and on health maintenance. Registered nurses hold a two- or four-year college degree. Other careers in the nursing field include licensed practical nurses and nursing aides. Licensed practical nurses take vital signs, give injections, and help keep patients comfortable. Their training usually includes a one-year program in a vocational school or community college. Nursing aides respond to patient's calls, serve meals, make beds, and assist patients. Training for nursing aides is offered through vocational schools and community colleges.

Additional information about nursing is available at **www.mcdougallittell.com**

Operations with Rational Numbers

Why are rational numbers important?

Rational numbers, which can be expressed as ratios of integers, are useful in describing fractional measurements, such as $\frac{1}{2}$ in. or 2.6 liters. Using operations with rational numbers is important when working with formulas and finding rates.

Operations with rational numbers are used in many careers, including nursing (page 267) and real estate (page 287). For example, nurses use operations with rational numbers when they calculate doses.

Meeting the California Standards

The skills you'll develop in this chapter will help you meet state standards and prepare for standardized tests. In this chapter you'll:

- **Simplify numerical expressions.** LESSONS 6.2, 6.3
- **Convert and use fractions, decimals, and percents.** LESSON 6.4
- **Solve problems that involve sales tax, commissions, and tips.** LESSON 6.4
- **Calculate with rational numbers by using exponent rules.** LESSON 6.7
- **Multiply and divide monomials by using the rules of exponents.** LESSON 6.7
- **Understand negative whole number exponents.** LESSON 6.8
- **Read, write, and compare numbers in scientific notation.** LESSON 6.9

Career Link **NURSE** A nurse uses operations with numbers when:

- administering medication to patients.
- calculating doses based on the patient's weight.

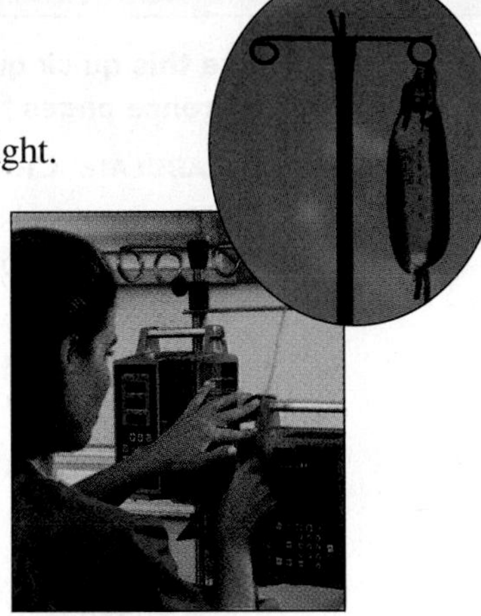

EXERCISES

An intravenous flow device administers drops of a solution that contains medicine. A nurse sets the frequency of the drops.

1. A patient needs 750 mg of medicine each day. There are 50 mg of medicine in each milliliter of solution. How many milliliters of solution should the patient be given each day? **15 ml**
2. There are 60 drops in a milliliter. How many drops of solution should the patient be given each day? **900 drops**
3. How many drops should the patient be given per hour? **37.5 drops/hour**

In Lesson 6.3, you will use the formula below to calculate the flow rate in drops per hour for another patient's medication.

$$\text{Flow rate} = \frac{M}{24} \cdot \frac{C}{S}$$

M = milligrams of medicine needed each day

C = drops needed to administer 1 mL of the solution

S = milligrams of medicine in 1 mL of the solution

Projects

A project covering Chapters 4–6 appears on pages 324–325 of the Student Edition. Additional projects for selected lessons in Chapter 6 are available in the *Assessment Book,* pp. 233–234.

Technology

Software

- Electronic Teacher Tools
- Online Lesson Planner
- Personal Student Tutor
- Test and Practice Generator

Internet Connections

- Application and Career Links 271, 287, 295, 307, 308
- Student Help 270, 277, 284, 292, 296, 302, 321

These Internet connections are available at **www.mcdougallittell.com**

Prepare

Diagnostic Tools

The **chapter readiness quiz** can help you diagnose whether students have the following skills needed in Chapter 6:

- Understand and identify fractions in simplest form.
- Write the prime factorization of a number.
- Find the least common multiple of two numbers.

Reteaching Materials

The following resources are available for students who need additional help with the skills on the chapter readiness quiz:

Chapter 6 Resource Book

- Reteaching with Practice (Lessons 5.1, 5.2, 5.3)

Personal Student Tutor

Additional Resources

The following resources are provided to help you prepare for the upcoming chapter and customize review materials:

Chapter 6 Resource Book

- Lesson Plans, pp. 1, 10, 19, 28, 36, 46, 55, 64, 73
- Lesson Plans for Block Scheduling, pp. 2, 11, 20, 29, 37, 47, 56, 65, 74

Technology

- Electronic Teacher Tools with Lesson Planning Software
- Test and Practice Generator

Chapter 6 Getting Ready

PREVIEW

What's the chapter about?

- Performing operations on **fractions**, and solving **equations** with **rational numbers**
- Multiplying with **percents**
- Multiplying and dividing **powers**, and using **scientific notation**
- Simplifying expressions with **negative** and **zero exponents**

WORDS TO KNOW

- **least common denominator,** *p. 273*
- **multiplicative inverses,** *p. 279*
- **inverse property of multiplication,** *p. 279*
- **reciprocals,** *p. 279*
- **zero exponent,** *p. 305*
- **negative exponent,** *p. 305*
- **scientific notation,** *p. 309*

PREPARE

Chapter Readiness Quiz

Take this quick quiz. If you are unsure of an answer, look back at the reference pages for help.

VOCABULARY CHECK *(refer to pp. 225, 233)*

1. If a fraction is in simplest form, then the numerator and denominator have a _?_ of 1. C

Ⓐ Common multiple Ⓑ Least common multiple

Ⓒ Greatest common factor Ⓓ Prime factor

2. Two fractions with the same simplest form are _?_. H

Ⓕ Identities Ⓖ Correlating Ⓗ Equivalent Ⓙ Equal

SKILL CHECK *(refer to pp. 220, 229–230)*

3. Which is the prime factorization of 324? C

Ⓐ $18 \cdot 18$ Ⓑ $2^2 \cdot 81$ Ⓒ $2^2 \cdot 3^4$ Ⓓ $2^3 \cdot 3^3$

4. Which is the least common multiple of $16xy^3$ and $28x^3y^2$? J

Ⓕ $4xy^2$ Ⓖ $64x^3y^2$ Ⓗ $112xy^2$ Ⓙ $112x^3y^3$

STUDY TIP

Keep a List of Assignments

A list of assignments will help you to stay organized and on task.

My Assignments

Date Due	Assignment	Done?
11/20	p. 271, Exs. 1-22	✓
11/22	p. 275, Exs. 2-30 evens	

6.1 Adding and Subtracting Fractions

California Standards

In this lesson you'll:

- Add and subtract positive and negative fractions. (NS 1.2)
- Add and subtract fractions by using factoring to find common denominators. (NS 2.2)

Goal 1 Using Common Denominators

In previous math courses you learned how to add and subtract fractions with the same and with different denominators. In this lesson you'll review those skills and extend them to negative fractions.

RULES FOR FRACTIONS WITH A COMMON DENOMINATOR

1. To add two fractions with a common denominator, add their numerators and write the sum over the denominator:

$$\frac{a}{c} + \frac{b}{c} = \frac{a+b}{c}$$

2. To subtract two fractions with a common denominator, subtract their numerators and write the difference over the denominator:

$$\frac{a}{c} - \frac{b}{c} = \frac{a-b}{c}$$

EXAMPLE 1 Adding Fractions

$\frac{5}{8} + \frac{7}{8} = \frac{5+7}{8}$ Add numerators.

$= \frac{12}{8}$ Simplify numerator.

$= \frac{3 \cdot \cancel{4}^{1}}{2 \cdot \cancel{4}_{1}}$ Factor numerator and denominator.

$= \frac{3}{2}$ Simplify.

Student Help

STUDY TIP
To rewrite $2\frac{1}{6}$ as an improper fraction, remember that
$2\frac{1}{6} = 2 + \frac{1}{6}$
$= \frac{12}{6} + \frac{1}{6} = \frac{13}{6}$.

EXAMPLE 2 Subtracting Mixed Numbers

$2\frac{1}{6} - 1\frac{5}{6} = \frac{13}{6} - \frac{11}{6}$ Rewrite as improper fractions.

$= \frac{13-11}{6}$ Subtract numerators.

$= \frac{2}{6}$ Simplify numerator.

$= \frac{1 \cdot \cancel{2}^{1}}{3 \cdot \cancel{2}_{1}}$ Factor numerator and denominator.

$= \frac{1}{3}$ Simplify.

1 Plan

Pacing

Suggested Number of Days

Transitional: 1 day
Average: 1 day
Advanced: 1 day
Block Schedule: 0.5 block with 6.2

Teaching Resources

Blacklines
(See page 266B.)

Transparencies
- Warm-Up Exercises
- Teacher Time-Savers
- English/Spanish Problem Solving
- Answers

Technology
- Electronic Teacher Tools
- Test and Practice Generator

2 Teach

Math Reasoning

For Mathematical Background Notes on mathematical reasoning related to this lesson, please refer to pages 266E and 266F in this Teacher's Edition.

Extra Examples 1 and 2
See next page.

California Standards and Assessment

CA Standards: NS 1.2, NS 2.2
CA Key Concepts Book: pp. S9–S11, S15, S36–S38, T12–T13

Math Reasoning

Understanding the terminology used for fractions helps clarify the addition and subtraction rules. The fraction $\frac{m}{n}$ represents m copies of $\frac{1}{n}$. The numerator m *enumerates,* or *counts,* the number of copies, while the denominator n *names,* or *denotes,* the denomination these copies have in common. *Equivalent fractions* represent the same number. To add or subtract fractions with different denominators, we replace them by equivalent fractions with the same denominator.

Extra Example 1

Find the sum. Then simplify.

$\frac{5}{12} + \frac{1}{12}$ $\frac{1}{2}$

Extra Example 2

Find the difference. Then simplify.

$3\frac{1}{8} - 2\frac{7}{8}$ $\frac{1}{4}$

Extra Example 3

Find the difference. Then simplify.

$\frac{2x}{9} - \left(-\frac{4x}{9}\right)$ $\frac{2x}{3}$

Extra Example 4

Find the sum or difference. Then simplify.

a. $\frac{3}{5} + \left(\frac{-1}{6}\right)$ $\frac{13}{30}$

b. $\frac{-3}{4} - \frac{5}{9}$ $\frac{-47}{36}$ or $-1\frac{11}{36}$

Teaching Tip

Emphasize that once a sum or difference is found, it is customary to simplify the result, if possible.

Concept Check

Explain how to add or subtract fractions. ***Sample answer:*** **Rewrite any mixed numbers as improper fractions. Rewrite the fractions so that they have a common denominator. Add or subtract the numerators and place the result over the common denominator. Simplify the resulting fraction.**

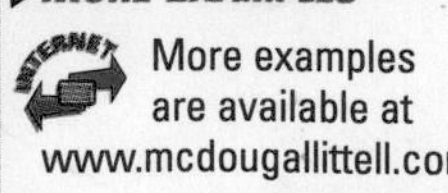

Student Help

▶ MORE EXAMPLES

More examples are available at www.mcdougallittell.com

EXAMPLE 3 Adding or Subtracting Variable Expressions

$$\frac{6x}{5} - \left(-\frac{3x}{5}\right) = \frac{6x}{5} + \frac{3x}{5}$$ To subtract $-\frac{3x}{5}$, add its opposite.

$$= \frac{6x + 3x}{5}$$ Add numerators.

$$= \frac{9x}{5}$$ Simplify numerator.

Goal 2 USING DIFFERENT DENOMINATORS

You can extend the rules for adding and subtracting fractions with like denominators to those with different denominators as described below.

RULES FOR FRACTIONS WITH DIFFERENT DENOMINATORS

One way to add or subtract fractions with different denominators is to rewrite the fractions using a common denominator as follows.

1. $\frac{a}{b} + \frac{c}{d} = \frac{ad}{bd} + \frac{bc}{bd} = \frac{ad + bc}{bd}$ **2.** $\frac{a}{b} - \frac{c}{d} = \frac{ad}{bd} - \frac{bc}{bd} = \frac{ad - bc}{bd}$

In both cases the common denominator is bd.

EXAMPLE 4 Adding and Subtracting Fractions

a. $$\frac{2}{3} + \left(-\frac{1}{8}\right) = \frac{2 \cdot 8}{3 \cdot 8} + \left(\frac{-1 \cdot 3}{8 \cdot 3}\right)$$ Use 8 • 3 as the common denominator.

$$= \frac{16}{24} + \left(\frac{-3}{24}\right)$$ Simplify.

$$= \frac{16 + (-3)}{24}$$ Add numerators.

$$= \frac{13}{24}$$ Simplify numerator.

Student Help

▶ STUDY TIP

A negative fraction such as $-\frac{1}{8}$ can also be written as $\frac{-1}{8}$ or as $\frac{1}{-8}$.

b. $$-\frac{4}{5} - \frac{1}{3} = \frac{-4}{5} + \frac{-1}{3}$$ Rewrite fractions and change to addition.

$$= \frac{-4 \cdot 3}{5 \cdot 3} + \frac{-1 \cdot 5}{3 \cdot 5}$$ Use 5 • 3 as the common denominator.

$$= \frac{-12}{15} + \frac{-5}{15}$$ Simplify.

$$= \frac{-12 + (-5)}{15}$$ Add numerators.

$$= \frac{-17}{15} \text{ or } -1\frac{2}{15}$$ Simplify numerator.

6.1 Exercises

Guided Practice

9. *Sample answer:* When the denominators are the same, add or subtract the numerators using the rules for adding or subtracting positive and negative numbers. Write the answer over the common denominator. $\frac{1}{9} + \frac{7}{9} = \frac{8}{9}$, $\frac{5}{11} - \frac{3}{11} = \frac{2}{11}$

25. Less than 1; since each denominator is more than twice its numerator, each fraction is less than $\frac{1}{2}$. Adding two fractions each less than $\frac{1}{2}$ will result in a sum that is less than 1.

Use fractions to write an equation that represents the indicated sum or difference.

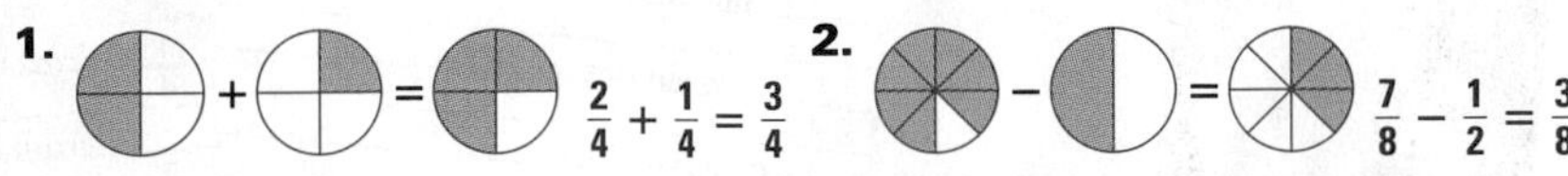

1. $\frac{2}{4} + \frac{1}{4} = \frac{3}{4}$

2. $\frac{7}{8} - \frac{1}{2} = \frac{3}{8}$

Add or subtract. Then simplify, if possible.

3. $\frac{1}{5} + \frac{3}{5}$ $\frac{4}{5}$

4. $3\frac{9}{10} - 1\frac{3}{10}$ $2\frac{3}{5}$

5. $\frac{2}{9} + \left(-\frac{5}{9}\right)$ $-\frac{1}{3}$

6. $\frac{1}{3} - 1\frac{4}{5}$ $-1\frac{7}{15}$

7. $\frac{5}{7} - \frac{2}{3}$ $\frac{1}{21}$

8. $\frac{-x}{4} + \frac{3x}{4}$ $\frac{x}{2}$

9. **WRITING** In your own words, write rules for adding and subtracting positive and negative fractions with the same denominator. Give examples to show how the rules work. See margin.

Practice and Problem Solving

Student Help

▶ **More Practice**
Extra practice to help you master skills is on page 700.

Add or subtract. Then simplify, if possible.

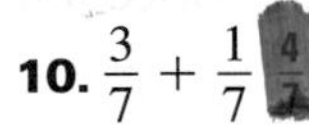

10. $\frac{3}{7} + \frac{1}{7}$ $\frac{4}{7}$

11. $\frac{4}{5} - \frac{2}{5}$ $\frac{2}{5}$

12. $2\frac{1}{8} - \frac{5}{8}$ $1\frac{1}{2}$

13. $\frac{7}{10} - \left(-\frac{1}{10}\right)$ $\frac{4}{5}$

14. $-\frac{6}{7} - \frac{3}{7}$ $-1\frac{2}{7}$

15. $\frac{1}{5} + \frac{3}{10}$ $\frac{1}{2}$

16. $\frac{5}{6} - \frac{1}{3}$ $\frac{1}{2}$

17. $-\frac{3}{8} + \frac{1}{5}$ $-\frac{7}{40}$

18. $3\frac{1}{2} + 1\frac{2}{5}$ $4\frac{9}{10}$

19. $2\frac{1}{2} + \frac{2}{3}$ $3\frac{1}{6}$

20. $\frac{11}{7} - \frac{3}{4}$ $\frac{23}{28}$

21. $8\frac{5}{6} - 2\frac{8}{9}$ $5\frac{17}{18}$

22. $\frac{x}{3} - \left(\frac{-2x}{3}\right)$ x

23. $\frac{m}{4} + \frac{5m}{6}$ $\frac{13m}{12}$

24. $\frac{2p}{7} - \frac{p}{2}$ $-\frac{3p}{14}$

25. **MATHEMATICAL REASONING** Suppose you have two positive fractions. In each fraction, the denominator is more than twice the numerator. Is the sum of the two fractions greater than or less than 1? How would you convince a classmate that you are correct? See margin.

26. **WEAVING** You finish weaving $5\frac{3}{4}$ inches of a carpet, then you find a mistake and pull out $1\frac{1}{8}$ inches of it. How much of the carpet remains? $4\frac{5}{8}$ in.

27. **EXERCISING** You run $3\frac{1}{2}$ miles and then walk $\frac{3}{4}$ mile to cool down. What distance do you cover while exercising? $4\frac{1}{4}$ mi

Link to Careers

TEXTILE DESIGNERS often use geometric patterns in their fabric designs.

More about textile designers available at www.mcdougallittell.com

3 Apply

Assignment Guide

Transitional
Day 1: pp. 271–272 Exs. 10–21, 26–27, 34–35

Average
Day 1: pp. 271–272 Exs. 10–24, 28–29, 34–35

Advanced
Day 1: pp. 271–272 Exs. 10–24, 30–31, 32–33*, 34–35

Block Schedule
pp. 271–272 Exs. 10–24, 28–29, 34–35 (with 6.2)

Extra Practice

- Student Edition, pp. 700–701
- Chapter 6 Resource Book, p. 6

Homework Check

To quickly check student understanding of key concepts, go over the following exercises:

Transitional: 10, 12, 16, 20, 26
Average: 10, 12, 16, 22, 28
Advanced: 10, 12, 16, 22, 30

Assess

Assessment Resources

- Assessment Book (Formal Assessment and Alternative Assessment)
- Test and Practice Generator

Mini-Quiz

Add or subtract. Then simplify.

1. $\frac{3x}{7}+\frac{2x}{7}$ $\frac{5x}{7}$
2. $3\frac{1}{5}-1\frac{3}{5}$ $\frac{8}{5}$ or $1\frac{3}{5}$
3. $\frac{5}{6}-\frac{2}{7}$ $\frac{23}{42}$
4. $2\frac{3}{5}-1\frac{1}{3}$ $\frac{19}{15}$ or $1\frac{4}{15}$
5. You walked $1\frac{3}{4}$ miles on Saturday and $1\frac{2}{3}$ miles on Sunday. How many miles did you walk over the weekend? $3\frac{5}{12}$ miles

28. HEALTH DRINKS Each recipe shown serves one person. You decide to combine both recipes and invite a friend over to taste your creation with you. Find the total amount of each ingredient you use.
See margin.

28. banana: 1 c, instant nonfat milk powder: $\frac{1}{4}$ c, frozen orange juice: $1\frac{1}{4}$ c, crushed ice: $\frac{2}{3}$ c, sparkling water: $\frac{1}{2}$ c, frozen pineapple juice: $\frac{1}{4}$ c

29. Yes; $1\frac{1}{4}+2\frac{3}{8}=3\frac{5}{8}$ ft, which is less than the total length of $4\frac{1}{2}$ ft.

29. CARPENTRY You find a wooden shelf $4\frac{1}{2}$ feet long. You want to cut it to make two smaller shelves. One will be $1\frac{1}{4}$ feet long, the other $2\frac{3}{8}$ feet long. Is the uncut shelf long enough? Explain your answer.
See margin.

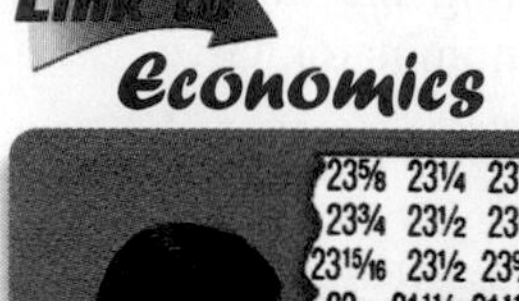

THE STOCK MARKET
Students can learn about saving, investing, and economics by choosing and tracking hypothetical investments in the stock market.

STOCK MARKET In Exercises 30 and 31, use the following information.
Stock prices are quoted in fractions of dollars. So, a stock price of $29\frac{3}{4}$ per share means $29.75 per share. You bought a stock on Monday at $38\frac{9}{16}$ per share. On Wednesday the stock price fell to $29\frac{3}{4}$. By Friday the price per share had risen to $55\frac{11}{16}$.

30. How much did the cost per share fall from Monday to Wednesday?

31. If you sold the stock on Friday, how much money would you have made per share? $17\frac{1}{8}$ or $17.125

CHALLENGE Find the missing fraction.

32. $\frac{3}{5}+\frac{4}{5}-$ **?** $=1$ $\frac{2}{5}$

33. $\frac{1}{8}+$ **?** $+\frac{3}{4}=3\frac{3}{8}$ $\frac{5}{2}$

Multiple-Choice Practice

34. What is the sum of $\frac{7}{8}$ and $\left(\frac{-1}{2}\right)$? C

Ⓐ $\frac{-11}{8}$ Ⓑ $\frac{-3}{8}$ Ⓒ $\frac{3}{8}$ Ⓓ $\frac{11}{8}$

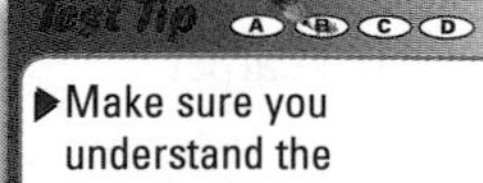

▶ Make sure you understand the question before you look for the answer.

35. A rain gauge outside a window measured $1\frac{3}{4}$ inches. One hour later, the gauge measured $2\frac{7}{8}$ inches. How much rain fell in one hour? G

Ⓕ 1 inch Ⓖ $1\frac{1}{8}$ inch Ⓗ $1\frac{1}{4}$ inch Ⓙ $1\frac{1}{2}$ inch

6.2 Using a Least Common Denominator

California Standards

In this lesson you'll:

- Add and subtract fractions by using factoring to find common denominators. (NS 2.2)
- Simplify numerical expressions by applying properties of rational numbers. (AF 1.3)

Goal 1 FINDING A LEAST COMMON DENOMINATOR

In Lesson 5.3 you learned how to find the least common multiple (LCM) of two or more integers. When you add or subtract fractions with different denominators, a convenient common denominator is the least common multiple of their denominators. This number is called the **least common denominator** (LCD) of the fractions.

EXAMPLE 1 Adding Fractions

Add $\frac{5}{6}$ and $-\frac{2}{9}$.

a. Use the product of the denominators as the common denominator.

b. Use the least common multiple as the least common denominator.

c. Compare the results.

Solution

a. $\frac{5}{6} + \left(-\frac{2}{9}\right) = \frac{5 \cdot \mathbf{9}}{6 \cdot \mathbf{9}} + \frac{-2 \cdot \mathbf{6}}{9 \cdot \mathbf{6}}$ Use 6 • 9 as the common denominator.

$= \frac{45 + (-12)}{54}$ Add numerators.

$= \frac{33}{54}$ Simplify.

$= \frac{11 \cdot \cancel{3}^{1}}{18 \cdot \cancel{3}_{1}}$ Factor numerator and denominator.

$= \frac{11}{18}$ Simplify fraction.

b. $\frac{5}{6} + \left(-\frac{2}{9}\right) = \frac{5 \cdot \mathbf{3}}{6 \cdot \mathbf{3}} + \frac{-2 \cdot \mathbf{2}}{9 \cdot \mathbf{2}}$ The LCM of 6 and 9 is 18.

$= \frac{15 + (-4)}{18}$ Add numerators.

$= \frac{11}{18}$ Simplify fraction.

c. The results are the same.

Student Help

▶ **LOOK BACK**
For help with finding the least common multiple, see page 229.

Notice that the common denominator 18 in part (b) of Example 1 is less than the common denominator 54 in part (a). Using the LCD as a common denominator usually lets you work with smaller numbers but you must find the LCM of the denominators first.

1 Plan

Pacing

Suggested Number of Days

Transitional: 1 day
Average: 1 day
Advanced: 1 day
Block Schedule: 0.5 block with 6.1

Teaching Resources

Blacklines
(See page 266B.)

Transparencies
- Warm-Up Exercises
- Teacher Time-Savers
- English/Spanish Problem Solving
- Answers

Technology
- Electronic Teacher Tools
- Test and Practice Generator

2 Teach

Math Reasoning

For Mathematical Background Notes on mathematical reasoning related to this lesson, please refer to pages 266E and 266F in this Teacher's Edition.

Extra Example 1
See next page.

California Standards and Assessment

CA Standards: NS 2.2, AF 1.3
CA Key Concepts Book: pp. S9–S11, S15, S36–S38, T12–T13

Math Reasoning

One reason for studying the LCM in previous lessons was that the least common denominator of the fractions $\frac{a}{b}$ and $\frac{c}{d}$ is the LCM of b and d.

Extra Example 1

Add $\frac{3}{4}$ and $\frac{-1}{6}$.

a. Use the product of the denominators as the common denominator. $\frac{7}{12}$

b. Use the LCM as the common denominator. $\frac{7}{12}$

c. Compare the results. **They are the same.**

Extra Example 2

Evaluate the expression $a + b - c$ when $a = \frac{2}{3}$, $b = \frac{5}{9}$, and $c = \frac{7}{18}$. $\frac{5}{6}$

Extra Example 3

Find the perimeter of the triangle.

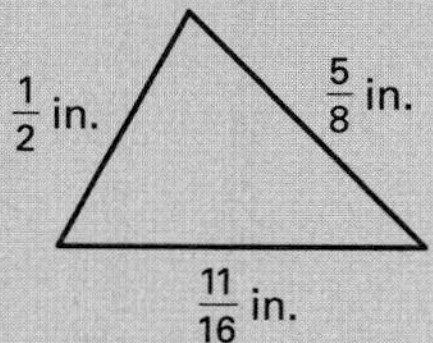

$\frac{29}{16}$ **in. or** $1\frac{13}{16}$ **in.**

Concept Check

How are least common multiples and least common denominators used to add unlike fractions? **You find the least common multiple of the denominators. This is the least common denominator. This denominator will be the denominator of the sum or difference before it is simplified (if possible).**

Goal 2 Working with Three or More Fractions

You can extend what you know about adding and subtracting fractions to simplify expressions with three or more fractions.

EXAMPLE 2 Evaluating Algebraic Expressions

Evaluate the expression $x - y + z$ when $x = \frac{1}{2}$, $y = \frac{3}{8}$, and $z = \frac{3}{4}$.

Solution

$x - y + z = \frac{1}{2} - \frac{3}{8} + \frac{3}{4}$ Substitute.

$= \frac{1 \cdot \mathbf{4}}{2 \cdot \mathbf{4}} - \frac{3}{8} + \frac{3 \cdot \mathbf{2}}{4 \cdot \mathbf{2}}$ The LCM of 2, 4, and 8 is 8.

$= \frac{4}{8} - \frac{3}{8} + \frac{6}{8}$ Simplify.

$= \frac{4}{8} + \left(\frac{-3}{8}\right) + \frac{6}{8}$ Rewrite as addition.

$= \frac{4 + (-3) + 6}{8}$ Add numerators.

$= \frac{7}{8}$ Simplify.

Student Help

▶ Vocabulary Tip
The *perimeter* of a triangle is the sum of the lengths of the sides of the triangle.

EXAMPLE 3 Adding Measures

Find the perimeter of the triangle.

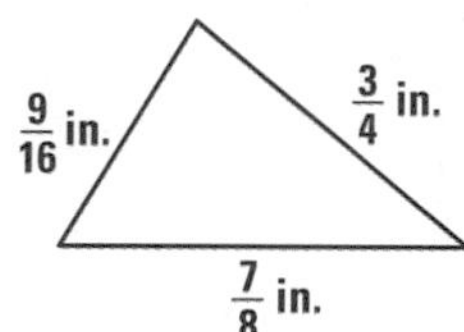

Solution

$\frac{3}{4} + \frac{7}{8} + \frac{9}{16} = \frac{3 \cdot \mathbf{4}}{4 \cdot \mathbf{4}} + \frac{7 \cdot \mathbf{2}}{8 \cdot \mathbf{2}} + \frac{9}{16}$ The LCM of 4, 8, and 16 is 16.

$= \frac{12}{16} + \frac{14}{16} + \frac{9}{16}$ Simplify.

$= \frac{12 + 14 + 9}{16}$ Add numerators.

$= \frac{35}{16}$ Add.

ANSWER ▶ The perimeter is $\frac{35}{16}$ inches, or $2\frac{3}{16}$ inches.

6.2 Exercises

Guided Practice

Use fractions to write an equation that represents the indicated sum or difference.

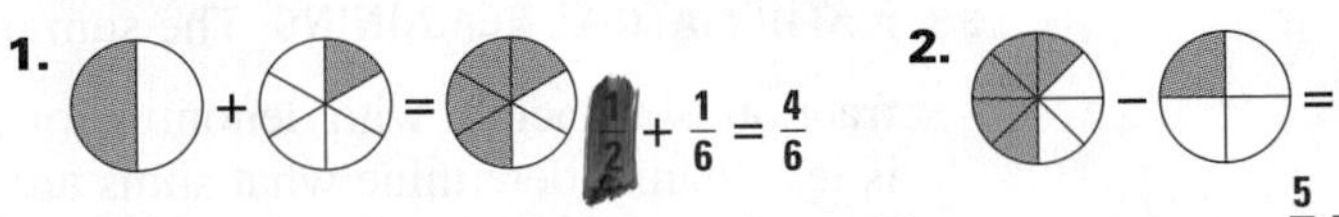

1. $\frac{1}{2} + \frac{1}{6} = \frac{4}{6}$

2. $\frac{5}{8} - \frac{1}{4} = \frac{3}{8}$

Add or subtract. Then simplify, if possible.

3. $\frac{3}{8} + \frac{1}{6}$ **$\frac{13}{24}$**

4. $-\frac{5}{8} + \frac{1}{16}$ **$-\frac{9}{16}$**

5. $\frac{1}{2} + \frac{3}{8} + \frac{1}{4}$ **$\frac{9}{8}$ or $1\frac{1}{8}$**

6. $\frac{2}{3} - \frac{1}{5} + \frac{1}{2}$ **$\frac{29}{30}$**

7. $\frac{1}{3} + \left(-\frac{4}{9}\right)$ **$-\frac{1}{9}$**

8. $\frac{3}{4} - 1\frac{1}{6}$ **$-\frac{5}{12}$**

9. $\frac{5}{12} + \frac{1}{2} - \frac{3}{4}$ **$\frac{1}{6}$**

10. $\frac{3}{5} - \left(-\frac{2}{15}\right)$ **$\frac{11}{15}$**

ALGEBRA Evaluate the variable expression when $m = \frac{2}{3}$, $n = \frac{1}{6}$, and $p = \frac{1}{9}$.

11. $m + n + p$ **$\frac{17}{18}$**

12. $m - n + p$ **$\frac{11}{18}$**

13. $m - n - p$ **$\frac{7}{18}$**

14. WRITING Write rules for adding and subtracting positive and negative fractions with different denominators. Give examples to show how the rules work. **See margin.**

Practice and Problem Solving

> **Student Help**
>
> ▶ **MORE PRACTICE** Extra practice to help you master skills is on page 700.

MODELING In Exercises 15 and 16, write a numerical expression corresponding to the model. Then evaluate the expression. **See margin.**

15.

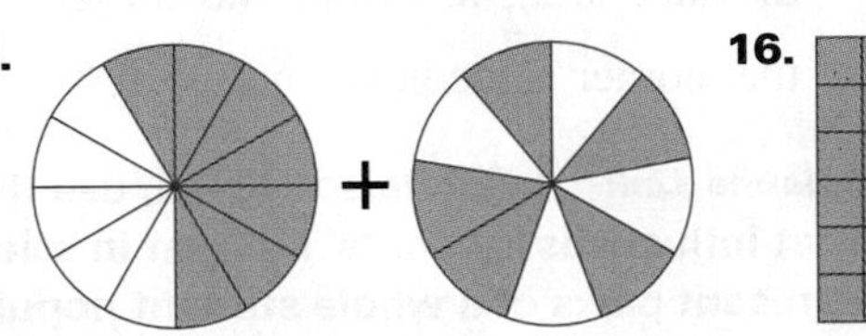

16.

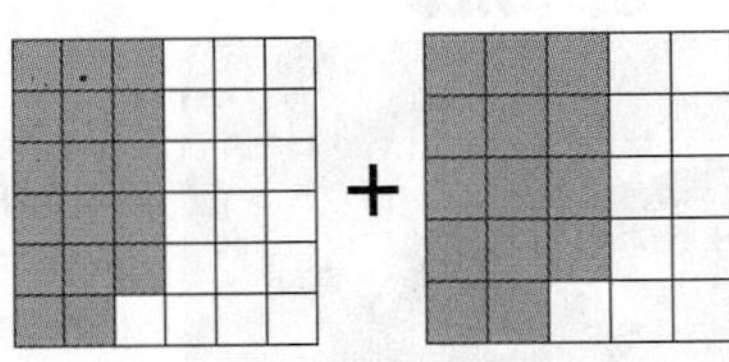

15. $\frac{7}{12} + \frac{5}{9}$; $\frac{41}{36}$ or $1\frac{5}{36}$

16. $\frac{17}{36} + \frac{14}{25}$; $\frac{929}{900}$ or $1\frac{29}{900}$

Add or subtract. Then simplify, if possible.

17. $\frac{2}{5} - \left(-\frac{1}{6}\right)$ $\frac{17}{30}$

18. $\frac{2}{3} + \left(-\frac{5}{9}\right)$ $\frac{1}{9}$

19. $-\frac{7}{12} + \frac{3}{18}$ $-\frac{5}{12}$

20. $-\frac{3}{7} - \frac{1}{14}$ $-\frac{1}{2}$

21. $-\frac{1}{2} + \left(-\frac{7}{12}\right)$ $-1\frac{1}{12}$

22. $\frac{9}{4} - \left(-\frac{5}{8}\right)$ $2\frac{7}{8}$

23. $\frac{29}{60} + \left(-\frac{3}{4}\right)$ $-\frac{4}{15}$

24. $3\frac{1}{4} + \left(-\frac{5}{6}\right)$ $2\frac{5}{12}$

25. $1\frac{2}{3} - \frac{7}{10}$ $\frac{29}{30}$

26. $-4\frac{4}{15} + \frac{2}{5}$ $-3\frac{13}{15}$

27. $2\frac{3}{8} + \left(-1\frac{3}{5}\right)$ $\frac{31}{40}$

28. $-\frac{3}{4} + \frac{1}{5} - \frac{7}{10}$ $-1\frac{1}{4}$

29. $\frac{1}{2} + \frac{3}{4} - \frac{7}{8}$ $\frac{3}{8}$

30. $3\frac{2}{5} - 1\frac{1}{10} + \frac{1}{2}$ $2\frac{4}{5}$

31. $1\frac{1}{9} + \left(-\frac{1}{3}\right) - \frac{1}{2}$ $\frac{5}{18}$

3 Apply

Assignment Guide

TRANSITIONAL
Day 1: EP p. 698 Exs. 35–40; pp. 275–277 Exs. 15–28, 32–34, 39–42, 59–60

AVERAGE
Day 1: pp. 275–277 Exs. 15–16, 20–28, 32–34, 39–40, 43–46, 59–60

ADVANCED
Day 1: pp. 275–277 Exs. 23–31, 35–40, 47–50, 55–58*, 59–60

BLOCK SCHEDULE
pp. 275–277 Exs. 15–16, 20–28, 32–34, 39–40, 43–46, 59–60 (with 6.1)

Extra Practice

- Student Edition, pp. 700–701
- Chapter 6 Resource Book, p. 15

Homework Check

To quickly check student understanding of key concepts, go over the following exercises:

Transitional: 18, 24, 28, 32, 40
Average: 22, 24, 28, 34, 40
Advanced: 24, 28, 30, 36, 40

14. ***Sample answer:*** **Find the least common denominator of the fractions. Rename each fraction to have the least common denominator. Follow the rules for adding and subtracting positive and negative numbers.**

$-\frac{1}{2} + \frac{3}{4} = -\frac{2}{4} + \frac{3}{4} = \frac{1}{4}$

Problem Solving

Exercises 35–37
Remind students to put parentheses around the value for r, since it is negative, to help avoid mistakes when adding or subtracting r.

Math Reasoning

Since $\frac{n}{18} - \frac{1}{9} = \frac{n-2}{18}$ is positive if $n > 3$ and $\frac{n}{18} < 1$ if $n < 18$, the required sums in Exercise 38 are of the form $\frac{n}{18}$, where $3 < n < 18$ and the GCF of n and 18 is 1.

ALGEBRA Evaluate the variable expression when $a = \frac{1}{4}$, $b = \frac{5}{6}$, $c = \frac{7}{8}$, $q = 1\frac{1}{5}$, $r = -\frac{3}{4}$, and $s = \frac{3}{10}$.

32. $a + b + c$ $\frac{47}{24}$ or $1\frac{23}{24}$ **33.** $a + b - c$ $\frac{5}{24}$ **34.** $a - b + c$ $\frac{7}{24}$

35. $q + r - s$ $\frac{3}{20}$ **36.** $q - r + s$ $\frac{9}{4}$ or $2\frac{1}{4}$ **37.** $q - r - s$ $\frac{33}{20}$ or $1\frac{13}{20}$

38. MATHEMATICAL REASONING The sum of $\frac{1}{9}$ and an unknown positive fraction is a fraction with denominator 18 when simplified. If the sum is less than 1, determine what sums are possible. $\frac{5}{18}, \frac{7}{18}, \frac{11}{18}, \frac{13}{18}, \frac{17}{18}$

GEOMETRY Find the perimeter of the figure.

39. 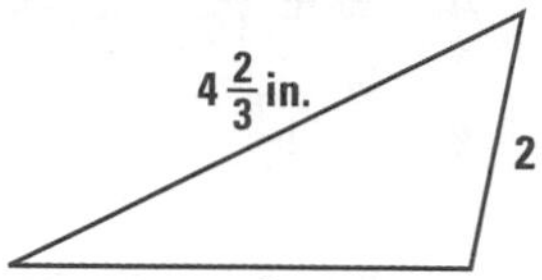 $4\frac{2}{3}$ in., $2\frac{1}{8}$ in., $3\frac{3}{4}$ in. $10\frac{13}{24}$ in.

40.

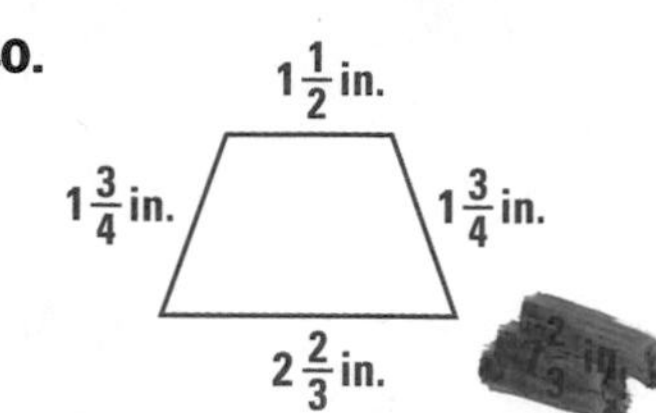

41. MANUFACTURING According to a manufacturer's specification, a spring should be $\frac{9}{32}$ inch long. You measure the spring and find it to be $\frac{5}{16}$ inch long. Is the actual spring longer or shorter than the specified measure? How much longer or shorter is it? longer; $\frac{1}{32}$ in.

42. CARPENTRY Walls typically have vertical boards, called *studs*, that are spaced $1\frac{1}{3}$ feet apart. When you mount a heavy object on a wall, you want to attach it to studs if possible. You have located one stud at a distance of $3\frac{1}{2}$ feet from one corner of a room. What distance from that corner is the next stud? $4\frac{5}{6}$ ft

46. $\frac{11}{100} + \frac{3}{20} + \frac{9}{50} + \frac{7}{25} + \frac{7}{25} = \frac{11}{100} + \frac{15}{100} + \frac{18}{100} + \frac{28}{100} + \frac{28}{100} = \frac{100}{100} = 1$

Science

NASA supports a variety of programs designed to spark students' interest in science and math.

Science Link In Exercises 43–46, use the diagram below. It shows what influences students' interest in science the most. The fractions represent parts of a whole student population.

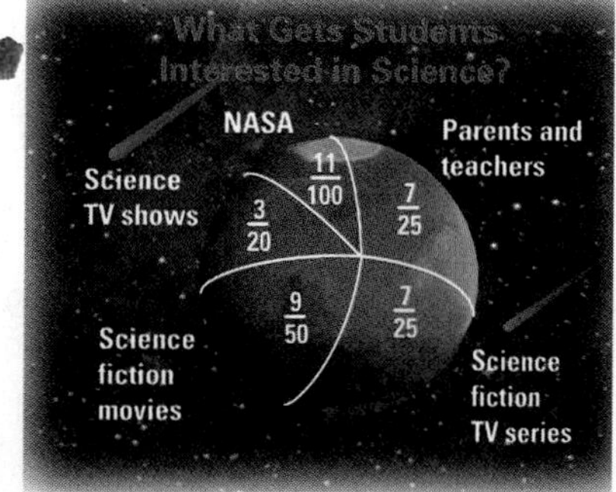

43. What influences students the most? the least? parents and teachers and science fiction TV series; NASA

44. What portion of students are influenced most by science fiction movies and science fiction TV series? $\frac{23}{50}$

45. Find the difference between the portion influenced by science TV shows and the portion influenced by NASA. $\frac{1}{25}$

46. Show that the sum of the parts of all students' responses is 1. **See margin.**

47. TUG OF WAR In a tug-of-war game, the other team pulls the rope $2\frac{1}{4}$ feet toward its side. Then your team pulls the rope $1\frac{2}{3}$ feet toward its side. After another minute, your team pulls the rope $4\frac{5}{6}$ feet more in its direction. Draw a diagram to determine how far from the starting point the middle of the rope is at this point in the game. **See margin.**

48. COMBINATION LOCK With the arrow on a combination lock pointing at 0, you turn the dial $\frac{2}{3}$ revolution clockwise, $1\frac{3}{4}$ revolution counterclockwise, and then $\frac{4}{5}$ revolution clockwise. In relation to the arrow, where is 0 now? Give your answer as a fraction of a revolution and a direction (clockwise or counterclockwise). **revolution counterclockwise**

Evaluate. Then simplify, if possible.

49. $\frac{53}{304} + \frac{126}{152}$ 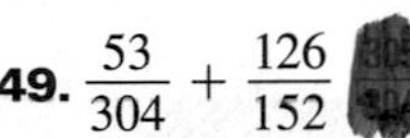

50. $-\frac{93}{255} + \frac{112}{340}$ 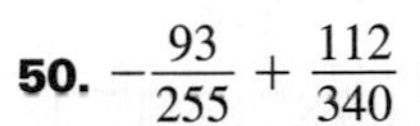

51. $\frac{88}{207} + \left(-\frac{49}{138}\right)$

52. $\frac{111}{540} - \frac{101}{126}$ 

53. $\frac{409}{435} - \frac{12}{290}$ 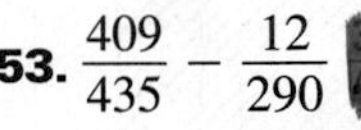

54. $-\frac{273}{324} - \frac{87}{405}$ 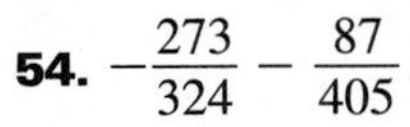

Student Help

▶ **HOMEWORK HELP**
Extra help with problem solving in Exs. 49–54 is available at www.mcdougallittell.com

CHALLENGE In Exercises 55–58, use the sequence.

$$\frac{1}{1 \cdot 2}, \frac{1}{2 \cdot 3}, \frac{1}{3 \cdot 4}, \frac{1}{4 \cdot 5}, \ldots$$

55. Find the sum of the first two terms in the sequence and simplify.

56. Find the sum of the first three terms and the first four terms and simplify.

57. If n is any positive integer, make a conjecture about the form of the sum of the first n terms of the sequence when simplified. **See margin.**

58. Test your conjecture for several values of n.

Multiple-Choice Practice

59. What is the sum of $12\frac{5}{6}$ and $8\frac{4}{9}$?

Ⓐ $4\frac{7}{18}$ Ⓑ $4\frac{7}{9}$ Ⓒ $21\frac{5}{18}$ Ⓓ $21\frac{5}{9}$

60. The triangle has a perimeter of $10\frac{3}{8}$ inches. What is the length of the side labeled x?

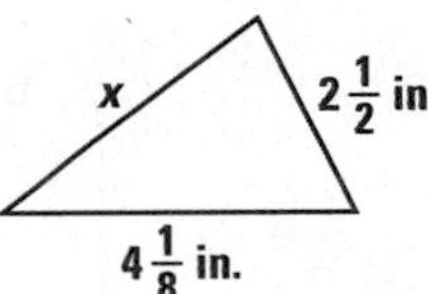

Ⓕ $1\frac{5}{8}$ in. Ⓖ $3\frac{1}{2}$ in. Ⓗ $3\frac{3}{4}$ in. Ⓙ $6\frac{1}{4}$ in.

4 Assess

Assessment Resources

- Assessment Book (Formal Assessment and Alternative Assessment)
- Test and Practice Generator

Mini-Quiz

Add or subtract. Then simplify.

1. $\frac{1}{8} + \frac{3}{16}$ $\frac{5}{16}$
2. $\frac{11}{14} - \frac{2}{7}$ $\frac{1}{2}$
3. $5\frac{3}{8} - 2\frac{1}{2}$ $\frac{23}{8}$ or $2\frac{7}{8}$
4. Evaluate the expression $x - y - z$ when $x = \frac{7}{8}$, $y = \frac{1}{3}$, and $z = \frac{1}{2}$. $\frac{1}{24}$
5. Find the perimeter of the figure.

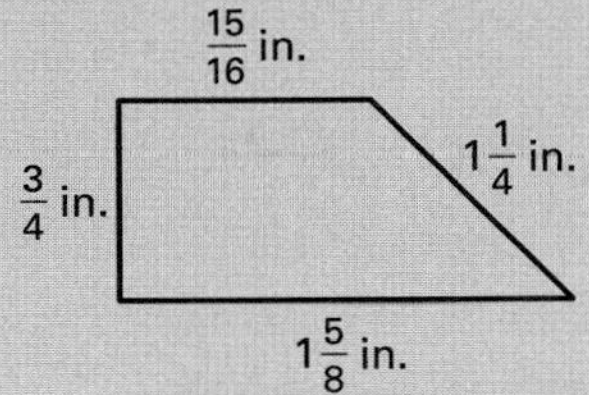

$\frac{73}{16}$ in. or $4\frac{9}{16}$ in.

Math Reasoning

In Exercises 55–58 the sums are $\frac{2}{3}, \frac{3}{4}, \frac{4}{5}, \ldots$, leading to the conjecture that the sum of the first n terms is $\frac{n}{n+1}$. To prove this, observe that the terms of the given sequence are $\frac{1}{1 \cdot 2} = 1 - \frac{1}{2}$, $\frac{1}{2 \cdot 3} = \frac{1}{2} - \frac{1}{3}$, $\frac{1}{3 \cdot 4} = \frac{1}{3} - \frac{1}{4}$, $\frac{1}{4 \cdot 5} = \frac{1}{4} - \frac{1}{5}, \ldots$. Therefore the sum of the first n terms is $\left(1 - \frac{1}{2}\right) + \left(\frac{1}{2} - \frac{1}{3}\right) + \left(\frac{1}{3} - \frac{1}{4}\right) + \ldots + \left(\frac{1}{n} - \frac{1}{n+1}\right)$. Cancellation of the inner terms gives the sum $1 - \frac{1}{n+1} = \frac{n}{n+1}$.

1 Plan

Pacing

Suggested Number of Days

Transitional: 2 days
Average: 2 days
Advanced: 2 days
Block Schedule: 1 block

Teaching Resources

(See page 266B.)

Transparencies

- Warm-Up Exercises
- Teacher Time-Savers
- English/Spanish Problem Solving
- Answers

Technology

- Electronic Teacher Tools
- Test and Practice Generator

2 Teach

For Mathematical Background Notes on mathematical reasoning related to this lesson, please refer to pages 266E and 266F in this Teacher's Edition.

California Standards and Assessment

CA Standards: NS 1.2, AF 1.3

CA Key Concepts Book: pp. S12, S14–S15, S51–S53, T12–T13

6.3 Multiplying Fractions

In this lesson you'll:

- Multiply rational numbers and take positive rational numbers to whole-number powers. (NS 1.2)
- Simplify numerical expressions by applying properties of rational numbers and justify the process used. (AF 1.3)

Goal 1 MULTIPLYING FRACTIONS

You can use an area model to represent the multiplication of fractions. For example, think of the product $\frac{1}{5} \cdot \frac{3}{4}$ as "one fifth of three fourths."

1. Shade three fourths of a unit square in one direction.
2. Shade one fifth of the square in the other direction.
3. The square has 3 of 20 equal parts doubly shaded. So, $\frac{1}{5} \cdot \frac{3}{4} = \frac{3}{20}$.

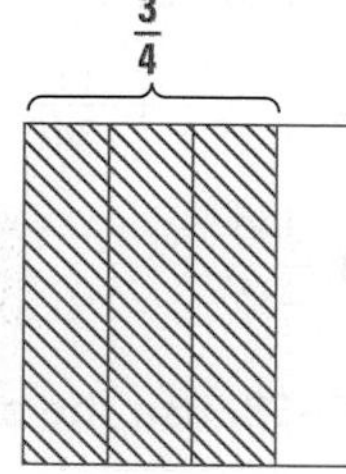

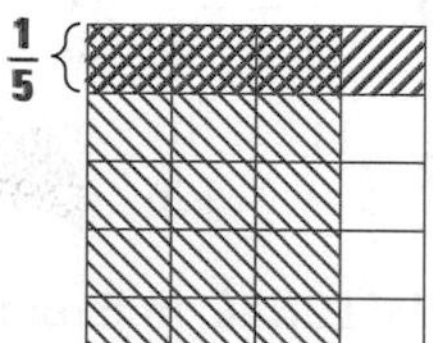

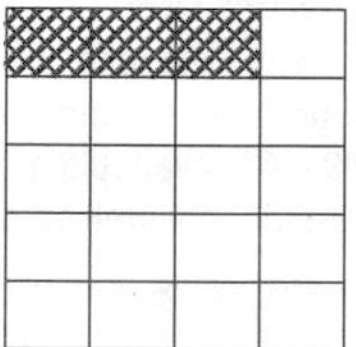

The area model suggests the following rule for multiplying fractions.

MULTIPLYING FRACTIONS

In Words To multiply two fractions, multiply the numerators to get the numerator of the product and multiply the denominators to get the denominator of the product.

In Algebra $\frac{a}{b} \cdot \frac{c}{d} = \frac{a \cdot c}{b \cdot d}$ **In Arithmetic** $\frac{3}{4} \cdot \frac{1}{5} = \frac{3 \cdot 1}{4 \cdot 5} = \frac{3}{20}$

Student Help

SKILLS REVIEW
For help with improper fractions, see page 678.

EXAMPLE 1 Multiplying Fractions

a. $\frac{-5}{8} \cdot \frac{3}{2} = \frac{-5 \cdot 3}{8 \cdot 2}$ Multiply numerators and multiply denominators.

$= \frac{-15}{16}$ or $-\frac{15}{16}$ Simplify.

b. $1\frac{2}{3} \cdot 3\frac{4}{5} = \frac{5}{3} \cdot \frac{19}{5}$ Rewrite as improper fractions.

$= \frac{5 \cdot 19}{3 \cdot 5}$ Multiply numerators and multiply denominators.

$= \frac{19}{3}$ or $6\frac{1}{3}$ Simplify.

EXAMPLE 2 Multiplying by a Whole Number

$\frac{6x}{5} \cdot 10 = \frac{6x}{5} \cdot \frac{10}{1}$ Rewrite 10 as $\frac{10}{1}$.

$= \frac{6x \cdot 10}{5 \cdot 1}$ Multiply numerators and multiply denominators.

$= \frac{6x \cdot \cancel{5}^{1} \cdot 2}{\cancel{5}_{1}}$ Factor numerator.

$= 12x$ Simplify fraction.

Goal 2 USING PROPERTIES OF RATIONAL NUMBERS

The properties that you learned about in Chapters 1–3, such as the commutative, associative, and distributive properties, are true for rational numbers as well as integers. You can use these properties and the rule for multiplying rational numbers to justify your work in Chapter 5 with equivalent fractions.

EXAMPLE 3 Justifying Equivalent Fractions

Show that $\frac{2}{3}$ is equivalent to $\frac{12}{18}$.

Solution

$\frac{2}{3} = \mathbf{1} \cdot \frac{2}{3}$ Identity property of multiplication

$= \frac{\mathbf{6}}{\mathbf{6}} \cdot \frac{2}{3}$ Substitute $\frac{6}{6}$ for 1.

$= \frac{6 \cdot 2}{6 \cdot 3}$ Multiply numerators and denominators.

$= \frac{12}{18}$ Simplify.

Student Help

▶ **STUDY TIP**
When using the identity property of multiplication, you may find it helpful to write $\frac{6}{6}$ as $\boxed{\frac{6}{6}}$ to remind you that the fraction is just another form of 1.

Two numbers whose product is 1 are **multiplicative inverses**, or **reciprocals**, of each other.

INVERSE PROPERTY OF MULTIPLICATION

In Words The product of a nonzero rational number and its multiplicative inverse is 1.

In Algebra $\frac{a}{b} \cdot \frac{b}{a} = 1$ where $a \neq 0$ and $b \neq 0$

In Arithmetic $\frac{2}{5} \cdot \frac{5}{2} = 1$

Math Reasoning

The geometric model at the beginning of this lesson interprets $\frac{1}{5} \cdot \frac{3}{4}$ as "one fifth of three fourths," and thereby shades $\frac{1}{5}$ of $\frac{3}{4}$ of the unit square to obtain $\frac{3}{20}$ of the square. One can be more explicit in bringing the actual concept of area into the model by noting that $\frac{1}{5} \cdot \frac{3}{4}$ represents the area of the rectangle at the last step, which also equals the sum of the areas of three smaller rectangles. Each of these smaller rectangles has area $\frac{1}{20}$, since the sum of the areas of 20 copies of one such rectangle is 1, the area of the unit square. Therefore $\frac{1}{5} \cdot \frac{3}{4} = 3 \cdot \frac{1}{20} = \frac{3}{20}$.

Extra Example 1

Multiply. Then simplify.

a. $\frac{-6}{11} \cdot \frac{22}{15}$ $\frac{-4}{5}$

b. $1\frac{1}{8} \cdot 2\frac{2}{5}$ $\frac{27}{10}$ or $2\frac{7}{10}$

Extra Example 2

Multiply. Then simplify.

$\frac{-7x}{3} \cdot 60$ $-140x$

Extra Example 3

Show that $\frac{4}{7}$ is equivalent to $\frac{32}{56}$.

$\frac{4}{7} = 1 \cdot \frac{4}{7}$ **Identity property of multiplication.**

$= \frac{8}{8} \cdot \frac{4}{7}$ **Substitute $\frac{8}{8}$ for 1.**

$= \frac{8 \cdot 4}{8 \cdot 7}$ **Multiply numerators and denominators.**

$= \frac{32}{56}$ **Simplify.**

Extra Example 4

Find the multiplicative inverse of the number.

a. $\frac{6}{7}$ $\frac{7}{6}$

b. $5\frac{1}{4}$ $\frac{4}{21}$

c. $\frac{-3}{8}$ $\frac{-8}{3}$

Concept Check

Explain how to multiply two fractions. ***Sample answer:*** **Rewrite any mixed numbers as improper fractions. Multiply the numerators and multiply the denominators. Simplify the resulting fraction, if possible.**

Student Help

▶STUDY TIP
One way to think about the reciprocal of a number like $\frac{4}{3}$ is to ask the question: What number can I multiply $\frac{4}{3}$ by to get 1?

EXAMPLE 4 ***Finding the Multiplicative Inverse***

Find the multiplicative inverse of the number.

a. $\frac{4}{3}$ **b.** $-2\frac{1}{3}$

Solution

To find the multiplicative inverse of a number, first write the number in the form $\frac{a}{b}$. The multiplicative inverse of $\frac{a}{b}$ is $\frac{b}{a}$.

a. The reciprocal of $\frac{4}{3}$ is $\frac{3}{4}$.

CHECK ✓ $\frac{4}{3} \cdot \frac{3}{4} = 1$

b. $-2\frac{1}{3}$ in the form $\frac{a}{b}$ is $-\frac{7}{3}$.

The reciprocal of $\frac{-7}{3}$ is $\frac{3}{-7}$ or $-\frac{3}{7}$.

CHECK ✓ $\left(-\frac{7}{3}\right) \cdot \left(-\frac{3}{7}\right) = 1$

6.3 Exercises

Guided Practice

In Exercises 1–3, write a multiplication expression represented by the area model. Then evaluate the expression.

1. 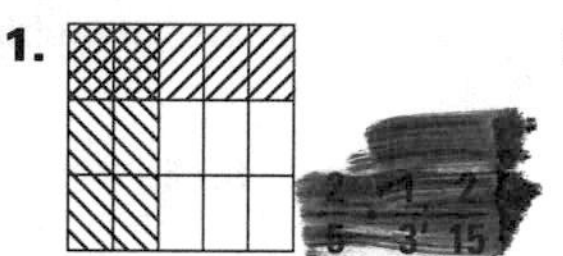

2. 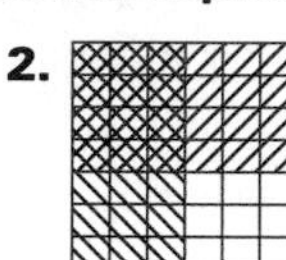

3. 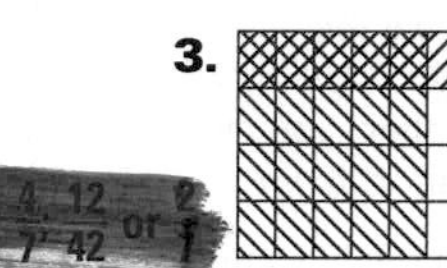 

Multiply. Then simplify, if possible.

4. $\frac{4}{7} \cdot \frac{3}{5}$ **5.** $\frac{2}{3} \cdot 6$ **6.** $\frac{5}{8} \cdot 15$ **7.** $1\frac{3}{5} \cdot 2\frac{1}{2}$

8. $\frac{-2}{3} \cdot \frac{2}{3}$ **9.** $6\frac{2}{3} \cdot 1\frac{1}{2}$ **10.** $\frac{y}{3} \cdot \left(-\frac{1}{5}\right)$ **11.** $24 \cdot \frac{x}{4}$

Name the property shown by the equation.

12. $\frac{3}{4} \cdot 1\frac{1}{2} = 1\frac{1}{2} \cdot \frac{3}{4}$ **commutative property of multiplication**

13. $\left(\frac{3}{5} \cdot 4\frac{2}{3}\right) \cdot 6 = \frac{3}{5} \cdot \left(4\frac{2}{3} \cdot 6\right)$ **associative property of multiplication**

14. $\frac{2}{-7} \cdot \frac{-7}{2} = 1$ **inverse property of multiplication**

15. $\frac{1}{2}\left(x + \frac{1}{3}\right) = \frac{1}{2}x + \frac{1}{6}$ **distributive property**

Find the multiplicative inverse of the rational number.

16. $-\frac{3}{8}$ **17.** $\frac{7}{2}$ **18.** -6 **19.** $2\frac{2}{3}$

Practice and Problem Solving

Student Help

▶**MORE PRACTICE** Extra practice to help you master skills is on page 700.

Multiply. Then simplify, if possible.

20. $\frac{1}{4} \cdot \frac{4}{5}$ 21. $\frac{-2}{3} \cdot \frac{8}{9}$ 22. $\frac{-5}{6} \cdot \left(\frac{-3}{4}\right)$

23. $1\frac{2}{5} \cdot 2\frac{2}{7}$ 24. $1\frac{1}{5} \cdot \left(-6\frac{2}{3}\right)$ 25. $-4\frac{1}{2} \cdot \left(-2\frac{5}{9}\right)$

26. $\frac{2}{3} \cdot \left(\frac{-4}{7}\right)$ 27. $\frac{-4}{9} \cdot \left(\frac{3}{-8}\right)$ 28. $\frac{5x}{6} \cdot 12$

29. $7 \cdot \frac{8y}{3}$ 30. $\frac{-13t}{20} \cdot \left(\frac{-1}{2}\right)$ 31. $\frac{-5}{6} \cdot \left(\frac{-6a}{15}\right)$

Use the fact that $a^2 = a \cdot a$ and $a^3 = a \cdot a \cdot a$ to evaluate the power.

32. $\left(\frac{1}{2}\right)^2$ 33. $\left(\frac{3}{5}\right)^2$ 34. $\left(\frac{4}{7}\right)^2$ 35. $\left(1\frac{2}{3}\right)^2$

36. $\left(\frac{1}{4}\right)^3$ 37. $\left(\frac{2}{3}\right)^3$ 38. $\left(\frac{7}{10}\right)^3$ 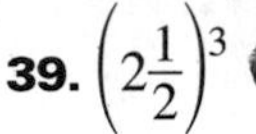 39. $\left(2\frac{1}{2}\right)^3$

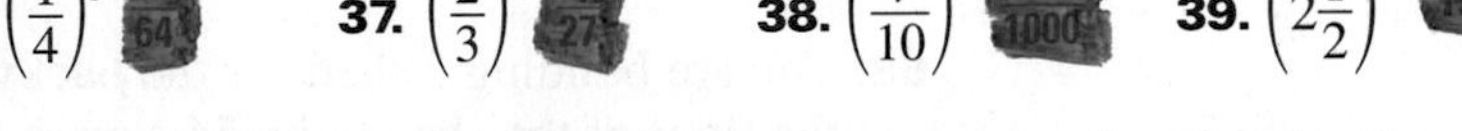

Using fractions, give an example of the property of multiplication.

40–43. See margin for sample answers.

40. Commutative property 41. Associative property

42. Identity property 43. Inverse property

41. $\frac{3}{4} \cdot \left(\frac{1}{2} \cdot \frac{2}{3}\right) = \left(\frac{3}{4} \cdot \frac{1}{2}\right) \cdot \frac{2}{3}$

42. $\frac{2}{9} \cdot 1 = \frac{2}{9}$

43. $\frac{2}{3} \cdot \frac{3}{2} = 1$

Find the multiplicative inverse. Justify your answer.

44. $-\frac{5}{8}$ 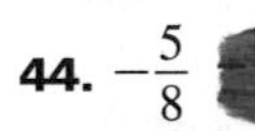 45. 4  46. $-1\frac{7}{12}$ 47. $\frac{15}{2}$

48. **Chapter Opener Link** Look back at the formula at the bottom of page 267. A patient needs 900 mg of medicine a day. Each milliliter of the solution contains 60 drops, and there are 45 mg of medicine in each milliliter of solution. What flow rate in drops per hour should the nurse set? 50 drops/h

49. **MATHEMATICAL REASONING** Explain why the reciprocal of the opposite of a nonzero number is the opposite of the reciprocal of the number. (*Hint*: Why is the product of $-\frac{1}{a}$ and $-a$ equal to 1 if $a \neq 0$?) See margin.

50. **COOKING** A recipe requires $\frac{3}{4}$ cup of sugar and $2\frac{1}{2}$ cups of flour. If you halve the recipe, how much sugar and flour should you measure? $\frac{3}{8}$ c sugar; $1\frac{1}{4}$ c flour

51. **EXERCISING** You ride a bike three times a week for exercise. On Mondays and Tuesdays you bike for $\frac{3}{4}$ hour, and on Thursdays you bike for $1\frac{1}{4}$ hours. If you burn about 450 Calories per hour biking, how many Calories do you burn per week from biking? 1237.5 Cal

Link to Exercise

CYCLING Serious cyclists improve their performance with aerodynamic and lightweight helmets, suits, and bicycles.

3 Apply

Assignment Guide

TRANSITIONAL
Day 1: SRH p. 678 Exs. 1–5, 11–15; pp. 281–282 Exs. 20–30, 32–34, 60–61
Day 2: pp. 281–282 Exs. 40–47, 52–53, 56, 58–59, 62–63

AVERAGE
Day 1: pp. 281–282 Exs. 23–36, 48, 50–51, 60–61
Day 2: pp. 281–282 Exs. 40–47, 52–56, 58–59, 62–63

ADVANCED
Day 1: pp. 281–282 Exs. 26–39, 48, 50–51, 60–61
Day 2: pp. 281–282 Exs. 40–47, 49, 52–56, 57*, 62–63

BLOCK SCHEDULE
pp. 281–282 Exs. 23–36, 40–48, 50–56, 58–63

Extra Practice

- Student Edition, pp. 700–701
- Chapter 6 Resource Book, p. 24

Homework Check

To quickly check student understanding of key concepts, go over the following exercises:

Transitional: 20, 24, 28, 32, 47, 52
Average: 22, 24, 30, 32, 47, 52
Advanced: 22, 24, 30, 32, 47, 52

Math Reasoning

For Exercise 44, keep in mind that the rule $(-1)a = -a$ holds for all real numbers.

49. By the inverse property of multiplication, if $a \neq 0$, $\frac{-a}{1} \cdot \frac{1}{-a} = 1$, so $\frac{1}{-a}$ is the multiplicative inverse of $-a$. Also, $(-a)(-\frac{1}{a}) = (-1 \cdot a)(-1 \cdot \frac{1}{a}) = [-1(-1)] \cdot (a \cdot \frac{1}{a}) = 1 \cdot 1 = 1$. Thus, $-\frac{1}{a}$ is the multiplicative inverse of $-a$. Then $\frac{1}{-a} = -\frac{1}{a}$.

4 Assess

Assessment Resources

- Assessment Book (Formal Assessment and Alternative Assessment)
- Test and Practice Generator

Mini-Quiz

Multiply. Then simplify, if possible.

1. $\frac{3}{8} \cdot \frac{4}{5}$ $\frac{3}{10}$
2. $\frac{-5}{9} \cdot \frac{3}{7}$ $\frac{-5}{21}$
3. $\frac{-2}{3} \cdot \left(\frac{-6}{7}\right)$ $\frac{4}{7}$
4. $5 \cdot \frac{7x}{30}$ $\frac{7x}{6}$
5. Find the multiplicative inverse of $2\frac{3}{4}$. Justify your answer. $\frac{4}{11}$; $2\frac{3}{4} = \frac{11}{4}$ and $\frac{11}{4} \cdot \frac{4}{11} = 1$

Math Reasoning

Although not required for its solution, Exercise 52 can be represented by a system of four linear equations in four variables:
$A = \frac{2}{3}B$, $B = C + 36$, $C = \frac{3}{5}D$, $D = 120$.

52. Show that $\frac{36}{48}$ is equivalent to $\frac{3}{4}$. Explain your reasoning. $\frac{36}{48} = \frac{3}{4} \cdot \frac{12}{12} = \frac{3}{4}$

MATHEMATICAL REASONING **Determine whether the statement is *true* or *false*. Justify your answer.**

53. $\frac{3}{7}$ is equivalent to $\frac{162}{376}$. false; $\frac{162}{376} = \frac{81}{188}$

54. $-\frac{84}{216}$ is equivalent to $-\frac{7}{18}$. true; $-\frac{84}{216} = \frac{12}{12} \cdot \left(-\frac{7}{18}\right) = -\frac{7}{18}$

55. $-\frac{15}{13}$ is the reciprocal of $-2\frac{3}{5}$. See margin.

56. 4 is the reciprocal of $-\frac{1}{4}$. See margin.

55. false; $-2\frac{3}{5} = \frac{-13}{5}$, which is not the reciprocal of $\frac{-15}{13}$.

56. false; reciprocal of $4 = \frac{1}{4}$

57. CHALLENGE Ann, Bob, Cara, and Dan each have coin collections. Ann has $\frac{2}{3}$ of Bob's number of coins. Bob has 36 more coins than Cara. Cara has $\frac{3}{5}$ of Dan's number of coins. Dan has 120 coins. How many coins does Ann have? 72 coins

Multiple-Choice Practice

58. You are building a shed for the backyard. You want the total area of the floor of the shed to be 54 square feet. Which of the following rectangular floors has an area equal to 54 square feet? A

Ⓐ 8 ft by $6\frac{3}{4}$ ft Ⓑ $8\frac{1}{4}$ ft by $6\frac{1}{2}$ ft

Ⓒ $8\frac{1}{2}$ ft by $6\frac{1}{4}$ ft Ⓓ $8\frac{3}{4}$ ft by 6 ft

59. What is the reciprocal of $5\frac{9}{10}$? F

Ⓕ $\frac{10}{59}$ Ⓖ $\frac{59}{10}$ Ⓗ $5\frac{10}{9}$ Ⓙ Not here

Mixed Review

Find the mean, median, and mode of the data. *(4.8)*

60. 2, 1, 3, 0, 2, 3, 4, 6, 5, 4, 1, 2 mean 2.75, median 2.5, mode 2

61. 98.7, 99.3, 98.2, 97.9, 98.6, 98.7, 99.0 mean about 98.6, median 98.7, mode 98.7

In Exercises 62 and 63, use the data which shows the number of candy bars sold by students participating in a school fundraiser. *(5.8)* 62–63. See margin.

51, 42, 10, 18, 58, 3, 35, 38, 20, 40, 48, 60, 65,
8, 80, 12, 47, 53, 33, 72, 45, 37, 48, 12, 22, 20

62. Make a stem-and-leaf plot of the data.

63. Use your stem-and-leaf plot to write two statements that describe the results of the fundraiser.

62.

0	3 8
1	0 2 2 8
2	0 0 2
3	3 5 7 8
4	0 2 5 7 8 8
5	1 3 8
6	0 5
7	2
8	0

Key: 5|1 represents 51 candy bars.

63. *Sample answer:* The fewest number of candy bars sold was 3, and the most sold was 80. Half of the students sold in the 30–59 range.

6.4 Multiplying with Percents

California Standards

In this lesson you'll:

- Convert fractions to decimals and percents, and use them in estimations, computations, and applications. (NS 1.3)
- Solve problems that involve sales tax, commissions, and tips. (NS 1.7)

Goal 1 Finding a Percent of a Number

You know that a percent can be written as an equivalent decimal or fraction. To find the percent of a number you can use either form.

Finding a Percent of a Number

In Words To find a percent of a number, rewrite the percent as a decimal or a fraction, and then multiply the numbers.

In Arithmetic 25% of $60 = 0.25 \cdot 60 = 15$ **or** 25% of $60 = \frac{1}{4} \cdot 60 = 15$

Example 1 Finding a Percent of a Number

a. Find 36% of 825. **b.** Find 40% of 70.

Solution

a. 36% of $825 = 0.36 \cdot 825$ Rewrite 36% as a decimal.

$= 297$ Multiply.

ANSWER ▶ 36% of 825 is 297.

b. 40% of $70 = \frac{2}{5} \cdot 70$ Rewrite 40% as a fraction.

$= 28$ Multiply.

ANSWER ▶ 40% of 70 is 28.

Student Help

▶**Skills Review**
For help with multiplying decimals, see page 676.

Example 2 Percents Greater than 100% and Less than 1%

a. Find 150% of 38. **b.** Find $\frac{1}{2}\%$ of 200.

Solution

a. 150% of $38 = 1.5 \cdot 38 = 57$

ANSWER ▶ 150% of 38 is 57.

b. $\frac{1}{2}\%$ of $200 = 0.005 \cdot 200 = 1$

ANSWER ▶ $\frac{1}{2}\%$ of 200 is 1.

CHECK ✓ Use estimation. For instance in part (a), $150\% > 100\%$, so an answer of 57 is reasonable, since $57 > 38$.

1 Plan

Pacing

Suggested Number of Days

Transitional: 2 days
Average: 2 days
Advanced: 2 days
Block Schedule: 1 block

Teaching Resources

Blacklines
(See page 266B.)

Transparencies
- Warm-Up Exercises
- Teacher Time-Savers
- English/Spanish Problem Solving
- Answers

Technology
- Electronic Teacher Tools
- Test and Practice Generator

2 Teach

Math Reasoning

For Mathematical Background Notes on mathematical reasoning related to this lesson, please refer to pages 266E and 266F in this Teacher's Edition.

Extra Examples 1 and 2
See next page.

California Standards and Assessment

CA Standards: NS 1.3, NS 1.7

Extra Example 1

a. Find 64% of 75. **48**
b. Find 80% of 45. **36**

Extra Example 2

a. Find 160% of 560. **896**
b. Find $\frac{1}{4}$% of 800. **2**

Extra Example 3

The sales tax rate where you live is 7.5%. You are buying a computer for $952. What will be the total cost of the computer? **$1,023.40**

Extra Example 4

You are buying a car for $12,500. The car salesman receives a 5% commission on the sale. How much commission will the salesman receive? **$625**

Extra Example 5

You eat supper at a nice restaurant and the bill is $33.95. Estimate the amount of a 15% tip for service. **$5.10**

Teaching Tip

Point out that estimating percents is a very useful skill to use in finding sales tax, discounts, and tips when a calculator or pencil and paper are not handy.

Concept Check

How can you find a percent of a number? ***Sample answer:*** **Multiply the number by the decimal form of the percent.**

Goal 2 FINDING SALES TAX, COMMISSIONS, AND TIPS

You can use percents to find the amount of sales tax, a commission, or a

Student Help

▶MORE EXAMPLES
More examples are available at www.mcdougallittell.com

EXAMPLE 3 Finding the Sales Tax

The sales tax rate where you live is 8.5%. Your family is buying a car for $28,540. What will be the total cost of the car?

Solution

First, find the sales tax.

8.5% of 28,540 = 0.085 • 28,540 — **Write percent as decimal.**
= 2,425.90 — **Multiply.**

Then, add the sales tax to the cost of the car.

$28,540 + $2,425.90 = $30,965.90

ANSWER▶ The total cost of the car is $30,965.90.

EXAMPLE 4 Finding a Commission

Your family is selling your house for $160,000. The realtor charges a commission of 6%. How much commission will the realtor receive?

Solution

$6\% \text{ of } 160{,}000 = \frac{6}{100} \cdot 160{,}000$ — **Write percent as a fraction.**
$= 9600$ — **Multiply.**

ANSWER▶ The realtor's commission is $9600.

EXAMPLE 5 Estimating to Find Tips

You and a friend go to lunch. The check comes to $24.85. Find the amount of a 15% tip for service.

Student Help

▶STUDY TIP
To find 10% of $25.00 using mental math, move the decimal point 1 place to the left.

Solution

When you leave a tip, you do not need to give an exact amount. Use estimation and mental math to find the tip. Begin by rounding $24.85 to $25.00 and thinking of 15% as 10% plus 5%.

$0.10 \cdot 25.00 = 2.50$ — **Find 10% of $25.00.**
$\frac{1}{2} \cdot 2.50 = 1.25$ — **5% is half of 10%.**
3.75 — **Add.**

ANSWER▶ A 15% tip of $24.85 is about $3.75.

6.4 Exercises

Guided Practice

Change the percent to a decimal or a fraction. Then evaluate.

1. 10% of 48 **4.8** **2.** $33\frac{1}{3}$% of 96 **32** **3.** 50% of 64 **32**

4. 200% of 23 **46** **5.** 45% of 380 **171** **6.** 0.5% of 38 **0.19**

7. SALES TAX The price of a new bicycle is $310. Find the total cost if you have to pay 6.5% sales tax on the bicycle. **$330.15**

8. COMMISSION A realtor charges a commission of 6%. What was the amount of commission on a property that sold for $250,000? **$15,000**

9. TIP The amount of a dinner check is $48.50. About how much should you leave the server as a 15% tip? **about $7.50**

Practice and Problem Solving

Student Help

▶ MORE PRACTICE
Extra practice to help you master skills is on page 700.

Change the percent to a decimal or a fraction. Then evaluate.

10. 16% of 50 **11.** 80% of 285 **228** **12.** 75% of 360 **270**

13. 340% of 5 **17** **14.** 120% of 35 **15.** 250% of 46 **115**

16. 0.8% of 500 **4** **17.** 6.5% of 800 **18.** $33\frac{1}{3}$% of 180 **60**

19. 0.025% of 1200 **0.3** **20.** 0.5% of 70 **0.35** **21.** 0.1% of 100 **0.1**

Match the percent phrase with the fraction phrase. Then find the percent of the number.

A. $\frac{1}{8}$ of 120 **B.** $\frac{1}{3}$ of 120 **C.** $\frac{3}{5}$ of 120 **D.** $\frac{1}{4}$ of 120

22. 25% of 120 **D; 30** **23.** 60% of 120 **C; 72** **24.** 12.5% of 120 **A; 15** **25.** $33\frac{1}{3}$% of 120 **B; 40**

Use mental math to find the percent of the number.

26. 10% of 100 **10** **27.** 5% of 80 **4** **28.** 20% of 300 **60**

29. 25% of 36 **9** **30.** 20% of 15 **3** **31.** 5% of 50 **2.5**

32. 5% of 6000 **300** **33.** 15% of 800 **120** **34.** 20% of 150 **30**

Estimate. Then multiply to check your estimate.
Exercises 35–40. Estimates will vary.

35. 26% of 80 **20; 20.8** **36.** 12% of 164 **16.4; 19.68** **37.** 48% of 92 **46; 44.16**

38. 78% of 63 **48; 49.14** **39.** 109% of 140 **154; 152.6** **40.** 2% of 1546 **30; 30.92**

3 Apply

Assignment Guide

TRANSITIONAL
Day 1: SRH p. 676 Exs. 1–5; pp. 285–286 Exs. 10–18, 22–28, 35–37, 41
Day 2: pp. 286–287 Exs. 45–52, 54–56, 60–62

AVERAGE
Day 1: pp. 285–286 Exs. 10–18, 22–25, 29–31, 35–37, 42–43
Day 2: pp. 286–287 Exs. 45–46, 60–62

ADVANCED
Day 1: pp. 285–286 Exs. 12–25, 32–34, 38–40, 42–44
Day 2: pp. 286–287 Exs. 45–46, 57–58, 59*, 60–62

BLOCK SCHEDULE
pp. 285–286 Exs. 10–18, 22–25, 29–31, 35–37, 42–43, 45–56, 60–62

Extra Practice

- Student Edition, pp. 700–701
- Chapter 6 Resource Book, p. 33

Homework Check

To quickly check student understanding of key concepts, go over the following exercises:

Transitional: 12, 26, 36, 46, 48
Average: 14, 30, 36, 46, 50
Advanced: 16, 34, 40, 46, 54

Problem Solving

Exercise 18
Ask students which is easier, multiplying $\frac{1}{3} \cdot 180$ or $0.3\overline{3} \cdot 180$.

Math Reasoning

If, as in Exercise 44, the value A of a quantity is increased by 10%, to become $A + \frac{1}{10}A$, and that in turn is decreased by 10%, to become $(A + \frac{1}{10}A) - \frac{1}{10}(A + \frac{1}{10}A)$, the end result is a value of $A - \frac{1}{100}A = \frac{99}{100}A$, which is less than the original value.

44. no; the 10% increase was based on \$18, or \$1.80. The 10% decrease was based on \$19.80, or \$1.98. The new price is now \$.18 lower than the original price.

41. FLOWER SHOW Of all the people attending a flower show, 40% received a discount coupon for food and beverages. Find how many received the coupon if there were 1840 people at the flower show. 736 people

SURFACE AREA In Exercises 42 and 43, use the information in the table.

42. Find the approximate number of square miles of land. about 57 million square miles

43. Find the percent of Earth's surface area that is water. Then find the approximate number of square miles of water. 71%; about 140 million square miles

Approximate Earth Measures	
Total surface area	197 million square miles
Land surface area	29%
Water surface area	?%

44. MATHEMATICAL REASONING The regular price of a concert ticket is \$18. The business office increases the price of the tickets 10% for the next concert. Then, because fewer people attend the next concert, the business office decreases the price of the ticket 10%. Are the tickets now the same price as they were originally? Explain your answer. See margin.

SALES TAX In Exercises 45 and 46, use the following information. In your county, a 7.25% sales tax is charged on *nonessential* items, such as prepared deli food. There is no sales tax on *essential* items such as bread, milk, and fruit. At the store, you buy one pound of bananas for \$.99 per pound, a gallon of milk for \$2.48, and a prepared ham sandwich for \$3.95.

45. Find the total amount of sales tax you pay on nonessential items. \$.29

46. Find the total amount of money you spent at the grocery store. \$7.71

Student Help

STUDY TIP
In Exercise 48, an alternative approach for finding the cost of the sweater after the discount is to find 65% of \$40.

SHOPPING In Exercises 47–49, use the following information. You buy a sweater on sale for 35% off the original price of \$40.

47. Find the amount that is taken off the original price for this sale. \$14

48. Determine the sale price of the sweater. \$26

49. An 8.5% sales tax on the sweater is applied to the sale price. Find the total cost of the sweater with this sales tax. \$28.21

COMMISSION In Exercises 50–52, use the following information. At your part-time job at an electronics store, you earn a 15.25% commission on all your sales.

50. Find how much you earn in a week if your sales total \$3000. \$457.50

51. Suppose your employer offers to pay you \$300 per week plus a 2.5% commission on everything you sell over \$500. Find how much you would earn if you sell \$3000 in one week. \$362.50

52. Compare the payment plans in Exercises 50 and 51. If your average weekly sales total is \$3000, which option would you choose? Explain. the straight 15.25% of all sales; I would make \$95 more each week under that plan.

53. MATHEMATICAL REASONING A clothing store advertises that the prices of all out-of-season apparel have been reduced by 30%. It also offers a coupon that reads, "Take an additional 15% off the sale price of all marked-down merchandise." If you use the coupon, will you get a 45% savings on out-of-season apparel? Explain, and give an example to illustrate. **See margin.**

RESTAURANTS In Exercises 54–56, use the following information. You and a friend are servers in a restaurant where the tips average 15%.

54. The check for the party you are serving comes to \$49.50. Estimate to find about how much you might be tipped. **\$7.50**

55. Your friend has a table where a large group has dined. The group's check comes to \$102.30. What tip might your friend expect? Explain how you can use mental math to solve the problem. **\$15.00; round \$102.30 down to \$100, then multiply by 15%.**

56. It is the policy for servers to put all their tips together to share equally at the end of the evening. There are three servers, including you. If all of the evening diners paid a total of \$1238.95 for their meals, estimate the amount of tip money collected. Approximately what amount should you expect to receive? **\$180; \$60**

Link to Careers

REAL ESTATE AGENTS
The main source of income for real estate professionals is commissions on sales. The rate of commission varies with the type of property and its value.

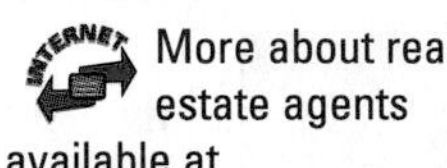
More about real estate agents available at www.mcdougallittell.com

REAL ESTATE In Exercises 57–59, use the following information. Your friend's family is selling their house. One realtor charges a commission of 7.5%. Another realtor charges a commission of \$5000 plus 4.5% of the selling price.

57. Let x represent the sale price of the house. Write an expression to find the commission that each realtor charges. **$0.075x$; $5000 + 0.045x$**

58. Your friend's family wants to sell their house for \$180,000. Find how much commission each realtor would earn. **\$13,500; \$13,100**

59. CHALLENGE Use the information in Exercise 57. Set the expressions equal and solve for x. Explain what your answer represents. **\$166,667; the selling price of the house for which both commission plans will charge the same.**

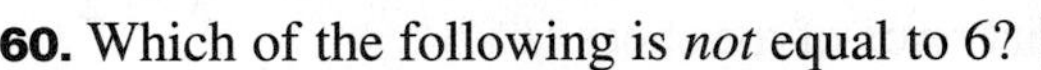

Multiple-Choice Practice

60. Which of the following is *not* equal to 6?  **D**

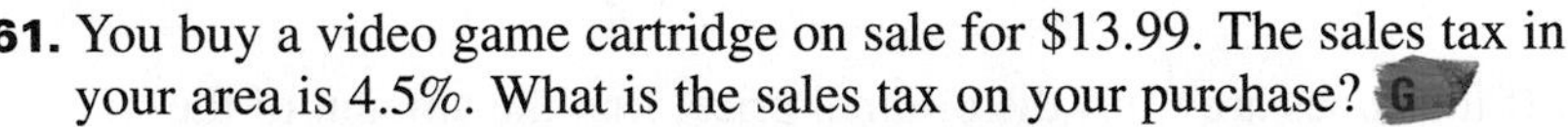

Ⓐ 4% of 150 Ⓑ $\frac{1}{2}$ of 12 Ⓒ 75% of 8 Ⓓ $\frac{1}{8}$ of 56

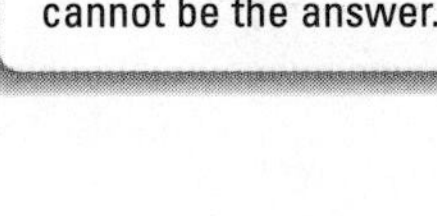

Test Tip A B C D

▶ Look for and eliminate choices that obviously cannot be the answer.

61. You buy a video game cartridge on sale for \$13.99. The sales tax in your area is 4.5%. What is the sales tax on your purchase? **G**

Ⓕ \$.58 Ⓖ \$.63 Ⓗ \$.68 Ⓙ \$14.62

62. The roller blades that you want to buy are on sale for 15% off the regular price of \$60. You have a coupon for an additional 15% off. What is the sale price of the roller blades? **C**

Ⓐ \$42.00 Ⓑ \$43.00 Ⓒ \$43.35 Ⓓ \$49.65

4 Assess

Assessment Resources

- Assessment Book (Formal Assessment and Alternative Assessment)
- Test and Practice Generator

Mini-Quiz

Find the percent of the number.

1. 45% of 625 **281.25**
2. 120% of 68 **81.6**
3. $\frac{1}{2}$% of 1200 **6**
4. The sales tax rate where you live is 8%. How much sales tax will you pay on a purchase of \$45? **\$3.60**
5. Estimate a 15% tip on a lunch costing \$14.79. **\$2.25**

53. No; you're taking the 15% off a different, lower, base number. \$100 • 30% = \$30 off. Sale price = \$70. \$70 • 15% = \$10.50. \$70 − 10.50 = \$59.50 final sale price. \$100 • 45% = \$45, and \$100 − 45 = \$55. The two amounts are not the same.

Additional Resources

A Mid-Chapter Test and a Mid-Chapter Partner Quiz are available in the *Assessment Book*, pp. 76–77 and p. 235.

Chapter 6 Mid-Chapter Test

Take this test as you would take a test in class. The answers to the exercises are given in the back of the book.

Add or subtract. Then simplify, if possible.

1. $\frac{1}{11} + \frac{3}{11}$ $\frac{4}{11}$ **2.** $\frac{5}{6} - \frac{1}{6}$ $\frac{2}{3}$ **3.** $4\frac{4}{5} + 1\frac{3}{5}$ $6\frac{2}{5}$ **4.** $\frac{3x}{8} - \frac{7x}{8}$ $-\frac{x}{2}$

5. $\frac{7}{10} - \frac{4}{25}$ $\frac{27}{50}$ **6.** $\frac{9}{10} - \frac{1}{2}$ $\frac{2}{5}$ **7.** $\frac{1}{12} + \frac{5}{6} - \frac{2}{3}$ $\frac{1}{4}$ **8.** $\frac{17}{30} - \frac{4}{5} + \frac{1}{6}$ $-\frac{1}{15}$

Multiply. Then simplify, if possible.

9. $\frac{-4}{7} \cdot \frac{7}{8}$ $-\frac{1}{2}$ **10.** $\frac{2}{3} \cdot \frac{3}{4} \cdot \frac{4}{5}$ $\frac{2}{5}$ **11.** $\frac{7}{10} \cdot 2$ $1\frac{2}{5}$ **12.** $\frac{2}{5} \cdot \left(\frac{-6}{5}\right)$ $-\frac{12}{25}$

13. $0 \cdot \frac{2}{11}$ 0 **14.** $\frac{5}{6} \cdot (-7)$ $-\frac{35}{6}$ **15.** $-\frac{2}{5} \cdot \left(-\frac{3}{4}\right)$ $\frac{3}{10}$ **16.** $-2\frac{1}{4} \cdot 1\frac{2}{3}$ $-\frac{15}{4}$

Find the multiplicative inverse. Justify your answer.

17. $\frac{6}{7}$ $\frac{7}{6}$ **18.** $-\frac{1}{4}$ -4 **19.** -12 $-\frac{1}{12}$ **20.** $3\frac{3}{5}$ $\frac{5}{18}$

Change the percent to a decimal or a fraction. Then multiply.

21. 60% of 90 **54** **22.** 25% of 220 **55** **23.** 120% of 65 **78** **24.** 0.2% of 28 **0.056**

GEOMETRY Find the perimeter and area of the figure.

25.

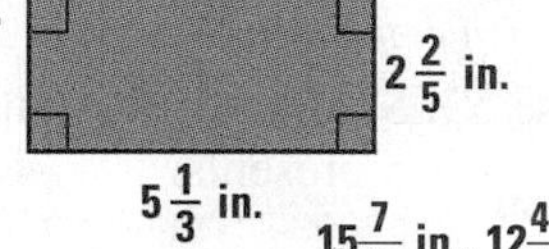

$15\frac{7}{15}$ in., $12\frac{4}{5}$ in.^{2}

26.

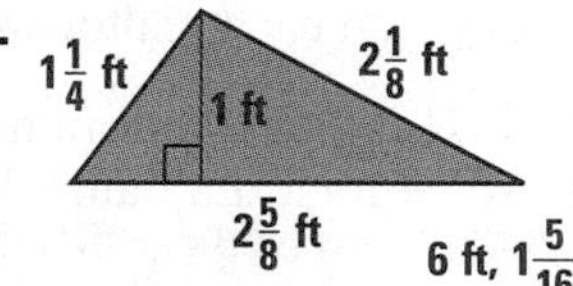

6 ft, $1\frac{5}{16}$ ft^2

27.

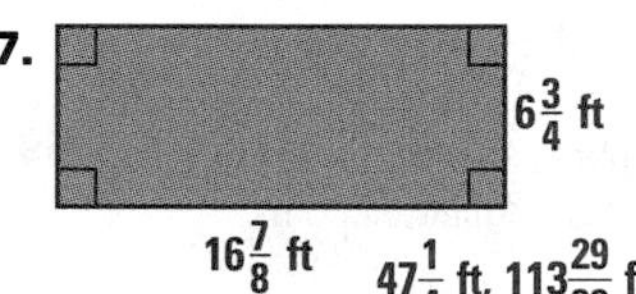

$47\frac{1}{4}$ ft, $113\frac{29}{32}$ ft^2

SHOES In Exercises 28 and 29, use the following information. You are shopping for shoes and find a clearance rack with shoes that are $\frac{1}{3}$ to $\frac{1}{2}$ off the original price. The original price of the shoes is $30.

28. If the shoes are $\frac{1}{3}$ off the original price, find the amount of the discount and determine how much you pay for the shoes. **$10, $20**

29. If the shoes are $\frac{1}{2}$ off the original price, find the amount of the discount and determine how much you pay for the shoes. **$15, $15**

30. CAMERA The price of a new camera is $189.00. Find the total cost if you have to pay 7.0% sales tax on the camera. **$202.23**

31. DINING OUT The amount of a check for lunch is $20.35. About how much should you leave the server as a 15% tip? **about $3.00**

6.5 Dividing Fractions

California Standards

In this lesson you'll:

- Divide rational numbers. (NS 1.2)
- Use measures expressed as rates to solve problems. Use unit analysis to check the reasonableness of the solution. (MG 1.3)

Goal 1 DIVIDING FRACTIONS

From your previous work with whole numbers and fractions, you know that dividing a number by 2 and multiplying the number by $\frac{1}{2}$ produce the same result. For instance, $6 \div 2 = 3$ and $6 \cdot \frac{1}{2} = 3$. Since 2 and $\frac{1}{2}$ are reciprocals, this suggests that a division problem can be rewritten as a multiplication problem by using a reciprocal.

DIVIDING FRACTIONS

In Words To divide by a fraction, multiply by its reciprocal.

In Algebra $\frac{a}{b} \div \frac{c}{d} = \frac{a}{b} \cdot \frac{d}{c}$

In Arithmetic $\frac{1}{5} \div \frac{3}{4} = \frac{1}{5} \cdot \frac{4}{3} = \frac{1 \cdot 4}{5 \cdot 3} = \frac{4}{15}$

EXAMPLE 1 Dividing Fractions

a. $\frac{3}{4} \div 3 = \frac{3}{4} \cdot \frac{1}{3}$ The reciprocal of 3 is $\frac{1}{3}$.

$= \frac{3}{12}$ Multiply fractions.

$= \frac{1 \cdot \cancel{3}^{1}}{4 \cdot \cancel{3}_{1}}$ Factor numerator and denominator.

$= \frac{1}{4}$ Simplify fraction.

CHECK ✓ Check a division problem by multiplying the divisor and the quotient to see if you get the dividend:

$3 \cdot \frac{1}{4} = \frac{3}{1} \cdot \frac{1}{4} = \frac{3}{4}$ ✓

b. $\frac{-2}{3} \div \frac{-4}{5} = \frac{-2}{3} \cdot \frac{5}{-4}$ The reciprocal of $\frac{-4}{5}$ is $\frac{5}{-4}$.

$= \frac{-10}{-12}$ Multiply fractions.

$= \frac{\cancel{-2}^{1} \cdot 5}{\cancel{-2}_{1} \cdot 6}$ Factor numerator and denominator.

$= \frac{5}{6}$ Simplify fraction.

Student Help

STUDY TIP
Remember that when you multiply or divide two numbers with the same sign, the answer is positive.

1 Plan

Pacing

Suggested Number of Days

Transitional: 2 days
Average: 2 days
Advanced: 2 days
Block Schedule: 1 block

Teaching Resources

Blacklines
(See page 266B.)

Transparencies
- Warm-Up Exercises
- Teacher Time-Savers
- English/Spanish Problem Solving
- Answers

Technology
- Electronic Teacher Tools
- Test and Practice Generator

2 Teach

Math Reasoning

For Mathematical Background Notes on mathematical reasoning related to this lesson, please refer to pages 266E and 266F in this Teacher's Edition.

Extra Example 1
See next page.

California Standards and Assessment

CA Standards: NS 1.2, MG 1.3
CA Key Concepts Book: pp. S13–S15, S77

Extra Example 1

Simplify the expression.

a. $\frac{-7}{10} \div 14$ $\frac{-1}{20}$

b. $\frac{5}{-12} \div \frac{-25}{36}$ $\frac{3}{5}$

Teaching Tip

Some students may wonder how we can multiply (by the reciprocal) to do a division problem. An explanation by way of an example follows.

$$\frac{1}{5} \div \frac{3}{4} = \frac{\frac{1}{5}}{\frac{3}{4}} \cdot 1 = \frac{\frac{1}{5}}{\frac{3}{4}} \cdot \frac{\frac{4}{3}}{\frac{4}{3}} =$$

$$\frac{\frac{1}{5} \cdot \frac{4}{3}}{\frac{3}{4} \cdot \frac{4}{3}} = \frac{\frac{1}{5} \cdot \frac{4}{3}}{1} = \frac{1}{5} \cdot \frac{4}{3}$$

Math Reasoning

The student should know the technique of converting mixed numbers to fractions or decimals before attempting arithmetic operations with them. However, this is not desirable in all cases. For instance it is easy to see directly that $3\frac{3}{4} - 2\frac{1}{2} = 1 + \frac{3}{4} - \frac{1}{2} = 1\frac{1}{4}$.

Extra Example 2

Simplify $5 \div 2\frac{2}{5}$. $\frac{25}{12}$

Extra Example 3

Simplify $\frac{-2}{3} \div \frac{6}{x}$. $\frac{-x}{9}$

Extra Example 4

You earned $8 for working $1\frac{1}{3}$ hours. What is your hourly rate? **$6.00 per hour**

EXAMPLE 2 Dividing by a Mixed Number

$2 \div 4\frac{1}{2} = 2 \div \frac{9}{2}$	Rewrite as an improper fraction.
$= 2 \cdot \frac{2}{9}$	The reciprocal of $\frac{9}{2}$ is $\frac{2}{9}$.
$= \frac{4}{9}$	Multiply.

EXAMPLE 3 Dividing by a Whole Number

$\frac{x}{2} \div 7 = \frac{x}{2} \cdot \frac{1}{7}$	The reciprocal of 7 is $\frac{1}{7}$.
$= \frac{x}{14}$	Multiply fractions.

Goal 2 SOLVING RATE PROBLEMS

To solve problems involving rates, you can use multiplication and division of fractions. Use unit analysis to check that the solution is reasonable.

EXAMPLE 4 Dividing Fractions

You earned $6 for baby-sitting $1\frac{2}{3}$ hours. What is your hourly rate?

Solution

Because your hourly rate is in *dollars per hour*, you divide money (in *dollars*) by time (in *hours*) to find the hourly rate.

Hourly rate $= 6 \div 1\frac{2}{3}$	Divide money by time.
$= 6 \div \frac{5}{3}$	Rewrite as an improper fraction.
$= 6 \cdot \frac{3}{5}$	The reciprocal of $\frac{5}{3}$ is $\frac{3}{5}$.
$= \frac{18}{5}$	Multiply.
$= 3.60$	Convert to a decimal.

ANSWER ▶ Your rate is $3.60 per hour.

CHECK ✓ Check by multiplying and using unit analysis:

$$\frac{5}{3}\cancel{h} \cdot 3.60\ \frac{\text{dollars}}{\cancel{h}} = 6 \text{ dollars} \checkmark$$

EXAMPLE 5 Multiplying and Dividing Fractions

RANCHING Your family owns a horse ranch. The pasture is a rectangle $\frac{1}{2}$ mile wide and $\frac{3}{4}$ mile long. You want to provide enough grazing area for each horse on your ranch. The recommended grazing area is 3 acres for every 2 horses. There are 640 acres in 1 square mile. What is the maximum number of horses you should have in the pasture?

Solution

The pasture has an area of $\frac{1}{2} \cdot \frac{3}{4} = \frac{3}{8}$ mi². Convert this area to acres.

$$\text{Number of acres in your pasture} = \frac{640 \text{ acres}}{1 \cancel{\text{mi}^2}} \cdot \frac{3}{8} \cancel{\text{mi}^2}$$

$$= 240 \text{ acres}$$

To find the maximum number of horses, divide the number of acres by the recommended acreage per horse.

$$240 \text{ acres} \div \frac{3 \text{ acres}}{2 \text{ horses}} = 240 \cancel{\text{acres}} \cdot \frac{2 \text{ horses}}{3 \cancel{\text{acres}}}$$

$$= 160 \text{ horses}$$

ANSWER ▶ The maximum number of horses is 160.

Math Reasoning

Encouraging students to use multiplication to check division problems reinforces their grasp of the inverse relation between the operations.

Extra Example 5

You have decided to buy a second horse ranch. This ranch has a small rectangular pasture that is $\frac{1}{4}$ mi wide and $\frac{3}{8}$ mi long. There are 640 acres in 1 square mile, and recommended grazing area is 3 acres for every 2 horses. What is the maximum number of horses you should have grazing in this second pasture?
40 horses

Concept Check

Explain how to divide rational numbers. ***Sample answer:*** **Rewrite any mixed numbers as improper fractions. Multiply the first fraction (the dividend) by the reciprocal of the second fraction (the divisor). Simplify the resulting fraction.**

6.5 Exercises

Guided Practice

Divide. Then simplify, if possible.

1. $\frac{1}{2} \div \frac{5}{6}$ **$\frac{3}{5}$**
2. $6 \div \frac{4}{9}$ **$\frac{27}{2}$ or $13\frac{1}{2}$**
3. $3\frac{1}{3} \div \frac{1}{9}$ **30**
4. $\frac{4}{5} \div 1\frac{1}{2}$ **$\frac{8}{15}$**
5. $\frac{n}{3} \div \frac{3}{2}$ **$\frac{2n}{9}$**
6. $3\frac{1}{2} \div \frac{4}{x}$ **$\frac{7x}{8}$**
7. $y \div \frac{3}{10}$ **$\frac{10y}{3}$**
8. $\frac{7}{8} \div m$ **$\frac{7}{8m}$**

9. **EXERCISING** You jogged 15 miles in $2\frac{1}{4}$ hours. Find your hourly rate of speed. **$6\frac{2}{3}$ mi/h**

10. **AQUARIUM** The classroom aquarium holds 20 gallons of water. If you use a $1\frac{1}{2}$ gallon container to fill the tank, how many times will you have to fill the container? **$13\frac{1}{3}$ times**

11. **WRITING** How can you check your answer to a division problem involving fractions? Give an example to illustrate. **See margin.**

11. ***Sample answer:*** **I can multiply the quotient by the divisor to see if I get the dividend.** $\frac{1}{3} \div \frac{1}{2} = \frac{1}{3} \cdot \frac{2}{1} = \frac{2}{3}$ **Check:** $\frac{2}{3} \cdot \frac{1}{2} = \frac{1}{3}$

3 Apply

Assignment Guide

TRANSITIONAL

Day 1: pp. 292–293 Exs. 12–23, 28–29, 40–44

Day 2: pp. 292–293 Exs. 30–35, 38–39, 47–53

AVERAGE

Day 1: pp. 292–293 Exs. 12–29, 40–44

Day 2: pp. 292–293 Exs. 30–36, 38–39, 47–53

ADVANCED

Day 1: pp. 292–293 Exs. 12–29, 37*, 41–46

Day 2: pp. 292–293 Exs. 30–36, 38–39, 47–53

BLOCK SCHEDULE

pp. 292–293 Exs. 12–36, 38–44, 47–53

Extra Practice

- Student Edition, pp. 700–701
- Chapter 6 Resource Book, p. 42

Homework Check

To quickly check student understanding of key concepts, go over the following exercises:

Transitional: 12, 14, 20, 22, 30
Average: 16, 18, 20, 26, 32
Advanced: 16, 18, 20, 26, 32

Problem Solving

Exercises 30–35

Remind students to write a verbal model. For example, in Exercise 30, students could write:

$\begin{pmatrix}\text{Number of}\\ \text{rest stops}\end{pmatrix} \cdot \begin{pmatrix}\text{Number of miles}\\ \text{between stops}\end{pmatrix}$

= Total miles.

Students can then decide what is given and what to solve for.

Practice and Problem Solving

Student Help

▶MORE PRACTICE
Extra practice to help you master skills in on page 701.

Divide. Then simplify, if possible.

12. $\frac{3}{2} \div \frac{1}{2}$ 3 **13.** $\frac{5}{2} \div 4$ $\frac{5}{8}$ **14.** $8 \div \frac{1}{4}$ 32 **15.** $2 \div 1\frac{1}{5}$

16. $\frac{3}{4} \div 2$ **17.** $3 \div \left(\frac{-5}{6}\right)$ **18.** $\frac{-1}{2} \div \frac{1}{3}$ **19.** $\frac{7}{4} \div \left(\frac{1}{-4}\right)$ −7

20. $\frac{4}{5} \div 1\frac{1}{2}$ $\frac{8}{15}$ **21.** $3\frac{1}{2} \div \frac{3}{4}$ **22.** $\frac{x}{2} \div (-4)$ **23.** $-\frac{3}{5} \div \frac{9}{x}$

24. $6\frac{2}{3} \div a$ **25.** $n \div 1\frac{1}{4}$ **26.** $\frac{1}{y} \div \frac{4}{y}$ **27.** $\frac{3b}{2} \div \frac{9b}{5}$

ERROR ANALYSIS **Describe and correct the error.** 28 and 29. See margin.

28. The person did not use the reciprocal of 3, $\frac{1}{3}$; $\frac{5}{18}$.

29. The person did not multiply the denominators; $-\frac{8}{9}$.

28. $\frac{5}{6} \div 3 = \frac{5}{6} \cdot \frac{3}{1} = \frac{5 \cdot 3}{2 \cdot 3} = \frac{5}{2}$

29. 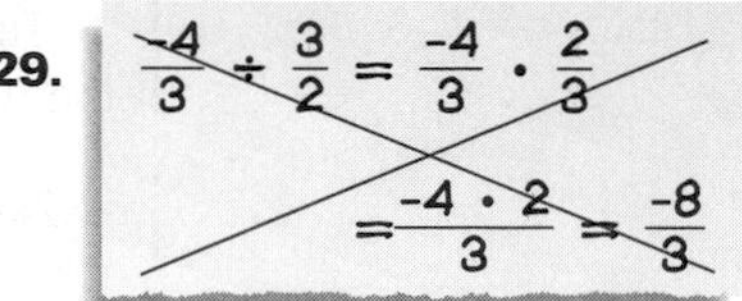

$\frac{-4}{3} \div \frac{3}{2} = \frac{-4}{3} \cdot \frac{2}{3} = \frac{-4 \cdot 2}{3} = \frac{-8}{3}$

Student Help

▶HOMEWORK HELP
Extra help with problem solving in Exs. 30–33 is available at www.mcdougallittell.com

In Exercises 30–33, decide whether to use multiplication or division to solve the problem. Solve the problem and explain why you selected that operation. Check your answer using unit analysis.

30. BICYCLING You are riding your bike on a trail that is 11 miles long. You stop to rest every $2\frac{3}{4}$ miles. How many rest stops will you make? 4 rest stops, which includes 1 at the end of the trail

31. JOGGING A running track is $\frac{1}{4}$ mile long. You run 15 times around the track. How far do you run?

32. BABY-SITTING You baby-sit your neighbor's children for $3\frac{3}{4}$ hours. You earn $12.00. Find your hourly wage. $3.20/h

33. CONSTRUCTION The distance between the floors of a building is $10\frac{1}{2}$ feet. The building has 5 floors. How tall is the building? (Assume the first floor is at ground level, and count the roof as a "floor.") 42 ft

DESIGNING **In Exercises 34 and 35, use the following information.** A designer is planning to make some pillows. The designer has a length of cotton cloth that is $5\frac{1}{4}$ feet long.

34. The designer wants to use the material to make three pillows. If the designer cuts the cloth into three pieces of equal length, how long is each piece of cloth?

35. Suppose the designer plans to make 12 more of the same pillows. How long a piece of cloth does he need to buy? Express the length in yards.

36. MATHEMATICAL REASONING A proper fraction is divided by an improper fraction. Can the quotient ever be greater than 1? Explain how you arrived at your conclusion. no; dividing a number less than 1 by a number greater than 1 can only result in a number even smaller yet.

37. CHALLENGE Simplify the expressions below. Write each result as a decimal, rounded to the hundredths place. Describe the pattern. Explain what happens when you divide a fraction by larger and larger whole numbers. $\frac{1}{8}, \frac{1}{12}, \frac{1}{16}, \frac{1}{20}$; 0.13, 0.08, 0.06, 0.05; the answer gets smaller and smaller.

$\frac{1}{4} \div 2$ $\qquad \frac{1}{4} \div 3$ $\qquad \frac{1}{4} \div 4$ $\qquad \frac{1}{4} \div 5$

Multiple-Choice Practice

38. Find the quotient $\frac{5}{6} \div \frac{2}{3}$. B

Ⓐ $\frac{5}{9}$ Ⓑ $\frac{5}{4}$ Ⓒ $\frac{3}{2}$ Ⓓ $\frac{9}{5}$

39. Suppose you are following a recipe to make rolls. The recipe calls for $5\frac{1}{3}$ cups of flour to make 40 rolls. How many rolls can you make with 32 cups of flour? J

Ⓕ 6 rolls Ⓖ $7\frac{1}{2}$ rolls Ⓗ 192 rolls Ⓙ 240 rolls

Mixed Review

40. You buy 100 shares of a stock on Monday morning. Each share of the stock loses 4 points on 2 days and gains 2 points on 3 days. Write your total gain or loss for the week as an integer. *(3.2)* −200

Write an equation for the area of the rectangle. Then solve for *x*. *(4.4)*

41. Area is 49 square inches.

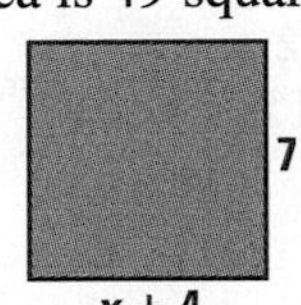

7(x + 4) = 49; 3 in.

42. Area is 20 square feet.

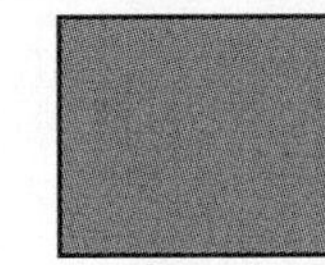

4(2x + 1) = 20; 2 ft

Write the prime factorization of the number. *(5.1)*

43. 26 $2 \cdot 13$ **44.** 78 $2 \cdot 3 \cdot 13$ **45.** 105 $3 \cdot 5 \cdot 7$ **46.** 210 $2 \cdot 3 \cdot 5 \cdot 7$

Find the greatest common factor of the expressions. *(5.2)*

47. 30 and 54 6 **48.** $12x$ and $15x$ $3x$ **49.** $10x^2y$ and $25xy^2$ $5xy$

Find the multiplicative inverse. *(6.3)*

50. 2 $\frac{1}{2}$ **51.** $-\frac{3}{7}$ $-\frac{7}{3}$ **52.** $4\frac{5}{12}$ $\frac{12}{53}$ **53.** $-1\frac{1}{9}$ $-\frac{9}{10}$

4 Assess

Assessment Resources

- Assessment Book (Formal Assessment and Alternative Assessment)
- Test and Practice Generator

Mini-Quiz

Simplify the expression.

1. $\frac{5}{6} \div \frac{2}{3}$ $\frac{5}{4}$
2. $\frac{4}{9} \div 3$ $\frac{4}{27}$
3. $4\frac{3}{8} \div \frac{3}{4}$ $\frac{35}{6}$
4. $\frac{2}{x} \div \frac{3}{5x}$ $\frac{10}{3}$
5. You have $5\frac{1}{3}$ yd of fabric. Each throw pillow you plan to make requires $1\frac{3}{8}$ ft of fabric. What is the maximum number of pillows you can make? **3 pillows**

Math Reasoning

In Exercise 37, the results obtained by dividing by 2, 3, 4 . . . not only get smaller and smaller, but in fact approach 0. It is a consequence of the order properties of real numbers that dividing by a larger number leads to a smaller result. If *a*, *b*, and *c* are positive numbers and $b > c$, then $\frac{a}{b} < \frac{a}{c}$.

1 Plan

Pacing

Suggested Number of Days

Transitional: 1 day
Average: 1 day
Advanced: 1 day
Block Schedule: 0.5 block with 6.7

Teaching Resources

Blacklines
(See page 266B.)

Transparencies
- Warm-Up Exercises
- Teacher Time-Savers
- English/Spanish Problem Solving
- Answers

Technology
- Electronic Teacher Tools
- Test and Practice Generator

2 Teach

Math Reasoning

For Mathematical Background Notes on mathematical reasoning related to this lesson, please refer to pages 266E and 266F in this Teacher's Edition.

California Standards and Assessment

CA Standards: AF 4.1, MG 1.1

6.6 Solving Equations with Rational Numbers

California Standards

In this lesson you'll:

- Compare weights, capacities, geometric measures, times, and temperatures within and between measurement systems. (MG 1.1)
- Solve two-step linear equations over the rational numbers and verify the reasonableness of the results. (AF 4.1)

Goal 1 Solving One-Step Equations

EXAMPLE 1 Solving an Addition Equation

$x + \frac{3}{4} = \frac{7}{8}$ Write original equation.

$x + \frac{3}{4} - \frac{3}{4} = \frac{7}{8} - \frac{3}{4}$ Subtract $\frac{3}{4}$ from each side.

$x = \frac{7}{8} - \frac{6}{8} = \frac{1}{8}$ Subtract using a common denominator.

ANSWER ▶ The solution is $\frac{1}{8}$.

CHECK ✓ $\frac{1}{8} + \frac{3}{4} \stackrel{?}{=} \frac{7}{8}$ Substitute in original equation.

$\frac{1}{8} + \frac{6}{8} = \frac{7}{8}$ Solution checks.

EXAMPLE 2 Solving a Subtraction Equation

$y - \frac{1}{3} = \frac{4}{5}$ Write original equation.

$y - \frac{1}{3} + \frac{1}{3} = \frac{4}{5} + \frac{1}{3}$ Add $\frac{1}{3}$ to each side.

$y = \frac{12}{15} + \frac{5}{15}$ Add using a common denominator.

$y = \frac{17}{15}$, or $1\frac{2}{15}$ Simplify.

Student Help

▶ **STUDY TIP**
To solve a multiplication equation, you can use the inverse property of multiplication and the identity property of multiplication to isolate the variable.

EXAMPLE 3 Solving a Multiplication Equation

$\frac{2}{3}m = \frac{5}{8}$ Write original equation.

$\left(\frac{3}{2} \cdot \frac{2}{3}\right)m = \frac{3}{2} \cdot \frac{5}{8}$ Multiply each side by the reciprocal of $\frac{2}{3}$.

$m = \frac{15}{16}$ Simplify.

Goal 2 SOLVING TWO-STEP EQUATIONS

To solve equations involving more than one operation, you use more than one inverse operation to get the variable isolated on one side.

Student Help

STUDY TIP
To solve an equation involving fractions, use inverse operations to isolate the variable on one side of equation, just like you did in Lesson 4.1 with integers.

EXAMPLE 4 Solving a Two-Step Equation

$\frac{1}{2}x + \frac{1}{3} = \frac{1}{6}$	Write original equation.
$\frac{1}{2}x + \frac{1}{3} - \frac{1}{3} = \frac{1}{6} - \frac{1}{3}$	Subtract $\frac{1}{3}$ from each side.
$\frac{1}{2}x = \frac{1}{6} - \frac{2}{6}$	Subtract using a common denominator.
$\frac{1}{2}x = -\frac{1}{6}$	Simplify.
$\frac{2}{1} \cdot \frac{1}{2}x = \frac{2}{1} \cdot \left(-\frac{1}{6}\right)$	Multiply each side by the reciprocal of $\frac{1}{2}$.
$x = -\frac{1}{3}$	Simplify.

Link to History

LORD KELVIN Another temperature scale, called the Kelvin scale, was developed by Lord Kelvin in 1847. A Kelvin temperature can be obtained by adding 273.15°C to a given Celsius temperature.

More about the Kelvin scale available at www.mcdougallittell.com

EXAMPLE 5 Using a Formula

TEMPERATURES Countries that use the metric system report temperatures using the Celsius scale. To convert Fahrenheit temperatures to Celsius temperatures, you can use the formula $F = \frac{9}{5}C + 32$. Use the formula to calculate the Celsius temperature that is equivalent to 77° Fahrenheit.

Solution

$F = \frac{9}{5}C + 32$	Write original equation.
$77 = \frac{9}{5}C + 32$	Substitute 77 for F.
$45 = \frac{9}{5}C$	Add −32 to each side.
$\frac{5}{9} \cdot 45 = \frac{5}{9} \cdot \frac{9}{5}C$	Multiply each side by $\frac{5}{9}$.
$25 = C$	Simplify.

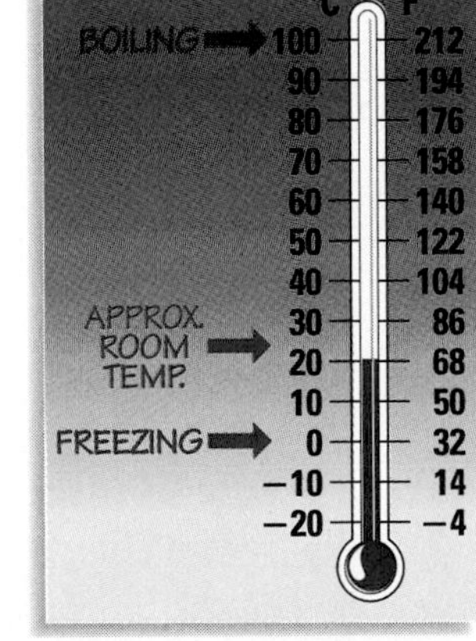

ANSWER ▶ 77° Fahrenheit is equivalent to 25° Celsius.

Note that this answer agrees with the chart, in which 77° Fahrenheit appears to fall about midway between 20° Celsius and 30° Celsius.

Math Reasoning

While this lesson provides practice with operations with fractions, the student should keep in mind that the rules governing the solution of algebraic equations hold for all real numbers, not only rational numbers.

Extra Example 1

Solve $x + \frac{5}{6} = \frac{11}{12}$. $\frac{1}{12}$

Extra Example 2

Solve $y - \frac{3}{4} = \frac{1}{7}$. $\frac{25}{28}$

Extra Example 3

Solve $\frac{3}{8}m = \frac{1}{5}$. $\frac{8}{15}$

Extra Example 4

Solve $\frac{1}{3}x - \frac{1}{4} = \frac{11}{12}$. $\frac{7}{2}$ or $3\frac{1}{2}$

Extra Example 5

Use the thermometer in Example 5 to estimate the Celsius temperature that is equivalent to 95°F. Then calculate its value using the formula $F = \frac{9}{5}C + 32$. 35°C

Extra Example 6

John can mow the yard in 2 hours. It takes Scott 3 hours to mow the same yard. How long would it take them to mow the yard together? **$\frac{6}{5}$ hours or $1\frac{1}{5}$ hours or 1 hour, 12 minutes**

Math Reasoning

There is an interesting pattern behind such rate of work problems. If *A* takes time *a* and *B* takes time *b* to do the same job, this means A can do $\frac{1}{a}$ of the job in unit time and *B* can do $\frac{1}{b}$ of the job in unit time. Therefore together *A* and *B* can do $\frac{1}{a} + \frac{1}{b}$ of the job in unit time. Therefore *A* and *B* together can do the entire job in time $\frac{1}{\frac{1}{a}+\frac{1}{b}} = \frac{ab}{a+b}$.

One expects that the time $\frac{ab}{a+b}$ is less than both *a* and *b*. This can be verified by confirming that if $a > 0$ and $b > 0$, then $\frac{ab}{a+b} < b$. To do this, divide both sides of the inequalities $a < a + b$ and $b < a + b$ by $a + b$. Then multiply both sides of the inequalities by *b* and *a*, respectively.

Concept Check

Explain how to solve an equation involving rational numbers. ***Sample answer:*** **Isolate the term that includes the variable. Combine terms by adding or subtracting fractions. Multiply both sides of the equation by the reciprocal of the coefficient of *x*. Simplify.**

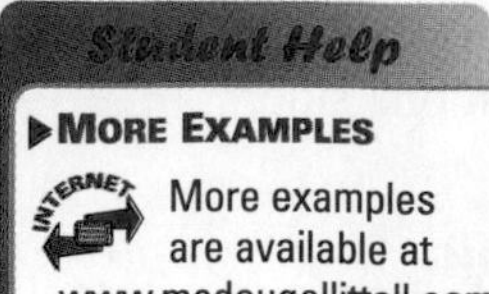

Student Help
▶MORE EXAMPLES
INTERNET
More examples are available at www.mcdougallittell.com

EXAMPLE 6 *Solving a Rate of Work Problem*

HOUSEWORK Maria can clean the house in 3 hours. It takes Paul 4 hours to do the same job. How long would it take them to clean the house together?

Solution

You can use algebra to solve this problem. Let x represent the number of hours Maria and Paul need to clean the house together. The fraction of the job that Maria can do in 1 hour is $\frac{1}{3}$. So, the fraction of the job that Maria can do in x hours is $\frac{1}{3}x$. Likewise, the fraction of the job that Paul can do in x hours is $\frac{1}{4}x$. These two fractions must add up to one whole job.

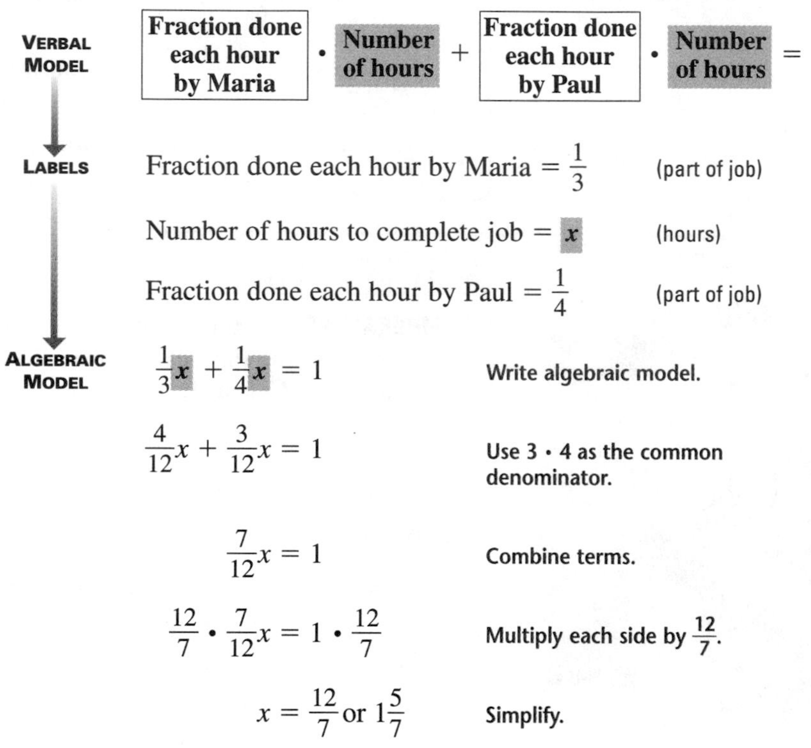

VERBAL MODEL
Fraction done each hour by Maria • Number of hours + Fraction done each hour by Paul • Number of hours = 1
LABELS
Fraction done each hour by Maria = $\frac{1}{3}$ (part of job)
Number of hours to complete job = x (hours)
Fraction done each hour by Paul = $\frac{1}{4}$ (part of job)
ALGEBRAIC MODEL
$\frac{1}{3}x + \frac{1}{4}x = 1$ Write algebraic model.
$\frac{4}{12}x + \frac{3}{12}x = 1$ Use 3 • 4 as the common denominator.
$\frac{7}{12}x = 1$ Combine terms.
$\frac{12}{7} \cdot \frac{7}{12}x = 1 \cdot \frac{12}{7}$ Multiply each side by $\frac{12}{7}$.
$x = \frac{12}{7}$ or $1\frac{5}{7}$ Simplify.

ANSWER ▶ Working together, Maria and Paul can clean the house in about 1 hour and 43 minutes.

When solving a real-life problem, you should always check that your answer is reasonable. In Example 6 above, Maria can clean the house in 3 hours alone. Two people working at this rate would take 1.5 hours to clean the house. Two people working at Paul's rate would clean the house in 2 hours. So, it is reasonable that together they can finish the job in less than 2 hours.

6.6 Exercises

Guided Practice

In Exercises 1–6, solve the equation. Check the solution.

1. $x + \frac{3}{4} = 6$ **$5\frac{1}{4}$** **2.** $y - \frac{5}{8} = 6\frac{1}{2}$ **$7\frac{1}{8}$** **3.** $\frac{1}{3}z = \frac{5}{8}$ **$\frac{15}{8}$ or $1\frac{7}{8}$**

4. $3a + \frac{1}{2} = \frac{7}{8}$ **$\frac{11}{24}$** **5.** $\frac{3}{5}b - \frac{1}{10} = \frac{29}{100}$ **$\frac{13}{20}$** **6.** $\frac{9}{16} - 2c = 1\frac{11}{32}$ **$-\frac{25}{64}$**

7. A charity reported that it had raised $10,000, which was $\frac{2}{3}$ of the goal for the year. Write and solve an equation to find how much money the charity's goal for the year was. **$\frac{2}{3}x = 10{,}000$, $15,000**

Practice and Problem Solving

Student Help

▶**MORE PRACTICE**
Extra practice to help you master skills is on page 701.

Solve the equation. Check the solution.

8. $x - \frac{7}{10} = \frac{4}{5}$ **$\frac{3}{2}$ or $1\frac{1}{2}$** **9.** $m + \frac{1}{16} = \frac{3}{8}$ **$\frac{5}{16}$** **10.** $\frac{2}{5}y = \frac{1}{10}$ **$\frac{1}{4}$**

11. $n + 1\frac{1}{2} = 2\frac{5}{8}$ **$1\frac{1}{8}$** **12.** $y - \frac{3}{8} = 1\frac{3}{4}$ **$2\frac{1}{8}$** **13.** $\frac{m}{3} = \frac{7}{9}$ **$\frac{7}{3}$ or $2\frac{1}{3}$**

14. $\frac{15}{32} = b + \frac{3}{8}$ **$\frac{3}{32}$** **15.** $4 = \frac{5}{8}c$ **$\frac{32}{5}$ or $6\frac{2}{5}$** **16.** $\frac{9}{16} = a - \frac{3}{4}$ **$\frac{21}{16}$ or $1\frac{5}{16}$**

17. $\frac{3}{8} + \frac{n}{4} = 2$ **$\frac{13}{2}$ or $6\frac{1}{2}$** **18.** $1\frac{3}{4} = \frac{a}{2} - \frac{1}{8}$ **$\frac{15}{4}$ or $3\frac{3}{4}$** **19.** $\frac{1}{2}y + \frac{2}{3} = 1\frac{5}{6}$ **$\frac{7}{3}$ or $2\frac{1}{3}$**

20. $\frac{9}{10} - z = -\frac{1}{2}$ **$\frac{7}{5}$ or $1\frac{2}{5}$** **21.** $1\frac{1}{5} = \frac{9}{10}c - \frac{3}{5}$ **2** **22.** $-\frac{3}{100} = \frac{1}{5} - 2m$ **$\frac{23}{200}$**

GEOMETRY **Write an equation to solve for *x*. Then solve the equation.**

23. Area $= \frac{63}{4}$ square units

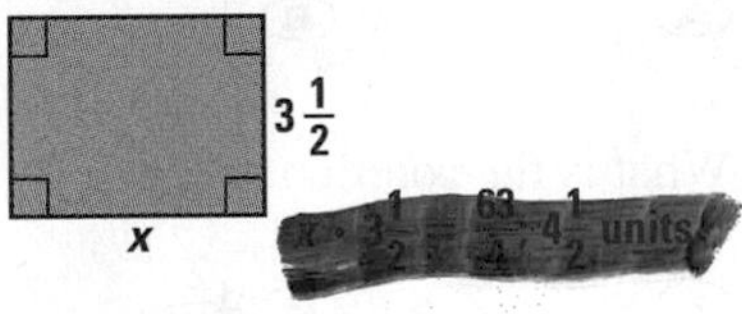

$x \cdot 3\frac{1}{2} = \frac{63}{4}$; $4\frac{1}{2}$ units

24. Area $= \frac{3}{40}$ square units

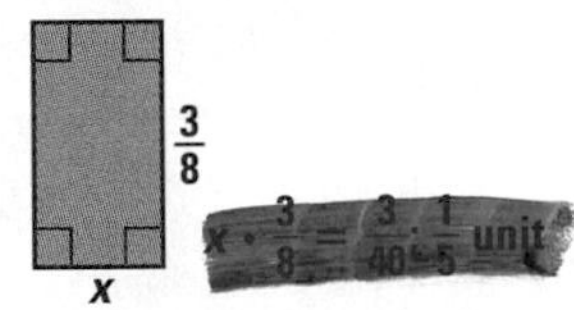

$x \cdot \frac{3}{8} = \frac{3}{40}$; $\frac{1}{5}$ unit

25. Area $= \frac{7}{15}$ square units

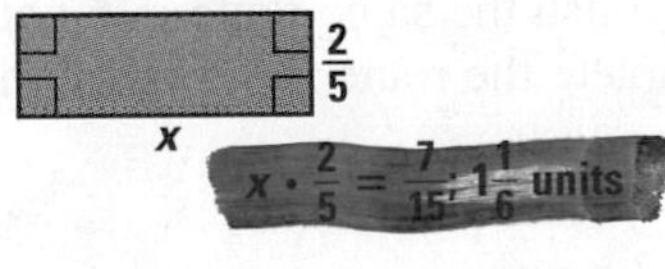

$x \cdot \frac{2}{5} = \frac{7}{15}$; $1\frac{1}{6}$ units

26. Area $= \frac{9}{8}$ square units

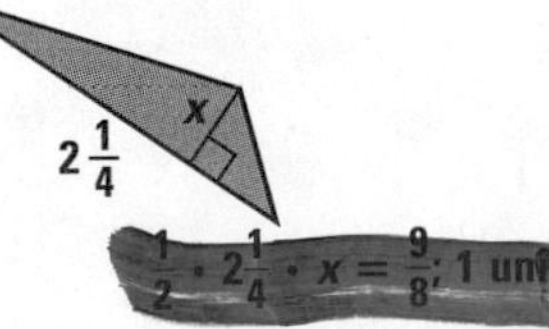

$\frac{1}{2} \cdot 2\frac{1}{4} \cdot x = \frac{9}{8}$; 1 unit

3 Apply

Assignment Guide

TRANSITIONAL
Day 1: pp. 297–298 Exs. 8–15, 18–19, 23–24, 27–28, 31–34, 39–40, 42–44

AVERAGE
Day 1: pp. 297–298 Exs. 8–18, 23–25, 27–29, 31–34, 39–40, 42–44

ADVANCED
Day 1: pp. 297–298 Exs. 11–22, 25–30, 35–40, 41*, 42–44

BLOCK SCHEDULE
pp. 297–298 Exs. 8–18, 23–25, 27–29, 31–34, 39–40, 42–44 (with 6.7)

Extra Practice

- Student Edition, pp. 700–701
- Chapter 6 Resource Book, p. 51

Homework Check

To quickly check student understanding of key concepts, go over the following exercises:

Transitional: 8, 10, 18, 34, 40
Average: 10, 12, 18, 34, 40
Advanced: 12, 18, 22, 36, 40

4 Assess

Assessment Resources

- Assessment Book (Formal Assessment and Alternative Assessment)
- Test and Practice Generator

Mini-Quiz

Solve each equation.

1. $x - \frac{3}{4} = \frac{1}{16}$ $\frac{13}{16}$
2. $x + \frac{1}{5} = \frac{7}{8}$ $\frac{27}{40}$
3. $\frac{2}{3}x = \frac{1}{8}$ $\frac{3}{16}$
4. $\frac{1}{5}x + \frac{1}{3} = \frac{3}{4}$ $\frac{25}{12}$ or $2\frac{1}{12}$
5. Use $F = \frac{9}{5}C + 32$ to find the Celsius temperature that is equivalent to 59°F. 15°C

30. $\frac{2}{3}\left(\frac{3}{2}x\right) = \left(\frac{2}{3} \cdot \frac{3}{2}\right)x$ Assoc. prop. of mult.
$= 1x$ Inv. prop. of mult.
$= x$ Identity prop. of mult.

In Exercises 27–29, write and solve the equation for the sentence.

27. Half of a number, plus 13, is 30. $\frac{x}{2} + 13 = 30$, 34

28. Three sevenths times a number, plus 6, is 33. $\frac{3}{7} \cdot x + 6 = 33$, 63

29. The sum of 86 and one fifth of a number is −24. $86 + \frac{x}{5} = -24$, −550

30. MATHEMATICAL REASONING Give reasons for each step in the following: $\frac{2}{3}\left(\frac{3}{2}x\right) = \left(\frac{2}{3} \cdot \frac{3}{2}\right)x = 1x = x$ See margin.

Science Link **Use the formula $F = \frac{9}{5}C + 32$ to find the equivalent Celsius temperature for the given Fahrenheit temperature. Use the chart on page 295 to check that your answer is reasonable.**

31. 180°F 82°C **32.** 0°F −18°C **33.** 90°F 32°C **34.** 42°F 6°C

35. −8°F −22°C **36.** 200°F 93°C **37.** 55°F 13°C **38.** 129°F 54°C

39. RAKING Mark can rake the yard in 3.5 hours. Joe takes 4 hours to do the same job. How long would it take them to rake the yard together? 1 h 52 min

40. FILLING A BUCKET To fill a bucket as fast as possible, you place it under two faucets. If one faucet is turned on alone, the bucket is filled in 2 minutes. If the other is turned on alone, the bucket is filled in 3 minutes. How long will it take to fill the bucket if both faucets are turned on? $\frac{6}{5}$ min or 1 min 12 s

41. CHALLENGE The perimeter of the triangle shown is $16\frac{1}{2}$ units. Write and solve an equation to find x. Then find the length of each side of the triangle.

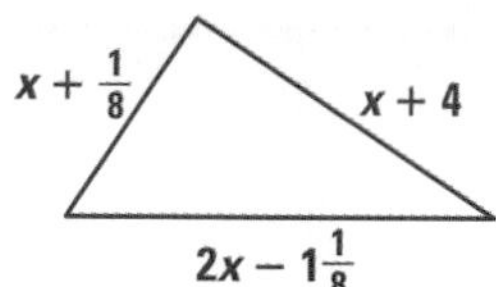

$x + \frac{1}{8} + x + 4 + 2x - 1\frac{1}{8} = 16\frac{1}{2}$, $x = \frac{27}{8}$; sides: $\frac{7}{2}, \frac{59}{8}, \frac{45}{8}$

Multiple-Choice Practice

42. What is the solution of $x - \frac{3}{8} = 1\frac{5}{16}$? D

Ⓐ $\frac{15}{16}$ Ⓑ $1\frac{1}{4}$ Ⓒ $1\frac{8}{24}$ Ⓓ $1\frac{11}{16}$

43. What is the solution of $\frac{1}{3}m + \frac{1}{6} = 4\frac{1}{2}$?

Ⓕ $4\frac{1}{3}$ Ⓖ $4\frac{2}{3}$ Ⓗ 13 Ⓙ 14

44. It takes Phil 5 hours to complete his bread delivery route. George can finish the same route in 6 hours. How long will it take them to complete the route if they both make bread deliveries? B

Ⓐ 2 hours 30 minutes Ⓑ 2 hours 44 minutes

Ⓒ 3 hours Ⓓ 2 hours 70 minutes

6.7 Multiplying and Dividing Powers

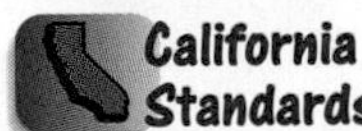

California Standards

In this lesson you'll:

- Multiply, divide, and simplify rational numbers by using exponent rules. (NS 2.3)
- Multiply and divide monomials. (AF 2.2)

Goal 1 MULTIPLYING POWERS

The following example suggests a rule for multiplying powers with the same base when the exponents are integers.

$$a^5 \cdot a^3 = \underbrace{\overbrace{(a \cdot a \cdot a \cdot a \cdot a)}^{\text{5 factors}} \cdot \overbrace{(a \cdot a \cdot a)}^{\text{3 factors}}}_{\text{8 factors}} = a^8$$

Notice that the exponent of a is **8**, which is equal to **5** + **3**.

Student Help

STUDY TIP
The exponent rule stated at the right is sometimes called the *product of powers* rule.

MULTIPLYING POWERS WITH THE SAME BASE

Let m and n be positive integers, and let a be any number.

In Words To multiply two powers with the same base, add their exponents.

In Algebra $a^m \cdot a^n = a^{m+n}$

In Arithmetic $3^2 \cdot 3^3 = 3^{2+3} = 3^5$

EXAMPLE 1 Multiplying Powers

Multiply the powers using repeated multiplication and exponent rules.

a. $4^4 \cdot 4^2$

b. $-\frac{1}{2} \cdot \left(-\frac{1}{2}\right)^2$

Solution

a. Use repeated multiplication: $4^4 \cdot 4^2 = (4 \cdot 4 \cdot 4 \cdot 4) \cdot (4 \cdot 4) = 4^6$

Use exponent rule: $4^4 \cdot 4^2 = 4^{4+2} = 4^6$

b. Use repeated multiplication: $-\frac{1}{2} \cdot \left(-\frac{1}{2}\right)^2 = -\frac{1}{2} \cdot \left(-\frac{1}{2}\right) \cdot \left(-\frac{1}{2}\right) = \left(-\frac{1}{2}\right)^3$

Use exponent rule: $-\frac{1}{2} \cdot \left(-\frac{1}{2}\right)^2 = \left(-\frac{1}{2}\right)^{1+2} = \left(-\frac{1}{2}\right)^3$

EXAMPLE 2 Multiplying Variable Expressions

$2x^2 \cdot 3x^4 = (2 \cdot 3) \cdot (x^2 \cdot x^4) = 6x^{2+4} = 6x^6$

1 Plan

Pacing

Suggested Number of Days

Transitional: 1 day
Average: 1 day
Advanced: 1 day
Block Schedule: 0.5 block with 6.6

Teaching Resources

Blacklines
(See page 266B.)

Transparencies
- Warm-Up Exercises
- Teacher Time-Savers
- English/Spanish Problem Solving
- Answers

Technology
- Electronic Teacher Tools
- Test and Practice Generator

2 Teach

Math Reasoning

For Mathematical Background Notes on mathematical reasoning related to this lesson, please refer to pages 266E and 266F in this Teacher's Edition.

Extra Examples 1 and 2
See next page.

California Standards and Assessment

CA Standards: NS 2.3, AF 2.2
CA Key Concepts Book: pp. S19, S21, S39–S41

Extra Example 1

Use repeated multiplication and then use an exponent rule to multiply the powers.

a. $3^5 \cdot 3$ 3^6

b. $\left(\frac{-2}{3}\right)^2 \cdot \left(\frac{-2}{3}\right)^5$ $\left(\frac{-2}{3}\right)^7$

Extra Example 2

Simplify the expression $5a^3 \cdot 4a$. $20a^4$

Extra Example 3

Use repeated multiplication and then use an exponent rule to divide the powers.

a. $\frac{(-2)^7}{(-2)^4}$ $(-2)^3$

b. $\frac{8^3}{8}$ 8^2

Extra Example 4

Simplify $\frac{3x^5}{18x^2}$. $\frac{x^3}{6}$ or $\frac{1}{6}x^3$

Concept Check

Explain how to divide powers with the same base. ***Sample answer:*** **Raise the common base to the power found by subtracting the exponent of the denominator from the exponent of the numerator.**

Goal 2 Dividing Powers

The following example suggests a rule for dividing powers with the same base when the exponents are integers.

$$\frac{c^5}{c^3} = \frac{\overbrace{c \cdot c \cdot c \cdot c \cdot c}^{\text{5 factors}}}{\underbrace{c \cdot c \cdot c}_{\text{3 factors}}} = \frac{\overset{1}{\cancel{c}} \cdot \overset{1}{\cancel{c}} \cdot \overset{1}{\cancel{c}} \cdot c \cdot c}{\underset{1}{\cancel{c}} \cdot \underset{1}{\cancel{c}} \cdot \underset{1}{\cancel{c}}} = \overbrace{c \cdot c}^{\text{2 factors}} = c^2$$

Notice that the exponent of c is **2**, which is equal to **5 − 3**.

Student Help

▶ **Study Tip**
The exponent rule stated at the right is sometimes called the *quotient of powers* rule.

Dividing Powers with the Same Base

Let m and n be positive integers where $m > n$, and let a be a nonzero number.

In Words To divide two powers with the same base, subtract the exponent of the denominator from the exponent of the numerator.

In Algebra $\frac{a^m}{a^n} = a^{m-n}$

In Arithmetic $\frac{2^5}{2^3} = 2^{5-3} = 2^2$

EXAMPLE 3 Dividing Powers

Divide the powers using repeated multiplication and exponent rules.

a. $\frac{(-5)^3}{-5}$

b. $\frac{6^4}{6^3}$

Use repeated multiplication:

a. $\frac{(-5)^3}{-5} = \frac{\overset{1}{\cancel{(-5)}} \cdot (-5) \cdot (-5)}{\underset{1}{\cancel{-5}}} = (-5)^2$

b. $\frac{6^4}{6^3} = \frac{\overset{1}{\cancel{6}} \cdot \overset{1}{\cancel{6}} \cdot \overset{1}{\cancel{6}} \cdot 6}{\underset{1}{\cancel{6}} \cdot \underset{1}{\cancel{6}} \cdot \underset{1}{\cancel{6}}} = 6$

Use exponent rule:

$\frac{(-5)^3}{-5} = (-5)^{3-1} = (-5)^2$

$\frac{6^4}{6^3} = 6^{4-3} = 6^1 = 6$

EXAMPLE 4 Dividing Variable Expressions

Simplify $\frac{2n^5}{4n}$.

Solution

$$\frac{2n^5}{4n} = \frac{2}{4} \cdot \frac{n^5}{n} = \frac{1}{2}n^{5-1} = \frac{1}{2}n^4$$

6.7 Exercises

Guided Practice

In Exercises 1–8, simplify the expression.

1. $4^3 \cdot 4^5$ 4^8 **2.** $\left(\frac{1}{4}\right)^2 \cdot \left(\frac{1}{4}\right)^3$ $\left(\frac{1}{4}\right)^5$ **3.** $(-a)^4 \cdot (-a)^3$ $(-a)^7$ **4.** $-2x^2 \cdot 3x^3$ $-6x^5$

5. $\frac{3^4}{3^2}$ 3^2 **6.** $\frac{8^6}{8^5}$ 8 **7.** $\frac{(-a)^5}{(-a)^2}$ $(-a)^3$ **8.** $\frac{3x^4}{6x^2}$ $\frac{1}{2}x^2$

9. WRITING Explain in your own words how to multiply and divide two powers that have the same base. Give examples to illustrate. **See margin.**

9. ***Sample answer:*** **Keep the same base. To multiply, add the exponents. To divide, subtract the exponents.** $4^3 \cdot 4^5 = 4^{3+5} = 4^8$; $\frac{4^5}{4^3} = 4^{5-3} = 4^2$

Practice and Problem Solving

Simplify the expression.

10. $5^2 \cdot 5^5$ **11.** $6^3 \cdot 6^2$ **12.** $b^3 \cdot b$ **13.** $(-2)^3 \cdot (-2)^3$ $(-2)^6$

14. $\left(\frac{x}{7}\right)^3 \cdot \left(\frac{x}{7}\right)^2$ **15.** $\left(-\frac{3}{5}\right)^2 \cdot \left(-\frac{3}{5}\right)^2$ **16.** $m^5 \cdot 5m^4$ $5m^9$ **17.** $3n^5 \cdot 2n^4$ $6n^9$

18. $\frac{(-10)^4}{(-10)^2}$ $(-10)^2$ **19.** $\frac{3^5}{3^4}$ 3 **20.** $\frac{(-x)^9}{(-x)^3}$ $(-x)^6$ **21.** $\frac{-15y^4}{3y^2}$ $-5y^2$

22. $\frac{10x^5}{x^3y}$ **23.** $\frac{25xy^2}{5xy}$ $5y$ **24.** $\frac{-16x^4}{-24x^2}$ $\frac{2x^2}{3}$ **25.** $\frac{5x^3}{100x^2}$ $\frac{x}{20}$

Write and simplify a numerical expression for the given phrase.

26. The product of seven squared and seven raised to the third power $7^2 \cdot 7^3$; 7^5

27. The product of six and six cubed $6 \cdot 6^3$, 6^4

28. The quotient of nine raised to the tenth power and nine raised to the eighth power $\frac{9^{10}}{9^8}$; 9^2

29. The quotient of three raised to the fifth power and three raised to the second power $\frac{3^5}{3^2}$; 3^3

ERROR ANALYSIS **Describe and correct the error.**

30. 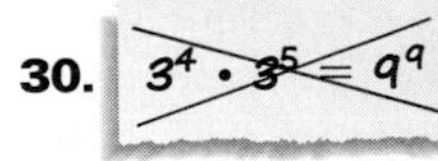

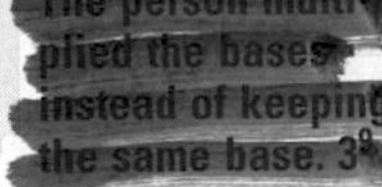

$3^4 \cdot 3^5 = 9^9$

The person multiplied the bases instead of keeping the same base. 3^9

31. 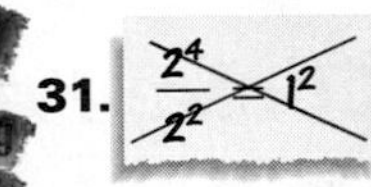

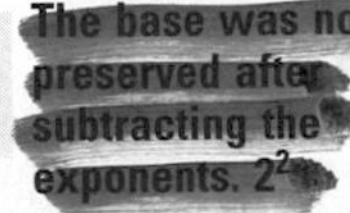

$\frac{2^4}{2^2} = 1^2$

The base was not preserved after subtracting the exponents. 2^2

MATHEMATICAL REASONING **Tell whether the statement is *true* or *false*. If it is false, rewrite the right side of the equation to make it true.**

32. $4^3 \cdot 4^2 = 4^6$ false; 4^5 **33.** $10^5 \cdot 10^6 \cdot 10^7 = 10^{18}$ true **34.** $a^2 \cdot a^3 \cdot a \cdot a^5 = a^{10}$ false; a^{11}

35. $\frac{6^6}{6^4} = 6^4$ false; 6^2 **36.** $\frac{x^5y^2z}{x^2yz} = x^3yz$ false; x^3y **37.** $\frac{(-2)^7}{(-2)^2} = (-2)^5$ true

3 Apply

Assignment Guide

TRANSITIONAL
Day 1: pp. 301–302 Exs. 10–23, 26–31, 38–39, 49–50

AVERAGE
Day 1: pp. 301–302 Exs. 10–24, 26–34, 38–41, 49–50

ADVANCED
Day 1: pp. 301–302 Exs. 12–28, 35–37, 43–44, 45–46*, 47–50

BLOCK SCHEDULE
pp. 301–302 Exs. 10–24, 26–34, 38–41, 49–50 (with 6.6)

Extra Practice

- Student Edition, pp. 700–701
- Chapter 6 Resource Book, p. 60

Homework Check

To quickly check student understanding of key concepts, go over the following exercises:

Transitional: 10, 12, 16, 18, 20
Average: 10, 12, 16, 20, 24
Advanced: 12, 16, 20, 24, 44

Student Help

▶**MORE PRACTICE**
Extra practice to help you master skills is on page 701.

4 Assess

Assessment Resources

- Assessment Book (Formal Assessment and Alternative Assessment)
- Test and Practice Generator

Mini-Quiz

Simplify each expression.

1. $7^4 \cdot 7$ 7^5
2. $(-2)^3 \cdot (-2)^4$ $(-2)^7$
3. $5x^6 \cdot 3x^2$ $15x^8$
4. $\frac{3^5}{3}$ 3^4
5. $\frac{6x^3}{9x}$ $\frac{2x^2}{3}$ or $\frac{2}{3}x^2$

Math Reasoning

In connection with Exercise 48, if the blue cube were to have edge length s and the green cube edge length ks, then the ratio of the volumes would be $\frac{(ks)^3}{s^3} = \frac{k^3s^3}{s^3} = k^3$. This is a special case of the general result that if C and C′ are solids such that C′ is similar to C with scale factor k, then the ratio of the volume of C′ to that of C is k^3. If C is a union of cubes of edge length s, then C′ will be a similar union of cubes of edge length ks, making the result easy to see in this case.

40. 10^9; *Sample answer:* There are 10 choices for each digit. $10^5 \cdot 10^4 = 10^9$

Student Help

HOMEWORK HELP

Extra help with problem solving in Exs. 41–44 is available at www.mcdougallittell.com

47. $\frac{10^6}{10^4}$; 10^2 or 100 times more PINs with the new system

ZIP CODES In Exercises 38–40, use the following information.
The United States Postal Service uses five digit ZIP codes. In 1981 it created the voluntary "ZIP + 4" system (five digits followed by four more digits). In both systems, each digit can be any integer from 0 to 9.

38. How many different ZIP codes are possible with the original ZIP code system? Use exponents to express your answer. (*Hint:* How many different numbers are there from 00000 to 99999?) 10^5

39. How many different 4 digit codes are possible? 10^4

40. MATHEMATICAL REASONING Multiply your answers from Exercises 38 and 39 to get the number of different ZIP codes possible with the "ZIP + 4" system. Explain why this result makes sense. See margin.

Use the quotient of powers rule to simplify. Then evaluate.

41. $\frac{\left(\frac{1}{3}\right)^4}{\left(\frac{1}{3}\right)^2}$ $\left(\frac{1}{3}\right)^2$; $\frac{1}{9}$ **42.** $\frac{\left(\frac{2}{5}\right)^6}{\left(\frac{2}{5}\right)^3}$ $\left(\frac{2}{5}\right)^3$; $\frac{8}{125}$ **43.** $\frac{\left(-\frac{3}{2}\right)^7}{\left(-\frac{3}{2}\right)^4}$ $\left(-\frac{3}{2}\right)^3$; $-\frac{27}{8}$ **44.** $\frac{\left(\frac{7}{8}\right)^{10}}{\left(\frac{7}{8}\right)^3}$ $\left(\frac{7}{8}\right)^7$; $\frac{823{,}543}{2{,}097{,}152}$

CHALLENGE Find the missing exponent that makes the statement true.

45. $2^3 \cdot 2^{?} = 2^8$ 5 **46.** $\frac{(-3)^7}{(-3)^{?}} = -3$ 6

47. ATMs A bank required its customers to enter a 4 digit personal identification number (PIN) when using one of its automatic teller machines (ATMs). To increase security, the bank increased the number of digits in the PIN to 6. Use powers of 10 to write and simplify an expression that gives the number of possible PINs under the new system compared to the old. See margin.

48. GEOMETRY Each edge of the blue cube is 2 units. Each edge of the green cube is double that of the blue cube. Write the volume of each cube as a power of 2. Then divide the volume of the green cube by the volume of the blue cube. Evaluate the result to find how many times greater the larger volume is than the smaller. blue 2^3, green $(2^2)^3$; $\frac{(2^2)^3}{2^3} = 2^3$ or 8 times as great

Multiple-Choice Practice

49. Simplify the expression $3a^2 \cdot 5a^4$. C

Ⓐ $15a^8$ Ⓑ $8a^6$ Ⓒ $15a^6$ Ⓓ Not here

50. Simplify the expression $\frac{4n^5}{2n^2}$. F

Ⓕ $2n^3$ Ⓖ $6n^7$ Ⓗ $8n^7$ Ⓙ $2n^{10}$

REASONING 6.8

DEVELOPING CONCEPTS
Integer Exponents

For use with Lesson 6.8

California Standards

- Understand negative whole number exponents. Multiply and divide expressions involving exponents with a common base. (NS 2.1)
- Analyze problems by observing patterns. (MR 1.1)
- Interpret negative whole-number powers as repeated division, and evaluate expressions that include exponents. (AF 2.1)

MATERIALS

- Paper and pencil

In Lesson 6.7 you simplified expressions involving positive integer exponents. You can look for a pattern to develop definitions for negative and zero exponents so that expressions involving them can be simplified.

SAMPLE 1 Looking for a Pattern

The diagram is a visual representation of several powers of 2. Use the diagram to complete the table.

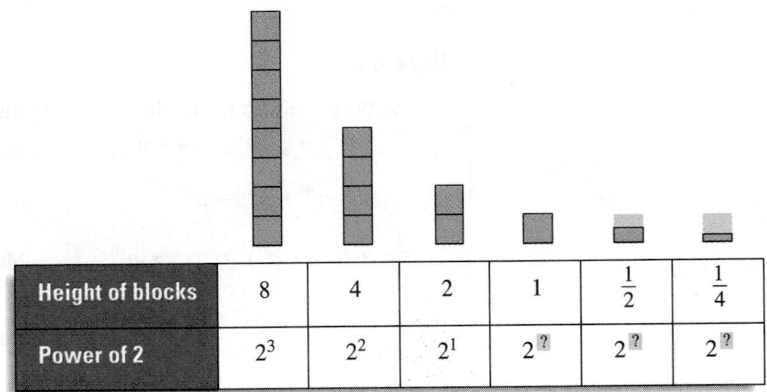

Height of blocks	8	4	2	1	$\frac{1}{2}$	$\frac{1}{4}$
Power of 2	2^3	2^2	2^1	$2^?$	$2^?$	$2^?$

Here's How

1. Notice that each time the height of the blocks is halved, the exponent of 2 decreases by 1.
2. To continue the pattern, decrease the exponent by 1 for each step.

ANSWER ▶ So, $2^0 = 1$, $2^{-1} = \frac{1}{2}$, and $2^{-2} = \frac{1}{4}$.

By generalizing the pattern in Sample 1, you can write the following definitions.

For any integer n and any number $a \neq 0$, $a^0 = 1$ and $a^{-n} = \frac{1}{a^n}$.

Try These

Find the missing exponent.

1. $16 = 4^?$ **2** **2.** $4 = 4^?$ **1** **3.** $1 = 4^?$ **0** **4.** $\frac{1}{4} = 4^?$ **−1**

Simplify the expression.

5. 5^{-2} $\frac{1}{5^2}$ or $\frac{1}{25}$ **6.** 3^0 **1** **7.** 2^{-5} $\frac{1}{2^5}$ or $\frac{1}{32}$ **8.** x^{-3} $\frac{1}{x^3}$

1 Planning the Activity

Purpose and Materials

See the margin of the student page.

▶ LINK TO LESSON

Students can apply the results of the activity to Example 1, part (a) in Lesson 6.8.

Math Reasoning

Students look for a pattern and apply the generalization to new problems. They apply deductive reasoning to justify rules.

2 Managing the Activity

Classroom Management

You may wish to have students look for the pattern in other powers. For example, in the sequence $3^3, 3^2, 3^1, \ldots$, each successive "height" is multiplied by one third. In the sequence $4^3, 4^2, 4^1, \ldots$, each successive "height" is multiplied by one fourth. Remind students that they are finding a pattern for a sequence, as they did in Lesson 1.6, Example 2(a).

California Standards and Assessment

CA Standards: NS 2.1, AF 2.1, MR 1.1

CA Key Concepts Book: pp. S20–S21

3 Closing the Activity

★ **KEY DISCOVERY**

A number raised to the zero power is 1. For a nonzero number a, $a^{-n} = \frac{1}{a^n}$ for any integer n.

Activity Assessment

Use Exercises 5–8 to assess student understanding.

In Lesson 6.7 you learned rules for multiplying and dividing powers having the same base and positive integer exponents. If you extend these rules so that *any* integers may be used as exponents, you can justify the definitions of a^0 and a^{-n} stated on the previous page.

SAMPLE 2 Justifying the Definition of Zero Exponents

Use the product of powers rule to write a justification of the definition of a^0.

Here's How

Let m be an integer, and let a be any nonzero number.

$a^m \cdot a^0 = a^{m+0}$	Product of powers rule
$a^m \cdot a^0 = a^m$	Identity property of addition
$\frac{1}{a^m} \cdot (a^m \cdot a^0) = \frac{1}{a^m} \cdot a^m$	Multiplication property of equality
$\left(\frac{1}{a^m} \cdot a^m\right) \cdot a^0 = \frac{1}{a^m} \cdot a^m$	Associative property of multiplication
$1 \cdot a^0 = 1$	Inverse property of multiplication
$a^0 = 1$	Identity property of multiplication

Try These

9. MATHEMATICAL REASONING Justify the definition of a^{-n} by giving a reason for each step. **See margin.**

Let n be an integer, and let a be any nonzero number.

$a^{-n} \cdot a^n = a^{-n+n}$	a. ___?___
$a^{-n} \cdot a^n = a^0$	b. ___?___
$a^{-n} \cdot a^n = 1$	c. ___?___
$(a^{-n} \cdot a^n) \cdot \frac{1}{a^n} = 1 \cdot \frac{1}{a^n}$	d. ___?___
$a^{-n} \cdot \left(a^n \cdot \frac{1}{a^n}\right) = 1 \cdot \frac{1}{a^n}$	e. ___?___
$a^{-n} \cdot 1 = 1 \cdot \frac{1}{a^n}$	f. ___?___
$a^{-n} = \frac{1}{a^n}$	g. ___?___

a. Product of powers rule
b. Inverse property of addition
c. Definition of zero exponenents
d. Multiplication property of equality
e. Associative property of multiplication
f. Inverse property of multiplication
g. Identity property of multiplication

6.8 Negative and Zero Exponents

California Standards

In this lesson you'll:

- Understand negative whole number exponents. (NS 2.1)
- Use measures expressed as products to solve problems and check the units of solutions. (MG 1.3)

Goal 1 Defining Negative and Zero Exponents

As you learned in Developing Concepts 6.8, page 303, zero and negative exponents are defined as follows.

Definition of Zero Exponent For any number $a \neq 0$, $a^0 = 1$.

Definition of Negative Exponent For any integer n and any number $a \neq 0$, a^{-n} is the reciprocal of a^n.

That is, $a^{-n} = \frac{1}{a^n}$.

Another way to write a^{-n} is $\left(\frac{1}{a}\right)^n$. You will prove this in Exercise 58.

To evaluate an expression involving negative or zero exponents, use the definitions above.

Student Help

Study Tip
Remember, two numbers are multiplicative inverses if their product is 1. For example, 4 and $\frac{1}{4}$ are multiplicative inverses because $4 \cdot \frac{1}{4} = 1$.

Example 1 Simplifying Numerical Expressions

Simplify the expression.

a. 2^{-4} **b.** $\left(\frac{2}{3}\right)^{-3}$ **c.** $\left(\frac{1}{5}\right)^0$

Solution

a. $2^{-4} = \frac{1}{2^4}$ Definition of negative exponent: $a^{-n} = \frac{1}{a^n}$.

$= \frac{1}{16}$ Evaluate power.

b. Use the definition $a^{-n} = \left(\frac{1}{a}\right)^n$. To simplify $\left(\frac{2}{3}\right)^{-3}$ let $a = \frac{2}{3}$, so $\frac{1}{a} = 1 \div \frac{2}{3} = 1 \cdot \frac{3}{2} = \frac{3}{2}$, which is the reciprocal of $\frac{2}{3}$.

$\left(\frac{2}{3}\right)^{-3} = \left(\frac{3}{2}\right)^3$ Definition of negative exponent: $a^{-n} = \left(\frac{1}{a}\right)^n$.

$= \frac{3}{2} \cdot \frac{3}{2} \cdot \frac{3}{2}$ Definition of exponent.

$= \frac{27}{8}$ Simplify.

c. $\left(\frac{1}{5}\right)^0 = 1$ Definition of zero exponent.

1 Plan

Pacing

Suggested Number of Days

Transitional: 1 day
Average: 1 day
Advanced: 1 day
Block Schedule: 0.5 block with 6.9

Teaching Resources

Blacklines
(See page 266B.)

Transparencies
- Warm-Up Exercises
- Teacher Time-Savers
- English/Spanish Problem Solving
- Answers

Technology
- Electronic Teacher Tools
- Test and Practice Generator

2 Teach

Math Reasoning

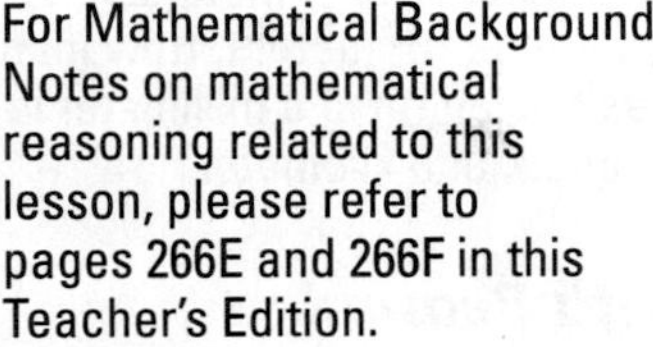

For Mathematical Background Notes on mathematical reasoning related to this lesson, please refer to pages 266E and 266F in this Teacher's Edition.

Extra Example 1
See next page.

California Standards and Assessment

CA Standards: NS 2.1, MG 1.3
CA Key Concepts Book: pp. S20–S21

Extra Example 1

Simplify each expression.

a. 5^{-2} $\frac{1}{25}$

b. -2^{-3} $-\frac{1}{8}$

c. $\left(\frac{1}{5}\right)^{-2}$ 25

d. $\left(\frac{13}{14}\right)^{0}$ 1

Extra Example 2

Simplify each expression.

a. a^{-2} $\frac{1}{a^2}$

b. $3x^0$ 3

c. $-2y^{-3}$ $\frac{-2}{y^3}$

Extra Example 3

Rewrite each expression using a prime base raised to a negative power.

a. $\frac{1}{27}$ 3^{-3}

b. $\frac{3}{x}$ $3x^{-1}$

Extra Example 4

A millimeter is 10^{-3} meters. A kilometer is 10^3 meters. How many times the length of a millimeter is the length of a kilometer? **10^6**

Math Reasoning

Example 4 and exercises similar to Exercises 46 and 47 on page 307 prepare the student for the study of scientific notation in the next lesson.

Concept Check

Is the value of an expression with a negative exponent always a negative number? Explain. **No, the negative exponent indicates that the power is the reciprocal of the power with the opposite (positive) exponent. The value of the expression may be positive or negative.**

To simplify a variable expression, rewrite the expression with positive exponents.

Student Help

STUDY TIP
In expressions such as $3x^2$ and $4y^{-5}$, the exponent is associated only with the variable.

EXAMPLE 2 Simplifying Variable Expressions

Simplify the expression.

a. $x^{-1} = \frac{1}{x^1} = \frac{1}{x}$ — Definition of negative exponent.

b. $-4n^0 = -4(n^0)$ — Exponent applies only to n.

$= -4 \cdot 1 = -4$ — Definition of zero exponent.

c. $3b^{-2} = 3(b^{-2})$ — Exponent applies only to b.

$= 3\left(\frac{1}{b^2}\right) = \frac{3}{b^2}$ — Definition of negative exponent.

Goal 2 USING NEGATIVE EXPONENTS

EXAMPLE 3 Rewriting Fractions using Negative Exponents

Rewrite the fraction as an expression using negative exponents. When a fraction contains numbers, write these numbers using a prime base raised to a power.

a. $-\frac{1}{16} = -\frac{1}{2^4}$ — Rewrite 16 as 2^4.

$= -2^{-4}$ — Definition of negative exponent.

b. $\frac{2}{x^3} = 2x^{-3}$ — Definition of negative exponent.

Student Help

STUDY TIP
As you saw in Developing Concepts 6.8, page 303, the exponent rules you learned in Lesson 6.7 also apply to negative exponents.

EXAMPLE 4 Comparing Relative Measures

BIOLOGY A field mouse has a mass of about 10^{-2} kilograms. A rhinoceros has a mass of about 10^3 kilograms. About how many times greater is the mass of the rhinoceros to the mass of the mouse?

Solution

Divide the mass of the rhinoceros by the mass of the mouse.

$\frac{10^3}{10^{-2}} = 10^{3-(-2)}$ — Quotient of powers rule: $\frac{a^m}{a^n} = a^{m-n}$.

$= 10^{3+2} = 10^5$ — Simplify exponent.

ANSWER ▶ The mass of the rhinoceros is about 10^5, or 100,000 times greater than the mass of the mouse.

6.8 Exercises

Guided Practice

In Exercises 1–8, simplify the expression.

1. 7^{-2} $\frac{1}{49}$ **2.** -4^{-3} $-\frac{1}{64}$ **3.** $\left(\frac{1}{2}\right)^{-5}$ 32 **4.** $\left(\frac{2}{5}\right)^{0}$ 1

5. x^{-2} $\frac{1}{x^2}$ **6.** $3a^{-3}$ $\frac{3}{a^3}$ **7.** $-2y^{-2}$ $-\frac{2}{y^2}$ **8.** $5x^0$ 5

9. *Sample answer:* $a^{-n} = \frac{1}{a^n}$, $\left(\frac{1}{a}\right)^{-n} = a^n$, and $a^0 = 1$ as long as $a \neq 0$.

9. WRITING In your own words give definitions for negative integer exponents and zero exponents. See margin.

Rewrite the fraction using prime bases raised to powers.

10. $\frac{1}{9}$ 3^{-2} **11.** $\frac{1}{36}$ $2^{-2} \cdot 3^{-2}$ **12.** $-\frac{1}{4}$ -2^{-2} **13.** $-\frac{1}{100}$ $-2^{-2} \cdot 5^{-2}$

Practice and Problem Solving

Student Help

▶**More Practice**
Extra practice to help you master skills is on page 701.

Simplify the expression.

14. 3^{-2} $\frac{1}{9}$ **15.** -10^{-3} $-\frac{1}{1000}$ **16.** 16^0 1 **17.** $(-9)^2$ 81

18. $(-3)^{-4}$ $\frac{1}{81}$ **19.** $(-6)^0$ 1 **20.** $\left(\frac{4}{5}\right)^{-2}$ $\frac{25}{16}$ **21.** $\left(\frac{3}{9}\right)^0$ 1

22. t^{-4} $\frac{1}{t^4}$ **23.** $2x^{-3}$ $\frac{2}{x^3}$ **24.** $3s^{-2}$ $\frac{3}{s^2}$ **25.** r^0 1

26. $-x^{-3}$ $-\frac{1}{x^3}$ **27.** $-3x^{-2}$ $-\frac{3}{x^2}$ **28.** $5y^0$ 5 **29.** xy^{-3} $\frac{x}{y^3}$

Rewrite the expression using a prime base raised to a power.

30. $\frac{1}{8}$ 

31. $-\frac{1}{125}$ -5^{-3} **32.** $-\frac{1}{3}$ -3^{-1} **33.** $\frac{1}{1024}$ 2^{-10}

34. $\frac{x}{343}$ 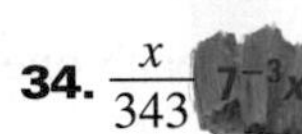

35. $-\frac{1}{121}$ -11^{-2} **36.** $\frac{5}{625}$ 5^{-3} **37.** $-\frac{3}{243}$ -3^{-4}

In Exercises 38–45, rewrite the expression using a negative exponent.

38. $\frac{1}{c^7}$ 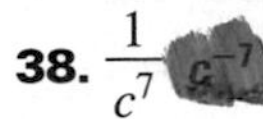

39. $\frac{1}{x^5}$ x^{-5} **40.** $\frac{1}{-(y^3)}$ 

41. $\frac{-1}{x^{10}}$ 

42. $\frac{1}{a}$ 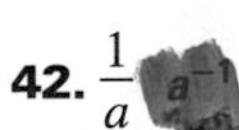

43. $\frac{5}{x^5}$ $5x^{-5}$ **44.** $\frac{12}{z^0}$ 12 **45.** $\frac{2^2}{x^2}$ 2^2x^{-2}

46. **Science Link** The diameter of a hydrogen atom is about 0.000000001 centimeter. Write this number as a fraction and then as a power of 10. $\frac{1}{1,000,000,000}$, 10^{-9}

47. **Science Link** A microsecond is 1 millionth of a second. Write the missing number in the equation below as a fraction and then as a power of 10. $\frac{1}{1,000,000}$, 10^{-6}

1 microsecond = **?** second

Link to Science

ELECTRON MICROSCOPES use a beam of electrons to magnify objects up to 1 million times their original size.

More about electron microscopes available at www.mcdougallittell.com

3 Apply

Assignment Guide

Transitional
Day 1: pp. 307–308 Exs. 14–25, 30–33, 38–41, 48–49, 52–53, 59–60

Average
Day 1: pp. 307–308 Exs. 18–29, 30–33, 38–41, 46–49, 52–53, 56, 59–60

Advanced
Day 1: pp. 307–308 Exs. 18–29, 34–37, 42–45, 50–53, 56–57, 58*, 59–60

Block Schedule
pp. 307–308 Exs. 18–29, 30–33, 38–41, 46–49, 52–53, 56, 59–60 (with 6.9)

Extra Practice

- Student Edition, pp. 700–701
- Chapter 6 Resource Book, p. 69

Homework Check

To quickly check student understanding of key concepts, go over the following exercises:

Transitional: 16, 20, 24, 32, 40, 52
Average: 18, 20, 24, 32, 40, 56
Advanced: 18, 20, 24, 36, 42, 56

Teaching Tip

In Exercises 14–29, remind students that a negative exponent does not cause the resulting expression to be negative. A negative coefficient, or a negative base raised to an odd power, will cause the resulting expression to be negative.

4 Assess

Assessment Resources

- Assessment Book (Formal Assessment and Alternative Assessment)
- Test and Practice Generator

Mini-Quiz

Simplify each expression.

1. 7^{-2} $\frac{1}{49}$
2. $\left(\frac{-1}{3}\right)^{-2}$ 9
3. $8a^0$ 8
4. $2x^{-4}$ $\frac{2}{x^4}$
5. Rewrite $\frac{1}{81}$ using a prime base raised to a negative exponent. 3^{-4}
6. A centimeter is 10^{-2} meters and a hectometer is 10^2 meters. How many times the length of a centimeter is the length of a hectometer? 10^4

58. $\left(\frac{1}{a}\right)^n = \frac{1}{a} \cdot \frac{1}{a} \cdot \ldots \cdot \frac{1}{a}$ **Definition of exponent**

$= \frac{1}{a \cdot a \cdot \ldots \cdot a}$ **Mult. of fractions**

$= \frac{1}{a^n}$ **Definition of exponent**

$= a^{-n}$ **Definition of neg. exponent**

48. $120 \frac{m}{sec} \cdot 5.6$ sec, 672 m

49. $15 \frac{lb}{ft} \cdot 24$ ft, 360 lb

50. $43 \frac{m}{sec^2} \cdot 8$ sec, 344 m/sec

51. $3600 \frac{sec}{h} \cdot 2.5$ h, 9000 sec

Link to Computers

COMPUTER SPEEDS
In 1950, a computer called ENIAC could add 5000 numbers in a second. Today's fastest computers can perform over 12 trillion calculations per second.

More about computer speeds available at www.mcdougallittell.com

In Exercises 48–51, write the expression using fractions instead of negative exponents, then evaluate the expression. 48–51. See margin.

EXAMPLE ***Units of Measure***

Evaluate the expression $50 \text{ mi} \cdot \text{h}^{-1} \times 3 \text{ h}$.

Solution

A unit of measure written using a negative exponent, such as $\text{mi} \cdot \text{h}^{-1}$ can be written as a fraction: $\text{mi} \cdot \text{h}^{-1} = \frac{\text{mi}}{\text{h}}$.

$$50 \text{ mi} \cdot \text{h}^{-1} \times 3 \text{ h} = 50 \frac{\text{mi}}{\cancel{\text{h}}} \cdot 3 \cancel{\text{h}} = 150 \text{ mi}$$

48. $120 \text{ m} \cdot \text{sec}^{-1} \times 5.6 \text{ sec}$

49. $15 \text{ lb} \cdot \text{ft}^{-1} \times 24 \text{ ft}$

50. $43 \text{ m} \cdot \text{sec}^{-2} \times 8 \text{ sec}$

51. $3600 \text{ sec} \cdot \text{h}^{-1} \times 2.5 \text{ h}$

Science Link **In Exercises 52–55, use the fact that the mass of a house spider is about 10^{-4} kilogram. About how many times greater is the mass of the given animal compared with the mass of a house spider?**

52. Evening bat: 10^{-3} kg 10 times greater

53. Black bear: 10^2 kg 1,000,000 times greater

54. Giraffe: 10^3 kg 10,000,000 times greater

55. Blue whale: 10^5 kg 1,000,000,000 times greater

56. COMPUTERS Many computers are so fast that their operation is measured in terms of nanoseconds and picoseconds. A nanosecond is 10^{-9} second. A picosecond is 10^{-12} second. How many picoseconds are in 1 nanosecond? 1000 picoseconds

57. MATHEMATICAL REASONING Explain whether $5x^2$ and $5x^{-2}$ are multiplicative inverses. Justify your answer. no; $5x^2 \cdot 5x^{-2} = (5 \cdot 5)x^2 \cdot x^{-2} = 25x^0 = 25(1) = 25 \neq 1$

58. CHALLENGE The following steps show that $\left(\frac{1}{a}\right)^n = a^{-n}$. Copy the steps and give a justification for each one. See margin.

$$\left(\frac{1}{a}\right)^n = \underbrace{\frac{1}{a} \cdot \frac{1}{a} \cdot \ldots \cdot \frac{1}{a}}_{n \text{ factors}} = \frac{1}{\underbrace{a \cdot a \cdot \ldots \cdot a}_{n \text{ factors}}} = \frac{1}{a^n} = a^{-n}$$

Multiple-Choice Practice

59. What is the multiplicative inverse of x^3? B

Ⓐ x^3 Ⓑ $\frac{1}{x^3}$ Ⓒ $\frac{1}{x^{-3}}$ Ⓓ $\frac{3}{x}$

60. Simplify the expression $4y^{-2}$. J

Ⓕ $2y$ Ⓖ $\frac{2}{y}$ Ⓗ $\frac{1}{4y^2}$ Ⓙ $\frac{4}{y^2}$

6.9 Scientific Notation

California Standards

In this lesson you'll:

- Read, write, and compare numbers in scientific notation. (NS 1.1)
- Simplify and evaluate expressions that include exponents. (AF 2.1)

Goal 1 WRITING SCIENTIFIC NOTATION

Numbers in real life can be very large or very small. For instance, the population of the world in 1998 was about 5,900,000,000. Instead of writing so many zeros, you can write

$$5{,}900{,}000{,}000 = 5.9 \times 1{,}000{,}000{,}000 = \mathbf{5.9 \times 10^9}$$

The form on the right is called *scientific notation.* A number is written in **scientific notation** if it has the form $c \times 10^n$, where c is greater than or equal to 1 and less than 10, and n is an integer.

Student Help

▶ STUDY TIP
You may find the following table of powers useful when you read and write numbers in scientific notation.

1000	10^3
100	10^2
10	10^1
1	10^0
0.1	10^{-1}
0.01	10^{-2}
0.001	10^{-3}

EXAMPLE 1 Reading Numbers in Scientific Notation

Write the number in decimal form.

a. 1.45×10^4 **b.** 2.07×10^{-5}

Solution

SCIENTIFIC NOTATION	PRODUCT FORM	DECIMAL FORM
a. 1.45×10^4	$1.45 \times 10{,}000$	14,500
b. 2.07×10^{-5}	2.07×0.00001	0.0000207

In Example 1 notice that the exponent of 10 tells you how many places to *move* the decimal point.

EXAMPLE 2 Writing Numbers in Scientific Notation

Write the number in scientific notation.

a. 0.00923 **b.** 73,000,000 **c.** $\frac{1}{8000}$

Solution

DECIMAL OR FRACTION FORM	PRODUCT FORM	SCIENTIFIC NOTATION
a. 0.00923	9.23×0.001	9.23×10^{-3}
b. 73,000,000	$7.3 \times 10{,}000{,}000$	7.3×10^7
c. $\frac{1}{8000} = 0.000125$	1.25×0.0001	1.25×10^{-4}

1 Plan

Pacing

Suggested Number of Days

Transitional: 1 day
Average: 1 day
Advanced: 1 day
Block Schedule: 0.5 block with 6.8

Teaching Resources

Blacklines
(See page 266B.)

Transparencies
- Warm-Up Exercises
- Teacher Time-Savers
- English/Spanish Problem Solving
- Answers

Technology
- Electronic Teacher Tools
- Test and Practice Generator

2 Teach

Math Reasoning

For Mathematical Background Notes on mathematical reasoning related to this lesson, please refer to pages 266E and 266F in this Teacher's Edition.

Extra Examples 1 and 2
See next page.

California Standards and Assessment

CA Standards: NS 1.1, AF 2.1

Extra Example 1

Write the number in decimal form.

a. 8.27×10^5 **827,000**

b. 5.69×10^{-3} **0.00569**

Extra Example 2

Write the number in scientific notation.

a. 0.0000037 **3.7×10^{-6}**

b. 8,210,000,000 **8.21×10^9**

c. $\frac{1}{25,000}$ **4.0×10^{-5}**

Extra Example 3

You buy paper by the carton for the copy machine in your home office. The carton holds ten 500-sheet packages of paper in two stacks side by side. If each sheet of paper is 4.4×10^{-3} in. thick, how tall is each stack of 5 packages? **11 in.**

Extra Example 4

Put the numbers in order from least to greatest.

$3.6 \times 10^{-5}, 3.06 \times 10^{-4}, 3.61 \times 10^{-6}$

$3.61 \times 10^{-6}, 3.6 \times 10^{-5}, 3.06 \times 10^{-4}$

Teaching Tip

Most scientific calculators represent very small and very large numbers using scientific notation. For example, 3.2 E 5 represents 3.2×10^5, and 3.2 E −5 represents 3.2×10^{-5}. Numbers in scientific notation can be easily entered using a button usually labeled E or EE.

Concept Check

You are given a number that is written as a decimal number times a power of 10. Is this number in scientific notation? Explain. **Not necessarily; the number is in scientific notation only if the decimal number is greater than or equal to 1 and less than 10.**

Goal 2 Using Scientific Notation

EXAMPLE 3 Multiplying with Scientific Notation

You work in a warehouse that stores recycled paper. Each sheet of paper is 4.4×10^{-3} inches thick. The paper comes in packages of 500 sheets. Disregarding the package wrap, estimate the height of a stack of 5 packages.

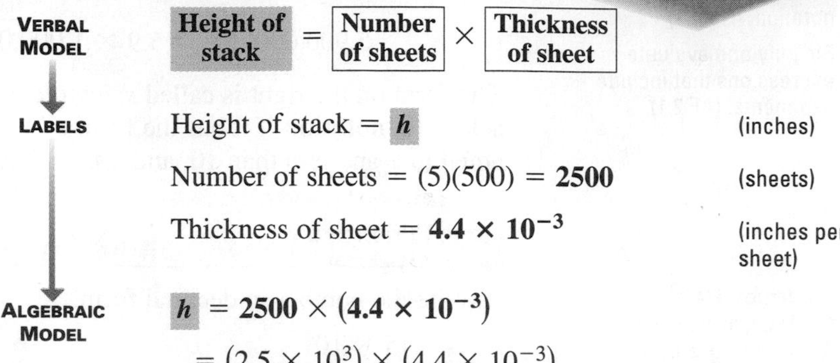

Solution

VERBAL MODEL: Height of stack = Number of sheets × Thickness of sheet

LABELS:

Height of stack = h (inches)

Number of sheets = (5)(500) = **2500** (sheets)

Thickness of sheet = **4.4×10^{-3}** (inches per sheet)

ALGEBRAIC MODEL:

$$h = \mathbf{2500} \times (\mathbf{4.4 \times 10^{-3}})$$
$$= (2.5 \times 10^3) \times (4.4 \times 10^{-3})$$
$$= (2.5 \times 4.4) \times (10^3 \times 10^{-3})$$
$$= 11 \times 10^0$$
$$= 11 \times 1$$
$$= 11$$

ANSWER ▶ The stack of 5 packages is about 11 inches high.

> **Student Help**
>
> ▶ **STUDY TIP**
> To multiply two numbers written in scientific notation, you can use the rule for multiplying powers with the same base.

EXAMPLE 4 Comparing Numbers in Scientific Notation

Order the numbers from least to greatest.

1.2×10^{-4}, 1.02×10^{-4}, 1.2×10^{-5}

Solution

Begin by writing each number in decimal form. It helps to line up decimal points, and compare the digits in each place.

$1.2 \times 10^{-4} = 0.00012$

$1.02 \times 10^{-4} = 0.000102$

$1.2 \times 10^{-5} = 0.000012$

ANSWER ▶ In decimal form, you can see that the order from least to greatest is 1.2×10^{-5}, 1.02×10^{-4}, 1.2×10^{-4}.

6.9 Exercises

Guided Practice

1. A. no; 12.3 > 10
B. Yes; the number is between 1 and 10, times a power of 10.
C. no; 0.123 < 1

1. Tell which of the following is written in scientific notation. Explain your answer. **See margin.**

A. 12.3×10^3 **B.** 1.23×10^4 **C.** 0.123×10^5

Find the missing exponent.

2. $350{,}000 = 3.5 \times 10^{?}$ **5** **3.** $0.00943 = 9.43 \times 10^{?}$ **−3**

Write the number in decimal form.

4. 6.25×10^5 **625,000** **5.** 8.7×10^{-6} **0.0000087** **6.** 1.365×10^{-3} **0.001365**

Write the number in scientific notation.

7. 870,000 **8.7×10^5** **8.** 0.000531 **5.31×10^{-4}** **9.** $\frac{3}{320}$ **9.375×10^{-3}**

10. POPULATION One of the following is the approximate 1998 population of China. The other is the approximate 1998 population of Canada. China has a greater population than Canada. Tell which is the population of China and which is the population of Canada.

a. 3.1×10^7 **Canada** **b.** 1.2×10^9 **China**

Practice and Problem Solving

Student Help

▶ More Practice
Extra practice to help you master skills is on page 701.

Write the number in scientific notation.

11. 100,000 1×10^5 **12.** 643,000 6.43×10^5 **13.** 0.00041 4.1×10^{-4} **14.** 0.18 1.8×10^{-1}

15. 32,610,000 3.261×10^7 **16.** 5,730,000,000 5.73×10^9 **17.** 0.000000012 1.2×10^{-8} **18.** 0.000008 8×10^{-6}

19. 0.006987 6.987×10^{-3} **20.** 563×10^3 5.63×10^5 **21.** 2 2×10^0 **22.** 5,472,300 5.4723×10^6

Write the number in decimal form.

23. 5.7×10^{-3} 0.0057 **24.** 3.41×10^{-6} 0.00000341 **25.** 2.50×10^4 25,000 **26.** 2.4×10^9 2,400,000,000

27. 6.3×10^8 630,000,000 **28.** 4.002×10^{-2} 0.04002 **29.** 5.16×10^5 516,000 **30.** 3.2×10^{-3} 0.0032

31. 9.86×10^3 9860 **32.** 2.0×10^1 20 **33.** 7.6×10^0 7.6 **34.** 8.5×10^{-1} 0.85

Tell whether the number is in scientific notation. If it is not, rewrite the number in scientific notation.

35. 5.3×10^{-5} yes **36.** 0.392×10^6 no; 3.92×10^5 **37.** 25.6×10^8 no; 2.56×10^9

38. 76.0×10^2 no; 7.6×10^3 **39.** 4.62×10^0 yes **40.** 0.8×10^{-1} no; 8×10^{-2}

41. 10.0×10^3 no; 1×10^4 **42.** 4.56×10^{-3} yes **43.** 76×10^{10} no; 7.6×10^{11}

3 Apply

Assignment Guide

Transitional
Day 1: pp. 311–313 Exs. 11–14, 23–26, 35–37, 44–45, 50–52, 58–59, 62–63, 69–73, 80–83

Average
Day 1: pp. 311–313 Exs. 15–18, 27–30, 38–40, 46–47, 50–52, 58–59, 63–64, 69–74, 80–83

Advanced
Day 1: pp. 311–313 Exs. 19–22, 31–34, 41–43, 48–49, 53–55, 60, 65–67, 68*, 69–74, 85–87

Block Schedule
pp. 311–313 Exs. 15–18, 27–30, 38–40, 46–47, 50–52, 58–59, 63–64, 69–74, 80–83 (with 6.8)

Extra Practice

- Student Edition, pp. 700–701
- Chapter 6 Resource Book, p. 78

Homework Check

To quickly check student understanding of key concepts, go over the following exercises:

Transitional: 12, 14, 24, 26, 58, 62
Average: 16, 18, 28, 58, 64
Advanced: 22, 34, 48, 60, 65

Math Reasoning

In converting $c \times 10^n$ to decimal form, as in Exercises 23–34, the decimal point is moved n places *to the right* if n is a positive integer and $|n|$ places *to the left* if n is a negative integer.

54. $\frac{(3.1 \times 10^{-4})(5.9 \times 10^{1})}{6.8 \times 10^{-3}}$;

2.69×10^{0}, 2.69

55. $\frac{(1 \times 10^{-3})(6.7 \times 10^{-4})}{}$;

8.86×10^{-2}, 0.0886

Evaluate the product. Write the result in scientific notation and in decimal form.

44. $(6.2 \times 10^2)(8 \times 10^3)$ 4.96×10^6, 4,960,000

45. $(4.5 \times 10^{-3})(3.4 \times 10^5)$ 1.53×10^3, 1530

46. $(2.3 \times 10^3)(1.9 \times 10^6)$ 4.37×10^9, 4,370,000,000

47. $(7.62 \times 10^{-2})(4.3 \times 10^{-6})$ 3.2766×10^{-7}, 0.00000032766

48. $(9.01 \times 10^{-1})(5.46 \times 10^7)$ 4.91946×10^7, 49,194,600

49. $(8.12 \times 10^4)(6.7 \times 10^{-3})$ 5.4404×10^2, 544.04

Convert each number in the expression to scientific notation. Then simplify and write the result in scientific notation and decimal form.
51–55. See margin.

50. $(30{,}000)(0.0006)$ $(3 \times 10^4)(6 \times 10^{-4})$; 1.8×10^1; 18

51. $\frac{(97{,}000)(240)}{0.25}$

52. $\frac{(0.0037)(0.0026)}{(120{,}000)(0.12)}$

53. $(520)(0.000867)$

54. $\frac{(0.00031)(59)}{0.0068}$

55. $\frac{(0.001)(0.00067)}{(0.0084)(0.0009)}$

Student Help

▶ **STUDY TIP**
In Exercises 50–55 you can use properties and the rules for multiplying and dividing powers with like bases to help find the result.

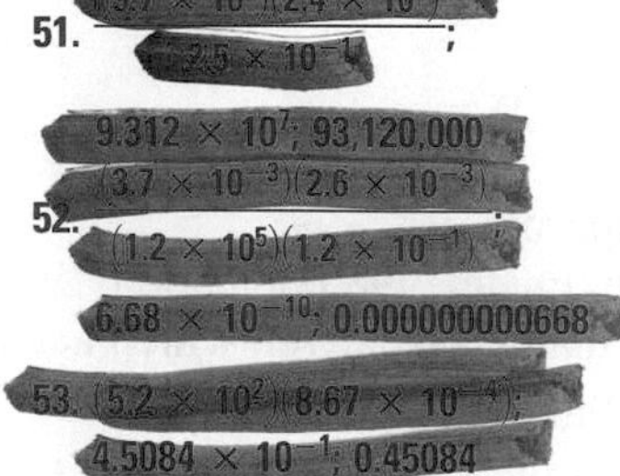

51. $\frac{(9.7 \times 10^4)(2.4 \times 10^2)}{2.5 \times 10^{-1}}$;
9.312×10^7; 93,120,000

52. $\frac{(3.7 \times 10^{-3})(2.6 \times 10^{-3})}{(1.2 \times 10^5)(1.2 \times 10^{-1})}$;
6.68×10^{-10}; 0.000000000668

53. $(5.2 \times 10^2)(8.67 \times 10^{-4})$;
4.5084×10^{-1}; 0.45084

In Exercises 56 and 57, write the number in scientific notation.

56. A thunderstorm cloud holds about 6,000,000,000,000 raindrops. 6×10^{12}

57. The adult human body contains about 100,000,000,000,000 cells. 1×10^{14}

In Exercises 58–60, order the numbers from least to greatest.

58. 3.4×10^{-4}, 3.4×10^{-5}, 3.4×10^{-6} 3.4×10^{-6}, 3.4×10^{-5}, 3.4×10^{-4}

59. 4.56×10^5, 4.65×10^5, 4.50×10^6, 4.60×10^4 4.6×10^4, 4.56×10^5, 4.65×10^5, 4.5×10^6

60. 7.89×10^{-3}, 7.98×10^{-2}, 7.90×10^{-4}, 7.98×10^3 7.9×10^{-4}, 7.89×10^{-3}, 7.98×10^{-2}, 7.98×10^3

Link to Music

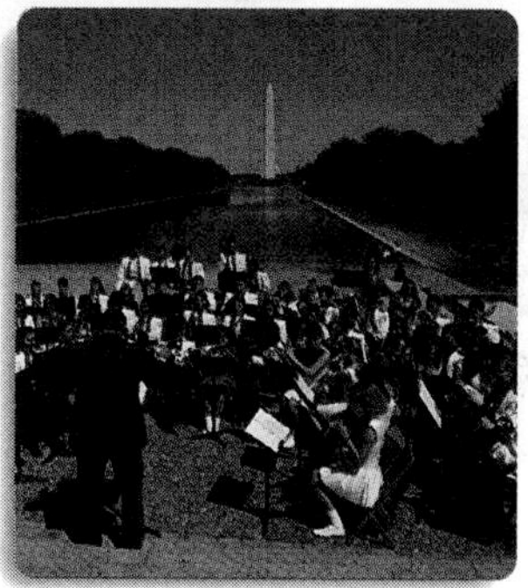

MUSIC About 44% of former and current musicians first learned to play a musical instrument in school.

61. MUSICAL INSTRUMENTS The table shows the number of people in the United States who play the five most popular instruments. Rewrite the table so the numbers are in decimal form. 82,000,000; 45,000,000; 15,000,000; 12,000,000; 12,000,000

Instrument	Piano	Guitar	Flute	Drums	Clarinet
Number	8.2×10^7	4.5×10^7	1.5×10^7	1.2×10^7	1.2×10^7

62. **Science Link** A white blood cell with a diameter of 6.0×10^{-4} centimeters is magnified 1×10^5 times. What is the magnified diameter? Express your answer in scientific notation. 6.0×10^1

63. ASTRONOMY The sun has a diameter of 1.39×10^6 kilometers. The diameter of Earth is 1.28×10^4 kilometers. How many times larger is the sun's diameter than the Earth's diameter? Express your answer in scientific notation. 1.09×10^2

64. ASTRONOMY The star Canis Majoris is about 2.7×10^3 light-years from Earth. A light-year is 5.88×10^{12} miles. Write 2.7×10^3 light-years in miles. about 1.59×10^{16} mi

65. GOVERNMENT In September 1998 the national debt was 5.5×10^{12} dollars, and the United States population was 2.7×10^8. What average amount per person did the government owe in 1998? Express your answer in scientific notation and in decimal form. 2.04×10^4 dollars/person, $20,400/person

MATHEMATICAL REASONING **In Exercises 66 and 67, explain how you can decide which number is greater without writing the numbers as decimals.** **66–67. See margin.**

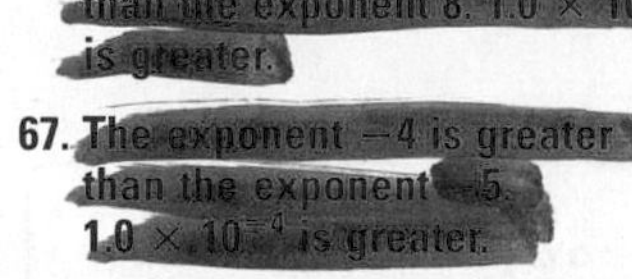

66. The exponent 9 is greater than the exponent 8. 1.0×10^9 is greater.

67. The exponent -4 is greater than the exponent -5. 1.0×10^{-4} is greater.

66. 1.0×10^9 or 9.0×10^8 **67.** 5.0×10^{-5} or 1.0×10^{-4}

68. CHALLENGE The energy corresponding to the mass of an electron is given by the equation $E = mc^2$. In this equation, c is the speed of light, 3.00×10^8 meters per second. The mass m of an electron is 9.11×10^{-31} kilograms. Calculate the energy corresponding to the mass of one electron. 8.20×10^{-14}

Multiple-Choice Practice

69. What is 0.00000456 written in scientific notation? C

Ⓐ 4.56×10^{-4} Ⓑ 4.56×10^{-5} Ⓒ 4.56×10^{-6} Ⓓ 4.56×10^{-7}

70. What is the area of the rectangle? G

Ⓕ 35.28×10^6 Ⓖ 3.528×10^6

Ⓗ 12.6×10^5 Ⓙ 3.528×10^5

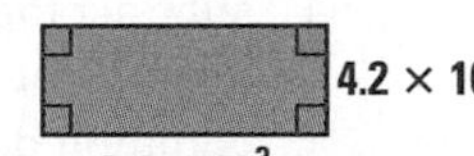

Not drawn to scale

Mixed Review

In Exercises 71–76, complete each statement using < or >. *(3.1)*

71. 0 ? −3 **72.** 5 ? −1 **73.** −8 ? −6

74. |−6| ? 5 **75.** |7| ? −2 **76.** |−10| ? |−11|

In Exercises 77–79, use the table which shows the average number of acres per farm in the United States. *(3.9)*

Year	1910	1920	1930	1940	1950	1960	1970	1980	1990
Acres per farm	139	149	157	175	216	297	373	426	460

77. Make a scatter plot of the data. **See margin.**

78. Determine whether the data shows a *positive correlation*, a *negative correlation*, or *no obvious correlation*. positive correlation

79. Draw a line that shows the trend in the data. Use your line to estimate the average number of acres per farm in 2000. about 500 acres per farm

Simplify the expression. *(5.4)*

80. $\frac{20}{25}$ $\frac{4}{5}$ **81.** $\frac{14}{27}$ $\frac{14}{27}$ **82.** $\frac{35}{14}$ $\frac{5}{2}$ **83.** $\frac{102}{200}$ $\frac{51}{100}$

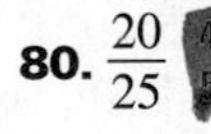

84. $\frac{2x}{4}$ $\frac{x}{2}$ **85.** $\frac{x^3}{x^2}$ x **86.** $\frac{x^4y^2}{x^3y}$ xy **87.** $\frac{15x^2y^2}{5xy^2}$ $3x$

4 Assess

Assessment Resources

- Assessment Book (Formal Assessment and Alternative Assessment)
- Test and Practice Generator

Mini-Quiz

Write the number in scientific notation.

1. 0.00034 3.4×10^{-4}
2. 34,000,000 3.4×10^7

Write the number in decimal form.

3. 3.51×10^5 351,000
4. 2.9×10^{-9} 0.0000000029
5. It is estimated that human hair grows at a rate of about 1×10^{-8} miles per hour. There are 6.336×10^4 in. in a mile. Find the rate of growth of human hair in inches per hour by multiplying $(1 \times 10^{-8}) \cdot (6.336 \times 10^4)$. 6.336×10^{-4} or 0.0006336 in./h

77, 79.

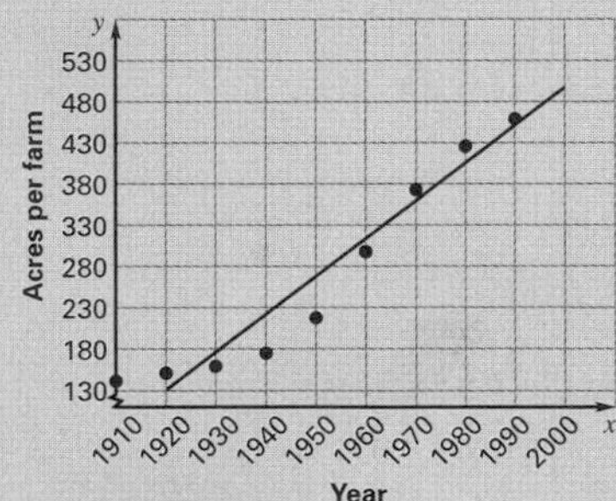

Additional Resources

The following resources are available to help review the material in this chapter:

Technology

- Personal Student Tutor
- Test and Practice Generator

Chapter Summary and Review

VOCABULARY

- **least common denominator,** *p. 273*
- **multiplicative inverses,** *p. 279*
- **reciprocals,** *p. 279*
- **inverse property of multiplication,** *p. 279*
- **zero exponent,** *p. 305*
- **negative exponent,** *p. 305*
- **scientific notation,** *p. 309*

6.1 ADDING AND SUBTRACTING FRACTIONS

Examples on pp. 269–270

To add or subtract fractions with a common denominator, add or subtract the numerators and use the common denominator. If the denominators are different, you can rewrite the fractions so that their common denominator is the product of the original denominators.

EXAMPLE **Find the difference $\frac{6}{7} - \frac{7}{12}$. Then simplify, if possible.**

$$\frac{6}{7} - \frac{7}{12} = \frac{6 \cdot 12}{7 \cdot 12} - \frac{7 \cdot 7}{12 \cdot 7}$$ The common denominator is 84.

$$= \frac{72}{84} - \frac{49}{84} = \frac{23}{84}$$ Simplify.

Add or subtract. Then simplify, if possible.

1. $\frac{19}{25} + \frac{24}{25}$ **$\frac{43}{25}$ or $1\frac{18}{25}$**
2. $1\frac{1}{3} - \frac{2}{3}$ **$\frac{2}{3}$**
3. $\frac{12y}{7} - \frac{10y}{7}$ **$\frac{2y}{7}$**
4. $\frac{1}{2} + \frac{1}{6}$ **$\frac{2}{3}$**
5. $\frac{5}{6} + \frac{2}{5}$ **$\frac{37}{30}$ or $1\frac{7}{30}$**
6. $1\frac{2}{3} - \frac{11}{12}$ **$\frac{3}{4}$**
7. $-\frac{9}{14} - \frac{11}{24}$ **$-\frac{185}{168}$ or $-1\frac{17}{168}$**
8. $\frac{2x}{4} + \left(-\frac{4x}{10}\right)$ **$\frac{x}{10}$**

6.2 USING A LEAST COMMON DENOMINATOR

Examples on pp. 273–274

The least common denominator (LCD) of two fractions is the least common multiple of their denominators.

EXAMPLE **Find the sum $-\frac{8}{9} + \frac{7}{15}$. Then simplify, if possible.**

$$-\frac{8}{9} + \frac{7}{15} = -\frac{8 \cdot 5}{9 \cdot 5} + \frac{3 \cdot 7}{3 \cdot 15}$$ The LCM of 9 and 15 is 45.

$$= \frac{-40 + 21}{45} = -\frac{19}{45}$$ Simplify numerator.

Add or subtract. Then simplify, if possible.

9. $\frac{1}{6} + \frac{4}{9}$ **$\frac{11}{18}$** **10.** $-\frac{2}{9} + \frac{5}{12}$ **$\frac{7}{36}$** **11.** $2\frac{1}{4} - 1\frac{1}{2}$ **$\frac{3}{4}$** **12.** $\frac{8}{15} + \left(-\frac{7}{9}\right)$ **$-\frac{11}{45}$**

13. $\frac{11}{14} - \left(-\frac{16}{21}\right)$ **$\frac{65}{42}$ or $1\frac{23}{42}$** **14.** $-3\frac{3}{8} - 2\frac{5}{6}$ **$-6\frac{5}{24}$** **15.** $\frac{1}{4} + \frac{1}{8} + \frac{1}{12}$ **$\frac{11}{24}$** **16.** $2\frac{4}{5} - 3\frac{7}{10} + \frac{13}{15}$ **$-\frac{1}{30}$**

6.3 MULTIPLYING FRACTIONS

Examples on pp. 278–280

For rational numbers $\frac{a}{b}$ and $\frac{c}{d}$, where $b \neq 0$ and $d \neq 0$, $\frac{a}{b} \cdot \frac{c}{d} = \frac{a \cdot c}{b \cdot d}$.

EXAMPLE **Find the product $-3\frac{2}{5} \cdot 2\frac{1}{3}$. Then simplify, if possible.**

$-3\frac{2}{5} \cdot 2\frac{1}{3} = -\frac{17}{5} \cdot \frac{7}{3}$ Rewrite as improper fractions.

$= -\frac{17 \cdot 7}{5 \cdot 3}$ Multiply numerators and multiply denominators.

$= -\frac{119}{15}$, or $-7\frac{14}{15}$ Simplify.

In Exercises 17–20, multiply. Then simplify, if possible.

17. $-\frac{1}{9} \cdot \frac{3}{4}$ **$-\frac{1}{12}$** **18.** $2\frac{2}{5} \cdot \left(-3\frac{1}{2}\right)$ **$-\frac{42}{5}$ or $-8\frac{2}{5}$** **19.** $\frac{4x}{5} \cdot 15$ **$12x$** **20.** $-\frac{11h}{15} \cdot \left(-\frac{5}{3}\right)$ **$\frac{11h}{9}$**

21. Find the area of the rectangle. **$\frac{55}{12}$m² or $4\frac{7}{12}$m²**

6.4 MULTIPLYING WITH PERCENTS

Examples on pp. 283–284

To multiply with percents, use either the decimal or the fraction equivalent.

EXAMPLE **a. Find 75% of 120.** **b. Find 127% of 44.**

a. 75% of 120 $= \frac{3}{4} \cdot 120 = 90$ **b.** 127% of 44 $= 1.27 \cdot 44 = 55.88$

In Exercises 22–25, change the percent to a decimal or a fraction. Then evaluate.

22. 30% of 120 **36** **23.** 0.8% of 900 **7.2** **24.** $66\frac{2}{3}$% of 162 **108** **25.** 165% of 68 **112.2**

26. A stockbroker earns 3.75% commission on stock sales. Find the commission for selling shares of one stock for \$1,050,000, shares of another for \$480,000, and shares of a third for \$13,890. **\$39,375; \$18,000; \$520.88**

6.5 DIVIDING FRACTIONS

Examples on pp. 289–291

To divide by a rational number, multiply by its reciprocal.

EXAMPLE **a. Find the quotient $-\frac{6}{7} \div \frac{2}{5}$.** **b. Find the quotient $\frac{2x}{3} \div 4$.**

a. The reciprocal of $\frac{2}{5}$ is $\frac{5}{2}$.

$$-\frac{6}{7} \div \frac{2}{5} = -\frac{6}{7} \cdot \frac{5}{2}$$

$$= -\frac{30}{14}, \text{ or } -\frac{15}{7}$$

b. The reciprocal of 4 is $\frac{1}{4}$.

$$\frac{2x}{3} \div 4 = \frac{2x}{3} \cdot \frac{1}{4}$$

$$= \frac{2x}{12}, \text{ or } \frac{x}{6}$$

Divide. Then simplify, if possible.

27. $\frac{n}{5} \div \frac{2}{3}$ **$\frac{3n}{10}$**

28. $4\frac{1}{2} \div 2\frac{1}{4}$ **2**

29. $\frac{8}{9} \div \left(\frac{-2}{3}\right)$ **$-\frac{4}{3}$ or $-1\frac{1}{3}$**

30. $-\frac{2x}{7} \div \frac{x}{21}$ **−6**

6.6 SOLVING EQUATIONS WITH RATIONAL NUMBERS

Examples on pp. 294–296

When solving equations with rational numbers, use inverse operations just as you would with integers, until the variable is isolated on one side of the equation.

EXAMPLE **Solve the equation $\frac{1}{6} + \frac{3}{4}y = \frac{5}{6}$.**

$\frac{1}{6} + \frac{3}{4}y = \frac{5}{6}$	Write original equation.
$\frac{3}{4}y = \frac{2}{3}$	Subtract $\frac{1}{6}$ from each side.
$\frac{4}{3} \cdot \frac{3}{4}y = \frac{4}{3} \cdot \frac{2}{3}$	Multiply each side by the reciprocal of $\frac{3}{4}$.
$y = \frac{8}{9}$	Simplify. y is by itself.

Solve the equation. Check the solution.

31. $\frac{3}{4} - q = \frac{7}{8}$ **$-\frac{1}{8}$**

32. $\frac{16}{7} + \frac{2}{3}n = \frac{11}{14}$ **$-\frac{9}{4}$ or $-2\frac{1}{4}$**

33. $\frac{4}{3}x - \frac{4}{5} = \frac{5}{6}$ **$\frac{49}{40}$ or $1\frac{9}{40}$**

34. The area of the triangle is $\frac{17}{12}$ square units. Write an equation that allows you to solve for x. Then solve the equation. **$\frac{17}{15}$**

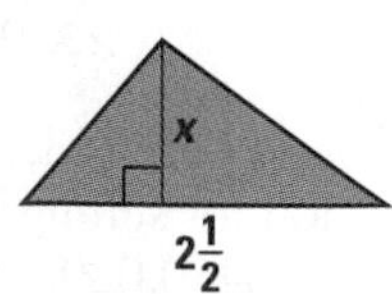

6.7 MULTIPLYING AND DIVIDING POWERS

Examples on pp. 299–300

To multiply powers with the same base, add their exponents. To divide powers with the same base, subtract the exponent of the denominator from the exponent of the numerator.

EXAMPLES $x^2 \cdot x^3 = x^{2+3} = x^5$ $\quad 2x \cdot 4x^3 = (2 \cdot 4)(x \cdot x^3) = 8x^{1+3} = 8x^4$

$\frac{4^7}{4^5} = 4^{7-5} = 4^2 = 16$ $\quad \frac{3y^5}{12y^2} = \frac{3 \cdot y^5}{12 \cdot y^2} = \frac{\cancel{3} \cdot y^{5-2}}{\cancel{3} \cdot 4} = \frac{y^3}{4}$

Simplify the expression.

35. $\left(\frac{2}{3}\right)^3 \cdot \left(\frac{2}{3}\right)^2$ $\left(\frac{2}{3}\right)^5$ **36.** $5y^2 \cdot 6y^4$ $30y^6$ **37.** $\frac{x^{10}}{x^4}$ x^6 **38.** $\frac{28a^4b}{42a^2}$ $\frac{2a^2b}{3}$

39. Write and simplify a numerical expression for the given phrase: *the quotient of seven raised to the fourth power and seven cubed.* $\frac{7^4}{7^3} = 7$

6.8 NEGATIVE AND ZERO EXPONENTS

Examples on pp. 305–308

For any integer n and nonzero number a, $a^{-n} = \frac{1}{a^n} = \left(\frac{1}{a}\right)^n$. Also, $a^0 = 1$.

EXAMPLES $2^{-5} = \frac{1}{2^5} = \frac{1}{32}$ $\quad \left(\frac{1}{4}\right)^{-3} = \left(\frac{4}{1}\right)^3 = 4^3 = 64$ $\quad \frac{1}{3}x^0 = \frac{1}{3} \cdot 1 = \frac{1}{3}$

Simplify the expression. Write your answer as a fraction in simplest form.

40. 3^{-2} $\frac{1}{9}$ **41.** $(-8)^{-2}$ $\frac{1}{64}$ **42.** $-\left(\frac{6}{x}\right)^{-4}$ $-\frac{x^4}{1296}$ **43.** x^{-5} $\frac{1}{x^5}$

44. $22x^{-4}$ $\frac{22}{x^4}$ **45.** $-5x^{-3}$ $-\frac{5}{x^3}$ **46.** $x^{-2}y^3$ $\frac{y^3}{x^2}$ **47.** $3y^0$ 3

6.9 SCIENTIFIC NOTATION

Examples on pp. 309–310

A number in scientific notation has the form $c \times 10^n$ for integer n, where $c \geq 1$ and $c < 10$.

EXAMPLES $2.2 \times 10^2 = 2.2 \times 100 = 220$ $\quad 0.0003 = 3.0 \times 0.0001 = 3.0 \times 10^{-4}$

Write the number in scientific notation.

48. 0.0896 8.96×10^{-2} **49.** 1,453,020 1.45302×10^6 **50.** 0.0000026 2.6×10^{-6} **51.** 87 8.7×10^1

52. 743,000 7.43×10^5 **53.** 0.00012 1.2×10^{-4} **54.** 11,203,000 1.1203×10^7 **55.** 0.0407 4.07×10^{-2}

Additional Resources

Assessment Book
- Formal Assessment, pp. 80–88
- Alternative Assessment, pp. 193–207

Test and Practice Generator

Chapter 6 Chapter Test

Add or subtract. Then simplify, if possible.

1. $-\frac{1}{5} + \frac{3}{5}$ [$\frac{2}{5}$] **2.** $\frac{11x}{12} - \frac{7x}{12}$ [$\frac{x}{3}$] **3.** $\frac{5}{6} + \frac{1}{10}$ [$\frac{14}{15}$] **4.** $\frac{11}{18} - 2\frac{2}{3}$ [$-\frac{37}{18}$]

MAIL In Exercises 5–7, use the circle graph which shows the makeup of the mail in the United States.

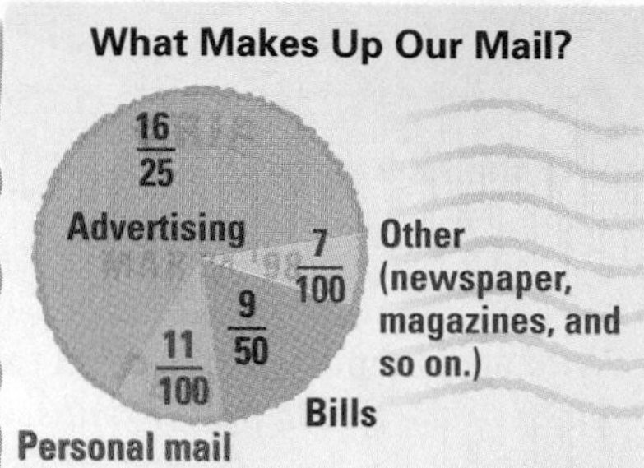

5. Find the sum of the portions representing personal mail and bills. [$\frac{29}{100}$]

6. Find the difference in the portions of mail that are advertising and personal mail. [$\frac{53}{100}$]

7. Find the sum of all the types of mail. Explain what your answer represents. [1; 100%, or all, types of mail have been included.]

Multiply or divide. Then simplify, if possible.

8. $\frac{4}{5} \cdot \frac{1}{2}$ [$\frac{2}{5}$] **9.** $\frac{4}{5} \div \left(\frac{-1}{2}\right)$ [$-\frac{8}{5}$ or $-1\frac{3}{5}$] **10.** $1\frac{1}{3} \cdot 1\frac{1}{2}$ [2] **11.** $-\frac{5s}{6} \div \frac{3s}{5}$  [$-\frac{25}{18}$ or $-1\frac{7}{18}$]

Change the percent to a decimal or a fraction. Then evaluate.

12. 58% of 30 [$0.58 \times 30 = 17.4$] **13.** 0.5% of 610 [$0.005 \times 610 = 3.05$] **14.** 126% of 25 [$1.26 \times 25 = 31.5$]

Solve the equation. Check the solution.

15. $\frac{7}{8} + y = \frac{5}{6}$ [$-\frac{1}{24}$] **16.** $\frac{9}{8}x - \frac{5}{6} = -\frac{2}{3}$ [$\frac{4}{27}$] **17.** $\frac{1}{8}x + \frac{3}{2} = \frac{5}{12}$ [$-\frac{26}{3}$ or $-8\frac{2}{3}$]

18. $\frac{4}{5}x = \frac{1}{9}$ [$\frac{5}{36}$] **19.** $1\frac{3}{4} + 6y = \frac{2}{7}$ [$-\frac{41}{168}$] **20.** $-\frac{11}{6}y - \frac{2}{9} = \frac{7}{12}$ [$-\frac{29}{66}$]

Simplify the expression.

21. $2z^4 \cdot 6z^2$ [$12z^6$] **22.** $\frac{8y^8}{20y^7}$ [$\frac{2y}{5}$] **23.** $(-2)^{-3}$ [$-\frac{1}{8}$] **24.** $a^{-2}b^2$ [$\frac{b^2}{a^2}$]

ASTRONOMY Light travels about 300,000 kilometers per second. It takes light about 500 seconds to travel from the sun to Earth.

25. Write the speed of light in scientific notation. [3×10^5 km/sec]

26. Write the time (in seconds) that it takes light to travel from the sun to Earth in scientific notation. [5×10^2 sec]

27. Approximate the distance between the sun and Earth using the following equation.

Distance = Speed of light • Time from sun to Earth. [1.5×10^8 km]

Multiple-Choice Practice

Test Tip If you find yourself getting frustrated by a test question, move on to the next question.

1. What is the perimeter of the figure?

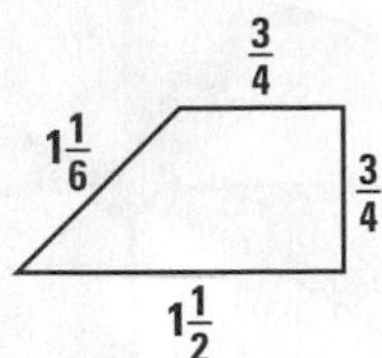

Ⓐ $3\frac{1}{2}$ Ⓑ $3\frac{2}{3}$

Ⓒ 4 Ⓓ $4\frac{1}{6}$

2. What is the difference of $3\frac{1}{6}$ and $-\frac{11}{8}$?

Ⓕ $-\frac{109}{24}$ Ⓖ $\frac{43}{24}$

Ⓗ $\frac{11}{6}$ Ⓙ $\frac{109}{24}$

3. What is the product of $-1\frac{3}{4}$ and $-2\frac{7}{8}$?

Ⓐ $-5\frac{11}{32}$ Ⓑ $2\frac{21}{32}$

Ⓒ $5\frac{1}{32}$ Ⓓ $5\frac{11}{32}$

4. Forty percent of the 50 people surveyed chose a cruise as their favorite type of vacation. How many people is this?

Ⓕ 2 Ⓖ 8

Ⓗ 20 Ⓙ 40

5. What is the quotient of $1\frac{4}{5}$ and $1\frac{1}{2}$?

Ⓐ $1\frac{1}{5}$ Ⓑ $1\frac{2}{5}$

Ⓒ $2\frac{3}{5}$ Ⓓ $2\frac{7}{10}$

6. The rectangle's area is $\frac{1}{2}$. What is its length?

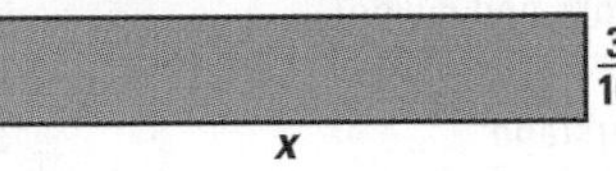

Ⓕ $\frac{3}{20}$ Ⓖ $\frac{3}{5}$

Ⓗ $1\frac{2}{3}$ Ⓙ $6\frac{2}{3}$

7. Solve the equation $\frac{2}{5} - \frac{2}{15}x = \frac{14}{15}$.

Ⓐ -4 Ⓑ 4

Ⓒ $-\frac{7}{3}$ Ⓓ $\frac{7}{2}$

8. Simplify $10y^{-3} \cdot 3y^2$.

Ⓕ $30y^{-6}$ Ⓖ $30y$

Ⓗ $30y^{-1}$ Ⓙ $30y^{-2}$

9. Simplify $5x^{-4}$.

Ⓐ $\frac{1}{5x^4}$ Ⓑ $\frac{5}{x^4}$

Ⓒ $-5x^4$ Ⓓ $\frac{-1}{5x^4}$

10. A lobster can lay 150,000 eggs at a time. Write this number in scientific notation.

Ⓕ 15×10^4 Ⓖ 1.5×10^5

Ⓗ 1.5×10^{-5} Ⓙ 0.15×10^{-3}

11. Simplify $(5 \times 10^{-7})(3.6 \times 10^4)$.

Ⓐ 1.8×10^{-4} Ⓑ 1.8×10^{-3}

Ⓒ 1.8×10^{-2} Ⓓ 1.8×10^{-1}

Teaching Tip

The Brain Games activity provides a motivating way to review selected content in the chapter. For a more comprehensive review, see the Chapter Summary and Review on pp. 314–317.

Brain 

California Standards

- Add, subtract, multiply, and divide fractions. (NS 1.2)
- Understand negative whole-number exponents. (NS 2.1)
- Analyze problems by identifying relationships. (MR 1.1)

Spinning Fractions

Materials

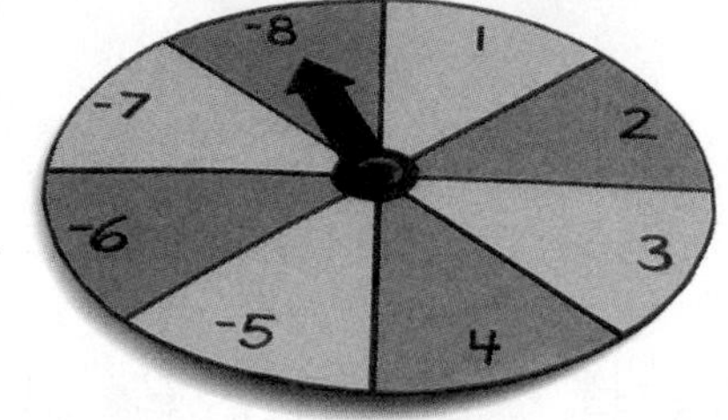

- **Spinner with eight equal sections labeled as shown**
- **Coin**

Directions

Object of the Game

Play the game in pairs. Each round the two players compare answers and the one with the greater answer earns a point. If the answers are the same, each player earns a point. The winner of the game is the player with the most points after a fixed time or a fixed number of rounds.

How to Play

STEP 1 Player A spins the spinner four times while Player B tosses the coin. (Next round reverse these rolls.) If the coin shows heads, the players add. If the coin shows tails, the players subtract.

STEP 2 Each player chooses how to arrange the four numbers that were spun into two proper fractions and then carries out the operation indicated by the coin.

Another Way to Play

The coin toss determines whether players multiply or divide. If the coin shows heads, the players multiply. If the coin shows tails, the players divide.

Brain Teaser

Find the Mystery Fraction $\frac{4}{5}$

- When it is added to a fraction with a numerator of 1, the sum is **1**.
- When it is raised to a power of -2, the numerator is **25**.
- When it is raised to the third power, the numerator is **64**.

California Standards and Assessment

CA Standards: NS 1.2, NS 2.1, MR 1.1

The basic skills you'll review on this page will help prepare you for the next chapter.

Reviewing the Basics

Additional Resources

Technology

- Personal Student Tutor
- Test and Practice Generator

EXAMPLE 1 Simplifying Numerical and Variable Expressions

Simplify the expression. **a.** $\frac{18}{60}$ **b.** $\frac{18xy^5}{12y^3}$

Solution

a. $\frac{18}{60} = \frac{\cancel{2} \cdot \cancel{3} \cdot 3}{2 \cdot \cancel{2} \cdot \cancel{3} \cdot 5} = \frac{3}{10}$

b. $\frac{18xy^5}{12y^3} = \frac{\cancel{2} \cdot \cancel{3} \cdot 3 \cdot x \cdot y^5}{2 \cdot \cancel{2} \cdot \cancel{3} \cdot y^3} = \frac{3 \cdot x \cdot y^{5-3}}{2} = \frac{3xy^2}{2}$

Try These

Simplify the expression.

1. $\frac{10}{18}$ $\frac{5}{9}$ **2.** $\frac{28}{26}$ $\frac{14}{13}$ or $1\frac{1}{13}$ **3.** $\frac{54}{28}$ $\frac{27}{14}$ or $1\frac{13}{14}$ **4.** $\frac{84}{112}$ $\frac{3}{4}$

5. $\frac{14x^3}{7x^2}$ $2x$ **6.** $\frac{81x^6y}{45x^3y}$ $\frac{9x^3}{5}$ **7.** $\frac{a^4bc^3}{a^2bc}$ a^2c^2 **8.** $\frac{120x^3y^5z^9}{168x^2y^3}$ $\frac{5xy^2z^9}{7}$

EXAMPLE 2 Solving Two-Step and Multi-Step Equations

Solve the equation $3x - 8 = 28$.

Solution

$3x - 8 = 28$	Write original equation.
$3x - 8 + 8 = 28 + 8$	Add 8 to each side.
$3x = 36$	Simplify.
$\frac{3x}{3} = \frac{36}{3}$	Divide each side by 3.
$x = 12$	Simplify. *x* is by itself.

Try These

Solve the equation.

9. $-x - 8 = -10$ **2** **10.** $6x + 7 = -37$ $-\frac{22}{3}$ or $-7\frac{1}{3}$

11. $4x + 5x - 10 = 35$ **5** **12.** $-8x + 2 = 5x + 15$ **−1**

13. $5(x + 1) = 75$ **14** **14.** $6(2 + x) = 5x + 15$ **3**

15. $3x - 8 = 40 - 5x$ **6** **16.** $7(x + 2) = 3x - 46$ **−15**

17. $-x + (-6) = 9x + 4$ **−1** **18.** $12x - 3 = -8x + 27$ $1\frac{1}{2}$

Student Help

MORE EXAMPLES More examples and practice exercises available at www.mcdougallittell.com

Additional Resources

A Cumulative Test for Chapters 1–6 is available in the *Assessment Book*, pp. 89–92.

Chapters 1-6 Cumulative Practice

Evaluate the expression. (1.3, 1.4)

1. $12 + 15(4)$ **72** **2.** 5^3 **125** **3.** $9^2 - 4^2$ **65** **4.** $(5^4 - 20) \div 11 + 9$ **64**

Write an equation that represents the verbal sentence. Then solve. (2.4)

5. The sum of a number and 5 is 21. **$x + 5 = 21$; 16**

6. The product of a number and 3 is 7. **$3x = 7$; $\frac{7}{3}$**

OIL PAINTING In Exercises 7 and 8, use the following information. For an oil painting course, you spend \$40.50 on tubes of paint that cost \$2.70 each. (2.7)

7. Write a verbal model to find the number of tubes of paint bought. Then assign labels to your model, and write an algebraic model. **Let n = the number of tubes of paint. $2.70n = 40.50$**

8. Solve the algebraic model and check your answer. **15 tubes**

Write an inequality that represents the verbal sentence. Then solve. (2.8)

9. The difference of z and 9 is less than -5. **$z - 9 < -5$; $z < 4$**

10. The quotient of x and 5 is greater than or equal to 25. **$\frac{x}{5} \geq 25$; $x \geq 125$**

RUNNING In Exercises 11 and 12, use the following information. (3.3) Your cousin tries to run an average of 7 miles a day for 5 days out of the week. She records her mileage in a training log. When she exceeds her goal, she records the extra miles. When she runs under her goal, she records the missed miles. When the sum of the week's numbers is greater than or equal to zero, then she has met her goal.

Day	Mon.	Tue.	Wed.	Thu.	Fri.	Sat.	Sun.
Miles	+4	No run	−4	+2	+3	−1	No run

11. Add the numbers in the table. Did your cousin meet her goal? **4; yes**

12. Find the number of miles that your cousin ran on each day and the total number of miles your cousin ran. **Mon 11 mi, Tue 0 mi, Wed 3 mi, Thu 9 mi, Fri 10 mi, Sat 6 mi, Sun 0 mi; total 39 mi**

In Exercises 13–15, simplify the expression. Then evaluate the expression when $x = -2$, $y = 4$, and $z = 5$. (1.8, 2.2, 3.2–3.5)

13. $3y - 6x + 3z - 5y$ **$-2y - 6x + 3z$; 19**

14. $-2(4x + 3x + y)$ **$-14x - 2y$; 20**

15. $2(3z - z) - y$ **$4z - y$; 16**

16. GEOMETRY Plot the points $A(-2, 2)$, $B(-2, 4)$, $C(-4, 4)$, and $D(-4, 2)$ to form the vertices of a rectangle. Find the perimeter and area of the rectangle. (3.8) **perimeter 8 units, area 4 square units**

Solve the equation. Check your solution. (4.1–4.5)

17. $5 - 4x = -11$ **4** **18.** $13x - 80 = 60 - 7x$ **7** **19.** $-3(y - 5) = 12$ **1**

20. WATER LEVELS During a drought, East Reservoir, which began the month 6 feet below full, is dropping at a rate of 4 inches per day. West Reservoir, which began the month 4 feet below full, is dropping at a rate of 6 inches per day. Use a table or solve an equation to find when the reservoirs will be the same amounts below full. **(4.6)** **12 days**

Find the mean, median, and mode of the data. (4.8)

21. 3, 2, 0, 3, 4, 2, 0, 2 **mean 2, median 2, mode 2**

22. 76, 92, 97, 98, 99, 101, 105, 110, 95 **mean 97, median 98, no mode**

Write the prime factorization of each number or factor each expression. Then use the results to find the least common multiple. (5.1, 5.3)

23. 14 and 49 **$2 \cdot 7$, 7^2; 98**

24. 270 and 450 **$2 \cdot 3^3 \cdot 5$, $2 \cdot 3^2 \cdot 5^2$; 1350**

25. $6x^2y$ and $8xy^3$ **$2 \cdot 3 \cdot x^2 \cdot y$, $2^3 \cdot x \cdot y^3$; $24x^2y^3$**

26. $9a^2b$ and $12ab^4$ **$3^2 \cdot a^2 \cdot b$, $2^2 \cdot 3 \cdot a \cdot b^4$; $36a^2b^4$**

Find the greatest common factor of the numerator and the denominator. Then use your answer to simplify the fraction. (5.2, 5.4)

27. $\frac{6}{48}$ **6; $\frac{1}{8}$**

28. $\frac{25}{45}$ **5; $\frac{5}{9}$**

29. $\frac{10}{15}$ **5; $\frac{2}{3}$**

30. $\frac{52}{54}$ **2; $\frac{26}{27}$**

Write the percent as a decimal and a fraction. Write the fraction as a decimal and a percent. (5.6, 5.7)

31. 160% **1.6, $\frac{8}{5}$**

32. 7.5% **0.075, $\frac{3}{40}$**

33. $\frac{24}{72}$ **$0.\overline{3}$, $33\frac{1}{3}$%**

34. $\frac{112}{80}$ **1.4, 140%**

35. The list below gives a bowler's scores for 16 games. Make a stem-and-leaf plot of the data, and use it to order the scores. **(5.8)** **See margin for graph.**

188, 206, 225, 216, 248, 231, 211, 180, 204, 221, 243, 216, 195, 209, 196, 219
180, 188, 195, 196, 204, 206, 209, 211, 216, 219, 221, 225, 231, 243, 248

In Exercises 36 and 37, use the circle graph. (6.1, 6.2)

36. What is the sum of all the shaded regions? **$\frac{3}{5}$**

37. What is the value of x? **$\frac{2}{5}$**

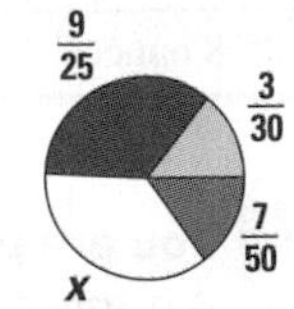

Find the perimeter and area of the figure. (6.1–6.3)

38.

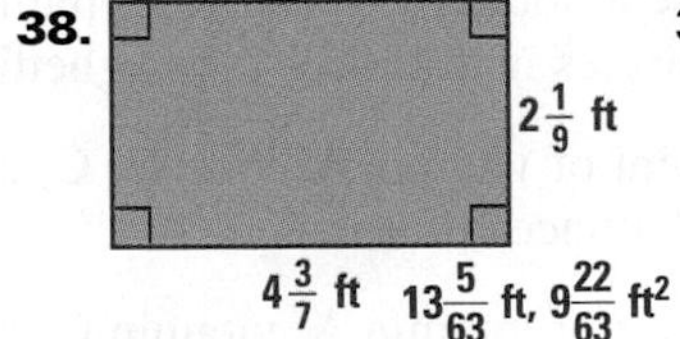

$13\frac{5}{63}$ ft, $9\frac{22}{63}$ ft²

39.

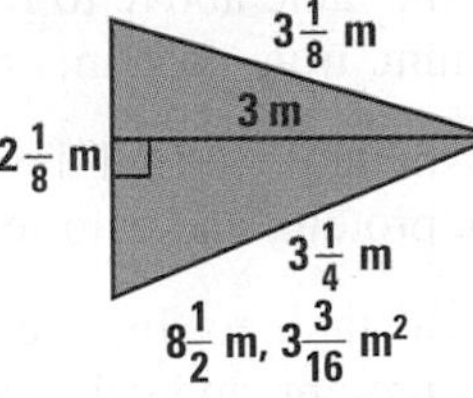

$8\frac{1}{2}$ m, $3\frac{3}{16}$ m²

40.

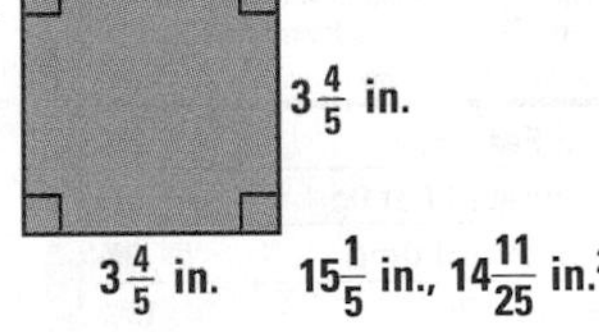

$15\frac{1}{5}$ in., $14\frac{11}{25}$ in.²

Simplify the expression. (6.7, 6.8)

41. a^{-4} **$\frac{1}{a^4}$**

42. 5^0 **1**

43. 10^3 **1000**

44. $4^2 \cdot 4^{-2}$ **1**

45. $x^7 \cdot x^{10}$ **x^{17}**

46. $\left(\frac{3}{4}\right)^{-3}$ **$\frac{64}{27}$**

47. $\frac{8a^4b}{10a^2}$ **$\frac{4a^2b}{5}$**

48. $6x^7 \cdot (-2x^4)$ **$-12x^{11}$**

Write the number in scientific notation. (6.9)

49. 26,473 **2.6473×10^4**

50. 0.1746 **1.746×10^{-1}**

51. 150,000,000 **1.5×10^8**

52. 0.0052100 **5.21×10^{-3}**

35.

Stem	Leaf
18	0 8
19	5 6
20	4 6 9
21	1 6 6 9
22	1 5
23	1
24	3 8

Key: 24 | 3 represents 243.

Project Overview

Mathematical Goals

- Read and interpret data given in tables.
- Perform operations with fractions.
- Write a ratio.
- Convert fractions to percents.

Managing the Project

Classroom Management
Students can complete the project individually or in pairs. If working in pairs, each student can find the amounts for three of the items. They should each explain to the other how they computed their results to check the accuracy of their methods.

Guiding Students' Work
Students should be reminded that the amounts given in the table may not be the same as the amount to be served at the dinner, so a conversion will be necessary. Students may wish, for example, to convert the Vitamin A percentage for 4 ounces of sauce to a percentage for 1 ounce, then multiply by 6. Or they may determine that 6 ounces is $\frac{3}{2}$ or 1.5 times 4 ounces, then multiply the numbers in the table by this fraction.

3. **Bread: 0%, 0%, 0%, 12%, 7.5 g, 180 Calories**
   Salad: 70%, 20%, 4%, 0%, 2 g, 30 Calories
   Dressing: 0%, 0%, 2%, 0%, 1 g, 25 Calories
   Milk: 10%, 4%, 30%, 0%, 8 g, 120 Calories

California Standards and Assessment

CA Standards: NS 1.2, NS 1.3, MR 3.0

Chapters 4-6 Project

Evaluating a Spaghetti Dinner

California Standards

- Use operations with rational numbers. (NS 1.2)
- Convert fractions to decimals and percents and use these representations in applications. (NS 1.3)
- Move beyond a problem by generalizing to other situations. (MR 3.0)

Materials

- Calculator
- Paper
- Pencil

OBJECTIVE Evaluate the nutritional content of a spaghetti dinner.

INVESTIGATION

It is recommended that you eat a certain amount of each vitamin or mineral each day. This amount is called the *daily value* of the vitamin or mineral. The percents in the table indicate the percent of the daily value of each vitamin or mineral that is in one serving of the given food.

Food, serving size	Vitamin A (% daily value)	Vitamin C (% daily value)	Calcium (% daily value)	Iron (% daily value)	Protein (in grams)	Calories
Spaghetti, 2 ounces	0	0	0	10	7	200
Sauce, 4 ounces	20	30	10	6	3	70
Bread, 2 ounces	0	0	0	8	5	120
Salad, 3 ounces	35	10	2	0	1	15
Dressing, 2 tablespoons	0	0	2	0	1	25
2% milk, 8 ounces	10	4	30	0	8	120

Nutrition Facts
Serving Size 1/2 cup (125g)
Servings per Container About 6
Calories 70 Calories from Fat 15

Amount per Serving	%DV*
Total Fat 1.5g	2%
Saturated Fat 0g	0%
Cholesterol 0mg	0%
Sodium 470mg	19%
Total Carbohydrate 12g	4%
Dietary Fiber 3g	11%
Sugars 11g	
Protein 3g	

Vitamin A 20% • Vitamin C 30%
Calcium 10% • Iron 6%

*Percent Daily Values (DV) are based on a 2,000 Calorie diet. Your daily values may be higher or lower depending on your calorie needs.

INGREDIENTS: TOMATO PUREE, WATER, DICED TOMATOES, SUGAR, ONIONS, SALT, OLIVE OIL, SOYBEAN OIL, PARSLEY, GARLIC, SPICE.

You are planning a spaghetti dinner. Each person will get about 4 ounces of spaghetti, 6 ounces of sauce, 3 ounces of bread, 6 ounces of salad, 2 tablespoons of dressing, and 8 ounces of milk.

1. Use the table above to find the amount of vitamin A, vitamin C, calcium, iron, protein, and calories in 4 ounces of spaghetti. **0%, 0%, 0%, 20%, 14 g, 400 Calories**
2. Use the table to find the amount of vitamin A, vitamin C, calcium, iron, protein, and calories in 6 ounces of sauce. **30%, 45%, 15%, 9%, 4.5 g, 105 Calories**
3. Use the table to find the amount of vitamin A, vitamin C, calcium, iron, protein, and calories in each of the other ingredients of the spaghetti dinner. **See margin.**
4. What is the total calorie content of the spaghetti dinner? Add up the number of calories you found for each ingredient in Exercises 1–3. **860 Calories**
5. The information in the table is based on the assumption that you need 2000 Calories each day. What percent of this number of calories will the spaghetti dinner provide? **43%**

6. How much protein is in the dinner? If you need 46 grams of protein in a day, what percent of this requirement does the dinner provide?
37 g; about 80%

7. What percent of the daily value does the dinner provide for vitamin A? for vitamin C? for calcium? for iron?
110%; 69%; 51%; 41%

Present Your Results

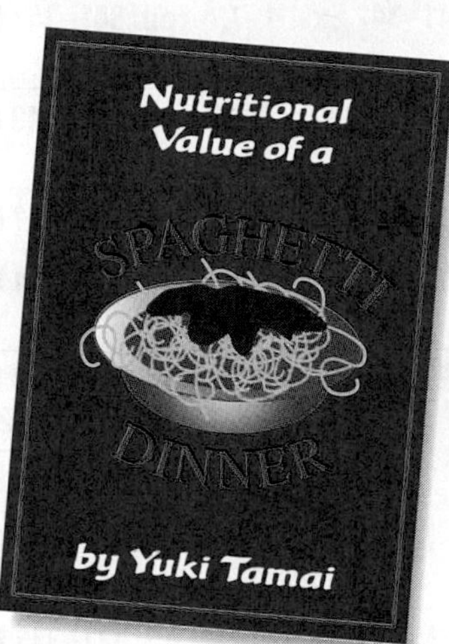

Write a report about the nutritional value of the spaghetti dinner.

- Include a discussion about the dinner in terms of nutrients and calories.
- Include your results from Exercises 1–7.
- Choose a purpose for changing the spaghetti dinner, such as consuming more iron. Then tell how you might alter the amount of each ingredient in the dinner to address your goal.

Extension

Materials Nutritional information for foods you eat

8. Record the food you eat during one day.

9. Find the nutritional information for each food you eat. Use the nutrition labels on the packages, or find the information on the Internet or in the library.

10. Are there any vitamins or minerals you don't get enough of? If so, what could you eat that contains those vitamins or minerals?

11. What foods are high in vitamin A? in vitamin C? in protein? in calcium? in iron? in calories? What patterns do you see? For example, do all fruits have similar nutritional strengths? Write a paragraph describing your observations.

Concluding the Project
Have the students present the report to the class by taking turns reporting parts of the project. For example, one student might present the number of calories and nutrients in the dinner and the other student could discuss the way the dinner could be changed to consume more iron or fewer calories.

Grading the Project

A well-written project will have the following characteristics:

- Complete and correct solutions to Exercises 1–7.
- A thorough and well-written report which answers all questions about the project.
- An extension to the project in which students complete the four exercises in the extension.

Pacing and Assignment Guide

Regular Schedule

Lesson	Les. Day	Transitional	Average	Advanced
7.1	Day 1	SRH p. 681 Exs. 1–4; pp. 331–332 Exs. 9–12, 15–25, 33–34	pp. 331–332 Exs. 9–23, 26, 28–29, 33–34	pp. 271–272 Exs. 15–23, 26, 27*, 28–31, 33–34
7.2	Day 1	pp. 336–337 Exs. 7–8, 11–14, 19–20, 24–26, 31–37	pp. 336–337 Exs. 9–10, 15–18, 21–27, 31–37	pp. 336–337 Exs. 9–10, 15–20, 26–28, 29*, 30–37
7.3	Day 1	SRH p. 671 Exs. 1–3; pp. 341–342 Exs. 4–7, 10, 12, 14–17, 20–21	pp. 341–342 Exs. 4–10, 12–17, 20–21	pp. 341–342 Exs. 4–10, 12–13, 18–19*, 20–21
7.4	Day 1	EP p. 699 Exs. 79–82; pp. 348–349 Exs. 7–12, 16–20, 27–28	pp. 348–349 Exs. 7–10, 13–20, 27–28	pp. 348–349 Exs. 7–10, 16–20, 24–25, 26*, 27–28
7.5	Day 1	pp. 352–354 Exs. 9–20, 32–33	pp. 352–354 Exs. 9–27, 32–33	pp. 352–354 Exs. 9–27, 32–33
	Day 2	SRH p. 688 Exs. 1–5; pp. 352–354 Exs. 28–31, 34–37, 43–44	pp. 352–354 Exs. 28–31, 34–39, 43–44	pp. 352–354 Exs. 28–31, 34–41, 42*, 43–44
7.6	Day 1	pp. 359–360 Exs. 8–9, 14–17, 22–28, 30, 36–40, 50–52, 58–60	pp. 359–360 Exs. 10–11, 18–23, 32–40, 52–55, 60–62	pp. 359–360 Exs. 12–13, 18–23, 29, 31*, 32–40, 52–55, 60–62
7.7	Day 1	pp. 363–364 Exs. 6–14, 19–21, 24–25	pp. 363–364 Exs. 6–14, 17–21, 24–25	pp. 363–364 Exs. 9–18, 22, 23*, 24–25
7.8	Day 1	pp. 367–368 Exs. 8–11, 14–16, 18–22, 28–29	pp. 367–368 Exs. 10–13, 15–20, 23–24, 28–29	pp. 367–368 Exs. 10–13, 15–17, 20, 23–26, 27*, 28–29
7.9	Day 1	pp. 371–373 Exs. 9–12, 14–16, 18, 22–24, 30–31	pp. 371–373 Exs. 9–17, 22–24, 28, 30–31	pp. 371–373 Exs. 11–18, 25–27, 29*, 30–31; EC: TE p. 326D*
Review	Day 1	pp. 374–377 Exs. 1–28	pp. 374–377 Exs. 1–28	pp. 374–377 Exs. 1–28
Assess	Day 1	Chapter 7 Test	Chapter 7 Test	Chapter 7 Test

Yearly Pacing *Chapter 7 Total* – **12 days** *Chapters 1–7 Total* – **92 days** *Remaining* – **68 days**

* Challenge Exercises EP = Extra Practice SRH = Skills Review Handbook EC = Extra Challenge

Block Schedule

Day 1	Day 2	Day 3	Day 4	Day 5	Day 6
7.1 pp. 331–332: Exs. 9–23, 26, 28–29, 33–34 **7.2** pp. 336–337: Exs. 9–10, 15–18, 21–27, 31–37	**7.3** pp. 341–342: Exs. 4–10, 12–17, 20–21 **7.4** pp. 348–349: Exs. 7–10, 13–20, 27–28	**7.5** pp. 352–354: Exs. 9–39, 43–44	**7.6** pp. 359–360: Exs. 10–11, 18–23, 32–40, 52–55, 60–62 **7.7** pp. 363–364: Exs. 6–14, 17–21, 24–25	**7.8** pp. 367–368: Exs. 10–13, 15–20, 23–24, 28–29 **7.9** pp. 371–373: Exs. 9–17, 22–24, 28, 30–31	**Review** pp. 374–377: Exs. 1–28 **Assess** Chapter 7 Test

Yearly Pacing *Chapter 7 Total* – **6 days** *Chapters 1–7 Total* – **46 days** *Remaining* – **34 days**

Support Materials

Chapter Resource Book

LESSON SUPPORT	7.1	7.2	7.3	7.4	7.5	7.6	7.7	7.8	7.9
Lesson Plans	p. 1	p. 10	p. 19	p. 28	p. 37	p. 46	p. 55	p. 64	p. 73
Lesson Plans for Block Scheduling	p. 2	p. 11	p. 20	p. 29	p. 38	p. 47	p. 56	p. 65	p. 74
Warm-Ups with Multiple-Choice Practice	p. 3	p. 12	p. 21	p. 30	p. 39	p. 48	p. 57	p. 66	p. 75
Problem of the Day	p. 4	p. 13	p. 22	p. 31	p. 40	p. 49	p. 58	p. 67	p. 76
Daily Cumulative Review	p. 5	p. 14	p. 23	p. 32	p. 41	p. 50	p. 59	p. 68	p. 77
Practice Masters	p. 6	p. 15	p. 24	p. 33	p. 42	p. 51	p. 60	p. 69	p. 78
Reteaching Masters	p. 7	p. 16	p. 25	p. 34	p. 43	p. 52	p. 61	p. 70	p. 79
Enrichment Masters	p. 9	p. 18	p. 27	p. 36	p. 45	p. 54	p. 63	p. 72	p. 81

Transparencies

	7.1	7.2	7.3	7.4	7.5	7.6	7.7	7.8	7.9
Warm-Ups with Multiple-Choice Practice	p. 51	p. 52	p. 53	p. 54	p. 55	p. 56	p. 57	p. 58	p. 59
Teacher Time-Saver Transparencies	✓	✓	✓	✓	✓	✓	✓	✓	✓
English/Spanish Problem Solving	p. 28		p. 29		p. 30		p. 31		
Answer Transparencies	✓	✓	✓	✓	✓	✓	✓	✓	✓

Technology

- Personal Student Tutor
- Time-Saving Test and Practice Generator
- Electronic Teacher Tools
- Technology: Using Calculators and Computers

Additional Resources

- Math Log
- Assessment Book
- Worked-Out Solution Key
- Practice Workbook (English/Spanish)
- Home and School Connection
- California Standards: Key Concepts Book

Correlation to the California Curriculum

Correlations to the California Standards
CA Standards: NS 1.3, NS 1.6, NS 1.7, AF 1.1, AF 4.0, AF 4.1, AF 4.2, MG 1.0, MG 1.1, MG 1.2, MG 2.0, SDP 1.0, MR 2.6, MR 3.1

California Curriculum Support

Key Concepts Book

- Pre-Course Review: Topic 1 Working with Decimals
  Topic 5 Measurement
- Key Standards: NS 1.7 Percent Problems *(Lesson 7.6)*
  NS 1.7 Simple and Compound Interest *(Lessons 7.8, 7.9)*
- Special Topics: Modeling Ratios and Proportions *(Lessons 7.1, 7.2)*
  Converting Units of Measure *(Lesson 7.1)*

California Standards Practice Workbook provides practice for each Standard that is covered in this chapter.

Providing Universal Access

Strategies for Strategic Learners

PROVIDE CONCRETE EXAMPLES

Concepts and Skills provides students with many practical problems in order to show how mathematics is applied every day. Additional connections are easy to make with the help of parents and community members. Proportion is a concept that adults use often in their home and work activities. Encourage parents to provide examples from cooking (doubling a recipe), carpentry (working from a blueprint or scale model to build something), gardening (determining how much fertilizer to purchase for a specific lawn size), and travel (understanding what the dollar is worth in different countries).

USE CROSS-CURRICULAR CONNECTIONS

In California, the seventh grade science standards asks students to construct scale models, maps, and diagrams to communicate scientific knowledge (Standard 7d). Proportion is a key concept in mathematics and science, and problems or activities that combine standards from math and science can be a way of extending the learning time. In Chapter 7 of *Concepts and Skills*, students learn about scale drawings (p. 338). If you collaborate with the science teacher, you could arrange for the mathematical concepts in Lesson 7.3 to be taught or reinforced in science class.

FOCUS ON KEY CONCEPTS

In order to understand proportion, students must be convinced that multiplying both numerator and denominator of a fraction by the same number does not change the value of the fraction. Some students may need lots of sample problems in order to be convinced. Word problems of the following type will be helpful:

"Which would you rather have, $\frac{2}{3}$ of a 10-inch pizza or $\frac{4}{6}$ of a 10-inch pizza?"

Then give examples which show the same concept with numbers.

$$\frac{2 \times 2}{3 \times 2} = \frac{4}{6}$$

And finally, substitute algebraic notation for the numbers.

$$\frac{A \cdot b}{C \cdot b} = \frac{A}{C}$$

Strategies for English Learners

USE PICTURES

Simple problems involving ratios can often be expressed with pictures rather than words. For example, Exercise 25 on page 336 can be drawn this way:

For students at the beginning and intermediate levels of English fluency, beginning the lesson with picture problems instead of word problems can help focus on the mathematical concepts. Students can then use their understanding of the mathematical concept to understand what is asked for in the word problems.

Another pictorial way to represent problems involving rates and ratios is with the following type of picture:

758 is what percent of 976?

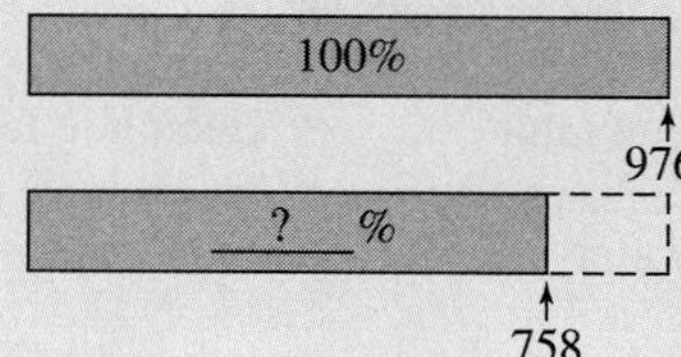

Strategies for Advanced Learners

DIFFERENTIATE INSTRUCTION IN TERMS OF COMPLEXITY

Most vocabulary is learned through reading. Teachers can help students build their mathematics vocabulary and understanding through the assignments of outside, independent reading. Books for children and young adults that discuss mathematical concepts are readily available and help students understand how mathematics is important in their daily lives. With the help of the school district or local library media teacher, teachers can find books that reinforce mathematical concepts, from the most simple to the most complex. Books by David Macaulay, such as *The Way Things Work*, discuss mathematical and scientific terms and concepts in the context of history, architecture, and science. Assigning reading that students do outside the mathematics instructional time not only builds understanding of mathematics concepts and vocabulary, but also helps students increase in reading ability. While the David Macaulay books are challenging in terms of the reading level, this strategy can be used with all students by selecting material at an appropriate reading level for each student.

SUBSTITUTE CHALLENGE PROBLEMS

Richard came home from school one day and asked his parents if he could help out by working at the family clothing store, sweeping the floors, stocking the clothing, etc. Richard's parents were delighted, and asked what he would expect to be paid. Richard said that the first day he would expect to be paid only a penny, but asked his parents if they would double his pay each day, so that he would be paid two cents on the second day, four cents on the third day, and so forth. How much would Richard earn on the tenth day? (*512 cents, or $5.12*) the fifteenth day? (*16,384 cents, or $163.84*)

The amount paid on the nth day can be represented by 2^{n-1}.

An ancient version of this involves a chessboard, where 1 grain of sand is placed on the first square, 2 on the second, 4 on the third, and so forth.

Mathematical Background Notes

Lessons 7.1–7.2

RATIO AND PROPORTION By definition, a **ratio** is simply the quotient $\frac{a}{b}$ of two numbers a and b, where $b \neq 0$. Common terminology is to describe $\frac{a}{b}$ as "a to b" which can be written $a{:}b$. In this chapter a and b tend to be taken as positive integers, although the concept of ratio does not require this.

A **proportion** is an equation of the form

$$\frac{a'}{a} = \frac{b'}{b},$$

which can be read as "a' is to a as b' is to b" and written as

$$a'{:}a = b'{:}b.$$

Suppose a, b, c, and d are numbers with $b \neq 0$ and $d \neq 0$. The cross products property in Lesson 7.2 states that if $\frac{a}{b} = \frac{c}{d}$, then $ad = bc$. With $b \neq 0$ and $d \neq 0$, the converse statement is also true, namely that if $ad = bc$, then $\frac{a}{b} = \frac{c}{d}$. Both statements are a consequence of the basic rules of arithmetic, as indicated in Exercise 30 on page 337.

The idea of proportion can be extended to include more than two ratios. Given two sequences of numbers,

$$a, b, c, d, \ldots \quad \text{and} \quad a', b', c', d', \ldots,$$

we say that the sequences are **proportional** if the ratios of corresponding terms are equal, that is, if

$$(*) \qquad \frac{a'}{a} = \frac{b'}{b} = \frac{c'}{c} = \frac{d'}{d} = \ldots.$$

In most applications the sequences are of finite length, but the definition can also be applied to infinitely long sequences.

If we denote the common ratio in (*) by k, then this is equivalent to

$$a' = ka, \quad b' = kb, \quad c' = kc, \quad d' = kd, \ldots.$$

It is a useful exercise to show that (*) is equivalent to

$$\frac{a}{a'} = \frac{b}{b'} = \frac{c}{c'} = \frac{d}{d'} = \ldots.$$

As an example, the two sequences

$$\mathbf{3, 12, 15, 27} \quad \textbf{and} \quad \mathbf{4, 16, 20, 36}$$

are proportional, since $\frac{4}{3} = \frac{16}{12} = \frac{20}{15} = \frac{36}{27}$.

Lesson 7.3

SIMILARITY Proportions arise naturally in geometry when dealing with similar figures. Two geometric figures F and F' are said to be **similar** if there is a one-to-one correspondence between the points of F and the points of F' and a number k such that for each pair of points P and Q belonging to F and corresponding points P' and Q' belonging to F', we have

$$\textbf{(distance from } P' \textbf{ to } Q') = k \cdot \textbf{(distance from } P \textbf{ to } Q).$$

This definition embodies the idea of enlarging (or shrinking) F by a **scale factor** k to obtain F'. For example, if F is a circle of diameter 3 and F' is a circle of diameter 6, then F and F' are similar with a scale factor of 2.

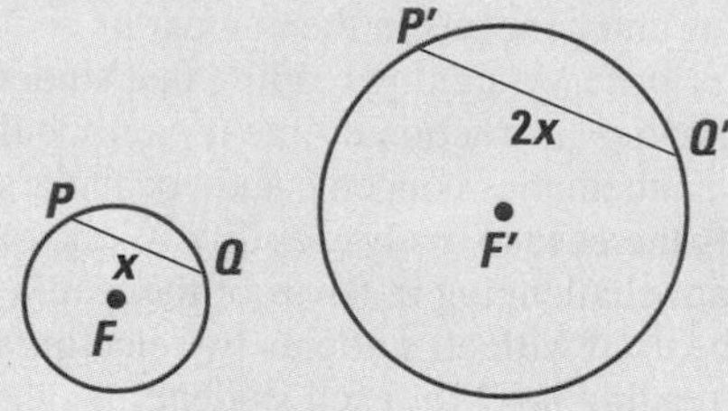

This means that the distance between every pair of points belonging to F' is twice the distance between the corresponding pair of points belonging to F.

In case F and F' are *similar polygons* and F has consecutive vertices A, B, C, D, . . . , while F' has corresponding vertices A', B', C', D', . . . , then

$$\frac{A'B'}{AB} = \frac{B'C'}{BC} = \frac{C'D'}{CD} = \ldots = k,$$

for some positive number k. That is, the sequences of side lengths AB, BC, CD, . . . and $A'B'$, $B'C'$, $C'D'$, . . . are proportional in the sense described above.

It can be shown that two polygons are **similar** if and only if

(1) the two sequences formed by the lengths of their corresponding sides are proportional,

and

(2) their corresponding angles have equal measures.

It is worth noting that the definition we have given for similar figures applies also to 3-dimensional figures. For example, a cube F of edge length 2 and a cube F' of edge length 6 are similar figures, with a scale factor $k = 3$. As a map represents an actual planar figure as a smaller similar figure, so do scale models represent actual 3-dimensional objects as similar 3-dimensional objects. The wooden model galleon in Exercises 5–7 on page 341 is a good example.

Lesson 7.4

Probability provides an important application of fractions, decimals, and percents. Here it is important to have in mind the way in which a given experiment generates both theoretical and experimental probabilities.

THEORETICAL PROBABILITY The calculation of theoretical probability is based on an experiment that generates a set of equally likely outcomes, for example, the roll of a fair die generates the set of outcomes $\{1, 2, 3, 4, 5, 6\}$. This set is called the **sample space** for the experiment.

When the sample space has N equally likely outcomes, it is natural to associate the probability $\frac{1}{N}$ with each of them, for example, the probability of a fair die coming up $\{5\}$ is $\frac{1}{6}$. However, we also want to assign probabilities to events such as an even roll as represented by $\{2, 4, 6\}$.

The actual definition of theoretical probability is formulated in terms of *events* such as $\{2, 4, 6\}$. Formally, an **event** is any subset of the sample space. In other words, an event is itself a set of outcomes. If the sample space for rolling a fair die is denoted by $S = \{1, 2, 3, 4, 5, 6\}$ and the event of an even roll is denoted by $A = \{2, 4, 6\}$, then the probability of an even roll is given by

$$P(A) = \frac{\textbf{Number of outcomes in } A}{\textbf{Number of outcomes in } S} = \frac{3}{6} = \frac{1}{2}.$$

To express this verbally, we sometimes refer to outcomes in A as *favorable outcomes*, in which case we arrive at the definition of theoretical probability that is given on page 345.

EXPERIMENTAL PROBABILITY Experimental probabilities are associated with experiments that can be repeated. Once the experiment has been described (for example, toss a dime and a penny) and the sample space defined (S= {(H, H), (H, T), (T, H), (T, T)}), we can calculate the experimental probability of "at least one head" by repeated tosses of the two coins and keeping track of how often the outcome belongs to A = {(H, H), (H, T), (T, H)}. By identifying outcomes in A with tosses with at least one head we would be led to the formula

$$\textbf{Experimental probability } P = \frac{\textbf{number of tosses with at least one head}}{\textbf{total number of trials}}.$$

Lessons 7.8–7.9

INTEREST Problems involving interest provide an important connection between fractions, decimals, and percents. We speak of eight percent interest as if the interest were a whole number. However, in actually computing interest, we make use of the fact that the rate r of interest is given by

$$8\% = \frac{8}{100} = 0.08.$$

Aside from providing an important application of the use of percents, the study of simple interest sets the stage for more realistic percentage-based growth problems, notably those involving compound interest and exponential growth.

As an example, consider \$850 invested at 8% interest for 1 year. At the end of the year, simple interest calls for an interest payment of \$850(0.08)(1) = \$68, leading to a new principal of \$850 + \$68 = \$918.

What if this money were left on deposit for a second year? If the \$68 interest is added to the account and the \$918 receives 8% interest, then at the end of the second year you would receive an interest payment of \$918(0.08)(1) = \$73.44. At the end of the second year the principal is

\$850 + \$68 + \$73.44 = \$991.44.

This is *not* the same as receiving simple interest for two years, in which case the final principal would be

\$850 + \$850(0.08)(2) = \$850 + \$136 = \$986.

In the first case the \$68 interest earned during the first year is allowed to accrue interest in the second, whereas under simple interest it is only the original principal of \$850 that accrues interest.

An important mathematical idea underlying compound interest is the fact that for any principal P invested at 8%, an annual interest payment of $P(0.08)(1)$ leads to a new principal of

$$P + P(0.08) = P(1 + 0.08) = P(1.08).$$

Thus allowing annual interest to earn interest corresponds to multiplying P by 1.08 at the end of each year that the original principal is left on deposit. In particular,

$$850(1.08) = 918$$

and

$$850(1.08)^2 = 991.44.$$

This can be a very good place to introduce technology, using a spreadsheet to do such calculations (see the example on page 372 where \$50 is invested at 6% interest compounded annually). As an alternative to a spreadsheet, many calculators have a capability for repeated multiplication. Repeated multiplication can be used to generate the sequence 56.18, 59.5508, 63.123848, 66.911279, and so on, that corresponds to the entries in the third spreadsheet column on page 372. In this way technology can be used to provide an informal introduction to the important concept of **exponential growth.**

By way of general formulation, suppose an amount P is invested at an annual interest rate r compounded annually. After n years there will have been n compoundings, resulting in a new balance

$$P(1 + r)^n.$$

Here it is important to keep in mind that r is to be expressed as a decimal. An interest rate of 8% corresponds to $r = \frac{8}{100} = 0.08$.

Chapter Overview

In this chapter, students will use percents to solve real-life situations and find the percent increase or decrease of a quantity. They will:

- Find ratios and rates.
- Write and solve proportions.
- Find the probability of an event.
- Calculate simple and compound interest.

Career Note

Stockbrokers buy and sell stocks, bonds, and other financial products for an investor. They also give advice to investors on building a strong financial future. When investors decide to buy or sell a stock, the stockbroker relays the order to the floor of the stock exchange where floor representatives buy and sell the stock. After the exchange has been made, the broker notifies the investor of the final price. Most stockbrokers have a college degree and have studied economics and finance.

Additional information about stockbrokers is available at **www.mcdougallittell.com**

Proportional Reasoning

Why is proportional reasoning important?

In a proportional relationship, the ratio of one variable to another is constant. You will use proportional reasoning as you study topics such as percents, similarity, and statistics.

Many people use proportional reasoning in their careers, including stockbrokers (page 327) and bank managers (page 373). For example, stockbrokers calculate the percent of increase in stock prices.

Meeting the California Standards

The skills you'll learn in this chapter will help you meet state standards and prepare for standardized tests. In this chapter you'll:

- **Solve problems involving rates.** LESSON 7.1
- **Construct and read drawings and models made to scale.** LESSON 7.3
- **Convert fractions to decimals and percents.** LESSON 7.4
- **Use percents in applications.** LESSON 7.5
- **Solve problems that involve markups and discounts.** LESSON 7.6
- **Calculate the percent of increase or decrease in a quantity.** LESSON 7.7
- **Compute simple interest and compound interest.** LESSONS 7.8, 7.9

Career Link **STOCKBROKER** A stockbroker uses proportional reasoning when:

- determining the value of an investment.
- finding the percent of increase or decrease in the value of an investment.

EXERCISES

You bought $1000 worth of stock in each company. A year later you sold the stocks. The graph shows the price per share when you bought and sold.

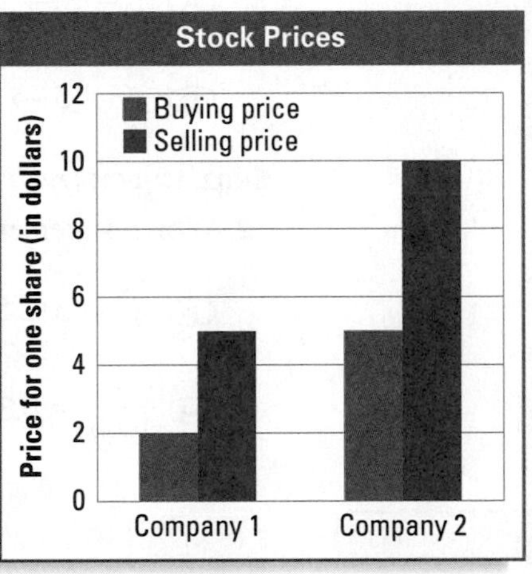

1. Which company's stock do you think was the better investment? Explain your reasoning. **See margin.**
2. How many shares of Company 1's stock could you buy with $1000? **500 shares**
3. How much money did you get when you sold the shares in Company 1? **$2500**
4. What was your profit selling shares in Company 1? **$1500**
5. Repeat Exercises 2–4 for Company 2. **200 shares; $2000; $1000**

In Lesson 7.7, you will learn how to use percent of increase to tell which company's stock was the better investment.

327

Projects

A project covering Chapters 7–9 appears on pages 504–505 of the Student Edition. Additional projects for selected lessons in Chapter 7 are available in the *Assessment Book*, pp. 238–239.

Technology

Software

- Electronic Teacher Tools
- Online Lesson Planner
- Personal Student Tutor
- Test and Practice Generator

Internet Connections

- Application and Career Links 332, 334, 341, 359, 373
- Student Help 331, 335, 342, 347, 354, 356, 362, 368, 372, 381

These Internet connections are available at **www.mcdougallittell.com**

1. ***Sample answer*: Company 1; it had the greater percent increase.**

Prepare

Diagnostic Tools

The **chapter readiness quiz** can help you diagnose whether students have the following skills needed in Chapter 7:
- Understand and apply the division property of equality.
- Write decimals as percents.
- Write fractions as percents.

Reteaching Materials

The following resources are available for students who need additional help with the skills on the chapter readiness quiz:

Chapter 7 Resource Book
- Reteaching with Practice (Lessons 2.6, 5.7)

Personal Student Tutor

Additional Resources

The following resources are provided to help you prepare for the upcoming chapter and customize review materials:

Chapter 7 Resource Book
- Lesson Plans, pp. 1, 10, 19, 28, 37, 46, 55, 64, 73
- Lesson Plans for Block Scheduling, pp. 2, 11, 20, 29, 38, 47, 56, 65, 74

Technology
- Electronic Teacher Tools with Lesson Planning Software
- Test and Practice Generator

Chapter 7 Getting Ready

PREVIEW

What's the chapter about?

- Using concepts of **ratio** and **rate** to write and solve **proportions**, including **scale drawings** and models
- Understanding **probability**
- Applying **percent** in proportions, **markup** and **discount**, and **simple** and **compound interest**

WORDS TO KNOW

- **ratio,** *p. 329*
- **rate,** *p. 330*
- **proportion,** *p. 333*
- **cross products,** *p. 333*
- **scale drawing,** *p. 338*
- **probability,** *p. 345*
- **interest,** *p. 365*
- **simple interest,** *p. 365*
- **compound interest,** *p. 369*

PREPARE

Chapter Readiness Quiz

Take this quick quiz. If you are unsure of an answer, look back at the reference pages for help.

VOCABULARY CHECK *(refer to p. 80)*

1. Which best illustrates the division property of equality? **B**

Ⓐ $\frac{x}{4} = \frac{5}{2} \rightarrow x = \frac{20}{2}$

Ⓑ $6x = 48 \rightarrow \frac{6x}{6} = \frac{48}{6}$

Ⓒ $\frac{75}{15} = 5 \rightarrow 5 \cdot 15 = 75$

Ⓓ $\frac{48}{9} = x \rightarrow \frac{16}{3} = x$

SKILL CHECK *(refer to p. 248)*

2. Which statement is false? **J**

Ⓕ $\frac{25}{8} = 312.5\%$

Ⓖ $333\frac{1}{3}\% = 3\frac{1}{3}$

Ⓗ $\frac{3}{1000} = 0.3\%$

Ⓙ $1.01 = 110\%$

STUDY TIP

Make Flash Cards

Make flash cards to use while you study with a classmate or family member.

What is 15% of 30?

7.1 Ratios and Rates

California Standards

In this lesson you'll:

- Solve problems involving rate, average speed, distance, and time. (AF 4.2)
- Choose an appropriate unit of measure and use ratios to convert within and between measurement systems. (MG 1.0)
- Compare measures within and between measurement systems. (MG 1.1)

Goal 1 FINDING RATIOS

A **ratio** is a comparison of a number a and a nonzero number b using division. The ratio of a to b can be written in three ways, as the fraction $\frac{a}{b}$ (or an equivalent decimal), as $a : b$, or as "a to b."

EXAMPLE 1 Writing a Ratio in Simplest Form

VOTING In the presidential election of 1904, Theodore Roosevelt won 336 electoral votes. Alton B. Parker won 140 electoral votes. What was the ratio of Roosevelt's electoral votes to Parker's electoral votes?

Solution

$$\text{Ratio} = \frac{\text{Roosevelt votes}}{\text{Parker votes}}$$

$$= \frac{336}{140} = \frac{\overset{1}{\cancel{28}} \cdot 12}{\underset{1}{\cancel{28}} \cdot 5} = \frac{12}{5}$$

ANSWER ▶ The ratio of Roosevelt's electoral votes to Parker's electoral votes was 12 : 5, or "12 to 5."

EXAMPLE 2 Rewriting with the Same Units

MODEL HOUSE You are building a model of a house. The actual house is 24 feet high. You want your model to be 8 inches high. What is the ratio of the height of the actual house to the height of the model house?

Solution

To find the ratio, you need to express both quantities in the same units of measure. Convert the height of the house from feet to inches.

$$24 \text{ feet} = 24 \cancel{\text{feet}} \cdot \frac{12 \text{ inches}}{1 \cancel{\text{foot}}} = 288 \text{ inches}$$

Now, find the ratio of the heights.

$$\text{Ratio} = \frac{\text{Height of the actual house}}{\text{Height of the model house}}$$

$$= \frac{288 \cancel{\text{inches}}}{8 \cancel{\text{inches}}} = \frac{\overset{1}{\cancel{8}} \cdot 36}{\underset{1}{\cancel{8}} \cdot 1} = \frac{36}{1}$$

ANSWER ▶ The ratio of the height of the actual house to the height of the model house is 36 : 1, or "36 to 1."

Student Help

▶ **SKILLS REVIEW**
For help with converting units of measure, see page 681.

1 Plan

Pacing

Suggested Number of Days

Transitional: 1 day
Average: 1 day
Advanced: 1 day
Block Schedule: 0.5 block with 7.2

Teaching Resources

Blacklines
(See page 326B.)

Transparencies
- Warm-Up Exercises
- Teacher Time-Savers
- English/Spanish Problem Solving
- Answers

Technology
- Electronic Teacher Tools
- Test and Practice Generator

2 Teach

Math Reasoning

For Mathematical Background Notes on mathematical reasoning related to this lesson, please refer to pages 326E and 326F in this Teacher's Edition.

Extra Examples 1 and 2
See next page.

California Standards and Assessment

CA Standards: AF 4.2, MG 1.0, MG 1.1

CA Key Concepts Book: pp. S78, T14–T21

Math Reasoning

Throughout this lesson, it is important to distinguish between ratios and rates. A ratio is a "pure number" in the sense that it does not express a relation between different units. A rate *does* express a numerical relation between units. For instance, in Example 2 it is possible to express both actual height and model height in terms of a common unit. In this form, "actual height to model height" is a ratio. However, in Example 3 it is not possible to express the quantities being compared in terms of a common unit.

Extra Example 1

In the 1860 presidential election, Abraham Lincoln won 180 electoral votes while John Breckenridge won 72 electoral votes. What was the ratio of Lincoln's electoral votes to Breckenridge's electoral votes? **5 : 2 or 5 to 2**

Extra Example 2

On a set of house plans, an architect wants to represent the 30 ft length of a living room by a 5 in. segment. What is the ratio of the length of the segment to the length of the living room? **1 : 72 or 1 to 72**

Extra Example 3

You drove 280 miles in 5 hours. The total amount of gas used was 14 gallons.

a. What was the average rate of fuel consumption? **20 mi/gal**

b. What was the average rate of speed? **56 mi/h**

Extra Example 4

A 6.5 oz jar of mustard costs $.49 and a 9 oz jar costs $.69. Which is the better buy? **the 6.5 oz jar**

Goal 2 FINDING RATES

A **rate of *a* per *b*** is a type of ratio that compares two quantities, *a* and *b*, that have different kinds of units of measure. A rate with a denominator of 1 unit is a *unit rate*. An example of a unit rate is $23 per foot.

EXAMPLE 3 Finding a Rate

DRIVING You and your family drove 400 miles in 8 hours. The total amount of fuel used was 20 gallons of gas.

a. What was the average rate of fuel consumption?

b. What was the average rate of speed?

Solution

a. To find the average rate of fuel consumption, divide the distance by the fuel used.

$$\text{Rate} = \frac{\text{Distance}}{\text{Fuel used}} = \frac{400 \text{ miles}}{20 \text{ gallons}} = \frac{\overset{1}{\cancel{20}} \cdot 20 \text{ miles}}{\underset{1}{\cancel{20}} \cdot 1 \text{ gallon}} = \frac{20 \text{ miles}}{1 \text{ gallon}}$$

ANSWER ▶ The result, $\frac{20 \text{ miles}}{1 \text{ gallon}}$, means 20 miles per gallon. So, the average rate of fuel consumption was 20 miles per gallon.

b. To find the average rate of speed, divide the distance by the time.

$$\text{Rate} = \frac{\text{Distance}}{\text{Time}} = \frac{400 \text{ miles}}{8 \text{ hours}} = \frac{\overset{1}{\cancel{8}} \cdot 50 \text{ miles}}{\underset{1}{\cancel{8}} \cdot 1 \text{ hour}} = \frac{50 \text{ miles}}{1 \text{ hour}}$$

ANSWER ▶ The result, $\frac{50 \text{ miles}}{1 \text{ hour}}$, means 50 miles per hour. So, the average rate of speed was 50 miles per hour.

Link to Economics

UNIT PRICING Many cities and states by law require stores to display unit prices to assist the consumer.

EXAMPLE 4 Finding a Unit Price

ECONOMICS A 16 ounce box of breakfast cereal costs $2.89, and a 20 ounce box costs $3.49. Which is the better buy?

Solution

Use a calculator to find the unit price for each cereal. Then compare the two unit prices to find which is smaller.

Price	Weight	Unit price
$2.89	16 ounces	$\frac{\$2.89}{16 \text{ ounces}} \approx 0.181$ dollars per ounce
$3.49	20 ounces	$\frac{\$3.49}{20 \text{ ounces}} \approx 0.175$ dollars per ounce

ANSWER ▶ The larger box has the smaller unit price so it is the better buy.

7.1 Exercises

Guided Practice

In Exercises 1 and 2, write the ratio as a fraction $\frac{a}{b}$ in simplest form.

1. 15 baskets in 30 attempts **$\frac{1}{2}$ basket per attempt**

2. 177 points scored in 5 games **$\frac{177}{5}$ points per game**

3. Describe six ratios that compare the colors of the nine triangles. **$\frac{4}{9}$, $\frac{5}{9}$, 4:5, 5:4, 9 to 5, 9 to 4**

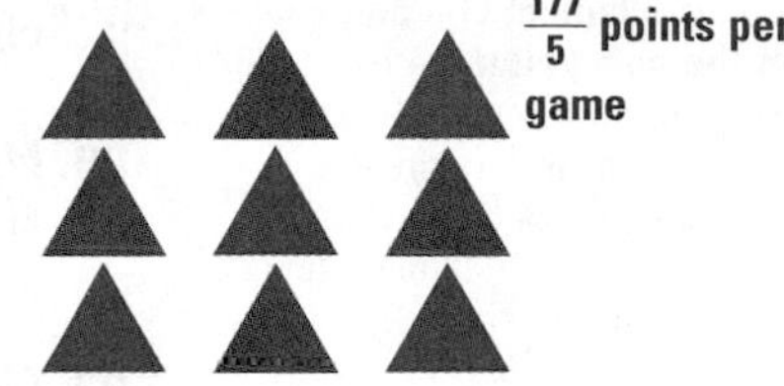

In Exercises 4–7, express both quantities in a common unit of measure, then write the ratio as a fraction $\frac{a}{b}$ in simplest form.

4. 5 inches to 2 feet **$\frac{5}{24}$**

5. 7 feet to 7 yards **$\frac{1}{3}$**

6. 18 ounces to 4 pounds **$\frac{9}{32}$**

7. 24 pints to 3 quarts **$\frac{4}{1}$**

8. Determine which of the following choices measures the rate at which an automobile uses gasoline. **A**

A. Miles per gallon **B.** Dollars per gallon **C.** Miles per hour

Practice and Problem Solving

> **Student Help**
> ▶**MORE PRACTICE**
> Extra practice to help you master skills is on page 702.

Write the ratio as a fraction $\frac{a}{b}$ in simplest form.

9. 5 out of 20 people $\frac{1}{4}$

10. 16 baskets in 18 attempts $\frac{8}{9}$ baskets per attempt

11. 19 out of 25 magazines $\frac{19}{25}$

12. 242 out of 364 cars $\frac{121}{182}$

13. 89 losses in 412 games $\frac{89}{412}$ losses per game

14. 125 rebounds in 13 games $\frac{125}{13}$ rebounds per game

In Exercises 15–18, express both quantities in a common unit of measure, then write the ratio as a fraction $\frac{a}{b}$ in simplest form.

15. $\frac{\text{2 feet}}{\text{18 inches}}$ $\frac{4}{3}$ **16.** $\frac{\text{1 hour}}{\text{3600 seconds}}$ $\frac{1}{1}$ **17.** $\frac{\text{2 minutes}}{\text{300 seconds}}$ $\frac{2}{5}$ **18.** $\frac{\text{2640 feet}}{\text{1 mile}}$ $\frac{1}{2}$

> **Student Help**
> ▶**HOMEWORK HELP**
> INTERNET Extra help with problem solving in Exs. 19–20 is available at www.mcdougallittell.com

19. CONCERT TICKETS A concert sold out in 6 hours. Nine thousand tickets were sold for the concert. Find the hourly rate at which the tickets sold. 1500 tickets per hour

20. SNOWFALL The record for snowfall in 24 hours is 78 inches at Mile 47 Camp, Cooper River Division, Alaska, on February 7, 1963. Find the average hourly rate at which the snow fell on that day. $3\frac{1}{4}$ in./h

Concept Check

What is the difference between a rate and a ratio? **A rate is the quotient of two quantities that have different units of measure; a ratio is a comparison of a number *a* and a nonzero number *b* using division.**

3 Apply

Assignment Guide

TRANSITIONAL
Day 1: SRH p. 681 Exs. 1–4; pp. 331–332 Exs. 9–12, 15–25, 33–34

AVERAGE
Day 1: pp. 331–332 Exs. 9–23, 26, 28–29, 33–34

ADVANCED
Day 1: pp. 331–332 Exs. 15–23, 26, 27*, 28–31, 33–34

BLOCK SCHEDULE
pp. 331–332 Exs. 9–23, 26, 28–29, 33–34 (with 7.2)

Extra Practice

- Student Edition, pp. 702–703
- Chapter 7 Resource Book, p. 6

Homework Check

To quickly check student understanding of key concepts, go over the following exercises:

Transitional: 10, 16, 20, 22, 24
Average: 12, 18, 20, 22, 28
Advanced: 18, 20, 22, 26, 28

Problem Solving

Exercise 19
Explain to students that when a problem asks for a "rate per hour," the hour units are in the denominator of the fraction, $\frac{\text{9000 tickets}}{\text{6 hours}}$. The word "per" can be interpreted as a fraction bar.

4 Assess

Assessment Resources

- Assessment Book (Formal Assessment and Alternative Assessment)
- Test and Practice Generator

Mini-Quiz

Write the verbal phrase as a rate or ratio. Explain why the phrase is a rate or ratio.

1. Preferred by 3 out of 7 students **3 : 7; ratio; same units**
2. Sold 120 rings in 8 h **15 rings/h; rate; different units**
3. You are drawing a map of your neighborhood. On the map, 2 feet represents 500 feet. What is the ratio of the map distance to actual distance? **1 : 250 or 1 to 250**
4. You drive 315 miles in 6 hours. You use 15 gallons of gas. What is your average rate of fuel consumption? **21 mi/gal**
5. A 20 ounce can of pineapple costs $1.29 and an 8 ounce can costs $.59. Which is the better buy? **the 20 ounce can**

Math Reasoning

In Exercise 34, as an explanation of why "average speed" is defined to be 448 ÷ 7, it may be useful to refer to the definition of "average" for a set of numbers. By recording the distance traveled each hour, one obtains a set of 7 numbers. Summing these 7 numbers, one obtains 448. The sum of these 7 numbers divided by 7 is 448 ÷ 7, which is the average speed.

30–32. See Additional Answers beginning on page AA1.

25. The 5 pounds, 2 ounces of chicken at $10.92 is the better buy. The unit price of the 2 pounds, 4 ounces at $6.50 is $.18/ounce; the unit price of the 5 pounds, 2 ounces of chicken at $10.92 is $.13/ounce.

26. The half-gallon bottle is the better buy. The unit price of the six 12-ounce cans for $5.79 is $.08 per ounce. The unit price of the half-gallon bottle is $.07 per ounce. It may be more convenient to buy the six 12-ounce cans if the juice is going to be consumed over a long period of time.

Link to Careers

VETERINARIAN Many veterinarians treat animals on farms or in zoos. Others do research for the U.S. Public Health Service.

More about veterinarians available at www.mcdougallittell.com

In Exercises 21–23, find the unit price.

21. 10 ounces at $3.59 $.359/oz **22.** $3.99 for a dozen $.333 per item **23.** 6 gallons for $6.75 $1.125/gal

UNIT PRICING In Exercises 24 and 25, decide which is the better buy. Explain your reasoning. Round to the nearest hundredth.

24. A 12 ounce box of cookies for $2.69 or an 18 ounce box of the same cookies for $3.99 Both have the same unit price of $.22 per ounce.

25. 2 pounds, 4 ounces of chicken for $6.50 or 5 pounds, 2 ounces of chicken for $10.92 See margin.

26. MATHEMATICAL REASONING A newspaper advertised apple juice in six 12 ounce cans for $5.79 and one 64 ounce bottle for $4.59. Which is the better buy? When might you choose not to buy the better buy? See margin.

27. CHALLENGE Two measures of fuel consumption for a car are gallons per mile and miles per gallon. What is the fuel consumption in gallons per mile for a car that gets 20 miles per gallon? Explain your reasoning. $\frac{1}{\frac{20 \text{ mi}}{\text{gal}}} = \frac{1 \text{ gal}}{20 \text{ mi}} = 0.05 \frac{\text{gal}}{\text{mi}}$

ANIMALS In Exercises 28 and 29, use the following information.
The heart of a horse beats 20 times in 40 seconds. The heart of a dog beats 5 times in 3 seconds.

28. Find the heart rate of each animal in beats per minute. horse: 30 beats/min dog: 100 beats/min

29. Determine which animal has a faster heartbeat. Justify your answer. See margin.

GEOMETRY Find the ratio of the green region's perimeter to the yellow region's perimeter. Then find the ratio of the green region's area to the yellow region's area. Record your data in a table. For each figure determine which ratio is greater. Explain your reasoning. 30–32. See margin.

30. **31.** **32.** $\frac{5}{2}$ 5 3 4

Multiple-Choice Practice

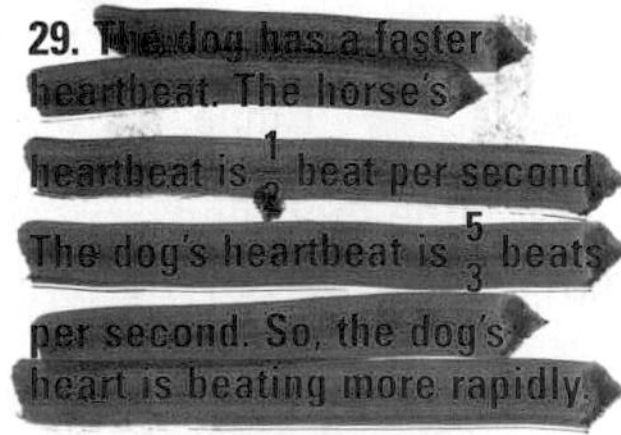

29. The dog has a faster heartbeat. The horse's heartbeat is $\frac{1}{2}$ beat per second. The dog's heartbeat is $\frac{5}{3}$ beats per second. So, the dog's heart is beating more rapidly.

33. Your soccer team finishes the regular season with a record of 20 wins and 8 losses. What is the ratio of wins to losses? B

Ⓐ 2 to 5 Ⓑ 5 to 2 Ⓒ 5 to 7 Ⓓ 2 to 7

34. Your family drives 448 miles in 7 hours on a vacation trip. What is the average rate of speed? H

Ⓕ 0.016 miles/hour Ⓖ 7 to 448 miles/hour

Ⓗ 64 miles/hour Ⓙ Not here

7.2 Writing and Solving Proportions

California Standards

In this lesson you'll:

- Use variables and appropriate operations to write an equation that represents a verbal description. (AF 1.1)
- Solve simple linear equations over rational numbers. (AF 4.0)
- Compare measures within and between measurement systems. (MG 1.1)

Goal 1 Solving Proportions

An equation that states that two ratios are equal is called a **proportion**. The proportion $\frac{a}{b} = \frac{c}{d}$ is read as "a is to b as c is to d." It has two **cross products**, ad and bc. The process of forming cross products is called *cross multiplying*.

$$\frac{a}{b} \times \frac{c}{d} \rightarrow b \cdot c, \quad a \cdot d$$

Cross products

In Exercise 30 you will show that the following property is true.

Cross Products Property

In Words In a proportion, the cross products are equal.

In Algebra If $\frac{a}{b} = \frac{c}{d}$ where $b \neq 0$ and $d \neq 0$ then $ad = bc$.

In Arithmetic Because $\frac{2}{5} = \frac{4}{10}$, you know that $2 \cdot 10 = 5 \cdot 4$.

When you know three numbers in a proportion, you can find the missing value by using cross products.

Example 1 Using the Cross Products Property

Use the cross products property to solve the proportion $\frac{3}{m} = \frac{5}{15}$.

Solution

$\frac{3}{m} = \frac{5}{15}$ Write original proportion.

$3 \cdot 15 = m \cdot 5$ Cross products property

$\frac{3 \cdot 15}{5} = \frac{m \cdot 5}{5}$ Divide each side by 5.

$9 = m$ Simplify. *m* is by itself.

ANSWER ▶ The solution is 9.

CHECK ✓ You can check the solution by showing that $\frac{3}{9}$ and $\frac{5}{15}$ simplify to the same fraction:

$$\frac{3}{9} = \frac{1}{3} \text{ and } \frac{5}{15} = \frac{1}{3}, \text{ so } \frac{3}{9} = \frac{5}{15}.$$

1 Plan

Pacing

Suggested Number of Days

Transitional: 1 day
Average: 1 day
Advanced: 1 day
Block Schedule: 0.5 block with 7.1

Teaching Resources

Blacklines

(See page 326B.)

Transparencies

- Warm-Up Exercises
- Teacher Time-Savers
- English/Spanish Problem Solving
- Answers

Technology

- Electronic Teacher Tools
- Test and Practice Generator

2 Teach

Math Reasoning

For Mathematical Background Notes on mathematical reasoning related to this lesson, please refer to pages 326E and 326F in this Teacher's Edition.

Extra Example 1
See next page.

California Standards and Assessment

CA Standards: AF 1.1, AF 4.0, MG 1.1

CA Key Concepts Book: pp. T14–T17

Extra Example 1

Use the cross products property to solve the proportion $\frac{8}{x} = \frac{5}{20}$. **32**

Math Reasoning

In connection with Example 2, it may be important to remind students that two fractions are compared by writing both over a common denominator. In this case an effort to determine which fraction is the larger leads to the fact that the fractions are equivalent.

Extra Example 2

A baby sitter makes $20 for working 6 hours. Another day she makes $30 for working 9 hours. What proportion could you write to find whether the baby sitter was paid consistently? **$\frac{20 \text{ dollars}}{6 \text{ hours}} \stackrel{?}{=} \frac{30 \text{ dollars}}{9 \text{ hours}}$ or $\frac{6 \text{ hours}}{20 \text{ dollars}} \stackrel{?}{=} \frac{9 \text{ hours}}{30 \text{ dollars}}$**

Extra Example 3

Asia occupies about $\frac{3}{10}$ of Earth's total land area. If Asia occupies about 17 million square miles of land area, what is the total land area of Earth? **about 57 million mi^2**

Teaching Tip

There are several ways to represent the same proportion, $\frac{a}{b} = \frac{c}{d}$: $\frac{a}{c} = \frac{b}{d}$, $\frac{d}{b} = \frac{c}{a}$, $\frac{d}{c} = \frac{b}{a}$.

Goal 2 USING PROPORTIONS IN REAL LIFE

Be sure you compare quantities in the same order in a proportion.

EXAMPLE 2 Writing a Proportion

READING You are reading a novel. One day you read 30 pages in 50 minutes. The next day you read 24 more pages in 40 minutes. What proportion could you write to see if you read at the same rate both days?

Solution

Method 1 You can write two ratios, each of which compares pages read to minutes spent reading:

$$\frac{30 \text{ (pages)}}{50 \text{ (minutes)}} \stackrel{?}{=} \frac{24 \text{ (pages)}}{40 \text{ (minutes)}}$$

Each ratio is a rate whose units are pages per minute.

Method 2 You can write two ratios, each of which compares minutes spent reading to pages read:

$$\frac{50 \text{ (minutes)}}{30 \text{ (pages)}} \stackrel{?}{=} \frac{40 \text{ (minutes)}}{24 \text{ (pages)}}$$

Each ratio is a rate whose units are minutes per page.

Student Help

▶ STUDY TIP
In Example 2 be sure you don't set up your proportion to compare pages to minutes in one ratio and minutes to pages in the other ratio.

Link to Science

ICEBERGS Once an Arctic iceberg reaches the relatively warmer waters of the North Atlantic, it loses height at a rate of 2 to 3 meters per day.

More about icebergs available at www.mcdougallittell.com

EXAMPLE 3 Writing and Solving a Proportion

SCIENCE LINK Only one seventh of the mass of an iceberg in the Arctic is visible above water. If about 70 tons of an iceberg is showing above water, what is the mass of the entire iceberg?

Solution

VERBAL MODEL $\frac{\text{Visible mass of the iceberg}}{\text{Entire mass of iceberg}} = \text{Ratio}$

LABELS
Visible mass of the iceberg = **70** (tons)
Entire mass of the iceberg = x (tons)
Ratio of visible mass of an iceberg to entire iceberg = $\frac{1}{7}$

ALGEBRAIC MODEL

$\frac{70}{x} = \frac{1}{7}$	Write algebraic model.
$70 \cdot 7 = x \cdot 1$	Cross products property
$490 = x$	Simplify. x is by itself.

ANSWER ▶ The mass of the iceberg is about 490 tons.

EXAMPLE 4 Writing a Proportion

HEALTH After exercising you check your heart rate. In 10 seconds you count 26 beats. What is your heart rate in beats per minute?

Solution

VERBAL MODEL

$$\frac{\text{Number of heart beats counted}}{\text{Amount of time}} = \frac{\text{Number of beats}}{\text{1 minute}}$$

LABELS

Number of heart beats counted = **26** (heart beats)

Amount of time spent counting = **10** (seconds)

Number of heart beats in 1 minute = x (heart beats)

Number of seconds in 1 minute = **60** (seconds)

ALGEBRAIC MODEL

$\frac{26}{10} = \frac{x}{60}$ Write algebraic model.

$x \cdot 10 = 26 \cdot 60$ Cross products property

$\frac{x \cdot 10}{10} = \frac{26 \cdot 60}{10}$ Divide each side by 10.

$x = 156$ Simplify. x is by itself.

ANSWER ▶ Your heart rate is 156 beats per minute.

Student Help

▶ **MORE EXAMPLES**

INTERNET More examples are available at www.mcdougallittell.com

Extra Example 4

On January 10, 1911, in Rapid City, South Dakota, the temperature fell 47°F in 15 minutes. What was the average rate of the temperature fall per hour? **188°F per hour**

Concept Check

How can the cross products property be used to solve a proportion? ***Sample answer:*** **Set the cross products equal and solve for the variable.**

7.2 Exercises

Guided Practice

Use the cross products property to solve the proportion.

1. $\frac{b}{3} = \frac{4}{12}$ **1** **2.** $\frac{9}{x} = \frac{3}{5}$ **15** **3.** $\frac{2}{3} = \frac{m}{36}$ **24** **4.** $\frac{7}{18} = \frac{21}{y}$ **54**

ERROR ANALYSIS Describe and correct the error.

5. If you earn $35 in 5 hours, how much money will you earn in 17 hours?

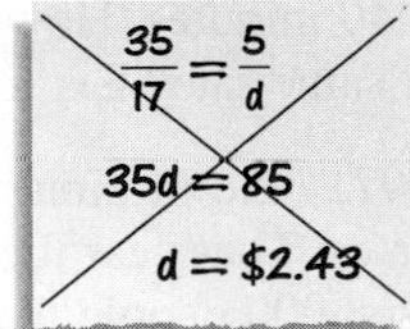

6. If you walk 2 miles in 30 minutes, how long will it take you to walk 5 miles?

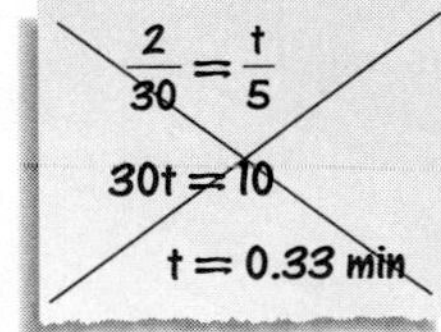

5. *Sample answer:* The student is setting two ratios equal that are not in proportion. $\frac{35}{5} = \frac{d}{17}$; **$119**

6. *Sample answer:* The student is setting two ratios equal that are not in proportion. $\frac{2}{30} = \frac{5}{t}$; **75 minutes**

3 Apply

Assignment Guide

TRANSITIONAL
Day 1: pp. 336–337 Exs. 7–8, 11–14, 19–20, 24–26, 31–37

AVERAGE
Day 1: pp. 336–337 Exs. 9–10, 15–18, 21–27, 31–37

ADVANCED
Day 1: pp. 336–337 Exs. 9–10, 15–20, 26–28, 29*, 30–37

BLOCK SCHEDULE
pp. 336–337 Exs. 9–10, 15–18, 21–27, 31–37 (with 7.1)

Extra Practice

- Student Edition, pp. 702–703
- Chapter 7 Resource Book, p. 15

Homework Check

To quickly check student understanding of key concepts, go over the following exercises:

Transitional: 12, 14, 20, 24, 26
Average: 16, 18, 22, 24, 26
Advanced: 16, 18, 20, 24, 26

Practice and Problem Solving

Student Help

▶ **MORE PRACTICE** Extra practice to help you master skills is on page 702.

Write the statement as a proportion. Then solve.

7. x is to 6 as 8 is to 9.

8. y is to 5 as 6 is to 17.

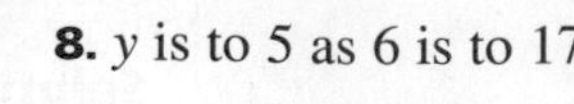

9. 3 is to 8 as m is to 24.

10. 2 is to 5 as 10 is to n.

In Exercises 11–18, solve the proportion. Check your solution.

11. $\frac{x}{3} = \frac{4}{9}$ **12.** $\frac{y}{5} = \frac{8}{5}$ **13.** $\frac{5}{7} = \frac{z}{2}$ **14.** $\frac{5}{12} = \frac{t}{2}$

15. $\frac{8}{m} = \frac{2}{5}$ **16.** $\frac{9}{x} = \frac{15}{2}$ **17.** $\frac{2}{3} = \frac{12}{b}$ **18.** $\frac{2.8}{y} = \frac{11}{2.5}$

19. DRIVING One car traveled 840 miles on 30 gallons of gas. Another car used 36 gallons of gas to travel 1008 miles. What proportion could you write to see if they are using fuel at the same rate?

20. RUNNING Lena can run 4 miles in 30 minutes. Rachel can run 7 miles in 56 minutes. What proportion could you write to see if they are running at the same rate?

Link to History

To EUROPE
To ASIA
To AFRICA

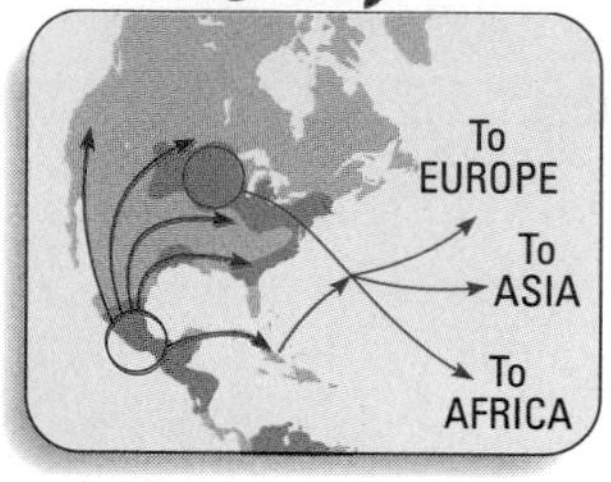

CORN Before 1492 corn was grown only in North America. European explorers brought corn back to Europe and also to Asia and Africa.

CORN BREAD RECIPE **In Exercises 21–23, use the recipe card.**

21. If you had 8 cups of corn meal, how many loaves of corn bread could you make?

22. To make 10 loaves of corn bread, how much sugar would you need?

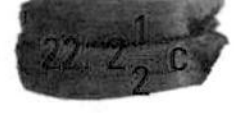

23. How many loaves of corn bread would you have to make if you wanted to serve 30 people?

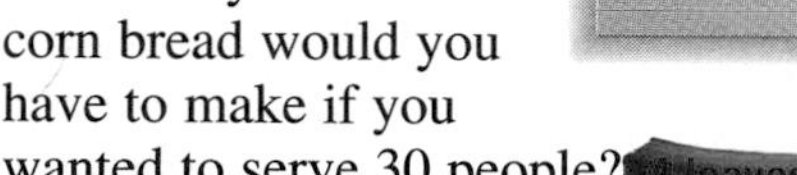

Easy Corn Bread (1 loaf)	
1 1/4 c flour	Preheat oven to 400°F.
3/4 c corn meal	Grease 8 by 8 inch pan.
1/4 c sugar	
2 t baking powder	Combine dry ingredients.
1/2 t salt	Mix in milk, oil, and egg.
1 c skim milk	Pour into pan. Bake 20
1/4 c vegetable oil	to 25 minutes.
1 egg, beaten	
	9 servings

In Exercises 24–27, write a proportion and solve.

24. DRIVING If a car is traveling at a speed of 45 miles per hour, how far can it travel in 40 minutes?

25. SHOPPING A supermarket advertises 3 pounds of tomatoes for $1.20. How much would it cost to buy 5 pounds of tomatoes?

26. READING RATE A teacher has 54 research papers to read. She can read three of them in 40 minutes. How long will it take her to read all of the papers at the same rate? Express your answer in hours.

27. BANANAS In 1997, 7450 million pounds of bananas were consumed in the United States. That year the U.S. population was 269 million people, and 32,268,000 people lived in California. Approximate the number of pounds of bananas eaten in California in 1997.

28. CORN You are husking corn for a cookout. Suppose it took 20 minutes to husk a total of 25 ears of corn. How long will it take to husk 30 more ears of corn? 24 min

29. CHALLENGE The ratio of Tom's age to Jill's age is 3 : 2. In 12 years the ratio will be 5 : 4. How old are Tom and Jill now? Tom is 18 years old; Jill is 12 years old

30. MATHEMATICAL REASONING The statements below prove the cross products property. Give a reason for each lettered step.

$\frac{a}{b} = \frac{c}{d}$; $b \neq 0, d \neq 0$	Given
$b \cdot d \cdot \frac{a}{b} = b \cdot d \cdot \frac{c}{d}$	**a.** ? Multiplication property of equality
$b \cdot d \cdot a \cdot \frac{1}{b} = b \cdot d \cdot c \cdot \frac{1}{d}$	Rewrite division as multiplication.
$\left(b \cdot \frac{1}{b}\right) \cdot a \cdot d = \left(d \cdot \frac{1}{d}\right) \cdot c \cdot b$	**b.** ? Associative and commutative properties of multiplication;
$1 \cdot a \cdot d = 1 \cdot c \cdot b$	**c.** ? Inverse property of multiplication
$a \cdot d = b \cdot c$	**d.** ? Identity property of multiplication; commutative property of multiplication

Multiple-Choice Practice

▶Be sure your answer is reasonable. In Exercise 32, is it reasonable to take 27,040 minutes to type 1040 words?

31. What is the solution of the proportion $\frac{x}{20} = \frac{3}{10}$? C

Ⓐ 1.5 Ⓑ 2 Ⓒ 6 Ⓓ 66.67

32. You can type at a rate of 26 words per minute. How long will it take you to type a report containing 1040 words? G

Ⓕ 30 minutes Ⓖ 40 minutes

Ⓗ 45 minutes Ⓙ 27,040 minutes

Mixed Review

In Exercises 33 and 34, use the picture at the right. The frame is 2 inches wide on all four sides. *(1.5)*

33. Find the perimeter of the picture frame. 60 in.

34. Find the perimeter and area of the picture inside the frame. perimeter: 44 in., area: 112 in.^{2}

Change the percent to a decimal or a fraction. Then multiply. *(6.4)*

35. 32% of 225 72 **36.** 14% of 550 77 **37.** 175% of 10 17.5

38. 240% of 60 144 **39.** 8.8% of 45 3.96 **40.** 3.05% of 90 2.745

41. 0.9% of 9 0.081 **42.** 0.25% of 100 0.25 **43.** 1.05% of 105 1.1025

4 Assess

Assessment Resources

- Assessment Book (Formal Assessment and Alternative Assessment)
- Test and Practice Generator

Mini-Quiz

Solve the proportion.

1. $\frac{4}{h} = \frac{10}{16}$ 6.4
2. $\frac{9}{21} = \frac{12}{b}$ 28
3. Three-fourths of the seventh graders voted in a school election. If 264 seventh graders voted, how many seventh grade students are enrolled? **352**
4. The temperature one day fell 2 degrees in 40 seconds. What is the average rate of temperature decrease per minute? **3° per min**

Math Reasoning

Note that the Challenge is asking students to anticipate problems involving "two equations in two unknowns." Referring to Tom's and Jill's ages by T and J, respectively, the first statement leads to $2T = 3J$ and the second to $4(T + 12) = 5(J + 12)$.

1 Plan

Pacing

Suggested Number of Days

Transitional: 1 day
Average: 1 day
Advanced: 1 day
Block Schedule: 0.5 block with 7.4

Teaching Resources

Blacklines
(See page 326B.)

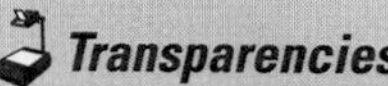

- Warm-Up Exercises
- Teacher Time-Savers
- English/Spanish Problem Solving
- Answers

Technology
- Electronic Teacher Tools
- Test and Practice Generator

2 Teach

Math Reasoning

For Mathematical Background Notes on mathematical reasoning related to this lesson, please refer to pages 326E and 326F in this Teacher's Edition.

California Standards and Assessment

CA Standards: MG 1.2, MG 2.0

7.3 Scale Drawings and Models

In this lesson you'll:

- Construct and read drawings and models made to scale. (MG 1.2)
- Compute the perimeter and area of common geometric objects; know how perimeter and area are affected by changes of scale. (MG 2.0)

Student Help

STUDY TIP
A scale drawing can be larger or smaller than the actual object. Maps and blueprints are common examples of scale drawings.

Goal 1 FINDING DIMENSIONS ON SCALE DRAWINGS

A **scale drawing** is a diagram of an object in which the length and width are proportional to the actual length and width of the object.

The **scale** for the drawing gives the relationship between the drawing's measurements and the actual measurements, such as "1 in. = 2 ft." This scale means that 1 inch in the drawing represents an actual distance of 2 feet.

The **scale factor** for a scale drawing is the ratio of the length and width in the drawing to the corresponding actual length and width.

EXAMPLE 1 Finding Actual Dimensions

Use the scale drawing of the theater stage.

a. Find the length of the back wall.

b. Find the scale factor.

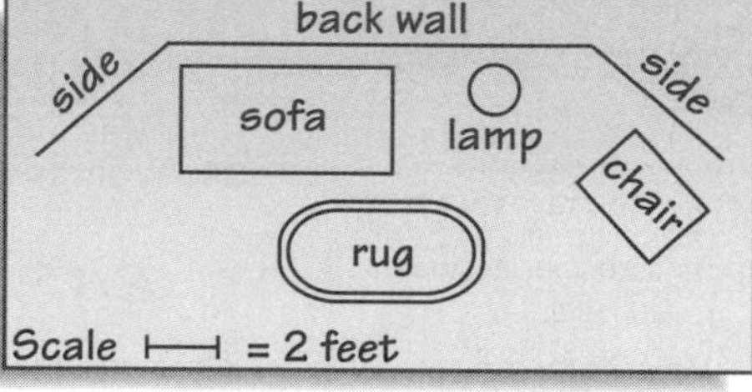

Solution

a. In the drawing, the scale measures 0.25 inch. When you measure the length of the back wall in the drawing, you find that it is 1.5 inches long. Let x be the actual length of the back wall.

$$\frac{\text{Actual length}}{\text{Length in drawing}} = \frac{2 \text{ feet}}{0.25 \text{ inches}}$$ Write a proportion.

$$\frac{x}{1.5 \text{ inches}} = \frac{24 \text{ inches}}{0.25 \text{ inches}}$$ Substitute and change units.

$$x \cdot 0.25 = 1.5 \cdot 24$$ Cross products property

$$x = 144$$ Divide each side by 0.25.

ANSWER ▶ The back wall is 144 inches, or 12 feet long. Check this in the original proportion.

b. Write the ratio of 0.25 inches and 2 feet. Convert feet to inches and simplify.

$$\frac{0.25 \text{ inches}}{2 \text{ feet}} = \frac{0.25 \text{ inches}}{24 \text{ inches}} = \frac{4 \cdot 0.25}{4 \cdot 24} = \frac{1}{96}$$

ANSWER ▶ So, each measurement in the scale drawing is $\frac{1}{96}$ of the corresponding measurement of the actual object.

Goal 2 DRAWING TO SCALE

To make a scale drawing you can take measurements of the actual objects, choose a scale, and then convert your measurements.

EXAMPLE 2 Making a Scale Drawing

You are making a scale drawing of your school computer room. The computer room is 20 feet long and 15 feet wide.

a. Find the length and width of the scale drawing of the computer room if the scale is $\frac{1}{2}$ inch = 10 feet.

b. Make a scale drawing of the computer room.

Solution

a. Find the length: Let x represent the room's length (in inches) on the drawing.

$\frac{\text{Length in diagram}}{\text{Actual length}} = \frac{0.5 \text{ inch}}{10 \text{ feet}}$ Write a proportion.

$\frac{x}{240 \text{ inches}} = \frac{0.5 \text{ inch}}{120 \text{ inches}}$ Substitute and change units. (20 ft = 240 in. and 10 ft = 120 in.)

$x \cdot 120 = 240 \cdot 0.5$ Cross products property

$x = 1$ Divide each side by 120.

ANSWER ▶ In the drawing, the computer room should be 1 inch long.

Find the width: Let x represent the room's width (in inches) on the drawing.

$\frac{\text{Width in diagram}}{\text{Actual width}} = \frac{0.5 \text{ inch}}{10 \text{ feet}}$ Write a proportion.

$\frac{x}{180 \text{ inches}} = \frac{0.5 \text{ inch}}{120 \text{ inches}}$ Substitute and change units. (15 ft = 180 in. and 10 ft = 120 in.)

$x \cdot 120 = 180 \cdot 0.5$ Cross products property

$x = 0.75$ Divide each side by 120.

ANSWER ▶ In the drawing, the computer room should be 0.75 inches wide.

b. To make the scale drawing, use $\frac{1}{8}$ inch graph paper. Then use a straightedge to draw a 1 inch by $\frac{3}{4}$ inch rectangle. Label the drawing using the scale.

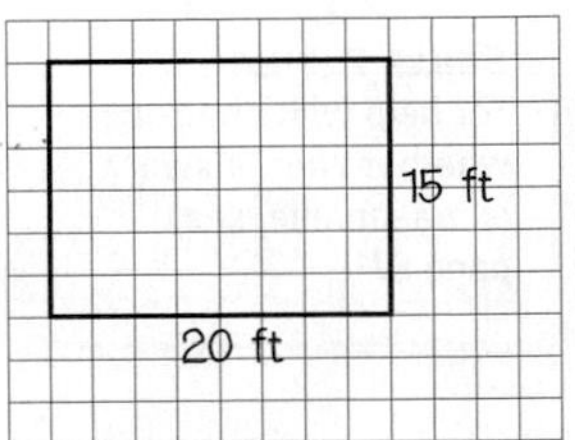

Link to Architecture

SCALE MODEL Architect Frank Gehry created a scale model of a design for a new computer center at the Massachusetts Institute of Technology.

Extra Example 1

Use the scale drawing of a school classroom.

a. Find the length of the wall behind the teacher's desk. **17.5 feet**

b. Find the scale factor. $\frac{1}{120}$

Teacher's Desk

Scale: 0.5 in. = 5 ft

Extra Example 2

You are making a scale drawing of your room. The room is 15 feet long by 12 feet wide.

a. Find the length and width of your room in the scale drawing if the scale is $\frac{1}{4}$ inch to 3 feet. **1.25 in. long by 1 in. wide**

b. Make a scale drawing of your room. **Check answers.**

Teaching Tip

When working with scale models, there are several ways to set up the proportion to result in the same answer. Two of those are:

$\frac{\text{Scale unit 1}}{\text{Actual unit 1}} = \frac{\text{Scale unit 2}}{\text{Actual unit 2}}$

and

$\frac{\text{Scale unit 1}}{\text{Scale unit 2}} = \frac{\text{Actual unit 1}}{\text{Actual unit 2}}.$

To see the other ways, refer to the Teaching Tip in Lesson 7.2.

Extra Example 3

Two triangles are shown. One has side lengths which are $\frac{1}{4}$ the lengths of the other. Are the perimeter and area of the smaller triangle $\frac{1}{4}$ the perimeter and area of the larger triangle?

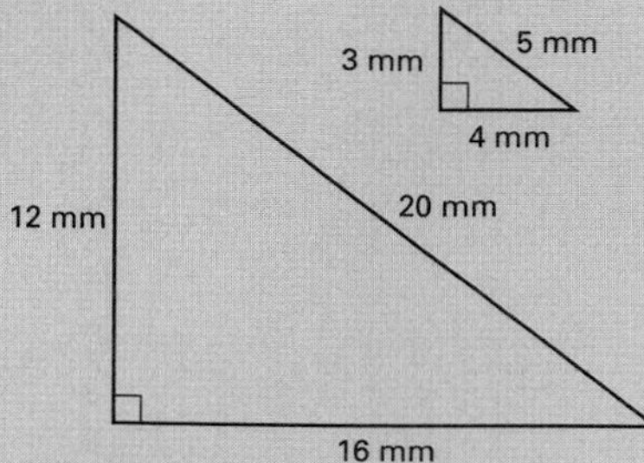

Perimeters are 12 mm and 48 mm. Areas are 6 mm^2 and 96 mm^2. The perimeter of the smaller triangle is $\frac{1}{4}$ the perimeter of the larger triangle, but the area is $\frac{1}{16}$ the area of the larger triangle.

Concept Check

Explain how to find an actual length from a scale drawing. ***Sample answer:*** **Find the length on the drawing by measuring. Set up a proportion using the measured length and the scale factor for the drawing. Solve the proportion.**

3. No; the enlarged photograph has twice the perimeter and four times the area of the wallet-sized photograph. Perimeter of wallet-sized photograph: 2(2) + 2(3) = 10 in.; perimeter of enlarged photograph: 2(4) + 2(6) = 20 in. The enlarged photograph has twice the perimeter of the wallet-sized photograph. Area of wallet-sized photograph: 2(3) = 6 in.^{2}; area of enlarged photograph: 4(6) = 24 in.^{2} The area of the enlarged photograph is four times the area of the wallet-sized photograph.

EXAMPLE 3 Comparing Perimeter and Area

PHOTOGRAPHS You use a photocopier to reduce an 8 inch by 10 inch photograph to 50% of its original size. Does the reduced photograph have half the perimeter and half the area of the original?

Solution

First find the perimeter and area of both figures.

	ORIGINAL PHOTOGRAPH	REDUCED PHOTOGRAPH
PERIMETER	$P = 2(8) + 2(10)$	$P = 2(4) + 2(5)$
	$= 36$ inches	$= 18$ inches
AREA	$A = 8(10)$	$A = 4(5)$
	$= 80$ square inches	$= 20$ square inches

Then write the ratios to compare the perimeters and areas.

PERIMETER

$$\text{Ratio} = \frac{\text{Perimeter of reduced}}{\text{Perimeter of original}} = \frac{18 \text{ inches}}{36 \text{ inches}} = \frac{1}{2}$$

AREA

$$\text{Ratio} = \frac{\text{Area of reduced}}{\text{Area of original}} = \frac{20 \text{ square inches}}{80 \text{ square inches}} = \frac{1}{4}$$

ANSWER ▶ The reduced photograph does have one half of the perimeter, but it has only one fourth the area.

7.3 Exercises

Guided Practice

In Exercises 1 and 2, use the following information.
The drawing of the bicycle has a scale of $\frac{3}{4}$ inch $= 2\frac{1}{4}$ feet. The distance between the centers of the wheels in the drawing is 1 inch.

1. Write a proportion to find the actual distance d between the centers of the wheels of the bicycle.

1. *Sample answer:* $\frac{2.25 \text{ ft}}{0.75 \text{ in.}} = \frac{x}{1 \text{ in.}}$ **(x meas. in ft)**

2. Solve the proportion in Exercise 1. Check the reasonableness of your answer. **$x = 3$ ft**

3. PHOTOGRAPHS You bring a 2 inch by 3 inch wallet-sized photograph to the photo shop to have it enlarged to a 4 inch by 6 inch photograph, twice its original size. Does the enlarged photograph have twice the perimeter and twice the area of the wallet-sized photograph? Explain. **See margin.**

Student Help

▶**SKILLS REVIEW**
For help with checking whether your answer is reasonable, see page 671.

Practice and Problem Solving

Student Help

▶**MORE PRACTICE** Extra practice to help you master skills is on page 702.

4. The floor plan at the right has a scale of $\frac{1}{4}$ inch = 4 feet. Find the actual measurements of three of the rooms. Record your data in a table. Show both the scale measurements and the actual measurements. See margin.

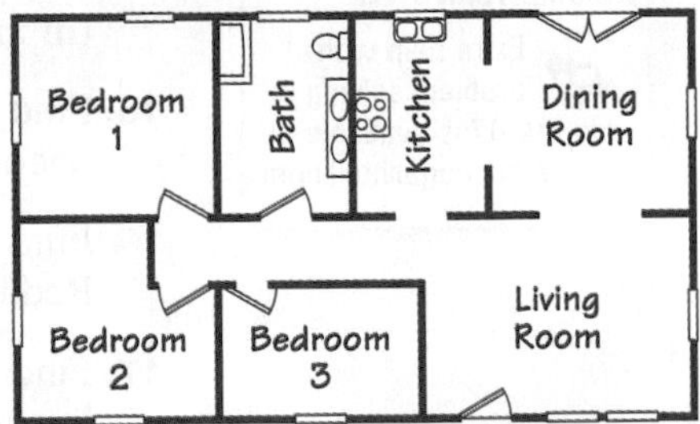

History Link **In Exercises 5–7, use the following information.** A wooden model galleon is built using a 1 : 90 scale. The length of the model is 520 millimeters, and the height is 615 millimeters.

Model galleon

5. Write the proportions to find the length ℓ and height h of the actual galleon. See margin.

6. Solve the proportions to find the actual length and height of the galleon. length: 46,800 millimeters, height: 55,350 millimeters

7. Rewrite the actual measurements in meters. length: 46.8 m, height: 55.35 m

In Exercises 8 and 9, use the following information. You are building a deck. You make a scale drawing with a scale of 2 feet = $\frac{1}{2}$ inch. The actual deck is 18 feet long and 12 feet wide. 8–9. See margin.

8. Determine the length and width of the deck in the scale drawing.

9. Use your answers from Exercise 8 to make a scale drawing.

10. **MATHEMATICAL REASONING** You have two maps of the same town. One uses a scale of 1 inch = 1000 feet, and the other uses the scale 1 inch = 1 mile. Which map is likely to show more detail? Explain your reasoning. See margin.

11. Choose a room in your home and construct a scale drawing of it. Be sure to include any furniture, closets, and doorways. What is the scale factor? Accept reasonable scale drawings that include appropriate scales.

12. **OFFICE SPACE** A company is moving to a smaller office. The original office was 60 feet long and 40 feet wide. The new office is 45 feet long and 30 feet wide, 75% of the original office's size. Does the new office have three fourths the area and three fourths the perimeter of the old office? Explain. See margin.

13. **DISTANCE** On a map the distance from Jacksonville, Florida, to Key West, Florida, measures $22\frac{1}{2}$ inches. The scale on the map is $1\frac{1}{8}$ inches = 25 miles. Find the actual distance between Jacksonville and Key West. 500 mi

SPANISH GALLEON The Spanish galleon was used as a trading ship in the late 1500s. Often it was used to sail up the coast of California and across the Pacific to the Philippine Islands.

INTERNET More about Spanish galleons available at www.mcdougallittell.com

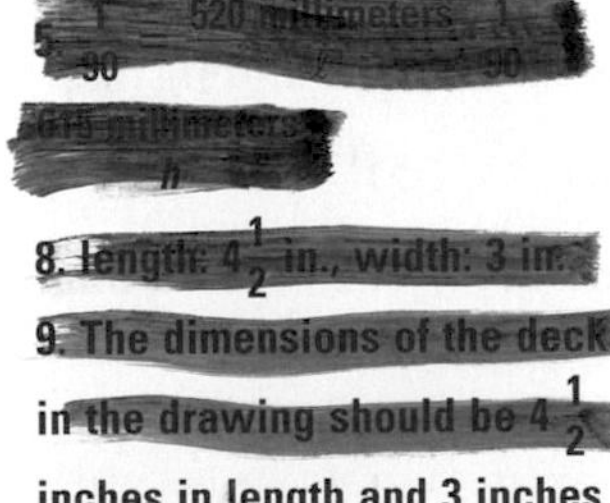

5. $\frac{1}{90} = \frac{520 \text{ millimeters}}{\ell}$, $\frac{1}{90} = \frac{615 \text{ millimeters}}{h}$

8. length: $4\frac{1}{2}$ in., width: 3 in.

9. The dimensions of the deck in the drawing should be $4\frac{1}{2}$ inches in length and 3 inches in width. The drawing must indicate that the scale is $\frac{1}{2}$ inch = 2 feet.

3 Apply

Assignment Guide

TRANSITIONAL
Day 1: SRH p. 671 Exs. 1–3; pp. 341–342 Exs. 4–7, 10, 12, 14–17, 20–21

AVERAGE
Day 1: pp. 341–342 Exs. 4–10, 12–17, 20–21

ADVANCED
Day 1: pp. 341–342 Exs. 4–10, 12–13, 18–19*, 20–21

BLOCK SCHEDULE
pp. 341–342 Exs. 4–10, 12–17, 20–21 (with 7.4)

Extra Practice

- Student Edition, pp. 702–703
- Chapter 7 Resource Book, p. 24

Homework Check

To quickly check student understanding of key concepts, go over the following exercises:

Transitional: 6, 8, 12, 14, 16
Average: 6, 8, 12, 14, 16
Advanced: 6, 8, 10, 12, 14

4. *Sample answer*:

	Map (in.)	Actual (ft)
Bedroom 1	$\frac{3}{4} \times \frac{3}{4}$	12 × 12
Bedroom 2	$\frac{3}{4} \times \frac{3}{4}$	12 × 12
Bedroom 3	$\frac{3}{4} \times \frac{1}{2}$	12 × 8

10. The map with the scale 1 inch = 1000 ft will show more detail. For example, a 200-foot long road will have a length of 0.2 inch on the map with a scale of 1 inch = 1000 feet. On a map with a scale of 1 inch = 1 mile, the length of the road will appear to be about 0.04 inch.

12. See Additional Answers beginning on page AA1.

4 Assess

Assessment Resources

- Assessment Book (Formal Assessment and Alternative Assessment)
- Test and Practice Generator

Mini-Quiz

The scale of a model is 1 to 60. Find the actual length for the given model length.

1. 11 in. **660 in. or 55 ft**
2. 1.5 ft **90 ft**
3. A map shows a distance of 2.5 inches between two cities. The scale for the map is $\frac{1}{4}$ inch = 15 miles. How far apart are the cities? **150 mi**
4. You have a scale model of a race car. The model was built using a 1-to-20 scale. The overall length of the actual race car is 18 ft. What is the length of the model? **0.9 ft or 10.8 in.**

18.

Celestial Body	Diameter of scale model to nearest 0.001 feet
Sun	25.950
Mercury	0.090
Venus	0.225
Earth	0.237
Mars	0.126
Jupiter	2.664
Saturn	2.247
Uranus	0.948
Neptune	0.924
Pluto	0.042

Student Help

▶**HOMEWORK HELP**

INTERNET Extra help with problem solving in Exs. 14–17 is available at www.mcdougallittell.com

14. $\frac{5}{8}$ in. = 100 mi

MAPS **In Exercises 14–17, use the map of Northern California.**

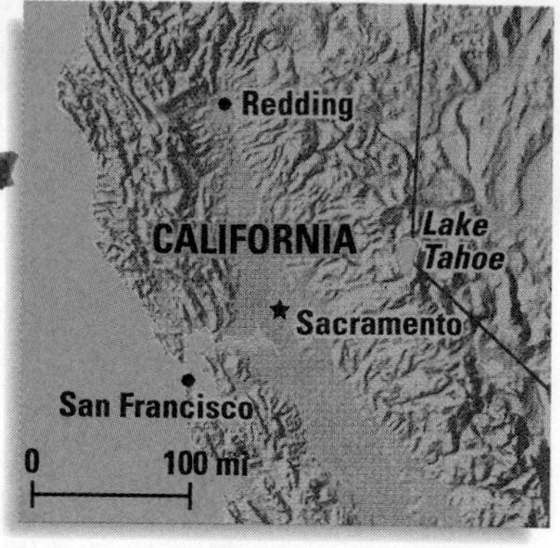

14. Measure the bar scale on the map (in inches). What is the map's scale?

15. Find the actual distance between Sacramento and San Francisco. **80 mi**

16. Find the actual distance between Redding and Lake Tahoe. **160 mi**

17. Find the actual distance between Sacramento and Redding. **140 mi**

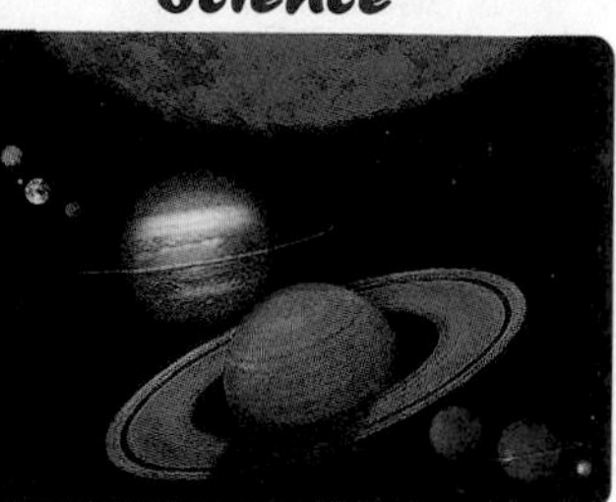

SOLAR SYSTEM The sun's mass is about 740 times as great as the masses of the 9 planets combined. Its mass provides the gravitational pull that keeps the planets in their orbits.

CHALLENGE **In Exercises 18 and 19, use the table, which shows the average diameters, to the nearest 100 miles, of the sun and planets in the solar system.**

Solar System	
Celestial body	Average diameter to nearest 100 miles
Sun	865,000
Mercury	3,000
Venus	7,500
Earth	7,900
Mars	4,200
Jupiter	88,800
Saturn	74,900
Uranus	31,600
Neptune	30,800
Pluto	1,400

18. Suppose you are asked to make scale models of the sun and all the planets using a scale of 3 feet = 100,000 miles. What are the scale model diameters? **See margin.**

19. What is the largest scale model diameter in Exercise 18? What is the smallest? Could you reasonably build all the models? Explain your reasoning. **25.95 ft, 0.042 ft; No, the model of the sun would be about 26 ft in diameter.**

Multiple-Choice Practice

20. A building design has a scale of 1 foot = $\frac{1}{4}$ inch. In the design, the building has a height of 16 inches. How tall is the actual building? **B**

(A) 16 feet (B) 64 feet (C) 192 feet (D) 768 feet

21. You are building a scale model of a car. The model is constructed on a scale of 1 inch = 28 inches. The height of the wheel on the model is $\frac{7}{8}$ inch. What is the height of the wheel on the actual car? **G**

(F) $20\frac{1}{2}$ inches (G) $24\frac{1}{2}$ inches

(H) 26 inches (J) 32 inches

DEVELOPING CONCEPTS
Experimental Probability

For use with Lesson 7.4

1 Planning the Activity

Purpose and Materials

See the margin of the student page.

▶ LINK TO LESSON

By performing this activity students will better understand how experimental probabilities are determined. Experimental probability is the topic of Goal 2 of Lesson 7.4.

Math Reasoning

Students use tables to organize data and to explain mathematical reasoning.

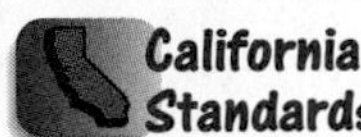

California Standards

- ▶ Collect, organize, and represent data sets and identify relationships through the use of an electronic spreadsheet. (SDP 1.0)
- ▶ Evaluate the reasonableness of the solution in the context of the original situation. (MR 3.1)

MATERIALS

- Number cube
- Paper and pencil

A statistic that is often used to analyze data is frequency. The *frequency* of an item is the number of times that the item occurs.

SAMPLE 1 Collecting and Organizing Data

Toss a number cube 24 times and record the results. Use a frequency table to organize the results.

Here's How

Suppose you got the following results.

3, 2, 1, 5, 6, 4, 2, 6, 6, 3, 2, 5, 5, 4, 5, 5, 3, 3, 5, 2, 3, 1, 6, 4

Go through the list and keep a running tally for each number on the number cube. When done, you can state the frequency of each, as shown in the table.

Number	Tally	Frequency
1	II	2
2	IIII	4
3	~~IIII~~	5
4	III	3
5	~~IIII~~ I	6
6	IIII	4

Try These

1. Work in small groups. Perform the experiment described in Sample 1.

2. The following are the results of the experiment from three groups. Do any of the results look unusual? Why or why not?

Number	Group 1	Group 2	Group 3
1	4	8	3
2	4	8	2
3	4	8	3
4	4	0	6
5	4	0	5
6	4	0	5

3. MATHEMATICAL REASONING Suppose you tossed a number cube 1200 times. Predict the frequency of each number. Explain.

1. Check tables.

2. Yes; In Group 1, all the tallies were the same number. In Group 2, all the tallies were either 8 or 0.

3. Each number should appear about 200 times. The chance of 1, 2, 3, 4, 5, or 6 appearing on one throw is $\frac{1}{6}$. The total number of times one of these numbers should appear in 1200 throws is about $1200\left(\frac{1}{6}\right)$.

California Standards and Assessment

CA Standards: SDP 1.0, MR 3.1

2 Managing the Activity

Group Work

Each group should assign members to perform the following tasks: rolling the number cube, recording the results, and making the frequency table. In addition, one group member should record the group's results on a chalkboard or transparency for the class to use in Exercise 4. The group should work together to make the spreadsheet, with one student typing while the others read numbers.

3 Closing the Activity

★ **KEY DISCOVERY**

As the number of rolls of the dice increases, the experimental probability and the theoretical probability of an event become nearly the same.

Activity Assessment

Use Exercises 3 and 5 to assess student understanding.

SAMPLE 2 Using a Spreadsheet

You can organize data using a spreadsheet. Enter the results from Sample 1 (labeled Group 1 below) and the four other groups shown. Find the sums of the frequencies for all groups, and express the sums as *relative* frequencies (percents of the total number of tosses).

Group 1: 3, 6, 2, 1, 5, 4, 2, 6, 6, 3, 2, 5, 5, 4, 5, 5, 3, 3, 5, 2, 3, 1, 6, 4

Group 2: 4, 2, 1, 5, 3, 2, 4, 6, 1, 3, 2, 6, 4, 3, 2, 5, 6, 1, 3, 3, 1, 4, 5, 3

Group 3: 5, 1, 3, 6, 5, 4, 2, 3, 1, 4, 2, 5, 3, 6, 5, 4, 1, 1, 2, 5, 4, 2, 6, 5

Group 4: 5, 2, 4, 1, 6, 5, 3, 2, 4, 6, 1, 4, 6, 5, 3, 4, 2, 3, 5, 4, 5, 1, 2, 4

Group 5: 2, 6, 1, 5, 3, 6, 2, 6, 4, 1, 3, 2, 3, 6, 2, 5, 1, 6, 3, 5, 3, 1, 2, 3

Here's How

Enter labels in Row 1 of the spreadsheet as shown below. In Column A, enter the numbers on the number cube. In Columns B–F, enter the data.

To calculate the sum of the frequencies, enter the formula = SUM(B2:F2) in Cell G2. Copy this formula into the remaining cells in Column G.

The total number of rolls is $5 \times 24 = 120$. Set the format for Column H to "Percent." Enter the formula = G2/120 in Cell H2. Copy this formula into the remaining cells in Column H.

	A	B	C	D	E	F	G	H
1	Number	Group 1	Group 2	Group 3	Group 4	Group 5	Totals	Percent
2	1	2	4	4	3	4	17	14%
3	2	4	4	4	4	5	21	18%
4	3	5	6	3	3	6	23	19%
5	4	3	4	4	6	1	18	15%
6	5	6	3	6	5	3	23	19%
7	6	4	3	3	3	5	18	15%

Student Help

▶ **TECHNOLOGY TIP**
A spreadsheet, like a table, is organized in rows and columns. Each position, called a *cell*, is designated by a letter (for the column) and a number (for the row). You can enter a label, a number, or a formula in a cell.

Try These

4. Enter the results from Exercise 1 into a spreadsheet along with results from the other groups in your class. Find the relative frequencies. Are your results similar to those shown in Sample 2? Explain.
The results should be similar to those shown in Sample 2.

5. MATHEMATICAL REASONING In Sample 2, what do you notice about the relative frequencies for 1, 2, 3, 4, 5, and 6? If data were collected for 1200 tosses, how would you expect the relative frequencies to change? Explain your reasoning. **The relative frequencies vary between 0.14 and 0.19. The relative frequencies should each be about $\frac{1}{6} \approx 0.17$.**

7.4 Probability

California Standards

In this lesson you'll:

- Convert fractions to decimals and percents and use these representations in estimations, computations, and applications. (NS 1.3)

Goal 1 Finding the Probability of an Event

When you perform an experiment, such as the one in Developing Concepts 7.4, page 343, the possible results are called **outcomes**. For example, the outcomes of rolling a number cube are 1, 2, 3, 4, 5, and 6.

An **event** is a collection of outcomes. The event "getting an even number" on a number cube consists of the outcomes 2, 4, and 6. The outcomes corresponding to a specified event are called **favorable outcomes**.

The **probability** P of an event is a measure of the likelihood that the event will occur. Probability is measured on a scale from 0 to 1.

$P = 0$	$P = 0.25$	$P = 0.5$	$P = 0.75$	$P = 1$
Impossible	Not likely	Equally likely	Quite likely	Certain

Student Help

▶ Look Back
Probability is a ratio that can be expressed as a fraction or percent. For help converting fractions to percents, see page 249.

When all outcomes of an experiment are equally likely, the probability of an event is given by this ratio:

$$\text{Probability of event} = \frac{\text{Number of favorable outcomes}}{\text{Total number of outcomes}}$$

Example 1 Finding a Probability

The spinner has 12 regions of equal size. You spin the spinner once.

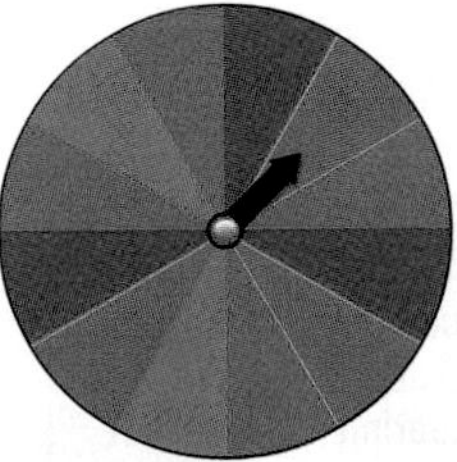

a. What is the probability that it will land on red?

b. What is the probability that it will land on green?

Solution

a. $P = \dfrac{\text{Number of red regions}}{\text{Total number of regions}}$

$= \dfrac{3}{12}$

$= \dfrac{1}{4} = 0.25 = 25\%$

b. $P = \dfrac{\text{Number of green regions}}{\text{Total number of regions}}$

$= \dfrac{2}{12}$

$= \dfrac{1}{6} \approx 0.17 = 17\%$

ANSWER ▶ The probability of spinning red is $\frac{1}{4} = 0.25$, and the probability of spinning green is $\frac{1}{6}$, or about 0.17.

1 Plan

Pacing

Suggested Number of Days

Transitional: 1 day
Average: 1 day
Advanced: 1 day
Block Schedule: 0.5 block with 7.3

Teaching Resources

Blacklines
(See page 326B.)

Transparencies
- Warm-Up Exercises
- Teacher Time-Savers
- English/Spanish Problem Solving
- Answers

Technology
- Electronic Teacher Tools
- Test and Practice Generator

2 Teach

Math Reasoning

For Mathematical Background Notes on mathematical reasoning related to this lesson, please refer to pages 326E and 326F in this Teacher's Edition.

Extra Example 1
See next page.

California Standards and Assessment

CA Standard: NS 1.3

Math Reasoning

In Example 1, the fact that the 12 regions of the spinner have equal central angles is used to indicate that the 12 colors are "equally likely."

Extra Example 1

The spinner below has 10 regions of equal size.

a. If you spin the spinner, what is the probability that it will land on a shaded region? $\frac{4}{10} = 0.4$

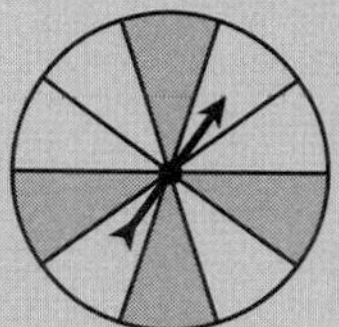

b. What is the probability that it will land on an unshaded region? $\frac{6}{10} = 0.6$

Extra Example 2

You have 24 marbles in a bag. Nine are yellow and the rest are blue. If you randomly choose one marble, what is the probability that it will be blue? $\frac{15}{24} = 0.625$

Extra Example 3

A scientist captures, marks, and releases 15 mountain goats. Later the scientist captured 9 mountain goats and found that 2 of them were marked. Find the experimental probability that a mountain goat was marked. $\frac{2}{9} \approx 0.22$ or 22%

Teaching Tip

Point out that the theoretical probability of an event and the experimental probability of the event are often not the same.

EXAMPLE 2 Finding a Probability

You have 15 coins in your pocket. Two are Canadian pennies, and the rest are United States pennies. If you select one coin at random, what is the probability that it will be a U.S. penny?

Solution

$$P = \frac{\text{Number of U.S. pennies}}{\text{Total number of coins}}$$

$$= \frac{13}{15} \approx 0.87 = 87\%$$

ANSWER ▶ The probability of selecting a U.S. penny is about 0.87.

Goal 2 FINDING AN EXPERIMENTAL PROBABILITY

The probabilities found in Examples 1 and 2 are called **theoretical probabilities** because they were found by mathematical reasoning without actually performing an experiment. Probabilities that are based on the repeated trials of an experiment are called **experimental probabilities**.

The relative frequencies that you calculated in Developing Concepts 7.4, page 343, are examples of experimental probabilities. In general, suppose an experiment consists of a certain number of *trials* (such as tosses of a number cube). For a given event (such as getting a 1), each trial where the event occurs is called a *success*. You can find the event's experimental probability using this formula:

$$\text{Experimental probability of event} = \frac{\text{Number of successes}}{\text{Number of trials}}$$

Student Help

▶ **STUDY TIP**
In probability, an "experiment" does not have to be a scientific procedure performed in a laboratory. Experimental probabilities can also be based on surveys, historical data, or simple activities like tossing a number cube.

EXAMPLE 3 Finding Experimental Probabilities

BUSES You take a bus to school. For 15 days you keep track of whether the bus picks you up on time, and you find that the bus is never early and is late on only 3 days. Find the experimental probability of the event.

a. The bus is on time. **b.** The bus is late.

Solution

a. There are 15 trials (bus arrivals) and 12 successes (on-time arrivals).

$$\begin{matrix}\text{Experimental probability} \\ \text{that bus is on time}\end{matrix} = \frac{12}{15} = \frac{4}{5} = 0.8$$

b. There are 15 trials (bus arrivals) and 3 successes (late arrivals).

$$\begin{matrix}\text{Experimental probability} \\ \text{that bus is late}\end{matrix} = \frac{3}{15} = \frac{1}{5} = 0.2$$

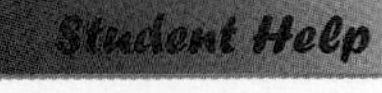

▶MORE EXAMPLES
More examples are available at www.mcdougallittell.com

EXAMPLE 4 Connecting Probability and Proportions

POLLS You are campaigning for class president. Your school newspaper conducts a poll of 64 of your classmates. 36 of those surveyed support you over your rival. Your class has 320 members.

a. Find the experimental probability that a classmate supports you.

b. Find about how many of your classmates support you.

Solution

a. The 64 classmates surveyed represent trials, and the 36 of these who support you represent successes. So the experimental probability that a classmates supports you is $\frac{36}{64} = \frac{9}{16}$.

b. Let x represent the number of classmates who support you. The ratio of your supporters to all classmates should be roughly the same for the entire class as for the group surveyed.

$\frac{x}{320} = \frac{9}{16}$ Write proportion.

$x \cdot 16 = 320 \cdot 9$ Cross products property.

$x = 180$ Divide each side by 16

ANSWER▶ About 180 of your classmates support you.

Math Reasoning

In Example 4 it is assumed that the school newspaper chose a *random sample* of students. In this way, asking students their opinions resembles repeated trials of an experiment, such as drawing a coin at random from a jar containing U.S. and Canadian pennies.

Extra Example 4

Use the information from Extra Example 3 to estimate the total number of mountain goats in the area. **about 68**

Concept Check

What is the difference between a theoretical probability and an experimental probability? **A theoretical probability can be found by mathematical reasoning. An experimental probability is based on repeated trials of an experiment.**

7.4 Exercises

Guided Practice

In Exercises 1–5, match the event with the letter in the diagram that indicates the event's probability.

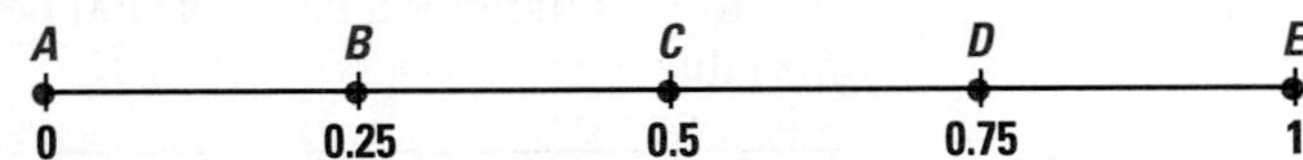

1. A Zip code ends with a digit greater than 4. **C**

2. You choose the letter E at random from a bag containing the letters of INTERNET written on slips of paper. **B**

3. You choose the letter F from the bag in Exercise 2. **A**

4. A spinner with 6 of 8 equal sections shaded red will land on red. **D**

5. The first digit of a telephone number is less than 10. **E**

6. You place 15 slips of paper in a bag. Five are blue, nine are red, and one is green. You choose one slip without looking. What is the probability that the slip is green? Express the probability as a fraction and as a percent. $\frac{1}{15}$ **or about 7%**

3 Apply

Assignment Guide

TRANSITIONAL
Day 1: EP p. 699 Exs. 79–82; pp. 348–349 Exs. 7–12, 16–20, 27–28

AVERAGE
Day 1: pp. 348–349 Exs. 7–10, 13–20, 27–28

ADVANCED
Day 1: pp. 348–349 Exs. 7–10, 16–20, 24–25, 26*, 27–28

BLOCK SCHEDULE
pp. 348–349 Exs. 7–10, 13–20, 27–28 (with 7.3)

Extra Practice

- Student Edition, pp. 702–703
- Chapter 7 Resource Book, p. 33

Homework Check

To quickly check student understanding of key concepts, go over the following exercises:

Transitional: 8, 10, 12, 16, 18, 20
Average: 8. 14, 16, 18, 20
Advanced: 8, 16, 18, 20, 24

15. *Sample answer:*

Letter	Experimental probability	Theoretical probability
A	60%	about 57%
B	about 13%	about 14%
L	10%	about 14%
M	about 17%	about 14%

The experimental probabilities were fairly close to the theoretical probabilities.

Practice and Problem Solving

Student Help

▶**MORE PRACTICE**
Extra practice to help you master skills is on page 702.

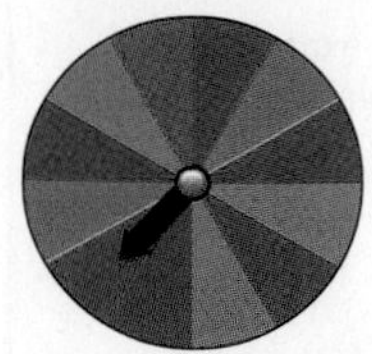

In Exercises 7–10, find the theoretical probability that the spinner at the right will land on the color. The spinner has 12 sections of equal size.

7. Green $\frac{1}{4}$ or 25% **8.** Red $\frac{5}{12}$ or about 42%

9. Purple $\frac{1}{12}$ or about 8% **10.** Blue $\frac{1}{6}$ or about 17%

In Exercises 11 and 12, suppose you tape a penny to a quarter using transparent tape. Toss this compound coin 30 times. For each toss, record whether the penny or the quarter lands on top.

11. Use the results to find the experimental probability that the penny lands on top. *Sample data:* $\frac{18}{30}$ or 60%

12. Suppose the compound coin is tossed to see who gets the ball in a sports game. If you want to win the toss, should you call "penny up" or "quarter up?" Explain your reasoning.

12. "penny up;" *Sample answer:* The compound coin favors "penny up" by a ratio of [illegible]

In Exercises 13–15, write each letter in the word ALABAMA on separate slips of paper and put them all in a bag. You intend to choose one slip of paper at random from the bag.

13. Find the theoretical probabilities of choosing an M, choosing an A, choosing a B, and choosing an L.

13. M: $\frac{1}{7}$ or about 14%, A: $\frac{4}{7}$ or about 57%, B: $\frac{1}{7}$ or about 14%, L: $\frac{1}{7}$ or about 14%.

14. Choose a slip of paper from the bag, record the letter, and replace it. Do this 30 times, recording the number of times you draw each letter. Find the experimental probability of choosing each letter.

14. *Sample data:* A: $\frac{18}{30}$ or 60%, B: $\frac{4}{30}$ or about 13%, L: $\frac{3}{30}$ or 10%, M: $\frac{5}{30}$ or about 17%

15. Compare your experimental probabilities with the theoretical probabilities found in Exercise 13. Explain your results. See margin.

MEDICINE In Exercises 16–20, use the following information. You take a poll to find the blood types of 200 people. You obtain the results shown in the table.

Blood type	O^+	O^-	A^+	A^-	B^+	B^-	AB^+	AB^-
Number of people	76	14	68	12	18	4	6	2

16. $\frac{19}{50}$ or 38%

17. $\frac{1}{50}$ or 2%

16. Find the experimental probability that a person has type O^+ blood.

17. Find the experimental probability that a person has type B^- blood.

18. Find the experimental probability that a person has type A blood (positive or negative). $\frac{2}{5}$ or 40%

19. In a town with 5000 people, about how many people would have type O^+ blood? 1900

20. In a town with 7500 people, about how many people would have type AB^+ blood? 225

In Exercises 21–23, use the following information. Suppose you forget a friend's post office box number. You know the box number has 2 digits and both digits are multiples of 3.

21. There are only 9 possible outcomes. List the outcomes, and find the theoretical probability that a random guess results in the correct box number.

22. To simulate guessing the box number, students wrote two sets of 3, 6, and 9 on pieces of paper and put each set in a bag. They chose a piece of paper from each bag and recorded the digits. Their results are shown in the table below. Compare the experimental probability of getting the correct box number with the theoretical probability in Exercise 21.

Number	33	36	39	63	66	69	93	96	99
Frequency	8	5	5	7	4	3	6	5	7

23. Perform the experiment described in Exercise 22, record your results, and find the experimental probability of getting the number 39.

24. You have a toy that answers questions you ask it with "Yes" or "No". You use the toy 30 times and find that it answers "Yes" 12 times. Find the experimental possibility that it answers "No."

25. MATHEMATICAL REASONING To predict who will win the next election for mayor, a reporter asks residents on one street which candidate they will vote for. On that street, 60% choose Candidate A and 40% choose Candidate B. The analyst concludes that Candidate A will win the election. Do you agree with this reasoning? Explain your answer.

26. CHALLENGE You have a rectangle that is 10.5 feet by 16 feet. You want to shade part of the rectangle blue so that the probability that a coin tossed at random on the rectangle lands in the blue area is $\frac{1}{3}$. Describe three different ways to do this.

21. 33, 36, 39, 63, 66, 69, 93, 96, and 99; the probability is $\frac{1}{9} \approx 0.11$ or 11%.

22. The experimental probability of guessing correctly can vary quite a bit, from 6% to 16%, while the theoretical probability is about 11%.

23. *Sample data:* 39: $\frac{6}{50}$ or 12%

25. No; the street may not be representative of the community. It would be better for the analyst to say that Candidate A will win 60% of the votes on that street than 60% of the votes cast citywide.

26. *Sample answer:* Area of the rectangle: 10.5 ft • 16 ft = 168 ft^2. Theoretical probability: $\frac{1}{3} = \frac{x}{168 \text{ ft}^2}$. A rectangular strip 3.5 feet by 16 feet or 7 ft by 8 ft or 4 ft by 14 ft will have an area of 56 square feet and when painted blue will give a theoretical probability of $\frac{1}{3}$ that a coin randomly tossed on the large rectangle will land on the blue area.

Multiple-Choice Practice

27. You want to color the spinner so that the probability of landing on blue is 0.25. How many of the equally-sized sections should you color blue?

Ⓐ 2 Ⓑ 3

Ⓒ 4 Ⓓ 6

28. When you roll a six-sided number cube, what is the probability of rolling a 4 or a 6?

Ⓕ $\frac{1}{6}$ Ⓖ $\frac{1}{3}$ Ⓗ $\frac{2}{3}$ Ⓙ $\frac{1}{2}$

4 Assess

Assessment Resources

- Assessment Book (Formal Assessment and Alternative Assessment)
- Test and Practice Generator

Mini-Quiz

1. A spinner has three blue sections and six red sections. All the sections are of equal size. Find the theoretical probability that the spinner will land on each color. **blue: $\frac{3}{9} \approx 0.33$; red: $\frac{6}{9} \approx 0.67$**
2. A poll is taken of pet owners to determine how many people own each type of animal. The results are shown below.

Cat	191
Dog	157
Rabbit	11
Bird	42
Fish	67
Other	19

a. If another pet owner is asked, what is the probability that he or she owns a bird? **$\frac{42}{487} \approx 0.09$**

b. Is the probability in part (a) *theoretical* or *experimental* probability? **experimental**

Math Reasoning

As a variant to Exercises 21–23, you might add the condition that the box number does not involve a repeated digit, as in 33, 66, and 99. Then ask students to develop their own design for a simulation (for example, drawing two slips from the same bag without replacement).

1 Plan

Pacing

Suggested Number of Days

Transitional: 2 days
Average: 2 days
Advanced: 2 days
Block Schedule: 1 block

Teaching Resources

Blacklines

(See page 326B.)

Transparencies

- Warm-Up Exercises
- Teacher Time-Savers
- English/Spanish Problem Solving
- Answers

Technology

- Electronic Teacher Tools
- Test and Practice Generator

2 Teach

Math Reasoning

For Mathematical Background Notes on mathematical reasoning related to this lesson, please refer to pages 326E and 326F in this Teacher's Edition.

Teaching Tip

Communicating Mathematics
Point out that the statement "*a* is *p* percent of *b*" can be restated as "*a* of *b* is *p* percent."

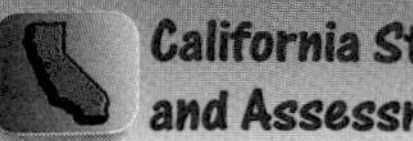

California Standards and Assessment

CA Standards: NS 1.3, AF 4.1

350

7.5 Solving Percent Problems

California Standards

In this lesson you'll:

- Solve two-step linear equations in one variable over the rational numbers, interpret the solution in the context from which it arose, and verify the reasonableness of the result. (AF 4.1)
- Use percents in estimations, computations, and applications. (NS 1.3)

Goal 1 Finding Percents

You can use a proportion to find what percent a number is of another number. The statement "a is p percent of b" is expressed by the proportion below, where a is part of the base, b is the base, and p is the percent.

$$\frac{a}{b} = \frac{p}{100} \qquad \frac{\text{Part of base}}{\text{Base}} = \frac{\text{Percent}}{100}$$

EXAMPLE 1 Finding a Percent

17 is what percent of 20?

Solution

$\frac{a}{b} = \frac{p}{100}$	Write proportion.
$\frac{17}{20} = \frac{p}{100}$	Substitute 17 for *a* and 20 for *b*.
$17 \cdot 100 = 20 \cdot p$	Cross products property
$1700 = 20p$	Simplify.
$85 = p$	Divide each side by 20.

ANSWER ▶ 17 is 85% of 20.

EXAMPLE 2 Finding a Percent

On a 50 point quiz, you received 48 points plus 5 bonus points. What percent did you receive?

Solution

$\frac{\text{Points received}}{\text{Points value of quiz}} = \frac{\text{Percent}}{100}$	Write verbal model.
$\frac{53}{50} = \frac{p}{100}$	Substitute 53 for points received and 50 for point value of quiz.
$53 \cdot 100 = 50 \cdot p$	Cross products property
$5300 = 50p$	Simplify.
$106 = p$	Divide each side by 50.

ANSWER ▶ You received 106% on the quiz.

Student Help

▶ STUDY TIP
Use estimation to help you check an answer. In Example 2, 53 is greater than 50, so the percent should be greater than 100%.

Goal 2 FINDING A PART OR THE BASE

In Examples 1 and 2, you used a proportion to find a percent. When the percent is known, you can use a proportion to find a part of the base or to find the base.

Student Help

▶ **LOOK BACK**
In Example 3, you can find 82% of 250 simply by multiplying 0.82 and 250 as you learned in Lesson 6.4.

EXAMPLE 3 Finding a Part of a Base

CLOTHING In a survey of 250 people, 82% said they prefer blue jeans to cargo pants. How many people said they prefer blue jeans?

Solution

$\frac{\text{Prefer blue jeans}}{\text{People surveyed}} = \frac{\text{Percent}}{100}$ Write verbal model.

$\frac{a}{250} = \frac{82}{100}$ Substitute 250 for people surveyed and 82 for percent.

$a \cdot 100 = 250 \cdot 82$ Cross products property

$100a = 20{,}500$ Simplify.

$a = 205$ Divide each side by 100.

ANSWER ▶ 205 people said they prefer blue jeans to cargo pants.

Student Help

▶ **SKILLS REVIEW**
Circle graphs are often used to display data. They are also referred to as pie charts. For help with reading circle graphs, see page 688.

EXAMPLE 4 Finding a Base

SCHOOL In a survey, parents of elementary school children were asked how many hours per week they spent helping their children with homework. Suppose 88 parents said they spent 1 to 4 hours. How many parents were surveyed?

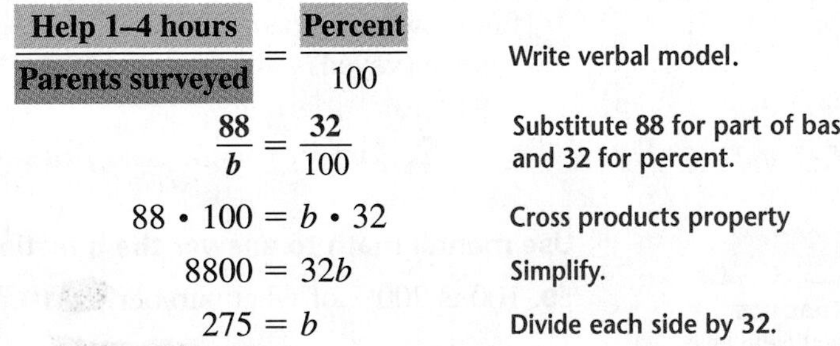

▶ Source: 20/20 Research

Solution

$\frac{\text{Help 1–4 hours}}{\text{Parents surveyed}} = \frac{\text{Percent}}{100}$ Write verbal model.

$\frac{88}{b} = \frac{32}{100}$ Substitute 88 for part of base and 32 for percent.

$88 \cdot 100 = b \cdot 32$ Cross products property

$8800 = 32b$ Simplify.

$275 = b$ Divide each side by 32.

ANSWER ▶ 275 parents were surveyed.

Math Reasoning

Percents need not have integer values. For example, 7 is $3\frac{1}{2}$% of 200, since $\frac{7}{200} = \frac{3.5}{100}$.

Extra Example 1

129 is what percent of 860? **15%**

Extra Example 2

On a 40-point quiz, you got 38 points plus 6 bonus points. Find the percent that you received. **110%**

Extra Example 3

In a survey of 400 people, 72% of them said they supported an increase in funding for public schools. How many supported an increase in funding? **288 people**

Extra Example 4

In a survey conducted by a local newspaper, adults were asked how many hours per week they spent exercising. The results are shown in the circle graph below. Suppose 18 adults said they exercised 7 or more hours per week. How many adults were surveyed? **360 adults**

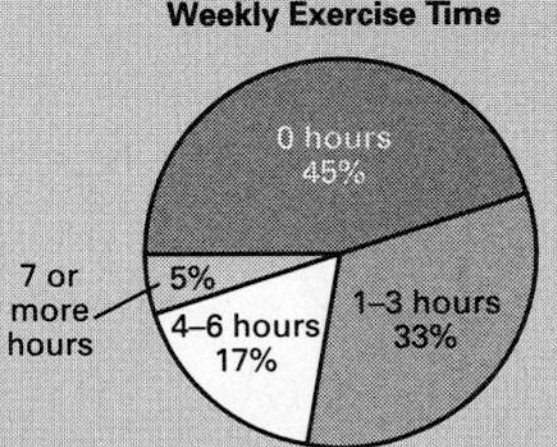

Concept Check

Can a percent problem involve more than 100%? Give an example, if possible. **Yes; *sample answer:* 100 is 200% of 50.**

3 Apply

Assignment Guide

TRANSITIONAL
Day 1: pp. 352–354 Exs. 9–20, 32–33
Day 2: SRH p. 688 Exs. 1–5; pp. 352–354 Exs. 28–31, 34–37, 43–44

AVERAGE
Day 1: pp. 352–354 Exs. 9–27, 32–33
Day 2: pp. 352–354 Exs. 28–31, 34–39, 43–44

ADVANCED
Day 1: pp. 352–354 Exs. 9–27, 32–33
Day 2: pp. 352–354 Exs. 28–31, 34–41, 42*, 43–44

BLOCK SCHEDULE
pp. 352–354 Exs. 9–39, 43–44

Extra Practice

- Student Edition, pp. 702–703
- Chapter 7 Resource Book, p. 42

Homework Check

To quickly check student understanding of key concepts, go over the following exercises:

Transitional: 10, 18, 22, 30, 32
Average: 10, 20, 22, 36, 38
Advanced: 14, 22, 24, 36, 40

4. $\frac{20}{25} = \frac{p}{100}$, 80%

7. $\frac{30}{150} = \frac{p}{100}$, 20%

The three types of percent problems presented in this lesson are summarized in the table below.

SOLVING PERCENT PROBLEMS

$\frac{a}{b} = \frac{p}{100}$ *a* is *p* percent of *b*.

Unknown	Question	Where to Look
p (percent)	*a* is what percent of *b*?	See Examples 1 and 2.
a (part of base)	What is *p* percent of *b*?	See Example 3.
b (base)	*a* is *p* percent of what?	See Example 4.

7.5 Exercises

Guided Practice

Solve the proportion. Tell what your answer represents.

1. $\frac{13}{25} = \frac{p}{100}$ **52%, the percent that 13 is of 25**

2. $\frac{a}{20} = \frac{85}{100}$ **17, the number that is 85 percent of 20**

3. $\frac{3}{b} = \frac{60}{100}$ **5, the number of which 3 is 60 percent**

In Exercises 4–7, write and solve a proportion to answer the question.

4. 20 is what percent of 25?

5. What is 16% of 50? $\frac{a}{50} = \frac{16}{100}$, 8

6. 90 is 75% of what? $\frac{90}{b} = \frac{75}{100}$, 120

7. 30 is what percent of 150?

8. The graph at the right shows the results of a survey in which people were asked how many hours per week they used their computers for fun. If 750 people said they spent 6 to 10 hours per week using their computer for fun, how many people were surveyed? **3750 people**

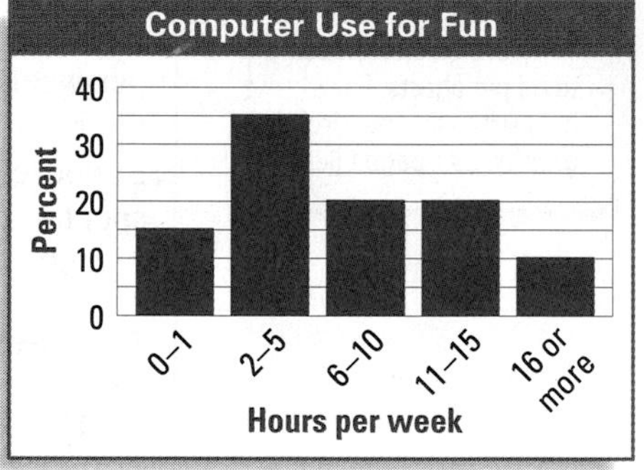

Practice and Problem Solving

Student Help
▶ **MORE PRACTICE**
Extra practice to help you master skills is on page 703.

Use mental math to answer the question.

9. 100 is 200% of what number? 50

10. What is 50% of 200? 100

11. 5 is what percent of 15? about 33%

12. 100 is 100% of what number? 100

13. What is 33% of 100? 33

14. 2 is what percent of 10? 20%

[redacted]

ERROR ANALYSIS **Describe and correct the error.**

15. 45 is what percent of 150?

$\frac{150}{45} = \frac{p}{100}$

$45p = 15{,}000$

$p = 333.33\%$

[redacted]

16. What is 24% of 50?

$\frac{24}{50} = \frac{p}{100}$

$50p = 24{,}000$

$p = 480\%$

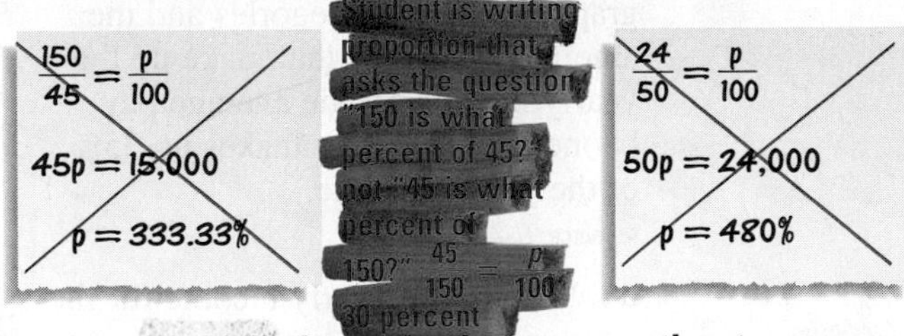

In Exercises 17–26, write and solve a proportion to answer the question.

17. 21 is what percent of 30?

18. What is 33% of 165?

19. 66 is 120% of what number?

20. What is 2% of 360?

21. 6.06 is 20.2% of what number?

22. 45 is what percent of 20?

23. 1 is what percent of 50?

24. What is 110% of 110?

25. 23 is 25% of what number?

26. 900 is what percent of 45?

27. MATHEMATICAL REASONING Solve the proportion $\frac{a}{b} = \frac{p}{100}$ for p. Explain why your answer makes sense.

MUSIC SURVEY **In Exercises 28–31, use the following information.** You take a survey in your class about favorite types of music. The circle graph shows the percent of students choosing each type. Nine students said that country music was their favorite.

28. Find the number of students who were surveyed. [redacted]

29. Find how many students said their favorite type of music was jazz and blues. [redacted]

30. Find how many students said their favorite type of music was hip-hop. [redacted]

31. Find how many students said their favorite type of music was rock/alternative. [redacted]

32. HEALTH STATISTICS According to a 1991 survey, about 20,295,000 Americans out of a total population of 235,688,000 were found to have some form of hearing loss. About what percent of the population has a hearing loss? [redacted]

33. REAL ESTATE The commission a realtor receives on the sale of a house is 7% of the sale price. The owners expected to sell the house for \$120,000. They ended up selling it for \$112,000. How much less commission did the realtor earn than expected? [redacted]

Link to Languages

AMERICAN SIGN LANGUAGE (ASL) is a visual/gestural language used by hearing-impaired individuals in face-to-face communication. The number of ASL users in the United States (including hearing individuals) is estimated to be between 500,000 and 2,000,000.

4 Assess

Assessment Resources

- Assessment Book (Formal Assessment and Alternative Assessment)
- Test and Practice Generator

Mini-Quiz

Solve the percent equation. Round your answer to two decimal places if necessary.

1. 38 is 57% of what number? **66.67**
2. 110 is what percent of 200? **55%**
3. What is 250% of 30? **75**
4. You paid \$58.36, which was 80% of the original price, for a watch. What was the original price? **\$72.95**
5. You got 19 points on a 25-point quiz. Find the percent that you received. **76%**

354

PAY PHONES In Exercises 34–37, use the following information. The circle graph shows the categories and the amounts of money that make up the yearly income for the average pay phone. Coin revenue makes up 35% of the yearly income.

▶ Source: *USA Today*

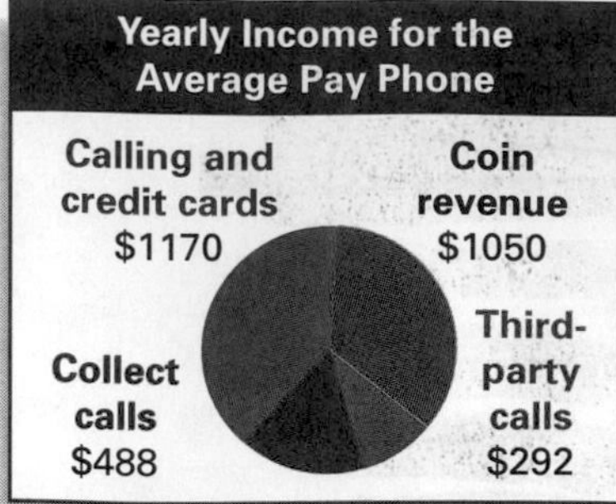

Student Help

▶ HOMEWORK HELP

INTERNET Extra help with problem solving in Exs. 34–37 is available at www.mcdougallittell.com

34. What is the yearly income for the average pay phone?

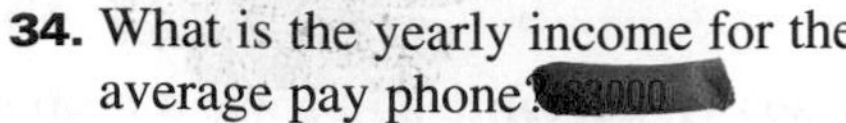

35. What percent of the yearly income is from calling and credit cards?

36. What percent of the yearly income is from collect calls?

37. What percent of the yearly income is from third-party calls?

38. SALES TAX You buy a new video game. You pay \$54.00 for the game plus \$2.70 in sales tax. Find the sales tax rate.

39. TIPS A customer leaves \$59.00 for a meal that costs \$50.00. What percent of the cost of the meal is the tip?

COMMISSION In Exercises 40 and 41, use the following information. Your sister works part-time at an electronics store. Her weekly salary is \$100 plus 5% commission on her total sales.

40. Find her total sales when her total income for the week is \$300.

41. When her sales are more than \$1500, she receives a \$150 bonus. Use your answer from Exercise 40 to determine whether she will receive this bonus.

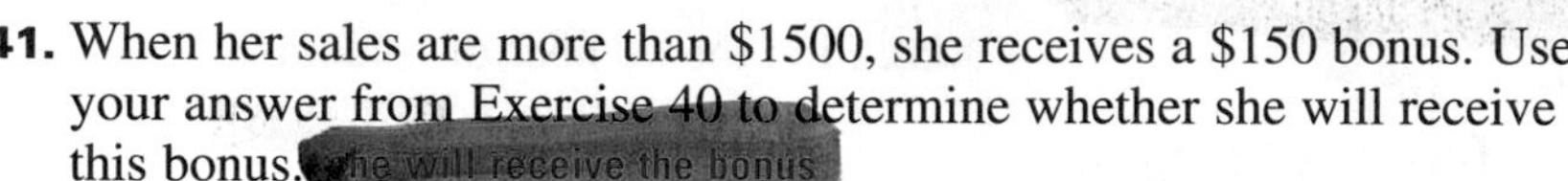

42. CHALLENGE Suppose the sales tax rate where you live is 6%. The cost of jeans is usually \$31.74 when the tax is added. When the jeans go on sale, their cost is \$21.04 including tax. How much did you save in sales tax by waiting to buy the jeans on sale?

Multiple-Choice Practice

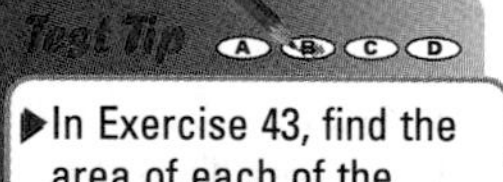

▶ In Exercise 43, find the area of each of the squares to find what percent of the figure is shaded.

In Exercises 43 and 44, use the figure shown, which consists of a square inside another square.

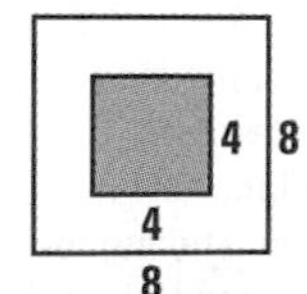

43. What percent of the figure is shaded?

Ⓐ 16%　Ⓑ 25%　Ⓒ 50%　Ⓓ 64%

44. The unshaded area is what percent of the shaded area in the figure?

Ⓕ 3%　Ⓖ 33.3%　Ⓗ 300%　Ⓙ 400%

Chapter 7 Mid-Chapter Test

Take this test as you would take a test in class. The answers to the exercises are given in the back of the book.

Write the ratio as a fraction $\frac{a}{b}$ in simplest form. When possible, express both quantities in a common unit of measure.

1. 100 meters in 18 seconds **2.** 18 lures to 6 fishermen **3.** 42 ounces to 3 pounds

4. 5 days to 1 week **5.** 12 feet to 4 yards **6.** 2 hours to 45 minutes

Find the unit price.

7. 4 apples for \$1.12 **8.** 2.5 pounds for \$6.50 **9.** \$6.72 for 6 gallons

In Exercises 10–13, solve the proportion. Check your solution.

10. $\frac{x}{4} = \frac{8}{2}$ **11.** $\frac{3}{7} = \frac{a}{9}$ **12.** $\frac{18}{b} = \frac{25}{36}$  **13.** $\frac{y}{3} = \frac{10}{2}$

14. Suppose you can read 30 pages of a book in 25 minutes. How long will it take you to read the entire book if it is 222 pages long?

15. You can walk 2 miles in 36 minutes. How far can you walk in one and a half hours?

16. You have a 3 inch by 5 inch photograph enlarged to 5 times its size so that it is 15 inches by 25 inches. Does the enlarged photograph have five times the perimeter and five times the area of the original photograph? Explain.

17. FLOOR PLAN In the floor plan at the right, the kitchen measures 1 inch by $\frac{1}{2}$ inch. The floor plan scale is 2 inches = 32 feet. Find the actual area of the kitchen.

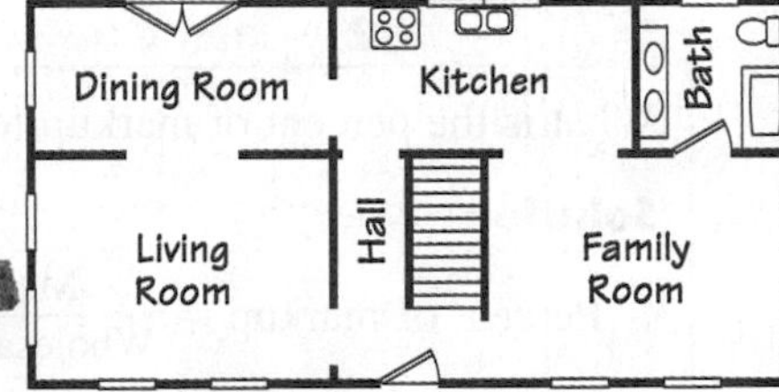

Find the theoretical probability of the event.

18. Rolling an even number on a number cube numbered 1 through 6

19. Choosing an A, E, I, O, or U out of all the letters of the alphabet

20. Landing on some color other than blue when a spinner has 4 of 12 equal sections colored blue

Write and solve a proportion to answer the question.

21. 15 is 125% of what number? **22.** What is 35% of 18?

23. 36 is what percent of 150? **24.** 25 is what percent of 250?

Additional Resources

A Mid-Chapter Test and a Mid-Chapter Partner Quiz are available in the *Assessment Book*, pp. 95–96 and p. 240.

1 Plan

Pacing

Suggested Number of Days

Transitional: 1 day
Average: 1 day
Advanced: 1 day
Block Schedule: 0.5 block with 7.7

Teaching Resources

Blacklines
(See page 326B.)

Transparencies
- Warm-Up Exercises
- Teacher Time-Savers
- English/Spanish Problem Solving
- Answers

Technology
- Electronic Teacher Tools
- Test and Practice Generator

2 Teach

Math Reasoning

For Mathematical Background Notes on mathematical reasoning related to this lesson, please refer to pages 326E and 326F in this Teacher's Edition.

California Standards and Assessment

CA Standard: NS 1.7

CA Key Concepts Book: pp. S28–S31, S35

356

7.6 Markup and Discount

California Standards

In this lesson you'll:

- Solve problems that involve markups and discounts. (NS 1.7)

Goal 1 Finding a Markup

A retail store buys items at *wholesale prices*. To cover expenses and make a profit, the store sells the items at higher *retail prices*. The difference between the retail and wholesale prices is called the **markup**.

$$\text{Markup} = \text{Retail price} - \text{Wholesale price}$$

EXAMPLE 1 Finding the Amount of Markup

CLOTHING A store buys a shirt at a wholesale price of \$13.50 and sells the shirt for \$24.95. What is the amount of markup?

Solution

$$\begin{aligned}\text{Markup} &= \text{Retail price} - \text{Wholesale price}\\ &= 24.95 - 13.50\\ &= 11.45\end{aligned}$$

ANSWER ▶ The amount of markup is \$11.45.

To find the *percent of markup*, use the wholesale price as the base and the amount of markup as the part of the base.

EXAMPLE 2 Finding a Percent of Markup

What is the percent of markup for the shirt in Example 1?

Solution

$$\begin{aligned}\text{Percent of markup} &= \frac{\text{Markup}}{\text{Wholesale price}}\\ &= \frac{11.45}{13.50}\\ &\approx 0.85 = 85\%\end{aligned}$$

ANSWER ▶ The percent of markup is about 85%.

Student Help

▶ **More Examples**

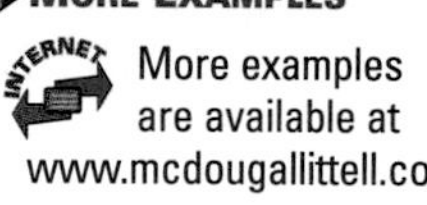

More examples are available at www.mcdougallittell.com

Often a store manager determines the retail price of an item by using a fixed percent of markup. In Example 3, you will determine what the retail price for a piece of jewelry should be by finding the amount of markup and adding it to the wholesale price.

Student Help

▶ **STUDY TIP**
You can also find the amount of markup in Example 3 by setting up a proportion:

$\frac{x}{180} = \frac{150}{100}$

EXAMPLE 3 Finding a Retail Price

JEWELRY You are the manager of a jewelry store. You buy a ring at a wholesale price of \$180. Your percent of markup is 150%. Find the retail price.

Solution

First find the amount of markup.

Markup = Percent of markup • Wholesale price

= 150% • 180 — **Substitute for percent and price.**

= 1.5 • 180 — **Write percent in decimal form.**

= 270 — **Multiply.**

Then find the sum of the amount of markup and the wholesale price.

Retail price = Wholesale price + Markup

= 180 + 270 = 450

ANSWER ▶ The retail price is \$450.

Goal 2 FINDING A DISCOUNT

When an item is on sale, the difference between the regular price and the sale price is called the **discount**.

Discount = Regular price − Sale price

To find the *percent of discount*, use the regular price as the base and the amount of discount as part of the base.

EXAMPLE 4 Finding a Percent of Discount

BOOKS A \$36 book is on sale for \$27.

a. Find the amount of discount. **b.** Find the percent of discount.

Solution

a. Discount = Regular price − Sale price

= 36 − 27 = 9

ANSWER ▶ The discount is \$9.

b. To find the percent of discount, use \$36 as the base.

$$\text{Percent of discount} = \frac{\text{Discount}}{\text{Regular price}} = \frac{9}{36}$$

$$= 0.25 = 25\%$$

ANSWER ▶ The percent of discount is 25%.

Extra Example 1

A store buys a pair of shoes at a wholesale price of \$37.50 and sells them for \$50. What is the amount of the markup? **\$12.50**

Extra Example 2

What is the percent markup for the pair of shoes in Extra Example 1? **about 33%**

Extra Example 3

You own an electronics store. You buy a CD player at a wholesale price of \$44. Your percent markup is 125%. Find the retail price. **\$99**

Extra Example 4

A \$55 pair of jeans is on clearance sale for \$22.

a. Find the amount of the discount. **\$33**

b. Find the discount percent. **60%**

Extra Example 5

Last weekend you bought a jacket on sale for $63.75. Today you are shopping in the same store and notice that the jacket is being sold at the regular price of $75.00. What was the discount percent you received last weekend? **15%**

Concept Check

Describe the method for finding the discount percent for an item when the regular price and sale price are given. **Find the discount by subtracting the sale price from the regular price. Then divide the discount by the regular price and write the result in percent form.**

EXAMPLE 5 *Finding a Percent of Discount*

SWEATSHIRT Last week you bought a sweatshirt on sale for $16.80. This week you find the sweatshirt is back at the regular price of $22.68. A friend tells you that you received a 35% discount because $22.68 - 16.80 = 5.88$ and $5.88 is 35% of $16.80.

a. Is your friend correct?

b. If not, what is the percent of discount?

Solution

a. Your friend is using the sale price as the base.

$$\frac{5.88}{16.80} = 0.35 = 35\%$$

ANSWER ▶ This is not correct. The regular price should be the base.

b. To find the percent of discount, use the regular price as the base.

$$\frac{5.88}{22.68} \approx 0.259$$ Divide discount by regular price.

$$= 25.9\%$$ Write percent.

ANSWER ▶ The percent of discount is about 25.9%.

7.6 Exercises

Guided Practice

In Exercises 1–4, find the percent of markup or the percent of discount.

1. Regular price: $35
Sale price: $30 **14.3% discount**

2. Wholesale price: $44
Retail price: $59 **34.1% markup**

3. Regular price: $24
Sale price: $20 **16.7% discount**

4. Wholesale price: $180
Retail price: $224 **24.4% markup**

5. DISCOUNT You are in a shoe store and see the sign at the right. Explain how you can find the original price of sneakers. Then find the original price.

5. sale price = original price − discount; sale price = original price − (percent of discount) • (original price); 29.99 = x − 0.25x; 29.99 = 0.75x; x = 39.99, original price is $39.99

MARKUP In Exercises 6 and 7, use the following information. The wholesale price of a sweater is $30. The clothing store sells the sweater for $78.

6. What is the amount of markup? **$48**

7. What is the percent of markup? **160%**

Practice and Problem Solving

Student Help

▶ **MORE PRACTICE** Extra practice to help you master skills is on page 703.

Find the amount of markup or the amount of discount. Round your answer to the nearest hundredth.

8. \$85 radio; 10% discount \$8.50 **9.** \$32 sweater; 55% off \$17.60

10. \$49.99 shoes; 33% off \$16.50 **11.** \$16.00 radio; 165% markup \$26.40

12. \$12.50 T-shirt; 155% markup \$19.38 **13.** \$.75 socks; 250% markup 

Find the cost of the item after the markup or discount described. Round your answer to the nearest hundredth.

14. \$34.50 sweatshirt; 20% off \$27.60 **15.** \$90 coat; 15% off \$76.50

16. \$6.99 toy; 125% markup \$15.73 **17.** \$15 movie; 162.5% markup \$39.38

18. \$145 stereo; 170% markup \$391.50 **19.** \$175.95 suit; 45% off \$96.77

20. \$175 chair; 75% off \$43.75 **21.** \$.33 sandwich; 300% markup 

Link to Careers

RETAIL BUYER When choosing merchandise to sell in a store, a retail buyer considers what customers want to buy, how much they will pay, and how much of a profit the store will make.

More about retail buyers available at www.mcdougallittell.com

RETAIL BUYER In Exercises 22 and 23, use the following information. A buyer for a store buys a television at a wholesale price of \$377.56. The store then sells the television to its customers for \$589.

22. Find the amount of markup for the television. \$211.44

23. Find the percent of markup for the television. 

In Exercises 24–29, use the following information. The receipt at the right shows your purchases during a recent sale.

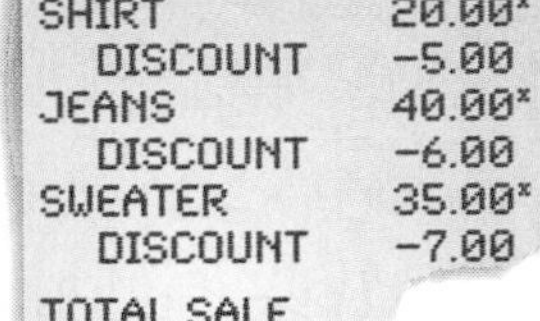

SHIRT	20.00*
DISCOUNT	-5.00
JEANS	40.00*
DISCOUNT	-6.00
SWEATER	35.00*
DISCOUNT	-7.00
TOTAL SALE	
TOTAL SAVINGS	

24. Find the percent of discount for the shirt. 25%

25. Find the percent of discount for the jeans. 15%

26. Find the percent of discount for the sweater. 20%

27. Find the total sales cost of your purchases. \$77.00

28. Find the total savings. \$18.00

29. MATHEMATICAL REASONING Describe the percent of discount using the total savings and the total regular cost. Is this percent of discount equal to the average of the percents of discount applied to the individual items? Explain your reasoning. See margin.

30. IN-LINE SKATES You buy a pair of in-line skates. The sign at the sporting goods store states that the price of the skates has been reduced 25%. The amount of discount is \$21.40. Find the regular price of the in-line skates. \$85.60

31. CHALLENGE A furniture store bought a table for \$200. The store offered it for sale with a regular price based on a markup of 150%. Later the table went on sale for 50% off the regular price. Can you buy it now for \$200? Justify your answer. See margin.

3 Apply

Assignment Guide

TRANSITIONAL
Day 1: pp. 359–360 Exs. 8–9, 14–17, 22–28, 30, 36–40, 50–52, 58–60

AVERAGE
Day 1: pp. 359–360 Exs. 10–11, 18–23, 32–40, 52–55, 60–62

ADVANCED
Day 1: pp. 359–360 Exs. 12–13, 18–23, 29, 31*, 32–40, 52–55, 60–62

BLOCK SCHEDULE
pp. 359–360 Exs. 10–11, 18–23, 32–40, 52–55, 60–62 (with 7.7)

Extra Practice

- Student Edition, pp. 702–703
- Chapter 7 Resource Book, p. 51

Homework Check

To quickly check student understanding of key concepts, go over the following exercises:

Transitional: 10, 14, 22, 26, 30
Average: 10, 18, 22, 32, 33
Advanced: 10, 20, 22, 32, 33

Problem Solving

Exercise 31
Neither the sale price nor the regular price is given. Students must use a two-step process, first calculating the regular (marked-up) price, then calculating the discounted price based on the regular price.

29. The percent of discount for the entire purchase is about 18.9%, but the average of the individual percents of discount is 20%.

31. See Additional Answers beginning on page AA1.

4 Assess

Assessment Resources

- Assessment Book (Formal Assessment and Alternative Assessment)
- Test and Practice Generator

Mini-Quiz

A store buys a hat at wholesale for \$9 and sells it for \$16.83.

1. Find the amount of the markup. **\$7.83**
2. What is the markup percent? **87%**
3. Find the discount percent for an \$85.00 watch that sold for \$63.75. **25%**
4. You paid \$39.96 for a new computer software game, which was on sale at a 20% discount. What was the full price? **\$49.95**

COMPUTERS In Exercises 32–35, use the following information. A local computer store buys a computer at a wholesale price of \$675. The store's retail price is \$1518.

32. Find the percent of markup for the computer. Round your answer to the nearest hundredth. 124.89%

33. The computer store is having a one-time sale and discounts the computer 25%. Find the new retail price for the computer.

34. The computer store is also required to add 8.25% sales tax on all computers sold. Determine the amount of sales tax due on the new retail price you found in Exercise 33. \$93.93

35. Find the total cost of the computer after the 25% discount and the 8.25% sales tax. \$1232.43

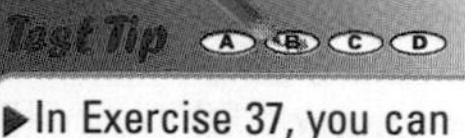

Multiple-Choice Practice

Test Tip Ⓐ Ⓑ Ⓒ Ⓓ

▶ In Exercise 37, you can eliminate H and J as possible answers because you know that \$386 is not less than half of \$585.

36. The wholesale price of a watch is \$12, and the retail price is \$18. What is the percent of markup?

Ⓐ 6% Ⓑ $33\frac{1}{3}\%$ Ⓒ 50% Ⓓ 66%

37. A \$585 bicycle is on sale for \$386. What is the percent of discount?

Ⓕ 27% Ⓖ 34% Ⓗ 52% Ⓙ 66%

Mixed Review

Solve the equation. Check your solution. *(4.1–4.5)*

38. $5y + 11 = -19$ **39.** $3y = 4y - 7$ **40.** $4(x + 2) = 12$

41. $3n + 7 = 22$ **42.** $8 + 2(q - 3) = 0$ **43.** $0.2s - 5.4 = 0$

44. $2r + 6r - 4 = 20$ **45.** $12 - 4x = 48$ **46.** $3(x + 2) = 12$

47. $25n - 7.3 = -2.05$ 0.21 **48.** $2.3s - 9.8 = 24.7$ **49.** $6r - 2 = 2r$

Write the percent as a decimal and as a fraction. *(5.7)*

50. 52% 0.52, $\frac{52}{100}$ **51.** 83% 0.83, $\frac{83}{100}$ **52.** 146% **53.** 206%

54. 2.4% 0.024, $\frac{24}{1000}$ **55.** 17.8% 0.178, $\frac{178}{1000}$ **56.** 0.13% 0.0013, $\frac{13}{10,000}$ **57.** 0.04% 0.0004, $\frac{4}{10,000}$

Express both quantities in a common unit of measure, then write the ratio as a fraction $\frac{a}{b}$ in simplest form. *(7.1)*

58. $\frac{\text{1 hour}}{\text{30 minutes}}$ **59.** $\frac{\text{5 minutes}}{\text{12 seconds}}$ **60.** $\frac{\text{4 feet}}{\text{9 inches}}$ **61.** $\frac{\text{16 yards}}{\text{8 feet}}$

62. $\frac{\text{3 pounds}}{\text{12 ounces}}$ **63.** $\frac{\text{3 cups}}{\text{5 pints}}$ $\frac{3}{10}$ **64.** $\frac{\text{8 centimeters}}{\text{2 meters}}$ **65.** $\frac{\text{9 gallons}}{\text{15 quarts}}$

7.7 Percent of Increase or Decrease

California Standards

In this lesson you'll:

- Calculate the percent of increase or decrease of a quantity. (NS 1.6)

Goal 1 Finding a Percent of Increase

A **percent of change** tells how much a quantity has increased or decreased relative to the original amount. You can use a ratio to find a percent of change.

$$\text{Percent of change} = \frac{\text{New amount} - \text{Original amount}}{\text{Original amount}}$$

When the new amount is greater than the original amount, the percent of change is positive and is called a percent of increase.

EXAMPLE 1 Finding a Percent of Change

The enrollment at a middle school for 1999 was 400 students and for 2000 it was 420 students. Find the percent of change from 1999 to 2000.

Solution

$$\text{Percent of change} = \frac{\text{2000 enrollment} - \text{1999 enrollment}}{\text{1999 enrollment}}$$

$$= \frac{420 - 400}{400}$$

$$= \frac{20}{400} = 0.05 = 5\%$$

ANSWER The percent of change in enrollment was 5%.

Student Help

STUDY TIP
In Example 2, notice that you can describe the increase in the width in two ways.

- 7 is 40% *more than* 5.
- 7 is 140% of 5.

EXAMPLE 2 Finding a Percent of Increase

PHOTOGRAPH You place a 5 inch by 7 inch photograph in a photo enlarger. You want to enlarge the photograph so it measures 7 inches by 9.8 inches to fit into a frame. What enlargement setting should you use?

Solution

Use either the width or the length to find the percent of increase.

$$\frac{\text{Enlarged width} - \text{Original width}}{\text{Original width}} = \frac{7 \text{ in.} - 5 \text{ in.}}{5 \text{ in.}}$$

$$= \frac{2 \text{ in.}}{5 \text{ in.}} = 0.4 = 40\%$$

ANSWER The percent of increase is 40%. This means that the enlarged size is 100% + 40% = 140% of the original size. You should choose an enlargement setting of 140%.

1 Plan

Pacing

Suggested Number of Days

Transitional: 1 day
Average: 1 day
Advanced: 1 day
Block Schedule: 0.5 block with 7.6

Teaching Resources

Blacklines
(See page 326B.)

Transparencies
- Warm-Up Exercises
- Teacher Time-Savers
- English/Spanish Problem Solving
- Answers

Technology
- Electronic Teacher Tools
- Test and Practice Generator

2 Teach

Math Reasoning

For Mathematical Background Notes on mathematical reasoning related to this lesson, please refer to pages 326E and 326F in this Teacher's Edition.

Extra Examples 1 and 2
See next page.

California Standards and Assessment

CA Standard: NS 1.6

Extra Example 1

During the first full year of business in 1995, the profits at a small investment business were $235,000. In 1996, the company's profits were $455,000. Find the percent of increase. **about 94%**

Extra Example 2

You place an 8 inch by 10 inch design in a photocopy machine. You want to enlarge it to 10 inches by $12\frac{1}{2}$ inches. What enlargement setting should you use? **125%**

Extra Example 3

The number of yearly memberships sold at a recreational center in 1996 was 422. In 1997, 394 yearly memberships were sold. Find the percent of decrease. **about 6.6%**

Extra Example 4

At a large retail clothing chain, prices were reduced on certain items by 25%. The items remaining unsold a month later were reduced by another 25%. The original price of an item was $20.

a. What is the price of the item after the first price reduction? **$15**

b. What is the price of the item after the second price reduction? **$11.25**

Concept Check

Is the calculation of the percent change different if it is a percent increase rather than a percent decrease? ***Sample answer:*** **The calculation is the same. If the percent is positive, it is an increase and if the percent is negative, it is a decrease.**

Goal 2 FINDING A PERCENT OF DECREASE

When the new amount is less than the original amount, the percent of change is negative and is called a percent of decrease.

Student Help

▶More Examples

More examples are available at www.mcdougallittell.com

EXAMPLE 3 Finding a Percent of Decrease

POPULATION In 1970 the population of New York was 18,241,000. In 1990 the population was 17,991,000. Find the percent of change from 1970 to 1990.

Solution

$$\text{Percent of change} = \frac{\text{1990 population} - \text{1970 population}}{\text{1970 population}}$$

$$= \frac{17{,}991{,}000 - 18{,}241{,}000}{18{,}241{,}000}$$

$$= \frac{-250{,}000}{18{,}241{,}000} \approx -0.014 = -1.4\%$$

ANSWER ▶ The population decreased about 1.4% from 1970 to 1990.

EXAMPLE 4 Using a Percent of Decrease

EMPLOYMENT AGENCY You manage an employment agency. At the beginning of 2001, your supervisor asked you to reduce the agency's travel expenses by 10% in 2001 and another 10% in 2002. In 2000, the expenses were $100,000.

a. What should the expenses be in 2001? **b.** In 2002?

Solution

a. Begin by finding 10% of the travel expenses in 2000.

10% of $100{,}000 = 0.1 \cdot 100{,}000$ Write 10% as a decimal.

$= 10{,}000$ Multiply.

Subtract to find the expenses for 2001.

$100{,}000 - 10{,}000 = 90{,}000$

ANSWER ▶ In 2001 your expenses should be $90,000.

b. Begin by finding 10% of the travel expenses in 2001.

10% of $90{,}000 = 0.1 \cdot 90{,}000$ Write 10% as a decimal.

$= 9000$ Multiply.

Subtract to find the expenses for 2001.

$90{,}000 - 9000 = 81{,}000$

ANSWER ▶ In 2002 your expenses should be $81,000.

Student Help

▶Study Tip

In Example 4, notice that decreasing an amount by 10% and then decreasing the result by 10% is not the same as decreasing the original amount by 20%.

7.7 Exercises

Guided Practice

In Exercises 1–3, identify the percent of change as an *increase* or a *decrease*. Then find the percent of change.

1. Before: 30
After: 45
increase, 50%

2. Before: 128
After: 32
decrease, −75%

3. Before: 250
After: 220
decrease, −12%

4. You are enlarging a sketch that measures 4 inches by 8 inches. You want the photocopy to measure 5 inches by 10 inches. What enlargement setting should you use on the photocopier? +125%

5. The population of Nevada in 1970 was 489,000. In 1990 it was 1,202,000. Find the percent of change to the nearest tenth.
145.81%, the population increased.

Practice and Problem Solving

Student Help

▶ MORE PRACTICE
Extra practice to help you master skills is on page 703.

Find the percent of change.

6. Before: 10
After: 12 +20%

7. Before: 14
After: 12 −14.3%

8. Before: 110
After: 143 +30%

9. Before: \$90
After: \$200 +122.2%

10. Before: \$260
After: \$160 −38.5%

11. Before: \$1085
After: \$1519 +40%

Chapter Opener Link Look back at page 327.

12. Find the percent of increase in the price of a share of Company 1's stock. 150%

13. Find the percent of increase in the price of a share of Company 2's stock. 100%

14. Which company's stock was the better investment? Explain.
Company 1's stock was the better investment. Rose the larger percentage.

Student Help

▶ STUDY TIP
Before calculating a percent of change, determine whether there has been an increase or a decrease. This will tell you whether the percent of change should be positive or negative.

In Exercises 15 and 16, use a percent to describe the pattern. List the next three numbers you expect to find in the sequence.

15. 1, 2, 4, 8, ?, ?, ? +100%; 16, 32, 64

16. 1024, 256, 64, 16, ?, ?, ? −75%; 4, 1, 0.25

17. WRITING You are writing an article for the school newspaper comparing the cost of a bag of groceries in 1949 with the cost of the same bag of groceries in 1999. Write the first sentence of your article stating the percent of increase in cost from 1949 to 1999. Round the percent to the nearest tenth.

Contents	1949	1999
Pork Chops, 1 lb	\$ .67	\$3.29
Chicken, 1 lb	\$ .63	\$ .79
Eggs, 1 dozen	\$ .73	\$1.19
Milk, 1 quart	\$ .22	\$ .99
Potatoes, 1 lb	\$ .05	\$ .36
Sugar, 1 lb	\$ .09	\$ .46

The cost of a bag of groceries increased from \$2.39 in 1949 to \$7.08 in 1999, which represents a 196.23% increase.

3 Apply

Assignment Guide

TRANSITIONAL
Day 1: pp. 363–364 Exs. 6–14, 19–21, 24–25

AVERAGE
Day 1: pp. 363–364 Exs. 6–14, 17–21, 24–25

ADVANCED
Day 1: pp. 363–364 Exs. 9–18, 22, 23*, 24–25

BLOCK SCHEDULE
pp. 363–364 Exs. 6–14, 17–21, 24–25 (with 7.6)

Extra Practice

- Student Edition, pp. 702–703
- Chapter 7 Resource Book, p. 60

Homework Check

To quickly check student understanding of key concepts, go over the following exercises:

Transitional: 8, 10, 12, 19, 20
Average: 8, 10, 12, 18, 20
Advanced: 8, 10, 16, 17, 18

4 Assess

Assessment Resources

- Assessment Book (Formal Assessment and Alternative Assessment)
- Test and Practice Generator

Mini-Quiz

Decide whether the change is an *increase* or a *decrease* and find the percent.

1. Before: 15, After: 10 **decrease; about 33.3%**
2. Before: 120, After: 150 **increase; 25%**
3. Before: 450, After: 415 **decrease; about 7.8%**
4. From one year to the next, the profits of company A increased from $350,000 to $425,000. The profits of company B increased from $32,000 to $40,000 during the same time. Which company had the greater percent increase in profits? **company B**

18. No. The marked up price, P_1, equals $P + 0.2P$, where P is the original price.
The sale price, P_2, equals $P_1 - 0.2P_1$.

$$P \stackrel{?}{=} P_2$$
$$\stackrel{?}{=} P_1 - 0.2P_1$$
$$= P + 0.2P - 0.2(P + 0.2P)$$
$$P \stackrel{?}{=} P + 0.2P - 0.2P + 0.04P$$
$$= P + 0.04P$$
$$P \neq P + 0.04P$$

18. MATHEMATICAL REASONING You want to buy a pair of in-line skates. Before you have time to save enough money to buy the skates, they are marked up 20%. A few weeks later they are on sale at 20% off. You buy them thinking they are back to the original price. Are you correct? **See margin.**

Link to Geography

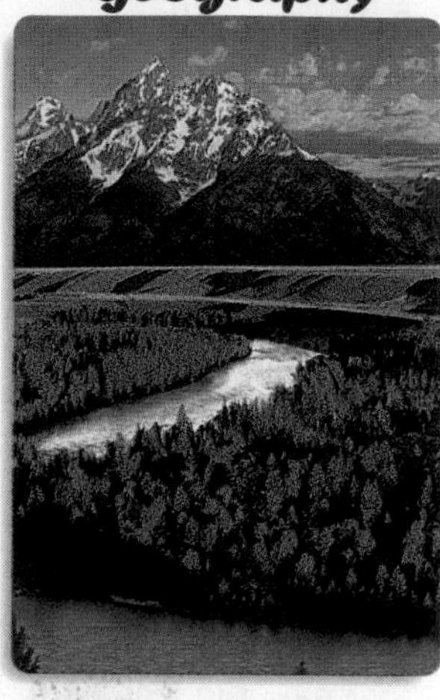

WYOMING Because of developments in Wyoming's mining industry, the state's population had a 42% increase between 1970 and 1980.

GEOGRAPHY In Exercises 19–21, use the table below which gives various state populations in 1970 and 1990.

Population of States in 1970 and 1990		
	1970	1990
Alaska	303,000	550,000
California	19,971,000	29,786,000
Florida	6,791,000	12,938,000
Iowa	2,825,000	2,777,000
Wyoming	332,000	454,000

19. Which state, California or Florida, had the greater percent of increase in population from 1970 to 1990? **Florida**

20. Which state had a decrease in population from 1970 to 1990? What was the percent of decrease? **Iowa, −1.7%**

21. Which state, Alaska or Wyoming, had the smaller percent of increase in population from 1970 to 1990? **Wyoming**

22. **ERROR ANALYSIS** Your friend finds a jacket on the clearance rack at a department store. It costs $50, but the store advertises that the price will be reduced 10% each day. Your friend claims that he will be able to buy the jacket for $25 in five days. Explain why your friend's reasoning is incorrect.

22. The friend is thinking that the price will be reduced 10% of the original price of $50 each day of the five sales days. So the price will be $50, $45, $40, $35, $30 and then $25 on the fifth day. However, the price is reduced by 10% of the previous day's price. So, the price will be $50, $45, $40.50, $36.45, $32.81, and then $29.52 on the fifth day.

23. **CHALLENGE** A department store has advertised a sweater sale for one day. All sweaters will be 35% off the regular price. You also have a coupon for $5.00 off the sale price. What percent will you save on a sweater with a regular price of $69.95? **42%**

Multiple-Choice Practice

24. A Company's stock was valued at $12 per share. After one year, the stock price increased to $15 per share. What is the percent of increase in the share price of the stock? **D**

Ⓐ 3% Ⓑ 15% Ⓒ 20% Ⓓ 25%

25. In 1990 the population of Bridgeton was 12,000. The town's population for the year 2000 was 10,800. By what percent did Bridgeton's population decrease? **F**

Ⓕ 10% Ⓖ 11.1% Ⓗ 12% Ⓙ 15%

7.8 Simple Interest

California Standards

In this lesson you'll:

- Use percents in applications. (NS 1.3)
- Compute simple interest. (NS 1.7)

Goal 1 FINDING SIMPLE INTEREST OR INTEREST RATE

Interest is money paid for the use of money. The amount you deposit or borrow is called the **principal**. The percent of increase in the principal is called the **interest rate**. When interest is paid only on the principal, it is called **simple interest**.

FINDING SIMPLE INTEREST

In Words To find the simple interest I, multlply the principal P, the annual interest rate r expressed as a decimal, and the time t in years.

In Algebra $I = Prt$

In Arithmetic Deposit $200 at 6% per year for 1 year. The interest earned is $I = (\$200)(0.06)(1) = \$12.00$.

EXAMPLE 1 Finding Simple Interest

You deposit $500 in a savings account for 9 months. If the annual simple interest rate is 1.5%, how much interest will you earn?

Solution

The principal is $500, the annual interest rate is 1.5% = 0.015, and the time is 9 months = 0.75 year.

$$I = Prt = (500)(0.015)(0.75) \approx 5.63$$

ANSWER ▶ The simple interest earned is $5.63.

Student Help

▶ **STUDY TIP**
Throughout this lesson, assume that no additional deposits or any withdrawals are made during the time period described.

EXAMPLE 2 Finding an Annual Interest Rate

You borrow $250 from your family. After 6 months, you pay back the $250 plus interest of $10. What is the annual simple interest rate?

Solution

$I = Prt$ Write formula for simple interest.

$10 = (250)(r)(\mathbf{0.5})$ Substitute. 6 months = 0.5 year

$10 = 125r$ Simplify.

$0.08 = r$ Divide each side by 125.

ANSWER ▶ The annual interest rate is 8%.

1 Plan

Pacing

Suggested Number of Days

Transitional: 1 day
Average: 1 day
Advanced: 1 day
Block Schedule: 0.5 block with 7.9

Teaching Resources

Blacklines
(See page 326B.)

Transparencies
- Warm-Up Exercises
- Teacher Time-Savers
- English/Spanish Problem Solving
- Answers

Technology
- Electronic Teacher Tools
- Test and Practice Generator

2 Teach

Math Reasoning

For Mathematical Background Notes on mathematical reasoning related to this lesson, please refer to pages 326E and 326F in this Teacher's Edition.

Extra Examples 1 and 2
See next page.

California Standards and Assessment

CA Standards: NS 1.3, NS 1.7

CA Key Concepts Book: pp. S32, S34–S35

Extra Example 1

You deposit \$2000 in a savings account for 3 months. If the annual simple interest rate is 4.1%, how much interest will you earn? **\$20.50**

Extra Example 2

You borrow \$120. After 9 months, you pay back the \$120 plus interest of \$5.40. What is the annual simple interest rate? **6%**

Extra Example 3

On January 1, a credit card has a balance of \$1900. The credit card company charges interest at an annual rate of 18%. If no payment or purchases are made, what will be the balance on Feburary 1? **\$1928.50**

Extra Example 4

A bank offers 3.5% annual simple interest on a special savings account. How much should you deposit to have \$1000 at the end of 5 years? **\$851.06**

Teaching Tip

Point out to students that the interest rate is normally given as an annual rate, so the time needs to be in years. If the interest rate is given as a monthly rate, then the time needs to be in months.

Concept Check

What do the words *principal*, *interest*, and *balance* mean when computing simple interest? ***Sample answer:*** **Principal is the amount of money you deposit or borrow. Interest is the amount of money paid for the use of the money. Balance is the sum of principal and interest.**

Goal 2 FINDING A BALANCE OR PRINCIPAL

Student Help

▶ STUDY TIP
In the formula for finding a balance, *Prt* represents the amount of interest, so $P + Prt$ represents the *principal plus the amount of interest.*

When you add the interest to the principal, the result is called the *balance* of your account. In this lesson balance is represented by A.

FINDING A BALANCE

In Words To find the balance in an account that earns simple interest, add the interest to the principal.

In Algebra $A = P + Prt$

In Arithmetic Deposit \$200 at 6% per year. After 1 year
$A = \$200 + (\$200)(0.06)(1) = \$200 + \$12 = \$212.$

EXAMPLE 3 Finding a Balance

On June 1, the balance on a credit card is \$2500. The credit card company charges interest at an annual rate of 21%. If no payment or purchases are made, what will the balance be on July 1?

Solution

$A = P + Prt$ — Write formula for balance.

$= 2500 + (2500)(0.21)\left(\frac{1}{12}\right)$ — Substitute. 1 month $= \frac{1}{12}$ year

$= 2500 + 43.75$ — Multiply.

$= 2543.75$ — Add.

ANSWER ▶ The balance on July 1 is \$2543.75.

EXAMPLE 4 Finding a Principal

A bank offers an annual interest rate of 5.5% on a one-year certificate of deposit. How much should you deposit to have a balance of \$1000 at the end of the year?

Hometown Bank
Certificate of Deposit
Annual Interest Rates

Account	Minimum Deposit	Interest Rate
91 days	\$500	3.69%
6 months	\$500	4.22%
12 months	\$500	5.5%
24 months	\$500	5.8%

Solution

The amount you deposit is the principal.

Student Help

▶ STUDY TIP
If you are given an interest rate and a balance, you can find the principal by solving $A = P + Prt$ for P.

$A = P + Prt$ — Write formula.

$1000 = P + P(0.055)(1)$ — Substitute.

$1000 = P(1 + 0.055)$ — Use distributive property.

$1000 = P(1.055)$ — Add.

$948 \approx P$ — Divide each side by 1.055.

ANSWER ▶ You would need to deposit approximately \$948 for one year.

7.8 Exercises

Guided Practice

In Exercises 1–4, find the simple interest.

1. \$400 at 6% for 1 year **\$24**

2. \$100 at 12% for 6 months **\$6**

3. \$5000 at 10% for 2 months **\$83.33**

4. \$25 at 25% for 3 months **\$1.56**

5. You deposit \$500 into an account that earns simple interest at an annual rate of 2.5%. What is your balance after one year? **\$512.50**

6. Your friend deposited \$400 in a savings account and received \$16 in simple interest after 1 year. Find the annual interest rate. **4%**

7. You want to invest in a one-year CD that pays simple interest at an annual rate of 5.25%. How much should you invest to have \$1500 at the end of the year? Round your answer to the nearest whole dollar. **\$1425**

Practice and Problem Solving

Student Help

▶MORE PRACTICE
Extra practice to help you master skills is on page 703.

Find the simple interest and the balance of the account.

8. \$1000 at 3% for 6 months **\$15, \$1015**

9. \$1250 at 12% for 2 months **\$25, \$1275**

10. \$4000 at 5% for 3 months **\$50, \$4050**

11. \$800 at 7.5% for 3 months **\$15, \$815**

12. \$5400 at 8% for 9 months **\$324, \$5724**

13. \$500 at 9.5% for 1 year **\$47.50, \$547.50**

Find the annual simple interest rate.

14. \$103.50 interest on \$2300 for 6 months **9%**

15. \$1600 interest on \$8000 for 1 year **20%**

16. \$25 interest on \$600 for 5 months **10%**

17. \$2100 interest on \$120,000 for 3 months **7%**

U.S. TREASURY In Exercises 18 and 19, use the following information. Your cousin purchased a two-year U.S. Treasury note for \$10,000. The simple annual interest rate is 6%. Your cousin receives interest payments every 6 months and will get his \$10,000 back at the end of 2 years.

18. What is the amount of simple interest that your cousin will earn every 6 months? **\$300**

19. What is the total amount, principal plus interest, that your cousin will have received at the end of the 2 years? **\$11,200**

20. MATHEMATICAL REASONING Which interest payment is larger, simple interest of 6% per year after one year or simple interest of 10% per year after six months? Justify your answer.

20. six percent per year for one year; *Sample answer:* At 6% per year for one year, $I = P(0.06)(1) = 0.06P$. At 10% per year for six months: $I = P(0.10)\left(\frac{1}{2}\right) = 0.05P$. The interest at 6% per year for one year is greater.

3 Apply

Assignment Guide

TRANSITIONAL
Day 1: pp. 367–368 Exs. 8–11, 14–16, 18–22, 28–29

AVERAGE
Day 1: pp. 367–368 Exs. 10–13, 15–20, 23–24, 28–29

ADVANCED
Day 1: pp. 367–368 Exs. 10–13, 15–17, 20, 23–26, 27*, 28–29

BLOCK SCHEDULE
pp. 367–368 Exs. 10–13, 15–20, 23–24, 28–29 (with 7.9)

Extra Practice

- Student Edition, pp. 702–703
- Chapter 7 Resource Book, p. 69

Homework Check

To quickly check student understanding of key concepts, go over the following exercises:

Transitional: 8, 10, 14, 16, 18
Average: 10, 12, 16, 18, 24
Advanced: 10, 12, 16, 23, 24

4 Assess

Assessment Resources

- Assessment Book (Formal Assessment and Alternative Assessment)
- Test and Practice Generator

Mini-Quiz

Find the simple interest and the balance of the account.

1. $250 at 4% for 9 months **interest: $7.50; balance: $257.50**
2. $3000 at 7% for 6 months **interest: $105; balance: $3105**

Find the annual simple interest rate.

3. $10 interest on $500 for 3 months **8%**
4. $315 interest on $6000 for 7 months **9%**
5. A credit card has a balance of $120 at the beginning of January. The card computes finance charges at an annual rate of 21%. If no payments or purchases are made, what will the balance be at the beginning of February? **$122.10**

ERROR ANALYSIS **In Exercises 21 and 22, describe and correct the error.**

21. Find the interest on $3400 at 6% simple interest for 3 months. **The value of t is incorrect. Instead of 0.5, it should be 0.25 for 3 months. $51.00**

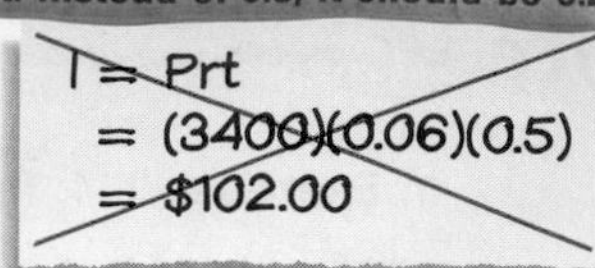

22. Find the principal that is invested at 5.5% simple interest for one year when the interest paid is $96.25. **The value of r is incorrect. Instead of 0.55, it should be 0.055 for 5.5%. $1750**

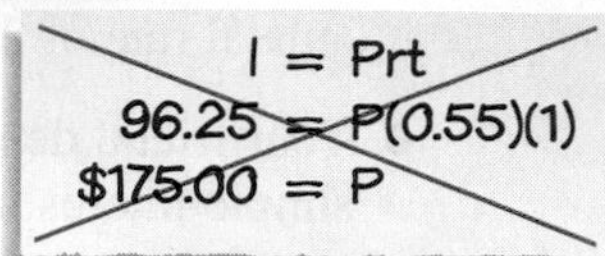

23. CREDIT CARDS At the beginning of May there is a balance of $3200 on a credit card account for which finance charges are computed at an annual rate of 18%. If no payments or purchases are made, what will the balance be at the beginning of June? **$3248**

24. SAVINGS At the end of 9 months you have $370.13 in your savings account. If the annual simple interest rate is 5.75%, what was the principal at the beginning of the 9 months? **$354.83**

Student Help

▶HOMEWORK HELP

Extra help with problem solving in Exs. 25–26 is available at www.mcdougallittell.com

CAR LOAN **In Exercises 25 and 26, use the following information.** Your brother wants to borrow $5000 to buy a used car. Your mother will lend him the money at 10% annual simple interest for 7 years. Your grandfather will also lend him the money at 12.5% annual simple interest for 4 years.

25. What is the amount of interest that your brother would pay to your mother? to your grandfather? **$3500, $2500**

26. From which relative should your brother borrow the money? Explain. **26. You should borrow the money from your grandfather because the amount of interest is less.**

27. CHALLENGE At the beginning of each month, you deposit $100 in a savings account that earns simple interest each month at an annual rate of 3%. What is the balance of the account one year after you make your first deposit, but before you make your 13th deposit? **about $1219.70**

Multiple-Choice Practice

28. You deposit $1000 in an account earning 7.5% annual simple interest. How much interest do you earn after 3 months? **A**

Ⓐ $18.75 Ⓑ $37.50 Ⓒ $50.50 Ⓓ $75.00

29. A bank lends you $1235 for 6 months. The amount of interest you must pay is $101.89. What is the annual simple interest rate? **H**

Ⓕ 8.25% Ⓖ 12% Ⓗ 16.5% Ⓙ 33%

7.9 Compound Interest

California Standards

In this lesson you'll:

- Compute compound interest. (NS 1.7)

Goal 1 FINDING COMPOUND INTEREST WITH A TABLE

Interest paid on the principal *and* on previously earned interest is **compound interest**. With compound interest, the interest earned is added to the principal at regular intervals (daily, monthly, quarterly, or annually). This sum becomes the new principal for the next earning period.

EXAMPLE 1 Finding Compound Interest

You deposit $500 in an account that pays 6% annual interest compounded quarterly. What is your balance at the end of one year?

Solution

Quarter	Beginning Balance	Interest	Ending Balance
1	$500.00	$I = (500.00)(0.06)(0.25)$ $= \$7.50$	$A = 500.00 + 7.50$ $= \$507.50$
2	$507.50	$I = (507.50)(0.06)(0.25)$ $\approx \$7.61$	$A = 507.50 + 7.61$ $= \$515.11$
3	$515.11	$I = (515.11)(0.06)(0.25)$ $\approx \$7.73$	$A = 515.11 + 7.73$ $= \$522.84$
4	$522.84	$I = (522.84)(0.06)(0.25)$ $\approx \$7.84$	$A = 522.84 + 7.84$ $= \$530.68$

ANSWER ▶ Your balance at the end of the 4 quarters (1 year) is $530.68.

Student Help

▶**STUDY TIP**
Throughout this lesson, assume that no additional deposits or any withdrawals are made during the time period described.

EXAMPLE 2 Comparing Compound and Simple Interest

Suppose the account in Example 1 paid only simple interest.

a. Find the balance at the end of a year using simple interest.

b. How much more interest was earned by compounding quarterly?

Solution

a. With simple interest, the balance at the end of the year would be:

$$A = P + Prt = 500 + (500)(0.06)(1) = 500 + 30 = \$530$$

b. The difference is $530.68 - 530 = 0.68$. You earned $.68 more when interested is compounded quarterly.

Student Help

▶**VOCABULARY TIP**
Monthly means 12 times a year.
Quarterly means 4 times a year.
Semiannually means 2 times a year.
Annually means 1 time a year.

1 Plan

Pacing
Suggested Number of Days
Transitional: 1 day
Average: 1 day
Advanced: 1 day
Block Schedule: 0.5 block with 7.8

Teaching Resources

Blacklines
(See page 326B.)

Transparencies
- Warm-Up Exercises
- Teacher Time-Savers
- English/Spanish Problem Solving
- Answers

Technology
- Electronic Teacher Tools
- Test and Practice Generator

2 Teach

Math Reasoning

For Mathematical Background Notes on mathematical reasoning related to this lesson, please refer to pages 326E and 326F in this Teacher's Edition.

Extra Examples 1 and 2
See next page.

California Standards and Assessment
CA Standard: NS 1.7
CA Key Concepts Book: pp. S33–S35

Extra Example 1

You deposit \$2000 in an account that pays 8% interest, compounded quarterly. If you make no additional deposits or withdrawals, what is your balance at the end of one year? **\$2164.86**

Extra Example 2

Suppose the account in Extra Example 1 paid only simple interest.

a. Find the balance at the end of one year using simple interest. **\$2160**

b. How much more interest did you earn from compound interest? **\$4.86**

Extra Example 3

Use the formula for compound interest to find the balance in the account described in Extra Example 1 at the end of one year. **\$2164.86**

Math Reasoning

Example 2 illustrates the advantage of compound interest after four compoundings. As a simpler example, one might compare two years of simple interest with two years of annual compounding. After two years of simple interest, an initial balance of P dollars would have a value of $P(1 + 2r)$. With annual compounding it would have a balance of $P(1 + r)^2$. Recalling that $(1 + r)^2 = 1 + 2r + r^2$, the difference between the two methods can be expressed as $P[(1 + 2r + r^2) - (1 + 2r)] = Pr^2$. It also should be noted that for the case of quarterly compounding, the formula $A = P(1 + rt)^n$ becomes $A = P\left(1 + \frac{r}{4}\right)^n$. Here it is important to recall that n refers to *quarters* that have elapsed. To find the balance after two years, it is necessary to set $n = 8$. Similar considerations apply to monthly or daily compounding.

Goal 2 A Formula for Compound Interest

Student Help

▶ Study Tip
In the table, notice that the ending balance in the first compounding period becomes the beginning balance in the second period. This pattern continues in the third and fourth compounding periods.

You can use the distributive property and exponents to develop a formula for finding compound interest. Let r represent the annual interest rate and t the time (in years) between compoundings.

Number of Compoundings	Beginning Balance	Interest	Ending Balance
1	P	$I = Prt$	$A = P + Prt$ $= P(1 + rt)$
2	$P(1 + rt)$	$I = P(1 + rt)(rt)$	$A = P(1 + rt) + P(1 + rt)(rt)$ $= P(1 + rt)(1 + rt)$ $= P(1 + rt)^2$
3	$P(1 + rt)^2$	$I = P(1 + rt)^2(rt)$	$A = P(1 + rt)^2 + P(1 + rt)^2(rt)$ $= P(1 + rt)^2(1 + rt)$ $= P(1 + rt)^3$
4	$P(1 + rt)^3$	$I = P(1 + rt)^3(rt)$	$A = P(1 + rt)^3 + P(1 + rt)^3(rt)$ $= P(1 + rt)^3(1 + rt)$ $= P(1 + rt)^4$

The table shows that after 4 compoundings the balance is $A = P(1 + rt)^4$. This formula can be generalized to compounding n times.

Finding Compound Interest

The balance after n compoundings is $A = P(1 + rt)^n$ where t is the time in years between compoundings.

Example 3 Finding Compound Interest

Use the formula for compound interest to find the balance in Example 1.

Solution

The principal is $P = \$500$. The annual interest rate is $r = 0.06$. Because the compounding occurs quarterly, the time is $t = 0.25$. Because there will be 4 quarterly compoundings during the year, $n = 4$.

$A = P(1 + rt)^n$ — **Write compound interest formula.**

$= (500)(1 + (0.06)(0.25))^4$ — **Substitute.**

$= (500)(1 + 0.015)^4$ — **Multiply inside the parentheses.**

$= (500)(1.015)^4$ — **Add inside the parentheses.**

$\approx (500)(1.06136)$ — **Raise 1.015 to the 4th power.**

≈ 530.68 — **Use a calculator and round.**

ANSWER ▶ The balance at the end of one year is \$530.68.

7.9 Exercises

Guided Practice

1. *Sample answers:* Simple interest is interest paid only on the principal; compound interest is interest paid on the principal and on previously earned interest. Example: six percent compounded quarterly

3.

Number of compoundings	Balance
1	$1020.00
2	$1040.40
3	$1061.21
4	$1082.43

5. $1000, 5%, 6 months, 12

1. WRITING Explain the difference between simple interest and compound interest. Give an example of compound interest.

In Exercises 2–4, use the following information. You deposit $1000 into a savings account at 8% annual interest for one year.

2. Find the balance in the account after one year using simple interest. **$1080**

3. Make a table to find the balance in the account after one year when the interest is compounded quarterly. Use the formula for compound interest to check your answer.

4. Did you earn more interest using simple or compound interest? How much more? **compound interest, $2.43**

From the given compound interest formula identify the principal, the annual interest rate, the time between compoundings, and the number of compoundings.

5. $A = 1000[1 + (0.05)(0.5)]^{12}$

6. $A = 4000[1 + (0.10)(0.25)]^{20}$ **$4000, 10%, 3 months, 20**

7. $A = 1200\left[1 + (0.09)\left(\frac{1}{12}\right)\right]^{24}$ **$1200, 9%, 1 month, 24**

8. $A = 9500[1 + (0.14)(0.25)]^{40}$ **9500, 14%, 3 months, 40**

Practice and Problem Solving

Student Help

▸ MORE PRACTICE
Extra practice to help you master skills is on page 703.

9. How many times each year is interest added to your account if interest is compounded monthly? quarterly? semiannually? annually? **12, 4, 2, 1**

10. How many times in five years is interest added to your account if interest is compounded monthly? quarterly? semiannually? annually? **60, 20, 10, 5**

In Exercises 11–13, use the information to find the balance in an account when $1000 is invested for one year.

11. 12% interest compounded monthly **$1126.83**

12. 20% interest compounded semiannually **$1210.00**

13. $5\frac{1}{2}\%$ interest compounded annually **$1055.00**

In Exercises 14 and 15, use the following information. You deposit $100 into a savings account for two years. The bank is offering an annual interest rate of 4% compounded monthly.

14. Determine how many compounding periods occur in two years. **24**

15. Use the formula for compound interest to find the balance in your account at the end of two years. **$108.31**

Concept Check

What is the difference between simple interest and compound interest? ***Sample answer:*** **Simple interest is paid only on principal while compound interest is paid on principal *and* on previously earned interest.**

3 Apply

Assignment Guide

TRANSITIONAL
Day 1: pp. 371–373 Exs. 9–12, 14–16, 18, 22–24, 30–31

AVERAGE
Day 1: pp. 371–373 Exs. 9–17, 22–24, 28, 30–31

ADVANCED
Day 1: pp. 371–373 Exs. 11–18, 25–27, 29*, 30–31; EC: TE p. 326D*

BLOCK SCHEDULE
pp. 371–373 Exs. 9–17, 22–24, 28, 30–31 (with 7.8)

Extra Practice

- Student Edition, pp. 702–703
- Chapter 7 Resource Book, p. 78

Homework Check

To quickly check student understanding of key concepts, go over the following exercises:

Transitional: 10, 12, 14, 16, 18
Average: 10, 12, 14, 16, 28
Advanced: 12, 14, 16, 26, 28

Teaching Tip

An interesting addition to Exercises 19–21 is the "Rule of 72." This common rule of thumb states that the time it takes your money to double can be approximated by dividing the interest rate (as a whole number) into 72. For example, at 9% money doubles in about $\frac{72}{9} = 8$ years.

26.

Year	Compound interest balance
0	$5000.00
1	$5469.03
2	$5982.07
3	$6543.23
4	$7157.03
5	$7828.41

27.

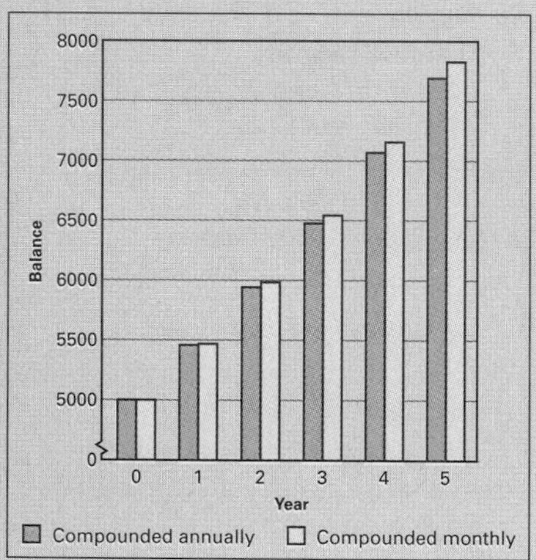

The difference becomes greater as the amount of time increases.

In Exercises 16 and 17, use the information to find the amount in the account after the given number of years.

16. Principal: $500; annual interest rate: 10%; compounded quarterly for 5 years **$819.31**

17. Principal: $1500; annual interest rate: 6%; compounded semiannually for 10 years **$2709.17**

Student Help

▶ STUDY TIP
Banks often calculate interest on the average daily balance of the account.

18. You will have more money in savings. (Your savings account: $760.06, your friend's: $757.49)

18. Your friend invests $600 in a savings account at 12% annual interest compounded semiannually. You invest $600 in another account at 12% annual interest compounded quarterly. At the end of two years, determine who will have more money in savings.

SPREADSHEET In Exercises 19–21, use a spreadsheet to find the number of years needed to double your money in the account described.

EXAMPLE

You deposit $50 in a savings account that earns 6% annual interest compounded annually.

Solution

The spreadsheet shows the interest added and the balance of the account after each compounding period. After you enter the data in Column A and in Rows 1 and 2, multiply the balance in Cell C2 by the interest rate to compute the amount in B3. To do this, enter the following formula in Cell B3:

$$= C2 * 0.06$$

To find the new balance in C3, add the amounts in C2 and B3. To do this, enter the following formula in Cell C3:

$$= C2 + B3$$

6% Interest

	A	B	C
1	Year	Interest	Balance
2	0	0	$50.00
3	1	$3.00	$53.00
4	2	$3.18	$56.18
5	3	$3.37	$59.55
6	4	$3.57	$63.12
7	5	$3.79	$66.91
8	6	$4.01	$70.93
9	7	$4.26	$75.18
10	8	$4.51	$79.69
11	9	$4.78	$84.47
12	10	$5.07	$89.54
13	11	$5.37	$94.91
14	12	$5.69	$100.61

Then use the "Fill Down" feature of your spreadsheet to copy these formulas into the remaining cells in Columns B and C.

ANSWER ▶ After 12 years the balance is over $100. It takes 12 years to double your money at 6% interest compounded annually.

Student Help

▶ HOMEWORK HELP
Extra help with problem solving in Exs. 19–21 is available at www.mcdougallittell.com

19. You deposit $100 in a savings account that earns 5% annual interest compounded annually. **15 years**

20. You deposit $1000 in a savings account that earns 5.5% annual interest compounded annually. **13 years**

21. You deposit $40 in a savings account that earns 6% annual interest compounded semiannually. **12 years**

Link to Careers

BANK MANAGER When assessing loan requests, bank managers need to determine how much a person can afford to pay each month. For example, a mortgage payment is usually no more than 28% to 36% of a person's monthly income.

More about bank managers available at www.mcdougallittell.com

25.

Year	Compound interest balance
0	$5,000.00
1	$5,450.00
2	$5,940.50
3	$6,475.15
4	$7,057.91
5	$7,693.12

MATHEMATICAL REASONING In Exercises 22–24, use the graph below. It shows the balance of a bank account over 12 years.

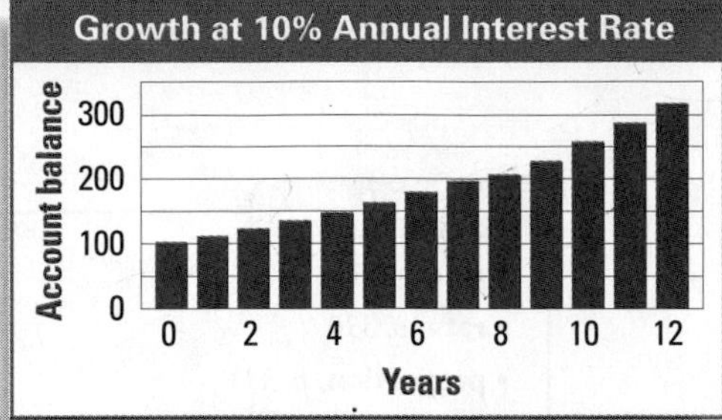

22. What is the interest rate? 10%

23. What was the initial deposit? Explain how you know. $100

24. How long did it take to double the money in the account? Explain how you know. 8 yr; balance reached $200 in year 8

In Exercises 25–27, use the following information. A bank has an annual interest rate of 9% for an account with a minimum deposit of $5000.

25. Make a table to record the balance after 1, 2, 3, 4, and 5 years if the bank pays interest compounded annually and you deposit $5000.

26. Make a table to record the balance after 1, 2, 3, 4 and 5 years if the bank pays interest compounded monthly and you deposit $5000. See margin.

27. Draw a double bar graph using your data from Exercises 25 and 26. What happens to the difference between annual compound interest and monthly compound interest as the amount of time increases? See margin.

28. COMPUTERS A computer store offers a financing plan that waives finance charges for one year. Interest is compounded monthly, but the interest does not have to be paid if the principal is paid within one year. Suppose a computer is purchased for $1500 and the store charges 20% annual interest. How much interest will accumulate after 6 months if no payments are made? $156.39

29. CHALLENGE The monthly payment M you must make on a loan is given by the formula $M = \left(\frac{rt(1 + rt)^n}{(1 + rt)^n - 1}\right)P$. Find the monthly payment on a $5000 loan at 7% interest compounded monthly for 3 years. How much will you pay in interest on the $5000 loan? The monthly payment is $154.39. It will cost $558.04 to borrow the money.

Multiple-Choice Practice

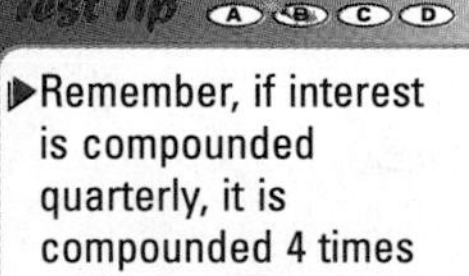

Test Tip Ⓐ Ⓑ Ⓒ Ⓓ

▶Remember, if interest is compounded quarterly, it is compounded 4 times each year.

In Exercises 30 and 31, use the following information. You deposit money in an account that pays interest compounded quarterly. You leave your money in the account for 15 years.

30. For how many compounding periods will interest be earned? C

Ⓐ 4 Ⓑ 15 Ⓒ 60 Ⓓ 75

31. By what number do you multiply the annual interest rate to determine the interest rate for each compounding period? G

Ⓕ 0.025 Ⓖ 0.25 Ⓗ 0.5 Ⓙ 4

4 Assess

Assessment Resources

- Assessment Book (Formal Assessment and Alternative Assessment)
- Test and Practice Generator

Mini-Quiz

Find the balance in an account when $1500 is invested for one year at the following interest rates.

1. 9% compounded monthly **$1640.71**
2. $8\frac{1}{2}$% compounded quarterly **$1631.62**
3. 10% compounded semiannually **$1653.75**
4. Your rich uncle deposits $20,000 in an account and tells you that you may keep the interest earned. If the account offers a $9\frac{1}{2}$% interest rate compounded monthly, how much interest will you earn at the end of one year? **$1984.95**

Additional Resources

The following resources are available to help review the material in this chapter:

Technology

- Personal Student Tutor
- Test and Practice Generator

Chapter 7 Chapter Summary and Review

VOCABULARY

- **ratio,** *p. 329*
- **rate,** *p. 330*
- **proportion,** *p. 333*
- **cross products,** *p. 333*
- **cross products property,** *p. 333*
- **scale drawing,** *p. 338*
- **scale,** *p. 338*
- **scale factor,** *p. 338*
- **outcomes,** *p. 345*
- **event,** *p. 345*
- **favorable outcomes,** *p. 345*
- **probability,** *p. 345*
- **theoretical probabilities,** *p. 346*
- **experimental probabilities,** *p. 346*
- **markup,** *p. 356*
- **discount,** *p. 357*
- **percent of change,** *p. 361*
- **interest,** *p. 365*
- **principal,** *p. 365*
- **interest rate,** *p. 365*
- **simple interest,** *p. 365*
- **compound interest,** *p. 369*

7.1 Ratios and Rates

Examples on pp. 329–330

EXAMPLES **a.** A 10 foot tall tree is 4 feet wide. Find the ratio of its height to its width.

b. You jog 10 miles in 2 hours. Find your rate of speed.

a. $\text{Ratio} = \dfrac{\text{Tree height}}{\text{Tree width}} = \dfrac{10\text{ feet}}{4\text{ feet}} = \dfrac{5}{2}$

b. $\text{Rate} = \dfrac{\text{Distance}}{\text{Time}} = \dfrac{10\text{ miles}}{2\text{ hours}} = 5\text{ miles per hour}$

1. Express 4 cups to 3 gallons in a ratio using a common unit of measure. $\frac{4}{48} = \frac{1}{12}$

2. Ground beef costs \$3.98 for 2 pounds, and ground turkey costs \$8.25 for 5 pounds. Which is a better buy? Explain your answer using unit rates.
The ground turkey is a better buy at \$1.65 per pound compared to the ground beef at \$1.99 per pound.

7.2 Writing and Solving Proportions

Examples on pp. 333–335

EXAMPLE **Solve the proportion $\frac{2}{b} = \frac{5}{8}$.**

$\frac{2}{b} = \frac{5}{8}$	Write original proportion.
$2 \cdot 8 = b \cdot 5$	Cross products property
$3.2 = b$	Divide each side by 5.

Solve the proportion. Check your solution.

3. $\frac{x}{4} = \frac{5}{8}$ **$\frac{5}{2}$** **4.** $\frac{10}{3} = \frac{12}{t}$ **$\frac{18}{5}$** **5.** $\frac{14}{s} = \frac{56}{9}$ **$\frac{9}{4}$** **6.** $\frac{5}{7} = \frac{m}{16}$ **$\frac{80}{7}$**

7.3 SCALE DRAWINGS AND MODELS

Examples on pp. 338–340

EXAMPLE Plans for a tree house have a scale of 1 inch = 0.75 feet. In the plans, the tree house is 12 inches wide. Find the actual width.

$\frac{\text{Actual width}}{\text{Width in drawing}} = \frac{0.75 \text{ ft}}{1 \text{ in.}}$ **Write proportion.**

$\frac{x}{12 \text{ in.}} = \frac{9 \text{ in.}}{1 \text{ in.}}$ **Substitute and change units.**

$x \cdot 1 = 12 \cdot 9$ **Cross products property**

$x = 108$ **Simplify. *x* is by itself.**

The tree house is 108 inches, or 9 feet, wide.

7. The Eiffel Tower in Paris, France, is 984 feet tall. If a model of the tower has a scale of 3 inches = 5 feet, how tall is the model? **49.2 ft tall**

8. On a map, you measure the distance from Dallas, Texas, to Portland, Maine to be about 7 inches. The scale on the map is 1.25 inches = 300 miles. Approximate the actual distance. **1680 mi**

7.4 PROBABILITY

Examples on pp. 345–347

EXAMPLE A bag contains each letter of EXCELLENCE on a separate slip of paper. What is the theoretical probability of drawing an E on a single slip of paper?

$$P = \frac{\text{Favorable outcomes}}{\text{Total outcomes}} = \frac{\text{Number of E's}}{\text{Total number of letters}} = \frac{4}{10} = \frac{\overset{1}{\cancel{2}} \cdot 2}{\underset{1}{\cancel{2}} \cdot 5} = \frac{2}{5} = 40\%$$

In Exercises 9–12, the spinner has 12 regions of equal size. Find the probability that the spinner will land on the color.

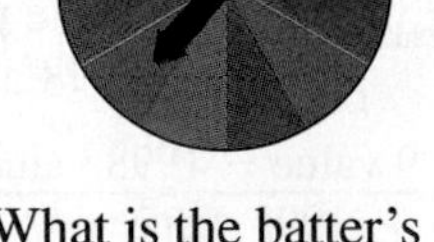

9. Green **$\frac{1}{12}$** **10.** Yellow **$\frac{1}{6}$**

11. Blue **$\frac{5}{12}$** **12.** Red **$\frac{1}{3}$**

13. A baseball player gets 105 hits in 300 times at bat. What is the batter's experimental probability of getting a hit? **0.35 or 35%**

7.5 SOLVING PERCENT PROBLEMS

Examples on pp. 350–352

EXAMPLE **What percent of 125 books is 25 books?**

$\frac{a}{b} = \frac{p}{100}$ Write proportion.

$\frac{25}{125} = \frac{p}{100}$ Substitute 25 for *a* and 125 for *b*.

$25 \cdot 100 = 125 \cdot p$ Cross products property

$20 = p$ Divide each side by 125.

In Exercises 14 and 15, write and solve a proportion.

14. 55 is what percent of 8? **687.5%**

15. 44 is 22% of what number? **200**

16. To earn an "A" on a test, you must get at least 92% of the questions correct. If you get 143 of 150 questions correct, do you earn an "A"? **yes**

7.6 MARKUP AND DISCOUNT

Examples on pp. 356–358

EXAMPLE The wholesale price of a car is \$22,790. The suggested retail price of the same car is \$25,090. Find the percent of markup.

$$\text{Markup} = \text{Retail price} - \text{Wholesale price} = 25{,}090 - 22{,}790 = 2300$$

$$\text{Percent of markup} = \frac{\text{Markup}}{\text{Wholesale price}} = \frac{2300}{22{,}790} \approx 0.10 = 10\%$$

Find the percent of markup or the percent of discount.

17. Regular: \$2000; sale: \$1500 **Discount of 25%**

18. Wholesale: \$.35; retail: \$.99 **Markup of 182.9%**

19. Wholesale: \$24.99; retail: \$34.99 **Markup of 40%**

20. Regular: \$153; sale: \$99 **Discount of 35.3%**

7.7 PERCENT OF INCREASE OR DECREASE

Examples on pp. 361–362

EXAMPLE Find the percent of decrease in the value of a car worth \$14,000 in 1998 and \$11,480 in 1999.

$$\frac{\text{1999 value} - \text{1998 value}}{\text{1998 value}} = \frac{11{,}480 - 14{,}000}{14{,}000} = \frac{-2520}{14{,}000} = -0.18 = -18\%$$

In Exercises 21 and 22, use the bar graph. The graph shows the number of pounds (in millions) of fish processed in the United States.

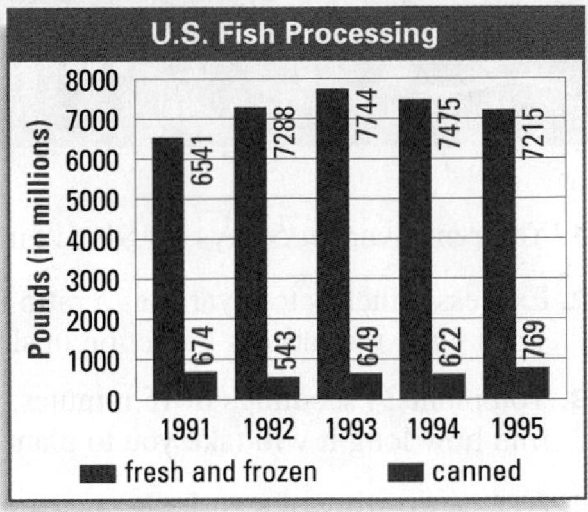

21. Find the percent of decrease in fresh and frozen fish from 1993 to 1995. **−6.8%**

22. Use the bar graph to find the percent of increase in canned fish from 1991 to 1995. **+14.1%**

23. GOVERNMENT In 1989, Texas had 27 representatives in the U.S. House of Representatives. In 1997, Texas had 30 representatives. Find the percent of increase from 1989 to 1997. **11.1%**

7.8 SIMPLE INTEREST

Examples on pp. 365–366

EXAMPLE You deposit $250 in an account that pays 6.75% annual simple interest. Find the new account balance after 3 months.

$$A = P + Prt = 250 + (250)(0.0675)(0.25) = 250 + 4.21875 \approx 254.22$$

The new account balance is $254.22.

In Exercises 24 and 25, find the simple interest and the balance of the account.

24. $100 at 5% annual simple interest for 1 year **$5, $105**

25. $1500 at 10% annual simple interest for 6 months **$75, $1575**

26. Find the annual simple interest rate if a deposit of $280 earns $13.65 in interest in 9 months. **6.5%**

7.9 COMPOUND INTEREST

Examples on pp. 369–370

EXAMPLE Find the balance of an account after one year when the principal is $1000 and the annual interest rate is 12%, compounded quarterly.

$$A = P(1 + rt)^n = 1000(1 + (0.12)(0.25))^4 = 1000(1.03)^4 \approx 1125.51$$

The new account balance is $1125.51.

27. Find the balance of an account after one year when the principal is $2500 and the annual interest rate is 12.5% compounded monthly. **$2,831.04**

28. Find the final balance on a 3 year certificate of deposit if the principal is $50,000 and the annual interest rate is 9.75%, compounded quarterly. **$66,754.06**

Additional Resources

Assessment Book

- Formal Assessment, pp. 99–107
- Alternative Assessment, pp. 193–207

Test and Practice Generator

Chapter 7 Chapter Test

1. You rent a car for 5 days for \$195. Find the daily rental rate. **\$39 per day**
2. Express 6 inches to 3 yards as a ratio in a common unit of measure. Then write the ratio as a fraction in simplest form. $\frac{6 \text{ inches}}{108 \text{ inches}}$; $\frac{1}{18}$
3. You plant 24 seedlings in 15 minutes. Write and solve a proportion to find how long it will take you to plant 120 seedlings. $\frac{15}{24} = \frac{t}{120}$; **75 min or** $1\frac{1}{4}$ **h**
4. A scale drawing of a park plan has a scale of 2 inches = 25 feet. If a walking bridge in the park is 140 feet long, how long is the bridge in the drawing? **11.2 in.**

In Exercises 5 and 6, use the rectangle at the right. Each small rectangle is the same size.

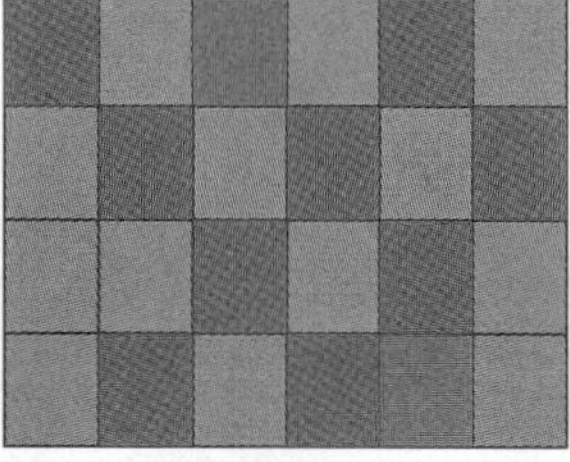

5. One small rectangle is chosen at random. Find the probability that it is red. **37.5%**
6. By choosing a rectangle at random 100 times, you find that the experimental probability that it is a certain color is about 20%. What color do you think this is? Explain. **Green;** $\frac{5}{24} \approx 20\%$

Write and solve a proportion to answer the question.

7. 102 is 85% of what number? **120**
8. 98 is what percent of 70? **140%**

In Exercises 9 and 10, use the following information. A store buys denim jeans at a wholesale price of \$15.00 and sells them for \$36.

9. Find the percent of markup for the jeans. **140%**
10. The jeans go on sale and are discounted 30%. Find the sale price. **\$25.20**

Identify the percent of change as an *increase* or a *decrease*. Then find the percent of change.

11. May rainfall: 4.8 inches
    June rainfall: 3.4 inches
    decrease, −29.2%
12. First mile: 7 minutes, 45 seconds
    Second mile: 8 minutes, 15 seconds
    increase, about 6.5%

In Exercises 13 and 14, use the following information. Your grandmother started a college fund for her grandchildren 15 years ago with an investment of \$15,000 at an annual interest rate of $6\frac{1}{2}\%$.

13. Find the balance of the account if the account earns simple interest. **\$29,625**
14. Find the balance of the account if interest is compounded quarterly. **\$39,457.06**

Multiple-Choice Practice

Test Tip Most standardized tests are based on concepts and skills taught in school. The best way to prepare is to keep up with your regular studies.

1. A 5 pound bag of potatoes costs \$1.99, and a 10 pound bag costs \$3.89. Which statement is *false*? **B**

(A) The price per pound is a unit rate.

(B) The 5 pound bag is the better buy.

(C) The unit price for the small bag is \$.398 per pound.

(D) The 10 pound bag is a better buy.

2. A model of the space vehicle *Saturn 5* has a 1: 484 scale. The height of the model is 9 inches. What is the height (in feet) of the actual *Saturn 5*? **H**

(F) $30\frac{1}{4}$ feet (G) $53\frac{7}{9}$ feet

(H) 363 feet (J) 4356 feet

3. A game that costs \$32 wholesale has a 120% markup. What is its retail price? **C**

(A) \$38.40 (B) \$57.60

(C) \$70.40 (D) \$72.00

4. What is the percent of decrease if a school's enrollment drops from 225 to 180 students? **F**

(F) −20% (G) −25%

(H) −44% (J) −45%

5. A principal of \$1500 earns \$45 simple interest in 6 months. What is the interest rate? **C**

(A) 3% (B) 4.5%

(C) 6% (D) 9%

6. The circle graph shows the favorite type of food of 250 people surveyed. Which statement is *false*? **H**

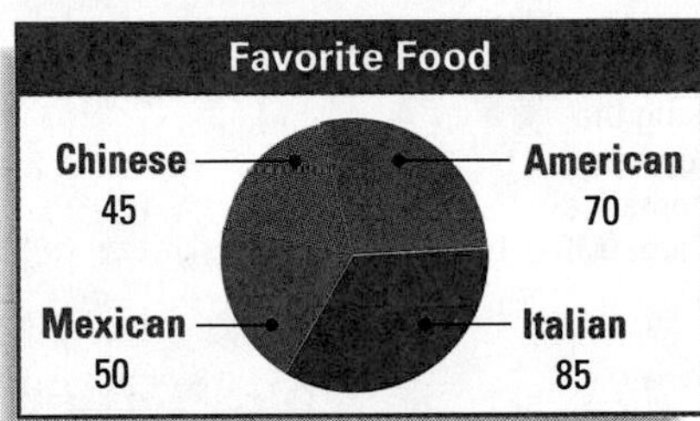

(F) The probability that a person chose Chinese is 0.18.

(G) The probability that a person chose Mexican is 0.2.

(H) The probability that a person chose American is 0.25.

(J) Based on the graph, 340 people out of 1000 would choose Italian.

7. Which proportion can be used to answer the following question?

50 is 125% of what number? **C**

(A) $\frac{a}{5} = \frac{125}{100}$ (B) $\frac{50}{b} = \frac{125}{1000}$

(C) $\frac{50}{b} = \frac{125}{100}$ (D) $\frac{a}{50} = \frac{125}{1000}$

8. A bank is offering a savings account earning 6% annual interest compounded monthly. You deposit \$500. What will your balance be after 9 months? **G**

(F) \$522.50 (G) \$522.96

(H) \$530.84 (J) \$570.58

Teaching Tip

The Brain Games activity provides a motivating way to review selected content in the chapter. For a more comprehensive review, see the Chapter Summary and Review on pp. 374–377.

Brain games

California Standards

- Solve two-step linear equations. (AF 4.1)
- Express the solution clearly and logically by using the appropriate mathematical notation. (MR 2.6)

Percent Questions

Materials

- 36 cards

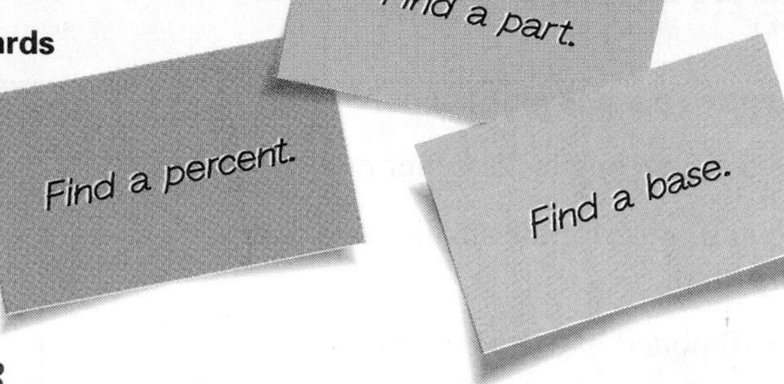

Directions

Object of the Game

Play in groups of three. Each round players score a point for writing a correct percent question. The winner is the player with the most points at the end of 9 rounds.

How to Play

STEP 1 Label 3 cards *Find a percent*, 3 cards *Find a part*, and 3 cards *Find a base*.

STEP 2 One player shuffles the labeled cards and places them face down. Another player deals 9 blank cards to each player.

STEP 3 One player chooses a labeled card. All players use one blank card to write a percent question of the type described on the card. Each player passes his or her card to the another player to check. A point is scored for each correct question.

Another Way to Play

Write an answer on each labeled card. Each player writes a percent question having the answer given.

Brain Teaser

16 oz or 1 lb
3/4 cheese
4 oz.
How much does a wheel of cheese weigh?

California Standards and Assessment

CA Standards: AF 4.1, MR 2.6

The basic skills you'll review on this page will help prepare you for the next chapter.

Reviewing the Basics

EXAMPLE 1 Solving Equations Using Subtraction

Solve $14 + y = -1$.

Solution

$14 + y = -1$ Write original equation.

$14 + y - \mathbf{14} = -1 - \mathbf{14}$ Subtract 14 from each side. (Subtraction property of equality)

$y = -15$ Simplify.

Try These

Solve the equation.

1. $23 + x = 35$ **12**

2. $y + 16 = 26$ **10**

3. $-15 = q + 15$ **−30**

4. $x + 75 = 180$ **105**

5. $60 + s = 360$ **300**

6. $-4 + n = 25$ **29**

EXAMPLE 2 Using Formulas

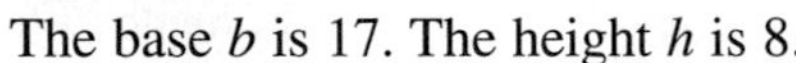

Find the area of the triangle.

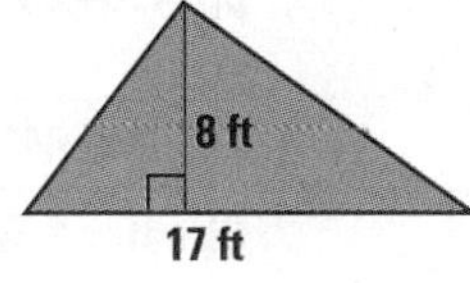

Solution

The base b is 17. The height h is 8.

$A = \frac{1}{2}bh$ Write area formula.

$= \frac{1}{2}(\mathbf{17})(\mathbf{8})$ Substitute 17 for b and 8 for h.

$= 68$ square feet Simplify.

Try These

Use the formulas to find the perimeter and area of the figure.

7. $P = a + b + c$
$A = \frac{1}{2}bh$
P = 40 m; A = 60 m²

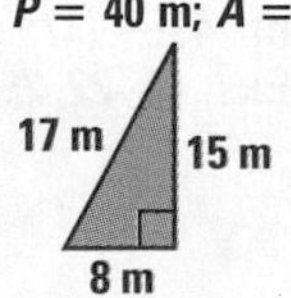

8. $P = 2w + 2\ell$
$A = \ell w$
P = 46 in., A = 126 in.²

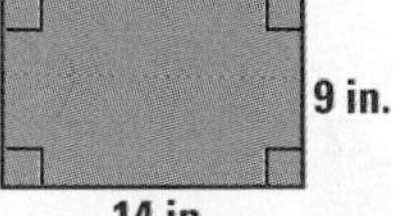

9. $P = 4s$
$A = s^2$
P = 44 ft, A = 121 ft²

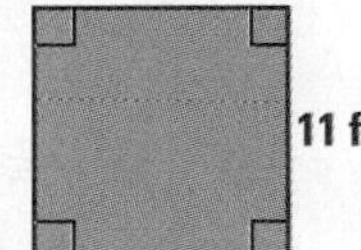

Student Help

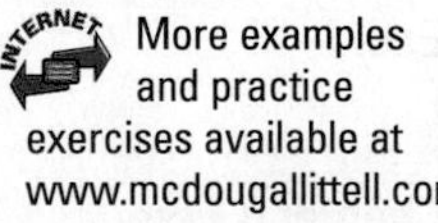

▶**MORE EXAMPLES**

More examples and practice exercises available at www.mcdougallittell.com

Additional Resources

Technology

- Personal Student Tutor
- Test and Practice Generator

Pacing and Assignment Guide

Regular Schedule

Lesson	Les. Day	Transitional	Average	Advanced
8.1	Day 1	pp. 387–389 Exs. 6–10, 15–18, 24–26, 33–36	pp. 387–389 Exs. 11–17, 19–26, 28–29, 33–36	pp. 387–389 Exs. 11–23, 26–31, 32*, 33–36
8.2	Day 1	pp. 393–394 Exs. 8–14, 19–20, 22–25, 30–33, 36–38, 47–48	pp. 393–394 Exs. 11–14, 19–33, 36–38, 40–45, 47–48	pp. 393–394 Exs. 14–16, 21–33, 36–38, 40–45, 46*, 47–48
8.3	Day 1	pp. 400–402 Exs. 6–8, 19–20, 32–36	pp. 400–402 Exs. 6–8, 19–20, 32–44	pp. 400–402 Exs. 6–8, 19–21, 32–44
	Day 2	pp. 400–402 Exs. 9–18, 21, 24–27, 29–31, 37–40	pp. 400–402 Exs. 9–18, 21, 23–27, 29–31	pp. 400–402 Exs. 9–12, 16–18, 21–27, 28*, 29–31
8.4	Day 1	pp. 407–409 Exs. 12–20, 24–37, 47–48	pp. 407–409 Exs. 12–20, 24–37, 41–45, 47–48	pp. 407–409 Exs. 12–17, 21–32, 41–45, 46*, 47–48
8.5	Day 1	pp. 415–416 Exs. 6–7, 10–11, 15–20, 23, 26–27	pp. 415–416 Exs. 6–18, 22–23, 26–27	pp. 415–416 Exs. 6–18, 23–24, 25*, 26–27
8.6	Day 1	pp. 421–422 Exs. 7–14, 16–17, 19, 24–25	pp. 421–422 Exs. 7–18, 20–22, 24–25	pp. 421–422 Exs. 8–18, 20–22, 23*, 24–25
8.7	Day 1	EP p. 695 Exs. 93–96; pp. 425–427 Exs. 3–8, 10–11, 14–15, 20–24, 31–33, 37–38	pp. 425–427 Exs. 3–16, 20–24, 31–33, 37–38	pp. 425–427 Exs. 3–15, 17–18, 19*, 20–24, 31–33, 37–38
8.8	Day 1	pp. 430–431 Exs. 6–12, 17–18, 21–22	pp. 430–431 Exs. 6–18, 21–22	pp. 430–431 Exs. 7–16, 19, 20*, 21–22
8.9	Day 1	EP p. 702 Exs. 20–23; pp. 435–437 Exs. 7–13, 23–25, 29–33, 38	pp. 435–437 Exs. 10–22, 29–33, 38	pp. 435–437 Exs. 10–22, 26–27, 28*, 29–31, 37–38
Review	Day 1	pp. 438–441 Exs. 1–23	pp. 438–441 Exs. 1–23	pp. 438–441 Exs. 1–23
Assess	Day 1	Chapter 8 Test	Chapter 8 Test	Chapter 8 Test

Yearly Pacing Chapter 8 Total – **12 days** Chapters 1–8 Total – **104 days** Remaining – **56 days**

* Challenge Exercises EP = Extra Practice SRH = Skills Review Handbook EC = Extra Challenge

Block Schedule

Day 1	Day 2	Day 3	Day 4	Day 5	Day 6
8.1 pp. 387–389: Exs. 11–17, 19–26, 28–29, 33–36 **8.2** pp. 393–394: Exs. 11–14, 19–33, 36–38, 40–45, 47–48	**8.3** pp. 400–402: Exs. 6–21, 23–27, 29–44	**8.4** pp. 407–409: Exs. 12–20, 24–37, 41–45, 47–48 **8.5** pp. 415–416: Exs. 6–18, 22–23, 26–27	**8.6** pp. 421–422: Exs. 7–18, 20–22, 24–25 **8.7** pp. 425–427: Exs. 3–16, 20–24, 31–33, 37–38	**8.8** pp. 430–431: Exs. 6–18, 21–22 **8.9** pp. 435–437: Exs. 10–22, 29–33, 38	**Review** pp. 438–441: Exs. 1–23 **Assess** Chapter 8 Test

Yearly Pacing Chapter 8 Total – **6 days** Chapters 1–8 Total – **52 days** Remaining – **28 days**

Support Materials

Chapter Resource Book

LESSON SUPPORT	8.1	8.2	8.3	8.4	8.5	8.6	8.7	8.8	8.9
Lesson Plans	p. 1	p. 10	p. 19	p. 28	p. 37	p. 46	p. 55	p. 64	p. 73
Lesson Plans for Block Scheduling	p. 2	p. 11	p. 20	p. 29	p. 38	p. 47	p. 56	p. 65	p. 74
Warm-Ups with Multiple-Choice Practice	p. 3	p. 12	p. 21	p. 30	p. 39	p. 48	p. 57	p. 66	p. 75
Problem of the Day	p. 4	p. 13	p. 22	p. 31	p. 40	p. 49	p. 58	p. 67	p. 76
Daily Cumulative Review	p. 5	p. 14	p. 23	p. 32	p. 41	p. 50	p. 59	p. 68	p. 77
Practice Masters	p. 6	p. 15	p. 24	p. 33	p. 42	p. 51	p. 60	p. 69	p. 78
Reteaching Masters	p. 7	p. 16	p. 25	p. 34	p. 43	p. 52	p. 61	p. 70	p. 79
Enrichment Masters	p. 9	p. 18	p. 27	p. 36	p. 45	p. 54	p. 63	p. 72	p. 81

Transparencies

	8.1	8.2	8.3	8.4	8.5	8.6	8.7	8.8	8.9
Warm-Ups with Multiple-choice Practice	p. 60	p. 61	p. 62	p. 63	p. 64	p. 65	p. 66	p. 67	p. 68
Teacher Time-Saver Transparencies	✓	✓	✓	✓	✓	✓	✓	✓	✓
English/Spanish Problem Solving			p. 32	p. 33	p. 34	p. 35	p. 36	p. 37	p. 38
Answer Transparencies	✓	✓	✓	✓	✓	✓	✓	✓	✓

Technology

- Personal Student Tutor
- Time-Saving Test and Practice Generator
- Electronic Teacher Tools
- Technology: Using Calculators and Computers

Additional Resources

- Math Log
- Assessment Book
- Worked-Out Solution Key
- Practice Workbook (English/Spanish)
- Home and School Connection
- California Standards: Key Concepts Book

Correlation to the California Curriculum

Correlations to the California Standards
CA Standards: MG 2.0, MG 2.1, MG 2.2, MG 3.0, MG 3.1, MG 3.2, MG 3.4, MG 3.6, MR 1.1, MR 2.5

California Curriculum Support

Key Concepts Book

- Pre-Course Review: Topic 1 Working with Decimals
  Topic 4 Angles and Polygons
  Topic 5 Measurement
- Key Standards: MG 3.4 Congruent Figures *(Lessons 8.5, 8.7, 8.8)*
  MG 3.4 Congruent Triangles *(Lesson 8.5)*

California Standards Practice Workbook provides practice for each Standard that is covered in this chapter.

Strategies for Strategic Learners

ANTICIPATE PROBLEM AREAS

CONGRUENT SHAPES The concepts of similar and congruent shapes may be confused by students. If two shapes can, through a series of rotations, reflections, and/or translations, be shown to be identical, they are called congruent. If two plane figures are congruent, then their corresponding angles are congruent, their corresponding sides are congruent, and their areas are equal. Two congruent triangles, for example, have three pairs of congruent angles, and three pairs of congruent sides, but one does not need that much information to decide that two shapes are congruent. Knowing any of the following is enough to determine that two triangles are congruent:

- Three sides are congruent.
- Two angles and the included side are congruent.
- Two sides and the included angle are congruent.

Have students verify this for themselves by drawing the shapes with just the information given in the list above.

SIMILAR SHAPES Similar shapes are similar in terms of their proportions, but generally one cannot be superimposed exactly on the other through rotation or flipping, the way congruent shapes can. Similar shapes are not necessarily the same size. It is as if you took two congruent shapes and then shrunk or enlarged one of them. Two figures are similar if their corresponding angles are congruent and the ratios of the lengths of their corresponding sides are equal.

Two triangles are similar if two angles of one triangle are congruent to two angles of the other triangle.

Again, have students demonstrate to themselves that this is true by drawing triangles, one bigger than the other, that satisfy the given condition.

Strategies for English Learners

BUILD ON WHAT STUDENTS KNOW

English learners who have arrived recently from other countries may have had adequate or excellent prior schooling in mathematics. They may be familiar with algorithms that are not commonly used in this country. Encourage recent immigrants to share alternate forms of describing mathematical concepts or algorithms and provide an opportunity for the whole class to understand and discuss these alternative methods. Such a discussion not only promotes respect for cultural diversity and gives the teacher a glimpse into the student's thinking, but it also allows all students an opportunity to build a deeper understanding of mathematics.

USE A PICTURE OR MODEL

Students who are not yet fluent in English can investigate the concepts of similarity and congruence, as well as the relationship between different shapes, by cutting up shapes. This is a fun activity for all students, and helps provide a concrete visualization of abstract concepts. Have students do the following:

Take a sheet of $8\frac{1}{2}$-by-11 inch paper. Draw a line between diagonal corners and cut the sheet into two right triangles. (You can do this by tearing the paper if you make really definite creases.) Then have students rotate and flip the shapes until the two triangles can be put one on top of the other. This illustrates the concept of congruence.

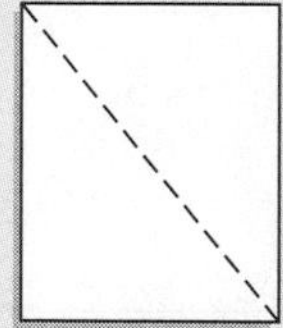

Now have the students take one of the large triangles and divide it into two smaller right triangles by folding the large triangle on the dotted line so that the hypotenuse of the triangle folds over on itself, and cutting or tearing.

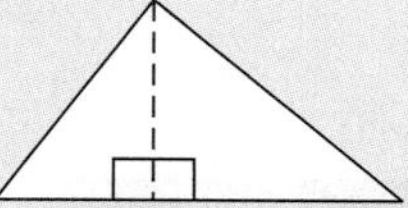

You will then have three right triangles that are similar, but not congruent. You can also illustrate the concept of proportion by having students measure the lengths of the sides of the triangles and comparing them. (If students have torn rather than cut the triangles, their measurements will not be very exact.)

Strategies for Advanced Learners

DIFFERENTIATE INSTRUCTION IN TERMS OF COMPLEXITY

The California History-Social Science Content Standards for seventh grade call for students to understand the significance of scientific theories (for example, those of Copernicus, Galileo, Kepler, and Newton) and the significance of inventions (for example, the telescope, microscope, thermometer, and barometer). It is impossible to separate these scientific theories from the advances in mathematics that, in many cases, made the scientific theories possible. Here is another opportunity to maximize learning time and to ensure that advanced students always have a challenging assignment on which they can be working when the daily or weekly assignments are too easy. These challenging assignments should be substituted for easier work; otherwise, you create an atmosphere in which students who finish early are rewarded with more work.

USE CROSS-CURRICULAR CONNECTIONS

Work with the science teacher to find out which theories and inventions will be discussed in science class. Have advanced students research mathematical discoveries that contributed to scientific ones. Galileo Galilei, a central figure in the Scientific Revolution, built on the thinking of those before him and advanced both fields by using mathematics to explain physics. He showed us that scientific phenomena can be explained in mathematical terms. He analyzed the movements of objects in space with lines, circles, triangles, and numbers. He described acceleration as a mathematical concept. A possible assignment for advanced students that would integrate their study of mathematics and science would be to research the following types of questions: "Who invented the compass? What did it allow scientists and mathematicians to do that they had not been able to do before?"

Isaac Newton, who was born in 1642, a few months after Galileo's death, built on the work of Galileo, Copernicus, Kepler, and others. His famous saying, "If I have seen further it is by standing on the shoulders of giants," shows his recognition that his contribution was to take the efforts of those before him and integrate them into unified theories. He developed scientific ideas in calculus, optics, and gravity, and invented the reflecting telescope in 1668. While Kepler based his laws of planetary motion on empirical observations, Newton derived them from his theories of motion and gravity.

Mathematical Background Notes

Lessons 8.1–8.3

BASIC TERMS The basic vocabulary of geometry contains the terms **line segment** and **ray.** At this early stage the student needs only an intuitive grasp of these terms. It is, however, helpful for the teacher to be aware of how these primitive terms can be given a precise definition.

By viewing a straight line as a number line, with each point on the line corresponding to a real number, we are able to define what it means for a point to be *between* two other points on a line. Given points *A*, *B*, and *C* on a line, we say

B is between A and C

if the *number* associated with *B* lies between the *numbers* associated with *A* and *C*. This corresponds to the picture below.

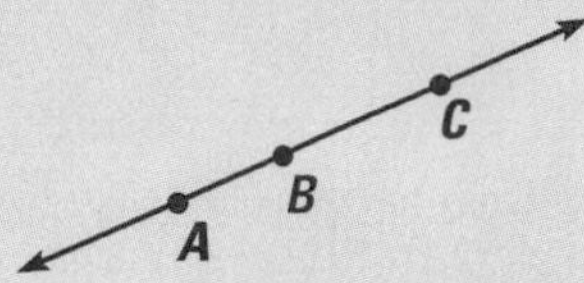

A **line segment** $\overline{AB}$ is the set of all points between *A* and *B* of the line determined by *A* and *B*.

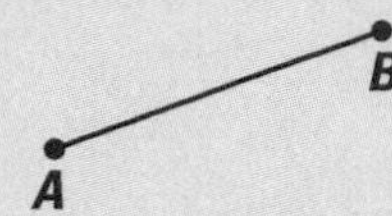

The points *A* and *B* are called the **endpoints** of $\overline{AB}$, and if *C* lies between *A* and *B*, then *A* and *C* are "on the same side of *B*."

Given a line ℓ and points *P* and *Q* on ℓ, the **ray** $\overrightarrow{PQ}$ consists of all points of ℓ that are on the same side of *P* as *Q*.

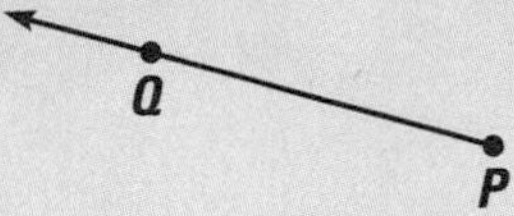

A ray is often called a **half-line** and the point *P* is the **endpoint** of $\overrightarrow{PQ}$. Each point *P* on a line determines two rays having *P* as their common endpoints. These two rays are called **opposite rays.**

Having defined what we mean by a ray, we are able to define an **angle** as the set of points lying on two rays with a common endpoint. It is traditional to say that a pair of opposite rays form a **straight angle.**

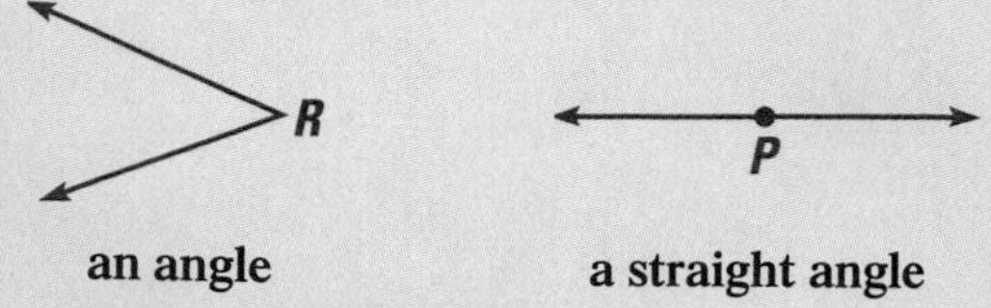

an angle　　　a straight angle

Angle measure is defined in a way that corresponds to our experience in measuring with a protractor. Here the measure of a straight angle is 180° and the measure of a right angle is 90°.

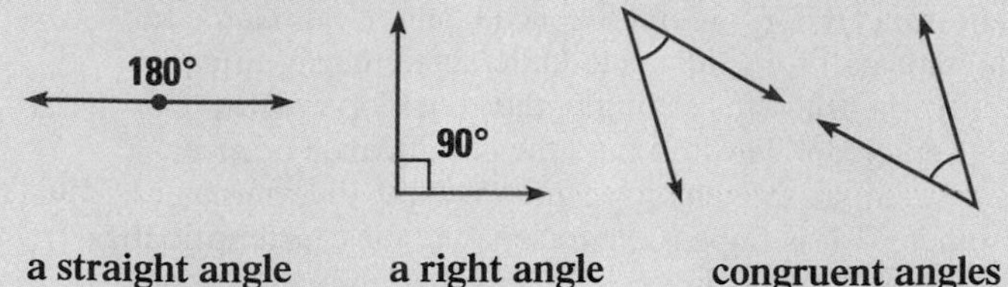

a straight angle　　　a right angle　　　congruent angles

Angles with the same measure are said to be **congruent.** (This corresponds to our intuition that if two angles have the same measure, then either can be moved and superimposed to coincide with the other.)

A pair of intersecting lines determine four nonstraight angles as in the picture below.

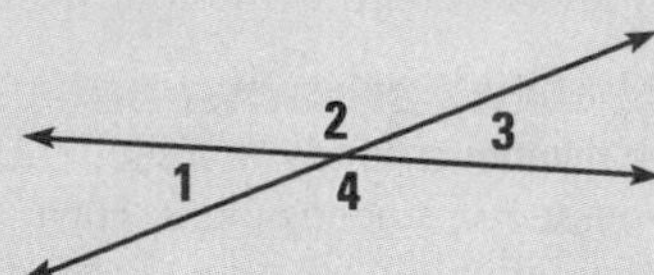

The opposite angles $\angle 2$ and $\angle 4$ are called **vertical angles,** as are $\angle 1$ and $\angle 3$. As shown in Developing Concepts in Lesson 8.3, vertical angles are congruent. That is, using the usual notation for congruence,

$$\angle 2 \cong \angle 4 \quad \text{and} \quad \angle 1 \cong \angle 3.$$

Another important congruence property of angles is that corresponding angles formed by a transversal crossing two parallel lines are congruent.

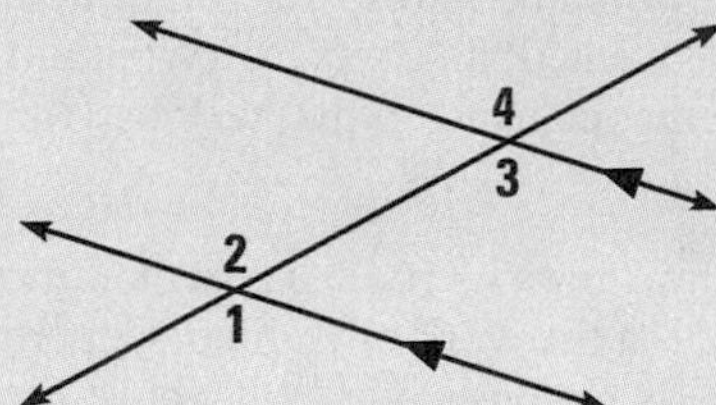

In the picture above, $\angle 1$ and $\angle 3$ are called **corresponding angles,** as are $\angle 2$ and $\angle 4$. When the lines being crossed by the transversal are parallel,

$$\angle 1 \cong \angle 3 \quad \text{and} \quad \angle 2 \cong \angle 4.$$

While this congruence property may strike us as intuitively obvious, it turns out to be a characteristic property of Euclidean geometry. As will be seen in Lesson 8.4, it is at the heart of the proof that the sum of the measures of the angles of a triangle is 180°. In non-Euclidean geometries these properties of corresponding angles and of triangles need not be true.

Lessons 8.4–8.5

ANGLE MEASURE SUMS The fact that the sum of the angle measures in a triangle is 180° has implications for other polygons as well. By partitioning a convex quadrilateral into two triangles, we see that the corresponding sum is 360°.

Since $m\angle B = m\angle 2 + m\angle 3$ and $m\angle D = m\angle 5 + m\angle 6$, we see that the sum of the measures of the angles of the quadrilateral equals the sum of the measures of the angles of *two* triangles or $2 \times 180° = 360°$.

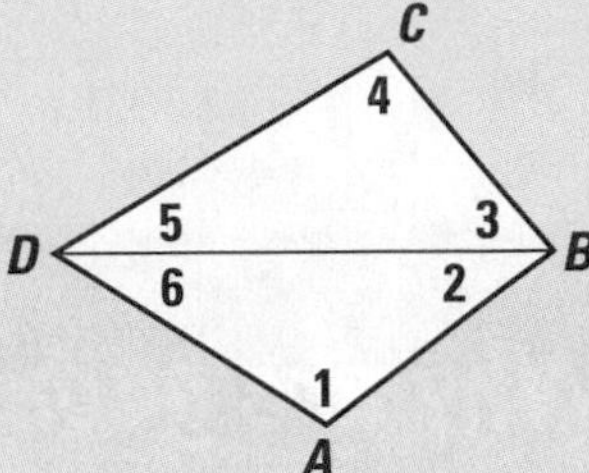

Similarly, any convex pentagon can be partitioned into 3 triangles using 2 diagonals.

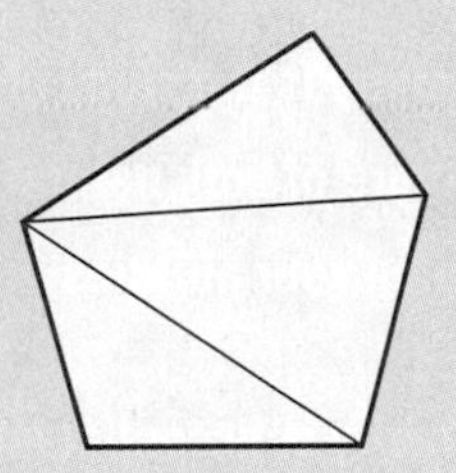

As before, we can see that the sum of the measures of the 5 angles of the pentagon is equal to the sum of the measures of 3 triangles, and therefore equal to $3 \times 180° = 540°$.

More generally, by partitioning a convex polygon with n sides into $n - 2$ triangles, we see that the sum of its angle measures is given by

$$(n - 2) \times 180°.$$

If this n-sided polygon is a **regular polygon** all of whose sides and angles are congruent, then each of its angles has measure

$$\frac{1}{n} \times (n - 2) \times 180° = \frac{n-2}{n} \times 180°.$$

Lesson 8.6

AREA OF A TRAPEZOID Starting with the formula for the area of a rectangle, it is possible to derive formulas for the areas of a parallelogram and a triangle. The same idea gives the area formula for a trapezoid of height h and bases b_1 and b_2. Two copies of such a trapezoid fit together to form a parallelogram of height h and base $b_1 + b_2$.

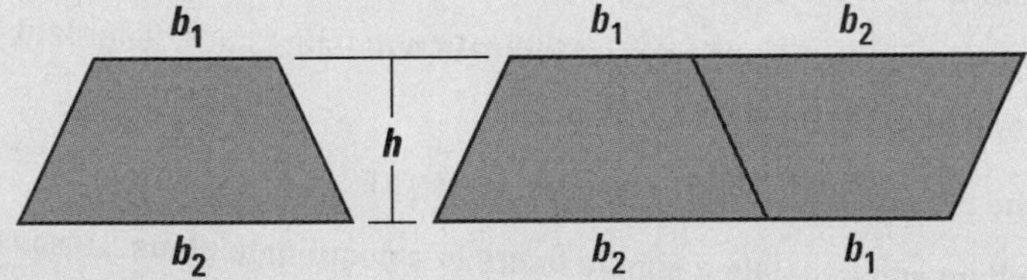

Since the parallelogram has area $h(b_1 + b_2)$, the trapezoid has area A given by

$$A = \frac{1}{2}h(b_1 + b_2).$$

A nice alternative proof is given in Sample 2 on page 418.

Lessons 8.8–8.9

REFLECTION These lessons rely on coordinate representations to introduce the student to some basic geometric transformations. The operation of **reflection,** described geometrically at the beginning of the lesson, has a simple coordinate representation if the line of reflection is one of the axes. Reflection about the x-axis sends each point (a, b) into $(a, -b)$, while reflection about the y-axis sends (a, b) into $(-a, b)$.

Reflection about an arbitrary line in the coordinate plane is more complicated, but reflection about the line $y = x$ is simple. Here each point (a, b) is sent into (b, a), as shown below.

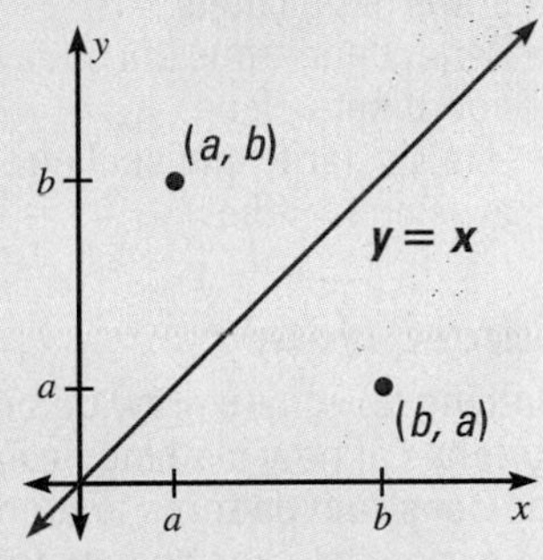

Other geometric transformations result from combining simple reflections. For example, it is a good challenge to show that following a reflection in the x-axis with a reflection in the line $y = x$ is equivalent to a 90° rotation (counterclockwise) about the origin. Here the first reflection sends (a, b) into $(a, -b)$, and the second sends $(a, -b)$ into $(-b, a)$. Thus, the transformation that sends (a, b) directly into $(-b, a)$ is a 90° rotation. It is useful to check this with some specific cases, such as $(a, b) = (1, 0)$ or $(a, b) = (1, 1)$.

TRANSLATION Another fundamental geometric transformation is **translation.** Given a fixed ordered pair (h, k), the translation that corresponds to (h, k) is one that sends each point (a, b) into $(a + h, b + k)$. When applied to all points of a given figure F, this translation slides F horizontally a distance h and then vertically a distance k. Connecting points in F with their image points in F' one obtains parallel line segments of equal length.

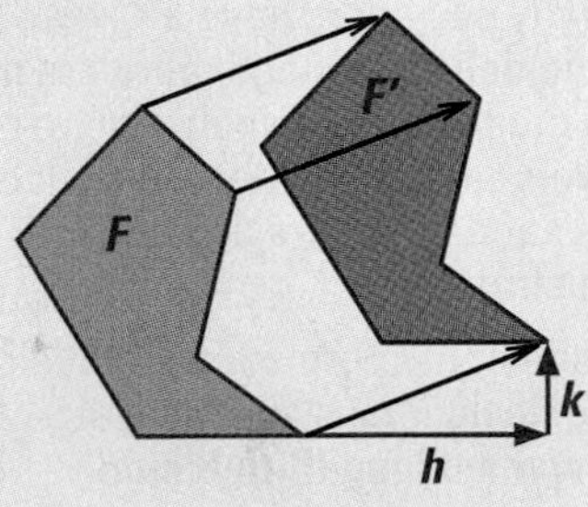

The transformation that corresponds to similarity can also be described in terms of coordinates. Given a figure F and a positive number k, the transformation that sends each point (a, b) into (ka, kb) in the image figure F' is called a **similarity transformation.** Here F' is similar to F with a scale factor of k. It is useful to experiment with simple examples, such as letting F denote a triangle and choosing $k = 2$.

An important relationship exists among the perimeters and areas of similar plane figures. If F' is similar to F with scale factor k, then the perimeters P' and P of F' and F, respectively, satisfy

$$P' = kP.$$

However, the relationship between their areas A' and A is given by

$$A' = k^2A.$$

Chapter Overview

Chapter Goals

In this chapter, students will identify points, lines, planes, angles, and parallel and perpendicular lines. They will:

- Classify triangles and special quadrilaterals.
- Recognize congruent polygons and regular polygons, and find areas of polygons.
- Reflect and translate lines in a coordinate plane.
- Use similarity and scaling to find missing lengths.

Career Note

Clothing designers draw detailed sketches of new clothing designs and construct patterns to produce the garments. They choose fabrics and colors for their designs, and oversee the production of the clothing. Designers are also involved in promoting and selling the design. Many designers have a 4-year college degree, though there are many related careers which require only two-year college degrees, such as pattern makers and fashion illustrators.

Additional information about clothing designers is available at **www.mcdougallittell.com**

Geometry Concepts

Why are geometry concepts important?

Geometry is the study of size and shape. It is useful in understanding the structure of both natural and artificial objects. Geometry also helps develop your abilities in mathematical reasoning.

Geometry is essential for many careers, including clothing design (page 383) and computer graphics (page 429). For example, clothing designers use geometry when they determine the best arrangement of a garment's pattern pieces on a piece of fabric.

Meeting the California Standards

The skills you'll learn in this chapter will help you meet state standards and prepare for standardized tests. In this chapter you'll:

- **Identify and construct basic elements of geometric figures.** LESSONS 8.1–8.4
- **Understand the conditions that indicate two figures are congruent.** LESSONS 8.1–8.3, 8.5, 8.7, 8.8
- **Find the areas of complex figures.** LESSON 8.6
- **Reflect and translate a simple figure in a coordinate plane.** LESSONS 8.7, 8.8
- **Understand how measures of similar figures are related.** LESSON 8.9

Career Link **CLOTHING DESIGNER**

A clothing designer uses geometry when:

- arranging pattern pieces on fabric.
- cutting fabric so that the garment hangs properly on a person.

vest front

vest front

vest back

EXERCISES

A designer is planning a vest like the one shown at the far right.

1. The front of the vest is made by cutting two shapes out of a piece of cloth. One shape is shown. Sketch the other. **See margin.**

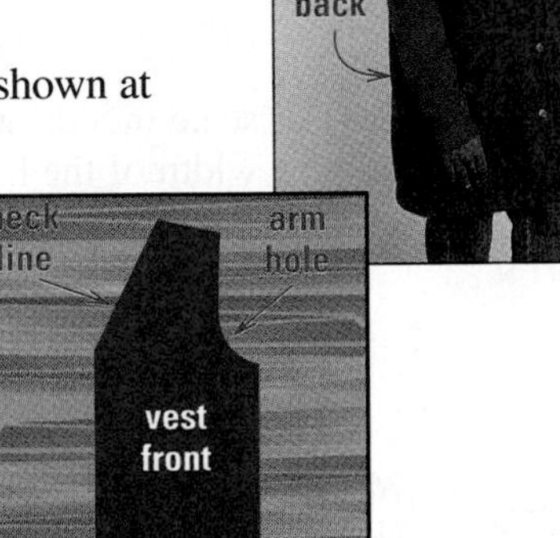

2. How are the two shapes in Exercise 1 alike? How are they different? **They are the same size and shape, but mirror images of each other.**

In Lesson 8.7, you will learn how to cut both shapes at once from folded cloth.

Projects

A project covering Chapters 7–9 appears on pages 504–505 of the Student Edition. Additional projects for selected lessons in Chapter 8 are available in the *Assessment Book,* pp. 243–244.

Technology

Software

- Electronic Teacher Tools
- Online Lesson Planner
- Personal Student Tutor
- Test and Practice Generator

Internet Connections

- Application and Career Links 388, 393, 422, 429
- Student Help 388, 399, 405, 413, 420, 429, 433, 436, 445

These Internet connections are available at **www.mcdougallittell.com**

1. ARM HOLE NECK LINE

Prepare

Diagnostic Tools

The **chapter readiness quiz** can help you diagnose whether students have the following skills needed in Chapter 8:

- Understand proportions and apply them to problem situations.
- Identify the four quadrants in the coordinate plane.

Reteaching Materials

The following resources are available for students who need additional help with the skills on the chapter readiness quiz:

Chapter 8 Resource Book

- Reteaching with Practice (Lessons 7.3)

Personal Student Tutor

Additional Resources

The following resources are provided to help you prepare for the upcoming chapter and customize review materials:

Chapter 8 Resource Book

- Lesson Plans, pp. 1, 10, 19, 28, 37, 46, 55, 64, 73
- Lesson Plans for Block Scheduling, pp. 2, 11, 20, 29, 38, 47, 56, 65, 74

Technology

- Electronic Teacher Tools with Lesson Planning Software
- Test and Practice Generator

Chapter 8 Getting Ready

PREVIEW

What's the chapter about?

- Introduction to important geometry concepts, including **classifying triangles** and **quadrilaterals**, and using simple reasoning
- Finding areas of **polygons**

WORDS TO KNOW

- **ray,** *p. 385*
- **congruent,** *pp. 385, 391, 412*
- **parallel lines,** *p. 386*
- **supplementary angles,** *p. 391*
- **complementary angles,** *p. 391*
- **vertical angles,** *p. 398*
- **perpendicular lines,** *p. 398*
- **quadrilateral,** *p. 405*
- **polygon,** *p. 412*
- **reflection,** *p. 423*
- **transformation,** *p. 428*
- **translation,** *p. 428*
- **similar,** *p. 432*

PREPARE

Chapter Readiness Quiz

Take this quick quiz. If you are unsure of an answer, look back at the reference pages for help.

VOCABULARY CHECK *(refer to p. 338)*

1. The ratio of a length in a drawing to the corresponding actual length is called the __?__. C

Ⓐ Proportion Ⓑ Scale Ⓒ Scale factor Ⓓ Scale rate

SKILL CHECK *(refer to pp. 144, 338)*

2. Which point is in Quadrant 4? J

Ⓕ $F(7, 8)$ Ⓖ $G(-3, -3)$ Ⓗ $H(0, -4)$ Ⓙ $J(5, -8)$

3. The scale in a drawing of a rectangular house is 2 inches = 3 feet. The width of the house in the drawing is 10 inches. Which proportion can you use to find the actual width of the house in feet? A

Ⓐ $\frac{w}{10} = \frac{3}{2}$ Ⓑ $\frac{10}{w} = \frac{3}{2}$ Ⓒ $\frac{w}{10} = \frac{36}{2}$ Ⓓ $\frac{10}{w} = \frac{36}{2}$

STUDY TIP

Make an Illustrated Glossary

An illustrated glossary will help you remember definitions.

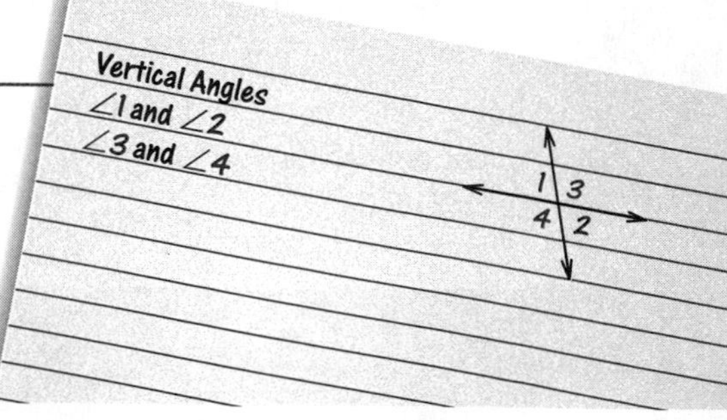

8.1 Points, Lines, and Planes

California Standards

In this lesson you'll:

- Identify and construct basic elements of geometric figures. (MG 3.1)
- Demonstrate an understanding of the conditions that indicate two line segments are congruent. (MG 3.4)
- Describe how two or more objects are related in space. (MG 3.6)

Goal 1 NAMING LINES, LINE SEGMENTS, AND RAYS

To become skilled in geometry, you must understand both the *words* and the *properties* of geometry.

The diagram at the right shows a **plane**, a **line**, a **point**, a **ray**, and a **line segment**, or segment. Their properties are suggested by the diagram. Points, lines, and planes are the basic building blocks of geometry and are not formally defined.

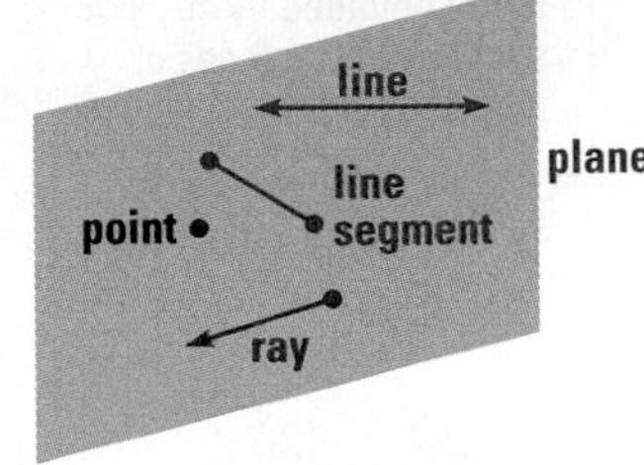

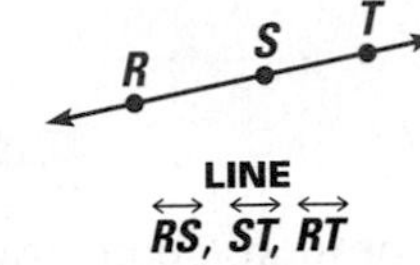

LINE
$\overleftrightarrow{RS}$, $\overleftrightarrow{ST}$, $\overleftrightarrow{RT}$

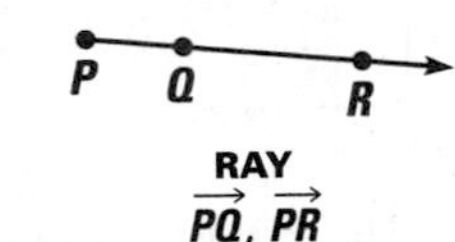

RAY
$\overrightarrow{PQ}$, $\overrightarrow{PR}$

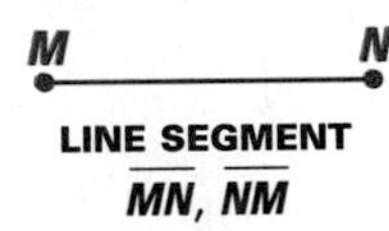

LINE SEGMENT
$\overline{MN}$, $\overline{NM}$

Lines, rays, and line segments are named using labeled points, as illustrated above.

Student Help

STUDY TIP
Notice that a line, a ray, and a segment can be named in more than one way. For instance, in Example 1, $\overrightarrow{AB}$ can also be named $\overrightarrow{AC}$. $\overline{AB}$ can also be named $\overline{BA}$.

EXAMPLE 1 Naming Rays and Segments

Name three different rays and three different line segments in the figure.

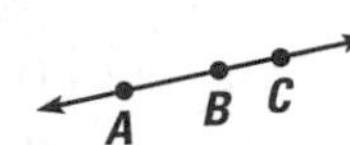

Solution

The endpoint of a ray is listed first to indicate where the ray begins.

$\overrightarrow{AB}$ 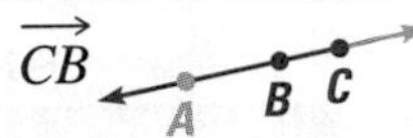 $\overrightarrow{CB}$ 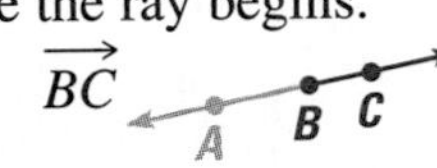 $\overrightarrow{BC}$

A line segment is named by its endpoints.

$\overline{AB}$ $\overline{BC}$ $\overline{AC}$ 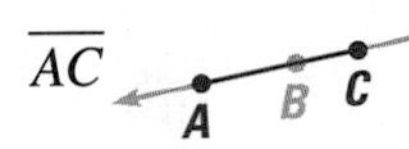

A line extends indefinitely in opposite directions. Because a given line segment has two endpoints, however, it has a definite length.

In the diagram at the right, the length of $\overline{XY}$ is 3 units. You can write this as $XY = 3$. Two line segments that have the same length are **congruent**. In the diagram, $\overline{XY}$ is congruent to $\overline{YZ}$. You can write this as $\overline{XY} \cong \overline{YZ}$.

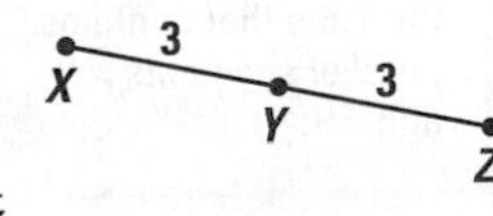

1 Plan

Pacing
Suggested Number of Days
Transitional: 1 day
Average: 1 day
Advanced: 1 day
Block Schedule: 0.5 block with 8.2

Teaching Resources

Blacklines
(See page 382B.)

Transparencies
- Warm-Up Exercises
- Teacher Time-Savers
- English/Spanish Problem Solving
- Answers

Technology
- Electronic Teacher Tools
- Test and Practice Generator

2 Teach

Math Reasoning

For Mathematical Background Notes on mathematical reasoning related to this lesson, please refer to pages 382E and 382F in this Teacher's Edition.

Extra Example 1
See next page.

California Standards and Assessment
CA Standards: MG 3.1, MG 3.4, MG 3.6

Math Reasoning

A point can be thought of as a "location" in the Euclidean plane. At a later stage, the Euclidean plane will be modeled by the coordinate plane, and the points, or locations, will be specified by their coordinates. Lines can be thought of as special sets of points having certain properties. For example, the points belonging to a line possess an order like numbers on a number line. This makes it possible to say that a point on a line is "between" two other points on the same line. Then a line segment can be defined as the set of all points between two points, including the two points.

Extra Example 1

Name three different rays and three different line segments in the figure.

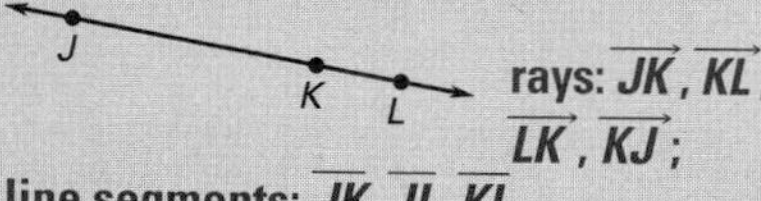

rays: $\overrightarrow{JK}$, $\overrightarrow{KL}$, $\overrightarrow{LK}$, $\overrightarrow{KJ}$; line segments: $\overline{JK}$, $\overline{JL}$, $\overline{KL}$

Extra Example 2

Use the diagram in Example 2.

a. Name a segment other than $\overline{AB}$, $\overline{AC}$, or $\overline{BD}$ that lies in the same plane as $\overline{CD}$. **$\overline{EH}$; $\overline{FG}$**

b. Name a segment other than $\overline{AB}$, $\overline{AF}$, or $\overline{BG}$ that lies in the same plane as $\overline{FG}$. **$\overline{EH}$; $\overline{CD}$**

c. Name a segment other than $\overline{FA}$ that lies in a different plane from $\overline{CD}$. **$\overline{GB}$; $\overline{FE}$; or $\overline{GH}$**

d. Name a segment other than $\overline{FA}$ that is not in the same plane as $\overline{BD}$. **$\overline{FG}$; $\overline{EH}$; or $\overline{EC}$;**

Extra Example 3

Use the diagram in Example 2.

a. Which line segments intersect $\overline{FG}$? **$\overline{FA}$, $\overline{GB}$, $\overline{FE}$, $\overline{GH}$**

b. Which line segments are parallel to $\overline{FG}$? **$\overline{AB}$, $\overline{CD}$, $\overline{EH}$**

Concept Check

Explain the difference between a line segment and a ray.
See answer at right.

Goal 2 IDENTIFYING OBJECTS IN A PLANE

As suggested by the diagram on page 385, you can think of a plane as a flat surface extending indefinitely in all directions.

Student Help

▶ VOCABULARY TIP
A *cube* is a three-dimensional figure bounded by six squares called *faces* of the cube.

EXAMPLE 2 Identifying Objects in Planes

Each face of the cube shown lies in a different plane. Two of these planes are represented in the diagram.

a. $\overline{AB}$ lies in the same plane as $\overline{CD}$.

b. $\overline{AB}$ lies in the same plane as $\overline{FG}$.

c. $\overline{CD}$ and $\overline{FA}$ are not in the same plane.

d. $\overline{FA}$ and $\overline{BD}$ are not in the same plane.

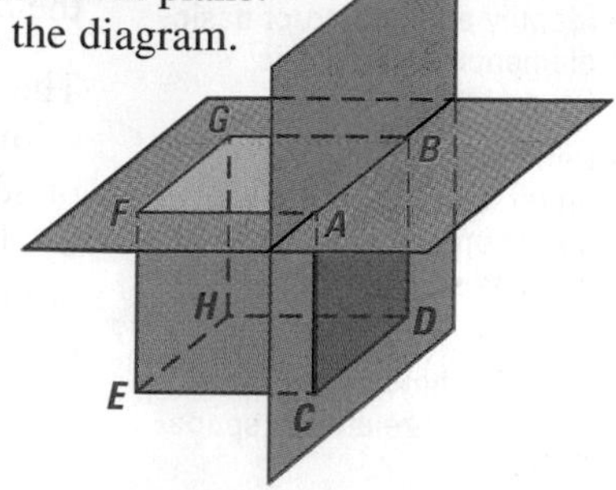

The **intersection** of two or more geometric figures is the set of points the figures have in common. In the diagram, line a and line b intersect at point P. Two lines are **parallel** if they are in the same plane and do not intersect. In the diagram, line c and line d are parallel. The red arrowheads indicate that the two lines are parallel.

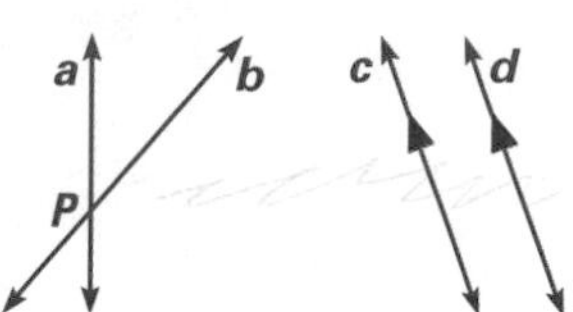

A theorem from geometry, which you may prove in a later course, states that if two lines are parallel to a third line, then the two lines are parallel to each other.

EXAMPLE 3 Identifying Intersecting and Parallel Segments

Use the diagram in Example 2.

a. Which line segments intersect $\overline{AB}$?

b. Which line segments are parallel to $\overline{AB}$?

Solution

a. The following line segments intersect $\overline{AB}$: $\overline{FA}$, $\overline{GB}$, $\overline{AC}$, and $\overline{BD}$.

b. $\overline{FG}$ is parallel to $\overline{AB}$ because the two segments are opposite sides of a square face of the cube. $\overline{CD}$ is parallel to $\overline{AB}$ for the same reason. Notice that $\overline{EH}$ and $\overline{CD}$ are opposite sides of a square face, so they are parallel. Because $\overline{EH}$ and $\overline{AB}$ are both parallel to $\overline{CD}$, they are parallel to each other.

Student Help

▶ STUDY TIP
In part (b) of Example 3, you can imagine a plane cutting through the cube that contains parallel segments $\overline{AB}$ and $\overline{EH}$.

Sample answer: **A line segment has a fixed length with two endpoints. A ray has one endpoint and extends indefinitely in one direction.**

8.1 Exercises

Guided Practice

In Exercises 1–3, match the term with the figure it best describes. Then name the figure.

A. Ray **B.** Line **C.** Line segment

1. A, B C

2. S R A

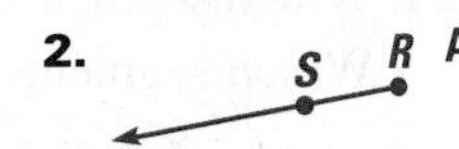

3. P Q B

4. C; $\overline{EC}$, $\overline{FA}$, $\overline{AC}$, and $\overline{EF}$

5. *Sample answer:* One pair of parallel lines is represented by the top and bottom of a rectangular window. A pair of intersecting lines is represented by one side of the window and the top. The plane that contains these lines can be represented by the window.

4. Use the diagram in Example 2 on page 386. Identify a fourth point in the same plane as points E, F, and A. Name four line segments in this plane.

5. Describe an example of parallel line segments in your classroom. Describe an example of intersecting line segments. In each case, describe the plane that contains the pair of line segments.

Practice and Problem Solving

Student Help

▶ More Practice
Extra practice to help you master skills is on page 704.

In Exercises 6–14, use the diagram at the right.

A B 2 C E F D G H J

6. Write four other names for $\overleftrightarrow{CF}$. *Sample answer:* $\overleftrightarrow{CE}$, $\overleftrightarrow{EF}$, $\overleftrightarrow{CD}$, and $\overleftrightarrow{DE}$

7. Name three different line segments that lie on $\overleftrightarrow{AG}$. $\overline{AC}$, $\overline{AG}$, and $\overline{CG}$

8. Name two parallel lines. $\overleftrightarrow{AG}$ and $\overleftrightarrow{BH}$

9. Name two pairs of intersecting lines. *Sample answer:* $\overleftrightarrow{AG}$ and $\overleftrightarrow{CF}$, $\overleftrightarrow{BE}$ and $\overleftrightarrow{CF}$

10. Name five rays with endpoint E. *Sample answer:* $\overrightarrow{EB}$, $\overrightarrow{EF}$, $\overrightarrow{EJ}$, $\overrightarrow{ED}$, and $\overrightarrow{EH}$

11. Are $\overrightarrow{EB}$ and $\overrightarrow{BE}$ the same ray? Explain your answer.

12. Are $\overline{EJ}$ and $\overline{JE}$ the same line segment? Explain your answer.

13. Are $\overleftrightarrow{EB}$ and $\overleftrightarrow{BE}$ the same line? Explain your answer.

14. Assume that $\overline{EB} \cong \overline{EJ}$. Find the length of $\overline{EJ}$. 2

11. No; they have different starting points and continue in opposite directions.

12. Yes; the line segments have the same endpoints.

13. Yes; a line continues indefinitely in both directions.

Sketch the indicated figure.

15. Three lines that intersect in one point See margin.

16. Two parallel lines that are intersected by a third line See margin.

17. Two intersecting lines are each intersected by a third line. There are exactly three intersection points. See margin.

18. Three lines in the same plane that do not intersect See margin.

3 Apply

Assignment Guide

Transitional
Day 1: pp. 387–389 Exs. 6–10, 15–18, 24–26, 33–36

Average
Day 1: pp. 387–389 Exs. 11–17, 19–26, 28–29, 33–36

Advanced
Day 1: pp. 387–389 Exs. 11–23, 26–31, 32*, 33–36

Block Schedule
pp. 387–389 Exs. 11–17,19–26, 28–29, 33–36 (with 8.2)

Extra Practice

- Student Edition, pp. 704–705
- Chapter 8 Resource Book, p. 6

Homework Check

To quickly check student understanding of key concepts, go over the following exercises:

Transitional: 6, 8,10, 16, 20, 24
Average: 12, 16, 20, 24, 26, 28
Advanced: 16, 20, 24, 28, 30

15.

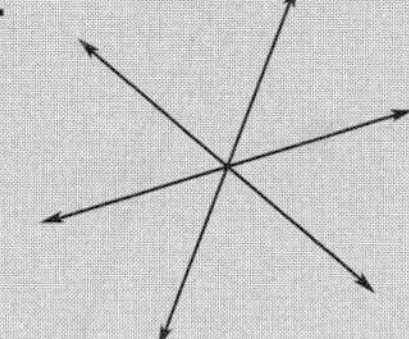

16.

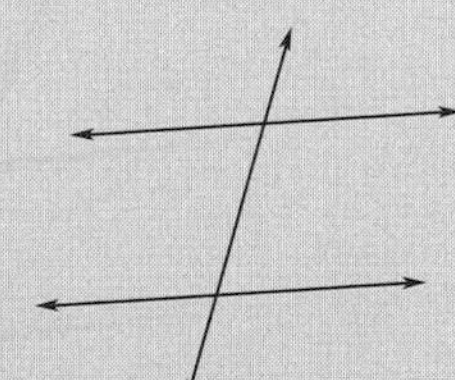

17.

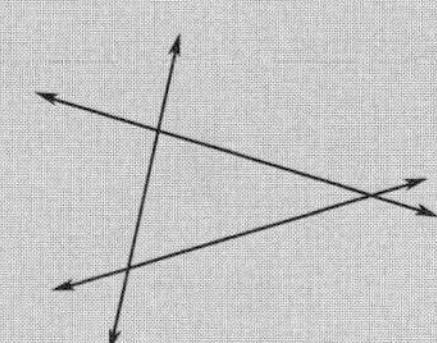

18. See Additional Answers beginning on page AA1.

Math Reasoning

In Exercise 23, points *P* and *V* determine a line that belongs to infinitely many different planes. In space, any three points not lying on the same line determine a unique plane containing them. For the cube shown in the diagram, there is a plane containing *P*, *Q*, *V*, and *W*. But no single plane contains *P*, *Q*, *V*, and *R*. (To see this, notice that *V* does not lie in the plane determined by *P*, *Q*, and *R*.)

DIGITAL ART Because computers use digits to process and store information (such as shape and color), computer-generated images like the one above are sometimes called *digital* images.

23. No; the plane containing *P*, *Q*, and *R* contains the whole top of the cube, and point *V* is not in that same plane.

DIGITAL ART In Exercises 19–23, use the diagram of a cube shown below. The diagram represents one of the cubes in the digital art shown at the left.

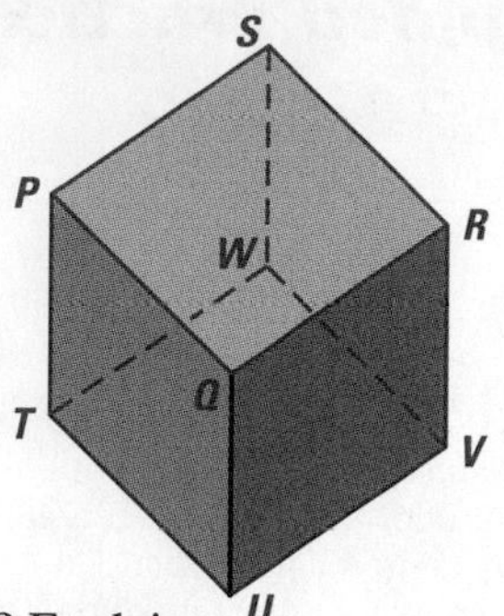

19. How many different planes form the faces of the cube? 6

20. Name a fourth point that lies in the same plane as points *P*, *Q* and *U*. T

21. Which segments intersect $\overline{PQ}$? Which segments are parallel to $\overline{PQ}$? $\overline{PT}$, $\overline{PS}$, $\overline{QU}$, and $\overline{QR}$; $\overline{SR}$, $\overline{WV}$ and $\overline{TU}$

22. Name two segments that are *not* in a common plane. Sample answer: $\overline{SR}$ and $\overline{UV}$

23. Are points *P*, *Q*, *R*, and *V* in the same plane? Explain. (See margin.)

ALGEBRA In Exercises 24–27, use the given information to write an equation. Then solve the equation to find the value of *x*.

24. $LN = 24$, $KN = 8$

25. $RU = 27$

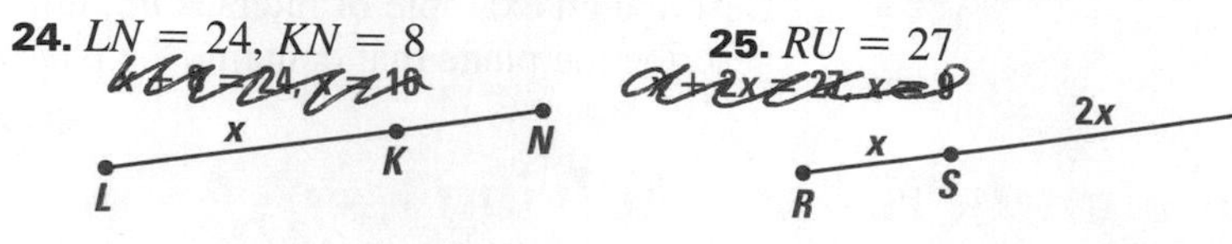

26. $BE = 20$, $\overline{BC} \cong \overline{CD}$, $DE = 3$

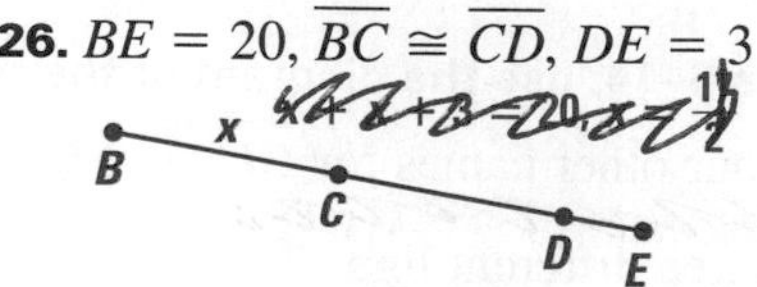

27. $\overline{AB} \cong \overline{CD}$, $AD = 9$, $AB = x - 3$

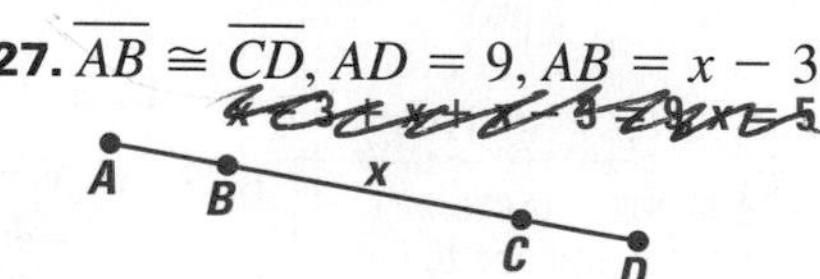

ARCHITECTURE In Exercises 28–32, use the brick building shown at the right and the information below.
Each window in the building is 10 feet wide and 7 feet high. The front doors of the building are 10 feet wide and 10 feet high. The space between the windows is 3 feet and the space between the windows and the edges of the building is 3 feet.

28. Find the length *BD* and the width *DF* of the building's base.

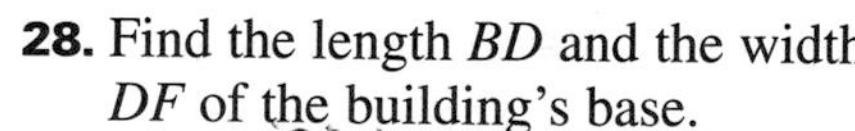

29. Find the height *CD* of the building.

30. MATHEMATICAL REASONING Determine whether the bottom edge of every window is parallel to the bottom edge of every other window. Explain your thinking. No; windows on the front of the building are not parallel to windows on the side of the building, so their bottom edges are not parallel.

31. Find the percent of the front of the building that is glass.

32. CHALLENGE Two lines that are not in the same plane are called *skew* lines. Identify as many pairs of skew lines as you can in the building.

32. $\overleftrightarrow{AB}$ and $\overleftrightarrow{CE}$, $\overleftrightarrow{AB}$ and $\overleftrightarrow{GE}$, $\overleftrightarrow{AB}$ and $\overleftrightarrow{DF}$, $\overleftrightarrow{AC}$ and $\overleftrightarrow{DF}$, $\overleftrightarrow{AC}$ and $\overleftrightarrow{EF}$, $\overleftrightarrow{AG}$ and $\overleftrightarrow{BD}$, $\overleftrightarrow{AG}$ and $\overleftrightarrow{EF}$, $\overleftrightarrow{AG}$ and $\overleftrightarrow{CD}$, $\overleftrightarrow{BD}$ and $\overleftrightarrow{CE}$, $\overleftrightarrow{BD}$ and $\overleftrightarrow{EF}$, $\overleftrightarrow{DF}$ and $\overleftrightarrow{EG}$, $\overleftrightarrow{CD}$ and $\overleftrightarrow{EG}$

Student Help

HOMEWORK HELP
Extra help with problem solving in Exs. 28–31 is available at www.mcdougallittell.com

Multiple-Choice Practice

In Exercises 33–36, use the figure shown.

33. Name the ray that begins at point *A*.

Ⓐ $\overrightarrow{DA}$ Ⓑ $\overline{AD}$

Ⓒ $\overrightarrow{AD}$ Ⓓ $\overleftrightarrow{AD}$

34. Which line is in the same plane as $\overleftrightarrow{CD}$?

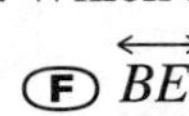

Ⓕ $\overleftrightarrow{BE}$ Ⓖ $\overleftrightarrow{FG}$

Ⓗ $\overleftrightarrow{BF}$ Ⓙ Not here

35. Which segments appear to be parallel?

Ⓐ $\overline{AB}$ and $\overline{BF}$ Ⓑ $\overline{BF}$ and $\overline{CF}$

Ⓒ $\overline{EF}$ and $\overline{DG}$ Ⓓ $\overline{BE}$ and $\overline{CF}$

36. Which line does *not* intersect $\overleftrightarrow{CD}$?

Ⓕ $\overleftrightarrow{DG}$ Ⓖ $\overleftrightarrow{BE}$ Ⓗ $\overleftrightarrow{AD}$ Ⓙ $\overleftrightarrow{CF}$

CONSTRUCTION Copying a Segment

Student Help

▶ **SKILLS REVIEW**
For help with using a compass and straightedge, see page 685.

You can use a compass and a straightedge to construct a segment that is congruent to a given segment. **See margin.**

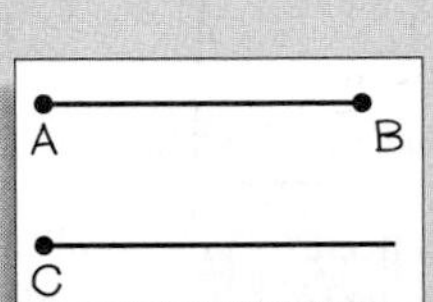

❶ Use a straightedge to draw a segment longer than $\overline{AB}$. Label the point *C* on the new segment.

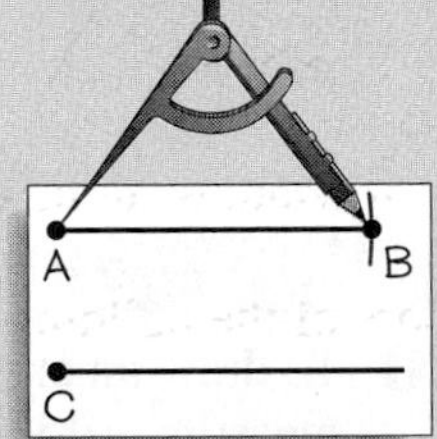

❷ Set your compass at the length of AB.

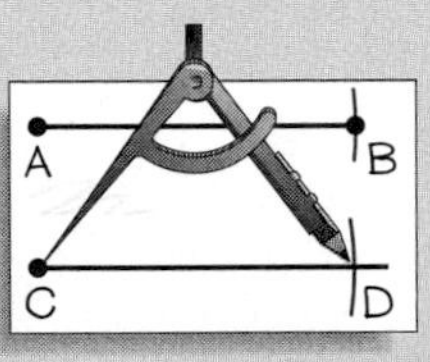

❸ Place the compass point at *C* and mark a second point, *D*, on the new segment. $\overline{CD} \cong \overline{AB}$.

Exercises **Use a compass and straightedge.**

1. Draw a segment that is about 2 inches long. Then copy the segment. **Check drawings.**

2. Draw segments that are 2 inches, 3 inches, and 4 inches long. Then use a compass and straightedge to draw a triangle with sides whose lengths are the same as the segments you drew. Describe your procedure. **Check drawings.**

4 Assess

Assessment Resources

- Assessment Book (Formal Assessment and Alternative Assessment)
- Test and Practice Generator

Mini-Quiz

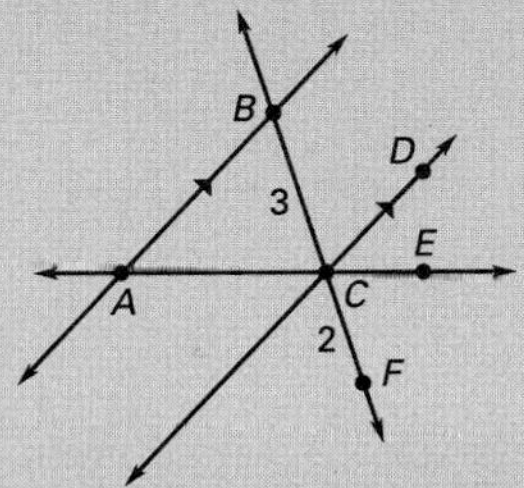

1. Name four different rays on line $\overleftrightarrow{AE}$. $\overrightarrow{AE}$, $\overrightarrow{CE}$, $\overrightarrow{CA}$, $\overrightarrow{EC}$ (or $\overrightarrow{EA}$)
2. What is the point of intersection of lines $\overleftrightarrow{AB}$ and $\overleftrightarrow{CF}$? *B*
3. Which lines are parallel? $\overleftrightarrow{AB}$ and $\overleftrightarrow{CD}$
4. Find *BF*. 5

Math Reasoning

The compass and straightedge construction of a segment congruent to a given segment is based on the fact that two segments are congruent if and only if they have the same length.

1 Plan

Pacing

Suggested Number of Days

Transitional: 1 day
Average: 1 day
Advanced: 1 day
Block Schedule: 0.5 block with 8.1

Teaching Resources

Blacklines
(See page 382B.)

Transparencies
- Warm-Up Exercises
- Teacher Time-Savers
- English/Spanish Problem Solving
- Answers

Technology
- Electronic Teacher Tools
- Test and Practice Generator

2 Teach

Math Reasoning

For Mathematical Background Notes on mathematical reasoning related to this lesson, please refer to pages 382E and 382F in this Teacher's Edition.

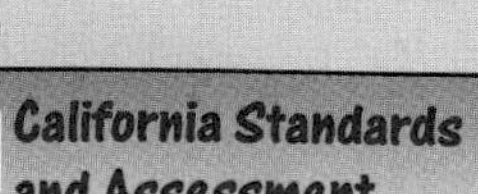

CA Standards: MG 3.1, MG 3.4

8.2 Naming, Measuring, and Drawing Angles

In this lesson you'll:

- Identify and construct basic elements of geometric figures, such as angles and angle bisectors. (MG 3.1)
- Demonstrate an understanding of the conditions that indicate two angles are congruent. (MG 3.4)

Student Help

STUDY TIP
Protractors may have two scales that go from 0° to 180° in reverse directions. Be sure to use the scale that starts at 0° for the angle you are measuring or drawing.

Goal 1 Measuring Angles

An **angle** consists of two rays with a common endpoint called the **vertex**. The rays form the sides of the angle. The angle at the right can be named $\angle BAC$, $\angle CAB$, or $\angle A$.

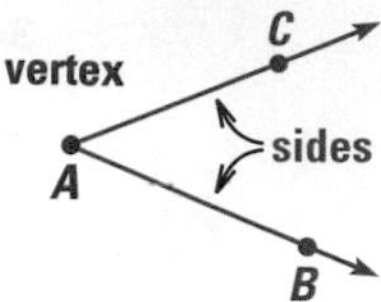

Angles are measured in *degrees*. For example, the measure of $\angle A$ is 45°. You can write this as $m\angle A = 45°$. A protractor can be used to find the approximate measure of an angle.

EXAMPLE 1 Measuring an Angle

1. To measure $\angle RST$, place the center of the protractor's base on the angle's vertex.
2. Position the protractor's 0° line with one side of the angle.
3. Read the angle measure from the protractor.

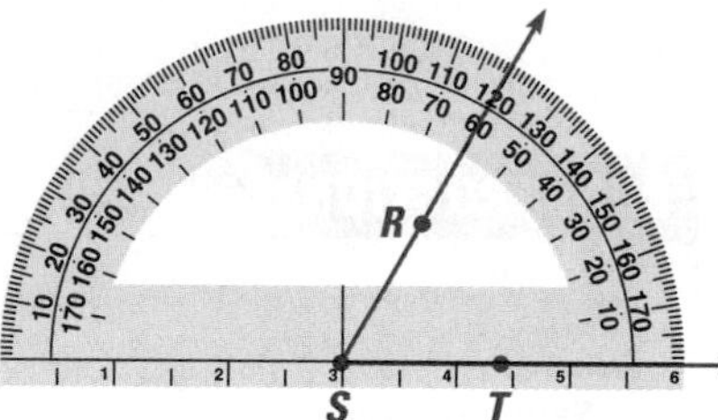

ANSWER ▶ $m\angle RST = 60°$

EXAMPLE 2 Drawing an Angle

1. To draw an angle A whose measure is 150°, first draw a ray and label its endpoint A.
2. Place the center of the protractor's base at the endpoint of the ray. Line up the protractor's 0° line with the ray.
3. Mark a point at 150°.
4. Draw a ray from A through the point.

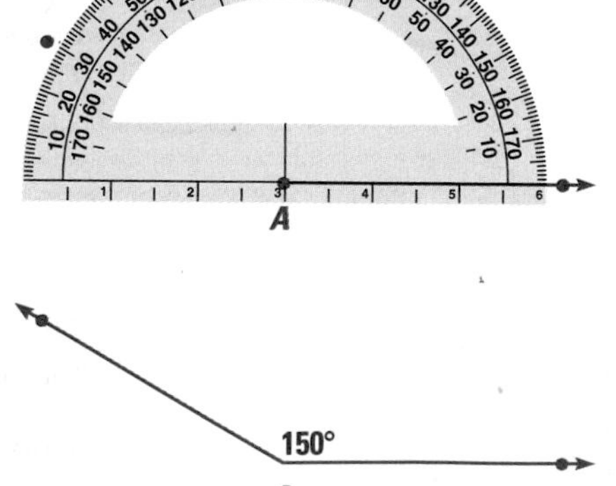

Goal 2 CLASSIFYING ANGLES

Angles are classified by their measures as follows.

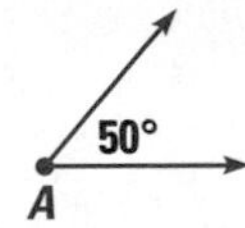

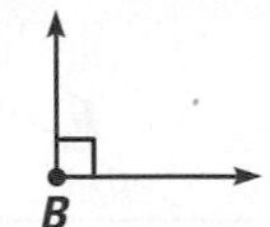

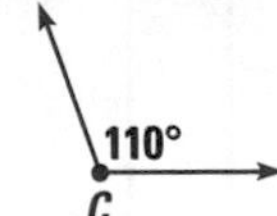

180°
D

ACUTE ANGLE	RIGHT ANGLE	OBTUSE ANGLE	STRAIGHT ANGLE
An angle having a measure between 0° and 90°	An angle having a measure of 90°	An angle having a measure between 90° and 180°	An angle having a measure of 180°

EXAMPLE 3 Classifying Angles

In the diagram at the right, there are

2 acute angles: $\angle TSV$, $\angle VSU$

2 obtuse angles: $\angle RST$, $\angle RSU$

1 straight angle: $\angle RSV$

1 right angle: $\angle TSU$

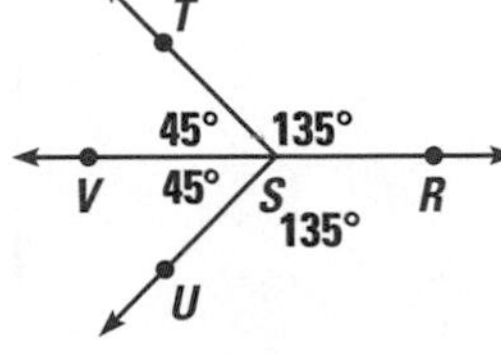

Two angles are **congruent** if they have the same measure. An **angle bisector** is a ray, line, or line segment that divides an angle into two congruent angles.

EXAMPLE 4 Identifying Congruent Angles

In the diagram in Example 3, $\angle TSV$ and $\angle VSU$ have the same measure. So, they are congruent. $\angle RST$ and $\angle RSU$ are also congruent. You can write $\angle TSV \cong \angle VSU$ and $\angle RST \cong \angle RSU$.

Because $\angle TSV \cong \angle VSU$, $\overrightarrow{SV}$ is an angle bisector of $\angle TSU$. You can also say that $\overrightarrow{SV}$ *bisects* $\angle TSU$.

Two angles are **complementary** if the sum of their measures is 90°. Two angles are **supplementary** if the sum of their measures is 180°.

COMPLEMENTARY ANGLES

$m\angle EFG + m\angle GFH = 90°$, so $\angle EFG$ and $\angle GFH$ are complementary.

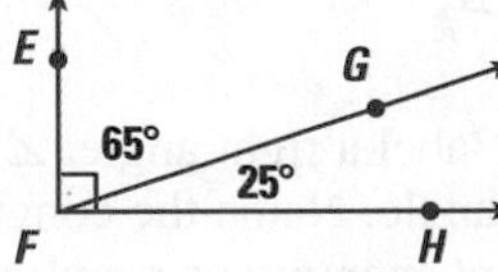

SUPPLEMENTARY ANGLES

$m\angle XYZ + m\angle UVW = 180°$, so $\angle XYZ$ and $\angle UVW$ are supplementary.

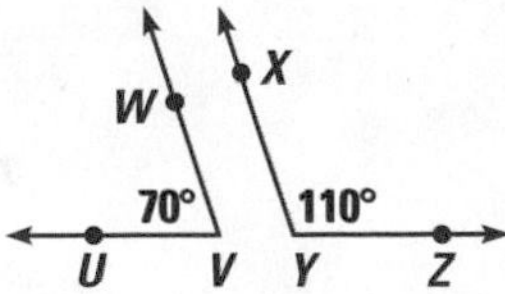

Student Help

▶STUDY TIP
A pair of complementary angles or a pair of supplementary angles do not necessarily share a side.

Extra Example 1

Use a protractor to measure $\angle GBS$.
$m\angle GBS = 130°$

G
B
S

Extra Example 2

Draw an angle B whose measure is 75°.

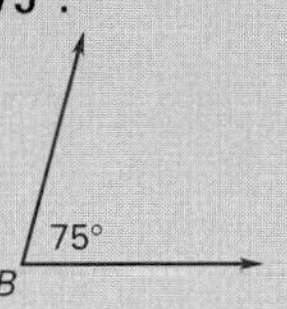

Extra Example 3

Classify each angle in the diagram as *acute, right, obtuse,* or *straight.*

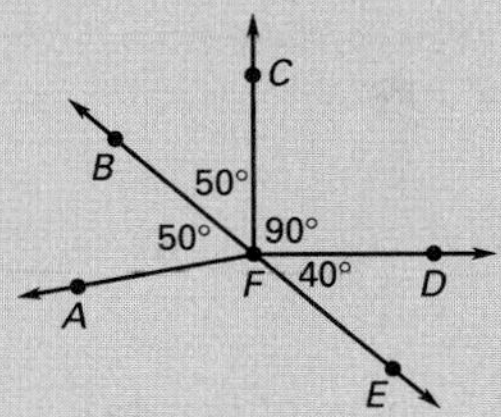

acute angles: $\angle AFB$, $\angle BFC$, and $\angle DFE$; right angle: $\angle CFD$; obtuse angles: $\angle AFE$, $\angle AFD$, $\angle AFC$, $\angle BFD$, and $\angle CFE$; straight angle: $\angle BFE$.

Extra Example 4

a. Name two congruent angles in the diagram in Extra Example 3. **$\angle BFA$ and $\angle CFB$**

b. Name the bisector of $\angle AFC$. **$\overrightarrow{FB}$**

Teaching Tip

Multiple Representations
Stress that two angles do not have to share a side in order to be supplementary. Visually, any two angles that can be placed so that they share a side and form a straight angle are supplementary. Numerically, any two angles whose measures add to 180° are supplementary.

Extra Example 5

Find the given angle measure.

a. Find $m\angle UVW$. **45°**

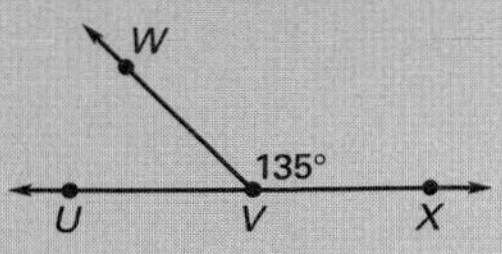

b. Find $m\angle FGH$. **22°**

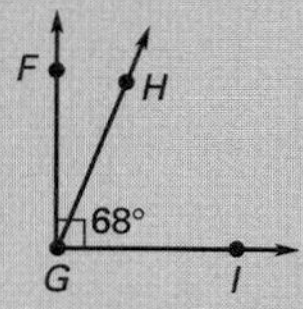

Concept Check

Can two obtuse angles be supplementary? Explain. **No; since each obtuse angle has a measure greater than 90°, the sum of the two measures would be greater than 180°.**

7.

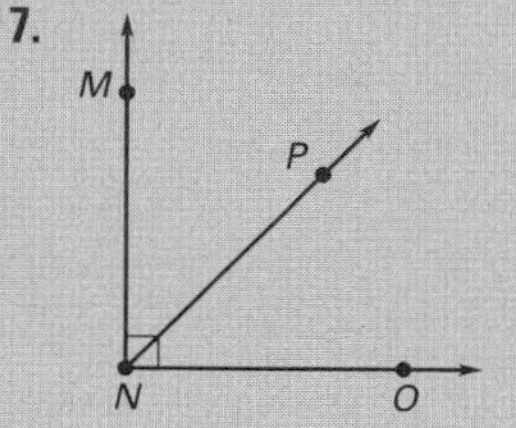

$\angle MNP$, $\angle PNO$; complementary

Student Help

▶VOCABULARY TIP
Two angles in the same plane that share a common side and a vertex and do not overlap are called *adjacent angles.* In Example 5, $\angle ABC$ and $\angle CBD$ are adjacent angles. So are $\angle PQS$ and $\angle SQR$.

EXAMPLE 5 Finding Angle Measures

Find the given angle measure.

a. Find $m\angle ABC$.

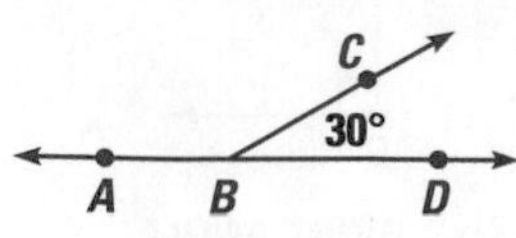

b. Find $m\angle PQS$.

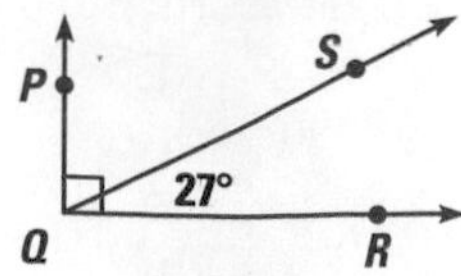

Solution

a. Because $\angle ABC$ and $\angle CBD$ share a common side and form a straight angle, they are supplementary angles.

$m\angle ABC + m\angle CBD = 180°$	Angles are supplementary.
$m\angle ABC + \mathbf{30°} = 180°$	Substitute 30° for $m\angle CBD$.
$m\angle ABC = 150°$	Subtract 30° from each side.

b. Because $\angle PQS$ and $\angle SQR$ share a common side and form a right angle, they are complementary.

$m\angle PQS + m\angle SQR = 90°$	Angles are complementary.
$m\angle PQS + \mathbf{27°} = 90°$	Substitute 27° for $m\angle RQS$.
$m\angle PQS = 63°$	Subtract 27° from each side.

8.2 Exercises

Guided Practice

In Exercises 1–3, use the diagram at the right.

1. Name the vertex of $\angle WXZ$. X

2. Name the sides of $\angle WXZ$. $\overrightarrow{XW}$, $\overrightarrow{XY}$, or $\overrightarrow{XZ}$

3. Give three other names for $\angle WXZ$.
any three of $\angle ZXW$, $\angle YXW$, $\angle WXY$ or $\angle X$

In Exercises 4–6, use a protractor to measure the angle. Determine whether the angle is *acute, obtuse, right,* or *straight*.

4. 90°, right

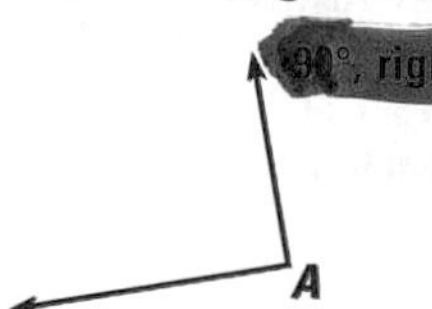

5. 70°, acute

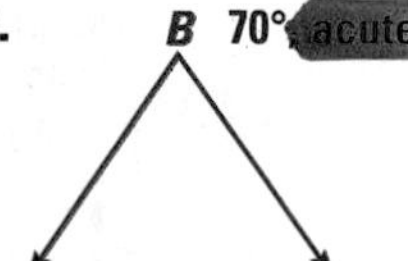

6. 180°, straight

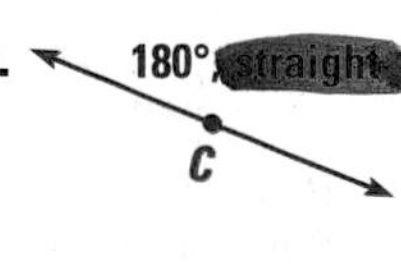

7. Sketch and label a right angle, $\angle MNO$. Then sketch a ray $\overrightarrow{NP}$ that bisects the angle. Name the congruent angles that are formed. Are the angles *complementary* or *supplementary*? See margin.

Practice and Problem Solving

Student Help

▸ MORE PRACTICE Extra practice to help you master skills is on page 704.

Copy the angle, extend its sides, and use a protractor to measure it to the nearest degree. Determine whether the angle is *acute, obtuse, right,* or *straight.*

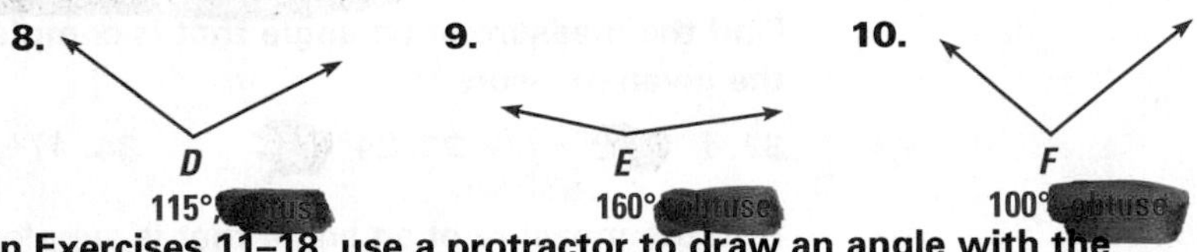

8. 115°, obtuse **9.** 160°, obtuse **10.** 100°, obtuse

In Exercises 11–18, use a protractor to draw an angle with the given measure. 11–21. See margin.

11. 30° **12.** 90° **13.** 125° **14.** 135°

15. 28° **16.** 110° **17.** 15° **18.** 45°

19. Use a protractor to draw two angles that are complementary.

20. Use a protractor to draw two nonadjacent angles that are supplementary.

21. Draw two angles that are congruent and complementary.

In Exercises 22–25, use the diagram at the right.

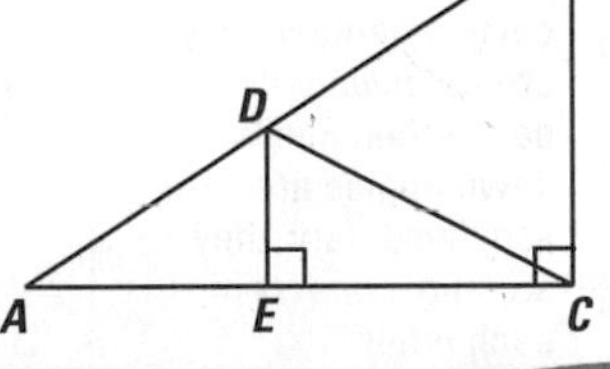

22. Name the angles that appear to be acute. Name the angles that appear to be obtuse.

22. acute: ∠DAE, ∠EDC, ∠DCB, ∠DCE, ∠ADE, ∠DBC, ∠CDB; obtuse: ∠ADC, ∠BDE

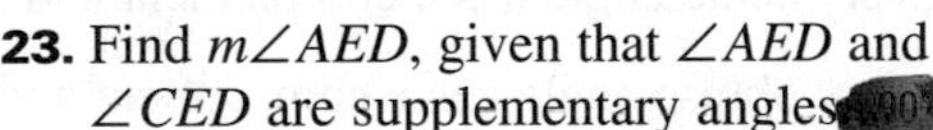

23. Find $m\angle AED$, given that $\angle AED$ and $\angle CED$ are supplementary angles. 90°

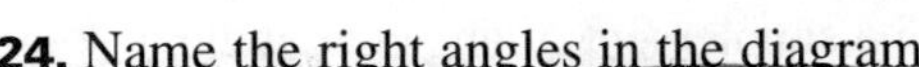

24. Name the right angles in the diagram. ∠DEA, ∠DEC, ∠BCA

25. Identify the vertex and the sides of $\angle CDE$. Explain why you should not use $\angle D$ as a name for this angle.

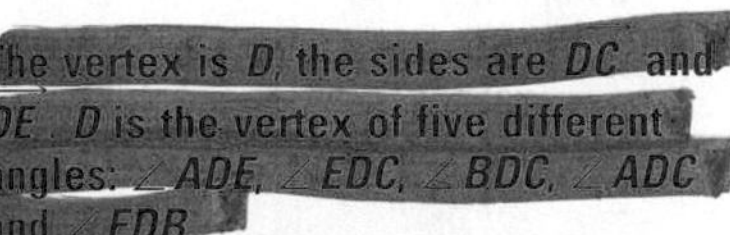

The vertex is *D*, the sides are $\overrightarrow{DC}$ and $\overrightarrow{DE}$. *D* is the vertex of five different angles: ∠ADE, ∠EDC, ∠BDC, ∠ADC and ∠EDB.

Link to Chemistry

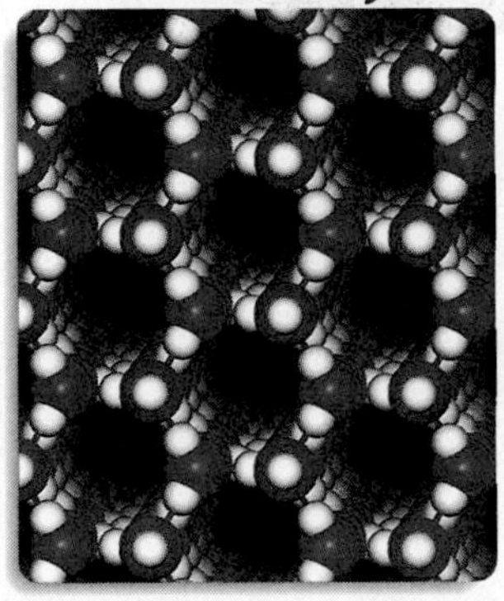

MOLECULES The image above is a model of the crystalline structure of frozen water. Each water molecule has two hydrogen atoms (shown in white) and one oxygen atom (shown in blue).

More about molecules and atoms available at www.mcdougallittell.com

Science Link **In Exercises 26–29, use the following information.** The properties of a molecule depend in part on the arrangement of its atoms. The diagrams below represent arrangements of the atoms in the molecules of four chemical compounds. Copy the angle in the diagram, extend its sides, and use a protractor to measure it to the nearest degree.

26. Water 100°

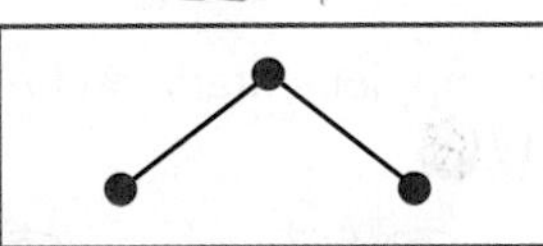

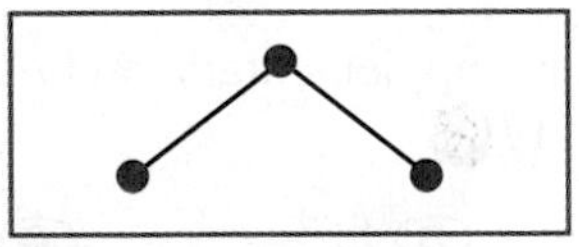

27. Carbon dioxide 180°

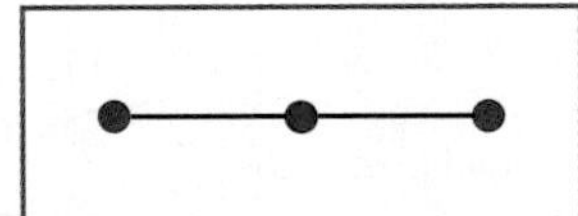

28. Sulfur dioxide 120°

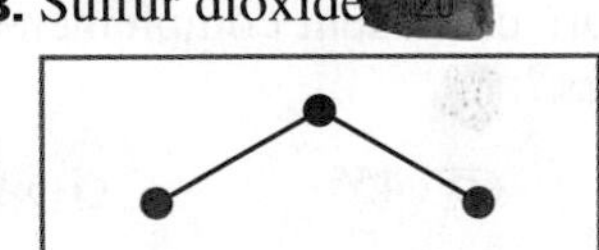

29. Oxygen chloride 110°

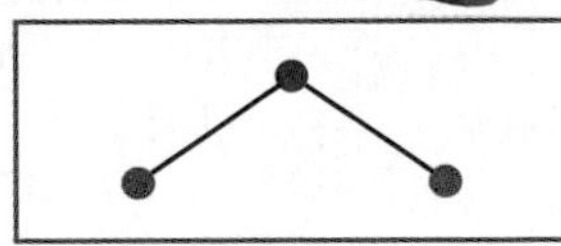

3 Apply

Assignment Guide

TRANSITIONAL
Day 1: pp. 393–394 Exs. 8–14, 19–20, 22–25, 30–33, 36–38, 47–48

AVERAGE
Day 1: pp. 393–394 Exs. 11–14, 19–33, 36–38, 40–45, 47–48

ADVANCED
Day 1: pp. 393–394 Exs. 14–16, 21–33, 36–38, 40–45, 46*, 47–48

BLOCK SCHEDULE
pp. 393–394 Exs. 11–14, 19–33, 36–38, 40–45, 47–48 (with 8.1)

Extra Practice

- Student Edition, pp. 704–705
- Chapter 8 Resource Book, p. 15

Homework Check

To quickly check student understanding of key concepts, go over the following exercises:

Transitional: 8, 20, 24, 30, 32, 36
Average: 14, 20, 26, 30, 32, 38
Advanced: 14, 28, 30, 34, 38, 44

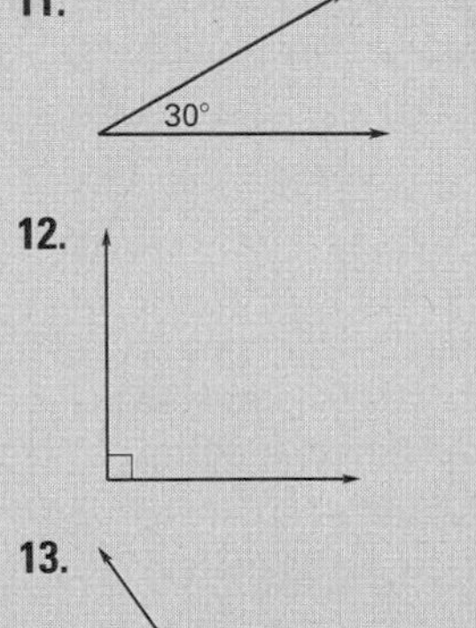

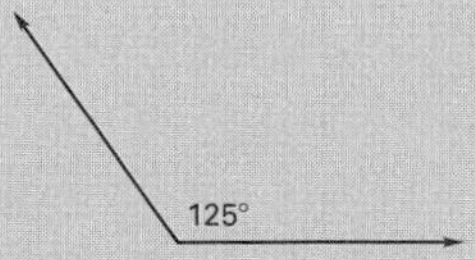

14–21. See Additional Answers beginning on page AA1.

Assessment Resources

- Assessment Book (Formal Assessment and Alternative Assessment)
- Test and Practice Generator

Mini-Quiz

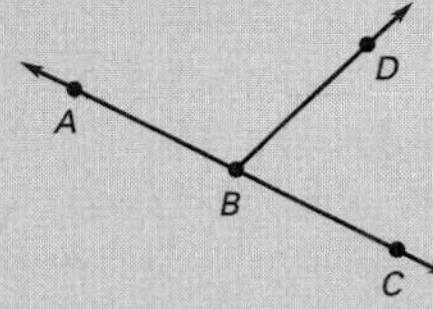

1. Use a protractor to measure $\angle ABD$. Is this angle *acute*, *obtuse*, or *right*? **110°; obtuse**
2. Name a straight angle in the figure. **$\angle ABC$**
3. Name a pair of supplementary angles. **$\angle ABD$ and $\angle DBC$**
4. Suppose $\angle JKL$ and $\angle TUV$ are supplementary. If $m\angle TUV = 115°$, find the measure of $\angle JKL$. **$m\angle JKL = 65°$**

Problem Solving

Prior Knowledge

In Exercise 40, remind students that they must combine like terms as the first step in solving the equation.

Math Reasoning

In connection with Exercise 46, it may be interesting to draw on the analogy between addition of measures of angles with a common vertex and addition of lengths of segments on a common line.

In Exercises 30 and 31, use the figure at the right. Assume that $m\angle 1 = 45°$.

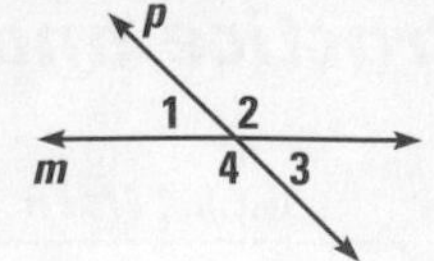

30. Find $m\angle 2$, $m\angle 3$, and $m\angle 4$. 135°, 45°, 135°

31. Describe the relationship between $\angle 1$ and $\angle 4$. They are supplementary angles.

Find the measure of an angle that is complementary to an angle with the given measure.

32. 1° **33.** 24° **34.** 47° **35.** 89°

Find the measure of an angle that is supplementary to an angle with the given measure.

36. 25° **37.** 90° **38.** 134° **39.** 178°

ALGEBRA In Exercises 40 and 41, use the angles shown below. The angles are supplementary.

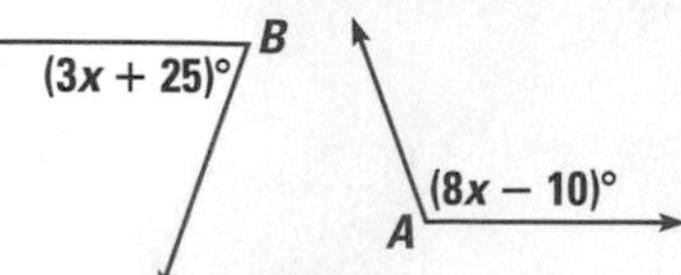

40. Write and solve an equation to find the value of x. See margin.

40. $3x + 25 + 8x - 10 = 180$; $x = 15$

41. Find the measure of each angle. $m\angle B = 70°$, $m\angle A = 110°$

MATHEMATICAL REASONING In Exercises 42–45, tell whether the statement is *true* or *false*. Explain your reasoning.

42. If an angle is a right angle, then its supplement is a right angle. True. The sum of the measures of two right angles is 180°.

43. Every acute angle has a complement and a supplement. See margin.

44. Every obtuse angle has a complement and a supplement. See margin.

45. The supplement of an acute angle is sometimes an acute angle. False. The supplement of an acute angle must be an obtuse angle.

Student Help

▶VOCABULARY TIP
If two angles are complementary, they are *complements* of each other. Similarly, if two angles are supplementary, they are *supplements* of each other.

43. True. An acute angle is less than 90° so there exist angles whose measures may be added to the measure of any acute angle so that they sum to 90° or to 180°.

46. CHALLENGE In the diagram shown, $m\angle AEB = 32.5°$, $m\angle AEC = 39°$, and $m\angle AED = 59°$. Find $m\angle BEC$, $m\angle BED$, and $m\angle CED$.
$m\angle BEC = 6.5°$, $m\angle BED = 26.5°$, $m\angle CED = 20°$

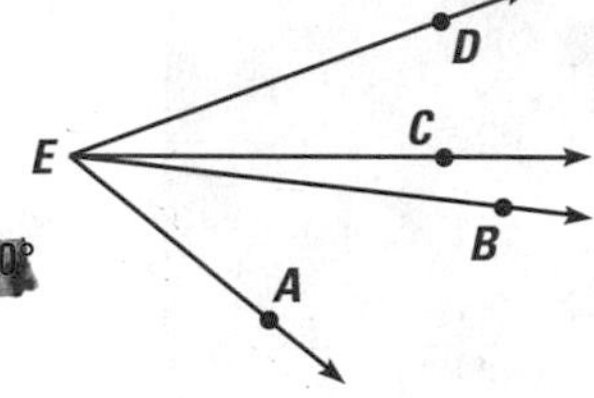

Multiple-Choice Practice

44. False. An obtuse angle is larger than 90° so there does not exist a complementary angle to it.

47. $\angle 1$ and $\angle 2$ are supplementary, and $m\angle 2 = 35°$. What is the measure of $\angle 1$? C

Ⓐ 35° Ⓑ 55° Ⓒ 145° Ⓓ 180°

48. $\angle A$ and $\angle B$ are congruent complementary angles. What is the measure of $\angle A$? G

Ⓕ 30° Ⓖ 45° Ⓗ 90° Ⓙ 180°

CONSTRUCTION Copying and Bisecting Angles

Student Help

▶ SKILLS REVIEW
For help with using a compass and straightedge, see page 685.

COPY AN ANGLE You can use a compass and a straightedge to construct an angle that is congruent to a given angle.

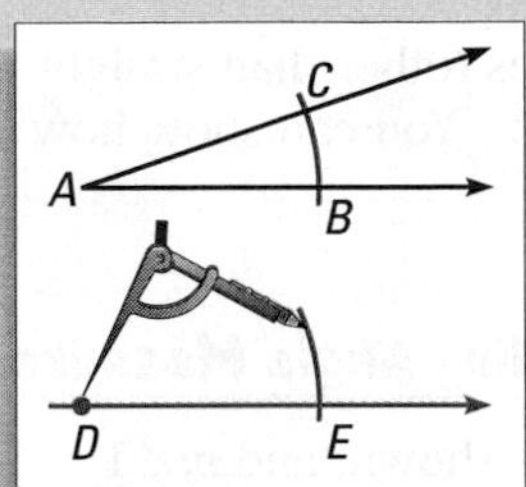

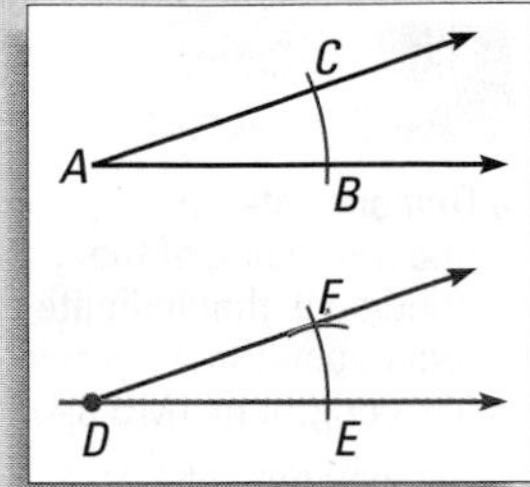

❶ To copy $\angle A$, first draw a ray with endpoint D. Then use the same compass setting to draw an arc with center A and an arc with center D. Label points B, C, and E.

❷ Draw an arc with radius BC and center E. Label the intersection F.

❸ Draw $\overrightarrow{DF}$. $\angle FDE \cong \angle CAB$.

BISECT AN ANGLE You can use a compass and a straightedge to bisect an angle.

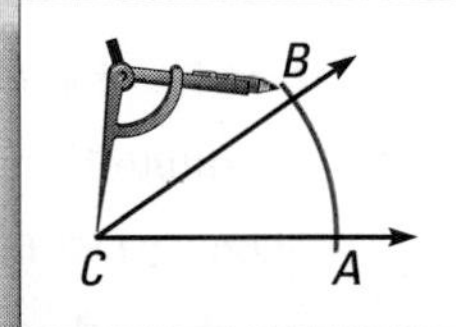

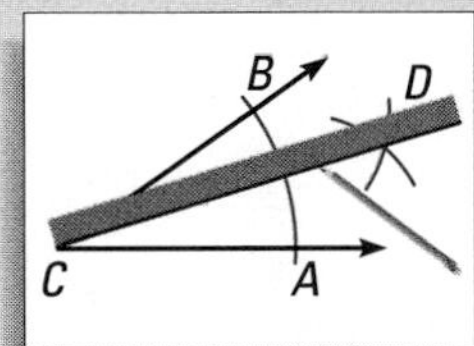

❶ Place the compass point at C. Draw an arc the intersects both sides of the angle. Label the intersections A and B.

❷ Place the compass point at A. Draw an arc. Then place the compass point at B. Using the same compass setting, draw another arc. Label the intersection D.

❸ Use a straightedge to draw a ray from C through D. This is the angle bisector.

Exercises Use a compass and straightedge.

In Exercises 1–3, draw the given type of angle. Construct an angle that is congruent to the one you drew. Then bisect the constructed angle and tell what type of angles are formed. **1–3. See margin.**

1. Acute angle **2.** Obtuse angle **3.** Straight angle

4. MATHEMATICAL REASONING Is it possible to bisect an obtuse angle to form two congruent obtuse angles? Explain your reasoning. **See margin.**

4. **No. An obtuse angle is an angle measuring between 90° and 180°. Since twice an obtuse angle will be more than 180°, it is not possible to bisect an obtuse angle to form two congruent obtuse angles.**

Math Reasoning

The construction of an angle congruent to a given angle is based on congruence properties of triangles. Here $\triangle DEF$ is constructed in such a way that $DE = AB$, $DF = AC$, and $EF = BC$, so $\triangle DEF$ is congruent to $\triangle ABC$ by the Side-Side-Side congruence property of triangles. Therefore, $m\angle FDE = m\angle CAB$. The construction for bisecting an angle also uses congruence properties of triangles. Points A and B are constructed so that $BC = AC$, and point D is constructed so that $DA = DB$. Thus $\triangle ACD$ is congruent to $\triangle BCD$ by the Side-Side-Side congruence property. Therefore, $m\angle ACD = m\angle BCD$.

1.

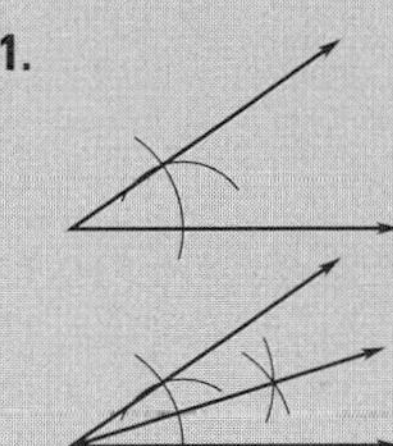

2 acute angles are formed.

2.

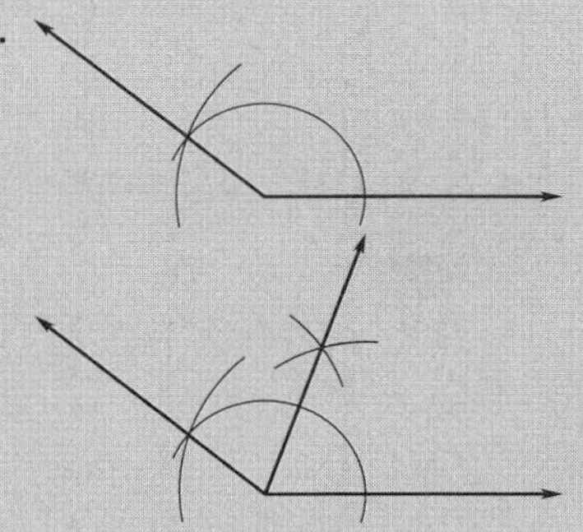

2 acute angles are formed.

3.

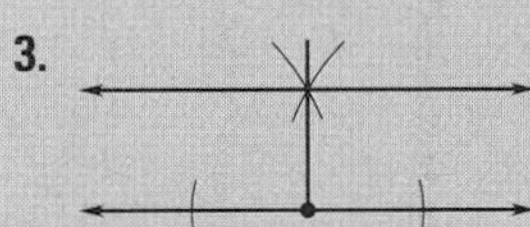

2 right angles are formed.

Planning the Activity

Purpose and Materials

See the margin of the student page.

▶ LINK TO LESSON

Students will use the results of this activity to solve Examples 1 and 2 in Lesson 8.3. Since students will have worked with vertical angles, you may wish to focus on the concept of corresponding angles in Goal 2.

Math Reasoning

Students use words, symbols, and diagrams to explain mathematical reasoning. They use deductive reasoning to prove a statement.

California Standards and Assessment

CA Standards: MG 3.4, MR 2.5

DEVELOPING CONCEPTS
Intersecting Lines

For use with Lesson 8.3

California Standards

- Demonstrate an understanding of the conditions that indicate two geometrical figures are congruent. (MG 3.4)
- Use a variety of methods, such as words, symbols, and diagrams to explain mathematical reasoning. (MR 2.5)

MATERIALS

- Paper and pencil

Consider the four angles (other than straight angles) that are formed when two lines intersect. You can show how the measures of these angles are related.

SAMPLE 1 Finding Angle Measures

Two lines intersect as shown, and $m\angle 1 = 35°$. You can use mathematical reasoning to find the measures of the other angles.

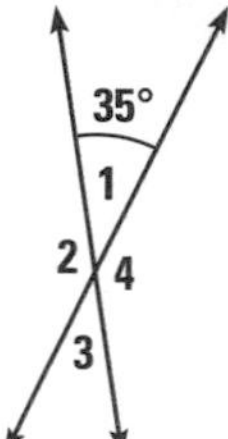

Here's How

$\angle 1$ and $\angle 2$ share a side and form a straight angle. So, you know that the sum of their measures is 180°. Therefore:

$m\angle 1 + m\angle 2 = 180°$	Measure of a straight angle is 180°.
$35° + m\angle 2 = 180°$	Substitute 35° for $m\angle 1$.
$m\angle 2 = 145°$	Subtract 35° from each side.

Similarly, $\angle 2$ and $\angle 3$ share a side and form a straight angle:

$m\angle 2 + m\angle 3 = 180°$	Measure of a straight angle is 180°.
$145° + m\angle 3 = 180°$	Substitute 145° for $m\angle 2$.
$m\angle 3 = 35°$	Subtract 145° from each side.

Using similar reasoning, you can show that $m\angle 4 = 145°$.

When two lines intersect, each pair of nonadjacent angles are called *vertical angles*. In the diagram above, $\angle 1$ and $\angle 3$ are vertical angles, as are $\angle 2$ and $\angle 4$. In Sample 1 you saw that $\angle 1 \cong \angle 3$ and $\angle 2 \cong \angle 4$.

Try These

In Exercises 1 and 2, use the diagram below.

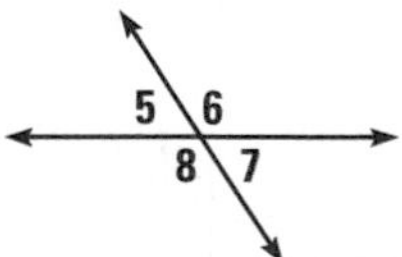
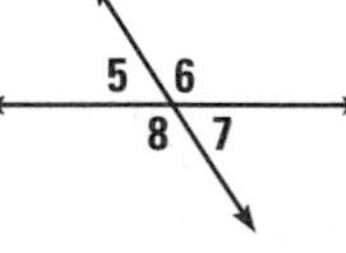

1. Identify each pair of vertical angles in the diagram shown at the right. **$\angle 5$ and $\angle 7$; $\angle 6$ and $\angle 8$**
2. **MATHEMATICAL REASONING** In the diagram, $m\angle 8 = 123°$. Find the measures of the other three angles. Explain how you found the angle measures. **$m\angle 5 = 57°$; $m\angle 6 = 123°$; $m\angle 7 = 57°$**

SAMPLE 2 Proving Vertical Angles are Congruent

You can use mathematical reasoning to prove that vertical angles are congruent.

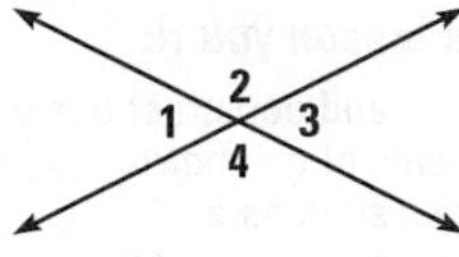

Here's How

In the diagram at the right, $\angle 1$ and $\angle 3$ are vertical angles. Prove that $\angle 1 \cong \angle 3$.

Statements	Reasons
1. $\angle 1$ and $\angle 3$ are vertical angles.	**1.** Given
2. $\angle 1$ and $\angle 2$ form a straight angle. $\angle 2$ and $\angle 3$ form a straight angle.	**2.** The sides that each pair of adjacent angles do not have in common form a straight angle.
3. $m\angle 1 + m\angle 2 = 180°$ $m\angle 3 + m\angle 2 = 180°$	**3.** Because each pair of angles form a straight angle, the angles are supplementary.
4. $m\angle 1 = 180° - m\angle 2$ $m\angle 3 = 180° - m\angle 2$	**4.** Subtract $m\angle 2$ from each side of both equations.
5. $m\angle 1 = m\angle 3$	**5.** $m\angle 1$ and $m\angle 3$ are both equal to $180° - m\angle 2$, so they are equal to each other.
6. $\angle 1 \cong \angle 3$	**6.** Definition of congruent angles

Student Help

▶**STUDY TIP**
The list of statements and reasons in Sample 2 is an example of a *two-column proof.* A two-column proof is often used in geometry to illustrate how mathematical reasoning is used to justify a conclusion.

Try These

MATHEMATICAL REASONING In Exercises 3–6, use the diagram below.

3–6. See margin.

5
6
8
7

3. The diagram indicates that $\angle 5$ is a right angle. Explain how you know that $\angle 7$ is a right angle.

4. Explain how you know that $\angle 6$ is a right angle.

5. Use your answer to Exercise 4 to explain how you know that $\angle 8$ is a right angle.

6. Based on the results of Exercises 3–5, what can you say about two lines that intersect to form a right angle?

3. Since $\angle 5$ and $\angle 7$ are vertical angles, $\angle 5 \cong \angle 7$. Therefore $m\angle 7 = m\angle 5 = 90°$.

4. $m\angle 6 + m\angle 7 = 180°$
$m\angle 6 + 90° = 180°$
$m\angle 6 = 90°$

5. $\angle 8$ and $\angle 6$ are vertical angles. Since $m\angle 6 = 90°$, $m\angle 8 = 90°$.

6. They form a total of 4 right angles.

2 Managing the Activity

Classroom Management

The use of an overhead is helpful when demonstrating concepts in this activity. Have volunteers come to the overhead to explain any patterns that they observe.

3 Closing the Activity

★ **KEY DISCOVERY**
Vertical angles are congruent.

Activity Assessment

Use Exercises 1 and 2 to assess student understanding.

1 Plan

Pacing

Suggested Number of Days

Transitional: 2 days
Average: 2 days
Advanced: 2 days
Block Schedule: 1 block

Teaching Resources

Blacklines
(See page 382B.)

Transparencies
- Warm-Up Exercises
- Teacher Time-Savers
- English/Spanish Problem Solving
- Answers

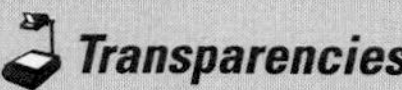

Technology
- Electronic Teacher Tools
- Test and Practice Generator

2 Teach

Math Reasoning

For Mathematical Background Notes on mathematical reasoning related to this lesson, please refer to pages 382E and 382F in this Teacher's Edition.

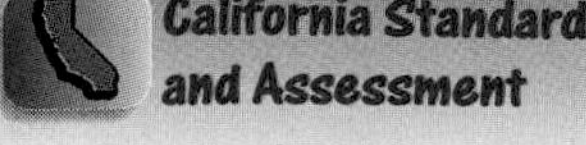

California Standards and Assessment

CA Standards: MG 3.1, MG 3.4

8.3 Parallel and Perpendicular Lines

California Standards

In this lesson you'll:

- Identify and construct basic elements of geometric figures, such as a perpendicular bisector and a perpendicular to a line. (MG 3.1)
- Demonstrate an understanding of conditions that indicate two angles are congruent. (MG 3.4)

Goal 1 Identifying Vertical Angles

When two lines intersect, four angles (other than straight angles) are formed. Each pair of nonadjacent angles are called **vertical angles**. $\angle 1$ and $\angle 3$ are vertical angles, as are $\angle 2$ and $\angle 4$. In Developing Concepts 8.3, page 396, you saw that vertical angles are congruent.

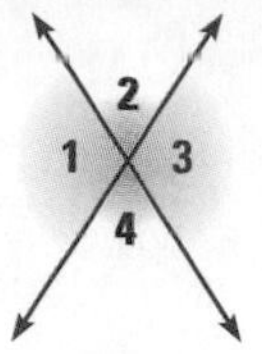

VERTICAL ANGLES
$\angle 1 \cong \angle 3$ **and** $\angle 2 \cong \angle 4$

EXAMPLE 1 Finding Angle Measures

In the diagram, $m\angle 1 = 50°$. Because $\angle 1$ and $\angle 3$ are vertical angles, they are congruent. So, $m\angle 3 = 50°$.

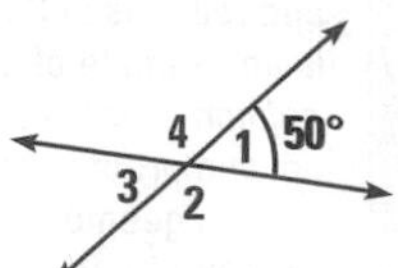

Because $\angle 1$ and $\angle 2$ share a side and form a straight angle, you know that the sum of their measures is 180°.

$$m\angle 2 = 180° - m\angle 1 = 180° - \mathbf{50°} = 130°$$

Because $\angle 2$ and $\angle 4$ are vertical angles, they are congruent. You can conclude that $m\angle 4 = 130°$.

When two lines intersect to form a right angle, as in Example 2 below, the lines are **perpendicular**.

EXAMPLE 2 Solving an Equation

In the diagram, $m\angle 2 = (x + 25)°$. Find the value of x.

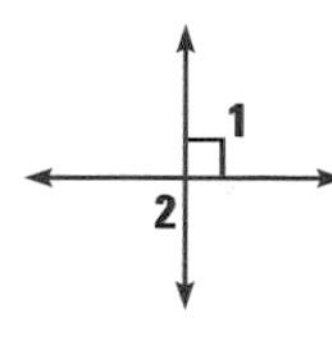

Solution

From the diagram, you know that $\angle 1$ and $\angle 2$ are vertical angles. Write and solve an equation to find the value of x.

$m\angle 1 = m\angle 2$	Vertical angles are congruent.
$90° = \mathbf{(x + 25)°}$	Substitute $(x + 25)°$ for $m\angle 2$.
$90 - 25 = x + 25 - 25$	Subtract 25 from each side.
$65 = x$	Simplify. x is by itself.

Goal 2 IDENTIFYING CORRESPONDING ANGLES

Student Help

VOCABULARY TIP
A *postulate* is a statement that is considered true without proof.

When a line, called a **transversal**, intersects two other lines, pairs of angles called **corresponding angles** are formed. In the diagrams below, $\angle 1$ and $\angle 2$ are corresponding angles, as are $\angle 3$ and $\angle 4$. If two *parallel* lines are intersected by a transversal, corresponding angles are congruent. In a later geometry course, you will learn that this statement is called a *postulate*.

Two nonparallel lines intersected by a transversal

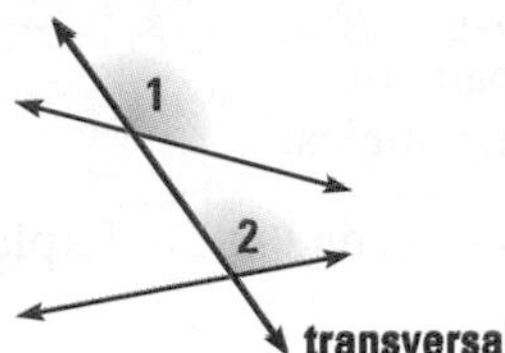

Two parallel lines intersected by a transversal

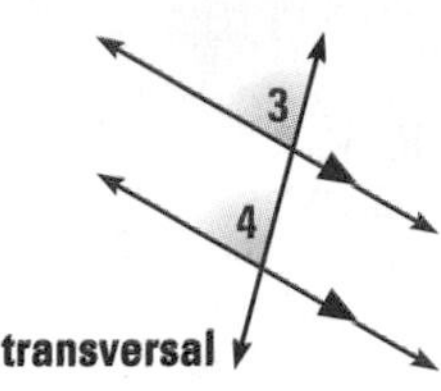

EXAMPLE 3 Identifying Corresponding Angles

In the diagram there are four pairs of corresponding angles. Because lines p and q are parallel, each pair of corresponding angles are congruent:

$\angle 1 \cong \angle 5$, $\angle 2 \cong \angle 6$,

$\angle 3 \cong \angle 7$, $\angle 4 \cong \angle 8$

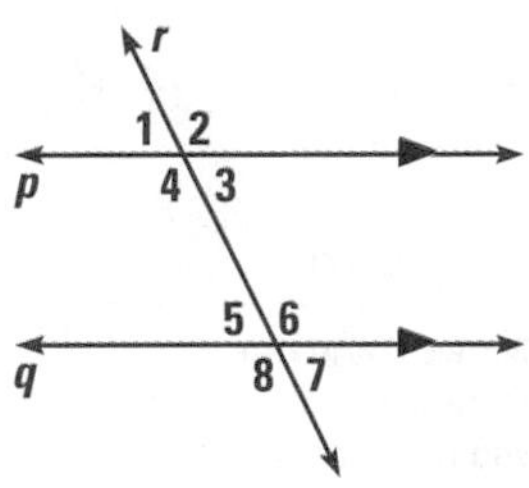

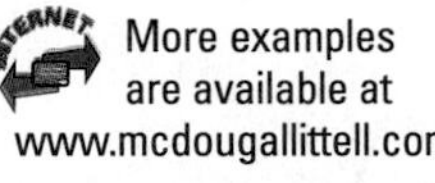

Student Help

MORE EXAMPLES
More examples are available at www.mcdougallittell.com

EXAMPLE 4 Finding Angle Measures

Use the diagram. Find $m\angle 1$, $m\angle 2$, and $m\angle 3$.

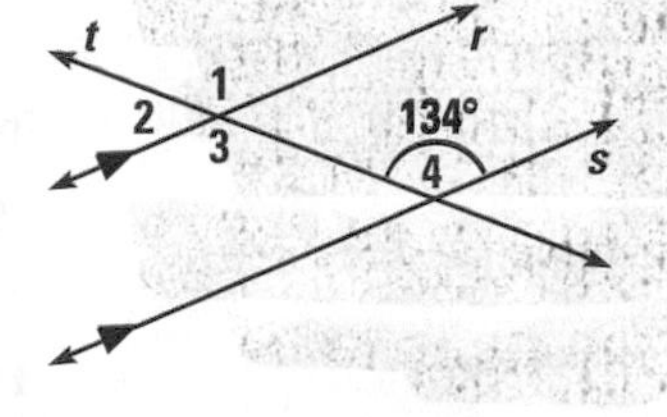

Solution

Because lines r and s are parallel, $\angle 1$ and $\angle 4$ are congruent corresponding angles. So, $m\angle 1 = 134°$.

Because $\angle 1$ and $\angle 3$ are vertical angles, $\angle 1 \cong \angle 3$. So, $m\angle 3 = 134°$.

$\angle 1$ and $\angle 2$ share a side and form a straight angle, so the sum of their measures is 180°.

$m\angle 1 + m\angle 2 = 180°$ Write equation.

$134° + m\angle 2 = 180°$ Substitute 134° for $m\angle 1$.

$m\angle 2 = 46°$ Subtract 134° from each side.

ANSWER ▶ $m\angle 1 = 134°$, $m\angle 2 = 46°$, and $m\angle 3 = 134°$.

Extra Example 1

Use the diagram to find the measures of angles 2, 3, and 4.

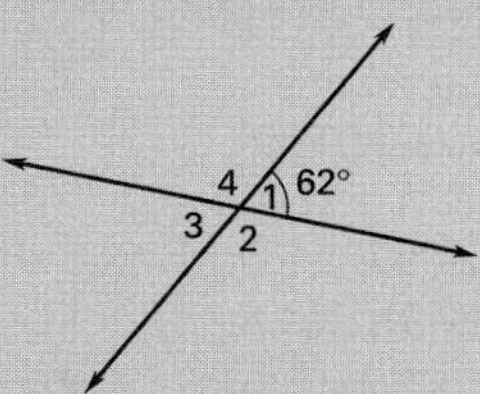

$m\angle 2 = 118°$; $m\angle 3 = 62°$; $m\angle 4 = 118°$

Extra Example 2

Use the diagram in Example 2. Suppose $m\angle 2 = (2x + 16)°$. Find the value of x. 37°

Extra Example 3

In the diagram, identify all congruent corresponding angles.

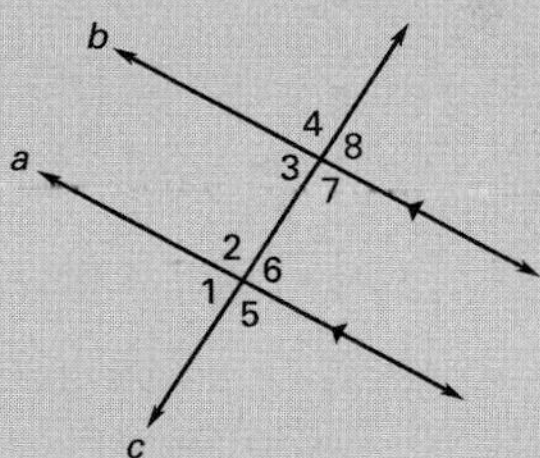

$\angle 1 \cong \angle 3$, $\angle 2 \cong \angle 4$, $\angle 5 \cong \angle 7$, $\angle 6 \cong \angle 8$

Extra Example 4

Use the diagram to find $m\angle 1$, $m\angle 2$, and $m\angle 3$. $m\angle 1 = 141°$, $m\angle 2 = 39°$, $m\angle 3 = 141°$

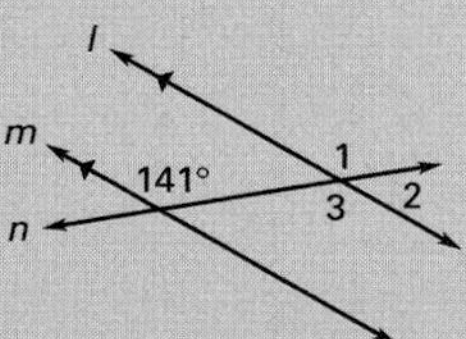

Concept Check

A pair of parallel lines is intersected by a third line. One of the angles formed by the third line and one of the parallel lines is a right angle. Draw a diagram to illustrate this situation. What can you say about the other angles? **All the angles are right angles.**

3 Apply

Assignment Guide

TRANSITIONAL
Day 1: pp. 400–402 Exs. 6–8, 19–20, 32–36
Day 2: pp. 400–402 Exs. 9–18, 21, 24–27, 29–31, 37–40

AVERAGE
Day 1: pp. 400–402 Exs. 6–8, 19–20, 32–44
Day 2: pp. 400–402 Exs. 9–18, 21, 23–27, 29–31

ADVANCED
Day 1: pp. 400–402 Exs. 6–8, 19–21, 32–44
Day 2: pp. 400–402 Exs. 9–12, 16–18, 21–27, 28*, 29–31

BLOCK SCHEDULE
pp. 400–402 Exs. 6–21, 23–27, 29–44

Extra Practice

- Student Edition, pp. 704–705
- Chapter 8 Resource Book, p. 24

Homework Check

To quickly check student understanding of key concepts, go over the following exercises:

Transitional: 8, 12, 16, 20, 26
Average: 8, 12, 18, 20, 26
Advanced: 8, 12, 18, 20, 26

5.

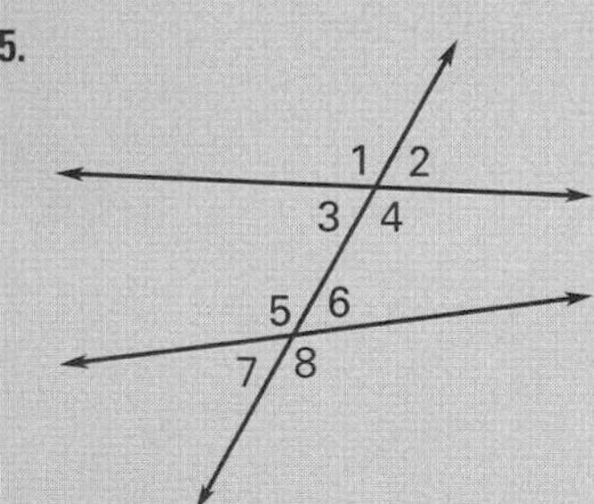

∠1 and ∠5, ∠2 and ∠6, ∠3 and ∠7, ∠4 and ∠8

8.3 Exercises

Guided Practice

In Exercises 1–4, use the figure below.

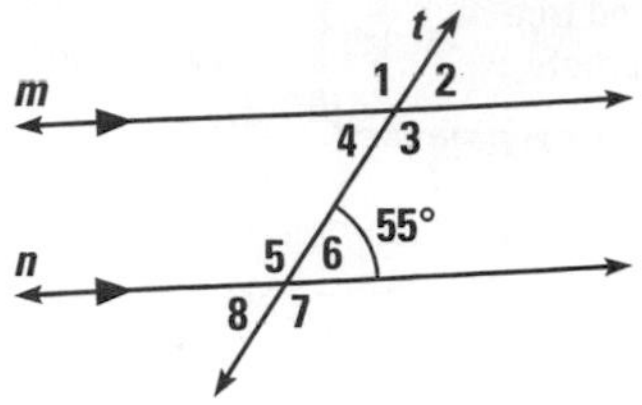

1. Which two lines are parallel? Which line is a transversal? **m and n are parallel; t is a transversal.**

2. Name four pairs of vertical angles. **∠1 and ∠3, ∠2 and ∠4, ∠5 and ∠7, ∠6 and ∠8**

3. Name four pairs of corresponding angles. **∠1 and ∠5, ∠2 and ∠6, ∠3 and ∠7, ∠4 and ∠8**

4. Find $m\angle 2$, $m\angle 4$, and $m\angle 8$. Explain your reasoning. **See margin.**

5. Sketch two lines intersected by a transversal where the corresponding angles are *not* congruent. Name all pairs of corresponding angles in your drawing. **See margin.**

4. $m\angle 2 = 55°$, $m\angle 4 = 55°$, and $m\angle 8 = 55°$; ∠2 and ∠6 are corresponding angles, so they are equal in measure. ∠2 and ∠4 and ∠6 and ∠8 are pairs of vertical angles. So all have a measure of 55°.

Practice and Problem Solving

Student Help

▶**MORE PRACTICE**
Extra practice to help you master skills is on page 704.

In Exercises 6–8, use the photograph.

6. Name all the pairs of vertical angles that are numbered in the photograph. See margin.

7. Which numbered angles are right angles? How do you know? See margin.

8. Find $m\angle 2$, $m\angle 3$, and $m\angle 4$ if $m\angle 1 = 82°$. $m\angle 2 = 98°$, $m\angle 3 = 82°$, $m\angle 4 = 98°$

6. ∠1 and ∠3, ∠2 and ∠4, ∠5 and ∠8, ∠6 and ∠7

7. ∠5, ∠8, ∠6, and ∠7; ∠8 is given to be a right angle; ∠5 and ∠8 are vertical angles and therefore congruent; ∠6 and ∠7 are both supplementary to ∠8 and therefore are right angles also.

In Exercises 9–15, use the figure at the right.

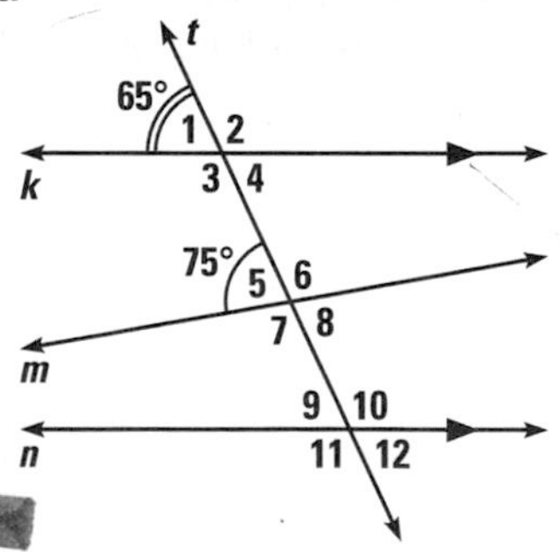

9. Explain why ∠4 is not congruent to ∠8. Line m is not parallel to line k.

10. Name all pairs of corresponding angles that have different measures. See margin.

11. Name two corresponding angles that have the same measure. *Sample answer:* ∠2 and ∠10

12. Name each angle whose measure is 65°. ∠1, ∠4, ∠9, and ∠12

13. Name each angle whose measure is 75°. ∠5 and ∠8

14. Name each angle whose measure is 115°. ∠2, ∠3, ∠10, and ∠11

15. Name each angle whose measure is 105°. ∠6 and ∠7

10. ∠1 and ∠5, ∠2 and ∠6, ∠3 and ∠7, ∠4 and ∠8, ∠5 and ∠9, ∠6 and ∠10, ∠7 and ∠11, ∠8 and ∠12

Explain why the angles with red numbers in the diagram are congruent. 16–18. See margin.

16.

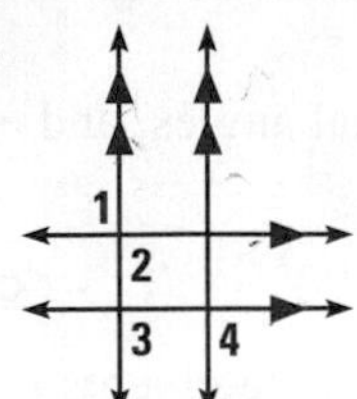

17.

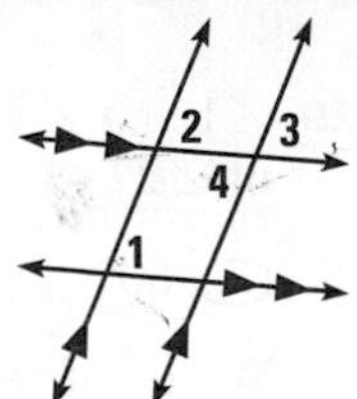

18.

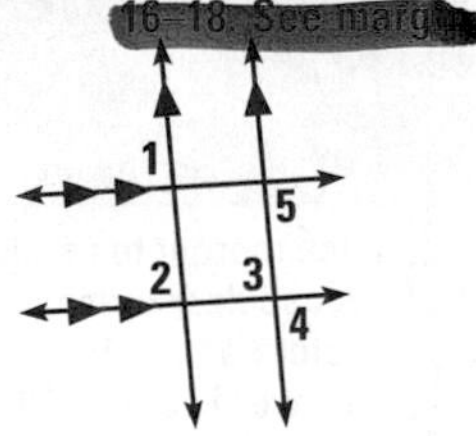

ALGEBRA In Exercises 19–21, find the value of *x*.

19.

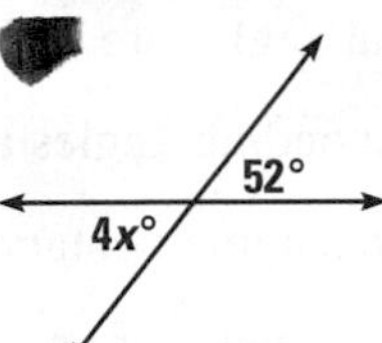

20.

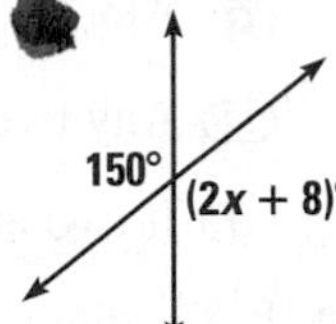

21. 25

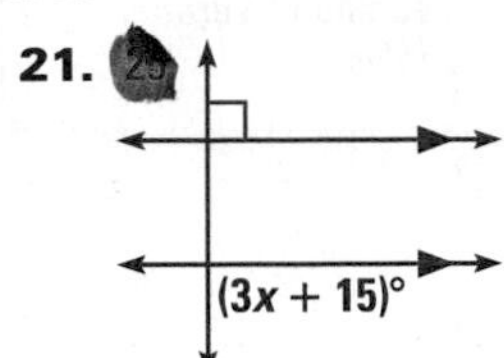

Link to History

England

Scotland

Ireland

UNION FLAG Three symbols were used to represent the countries of England, Scotland, and Ireland in the Union Flag established in 1801. These symbols are contained in the flag that is still used in the United Kingdom today.

22. FLAG DESIGN Assume that every line segment in the simplified line drawing of the flag is parallel to the top of the flag, the right side of the flag, or one of its two diagonals. (A *diagonal* is a segment drawn from one corner of the flag to the opposite corner.) Use a protractor to measure several of the angles in the flag. What is the minimum number of angles you need to measure to determine the measure of every angle in the drawing? Explain your reasoning. **See margin.**

Union Flag

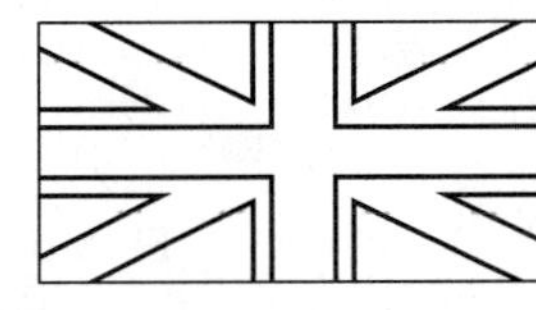

Line Drawing

23. MATHEMATICAL REASONING If two lines intersect in such a way that one of the angles formed is acute, what can you conclude about the other three angles that are formed? Explain your reasoning. Include a sketch. See margin.

In Exercises 24–27, use the figure at the right.

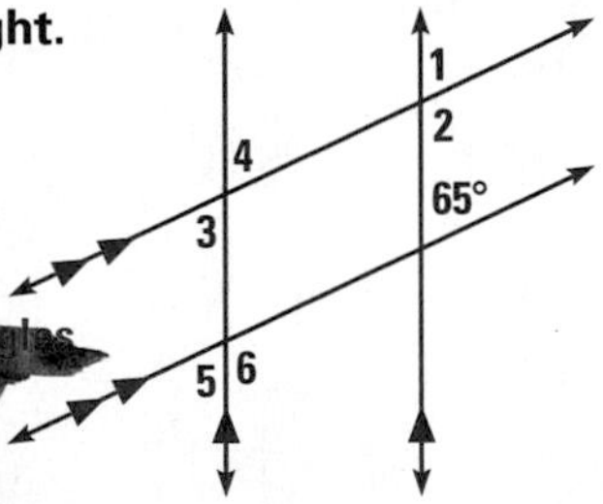

24. Find $m\angle 1$ and $m\angle 4$. Explain your reasoning. See margin.

25. Describe the relationship between $\angle 4$ and $\angle 3$. They are vertical angles and are congruent.

26. Find $m\angle 3$ and $m\angle 5$. Explain your reasoning. 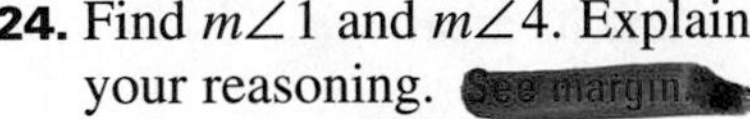

27. Find $m\angle 6$. 

28. CHALLENGE Use the diagram at the right. Find the values of *a* and *b*. Explain your reasoning. a = 130, b = 50

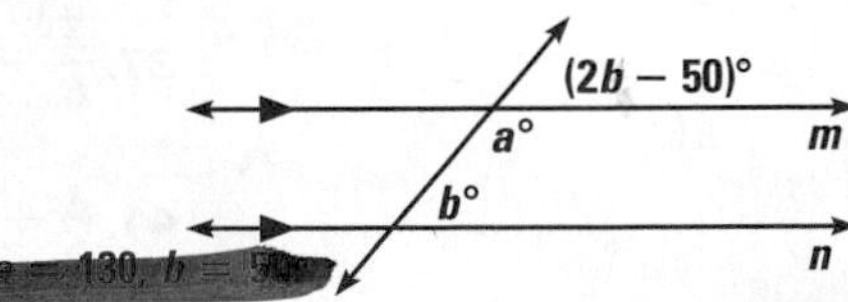

16. $\angle 1 \cong \angle 2$ because they are vertical angles; $\angle 2 \cong \angle 3$ and $\angle 3 \cong \angle 4$ because they are corresponding angles. Therefore, $\angle 1 \cong \angle 2 \cong \angle 3 \cong \angle 4$ or $\angle 1 \cong \angle 4$.

17. $\angle 1 \cong \angle 2$ because they are corresponding angles, $\angle 2 \cong \angle 3$ because they are corresponding angles, and $\angle 3 \cong \angle 4$ because they are vertical angles. Therefore, $\angle 1 \cong \angle 2 \cong \angle 3 \cong \angle 4$ or $\angle 1 \cong \angle 4$.

18. $\angle 1 \cong \angle 2$ because they are corresponding angles; $\angle 2 \cong \angle 3$ because they are corresponding angles, $\angle 3 \cong \angle 4$ because they are vertical angles, and $\angle 4 \cong \angle 5$ because they are corresponding angles. Therefore, $\angle 1 \cong \angle 2 \cong \angle 3 \cong \angle 4 \cong \angle 5$ or $\angle 1 \cong \angle 3 \cong \angle 5$.

22. 1; many of the angles are 90° angles, several are complementary angles, and since the patterns are identical in the four regions, the angles are the same in similar parts of the four regions.

23. When two lines intersect, each pair of nonstraight angles either are vertical or supplementary angles. Vertical angles are congruent, hence $\angle 1 \cong \angle 3$ and $\angle 2 \cong \angle 4$. If $\angle 1$ is acute, then $\angle 3$ is acute, since they are congruent. $\angle 1$ and $\angle 2$ are supplementary, so $m\angle 1 + m\angle 2 = 180°$. Since $m\angle 1 < 90°$, $m\angle 2 > 90°$, so $\angle 2$ is obtuse. $\angle 2 \cong \angle 4$, so $\angle 4$ is also obtuse.

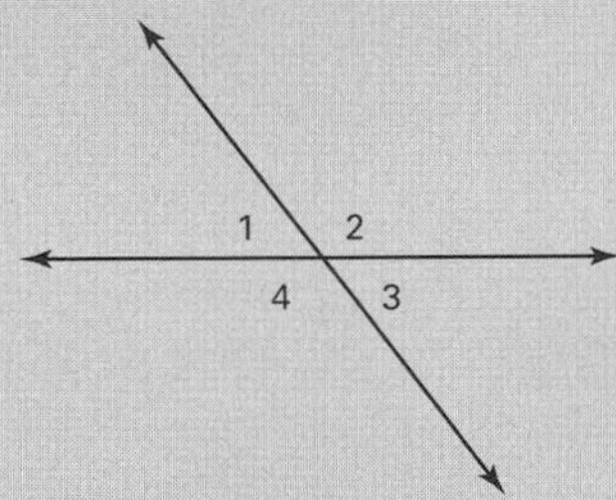

24. $m\angle 1 = m\angle 4 = 65°$. $\angle 1$ and $\angle 4$ are corresponding angles and $\angle 1$ and the 65° angle are corresponding angles also.

26. $m\angle 3 = m\angle 5 = 65°$; $\angle 3$ and $\angle 4$ are vertical and therefore congruent. $\angle 3$ and $\angle 5$ are corresponding angles and are congruent.

4 Assess

Assessment Resources

- Assessment Book (Formal Assessment and Alternative Assessment)
- Test and Practice Generator

Mini-Quiz

1. Angles 1 and 5 form a corresponding pair. With what other angle does $\angle 1$ form a corresponding pair? **$\angle 9$**

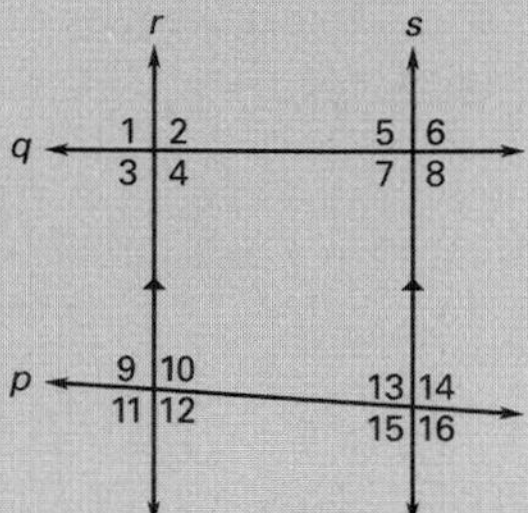

2. Explain why $\angle 3$ is not congruent to $\angle 11$. **Lines *p* and *q* that form these corresponding angles are not parallel.**
3. Lines *r* and *s* are parallel. If $m\angle 10 = 97°$, find $m\angle 12$, $m\angle 16$, and $m\angle 13$. **83°; 83°; 83°**

36. ***Sample answer:***

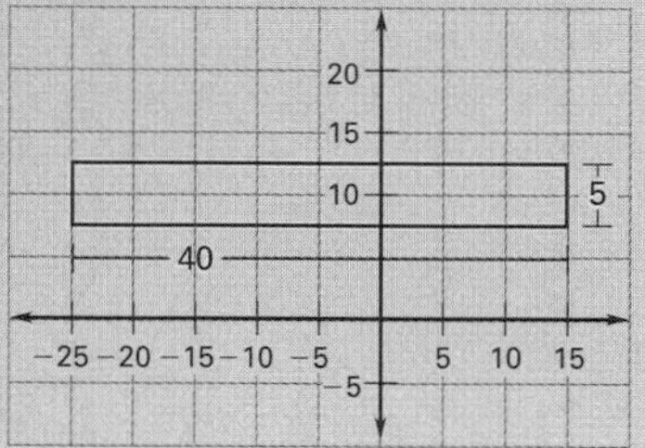

Multiple-Choice Practice

Test Tip

▶ Don't forget to review vocabulary terms before a test. To answer Exercise 29 correctly, for example, you need to know the meaning of *vertical angles.*

29. $\angle 1$ and $\angle 2$ are vertical angles, and $m\angle 1 = 30°$. What is the measure of $\angle 2$?

Ⓐ 60° Ⓑ 90° Ⓒ 150° Ⓓ Not here

30. Which of the following statements is *false*?

Ⓕ Any two right angles are congruent.

Ⓖ Any two vertical angles are congruent.

Ⓗ Any two corresponding angles are congruent.

Ⓙ If two angles are supplementary, then their sum is 180°.

31. In the diagram, lines *p* and *q* are parallel lines. They are intersected by a transversal that is not perpendicular to either line. Which of the following statements is *true*?

Ⓐ $\angle 1 \cong \angle 2$

Ⓑ The sum of $m\angle 1$ and $m\angle 4$ is 180°.

Ⓒ $\angle 6$ and $\angle 7$ are vertical angles.

Ⓓ $\angle 3$ and $\angle 5$ are corresponding angles.

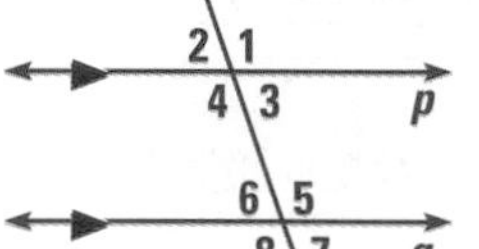

Mixed Review

Find the average of the integers. *(3.6)*

32. −10, 6, −3, 4, −12, 13, 15, 11 **3**

33. −27, 34, −35, 12, −19, −28, 14, 14, 0, −5 **−4**

34. −7, −9, −12, 2, −10, −6 **−7**

In Exercises 35 and 36, use the coordinate plane shown. *(3.8)*

35. Find the length and the width of the rectangle. Then find its perimeter and its area.
$l = 20$, $w = 10$; $P = 60$, $A = 200$

36. Draw a coordinate plane. Draw a rectangle that has the same area but a different perimeter than the rectangle shown. **See margin.**

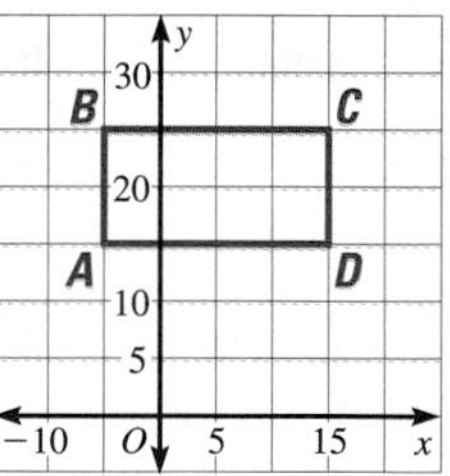

Add or subtract. Then simplify, if possible. *(6.1, 6.2)*

37. $\frac{5}{6} + \left(-\frac{1}{6}\right)$ $\mathbf{\frac{2}{3}}$ **38.** $\frac{2}{3} + \frac{3}{6}$ $\mathbf{\frac{7}{6}}$ **39.** $\frac{-3}{5} - \frac{1}{3}$ $\mathbf{-\frac{14}{15}}$ **40.** $4\frac{1}{2} + 1\frac{1}{2}$ **6**

41. $\frac{x}{6} + \frac{x}{6}$ $\mathbf{\frac{2x}{6} = \frac{x}{3}}$ **42.** $\frac{z}{3} + \frac{z}{6}$ $\mathbf{\frac{z}{2}}$ **43.** $\frac{y}{2} - \frac{5}{3}$ $\mathbf{\frac{(3y-10)}{6}}$ **44.** $\frac{a}{5} - \frac{a}{10}$ $\mathbf{\frac{a}{10}}$

CONSTRUCTION Constructing Perpendiculars

Student Help

▶ **SKILLS REVIEW**
For help with using a compass and straightedge, see page 685.

BISECT A SEGMENT The **midpoint** of a segment is the point that divides the segment into two congruent segments. A line, a segment, or a ray that is perpendicular to a line segment at its midpoint is called a **perpendicular bisector** of the segment. You can use a compass and a straightedge to construct the perpendicular bisector of a given segment.

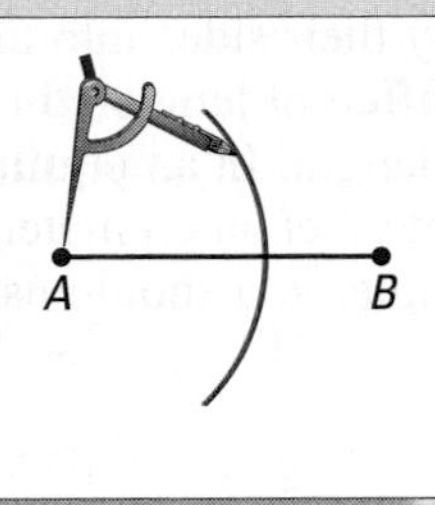

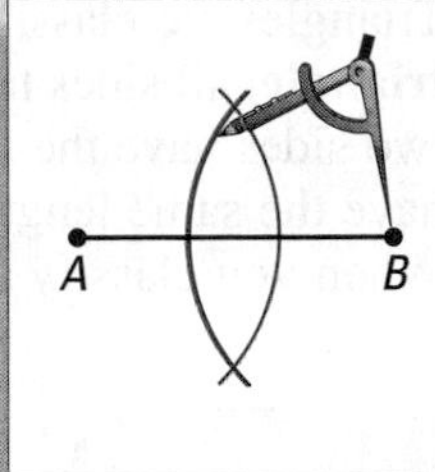

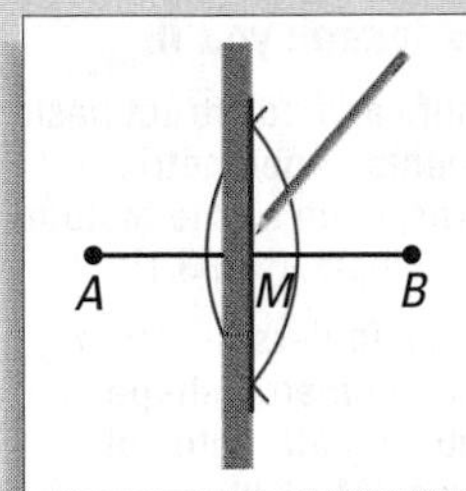

1. Place the compass point at A. Use a compass setting greater than half the length of $\overline{AB}$. Draw an arc.
2. Keep the same compass setting. Place the compass point at B. Draw an arc. It should intersect the other arc in two places.
3. Draw a segment through the points of intersection. This segment bisects $\overline{AB}$ at M, the midpoint of $\overline{AB}$.

CONSTRUCT A PERPENDICULAR TO A LINE You can use a compass and a straightedge to construct a line that is perpendicular to a given line and passes through a given point not on the line.

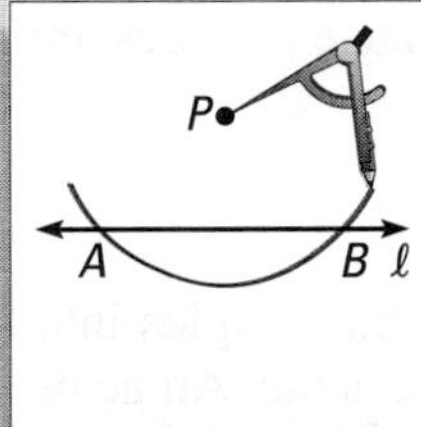

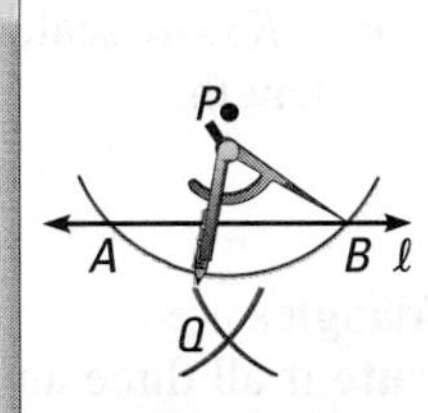

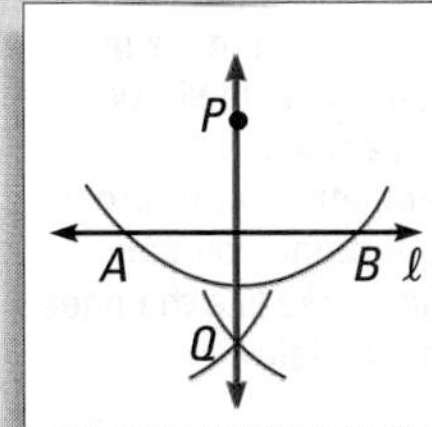

1. Place the compass point at P and draw an arc that intersects line ℓ twice. Label the intersections A and B.
2. Draw an arc with center A. Using the same radius, draw an arc with center B. Label the intersection of the arcs Q.
3. Use a straightedge to draw $\overleftrightarrow{PQ}$. $\overleftrightarrow{PQ}$ is perpendicular to ℓ.

Exercises Use a compass and straightedge.

1. Draw a segment that is about $3\frac{1}{2}$ inches long. Construct the perpendicular bisector of the segment. **Check drawings.**
2. Draw a line and a point not on the line. Construct a line through the point that is perpendicular to the line you drew. **Check drawings.**

Math Reasoning

Note that the construction for the line through a given point P and perpendicular to a given line begins by constructing a line segment $\overline{AB}$ in such a way that P will be one of the points used in the preceding construction for bisecting a segment. As a challenge, ask students to construct the line perpendicular to a given line through a given point P that is *on* the given line.

1 Plan

Pacing

Suggested Number of Days

Transitional: 1 day
Average: 1 day
Advanced: 1 day
Block Schedule: 0.5 block with 8.5

Teaching Resources

Blacklines
(See page 382B.)

Transparencies

- Warm-Up Exercises
- Teacher Time-Savers
- English/Spanish Problem Solving
- Answers

Technology

- Electronic Teacher Tools
- Test and Practice Generator

2 Teach

Math Reasoning

For Mathematical Background Notes on mathematical reasoning related to this lesson, please refer to pages 382E and 382F in this Teacher's Edition.

California Standards and Assessment

CA Standards: MG 3.0, MG 3.1

8.4 Triangles and Quadrilaterals

California Standards

In this lesson you'll:

- Identify and construct basic elements of geometric figures, such as the altitude of a triangle. (MG 3.1)
- Deepen understanding of plane geometric shapes by identifying attributes of figures. (MG 3.0)

Student Help

▶ STUDY TIP
Tick marks are used to show that the sides of a geometric figure are congruent, as in Example 1. To show that angles in a geometric figure are congruent, you can use marks like the ones shown below.

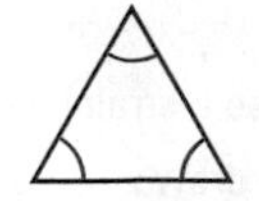

Goal 1 CLASSIFYING TRIANGLES

Triangles are classified by their sides into three categories. In a **scalene triangle**, all sides have different lengths. In an **isosceles triangle**, at least two sides have the same length. In an **equilateral triangle**, all three sides have the same length. Note that an equilateral triangle is also isosceles. When you classify a triangle, you should use the most specific name.

EXAMPLE 1 *Classifying Triangles*

Classify the triangle according to its sides.

a. C, 5, 5, A, 4, B

b.

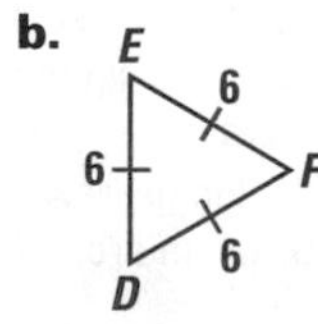

c.

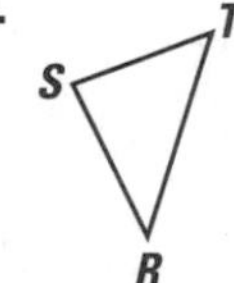

Solution

a. $\triangle ABC$ is isosceles because it has two sides of length 5.

b. $\triangle DEF$ is equilateral because each side has a length of 6.

c. $\triangle RST$ is scalene because no sides are marked as having the same length.

Triangles are classified by their angles into four categories. A triangle is **acute** if all three angles are acute. An acute triangle is **equiangular** if all three angles have the same measure. A triangle is **obtuse** if one of its angles is obtuse. A triangle is **right** if one of its angles is a right angle.

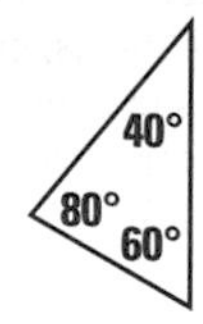

ACUTE TRIANGLE
All angles have measures less than 90°.

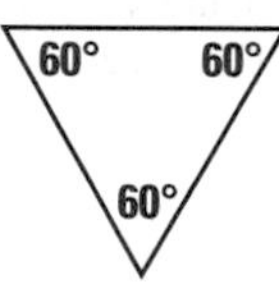

EQUIANGULAR TRIANGLE
Every angle measures 60°.

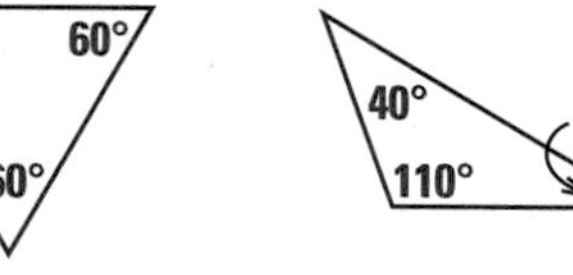

OBTUSE TRIANGLE
One angle has a measure greater than 90°.

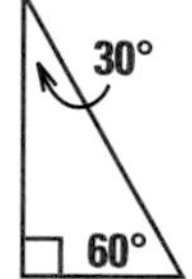

RIGHT TRIANGLE
One angle has a measure of 90°.

You may recall from a previous course that the sum of the angle measures of a triangle is 180°. In Exercises 21–23 on page 408, you will develop an argument for the truth of this statement.

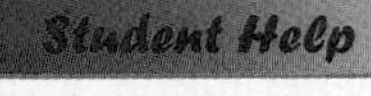

▶ MORE EXAMPLES

More examples are available at www.mcdougallittell.com

EXAMPLE 2 Finding an Angle Measure

Find $m\angle B$.

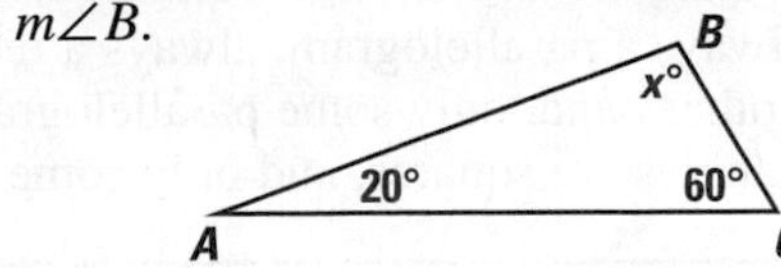

Solution

$m\angle A + m\angle B + m\angle C = 180°$	The sum of the angle measures of a triangle is 180°.
$20° + x° + 60° = 180°$	Substitute.
$80 + x = 180$	Simplify.
$x = 100$	Subtract 80 from each side.

ANSWER ▶ $m\angle B = 100°$

Goal 2 CLASSIFYING QUADRILATERALS

A **quadrilateral** is a closed figure with four sides that are line segments. The segments are joined at their endpoints. A quadrilateral is *convex* if for every pair of interior points, the segment joining them lies completely within the quadrilateral.

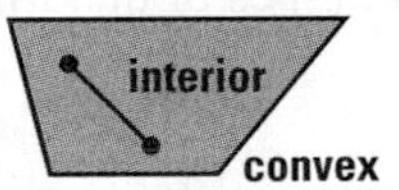

Seven special kinds of convex quadrilaterals are shown below.

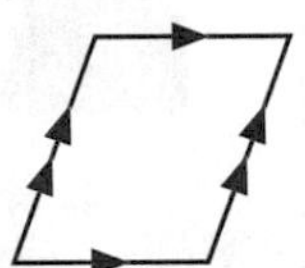

PARALLELOGRAM
Opposite sides are parallel.

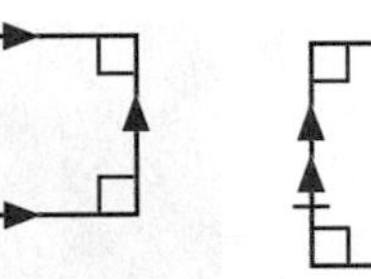

RECTANGLE
Parallelogram with four right angles

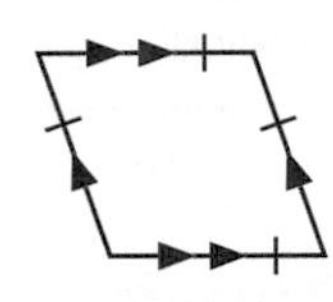

SQUARE
Rectangle with all sides congruent

RHOMBUS
Parallelogram with all sides congruent

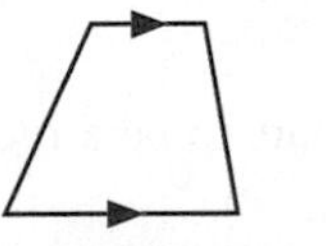

TRAPEZOID
Exactly one pair of parallel sides

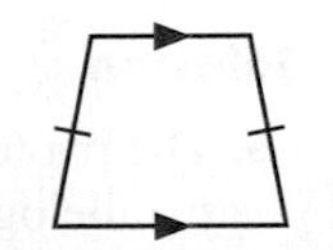

ISOSCELES TRAPEZOID
Trapezoid with nonparallel sides congruent

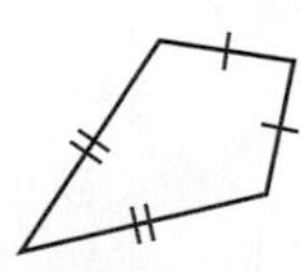

KITE
Two pairs of sides (not opposite sides) are congruent.

Extra Example 1

Classify each triangle according to its sides.

a. **b.**

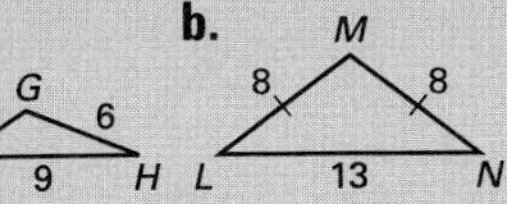

c.

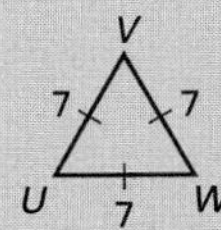

a. scalene b. isosceles c. equilateral

Extra Example 2

In triangle ABC, $m\angle A = 35°$ and $m\angle B = 70°$. Find $m\angle C$. **75°**

Math Reasoning

A set S is said to be convex if for every pair of points belonging to S, the line segment joining the two points also is in S. Therefore a convex quadrilateral is one whose interior region is a convex set.

Extra Example 3

Name all types of quadrilaterals that describe each shape.

a. 

b.

c. 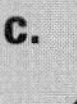 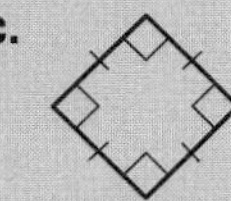

a. **rhombus, parallelogram**

b. **kite**

c. **square, rhombus, rectangle, parallelogram**

Teaching Tip

Students may have difficulty understanding the relationships between squares, rhombuses, rectangles, and parallelograms. Ask them to name a property of one of the figures. Then have them list the other quadrilaterals that have the same property.

Concept Check

Is a rectangle always a square or always a parallelogram? ***Sample answer:*** **A rectangle is always a parallelogram, but it is not always a square.**

The Venn diagram below shows how the different types of quadrilaterals are related, based on their definitions. For example, by definition, a square is always a parallelogram, always a rectangle, and always a rhombus. On the other hand, only some parallelograms are squares, only some rectangles are squares, and only some rhombuses are squares.

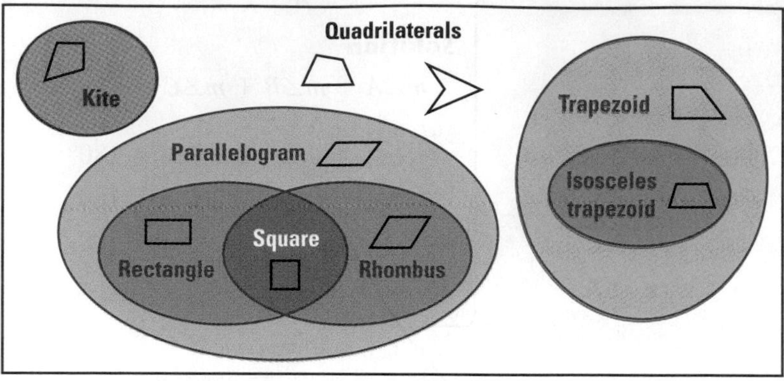

The white region of the Venn diagram contains all quadrilaterals that do not have any of the characteristics of the quadrilaterals in the shaded regions.

Student Help

▶ STUDY TIP
When you classify a quadrilateral, you should use the most descriptive name. For instance, although the rectangle in Example 3 is also a parallelogram, it is classified as a rectangle.

EXAMPLE 3 Classifying Quadrilaterals

GRAPHIC DESIGN You display a yearbook photo for the school in different ways. Name all types of quadrilaterals that describe each shape.

a. 

b. 

c. 

Solution

a. The photo appears to be a rectangle. This means that it is also a parallelogram.

b. The photo appears to be a square. This means that it is also a rectangle, a rhombus, and a parallelogram.

c. The photo appears to be an isosceles trapezoid. This means it is also a trapezoid.

8.4 Exercises

Guided Practice

Match the triangle with all the words that describe the triangle.

A. Isosceles **B.** Equiangular **C.** Scalene **D.** Obtuse

E. Equilateral **F.** Right **G.** Acute

1. C, G
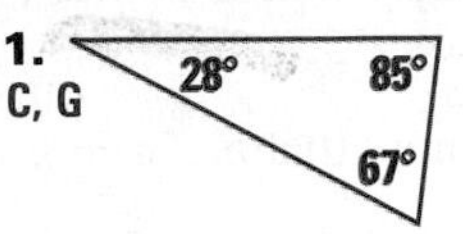

2. B, E, G
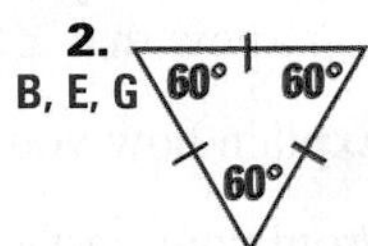

3. C, G
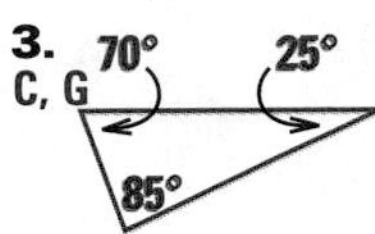

4. A, G
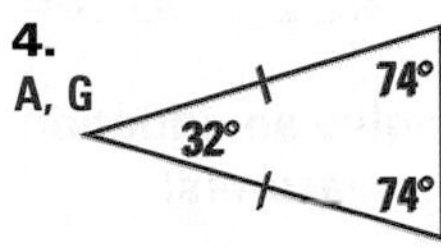

5. C, F
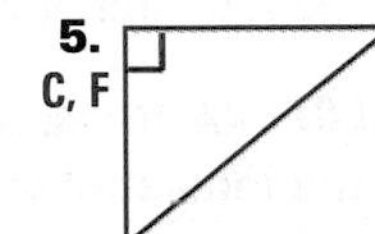

6. A, D
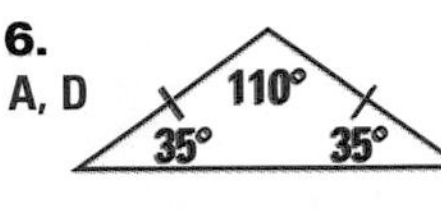

Name all the types of quadrilaterals that fit the given description.

7. Two pairs of sides are parallel. **parallelogram, rectangle, square, rhombus**

8. Exactly two sides are parallel. **trapezoid, isosceles trapezoid**

9. All four sides are congruent. **rhombus, square**

10. It has four right angles. **rectangle, square**

11. Two pairs of sides are congruent, but opposite sides are not congruent. **kite**

Practice and Problem Solving

Student Help

▸ MORE PRACTICE Extra practice to help you master skills is on page 704.

Classify the triangle by its angles and by its sides.

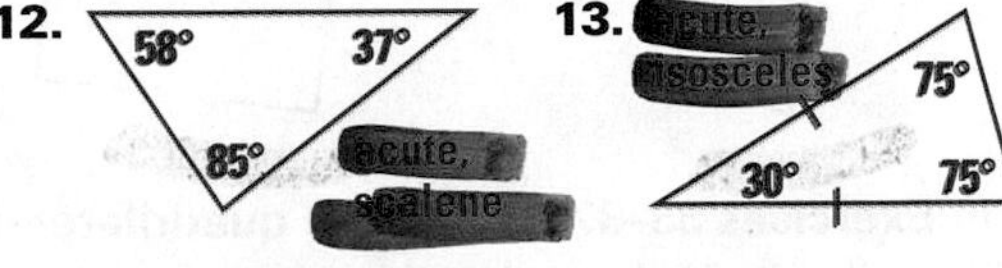

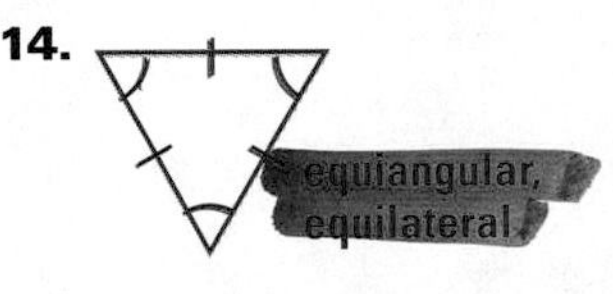

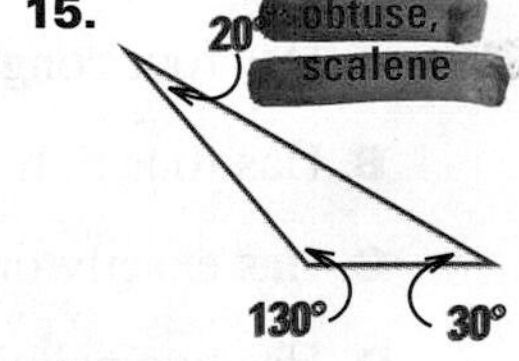

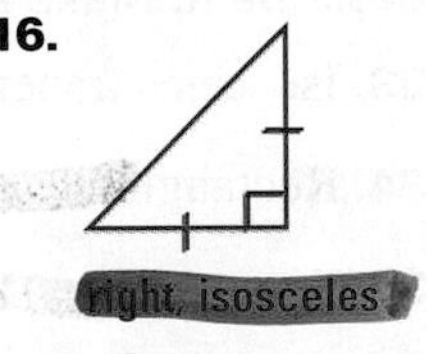

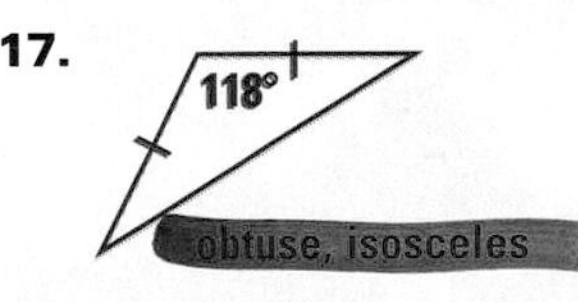

Sketch a triangle that is an example of the indicated type. Then label it with appropriate angle measures and congruence tick marks. 18–20. See margin.

18. Acute **19.** Right isosceles **20.** Obtuse scalene

3 Apply

Assignment Guide

TRANSITIONAL
Day 1: pp. 407–409 Exs. 12–20, 24–37, 47–48

AVERAGE
Day 1: pp. 407–409 Exs. 12–20, 24–37, 41–45, 47–48

ADVANCED
Day 1: pp. 407–409 Exs. 12–17, 21–32, 41–45, 46*, 47–48

BLOCK SCHEDULE
pp. 407–409 Exs. 12–20, 24–37, 41–45, 47–48 (with 8.5)

Extra Practice

- Student Edition, pp. 704–705
- Chapter 8 Resource Book, p. 33

Homework Check

To quickly check student understanding of key concepts, go over the following exercises:

Transitional: 12, 14, 20, 24, 28, 30
Average: 14, 16, 20, 26, 28, 30
Advanced: 14, 16, 22, 26, 28, 30

18. ***Sample answer:***

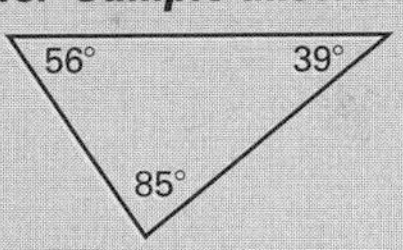

19.

45°
45°

20. ***Sample answer:***

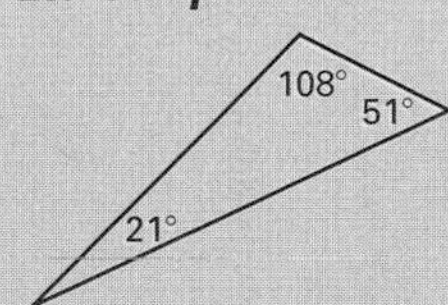

Math Reasoning

The Parallel Postulate states that given any line and a point not on that line, there is one and only one line through that point parallel to the given line. This is used in the proof that the sum of the angle measures of a triangle is 180°, when $\overleftrightarrow{CD}$ is drawn through C parallel to $\overleftrightarrow{AB}$.

Problem Solving

Exercises 43–45

Have students refer to the Venn diagram on page 406.

21. $\angle 1 \cong \angle 4$ **and** $\angle 2 \cong \angle 6$ **since they are corresponding angles and their transversals intersect parallel line segments.** $\angle 3 \cong \angle 5$ **since they are vertical angles.**

22. Together, $\angle 4$, $\angle 5$ **and** $\angle 6$ **form a straight angle. A straight angle measures 180°.**

23. From Exercise 21 we know that $m\angle 1 = m\angle 4$, $m\angle 2 = m\angle 6$, **and** $m\angle 3 = m\angle 5$. **By substitution,** $m\angle 1 + m\angle 2 + m\angle 3 = 180°$.

MATHEMATICAL REASONING In Exercises 21–23, use the diagram.

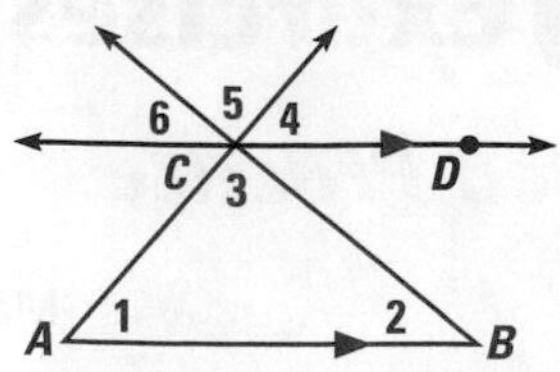

In the diagram, $\overleftrightarrow{CD}$ has been drawn through point C parallel to $\overline{AB}$. Sides $\overline{AC}$ and $\overline{BC}$ of $\triangle ABC$ have been extended. You can use the diagram to prove that the sum of the angle measures of a triangle is 180°.

21. Explain how you know that $\angle 1 \cong \angle 4$ and $\angle 2 \cong \angle 6$. Explain how you know that $\angle 3 \cong \angle 5$. See margin.

22. Explain how you know that $m\angle 4 + m\angle 5 + m\angle 6 = 180°$. See margin.

23. From your answers to Exercises 21 and 22, explain how you can conclude that $m\angle 1 + m\angle 2 + m\angle 3 = 180°$. See margin.

ALGEBRA Write and solve an equation to find the value of *x*. Then find the indicated angle measure(s).

24. Find $m\angle E$.

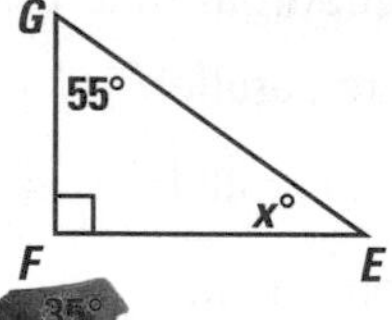

35°

25. Find $m\angle N$ and $m\angle P$.

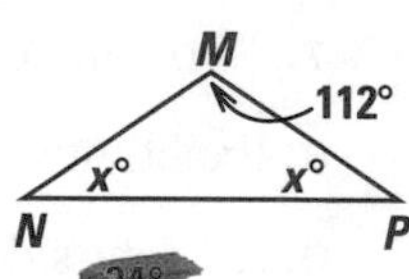

34°

26. Find $m\angle R$, $m\angle S$, and $m\angle T$.

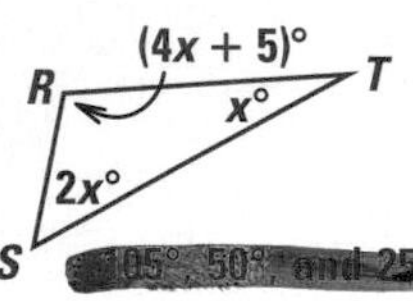

105°, 50°, and 25°

Use the given markings to classify the quadrilateral.

27.

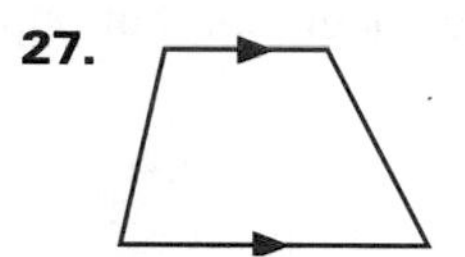

trapezoid

28.

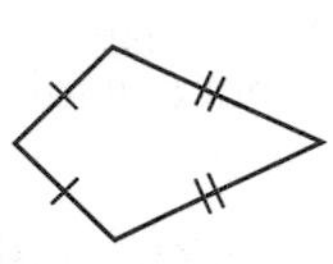

kite

29.

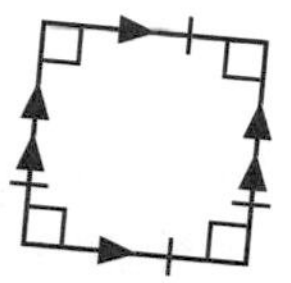

square

30.

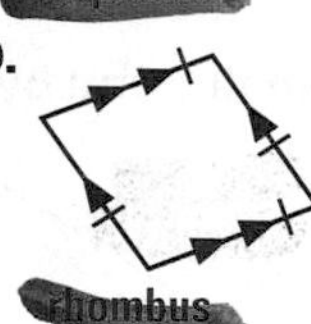

rhombus

31.

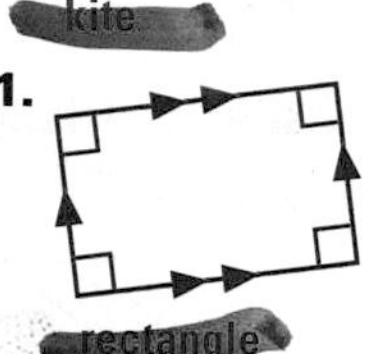

rectangle

32.

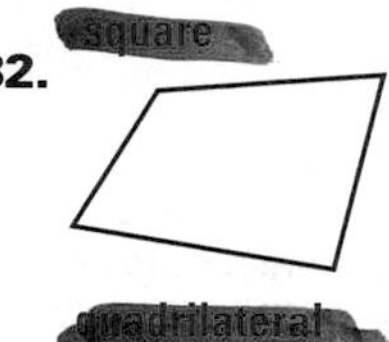

quadrilateral

In Exercises 33–37, match the quadrilateral with all the statements that describe it. Make a sketch to support your answer.

33. Isosceles trapezoid C, E

34. Rectangle B, D

35. Square A, B, D

36. Rhombus A, D

37. Trapezoid C

A. Has four congruent sides.

B. Has four right angles.

C. Has exactly one pair of parallel sides.

D. Has two pairs of parallel sides.

E. Has only one pair of congruent sides.

STRUCTURAL DESIGN **In Exercises 38–40, refer to the figures below. The figures are made with popsicle sticks and fasteners.**

38. Is the triangle rigid? In other words, can you adjust the sticks to form a different triangular shape? Yes; No

39. Is the rectangle rigid? In other words, can you adjust the sticks to form a different type of quadrilateral? No; Yes

40. Triangles are often used in the design of structures like the tandem bicycle shown. Why do you think triangles appear in the frame of a bicycle? Triangles are used because they are rigid.

MATHEMATICAL REASONING **In Exercises 41–45, complete the statement with *always, sometimes,* or *never*. Explain your reasoning.**

41. An isosceles triangle is __?__ an acute triangle. sometimes

42. An obtuse triangle __?__ has a right angle. never

43. A quadrilateral is __?__ a parallelogram. sometimes

44. A rectangle is __?__ a rhombus. sometimes

45. A rhombus is __?__ a square. sometimes

46. CHALLENGE Use the diagram at the right. Find the value of x. (*Hint*: Notice that $\overline{BD}$ is a transversal that intersects two parallel line segments.) 118

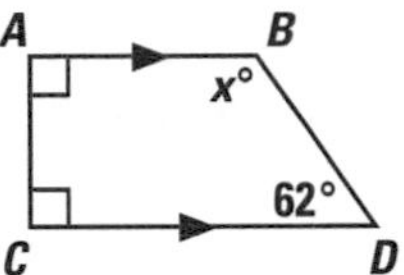

Multiple-Choice Practice

47. An obtuse triangle can have which of the following measures? 

Ⓐ 60°, 60°, 60° Ⓑ 120°, 90°, 60°

Ⓒ 120°, 60°, 30° Ⓓ 120°, 50°, 10°

48. Which statement is *true*? 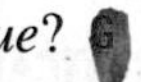

Ⓕ An obtuse triangle must have two obtuse angles.

Ⓖ An equiangular triangle must have three acute angles.

Ⓗ An equilateral triangle can have one obtuse angle.

Ⓙ An isosceles triangle must have one obtuse angle.

4 Assess

Assessment Resources

- Assessment Book (Formal Assessment and Alternative Assessment)
- Test and Practice Generator

Mini-Quiz

1. Classify the triangle according to its sides and angles.

   a. 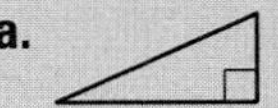 **b.** 

   a. scalene right triangle
   b. acute isosceles triangle

2. Identify the quadrilateral from its appearance. Use the name that *best* describes the quadrilateral.

   a. 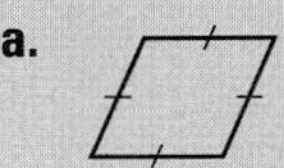 **b.** 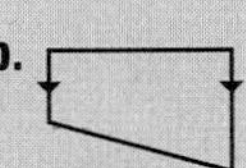

   a. rhombus
   b. trapezoid

3. Complete the statement with *always*, *sometimes*, or *never*.

   a. A kite is __?__ a rhombus. **never**

   b. A parallelogram is __?__ a square. **sometimes**

Math Reasoning

The triangle in Exercise 38 is rigid because of the Side-Side-Side congruence property. Any other triangle with the same side lengths would have to be congruent to the given triangle. On the other hand, the angles of the parallelogram can be changed without changing the lengths of the sides, because two parallelograms with corresponding sides of equal lengths need *not* be congruent.

Math Reasoning

By constructing all three altitudes in a variety of triangles, students will discover that the altitudes of a triangle always meet in a single point (called the orthocenter of the triangle). Students can also make such discoveries by experimenting with computer software such as The Geometer's Sketchpad. However experience with manual constructions using compass and straightedge is important in instilling geometric skills and understanding.

CONSTRUCTION Altitude of a Triangle

Student Help

▶ SKILLS REVIEW
For help with using a compass and straightedge, see page 685.

A perpendicular segment from a vertex of a triangle to the line containing the side opposite the vertex is called an **altitude of a triangle**. An altitude can lie inside, on, or outside a triangle, as shown in red in the triangles at the right.

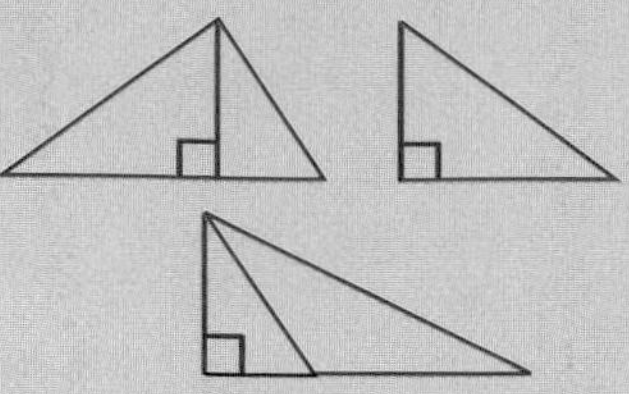

You can use a compass and a straightedge to construct an altitude of a triangle. The construction is based on the one you learned for constructing a perpendicular to a line from a point not on the line (see page 403).

To construct an altitude from point C to side $\overline{AB}$ of $\triangle ABC$ shown below, begin by extending side $\overline{AB}$ through points A and B to form $\overleftrightarrow{AB}$. Then follow the steps below.

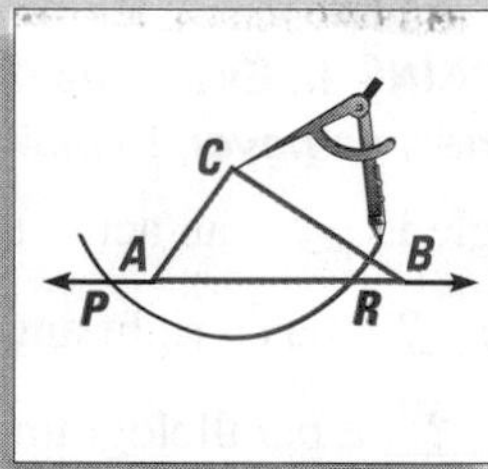

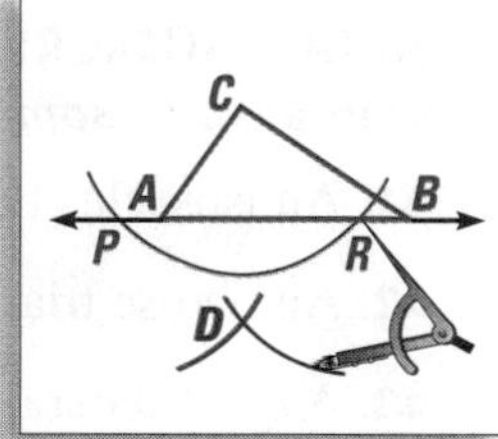

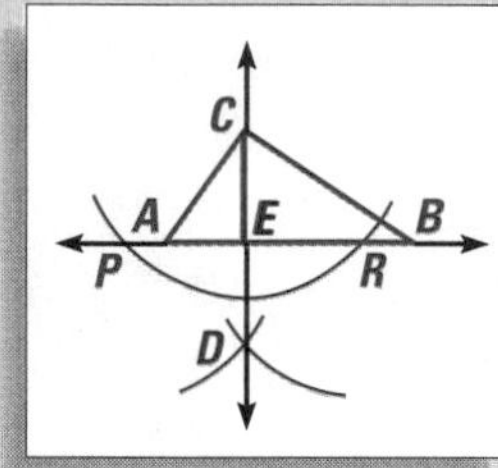

1. Place the compass point at C and draw an arc that intersects $\overleftrightarrow{AB}$ twice. Label the intersections P and R.
2. Draw an arc with center P. Using the same radius, draw an arc with center R. Label the intersection of the arcs D.
3. Use a straightedge to draw $\overleftrightarrow{CD}$. Label the intersection of $\overleftrightarrow{AB}$ and $\overleftrightarrow{CD}$ point E. $\overline{CE}$ is an altitude of $\triangle ABC$.

Exercises Use a compass and straightedge.

1. Draw a triangle. Construct an altitude from one of the vertices. **Check drawings.**
2. Draw a triangle whose sides are about 8 centimeters, 9 centimeters, and 10 centimeters long. Then construct an altitude from each vertex. What do you notice about the three altitudes? **Check drawings; all altitudes intersect in a point.**
3. Draw an obtuse triangle. Label the vertices. Determine which vertices, if any, have corresponding altitudes that lie *outside* the triangle. Construct one of these altitudes. **See margin.**

3. Check drawings. The altitudes from the vertices of the two acute angles of the triangle lie outside the triangle.

4. **MATHEMATICAL REASONING** You want to construct an altitude from each vertex to the opposite side in $\triangle ABC$, shown at the right. How many altitudes do you actually have to construct? Explain.
1, because $\overline{AC}$ is an altitude to $\overline{BC}$ and $\overline{BC}$ is an altitude to $\overline{AC}$.

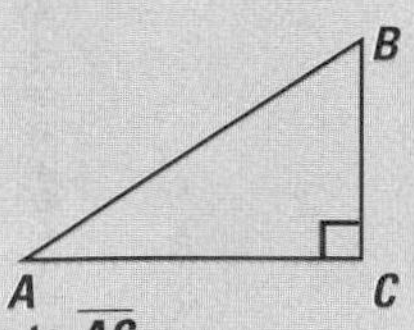

Chapter 8 Mid-Chapter Test

Take this test as you would take a test in class. The answers to the exercises are given in the back of the book.

In Exercises 1–4, use the cube at the right.

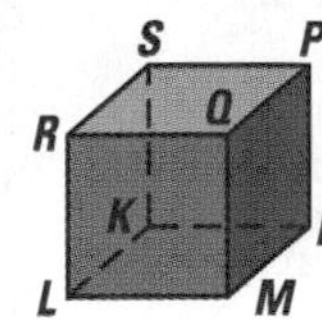

1. Name another point that lies in the same plane as M, N, and P. ***Q***

2. Name two lines that are parallel to $\overline{SR}$. ***$\overleftrightarrow{PQ}$ and $\overleftrightarrow{KL}$***

3. Name two lines that intersect. ***Sample answer: $\overrightarrow{RS}$ and $\overrightarrow{RL}$***

4. Name the point of intersection of $\overline{SP}$ and $\overline{PQ}$. ***P***

In Exercises 5–10, use the photograph at the right.

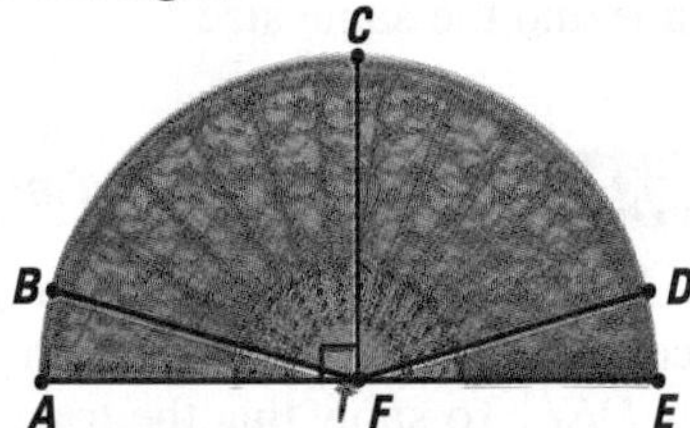

5. Name the right angles. ***$\angle AFC$, $\angle CFE$***

6. Name the acute angles.
$\angle AFB$, $\angle BFC$, $\angle CFD$ and $\angle DFE$

7. Name the obtuse angles.
$\angle AFD$, $\angle BFD$ and $\angle BFE$

8. Name the straight angle. ***$\angle AFE$***

9. Name two complementary angles. ***$\angle AFB$ and $\angle CFB$ or $\angle CFD$ and $\angle DFE$***

10. Name two supplementary angles. ***$\angle AFB$ and $\angle BFE$ or $\angle AFD$ and $\angle DFE$ or $\angle AFC$ and $\angle CFE$***

In Exercises 11–14, use the figure shown. For Exercises 11–13, complete the sentences with the words *vertical* or *corresponding*.

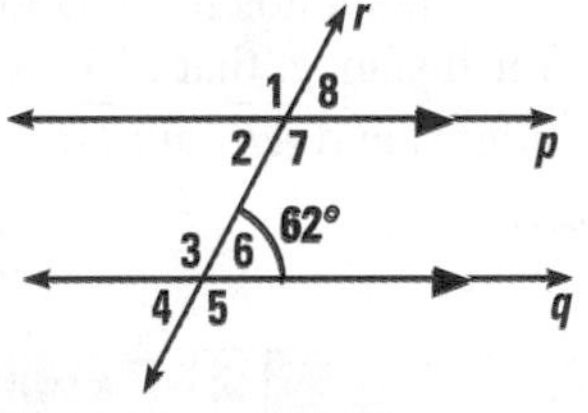

11. $\angle 1$ and $\angle 7$ are __?__ angles. ***vertical***

12. $\angle 8$ and $\angle 6$ are __?__ angles. ***corresponding***

13. $\angle 2$ and $\angle 4$ are __?__ angles. ***corresponding***

14. Find the measure of each angle.

14. $m\angle 1 = m\angle 7 = m\angle 3 = m\angle 5 = 118°$; $m\angle 2 = m\angle 8 = m\angle 4 = m\angle 6 = 62°$

Classify the triangle by its angles and by its sides.

15. 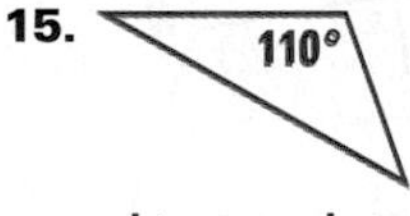

obtuse, scalene

16. 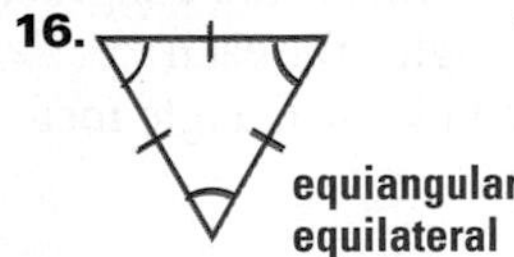
equiangular, equilateral

17. 
right, scalene

18. 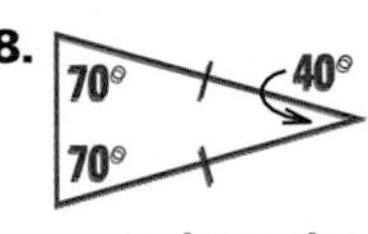

acute, isosceles

MATHEMATICAL REASONING In Exercises 19–22, complete the statement using *sometimes, always,* or *never*.

19. A rhombus is __?__ a rectangle. ***sometimes***

20. A square is __?__ a trapezoid. ***never***

21. A parallelogram is __?__ a quadrilateral. ***always***

22. A square is __?__ a rhombus. ***always***

23. $\angle 1$ and $\angle 2$ are vertical angles. If $m\angle 1 = (x + 10)°$ and $m\angle 2 = 2x°$, find the value of x. ***10***

Additional Resources

A Mid-Chapter Test and a Mid-Chapter Partner Quiz are available in the *Assessment Book*, pp. 110–111 and 245.

1 Plan

Pacing

Suggested Number of Days

Transitional: 1 day
Average: 1 day
Advanced: 1 day
Block Schedule: 0.5 block with 8.4

Teaching Resources

(See page 382B.)

Transparencies

- Warm-Up Exercises
- Teacher Time-Savers
- English/Spanish Problem Solving
- Answers

Technology

- Electronic Teacher Tools
- Test and Practice Generator

2 Teach

For Mathematical Background Notes on mathematical reasoning related to this lesson, please refer to pages 382E and 382F in this Teacher's Edition.

California Standards and Assessment

CA Standard: MG 3.4

CA Key Concepts Book: pp. S87–S92

8.5 Polygons and Congruence

California Standards

In this lesson you'll:

- Demonstrate an understanding of the conditions that indicate that two geometric figures are congruent. (MG 3.4)
- Demonstrate an understanding of what congruence means about the relationships between the sides and the angles of two congruent figures. (MG 3.4)

Student Help

STUDY TIP
There is more than one way to state a congruence. For instance, in Example 1 you can also write $\triangle BCA \cong \triangle EFD$, $\triangle CAB \cong \triangle FDE$, $\triangle CBA \cong \triangle FED$, $\triangle BAC \cong \triangle EDF$, or $\triangle ACB \cong \triangle DFE$.

Goal 1 RECOGNIZING CONGRUENT POLYGONS

A **polygon** is a closed figure whose sides are line segments in the same plane that are joined at their endpoints. The number of sides determines the name of the polygon. The point where two sides meet is called a **vertex** of the polygon. The plural of vertex is *vertices*. Polygons are named by listing their vertices in order, such as triangle *ABC* or quadrilateral *LMNQ* in the examples below.

Two polygons are **congruent** if their *corresponding sides* and their *corresponding angles* are congruent. Congruent polygons are the same shape and the same size.

EXAMPLE 1 Naming Congruent Polygons

All three sides and all three angles of $\triangle ABC$ are congruent to the corresponding sides and angles of $\triangle DEF$. To show that the triangles are congruent, you can write $\triangle ABC \cong \triangle DEF$.

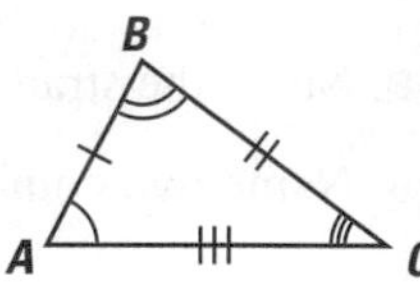

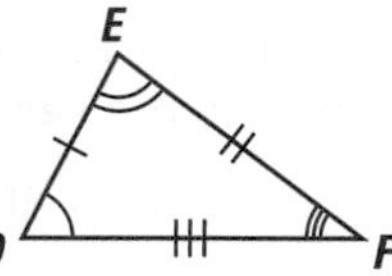

In a congruence statement, the corresponding vertices of the triangles are written in the same order to indicate which angles and sides are corresponding. In the statement $\triangle ABC \cong \triangle DEF$, *A* corresponds to *D*, *B* to *E*, and *C* to *F*. This means, for instance, that $\angle A$ and $\angle D$ are corresponding angles and $\overline{AB}$ and $\overline{DE}$ are corresponding sides.

EXAMPLE 2 Finding Angle Measures

Quadrilaterals *LMNQ* and *RSTU* are congruent. List the corresponding angles for each quadrilateral to find the unknown angle measures.

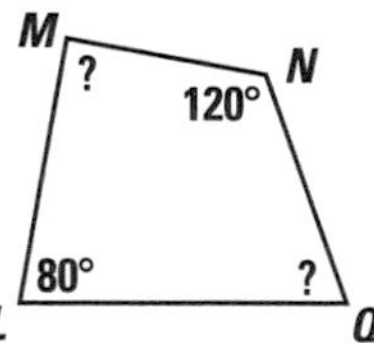

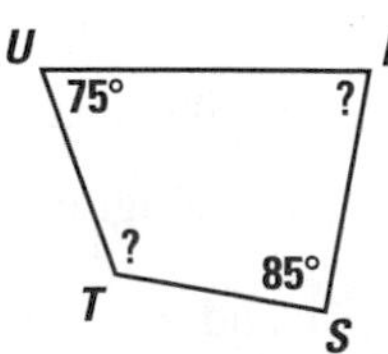

Solution

$\angle L \cong \angle R$, so $m\angle R = m\angle L = 80°$.

$\angle M \cong \angle S$, so $m\angle M = m\angle S = 85°$.

$\angle N \cong \angle T$, so $m\angle T = m\angle N = 120°$.

$\angle Q \cong \angle U$, so $m\angle Q = m\angle U = 75°$.

To show that two polygons are congruent, you must show that all of their corresponding sides and corresponding angles are congruent.

In a later geometry course, you will learn the *side-angle-side* (SAS) congruence postulate, which states that two *triangles* are congruent if two sides and the angle included between the sides of one triangle are congruent to two sides and the angle included between the sides of the second triangle. Another postulate, the *side-side-side* (SSS) congruence postulate, states that two triangles are congruent if all three sides of one triangle are congruent to all three sides of the other.

EXAMPLE 3 Showing that Two Triangles are Congruent

You draw $\triangle PQR$ with $\overline{PQ} \cong \overline{RQ}$. You construct a segment that bisects $\angle PQR$ to form $\triangle PQM$ and $\triangle RQM$, as shown. Show that $\triangle PQM \cong \triangle RQM$.

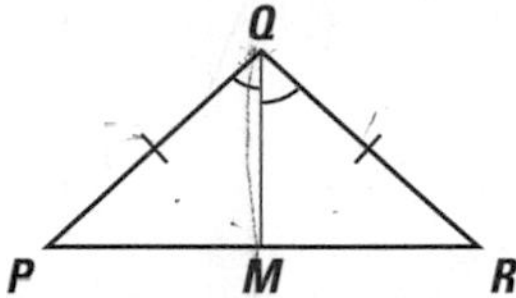

Solution

You are given that $\overline{PQ} \cong \overline{RQ}$. Also, $\angle PQM \cong \angle RQM$ because $\overline{QM}$ bisects $\angle PQR$. And because the triangles share side $\overline{QM}$, you can write $\overline{QM} \cong \overline{QM}$. Thus, two sides and an included angle of $\triangle PQM$ are congruent to two sides and an included angle of $\triangle RQM$. So, $\triangle PQM \cong \triangle RQM$ by the SAS congruence postulate.

Goal 2 IDENTIFYING REGULAR POLYGONS

A polygon is **regular** if all of its sides have the same length and all of its angles have the same measure. Four examples are shown below.

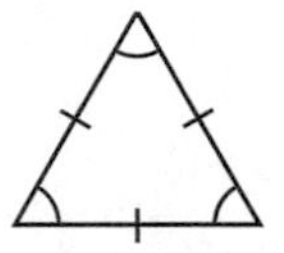

REGULAR TRIANGLE

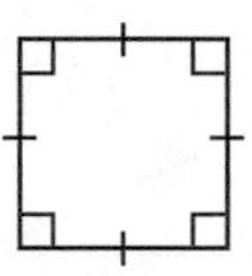

REGULAR QUADRILATERAL

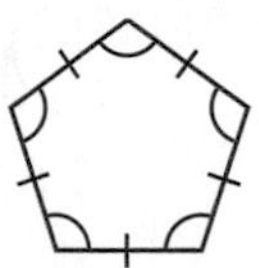

REGULAR PENTAGON

REGULAR HEXAGON

EXAMPLE 4 Using Measures in Polygons

In a regular pentagon, all sides have the same length, and all angles have the same measure. The perimeter of the regular pentagon shown is $5 \cdot 15 = 75$ feet. The sum of the angle measures is $5 \cdot 108° = 540°$.

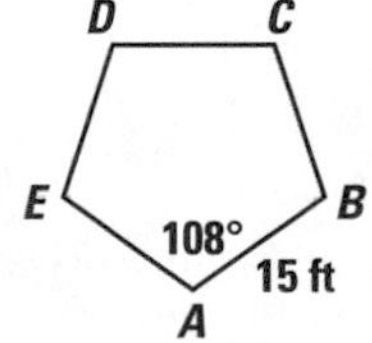

Student Help

▶ **MORE EXAMPLES**

More examples are available at www.mcdougallittell.com

Extra Example 1

Write a congruence statement for the following triangles.

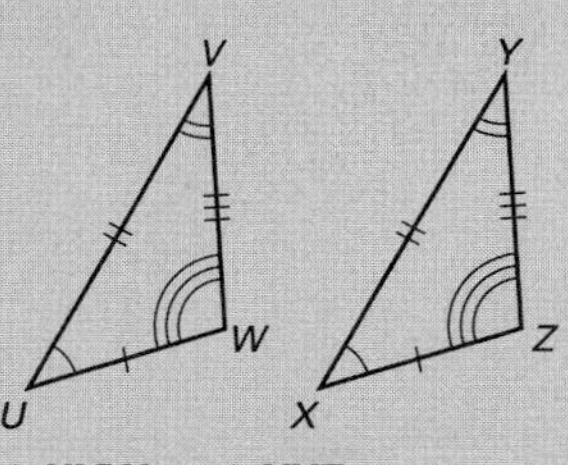

$\triangle UVW \cong \triangle XYZ$

Extra Example 2

Quadrilaterals *ABCD* and *EFGH* are congruent. List the corresponding angles for each quadrilateral to find the unknown angle measures.

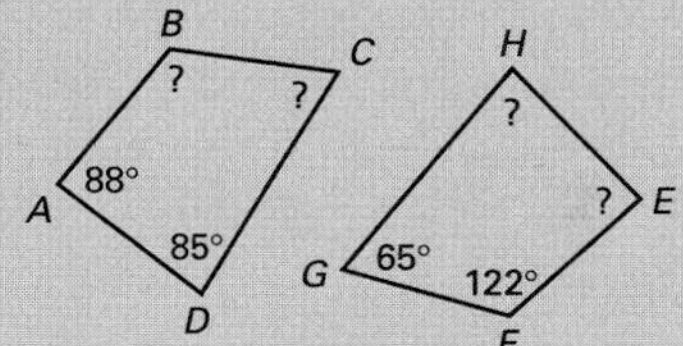

$\angle B \cong \angle F$, $\angle C \cong \angle G$, $\angle D \cong \angle H$, $\angle A \cong \angle E$; $m\angle B = 122°$, $m\angle C = 65°$, $m\angle H = 85°$, $m\angle E = 88°$

Extra Example 3

Suppose you draw a triangle so that $\overline{BD}$ both bisects the base and is perpendicular to it. Show that $\triangle ABD \cong \triangle CBD$.

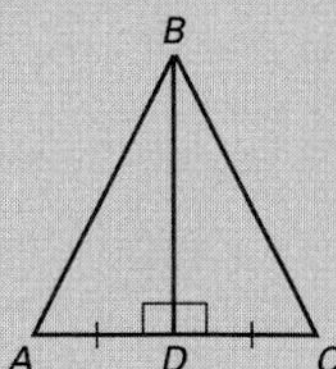

$\overline{AD} \cong \overline{CD}$ is given. $\angle BDA \cong \angle BDC$ since both are right angles. The triangles share a side, so $\overline{BD} \cong \overline{BD}$. So $\triangle ABD \cong \triangle CBD$ by the SAS congruence postulate.

Extra Example 4

The perimeter of a regular hexagon is 72 mm and the sum of its angle measures is 720°. What is the length of each side and the measure of each angle? **12 mm; 120°**

Extra Example 5

Suppose you sketch one diagonal in a square to form $\triangle FGH$ and $\triangle FJH$ as shown. Show that $\triangle FGH \cong \triangle FJH$.

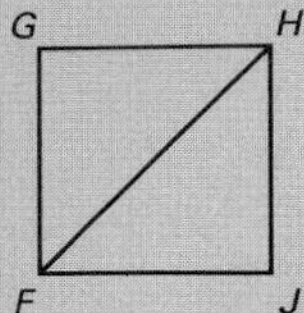

$\overline{FG} \cong \overline{FJ}$ and $\overline{GH} \cong \overline{JH}$ since all sides are congruent in a square. $\angle FGH \cong \angle FJH$ since both are right angles. So $\triangle FGH \cong \triangle FJH$ by the SAS congruence postulate.

Math Reasoning

As students experiment by drawing diagonals, they might discover that in a convex polygon with n sides, the number of diagonals added to the number of sides gives the triangular number $\frac{n(n-1)}{2}$. It is interesting to relate this to the formula $1 + 2 + 3 + \ldots + (n-1) = \frac{n(n-1)}{2}$.
(In drawing diagonals and sides, we can begin by connecting a vertex to the other $n-1$ vertices, then go to another vertex and connect that to the remaining $n-2$ vertices, and so on.)

Concept Check

Is a rectangle a regular polygon? ***Sample answer:*** **No. It has all angles of equal measure but it does not have equal side lengths.**

Student Help

STUDY TIP
The number of diagonals in a polygon depends on the number of sides. A rectangle has 2 diagonals. A pentagon has 5 diagonals.

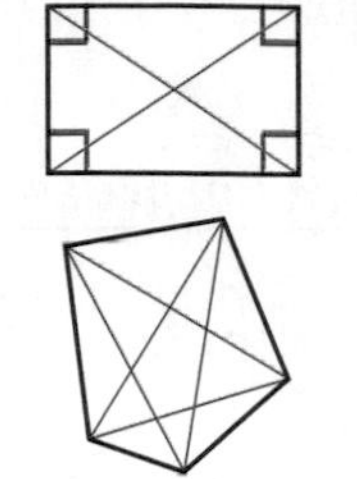

A **diagonal** of a polygon is a segment joining two nonconsecutive vertices.

EXAMPLE 5 Using Diagonals in a Polygon

You sketch two diagonals in a regular hexagon to form $\triangle ABC$ and $\triangle DEF$ as shown. Show that $\triangle ABC \cong \triangle DEF$.

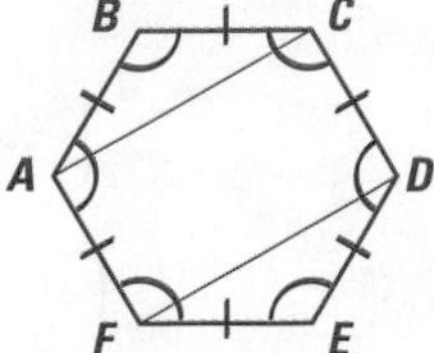

Solution

Two sides of each triangle are sides of a regular hexagon, so you know that $\overline{AB} \cong \overline{DE}$ and $\overline{BC} \cong \overline{EF}$. The angle included between sides $\overline{AB}$ and $\overline{BC}$ and the angle included between sides $\overline{DE}$ and $\overline{EF}$ are congruent because they are the angles of a regular hexagon.

Thus, two sides and an included angle of $\triangle ABC$ are congruent to two sides and an included angle of $\triangle DEF$. You can conclude that $\triangle ABC \cong \triangle DEF$ by the SAS congruence postulate.

8.5 Exercises

Guided Practice

In Exercises 1 and 2, complete the congruence statement. Then list the corresponding angles and the corresponding sides of each pair of congruent polygons.

1. $\triangle MNP \cong$ __?__

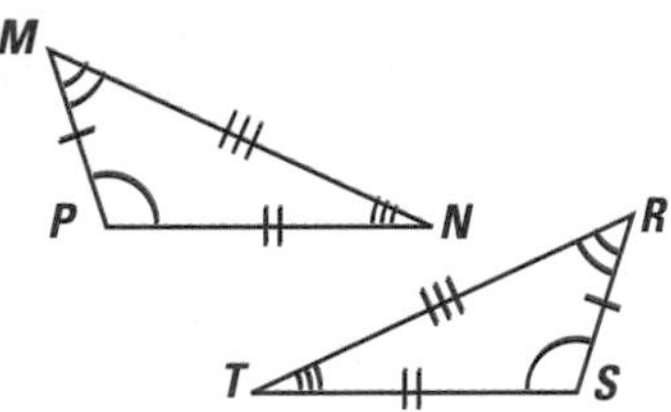

2. Quadrilateral $ABCD \cong$ __?__

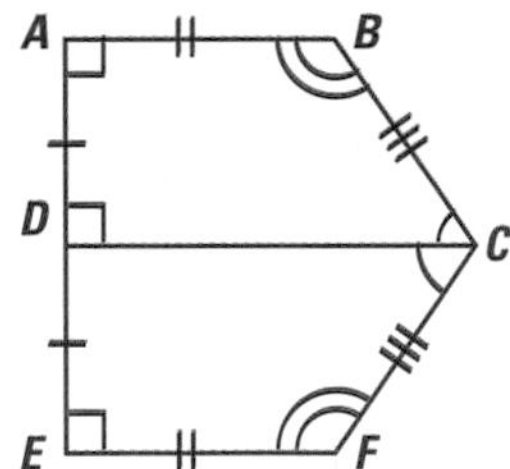

3. In Exercise 1, $m\angle M = 56°$ and $m\angle N = 29°$. Find $m\angle P$ and the measures of the angles of the second triangle in Exercise 1. **95°; $m\angle R = 56°$, $m\angle T = 29°$, $m\angle S = 95°$**

4. What is another name for a regular quadrilateral? What is the sum of the angle measures of a regular quadrilateral? **square; 360°**

5. MATHEMATICAL REASONING Draw a rectangle and mark the congruent sides and right angles. Label the vertices. Then draw a diagonal. Explain how you know that the two triangles formed are congruent. **See margin.**

1. $\triangle RTS$; $\angle M \cong \angle R$, $\angle N \cong \angle T$ and $\angle P \cong \angle S$, $\overline{MN} \cong \overline{RT}$, $\overline{MP} \cong \overline{RS}$ and $\overline{NP} \cong \overline{TS}$

2. Quadrilateral $EFCD$; $\angle A \cong \angle E$, $\angle B \cong \angle F$, $\angle BCD \cong \angle FCD$, $\angle ADC \cong \angle EDC$, $\overline{AD} \cong \overline{ED}$, $\overline{AB} \cong \overline{EF}$, $\overline{BC} \cong \overline{FC}$, $\overline{DC} \cong \overline{DC}$

5. Check drawings. The two triangles formed are congruent because of SSS or SAS. (Either is correct.)

Practice and Problem Solving

Student Help

▶MORE PRACTICE Extra practice to help you master skills is on page 705.

Determine whether the figures are congruent. If they are, write a congruence statement. Then list the corresponding angles and the corresponding sides.

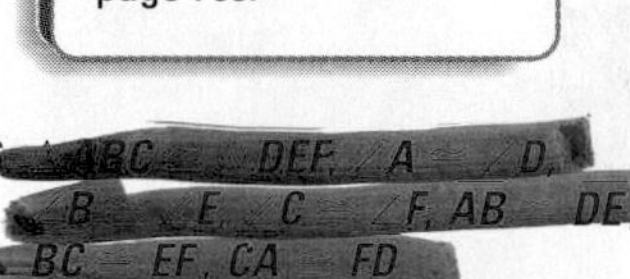

6.

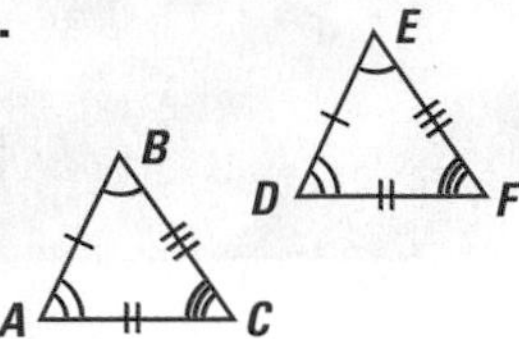

7.

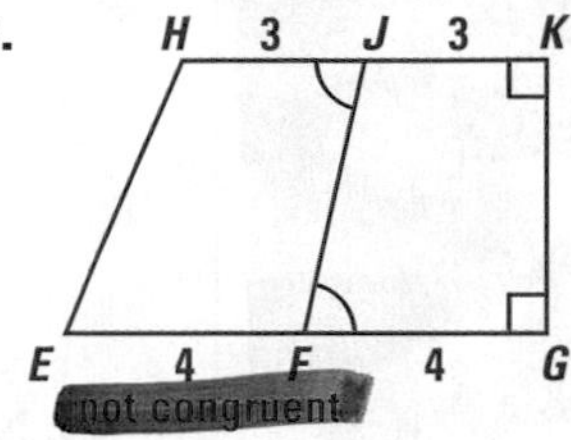

not congruent

8. G J 8 K; 8, 10, 10, 6; F 6 H; M

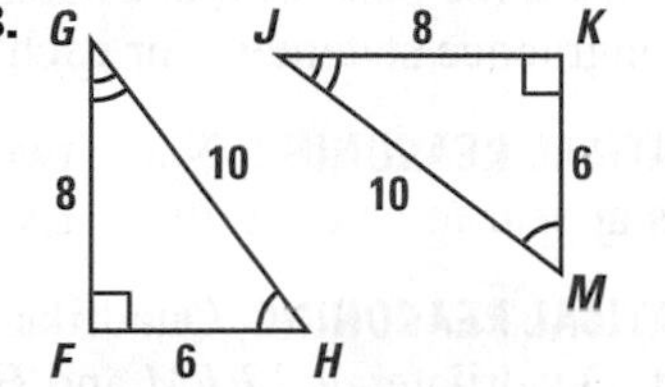

9.

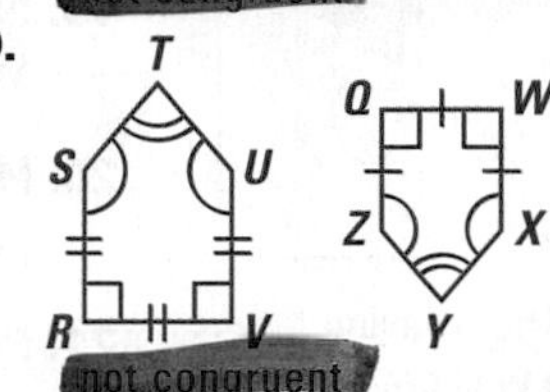

not congruent

In Exercises 10–13, find the indicated angle measures and side lengths.

10. $\triangle ABC \cong \triangle FED$ $m\angle B = 60°$, $m\angle D = 55°$, $m\angle F = 65°$

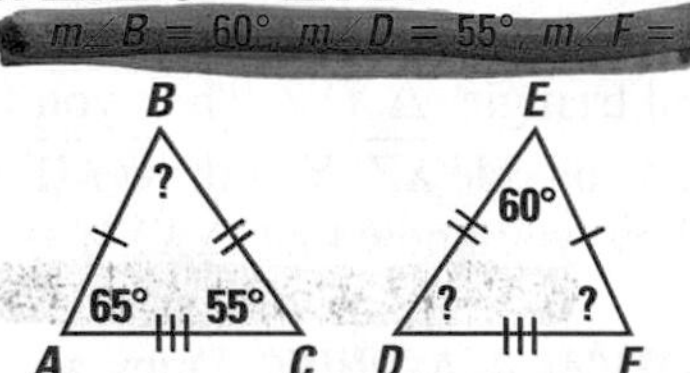

11. Figure $EHJK \cong$ Figure $MNPQ$ $m\angle K = 102°$, $m\angle M = 92°$, $PN = 8$

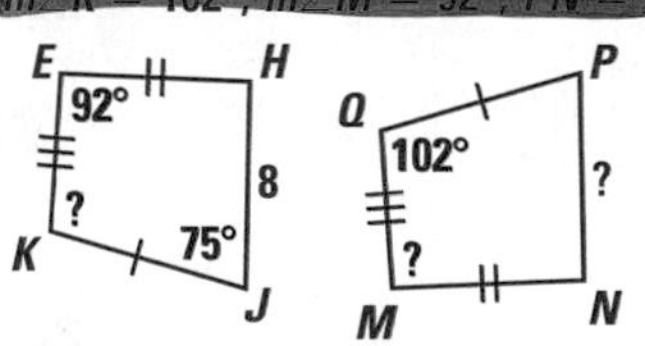

12. $\triangle RST \cong \triangle VXW$ $m\angle S = 90°$, $ST = 12$ and $RT = 13$

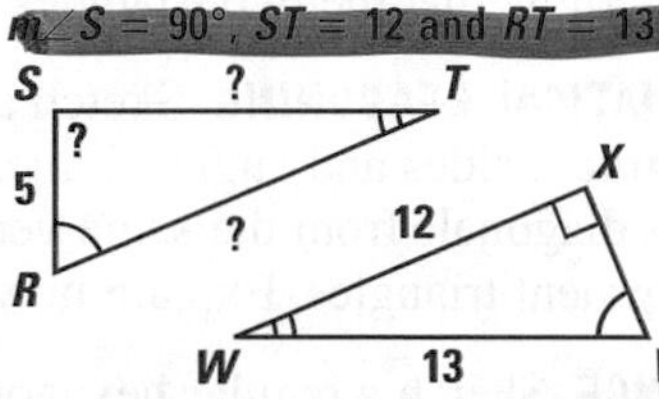

13. $\triangle ABC \cong \triangle CDA$ $m\angle D = 84°$, $AD = 13$ and $AB = 9$

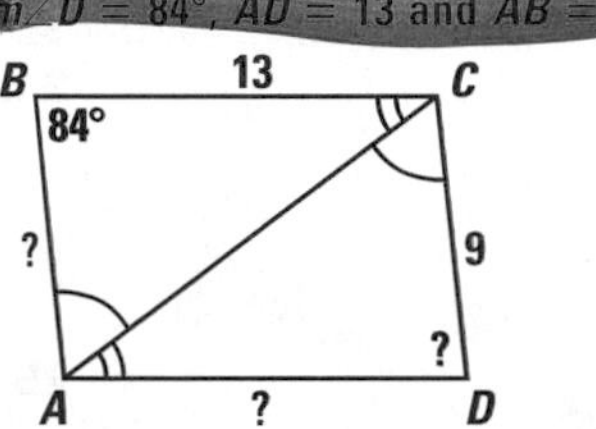

14. MATHEMATICAL REASONING Sketch two polygons whose corresponding sides are congruent but whose corresponding angles are *not* congruent. Then sketch two polygons whose angles are congruent but whose side lengths are *not* congruent. See margin.

In Exercises 15–18, use the figure shown.

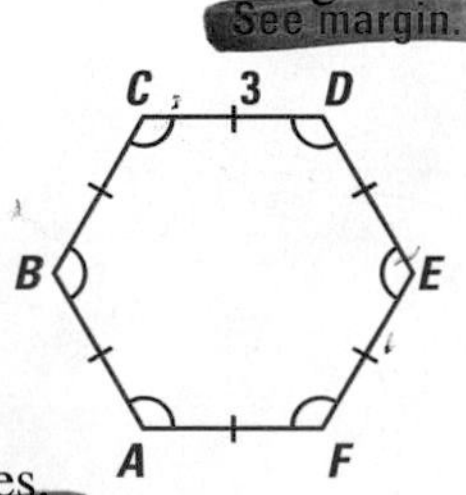

15. What kind of polygon is the figure? Regular hexagon

16. $m\angle A = 120°$. Find $m\angle C$. 120°

17. Find the perimeter of the figure. 18

18. Find the sum of the figure's angle measures. 720°

3 Apply

Assignment Guide

TRANSITIONAL
Day 1: pp. 415–416 Exs. 6–7, 10–11, 15–20, 23, 26–27

AVERAGE
Day 1: pp. 415–416 Exs. 6–18, 22–23, 26–27

ADVANCED
Day 1: pp. 415–416 Exs. 6–18, 23–24, 25*, 26–27

BLOCK SCHEDULE
pp. 415–416 Exs. 6–18, 22–23, 26–27 (with 8.4)

Extra Practice

- Student Edition, pp. 704–705
- Chapter 8 Resource Book, p. 42

Homework Check

To quickly check student understanding of key concepts, go over the following exercises:

Transitional: 8, 10, 12, 16, 18
Average: 8, 10, 12, 18, 23
Advanced: 8, 10, 12, 18, 23

Problem Solving

Exercises 10 and 11
Have students copy the figures and use colored pens to mark the angles between two congruent sides. Matching colors represent congruent angles.

14. *Sample answer:*

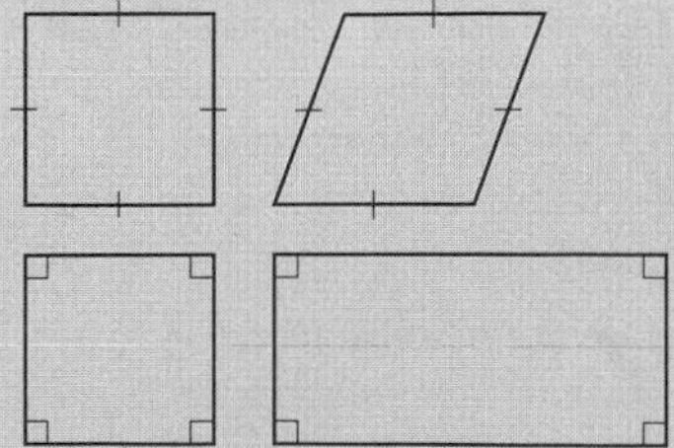

Assess

Assessment Resources

- Assessment Book (Formal Assessment and Alternative Assessment)
- Test and Practice Generator

Mini-Quiz

The triangles below are congruent.

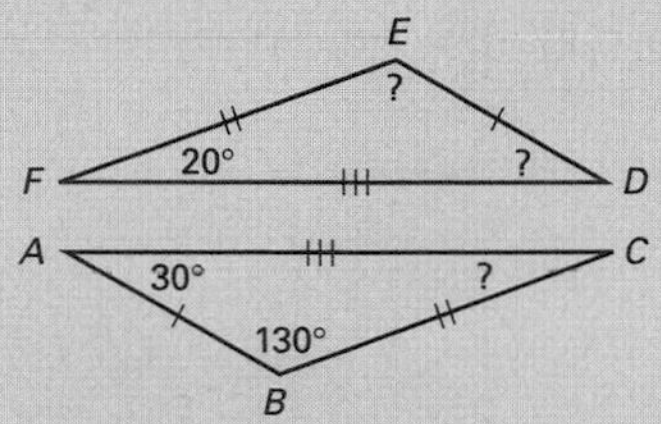

1. Write a congruence statement. ***Sample answer:*** **$\triangle ABC \cong \triangle DEF$**
2. Find the missing angle measures. **$m\angle C = 20°$, $m\angle D = 30°$, $m\angle E = 130°$**
3. Draw a rectangle and mark congruent sides. Label the vertices. Then draw a diagonal. Explain why the two triangles formed are congruent. ***Sample answer:*** **In a rectangle opposite sides are congruent, so two sides of one triangle are congruent to the two corresponding sides of the other triangle. Since all angles are 90°, the angles between the two sides are congruent. So the triangles are congruent by the SAS congruence postulate.**

19. *Sample Answer:* $CELK \cong CEHB$; $CDJK \cong CDAB$; $EDJL \cong EDAH$

20. *Sample Answer:* figure *ABCKJ* and figure *AHELJ*. The sides of the pentagons have different corresponding lengths, so they are not congruent.

21. They are congruent. If the two sets of parts are congruent with each other, then the figures made up from the parts are congruent.

23–25. See Additional Answers beginning on page AA1.

Link to Art

WEAVING The weaving shown above was created by Erica Licea-Kane, an artist who frequently uses geometric shapes to establish visual structure in her work.

ART In Exercises 19–21, use the photo and diagram below. The diagram is based on a portion of the fabric design in the woven tapestry at the left. 19–21. See margin.

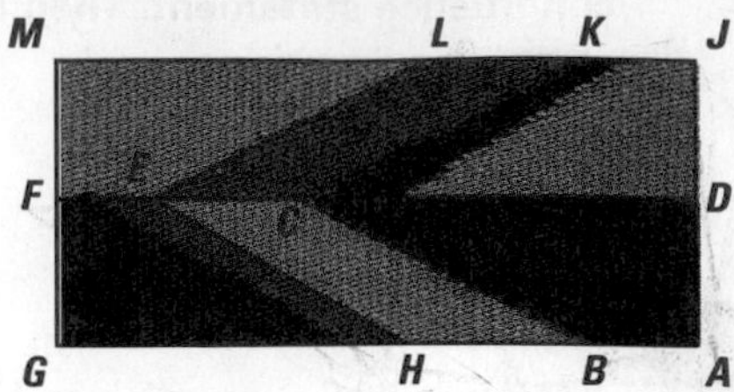

19. Name at least three pairs of quadrilaterals that appear to be congruent. Write a congruence statement for each pair of quadrilaterals.

20. MATHEMATICAL REASONING Name two different pentagons. Do these pentagons appear to be congruent? Explain.

21. MATHEMATICAL REASONING Quadrilaterals *KCEL* and *BCEH* are congruent. Quadrilaterals *LEFM* and *HEFG* are congruent. What can you conclude about quadrilaterals *KCFM* and *BCFG*? Explain your reasoning.

22. MATHEMATICAL REASONING You construct an equilateral triangle, $\triangle XYZ$. Then you find the midpoint *M* of side $\overline{XZ}$. You draw $\overline{MY}$ as shown. Explain how you know that $\triangle XYM \cong \triangle ZYM$. $\overline{XY} \cong \overline{YZ}$, $\overline{XM} \cong \overline{MZ}$, $\overline{YM} \cong \overline{YM}$; SSS

23. MATHEMATICAL REASONING Draw a parallelogram and mark the congruent sides. Label the vertices. Then draw a diagonal. Explain how you know that the two triangles formed are congruent. SSS; See margin.

24. MATHEMATICAL REASONING Sketch a regular pentagon and mark the congruent sides and angles. Label the vertices. Then draw two different diagonals from the same vertex of the pentagon. Identify two congruent triangles. Explain how you know they are congruent. See margin.

25. CHALLENGE Sketch a regular hexagon. Show how to create an equilateral triangle using diagonals of the hexagon. Then explain how you know that the triangle is equilateral. See margin.

Multiple-Choice Practice

26. If quadrilateral $ABCD \cong$ quadrilateral $JKLM$, which side of $JKLM$ corresponds to $\overline{AD}$ from $ABCD$? D

Ⓐ $\overline{JK}$ Ⓑ $\overline{KL}$ Ⓒ $\overline{LM}$ Ⓓ $\overline{JM}$

27. A regular pentagon has a perimeter of 75 millimeters. What is the length of each side of the pentagon?

Ⓕ 12.50 mm Ⓖ 18.75 mm Ⓗ 15.50 mm Ⓙ Not here

DEVELOPING CONCEPTS
Area Formulas

For use with Lesson 8.6

California Standards

- Use formulas routinely for finding the area of basic two-dimensional figures, such as parallelograms and trapezoids. (MG 2.1)
- Use a variety of methods, such as words, symbols, and diagrams to explain mathematical reasoning. (MR 2.5)

MATERIALS
- Paper and pencil

You already know many area formulas. Here you will use the formula for the area of a triangle to develop formulas for the area of a parallelogram and the area of a trapezoid.

SAMPLE 1 Finding the Area of a Parallelogram

You can use the length of any side of a parallelogram as its *base*. The perpendicular distance between that side and the opposite side is the *height* of the parallelogram. You can find the area of a parallelogram if you know its base and its height.

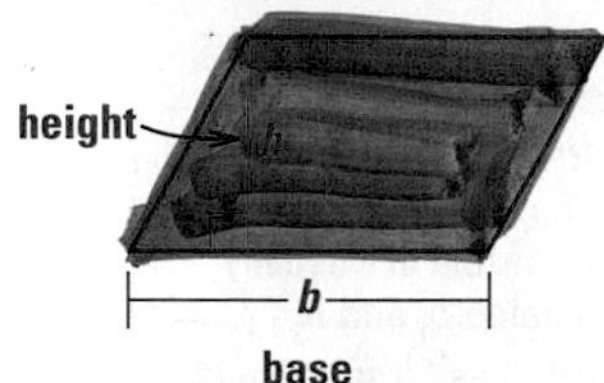

Here's How

Divide the parallelogram into two congruent triangles by drawing a diagonal. (You will be able to prove the triangles are congruent in a later geometry course.) The area of the parallelogram is the sum of the areas of the two triangles.

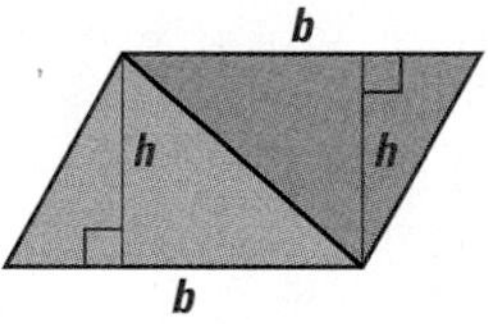

$$\text{Area} = \textbf{Area of Triangle 1} + \textbf{Area of Triangle 2}$$
$$= \frac{1}{2}bh + \frac{1}{2}bh$$
$$= bh$$

So, to find the area of a parallelogram, multiply its base by its height.

Student Help

SKILLS REVIEW
For help with finding the area of a triangle, see page 683.

Try These

In Exercises 1–3, find the area of the parallelogram.

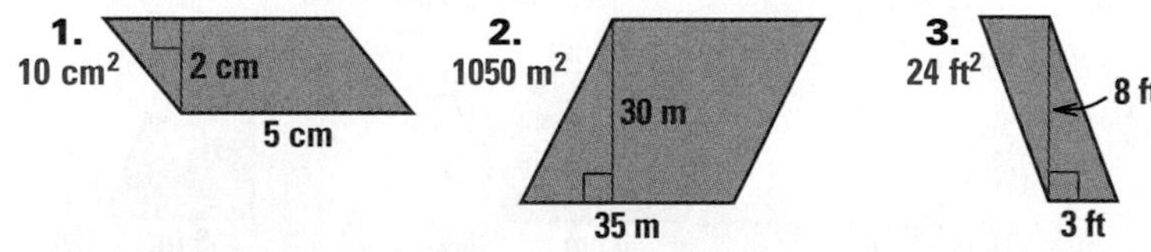

4. **MATHEMATICAL REASONING** Can you use the formula $A = bh$ to find the area A of a rectangle? Explain your reasoning.
Yes; the sides are perpendicular and can be used as the base and the height.
5. **MATHEMATICAL REASONING** In Sample 1, does it matter which diagonal you draw? Explain your reasoning. Include a diagram.
See margin.

1 Planning the Activity

Purpose and Materials
See the margin of the student page.

LINK TO LESSON
Students apply the results of the activity in Example 1 of Lesson 8.6.

Math Reasoning
Students use words, symbols, and diagrams to explain mathematical reasoning. They develop generalizations and apply the results to new situations.

2 Managing the Activity

Classroom Management
Have student volunteers come forward to demonstrate drawing the diagonals and identifying the base and height of each triangle.

5. The triangles formed by drawing the diagonal are congruent regardless of which diagonal is drawn.

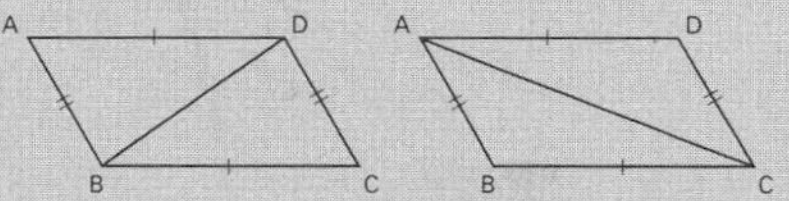

California Standards and Assessment

CA Standards: MG 2.1, MR 2.5

3 Closing the Activity

★ **KEY DISCOVERY**

The area of a parallelogram can be found by multiplying the base times the height. The area of a trapezoid can be found by multiplying the sum of *both* bases times one-half the height.

Activity Assessment

Use Exercises 1 and 6 to assess student understanding.

SAMPLE 2 Finding the Area of a Trapezoid

The length of each parallel side of a trapezoid is called a *base*. The *height* of a trapezoid is the perpendicular distance between the parallel sides. You can find the area of a trapezoid if you know its bases and its height.

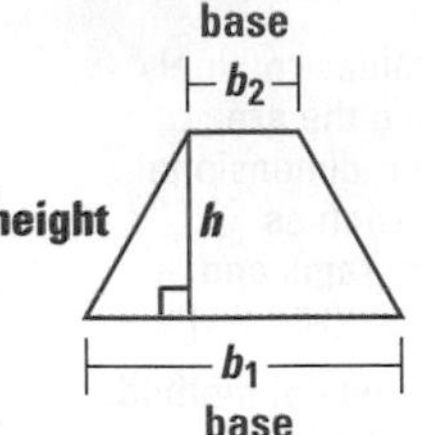

Student Help

▶ **READING TIP**
The bases of a trapezoid are usually labeled b_1 and b_2 (read as "b sub 1" and "b sub 2").

Here's How

Divide the trapezoid into two triangles by drawing a diagonal. The area of the first triangle is given by $\frac{1}{2}b_1h$. The area of the second is given by $\frac{1}{2}b_2h$. The area of the trapezoid is the sum of the areas of the two triangles.

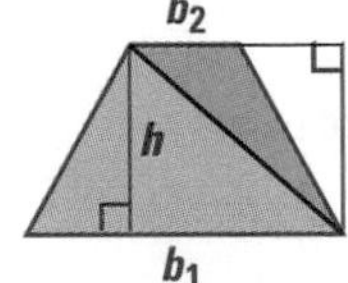

Area = **Area of Triangle 1 + Area of Triangle 2**

$$= \frac{1}{2}b_1h + \frac{1}{2}b_2h$$

$$= \frac{1}{2}h(b_1 + b_2) \quad \text{Distributive property}$$

So, you can find the area of a trapezoid by taking $\frac{1}{2}$ times the height times the sum of the bases.

Try These

In Exercises 6–8, find the area of the trapezoid.

6. 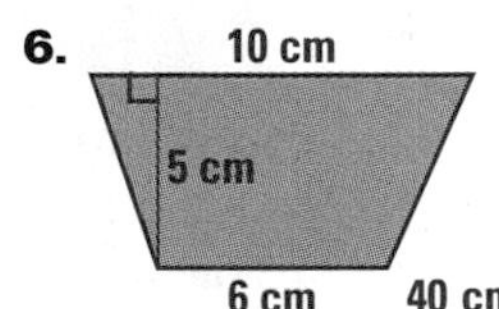

40 cm²

7. 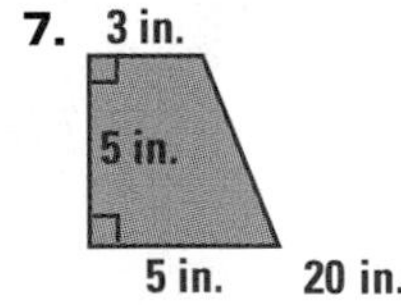

20 in.²

8. 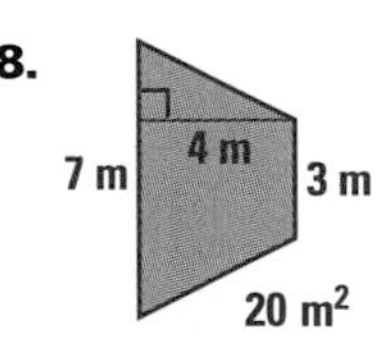

20 m²

9. **MATHEMATICAL REASONING** Is the following rule accurate? The area of a trapezoid is equal to the product of its height and the average of the bases. Explain your reasoning. **See margin.**

9. Yes, the product of the height and the average of the two bases is $h \cdot \frac{(b_1 + b_2)}{2} = \frac{1}{2}h(b_1 + b_2)$, which is the area of a trapezoid.

8.6 Areas of Polygons

In this lesson you'll:

- Use formulas routinely for finding the area of basic two-dimensional figures, such as rectangles, parallelograms, trapezoids, squares, and triangles. (MG 2.1)
- Estimate and compute the area of more complex two-dimensional figures by breaking them down into basic polygons. (MG 2.2)

Goal 1 Finding the Areas of Polygons

The first diagram below shows the height h and the base b of a parallelogram. The second diagram shows the height h and the two bases b_1 and b_2 of a trapezoid. The variable b_1 is read "b sub 1."

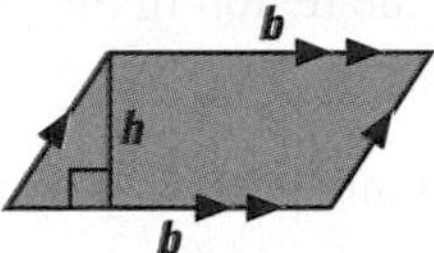

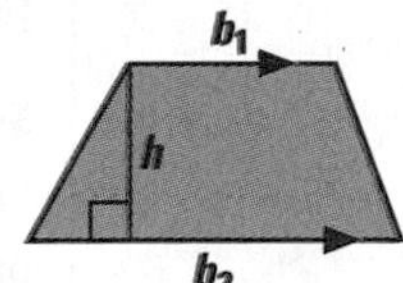

In Developing Concepts 8.6, page 417, you saw how to find the area of a parallelogram and the area of a trapezoid.

Areas of Parallelograms and Trapezoids

Parallelogram Area = bh

Trapezoid Area = $\frac{1}{2}(b_1 + b_2)h$

EXAMPLE 1 Finding Areas

Find the area of the figure.

a.

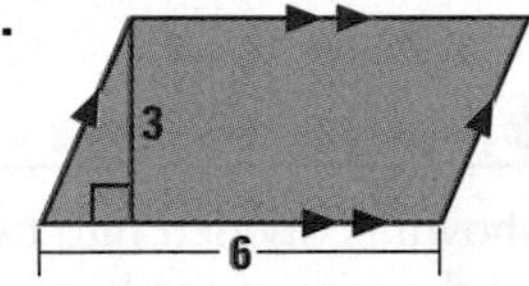

b.

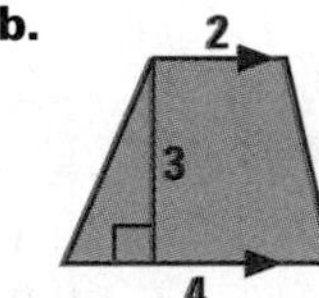

Solution

a. Use the formula for the area of a parallelogram.

Area = bh	**Write area formula.**
$= 6 \cdot 3$	**Substitute for b and h.**
= 18 square units	**Simplify.**

b. Use the formula for the area of a trapezoid.

Area = $\frac{1}{2}(b_1 + b_2)h$	**Write area formula.**
$= \frac{1}{2}(4 + 2)3$	**Substitute for b_1, b_2, and h.**
= 9 square units	**Simplify.**

1 Plan

Pacing

Suggested Number of Days

Transitional: 1 day
Average: 1 day
Advanced: 1 day
Block Schedule: 0.5 block with 8.7

Teaching Resources

Blacklines
(See page 382B.)

Transparencies
- Warm-Up Exercises
- Teacher Time-Savers
- English/Spanish Problem Solving
- Answers

Technology
- Electronic Teacher Tools
- Test and Practice Generator

2 Teach

Math Reasoning

For Mathematical Background Notes on mathematical reasoning related to this lesson, please refer to pages 382E and 382F in this Teacher's Edition.

Extra Example 1
See next page.

California Standards and Assessment

CA Standards: MG 2.1, MG 2.2

Extra Example 1

Find the area of the figure.

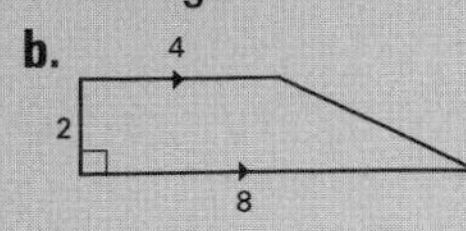

a. 6 square units

b. 12 square units

Teaching Tip

Emphasize that the subscripts used in the variables b_1 and b_2 indicate that there are two different bases in a trapezoid.

Extra Example 2

The plan for another putting green of the miniature golf course is shown. Each square represents 1 ft². What is the total area of the green? **40.5 ft²**

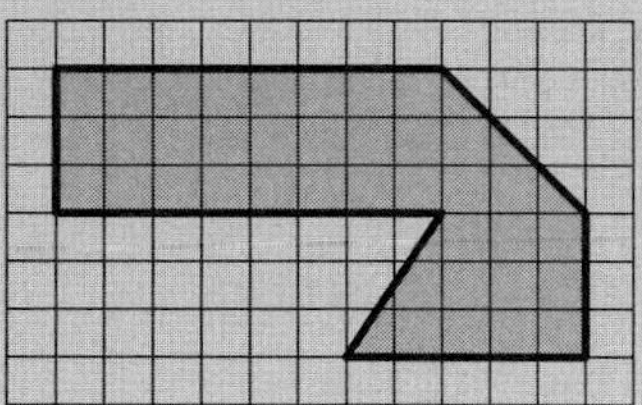

Extra Example 3

Find the area of the polygon by dividing it into smaller polygons.

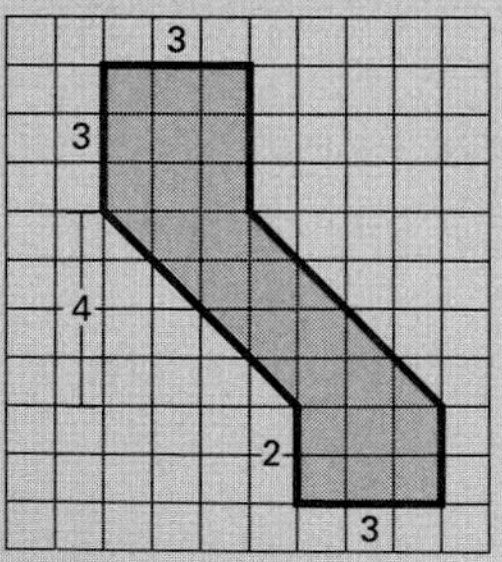

27 square units

Concept Check

Explain how to find the height of a parallelogram or a trapezoid. ***Sample answer:*** **Find the perpendicular distance between two parallel sides.**

Goal 2 Finding Areas of Polygons

When you solve real-life area problems, you may need to find areas of polygons that are more complex than the ones you have seen so far. You may be able to divide such polygons into smaller regions whose areas you can find using familiar area formulas.

EXAMPLE 2 Finding an Area of a Polygon

GOLF COURSE You are designing a putting green for a miniature golf course, as shown. Find the area of the region in the picture.

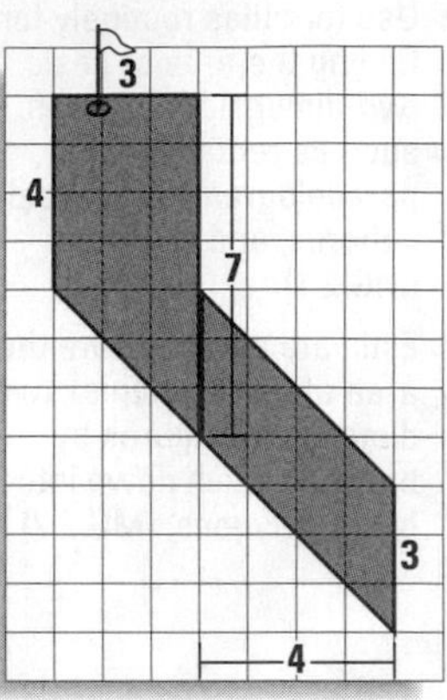

Each grid square represents 1 square foot.

Solution

Divide the green into a trapezoid and a parallelogram.

$$\text{Area of trapezoid} = \frac{1}{2}(b_1 + b_2)h$$
$$= \frac{1}{2}(4 + 7)3$$
$$= 16.5 \text{ ft}^2$$

$$\text{Area of parallelogram} = bh$$
$$= 3 \cdot 4$$
$$= 12 \text{ ft}^2$$

ANSWER ▶ The total area of the green is 16.5 + 12 = 28.5 square feet.

Student Help

▶ **STUDY TIP**
You can check the answer in Example 2 by counting unit squares in the diagram.

EXAMPLE 3 Finding an Area of a Hexagon

The hexagon shown is divided into two trapezoids. Find the area of the hexagon.

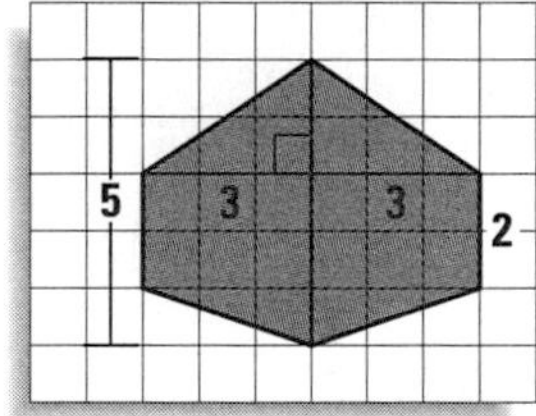

Solution

The area of the hexagon is twice the area of one trapezoid. The height of each trapezoid is 3 units. The bases of each trapezoid are 5 and 2 units.

$$\text{Area of trapezoid} = \frac{1}{2}(b_1 + b_2)h \quad \text{Write area formula.}$$
$$= \frac{1}{2}(5 + 2)3 \quad \text{Substitute for } b_1, b_2, \text{ and } h.$$
$$= 10.5 \text{ square units} \quad \text{Simplify.}$$

ANSWER ▶ Area of hexagon = 2 • 10.5 = 21 square units.

Student Help

▶ **MORE EXAMPLES**
More examples are available at www.mcdougallittell.com

8.6 Exercises

Guided Practice

Match the polygon with one or more formulas that can be used to find its area *A*. Then find the area of the polygon.

A. $A = \frac{1}{2}bh$ **B.** $A = \frac{1}{2}(b_1 + b_2)h$ **C.** $A = bh$ **D.** $A = s^2$

1.

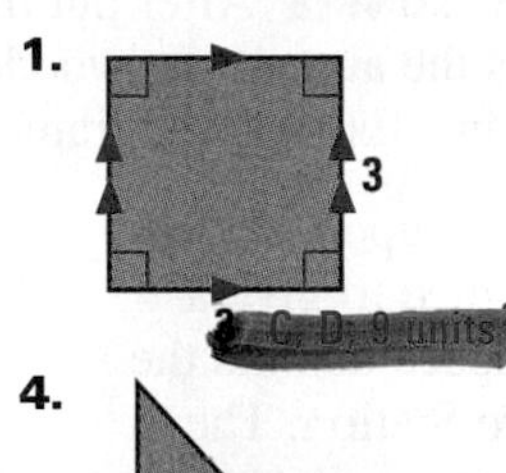

2.

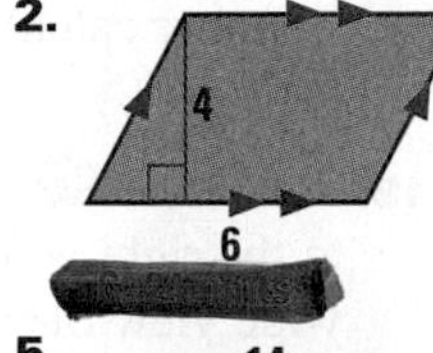

3.

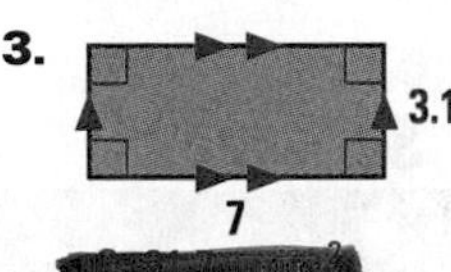

4.

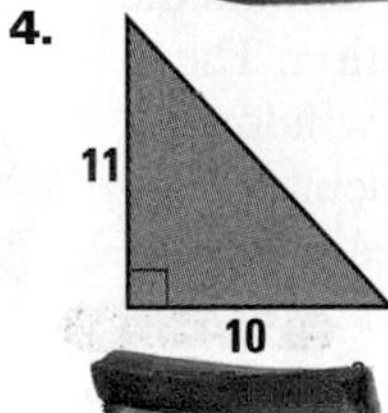

5.

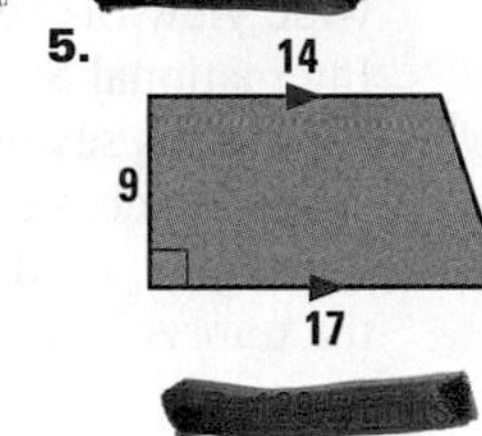

6.

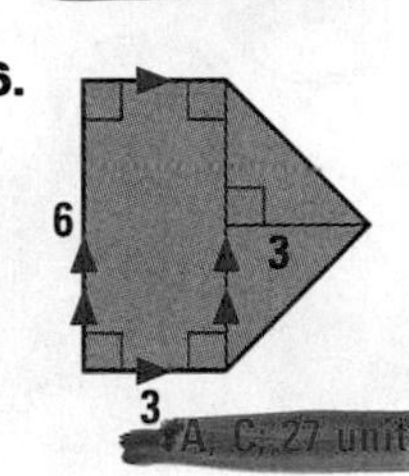

Practice and Problem Solving

Student Help

▶ **MORE PRACTICE**
Extra practice to help you master skills is on page 705.

Find the area of the polygon.

7. **8.** **9.** **10.** **11.** **12.**

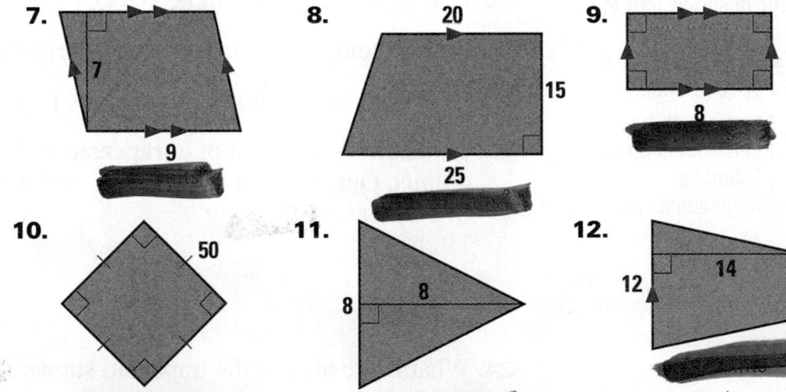

Copy the polygon onto grid paper. Find the area of the polygon by dividing it into smaller polygons. Tell what area formulas you used.

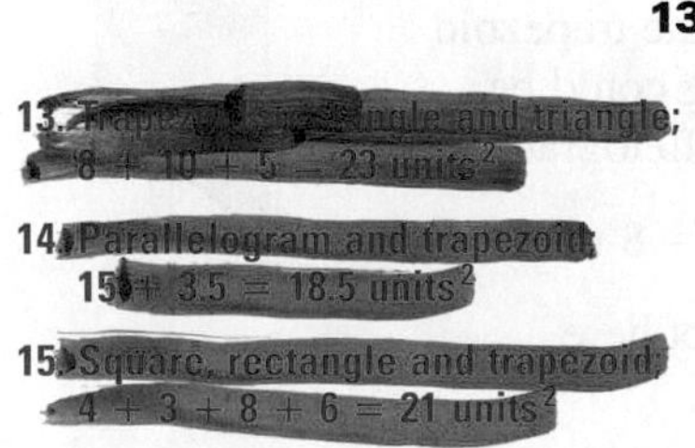

13.

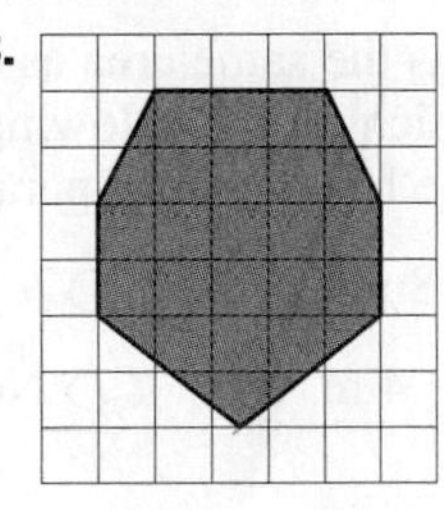

14.

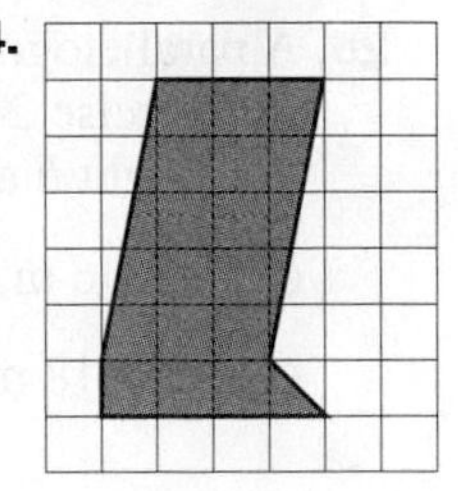

15.

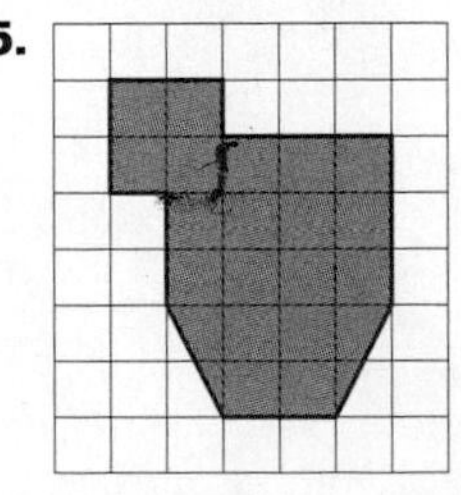

3 Apply

Assignment Guide

TRANSITIONAL
Day 1: pp. 421–422 Exs. 7–14, 16–17, 19, 24–25

AVERAGE
Day 1: pp. 421–422 Exs. 7–18, 20–22, 24–25

ADVANCED
Day 1: pp. 421–422 Exs. 8–18, 20–22, 23*, 24–25

BLOCK SCHEDULE
pp. 421–422 Exs. 7–18, 20–22, 24–25 (with 8.7)

Extra Practice

- Student Edition, pp. 704–705
- Chapter 8 Resource Book, p. 51

Homework Check

To quickly check student understanding of key concepts, go over the following exercises:

Transitional: 8, 10, 12, 14, 16
Average: 8, 10, 12, 14, 20
Advanced: 8, 10, 12 14, 20

Problem Solving

Exercises 13–15
Tell students that while many different divisions are possible, they should divide the polygons so that they can easily find the base and height of the smaller polygons.

Assess

Assessment Resources

- Assessment Book (Formal Assessment and Alternative Assessment)
- Test and Practice Generator

Mini-Quiz

Find the area of the polygon.

1. 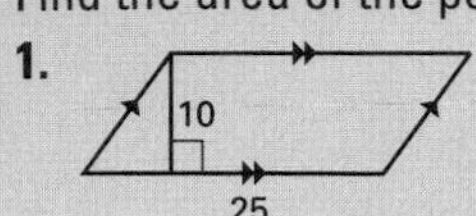

250 square units

2. 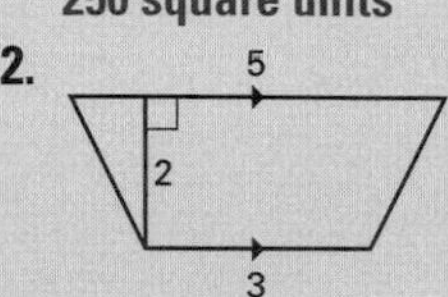

8 square units

3. 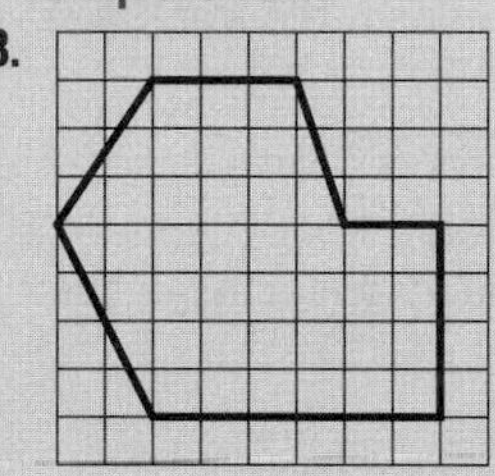

41.5 square units

17. 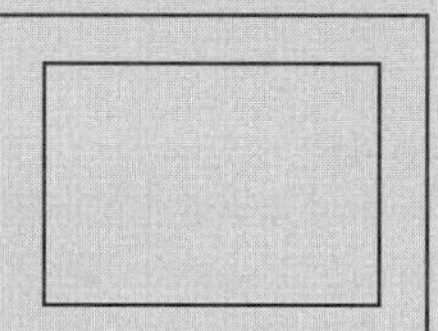

20. Areas will vary.

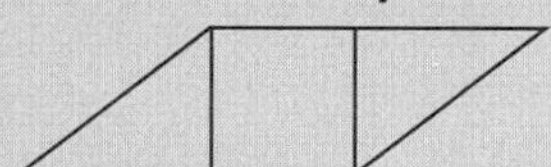

21. Areas will vary.

22. Areas will vary.

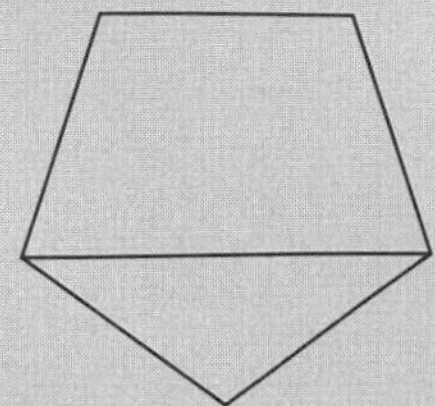

18. The outer rectangle is 63 in.^{2} and the inner rectangle (the opening) is 35 in.^{2} The area of the frame itself is the difference between these two measurements.

SPACE STATION In the future, astronauts may work at an international space station that orbits Earth. The photo above shows part of a full-scale training module for the space station at the Johnson Space Center.

More about the International Space Station available at www.mcdougallittell.com

PICTURE FRAME In Exercises 16–18, use the diagram below. Each trapezoid in the diagram is a piece of a wooden picture frame.

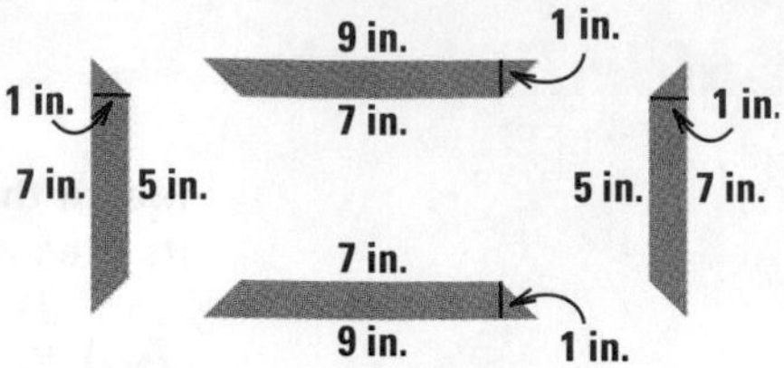

16. Find the area of each piece. Then find the total area of the wooden frame. 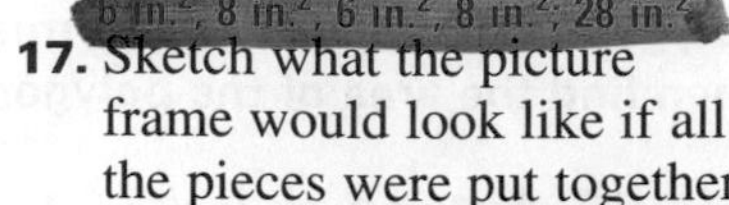 6 in.^{2}, 8 in.^{2}, 6 in.^{2}, 8 in.^{2}; 28 in.^{2}

17. Sketch what the picture frame would look like if all the pieces were put together. See margin.

18. MATHEMATICAL REASONING After putting the frame together, a framer calculates the area of the wooden frame as follows: $9(7) - 7(5) = 28$ in.^{2} Explain the framer's reasoning. See margin.

19. Science Link The cupola shown at the right is designed to give a wide view of the space outside the International Space Station. The cupola has seven glass windows, six of which are congruent trapezoids. Find the area of one of the trapezoidal windows. 391.68 in.^{2}

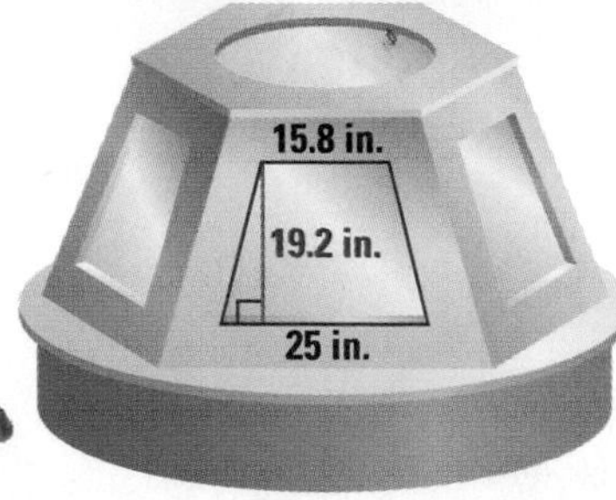

In Exercises 20–22, make a sketch on graph paper to represent the "equation." Then find the area of the final figure, assuming that each grid square equals one square unit.

20. (2 congruent right triangles) + (1 square) = (1 parallelogram) See margin.

21. (1 trapezoid) + (1 triangle) = (1 parallelogram) See margin.

22. (1 isosceles triangle) + (1 isosceles trapezoid) = (1 pentagon) See margin.

23. CHALLENGE The area of a trapezoid is 18 square units. Its height is 4 units. One base is twice as long as the other base. Find the lengths of both bases. 3 and 6

Multiple-Choice Practice

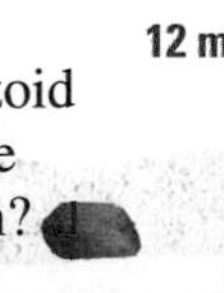

24. What is the area of the trapezoid shown? B

Ⓐ 24 m^2 Ⓑ 36 m^2

Ⓒ 48 m^2 Ⓓ 72 m^2

25. A parallelogram has the same area as the trapezoid in Exercise 24. Which of the following could be the height h and the base b of the parallelogram? H

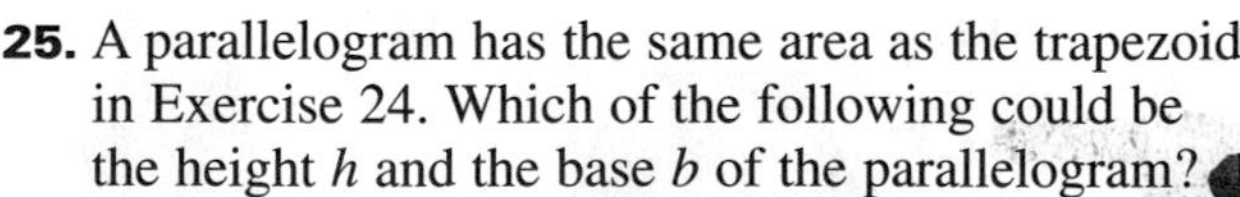

Ⓕ $h = 6$ m, $b = 8$ m Ⓖ $h = 8$ m, $b = 6$ m

Ⓗ $h = 18$ m, $b = 4$ m Ⓙ Not here

8.7 Line Reflections

California Standards

In this lesson you'll:

- Understand and use coordinate graphs to plot simple figures and determine their image under reflections. (MG 3.2)
- Demonstrate an understanding of conditions that indicate two geometrical figures are congruent. (MG 3.4)

Goal 1 REFLECTING FIGURES IN LINES

In the diagram below, $\triangle ABC$ is *reflected* in a line, called the *line of reflection,* to produce an *image* $\triangle A'B'C'$ on the other side of the line. A **reflection** is an operation that maps every point P in a figure to its image point P' (read as *P prime*) so that the following are true:

- If P is not on the line of reflection, then the line of reflection is the perpendicular bisector of $\overline{PP'}$.
- If P is *on* the line of reflection, then $P = P'$.

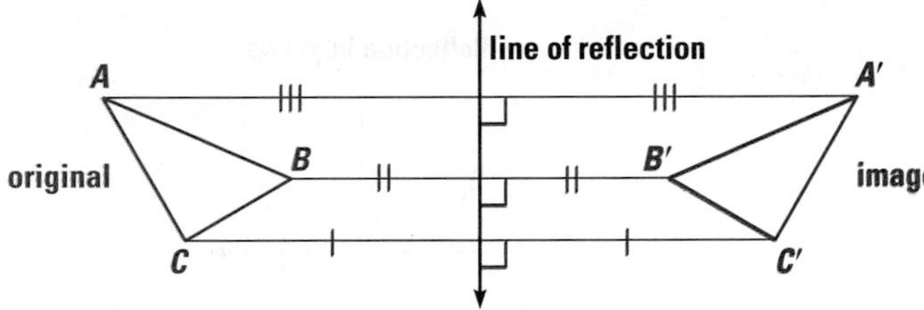

When a figure is reflected in a line, its image is congruent to the original figure. You will prove this statement is true in a later geometry course.

Student Help

VOCABULARY TIP
A geometric reflection can be compared with an actual reflection in a mirror. You reflect a point in a line to produce an *image point.* You look in a mirror to see an *image* of yourself.

EXAMPLE 1 Reflecting in a Coordinate Plane

Graph the triangle with vertices $R(2, 6)$, $S(3, 4)$, and $T(0, 2)$ in a coordinate plane. Reflect $\triangle RST$ in the y-axis.

Solution

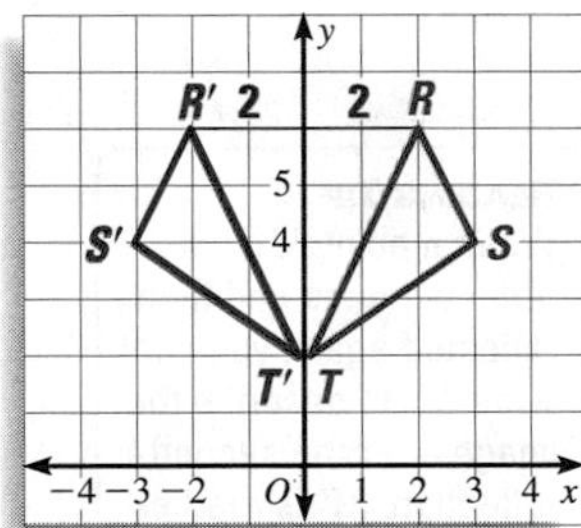

First graph points R, S, and T. Connect the points to form $\triangle RST$.

To find the image point R', imagine drawing a line through point R and perpendicular to the y-axis. Point R lies on this line 2 units to the right of the y-axis. Therefore the image point R' lies on the line 2 units to the left of the y-axis. You can use similar reasoning to plot point S'.

Because T is *on* the line of reflection, T and T' have the same coordinates.

Connect R', S', and T' to form $\triangle R'S'T'$.

1 Plan

Pacing

Suggested Number of Days

Transitional: 1 day
Average: 1 day
Advanced: 1 day
Block Schedule: 0.5 block with 8.6

Teaching Resources

Blacklines
(See page 382B.)

Transparencies
- Warm-Up Exercises
- Teacher Time-Savers
- English/Spanish Problem Solving
- Answers

Technology
- Electronic Teacher Tools
- Test and Practice Generator

2 Teach

Math Reasoning

For Mathematical Background Notes on mathematical reasoning related to this lesson, please refer to pages 382E and 382F in this Teacher's Edition.

Extra Example 1
See next page.

California Standards and Assessment

CA Standards: MG 3.2, MG 3.4
CA Key Concepts Book: pp. S87–S89, S92

Extra Example 1

Graph the quadrilateral with vertices $E(1, 2)$, $F(1, 4)$, $G(3, 6)$, and $H(4, 1)$ in a coordinate plane. Reflect each point in the y-axis.

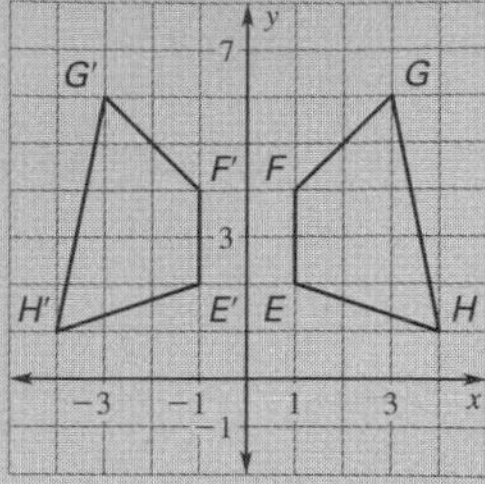

Extra Example 2

Refer to Extra Example 1. Use the motion rule $(x, y) \rightarrow (x, -y)$ to find the coordinates of the vertices of the image of quadrilateral $EFGH$ if the reflection had been in the x-axis. **$E'(1, -2)$, $F'(1, -4)$, $G'(3, -6)$, $H'(4, -1)$**

Math Reasoning

A *distance-preserving* transformation maps any figure to a congruent figure. Reflections across lines and translations (to be studied in Lesson 8.8) are examples of such transformations. Rotations also have this property. It can be shown that given any distance-preserving transformation in the plane, there exist three or fewer lines in the plane such that the same transformation results by successive reflections across the lines.

Concept Check

Explain how coordinates can be used to reflect a figure in the x-axis and y-axis. **When reflecting in the x-axis, the x-coordinate of an image point is the same as the x-coordinate of the original figure, and its y-coordinate is the opposite. When reflecting in the y-axis, the y-coordinate of an image point is the same and its x-coordinate is the opposite.**

A figure has **line symmetry** if you can draw a line through the figure such that the part of the figure on one side of the line is the reflection of the part on the other side. For example, rectangle $RSTU$ has two lines of symmetry.

The parts of the rectangle to the left and right of the y-axis are reflections in the y-axis, so the y-axis is one line of symmetry. The parts of the rectangle above and below the x-axis are reflections in the x-axis, so the x-axis is another line of symmetry.

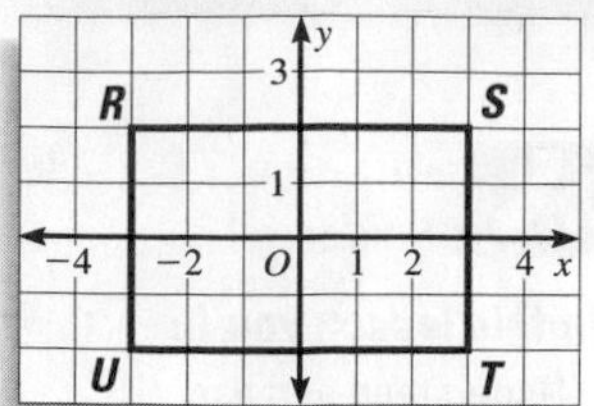

Goal 2 DESCRIBING A REFLECTION

You can use coordinate notation to describe a reflection in a coordinate plane.

Reflection in y-axis

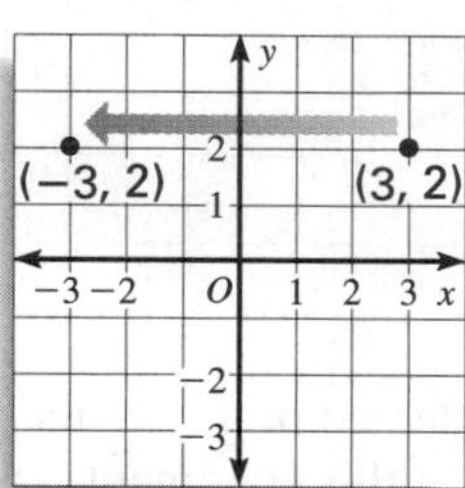

$(3, 2) \rightarrow (-3, 2)$

The y-coordinate is the same and the x-coordinate is the opposite. Describe this as $(x, y) \rightarrow (-x, y)$.

Reflection in x-axis

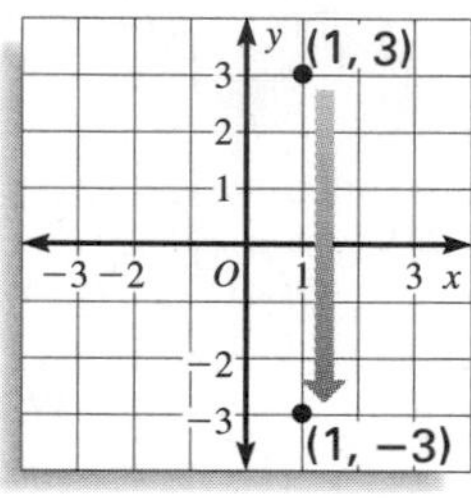

$(1, 3) \rightarrow (1, -3)$

The x-coordinate is the same and the y-coordinate is the opposite. Describe this as $(x, y) \rightarrow (x, -y)$.

EXAMPLE 2 Using Coordinate Notation

$\overline{MN}$ has endpoints at $M(-4, 1)$ and $N(-1, 3)$. The diagram shows $\overline{MN}$ reflected first in the y-axis to produce the image $\overline{M'N'}$. Then this image is reflected in the x-axis to produce the image $\overline{M''N''}$.

Reflection in y-axis:

$(x, y) \rightarrow (-x, y)$
$M(-4, 1) \rightarrow M'(4, 1)$
$N(-1, 3) \rightarrow N'(1, 3)$

Reflection in x-axis:

$(x, y) \rightarrow (x, -y)$
$M'(4, 1) \rightarrow M''(4, -1)$
$N'(1, 3) \rightarrow N''(1, -3)$

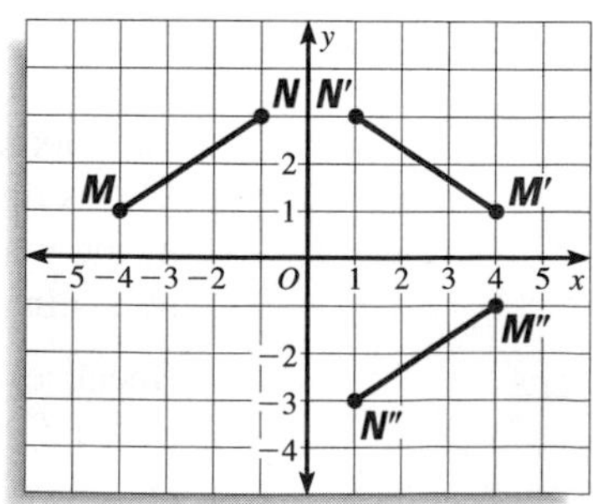

Student Help

READING TIP
When a point M is reflected once and then reflected again, you can write M'' to describe the image after the second reflection. M'' is read as *M double prime*.

8.7 Exercises

Guided Practice

1. $(x, y) \to (-x, y)$ The line of reflection is the y-axis.

2. Quadrant 3; $(x, y) \to (x, -y)$; $L'' = (-1, -1)$, $M'' = (-4, -5)$, $N'' = (-4, -1)$

In Exercises 1 and 2, $\triangle LMN$ is reflected to produce $\triangle L'M'N'$.

1. Use coordinate notation to describe the reflection shown in the diagram. Describe the line of reflection.

2. Suppose $\triangle L'M'N'$ is reflected in the x-axis to produce $\triangle L''M''N''$. In which quadrant would $\triangle L''M''N''$ lie? Use coordinate notation to describe this reflection and find the coordinates of the vertices of $\triangle L''M''N''$.

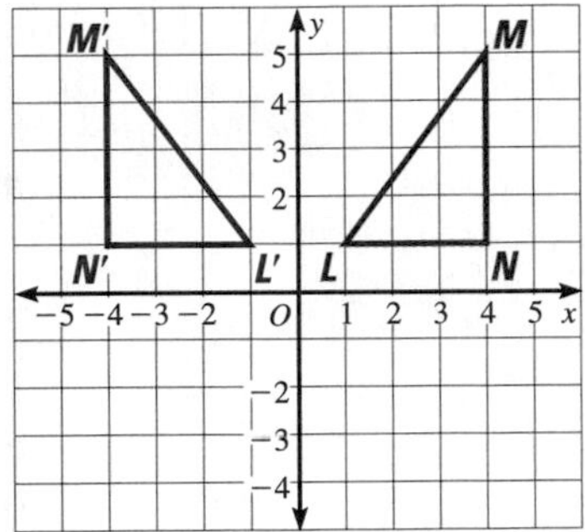

Practice and Problem Solving

Student Help

▸**MORE PRACTICE** Extra practice to help you master skills is on page 705.

Determine whether the red figure is a reflection of the blue figure in line k. If it is not, sketch the reflection of the blue figure in line k.

3.

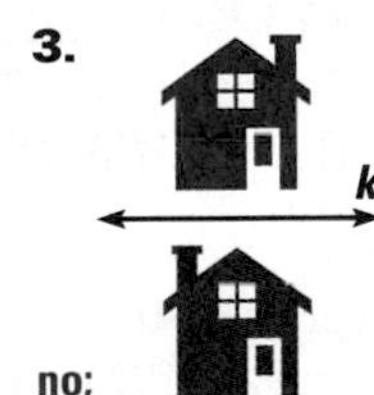

no; see margin.

4.

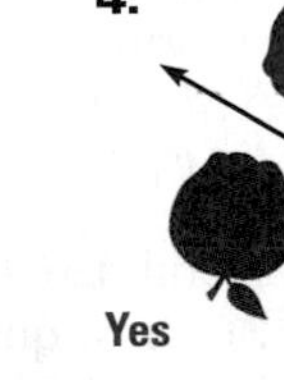

Yes

5.

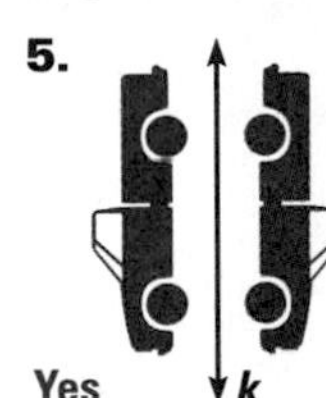

Yes

In Exercises 6 and 7, copy the diagram on a piece of graph paper. Draw the image after the indicated reflection.

6. Reflect rectangle $RSTV$ in the y-axis. **See margin.**

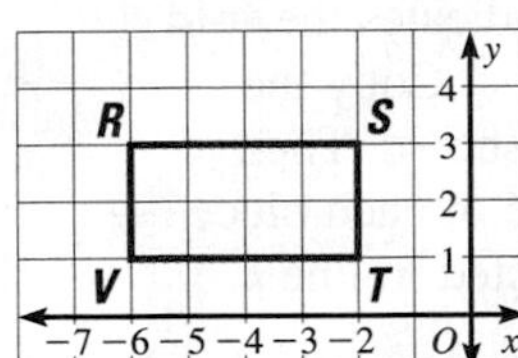

7. Reflect $\triangle EFG$ in the x-axis. **See margin.**

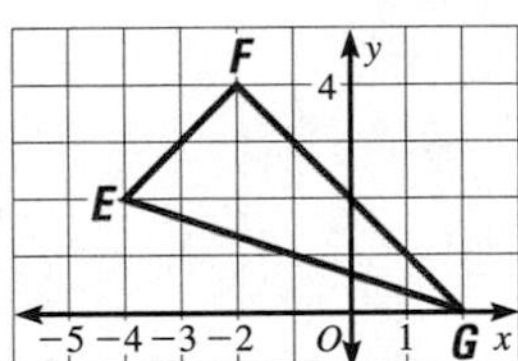

8. $RS = VT = R'S' = V'T' = 4$, $RV = ST = R'V' = S'T' = 2$; The rectangles are congruent because their corresponding sides and angles are congruent.

8. MATHEMATICAL REASONING Use your drawing from Exercise 6. Find the side lengths of rectangle $RSTV$ and the side lengths of its image. Are the rectangles congruent? Explain. **See margin.**

9. You come back to the original figure; $(x, y) \to (-x, y) \to (-(-x), y)$ or (x, y) $(x, y) \to (x, -y) \to (x, -(-y))$ or (x, y).

9. MATHEMATICAL REASONING Describe what happens when you reflect a figure in a line and then reflect the image in the same line. Show how coordinate notation can be used to justify this result for a reflection in the y-axis or in the x-axis. **See margin.**

3 Apply

Assignment Guide

TRANSITIONAL
Day 1: EP p. 695 Exs. 93–96; pp. 425–427 Exs. 3–8, 10–11, 14–15, 20–24, 31–33, 37–38

AVERAGE
Day 1: pp. 425–427 Exs. 3–16, 20–24, 31–33, 37–38

ADVANCED
Day 1: pp. 425–427 Exs. 3–15, 17–18, 19*, 20–24, 31–33, 37–38

BLOCK SCHEDULE
pp. 425–427 Exs. 3–16, 20–24, 31–33, 37–38 (with 8.6)

Extra Practice

- Student Edition, pp. 704–705
- Chapter 8 Resource Book, p. 60

Homework Check

To quickly check student understanding of key concepts, go over the following exercises:

Transitional: 4, 6, 7, 10, 14
Average: 4, 6, 10, 14, 16
Advanced: 4, 6, 12, 14, 17

3.

6.

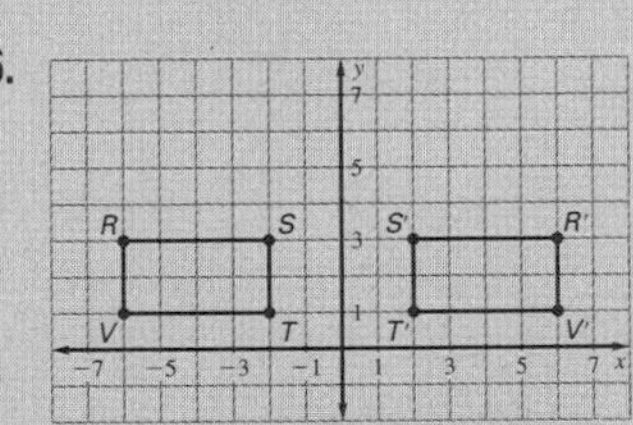

7.

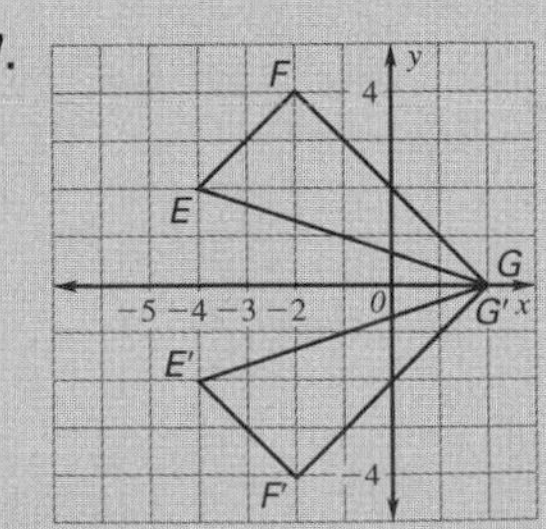

14.

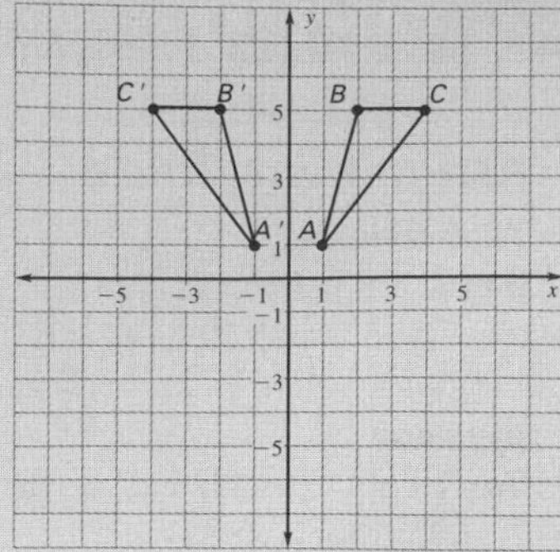

15.

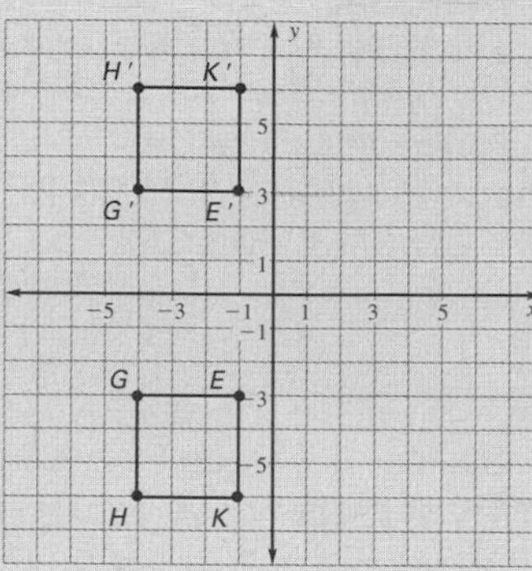

16.

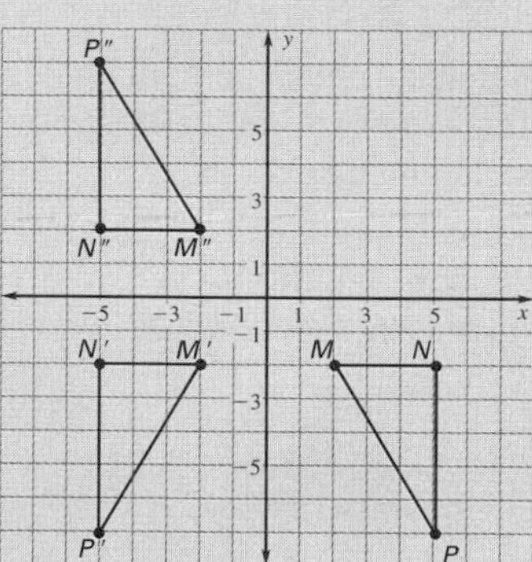

17.

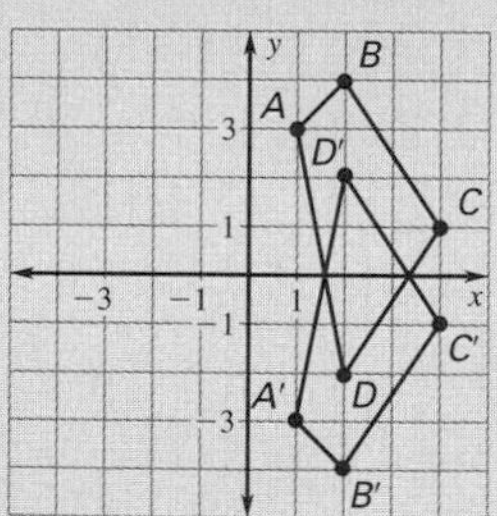

18–19. See Additional Answers beginning on page AA1.

MATHEMATICAL REASONING **In Exercises 10–13, use the figure below. Tell whether the statement is *true* or *false*. Explain your reasoning.**

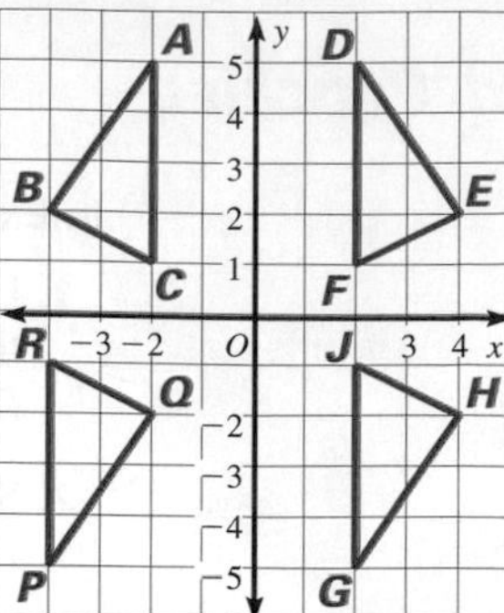

10. $\triangle DEF$ is the reflection of $\triangle ABC$ in the y-axis.
True, each vertex is reflected in the *y*-axis.

11. $\triangle DEF$ is the reflection of $\triangle GHJ$ in the y-axis.

11. False; $\triangle$ *DEF* is the reflection of $\triangle$ *GHJ* in the *x*-axis.

12. $\triangle GHJ$ is the reflection of $\triangle PQR$ in the y-axis.

12. False; *sample answer:* (–2, –2) should be reflected to (2, –2), but the corresponding vertex *H* has coordinates (4, –2).

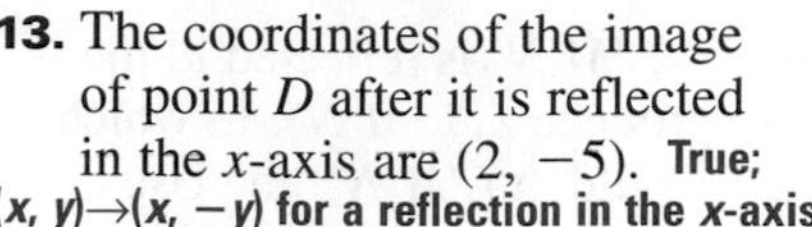

13. The coordinates of the image of point D after it is reflected in the x-axis are $(2, -5)$. **True; $(x, y) \to (x, -y)$ for a reflection in the *x*-axis.**

In Exercises 14 and 15, plot the given points and connect them to form a polygon. Then draw the image of the polygon after the indicated reflection. Identify the line of reflection.

14. $A(1, 1)$, $B(2, 5)$, $C(4, 5)$ **See margin.**
reflection: $(x, y) \to (-x, y)$ **line of reflection = *y*-axis**

15. $E(-1, -3)$, $G(-4, -3)$, $H(-4, -6)$, $K(-1, -6)$ **See margin.**
reflection: $(x, y) \to (x, -y)$ **line of reflection = *x*-axis**

16. Plot the points $M(2, -2)$, $N(5, -2)$, and $P(5, -7)$. Then connect the points to form a triangle. Reflect $\triangle MNP$ in the y-axis to form the image $\triangle M'N'P'$. Then reflect $\triangle M'N'P'$ in the x-axis to form the image $\triangle M''N''P''$. **See margin.**

17. Quadrilateral $ABCD$ has vertices $A(1, 3)$, $B(2, 4)$, $C(4, 1)$, and $D(2, -2)$. Draw quadrilateral $ABCD$ in a coordinate plane. Then draw the image of $ABCD$ after the following reflection: $(x, y) \to (x, -y)$. Identify the line of reflection. **See margin. line of reflection = *x*-axis**

18. *Chapter Opener Link* Sewing patterns are often laid on a piece of folded cloth as shown at the right. Line k indicates the fold line of the fabric. Copy the pattern pieces shown. Then draw the image of each piece after it is reflected in line k. **See margin.**

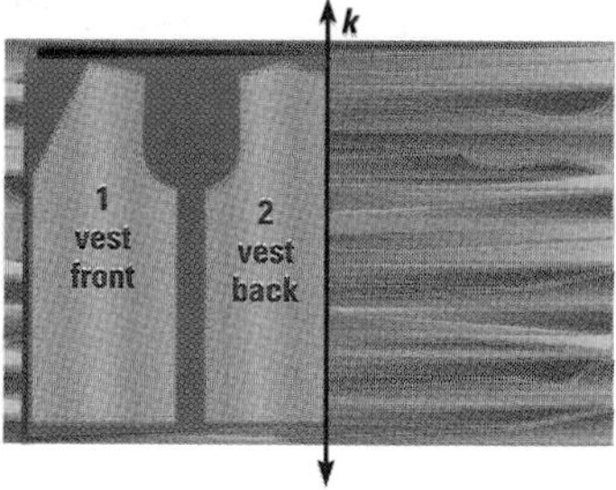

19. CHALLENGE Draw a triangle whose vertices are all in one quadrant of a coordinate plane. The vertices should have integer coordinates.

a. Draw the image of the triangle after the following reflection: $(x, y) \to (y, x)$. Then draw the line of reflection. **See margin.**

b. Repeat part (a) for several different triangles. In each case, what do you notice about the coordinates of the points on the line of reflection? **The *x*-and *y*-coordinates are equal.**

Multiple-Choice Practice

20. Point $M(1, 5)$ is reflected in the y-axis. Its image M' is then reflected in the x-axis. What are the coordinates of the second image, M''? **C**

Ⓐ $(1, -5)$ Ⓑ $(-1, 5)$ Ⓒ $(-1, -5)$ Ⓓ Not here

21. Points $A(-1, 3)$, $B(-2, 1)$, and $C(-3, 2)$ are the vertices of a triangle. $\triangle ABC$ is reflected in the y-axis. What are the coordinates of the vertices of its image, $\triangle A'B'C'$? **G**

Ⓕ $A'(1, -3)$, $B'(2, -1)$, and $C'(3, -2)$

Ⓖ $A'(1, 3)$, $B'(2, 1)$, and $C'(3, 2)$

Ⓗ $A'(-1, -3)$, $B'(-2, -1)$, and $C'(-3, -2)$

Ⓙ $A'(-1, 3)$, $B'(-2, 1)$, and $C'(-3, 2)$

22. Use the figure below. Which statement describes how to reflect quadrilateral $ABCD$ to produce quadrilateral $LMNP$? **C**

Ⓐ $(x, y) \rightarrow (-x, -y)$

Ⓑ $(x, y) \rightarrow (x, -y)$

Ⓒ $(x, y) \rightarrow (-x, y)$

Ⓓ $(x, y) \rightarrow (y, x)$

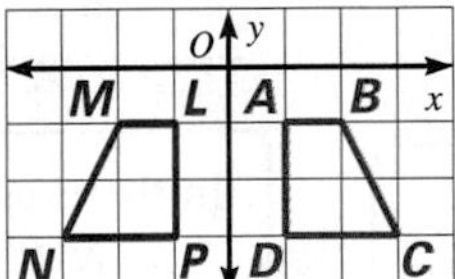

Mixed Review

Solve the equation. *(4.1–4.5, 4.7, 6.6)*

23. $2b - 2 = -2b$ **$b = \frac{1}{2}$**

24. $2p - 20 = 10 - 8p$ **$p = 3$**

25. $2a + 4.04 = 16.08$ **$a = 6.02$**

26. $3r - 1 = 8$ **$r = 3$**

27. $6m - 12 = 6 - 3m$ **$m = 2$**

28. $14 - (2 - t) = -2t$ **$t = -4$**

29. $t - \frac{4}{3} = \frac{2}{5}$ **$t = \frac{26}{15}$**

30. $q - \frac{1}{2} = \frac{1}{3}$ **$q = \frac{5}{6}$**

Write the number in scientific notation. *(6.9)*

31. 2100 **2.1×10^3**

32. 0.00092 **9.2×10^{-4}**

33. 16,000,000 **1.6×10^7**

34. 0.00000046 **4.6×10^{-7}**

35. 1793 **1.793×10^3**

36. 0.0704 **7.04×10^{-2}**

Identify the percent of change as an *increase* or *decrease*. Then find the percent of change. *(7.7)*

37. Before: \$42.12
After: \$40.18 **decrease; −4.6%**

38. Before: 3.6 pounds
After: 7.6 pounds **increase; 111%**

39. Before: 77.1 kilograms
After: 66.1 kilograms **decrease; −14.3%**

40. Before: 4.4 feet
After: 6.3 feet **increase; 43.2%**

4 Assess

Assessment Resources

- Assessment Book (Formal Assessment and Alternative Assessment)
- Test and Practice Generator

Mini-Quiz

1. Graph $\triangle ABC$ in a coordinate plane: $A(-3, 1)$, $B(4, -1)$, $C(0, 2)$. Then graph the image when $\triangle ABC$ is reflected in the x-axis and the image when $\triangle ABC$ is reflected in the y-axis.

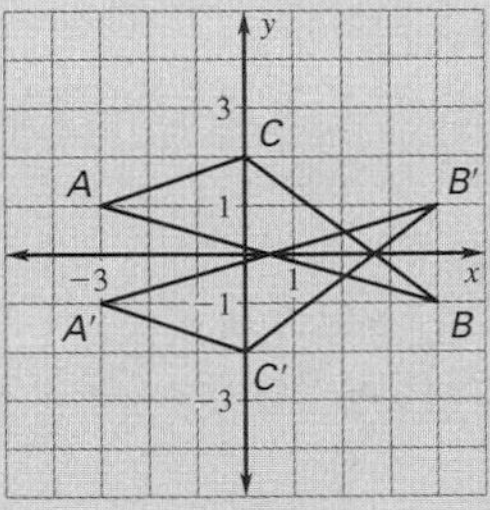

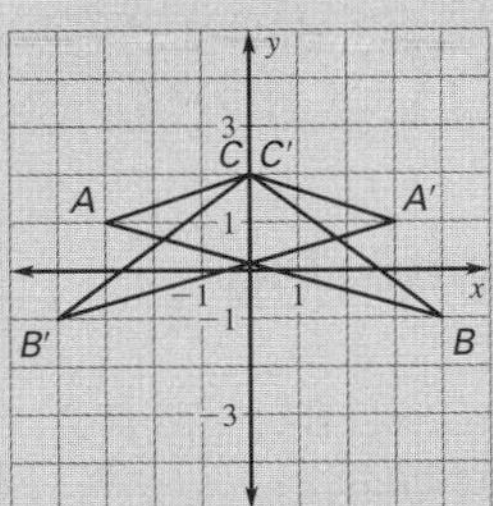

2. What happened to point C in Exercise 1 when the figure was reflected in the y-axis? Explain. **Point C was its own reflection. This happened because point C was on the line of reflection.**

1 Plan

Pacing

Suggested Number of Days

Transitional: 1 day
Average: 1 day
Advanced: 1 day
Block Schedule: 0.5 block with 8.9

Teaching Resources

Blacklines
(See page 382B.)

Transparencies
- Warm-Up Exercises
- Teacher Time-Savers
- English/Spanish Problem Solving
- Answers

Technology
- Electronic Teacher Tools
- Test and Practice Generator

2 Teach

Math Reasoning

For Mathematical Background Notes on mathematical reasoning related to this lesson, please refer to pages 382E and 382F in this Teacher's Edition.

California Standards and Assessment

CA Standards: MG 3.2, MG 3.4
CA Key Concepts Book: pp. S87–S89, S92

8.8 Translations

California Standards

In this lesson you'll:
- Understand and use coordinate graphs to plot simple figures and determine their image under translations. (MG 3.2)
- Demonstrate an understanding of conditions that indicate two geometrical figures are congruent. (MG 3.4)

Goal 1 Translating in a Coordinate Plane

A **transformation** is an operation that makes a figure correspond to another figure, called the *image*. Reflections and *translations*, which you will learn about in this lesson, are two kinds of transformations.

In a **translation** (sometimes called a *slide*), each point of a figure is moved the same distance in the same direction. The image of a figure after a translation is congruent to the original figure, a statement you will prove in a later geometry course.

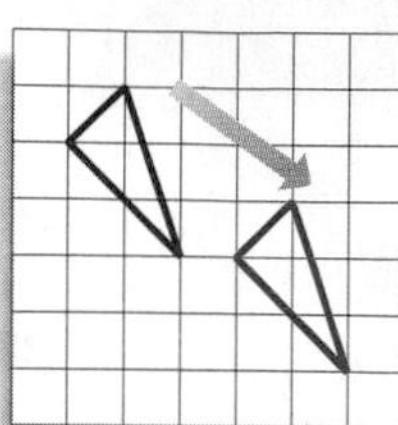

Student Help

Study Tip
It is often convenient to describe a translation as a combination of two translations, one that slides the figure in a horizontal direction, and one that slides it in a vertical direction.

Example 1 Describing a Translation

In the diagram at the right, $\triangle M'N'P'$ is the image of $\triangle MNP$ after a translation. Give a verbal description of the translation.

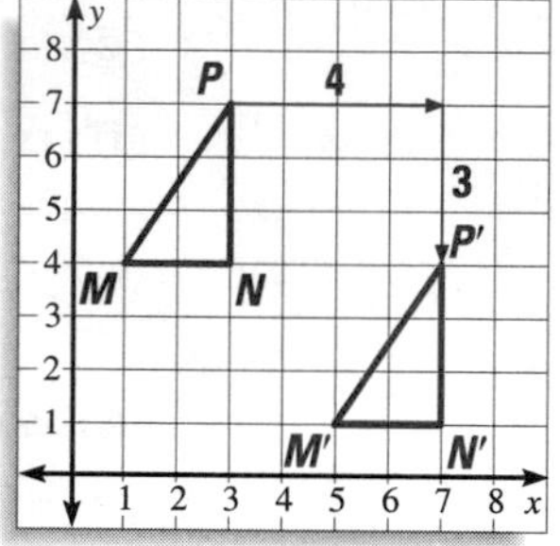

Solution

Each point on $\triangle MNP$ has been translated 4 units to the right and 3 units down.

Example 2 Translating in the Coordinate Plane

$\overline{AB}$ has endpoints at $A(-5, -4)$ and $B(-3, -1)$. Draw $\overline{AB}$ and its image after a translation of 6 units to the right and 1 unit up.

Solution

Draw $\overline{AB}$. Then move 6 units to the right and 1 unit up from point A to plot point $A'(1, -3)$. Move 6 units to the right and 1 unit up from point B to plot point $B'(3, 0)$. Connect these points to form $\overline{A'B'}$.

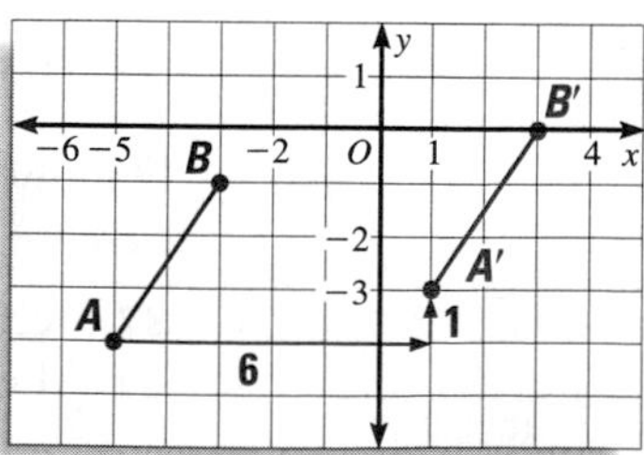

Goal 2 DESCRIBING A TRANSLATION

You can use coordinate notation to describe a translation.

Student Help

▶ **MORE EXAMPLES**

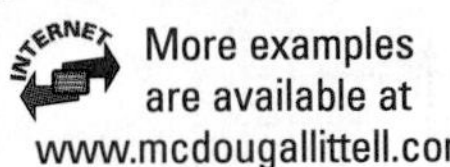

More examples are available at www.mcdougallittell.com

EXAMPLE 3 Using Coordinate Notation

Parallelogram $ABCD$ has vertices $A(-4, 3)$, $B(-1, 4)$, $C(3, 3)$, and $D(0, 2)$. The following coordinate notation describes a translation.

$$(x, y) \to (x + 2, y - 5)$$

Translate parallelogram $ABCD$. Then write a verbal description of the translation.

Solution

Add 2 to each x-coordinate and subtract 5 from each y-coordinate.

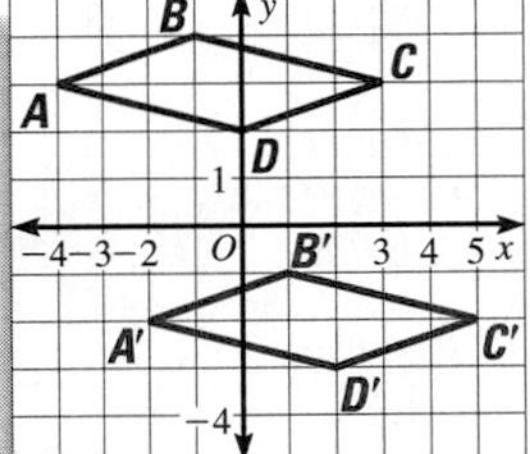

Original	Image
(x, y)	$\to (x + 2, y - 5)$
$A(-4, 3)$	$\to A'(-2, -2)$
$B(-1, 4)$	$\to B'(1, -1)$
$C(3, 3)$	$\to C'(5, -2)$
$D(0, 2)$	$\to D'(2, -3)$

Each point is translated 2 units to the right and 5 units down.

Link to Careers

COMPUTER GRAPHICS Computer graphics artists often use transformations in their work. Translations were used to create the image above from a single photo of a skier.

More about computer graphics available at www.mcdougallittell.com

EXAMPLE 4 Using Coordinate Notation

COMPUTER GRAPHICS In computer graphics, translations are used to create patterns and animations. Use coordinate notation to describe each translation.

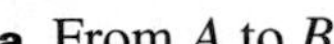

a. From A to B

b. From B to C

c. From C to D

Solution

a. The hand moves from (3, 2) to (5, 4). So, each point moves 2 units to the right and 2 units up: $(x, y) \to (x + 2, y + 2)$.

b. The hand moves from (5, 4) to (8, 6). So, each point moves 3 units to the right and 2 units up: $(x, y) \to (x + 3, y + 2)$.

c. The hand moves from (8, 6) to (9, 3). So, each point moves 1 unit to the right and 3 units down: $(x, y) \to (x + 1, y - 3)$.

Extra Example 1

In the diagram below, $\triangle A'B'C'$ is the image of $\triangle ABC$ after a translation. Give a verbal description of the translation.

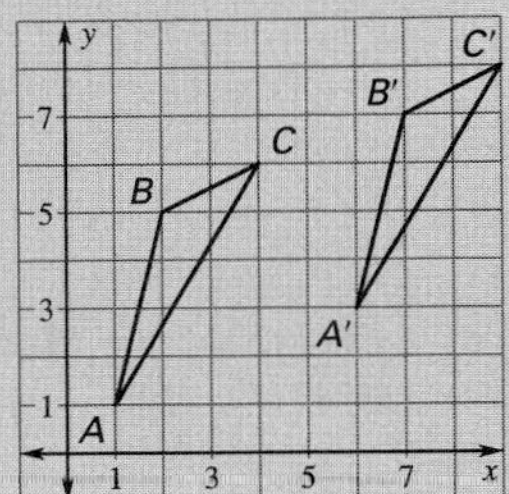

Each point on $\triangle ABC$ has been translated 5 units right and 2 units up.

Extra Example 2

$\overline{CD}$ has endpoints $C(0, 3)$ and $D(1, -1)$. Draw $\overline{CD}$ and its image after a translation of 2 units left and 1 unit down.

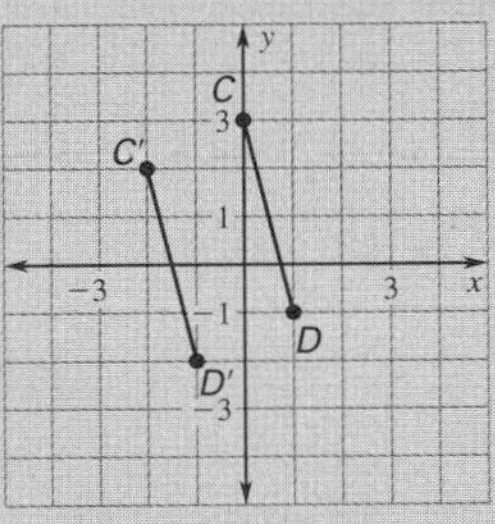

Extra Example 3

Trapezoid $PQRS$ has vertices $P(1, -1)$, $Q(1, -2)$, $R(-1, -2)$, and $S(-1, 0)$. The following coordinate notation describes a translation.

$$(x, y) \to (x - 3, y + 3)$$

Translate trapezoid $PQRS$. Then write a verbal description of the translation.

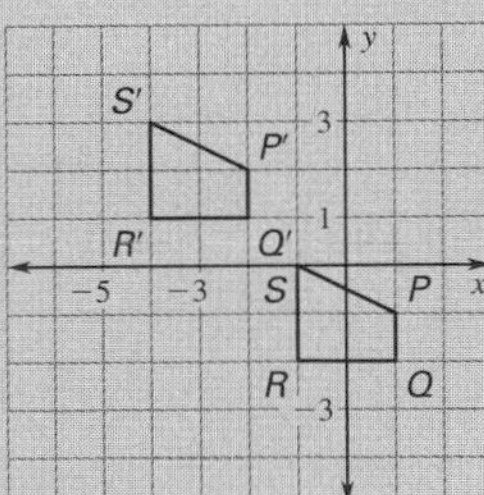

Verbal description: Each point moves 3 units to the left and 3 units up.

Extra Example 4
See next page.

Extra Example 4

Refer to Example 4. Describe the translation of the hand from *D* back to *A*. **It moves from (9, 3) to (3, 2). So it moves 6 units to the left and 1 unit down.**

Concept Check

What is the difference between a translation and a reflection? **In a translation, the figure is moved or slid. The vertices have the same orientation. In a reflection, the figure is flipped over a line of reflection and the vertices have the opposite orientation.**

3 Apply

Assignment Guide

TRANSITIONAL

Day 1: pp. 430–431 Exs. 6–12, 17–18, 21–22

AVERAGE

Day 1: pp. 430–431 Exs. 6–18, 21–22

ADVANCED

Day 1: pp. 430–431 Exs. 7–16, 19, 20*, 21–22

BLOCK SCHEDULE

pp. 430–431 Exs. 6–18, 21–22 (with 8.9)

Extra Practice

- Student Edition, pp. 704–705
- Chapter 8 Resource Book, p. 69

Homework Check

To quickly check student understanding of key concepts, go over the following exercises:

Transitional: 6, 8, 10, 12, 14
Average: 6, 8, 10, 12, 14
Advanced: 6, 8, 10, 12, 14

8–10. See Additional Answers beginning on page AA1.

8.8 Exercises

Guided Practice

1. Translation; Each point on the red figure has been translated 5 units to the right and 4 units down.

2. Translation; Each point on the red figure has been translated 2 units to the left and 3 units up.

3. Reflection; Each point in the red figure is a reflection of the blue figure in the *y*-axis.

4. Translation; Each point on the red figure has been translated 2 units to the right.

In Exercises 1–4, tell whether the red figure is a *reflection* or a *translation* of the blue figure. Describe the transformation verbally.

1.

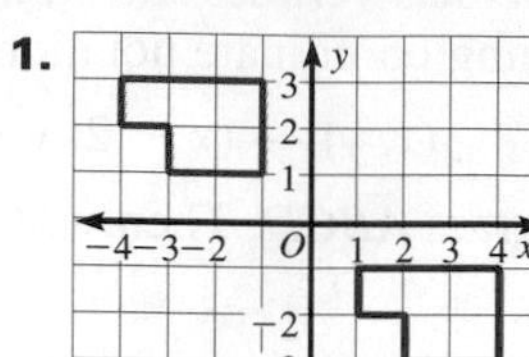

2.

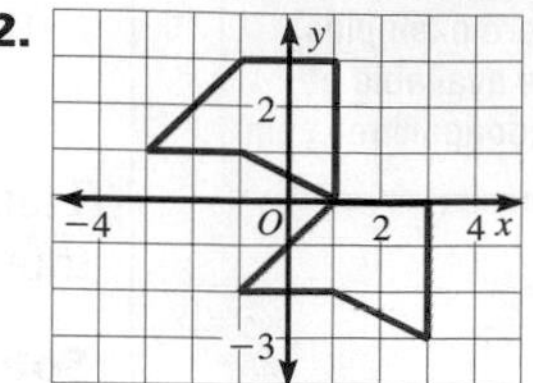

3.

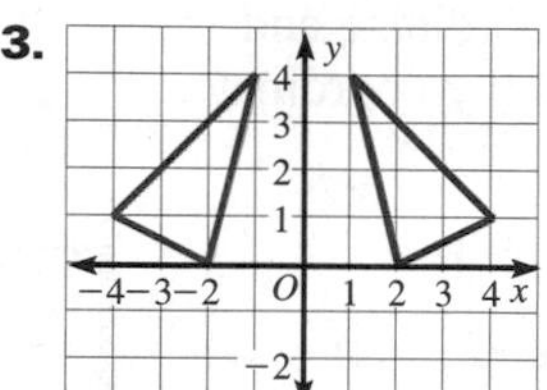

4.

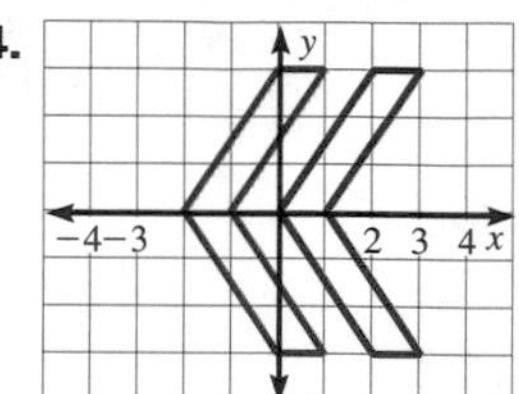

5. Match each diagram in Exercises 1–4 with one of the transformations below.

A. $(x, y) \to (x + 2, y)$ **4**

B. $(x, y) \to (-x, y)$ **3**

C. $(x, y) \to (x + 5, y - 4)$ **1**

D. $(x, y) \to (x - 2, y + 3)$ **2**

Practice and Problem Solving

Student Help

▶MORE PRACTICE
Extra practice to help you master skills is on page 705.

6. Each point on the blue figure has been translated 4 units to the right and 2 units down.

7. Each point on the blue figure has been translated 2 units to the left and 4 units up.

Write a verbal description of the transformation that maps the blue figure to the red figure.

6.

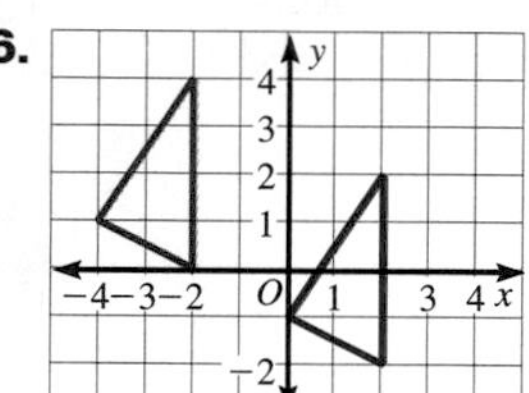

7.

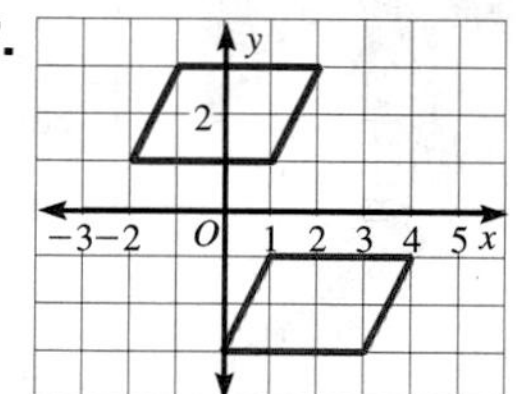

The vertices of a triangle are given. Draw the triangle in a coordinate plane. Then draw its image after the indicated translation. Use coordinate notation to describe the translation.

8. $P(1, 1)$, $Q(3, 5)$, $R(5, 4)$; Translate 2 units left and 4 units down. **$(x, y) \to (x - 2, y - 4)$; see margin.**

9. $L(-6, 0)$, $M(-6, -4)$, $N(-3, -4)$; Translate 0 units right and 5 units up. **$(x, y) \to (x, y + 5)$; see margin.**

10. $U(0, 3)$, $V(3, 0)$, $W(6, 6)$; Translate 8 units left and 8 units down. **$(x, y) \to (x - 8, y - 8)$; see margin.**

In Exercises 11–14, you are given that trapezoid *EFGH* has vertices *E*(−2, 1), *F*(−1, 3), *G*(1, 3), and *H*(4, 1). Draw trapezoid *EFGH*. Then draw the image of the trapezoid after the indicated translation.

11. $(x, y) \rightarrow (x - 3, y - 6)$ **See margin.**

12. $(x, y) \rightarrow (x + 4, y - 3)$ **See margin.**

13. $(x, y) \rightarrow (x + 5, y + 2)$ **See margin.**

14. $(x, y) \rightarrow (x, y + 4)$ **See margin.**

15. Write a verbal description of each transformation in Exercises 11–14.

15. Trapezoid *EFGH* is translated 3 units to the left and 6 units down; Trapezoid *EFGH* is translated 4 units to the right and 3 units down; Trapezoid *EFGH* is translated 5 units to the right and 2 units up; Trapezoid *EFGH* is translated 4 units up.

16. Find the area of trapezoid *EFGH* in Exercises 11–14. Then find the area of each image of trapezoid *EFGH*. What do you notice? **In each case the area is 8 square units.**

MAP DIRECTIONS In Exercises 17 and 18, use the map shown at the right.

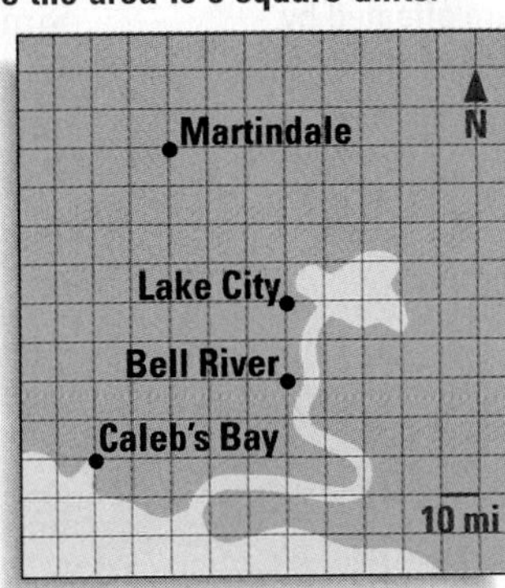

17. You leave Martindale and drive 20 miles west and 80 miles south. Find the city you reach. **Caleb's Bay**

18. You drive from Caleb's Bay to Bell River. Describe the translation verbally using east-west and north-south movements. **Drive 50 mi east and 20 mi north.**

19. MATHEMATICAL REASONING A square lies in the second quadrant of a coordinate plane. Write possible coordinates for the vertices of the square. Then use coordinate notation to describe two transformations, one that translates the square to its image in the fourth quadrant, and one that translates this image back to the original square. How is the coordinate notation for one of the translations related to the coordinate notation for the other?

19. One set of vertices for a square is (−5, 4), (−2, 4), (−2, 1) and (−5, 1). If the square is translated using $(x, y) \rightarrow (x + 7, y - 5)$, the image vertices are (2, −1), (5, −1), (5, −4), and (2, −4). To translate back to the original square, use $(x, y) \rightarrow (x - 7, y + 5)$. The coordinate notations use inverse operations such as add 7 and subtract 7.

20. CHALLENGE $\triangle ABC$ has vertices $A(0, 1)$, $B(3, 4)$, and $C(1, 5)$. The coordinates of its image after two transformations are $A''(-4, 1)$, $B''(-1, -2)$, and $C''(-3, -3)$. Describe how this result can be produced by a combination of two transformations. (*Hint:* Try a reflection followed by a translation.)

20. *Sample answer:* reflect $\triangle ABC$ in the *x*-axis, then perform the translation $(x, y) \rightarrow (x - 4, y + 2)$.

Multiple-Choice Practice

21. When the figure at the right is translated 3 units to the right and 5 units up, which point is *not* a vertex of the translated image? **B**

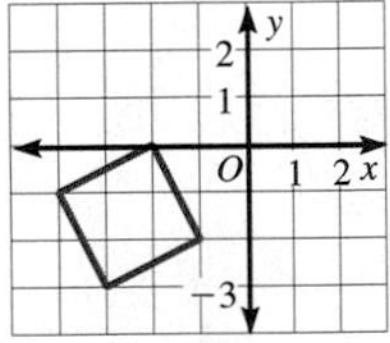

Ⓐ (1, 5) Ⓑ (2, 0) Ⓒ (2, 3) Ⓓ (−1, 4)

22. Which of the following describes the translation in Exercise 21? **J**

Ⓕ $(x, y) \rightarrow (x - 3, y - 5)$ Ⓖ $(x, y) \rightarrow (x + 3, y - 5)$

Ⓗ $(x, y) \rightarrow (x - 3, y + 5)$ Ⓙ $(x, y) \rightarrow (x + 3, y + 5)$

4 Assess

Assessment Resources

- Assessment Book (Formal Assessment and Alternative Assessment)
- Test and Practice Generator

Mini-Quiz

1. Graph the triangle whose vertices are *K*(−2, 3), *L*(1, 4), and *M*(0, −2). Then translate the triangle 3 units to the right and 2 units down. Give the coordinates of the vertices of the image. ***K*′(1, 1), *L*′(4, 2), *M*′(3, −4)**

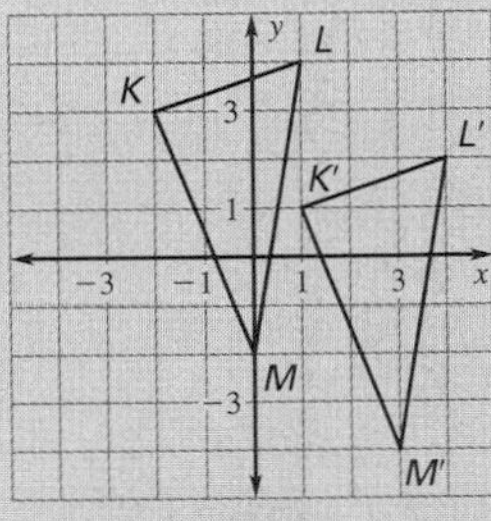

2. Write a motion rule for the translation described above. $(x, y) \rightarrow (x + 3, y - 2)$

11.

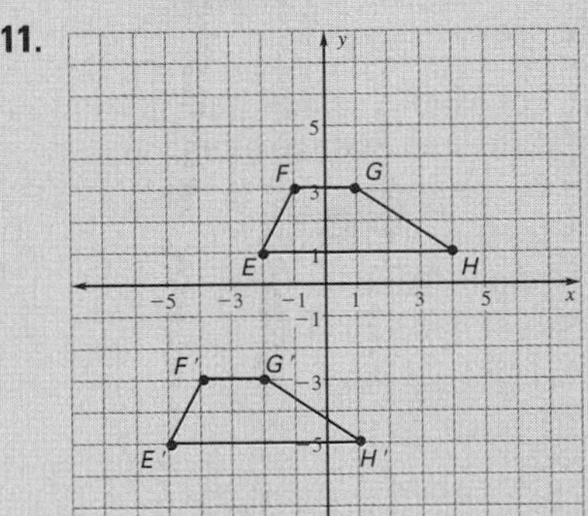

12.

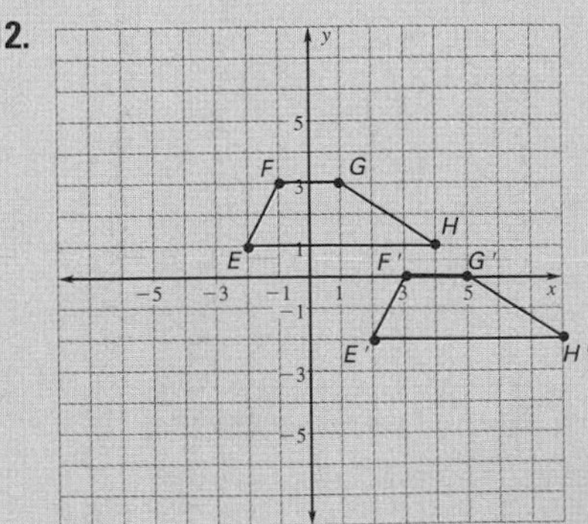

13–14. See Additional Answers beginning on page AA1.

1 Plan

Pacing

Suggested Number of Days

Transitional: 1 day
Average: 1 day
Advanced: 1 day
Block Schedule: 0.5 block with 8.8

Teaching Resources

Blacklines
(See page 382B.)

Transparencies
- Warm-Up Exercises
- Teacher Time-Savers
- English/Spanish Problem Solving
- Answers

Technology
- Electronic Teacher Tools
- Test and Practice Generator

2 Teach

Math Reasoning

For Mathematical Background Notes on mathematical reasoning related to this lesson, please refer to pages 382E and 382F in this Teacher's Edition.

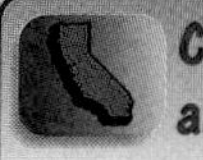

California Standards and Assessment

CA Standard: MG 2.0

8.9 Similarity

California Standards

In this lesson you'll:

- Know how perimeter and area are affected by changes of scale. (MG 2.0)

Goal 1 Using Properties of Similar Figures

If the corresponding angles of two figures are congruent and the ratios of the lengths of their corresponding sides are equal, the figures are **similar**. Similar figures are the same shape, but are not necessarily the same size. So, two congruent figures are always similar, but two similar figures are not necessarily congruent. In the diagram below, quadrilateral *ABCD* is similar to quadrilateral *EFGH*. You can write this statement as quadrilateral $ABCD \sim$ quadrilateral $EFGH$.

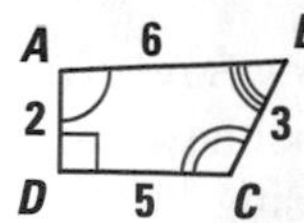

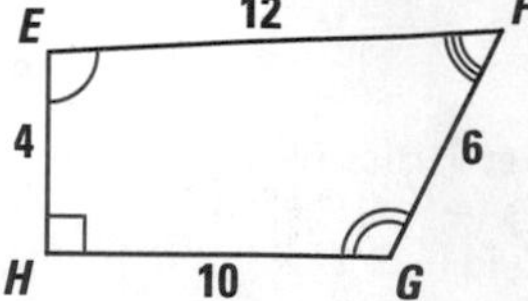

CORRESPONDING ANGLES

$\angle A \cong \angle E \quad \angle C \cong \angle G$

$\angle B \cong \angle F \quad \angle D \cong \angle H$

CORRESPONDING SIDES

$$\frac{AB}{EF} = \frac{BC}{FG} = \frac{CD}{GH} = \frac{AD}{EH} = \frac{1}{2}$$

EXAMPLE 1 Properties of Similarity

$\triangle ABC \sim \triangle DEF$. Describe the relationships among the angles and sides of the triangle.

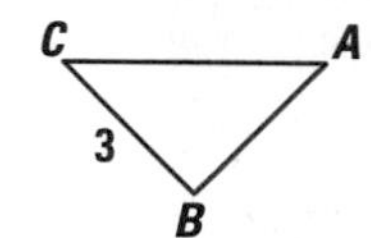

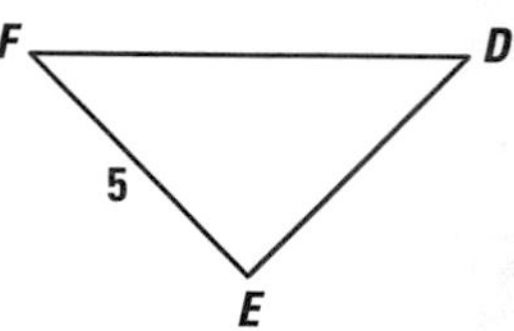

Solution

Corresponding angles are congruent. That is, $\angle A \cong \angle D$, $\angle B \cong \angle E$, and $\angle C \cong \angle F$.

The ratios of the lengths of corresponding sides are equal. The lengths of corresponding sides $\overline{BC}$ and $\overline{EF}$ are given, so this ratio is 3 : 5.

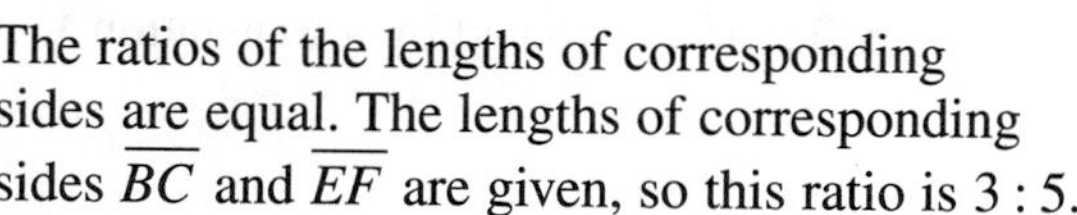

$$\frac{BC}{EF} = \frac{AB}{DE} = \frac{AC}{DF} = \frac{3}{5}$$

To show that two polygons are similar, you must show that their corresponding angles are congruent and that the ratios of the lengths of their corresponding sides are equal. To show that two *triangles* are similar, you can use the *angle-angle* (AA) similarity postulate:

If two angles of one triangle are congruent to two angles of another triangle, then the triangles are similar.

Student Help

▶ **LOOK BACK**
For help with writing and solving a proportion, see page 334.

Student Help

▶ **MORE EXAMPLES**

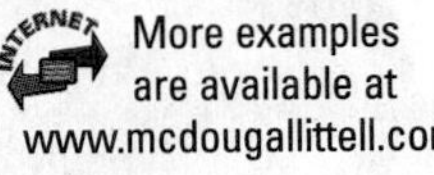

More examples are available at www.mcdougallittell.com

EXAMPLE 2 Finding Side Lengths

Find the length of $\overline{RS}$.

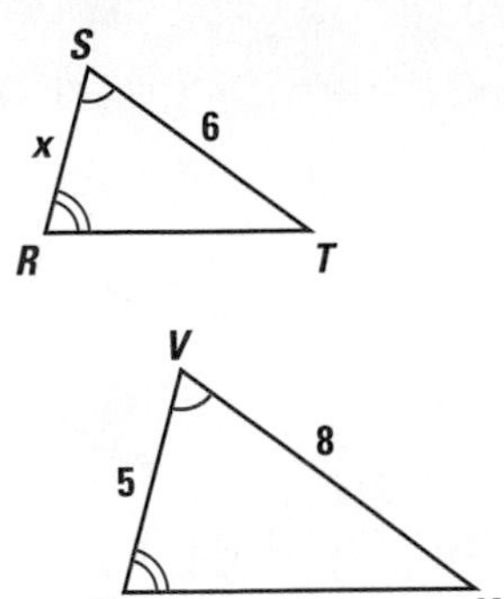

Solution

Because two angles of $\triangle RST$ are congruent to two angles of $\triangle UVW$, $\triangle RST \sim \triangle UVW$ by the AA similarity postulate. Write and solve a proportion to find the length of $\overline{RS}$.

$\frac{RS}{UV} = \frac{ST}{VW}$ Write proportion.

$\frac{x}{5} = \frac{6}{8}$ Substitute.

$8x = 30$ Cross product property

$x = 3.75$ Divide each side by 8.

ANSWER ▶ The length of $\overline{RS}$ is 3.75 units.

If two polygons are similar, the ratio of the lengths of two corresponding side lengths is called the **scale factor**. In the triangles above, the scale factor of $\triangle RST$ to $\triangle UVW$ is $\frac{6}{8}$, or $\frac{3}{4}$.

EXAMPLE 3 Using a Scale Factor

You are designing a poster to advertise the next meeting of the Space Club. You begin by sketching the design shown at the right. The scale factor of the actual poster to your sketch is 4 : 1. Find the height and the width of the actual poster.

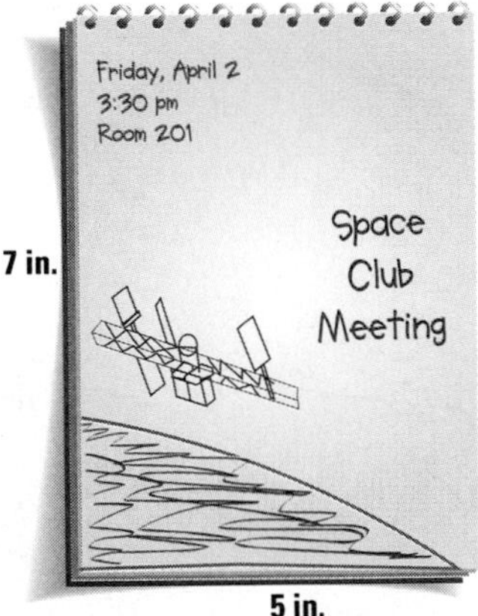

Solution

Use the scale factor to find the height h and the width w of the poster.

$\frac{\text{Poster height}}{\text{Sketch height}} = \text{Scale factor}$ $\qquad$ $\frac{\text{Poster width}}{\text{Sketch width}} = \text{Scale factor}$

$\frac{h}{7 \text{ inches}} = \frac{4}{1}$ $\qquad$ $\frac{w}{5 \text{ inches}} = \frac{4}{1}$

$h = 4(7)$ $\qquad$ $w = 4(5)$

$h = 28$ $\qquad$ $w = 20$

ANSWER ▶ The poster has a height of 28 inches and a width of 20 inches.

Teaching Tip

The order of the vertices in a similarity statement is important. The similarity statement in Example 1 indicates these correspondences: $A \leftrightarrow D$, $B \leftrightarrow E$, and $C \leftrightarrow F$. Point out that these correspondences can be seen in both the angle measure statements and the ratios of lengths.

Extra Example 1

Given that $\triangle JKL \sim \triangle XYZ$, write statements describing the relationships among their angles and sides. **$m\angle J = m\angle X$, $m\angle K = m\angle Y$, $m\angle L = m\angle Z$, and $\frac{JK}{XY} = \frac{KL}{YZ} = \frac{JL}{XZ}$**

Extra Example 2

Find the length of $\overline{AB}$.

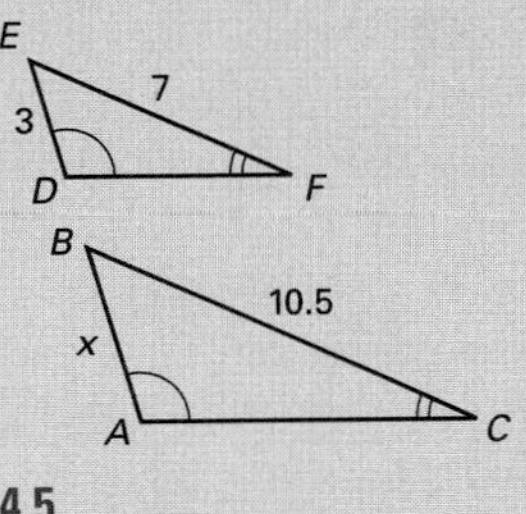

4.5

Extra Example 3

You are designing a poster to advertise the next meeting of the Math Club. You begin by drawing a sketch of the poster that is 6 in. wide and 8 in. high. You decide that the scale factor of the actual poster to your sketch is 6 : 1. Find the height and width of the actual poster. **The poster will have a width of 36 in. and a height of 48 in.**

Extra Example 4

Find the perimeters of the sketch and the actual poster in Extra Example 3. Then find the ratio of the perimeter of the actual poster to the perimeter of the sketch. Compare this ratio with the scale factor. **28 in., 168 in.; the ratio, $\frac{6}{1}$, is the same as the scale factor.**

Extra Example 5

Find the areas of the sketch and the actual poster in Extra Example 3. Then find the ratio of the area of the actual poster to the area of the sketch. Compare this ratio with the scale factor. **48 in.^{2}, 1728 in.^{2}; the ratio, $\frac{36}{1}$, is the square of the scale factor.**

Math Reasoning

The precise definitions of congruence and similarity are as follows.

Two figures F and F' are congruent if there is a one-to-one correspondence between their points such that if P and Q are points of F and P' and Q' the corresponding points of F', then the distance from P' to Q' is equal to the distance from P to Q.

Two figures F and F' are similar, with scale factor $k > 0$, if there is a one-to-one correspondence between them such that for each pair of points P and Q of F and the corresponding pair P' and Q' of F', the ratio of the distance between P' and Q' to the distance between P and Q is k. It can be shown that two polygons whose corresponding angles are congruent and whose corresponding sides have lengths in a fixed ratio are similar in the sense just described.

Concept Check

If two figures are similar, what is the relationship of their perimeters and of their areas? **The ratio of the perimeters is equal to the scale factor; the ratio of the areas is equal to the square of the scale factor.**

Goal 2 COMPARING PERIMETERS AND AREAS

EXAMPLE 4 Comparing Perimeters

Using the information from Example 3, find the perimeter of your sketch of the poster and the perimeter of the actual poster. Then find the ratio of the poster's perimeter to the sketch's perimeter. Compare this ratio with the scale factor.

Solution

Sketch:

Perimeter $= 2(5) + 2(7) = 24$ inches

Poster:

Perimeter $= 2(20) + 2(28) = 96$ inches

The ratio of the poster's perimeter to the sketch's perimeter is:

$$\frac{\text{Perimeter of poster}}{\text{Perimeter of sketch}} = \frac{96 \text{ inches}}{24 \text{ inches}} = \frac{4}{1}$$

ANSWER ▶ The ratio is the same as the scale factor.

EXAMPLE 5 Comparing Areas

Using the information from Example 3, find the area of your sketch of the poster and the area of the actual poster. Then find the ratio of the poster's area to the sketch's area. Compare this ratio with the scale factor.

Solution

Area of sketch $= 5 \times 7 = 35$ square inches

Area of poster $= 20 \times 28 = 560$ square inches

The ratio of the poster's area to the sketch's area is:

$$\frac{\text{Area of poster}}{\text{Area of sketch}} = \frac{560 \text{ in.}^2}{35 \text{ in.}^2} = \frac{16}{1}$$

ANSWER ▶ The ratio of the areas is the square of the scale factor.

The results you saw in Examples 4 and 5 are true in general for all pairs of similar figures.

- If two figures are similar, then the ratio of their perimeters is equal to the scale factor.
- If two figures are similar, then the ratio of their areas is the square of the scale factor.

8.9 Exercises

Guided Practice

In Exercises 1–6, use the triangles below.

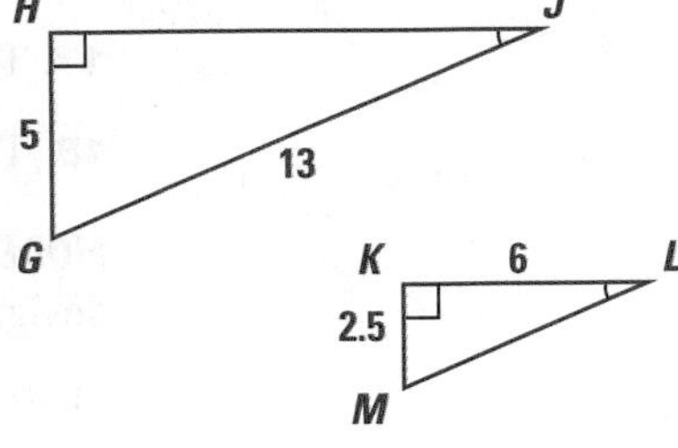

1. Explain how you know that $\triangle HJG \sim \triangle KLM$. **AA**

2. Copy and complete the statement: $m\angle H = m\angle$ __?__. **$m\angle H = m\angle K$**

3. Copy and complete the statement: $\frac{GH}{MK} = \frac{HJ}{?} = \frac{?}{LM}$ **$\frac{GH}{MK} = \frac{HJ}{KL} = \frac{JG}{LM}$**

4. Find the scale factor of $\triangle HJG$ to $\triangle KLM$. **2:1**

5. Find the lengths of $\overline{ML}$ and $\overline{HJ}$. **$ML = 6.5$ and $HJ = 12$**

6. Find the ratio of the perimeters of $\triangle HJG$ and $\triangle KLM$ and the ratio of the areas of $\triangle HJG$ and $\triangle KLM$. How are these ratios related to the scale factor from Exercise 5? **The ratio of the perimeters is 2:1 and the ratio of the areas is 4:1. The ratio of the perimeters is equal to the scale factor and the ratio of the areas is the square of the scale factor.**

Practice and Problem Solving

Student Help

▸MORE PRACTICE Extra practice to help you master skills is on page 705.

In Exercises 7–9, quadrilateral *QRST* ~ quadrilateral *WXYZ*.

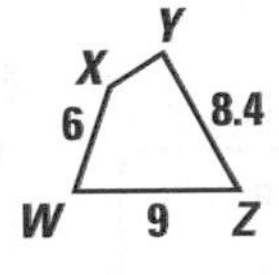

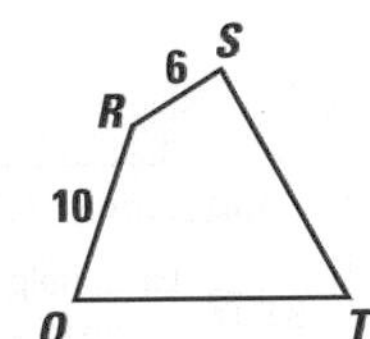

7. Write a statement describing the relationships between the corresponding angles of quadrilaterals *QRST* and *WXYZ*. **The corresponding angles are congruent.**

8. Write a statement describing the relationships between the corresponding sides of quadrilaterals *QRST* and *WXYZ*.

8. The corresponding sides of quadrilateral *QRST* and quadrilateral *WXYZ* are in the ratio 5:3.

9. Find the lengths of $\overline{QT}$, $\overline{ST}$, and $\overline{XY}$. **$QT = 15$, $ST = 14$, $XY = 3.6$**

In Exercises 10–13, you are given a pair of similar figures. Solve for *x*.

10.

$x = 12$

11.

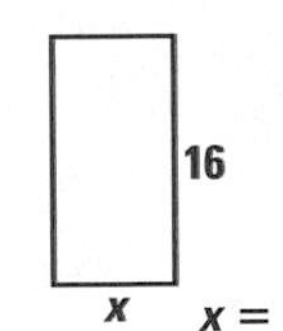

$x = 8$

12.

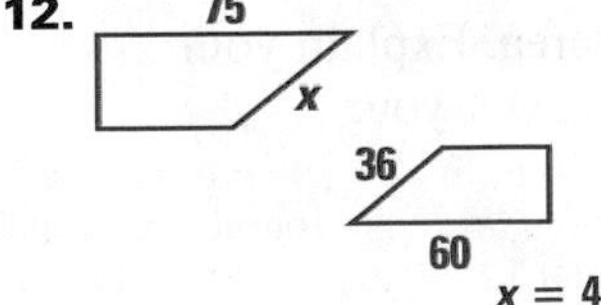

$x = 45$

13.

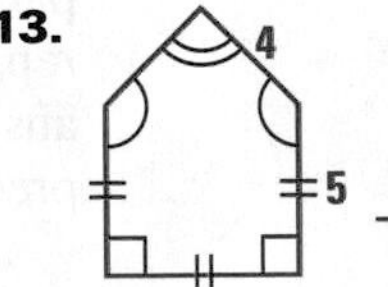

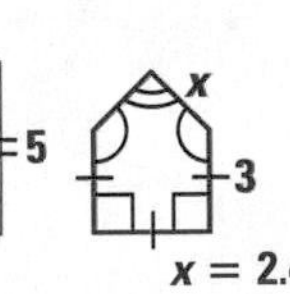

$x = 2.4$

3 Apply

Assignment Guide

TRANSITIONAL
Day 1: EP p. 702 Exs. 20–23; pp. 435–437 Exs. 7–13, 23–25, 29–33, 38

AVERAGE
Day 1: pp. 435–437 Exs. 10–22, 29–33, 38

ADVANCED
Day 1: pp. 435–437 Exs. 10–22, 26–27, 28*, 29–31, 37–38

BLOCK SCHEDULE
pp. 435–437 Exs. 10–22, 29–33, 38 (with 8.8)

Extra Practice

- Student Edition, pp. 704–705
- Chapter 8 Resource Book, p. 78

Homework Check

To quickly check student understanding of key concepts, go over the following exercises:

Transitional: 9, 10, 12, 23, 24
Average: 10, 11, 12, 20, 22
Advanced: 10, 11, 12, 20, 22

Problem Solving

Exercises 11 and 12
Have students trace the figures, turning their paper so that the figures have the same orientation.

MATHEMATICAL REASONING In Exercises 14–18, complete the statement using *sometimes, always,* or *never*. Explain your reasoning.

14. A right triangle and an equilateral triangle are __?__ similar. **never**

15. Two rectangles are __?__ similar. **sometimes**

16. If one acute angle of a right triangle is congruent to an acute angle of another right triangle, the triangles are __?__ similar. **always**

17. Two congruent polygons are __?__ similar. **always**

18. Two regular triangles are __?__ similar. **always**

MODEL CAR In Exercises 19–22, use the following information. You are designing a model car that is a scale replica of a full-sized car. The scale factor of the model to the actual car is $\frac{1}{6}$. The license plate on the full-sized car is 6 inches high and 12 inches wide.

19. Find the height and width of the license plate on the model car. **1 in. high and 2 in. wide**

20. Find the perimeter and area of the license plate on the actual car. Then find the perimeter and area of the license plate on the model car.

20. On the actual car the perimeter is 36 inches and the area is 72 square inches. On the model car the perimeter is 6 inches and the area is 2 square inches.

21. Find the ratio of the perimeter of the model car's license plate to the perimeter of the actual car's license plate. How does this ratio compare with the scale factor? **The ratio is $\frac{1}{6}$; the same as the scale factor.**

22. Find the ratio of the area of of the model car's license plate to the area of the actual car's license plate. How does this ratio compare with the scale factor? **The ratio is $\frac{1}{36}$; the square of the scale factor.**

Student Help

▶ HOMEWORK HELP

INTERNET Extra help with problem solving in Exs. 23–25 is available at www.mcdougallittell.com

PAINTING In Exercises 23–25, use the following information. You work in a museum that sells the postcard below. The postcard shows a reproduction of a painting. The actual painting is about 28.9 centimeters wide.

23. Find the scale factor of the actual painting to the reproduction. Write the scale factor as a decimal rounded to the nearest tenth. **3.7**

24. Find the height of the actual painting rounded to the nearest tenth of a centimeter. **45.7 cm**

25. Predict how many times greater the actual painting's perimeter is than the reproduction's perimeter. Predict how many times greater the painting's area is than the reproduction's area. Explain your answers. Then check your predictions. **The painting's perimeter is about 3.7 times the perimeter of the reproduction and the area is about 13.4 times the area of the reproduction.**

7.9 cm

12.5 cm

***Jeanne Hébuterne* (1918), Amedeo Modigliani**

LAUNCH TOWERS In Exercises 26 and 27, use the following information. A woman 5 feet tall is standing near a rocket launch tower, as shown at the right. The right triangles formed by the tower and its shadow and the woman and her shadow are similar. The woman's shadow is 3 feet long, and the tower's shadow is 240 feet long.

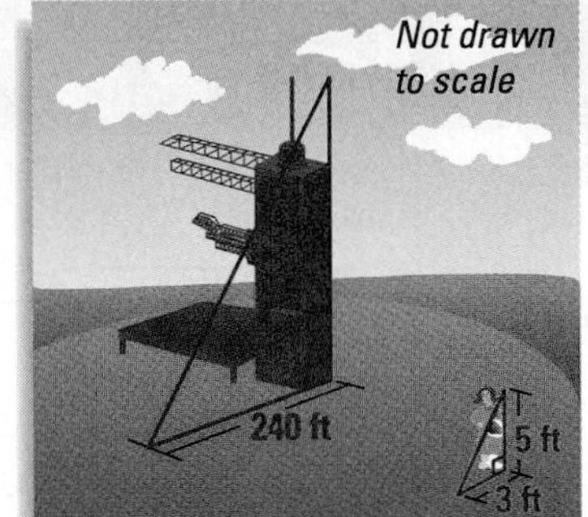

26. The ratios are equal because they are corresponding sides of similar triangles.

26. Explain why the ratio of the tower's height to the woman's height is equal to the ratio of their shadows.

27. Find the height of the launch tower. **400 ft**

28. CHALLENGE Two rectangles are similar. The area of the first rectangle is 108 square inches. Its width is 9 inches. The area of the second rectangle is 12 square inches. Find its length and width.
The width is 3 inches and the height is 4 inches.

Multiple-Choice Practice

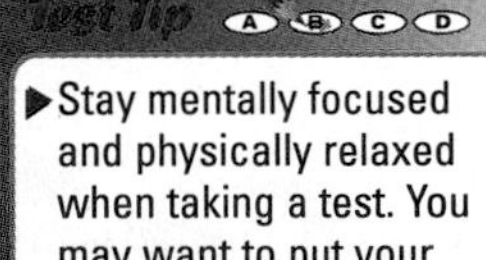

▶Stay mentally focused and physically relaxed when taking a test. You may want to put your pencil down and take a couple of deep breaths before going on to new exercises.

29. What is the value of x? **D**

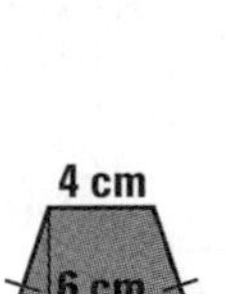

Ⓐ 2 Ⓑ 3

Ⓒ 5 Ⓓ 8

30. The two trapezoids at the right are similar. What is the area of the larger trapezoid? **H**

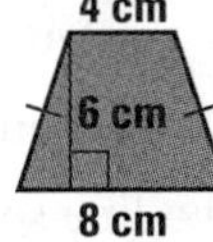

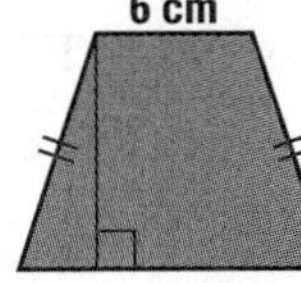

Ⓕ 11 cm^2 Ⓖ 36 cm^2

Ⓗ 81 cm^2 Ⓙ 162 cm^2

Mixed Review

31. Rectangle $ABCD$ has vertices $A(-2, -2)$, $B(-2, 5)$, $C(3, 5)$, and $D(3, -2)$. Draw rectangle $ABCD$ in a coordinate plane and find its perimeter. *(3.8)* **The perimeter is 24**
See margin.

In Exercises 32–37, solve the equation. Round your answer to the nearest tenth. *(4.7)*

32. $4x + 5 = 11.3$ **1.6**

33. $22m + 12 = 14.3$ **0.1**

34. $23n - 9.5 = 24$ **1.5**

35. $8.3 - 12t = 97$ **−7.4**

36. $5(3s - 4.1) = 5s + 0.3$ **2.1**

37. $15w - 7.7 = 2(10w + 20)$ **−9.5**

38. Find the area of a trapezoid whose bases are 3 feet and 6 feet and whose height is 5 feet. *(8.6)* **22.5 ft^2**

4 Assess

Assessment Resources

- Assessment Book (Formal Assessment and Alternative Assessment)
- Test and Practice Generator

Mini-Quiz

A scale drawing of a rectangular swimming pool is $1\frac{1}{4}$ ft by $1\frac{3}{4}$ ft. The scale factor of the swimming pool to the drawing is 16 : 1.

1. Find the dimensions of the actual swimming pool. **20 ft by 28 ft**
2. Find the area of the drawing and the area of the actual swimming pool. Then find the ratio of the area of the swimming pool to the area of the drawing.
   drawing area: $2\frac{3}{16}$ ft^2 or 2.1875 ft^2
   pool area: 560 ft^2
   ratio of the areas: 256 : 1 or 16^2 : 1

31.

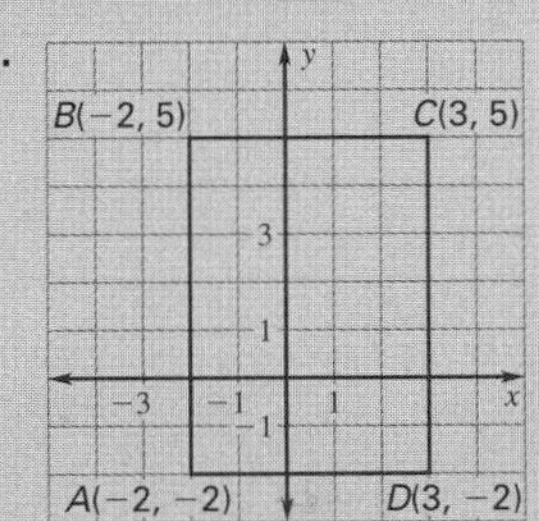

Additional Resources

The following resources are available to help review the material in this chapter:

Technology

- Personal Student Tutor
- Test and Practice Generator

Chapter 8 Chapter Summary and Review

VOCABULARY

- **point, line, plane,** *p. 385*
- **ray,** *p. 385*
- **line segment,** *p. 385*
- **congruent,** *pp. 385, 391, 412*
- **intersection,** *p. 386*
- **parallel lines,** *p. 386*
- **angle, vertex of angle,** *p. 390*
  - **acute angle,** *p. 391*
  - **right angle,** *p. 391*
  - **obtuse angle,** *p. 391*
  - **straight angle,** *p. 391*
- **angle bisector,** *pp. 391, 395*
- **complementary angles,** *p. 391*
- **supplementary angles,** *p. 391*
- **vertical angles,** *p. 398*
- **perpendicular lines,** *p. 398*
- **transversal,** *p. 399*
- **corresponding angles,** *p. 399*
- **triangle (scalene, isosceles, equilateral, acute, obtuse, equiangular, right),** *p. 404*
- **quadrilateral,** *p. 405*
  - **parallelogram,** *p. 405*
  - **rhombus,** *p. 405*
  - **trapezoid,** *p. 405*
  - **isosceles trapezoid,** *p. 405*
  - **kite,** *p. 405*
- **midpoint,** *p. 403*
- **perpendicular bisector,** *p. 403*
- **altitude of a triangle,** *p. 410*
- **polygon, vertex of a polygon,** *p. 412*
- **regular polygon,** *p. 413*
- **diagonal of polygon,** *p. 414*
- **reflection,** *p. 423*
- **line symmetry,** *p. 424*
- **transformation,** *p. 428*
- **translation,** *p. 428*
- **similar,** *p. 432*
- **scale factor,** *p. 433*

8.1 POINTS, LINES, AND PLANES

Examples on pp. 385–386

EXAMPLES $\overleftrightarrow{AG}$ and $\overleftrightarrow{BH}$ are parallel. $\overleftrightarrow{CF}$ and $\overleftrightarrow{BH}$ intersect at point D. Two other names for $\overleftrightarrow{EG}$ are $\overleftrightarrow{GA}$ and $\overleftrightarrow{EA}$. $\overline{BD}$ and $\overline{BH}$ are two line segments on $\overleftrightarrow{HD}$. $\overrightarrow{DB}$ and $\overrightarrow{DH}$ extend in opposite directions from point D.

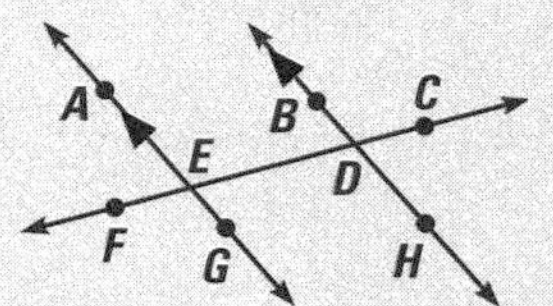

1. Write two other names for $\overrightarrow{FE}$. $\overrightarrow{FD}$ **and** $\overrightarrow{FC}$
2. Name five line segments that have D as an endpoint. $\overline{CD}$, $\overline{BD}$, $\overline{DH}$, $\overline{ED}$, $\overline{FD}$

8.2 NAMING, MEASURING, AND DRAWING ANGLES

Examples on pp. 390–392

EXAMPLES Angles are classified by their measures.

$m\angle ABD = 145°$, so $\angle ABD$ is obtuse.
$m\angle DBC = 35°$, so $\angle DBC$ is acute.
$m\angle ABC = 180°$, so $\angle ABC$ is straight.

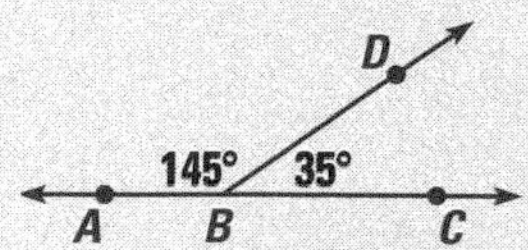

In Exercises 3 and 4, use the diagram.

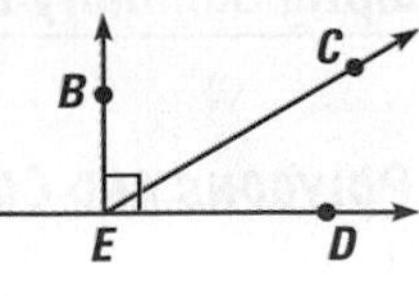

3. Name an obtuse angle and a right angle. **obtuse: $\angle AEC$, right: $\angle BED$**

4. Name two complementary angles. Name two supplementary angles. **$\angle CED$ and $\angle BEC$; $\angle AEC$ and $\angle CED$ or $\angle AEB$ and $\angle DEB$**

8.3 Parallel and Perpendicular Lines

Examples on pp. 398–399

EXAMPLE **Find each angle whose measure is 60°. Explain your reasoning.**

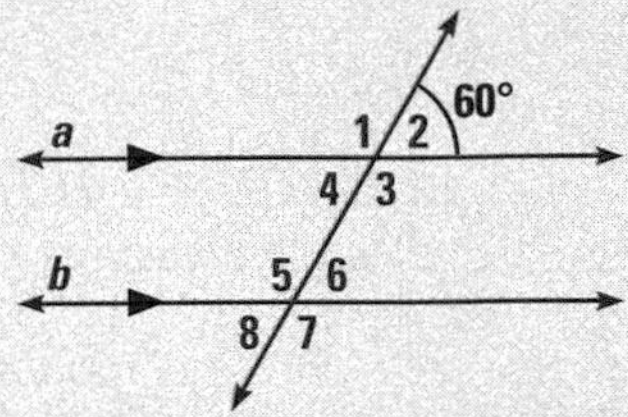

Because lines a and b are parallel, $\angle 6$ and $\angle 2$ are congruent corresponding angles. So $m\angle 6 = 60°$.

Because $\angle 4$ and $\angle 2$ are vertical angles, $\angle 4 \cong \angle 2$, and $m\angle 4 = 60°$. Similarly, $\angle 8 \cong \angle 6$, so $m\angle 8 = 60°$.

5. Find $m\angle 7$. Then name each angle that has the same measure as $\angle 7$. Explain your reasoning. **$m\angle 7 + m\angle 6 = 180°$; $m\angle 7 = 120°$; $\angle 5$, $\angle 3$, $\angle 1$; $\angle 5$ and $\angle 7$ are vertical angles, $\angle 3$ and $\angle 7$ are congruent corresponding angles, $\angle 3$ and $\angle 1$ are vertical angles.**

8.4 Triangles and Quadrilaterals

Examples on pp. 404–406

EXAMPLES **Classify the triangle by its angles and by its sides. Classify the quadrilateral using the given markings.**

a.

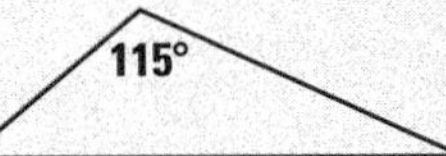

No sides are marked as having the same length, and one angle is greater than 90°: obtuse scalene triangle

b.

Exactly one pair of sides are parallel, and the nonparallel sides are congruent: isosceles trapezoid

Classify each triangle by its angles and by its sides. Classify each quadrilateral using the given markings.

6. 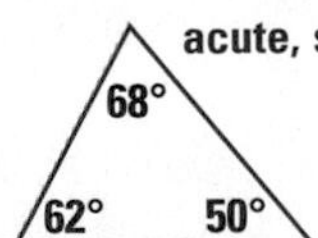

acute, scalene

7. 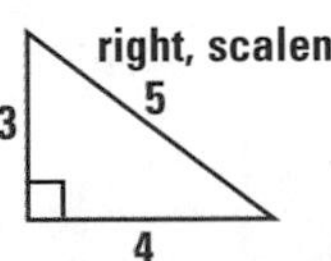

right, scalene

8. 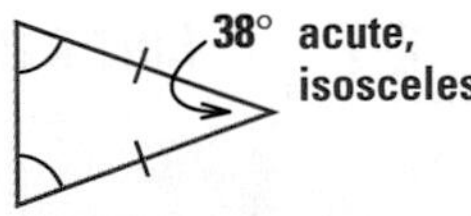

acute, isosceles

9. 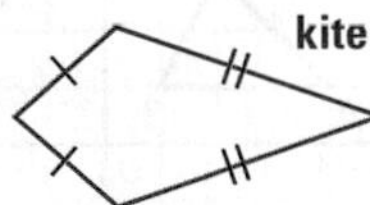
kite

10. 
rhombus

11. 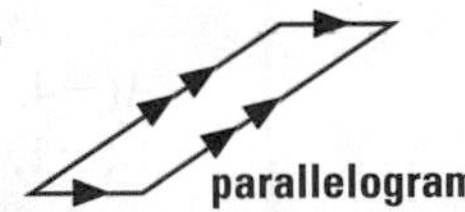
parallelogram

8.5 POLYGONS AND CONGRUENCE

Examples on pp. 412–414

EXAMPLE **Given that quadrilateral *PQRS* ≅ quadrilateral *EFGH*, list all congruences.**

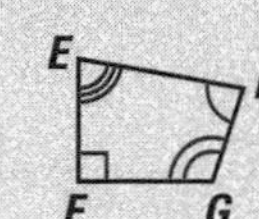

$\angle P \cong \angle E$ $\quad \angle Q \cong \angle F$ $\quad \angle R \cong \angle G$ $\quad \angle S \cong \angle H$

$\overline{PQ} \cong \overline{EF}$ $\quad \overline{QR} \cong \overline{FG}$ $\quad \overline{RS} \cong \overline{GH}$ $\quad \overline{SP} \cong \overline{HE}$

12. $\triangle BCD \cong \triangle HGF$. Find the indicated angle measures. **$m\angle B = 45°$, $m\angle D = 85°$, $m\angle G = 50°$**

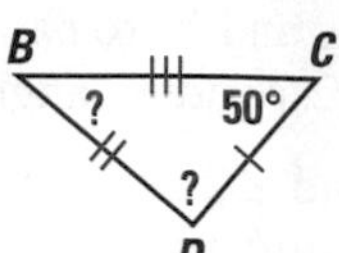

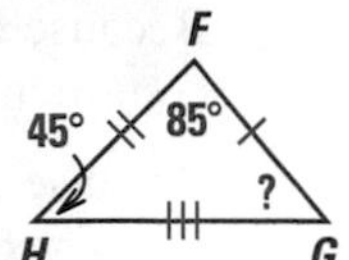

8.6 AREAS OF POLYGONS

Examples on pp. 419–420

EXAMPLES **Find the area of the polygon.**

a.

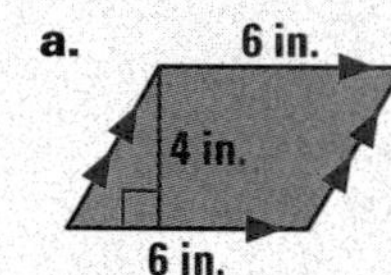

$A = bh$
$= 6(4)$
$= 24 \text{ in.}^2$

b.

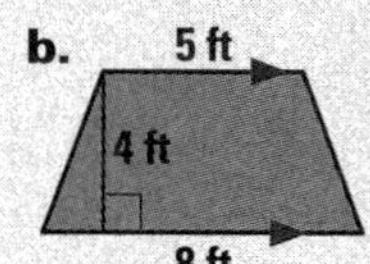

$A = \frac{1}{2}(b_1 + b_2)h$
$= \frac{1}{2}(5 + 8)(4)$
$= 26 \text{ ft}^2$

Find the area of the polygon.

13. **4500 ft²**

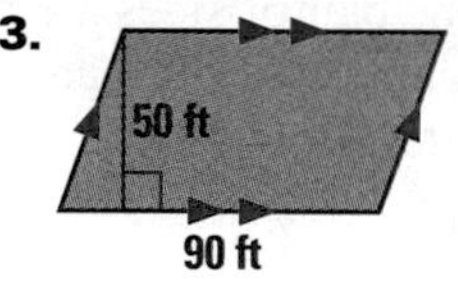

14. **4200 ft²**

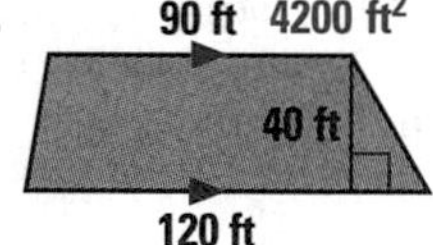

15. **1550 m²**

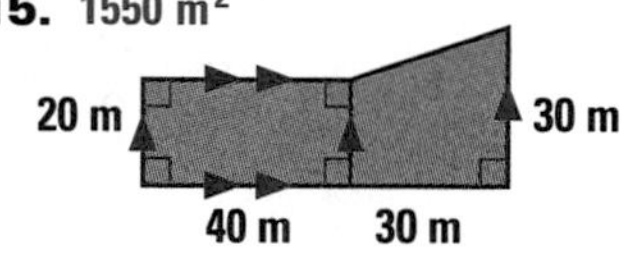

8.7 LINE REFLECTIONS

Examples on pp. 423–424

EXAMPLE **Use coordinate notation to describe the reflection.**

$A(-4, 1) \to A'(4, 1)$, $B(-2, 3) \to B'(2, 3)$, and $C(-1, 1) \to C'(1, 1)$. So, $(x, y) \to (-x, y)$.

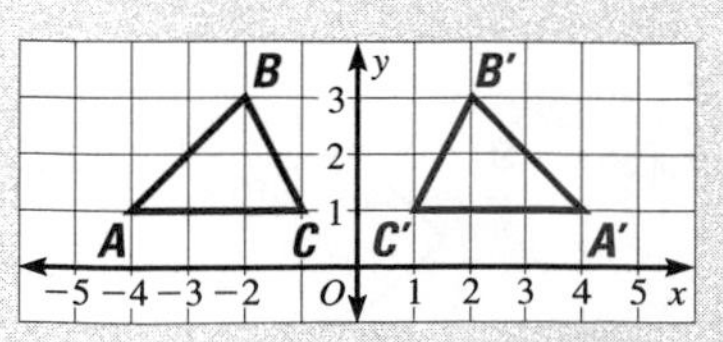

Plot the given points and connect them to form a polygon. Then perform the indicated reflection. Identify the line of reflection.

16. $A(-4, 0)$, $B(0, 3)$, $C(3, 1)$; reflection: $(x, y) \to (-x, y)$ **Line of reflection is *y*-axis; see margin.**

17. $Q(-3, -3)$, $R(-3, 3)$, $S(4, 3)$, $T(1, -3)$; reflection: $(x, y) \to (x, -y)$ **Line of reflection is *x*-axis; see margin.**

8.8 TRANSLATIONS

Examples on pp. 428–429

EXAMPLE **Draw the image of $\triangle FGH$ after the translation $(x, y) \to (x + 3, y - 2)$.**

$F(-4, 1) \to F'(-1, -1)$

$G(-1, 3) \to G'(2, 1)$

$H(-2, -1) \to H'(1, -3)$

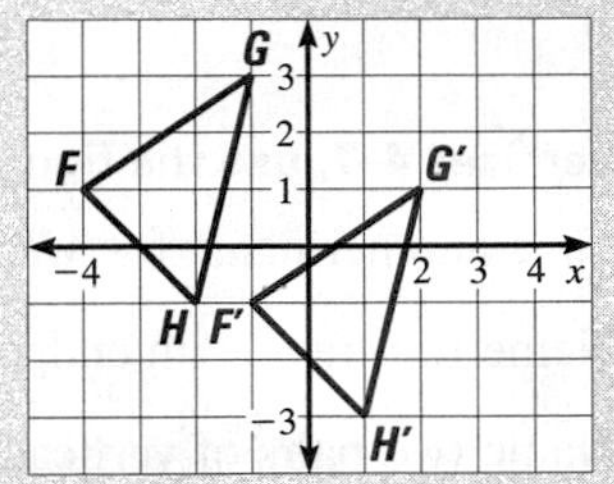

18. $\triangle XYZ$ has vertices $X(-1, 1)$, $Y(4, -1)$, and $Z(3, 3)$. Draw $\triangle XYZ$ in a coordinate plane. Then draw its image after a translation 3 units left and 4 units down. Use coordinate notation to describe the translation. **$(x, y) \to (x - 3, y - 4)$; see margin.**

Parallelogram *CDEF* has vertices $C(-1, -1)$, $D(-2, 1)$, $E(1, 3)$, and $F(2, 1)$. Draw the parallelogram and its image after the indicated translation.

19. $(x, y) \to (x - 1, y - 3)$ **See margin.** **20.** $(x, y) \to (x + 3, y - 4)$ **See margin.**

8.9 SIMILARITY

Examples on pp. 432–434

EXAMPLE **Quadrilateral *KLMN* ~ quadrilateral *QRST*. List the pairs of corresponding angles. Find the scale factor of *QRST* to *KLMN*.**

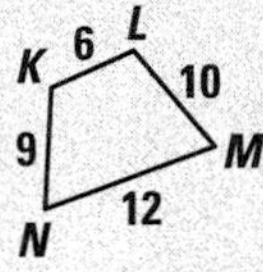

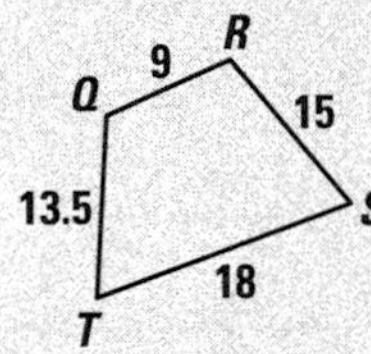

$m\angle K = m\angle Q$ $m\angle L = m\angle R$
$m\angle M = m\angle S$ $m\angle N = m\angle T$

The ratios of the corresponding side lengths are equal. This ratio is the scale factor.

$\frac{QR}{KL} = \frac{RS}{LM} = \frac{ST}{MN} = \frac{TQ}{NK} = \frac{3}{2}$ Scale factor

Use the diagram, in which $\triangle UVW \sim \triangle XYZ$.

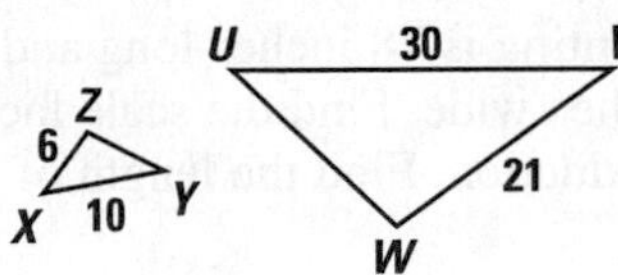

21. Find the scale factor of $\triangle UVW$ to $\triangle XYZ$. **3:1**

22. Find the length of $\overline{UW}$. **18**

23. Find the length of $\overline{YZ}$. **7**

16.

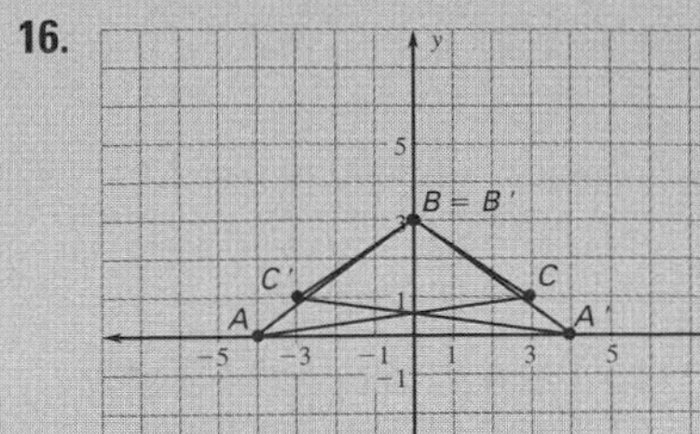

17.

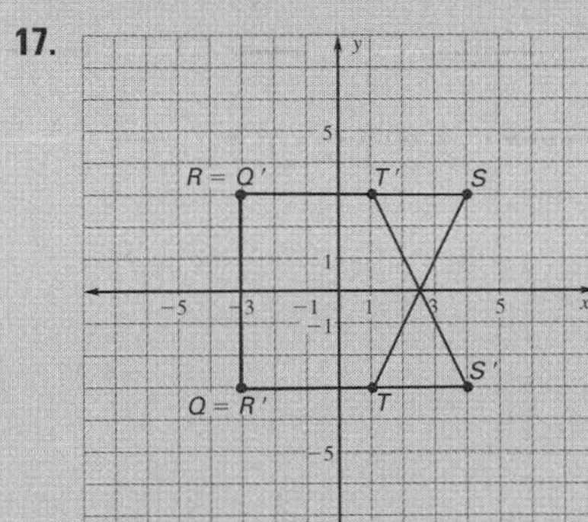

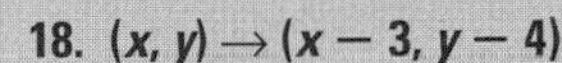
18. $(x, y) \to (x - 3, y - 4)$

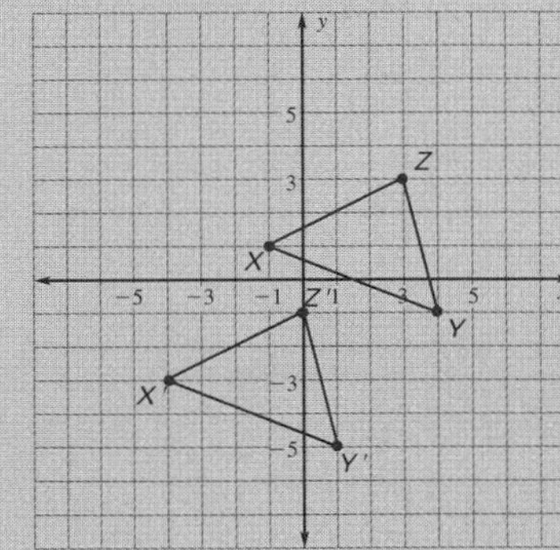

19.

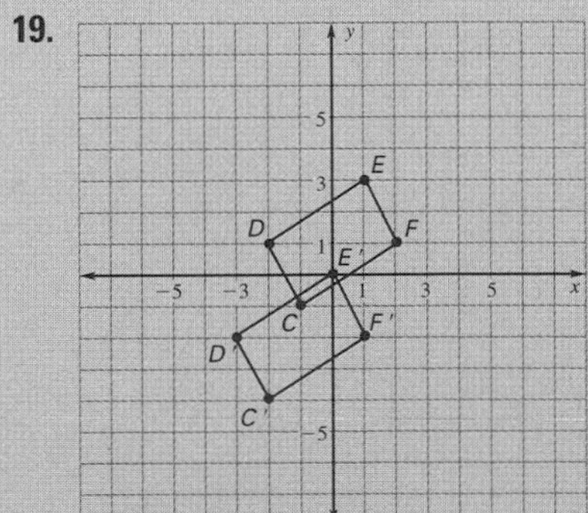

20. See Additional Answers beginning on page AA1.

Additional Resources

☐ ***Assessment Book***

- Formal Assessment, pp. 114–125
- Alternative Assessment, pp. 193–207

Test and Practice Generator

16.

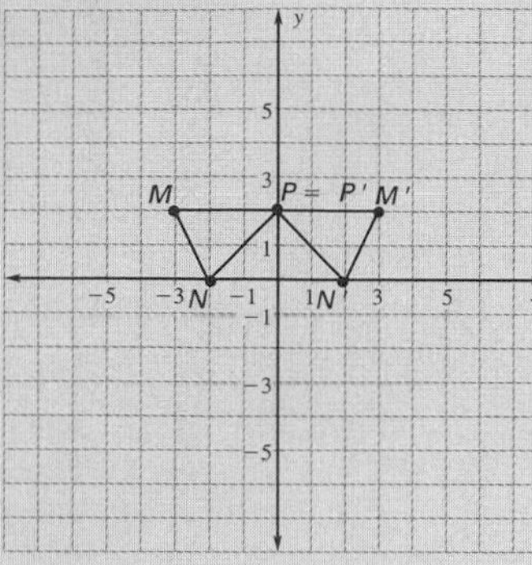

17.

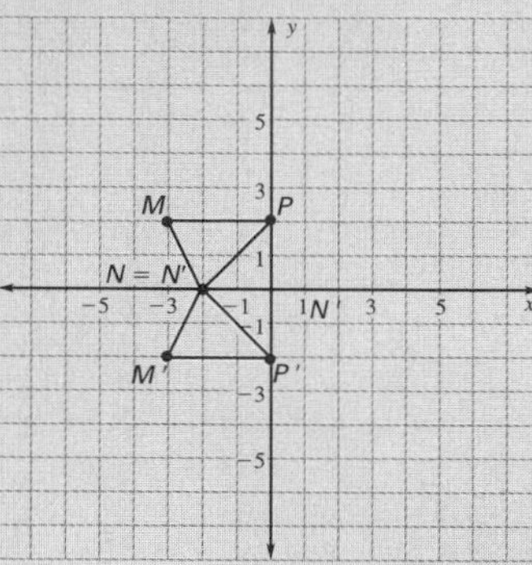

18.

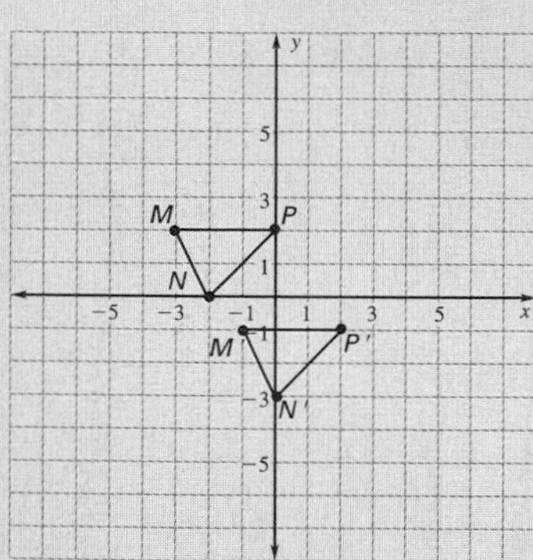

Chapter 8 Chapter Test

Match the angle with its measure.

A. 155° **B.** 135° **C.** 42°

1. B

2. C

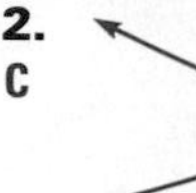

3. A

In Exercises 4–7, use the figure at the right.

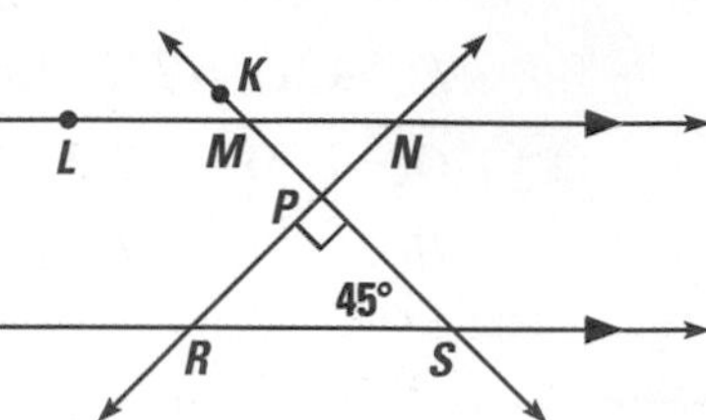

4. Give another name for $\overleftrightarrow{MP}$. ***Sample answer:*** $\overleftrightarrow{MS}$

5. Name four rays with endpoint P. ***Sample answer:*** $\overrightarrow{PM}$, $\overrightarrow{PN}$, $\overrightarrow{PS}$, $\overrightarrow{PR}$

6. Name two pairs of vertical angles. ***Sample answer:*** $\angle MPN$ **and** $\angle RPS$, $\angle NPS$ **and** $\angle MPR$

7. Find the measure of $\angle KML$. Explain your answer. **45°; corresponding with** $\angle PSR$

Classify the triangle by its angles and by its sides.

8. **right, isosceles**

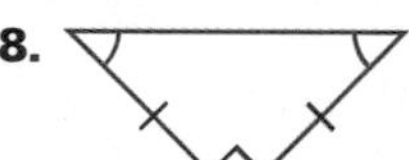

9. **obtuse, scalene**

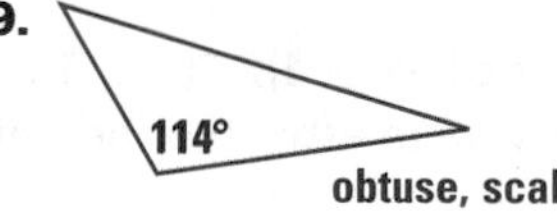

10. **acute, isosceles**

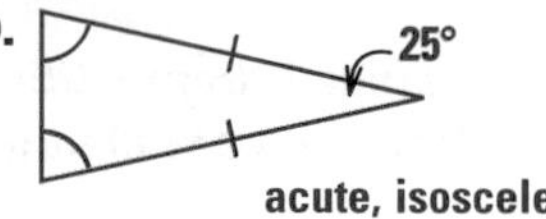

Tell whether the statement is *true* or *false*.

11. A regular quadrilateral is a square. **true**

12. All regular triangles are congruent. **false**

Find the area of the polygon.

13. 18

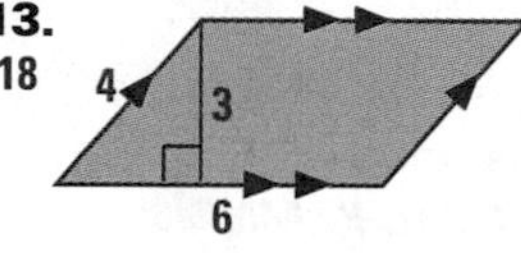

14. 180

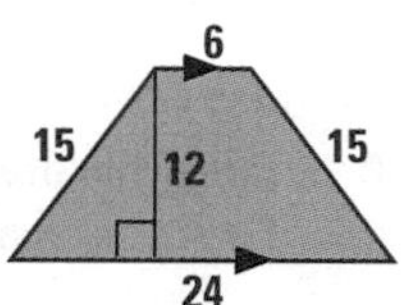

15. 26

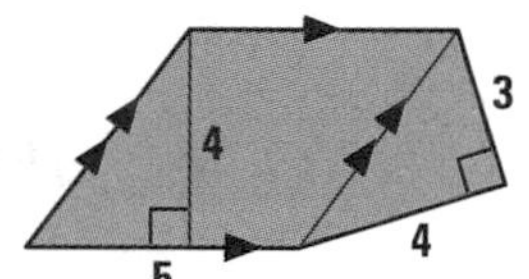

In Exercises 16–18, copy $\triangle MNP$ on graph paper. Then draw its image after the indicated transformation.

16. Reflection in the y-axis **See margin.**

17. $(x, y) \rightarrow (x, -y)$ **See margin.**

18. $(x, y) \rightarrow (x + 2, y - 3)$ **See margin.**

19. A painting is 78 inches long and 24 inches wide. A reproduction is 6 inches wide. Find the scale factor of the painting to the reproduction. Find the length of the reproduction. **4:1; 19.5 in.**

Multiple-Choice Practice

Test Tip Be careful about choosing an answer that seems obvious. Read the problem and all the choices carefully before answering.

1. Which statement is *false*? **D**

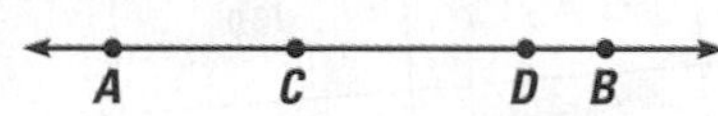

Ⓐ $\overline{AC}$ lies on $\overleftrightarrow{AB}$.

Ⓑ The line above can be called $\overleftrightarrow{CB}$.

Ⓒ $\overrightarrow{DC}$ is the same as $\overrightarrow{DA}$.

Ⓓ $\overrightarrow{CB}$ is the same as $\overrightarrow{BC}$.

2. What type of angle is made by a clock's hands at 8:00 P.M.? **H**

Ⓕ Acute Ⓖ Right

Ⓗ Obtuse Ⓙ Straight

3. Which statement about the figure is *true*? **C**

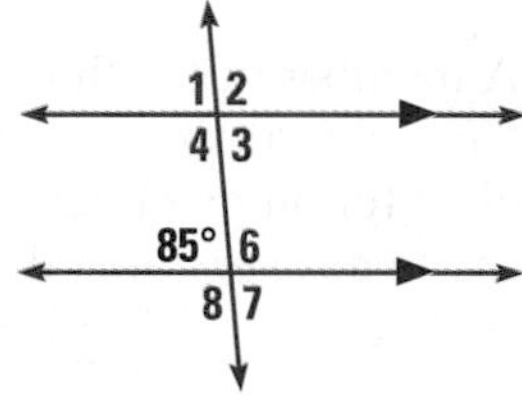

Ⓐ ∠1 and ∠8 are congruent.

Ⓑ ∠4 and ∠6 are corresponding angles.

Ⓒ The measure of ∠7 is 85°.

Ⓓ ∠2 and ∠3 are vertical angles.

4. Which statement is *false*? **G**

Ⓕ Some parallelograms are rectangles.

Ⓖ All rhombuses are squares.

Ⓗ All squares are rhombuses.

Ⓙ No trapezoid is a parallelogram.

5. Find the area of a parallelogram with base 7 feet and height 2 feet. **C**

Ⓐ 7 ft^2 Ⓑ 9 ft^2

Ⓒ 14 ft^2 Ⓓ 18 ft^2

6. $\triangle ABC \cong \triangle DEF$. Which statement is *false*? **J**

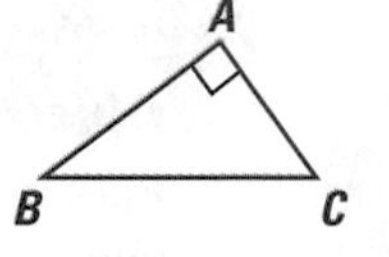

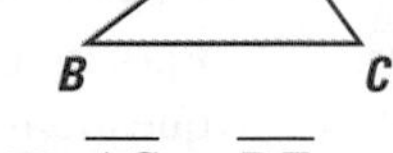

Ⓕ $\overline{AC} \cong \overline{DF}$ Ⓖ $\angle A \cong \angle D$

Ⓗ $\overline{BC} \cong \overline{EF}$ Ⓙ $\angle A \cong \angle E$

In Exercises 7 and 8, use the graph below.

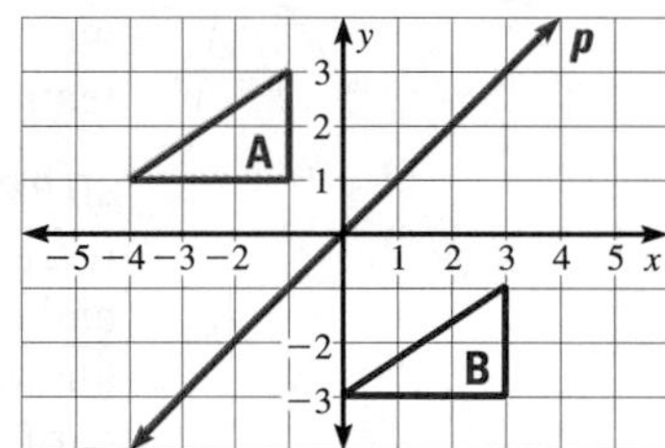

7. What reflection (if any) could describe a transformation from Figure A to Figure B? **D**

Ⓐ In the *y*-axis Ⓑ In the *x*-axis

Ⓒ In the line *p* Ⓓ No reflection

8. Which of the following describes a transformation from Figure A to Figure B? **G**

Ⓕ $(x, y) \rightarrow (x + 4, y + 4)$

Ⓖ $(x, y) \rightarrow (x + 4, y - 4)$

Ⓗ $(x, y) \rightarrow (x - 4, y + 4)$

Ⓙ $(x, y) \rightarrow (x - 4, y - 4)$

443

Teaching Tip

The Brain Games activity provides a motivating way to review selected content in the chapter. For a more comprehensive review, see the Chapter Summary and Review on pp. 438–441.

Brain games

California Standards

- Identify basic elements of geometric figures. (MG 3.1)
- Analyze problems by identifying relationships. (MR 1.1)

Geometry Bowl

Materials

- **Blank cards**
- **Poster board divided into columns and rows, labeled as shown**

Points	Lines and Angles	Triangles	Polygons
100	Lines and Angles 100	Triangles 100	Polygons 100
200	Lines and Angles 200	Triangles 200	Polygons 200
300	Lines and Angles 300	Triangles 300	True or false? Two squares are always similar.

Directions

Scores		
Turn	Team 1	Team 2
1	100	−100
2	200	300
3	−200	300
4	100	

Object of the Game

Play in teams of 4. Two teams compete and answer nine questions written by a third team. The team with the most points after all nine questions have been asked wins.

How to Play

STEP 1 Each team takes nine cards. On one side of each card, write the category and number of points. On the other side, write a question. Two teams are chosen to compete. The third team places its questions on the poster board.

STEP 2 One team chooses a card. A member of the third team reads the question. The team has 1 minute to answer correctly and earn points. The team loses points for an incorrect answer. The other team has 1 minute to answer correctly and earn points without risk of losing any.

Another Way to Play

Three different topics from the chapter are chosen, and each team writes three questions for each of the topics.

Brain Teaser

Brain teaser answer: isosceles trapezoid

Find the mystery figure.

- I have one line of symmetry.
- My two nonparallel sides are congruent.
- Two of my sides are parallel.
- My two diagonals are congruent.

California Standards and Assessment

CA Standards: MG 3.1, MR 1.1

The basic skills you'll review on this page will help prepare you for the next chapter.

Reviewing the Basics

EXAMPLE 1 Evaluating an Expression

Simplify the expression $-5x + y + 3x + 2y$. Then evaluate it when $x = 2$ and $y = 3$.

Solution

$-5x + y + 3x + 2y = -5x + 3x + y + 2y$ Commutative property.

$= (-5x + 3x) + (y + 2y)$ Associative property.

$= -2x + 3y$ Simplify.

ANSWER ▶ When $x = 2$ and $y = 3$,
$-2\mathbf{x} + 3\mathbf{y} = -2(\mathbf{2}) + 3(\mathbf{3}) = 5$

Try These

Simplify the expression. Evaluate it for the given value(s).

1. $8x + 3 + 2x - 5$, when $x = -3$ **$10x - 2$; -32**

2. $a + 6b + a - 8b + 2a$, when $a = -2$ and $b = -6$ **$4a - 2b$; 4**

3. $3x + 12y - 5x - 10y$, when $x = 7$ and $y = -3$ **$-2x + 2y$; -20**

4. $4z + z + 5y - 3$, when $y = 4$ and $z = -1$ **$5z + 5y - 3$; 12**

5. $3m - 5m + m^2$, when $m = -8$ **$m^2 - 2m$; 80**

EXAMPLE 2 Solving Equations with Variables on Both Sides

Solve the equation $9x - 5 = 2(5 + 4x)$.

Solution

$9x - 5 = 2(5 + 4x)$ Write original equation.

$9x - 5 = 10 + 8x$ Use distributive property.

$9x - 5 \mathbf{- 8x} = 10 + 8x \mathbf{- 8x}$ Subtract $8x$ from each side.

$x - 5 = 10$ Simplify.

$x - 5 \mathbf{+ 5} = 10 \mathbf{+ 5}$ Add 5 to each side.

$x = 15$ Simplify. x is by itself.

Student Help

▶ **MORE EXAMPLES**
INTERNET More examples and practice exercises available at www.mcdougallittell.com

Try These

Solve the equation. Then check your solution.

6. $5x - 7 = 9 + x$ **4**

7. $-3y - 9 = 11 - y$ **-10**

8. $7n - 18 = 2n - 4$ **$\frac{14}{5}$**

9. $17 - a = -11 - 5a$ **-7**

10. $2(3 + 2x) = 3 - 2x$ **$-\frac{1}{2}$**

11. $5(b - 5) = 10b$ **-5**

Additional Resources

Technology
- Personal Student Tutor
- Test and Practice Generator

Pacing and Assignment Guide

Regular Schedule

Lesson	Les. Day	Transitional	Average	Advanced
9.1	Day 1	pp. 451–452 Exs. 14–25, 41–50	pp. 451–452 Exs. 14–21, 26–29, 43–52	pp. 451–452 Exs. 14–21, 26–29, 43–52
	Day 2	pp. 451–452 Exs. 30–31, 33–40, 56–57, 60–61	pp. 451–452 Exs. 30–40, 53–57, 60–61	pp. 451–452 Exs. 30–40, 56–58, 59*, 60–61
9.2	Day 1	pp. 455–457 Exs. 17–26, 30–34, 50, 60–62	pp. 455–457 Exs. 17–34, 50, 60–62	pp. 455–457 Exs. 17–34, 50, 60–62
	Day 2	SRH p. 674 Exs. 1–5; pp. 455–457 Exs. 12–16, 35–37, 44–45, 58–59, 63–68	pp. 455–457 Exs. 12–16, 38–40, 46–47, 51–52, 58–59, 63–68	pp. 455–457 Exs. 12–16, 41–43, 48–49, 53, 54–57*, 58–59, 63–68
9.3	Day 1	EP p. 704 Exs. 10–23; pp. 462–464 Exs. 8–21, 27–29, 37–38	pp. 462–464 Exs. 8–19, 21–22, 25–26, 30, 37–38	pp. 462–464 Exs. 10–22, 25–26, 32–33, 34–36, 37–38; EC: TE p. 446D*
9.4	Day 1	pp. 467–468 Exs. 7–16, 20, 22–23	pp. 467–468 Exs. 7–18, 22–23	pp. 467–468 Exs. 8–19, 21*, 22–23
9.5	Day 1	pp. 472–474 Exs. 9–10, 17–19, 34–46	pp. 472–474 Exs. 9–10, 17–19, 23, 34–46	pp. 472–474 Exs. 9–10, 17–19, 23, 34–46
	Day 2	pp. 472–474 Exs. 11–14, 20, 26–29, 31–33	pp. 472–474 Exs. 11–14, 20, 26–29, 31–33	pp. 472–474 Exs. 13–16, 20, 24–26, 30*, 31–33
9.6	Day 1	pp. 478–479 Exs. 12–17, 21–24, 29–34, 44–45, 49–51	pp. 478–479 Exs. 14–18, 21–24, 32–37, 44–45, 47–51	pp. 478–479 Exs. 14–20, 25–28, 38–45, 46*, 47–51
9.7	Day 1	pp. 482–483 Exs. 16–31, 38, 45–47	pp. 482–483 Exs. 16–19, 21–33, 39–40, 45–47	pp. 482–483 Exs. 15–19, 21–24, 32–37, 40–43, 44*, 45–47
9.8	Day 1	pp. 486–488 Exs. 9–23, 50–53, 58–59, 62–63	pp. 486–488 Exs. 10–14, 18–26, 50–53, 58–59, 62–63	pp. 486–488 Exs. 10–14, 20–29, 50–53, 58–59, 62–63
	Day 2	pp. 486–488 Exs. 30, 37–38, 41–43, 47–49, 64–67, 70–72	pp. 486–488 Exs. 30, 37–38, 42–45, 47–49, 64–67, 70–72	pp. 486–488 Exs. 30, 39–40, 42–45, 46*, 47–49, 64–67, 70–72
9.9	Day 1	EP p. 697 Exs 66–69; pp. 491–493 Exs. 18–20, 24–25	pp. 491–493 Exs. 18–20, 24–25	pp. 491–493 Exs. 18–20, 24–25
	Day 2	pp. 491–493 Exs. 10–17, 21–23, 29–30	pp. 491–493 Exs. 10–17, 21–23, 26, 29–30	pp. 491–493 Exs. 10–17, 23, 26, 27–28*, 29–30
Review	Day 1	pp. 494–497 Exs. 1–40	pp. 494–497 Exs. 1–40	pp. 494–497 Exs. 1–40
Assess	Day 1	Chapter 9 Test	Chapter 9 Test	Chapter 9 Test

Yearly Pacing Chapter 9 Total – **16 days** Chapters 1–9 Total – **120 days** Remaining – **40 days**

* Challenge Exercises EP = Extra Practice SRH = Skills Review Handbook EC = Extra Challenge

Block Schedule

Day 1	Day 2	Day 3	Day 4	Day 5	Day 6	Day 7	Day 8
9.1 pp. 451–452: Exs. 14–21, 26–40, 43–57, 60–61	**9.2** pp. 455–457: Exs. 12–34, 38–40, 46–47, 50–52, 58–68	**9.3** pp. 462–464: Exs. 8–19, 21–22, 25–26, 30, 37–38 **9.4** pp. 467–468: Exs. 7–18, 22–23	**9.5** pp. 472–474: Exs. 9–14, 17–20, 23–26, 30–46	**9.6** pp. 478–479: Exs. 14–18, 21–24, 32–37, 44–45, 47–51 **9.7** pp. 482–483: Exs. 16–19, 21–33, 39–40, 45–47	**9.8** pp. 486–488: Exs. 10–14, 18–26, 30, 37–38, 42–45, 47–53, 58–59, 62–67, 70–72	**9.9** pp. 491–493: Exs. 10–26, 29–30	**Review** pp. 494–497: Exs. 1–40 **Assess** Chapter 9 Test

Yearly Pacing Chapter 9 Total – **8 days** Chapters 1–9 Total – **60 days** Remaining – **20 days**

Support Materials

Chapter Resource Book

LESSON SUPPORT	9.1	9.2	9.3	9.4	9.5	9.6	9.7	9.8	9.9
Lesson Plans	p. 1	p. 10	p. 19	p. 28	p. 37	p. 46	p. 55	p. 64	p. 73
Lesson Plans for Block Scheduling	p. 2	p. 11	p. 20	p. 29	p. 38	p. 47	p. 56	p. 65	p. 74
Warm-Ups with Multiple-Choice Practice	p. 3	p. 12	p. 21	p. 30	p. 39	p. 48	p. 57	p. 66	p. 75
Problem of the Day	p. 4	p. 13	p. 22	p. 31	p. 40	p. 49	p. 58	p. 67	p. 76
Daily Cumulative Review	p. 5	p. 14	p. 23	p. 32	p. 41	p. 50	p. 59	p. 68	p. 77
Practice Masters	p. 6	p. 15	p. 24	p. 33	p. 42	p. 51	p. 60	p. 69	p. 78
Reteaching Masters	p. 7	p. 16	p. 25	p. 34	p. 43	p. 52	p. 61	p. 70	p. 79
Enrichment Masters	p. 9	p. 18	p. 27	p. 36	p. 45	p. 54	p. 63	p. 72	p. 81

Transparencies

	9.1	9.2	9.3	9.4	9.5	9.6	9.7	9.8	9.9
Warm-Ups with Multiple-Choice Practice	p. 69	p. 70	p. 71	p. 72	p. 73	p. 74	p. 75	p. 76	p. 77
Teacher Time-Saver Transparencies	✓	✓	✓	✓	✓	✓	✓	✓	✓
English/Spanish Problem Solving	p. 39		p. 40		p. 41	p. 42		p. 43	p. 44
Answer Transparencies	✓	✓	✓	✓	✓	✓	✓	✓	✓

Technology

- Personal Student Tutor
- Time-Saving Test and Practice Generator
- Electronic Teacher Tools
- Technology: Using Calculators and Computers

Additional Resources

- Math Log
- Assessment Book
- Worked-Out Solution Key
- Practice Workbook (English/Spanish)
- Home and School Connection
- California Standards: Key Concepts Book

Correlation to the California Curriculum

Correlations to the California Standards
CA Standards: NS 1.4, NS 1.7, NS 2.0, NS 2.4, AF 1.0, AF 1.1, AF 4.0, AF 4.1, AF 4.2, MG 3.0, MG 3.2, MG 3.3, SDP 1.1, SDP 1.3, MR 1.1, MR 2.3, MR 3.3

California Curriculum Support
Key Concepts Book
- Pre-Course Review: Topic 1 Working with Decimals
  Topic 5 Measurement
- Key Standards: NS 1.4 Rational and Irrational Numbers *(Lesson 9.2)*
  AF 4.1 Solving Two-Step Inequalities *(Lesson 9.8)*
  MG 3.3 The Pythagorean Theorem *(Lesson 9.3)*
  MG 3.3 Converse of the Pythagorean Theorem *(Lesson 9.4)*
  SDP 1.3 Box-and-Whisker Plots *(Lesson 9.9)*

California Standards Practice Workbook provides practice for each Standard that is covered in this chapter.

Providing Universal Access

Strategies for Strategic Learners

SEPARATE CONFUSING ELEMENTS

Some students grasp a concept with one or two examples, but most students need many more. If students are confused about the different aspects of lines they are learning in this chapter, take one really good problem and spend some time on it. Encourage students to ask questions, and as they are solving a problem, circulate around the room to see their work. Have students work on only one kind of problem before going on to the next. Do not introduce confusing formulas or concepts on the same day—in fact, space them over several days a week in order to ensure that students understand one formula or concept before you go on to the next. As part of a general weekly or monthly review, include an appropriate problem or two to remind students of particularly difficult concepts.

PROVIDE AN OVERVIEW

Explain to students that in algebra, they will study many concepts related to lines. They will be finding an equation of a line given two points on the line, finding the slope of a line, or using the Pythagorean theorem to determine the distance between two points on a line. They will be finding out whether a given point is, or is not, on a given line. They will be given two lines and asked to find the point at which they intersect, the only point that satisfies the equations for both lines. Point out to students that the distance formula

$$d = \sqrt{(x_2 - x_1)^2 + (y_2 - y_1)^2}$$

is derived using the Pythagorean theorem.

ANTICIPATE PROBLEM AREAS

Students may be confused by differences in the way things are labeled. The letter *c*, for example, may be used to represent a side of a triangle opposite an angle labeled *C*.

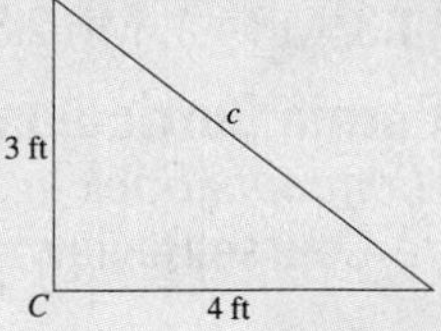

A typical problem might ask students to find the value of *c*. That same side, however, might be named by its endpoints; in another problem students might be asked to calculate the length of line segment *AB*.

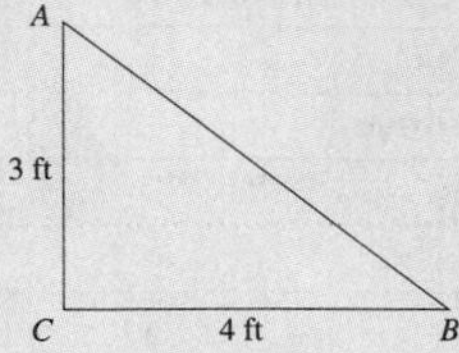

And in still another problem, the letter *d*, for distance, might be used to represent the length of the side opposite a right angle.

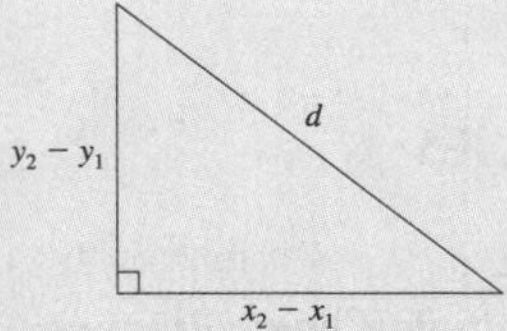

Students must study each problem carefully.

Strategies for English Learners

VOCABULARY DEVELOPMENT

Certain letters are commonly (but not always) used in formulas to represent specific things. Review with your English learners common abbreviations used in mathematics formulas. Page 470 uses the distance formula and the common abbreviation for distance (d). Abbreviations may be in capital or lower case letters and include:

distance (d)
diameter (d)
rate (r)
time (t)
perimeter (P)
probability (P)
area (A)
base (b)
height or altitude (h)
length (ℓ)
width (w)
circumference (C)
radius (r)
degrees Fahrenheit (°F)
degrees Celsius (°C)
volume (V)

Note that some letters commonly stand for more than one thing, and students will need to look at the context to understand the abbreviation. Ask students to tell you what the variables represent in the following common formulas:

$d = rt$ (d is distance; r is rate; t is time)
$d = 2r$ (d is diameter; r is radius)
$A = \frac{1}{2}bh$ (A is area of a triangle; b is base; h is height)
$A = \pi r^2$ (A is area of a circle; r is radius)
$A = \ell w$ (A is area of a rectangle; ℓ is length; w is width)

You can also have students review the common abbreviations of units of measurement.

Strategies for Advanced Learners

DIFFERENTIATE INSTRUCTION IN TERMS OF DEPTH

The Pythagorean theorem is a key concept in mathematics; many other geometric proofs build upon this theorem. Ask students to research these proofs for the Pythagorean theorem:

1. The classical proof given by Euclid in 300 B.C.

2. Bhaskara's proof, given by the Indian mathematician about 1150 B.C.

Most students do not know enough mathematics at this point to prove the Pythagorean theorem or to fully understand these proofs. Nevertheless, they may be interested in looking at the proofs, studying the illustrations that accompany them, and reading about the mathematicians that developed them. They should understand at this point that proofs underlie everything taught in mathematics and that a proof is just the formal display of mathematical reasoning.

CHAPTER 9 Mathematical Background Notes

Lessons 9.1–9.2

IRRATIONAL NUMBERS The operation of taking square roots creates a need to enlarge the system of rational numbers to include **irrational numbers,** that is, numbers that are not rational. One of the most familiar examples of an irrational number is $\sqrt{2}$. This number is encountered geometrically as the side length of a square of area 2. This can be seen geometrically without the Pythagorean theorem by considering a square built on the diagonal of a unit square.

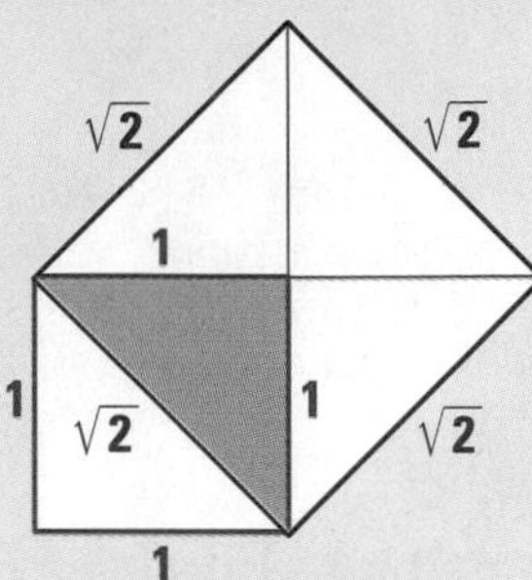

Since the large square contains 4 copies of a triangle of area $\frac{1}{2}$, its area is 2. Denoting the length of its sides by s, we arrive at $s^2 = 2$, or $s = \sqrt{2}$.

To show that $\sqrt{2}$ is not rational, we must show that a number s satisfying $s^2 = 2$ cannot be written in the form $s = \frac{a}{b}$, where a and b are positive integers. Here we may assume that $\frac{a}{b}$ has been simplified and, in particular, that not both a and b are *even* integers (both are odd, or one is even and the other odd). Now the condition $\left(\frac{a}{b}\right)^2 = 2$ leads us to

$$\frac{a^2}{b^2} = 2, \text{ or } a^2 = 2b^2.$$

Thus a^2 is even, being twice an integer. But then a itself could not be odd, since the square of an odd number is always odd. Therefore, *a must be even.* But if a is even, then $a = 2k$ for some integer k, leading to

$$2b^2 = a^2 = (2k)^2 = 4k^2.$$

From this we get $b^2 = 2k^2$, so b^2 is even. But then, by the same reasoning already applied to *a, b itself would have to be even.* Thus, the assumption $\left(\frac{a}{b}\right)^2 = 2$ has led to a contradiction that shows the irrationality of $\sqrt{2}$.

An alternate proof that $\sqrt{2}$ is irrational can be based on *the uniqueness of prime factorization.* It has the advantage that an analogous argument can be used to show that if N is not a perfect square, then $\sqrt{N}$ is irrational. As before, one proceeds with an indirect proof, assuming that $\sqrt{2}$ is rational and arriving at a contradiction.

If $\sqrt{2} = \frac{a}{b}$, where a and b are integers, then $2b^2 = a^2$.

Now let $a = p_1 \cdot p_2 \cdot \ldots \cdot p_m$ and $b = q_1 \cdot q_2 \cdot \ldots \cdot q_n$ be the prime factorizations of a and b. Then a^2 is the product of $2m$ primes and b^2 is the product of $2n$ primes. The equation $2b^2 = a^2$ then has a product of $2n + 1$ primes on the left side and a product of $2m$ primes on the right side. An important theorem from number theory (called the Fundamental Theorem of Arithmetic) tells us that the factorization of an integer into primes is *unique* (up to the order of the factors). Yet the equation $2b^2 = a^2$ has led us to conclude that the same integer has been factored into an odd number of primes (on the left side) and an even number of primes (on the right side). This contradicts the Fundamental Theorem of Arithmetic and shows that our initial assumption is wrong. Therefore $\sqrt{2}$ is an irrational number.

This argument readily extends to a proof that if N is a prime number, then $\sqrt{N}$ is irrational. Indeed, as long as N is a positive integer that is not itself a perfect square, then the prime factorization of N will contain some prime that is repeated an odd number of times. This alone will trigger a contradiction of the Fundamental Theorem of Arithmetic and lead to the following conclusion: **If N is a positive integer that is not a perfect square, then $\sqrt{N}$ is irrational.**

Irrational numbers can also be characterized as those whose decimal expansions are nonrepeating. We can think of these as filling the "gaps" on the number line that are not occupied by rational numbers. The fact that π is irrational (the proof requires more advanced techniques than those used for $\sqrt{2}$) means that its decimal expansion

$$\pi = 3.14159265\ldots$$

does not terminate or fall into a repeating pattern. There are, however, many good rational approximations of π, the number $\frac{22}{7}$ being one of the better known.

This is a good place to pause and ask why decimal expansions of rational numbers are either terminating or repeating. The answer lies in the long division algorithm, which we could use to find the decimal expansion of $\frac{22}{7}$.

```
     3.142857 . . .
  7)22.000000 . . .
    21
     10
      7
      30
      28
       20
       14
        60
        56
         40
         35
          50
          49
           10 . . .
```

Because the remainders being generated are whole numbers less than 7, there must be a point where a previous remainder is repeated. Once we are bringing down zeros and a remainder repeats, the process will lead to the same sequence of digits as before, repeating the same pattern endlessly. In this way we obtain the decimal representation

$$\frac{22}{7} = 3.\overline{142857},$$

giving the rational approximation $\pi \approx \frac{22}{7}$, accurate to two decimal places. This line of argument can be used to show that the quotient $\frac{a}{b}$ of *any* pair of positive integers corresponds to a terminating or repeating decimal.

The converse is also true. That is, a real number with a terminating or repeating decimal expansion must be a rational number. The general idea behind this is embodied in the following example. Suppose $x = 0.21353535\ldots = 0.21\overline{35}$. Then

$$\begin{aligned} 100x &= 21.35353535\ldots = 21.35\overline{35} \\ x &= 0.21353535\ldots = 0.21\overline{35} \end{aligned}$$

so that subtraction gives $99x = 21.14$ and $9900x = 2114$. This shows that

$$x = \frac{2114}{9900} = \frac{1057}{4950},$$

a rational number.

Lessons 9.3–9.4

PYTHAGOREAN THEOREM A discussion of the Pythagorean theorem will prepare the student for the distance formula in the coordinate plane. In its numerical form, the Pythagorean theorem tells us that if a and b are the lengths of the legs of a right triangle and c is the length of the hypotenuse, then the numbers a, b, and c satisfy

$$a^2 + b^2 = c^2.$$

The geometric form of this theorem interprets a^2, b^2, and c^2 as the areas of squares built on the sides of a right triangle.

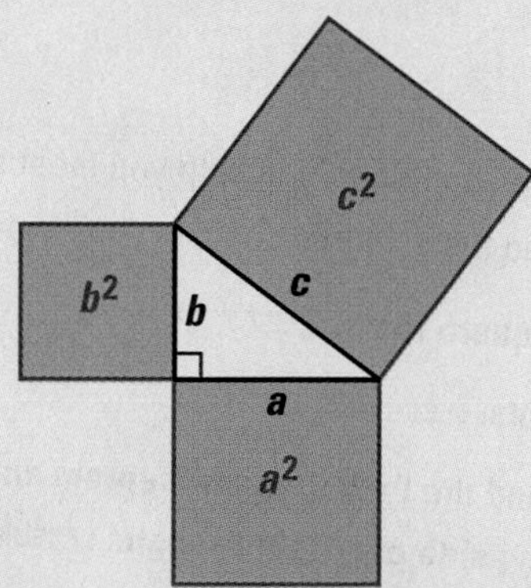

While this area interpretation provides a basis for some of the many known proofs of the Pythagorean theorem, a proof closer to the ideas that students have encountered can be based on similar triangles. The picture below shows a right triangle ABC with altitude $\overline{CD}$ dropped from the right angle vertex C to the hypotenuse $\overline{AB}$.

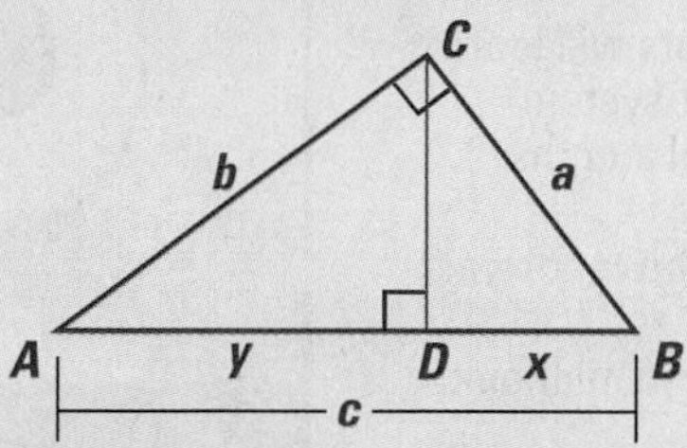

The legs of the triangle have lengths a and b, respectively, and the hypotenuse has length c. Letting x be the length of $\overline{BD}$ and y the length of $\overline{AD}$, we have

$$x + y = c.$$

Since triangles ABC and ACD are right triangles with $\angle A$ in common, they are similar by the AA similarity postulate. The fact that corresponding sides of these similar triangles are proportional implies that

$$\frac{y}{b} = \frac{b}{c}, \text{ so } cy = b^2.$$

Also, triangle CBD is similar to triangle ABC, giving

$$\frac{x}{a} = \frac{a}{c}, \text{ so } cx = a^2.$$

These results can be combined to give the desired result

$$a^2 + b^2 = cx + cy = c(x + y) = c \cdot c = c^2.$$

The *converse* of the Pythagorean theorem asserts that if a, b, and c are the sides of a triangle, and if $a^2 + b^2 = c^2$, then the triangle is a right triangle. It is interesting that this converse can be proved using the Pythagorean theorem itself, as follows.

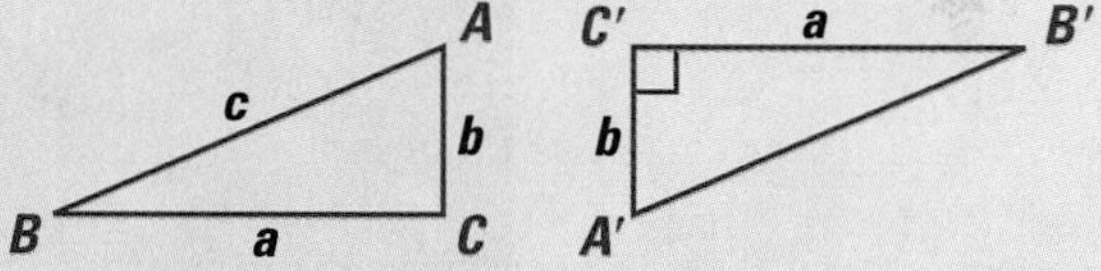

In the picture above, suppose $\triangle ABC$ is a triangle whose sides satisfy $a^2 + b^2 = c^2$. Let $\triangle A'B'C'$ be a *right* triangle whose two legs satisfy $B'C' = a$ and $A'C' = b$. By the Pythagorean theorem,

$$(A'B')^2 = (B'C')^2 + (A'C')^2 = a^2 + b^2.$$

Since $a^2 + b^2 = c^2$, we have $A'B' = c$. This shows that the two triangles have corresponding sides of equal length, and the SSS congruence postulate tells us that $\triangle ABC$ is congruent to $\triangle A'B'C'$. Hence $\triangle ABC$ is a right triangle.

Chapter Overview

Career Note

In this chapter, students will learn about the real number system and estimate irrational lengths. They will:

- Use the Pythagorean theorem and its converse.
- Use the distance and midpoint formulas.
- Solve inequalities.
- Make box-and-whisker plots of data.

Career Note

Geologists study Earth, its surfaces, and its interior. They search for natural resources, such as petroleum and natural gas, and study groundwater quality. Geologists study earthquakes and volcanoes, and try to predict their behavior. Those interested in geology careers should possess strong analytical abilities. A four-year college degree is usually required, but most geologists hold higher degrees.

Additional information about geologists is available at **www.mcdougallittell.com**

Real Numbers and Solving Inequalities

Why are real numbers important?

Unlike a rational number, an *irrational* number cannot be written as a ratio of two integers. Rational and irrational numbers together constitute the set of real numbers. Real numbers are the basis for the real number line, which is used for graphing in algebra.

Many people use real numbers and inequalities in their careers, including geologists (page 447), telephone workers (page 471), and ornithologists (page 487). For example, geologists measure changes in gravity to tell how quickly the ground is rising or falling.

Meeting the California Standards

The skills you'll learn in this chapter will help you meet state standards and prepare for standardized tests. In this chapter you'll:

- **Find and estimate square roots.** LESSON 9.1
- **Use powers and roots.** LESSON 9.2
- **Know and understand the Pythagorean theorem and use it to find the length of the missing side of a right triangle.** LESSONS 9.3, 9.5
- **Use the converse of the Pythagorean theorem to deepen understanding of geometric shapes by identifying attributes of figures.** LESSON 9.4
- **Solve simple linear inequalities.** LESSONS 9.6, 9.7

Career Link **GEOLOGIST** A geologist uses real numbers when:

- calculating the distance of Earth's surface from its center.
- determining how quickly the ground in a particular location is rising or falling.

EXERCISES

In some places, such as mountain ranges, the ground is rising very slowly. As the ground moves farther away from the center of Earth, the strength of gravity decreases. Geologists can use the formula below to find the distance r (in meters) to the center of Earth. In the formula, g is a measure of gravity.

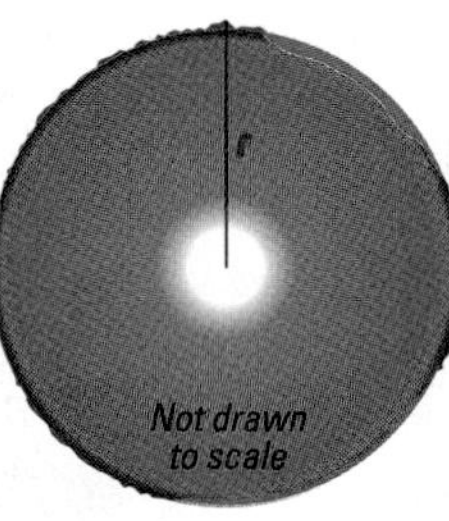

$$r = \sqrt{\frac{3.99 \times 10^{14}}{g}}$$

In one location, the value of g changed from 9.83271126 to 9.83271123 in one year.

1. Did the value of g increase or decrease? By how much? **g decreased by 0.00000003.**

2. Did the value of $\frac{3.99 \times 10^{14}}{g}$ increase or decrease? Explain. **Increased; the denominator decreased, so the value increased.**

In Lesson 9.1, you'll learn how to calculate how much the ground rose or fell in a year.

Projects

A project covering Chapters 7–9 appears on pages 504–505 of the Student Edition. Additional projects for selected lessons in Chapter 9 are available in the *Assessment Book,* pp. 248–249.

Technology

Software

- Electronic Teacher Tools
- Online Lesson Planner
- Personal Student Tutor
- Test and Practice Generator

Internet Connections

- Application and Career Links 461, 471, 483, 487
- Student Help 450, 456, 463, 466, 474, 481, 485, 493, 501

These Internet connections are available at **www.mcdougallittell.com**

Prepare

Diagnostic Tools

The **chapter readiness quiz** can help you diagnose whether students have the following skills needed in Chapter 9:

- Understand and apply multiplicative inverses.
- Identify rational numbers.
- Solve linear equations.

Reteaching Materials

The following resources are available for students who need additional help with the skills on the chapter readiness quiz:

Chapter 9 Resource Book

- Reteaching with Practice (Lessons 4.2, 4.4, 5.5, 6.3)

Personal Student Tutor

Additional Resources

The following resources are provided to help you prepare for the upcoming chapter and customize review materials:

Chapter 9 Resource Book

- Lesson Plans, pp. 1, 10, 19, 28, 37, 46, 55, 64, 73
- Lesson Plans for Block Scheduling, pp. 2, 11, 20, 29, 38, 47, 56, 65, 74

Technology

- Electronic Teacher Tools with Lesson Planning Software
- Test and Practice Generator

Chapter 9 Getting Ready

PREVIEW

What's the chapter about?

- Using **square roots**, the **real number system**, the **Pythagorean theorem**, and the **distance** and **midpoint formulas**
- Solving inequalities and **graphing their solutions**
- Using **box-and-whisker plots**

WORDS TO KNOW

- **square root,** *p. 449*
- **perfect square,** *p. 449*
- **irrational numbers,** *p. 453*
- **real numbers,** *p. 453*
- **Pythagorean theorem,** *p. 460*
- **distance formula,** *p. 470*
- **midpoint formula,** *p. 471*
- **lower quartile,** *p. 489*
- **upper quartile,** *p. 489*
- **box-and-whisker plot,** *p. 489*
- **range,** *p. 489*
- **interquartile range,** *p. 489*

PREPARE

Chapter Readiness Quiz

Take this quick quiz. If you are unsure of an answer, look back at the reference pages for help.

VOCABULARY CHECK *(refer to pp. 239, 279)*

1. What is another name for the reciprocal of a number? **C**

Ⓐ Additive inverse Ⓑ Base

Ⓒ Multiplicative inverse Ⓓ Multiplicative identity

2. A __?__ is the quotient of two integers a and b where $b \neq 0$. **J**

Ⓕ Rate Ⓖ Proportion

Ⓗ Reciprocal Ⓙ Rational number

SKILL CHECK *(refer to pp. 175, 183)*

3. What is the solution of the equation $3(y - 2) + 2 = -y$? **C**

Ⓐ -2 Ⓑ 0 Ⓒ 1 Ⓓ 2

STUDY TIP

Check Your Work

Checking your work will help you catch any mistakes you make. Be sure to correct any mistakes you find.

Remember to Check My Work
- Write out all steps when doing homework.
- Check each step carefully.

9.1 Square Roots

California Standards

In this lesson you'll:

- Use the inverse relationship between raising to a power and extracting the root of a perfect square integer. (NS 2.4)
- For an integer that is not square, determine without a calculator the two integers between which its square root lies. (NS 2.4)

Goal 1 Finding Square Roots

In Chapter 1 you learned that 9 is the *square* of 3 because $3^2 = 9$. You can also say that 3 is a *square root* of 9. A **square root** of a number is a number which, when multiplied by itself, produces the given number.

If $m^2 = n$, then m is a square root of n.

Every positive number has a positive square root and a negative square root. The *radical sign* $\sqrt{\ }$ is used to represent the positive square root. For example, $\sqrt{4} = 2$ is the positive square root of 4. The negative square root of 4 is $-\sqrt{4} = -2$ because $(-2)^2 = (-2)(-2) = 4$.

Negative numbers have no square roots because the square of a number is never negative. Zero has one square root, which is itself.

Example 1 Finding Square Roots

Find the square roots of 36.

Solution

$\sqrt{36} = 6$ because $6^2 = 36$.

$-\sqrt{36} = -6$ because $(-6)^2 = 36$.

ANSWER ▶ So, the square roots of 36 are 6 and -6.

Example 1 shows that 36 is a *perfect square*. A **perfect square** is any number that has integer square roots. You can use a calculator to approximate the square roots of a number that is not a perfect square.

Example 2 Using a Calculator

Use a calculator to approximate $\sqrt{3}$. Round to the nearest hundredth.

Solution

KEYSTROKES	DISPLAY
3 	1.732050808

Rounded to the nearest hundredth, $\sqrt{3}$ is 1.73. Check if this is reasonable by squaring 1.73:

$$1.73^2 = 2.9929$$

ANSWER ▶ Since 2.9929 is close to 3, it is reasonable that $\sqrt{3} \approx 1.73$.

Student Help

▶ **Technology Tip**
When you use the √ key to find $\sqrt{3}$, a calculator gives a rounded value. The decimal for $\sqrt{3}$ actually continues without end.

$\sqrt{3} = 1.732050808\ldots$

$\sqrt{3} \approx 1.732050808$

1 Plan

Pacing
Suggested Number of Days

Transitional: 2 days
Average: 2 days
Advanced: 2 days
Block Schedule: 1 block

Teaching Resources

Blacklines
(See page 446B.)

Transparencies
- Warm-Up Exercises
- Teacher Time-Savers
- English/Spanish Problem Solving
- Answers

Technology
- Electronic Teacher Tools
- Test and Practice Generator

2 Teach

Math Reasoning

For Mathematical Background Notes on mathematical reasoning related to this lesson, please refer to pages 446E and 446F in this Teacher's Edition.

Extra Examples 1 and 2
See next page.

California Standards and Assessment

CA Standard: NS 2.4

Math Reasoning

An equivalent definition of perfect squares states that a perfect square is the square of an integer. For instance, 529 is a perfect square, because $529 = (23)^2$.

Extra Example 1

Find the square roots of 64. **8 and −8**

Extra Example 2

Use a calculator to approximate $\sqrt{5}$. Round to the nearest hundredth. **2.24**

Extra Example 3

a. Approximate $\sqrt{150}$ to the nearest whole number. **12**

b. Approximate $\sqrt{150}$ to the nearest tenth. **12.2**

Extra Example 4

A square has an area of 50 square centimeters. About how long is one side of the square? **about 7.1 centimeters**

Teaching Tip

Multiple Representations

Emphasize that a calculator gives an *approximation* of a square root of a number that is not a perfect square. The actual square root of a is the *exact* number x so that $x^2 = a$.

Concept Check

Explain how to approximate the square root of a number that is not a perfect square to the nearest whole number without using a calculator. ***Sample answer:*** **Find two consecutive whole numbers whose squares are smaller than and larger than the number under the radical. Square the number halfway between these two whole numbers to determine whether the square root is closer to the smaller or the larger consecutive whole number.**

Goal 2 APPROXIMATING SQUARE ROOTS

You can also approximate a square root without using a calculator.

Student Help

▶STUDY TIP
For help with finding the square roots of a number, see page 718.

EXAMPLE 3 Approximating a Square Root

a. Approximate $\sqrt{128}$ to the nearest whole number.

b. Approximate $\sqrt{128}$ to the nearest tenth.

Solution

a. Find the whole number whose square is closest to 128. As you can see on the number line below, 128 is between $121 = 11^2$ and $144 = 12^2$. So, $\sqrt{128}$ is between 11 and 12.

To tell whether $\sqrt{128}$ is closer to 11 or to 12, find $11.5^2 = 132.25$. Since $128 < 11.5^2$, $\sqrt{128}$ is closer to 11 than it is to 12.

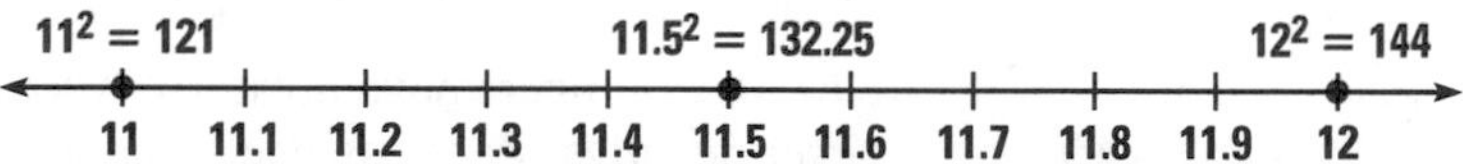

ANSWER ▶ So, to the nearest whole number, $\sqrt{128} \approx 11$.

b. Make a list like the one at the right. From the list you can see that 128 is between $127.69 = 11.3^2$ and $129.96 = 11.4^2$. So, $\sqrt{128}$ is between 11.3 and 11.4.

$11.2^2 = 125.44$
$11.3^2 = 127.69$ ← 128
$11.4^2 = 129.96$

To tell whether $\sqrt{128}$ is closer to 11.3 or 11.4, find $11.35^2 \approx 128.82$. Since $128 < 11.35^2$, $\sqrt{128}$ is closer to 11.3 than it is to 11.4.

ANSWER ▶ So, to the nearest tenth, $\sqrt{128} \approx 11.3$.

Student Help

▶MORE EXAMPLES

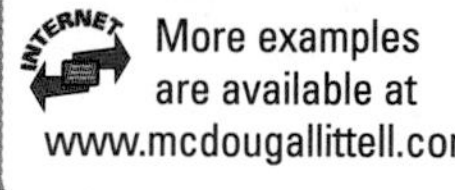

More examples are available at www.mcdougallittell.com

EXAMPLE 4 Approximating the Side of a Square

A square has an area of 90 square centimeters. To the nearest tenth, how long is one side of the square?

Solution

Use the area to find the length of one side.

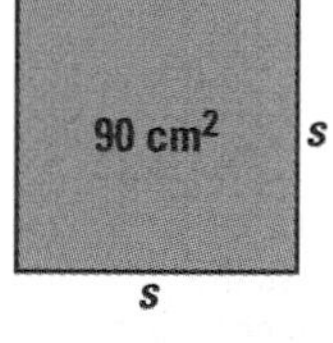

$$\text{Area} = s^2$$
$$90 = s^2$$
$$-\sqrt{90} \text{ or } \sqrt{90} = s$$

Since length is positive, $s = \sqrt{90}$. To approximate s, note that $9^2 = 81$ and $10^2 = 100$ so you know that $\sqrt{90}$ is between 9 and 10.

ANSWER ▶ Since $9.4^2 = 88.36$ and $9.5^2 = 90.25$, the length of each side is about 9.5 centimeters.

9.1 Exercises

Guided Practice

Write the two square roots of the number.

1. 25 **5, −5** **2.** 49 **7, −7** **3.** 100 **10, −10** **4.** 121 **11, −11**

CALCULATOR Using a calculator, find the two square roots of the number. Round your answers to the nearest tenth.

5. 5 **2.2, −2.2** **6.** 0.26 **0.5, −0.5** **7.** 19 **4.4, −4.4** **8.** 30 **5.5, −5.5**

In Exercises 9–12, approximate the positive square root of the number to the nearest whole number and the nearest tenth. Do not use a calculator.

9. 15 **4; 3.9** **10.** 27 **5; 5.2** **11.** 300 **17; 17.3** **12.** 7 **3; 2.6**

13. The area of a square field is 70 square meters. Find the length of one side of the field. **about 8.4 m**

Practice and Problem Solving

Student Help

▶More Practice
Extra practice to help you master skills is on page 706.

Write the two square roots of the number.

14. 64 **8, −8** **15.** 169 **13, −13** **16.** 256 **16, −16** **17.** 400 **20, −20**

18. 1600 **40, −40** **19.** 0.04 **0.2, −0.2** **20.** 0.36 **0.6, −0.6** **21.** 1.21 **1.1, −1.1**

CALCULATOR Use a calculator to approximate the square root. Round your answer to the nearest tenth.

22. $\sqrt{39}$ **6.2** **23.** $\sqrt{72.25}$ **8.5** **24.** $\sqrt{105}$ **10.2** **25.** $\sqrt{200}$ **14.1**

26. $\sqrt{1352}$ **36.8** **27.** $\sqrt{0.89}$ **0.9** **28.** $\sqrt{2026}$ **45.0** **29.** $\sqrt{8052}$ **89.7**

Use the given area of the green square to approximate the length of one of its sides to the nearest tenth. Use the grid to check your answer. The small squares in the grid are each 1 square unit.

30. Area of green square is 20 square units.

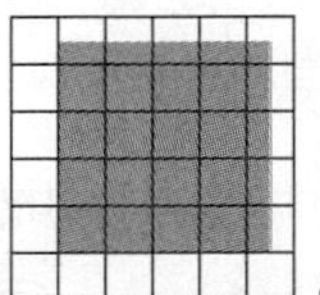

4.5 units

31. Area of green square is 56 square units.

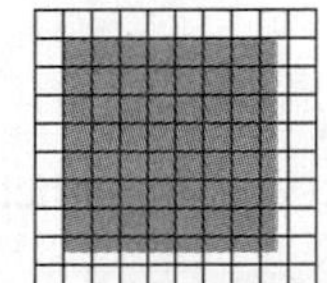

7.5 units

32. Area of green square is 31 square units.

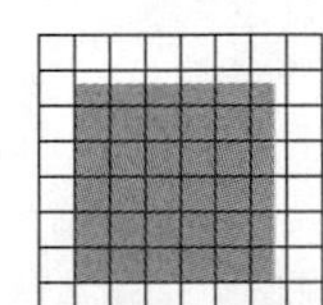

5.6 units

Without using a calculator, approximate the square roots of the number to the nearest whole number and the nearest tenth.

33. 8 **3, 2.8** **34.** 12 **3, 3.5** **35.** 42 **6, 6.5** **36.** 88 **9, 9.4**

3 Apply

Assignment Guide

Transitional
Day 1: pp. 451–452 Exs. 14–25, 41–50
Day 2: pp. 451–452 Exs. 30–31, 33–40, 56–57, 60–61

Average
Day 1: pp. 451–452 Exs. 14–21, 26–29, 43–52
Day 2: pp. 451–452 Exs. 30–40, 53–57, 60–61

Advanced
Day 1: pp. 451–452 Exs. 14–21, 26–29, 43–52
Day 2: pp. 451–452 Exs. 30–40, 56–58, 59*, 60–61

Block Schedule
pp. 451–452 Exs. 14–21, 26–40, 43–57, 60–61

Extra Practice

- Student Edition, pp. 706–707
- Chapter 9 Resource Book, p. 6

Homework Check

To quickly check student understanding of key concepts, go over the following exercises:

Transitional: 14, 22, 38, 42, 56
Average: 16, 26, 40, 46, 56
Advanced: 18, 28, 40, 48, 56

4 Assess

Assessment Resources

- Assessment Book (Formal Assessment and Alternative Assessment)
- Test and Practice Generator

Mini-Quiz

1. Find the square roots of 225. **15 and −15**
2. Use a calculator to estimate $\sqrt{31}$. Round to the nearest hundredth. **5.57**
3. Without using a calculator, estimate $\sqrt{112}$ to the nearest whole number. Explain your procedure. **11; $10^2 = 100$, $11^2 = 121$, and $10.5^2 = 110.25$. Since $110.25 < 112 < 121$, $\sqrt{112}$ is closer to 11 than to 10.**
4. A square has an area of 10 square inches. About how long is one side of the square? **3.2 inches**

Math Reasoning

In Exercise 58, we can determine the perimeter of a square once we know its area because any two squares are similar, that is, have the same shape, though their sizes might differ. In connection with this exercise, students might be asked why the perimeter of a rectangle cannot be determined solely from a knowledge of its area. In Exercise 59, we can determine the volume of a cube from a knowledge of its surface area. But it would not be possible to determine the volume of a rectangular box solely from the knowledge of its surface area.

Student Help

▶ STUDY TIP In Exercise 41 you can solve the equation $t^2 = 16$ by asking the question "What number(s) can I square to get 16?"

The area of a square is given. Approximate the length of one side of the square. Round your answer to the nearest tenth.

37. 40 square inches **6.3 in.**

38. 120 square centimeters **11.0 cm**

39. 70 square feet **8.4 ft**

40. 55 square meters **7.4 m**

Solve the equation using mental math.

41. $t^2 = 16$ **4, −4**

42. $100 = x^2$ **10, −10**

43. $625 = p^2$ **25, −25**

44. $h^2 = 81$ **9, −9**

45. $s^2 = 36$ **6, −6**

46. $y^2 = 225$ **15, −15**

47. $25 = z^2$ **5, −5**

48. $144 = r^2$ **12, −12**

49. $t^2 = \frac{1}{4}$ **$\frac{1}{2}, -\frac{1}{2}$**

50. $x^2 = \frac{1}{9}$ **$\frac{1}{3}, -\frac{1}{3}$**

51. $p^2 = \frac{4}{9}$ **$\frac{2}{3}, -\frac{2}{3}$**

52. $a^2 = \frac{81}{100}$ **$\frac{9}{10}, -\frac{9}{10}$**

Chapter Opener Link **In Exercises 53–55, look back at the exercises on page 447.**

53. Find the value of r when $g = 9.83271126$. **6,370,152.139 m**

54. Find the value of r when $g = 9.83271123$. **6,370,152.149 m**

55. Did the value of r increase or decrease when g changed from 9.83271126 to 9.83271123? By about how much? **increase by 0.01 m**

Link to Aviation

HORIZON A typical cruising altitude for a long-distance airplane flight is 33,000 feet. At this altitude, the distance to the horizon is about 222.5 miles.

HORIZON In Exercises 56 and 57, use the following information. You can approximate the distance to the horizon when looking out across the ocean if you know the height from sea level to your eyes. On a clear day, that distance squared is 1.5 times the height. So, $d^2 = 1.5h$ where the distance d is in miles and the height h is in feet.

56. You are on an observation deck on a clear day. Your eyes are 10 feet above sea level. How far can you see? Round your answer to the nearest tenth. **3.9 mi**

57. You climb to the top of an observation tower on a clear day. Your eyes are 30 feet above sea level. How far can you see? Round your answer to the nearest tenth. **6.7 mi**

58. MATHEMATICAL REASONING Explain how to find the perimeter of a square when you know its area. Give an example. **See margin.**

59. CHALLENGE The surface area of a cube is the sum of the areas of its faces. Find the volume of the cube shown if the surface area is 216 square centimeters. **216 cm³**

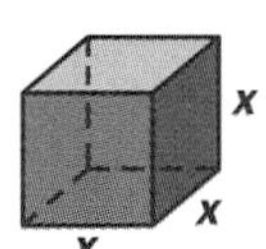

Multiple-Choice Practice

60. $\sqrt{72.25}$ is between which two positive integers? **C**

Ⓐ 6 and 7 Ⓑ 7 and 8 Ⓒ 8 and 9 Ⓓ Not here

61. What is the positive square root of 196? **G**

Ⓕ 13 Ⓖ 14 Ⓗ 14.5 Ⓙ 19.9

58. Multiply 4 times the square root of the area. *Sample answer:* If $A = 100$ m², then each side has length $\sqrt{100} = 10$ m. $P = 4(10) = 40$ m.

9.2 The Real Number System

California Standards

In this lesson you'll:

- Differentiate between rational and irrational numbers. (NS 1.4)
- Know that every rational number is either a terminating or a repeating decimal. (NS 1.5)
- Use powers and roots in working with fractions. (NS 2.0)

Goal 1 CLASSIFYING REAL NUMBERS

In Chapter 5 you learned that a rational number is a number that can be written as the quotient of two integers a and b where $b \neq 0$. Numbers that cannot be written as the quotient of two integers are called **irrational numbers**.

Any rational number can be written either as a terminating decimal or as a repeating decimal. The decimal form of an irrational number neither terminates nor repeats. The number below is an irrational number.

1.101001000100001000001000000100000001000000001000000000001. . .

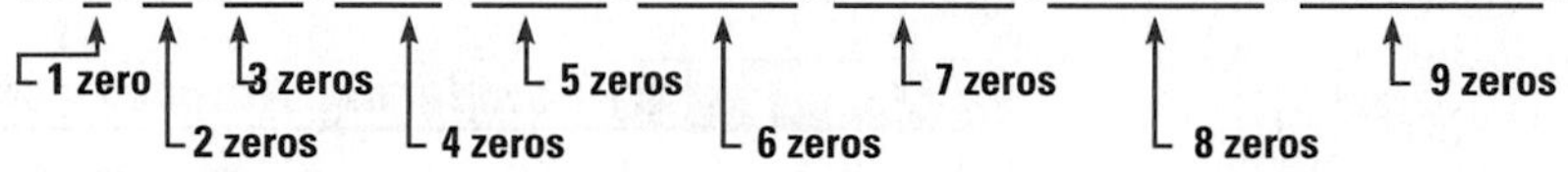

Together, the rational and irrational numbers make up the set of **real numbers**. The Venn diagram at the right illustrates the relationships among the different types of numbers you have studied so far.

Real Numbers

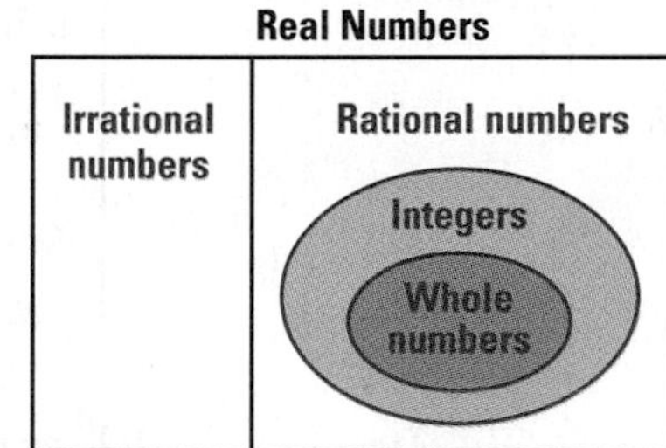

EXAMPLE 1 *Finding Irrational Lengths*

QUILTING You are designing a small quilt. Each piece of cloth is a right triangle. Eight of the pieces form a square that is 2 inches by 2 inches, as shown. To the nearest tenth of an inch, how long are the sides of the black square?

2 in.

2 in.

Solution

The large square has an area of 4 square inches. The black square has half that area, or 2 square inches.

$$\text{Area of black square} = x^2$$

$$2 = x^2$$

$$-\sqrt{2} \text{ or } \sqrt{2} = x$$

ANSWER ▶ Since length is positive, $x = \sqrt{2}$. So, each side of the black square is $\sqrt{2} \approx 1.4$ inches long.

Student Help

▶ **STUDY TIP**
Some square roots are rational and others are irrational. $\sqrt{4} = 2$ and $\sqrt{1.21} = 1.1$ are both rational, but $\sqrt{2} = 1.414213\ldots$ and $\sqrt{11} = 3.316624\ldots$ are irrational.

1 Plan

Pacing

Suggested Number of Days

Transitional: 2 days
Average: 2 days
Advanced: 2 days
Block Schedule: 1 block

Teaching Resources

Blacklines
(See page 446B.)

Transparencies
- Warm-Up Exercises
- Teacher Time-Savers
- English/Spanish Problem Solving
- Answers

Technology
- Electronic Teacher Tools
- Test and Practice Generator

2 Teach

Math Reasoning

For Mathematical Background Notes on mathematical reasoning related to this lesson, please refer to pages 446E and 446F in this Teacher's Edition.

Extra Example 1
See next page.

Teaching Tip

It can be proved that if n is a positive integer and n is not a perfect square, then $\sqrt{n}$ is an irrational number. There are many other irrational numbers as well.

California Standards and Assessment

CA Standards: NS 1.4, NS 2.0
CA Key Concepts Book: pp. S79–S82, S86

Extra Example 1

Refer to the figure in Example 1. Suppose the eight pieces form a square that is 4 inches by 4 inches. How long would the sides of the black square be then, to the nearest tenth of an inch? **$\sqrt{8} \approx 2.8$ inches**

Extra Example 2

Graph $-\frac{2}{3}, \frac{1}{5}, \sqrt{8}$, and $\frac{10}{3}$ on a number line.

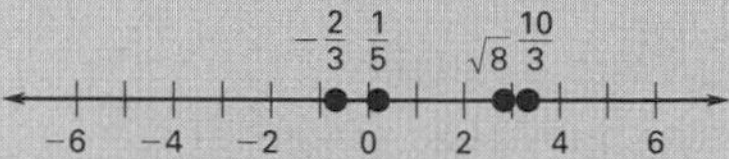

Extra Example 3

Graph the numbers on a number line. Then complete the statement using <, >, or =.

a. $\sqrt{3}$ _?_ 3

b. $\sqrt{\frac{1}{16}}$ _?_ $\frac{1}{4}$

c. $\sqrt{\frac{8}{9}}$ _?_ $\frac{8}{9}$

Solutions:

a. $\sqrt{3} \approx 1.73$ $3 = 3.0$

1.6 2.0 2.4 2.8 3.2 3.6 4.0

$\sqrt{3} < 3$

b.

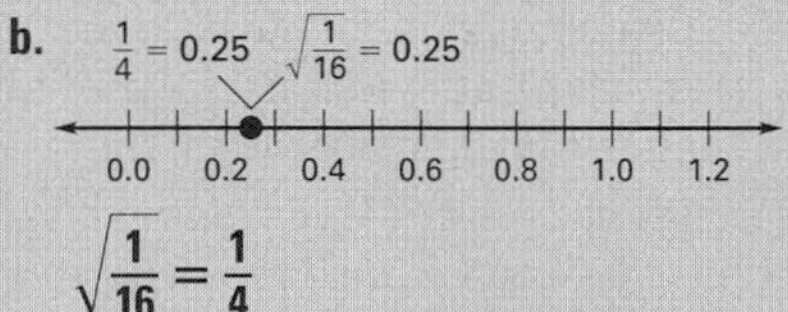

$\sqrt{\frac{1}{16}} = \frac{1}{4}$

c.

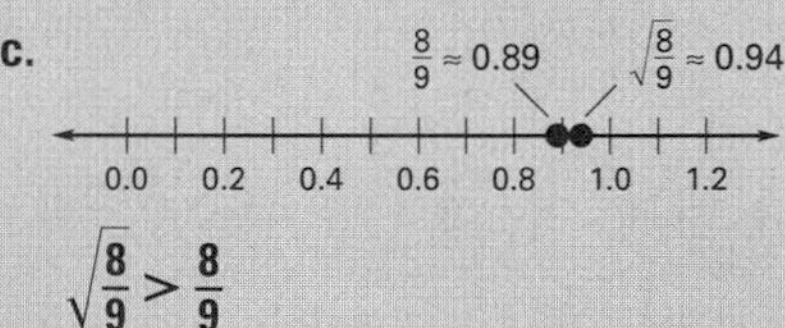

$\sqrt{\frac{8}{9}} > \frac{8}{9}$

Concept Check

Is every number written with a radical sign an irrational number? Explain. ***Sample answer:*** **No; for example, $\sqrt{9}$ is a rational number because $\sqrt{9} = 3$, which can be written as $\frac{3}{1}$.**

Goal 2 Using a Number Line

You can use a number line to compare real numbers.

EXAMPLE 2 Graphing Real Numbers

Graph $-\frac{3}{2}$, -0.5, $\sqrt{3}$, and $\frac{8}{3}$ on a number line.

Solution

Find decimal approximations of the numbers to help you graph them.

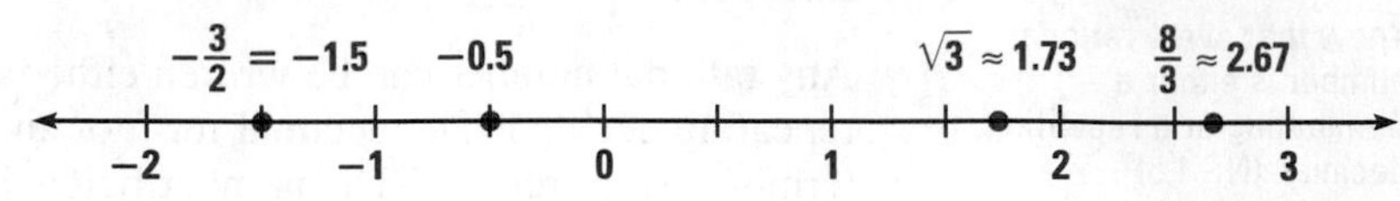

EXAMPLE 3 Comparing Numbers on a Number Line

Graph the numbers on a number line. Then complete the statement using <, >, or =.

a. $\sqrt{2}$ **?** 2

b. $\sqrt{\frac{1}{2}}$ **?** $\frac{1}{2}$

c. $\sqrt{\frac{9}{4}}$ **?** $\frac{3}{2}$

Solution

a. As decimals, $\sqrt{2} \approx 1.41$ and $2 = 2.0$.

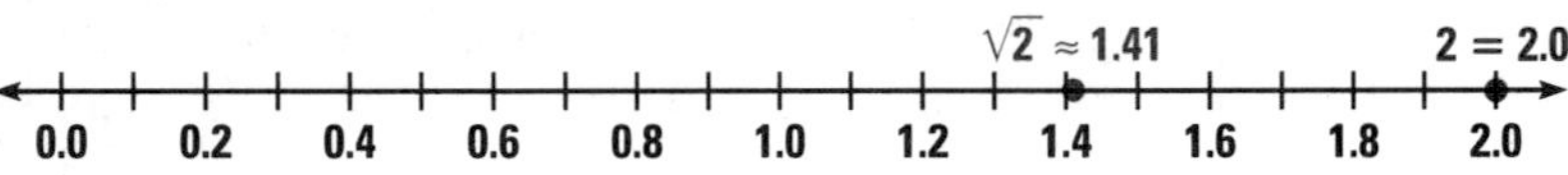

ANSWER ▶ Because $\sqrt{2}$ appears to the left of 2, $\sqrt{2} < 2$.

b. As decimals, $\sqrt{\frac{1}{2}} \approx 0.71$ and $\frac{1}{2} = 0.5$.

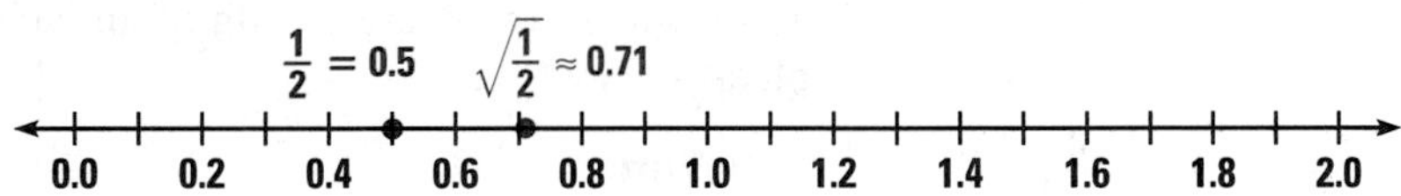

ANSWER ▶ Because 0.71 appears to the right of 0.5, $\sqrt{\frac{1}{2}} > \frac{1}{2}$.

c. As decimals, $\sqrt{\frac{9}{4}} = \sqrt{2.25} = 1.5$ and $\frac{3}{2} = 1.5$.

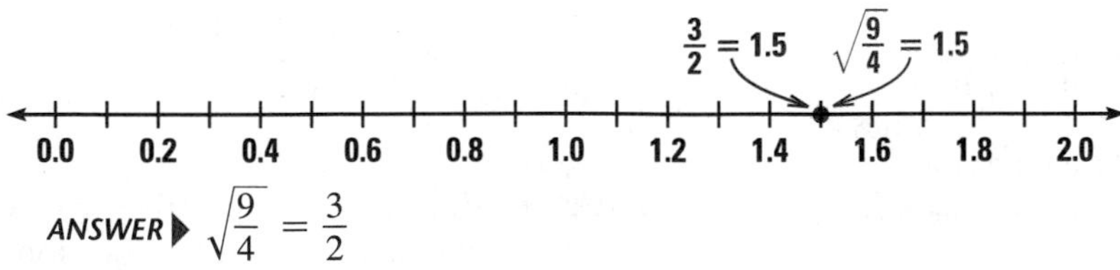

ANSWER ▶ $\sqrt{\frac{9}{4}} = \frac{3}{2}$

Student Help

▶ **Skills Review**
For help with comparing numbers on a number line, see page 674.

9.2 Exercises

Guided Practice

1. **WRITING** Describe how the decimal form of a rational number is different from the decimal form of an irrational number. Give examples to illustrate your answer. **See margin.**

In Exercises 2–9, tell whether each number is *rational* or *irrational*. Give a reason for your answer. **2–9. See margin.**

2. $\frac{7}{3}$ **3.** $\sqrt{5}$ **4.** $\sqrt{9}$ **5.** $-\sqrt{\frac{2}{9}}$

6. 0.567 **7.** 0.12 **8.** 1.121131114. . . **9.** −8.4

10. The floor area of a room is 160 square yards. The floor is in the shape of a square. What is the approximate length of one edge of the floor? **12.6 yd**

11. Graph the numbers on a number line. Determine the greatest and least numbers. **See margin. 3, $-\sqrt{8}$**

$$0, \frac{1}{2}, -\frac{5}{3}, -2.1, \sqrt{4}, \sqrt{6}, -\sqrt{8}, 3$$

1. The decimal form of a rational number either terminates or is a repeating decimal. The decimal form of an irrational number neither terminates nor repeats. Check examples.
2. rational; in form $\frac{a}{b}$, a and b integers and b nonzero
3. irrational; non-repeating, non-terminating decimal equivalent
4. rational; can be written as $\frac{3}{1}$
5. irrational; non-repeating, non-terminating decimal equivalent
6. rational; terminating decimal
7. rational; terminating decimal
8. irrational; non-repeating, non-terminating decimal
9. rational; terminating decimal

Practice and Problem Solving

Student Help

▶**MORE PRACTICE**
Extra practice to help you master skills is on page 706.

Match each number with a point on the number line.

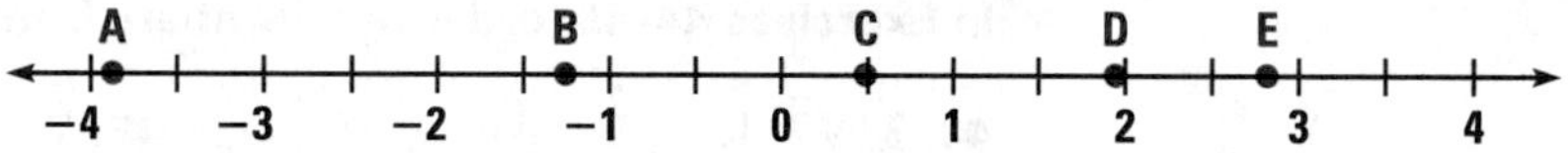

12. $\sqrt{8}$ **E** **13.** $-\sqrt{15}$ **A** **14.** 0.49 **C** **15.** $\sqrt{3.8}$ **D** **16.** $-\sqrt{\frac{25}{16}}$ **B**

MATHEMATICAL REASONING **Copy the table. Put a check mark in all the columns that describe the number.** **17–23. See margin.**

	Number	Integer	Rational	Irrational	Real
17.	26	?	?	?	?
18.	$\frac{7}{2}$	?	?	?	?
19.	$\sqrt{7}$	?	?	?	?
20.	$-\sqrt{144}$	?	?	?	?
21.	0.98	?	?	?	?
22.	0.3030030003. . .	?	?	?	?
23.	0.51515151. . .	?	?	?	?

17. integer, rational, real
18. rational, real
19. irrational, real
20. integer, rational, real
21. rational, real
22. irrational, real
23. rational, real

3 Apply

Assignment Guide

TRANSITIONAL
Day 1: pp. 455–457 Exs. 17–26, 30–34, 50, 60–62
Day 2: SRH p. 674 Exs. 1–5; pp. 455–457 Exs. 12–16, 35–37, 44–45, 58–59, 63–68

AVERAGE
Day 1: pp. 455–457 Exs. 17–34, 50, 60–62
Day 2: pp. 455–457 Exs. 12–16, 38–40, 46–47, 51–52, 58–59, 63–68

ADVANCED
Day 1: pp. 455–457 Exs. 17–34, 50, 60–62
Day 2: pp. 455–457 Exs. 12–16, 41–43, 48–49, 53, 54–57*, 58–59, 63–68

BLOCK SCHEDULE
pp. 455–457 Exs. 12–34, 38–40, 46–47, 50–52, 58–68

Extra Practice

- Student Edition, pp. 706–707
- Chapter 9 Resource Book, p. 15

Homework Check

To quickly check student understanding of key concepts, go over the following exercises:

Transitional: 18, 22, 26, 36, 44
Average: 18, 22, 26, 38, 46
Advanced: 18, 22, 28, 42, 48, 50

11.

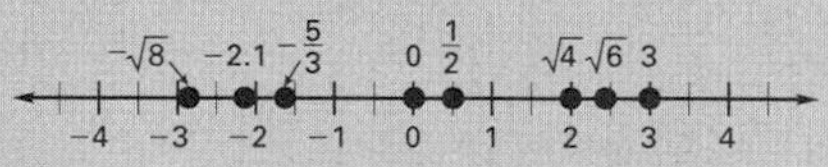

Problem Solving

Exercises 24–27
Have students refer to the Venn diagram on page 453.

35. 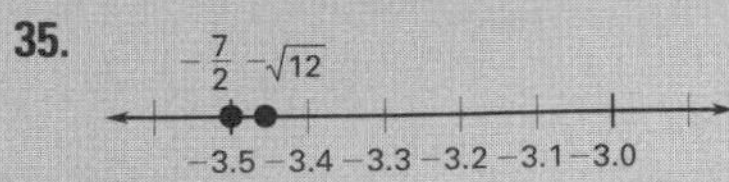

36. 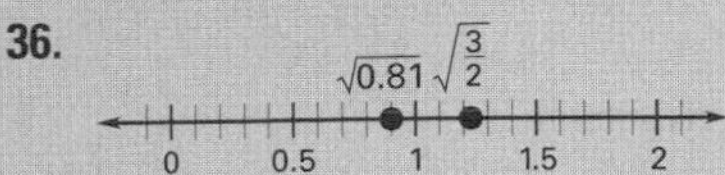

37. 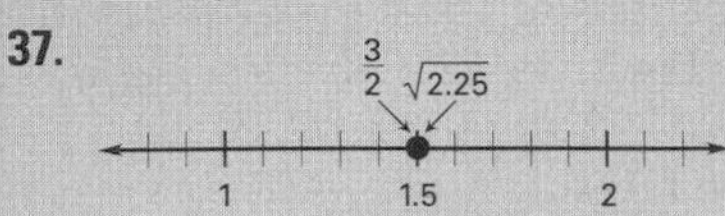

38. 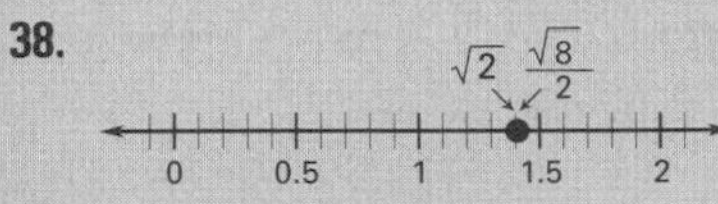

39. 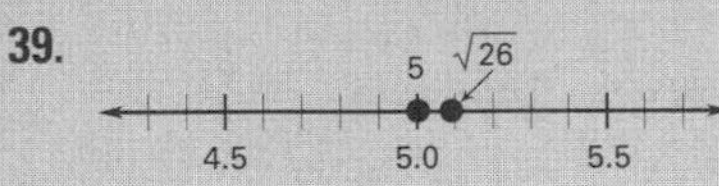

40. 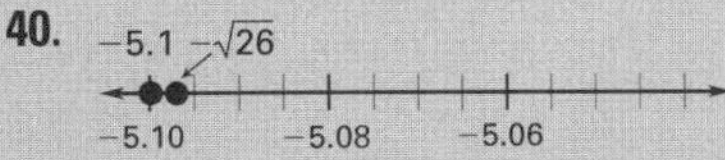

41. 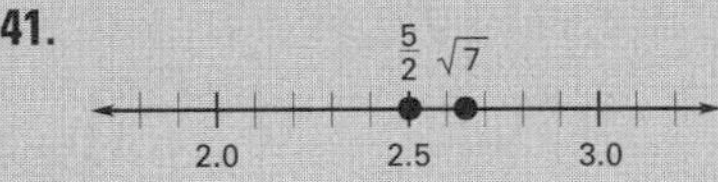

42. 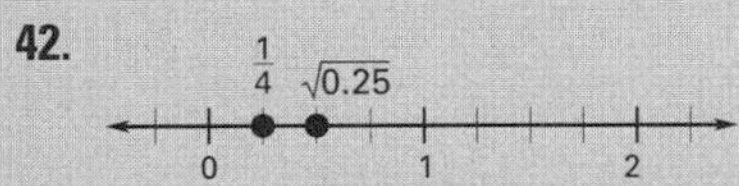

43. 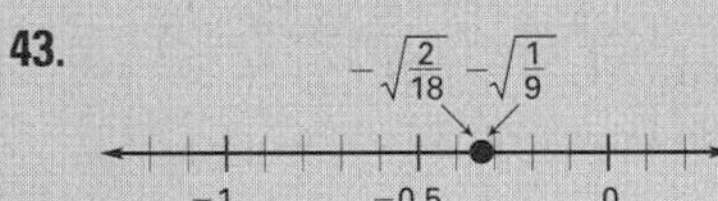

24. Irrational; 5 is not a perfect square.

25. Irrational; $\frac{1}{2}$ is not a perfect square.

26. Rational; 9 is a perfect square.

27. Irrational; 8 is not a perfect square.

28. Rational; 16 is a perfect square.

29. Rational; 25 is a perfect square.

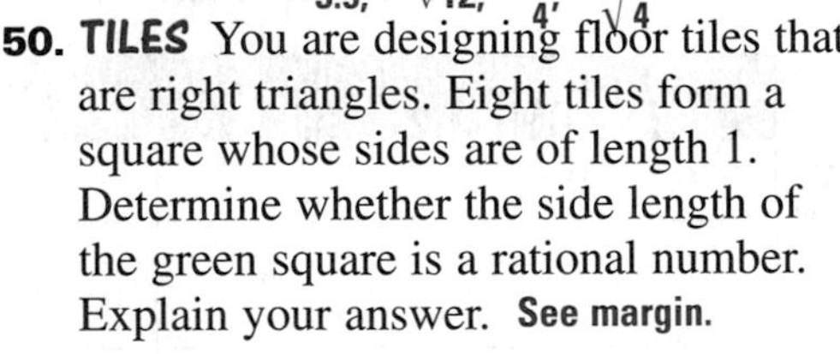

Student Help
HOMEWORK HELP
INTERNET
Extra help with problem solving in Exs. 35–43 is available at www.mcdougallittell.com

50. Not a rational number. The green square contains 4 tiles, so its area is half the area of the large square, or 0.5 square units. The side length of the green square is $\sqrt{0.5}$, which is irrational.

Tell whether the number is *rational* or *irrational*. Give a reason for your answer. 24–29. See margin.

24. $\sqrt{\frac{1}{5}}$ **25.** $\sqrt{\frac{5}{10}}$ **26.** $\sqrt{\frac{27}{3}}$

27. $\sqrt{\frac{400}{50}}$ **28.** $\sqrt{\frac{512}{32}}$ **29.** $\sqrt{\frac{625}{25}}$

MATHEMATICAL REASONING Complete the statement using *always, sometimes,* or *never.* Explain your answer.

30. A real number is __?__ a rational number.
sometimes; It could also be irrational.

31. An irrational number is __?__ a real number.
always; All irrational numbers are real numbers.

32. A negative integer is __?__ an irrational number.
never; Any integer can be written as $\frac{a}{b}$, with a and b integers, b nonzero.

33. The square root of a number is __?__ an irrational number.
sometimes; The square root of a perfect-square number is rational.

34 An integer is __?__ a whole number.
sometimes; A negative integer is not a whole number.

Graph the numbers on a number line. Then complete the statement using <, >, or =. 35–43. See margin.

35. $-\frac{7}{2}$? $-\sqrt{12}$ < **36.** $\sqrt{0.81}$? $\sqrt{\frac{3}{2}}$ < **37.** $\sqrt{2.25}$? $\frac{3}{2}$ =

38. $\sqrt{2}$? $\frac{\sqrt{8}}{2}$ = **39.** 5 ? $\sqrt{26}$ < **40.** -5.1 ? $-\sqrt{26}$ <

41. $\sqrt{7}$? $\frac{5}{2}$ > **42.** $\sqrt{0.25}$? $\frac{1}{4}$ > **43.** $-\sqrt{\frac{2}{18}}$? $-\sqrt{\frac{1}{9}}$ =

In Exercises 44–49, order the numbers from least to greatest.

44. $3, \sqrt{7}, 1.75, \frac{2}{3}$ $\frac{2}{3}, 1.75, \sqrt{7}, 3$

45. $\sqrt{8}, -4, \frac{5}{2}, -3.75$ $-4, -3.75, \frac{5}{2}, \sqrt{8}$

46. $\sqrt{221}, \sqrt{81}, 10.3, -12$
$-12, \sqrt{81}, 10.3, \sqrt{221}$

47. $1.02, -2, \sqrt{2.5}, \sqrt{1.25}$
$-2, 1.02, \sqrt{1.25}, \sqrt{2.5}$

48. $-\sqrt{\frac{1}{4}}, -3.5, -\frac{3}{4}, -\sqrt{12}$
$-3.5, -\sqrt{12}, -\frac{3}{4}, -\sqrt{\frac{1}{4}}$

49. $\frac{10}{9}, \sqrt{10}, \sqrt{7.2}, 1.8$ $\frac{10}{9}, 1.8, \sqrt{7.2}, \sqrt{10}$

50. TILES You are designing floor tiles that are right triangles. Eight tiles form a square whose sides are of length 1. Determine whether the side length of the green square is a rational number. Explain your answer. See margin.

51. List all of the whole numbers from 1 to 100 that have rational square roots. What percent of the whole numbers from 1 to 100 have rational square roots? 1, 4, 9, 16, 25, 36, 49, 64, 81, 100; 10%

52. How can you use your answer from Exercise 51 to find the percent of the whole numbers from 1 to 100 that have irrational square roots?
Subtract the percentage in Exercise 51 from 100%.

53. MATHEMATICAL REASONING Give an example of a decimal that neither terminates nor repeats. Explain how you know that it will never repeat. ***Sample answer:*** **0.04004000400004...**

CHALLENGE Evaluate the expression when $a = 2$, $b = 4$, and $c = 9$. Determine whether the result is a *rational* or an *irrational* number.

54. $\sqrt{a} + \sqrt{b}$ **$2 + \sqrt{2}$, or about 3.41; irrational**

55. $\sqrt{b} - \sqrt{c}$ **−1; rational**

56. $\sqrt{a} \cdot \sqrt{c}$ **$\sqrt{2} \cdot 3$ or about 4.24; irrational**

57. $\sqrt{c} \div \sqrt{b}$ **$\frac{3}{2}$; rational**

Multiple-Choice Practice

Test Tip Ⓐ Ⓑ Ⓒ Ⓓ

▶Since you know an irrational number can not be expressed as a quotient of two integers, you can eliminate $\frac{41}{19}$ as a possible answer in Exercise 48.

58. Which number is irrational? **D**

Ⓐ $\frac{41}{19}$ Ⓑ $-\sqrt{36}$ Ⓒ $\sqrt{2.25}$ Ⓓ Not here

59. Which statement is *false*? **G**

Ⓕ All whole numbers are integers.

Ⓖ The decimal form of an irrational number repeats.

Ⓗ All real numbers are either rational or irrational.

Ⓙ A number cannot be both rational and irrational.

Mixed Review

FUNDRAISING In Exercises 60–62, use the following information. Your class is selling sandwiches to raise money. The class spent $400 to buy food to make the sandwiches, and it is selling them for $2.50 each. *(2.4)*

60. Use the verbal model below to write an equation for the profit P if you sell x sandwiches. **$P = 2.50x - 400$**

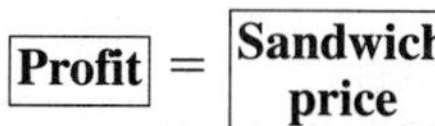

VERBAL MODEL Profit = Sandwich price • Number of sandwiches sold − Expenses

61. You have sold 200 sandwiches. What is your profit? Explain. **\$100; 2.50(200) − 400 = 100**

62. You will break even if the profit is \$0. How many sandwiches must you sell to break even? **160 sandwiches**

Find the greatest common factor. *(5.2)*

63. 24, 39 **3** **64.** 15, 175 **5** **65.** $10xy$, $22y$ **2y** **66.** $36a$, 48 **12**

67. SPANISH In 1998 about 656,600 Americans took a language course in Spanish. This represented 55% of those who took a language course. Find the total number of Americans who took a language course. *(7.5)* **1,193,818 Americans**

68. FRENCH In 1998 about 17% of Americans who took a language course took a course in French. Use your answer from Exercise 67 to find the number of Americans who took a course in French. *(7.5)* **202,949 Americans**

4 Assess

Assessment Resources

- Assessment Book (Formal Assessment and Alternative Assessment)
- Test and Practice Generator

Mini-Quiz

Tell whether the number is *rational* or *irrational.*

1. $-\frac{2}{5}$ **rational**
2. $\sqrt{23}$ **irrational**
3. $\sqrt{49}$ **rational**

Complete the statement with <, >, or =.

4. $\sqrt{6}$? 6 **<**
5. $\sqrt{0.4}$? 0.4 **>**
6. $\sqrt{4.84}$? 2.2 **=**

Math Reasoning

In Exercise 54 we know that $\sqrt{2} + 2$ is not rational, for if $\sqrt{2} + 2 = \frac{a}{b}$, with a and b integers, then we would have $\sqrt{2} = \frac{a}{b} - 2 = \frac{a - 2b}{b}$, a ratio of integers, contradicting the fact that $\sqrt{2}$ is irrational. In Exercise 56 we know that $3\sqrt{2}$ is irrational, because if $3\sqrt{2} = \frac{a}{b}$, with a and b integers, then $\sqrt{2} = \frac{a}{3b}$, which contradicts the fact that $\sqrt{2}$ is irrational.

1 Planning the Activity

Purpose and Materials

See the margin of the student page.

▶ LINK TO LESSON

Students apply the results of the activity in Lesson 9.3 to see that the Pythagorean theorem is true. They can then apply the theorem in Examples 1–3.

Math Reasoning

Students analyze a problem and use deductive reasoning to prove the Pythagorean theorem. They develop generalizations to apply to new situations.

4. Since $m\angle 4 = 90$ degrees and the sum of the angles of a triangle is 180 degrees, $m\angle 1 + m\angle 2 = 90$ degrees. $m\angle 1 + m\angle 2 + m\angle 3 = 180$ degrees. Therefore, $90° + m\angle 3 = 180°$ or $m\angle 3 = 90°$. Since all the sides are congruent and all angles labeled 3 measure 90 degrees, the figure is a square.

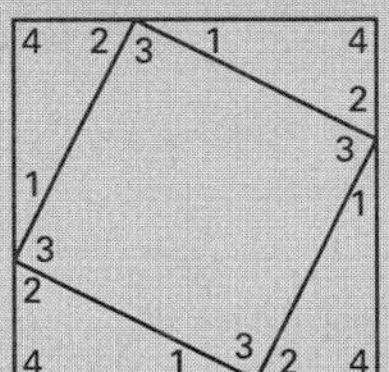

California Standards and Assessment

CA Standards: MG 3.3, MR 1.1

CA Key Concepts Book: pp. S79–S82

REASONING 9.3

DEVELOPING CONCEPTS
Right Triangles

For use with Lesson 9.3

California Standards

- Know and understand the Pythagorean theorem and use it to find the length of the missing side of a right triangle. (MG 3.3)
- Analyze problems by identifying relationships, identifying missing information, and observing patterns. (MR 1.1)

MATERIALS:

- Paper and pencil
- Scissors

Given the lengths of the two *legs* of a right triangle, it is possible to find the length of the *hypotenuse*.

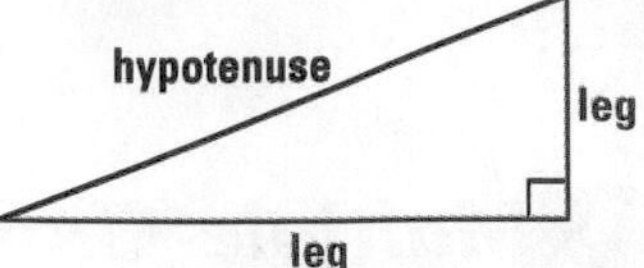

SAMPLE 1 Finding the Length of the Hypotenuse

A right triangle has legs of length 3 and 4. Find the length of the hypotenuse.

Here's How

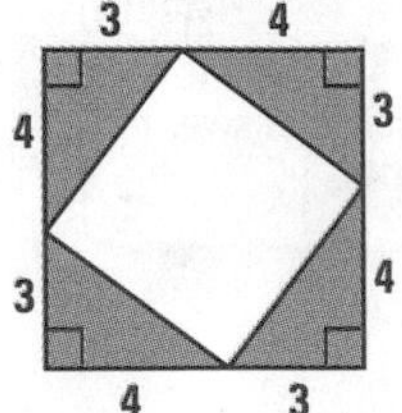

1. First draw a right triangle with legs of length 3 and 4. Then make three copies of the triangle.
2. Arrange the four triangles to form a large square, as shown.
3. You can show through an argument using complementary and supplementary angles that the inner figure formed by the hypotenuses is a square. Find the area of the inner square by finding the difference of the area of the outer square and the areas of the four triangles.

$$\begin{aligned}\text{Area of inner square} &= \text{Area of outer square} - 4(\text{Area of triangle})\\ &= 7^2 - 4\left(\frac{1}{2} \cdot 3 \cdot 4\right)\\ &= 49 - 24\\ &= 25\end{aligned}$$

Because the area of the inner square is 25, the length of each side must be $\sqrt{25} = 5$. So, the hypotenuse has a length of 5.

Try These

For Exercises 1–3, use the method shown above to find the length of the hypotenuse of a right triangle having legs of the given lengths.

1. 5 and 12 **13** **2.** 6 and 8 **10** **3.** 8 and 15 **17**

4. MATHEMATICAL REASONING By using what you know about complementary and supplementary angles, show that the inner figure formed by the hypotenuses in the diagram above is a square. **See margin.**

SAMPLE 2 Proving the Pythagorean Theorem

A right triangle has legs of length a and b. Find the length of the hypotenuse.

Here's How

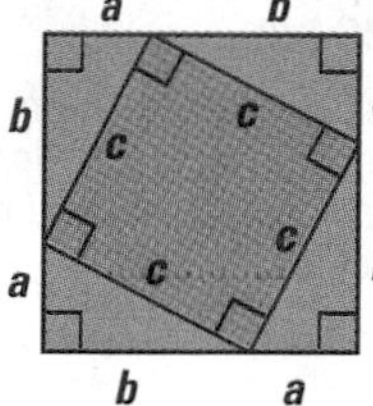

1. First draw a right triangle with legs of length a and b and hypotenuse of length c. Then make three copies of the triangle.
2. Arrange the triangles as shown and express the area of the inner square as a difference of areas.

c^2 = Area of inner square

= (Area of outer square) − 4(Area of triangle)

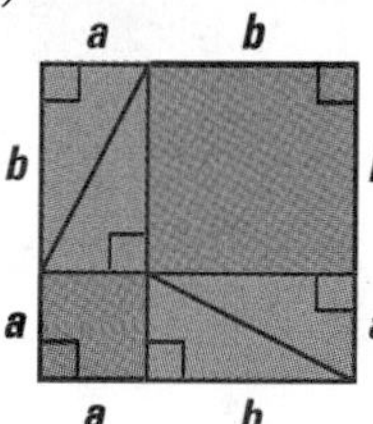

3. Draw two squares with sides of length a and b.
4. Arrange the four triangles from Step 1 and the two squares from Step 3 as shown and express the sum of the areas of the two smaller squares as a difference of areas.

$a^2 + b^2$ = Areas of two smaller squares

= (Area of outer square) − 4(Area of triangle)

Since the expressions c^2 and $a^2 + b^2$ both represent the same difference of areas, $a^2 + b^2 = c^2$. This gives the following result, called the *Pythagorean theorem*:

> If a right triangle has legs of length a and b and a hypotenuse of length c, then $a^2 + b^2 = c^2$.

Try These

5. Go back to Sample 1 and use the Pythagorean theorem to find the length of the hypotenuse. **5**
6. **MATHEMATICAL REASONING** Can you use the Pythagorean theorem to find the length of *any* side of a right triangle if you know the lengths of the other two sides? Explain and give an example. **See margin.**
7. **MATHEMATICAL REASONING** Do you think that the Pythagorean theorem applies to *any* triangle? Explain and give an example.

6. Yes. Since we know 2 of the 3 sides we can solve for the third side.
$a^2 = b^2 + c^2$
$5^2 = 4^2 + b^2$
$b^2 = 5^2 - 4^2 = 9$
$b = 3$

7. no; The theorem depends on the fact that one angle is a right angle, and that the other two angles are complementary.

2 Managing the Activity

Classroom Management

Use an overhead to model how the squares and triangles are arranged in Sample 2. You may wish to make 8 copies of the right triangle with legs a and b so that the two large squares can be shown side-by-side. The squares and triangles could be cut from a colored transparency so that they are easily visible on an overhead.

3 Closing the Activity

★ Key Discovery

In a right triangle, the sum of the squares of the lengths of the legs is equal to the square of the length of the hypotenuse.

Activity Assessment

Use Exercises 1–3 to assess student understanding.

1 Plan

Pacing

Suggested Number of Days

Transitional: 1 day
Average: 1 day
Advanced: 1 day
Block Schedule: 0.5 block with 9.4

Teaching Resources

Blacklines

(See page 446B.)

Transparencies

- Warm-Up Exercises
- Teacher Time-Savers
- English/Spanish Problem Solving
- Answers

Technology

- Electronic Teacher Tools
- Test and Practice Generator

2 Teach

Math Reasoning

For Mathematical Background Notes on mathematical reasoning related to this lesson, please refer to pages 446E and 446F in this Teacher's Edition.

California Standards and Assessment

CA Standard: MG 3.3

CA Key Concepts Book: pp. S22–S23

9.3 The Pythagorean Theorem

California Standards

In this lesson you'll:

- Know and understand the Pythagorean theorem. (MG 3.3)
- Use the Pythagorean theorem to find the length of the missing side of a right triangle. (MG 3.3)

Goal 1 Using the Pythagorean Theorem

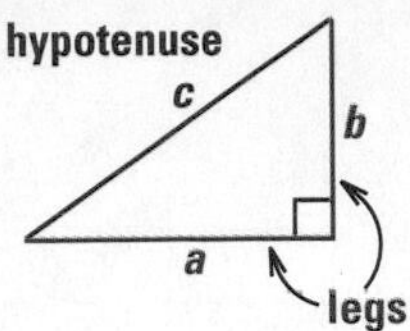

As you learned in Chapter 8, a right triangle is a triangle that has a right angle. The sides that form the right angle are the **legs** of the triangle. The side opposite the right angle is the **hypotenuse**.

As you saw in Developing Concepts 9.3, page 458, the lengths of the legs and hypotenuse of any right triangle are related by the Pythagorean theorem. Mathematicians have known about this theorem for thousands of years, and many different proofs of it exist.

Pythagorean Theorem

For any right triangle, the sum of the squares of the lengths of the legs, a and b, equals the square of the length of the hypotenuse, c.

$$a^2 + b^2 = c^2$$

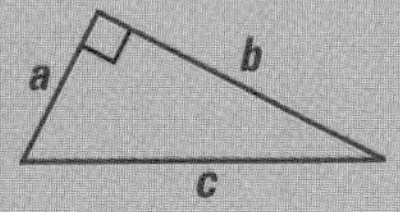

EXAMPLE 1 Finding the Length of the Hypotenuse

Find the length of the hypotenuse of the right triangle.

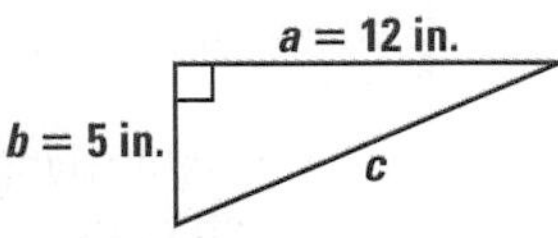

Solution

The lengths of the legs are 12 inches and 5 inches. Let $a = 12$ and $b = 5$.

$a^2 + b^2 = c^2$	Use Pythagorean theorem.
$12^2 + 5^2 = c^2$	Substitute 12 for a and 5 for b.
$144 + 25 = c^2$	Square 12 and 5.
$169 = c^2$	Add.
$\sqrt{169} = c$	Take positive square root of each side.
$13 = c$	Simplify.

ANSWER ▶ The hypotenuse has a length of 13 inches.

Link to History

PYTHAGOREAN THEOREM The Pythagorean theorem is named after the Greek mathematician Pythagoras, who lived about 585–500 B.C.

More about Pythagoras available at www.mcdougallittell.com

Goal 2 SOLVING A RIGHT TRIANGLE

If you know the lengths of two sides of a right triangle, you can use the Pythagorean theorem to find the length of the third side. This is called **solving a right triangle**.

EXAMPLE 2 Solving a Right Triangle

In a right triangle, the length of the hypotenuse is 10, and the length of one leg is 6. Find the length of the other leg.

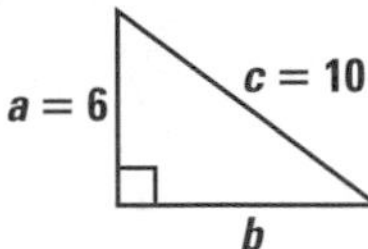

Solution

$a^2 + b^2 = c^2$	Use Pythagorean theorem.
$6^2 + b^2 = 10^2$	Substitute 6 for a and 10 for c.
$36 + b^2 = 100$	Square 6 and 10.
$b^2 = 64$	Subtract 36 from each side.
$b = 8$	Take positive square root of each side.

ANSWER ▶ The length of the other leg is 8.

EXAMPLE 3 Solving an Isosceles Right Triangle

LANDSCAPING You want to attach guy wires to a young tree. Each wire is 8 feet long. The distance from the base of the tree to the point of attachment is equal to the distance from the base of the tree to the stakes in the ground. How far up the tree should you attach the wires?

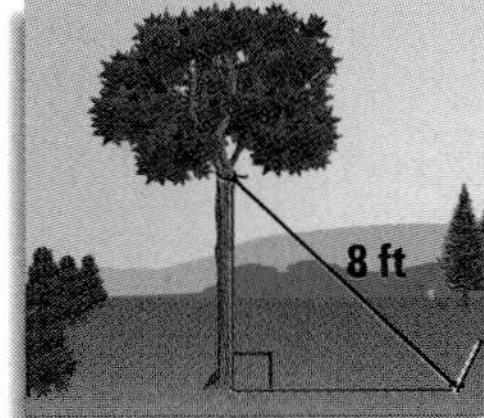

Solution

Because the distance from the base of the tree to the point of attachment is equal to the distance from the base of the tree to the stakes, the right triangle is isosceles. Using the Pythagorean theorem, you can see that the length of the hypotenuse is enough information to find the length of each leg.

$a^2 + b^2 = c^2$	Use Pythagorean theorem.
$a^2 + a^2 = 8^2$	$a = b$, so substitute a for b. Substitute 8 for c.
$2a^2 = 64$	Simplify.
$a^2 = 32$	Divide each side by 2.
$a = \sqrt{32}$	Take positive square root of each side.

ANSWER ▶ You can use a calculator to find that $\sqrt{32} \approx 5.7$. So, the length of each leg is about 5.7 feet. You should attach the wires about 5.7 feet up the tree.

Student Help

▶ **LOOK BACK**
A triangle is isosceles if at least two of its sides have the same length. In an *isosceles right* triangle, both legs have the same length. For help with isosceles triangles, see page 404.

Extra Example 1

Find the length of the hypotenuse of the right triangle.

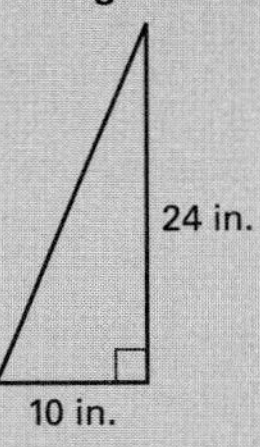

26 in.

Extra Example 2

In a right triangle, the length of the hypotenuse is 34, and the length of one leg is 30. Find the length of the other leg. **16**

Extra Example 3

Suppose the guy wires in Example 3 are 10 feet long. How far up the tree should you attach the wires?
$\sqrt{50} \approx 7.1$ ft

Teaching Tip

Common Error
Students often think that $\sqrt{a^2 + b^2} = \sqrt{a^2} + \sqrt{b^2}$. Remind them that this is not true by doing several examples.

Concept Check

Can the Pythagorean theorem be used to solve any triangle? Explain.
No. The Pythagorean theorem applies only to right triangles.

3 Apply

Assignment Guide

TRANSITIONAL
Day 1: pp. 462–464 Exs. 8–21, 27–29, 37–38

AVERAGE
Day 1: pp. 462–464 Exs. 8–19, 21–22, 25–26, 30, 37–38

ADVANCED
Day 1: pp. 462–464 Exs. 10–22, 25–26, 32–33, 34–36, 37–38; EC: TE p. 446D*

BLOCK SCHEDULE
pp. 462–464 Exs. 8–19, 21–22, 25–26, 30, 37–38 (with 9.4)

Extra Practice

- Student Edition, pp. 706–707
- Chapter 9 Resource Book, p. 24

Homework Check

To quickly check student understanding of key concepts, go over the following exercises:

Transitional: 10, 12, 14, 20, 28
Average: 10, 12, 18, 22, 30
Advanced: 16, 20, 28, 32, 33

9.3 Exercises

Guided Practice

In Exercises 1–6, let *a* and *b* be the lengths of the legs of a right triangle. Let *c* be the length of the hypotenuse. Use the Pythagorean theorem to find the missing length. Round your answer to the nearest tenth.

1. $a = 8, b = 15$ **17** **2.** $a = 16, c = 34$ **30** **3.** $b = 12, c = 15$ **9**

4. $a = 7, b = 11$ **13.0** **5.** $b = 13, c = 15$ **7.5** **6.** $a = 6, c = 12$ **10.4**

7. An isosceles right triangle has a hypotenuse whose length is 6 feet. What is the length of each leg? **about 4.2 ft**

Practice and Problem Solving

Student Help
▶MORE PRACTICE
Extra practice to help you master skills is on page 706.

Find the length of the hypotenuse of the right triangle.

8.
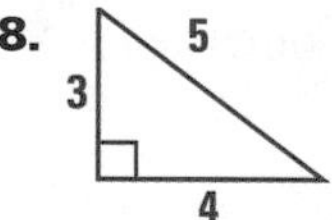

9.
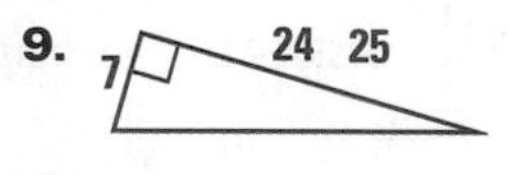

10. 35 37 12

The length of a leg of an isosceles right triangle is given. Find the length of the hypotenuse. Round your answer to the nearest tenth.

11. 25 **35.4** **12.** 1.5 **2.1** **13.** 12.75 **18.0**

In Exercises 14–19, use the Pythagorean theorem to solve the right triangle.

14.
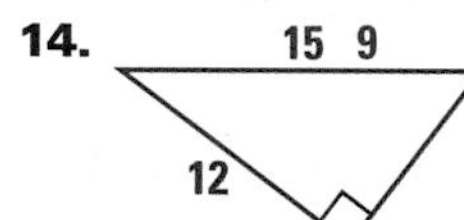

15.
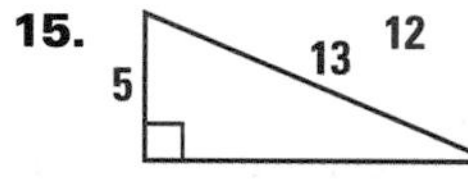

16.
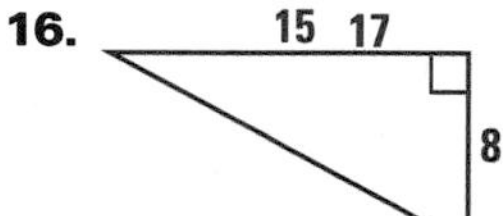

17.
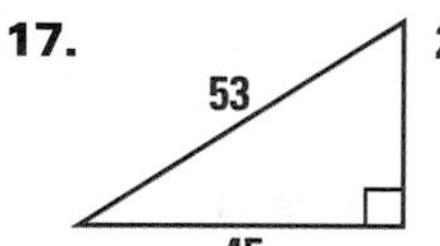

18.
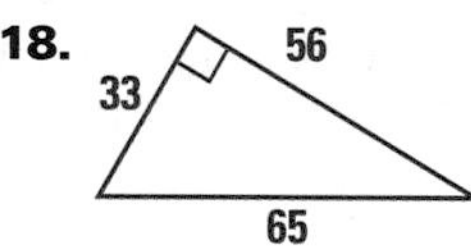

19.
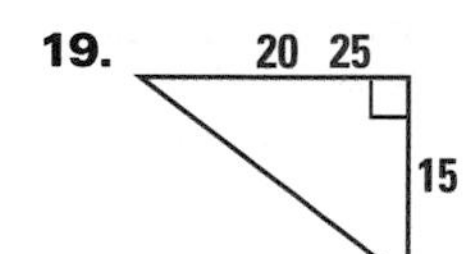

Student Help
▶STUDY TIP
In Exercises 20–22, you may want to sketch a right triangle and label the sides using the given information.

20. One leg of a right triangle is twice as long as the other leg. The length of the hypotenuse is $\sqrt{20}$. What is the length of each leg? **2, 4**

21. One leg of a right triangle is five times as long as the other leg. The length of the hypotenuse is $\sqrt{416}$. What is the length of each leg? **4, 20**

22. The length of the hypotenuse of a right triangle is three times the length of one of the legs. The length of the other leg is $\sqrt{72}$. What is the length of the hypotenuse? **9**

Student Help

▶ HOMEWORK HELP
Extra help with problem solving in Exs. 23–24 is available at www.mcdougallittell.com

Let a and b be the lengths of the legs of a right triangle. Let c be the length of the hypotenuse. Use the given lengths to draw the right triangle on graph paper and estimate the missing length. Then use the Pythagorean theorem to check your estimate.

23. $a = 6$, $b = 7$, $c =$ **?** about 9.2 **24.** $a = 4$, $b =$ **?**, $c = 5$ 3

MATHEMATICAL REASONING Complete the statement with *always*, *sometimes*, or *never*.

25. If you know the lengths of two sides of a right triangle, then you can __?__ find the length of the third side. always

26. In a right triangle, if the lengths of the legs are integers, then the length of the hypotenuse is __?__ an integer. sometimes

VOLLEYBALL In Exercises 27–29, use the following information. You are setting up a volleyball net. To keep each pole standing straight, you use two ropes and two stakes as shown at the right.

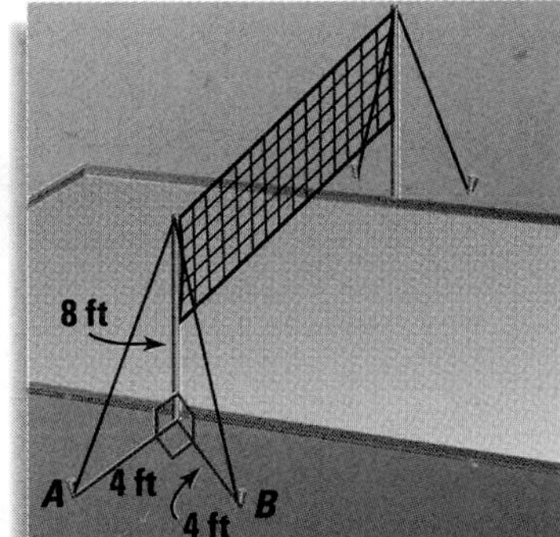

27. Find the length of each rope. about 8.9 ft

28. What is the total length of rope you will need for both poles? about 35.8 ft

29. Find the distance between the stakes, marked A and B. about 5.7 ft

30. CELLULAR TELEPHONE A cellular telephone tower is anchored by four wires, each 190 feet long. The points where the wires are attached to concrete blocks embedded in the ground are all 102.5 feet from the base of the tower. Find the height of the point where the wires are attached to the tower. about 160.0 ft

31. ERROR ANALYSIS Describe and correct the error. should solve for b, not c;
$6^2 + b = 8^2$
$b^2 = 8^2 - 6^2$
$b = \sqrt{64 - 36}$
$b \approx 5.3$

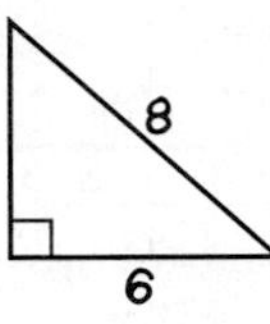

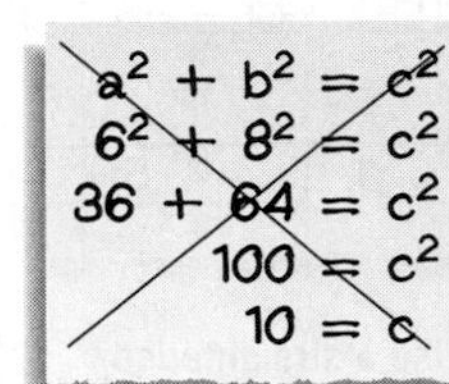

32. DRIVING From the junction of Highways 330 and 30, you drive to Ames, Iowa. Then you turn south and drive on Highway 35 to Des Moines, Iowa. How many miles would you have saved if you had driven on Highways 330 and 65 to Des Moines instead? about 16.7 mi

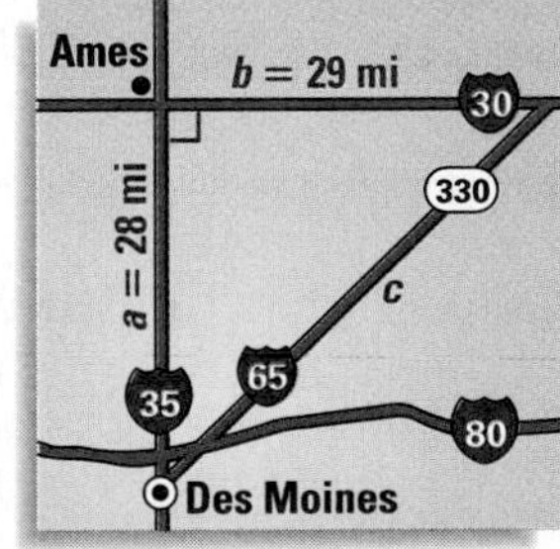

4 Assess

Assessment Resources

- Assessment Book (Formal Assessment and Alternative Assessment)
- Test and Practice Generator

Mini-Quiz

Suppose a and b are the lengths of the legs of a right triangle, and c is the length of the hypotenuse. Find the missing length. If necessary, round your answer to two decimal places.

1. $a = 14, b = 28$ **$c \approx 31.30$**
2. $a = 5, b = 17$ **$c \approx 17.72$**
3. $a = 12, c = 20$ **$b = 16$**
4. $b = 31, c = 39$ **$a \approx 23.66$**
5. Find the length of the diagonal of a square whose sides are 4 cm long. Round your answer to two decimal places. **5.66 cm**

33. LADDER For safety purposes, the base of a 40 foot ladder should be between 10 feet and 18 feet from the base of the wall. Find the maximum and minimum heights that the ladder will reach. **about 38.7 ft, about 35.7 ft**

CHALLENGE The lengths of two sides of a right triangle are given. Draw two *different* right triangles whose sides have these lengths. Then find the length of the missing side of each triangle.

34. 8 cm and 10 cm **about 12.8 cm, 6 cm**
35. 5 cm and 6 cm **about 3.3 cm, about 7.8 cm**
36. 5 cm and 12 cm **13 cm, about 10.9 cm**

Multiple-Choice Practice

Test Tip A B C D

▶ In Exercises 37 and 38, be sure to notice whether you are finding a leg or the hypotenuse.

37. What is the value of x for the triangle shown? **C**

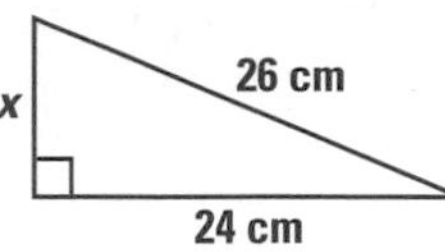

Ⓐ 2 cm Ⓑ 4 cm
Ⓒ 10 cm Ⓓ 11.38 cm

38. What is the approximate value of y for the the triangle shown? **G**

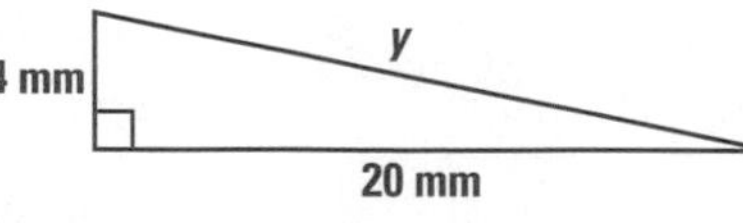

Ⓕ 19.7 mm Ⓖ 20.4 mm
Ⓗ 21 mm Ⓙ 21.7 mm

CONSTRUCTION — Graphing Irrational Numbers

You can use a compass and graph paper to graph some irrational numbers like $\sqrt{20}$ on a number line. Because 20 is the sum of two squares, 4 and 16, you begin by constructing a right triangle with a hypotenuse of length $\sqrt{20}$.

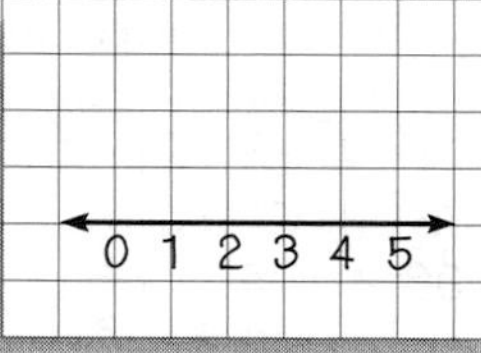

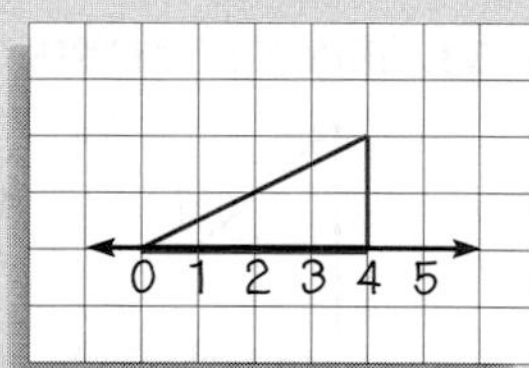

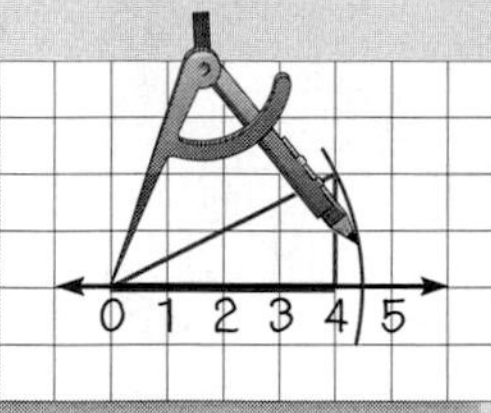

❶ Use a straightedge to draw a number line on graph paper. Number the line from 0 to 5.

❷ Draw a right triangle whose legs have lengths 2 and 4. Using the Pythagorean theorem, you know $c = \sqrt{2^2 + 4^2} = \sqrt{20}$.

❸ Use a compass to copy the length of the hypotenuse onto the number line. You can see that $\sqrt{20} \approx 4.5$.

Student Help

▶ **LOOK BACK** For help with copying a segment, see page 389.

Exercises **Use the construction to graph the number.** **1–5. Check constructions.**

1. $\sqrt{53}$ **2.** $\sqrt{34}$ **3.** $\sqrt{61}$ **4.** $\sqrt{2}$

5. Use the graph in Exercise 4 to graph $\sqrt{3}$.

9.4 The Converse of the Pythagorean Theorem

California Standards

In this lesson you'll:

- Know the Pythagorean theorem and deepen understanding of geometric shapes by identifying attributes of figures. (MG 3.0)
- Know and use the converse of the Pythagorean theorem. (MG 3.3)

Goal 1 Using the Converse of the Theorem

The Pythagorean theorem is an *if-then* statement with two parts, the **hypothesis** (the *if* part) and the **conclusion** (the *then* part):

If a and b are the lengths of the legs and c is the length of the hypotenuse of a right triangle, then $a^2 + b^2 = c^2$.

When you reverse the hypothesis and conclusion of an if-then statement, the new statement is called the **converse** of the original statement. The converse of a true statement may or may not be true. Exercise 19 on page 468 shows that the converse of the Pythagorean theorem is true.

Converse of the Pythagorean Theorem

Let a, b, and c be the lengths of the sides of a triangle with c the length of the longest side. If $a^2 + b^2 = c^2$, then the triangle is a right triangle.

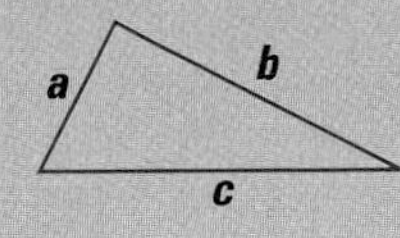

Example 1 Identifying a Right Triangle

Determine if the triangle with the given side lengths is a right triangle.

a. 7, 11, $\sqrt{170}$ **b.** 10, 23, 25

Solution

a. $a^2 + b^2 \stackrel{?}{=} c^2$ Write equation to be tested.

$7^2 + 11^2 \stackrel{?}{=} (\sqrt{170})^2$ Substitute for a, b, and c.

$49 + 121 \stackrel{?}{=} 170$ Square 7, 11, and $\sqrt{170}$.

$170 = 170$ Add and compare.

ANSWER ▶ Since $7^2 + 11^2 = (\sqrt{170})^2$, the triangle is a right triangle.

b. $a^2 + b^2 \stackrel{?}{=} c^2$ Write equation to be tested.

$10^2 + 23^2 \stackrel{?}{=} 25^2$ Substitute for a, b, and c.

$100 + 529 \stackrel{?}{=} 625$ Square 10, 23, and 25.

$629 \neq 625$ Add and compare.

ANSWER ▶ Since $10^2 + 23^2 \neq 25^2$, the triangle is *not* a right triangle.

Student Help

▶ **Study Tip**
When you use the converse of the Pythagorean theorem to test a triangle, always substitute the length of the longest side for c. Substitute the other lengths for a and b.

1 Plan

Pacing

Suggested Number of Days

Transitional: 1 day
Average: 1 day
Advanced: 1 day
Block Schedule: 0.5 block with 9.3

Teaching Resources

Blacklines
(See page 446B.)

Transparencies
- Warm-Up Exercises
- Teacher Time-Savers
- English/Spanish Problem Solving
- Answers

Technology
- Electronic Teacher Tools
- Test and Practice Generator

2 Teach

Math Reasoning

For Mathematical Background Notes on mathematical reasoning related to this lesson, please refer to pages 446E and 446F in this Teacher's Edition.

Extra Example 1
See next page.

California Standards and Assessment

CA Standards: MG 3.0, MG 3.3
CA Key Concepts Book: pp. S83–S86

Math Reasoning

Observe that the proof of the converse of the Pythagorean theorem given in Exercise 19 on page 468 uses the theorem itself.

Extra Example 1

Determine if the triangle with the given side lengths is a right triangle.

a. 11, 18, 21 **no**

b. $\sqrt{11}$, 5, 6 **yes**

Extra Example 2

Determine whether each triangle is an acute triangle, an obtuse triangle, or a right triangle.

a.

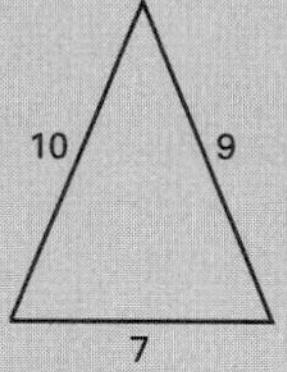

acute

b.

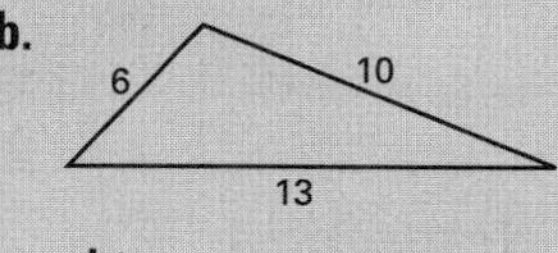

obtuse

Teaching Tip

Common Error

Many students believe that if an angle *looks* like a right angle, it *is* a right angle. Remind them that an angle of 89.5° is acute, but will *look* like a right angle. This is why the method of identifying acute and right triangles is important.

Concept Check

How can you determine whether a triangle is a right triangle? ***Sample answer:*** **Use the converse of the Pythagorean theorem. If lengths *a*, *b*, and *c* satisfy $a^2 + b^2 = c^2$, then the triangle is a right triangle.**

Goal 2 CLASSIFYING TRIANGLES

The converse of the Pythagorean theorem allows you to determine whether a triangle is a right triangle if you know the lengths of the sides. In a later course, you will prove the following theorems, which allow you to determine whether a triangle is acute or obtuse.

IDENTIFYING ACUTE AND OBTUSE TRIANGLES

In $\triangle ABC$, let c be the length of the longest side and a and b be the lengths of the other sides.

If $a^2 + b^2 > c^2$, then $\triangle ABC$ is acute.

If $a^2 + b^2 < c^2$, then $\triangle ABC$ is obtuse.

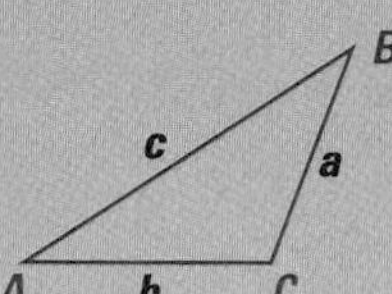

EXAMPLE 2 *Identifying Acute and Obtuse Triangles*

Determine whether each triangle is an acute triangle, an obtuse triangle, or a right triangle.

a.

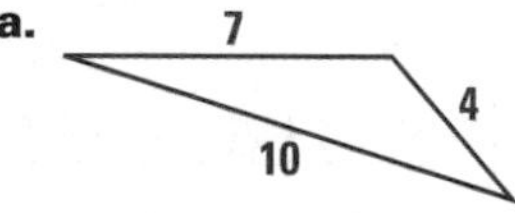

b.

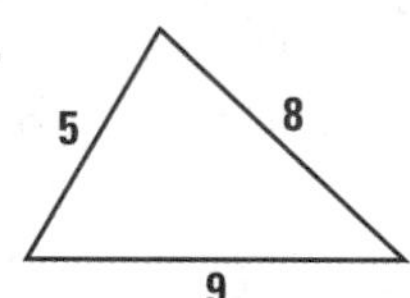

Solution

a. $a^2 + b^2 \; ? \; c^2$ Write expressions to be compared.

$4^2 + 7^2 \; ? \; 10^2$ Substitute for *a*, *b*, and *c*.

$16 + 49 \; ? \; 100$ Square 4, 7, and 10.

$65 \; ? \; 100$ Add.

$65 < 100$ Compare.

ANSWER ▶ Since $a^2 + b^2 < c^2$, the triangle is an obtuse triangle.

b. $a^2 + b^2 \; ? \; c^2$ Write expressions to be compared.

$5^2 + 8^2 \; ? \; 9^2$ Substitute for *a*, *b*, and *c*.

$25 + 64 \; ? \; 81$ Square 5, 8, and 9.

$89 \; ? \; 81$ Add.

$89 > 81$ Compare.

ANSWER ▶ Since $a^2 + b^2 > c^2$, the triangle is an acute triangle.

Student Help

▶ **MORE EXAMPLES**

INTERNET More examples are available at www.mcdougallittell.com

9.4 Exercises

Guided Practice

1. *Sample answer:* With the Pythagorean theorem, you know that a triangle is a right triangle, and can use this fact to find the length of a side. With the converse of the Pythagorean theorem, you know the lengths of all of the sides, and can use this to find out if the triangle is a right triangle.

1. WRITING In your own words, explain the difference between the Pythagorean theorem and the converse of the Pythagorean theorem. **See margin.**

Use the converse of the Pythagorean theorem to determine whether the triangle is a right triangle.

2.

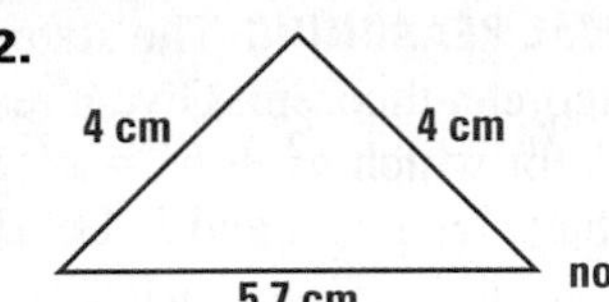

no

3.

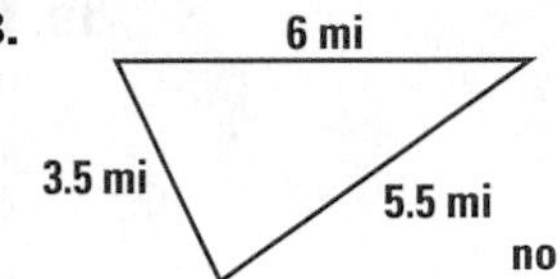

no

The lengths of the sides of a triangle are given. Determine whether the triangle is an *obtuse triangle* or an *acute triangle*.

4. 9, 13, 15 **acute triangle** **5.** 5, 8, $\sqrt{88}$ **acute triangle** **6.** 5, 6, 8 **obtuse triangle**

Practice and Problem Solving

Student Help

▶MORE PRACTICE Extra practice to help you master skills is on page 706.

Determine whether the triangle with the given side lengths is a right triangle.

7. 7, 24, 25 **yes** **8.** 4, 6, $\sqrt{52}$ **yes** **9.** 5, $\sqrt{47}$, 8 **no**

In Exercises 10–16, copy and complete the table. Determine whether a triangle with side lengths *a*, *b*, and *c* is a *right triangle*, an *acute triangle*, or an *obtuse triangle*.

	a	b	c	$a^2 + b^2$	c^2	Type of triangle	
10.	2	3	4	?	?	?	13; 16; obtuse
11.	3	4	5	?	?	?	25; 25; right
12.	2	2	3	?	?	?	8; 9; obtuse
13.	3	3	4	?	?	?	18; 16; acute
14.	5	12	13	?	?	?	169; 169; right
15.	1	$\sqrt{5}$	2	?	?	?	6; 4; acute
16.	4	$\sqrt{11}$	6	?	?	?	27; 36; obtuse

17. yes; Let k = the nonzero whole number. Then $(ka)^2 + (kb)^2 = k^2a^2 + k^2b^2 = k^2(a^2 + b^2) = k^2(c^2) = (kc)^2$.

17. MATHEMATICAL REASONING Pythagorean triples are sets of integers a, b, and c such that $a^2 + b^2 = c^2$. The numbers 3, 4, and 5 form a Pythagorean triple. Will the three numbers formed by multiplying 3, 4, and 5 by the same nonzero whole number form a Pythagorean triple? Explain your reasoning. **See margin.**

3 Apply

Assignment Guide

TRANSITIONAL
Day 1: pp. 467–468 Exs. 7–16, 20, 22–23
AVERAGE
Day 1: pp. 467–468 Exs. 7–18, 22–23
ADVANCED
Day 1: pp. 467–468 Exs. 8–19, 21*, 22–23
BLOCK SCHEDULE
pp. 467–468 Exs. 7–18, 22–23 (with 9.3)

Extra Practice

- Student Edition, pp. 706–707
- Chapter 9 Resource Book, p. 33

Homework Check

To quickly check student understanding of key concepts, go over the following exercises:

Transitional: 8, 10, 13, 14, 20
Average: 8, 10, 13, 14, 18
Advanced: 8, 10, 13, 14, 18

4 Assess

Assessment Resources

- Assessment Book (Formal Assessment and Alternative Assessment)
- Test and Practice Generator

Mini-Quiz

Determine if the triangle with the given side lengths is an *acute triangle*, an *obtuse triangle*, or a *right triangle*.

1. $a = 8, b = 9, c = 12$ **acute**
2. $a = 3, b = 5, c = 6$ **obtuse**
3. $a = \sqrt{17}, b = 8, c = 9$ **right**
4. A doorway is being framed for a new house. The doorway measures 6.7 feet by 2.5 feet. The diagonal is measured to be 7.3 feet. Are the angles of the doorway all 90°? **No. $6.7^2 + 2.5^2 \neq 7.3^2$.**

18. CARPENTRY The doors on an old cabinet no longer close properly because the cabinet leans slightly. Hooks are placed at opposite corners on the back of the cabinet as shown. The hooks are joined by a wire that will be tightened until it pulls the cabinet back into a rectangular shape. The cabinet is 32 inches wide and 60 inches high. How long should the wire be when the job is finished? **68 in.**

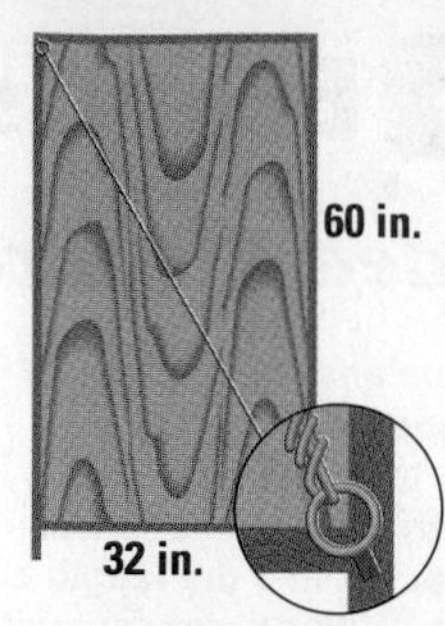

19. MATHEMATICAL REASONING The statements below prove the converse of the Pythagorean theorem. Give a reason for each lettered step. Start with $\triangle ABC$, for which $a^2 + b^2 = c^2$. Let $\triangle FED$ be a right triangle whose legs have lengths a and b. Let d be the hypotenuse of this triangle. **See margin.**

$a^2 + b^2 = d^2$ **a.** ___?___

$c^2 = d^2$ **b.** ___?___

$c = d$ **c.** ___?___

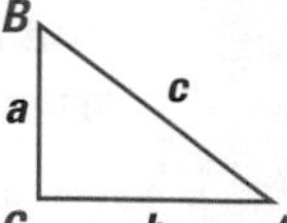

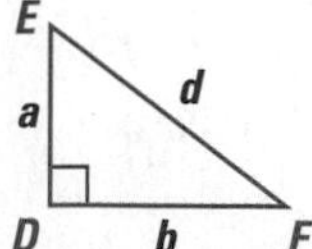

19a. Pythagorean theorem

19b. Substitution

19c. Taking the positive square root of each side of an equation retains the equality and c and d are both positive.

From Lesson 8.5 you know that the side-side-side congruence postulate states that two triangles are congruent if all three sides of one triangle are congruent to all three sides of the other. Therefore, $\triangle ABC$ and $\triangle FED$ are congruent, so $\triangle ABC$ must be a right triangle.

Student Help

READING TIP
In carpentry *being square* means *meeting at a right angle.*

20. CARPENTRY The corners of an old house may not be exactly square. This shelf is parallel to the floor and fits exactly into one corner of the house. The sides of the shelf are 20 inches, 21 inches, and 29 inches long. Is the corner square? **yes**

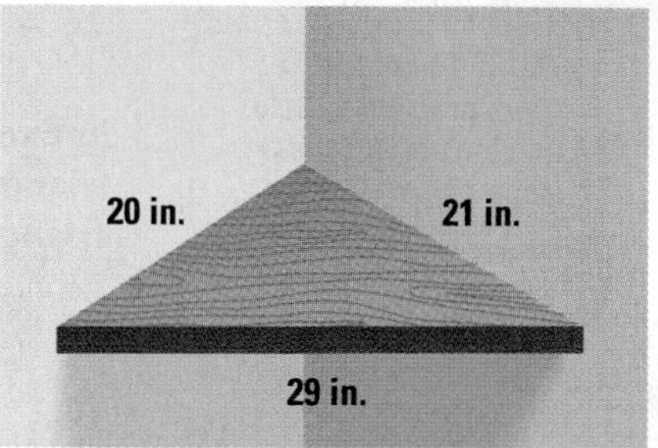

21. CHALLENGE Two opposite sides of a quadrilateral are each 8 inches long. The other two opposite sides are each 9 inches long. One diagonal is $\sqrt{145}$ inches long. Your friend says that the quadrilateral is a rectangle. Do you agree? Explain your reasoning. **yes; $8^2 + 9^2 = 64 + 81 = 145$. $(\sqrt{145})^2 = 145$. Since $8^2 + 9^2 = (\sqrt{145})^2$, the angle is a right angle and the figure is a parallelogram with a right angle, or a rectangle.**

Multiple-Choice Practice

22. Which numbers represent the lengths of the sides of a right triangle? **C**

(A) 4, 4, 4 (B) 3, 4, 6 (C) 9, 12, 15 (D) 8, 11, 14

23. What type of triangle has sides that measure 6 inches, 9 inches, and 11 inches? **F**

(F) Obtuse (G) Isosceles (H) Right (J) Acute

DEVELOPING CONCEPTS
Distance Formula

For use with Lesson 9.5

California Standards

- Understand and use coordinate graphs to plot simple figures and determine lengths. (MG 3.2)
- Develop generalizations of the results obtained and the strategies used and apply them to new problem situations. (MR 3.3)

MATERIALS:
- Graph paper
- Paper and pencil

You already know how to find the lengths of vertical and horizontal line segments from Lesson 3.8. You can use this information to find the distance between any two points in a coordinate plane.

SAMPLE 1 Finding the Distance Between Two Points

Find the distance between $A(x_1, y_1)$ and $B(x_2, y_2)$.

Here's How

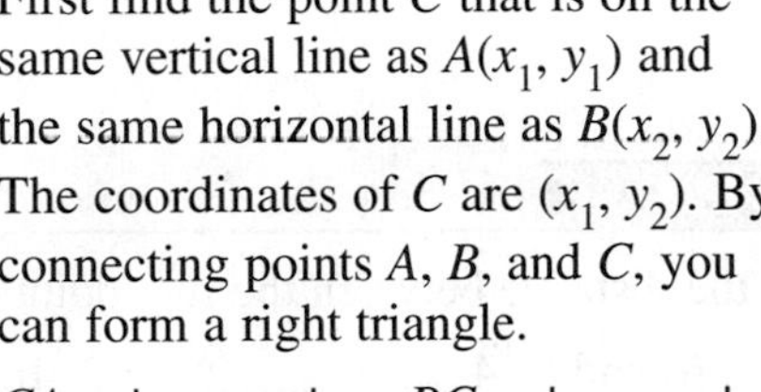

First find the point C that is on the same vertical line as $A(x_1, y_1)$ and the same horizontal line as $B(x_2, y_2)$. The coordinates of C are (x_1, y_2). By connecting points A, B, and C, you can form a right triangle.

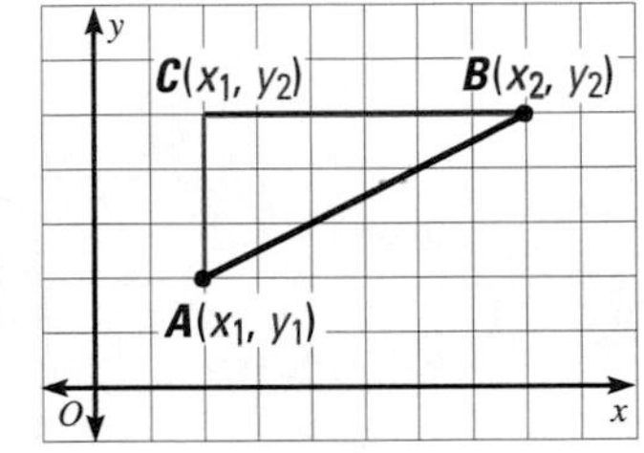

$CA = |y_2 - y_1|$ $\quad BC = |x_2 - x_1|$

Because you know the lengths of both legs of a right triangle, you can use the Pythagorean theorem to find the length of the hypotenuse $\overline{AB}$.

$a^2 + b^2 = c^2$ Use Pythagorean theorem.

$|x_2 - x_1|^2 + |y_2 - y_1|^2 = c^2$ Substitute BC for a and CA for b.

$(x_2 - x_1)^2 + (y_2 - y_1)^2 = c^2$ Drop the absolute value signs.

$\sqrt{(x_2 - x_1)^2 + (y_2 - y_1)^2} = c$ Take positive square root of each side.

The last equation is known as the *distance formula*.

Student Help

STUDY TIP
Since it doesn't matter whether the difference in the x-coordinates (or the y-coordinates) is nonnegative when you square, you don't need to use the absolute value signs once you substitute for a and b in $a^2 + b^2 = c^2$.

Try These

1. If $A(x_1, y_1) = A(5, 7)$ and $B(x_2, y_2) = B(2, 3)$, show that the distance between A and B is 5.

2. If $A(x_1, y_1) = A(-3, 6)$ and $B(x_2, y_2) = B(-4, -2)$, show that the distance between A and B is approximately 8.06.

3. **MATHEMATICAL REASONING** In Sample 1 suppose you chose point C to be on the same horizontal line as (x_1, y_1) and the same vertical line as (x_2, y_2). How would Sample 1 change?

4. **MATHEMATICAL REASONING** Suppose you use the distance formula to find the distance between two points on the same vertical line, such as $(2, y_1)$ and $(2, y_2)$. What result do you get? How does this agree with what you already know about distance on a vertical line?

1. $c = \sqrt{(2-5)^2 + (3-7)^2} = \sqrt{3^2 + 4^2} = \sqrt{9 + 16} = \sqrt{25} = 5$

2. $c = \sqrt{(-4-(-3))^2 + (-2-6)^2} = \sqrt{(-1)^2 + (-8)^2} = \sqrt{1 + 64} = \sqrt{65} \approx 8.06$

3. AC becomes $|x_2 - x_1|$ and BC becomes $|y_2 - y_1|$; the answer is the same.

4. $c = \sqrt{(y_2 - y_1)^2}$; $\sqrt{(y_2 - y_1)^2}$ is the same as $|y_2 - y_1|$.

1 Planning the Activity

Purpose and Materials
See the margin of the student page.

LINK TO LESSON
Students apply the results of the activity to Example 1 in Lesson 9.5. Since students will have seen the distance formula, you may wish to focus on the midpoint formula in Goal 2.

Math Reasoning
Students analyze a problem and use deductive reasoning to derive the distance formula. They develop generalizations of the results to apply to new situations.

2 Managing the Activity

Classroom Management
You may wish to use an overhead to demonstrate the derivation of the distance formula.

3 Closing the Activity

KEY DISCOVERY
To find the distance between two points in a coordinate plane, you can use the formula $\sqrt{(x_2 - x_1)^2 + (y_2 - y_1)^2}$.

Activity Assessment
Use Exercises 1 and 2 to assess student understanding.

California Standards and Assessment

CA Standards: MG 3.2, MR 3.3

1 Plan

Pacing

Suggested Number of Days

Transitional: 2 days
Average: 2 days
Advanced: 2 days
Block Schedule: 1 block

Teaching Resources

Blacklines
(See page 446B.)

Transparencies
- Warm-Up Exercises
- Teacher Time-Savers
- English/Spanish Problem Solving
- Answers

Technology
- Electronic Teacher Tools
- Test and Practice Generator

2 Teach

Math Reasoning

For Mathematical Background Notes on mathematical reasoning related to this lesson, please refer to pages 446E and 446F in this Teacher's Edition.

California Standards and Assessment

CA Standards: AF 4.2, MG 3.2

9.5 The Distance and Midpoint Formulas

California Standards

In this lesson you'll:
- Determine lengths in a coordinate plane. (MG 3.2)
- Solve multi-step problems involving distance. (AF 4.2)

Goal 1 USING THE DISTANCE FORMULA

As you saw in Developing Concepts 9.5, you can use the Pythagorean theorem to find the distance between two points in a coordinate plane.

THE DISTANCE FORMULA

The distance d between the points (x_1, y_1) and (x_2, y_2) is

$$d = \sqrt{(x_2 - x_1)^2 + (y_2 - y_1)^2}.$$

EXAMPLE 1 *Using the Distance Formula*

Find the distance between the two points.

a. (1, 6) and (−4, 2) **b.** (−3, −2) and (−4, 7)

Solution

a. Let (x_1, y_1) be (1, 6), so $x_1 = 1$ and $y_1 = 6$.

Let (x_2, y_2) be (−4, 2), so $x_2 = -4$ and $y_2 = 2$.

$$\begin{aligned} d &= \sqrt{(x_2 - x_1)^2 + (y_2 - y_1)^2} \\ &= \sqrt{(-4 - 1)^2 + (2 - 6)^2} \\ &= \sqrt{(-5)^2 + (-4)^2} \\ &= \sqrt{41} \\ &\approx 6.4 \end{aligned}$$

ANSWER ▶ The distance between the points is about 6.4 units.

Student Help

STUDY TIP
It does not matter which point you call (x_1, y_1) and which point you call (x_2, y_2). Your answer will be the same.

b. Let (x_1, y_1) be (−4, 7), so $x_1 = -4$ and $y_1 = 7$.

Let (x_2, y_2) be (−3, −2), so $x_2 = -3$ and $y_2 = -2$.

$$\begin{aligned} d &= \sqrt{(x_2 - x_1)^2 + (y_2 - y_1)^2} \\ &= \sqrt{(-3 - (-4))^2 + (-2 - 7)^2} \\ &= \sqrt{(1)^2 + (-9)^2} \\ &= \sqrt{82} \\ &\approx 9.1 \end{aligned}$$

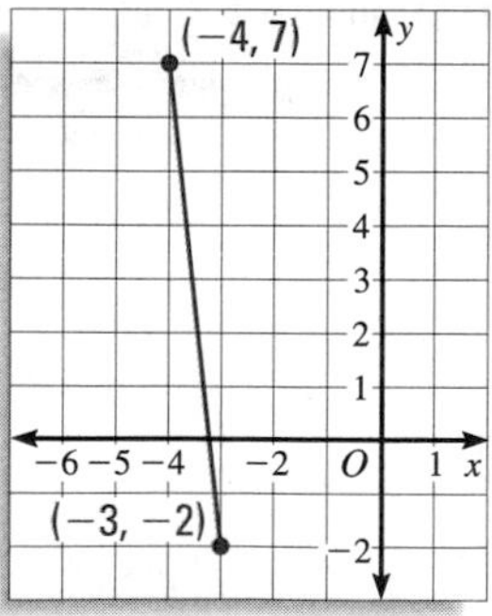

ANSWER ▶ The distance between the points is about 9.1 units.

Goal 2 USING THE MIDPOINT FORMULA

As you learned in Chapter 8, the midpoint of a line segment is the point that divides the segment into two congruent segments. In Exercise 24, on page 473 you will show that the following formula is true.

THE MIDPOINT FORMULA

The midpoint of the segment with endpoints (x_1, y_1) and (x_2, y_2) is

$$\left(\frac{x_1 + x_2}{2}, \frac{y_1 + y_2}{2}\right).$$

EXAMPLE 2 Finding the Midpoint

Find the midpoint of $\overline{AB}$ given $A(-2, 5)$ and $B(4, 1)$.

Solution

Let (x_1, y_1) be $(-2, 5)$ and (x_2, y_2) be $(4, 1)$.

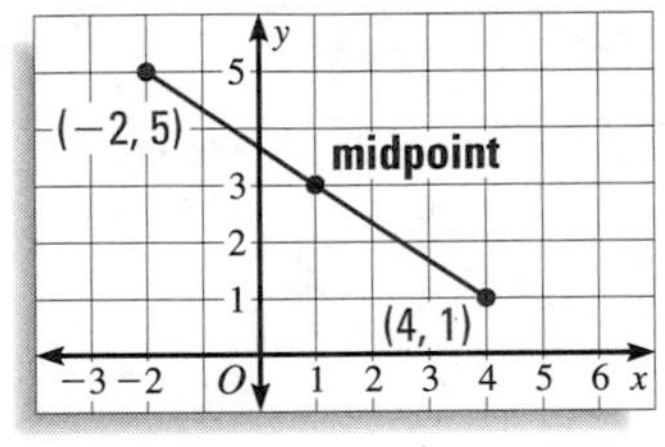

$$\text{Midpoint} = \left(\frac{x_1 + x_2}{2}, \frac{y_1 + y_2}{2}\right)$$

$$= \left(\frac{-2 + 4}{2}, \frac{5 + 1}{2}\right)$$

$$= (1, 3)$$

ANSWER ▶ The midpoint is **(1, 3)**.

EXAMPLE 3 Using the Midpoint Formula

You work for a telephone company. You want to find the coordinates of a telephone pole that will be halfway between two other poles at (20, 20) and (94, 40). Describe the location of the middle pole.

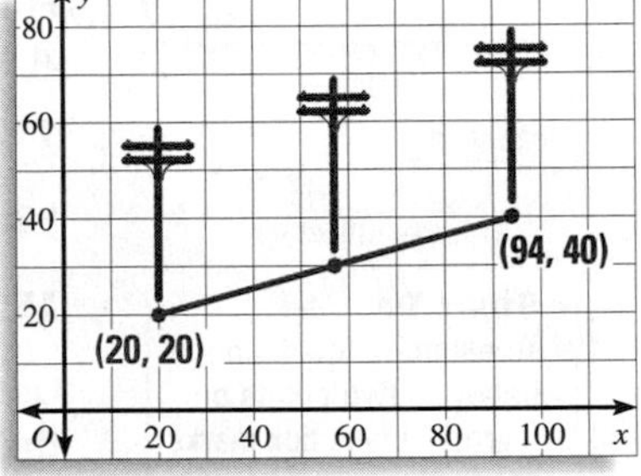

Solution

Let (x_1, y_1) be (20, 20) and (x_2, y_2) be (94, 40).

$$\text{Midpoint} = \left(\frac{x_1 + x_2}{2}, \frac{y_1 + y_2}{2}\right) \quad \text{Use midpoint formula.}$$

$$= \left(\frac{20 + 94}{2}, \frac{20 + 40}{2}\right) \quad \text{Substitute.}$$

$$= (57, 30) \quad \text{Simplify.}$$

ANSWER ▶ The coordinates of the middle pole are (57, 30).

Link to Careers

LINE INSTALLER After setting poles, line installers attach lines for electricity, telephone, and cable television. They also maintain and repair these lines.

More about line installers available at www.mcdougallittell.com

Math Reasoning

If $(x_1, 0)$ and $(x_2, 0)$ are points on the x-axis, notice that the distance formula gives $\sqrt{(x_2 - x_1)^2 + (0 - 0)^2} = \sqrt{(x_2 - x_1)^2} = |x_2 - x_1|$, the expected result for the distance between the two points when we view the x-axis as a number line.

Extra Example 1

Find the distance between the two points.

a. (3, −5) and (−4, 1)
$\sqrt{85} \approx 9.2$ units

b. (5, 6) and (−3, −1)
$\sqrt{113} \approx 10.6$ units

Extra Example 2

Find the midpoint of $\overline{AB}$ given $A(3, -5)$ and $B(-4, 1)$. $\left(-\frac{1}{2}, -2\right)$

Extra Example 3

You are building a fence, and want to place a fence post halfway between posts at (0, 10) and (80, 30). Describe the location of the post. **(40, 20)**

Concept Check

Describe how to find the midpoint of a line segment. ***Sample answer:*** **Add the x-coordinates of the segment's endpoints and divide the sum by 2 to get the x-coordinate of the midpoint. Add the y-coordinates of the endpoints and divide the sum by 2 to get the y-coordinate of the midpoint.**

3 Apply

Assignment Guide

TRANSITIONAL
Day 1: pp. 472–474 Exs. 9–10, 17–19, 34–46
Day 2: pp. 472–474 Exs. 11–14, 20, 26–29, 31–33

AVERAGE
Day 1: pp. 472–474 Exs. 9–10, 17–19, 23, 34–46
Day 2: pp. 472–474 Exs. 11–14, 20, 26–29, 31–33

ADVANCED
Day 1: pp. 472–474 Exs. 9–10, 17–19, 23, 34–46
Day 2: pp. 472–474 Exs. 13–16, 20, 24–26, 30*, 31–33

BLOCK SCHEDULE
pp. 472–474 Exs. 9–14, 17–20, 23–26, 30–46

Extra Practice

- Student Edition, pp. 706–707
- Chapter 9 Resource Book, p. 42

Homework Check

To quickly check student understanding of key concepts, go over the following exercises:

Transitional: 12, 14, 18, 20, 26
Average: 12, 14, 18, 20, 26
Advanced: 14, 16, 18, 20, 26

9.5 Exercises

Guided Practice

Find the distance between the points, rounding your answer to the nearest tenth if necessary. Then find the midpoint of the segment that connects the points.

1. (5, 4) and (2, 0) **5; (3.5, 2)**

2. (−1, −3) and (−1, −7) **4; (−1, −5)**

3. (2, 3) and (−2, 5) **4.5; (0, 4)**

4. (−3, 3) and (0, 9) **6.7; (−1.5, 6)**

GEOMETRY In Exercises 5–8, use the figure shown.

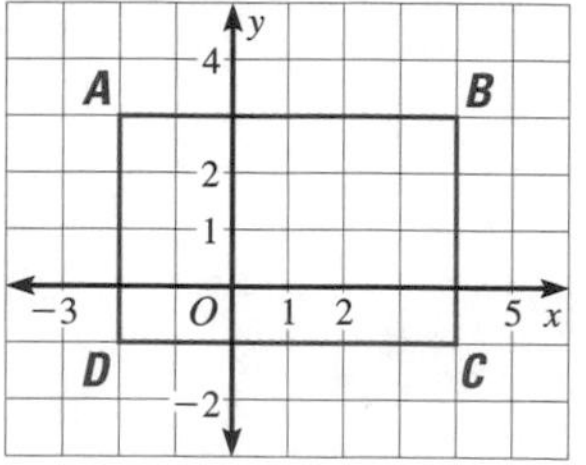

5. Find the coordinates of the labeled points. **A(−2, 3); B(4, 3); C(4, −1); D(−2, −1)**

6. Find the length of each segment. Add the lengths to find the perimeter. **AB = 6, BC = 4, CD = 6, DA = 4; 20**

7. Draw the two diagonals connecting opposite corners of the rectangle. Find the midpoint of each diagonal. **(1, 1); (1, 1)**

8. What can you conclude about the midpoints of the diagonals? **The midpoints are the same point.**

Practice and Problem Solving

> **Student Help**
>
> ▶ **MORE PRACTICE**
> Extra practice to help you master skills is on page 706.

The expression represents the distance between two points. Name the coordinates of the points.

9. $\sqrt{(5-3)^2 + (6-1)^2}$ **(5, 6) and (3, 1)**

10. $\sqrt{(-4-7)^2 + (-8-(-2))^2}$ **(−4, −8) and (7, −2)**

Find the length and the midpoint of $\overline{AB}$ given the coordinates of *A* and *B*. If necessary, round your answer to the nearest tenth.

11. *A*(8, 3) and *B*(12, 11) **8.9; (10, 7)**

12. *A*(3, 7) and *B*(9, −5) **13.4; (6, 1)**

13. *A*(−4, 16) and *B*(−10, 12) **7.2; (−7, 14)**

14. *A*(−6, −1) and *B*(−8, 11) **12.2; (−7, 5)**

15. *A*(15, 20) and *B*(14, −5) **25.0; (14.5, 7.5)**

16. *A*(−13, −2) and *B*(−3, −17) **18.0; (−8, −9.5)**

> **Student Help**
>
> ▶ **STUDY TIP**
> To estimate the distance between two points on a graph, make tick marks spaced according to the grid on the edge of a piece of paper. Use the paper as a ruler.

Use the graph to estimate the distance between the points. Then use the distance formula to find the actual distance between the points. Compare your estimate and the actual distance between the points.

17.
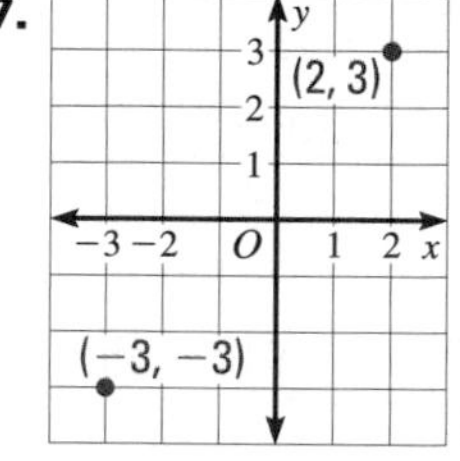

7.8

18.
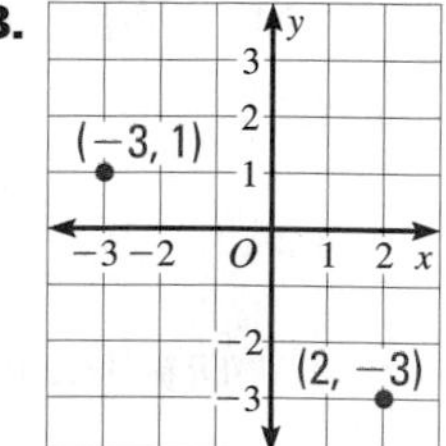

6.4

19.
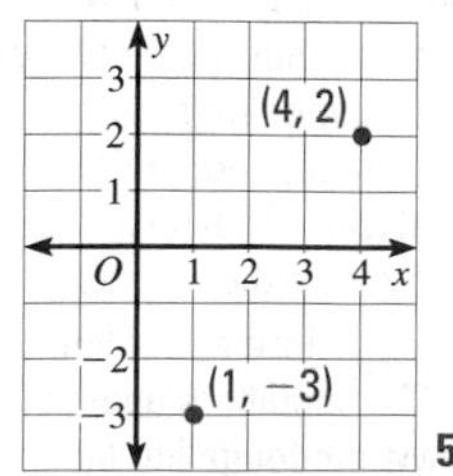

5.8

20. CABLE CAR You and a friend are visiting San Francisco. You are at the cable car turnaround. Your friend is at the Transamerica Pyramid. You agree to meet halfway between the two locations. Which landmark would be closer to the midpoint, North Beach Playground or Washington Square? Explain. **Washington Square; midpoint = $(5, \frac{7}{2})$**

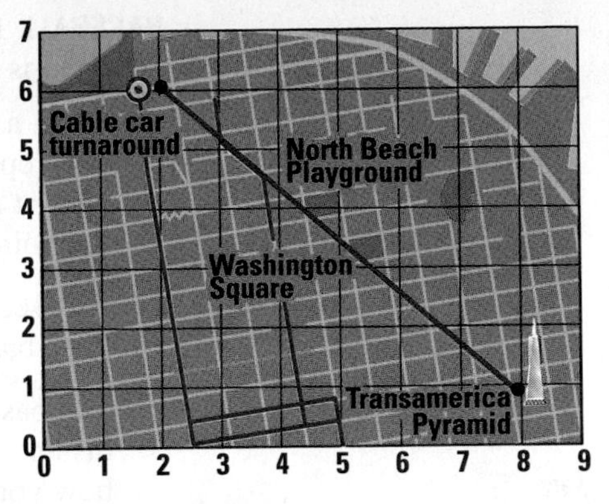

In Exercises 21 and 22, the expression represents the midpoint between two points. Name the coordinates of the points.

21. $\left(\frac{3+4}{2}, \frac{1-5}{2}\right)$ **(3, 1) and (4, −5)**

22. $\left(\frac{-4+6}{2}, \frac{7-3}{2}\right)$ **(−4, 7) and (6, −3)**

23. $\sqrt{(14-2)^2+(3-8)^2} = 13$, $\sqrt{(2-2)^2+(8-3)^2} = 5$, $\sqrt{(14-2)^2+(3-3)^2} = 12$; $5^2 + 12^2 = 169 = 13^2$

23. MATHEMATICAL REASONING Your friend claims that the points (2, 8), (14, 3), and (2, 3) form a right triangle. Use the distance formula and the converse of the Pythagorean theorem to prove that your friend is correct. **See margin.**

Student Help

▶LOOK BACK
Refer to Exercise 30 on page 337 for help in justifying the midpoint formula.

24. MATHEMATICAL REASONING The statements below justify part of the midpoint formula. Give a reason for each lettered step. Start with right $\triangle ABC$ having vertices $A(x_1, y_1)$, $B(x_2, y_2)$, and $C(x_2, y_1)$. Midpoint M is (x, y). If you let the distance between A and B be 2 units, then the distance between A and midpoint M is 1 unit. **See margin.**

$\frac{1}{2} = \frac{x - x_1}{x_2 - x_1}$ Similar triangles

$2(x - x_1) = 1(x_2 - x_1)$ **a.** ?

$2x - 2x_1 = x_2 - x_1$ **b.** ?

$2x = x_1 + x_2$ **c.** ?

$x = \frac{x_1 + x_2}{2}$ **d.** ?

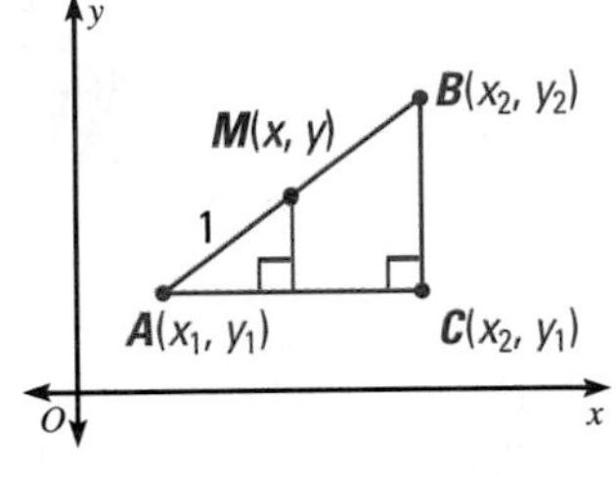

24a. Cross products property
24b. Distributive property
24c. Add $2x_1$ to each side.
24d. Divide each side by 2.

25. MATHEMATICAL REASONING Complete the proof in Exercise 24 by showing that the y-coordinate of the midpoint is $\frac{y_1 + y_2}{2}$. Give statements and reasons for each step. **See margin.**

26. PLANNING A TRIP You live in Nashville, Tennessee, and are planning a trip to Wichita, Kansas. The latitude-longitude coordinates of each city are shown on the map. You decide to stop halfway between the two cities. Estimate the coordinates of the halfway point. **(37 N, 92 W)**

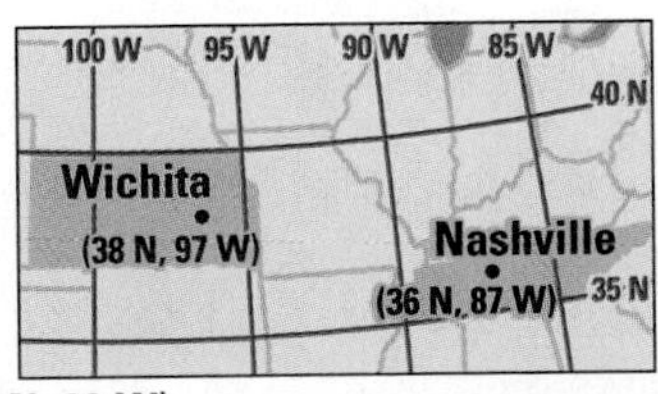

25. $\frac{1}{2} = \frac{y - y_1}{y_2 - y_1}$
Similar triangles.
$2(y - y_1) = 1(y_2 - y_1)$
Cross Products Property
$2y - 2y_1 = y_2 - y_1$
Distributive Property
$2y = y_2 + y_1$
Add $2y_1$ to each side.
$y = \frac{y_1 + y_2}{2}$
Divide each side by 2.

Assess

Assessment Resources

- Assessment Book (Formal Assessment and Alternative Assessment)
- Test and Practice Generator

Mini-Quiz

Find the midpoint of the segment with the given endpoints and the distance between the endpoints.

1. (2, 1), (1, 4) **(1.5, 2.5); about 3.2**
2. (−1, −3), (−4, 2) **(−2.5, −0.5); about 5.8**
3. Suppose you are hanging paintings in a museum. The center of one painting is at (52, 34) and the center of another painting is at (124, 58). What is the location of a painting that is to be placed halfway between these points? **(88, 46)**

Math Reasoning

As a tip for Exercise 30, you may wish to tell students that if you double the average of two numbers and subtract from that one of the original numbers, you get the other number. That is, $2 \cdot \left(\frac{a+b}{2}\right) - a = b$.

27.

3rd base (0, 9)
2nd base (9, 9)
home plate (0, 0)
1st base (9, 0)

BASEBALL In Exercises 27–29, use the following information. A baseball diamond is a square. It measures 90 feet between consecutive bases.

Student Help

▶HOMEWORK HELP
Extra help with problem solving in Exs. 27–29 is available at www.mcdougallittell.com

27. Draw a baseball diamond on a coordinate plane as follows: Let each unit represent 10 feet. Plot the point for first base at (9, 0), second base at (9, 9), third base at (0, 9), and home plate at (0, 0). Connect the points to form a square. **See margin.**

28. A baseball player catches the baseball halfway between second and third bases. Find the coordinates of that point. **(4.5, 9)**

29. The baseball player then throws the baseball to first base. Use the distance formula to determine how far the baseball is thrown. Explain how you found the answer. **100.6 ft; the distance formula gave $\sqrt{101.25}$, or about 10.06 units. Each unit is 10 ft, so 10.06 × 10 = 100.6 ft.**

30. CHALLENGE The midpoint of a line segment is (4, −8). One endpoint of the segment is (10, 15). What are the coordinates of the other endpoint? **(−2, −31)**

Multiple-Choice Practice

In Exercises 31 and 32, use the graph shown.

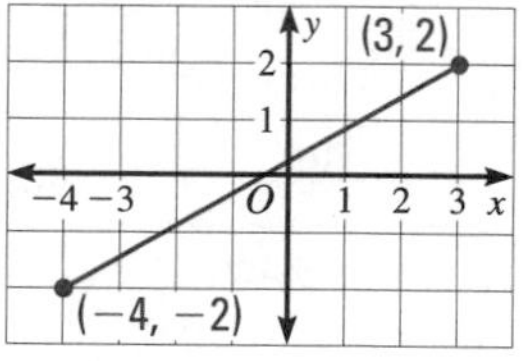

Test Tip

▶In Exercise 31 you can eliminate the point (1, 2) because it doesn't lie on the line segment.

31. What is the midpoint of the line segment? **B**

Ⓐ (1, 2) Ⓑ $\left(-\frac{1}{2}, 0\right)$ Ⓒ $\left(0, -\frac{1}{2}\right)$ Ⓓ $\left(0, \frac{1}{2}\right)$

32. Which number best approximates the distance between the points? **H**

Ⓕ 6 Ⓖ 7 Ⓗ 8 Ⓙ 9

33. A line segment has endpoints at (2, 7) and (−4, 5). Which point is the midpoint of the segment? **A**

Ⓐ (−1, 6) Ⓑ (3, 1) Ⓒ (−1, −1) Ⓓ (−3, 1)

Mixed Review

Solve the inequality. *(2.8)*

34. $x + 2 \geq 9$ **$x \geq 7$** **35.** $2p < 14$ **$p < 7$** **36.** $x - 7 \geq 3$ **$x \geq 10$**

37. $5n > 8$ **$n > \frac{8}{5}$** **38.** $y - 7 \leq 4$ **$y \leq 11$** **39.** $3s < 21$ **$s < 7$**

40. $5 + m \leq 15$ **$m \leq 10$** **41.** $r - 9 > 1$ **$r > 10$** **42.** $4t \geq 16$ **$t \geq 4$**

Simplify the expression. *(6.7, 6.8)*

43. $2n^2 \cdot 4n^7$ **$8n^9$** **44.** $\frac{15p^6}{5p^3}$ **$3p^3$** **45.** $4s^{-10}$ **$\frac{4}{s^{10}}$** **46.** $9r^0$ **9**

Chapter 9 Mid-Chapter Test

Take this test as you would take a test in class. The answers to the exercises are given in the back of the book.

Write the two square roots of the number.

1. 16 **4, −4** **2.** 121 **11, −11** **3.** 0.49 **0.7, −0.7** **4.** 0.36 **0.6, −0.6**

Determine the length of each side of the square.

5.

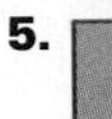

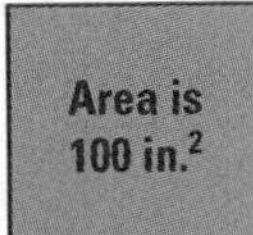

10 in.

6.

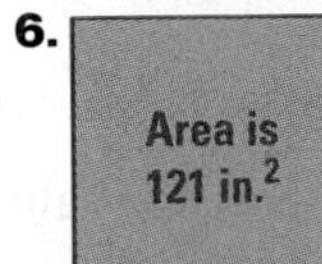

11 in.

7.

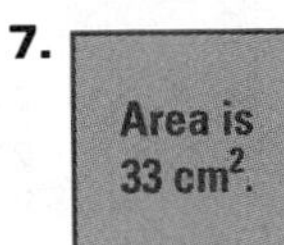

$\sqrt{33}$ cm, or about 5.7 cm

Tell whether the number is *rational* or *irrational*. Explain your reasoning.

8. $\sqrt{250}$ **irrational; non-terminating, non-repeating decimal equivalent**

9. $\sqrt{25}$ **rational; $\sqrt{25} = 5 = \frac{5}{1}$**

10. $\sqrt{2.5}$ **irrational; non-terminating, non-repeating decimal equivalent**

11. $\sqrt{0.25}$ **rational; $\sqrt{0.25} = 0.5 = \frac{1}{2}$**

Complete the statement using <, >, or =.

12. $\sqrt{7}$? 7 **<** **13.** −5 ? $-\sqrt{5}$ **<** **14.** 3 ? $\sqrt{11}$ **<** **15.** 9.2 ? $\sqrt{85}$ **<**

Use the Pythagorean theorem to solve the right triangle.

16.

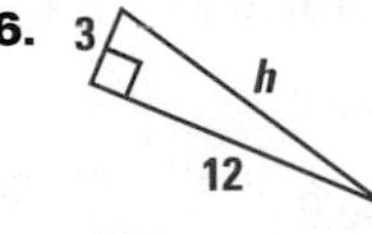

$\sqrt{153}$, or about 12.4

17.

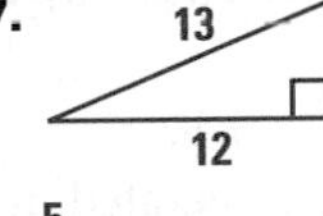

5

18.

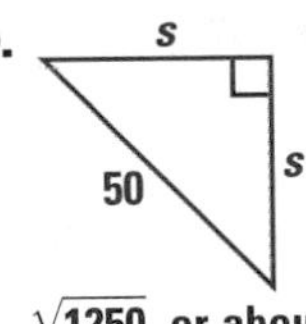

$\sqrt{8192}$, or about 90.5

19. (s, s, 50)

$\sqrt{1250}$, or about 35.4

In Exercises 20–23, the length of the hypotenuse of an isosceles right triangle is given. Find the length of the legs.

20. 6 **$\sqrt{18}$, or about 4.2** **21.** 14 **$\sqrt{98}$, or about 9.9** **22.** 21 **$\sqrt{220.5}$, or about 14.8** **23.** 25 **$\sqrt{312.5}$, or about 17.7**

24. The length of one leg of a right triangle is 4 times the length of the other leg. The length of the hypotenuse is $\sqrt{17}$. What is the length of each leg? **1, 4**

The lengths of the sides of a triangle are given. Determine whether the triangle is an *acute triangle*, a *right triangle*, or an *obtuse triangle*.

25. 2, 4, 5 **obtuse** **26.** 5, 12, 13 **right** **27.** 6, 8, 10 **right** **28.** 8, 10, 12 **acute**

Find the length and the midpoint of $\overline{AB}$ given the coordinates of *A* and *B*. If necessary, round your answer to the nearest tenth.

29. $A(1, 3)$ and $B(4, 1)$ **3.6; (2.5, 2)**

30. $A(-4, 3)$ and $B(-2, 5)$ **2.8; (−3, 4)**

31. $A(5, -6)$ and $B(-2, 7)$ **14.8; (1.5, 0.5)**

32. $A(-4, -1)$ and $B(-6, -1)$ **2; (−5, −1)**

33. $A(0, -4)$ and $B(2, 0)$ **4.5; (1, −2)**

34. $A(8, -9)$ and $B(-3, -6)$ **11.4; (2.5, −7.5)**

Additional Resources

A Mid-Chapter Test and a Mid-Chapter Partner Quiz are available in the *Assessment Book*, pp. 128–129 and p. 250.

1 Plan

Pacing

Suggested Number of Days

Transitional: 1 day
Average: 1 day
Advanced: 1 day
Block Schedule: 0.5 block with 9.7

Teaching Resources

Blacklines
(See page 446B.)

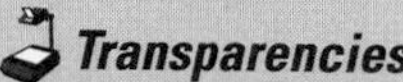

Transparencies
- Warm-Up Exercises
- Teacher Time-Savers
- English/Spanish Problem Solving
- Answers

Technology
- Electronic Teacher Tools
- Test and Practice Generator

2 Teach

Math Reasoning

For Mathematical Background Notes on mathematical reasoning related to this lesson, please refer to pages 446E and 446F in this Teacher's Edition.

California Standards and Assessment

CA Standards: AF 1.1, AF 4.0

9.6 Solving Inequalities Using Addition or Subtraction

California Standards

In this lesson you'll:

- Use variables and appropriate operations to write an inequality that represents a verbal description. (AF 1.1)
- Solve linear inequalities over the rational numbers. (AF 4.0)

Goal 1 Writing and Graphing Inequalities

As you learned in Lesson 2.8, an inequality is formed when an inequality symbol is placed between two expressions. Inequalities may have many solutions. Graphing the solutions of an inequality on a number line can help you visualize the values of x that make the inequality true.

EXAMPLE 1 Writing an Inequality

The graph shows all possible values for x. Write an inequality.

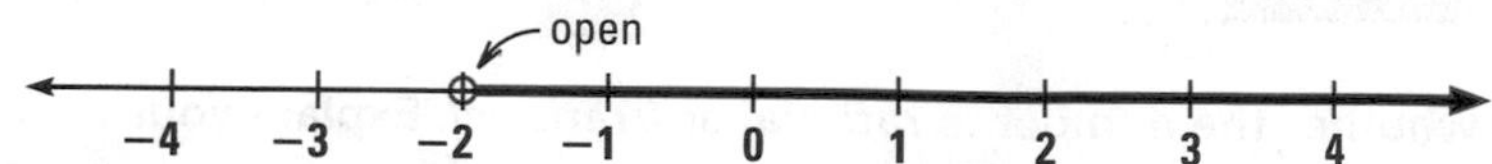

Solution

Notice that the circle at -2 is an open circle. This means that $x = -2$ is not part of the graph of the inequality.

Since the shading extends to the right of -2, x can be any number *greater* than -2.

ANSWER ▶ The inequality is $x > -2$. This may also be written as $-2 < x$.

Four basic types of inequalities are illustrated in Example 2.

Student Help

▶ Study Tip
Remember these inequality symbols:
$>$ means *is greater than*
$\geq$ means *is greater than or equal to*
$<$ means *is less than*
$\leq$ means *is less than or equal to*

EXAMPLE 2 Graphing Inequalities on a Number Line

VERBAL PHRASE	INEQUALITY	GRAPH
All real numbers less than 2	$x < 2$	open; −4 −2 0 2 4
All real numbers greater than -3	$x > -3$	open; −4 −2 0 2 4
All real numbers less than or equal to -1	$x \leq -1$	closed; −4 −2 0 2 4
All real numbers greater than or equal to 0	$x \geq 0$	closed; −4 −2 0 2 4

Goal 2 SOLVING INEQUALITIES

Student Help

STUDY TIP
To check the solution of an inequality, substitute several numbers from the solution into the original inequality. If the numbers make the inequality true, they confirm the solution.

Solving an inequality involving addition or subtraction is similar to solving an equation. Use an inverse operation to isolate the variable.

EXAMPLE 3 Using Addition or Subtraction to Solve

Solve the inequality. Then graph the solution.

a. $n + 8 \le 12$ **b.** $n - 2 > 4$

Solution

a. $n + 8 \le 12$ Write original inequality.

$n + 8 \mathbf{- 8} \le 12 \mathbf{- 8}$ Subtract 8 from each side.

$n \le 4$ Simplify. n is by itself.

To graph $n \le 4$, draw a closed circle at 4 and shade the number line to the left of 4.

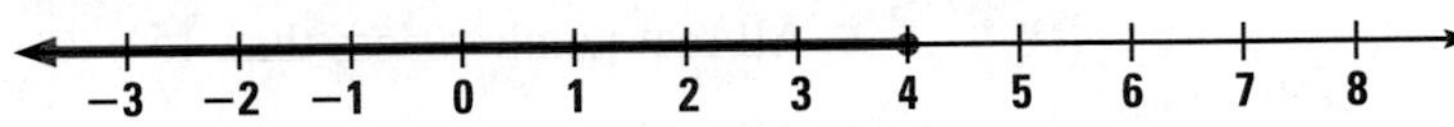

b. $n - 2 > 4$ Write original inequality.

$n - 2 \mathbf{+ 2} > 4 \mathbf{+ 2}$ Add 2 to each side.

$n > 6$ Simplify. n is by itself.

To graph $n > 6$, draw an open circle at 6 and shade the number line to the right of 6.

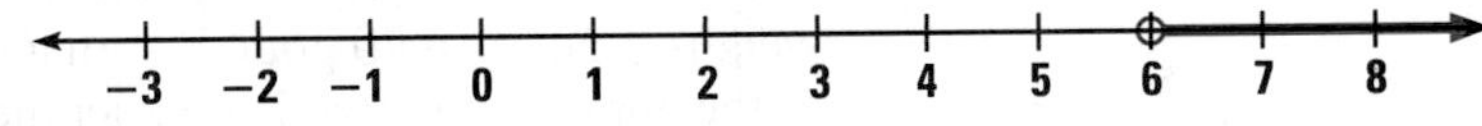

Link to Health

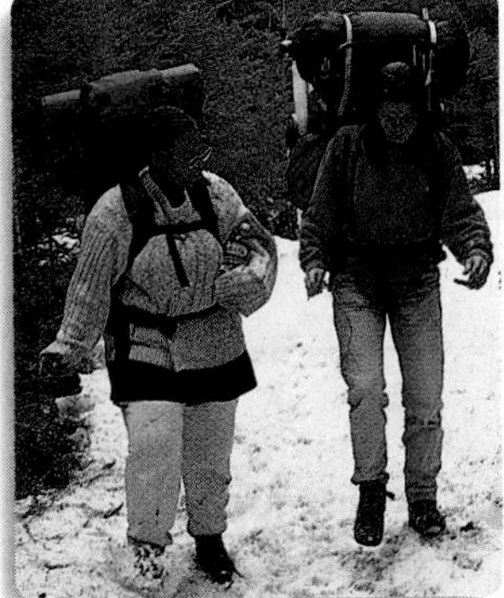

BACKPACKS If you often carry more than 10%–15% of your body weight, you may hurt your back. As shown above, frame packs can help because the frame puts the weight on your hips instead of your shoulders.

EXAMPLE 4 Writing and Solving an Inequality

BACKPACKS Your backpack weighs 2 pounds when it is empty. To avoid back injury, the weight of your pack and books together should be at most 15 pounds. How many pounds of books can you carry?

Solution

Let b represent the weight of your books. Then $b + 2$ represents the combined weight of your books and backpack.

$b + 2 \le 15$ Write inequality.

$b + 2 \mathbf{- 2} \le 15 \mathbf{- 2}$ Subtract 2 from each side.

$b \le 13$ Simplify. b is by itself.

ANSWER ▶ You can carry at most 13 pounds of books.

CHECK ✓ Choose any number less than 13, such as 10. Is $10 + 2$ less than or equal to 15? Yes, because $12 \le 15$.

Extra Examples 1 and 2

Write and graph an inequality that models the verbal phrase.

a. All real numbers less than −1
$x < -1$

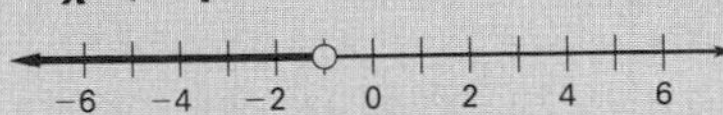

b. All real numbers greater than 3
$x > 3$

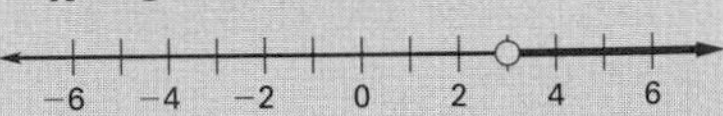

c. All real numbers less than or equal to 1 **$x \le 1$**

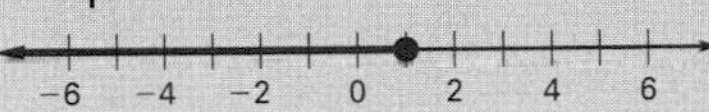

d. All real numbers greater than or equal to −2 **$x \ge -2$**

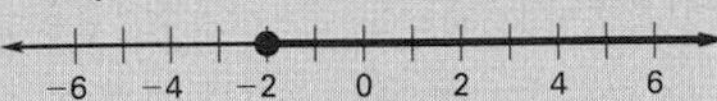

Extra Example 3

Solve each inequality. Then graph the solution.

a. $x - 5 \ge -3$ **$x \ge 2$**

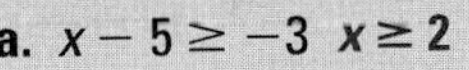

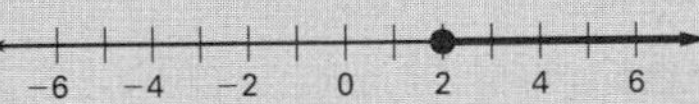

b. $x + 4 < -6$ **$x < -10$**

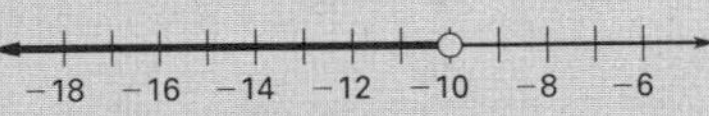

Extra Example 4

A hanging flower pot weighs one pound. When filled it should weigh no more than 10 pounds. How many pounds of dirt and flowers can it hold? **no more than 9 lb**

Concept Check

Explain how to graph an inequality. ***Sample answer:*** **If the variable is *less than* a number, draw an open circle at the number and shade to the left of the number. If the variable is *greater than* a number, draw an open circle at the number and shade to the right of the number. If the variable is *less than or equal* or *greater than or equal* to the number, use a closed circle and shade appropriately.**

3 Apply

Assignment Guide

TRANSITIONAL
Day 1: pp. 478–479 Exs. 12–17, 21–24, 29–34, 44–45, 49–51
AVERAGE
Day 1: pp. 478–479 Exs. 14–18, 21–24, 32–37, 44–45, 47–51
ADVANCED
Day 1: pp. 478–479 Exs. 14–20, 25–28, 38–45, 46*, 47–51
BLOCK SCHEDULE
pp. 478–479 Exs. 14–18, 21–24, 32–37, 44–45, 47–51 (with 9.7)

Extra Practice

- Student Edition, pp. 706–707
- Chapter 9 Resource Book, p. 51

Homework Check

To quickly check student understanding of key concepts, go over the following exercises:

Transitional: 14, 16, 22, 30, 44
Average: 14, 18, 24, 34, 44
Advanced: 14, 18, 26, 40, 44

5.
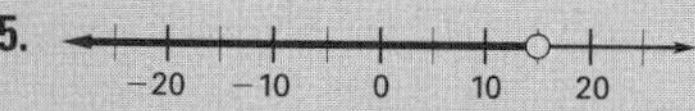

6.
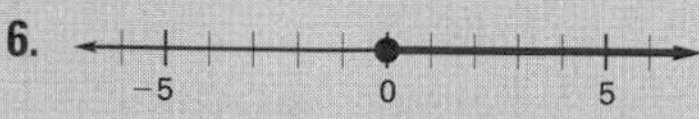

7.
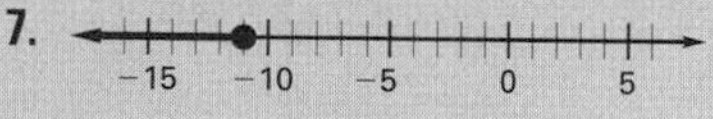

8.
−10 −5 0 5 10

9.
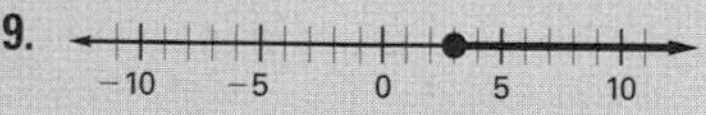

10.
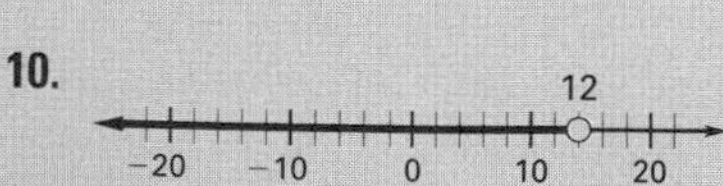

16–20. See Additional Answers beginning on page AA1.

9.6 Exercises

Guided Practice

Match the inequality with its graph.

1. $x < 10$ **C**

2. $x \geq -4$ **D**

3. $x \leq -4$ **B**

4. $x > 10$ **A**

A.
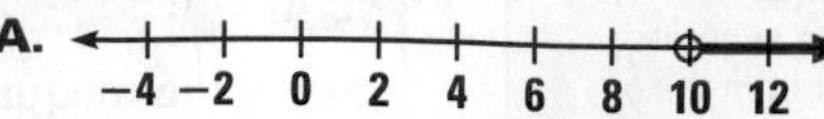

B. −6 −5 −4 −3 −2 −1 0 1

C. −4 −2 0 2 4 6 8 10 12

D. −6 −5 −4 −3 −2 −1 0 1

Write two inequalities for the phrase. Then graph the inequalities.

5. All real numbers less than 15 **$x < 15$; $15 > x$; See margin.**

6. All real numbers greater than or equal to 0 **$x \geq 0$; $0 \leq x$; See margin.**

7. All real numbers less than or equal to -11 **$x \leq -11$; $-11 \geq x$; See margin.**

In Exercises 8–10, solve the inequality. Then graph the solution.

8. $n + 5 < -2$ **$n < -7$; See margin.**

9. $x - 5 \geq -2$ **$x \geq 3$; See margin.**

10. $9 > y - 3$ **$12 > y$; See margin.**

11. An empty basket weighs 3 pounds. Filled with apples, the basket weighs more than 40 pounds. What can you say about the weight of the apples? Write and solve an inequality. **$x + 3 > 40$; $x > 37$; The weight of the apples is greater than 37 lb.**

Practice and Problem Solving

Student Help

▶**MORE PRACTICE**
Extra practice to help you master skills is on page 707.

Write the inequality represented by the graph.

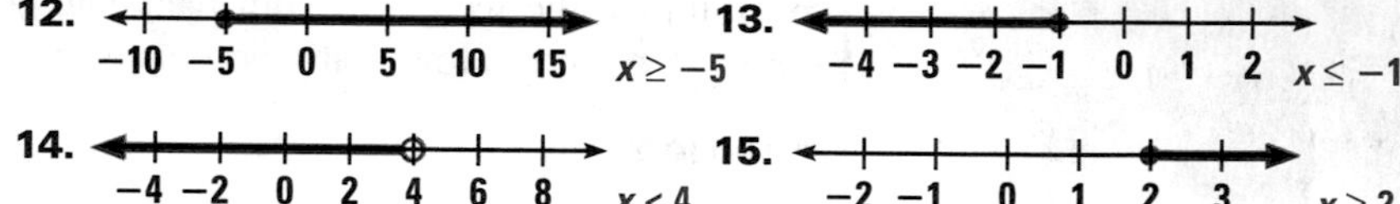

12. **$x \geq -5$** **13.** **$x \leq -1$**

14. **$x < 4$** **15.** **$x \geq 2$**

Write two inequalities for the phrase. Then graph the inequalities. **16–20. See margin for graphs.**

16. All real numbers greater than or equal to 4 **$x \geq 4$; $4 \leq x$**

17. All real numbers less than or equal to -2 **$x \leq -2$; $-2 \geq x$**

18. All real numbers greater than -5 **$x > -5$; $-5 < x$**

19. All real numbers less than 10 **$x < 10$; $10 > x$**

20. All real numbers greater than or equal to -1 **$x \geq -1$; $-1 \leq x$**

Recreation

CYCLING When you go uphill, low gears make it easier to pedal, but you go slowly. On level ground, you can use a high gear to go faster.

Graph the inequality. **21–28. See margin.**

21. $x \geq 1$ **22.** $x < 0$ **23.** $x > 7$ **24.** $x \leq -2$

25. $x < 5$ **26.** $x \geq -9$ **27.** $x \leq -1$ **28.** $x > 7$

In Exercises 29–43, solve the inequality. Then graph the solution. **29–43. See margin for graphs.**

29. $w - 4 < 5$ $w < 9$ **30.** $n - 3 > 1$ $n > 4$ **31.** $y + 2 \leq 5$ $y \leq 3$

32. $b + 6 \geq 11$ $b \geq 5$ **33.** $5 \geq t - 1$ $6 \geq t$ **34.** $2 \geq p - 8$ $10 \geq p$

35. $x + 4 \geq 2$ $x \geq -2$ **36.** $z + 7 > -2$ $z > -9$ **37.** $1 > a + 5$ $-4 > a$

38. $c - 8 \leq 0$ $c \leq 8$ **39.** $d + 5 \geq -3$ $d \geq -8$ **40.** $3 > r + 4$ $-1 > r$

41. $15 \geq k - 2$ $17 \geq k$ **42.** $s + 12 \geq 0$ $s \geq -12$ **43.** $1 < q - 1$ $2 < q$

44. CYCLING The fastest you can bicycle on level ground is 25 miles per hour. Which of the following inequalities best describes your speed s (in miles per hour)? Explain your reasoning. **D**

A. $25 < s$ **B.** $25 > s$ **C.** $25 \leq s$ **D.** $25 \geq s$

45. FISHING Your local newspaper reports that the winner of a fishing contest caught two fish weighing more than 50 pounds total. The smaller fish alone weighed 19 pounds. What can you say about the weight of the larger fish? Write and solve an inequality.
$19 + x > 50$; The larger fish weighed more than 31 pounds.

46. CHALLENGE The longest side of an obtuse triangle is 12 inches. Another side measures 8 inches. The length of the third side must be less than what measure? Explain your reasoning. **See margin.**

46. $\sqrt{80} \approx 8.9$ **in.; A side equal to** $\sqrt{80} \approx 8.9$ **inches would result in a right triangle; greater than** $\sqrt{80} \approx 8.9$ **inches, an acute triangle.**

MATHEMATICAL REASONING **Match the statement with a graph. Explain.**

A. 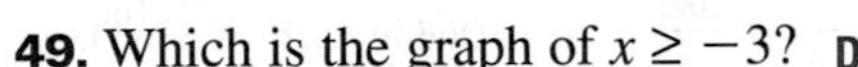

B. 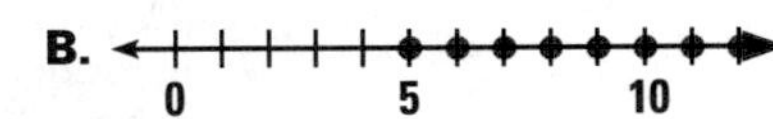

47. At least 5 students attended.
B; The number of students must be an integer.

48. The temperature is at least 5°.
A; Temperature does not have to be integral.

Multiple-Choice Practice

49. Which is the graph of $x \geq -3$? **D**

Ⓐ 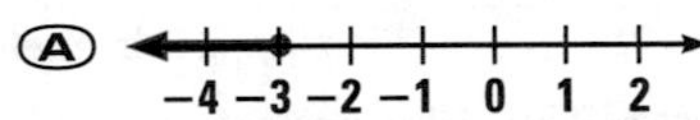 Ⓑ 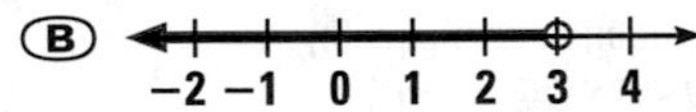

Ⓒ –4 –3 –2 –1 0 1 2 Ⓓ –4 –3 –2 –1 0 1 2

50. Decide which inequality represents the following verbal phrase: *all real numbers greater than* -2. **H**

Ⓕ $x < -2$ Ⓖ $x \leq -2$ Ⓗ $x > -2$ Ⓙ $x \geq -2$

51. What is the solution of $8 + x > -9$? **B**

Ⓐ $x > -1$ Ⓑ $x > -17$ Ⓒ $x > 1$ Ⓓ $17 > x$

4 Assess

Assessment Resources

- Assessment Book (Formal Assessment and Alternative Assessment)
- Test and Practice Generator

Mini-Quiz

Write the inequality represented by the graph.

1. 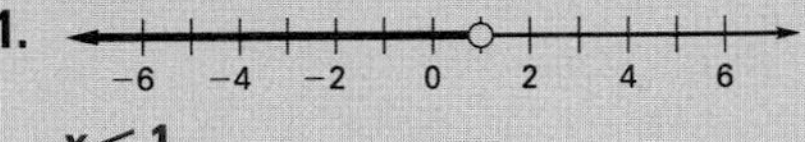
$x < 1$

2. –6 –4 –2 0 2 4 6
$x \geq -3$

Solve the inequality. Then graph the solution.

3. $x + 12 \geq 8$ $x \geq -4$

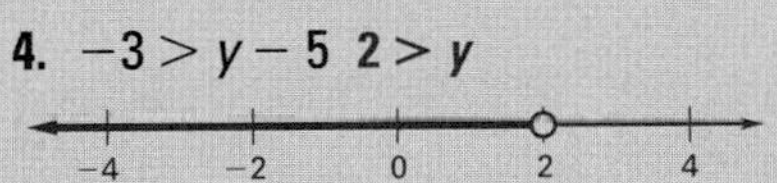

4. $-3 > y - 5$ $2 > y$

–4 –2 0 2 4

5. A wall cabinet weighs 50 pounds. The weight of the filled cabinet can be no more than 120 pounds. Write and solve an inequality to determine how much the cabinet can hold. **$x + 50 \leq 120$; $x \leq 70$; the cabinet can hold no more than 70 lb.**

21. 

22. 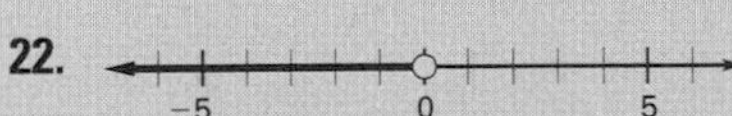

23. –10 –5 0 5 10

24. 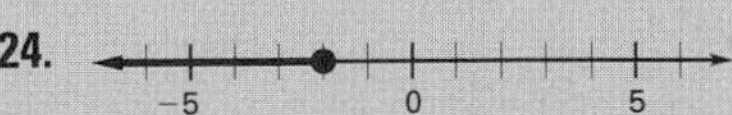

25. –10 –5 0 5 10

26. 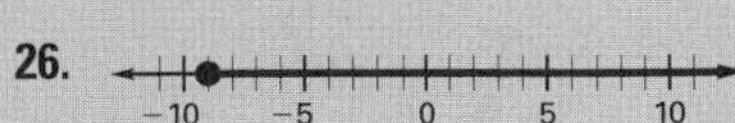

27–43. See Additional Answers beginning on page AA1.

1 Plan

Pacing

Suggested Number of Days

Transitional: 1 day
Average: 1 day
Advanced: 1 day
Block Schedule: 0.5 block with 9.6

Teaching Resources

Blacklines
(See page 446B.)

Transparencies
- Warm-Up Exercises
- Teacher Time-Savers
- English/Spanish Problem Solving
- Answers

Technology
- Electronic Teacher Tools
- Test and Practice Generator

2 Teach

Math Reasoning

For Mathematical Background Notes on mathematical reasoning related to this lesson, please refer to pages 446E and 446F in this Teacher's Edition.

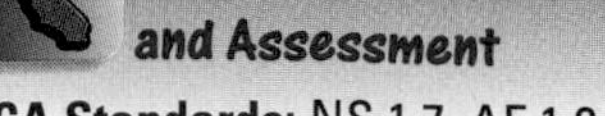

California Standards and Assessment

CA Standards: NS 1.7, AF 1.0, AF 4.0

9.7 Solving Inequalities Using Multiplication or Division

California Standards

In this lesson you'll:

- Solve simple linear inequalities over the rational numbers. (AF 4.0)
- Express quantitative relationships by using inequalities. (AF 1.0)
- Solve problems that involve commissions. (NS 1.7)

Goal 1 SOLVING AN INEQUALITY BY DIVIDING

Solving an inequality is similar to solving an equation. You use the four arithmetic operations to isolate the variable on one side of the inequality. There is one important difference, however. When you multiply or divide an inequality by a negative number, you must reverse the inequality symbol.

Multiply by −2: $5 > -4$ becomes $-10 < 8$.

Divide by −3: $-6 < 3$ becomes $2 > -1$.

PROPERTIES OF INEQUALITIES

1. Adding or subtracting the same number on each side of an inequality produces an equivalent inequality.
2. Multiplying or dividing each side of an inequality by the same *positive* number produces an equivalent inequality.
3. Multiplying or dividing each side of an inequality by the same *negative* number and *reversing the direction of the inequality symbol* produces an equivalent inequality.

EXAMPLE 1 Solving an Inequality by Dividing

Solve the inequality. **a.** $12 < 3m$ **b.** $-2x < 6$

Solution

a. $12 < 3m$ Write original inequality.

$\frac{12}{3} < \frac{3m}{3}$ Divide each side by 3.

$4 < m$ Simplify. *m* is by itself.

ANSWER ▶ The solution is $4 < m$, which is all real numbers that are greater than 4.

b. $-2x < 6$ Write original inequality.

$\frac{-2x}{-2} > \frac{6}{-2}$ Divide each side by −2. Reverse the inequality.

$x > -3$ Simplify. *x* is by itself.

ANSWER ▶ The solution is $x > -3$, which is all real numbers that are greater than −3.

Student Help

▶ **STUDY TIP**
In Example 1 check the solution of an inequality by substituting several numbers from the solution into the original inequality. The numbers should make the original inequality true.

Goal 2 SOLVING AN INEQUALITY BY MULTIPLYING

EXAMPLE 2 Solving an Inequality by Multiplying

Solve the inequality.

a. $\frac{n}{3} \leq 4$ **b.** $-\frac{1}{2}x \geq 6$

Solution

a. When multiplying by a positive number, do not reverse the inequality.

$\frac{n}{3} \leq 4$ Write original inequality.

$3 \cdot \frac{n}{3} \leq 3 \cdot 4$ Multiply each side by 3.

$n \leq 12$ Simplify. *n* is by itself.

ANSWER ▶ The solution is $n \leq 12$, which is all real numbers that are less than or equal to 12.

b. When multiplying by a negative number, reverse the inequality.

$-\frac{1}{2}x \geq 6$ Write original inequality.

$-2 \cdot \left(-\frac{1}{2}\right)x \leq -2 \cdot 6$ Multiply each side by −2. Reverse the inequality.

$x \leq -12$ Simplify. *x* is by itself.

ANSWER ▶ The solution is $x \leq -12$, which is all real numbers that are less than or equal to −12.

Student Help

▶ **MORE EXAMPLES**
More examples are available at www.mcdougallittell.com

EXAMPLE 3 Using an Inequality to Solve a Problem

REAL ESTATE A real estate agent earns a 5% commission for each house he sells. What house prices will earn him a commission of at least $4000?

Solution

Let *H* represent the price of the house. Then the agent's commission is 5% of *H*, or 0.05*H*.

$0.05H \geq 4000$ Commission is *at least* $4000.

$\frac{0.05H}{\mathbf{0.05}} \geq \frac{4000}{\mathbf{0.05}}$ Divide each side by 0.05.

$H \geq 80{,}000$ Simplify. *H* is by itself.

ANSWER ▶ The prices of the houses he sells must be at least $80,000.

Student Help

▶ **VOCABULARY TIP**
Phrases like *at least* and *no less than* mean "is greater than or equal to" (≥). Phrases like *at most* and *no more than* mean "is less than or equal to" (≤). So in Example 3, a commission of *at least* $4000 means it is $4000 or more.

Extra Example 1

Solve the inequality.

a. $64 > 4x$ **$16 > x$**

b. $-42 < -6w$ **$7 > w$**

Extra Example 2

Solve the inequality.

a. $-\frac{3}{4}d \geq 21$ **$d \leq -28$**

b. $5 \geq -\frac{r}{5}$ **$r \geq -25$**

Extra Example 3

You are a car salesman. You earn a 4% commission on each car you sell. What car prices will earn you a commission of at least $500? **car prices of at least $12,500**

Concept Check

How is solving an inequality different from solving an equation? ***Sample answer:*** **If you multiply or divide by a negative number, you must reverse the inequality symbol; otherwise, the procedure is the same.**

3 Apply

Assignment Guide

TRANSITIONAL
Day 1: pp. 482–483 Exs. 16–31, 38, 45–47
AVERAGE
Day 1: pp. 482–483 Exs. 16–19, 21–33, 39–40, 45–47
ADVANCED
Day 1: pp. 482–483 Exs. 15–19, 21–24, 32–37, 40–43, 44*, 45–47
BLOCK SCHEDULE
pp. 482–483 Exs. 16–19, 21–33, 39–40, 45–47 (with 9.6)

Extra Practice

- Student Edition, pp. 706–707
- Chapter 9 Resource Book, p. 60

Homework Check

To quickly check student understanding of key concepts, go over the following exercises:

Transitional: 16, 20, 26, 28, 38
Average: 16, 18, 28, 30, 40
Advanced: 16, 32, 34, 40, 42

Problem Solving

Exercise 25
Students may think incorrectly that $A > l \cdot w$ and then write $216 > 8 \cdot w$, rather than thinking that $A = l \cdot w$, which means that $8 \cdot w > 216$.

9.7 Exercises

Guided Practice

Tell whether the operation reverses the sign of the inequality.

1. Multiply each side by -1. **yes**
2. Divide each side by 4. **no**
3. Multiply each side by $\frac{1}{4}$. **no**
4. Divide each side by -5. **yes**

Use <, >, ≤, or ≥ to complete the solution.

5. $3y > 15$ — $y \; ? \; 5$ **>**
6. $4 > -x$ — $-4 \; ? \; x$ **<**
7. $-2 \ge -\frac{1}{2}a$ — $4 \; ? \; a$ **≤**
8. $-3 \ge -6t$ — $\frac{1}{2} \; ? \; t$ **≤**

In Exercises 9–12, solve the inequality.

9. $4b > 24$ **$b > 6$**
10. $\frac{n}{2} > 1$ **$n > 2$**
11. $36 \ge -\frac{1}{2}f$ **$-72 \le f$**
12. $-5 < 0.2h$ **$-25 < h$**

13. Suppose sales tax is 5% of the total purchase where you live. If you pay at least $2 in sales tax, what can you say about the amount of your total purchase before sales tax is included? **It must be at least $40.**

Practice and Problem Solving

Student Help
▶MORE PRACTICE
Extra practice to help you master skills is on page 707.

ERROR ANALYSIS Describe and correct the error. **14–16. See margin.**

14.
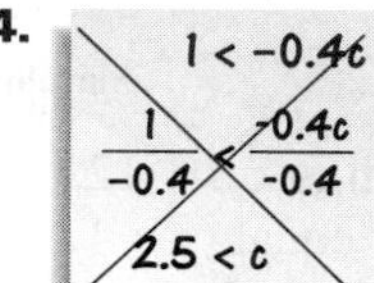

15.
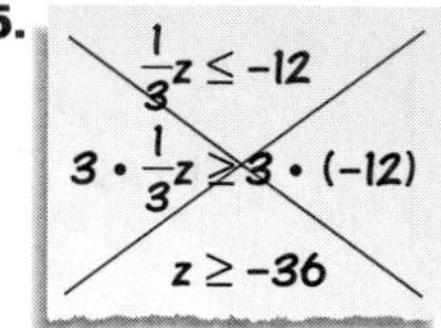

16.
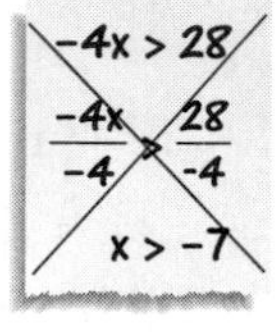

14. Dividing by a negative number reverses the direction of the inequality. Also, the quotient of a positive number and a negative number is negative. The left-hand side is $-\frac{1}{0.4}$. Hence, $-2.5 > c$.

15. Multiplying each side of an inequality by the same positive number does not reverse the direction of the inequality; $z \le -36$.

16. Dividing each side of an inequality by the same negative number must reverse the direction of the inequality; $x < -7$.

Use <, >, ≤, or ≥ to complete the solution.

17. $-4b < 24$ — $b \; ? \; -6$ **>**
18. $6x \ge -42$ — $x \; ? \; -7$ **≥**
19. $10 \le \frac{-1}{4}m$ — $-40 \; ? \; m$ **≥**
20. $-9 > -3x$ — $3 \; ? \; x$ **<**

In Exercises 21–24, match the inequality with the graph of its solution.

A.
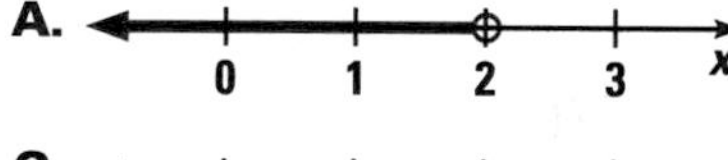

B.
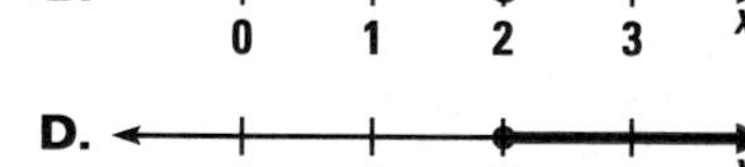

C.

D.

21. $0.7x \le 1.4$ **C**
22. $-1 > -\frac{1}{2}x$ **B**
23. $\frac{1}{8} \le \frac{1}{16}x$ **D**
24. $-3x > -6$ **A**

25. GEOMETRY The length of a rectangle is 8 inches. Its area is greater than 216 square inches. Write and solve an inequality for the width of the rectangle. **$8w > 216$; The width is more than 27 inches.**

RAIN FORESTS Many medicines come from rain forest plants. One example is quinine, which comes from the bark of a cinchona tree found in Latin America and Africa. Quinine was used to treat malaria.

More about rain forests available at www.mcdougallittell.com

In Exercises 26–37, solve the inequality. Then graph the solution. **See margin for graphs.**

26. $3m < 4$ **$m < \frac{4}{3}$** **27.** $2n \geq 5$ **$n \geq \frac{5}{2}$** **28.** $-5b < 35$ **$b > -7$**

29. $\frac{y}{8} > 4$ **$y > 32$** **30.** $\frac{x}{2} \leq 8$ **$x \leq 16$** **31.** $-2a > \frac{1}{2}$ **$a < -\frac{1}{4}$**

32. $-\frac{1}{2}z > 5$ **$z < -10$** **33.** $-\frac{1}{5}p \geq 2$ **$p \leq -10$** **34.** $-\frac{3}{2} < -\frac{1}{4}x$ **$6 > x$**

35. $0.5y \geq -6$ **$y \geq -12$** **36.** $-5.6 \leq -1.4m$ **$4 \geq m$** **37.** $-3a \leq -6$ **$a \geq 2$**

In Exercises 38–42, write and solve an inequality for the situation described.

38. FUNDRAISER Your softball team sells sandwiches to raise money. The profit is \$.75 per sandwich. The team needs to raise at least \$300. How many sandwiches must the team sell? **$0.75s \geq 300$; Sell 400 or more sandwiches.**

39. BICYCLING You plan to ride your bike more than 12 miles. You bike at a speed of 15 miles per hour. What can you say about how long you will ride your bike? **$15t > 12$; Ride more than 0.8 of an hour or 48 minutes.**

40. Science Link At one time, rain forests covered about 14% of Earth's land area. Today they cover about 3,435,500 square miles, or less than 6% of Earth's land area. What is the total land area on Earth? **The total area of Earth's land is more than 57,258,333 square miles.**

41. GARDENING You want to plant a rectangular flower bed in front of the school. The bed will be 3 feet wide. You have enough seedlings to plant an area of at most 60 square feet. How long can the bed be? **Less than or equal to 20 feet**

42. COMMISSIONS A real estate agent earns a 6% commission for each house sold. What house prices will earn her a commission of at least \$4500? **The prices of the houses she sells must be at least \$75,000.**

43. MATHEMATICAL REASONING What is the greatest integer solution of $-6n > -60$? Justify your answer. **9; Since the solution is $n < 10$, the greatest integer less than 10 is 9.**

44. CHALLENGE Find all integers n such that $\frac{n}{2} < 3$ *and* $-4n \leq -4$. **1, 2, 3, 4, 5**

Multiple-Choice Practice

45. What is the solution of $-3n \geq 210$? **B**

Ⓐ $n \leq 70$ Ⓑ $n \leq -70$ Ⓒ $n \geq 70$ Ⓓ $n \geq -70$

46. What is the solution of $-60 < -12y$? **J**

Ⓕ $-5 < y$ Ⓖ $-5 > y$ Ⓗ $5 < y$ Ⓙ $5 > y$

47. You plan to invest money for one year at an annual simple interest rate of 5%. Which inequality shows how much money provides at least \$100 in interest? **C**

Ⓐ $x \geq \$200$ Ⓑ $x < \$2000$ Ⓒ $x \geq \$2000$ Ⓓ $x \geq \$20,000$

4 Assess

Assessment Resources

- Assessment Book (Formal Assessment and Alternative Assessment)
- Test and Practice Generator

Mini-Quiz

Solve the inequality. Then graph the solution.

1. $-5x \geq 15$ **$x \leq -3$;**

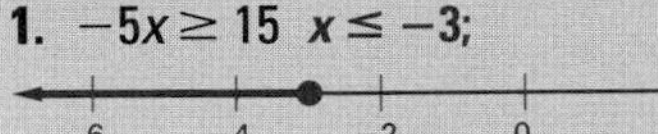

2. $\frac{t}{9} < -2$ **$t < -18$;**

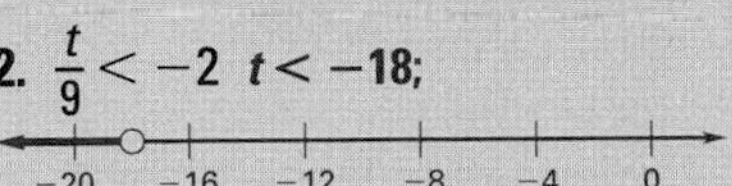

3. $-8.4 > -1.4d$ **$6 < d$;**

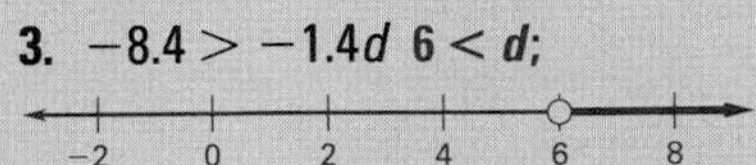

4. You and a friend are going to a restaurant for dinner. You agree to pay for the meals and your friend plans to leave a 15% tip. If your friend is limited to \$4.00 for the tip, what can be the range of the cost, m, for the meals? **$m \leq 26.67$; the cost of the meals must be no more than \$26.67.**

26.

27.

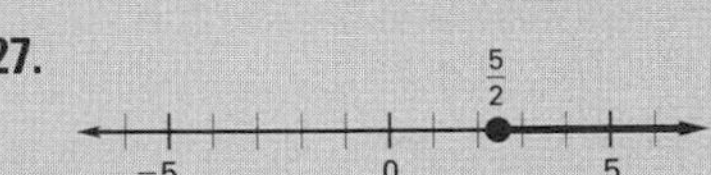

28.

29.

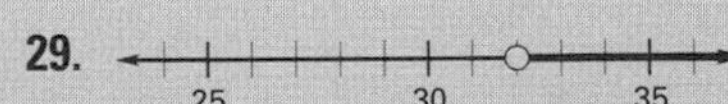

30. 12 14 16 18 20

31.

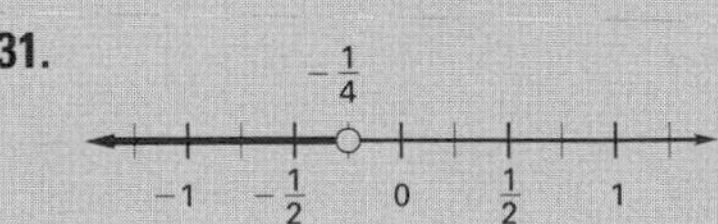

32.

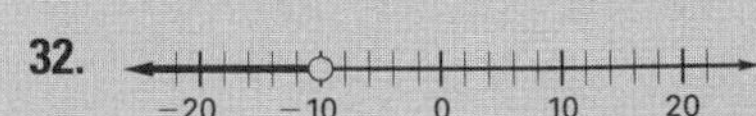

33–37. See Additional Answers beginning on page AA1.

1 Plan

Pacing

Suggested Number of Days

Transitional: 2 days
Average: 2 days
Advanced: 2 days
Block Schedule: 1 block

Teaching Resources

Blacklines
(See page 446B.)

Transparencies
- Warm-Up Exercises
- Teacher Time-Savers
- English/Spanish Problem Solving
- Answers

Technology
- Electronic Teacher Tools
- Test and Practice Generator

2 Teach

Math Reasoning

For Mathematical Background Notes on mathematical reasoning related to this lesson, please refer to pages 446E and 446F in this Teacher's Edition.

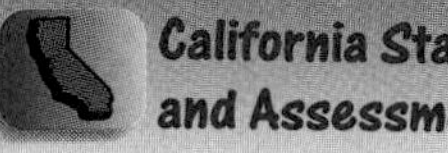

California Standards and Assessment

CA Standard: AF 4.1
CA Key Concepts Book: pp. S70–S73

9.8 Solving Two-Step Inequalities

California Standards

In this lesson you'll:

- Solve two-step linear inequalities in one variable over the rational numbers. (AF 4.1)
- Interpret the solutions of an inequality in the context from which it arose and verify the reasonableness of results. (AF 4.1)

Goal 1 Solving Two-Step Inequalities

In this lesson you will solve inequalities that require two or more steps.

EXAMPLE 1 Solving a Two-Step Inequality

Solve $2x + 1 \le 4$ and graph the solution.

Solution

$2x + 1 \le 4$	Write original inequality.
$2x + 1 - \mathbf{1} \le 4 - \mathbf{1}$	Subtract 1 from each side.
$2x \le 3$	Simplify.
$\frac{2x}{\mathbf{2}} \le \frac{3}{\mathbf{2}}$	Divide each side by 2.
$x \le \frac{3}{2}$	Simplify. *x* is by itself.

ANSWER ▶ The solution is all real numbers less than or equal to $\frac{3}{2}$.

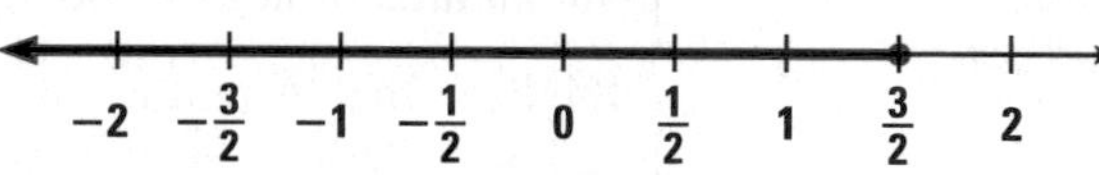

EXAMPLE 2 Solving a Two-Step Inequality

Solve $-\frac{1}{3}m - 5 > 2$.

Solution

$-\frac{1}{3}m - 5 > 2$	Write original inequality.
$-\frac{1}{3}m - 5 + \mathbf{5} > 2 + \mathbf{5}$	Add 5 to each side.
$-\frac{1}{3}m > 7$	Simplify.
$\mathbf{-3} \cdot \left(-\frac{1}{3}\right)m < \mathbf{-3} \cdot 7$	Multiply each side by −3. Reverse the inequality symbol.
$m < -21$	Simplify. *m* is by itself.

ANSWER ▶ The solution is all real numbers less than −21.

Goal 2 SOLVING PROBLEMS

You may be able to solve a real-life problem using a two-step inequality.

EXAMPLE 3 Writing and Solving an Inequality

BAKING You are baking 36 bran muffins with raisins. Without raisins, each muffin contains 105 Calories. You want each muffin to have fewer than 115 Calories. Each raisin has 1.3 Calories. How many raisins can you have in each muffin?

Solution

Method 1 Write and solve an inequality.

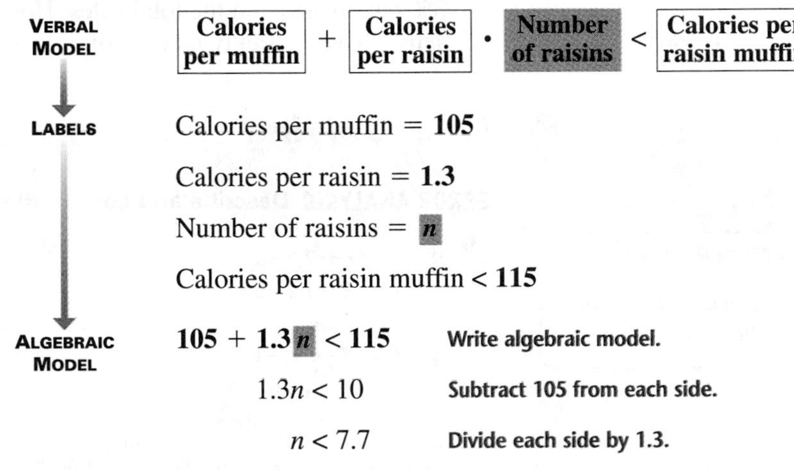

VERBAL MODEL
Calories per muffin + Calories per raisin • Number of raisins < Calories per raisin muffin
LABELS
Calories per muffin = 105
Calories per raisin = 1.3
Number of raisins = n
Calories per raisin muffin < 115
ALGEBRAIC MODEL
105 + 1.3n < 115 Write algebraic model.
1.3n < 10 Subtract 105 from each side.
n < 7.7 Divide each side by 1.3.

ANSWER ▶ You can have up to 7 raisins per muffin.

Method 2 Use a table or a graph.

Raisins	Calories
0	105
1	106.3
2	107.6
3	108.9
4	110.2
5	111.5
6	112.8
7	114.1
8	115.4

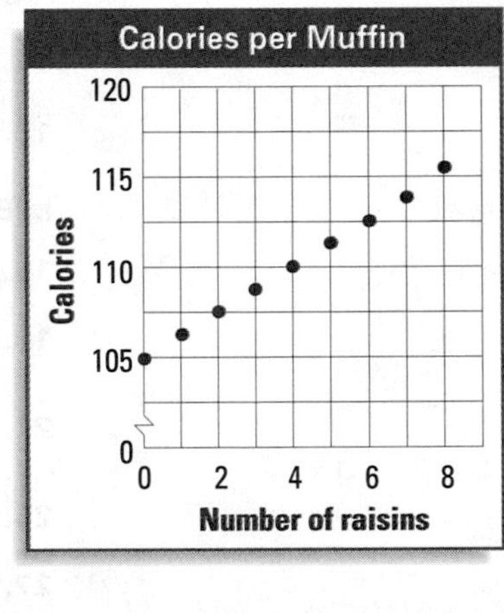

ANSWER ▶ Notice that the number of calories exceeds 115 when the number of raisins is greater than 7.

Student Help

▶**MORE EXAMPLES**
More examples are available at www.mcdougallittell.com

Student Help

▶**SKILLS REVIEW**
For help with using a table or a graph to solve problems, see pages 668–669.

Extra Example 1

Solve $3x + 5 \geq -4$ and graph the solution. $x \geq -3$

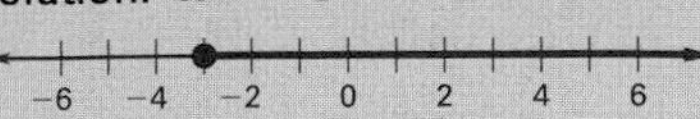

Extra Example 2

Solve $-\frac{1}{2}x - 9 < -1$. $x > -16$

Extra Example 3

You are baking a batch of 36 oatmeal chocolate chip cookies. Without the chips, the recipe has 1000 calories (Cal). You want each cookie to have less than 45 Cal. Each chocolate chip has 2.4 Cal. How many chips can you have in each cookie? **$n < 7.2$; You can use up to 7 chocolate chips in each cookie.**

Concept Check

You are asked to solve an inequality that contains a negative number. Does this mean you will need to reverse the direction of the inequality symbol? Explain. ***Sample answer:*** **Not necessarily. For example, solving $2x + 1 < -4$ does not involve a step in which the inequality symbol is reversed.**

3 Apply

Assignment Guide

TRANSITIONAL
Day 1: pp. 486–488 Exs. 9–23, 50–53, 58–59, 62–63
Day 2: pp. 486–488 Exs. 30, 37–38, 41–43, 47–49, 64–67, 70–72

AVERAGE
Day 1: pp. 486–488 Exs. 10–14, 18–26, 50–53, 58–59, 62–63
Day 2: pp. 486–488 Exs. 30, 37–38, 42–45, 47–49, 64–67, 70–72

ADVANCED
Day 1: pp. 486–488 Exs. 10–14, 20–29, 50–53, 58–59, 62–63
Day 2: pp. 486–488 Exs. 30, 39–40, 42–45, 46*, 47–49, 64–67, 70–72

BLOCK SCHEDULE
pp. 486–488 Exs. 10–14, 18–26, 30, 37–38, 42–45, 47–53, 58–59, 62–67, 70–72

Extra Practice

- Student Edition, pp. 706–707
- Chapter 9 Resource Book, p. 69

Homework Check

To quickly check student understanding of key concepts, go over the following exercises:

Transitional: 16, 18, 22, 30, 42
Average: 18, 22, 24, 42, 44
Advanced: 20, 22, 24, 42, 44

1. 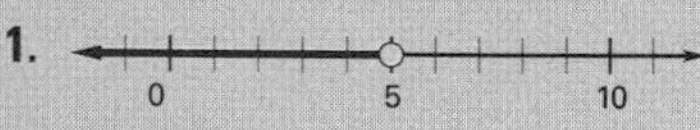

2. 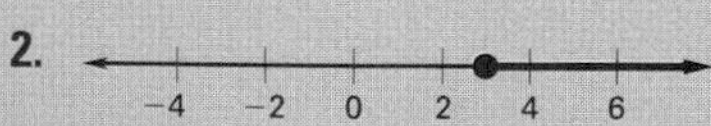

3. 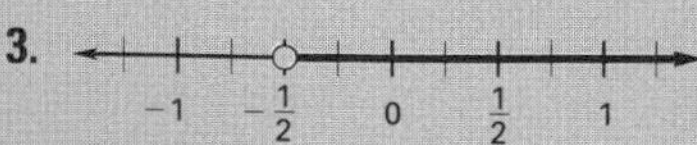

4. −5 0 5

5. −5 0 5 10 15

6. −10 −5 0 5 10

9.8 Exercises

Guided Practice

Solve the inequality and explain your steps. Then graph the solution. **See margin for graphs.**

1. $3x - 2 < 13$ **$x < 5$** **2.** $-18 + 10y \geq 12$ **$y \geq 3$** **3.** $4y - 1 > -3$ **$y > -\frac{1}{2}$**

4. $3 + 6x \leq 21$ **$x \leq 3$** **5.** $2y - 5 > 15$ **$y > 10$** **6.** $-7 - 4x < 9$ **$x > -4$**

7. Tell when you should reverse the direction of the inequality sign when solving an inequality. Give examples to illustrate. **When multiplying or dividing both sides of the inequality by a negative number. Examples will vary.**

8. COMMISSION A salesperson earns a salary of \$100 per week plus a 3% commission on the total sales. How much must the salesperson sell to have a weekly income of at least \$500? **Total sales should be at least \$13,333.33.**

Practice and Problem Solving

Student Help

▶MORE PRACTICE
Extra practice to help you master skills is on page 707.

10. **The subtraction of $\frac{3}{4}x$ from $\frac{1}{2}x$ results in a negative $\frac{1}{4}x$ on the third line. $x \geq -1$**

ERROR ANALYSIS Describe and correct the error.

9.

$-4x + 7 \geq -5$
$-4x + 7 - 7 \geq -5 - 7$
$\frac{-4x}{-4} \geq \frac{-12}{-4}$
$x \geq 3$

When dividing both sides of an inequality by a negative number the direction of the inequality must be reversed; $x \leq 3$.

10.

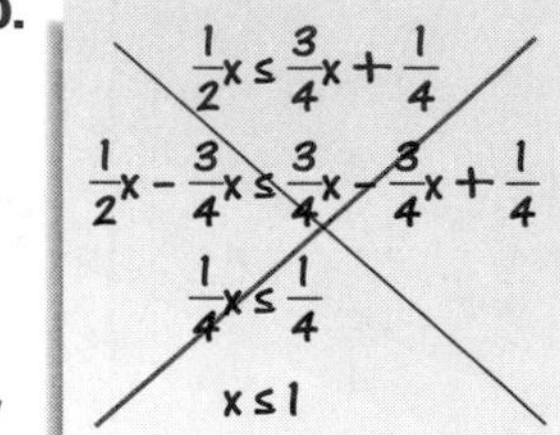

See margin.

Match the inequality with its solution.

A. $x < -2$ **B.** $x < 2$ **C.** $x > -2$ **D.** $x > 2$

11. $2x + 13 > 9$ **C** **12.** $-2x - 8 > -4$ **A**

13. $6 < 18 - 6x$ **B** **14.** $16 - 10x < 4 - 4x$ **D**

In Exercises 15–29, solve the inequality. Then graph the solution. **See margin for graphs.**

15. $-11x + 3 < -30$ **$x > 3$** **16.** $-9 < 2b - 13$ **$2 < b$** **17.** $5a + 6 \geq -9$ **$a \geq -3$**

18. $-3a + 4 > -11$ **$a < 5$** **19.** $2c - 6 \geq 12$ **$c \geq 9$** **20.** $-3m + 5 < 17$ **$m > -4$**

21. $\frac{y}{5} + 12 \leq 8$ **$y \leq -20$** **22.** $\frac{3}{4}m \leq \frac{1}{4}m + 2$ **$m \leq 4$** **23.** $-\frac{1}{5}x > \frac{4}{5}x + 3$ **$x < -3$**

24. $-4x + 3 \geq -5x$ **$x \geq -3$** **25.** $3p - 4 \leq 2p - 11$ **$p \leq -7$** **26.** $6w - 5 > -4w - 9$ **$w > -\frac{2}{5}$**

27. $-3k - 4 < 2k + 9$ **$k > -\frac{13}{5}$** **28.** $2(x + 1) \geq -2$ **$x \geq -2$** **29.** $4x + 1 \leq 2(x + 2)$ **$x \leq \frac{3}{2}$**

30. PARKING FEES Parking fees in the municipal lot are \$3.50 plus \$.75 for each hour or fraction of an hour. If you want to spend less than \$6.00, how long can you park? **3 hours or less**

MATHEMATICAL REASONING **In Exercises 31–36, the values of x are restricted to the numbers −2, −1, 0, 1, and 2. Determine which values of x are solutions of the inequality.**

31. $-5x - 9 < 11$ **−2, −1, 0, 1, 2**

32. $-7 - 2x \geq -9$ **−2, −1, 0, 1**

33. $6x - 7 \geq 4$ **2**

34. $5y + 20 > 15$ **0, 1, 2**

35. $4x - 3 \leq -11$ **−2**

36. $-3x + 4 < 5$ **0, 1, 2**

In Exercises 37–40, let n and $n + 1$ represent two consecutive integers. Write an inequality for the sentence. Then solve the inequality.

37. The sum of two consecutive integers is at least 7. $n + n + 1 \geq 7;\ n \geq 3$

38. The sum of two consecutive integers is more than 18. $n + n + 1 > 18;\ n > \frac{17}{2}$

39. The sum of two consecutive integers is less than 20. $n + n + 1 < 20;\ n < \frac{19}{2}$

40. The sum of two consecutive integers is at most 29. $n + n + 1 \leq 29;\ n \leq 14$

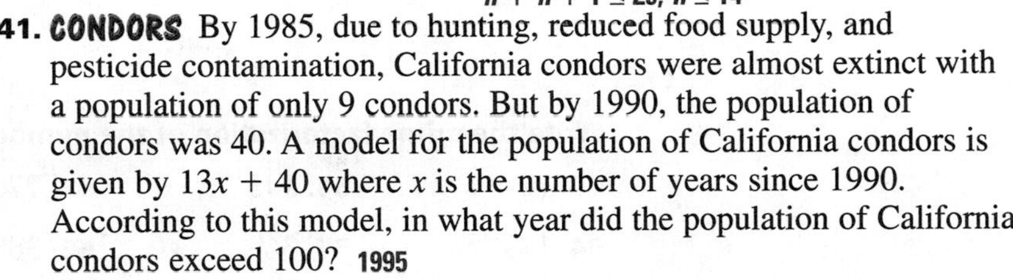

Link to Careers

ORNITHOLOGISTS study bird behavior, birds and their environments, and bird anatomy. They also study birds' migration habits and song patterns.

More about ornithologists available at www.mcdougallittell.com

41. CONDORS By 1985, due to hunting, reduced food supply, and pesticide contamination, California condors were almost extinct with a population of only 9 condors. But by 1990, the population of condors was 40. A model for the population of California condors is given by $13x + 40$ where x is the number of years since 1990. According to this model, in what year did the population of California condors exceed 100? **1995**

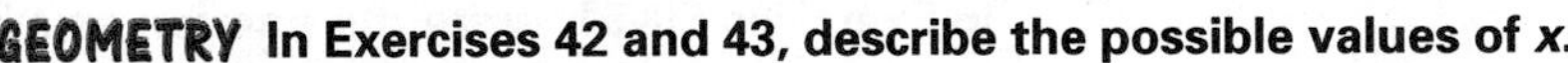

GEOMETRY **In Exercises 42 and 43, describe the possible values of x.**

42. The area of the rectangle is at least 28 square centimeters. $x \geq 4$

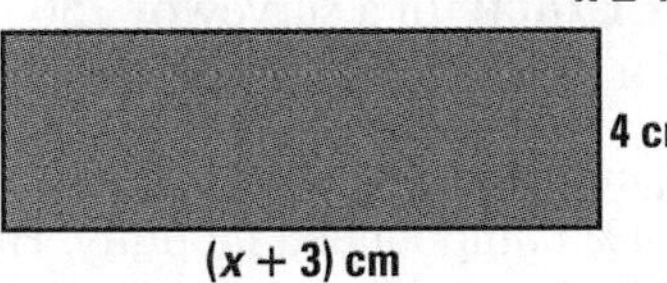

43. The perimeter of the triangle is less than or equal to 36 feet. $3 \leq x < 5.5$

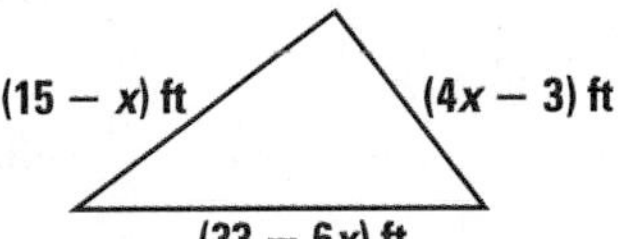

44. NUTRITION You want to plan a macaroni and cheese school lunch that is to contain at least 20 grams of protein. Without the macaroni and cheese, the lunch has 6 grams of protein. The macaroni and cheese has 2 grams of protein per ounce. Write and solve an inequality to find the amount of macaroni and cheese that should be served in order to have the desired amount of protein. $6 + 2x \geq 20$; **7 oz or more**

45. CARNIVAL You are going to a carnival. It costs $10 to enter, and tickets for games and rides cost $.25 each. You don't want to spend more than $20. Write and solve an inequality to find the number of tickets you can buy. $10 + 0.25t \leq 20$; **You can buy at most 40 tickets.**

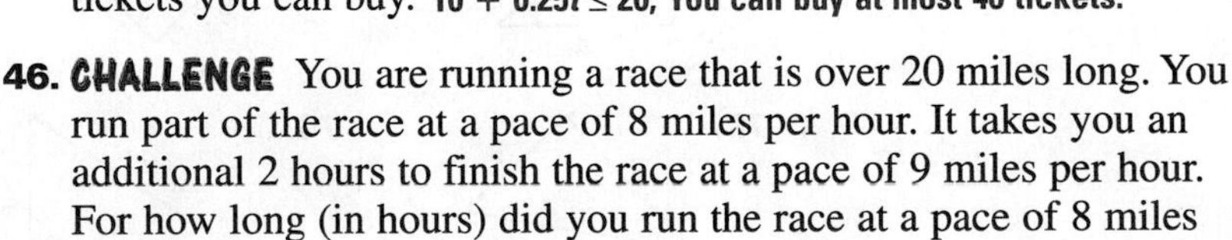

46. CHALLENGE You are running a race that is over 20 miles long. You run part of the race at a pace of 8 miles per hour. It takes you an additional 2 hours to finish the race at a pace of 9 miles per hour. For how long (in hours) did you run the race at a pace of 8 miles per hour? **more than $\frac{1}{4}$ of an hour**

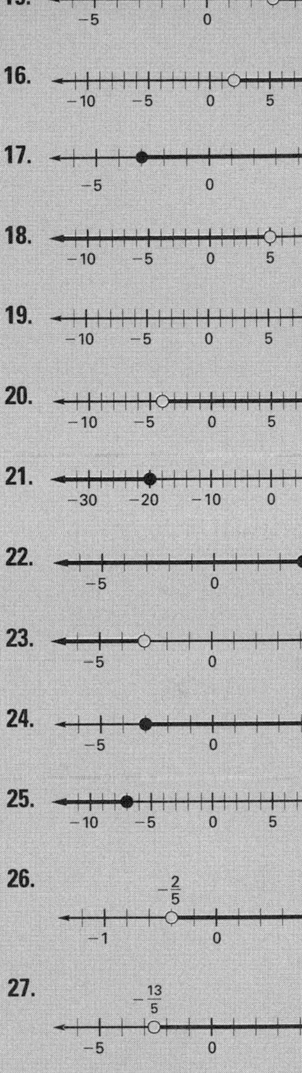

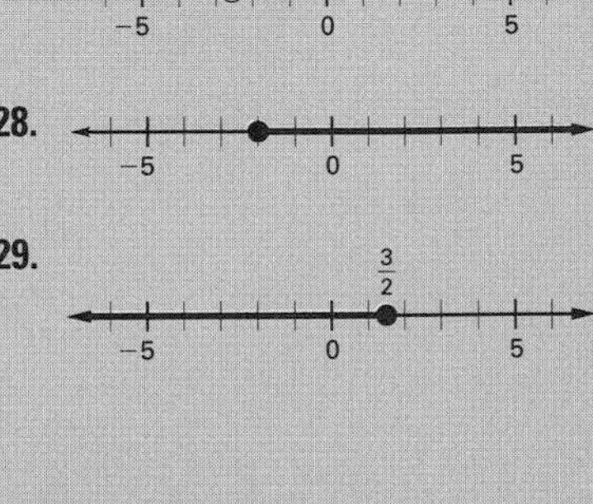

4 Assess

Assessment Resources

- Assessment Book (Formal Assessment and Alternative Assessment)
- Test and Practice Generator

Mini-Quiz

Solve the inequality.

1. $-8 \le 4m + 7$ $m \ge -\frac{15}{4}$
2. $-\frac{2}{3}x + \frac{2}{9} \ge \frac{1}{9}$ $x \le \frac{1}{6}$
3. $3(x - 2) > 4x$ $x < -6$
4. The sum of three consecutive integers is greater than 36. Write the inequality that represents the verbal sentence. Solve the inequality. $n + (n + 1) + (n + 2) > 36$; $n > 11$

Multiple-Choice Practice

▶In Exercise 48 remember *increased by* is a verbal phrase that indicates addition so you can eliminate F and H.

47. What is the solution of $20 \ge 10 + 2x$? **C**

Ⓐ $x < 5$ Ⓑ $x > 5$ Ⓒ $x \le 5$ Ⓓ $x \ge 5$

48. Decide which inequality represents the following verbal phrase: *a number increased by 2 is no more than 16.* **J**

Ⓕ $16 \le x - 2$ Ⓖ $16 \le x + 2$ Ⓗ $16 \ge x - 2$ Ⓙ $16 \ge x + 2$

49. At the grocery store, you buy ground meat for \$3.38, bread for \$1.79, and some oranges. Oranges are \$.25 each. How many oranges can you buy if you want to spend less than \$7.00? **B**

Ⓐ 5 Ⓑ 7 Ⓒ 8 Ⓓ 10

Mixed Review

Write the prime factorization of the number. *(5.1)*

50. 70 $5 \cdot 2 \cdot 7$ **51.** 145 $5 \cdot 29$ **52.** 270 $2 \cdot 3^3 \cdot 5$ **53.** 205 $5 \cdot 41$

54. 189 $3^3 \cdot 7$ **55.** 369 $3^2 \cdot 41$ **56.** 368 $2^4 \cdot 23$ **57.** 440 $2^3 \cdot 5 \cdot 11$

In Exercises 58–61, write the fraction as a decimal. *(5.5)*

58. $\frac{7}{9}$ $0.\overline{7}$ **59.** $-\frac{2}{15}$ $-0.1\overline{3}$ **60.** $4\frac{3}{4}$ 4.75 **61.** $-2\frac{8}{9}$ $-2.\overline{8}$

62. **SCHOOL LUNCH** In a survey of 350 students, 36% said they pack their lunch for school. How many students surveyed pack their lunch? *(6.4)* **126 students**

63. Your friend deposits \$500 in a savings account with an annual interest rate of 4% compounded monthly. How much interest will your friend earn in 2 years? *(7.9)* **\$41.57**

State whether each number is *rational* or *irrational*. *(9.2)*

64. 3.5 rational **65.** $\sqrt{17}$ irrational **66.** 1.020020002. . . irrational

67. $4.\overline{67}$. . . rational **68.** $\sqrt{11}$ irrational **69.** 5 rational

Use the Pythagorean theorem to solve the right triangle. Round your answer to the nearest tenth. *(9.3)*

70.
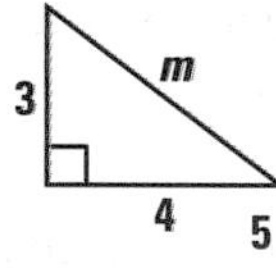

5

71.
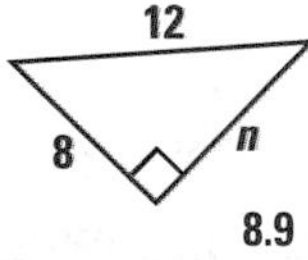

8.9

72.
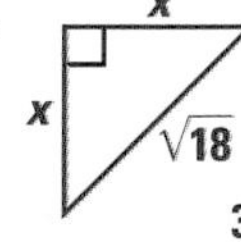

3

73.
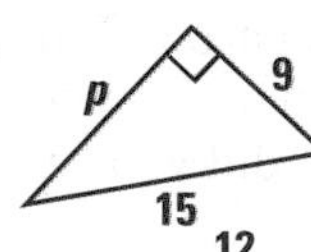

12

74.
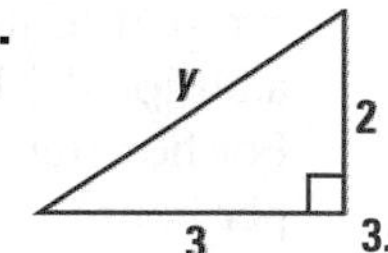

3.6

75.
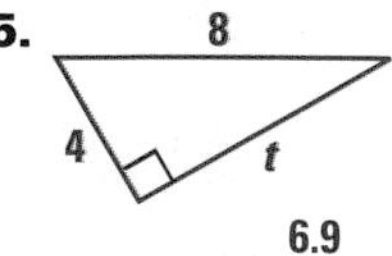

6.9

9.9 Box-and-Whisker Plots

California Standards

In this lesson you'll:

- Know and use a box-and-whisker plot to display a single set of data or compare two sets of data. (SDP 1.1)
- Understand the meaning of, and be able to compute the minimum, the lower quartile, the median, the upper quartile, and the maximum of a data set. (SDP 1.3)

Student Help

LOOK BACK
Since the data set in Example 1 consists of an even number of numbers, the median lies between the two middle values. For help finding the median, see page 203.

Goal 1 DRAWING BOX-AND-WHISKER PLOTS

The median of a set of ordered data divides the data into a lower and an upper half. The median of the lower half of the data is called the **lower quartile**. The median of the upper half is called the **upper quartile**. Data that have been divided into four parts using the median and quartiles can be displayed in a **box-and-whisker plot**.

EXAMPLE 1 Drawing a Box-and-Whisker Plot

A survey of 14 ski resorts recorded the number of lifts at each resort. Draw a box-and-whisker plot of the data.

17, 27, 19, 8, 25, 18, 11, 9, 7, 30, 8, 11, 11, 13

Solution

Write the data in increasing order, then find the median and quartiles.

$$\textbf{Median} = \frac{11 + 13}{2} = 12$$

7, 8, 8, **9**, 11, 11, **11**, **13**, 17, 18, **19**, 25, 27, 30

Lower quartile = **9** **Upper quartile** = **19**

Draw a number line that includes the minimum value, 7, and the maximum value, 30. Plot each of the following five numbers below the number line: the minimum, the lower quartile, the median, the upper quartile, and the maximum. Draw a box from the lower quartile to the upper quartile. Draw a vertical line through the median. Finally, draw "whiskers" from the quartiles to the minimum and the maximum.

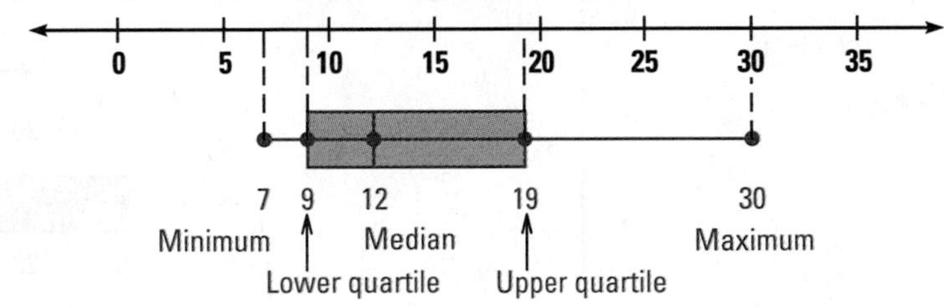

A box-and-whisker plot helps to show the variation of a data set, that is, how spread out the data are. One measure of variation is the *range*. The **range** of a set of data is the difference between the maximum and minimum values. The **interquartile range** is the difference between the upper quartile and lower quartile.

1 Plan

Pacing

Suggested Number of Days

Transitional: 2 days
Average: 2 days
Advanced: 2 days
Block Schedule: 1 block

Teaching Resources

Blacklines
(See page 446B.)

Transparencies
- Warm-Up Exercises
- Teacher Time-Savers
- English/Spanish Problem Solving
- Answers

Technology
- Electronic Teacher Tools
- Test and Practice Generator

2 Teach

Math Reasoning

For Mathematical Background Notes on mathematical reasoning related to this lesson, please refer to pages 446E and 446F in this Teacher's Edition.

Extra Example 1
See next page.

California Standards and Assessment

CA Standards: SDP 1.1, SDP 1.3
CA Key Concepts Book: pp. S100–S103

Extra Example 1

Draw a box-and-whisker plot for the following data.

54, 59, 39, 41, 46, 37, 36, 34, 22, 40, 61, 48, 45, 50, 28

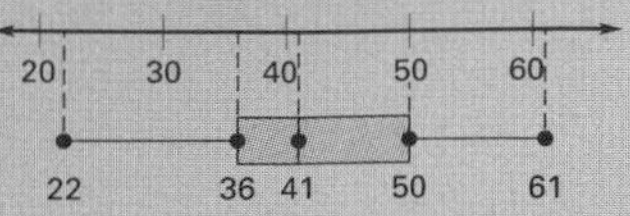

Extra Example 2

The box-and-whisker plots below show the age distribution in Louisiana and Washington, D.C. What do the plots tell you about age differences in the populations?

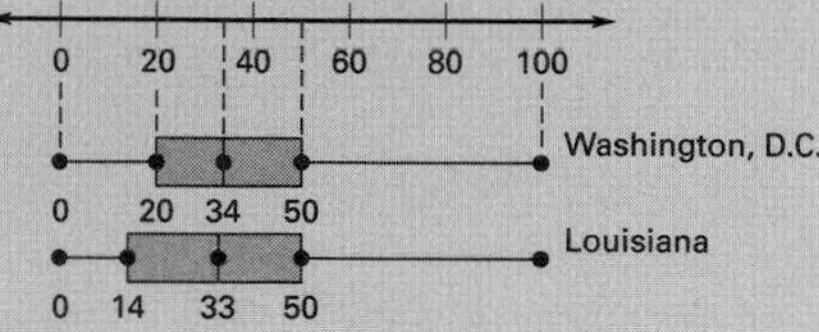

Sample answer: **Washington has a smaller age interquartile range; 50% of its population is between the ages of 20 and 50, while Louisiana has 50% of its population between ages 14 and 50.**

Concept Check

Write a list of steps to follow when drawing a box-and-whisker plot.
Sample answer: **1. Order the data from least to greatest. 2. Find the median of all the data. 3. Find the lower and upper quartiles. 4. Plot the minimum and maximum values, the median, and the lower and upper quartiles. 5. Draw a box from the lower to the upper quartile, with a vertical line at the median. 6. Draw the whiskers connecting the box to the minimum and maximum values.**

Goal 2 Using Box-and-Whisker Plots

Box-and-whisker plots can be used to compare two or more data sets.

Student Help

▶ Study Tip
The box in a box-and-whisker plot represents about 50% of the data. Each whisker represents about 25% of the data.

EXAMPLE 2 Interpreting Box-and-Whisker Plots

The box-and-whisker plots below represent the ages of the populations of Alaska and Rhode Island. What do the plots tell you about age differences in the populations of the two states?

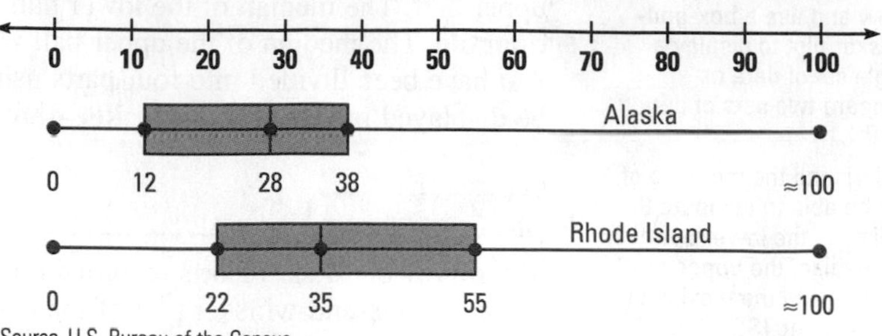

▶ Source U.S. Bureau of the Census

Solution

In general, Rhode Island's population is older than Alaska's. For example, 50% of Alaska's population is between 12 and 38, while 50% of Rhode Island's is between 22 and 55. If you choose 30 as an age that separates young and old, more than 50% of Rhode Island's population is over 30, while less than 50% of Alaska's population is over 30.

EXAMPLE 3 Interpreting Box-and-Whisker Plots

The box-and-whisker plots represent speeds (in miles per hour) of cars at midnight and noon on one city street. Which plot is more likely to represent noon?

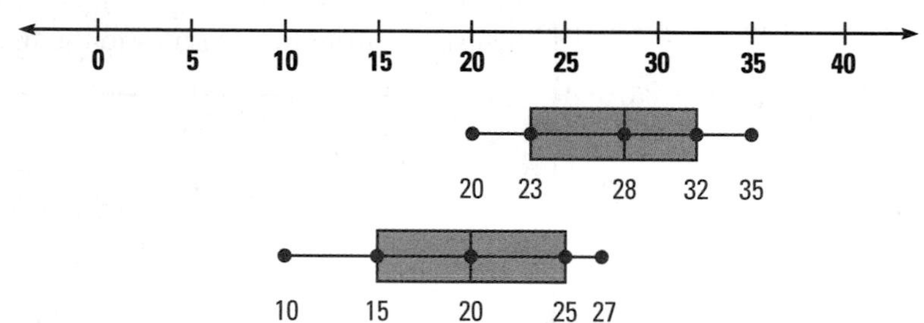

Solution

Since there is generally more traffic on city streets at noon than at midnight, speeds would generally be slower at noon. On the bottom plot, 50% of the speeds are under 20 miles per hour. On the top plot, all the speeds are 20 miles per hour or more. It is reasonable to assume that the bottom plot represents noon.

9.9 Exercises

Guided Practice

In Exercises 1–8, use the box-and-whisker plot below, which shows video game scores. Name the value.

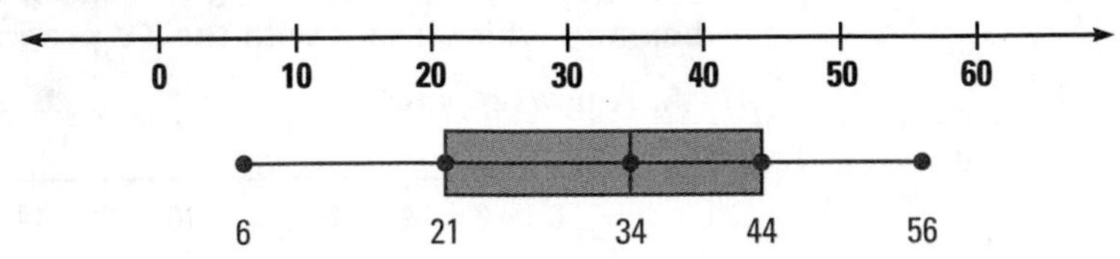

1. Minimum score **6**

2. Maximum score **56**

3. Median **34**

4. Lower quartile **21**

5. Upper quartile **44**

6. Range **50**

7. Percent of scores above 44 **25%**

8. Percent of scores between 21 and 44 **50%**

9. You asked 12 friends how many books they read in the past year. Draw a box-and-whisker plot that represents the results below.
3, 4, 8, 10, 13, 17, 21, 26, 29, 31, 32, 36. **See margin.**

Practice and Problem Solving

Student Help

▶MORE PRACTICE
Extra practice to help you master skills is on page 707.

In Exercises 10–17, use the box-and-whisker plot, which shows the numbers of baseball cards owned by card collectors in one school. Name the value.

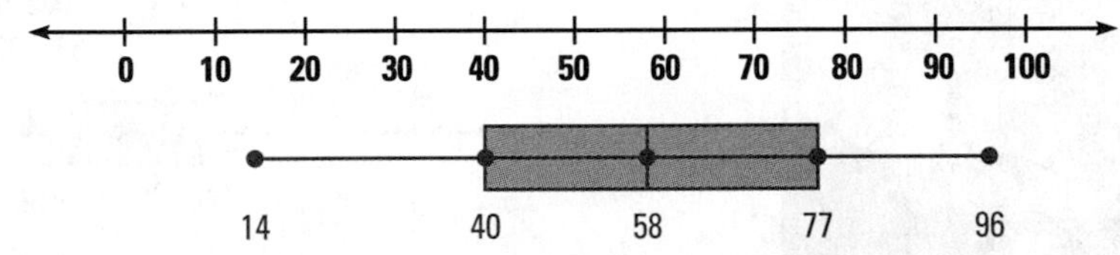

10. Minimum number **14**

11. Maximum number **96**

12. Median **58**

13. Lower quartile **40**

14. Upper quartile **77**

15. Range **82**

16. Interquartile range **37**

17. Percent of numbers between 58 and 96 **50%**

The data set represents the ages of children at a family gathering. Draw a box-and-whisker plot for the data. Describe the variation.

18. 9, 7, 12, 15, 11, 11, 13, 8, 9, 8, 7, 13, 8, 14, 6, 11, 5
See margin. The range is 10. The interquartile range is 5.

19. 4, 8, 10, 13, 3, 2, 7, 6, 5, 4, 8, 1, 14, 9, 2, 10, 9, 2
See margin. The range is 13. The interquartile range is 6.

3 Apply

Assignment Guide

TRANSITIONAL
Day 1: EP p. 697 Exs. 66–69; pp. 491–493 Exs. 18–20, 24–25
Day 2: pp. 491–493 Exs. 10–17, 21–23, 29–30

AVERAGE
Day 1: pp. 491–493 Exs. 18–20, 24–25
Day 2: pp. 491–493 Exs. 10–17, 21–23, 26, 29–30

ADVANCED
Day 1: pp. 491–493 Exs. 18–20, 24–25
Day 2: pp. 491–493 Exs. 10–17, 23, 26, 27–28*, 29–30

BLOCK SCHEDULE
pp. 491–493 Exs. 10–26, 29–30

Extra Practice

- Student Edition, pp. 706–707
- Chapter 9 Resource Book, p. 78

Homework Check

To quickly check student understanding of key concepts, go over the following exercises:

Transitional: 16, 18, 22, 24, 25
Average: 16, 18, 22, 24, 25
Advanced: 16, 18, 23, 24, 25

9.

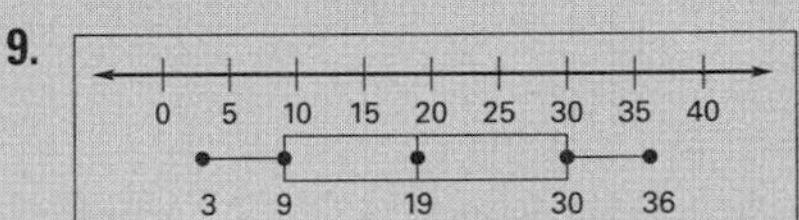

18.

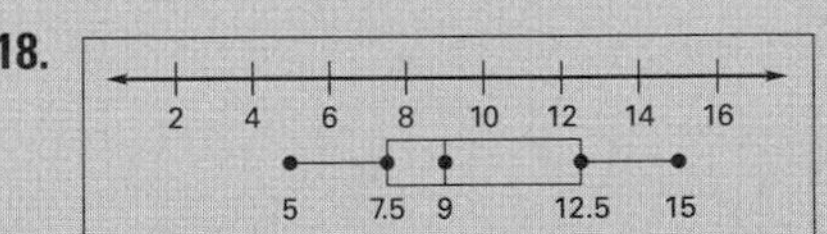

19.

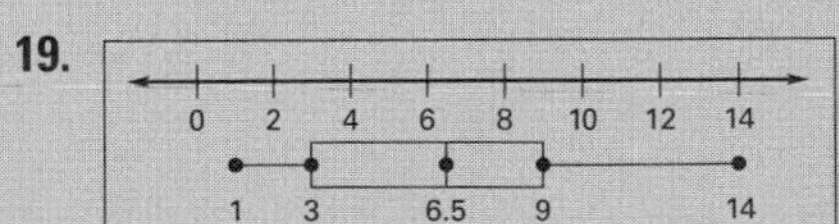

24.

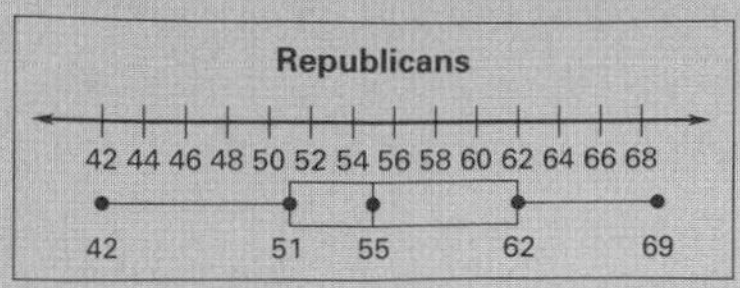

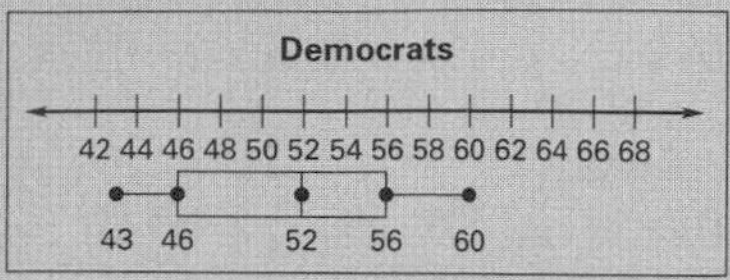

25. ***Sample answer:*** **The maximum age for the Democrats is almost the upper quartile age for the Republicans. The median age for the Democrats is nearly the lower quartile for the Republicans. The range of the Republicans is more than the range for the Democrats. In general, Republican presidents are older. Half of the Democrats are between 46 and 56, while half of the Republicans are between 51 and 62.**

21. B; The range of the watchers is 20 years. 50% of these are between 6 and 12 years old. This suggests that these are children who are more likely to watch cartoons.

22. A; 50% of this group are between the ages of 32 and 65, a much older group suggesting a news report rather than a cartoon.

23. City B; ***Sample answer:*** **The median of City B is colder than the median of City A. 25% of the temperatures are between 5 and 40 degrees in City B whereas in City A practically all of the temperatures are above that. Although they both have interquartile ranges of 20 degrees, City B has 50% between 40 and 60 degrees while City A has 50% between 55 and 75 degrees.**

Link to Politics

RONALD REAGAN was 69 years old when he took the oath of office as President of the United States in 1981. He was older than any previous newly inaugurated American President.

20. Collect wrist size data from a dozen girls and a dozen boys in your class. Use a string and a ruler to measure the distance around each person's right wrist. Measure to the nearest half centimeter. Draw a box-and-whisker plot of the girls' data and draw another of the boys' data. Compare the plots and describe the variation. **Data will vary.**

MATHEMATICAL REASONING The box-and-whisker plots below show the ages of people watching a TV program. Match the most reasonable box-and-whisker plot with the TV program. Explain your choices.

A. A news report **B.** A cartoon

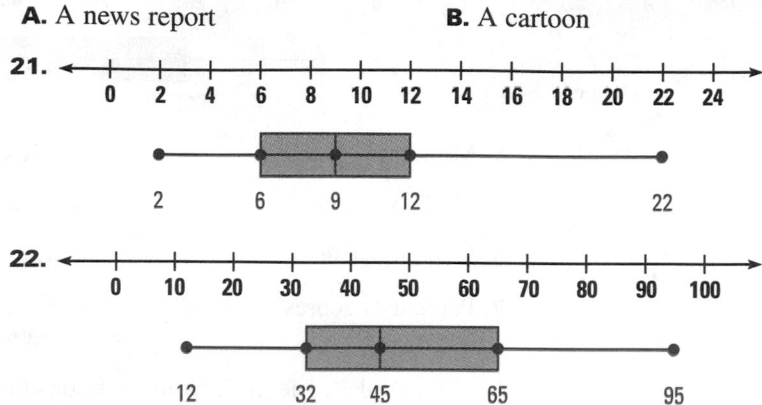

23. WRITING The box-and-whisker plots represent average daily temperatures in degrees Fahrenheit for two cities. Write a short paragraph comparing the data in as many ways as you can. Which city is more likely to be farther north? Explain your reasoning.

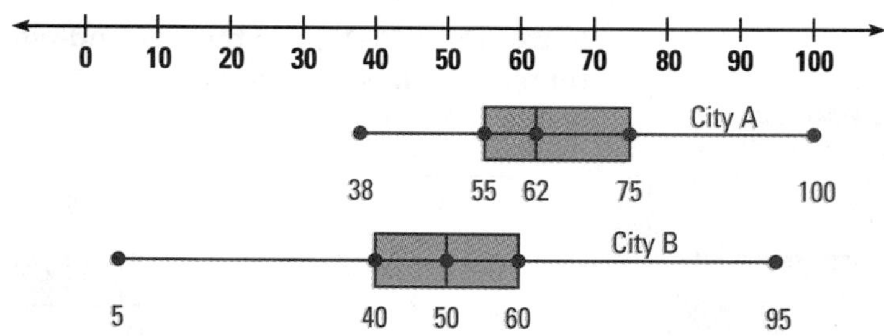

POLITICS In Exercises 24 and 25, use the following information. For the period 1900–1999, the table lists the age of each President of the United States at his first inauguration and his political party.

Age at First Inauguration of American Presidents 1900-1999	
Democrats	**Republicans**
56, 51, 60, 43, 55, 52, 46	54, 42, 51, 55, 51, 54, 62, 56, 61, 69, 64

24–25. See margin.

24. Use a single number line to draw two box-and-whisker plots, one for Democrats and one for Republicans.

25. Compare the plots. What conclusions can you make between the ages of Republican and Democratic Presidents in the 1900s?

26. ERROR ANALYSIS The number of hours worked in one week by part-time employees at a company are 26, 10, 19, 34, 2, 5, 21, 12, 1, 39, 14, 30, 18, 37, 7, 24. The box-and-whisker plot below, which is supposed to represent the data, contains three errors. Describe the errors and correct them. **8.5 is the lower quartile not 8. 18.5 is the median not 18, and 39 is the maximum not 37.**

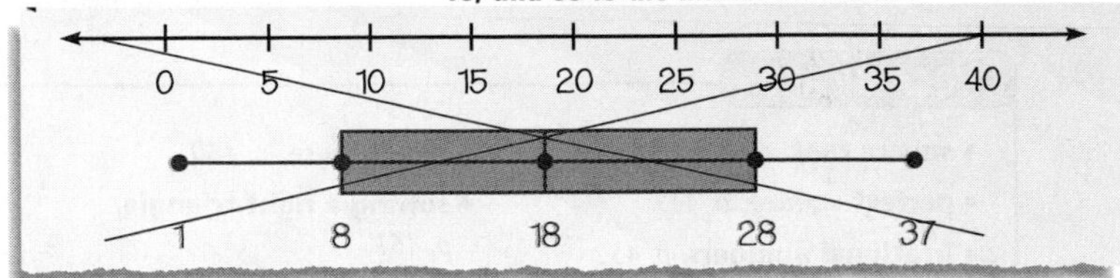

Student Help

▶ HOMEWORK HELP

Extra help with problem solving in Exs. 27–28 is available at www.mcdougallittell.com

CHALLENGE In Exercises 27 and 28, use the lists of prices (in dollars) of three types of stereo components.

Receivers: 165, 200, 260, 180, 300, 460, 390, 445, 225, 325, 400, 280

CD players: 170, 270, 180, 140, 240, 195, 255, 160, 200, 290, 230, 280

Tape decks: 200, 225, 150, 285, 260, 230, 295, 255, 290, 195, 265, 280

27. Using the same number line, draw a box-and-whisker plot for each stereo component. **See margin.**

28. Which type of component shows the most variation in price? Which shows the least? **See margin.**

Multiple-Choice Practice

Test Tip Ⓐ Ⓑ Ⓒ Ⓓ

▶ Be sure you pay careful attention to vocabulary. For example, if a test question asks about the upper quartile, don't confuse it with the lower quartile.

29. Which statement is true about the data? **C**

15, 17, 25, 10, 21, 19, 8, 14, 23, 20, 16, 4, 19, 27, 24, 19

Ⓐ The median is 18.5. Ⓑ The range is 4.

Ⓒ The upper quartile is 22. Ⓓ The interquartile range is 23.

30. The prices (in dollars) of 13 software packages are given. Which box-and-whisker plot correctly displays the data? **G**

59, 63, 65, 70, 75, 77, 65, 71, 59, 75, 80, 70, 63

Ⓕ
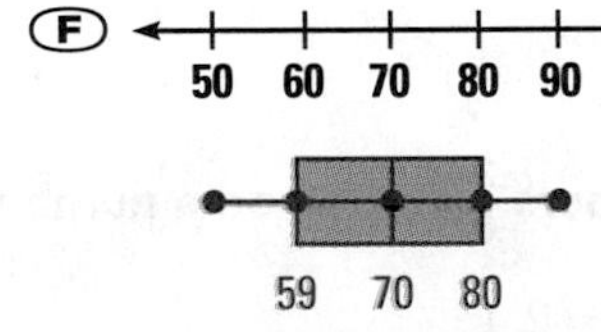

Ⓖ
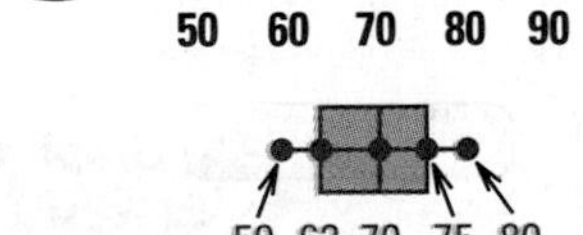

Ⓗ
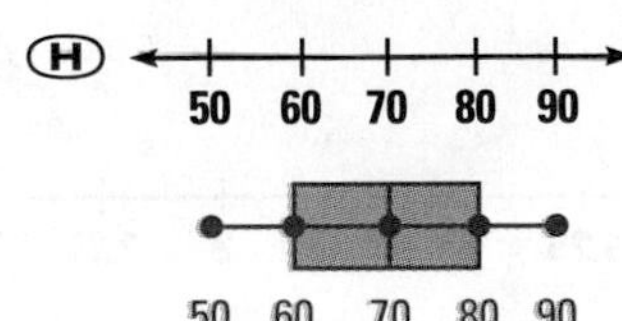

Ⓙ
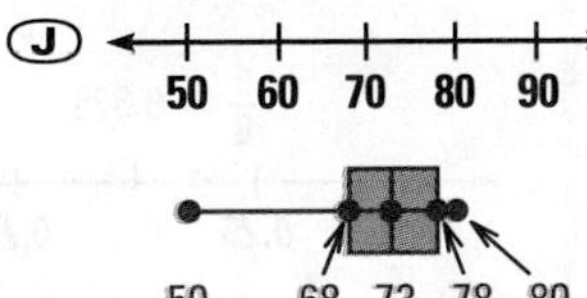

4 Assess

Assessment Resources

- Assessment Book (Formal Assessment and Alternative Assessment)
- Test and Practice Generator

Mini-Quiz

1. The prices (to the nearest dollar) for the different women's aerobics shoes sold at a store are given below. Draw a box-and-whisker plot of the data.

$50, $45, $39, $37, $40, $67, $45, $25, $59, $49, $50, $55

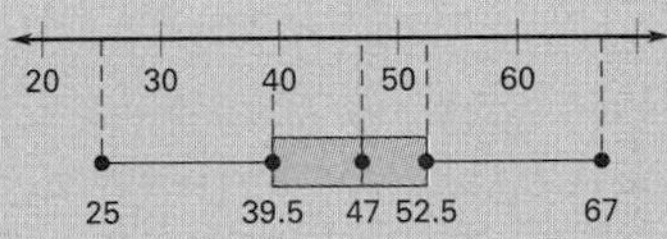

Use your box-and-whisker plot from question 1.

2. What percent of the shoes are priced between $39.50 and $52.50? **50%**

3. Below what price are 25% of the shoes? **$39.50**

27.

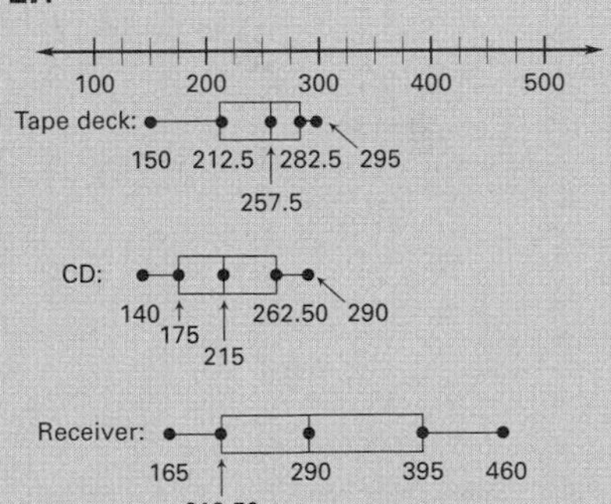

28. Receivers show the most variation in price, with a range of nearly $300. Tape decks show the least variation, with a difference of only $70 between the upper and lower quartiles.

Additional Resources

The following resources are available to help review the material in this chapter:

Technology
- Personal Student Tutor
- Test and Practice Generator

Chapter 9 Chapter Summary and Review

VOCABULARY

- **square root,** *p. 449*
- **perfect square,** *p. 449*
- **irrational numbers,** *p. 453*
- **real numbers,** *p. 453*
- **Pythagorean theorem,** *p. 460*
- **legs of a triangle,** *p. 460*
- **hypotenuse,** *p. 460*
- **solving a right triangle,** *p. 461*
- **converse,** *p. 465*
- **distance formula,** *p. 470*
- **midpoint formula,** *p. 471*
- **lower quartile,** *p. 489*
- **upper quartile,** *p. 489*
- **box-and-whisker plot,** *p. 489*
- **range,** *p. 489*
- **interquartile range,** *p. 489*

9.1 SQUARE ROOTS

Examples on pp. 449–450

EXAMPLE **Find the square roots of 196.**

$\sqrt{196} = 14$ because $14^2 = 196$. $-\sqrt{196} = -14$ because $(-14)^2 = 196$.

So, the square roots of 196 are 14 and −14. The number 196 is a perfect square.

Solve the equation using mental math.

1. $49 = n^2$ **7, −7** **2.** $y^2 = 81$ **9, −9** **3.** $121 = r^2$ **11, −11** **4.** $x^2 = \frac{49}{64}$ $\frac{7}{8}, -\frac{7}{8}$

In Exercises 5–8, approximate the square roots of the number. Round your answer to the nearest tenth.

5. 41 **6.4, −6.4** **6.** 77 **8.8, −8.8** **7.** 92 **9.6, −9.6** **8** 27 **5.2, −5.2**

9. How long is a side of a square that has an area of 45 square feet? Round your answer to the nearest tenth. **6.7 ft**

9.2 THE REAL NUMBER SYSTEM

Examples on pp. 453–454

EXAMPLE **Graph the numbers $\frac{3}{8}$ and $\sqrt{6}$ on a number line.**

As decimals, $\frac{3}{8} = 0.375$ and $\sqrt{6} \approx 2.45$.

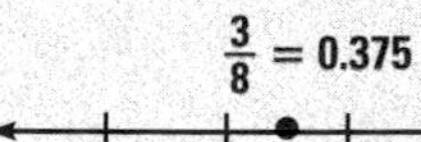

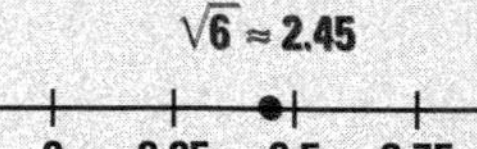

0 0.25 0.5 0.75 1 1.25 1.5 1.75 2 2.25 2.5 2.75

Graph the numbers on a number line. Then complete the statement using <, >, or =. **10–13. See margin for graphs.**

10. $-\sqrt{36}$ **?** $-\sqrt{40}$ **>** **11.** $\sqrt{1.6}$ **?** 0.4 **>** **12.** $-\sqrt{420}$ **?** -4.5 **<** **13.** $\sqrt{\frac{1}{4}}$ **?** $\sqrt{\frac{1}{2}}$ **<**

9.3 THE PYTHAGOREAN THEOREM

Examples on pp. 460–461

EXAMPLE **Find *c* in the triangle shown.**

$a^2 + b^2 = c^2$ Use Pythagorean theorem.

$7^2 + 4^2 = c^2$ Substitute 7 for *a* and 4 for *b*.

$65 = c^2$ Square 7 and 4. Then add.

$8.06 \approx c$ Take positive square root of each side.

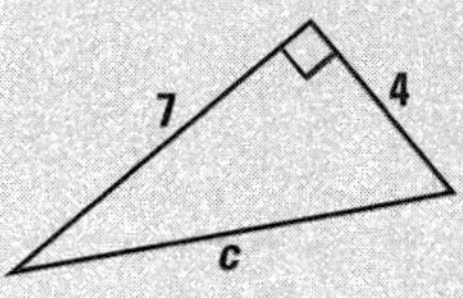

Use the Pythagorean theorem to solve the right triangle. Round your answer to the nearest tenth.

14. 

10.6

15. 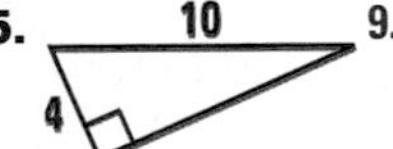

9.2

16. 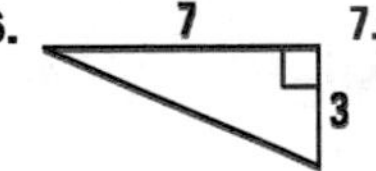

7.6

17. 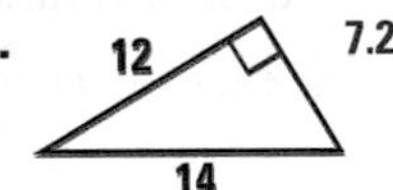

7.2

9.4 THE CONVERSE OF THE PYTHAGOREAN THEOREM

Examples on pp. 465–466

EXAMPLE **Determine whether the triangle is a right triangle.**

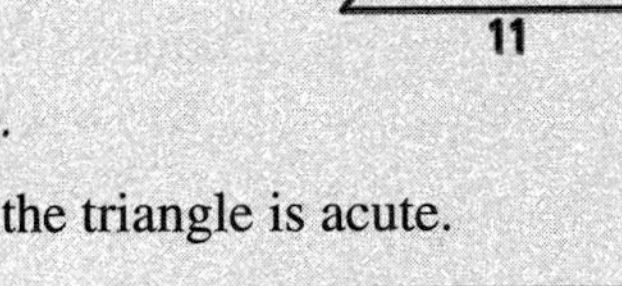

$a^2 + b^2 \stackrel{?}{=} c^2$ Write equation to be tested.

$7^2 + 9^2 \stackrel{?}{=} 11^2$ Substitute for *a*, *b*, and *c*.

$130 \neq 121$ Square 7, 9, and 11. Then add and compare.

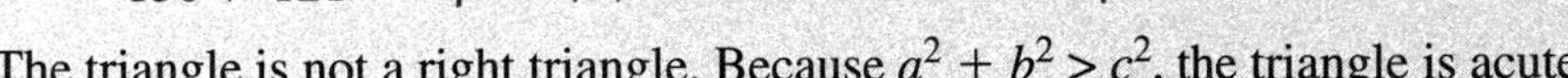

The triangle is not a right triangle. Because $a^2 + b^2 > c^2$, the triangle is acute.

18. It was once believed that ancient Egyptians tightly held a rope with equally spaced knots to form a triangle as shown at the right. For the triangle to be a right triangle, what must be true about the number of spaces on each side? Explain. **They must satisfy the Pythagorean theorem.**

Determine whether the triangle with the given side lengths is right, acute, or obtuse.

19. 4, 5, 6 **acute** **20.** 5, 12, 13 **right** **21.** 5, 7, 9 **obtuse**

10.

11.

12.

13.
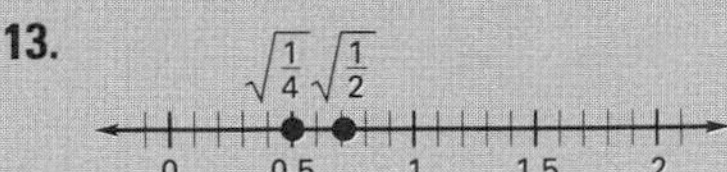

25. 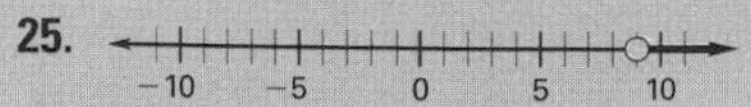

26. 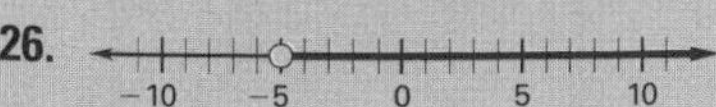

27. 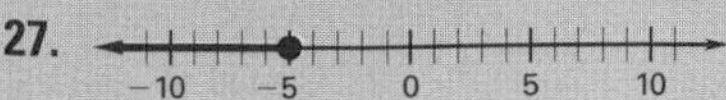

28. −10 −5 0 5 10

9.5 THE DISTANCE AND MIDPOINT FORMULAS

Examples on pp. 470–471

EXAMPLES **Find the distance between (−3, 4) and (−5, 8). Find the midpoint of the segment that connects the two points.**

Let (x_1, y_1) be $(-3, 4)$ and (x_2, y_2) be $(-5, 8)$.

Distance $= \sqrt{(x_2 - x_1)^2 + (y_2 - y_1)^2}$

$= \sqrt{(-5 - (-3))^2 + (8 - 4)^2}$

$= \sqrt{(-2)^2 + (4)^2}$

$= \sqrt{20} \approx 4.47$

Midpoint $= \left(\frac{x_1 + x_2}{2}, \frac{y_1 + y_2}{2}\right)$

$= \left(\frac{-3 - 5}{2}, \frac{4 + 8}{2}\right)$

$= (-4, 6)$

Find the length and the midpoint of $\overline{AB}$ given the coordinates of A and B. Round your answer to the nearest tenth.

22. $A(5, 7)$ and $B(8, 12)$ **5.8; (6.5, 9.5)**

23. $A(-2, 0)$ and $B(1, 9)$ **9.5; (−0.5, 4.5)**

24. $A(1, -7)$ and $B(-5, -6)$ **6.1; (−2, −6.5)**

9.6 SOLVING INEQUALITIES USING ADDITION OR SUBTRACTION

Examples on pp. 476–477

EXAMPLE **Solve the inequality $n - 7 \ge -9$. Then graph the solution.**

$n - 7 \ge -9$ **Write original inequality.**

$n \ge -2$ **Add 7 to each side.**

To graph $n \ge -2$, draw a closed circle at -2 and shade the number line to the right of -2.

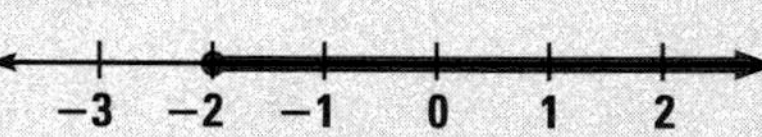

Solve the inequality. Then graph the solution. **See margin for graphs.**

25. $6 < x - 3$ **$x > 9$**

26. $a + 3 > -2$ **$a > -5$**

27. $4 + b \le -1$ **$b \le -5$**

28. $x - 1 \ge -5$ **$x \ge -4$**

9.7 SOLVING INEQUALITIES USING MULTIPLICATION OR DIVISION

Examples on pp. 480–481

EXAMPLE **Solve the inequality $-12x < 84$.**

$-12x < 84$ **Write original inequality.**

$x > -7$ **Divide each side by −12. Reverse the inequality.**

In Exercises 29–32, solve the inequality. Then graph the solution. **See margin for graphs.**

29. $-4x \geq 16$ $x \leq -4$ **30.** $10 < -5x$ $x < -2$ **31.** $\frac{x}{2} > -3$ $x > -6$ **32.** $-\frac{1}{4}x \leq \frac{3}{8}$ $x \geq -\frac{3}{2}$

33. You have $8.05 left on a calling card. Write and solve an inequality to find how long you can talk if you are making a long distance call that costs $.08 per minute. **$0.08x < 8.05$. You can talk up to about 100.6 min.**

9.8 SOLVING TWO-STEP INEQUALITIES

Examples on pp. 484–485

EXAMPLE **Solve the inequality $6x - 7 \leq 23$.**

$6x - 7 \leq 23$	Write original inequality.
$6x \leq 30$	Add 7 to each side.
$x \leq 5$	Divide each sides by 6.

In Exercises 34–37, solve the inequality. Then graph the solution. **See margin for graphs.**

34. $-4x - 5 \geq 3$ $x \leq -2$ **35.** $13 < 2z - 9$ $z > 11$ **36.** $4x + 7 \leq 2x + 4$ $x \leq -\frac{3}{2}$ **37.** $5 + 8(x - 2) > 3$ $x > \frac{7}{4}$

38. BACKPACKING On your backpacking trip, you are taking an emergency food supply that you don't want to weigh more than 1.5 pounds. Of this, 5 ounces will be a trail mix. The rest will be high energy nutrition bars that weigh 2.2 ounces each. Write and solve an inequality to find possible numbers of energy bars you can take. **$5 + 2.2n \leq 24$. You can take 8 or fewer energy bars.**

9.9 BOX-AND-WHISKER PLOTS

Examples on pp. 489–490

EXAMPLE **Draw a box-and-whisker plot of the data: 23, 84, 53, 63, 75, 29, 19, 38, 47, 57**

19, 23, 29, 38, 47, 53, 57, 63, 75, 84 — List numbers in increasing order.

The minimum is 19. The maximum is 84.

The median is $\frac{47 + 53}{2} = 50$.

The lower quartile is 29. The upper quartile is 63.

Draw a box-and-whisker plot of the data.

39. 25, 27, 5, 8, 9, 12, 16, 18, 21, 22, 14, 11 **See margin.**

40. 35, 67, 95, 100, 47, 82, 50, 0, 89, 71, 16, 47, 63, 33, 80, 55, 40, 77, 60 **See margin.**

29. 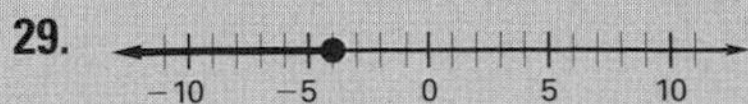

30. 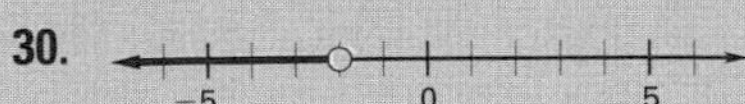

31. 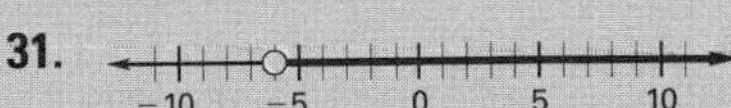

32. 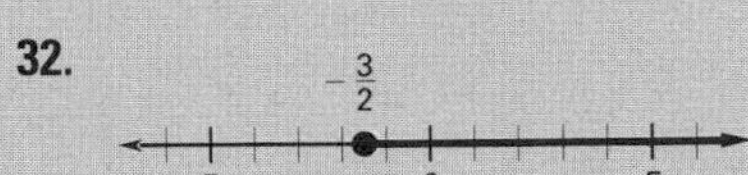

34. 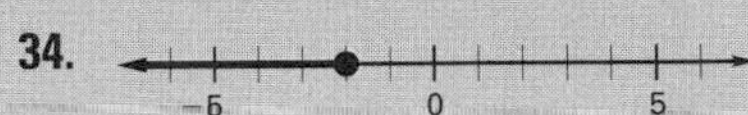

35. 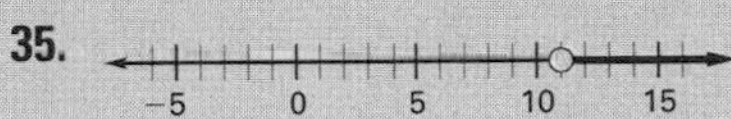

36. 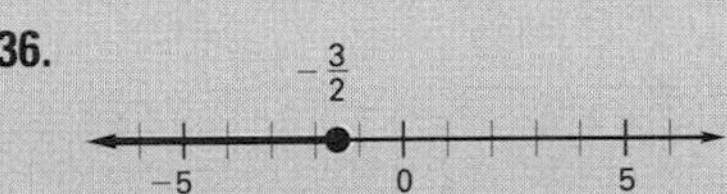

37. 

39. 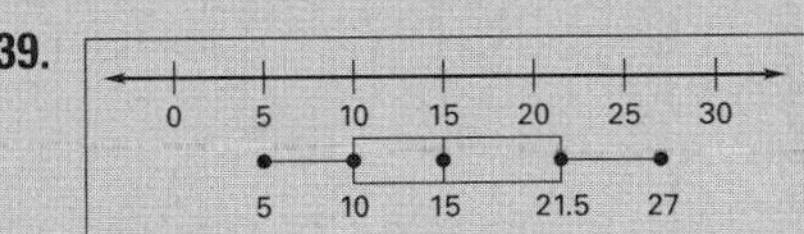

40. 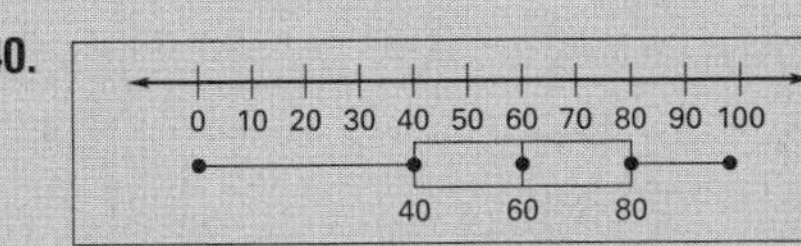

Additional Resources

Assessment Book

- Formal Assessment, pp. 132–140
- Alternative Assessment, pp. 193–207

Test and Practice Generator

18. 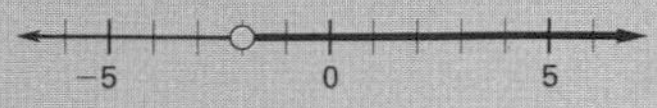

19. 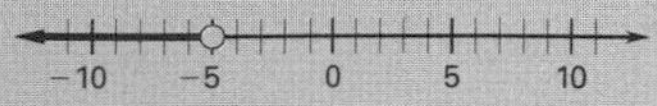

20. 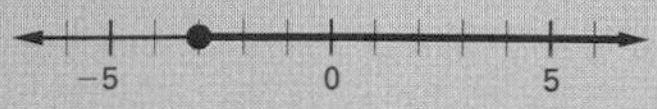

21. 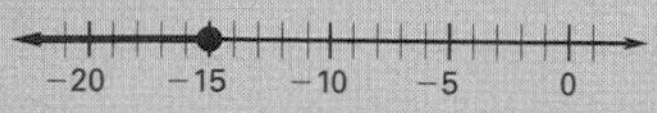

22. 

23. 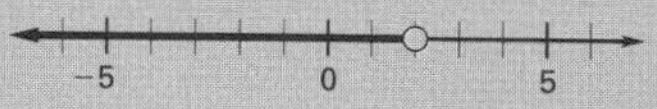

25. 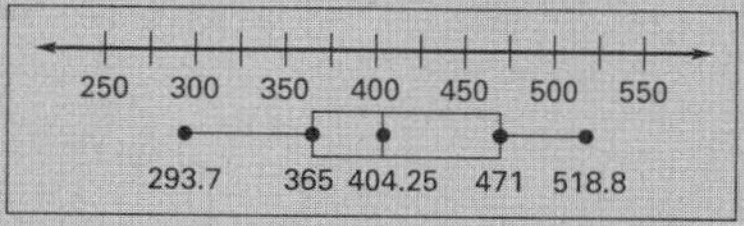

Chapter 9 Chapter Test

Write the two square roots of the number. If necessary, approximate the square roots to the nearest tenth without using a calculator.

1. 225 **15, –15** **2.** 48 **6.9, –6.9** **3.** 0.16 **0.4, –0.4** **4.** $\frac{25}{49}$ $\frac{5}{7}$, $-\frac{5}{7}$

Match each number with a point on the number line.

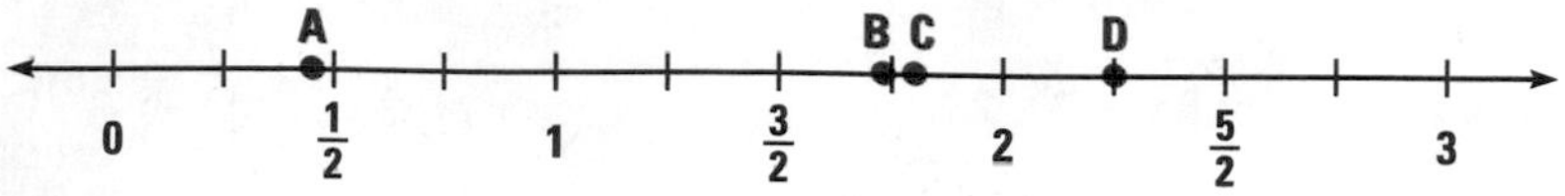

5. $\frac{9}{5}$ **C** **6.** $\frac{9}{4}$ **D** **7.** $\sqrt{3}$ **B** **8.** $\sqrt{0.2}$ **A**

Use the Pythagorean theorem to solve the right triangle.

9. 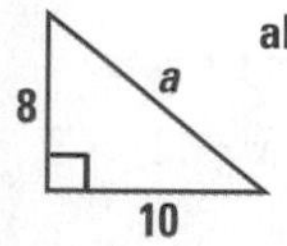

about 12.8

10. 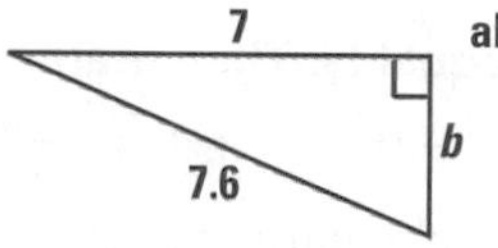

about 3

11. 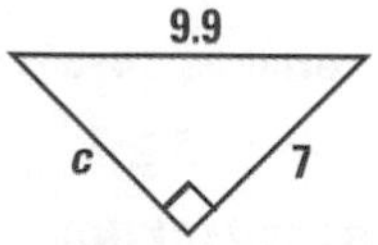

about 7

GARDENING **You are laying out a frame for a triangular garden. If your frame has the side lengths given, tell whether it is a right triangle.**

12. 3 m, 3 m, 4 m **no** **13.** 10.5 ft, 14 ft, 17.5 ft **yes** **14.** 2.5 yd, 3.5 yd, 4.5 yd **no**

Find the length and the midpoint of $\overline{AB}$ given the coordinates of *A* and *B*. Round your answer to the nearest tenth.

15. $A(-3, -2)$ and $B(5, 6)$ **11.3; (1, 2)** **16.** $A(1, 5)$ and $B(8, 0)$ **8.6; (4.5, 2.5)** **17.** $A(4, -9)$ and $B(-1, -7)$ **5.4; (1.5, –8)**

Solve the inequality. Then graph the solution. **See margin for graphs.**

18. $-x < 2$ **$x > -2$** **19.** $-16 > y - 11$ **$y < -5$** **20.** $-8r - 16 \le 8$ **$r \ge -3$**

21. $-\frac{1}{3}p \ge 5$ **$p \le -15$** **22.** $14 - \frac{3}{2}w > 5$ **$w < 6$** **23.** $5(x - 2) < 3x - 6$ **$x < 2$**

In Exercises 24 and 25, use the table below, which shows the numbers of recreational vehicles (RVs) in thousands from 1989 to 1996.

Year	1989	1990	1991	1992	1993	1994	1995	1996
RVs	388.3	347.3	293.7	382.7	420.2	518.8	475.2	466.8

24. Find the median and the lower and upper quartiles of the data. **median = 404.25, lower quartile = 365, upper quartile = 471**

25. Draw a box-and-whisker plot of the data. **See margin.**

Multiple-Choice Practice

Test Tip You can make notes, sketches, or graphs in your test booklet to help you solve problems, but you must keep your answer sheet neat.

1. A square sandbox has an area of 16 square feet. How long is each side? **B**

Ⓐ 4 ft^2 Ⓑ 4 ft

Ⓒ 8 ft Ⓓ 16 ft

2. Which statement about the number 1.69 is false? **H**

Ⓕ The number is rational.

Ⓖ The number is real.

Ⓗ The number is an integer.

Ⓙ The number is terminating.

3. What is the length of the unknown side of the triangle? **C**

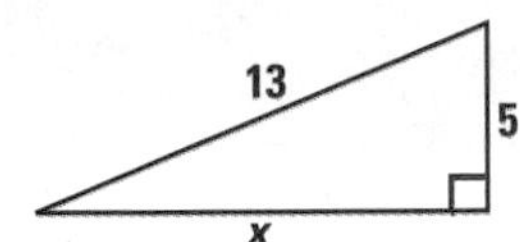

Ⓐ 4 Ⓑ 8

Ⓒ 12 Ⓓ 14

4. A triangle has sides of length 8, 14, and 16. Which statement about the triangle is true? **H**

Ⓕ It is right. Ⓖ It is obtuse.

Ⓗ It is acute. Ⓙ It is isosceles.

5. If you graph $(-1, 2)$ and $(3, -4)$ in a coordinate plane, about how far apart will the two points be? **D**

Ⓐ 4 units Ⓑ 4.5 units

Ⓒ 6.3 units Ⓓ 7.2 units

6. What is the midpoint of the segment connecting $(-2, 5)$ and $(3, -4)$? **J**

Ⓕ (1.5, –0.5) Ⓖ (–0.5, 0.5)

Ⓗ (0.5, –0.5) Ⓙ (0.5, 0.5)

7. Which statement correctly describes the graph? **D**

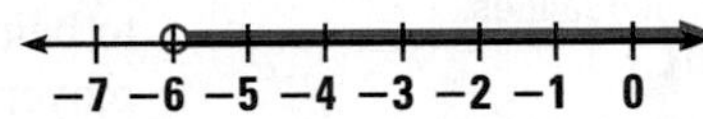

Ⓐ x is at least -6.

Ⓑ x is less than -6.

Ⓒ x is no more than -6.

Ⓓ x is greater than -6.

8. At a fair, you play a game to win a giant stuffed animal. You have \$5.50. Each game costs \$.50. Which inequality can you use to find how many games you can play? **H**

Ⓕ $0.5x > 5.5$ Ⓖ $5.5x \geq 0.5$

Ⓗ $0.5x \leq 5.5$ Ⓙ $5.5x < 0.5$

9. What is the solution of the inequality? **B**

$-3x + 3 \geq 9$

Ⓐ $x \geq -2$ Ⓑ $x \leq -2$

Ⓒ $x \geq -4$ Ⓓ $x \leq -4$

10. What is the interquartile range of the data?

0, 3, 4, 4, 6, 7, 9, 13, 15, 18 **H**

Ⓕ 6.5 Ⓖ 8

Ⓗ 9 Ⓙ 18

Teaching Tip

The Brain Games activity provides a motivating way to review selected content in the chapter. For a more comprehensive review, see the Chapter Summary and Review on pp. 494–497.

Brain games

California Standards

- Understand the Pythagorean theorem and its converse. (MG 3.3)
- Differentiate between rational and irrational numbers. (NS 1.4)
- Solve two-step linear inequalities. (AF 4.1)
- Estimate quantities and solve for them. (MR 2.3)

Spaghetti Triangles

Materials

- **Uncooked spaghetti**
- **Ruler**

Directions

Object of the Game

Play in pairs. Each player tries to form a right triangle using pieces of spaghetti. The player whose hypotenuse is the closest to being the correct length earns a point. The winner is the player with the most points after a fixed number of rounds.

How to Play

STEP 1 Each player takes a piece of spaghetti, breaks it into 3 pieces, and uses 2 pieces to form the legs of a right triangle.

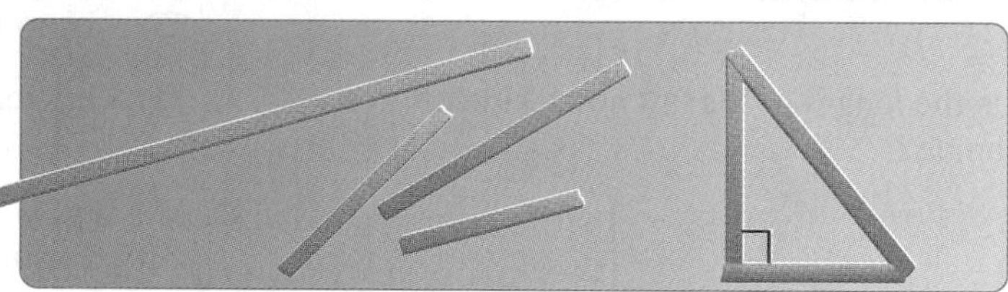

STEP 2 Each player uses the third piece as the hypotenuse and then uses the Pythagorean theorem to find what the length of the hypotenuse should be. Each player compares the calculated length with the actual length of the spaghetti.

Another Way to Play

Use the longest piece of spaghetti as the hypotenuse and one other piece as a leg. See how close the third piece comes to being the correct length for the other leg.

Brain Teaser Answer: $\sqrt{a}$, **where** a **is rational and** $4 < a < 6.25$

Brain Teaser

What number am I ?

An irrational number unless I am squared.

2 ? 3

On the number line between 2 and 3

A solution of the inequality

$2x - 4 < 1$

California Standards and Assessment

CA Standards: NS 1.4, MG 3.3, AF 4.1, MR 2.3

The basic skills you'll review on this page will help prepare you for the next chapter.

Reviewing the Basics

EXAMPLE 1 Finding the Area of a Polygon

Find the area of the trapezoid.

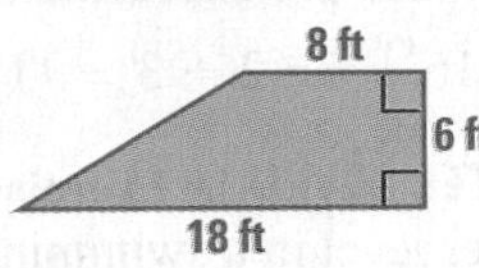

Solution

$$\text{Area} = \frac{1}{2}(b_1 + b_2)h$$ Write area formula.

$$= \frac{1}{2}(18 + 8)(6)$$ Substitute 18 for b_1, 8 for b_2, and 6 for h.

$$= 78 \text{ ft}^2$$ Simplify.

Try These

Find the area of the polygon.

1. 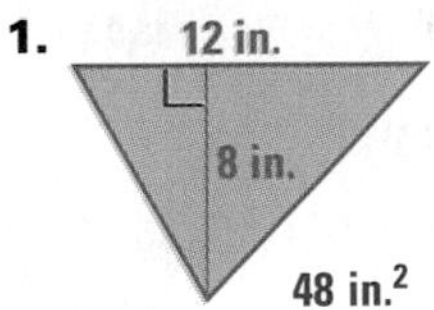

48 in.^{2}

2. 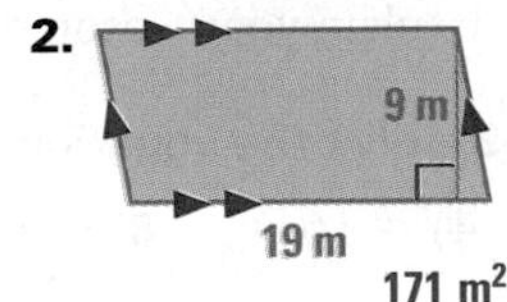

171 m^2

3. 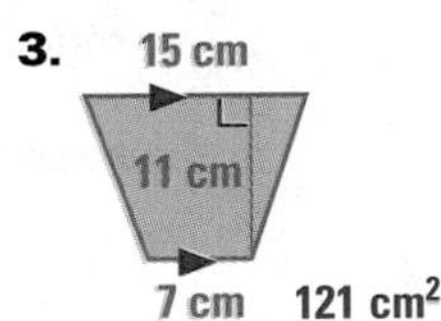

121 cm^2

EXAMPLE 2 Solving Proportions

Solve the proportion $\frac{2}{3} = \frac{x}{15}$.

Solution

$$\frac{2}{3} = \frac{x}{15}$$ Write original proportion.

$$3 \cdot x = 2 \cdot 15$$ Cross products property

$$\frac{3 \cdot x}{\mathbf{3}} = \frac{2 \cdot 15}{\mathbf{3}}$$ Divide each side by 3.

$$x = 10$$ Simplify. x is by itself.

Try These

Solve the proportion.

4. $\frac{14}{x} = \frac{28}{12}$ 6 **5.** $\frac{y}{20} = \frac{3}{10}$ 6 **6.** $\frac{4.2}{3} = \frac{t}{10}$ 14

7. $\frac{s}{18} = \frac{3.5}{9}$ 7 **8.** $\frac{6}{1.2} = \frac{5}{z}$ 1 **9.** $\frac{12}{15} = \frac{24}{x}$ 30

10. $\frac{5}{7} = \frac{p}{15.4}$ 11 **11.** $\frac{6.4}{m} = \frac{8}{5}$ 4 **12.** $\frac{11}{5.5} = \frac{k}{11}$ 22

Student Help

▶ MORE EXAMPLES

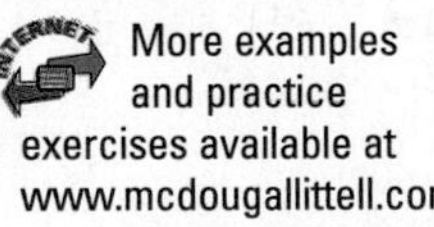
More examples and practice exercises available at www.mcdougallittell.com

Additional Resources

Technology
- Personal Student Tutor
- Test and Practice Generator

Additional Resources

A Cumulative Test for Chapters 1–9 is available in the *Assessment Book*, pp. 141–144.

4.

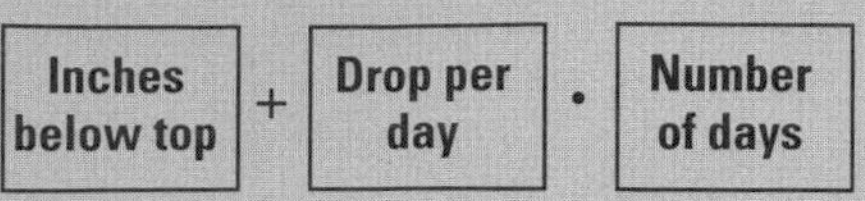

Inches below the top = 12 (in.)
Drop per day = 0.75 (in./day)
Number of days = d (days)
Total inches below the top = 21 (in.)

Chapters 1-9 Cumulative Practice

Evaluate the expression. (1.4)

1. $16 + 6 \cdot 2 \div 3 - 11$ **9** **2.** $4 \cdot (14 - 9)^2 \div 10$ **10** **3.** $11 - 6^2 \div 9 \cdot 2$ **3**

WATER LEVEL In Exercises 4 and 5, use the following information. The water level in a swimming pool has been dropping 0.75 inches per day. The first time you check it, the level is 12 inches below the top. (2.7)

4. Write a verbal model to find how long it will take the water to reach a level of 21 inches below the top if no water is added. Assign labels to each part of the verbal model. **See margin.**

5. Write and solve an algebraic model using the verbal model and labels from Exercise 4. **$12 + .75d = 21$; 12 days**

6. Decide whether the distance a person drives and the amount of fuel she will need has a *positive correlation*, a *negative correlation*, or *no obvious correlation*. Explain your reasoning. (3.9) **Positive correlation. The more a person drives, the more fuel is used.**

In Exercises 7–9, solve the equation. (4.4, 4.5)

7. $3n - 5(n - 4) = 16$ **2** **8.** $-(x - 5) = 6(x + 2)$ **−1** **9.** $-7z = 5 - 3(z + 2)$ $\frac{1}{4}$

10. Find the mean, median, and mode(s) of the data, which are peak wind gusts (in miles per hour) for a two-week period. (4.8) **mean 19.9, median 19.5, mode 22**

11, 18, 9, 21, 39, 16, 22, 10, 8, 31, 27, 22, 30, 15

In Exercises 11–14, write the prime factorization of the number. Use exponents for repeated factors. (5.1)

11. 83 **83** **12.** 210 **$2 \cdot 3 \cdot 5 \cdot 7$** **13.** 144 **$2^4 \cdot 3^2$** **14.** 600 **$2^3 \cdot 3 \cdot 5^2$**

15. The spinner at the right is divided into 15 equal sections. Determine what portion of the spinner is shaded green. Express your answer as a percent and as a decimal. (5.6, 5.7) **40%, 0.4**

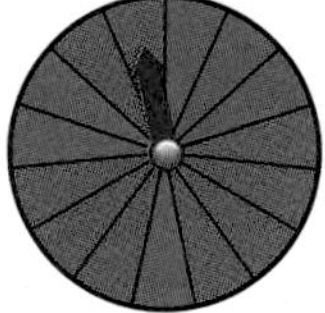

Write the perimeter and the area of the rectangle or square. (6.1–6.3)

16. Rectangle: $5\frac{5}{6}$ ft by $4\frac{1}{9}$ ft. **$19\frac{8}{9}$ ft, $23\frac{53}{54}$ ft^2**

17. Square: $6\frac{7}{8}$ in. by $6\frac{7}{8}$ in. **$27\frac{1}{2}$ in., $47\frac{17}{64}$ in.^{2}**

18. Rectangle: 10 m by $3\frac{1}{2}$ m. **27 m, 35 m^2**

Multiply or divide. Then simplify if possible. (6.3, 6.5)

19. $\frac{5}{12} \cdot \frac{10}{3}$ $\frac{25}{18}$ **20.** $\frac{5}{2} \div \frac{1}{5}$ $\frac{25}{2}$ **21.** $\frac{7n}{4} \cdot 16$ **$28n$** **22.** $-\frac{6}{10} \div \frac{z}{5}$ $-\frac{3}{z}$

23. PROPERTY TAX If \$2100 is the property tax for a house worth \$105,000, find the property tax for a house worth \$140,000. (7.2) **\$2800**

Use a proportion to answer the question. (7.5)

24. 63 is what percent of 90? **70%**

25. What is 85% of 40? **34**

26. What is 62.5% of 320? **200**

27. 105 is 150% of what number? **70**

In Exercises 28–30, find the percent of change. (7.7)

28. Before: 207,100 units
After: 215,025 units **increase, 3.8%**

29. Before: \$39.99
After: \$25.99 **decrease, 35%**

30. Before: 750 students
After: 1275 students **increase, 70%**

31. COMPOUND INTEREST A credit union offers a 2 year certificate of deposit with an annual interest rate of 12.5% on deposits of \$3500 or more. What is the balance on a \$3500 deposit after 2 years if the interest is compounded monthly? (7.9) **\$4488.28**

Tell whether the statement is *true* or *false*. Explain. (8.1–8.3)

32. The endpoint of a ray is always the second point in the ray's name. **False**

33. An angle supplementary to an obtuse angle is sometimes a right angle. **False**

34. An angle complementary to an acute angle is always acute. **True**

35. Vertical angles cannot be supplementary. **False**

In Exercises 36–38, copy the diagram on a piece of grid paper. (8.7, 8.8)

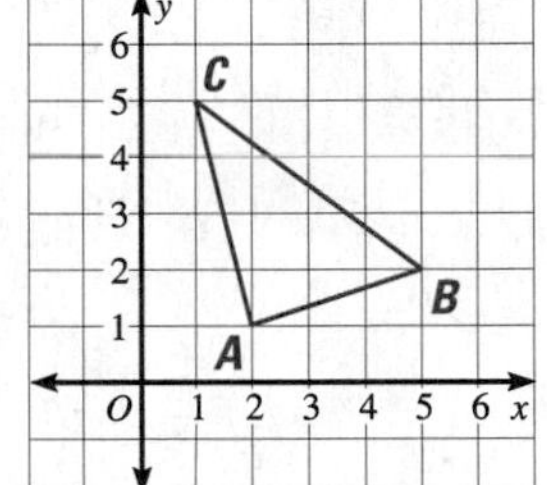

36. Draw the image of $\triangle ABC$ after being reflected in the x-axis. What are the coordinates of the vertices of the image?
$A' = (2, -1)$, $B' = (5, -2)$, $C' = (1, -5)$; See margin.

37. Draw the image of $\triangle ABC$ after the reflection $(x, y) \rightarrow (-x, y)$. What are the coordinates of the vertices of the image? **$A' = (-2, 1)$, $B' = (-5, 2)$, $C' = (-1, 5)$; See margin.**

38. Draw the image of $\triangle ABC$ after being translated 4 units to the right and 2 units down. Use coordinate notation to describe the translation. **$(x, y) \rightarrow (x + 4, y - 2)$; See margin.**

Use the Pythagorean theorem to solve the right triangle. (9.3)

39. 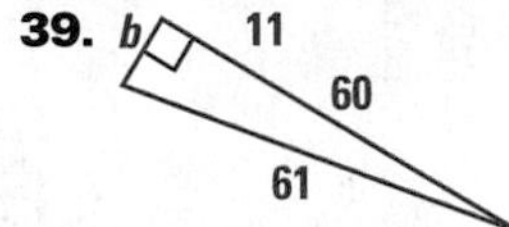

40. 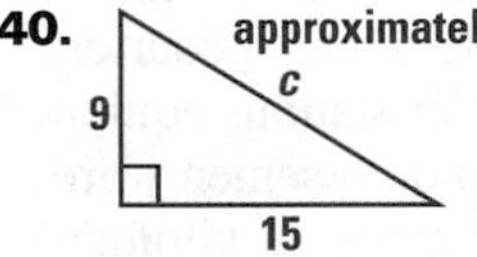

approximately 17.5

41. 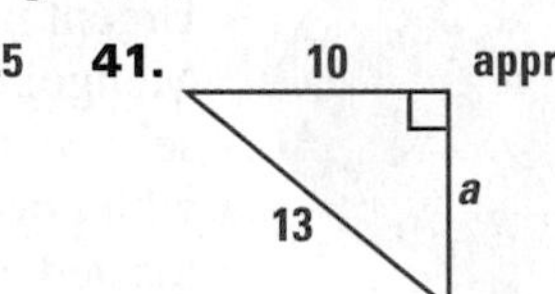

approximately 8.3

Find the distance between the points. Then find the midpoint of the segment that connects the points. (9.5)

42. (0, 0) and (1, 4) **4.1, (0.5, 2)**

43. $(-1, 5)$ and $(3, -1)$ **7.2, (1, 2)**

44. (0, 4) and $(-1, -3)$ **7.1, (−0.5, 0.5)**

Solve the inequality. Then graph the solution. (9.6 – 9.8) **See margin for graphs.**

45. $a + 12 < 7$ **$a < -5$**

46. $2b - 19 \geq -15$ **$b \geq 2$**

47. $-4 \leq 5 - 6m$ **$m \leq \frac{3}{2}$**

48. $\frac{n}{8} > \frac{2}{3}$ **$n > \frac{16}{3}$**

36.

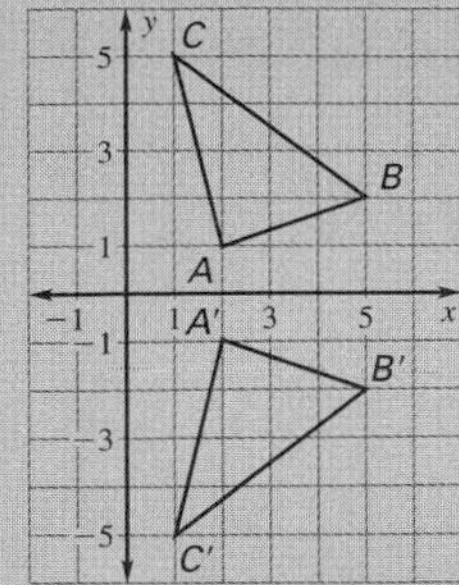

37.

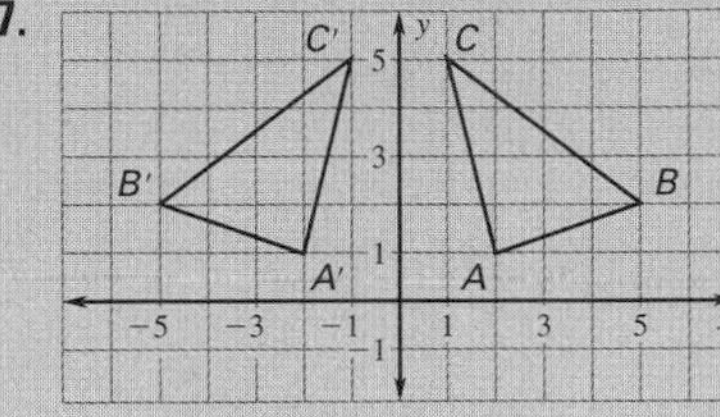

38.

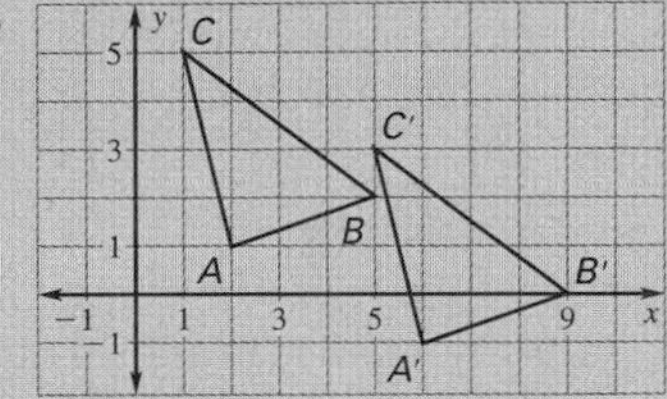

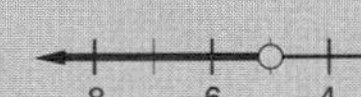

45.

46.

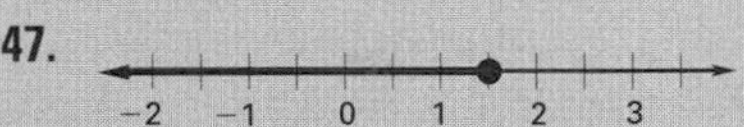

47.

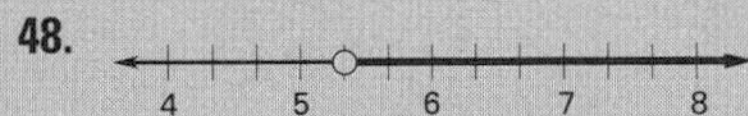

48.

4 5 6 7 8

Project Overview

Mathematical Goals

- Estimate areas of irregular figures, and compare them as percents.
- Use scale factors to find distances.
- Solve rate problems.

Managing the Project

Classroom Management
Students can work individually or in small groups. If working in groups, they should decide together how to estimate the areas. Part of the group could work on one of the areas, while the rest of the group works on the other area. They should then check each others' work. All group members should work together to answer questions 3–7.

Group members should work together to create an outline for the report. They should collaborate on writing the draft and the final report.

Guiding Students' Work
Students may need suggestions on the best way to estimate the areas of the empires. Point to the illustrations beside the "Present Your Results" header and remind them that they know formulas for calculating areas of rectangles and triangles. You may wish to ask them why the illustrations do not show a larger rectangle or triangle.

If students have difficulty determining the time it takes for a message to travel from one city to another, remind them of the formula distance = rate × time.

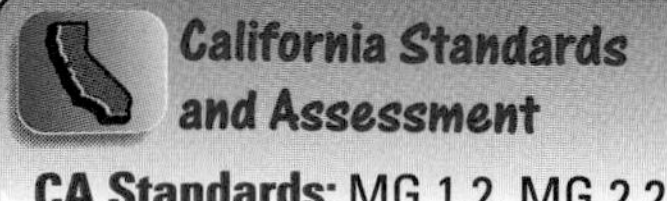

CA Standards: MG 1.2, MG 2.2, MR 1.3

Chapters 7-9 Project

California Standards

- ▶ Construct and read drawings and models made to scale. (MG 1.2)
- ▶ Determine when and how to break a problem into simpler parts. (MR 1.3)
- ▶ Estimate the areas of complex figures. (MG 2.2)

Materials

- Metric ruler
- Calculator

Comparing Ancient Empires

OBJECTIVE To compare the areas and communication systems of the Mongol and Inca empires.

INVESTIGATION

In Exercises 1–7, use the maps below.

1. Estimate the area of the Mongol empire. Explain the method you used. ***Sample answer:* 27,000,000 km²**
2. Estimate the area of the Inca empire. Explain the method you used. ***Sample answer:* 2,200,000 km²**
3. Compare the areas of the empires. Which was larger? Write the area of the smaller empire as a percent of the area of the larger empire. **Mongol Empire; *Sample answer:* about 8%**

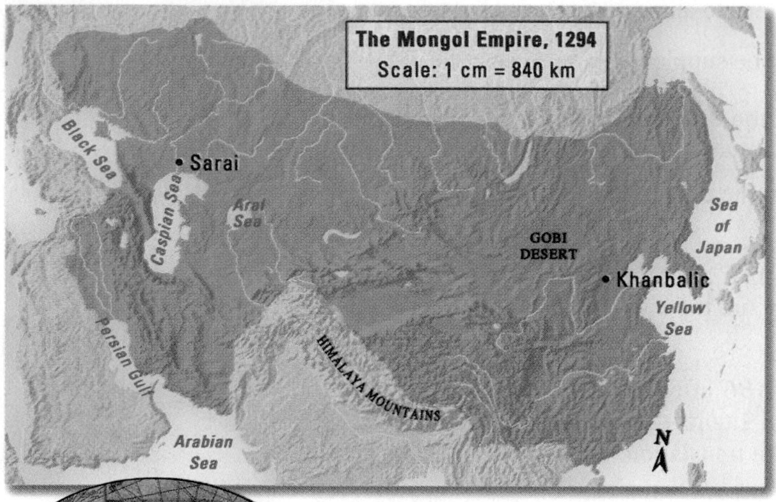

The Inca Empire, 1532
Scale: 1 cm = 410 km
Inca roads
Cuzco
Pacific Ocean
N

Merchants traveling through the Mongol empire.

Urgent messages traveled through the Mongol empire using a courier service. Courier stations equipped with horses and horsemen were located about every 40 kilometers. One horseman would ride to the next courier station and pass the message to another horseman. The process continued until the message reached its destination. With this method, a message traveled about 320 kilometers per day.

4. Estimate the straight-line distance from the capitol, Khanbalic, to Sarai. ***Sample answer:* about 5540 km**
5. About how long did it take a message to go from Khanbalic to Sarai? ***Sample answer:* about $17\frac{1}{3}$ days**

The Incas did not have horses. Urgent messages were delivered by runners. Messenger huts were about 1.6 kilometers apart. One messenger, or *chasquis,* would run to the next hut and give the message to the next messenger. The process continued until the destination was reached. With this method, a message traveled about 240 kilometers per day.

6. Estimate the distance from the capital city, Cuzco, to the southern edge of the Inca empire along the Inca roads.
Sample answer: **about 2670 km**

7. Estimate the number of days it took for a message to travel from Cuzco to the southern edge of the Inca empire.
Sample answer: **about 11 days**

PRESENT YOUR RESULTS

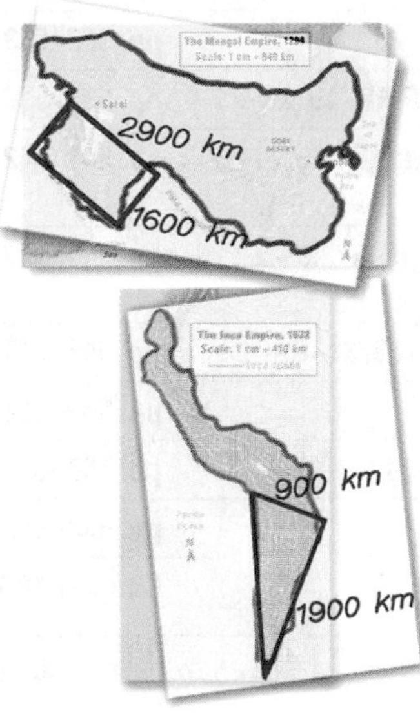

Which empire do you think had a more effective communication system? Write a report to support your answer.

- Discuss the location of the capital city relative to other cities in the empire.
- Discuss the area of each empire. How did the size of the empire affect the communication?
- Consider the method of communication.
- Include your answers to Exercises 1–7.

EXTENSION

Materials
- Map of the United States

In 1860 in the United States, mail could travel about 320 kilometers a day by Pony Express.

8. Find a map of the United States. Estimate the distance in kilometers from St. Joseph, Missouri, to Sacramento. If necessary, use the conversion 1 mile ≈ 1.6 kilometers. ***Sample answer:*** **about 3200 km**

9. How long would it take a message to be delivered by Pony Express from St. Joseph, Missouri, to Sacramento? ***Sample answer:*** **about 10 days**

10. How did the Pony Express compare with the communication systems in the Inca and Mongol empires? ***Sample answer:*** **It was almost twice as fast as Inca messengers and slightly faster than the Mongol couriers.**

Concluding the Project
Students should present their reports to the class by having group members report separately on different parts of the project. One member may show how the group estimated the area, while other members discuss the answers to the questions and the other components of the report. You can use questions like these for class discussion:
- Do you think that using many small rectangles and triangles would give you a better estimate of the area?
- Do you think grid paper would help with your area estimate?

Grading the Project

A well-written project will have the following characteristics:
- Complete and correct solutions to Exercises 1–7.
- A thorough and well-written report which addresses the key points affecting the communication within the empire.
- A clear description and diagrams illustrating the method of estimating the areas of the empires.
- An extension to the project in which students present their ideas clearly.

Pacing and Assignment Guide

Regular Schedule

Lesson	Les. Day	Transitional	Average	Advanced
10.1	Day 1	pp. 514–515 Exs. 6–11, 18–20	pp. 514–515 Exs. 6–11, 18–21, 29*	pp. 514–515 Exs. 6–11, 18–21, 29–31*
	Day 2	pp. 514–515 Exs. 12–13, 15–16, 22–27, 32–34	pp. 514–515 Exs. 12–17, 22–28, 32–34	pp. 514–515 Exs. 12–17, 22–28, 32–34
10.2	Day 1	pp. 520–521 Exs. 9–12, 14–15, 21–22	pp. 520–521 Exs. 9–16, 21–22	pp. 520–521 Exs. 9–16, 21–22
	Day 2	pp. 520–521 Exs. 17–20, 23–31, 37–38	pp. 520–521 Exs. 17–20, 23–34, 37–38	pp. 520–521 Exs. 17–20, 23–34, 35*, 36–38; EC: TE p. 506D*
10.3	Day 1	pp. 526–527 Exs. 7–12, 25–32	pp. 526–527 Exs. 7–12, 25–35	pp. 526–527 Exs. 7–12, 25–35
	Day 2	pp. 526–527 Exs. 13–16, 20–24	pp. 526–527 Exs. 13–17, 20–24	pp. 526–527 Exs. 13–17, 19*, 20–24
10.4	Day 1	pp. 532–533 Exs. 8–13, 20–21	pp. 532–533 Exs. 8–13, 20–21, 23–25	pp. 532–533 Exs. 8–13, 20–25
	Day 2	pp. 532–533 Exs. 15–18, 27–28	pp. 532–533 Exs. 14–19, 22, 27–28	pp. 532–533 Exs. 14–19, 26*, 27–28
10.5	Day 1	pp. 537–538 Exs. 7–8, 11–16, 18–19, 23–25	pp. 537–538 Exs. 8–11, 13–16, 18–19, 23–25	pp. 537–538 Exs. 8–11, 16–19, 20*, 21–25
10.6	Day 1	pp. 541–542 Exs. 11–12, 14–15, 18–19, 21–22, 26–27	pp. 541–542 Exs. 12–13, 15–22, 26–27	pp. 541–542 Exs. 12–15, 19–23, 24*, 25–27
10.7	Day 1	pp. 545–547 Exs. 5–6, 8–9, 15–17, 20–21, 40–43	pp. 545–547 Exs. 5–10, 15–17, 20–22, 40–43	pp. 545–547 Exs. 6–9, 15–17, 20–22, 40–43
	Day 2	pp. 545–547 Exs. 11–14, 23–25, 31–39	pp. 545–547 Exs. 11–14, 23–25, 30–39	pp. 545–547 Exs. 11–14, 26–28, 29*, 30–39
10.8	Day 1	pp. 550–551 Exs. 7–8, 11–17	pp. 550–551 Exs. 7–8, 11–17	pp. 550–551 Exs. 7–8, 11–17
	Day 2	pp. 550–551 Exs. 9–10, 18–20, 22–23	pp. 550–551 Exs. 9–10, 18–20, 22–23	pp. 550–551 Exs. 9–10, 18–20, 21*, 22–23
Review	Day 1	pp. 552–555 Exs. 1–25	pp. 552–555 Exs. 1–25	pp. 552–555 Exs. 1–25
Assess	Day 1	Chapter 10 Test	Chapter 10 Test	Chapter 10 Test

Yearly Pacing *Chapter 10 Total* – 16 days *Chapters 1–10 Total* – 136 days *Remaining* – 24 days

* Challenge Exercises EP = Extra Practice SRH = Skills Review Handbook EC = Extra Challenge

Block Schedule

Day 1	Day 2	Day 3	Day 4	Day 5	Day 6	Day 7	Day 8
10.1 pp. 514–515: Exs. 6–28, 29*, 32–34	**10.2** pp. 520–521: Exs. 9–34, 37–38	**10.3** pp. 526–527: Exs. 7–17, 20–35	**10.4** pp. 532–533: Exs. 8–25, 27–28	**10.5** pp. 537–538: Exs. 8–11, 13–16, 18–19, 23–25 **10.6** pp. 541–542: Exs. 12–13, 15–22, 26–27	**10.7** pp. 545–547: Exs. 5–17, 20–25, 30–43	**10.8** pp. 550–551: Exs. 7–20, 22–23	**Review** pp. 552–555: Exs. 1–25 **Assess** Chapter 10 Test

Yearly Pacing *Chapter 10 Total* – 8 days *Chapters 1–10 Total* – 68 days *Remaining* – 12 days

Support Materials

Chapter Resource Book

LESSON SUPPORT	10.1	10.2	10.3	10.4	10.5	10.6	10.7	10.8
Lesson Plans	p. 1	p. 10	p. 19	p. 28	p. 37	p. 46	p. 55	p. 64
Lesson Plans for Block Scheduling	p. 2	p. 11	p. 20	p. 29	p. 38	p. 47	p. 56	p. 65
Warm-Ups with Multiple-Choice Practice	p. 3	p. 12	p. 21	p. 30	p. 39	p. 48	p. 57	p. 66
Problem of the Day	p. 4	p. 13	p. 22	p. 31	p. 40	p. 49	p. 58	p. 67
Daily Cumulative Review	p. 5	p. 14	p. 23	p. 32	p. 41	p. 50	p. 59	p. 68
Practice Masters	p. 6	p. 15	p. 24	p. 33	p. 42	p. 51	p. 60	p. 69
Reteaching Masters	p. 7	p. 16	p. 25	p. 34	p. 43	p. 52	p. 61	p. 70
Enrichment Masters	p. 9	p. 18	p. 27	p. 36	p. 45	p. 54	p. 63	p. 72

Transparencies

	10.1	10.2	10.3	10.4	10.5	10.6	10.7	10.8
Warm-Ups with Multiple-Choice Practice	p. 78	p. 79	p. 80	p. 81	p. 82	p. 83	p. 84	p. 85
Teacher Time-Saver Transparencies	✓	✓	✓	✓	✓	✓	✓	✓
English/Spanish Problem Solving	p. 45		p. 46			p. 47		p. 48
Answer Transparencies	✓	✓	✓	✓	✓	✓	✓	✓

Technology

- Personal Student Tutor
- Time-Saving Test and Practice Generator
- Electronic Teacher Tools
- Technology: Using Calculators and Computers

Additional Resources

- Math Log
- Assessment Book
- Worked-Out Solution Key
- Practice Workbook (English/Spanish)
- Home and School Connection
- California Standards: Key Concepts Book

Correlation to the California Curriculum

Correlations to the California Standards
CA Standards: MG 1.1, MG 2.1, MG 2.2, MG 2.3, MG 2.4, MG 3.1, MG 3.5, MG 3.6, MR 1.1, MR 2.5, MR 3.2, MR 3.3

California Curriculum Support

Key Concepts Book

- Pre-Course Review: Topic 1 Working with Decimals
  Topic 5 Measurement
- Key Standards: MG 3.6 Classifying Lines in Space *(Lesson 10.2)*
  MG 3.6 Exploring Solids *(Lessons 10.2, 10.6, 10.7)*

California Standards Practice Workbook provides practice for each Standard that is covered in this chapter.

Strategies for Strategic Learners

USE A GRAPHIC ORGANIZER

It is easy at this stage for students to confuse *true* and *equal*. It might help students to draw a grid like this on the board, and to put examples in each box:

	True	Not True
Equal	$a = a$	$2 = 4$
Unequal	$2 \neq 3$	$2 \neq 1 + 1$

Have students generate their own examples, until they can see that a statement might be an equation or an inequality, and that the statements might be true or false.

FOCUS ON KEY CONCEPTS

A key concept in mathematics is the idea of inverse operations. Inverse operations "undo" each other. For example, addition and subtraction are inverse operations, as are multiplication and division. Squaring a number and finding the positive square root of a number are inverse operations. Multiplication and factoring of polynomials can be thought of as inverse operations. Sometimes one of the two operations is more difficult for students than the other is. Squaring a number, for example, is simply multiplying the number by itself. But finding a square root involves some thought, and some choices. If we want to find the square root of 169, for example (without a calculator), we might work forwards and backwards from numbers we know. If we know that 10×10 equals 100, then we know that the square root of 169 is greater than 10. If we know that 15 squared is 225, we might work backwards and try a number between 10 and 15—say 12 or 13.

Help students understand the idea of inverse by having them do and undo operations. Asking them to square all whole numbers between 1 and 12, and then find the square roots of those numbers, will help them understand the concept of inverses. This exercise will also help them make informed choices when they encounter more difficult problems.

Strategies for English Learners

VOCABULARY STUDY OF ROOTS

Many mathematical terms share a Greek or Latin root. Recognizing the root can help students understand the meaning of new words. For example:

Greek or Latin Root	Mathematical Terms
congruere (Latin, *to agree*)	*congru*ent, *congru*ence,
polys (Greek, *many*)	*poly*gon, *poly*hedron, *poly*hedral
hedra (Greek, *surface*)	poly*hedr*on, octa*hedr*al
circum (Latin, *around*)	*circum*ference
circulus (Latin, *circle* or *ring*)	*circ*le, *circul*ar
ferre (Latin, *bear*, *carry*)	circum*fer*ence, peri*phery*
secare (Latin, *to cut*)	inter*sect*, inter*section*
capere (Latin, *to seize* or *stop*)	inter*cept*, inter*cept*ion

Tell students that the Latin prefix *inter*– means between. Then ask them to give you the meaning of the word *intercept*. Encourage students to look for the similarities in words, and to watch for prefixes, suffixes, or roots that may give them clues to a word's meaning.

Have students use the meanings of roots and prefixes to guess the meanings of the following words, and then check their guesses by looking them up in the dictionary:

polyphonic (*many sounds*)
polynomial (*many names or terms*)
polysyllabic (*many syllables*)
circumnavigate (*to sail around*)
encircle (*to make a circle around*)

Strategies for Advanced Learners

DIFFERENTIATE INSTRUCTION IN TERMS OF COMPLEXITY

Advanced learners may be interested in investigating the relationships between regular plane figures and regular three-dimensional figures. The five regular three-dimensional figures, or polyhedrons, are shown below.

Tetrahedron
4 faces that are equilateral triangles.

Cube
6 faces that are squares.

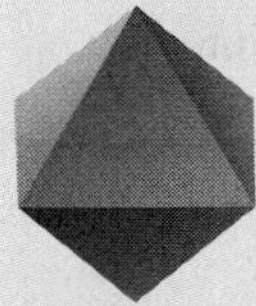

Octahedron
8 faces that are equilateral triangles.

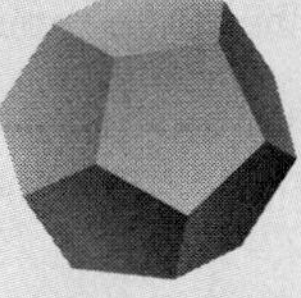

Dodecahedron
12 faces that are regular pentagons.

Icosahedron
20 faces that are equilateral triangles.

Students may notice, or you may point out, that all the faces on each given figure are congruent. Have students examine the figures above and try to identify the number of faces and the shape of each face.

Students may research the figures to determine their names, or given the names, the students can research the origin of each name. (For example, an icosahedron has twenty faces, and *eikosi* is Greek for "twenty.")

CHAPTER 10 Mathematical Background Notes

Much as the study of polygons, perimeter, and area helps students develop spatial intuition in the plane, so does the study of polyhedra help develop spatial intuition in three dimensions. This chapter introduces students to formulas for the volume of pyramids and cones. These can be related to the formula for the volume of a sphere, as first established by Archimedes over 2000 years ago.

Lesson 10.1

CIRCUMFERENCE Since all circles are similar, and the ratio of distances between corresponding points in similar figures is constant, we know that the ratio of the circumference to the diameter is the same for all circles. This ratio is denoted by the symbol π. Thus, if C is the circumference and d the diameter, then $\frac{C}{d} = \pi$. From this we obtain the well-known formula for the circumference of a circle

$$C = \pi d.$$

For a circle of radius r we have $d = 2r$ and

$$C = 2\pi r.$$

The number π is an irrational number whose decimal expansion begins $\pi = 3.1415926\ldots.$

In applications, the approximation $\pi \approx 3.14$ is often convenient. Another useful approximation is $\pi \approx \frac{22}{7}$. Since $\frac{22}{7} = 3.\overline{142857}$ (the bar denotes a repeating decimal), this is accurate to two decimal places and slightly more accurate than 3.14. The following approximation, originating with Chinese mathematicians from the fifth century, is accurate to six decimal places.

$$\pi \approx \frac{355}{113} = 3.1415929\ldots.$$

AREA A compelling way to arrive at the formula for the area of a circle is to consider regular polygons with 3, 4, 5, . . . sides circumscribed about a given circle of radius r. If such a polygon has n sides, each side having length s, then the polygon can be partitioned into n triangles with a vertex at the center, altitude r, and base of length s. Since each of these triangles has area $\frac{1}{2}rs$, the polygon has area $n \cdot \frac{1}{2}rs = \frac{1}{2}r(ns) = \frac{1}{2}rP$, where P is the perimeter of the polygon.

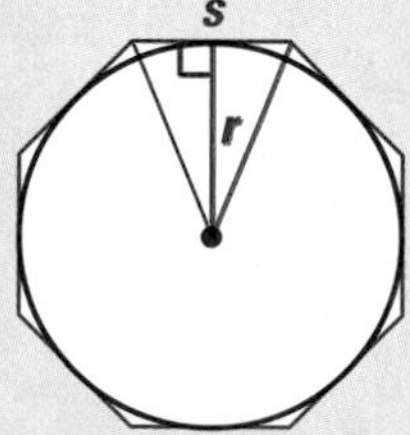

circle inscribed in a regular polygon with 8 sides

When the number n of sides is very large, the perimeter of the polygon is very close to the circumference of the circle, so $P \approx 2\pi r$. Therefore, the area $\frac{1}{2}rP$ of the polygon is close to $\frac{1}{2}r(2\pi r) = \pi r^2$. But for large n the area of the polygon is close to that of the circle. On this basis we expect the area of the circle to be given by

$$A = \pi r^2.$$

Lessons 10.2–10.3

The student's spatial intuition can be developed by viewing and handling physical models of a variety of three-dimensional solids. Practice in the construction of polyhedra from their planar nets also helps to relate a solid to its boundary. The surface area of a polyhedron is defined to be the sum of the areas of its faces, and the concept of planar net is an effective way of helping the student to remember and apply this definition.

Lessons 10.4–10.5

VOLUME In analogy with the formula for the area of a parallelogram, we find that the volume of a prism (either right or oblique) is *base times height.* For some simple polyhedra, it is possible to establish this fact on the basis of two intuitive properties.

(1) Congruent polyhedra have the same volume.

(2) The volume of a polyhedron that has been dissected into smaller polyhedral pieces is the sum of the volumes of the pieces.

Unfortunately, in contrast to the situation in plane geometry, it is *not* the case that every polyhedron can be dissected into polyhedral pieces that can be reassembled to form a box. As a consequence, establishing formulas for the volumes of polyhedra requires more advanced mathematical tools.

Cavalieri's principle is a powerful tool for establishing formulas for the volumes of a variety of solids. As illustrated below, it can be used to establish formulas for the volume of an oblique circular cylinder, as given in Lesson 10.5. However, the same idea leads to formulas for the volumes of prisms, pyramids, cones, and even a sphere.

Given a circular cylinder of height h whose base circle has area B, construct a box of the same height whose base rectangle also has area B. Position the two solids so that their base planes coincide. Observe then that all areas of cross sections of the cylinder by planes parallel to the base are equal to the corresponding areas of cross sections of the box.

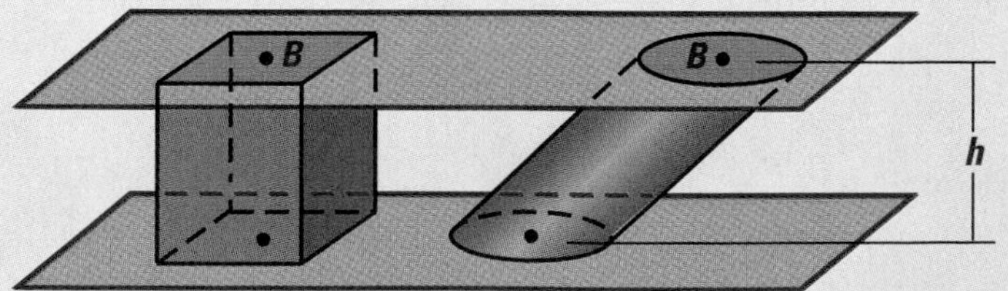

On this basis, Cavalieri's principle asserts that the volume of the cylinder is equal to the volume of the box. This volume is

$$V = B \times h.$$

Note that the argument does not depend on the fact that the base of the cylinder is a circle. Indeed, the same method can be used to establish that the above formula gives the volume of any prism of height h whose base has area B.

Lesson 10.6

PYRAMIDS The fact that the volume of a pyramid is given by

$$V = \frac{1}{3}Bh$$

means that a box of height h and base area B has volume 3 times that of the pyramid. This is the fact that is illustrated by the sand filling experiment in Lesson 10.6.

In some special cases, this formula can be obtained by elementary methods. For example, the picture below shows that a cube can be dissected into three congruent pyramids.

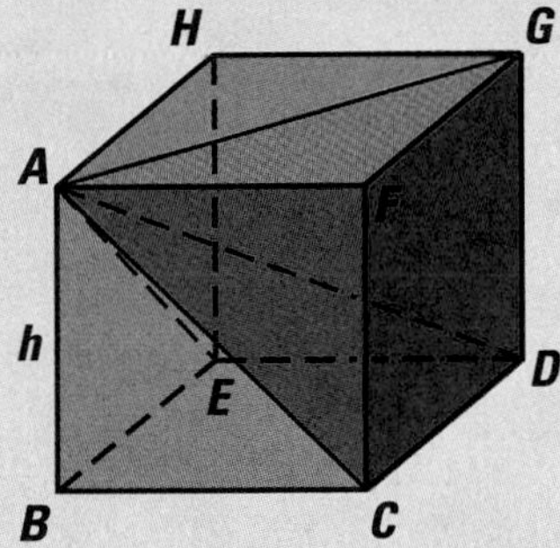

In the picture above one sees a pyramid with vertex at A and square base $BCDE$. In fact, we also see a second pyramid with vertex A and base $FCDG$ and yet a third pyramid with vertex A and base $HEDG$. These three pyramids are congruent and form a dissection of the cube. A good way to reinforce this visual image is to build a model of such a pyramid and then fit three copies into a cube. The net below can be folded to give a model of such a pyramid.

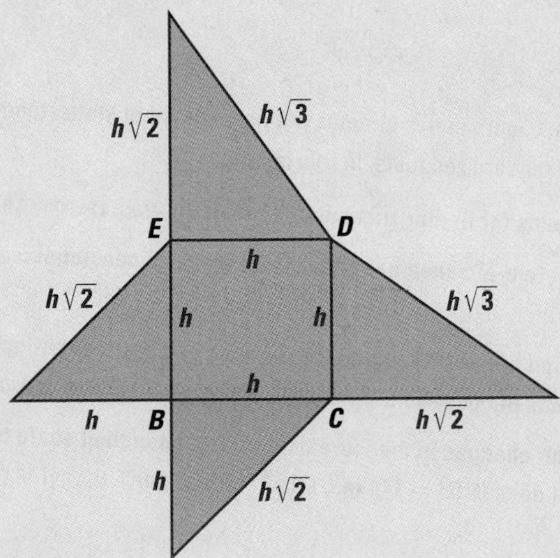

The height of the resulting pyramid is equal to the edge length h of the cube, and the base of the pyramid has area $B = h^2$. Since the volume of the cube is h^3, and the volume of the pyramid is $\frac{1}{3}$ that of the cube, we have

$$V = \frac{1}{3}h^3 = \frac{1}{3}h^2 \cdot h = \frac{1}{3}Bh,$$

which is the desired formula. Of course, the pyramid for which we have established this formula is of a very special type. However, Cavalieri's principle makes it possible to extend this formula to general pyramids and to cones with bases of general shape.

Lesson 10.7

SPHERES Archimedes viewed his derivation of the formula for the volume of a sphere as his crowning mathematical achievement. He phrased this result as *the volume of a sphere is $\frac{2}{3}$ the volume of the circumscribed cylinder*. This is to be interpreted as in the picture below.

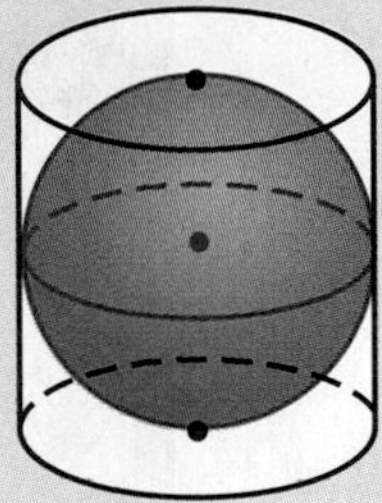

Volume of Sphere $= \frac{2}{3}$ (Volume of Cylinder)

Note that if the radius of the sphere is r, then the cylinder has height $2r$ and base area πr^2. Therefore the cylinder has volume $\pi r^2 \cdot 2r = 2\pi r^3$. The volume of the sphere is therefore

$$V = \frac{2}{3}(2\pi r^3) = \frac{4}{3}\pi r^3.$$

The method used by Archimedes corresponds to applying Cavalieri's principle to a hemisphere of radius r and the solid obtained by removing a cone from the cylinder in the figure below.

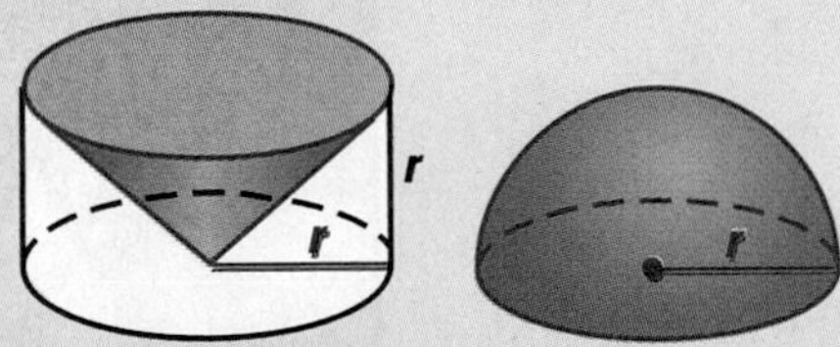

He showed that horizontal planes intersect these two solids in plane regions of equal area (an annulus of area $\pi r^2 - \pi x^2$ on the left and a circle of area $\pi(\sqrt{r^2 - x^2})^2$ on the right). Therefore, by Cavalieri's principle, the two solids have equal volumes. But the volume on the left is

$$\text{Volume(cylinder)} - \text{Volume(cone)} = (\pi r^2)r - \frac{1}{3}(\pi r^2)r = \frac{2}{3}\pi r^3.$$

Then Volume (sphere) $= 2(\frac{2}{3}\pi r^3) = \frac{4}{3}\pi r^3$.

Chapter Overview

Chapter Goals

In the chapter, students will identify three-dimensional figures—polyhedrons, spheres, cylinders, and cones. They will:

- Find the circumference and area of a circle.
- Find the surface area of a prism or a cylinder.
- Find the volume of a prism, pyramid, cylinder, cone, or sphere.
- Recognize similar solids and find scale factors.

Career Note

Civil engineers plan, design, and build highways, canals, dams, bridges, buildings, and water treatment systems, among other things. Some civil engineers work for government agencies, while others work for private companies.

Those interested in careers as civil engineers should have a strong math and science background. A four- or five-year college degree is required, as well as field training and state licensing.

Additional information about civil engineering is available at **www.mcdougallittell.com**

Geometry and Measurement

Why are geometry and measurement important?

Finding volumes and surface areas of three-dimensional objects, the subject of this chapter, helps you solve problems about storage capacity and economical use of materials in manufacturing.

Geometry and measurement are important in many careers, including civil engineering (page 507) and architecture (page 551). For example, when civil engineers design buildings, they use formulas for surface area and volume to calculate the amount of materials needed.

Meeting the California Standards

The skills you'll learn in this chapter will help you meet state standards and prepare for standardized tests. In this chapter you'll:

- **Use formulas for finding measures of basic figures.** LESSONS 10.1, 10.3–10.7
- **Construct two-dimensional patterns for three-dimensional models.** LESSON 10.2
- **Understand how surface area and volume of a solid are affected when the dimensions of the solid are multiplied by a scale factor.** LESSONS 10.7, 10.8
- **Relate the changes in measurement with a change of scale to conversions between units ($1 \text{ ft}^2 = 144 \text{ in.}^2$, $1 \text{ in.}^3 \approx 16.38 \text{ cm}^3$).** LESSON 10.8

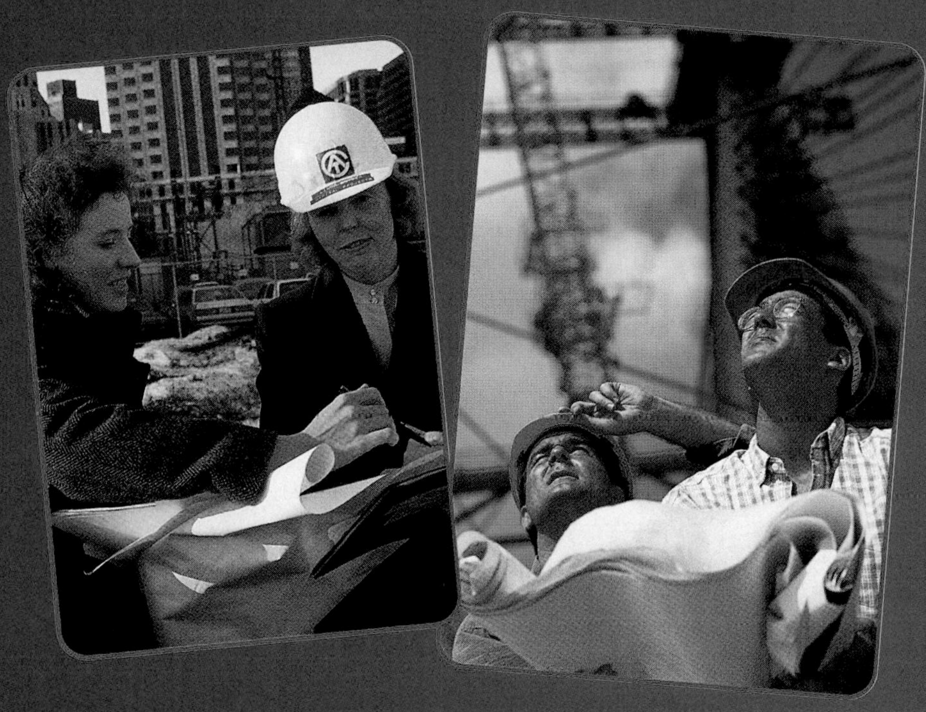

Career Link **CIVIL ENGINEER** A civil engineer uses geometry and measurement when:

- planning the materials needed to build something.
- calculating the volume of a building to estimate ventilation and climate-control needs.

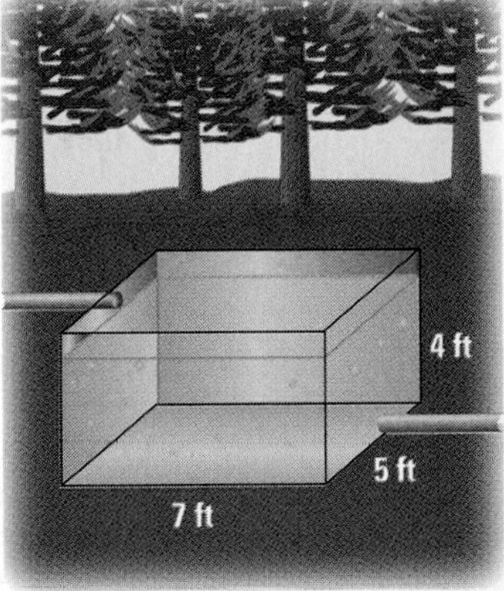

EXERCISES

A civil engineer is designing an enclosed holding tank for water and must estimate the amount of materials needed. The tank will be 7 feet long, 5 feet wide, and 4 feet tall.

1. Find the area of each side of the tank, including the top and the bottom. Each side is a rectangle.
front/back: 28 ft^2, sides: 20 ft^2, top/bottom: 35 ft^2

2. Find the sum of the areas of the sides, top, and bottom of the tank. **166 ft^2**

In Lesson 10.3, you will use a formula for finding the surface area of the tank.

Projects

A project covering Chapters 10–12 appears on pages 664–665 of the Student Edition. Additional projects for selected lessons in Chapter 10 are available in the *Assessment Book,* pp. 253–254.

Technology

Software

- Electronic Teacher Tools
- Online Lesson Planner
- Personal Student Tutor
- Test and Practice Generator

Internet Connections

- Application and Career Links
  515, 531, 533, 544, 551
- Student Help
  511, 518, 526, 532, 536, 539, 546, 550, 559

These Internet connections are available at **www.mcdougallittell.com**

Prepare

Diagnostic Tools

The **chapter readiness quiz** can help you diagnose whether students have the following skills needed in Chapter 10:

- Understand the meaning of congruent polygons.
- Determine the area of triangles.
- Understand the use and construction of scale drawings.

Reteaching Materials

The following resources are available for students who need additional help with the skills on the chapter readiness quiz:

Chapter 10 Resource Book

- Reteaching with Practice (Lessons 1.5, 7.3, 8.9)

Personal Student Tutor

Additional Resources

The following resources are provided to help you prepare for the upcoming chapter and customize review materials:

Chapter 10 Resource Book

- Lesson Plans, pp. 1, 10, 19, 28, 37, 46, 55, 64
- Lesson Plans for Block Scheduling, pp. 2, 11, 20, 29, 38, 47, 56, 65

Technology

- Electronic Teacher Tools with Lesson Planning Software
- Test and Practice Generator

Chapter 10 Getting Ready

PREVIEW

What's the chapter about?

- Finding the **circumference** and **area** of circles
- Finding the **surface area** and **volume** of various solids
- Exploring the relationships of **similar solids**

WORDS TO KNOW

- **circle,** *p. 511*
- **circumference,** *p. 511*
- **central angle,** *p. 513*
- **sector,** *p. 513*
- **polyhedron,** *p. 518*
- **net,** *p. 518*
- **prism,** *p. 523*
- **cylinder,** *p. 523*
- **surface area,** *p. 523*
- **volume,** *p. 530*
- **pyramid,** *p. 539*
- **cone,** *p. 539*
- **sphere,** *p. 543*
- **similar solids,** *p. 548*

PREPARE

Chapter Readiness Quiz

Take this quick quiz. If you are unsure of an answer, look back at the reference pages for help.

VOCABULARY CHECK *(refer to p. 432)*

1. Polygons whose corresponding angles have the same measures and whose corresponding sides have the same ratio are __?__ polygons. **D**

Ⓐ Congruent Ⓑ Regular Ⓒ Four-sided Ⓓ Similar

SKILL CHECK *(refer to pp. 22, 338)*

2. What is the area of the triangle shown? **G**

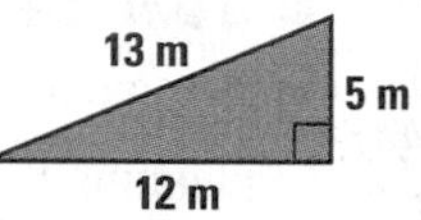

Ⓕ 15 m^2 Ⓖ 30 m^2

Ⓗ 60 m^2 Ⓙ 78 m^2

3. A park map has a scale of 3 inches = 100 yards. A path on the map measures 5.1 inches. What is the length of the actual path? **C**

Ⓐ 17 yd Ⓑ 60 yd Ⓒ 170 yd Ⓓ 300 yd

STUDY TIP

Take Notes

Take notes during class and while you are studying on your own. Your notes will help you quickly review the concepts you have studied.

3/8

Notes for 10.1

Diameter: distance across circle through center

Radius: distance from center to point on circle

radius

diameter

DEVELOPING CONCEPTS Circles

For use with Lesson 10.1

California Standards

- Use formulas routinely for finding the circumference and area of circles. (MG 2.1)
- Use a variety of methods, such as words, numbers, symbols, tables, diagrams, and models, to explain mathematical reasoning. (MR 2.5)

MATERIALS

- Paper and pencil

Student Help

STUDY TIP The circumference of the circle is *greater* than the perimeters of the inside polygons and *less* than the perimeters of the outside polygons.

A *circle* is the set of all points in a plane that are the same distance from a given point, called the *center* of the circle. The *radius* is the distance from the center to a point on the circle. The *diameter* is the distance across the circle through its center. The diameter is twice the radius. The *circumference* is the distance around the circle.

SAMPLE 1 Comparing Circumference and Diameter

Consider a group of regular polygons drawn **inside** and **outside** of a circle. The more sides a polygon has, the closer it approximates the curve of the circle. You can use these polygons to approximate the ratio of the circumference of the circle to its diameter. (The side lengths of the polygons have been measured to the nearest hundredth.)

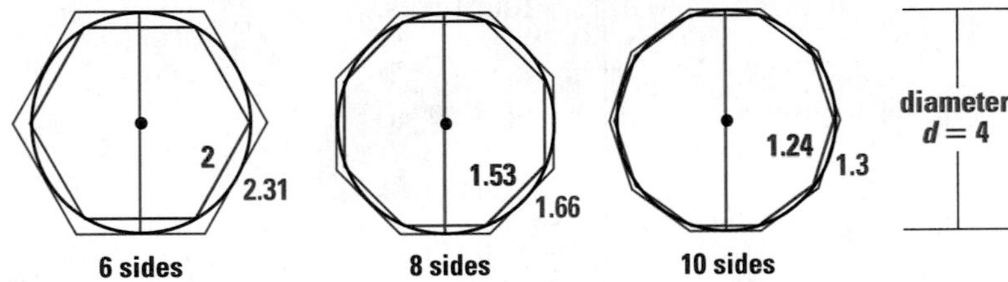

Here's How

Find the perimeter P of each polygon. Then find the ratio of P to the diameter d of the circle.

POLYGONS INSIDE CIRCLE		POLYGONS OUTSIDE CIRCLE	
Perimeter	Ratio $= \frac{P}{d}$	Perimeter	Ratio $= \frac{P}{d}$
$\mathbf{2} \cdot 6 = 12$	$\frac{12}{4} = 3$	$\mathbf{2.31} \cdot 6 = 13.86$	$\frac{13.86}{4} = 3.465$
$\mathbf{1.53} \cdot 8 = 12.24$	$\frac{12.24}{4} = 3.06$	$\mathbf{1.66} \cdot 8 = 13.28$	$\frac{13.28}{4} = 3.32$
$\mathbf{1.24} \cdot 10 = 12.4$	$\frac{12.4}{4} = 3.1$	$\mathbf{1.3} \cdot 10 = 13$	$\frac{13}{4} = 3.25$

Because the circumference C of the circle is a number that is between the perimeter of the inside and outside polygons, the ratio of C to d is between the ratios for the polygons. In particular, $\frac{C}{d}$ is between 3.1 and 3.25. The ratio of the circle's circumference C to its diameter d is in fact the same for all circles. This ratio is defined by the Greek letter *pi*, written as π. A decimal approximation of π is 3.14. You can use this information to write a formula for the circumference: $C = \pi d$, because $\frac{C}{d} = \pi$.

1 Planning the Activity

Purpose and Materials

See the margin of the student page. See also the Activity Support Master in the Chapter 10 Resource Book.

LINK TO LESSON
In this activity students will see that the number π is the ratio of a circle's circumference to its diameter. This relationship leads to the formula for finding the circumference of a circle, $C = \pi d$. The application of this formula is seen in Example 1 of Lesson 10.1.

Math Reasoning

Students are
- Formulating and justifying mathematical conjectures
- Testing conjectures using deductive reasoning
- Developing generalizations and applying them to new problem situations

2 Managing the Activity

Classroom Management

Step through Sample 1 with the whole class. Point out that the more sides you add to a polygon, the more it resembles a circle, and P, the perimeter of the polygon, gets closer and closer to C, the circumference of the circle. Emphasize that the class is studying the polygons in order to discover something about circles.

Teaching Tip

Inform students that the side lengths of the polygons can be calculated with more advanced mathematical methods.

California Standards and Assessment

CA Standards: MG 2.1, MR 2.5

3 Closing the Activity

★ **KEY DISCOVERY**

Students should have an understanding of the meaning of π, the formula for the circumference of a circle, and the formula for the area of a circle.

Activity Assessment

Use Exercises 1 and 4–6 to assess student understanding.

Try These

Find the circumference of a circle with the given diameter *d*. Use 3.14 for π.

1. $d = 11$ cm **34.54 cm** **2.** $d = 4$ ft **12.56 ft** **3.** $d = 18$ in. **56.52 in.**

SAMPLE 2 Approximating the Area of a Circle

You can approximate the area of a circle by cutting it into wedges.

Here's How

❶ Fold the circle in half, four times.

❷ Cut the circle into 16 wedges.

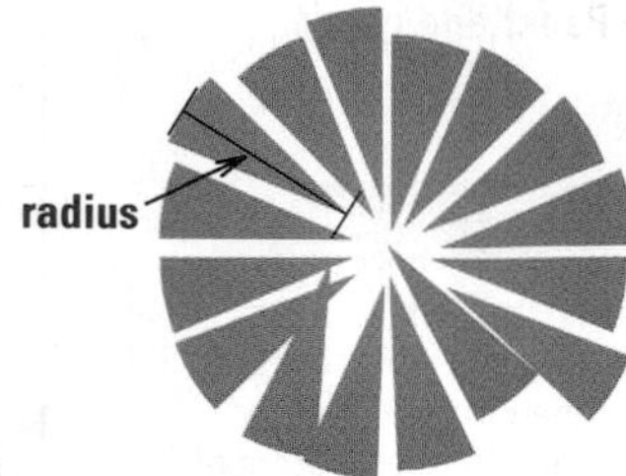

❸ Arrange the wedges as shown.

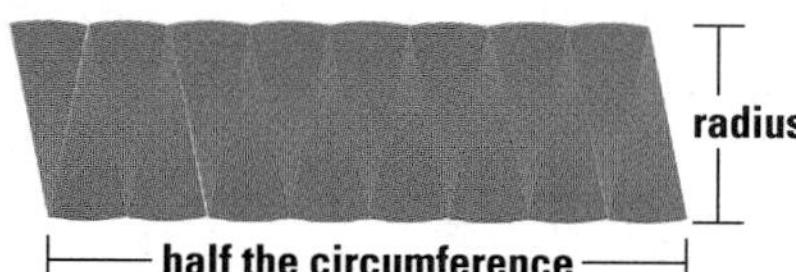

Because the figure resembles a parallelogram, use the formula for the area of a parallelogram to approximate the area of the circle.

Area of a circle ≈ (Base) • (Height)

= (Half the circumference) • (Radius)

Try These

4. MATHEMATICAL REASONING Translate the verbal model in Sample 2 as an algebraic model using only the variables *A* (for area) and *r* (for radius). (*Hint:* Begin by writing the circumference in terms of *r*.)
$A = \pi r^2$

5. Find the area of a circle with a radius of 3 feet. Use 3.14 for π. **28.26 ft²**

10.1 Circumference and Area of a Circle

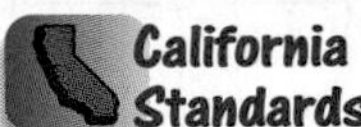

California Standards

In this lesson you'll:

- Use formulas routinely for finding the circumference and area of circles. (MG 2.1)
- Identify and construct central angles, radii, diameters, and chords of circles using a compass and straightedge. (MG 3.1)

Goal 1 Finding the Circumference of a Circle

A **circle** is the set of all points in a plane that are the same distance from a given point, called the **center** of the circle. The distance from the center to a point on the circle is the **radius** of the circle. The distance across the circle through its center is the **diameter**. The diameter is twice the radius.

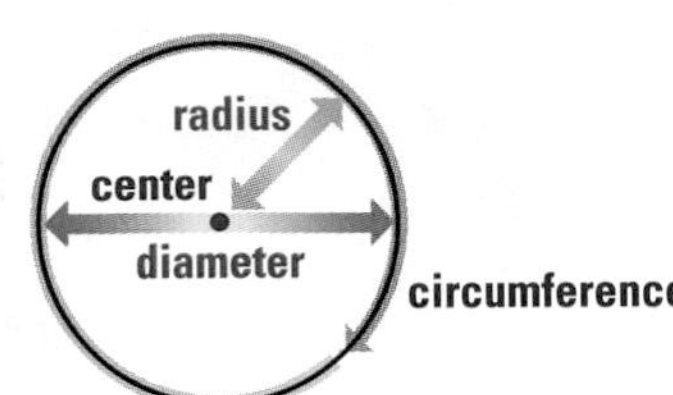

The **circumference** of a circle is the distance around the circle. As you learned in Developing Concepts 10.1, page 509, the ratio of the circumference of any circle to its diameter is denoted by the Greek letter π (or *pi*). The number π is an irrational number approximately equal to 3.14.

The Circumference of a Circle

Let d be the diameter of a circle, and let r be its radius. The circumference C of the circle is

$$C = \pi d \text{ or, because } d = 2r,\ C = 2\pi r.$$

Student Help

▶ Reading Tip
The radius and diameter of a circle are also segments. Whether the words refer to segments or their lengths depends on the context in which they appear.

Example 1 Finding a Circumference

Find the circumference of the circle.

a. A circle of diameter 26 inches

b. A circle of radius 4 feet

Solution

a. $C = \pi d$ — Write formula for circumference.

$\approx 3.14 \cdot 26$ — Substitute for π and d.

$= 81.64$ — Simplify.

ANSWER ▶ The circumference is about 82 inches.

b. $C = 2\pi r$ — Write formula for circumference.

$\approx 2(3.14)(4)$ — Substitute for π and r.

$= 25.12$ — Simplify.

ANSWER ▶ The circumference is about 25 feet.

Student Help

▶ More Examples
More examples are available at www.mcdougallittell.com

1 Plan

Pacing

Suggested Number of Days

Transitional: 2 days
Average: 2 days
Advanced: 2 days
Block Schedule: 1 block

Teaching Resources

Blacklines
(See page 506B.)

Transparencies
- Warm-Up Exercises
- Teacher Time-Savers
- English/Spanish Problem Solving
- Answers

Technology
- Electronic Teacher Tools
- Test and Practice Generator

2 Teach

Math Reasoning

For Mathematical Background Notes on mathematical reasoning related to this lesson, please refer to pages 506E and 506F in this Teacher's Edition.

Extra Example 1
See next page.

California Standards and Assessment

CA Standards: MG 2.1, MG 3.1

Math Reasoning

Students should develop the habit of retaining the symbol for π until the very end of a calculation, at which point they can substitute an approximation for π. For instance, $3\pi + 7\pi = 10\pi \approx 10(3.14) = 31.4$ is preferable to $3\pi + 7\pi \approx 3(3.14) + 7(3.14) = 9.42 + 21.98 = 31.4$.

Extra Example 1

Find the circumference of the circle.

a. A circle has a diameter of 14 inches. **about 43.96 in.**

b. A circle has a radius of 10 feet. **about 62.8 ft**

Extra Example 2

The lid of a can has a diameter of 8 cm. Find the area of the lid. **about 50.24 cm^2**

Extra Example 3

A circle has an area of 49π square inches. What is its radius? **7 in.**

Goal 2 FINDING THE AREA OF A CIRCLE

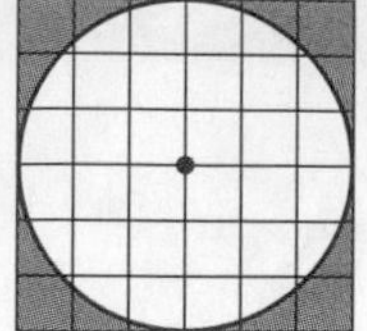

The circle at the right has a radius of 3 units. To estimate the area of the circle, you can estimate the area of each of the four blue corner regions to be 2 square units. Because the area of the entire square is $6 \cdot 6 = 36$ square units, you find that the area of the circle is about $36 - 4(2) = 28$ square units.

The following formula, which you learned in Developing Concepts 10.1, page 509, states that the exact area of the circle shown above is πr^2, or $9\pi \approx 28.3$ square units.

THE AREA OF A CIRCLE

Let r be the radius of a circle. The area A of the circle is

$$A = \pi r^2.$$

Link to Architecture

CIRCULAR BUILDINGS The Space Needle in Seattle, Washington, has a circular restaurant that rotates every 58 minutes.

EXAMPLE 2 Finding the Area of a Circle

ARCHITECTURE The floor of a restaurant has a circular shape with a diameter of 96 feet. Find the area of the floor.

Solution

The radius is half of the diameter.

$$r = \frac{96}{2} = 48 \text{ feet}$$

Using this measurement, you can find the area of the floor.

$A = \pi r^2$	Write formula for area of a circle.
$\approx 3.14 \cdot (48)^2$	Substitute for π and r.
$= 7234.56$	Use a calculator.

ANSWER ▶ The area of the floor is about 7235 square feet.

EXAMPLE 3 Finding the Radius of a Circle

A circle has an area of 16π square feet. What is its radius?

Solution

$A = \pi r^2$	Write formula for area of a circle.
$16\pi = \pi r^2$	Substitute for A.
$16 = r^2$	Divide each side by π.
$4 = r$	Take positive square root.

ANSWER ▶ The radius is 4 feet.

Student Help

▶ **STUDY TIP** If you are given the circumference or area of a circle, you can find the radius by solving $C = 2\pi r$ or $A = \pi r^2$ for r.

An angle whose sides are radii and whose vertex is the center of a circle is a **central angle** of the circle. There are 360° in a circle, so the measure of a central angle is between 0° and 360°. The part of a circle determined by two radii is called a **sector** of the circle.

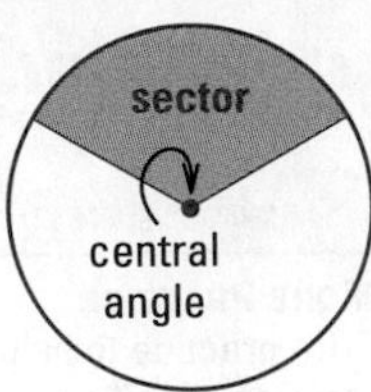

EXAMPLE 4 Finding the Area of a Sector

The area of the circle shown is 255 square meters. Find the area of the blue sector.

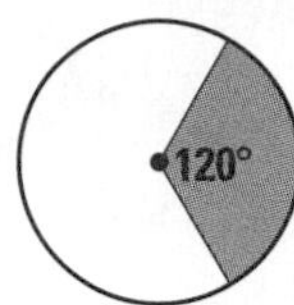

Solution

You can find the area of the sector by setting up and solving a proportion.

$$\frac{\text{Area of sector}}{\text{Area of entire circle}} = \frac{\text{Measure of central angle}}{\text{Measure of entire circle}}$$

$$\frac{x}{255} = \frac{120}{360}$$ Substitute.

$$360x = 255 \cdot 120$$ Cross products property.

$$360x = 30{,}600$$ Simplify.

$$\frac{360x}{360} = \frac{30{,}600}{360}$$ Divide each side by 360.

$$x = 85$$ Simplify. x is by itself.

ANSWER ▶ The area of the blue sector is 85 square meters.

Student Help

▶**LOOK BACK**
For extra help with writing and solving proportions, see page 333.

10.1 Exercises

Guided Practice

In Exercises 1–4, use the circle with center A.

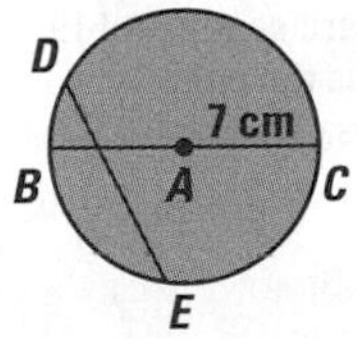

1. Name a segment that is a radius. **$\overline{AB}$ or $\overline{AC}$**
2. Name a segment that is a diameter. **$\overline{BC}$**
3. Find the circumference. Leave your answer in terms of π. **14π cm**
4. Find the area. Leave your answer in terms of π. **49π cm^2**
5. **BICYCLES** One bicycle wheel has a radius of 14 inches and another has a radius of 13 inches. Which wheel has a greater circumference? Find the circumference of each to check your answer.

5. The wheel with radius 14 inches has circumference 28π inches, which is greater than the circumference of the wheel with radius 13 inches which is 26π inches.

Math Reasoning

Technically, an angle is the union of two rays with a common endpoint, and the degree measure of an angle is never more than 180°. However, the context here makes it clear what is meant by a central angle with measure larger than 180°. We would like, for example, to be able to say that a central angle with measure 270° determines a sector whose area is $\frac{3}{4}$ that of the circle.

Extra Example 4

The area of the circle shown is 64 square feet. Find the area of the shaded sector if its central angle measures 90°.

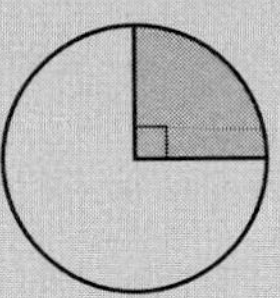

16 ft^2

Teaching Tip

You can also solve $\frac{x}{255} = \frac{120}{360}$ as follows:

$$\frac{x}{255} = \frac{120}{360} = \frac{1}{3}$$

$$255\left(\frac{x}{255}\right) = 255\left(\frac{1}{3}\right)$$

$$x = \frac{255}{3} = 85$$

Concept Check

Find the circumference and area of a circle with radius y. **$C = 2\pi y$, $A = \pi y^2$**

3 Apply

Assignment Guide

TRANSITIONAL
Day 1: pp. 514–515 Exs. 6–11, 18–20
Day 2: pp. 514–515 Exs. 12–13, 15–16, 22–27, 32–34

AVERAGE
Day 1: pp. 514–515 Exs. 6–11, 18–21, 29*
Day 2: pp. 514–515 Exs. 12–17, 22–28, 32–34

ADVANCED
Day 1: pp. 514–515 Exs. 6–11, 18–21, 29–31*
Day 2: pp. 514–515 Exs. 12–17, 22–28, 32–34

BLOCK SCHEDULE
pp. 514–515 Exs. 6–28, 29*, 32–34

Extra Practice

- Student Edition, pp. 708–709
- Chapter 10 Resource Book, p. 6

Homework Check

To quickly check student understanding of key concepts, go over the following exercises:

Transitional: 6, 8, 12, 16, 22
Average: 8, 10, 12, 16, 22
Advanced: 8, 10, 14, 16, 22

18. and 19.

radius	circumference	area
1	2π	π
2	4π	4π
3	6π	9π
4	8π	16π
5	10π	25π
6	12π	36π

If you multiply the radius by a factor of n, you multiply the circumference by a factor of n and you multiply the area by a factor of n^2.

20. If the diameter of a circle is doubled, its circumference is doubled since circumference is proportional to diameter. If the diameter of a circle is doubled, its area is four times as large, since area is proportional to the square of the diameter.

Practice and Problem Solving

Student Help

▶MORE PRACTICE
Extra practice to help you master skills is on page 708.

Find the circumference and area of the clock face. Use 3.14 for π. Round your result to the nearest tenth.

6. $r = 2$ in. **$C \approx 12.6$ in.; $A \approx 12.6$ in.^{2}**

7. $r = 3$ cm **$C \approx 18.8$ cm; $A \approx 28.3$ cm^2**

8. $d = 5.8$ cm **$C \approx 18.2$ cm; $A \approx 26.4$ cm^2**

Find the area of the shaded portion of the figure. Use 3.14 for π. Round your result to the nearest tenth.

9. **9.4 ft^2**

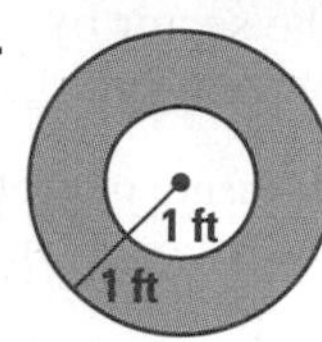

10. **13.8 mm^2**

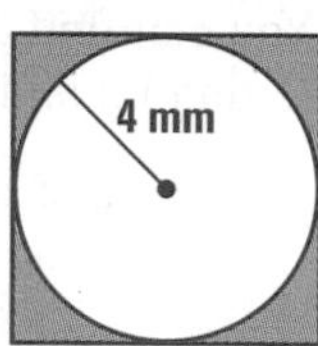

11. **4.6 m^2**

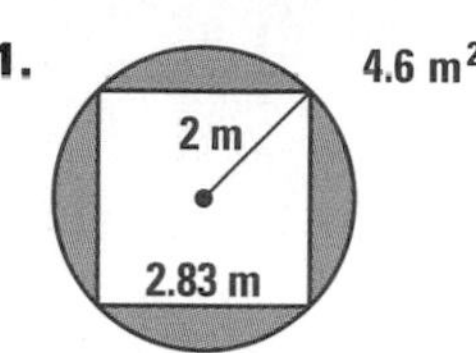

Find the radius and diameter of the figure. Use 3.14 for π. Round your result to the nearest tenth.

12. $A = 36\pi$ in.^{2} **$r = 6$ in.; $d = 12$ in.**

13. $A = 113.10$ cm^2 **$r \approx 6$ cm; $d \approx 12$ cm**

14. $C = 11$ in. **$r \approx 1.8$ in.; $d \approx 3.5$ in.**

Find the area of the entire circle given the area S of the sector.

15. $S = 9.5$ m^2 **38 m^2**

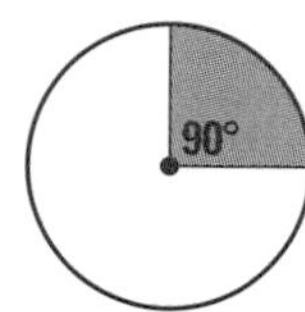

16. $S = 4$ ft^2 **6 ft^2**

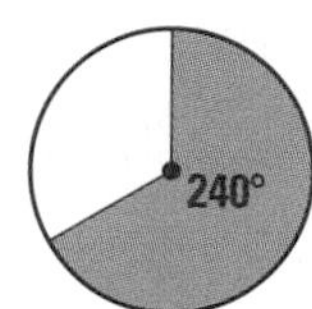

17. $S = 18$ cm^2 **90 cm^2**

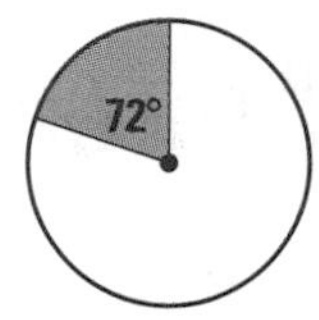

Student Help

▶VOCABULARY TIP
In Exercises 18 and 19, *radii* is the plural of *radius.*

In Exercises 18 and 19, create a table. Then describe the pattern.

18. Find the circumferences of the circles whose radii are 1, 2, 3, 4, 5, and 6. **18, 19. See margin.**

19. Find the areas of the circles whose radii are 1, 2, 3, 4, 5, and 6.

20. MATHEMATICAL REASONING If the diameter of a circle is doubled, does the circumference of the circle double? Does the area of the circle double? Explain your reasoning.

21. MATHEMATICAL REASONING Express the area A of a circle in terms of its diameter d. $A = \frac{\pi d^2}{4}$

PIZZA In Exercises 22–24, use the following information. A pizza has a diameter of 12 inches and costs $12.

22. Find the area of the entire pizza. **$A \approx 113$ in.^{2}**

23. The pizza is cut into six pieces. Find the area of each piece. **18.8 in.^{2}**

24. Find the cost of each piece. **$2**

History Link **In Exercises 25–28, use the map below.**

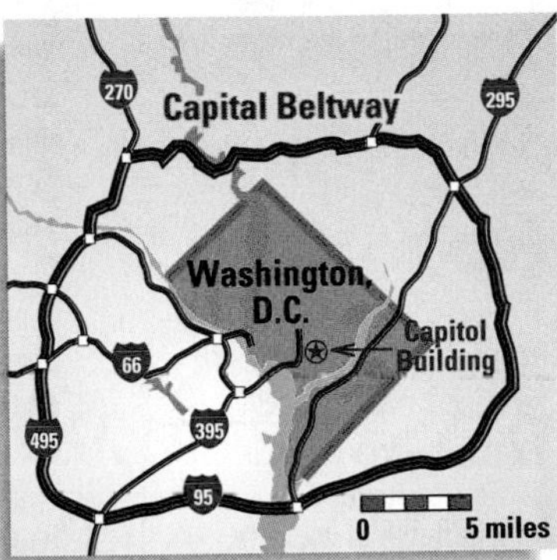

25. The road around Washington, D.C., is called the *Capital Beltway*. Estimate the distance from the Beltway into the center of Washington, D.C., on Interstate 395. **10 mi**

26. Estimate the length of a trip on the Beltway going around Washington, D.C., entirely. **63 mi**

27. Estimate the area inside the Beltway. **314 mi^2**

28. Estimate the percent of the region inside the Beltway that is Washington, D.C. **about 20%**

CHALLENGE In Exercises 29–31, the segment joining the labeled points contains the center of the circle. Use the distance formula to find the diameter of the circle. Then use the diameter to find the circumference and the area of the circle.

29.

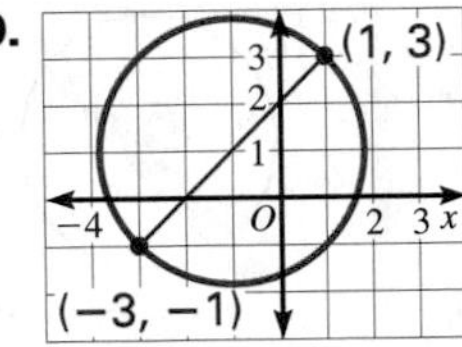

$d \approx 5.7$; $C \approx 17.8$; $A \approx 25.1$

30. (−3, 2), (3, 1)

$d \approx 6.1$; $C \approx 19.1$; $A \approx 29.0$

31. (3, 0), (−1, −2)

$d \approx 4.5$; $C \approx 14.0$; $A \approx 15.7$

Multiple-Choice Practice

In Exercises 32–34, suppose the diameter of a circle is 5 inches.

32. What is the approximate circumference of the circle? **C**

Ⓐ 31.40 in. Ⓑ 19.63 in. Ⓒ 15.70 in. Ⓓ 7.85 in.

33. What is the approximate area of the circle? **G**

Ⓕ 31.40 in.^{2} Ⓖ 19.63 in.^{2} Ⓗ 15.70 in.^{2} Ⓙ 7.85 in.^{2}

34. A sector of the circle has an area of 4.9 square inches. What is the measure of the central angle that forms the sector? **B**

Ⓐ 45° Ⓑ 90° Ⓒ 180° Ⓓ 270°

Link to History

WASHINGTON, D.C. French engineer Pierre L'Enfant was employed by George Washington to plan Washington, D.C.

More about Washington, D.C., at www.mcdougallittell.com

4 Assess

Assessment Resources

- Assessment Book (Formal Assessment and Alternative Assessment)
- Test and Practice Generator

Mini-Quiz

1. Find the circumference of a circle with a radius of 5 meters. **about 31.4 m**
2. Find the circumference of a circle with a diameter of 24 feet. **about 75.36 ft**
3. A quarter has a diameter of about 24 mm. Find the area of a quarter. **about 452.16 mm^2**
4. A circle has an area of 121π square inches. What is its radius? **11 in.**
5. The area of the sector shown is 36π cm^2. If the sector's central angle is 45°, what is the area of the entire circle?

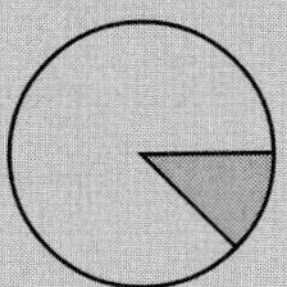

288π cm^2

Math Reasoning

Given a circle drawn on a piece of paper, without its center being given, an entertaining challenge is to find the center using only compass and straightedge. (*Hint:* the perpendicular bisector of any chord of a circle passes through the center.)

1. Check constructions. Use a straightedge to draw $\overleftrightarrow{AQ}$, intersecting the circle at point B. Bisect $\overline{AB}$ (see p. 403) to form $\overleftrightarrow{QC}$, with C a point on the circle. $\angle AQC$ and $\angle BQC$ are 90° central angles.

2. No, the length of the longest chord is equal to the diameter which is only 3 inches.

3. Draw point A on the circle.

CONSTRUCTION *Constructing Chords and Radii*

Student Help

▶ **SKILLS REVIEW**
For help with using a compass and a straightedge, see page 685.

CONSTRUCTING CHORDS A line segment whose endpoints lie on a circle is called a **chord**. A chord that contains the center of the circle is a diameter of the circle. You can use a compass and straightedge to construct a chord of a given length.

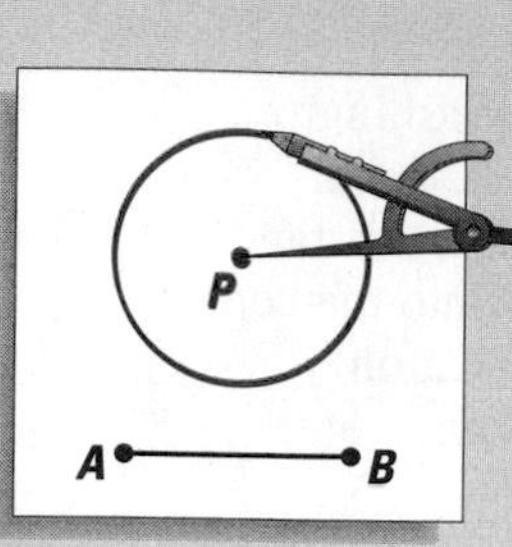

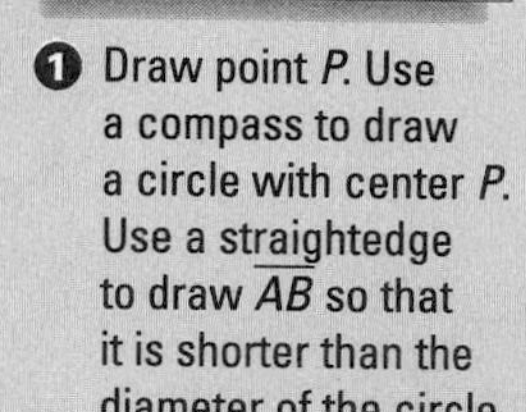

1 Draw point P. Use a compass to draw a circle with center P. Use a straightedge to draw $\overline{AB}$ so that it is shorter than the diameter of the circle.

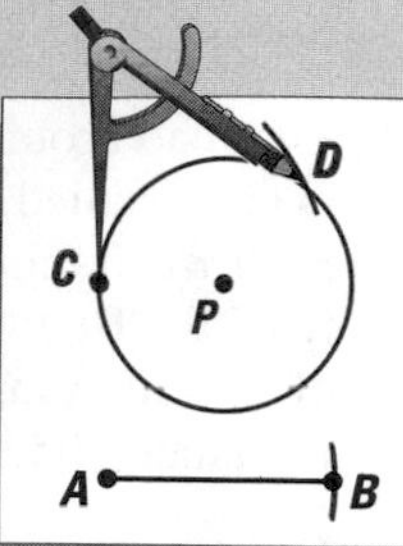

2 Draw point C on the circle. Set your compass at the length of $\overline{AB}$. Then use the same compass setting to draw an arc with center C. Label the intersection D.

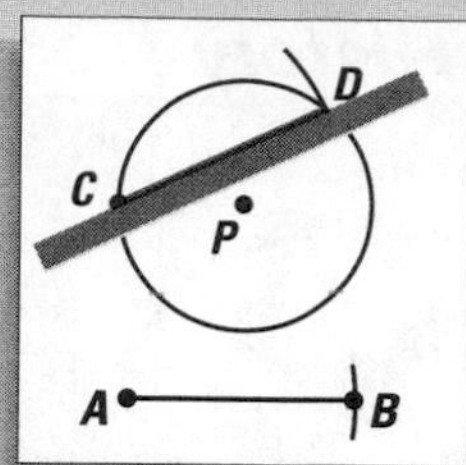

3 Use a straightedge to draw chord $\overline{CD}$.

Student Help

▶ **STUDY TIP**
To construct a diameter of a circle, draw a point on the circle. Then use a straightedge to draw a chord from that point through the center to the other side of the circle.

CONSTRUCTING RADII You can use a compass and a straightedge to construct a radius of a circle and a central angle of a circle.

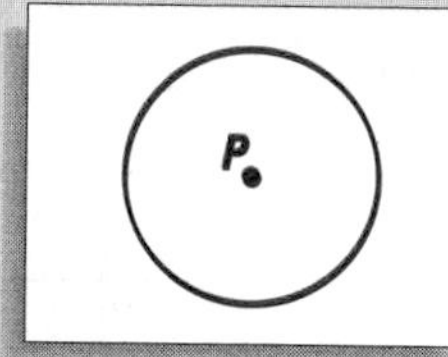

1 Draw point P. Use a compass to draw a circle with center P.

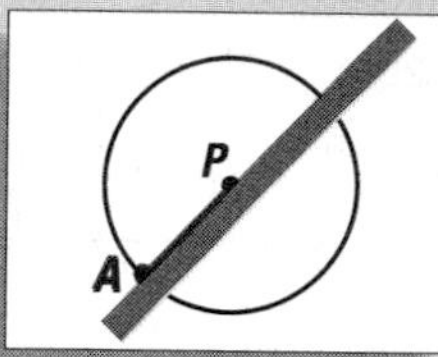

2 Draw point A on the circle. To draw radius $\overline{AP}$, use a straightedge to connect points A and P.

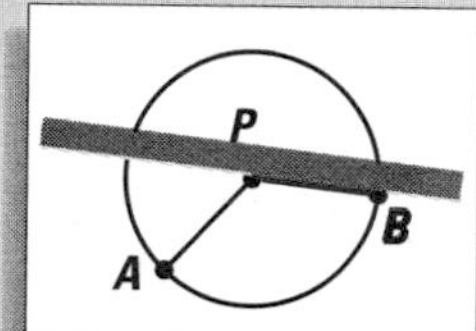

3 Draw point B on the circle. Draw radius $\overline{PB}$. $\angle APB$ is a central angle of the circle.

Exercises

Use a compass and a straightedge. Construct a circle with center Q and a radius of 1.5 inches. **1–3. See margin.**

1. Use a ruler to draw a chord that is 2.5 inches long.

2. Is it possible to construct a chord that is 3.5 inches long? Explain.

3. MATHEMATICAL REASONING Construct a central angle with a measure of 90°. Describe your steps.

10.2 Three-Dimensional Figures

California Standards

In this lesson you'll:

- Construct two-dimensional patterns for three-dimensional models, such as prisms, cylinders, and cones. (MG 3.5)
- Describe how two or more objects are related in space. (MG 3.6)

Student Help

STUDY TIP
Sometimes the lines in a diagram of a three-dimensional figure intersect on the page. This does not necessarily mean that the lines intersect in space.

Goal 1 CLASSIFYING LINES IN SPACE

Points and lines that lie in the same plane are **coplanar**. In particular, a pair of intersecting lines or a pair of parallel lines are coplanar. Lines that do not intersect and are not parallel are **skew lines**. Skew lines do not lie in the same plane. In the diagram, lines m and n are coplanar, and lines k and m are skew.

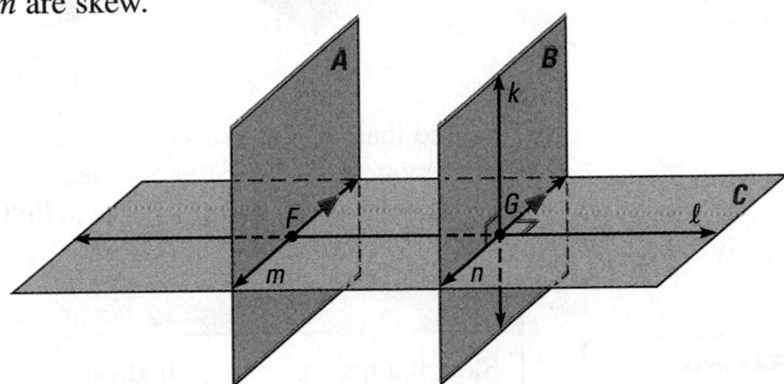

A line perpendicular to a plane intersects the plane in a point and is perpendicular to every line in the plane that passes through the point. For example, line ℓ is perpendicular to plane B, and line ℓ is perpendicular to both lines k and n.

Planes that do not intersect are parallel. The distance between parallel planes refers to the distance measured along a line perpendicular to both planes. In the diagram above, planes A and B are parallel and the distance between planes A and B is the length of $\overline{FG}$.

EXAMPLE 1 Relating Lines in Space

Use the diagram of the solid.

a. Name a pair of coplanar lines.

b. Name a pair of any skew lines.

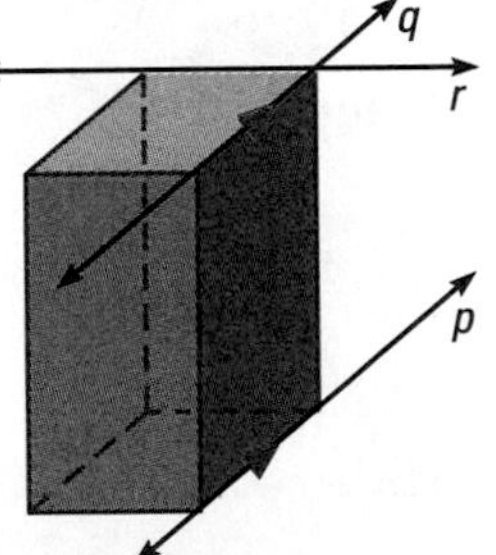

Solution

a. Because lines p and q are parallel, they are coplanar. Because lines q and r intersect, they are coplanar.

b. Lines p and r are skew because they do not intersect, are not parallel, and do not lie in the same plane.

1 Plan

Pacing

Suggested Number of Days

Transitional: 2 days
Average: 2 days
Advanced: 2 days
Block Schedule: 1 block

Teaching Resources

Blacklines
(See page 506B.)

Transparencies
- Warm-Up Exercises
- Teacher Time-Savers
- English/Spanish Problem Solving
- Answers

Technology
- Electronic Teacher Tools
- Test and Practice Generator

2 Teach

Math Reasoning

For Mathematical Background Notes on mathematical reasoning related to this lesson, please refer to pages 506E and 506F in this Teacher's Edition.

Extra Example 1
See next page.

California Standards and Assessment

CA Standards: MG 3.5, MG 3.6
CA Key Concepts Book: pp. S93–S99

Extra Example 1

Use the diagram of the solid.

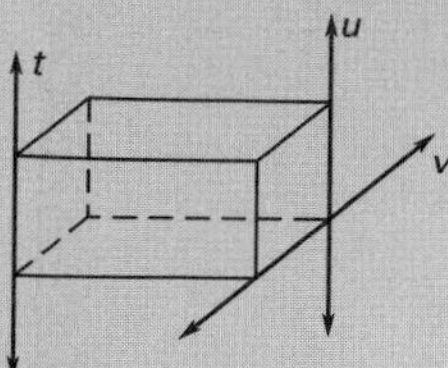

a. Name any coplanar lines. *t* and *u*, *u* and *v*

b. Name any skew lines. *t* and *v*

Extra Example 2

Sketch the net for the polyhedron.

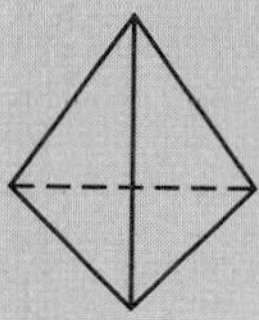

The pyramid has 4 triangular faces.

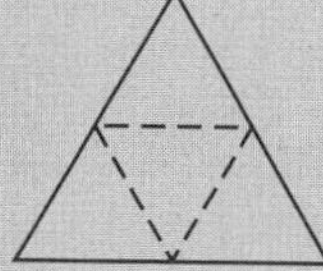

Teaching Tip

Have students cut out a paper triangle and connect the midpoints of the sides to form the "midpoint triangle." This configuration may be viewed as the net for a tetrahedron. By folding an acute-angled triangle along the edges of its midpoint triangle, a tetrahedron can be formed. If the initial triangle is equilateral, this gives a regular tetrahedron. Let students experiment with triangles of various shapes. What happens if you start with a right triangle?

Goal 2 EXPLORING SOLIDS

> **Student Help**
>
> ▶**VOCABULARY TIP**
> The plural of the term polyhedron is *polyhedra* or *polyhedrons.* The plural of vertex is *vertices.*

A **polyhedron** is a closed solid that is bounded by polygons, called the **faces** of the polyhedron. Adjacent faces meet at the **edges** of the polyhedron. A **vertex** of a polyhedron is a point where three or more edges meet. Two common types of polyhedrons are *prisms* and *pyramids*.

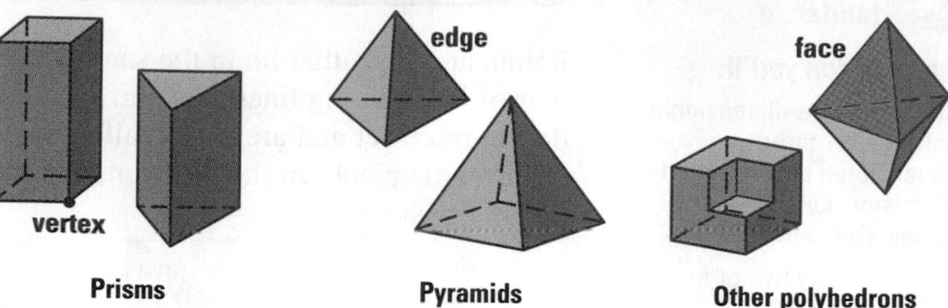

Imagine that you have used cardboard to make a polyhedron. You then cut along enough edges of the polyhedron so that you can lay it flat. The two-dimensional figure that results is called a **net**.

> **Student Help**
>
> ▶**MORE EXAMPLES**
> 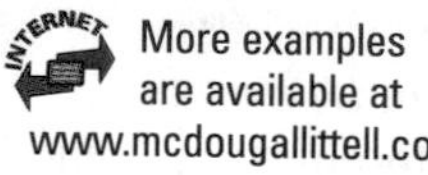
>
> More examples are available at www.mcdougallittell.com

EXAMPLE 2 Drawing Nets

Sketch a net for the polyhedron.

a. 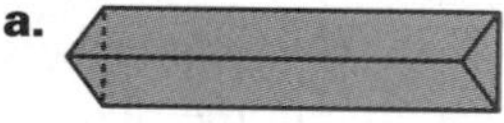

b. 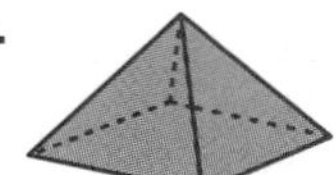

Solution

a. The prism has five faces: three rectangles and two triangles.

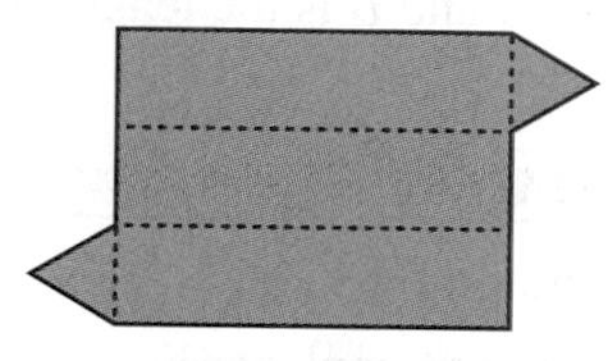

b. The pyramid has five faces: one square and four triangles.

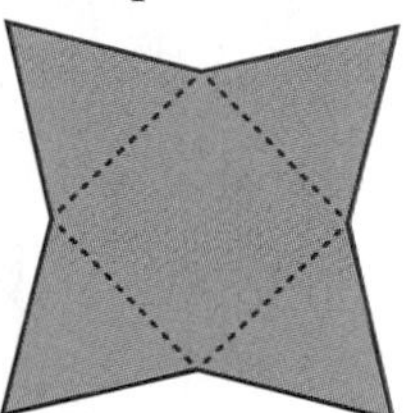

Three other types of solids, a *sphere*, a *cylinder*, and a *cone*, are shown below. These solids are not polyhedrons because they are not bounded by polygons. You will learn more about these solids later in this chapter.

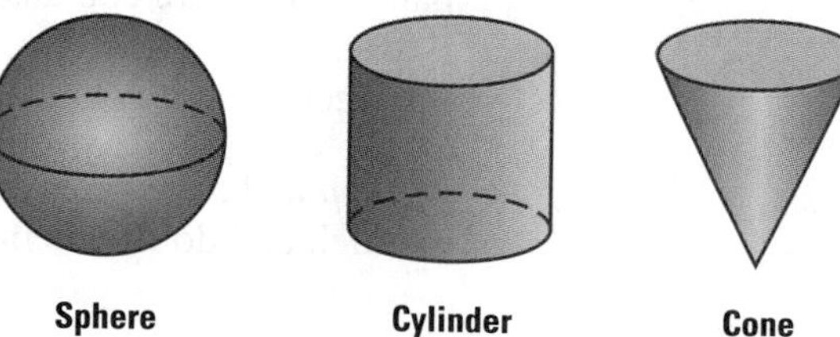

You can construct a solid by folding up its net and taping its edges.

EXAMPLE 3 ***Constructing Solids***

Describe the solid that results from folding each net.

a.

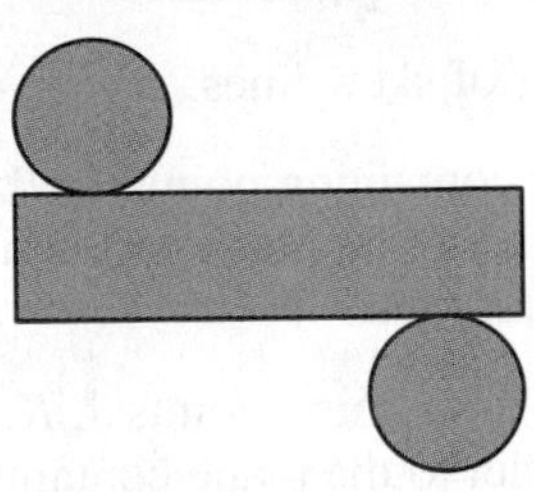

b.

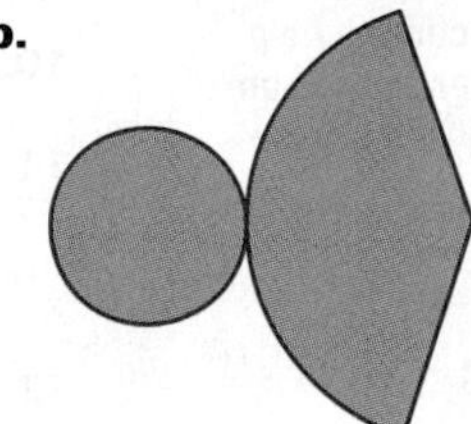

Solution

a. When the net is folded, it forms a cylinder.

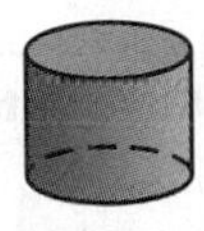

b. When the net is folded, it forms a cone.

Extra Example 3

Describe the solid that results from folding the net.

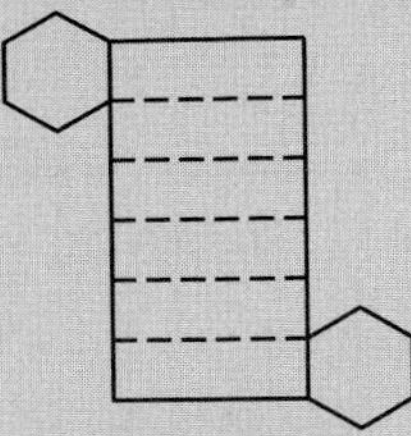

hexagonal prism

Concept Check

Complete each phrase with *always*, *sometimes*, or *never* to make a true statement.

1. Parallel lines are _?_ coplanar. **always**
2. Coplanar lines are _?_ parallel. **sometimes**
3. Skew lines are _?_ coplanar. **never**
4. Parallel lines are _?_ skew. **never**

10.2 Exercises

Guided Practice

MATHEMATICAL REASONING Tell whether the statement is *true* or *false*. Explain your answer.

1. Parallel lines are coplanar.

2. Skew lines intersect.

1. **True; parallel lines lie in the same plane.**
2. **False; skew lines do not lie in the same plane and therefore cannot intersect.**

In Exercises 3–5, match the solid with its name.

A. Prism **B.** Cone **C.** Sphere

3. **C**

4. **A**

5. **B**

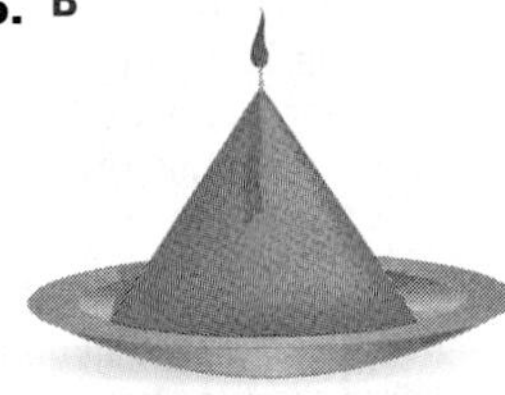

In Exercises 6–8, use the pyramid shown.

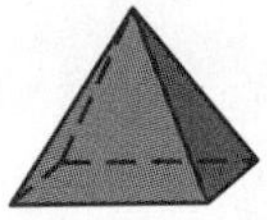

6. How many faces does the pyramid have? **5**

7. How many vertices does the pyramid have? **5**

8. How many edges does the pyramid have? **8**

3 Apply

Assignment Guide

TRANSITIONAL
Day 1: pp. 520–521 Exs. 9–12, 14–15, 21–22
Day 2: pp. 520–521 Exs. 17–20, 23–31, 37–38
AVERAGE
Day 1: pp. 520–521 Exs. 9–16, 21–22
Day 2: pp. 520–521 Exs. 17–20, 23–34, 37–38
ADVANCED
Day 1: pp. 520–521 Exs. 9–16, 21–22
Day 2: pp. 520–521 Exs. 17–20, 23–34, 35*, 36–38; EC: TE p. 506D*
BLOCK SCHEDULE
pp. 520–521 Exs. 9–34, 37–38

Extra Practice

- Student Edition, pp. 708–709
- Chapter 10 Resource Book, p. 15

Homework Check

To quickly check student understanding of key concepts, go over the following exercises:

Transitional: 10, 18, 25, 26, 30
Average: 10, 24, 30, 31, 32
Advanced: 10, 24, 26, 28, 32

Modeling Problem Solving

Exercises 14–16 and 23–24
Students who have difficulty with spatial visualization may benefit from modeling the situation described. Paper can be used to model planes in space or can be folded to model a solid. For other exercises, tracing a net and folding where indicated can help students recognize the solid figure represented.

23–25. See Additional Answers beginning on page AA1.

Practice and Problem Solving

Student Help

▶ MORE PRACTICE
Extra practice to help you master skills is on page 708.

In Exercises 9–13, use the solid shown.

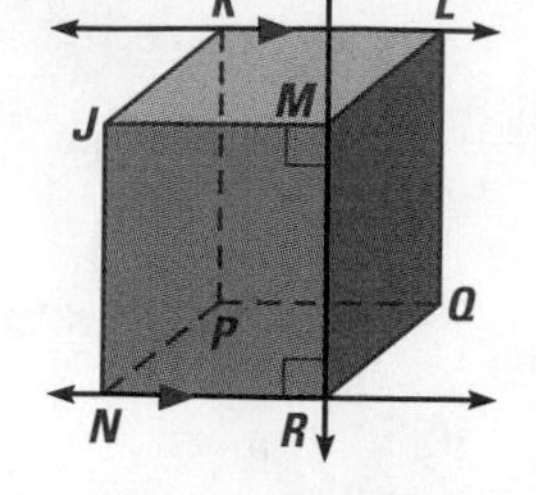

9. Name a pair of coplanar lines. **$\overleftrightarrow{NR}$ and $\overleftrightarrow{RM}$, or $\overleftrightarrow{NR}$ and $\overleftrightarrow{KL}$**

10. Name a pair of skew lines. **$\overleftrightarrow{KL}$ and $\overleftrightarrow{RM}$**

11. Is the plane containing points M, L, Q, and R parallel to the plane containing points J, M, R, and N? **No**

12. Is the plane containing points J, K, L, and M parallel to the plane containing points N, P, Q, and R? **Yes**

13. Name a segment whose length represents the distance between the planes containing points J, K, P, N and points M, L, Q, R. **$\overline{NR}$, $\overline{KL}$, $\overline{JM}$, or $\overline{PQ}$**

Determine whether there is a common intersection of the three planes. If so, tell whether the three planes intersect in a point or a line.

14. **Yes; line**

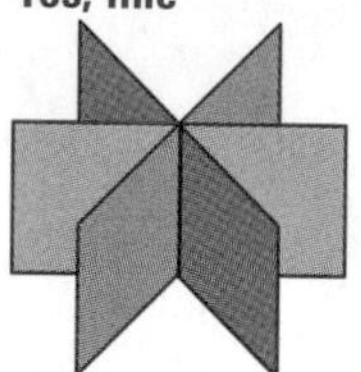

15. **No**

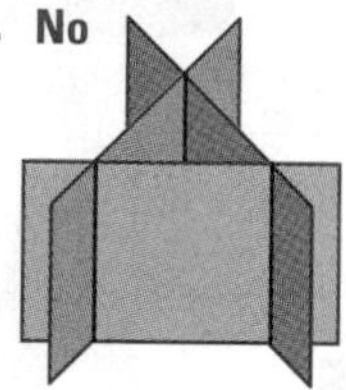

16. **Yes; point**

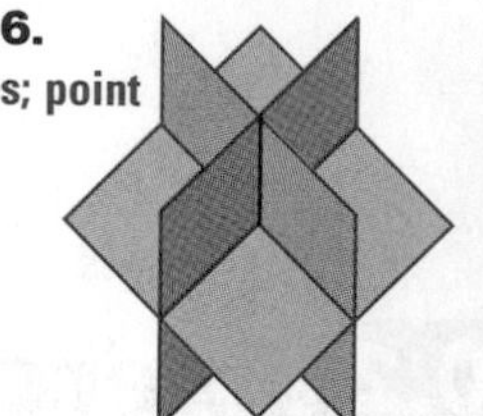

WRITING Sketch and label a net for a prism, pyramid, cylinder, and cone. Compare and contrast the nets of the two solids. **17–20. See margin.**

17. Pyramid and prism
18. Cone and cylinder
19. Pyramid and cone
20. Cylinder and prism

17–20. Sample answers are given.

17. Both nets have only straight sides.

18. Both have circular bases; a cone has a sector of a circle for a body while a cylinder has a rectangle.

19. Both have triangular or triangle-like components; the cone has a circular base while a pyramid has a base that is a polygon.

20. Both have rectangular components; the cylinder has a circular base.

In Exercises 21 and 22, use the following information. A *diagonal* of a prism connects two vertices that do <u>not</u> lie on the same face. In the prism shown, $\overline{FD}$ is a diagonal of the prism.

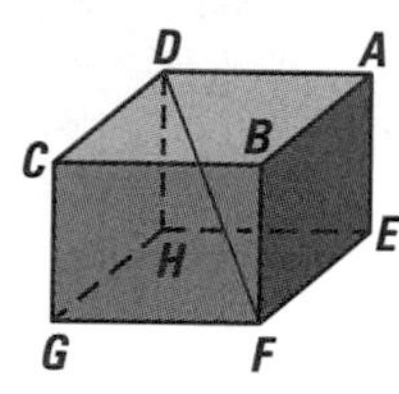

21. Name another diagonal of the prism. **$\overline{AG}$, $\overline{EC}$, or $\overline{BH}$**

22. Explain why $\overline{AH}$ is not a diagonal of the prism. **$\overline{AH}$ lies in the plane of $ADHE$.**

Sketch and label a net for the solid. **23–25. See margin.**

23.

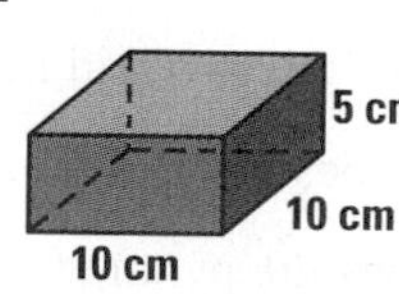

24.

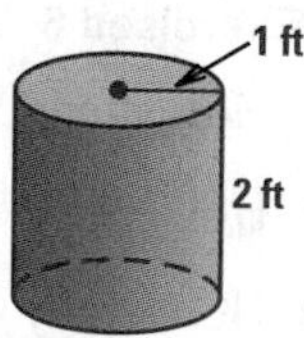

25.

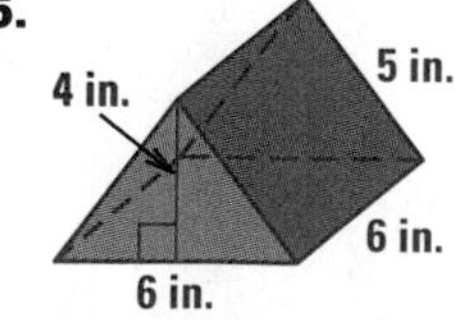

Identify the solid formed by folding the net.

26. Pyramid

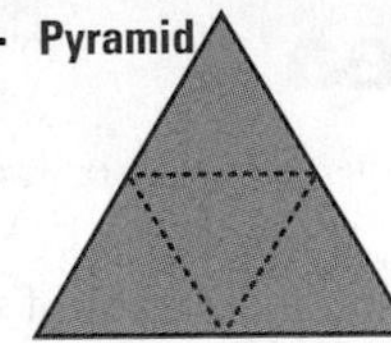

27. Cone

28. Pyramid

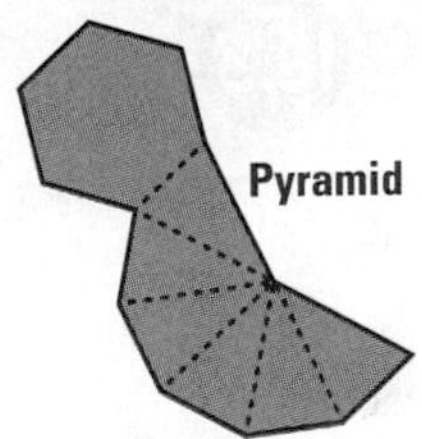

PACKAGE DESIGN Sketch the gift box that results after the net has been folded. Use the shaded face as the bottom of the box. 29–31. See margin.

29.

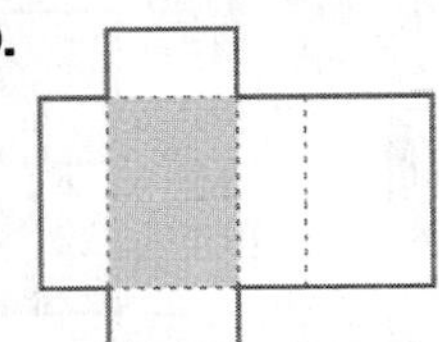

30.

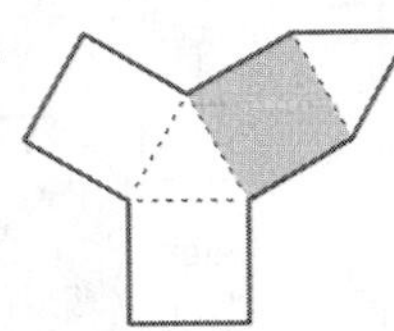

31.

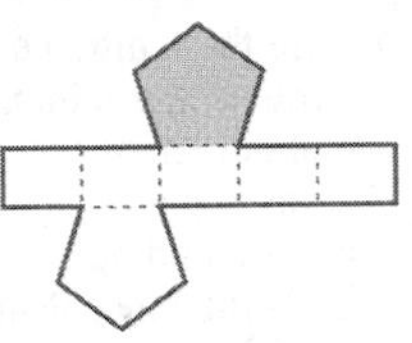

MATHEMATICAL REASONING In Exercises 32–34, determine whether the net can be folded to form a cube. If not, explain why.

32. No; If you try to fold it into a cube, two of the faces will overlap.

32.

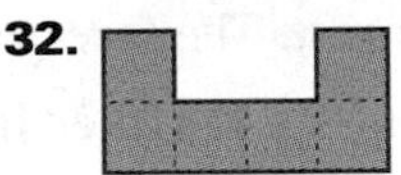

33. No; If you try to fold it into a cube, two of the faces will overlap.

34. Yes

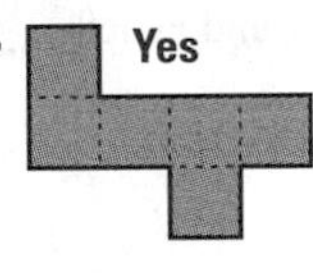

35. CHALLENGE Sketch all possible nets that can be folded to form a cube. See margin.

36. What is the least number of edges of a cube that must be cut in order to unfold it and lay it flat? 7

Multiple-Choice Practice

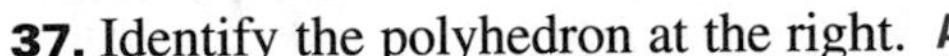

37. Identify the polyhedron at the right. A

Ⓐ Prism Ⓑ Cone

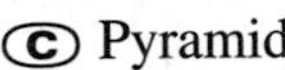

Ⓒ Pyramid Ⓓ Triangle

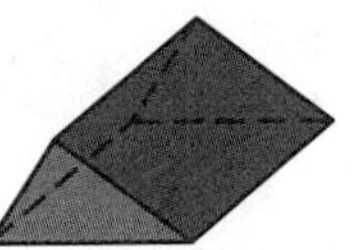

38. Decide which cube matches the net below. G

Test Tip

▶Some questions are easier to answer if you work backwards from the answer choices.

Ⓕ

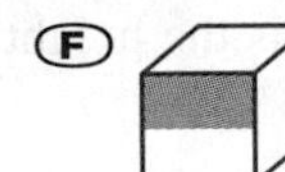

Ⓖ

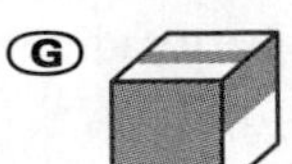

Ⓗ

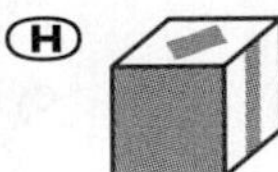

Ⓙ

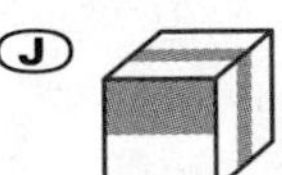

4 Assess

Assessment Resources

- Assessment Book (Formal Assessment and Alternative Assessment)
- Test and Practice Generator

Mini-Quiz

Use the diagram of the solid.

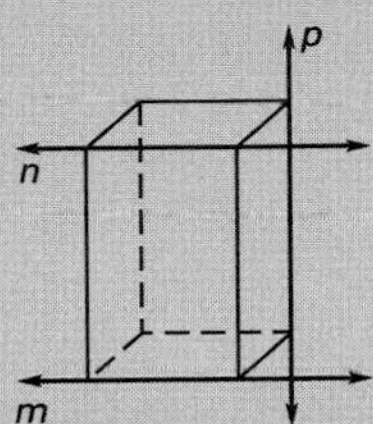

1. Name any coplanar lines. **m and n**
2. Name any skew lines. **m and p, n and p**
3. Sketch a net for the polyhedron. **Answers may vary. Sample answer is shown.**

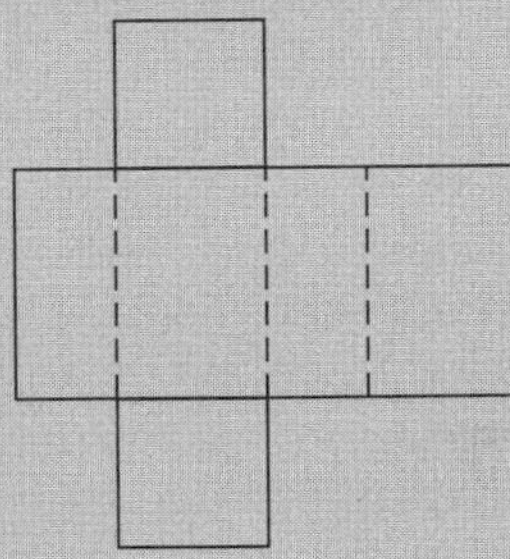

4. Describe the solid that results from folding the net shown.

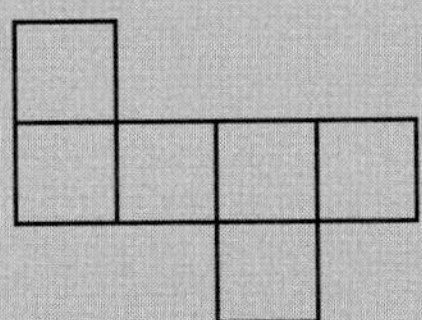

a cube

29.

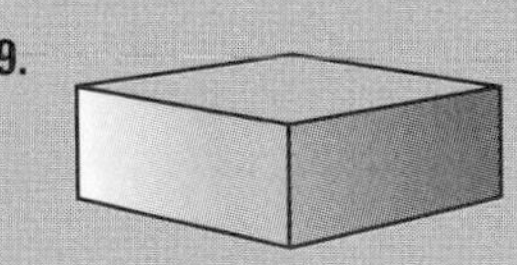

30–31, 35. See Additional Answers beginning on page AA1.

1 Planning the Activity

Purpose and Materials

See the margin of the student page. See also the Activity Support Master in the Chapter 10 Resource Book.

▶ **LINK TO LESSON**

Students will use nets to understand surface area and to develop a formula. This formula is applied to cylinders and prisms in Examples 1 and 2 of Lesson 10.3.

Math Reasoning

Students break a problem into simpler parts and develop generalizations which they apply to new situations.

2 Managing the Activity

Classroom Management

Have students work with actual nets to demonstrate the concept in the sample.

3 Closing the Activity

★ **KEY DISCOVERY**

- For a Prism: $S = 2B + Ph$
- For a Cylinder: $S = 2B + Ch$

Activity Assessment

Use Exercises 1–2 to assess student understanding.

CA Standards: MG 2.1, MR 3.2

REASONING 10.3

DEVELOPING CONCEPTS
Surface Area

For use with Lesson 10.3

California Standards

- Use formulas routinely for finding the surface area of prisms and cylinders. (MG 2.1)
- Note the method of deriving the solution and demonstrate a conceptual understanding of the derivation by solving similar problems. (MR 3.2)

MATERIALS

- Paper and pencil

The *surface area* of a prism is the sum of the areas of all its faces.

SAMPLE 1 Finding Surface Area

You can use the net for the prism shown to find its surface area.

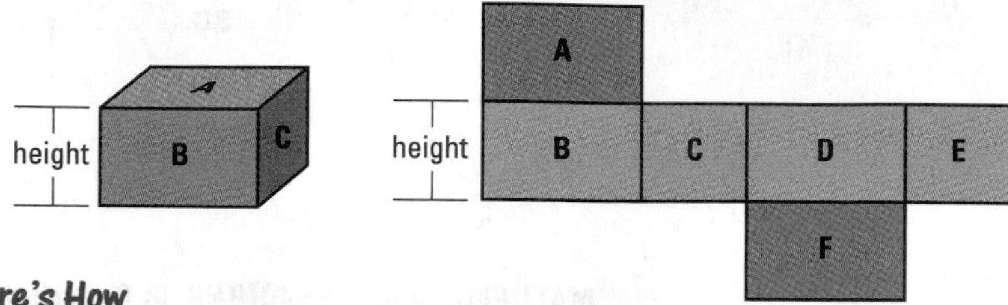

Here's How

Add the areas of the faces. The top and bottom faces (A and F) are called *bases* and are congruent. The faces can be grouped as follows:

Net = **Two congruent bases + Other faces**

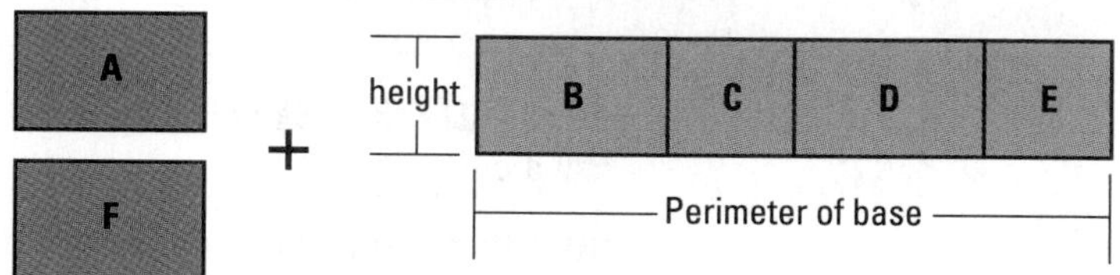

Notice that the area of the four remaining faces is equal to the base perimeter multiplied by the height of the prism. You can use this fact to write the following formula for the surface area S of a prism:

$$S = 2(\text{Base area}) + (\text{Base Perimeter}) \cdot (\text{Height of prism})$$

Try These

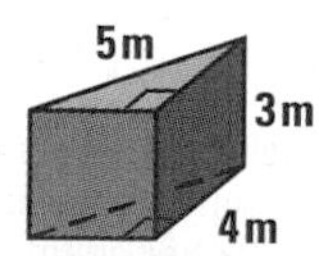

1. Use the formula from Sample 1 to find the surface area of the prism at the right. Check your answer by adding the areas of the faces. **48 m²**

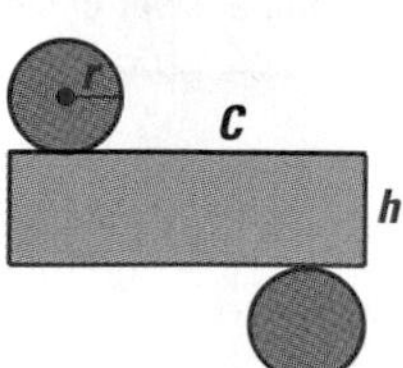

2. **MATHEMATICAL REASONING** Use the net of the cylinder shown to write a formula for the surface area. In the diagram, C is the base circumference, r is the base radius, and h is the height of the cylinder. $S = 2\pi r^2 + Ch$

10.3 Surface Areas of Prisms and Cylinders

California Standards

In this lesson you'll:

- Use formulas routinely for finding the surface area of prisms and cylinders. (MG 2.1)

Goal 1 Finding Surface Area

A **prism** is a polyhedron with two congruent faces, called **bases,** that lie in parallel planes. A **rectangular prism** is a prism whose bases are rectangles. A **circular cylinder** is a solid with congruent circular bases that lie in parallel planes. All cylinders in this book are circular. The radius of a base is also called the radius of the cylinder. The height of a prism or a cylinder is the perpendicular distance between its bases.

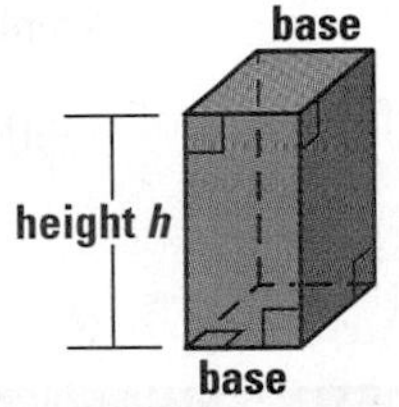

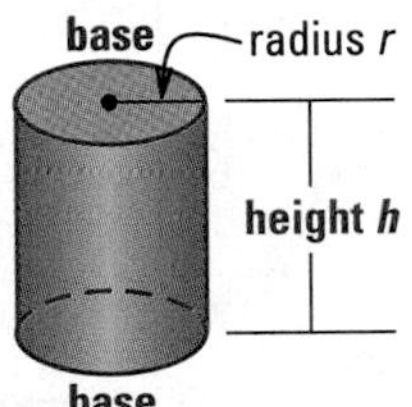

Student Help

Reading Tip
Prisms are named according to the shapes of their bases. For example, a right *triangular* prism is a right prism whose bases are *triangles.*

In a **right prism,** shown above on the left, the edges connecting the bases are perpendicular to the bases. In a **right cylinder,** the segment joining the centers of the bases is perpendicular to the bases. The **surface area** of a solid is the sum of the areas of all the surfaces that bound the solid. The formulas for the surface area of a right prism and a right cylinder, as you learned in Developing Concepts 10.3, page 522, are given below.

Surface Area of a Right Prism and a Right Cylinder

Prism The surface area S of a right prism is $S = 2B + Ph$ where B is the base area, P is the base perimeter, and h is the height of the prism.

Cylinder The surface area S of a right cylinder is $S = 2B + Ch$ where B is the base area, C is the base circumference, and h is the height of the cylinder.

Student Help

Technology Tip
If your calculator has a π key, it will use a value of π with many decimal places. So, you will need to round your final answer. Throughout the rest of this chapter, the calculator value of π will be used in examples.

Example 1 Finding the Surface Area of a Cylinder

You can find the surface area of the right cylinder as follows.

$S = 2B + Ch$	Write formula.
$= 2(9\pi) + 6\pi(10)$	Substitute.
$= 18\pi + 60\pi$	Multiply.
$= 78\pi$	Add.
≈ 245.04	Use a calculator.

ANSWER ▶ The surface area is about 245 square meters.

1 Plan

Pacing
Suggested Number of Days
Transitional: 2 days
Average: 2 days
Advanced: 2 days
Block Schedule: 1 block

Teaching Resources

Blacklines
(See page 506B.)

Transparencies
- Warm-Up Exercises
- Teacher Time-Savers
- English/Spanish Problem Solving
- Answers

Technology
- Electronic Teacher Tools
- Test and Practice Generator

2 Teach

Math Reasoning

For Mathematical Background Notes on mathematical reasoning related to this lesson, please refer to pages 506E and 506F in this Teacher's Edition.

Extra Example 1
See next page.

California Standards and Assessment
CA Standard: MG 2.1

Extra Example 1

Find the surface area of a right cylinder with a base area of 25π ft^2, a circumference of 10π ft, and a height of 4 ft. 90π ft$^2 \approx 282.7$ ft^2

Teaching Tip

Explain to students that 3.14 is just an approximation of π. Many calculators have a key for π that will display up to 8 decimal places. This will give a more precise calculation than using 3.14.

Extra Example 2

Find the surface area of a right rectangular prism with length 10 inches, width 3 inches, and height 8 inches. 268 in.^{2}

Extra Example 3

Estimate the amount of material needed to make the cylindrical pillow shown.

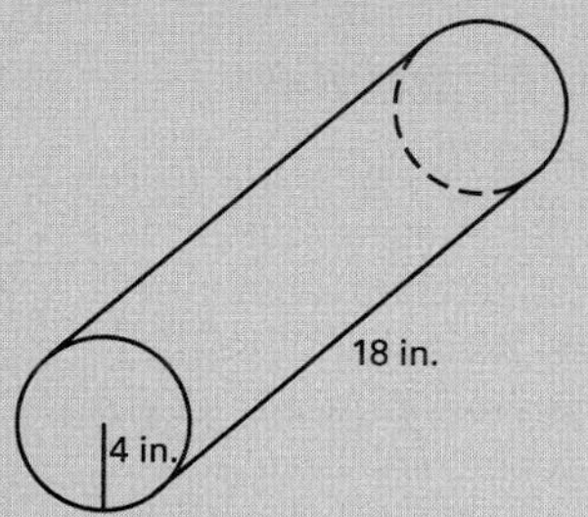

about 552.92 in.^{2}

Student Help

▶LOOK BACK
For help with finding the area of a triangle, see page 22.

EXAMPLE 2 Finding the Surface Area of a Prism

Find the surface area of the right prism.

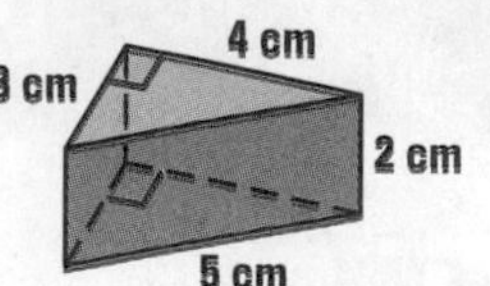

Solution

Find its base area using the formula for the area of a triangle. The base area is:

$$B = \frac{1}{2}bh = \frac{1}{2} \cdot 3 \cdot 4 = 6 \text{ cm}^2$$

The base perimeter P is $3 + 4 + 5 = 12$ centimeters. Use the base perimeter and base area to find the surface area.

$S = 2B + Ph$	Write formula.
$= 2 \cdot 6 + 12 \cdot 2$	Substitute for B, P, and h.
$= 36$	Simplify.

ANSWER ▶ The surface area of the prism is 36 square centimeters.

Goal 2 SOLVING REAL-LIFE PROBLEMS

EXAMPLE 3 Using Surface Area

CANNED GOODS Estimate the amount of material needed to make the cylindrical can.

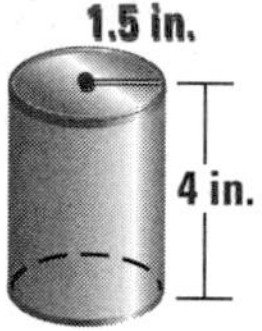

Solution

To estimate the amount of material, find the surface area of the can. Start by finding the base area and base circumference.

$B = \pi r^2$	$C = 2\pi r$	Write formula.
$= \pi(1.5)^2$	$= 2\pi(1.5)$	Substitute for r.
$= 2.25\pi$ in.^{2}	$= 3\pi$ in.	Simplify.

Use the base area and base circumference to find the surface area.

$S = 2B + Ch$	Write formula for surface area.
$= 2 \cdot 2.25\pi + 3\pi \cdot 4$	Substitute for B, C, and h.
$= 4.5\pi + 12\pi$	Multiply.
$= 16.5\pi$	Add.
≈ 51.84	Use a calculator.

ANSWER ▶ The surface area is about 52 square inches. This means that it will take about 52 square inches of material to make the can, if you assume there is no waste in the manufacturing process.

EXAMPLE 4 Comparing Surface Areas

Student Help

▶ READING TIP
A *box* is understood to be a right prism with rectangular bases.

CONTAINERS The two containers shown hold about the same amount of cereal. The surface area of the cylindrical container is about 206 square inches. Is the surface area of the box more or less? What does this imply?

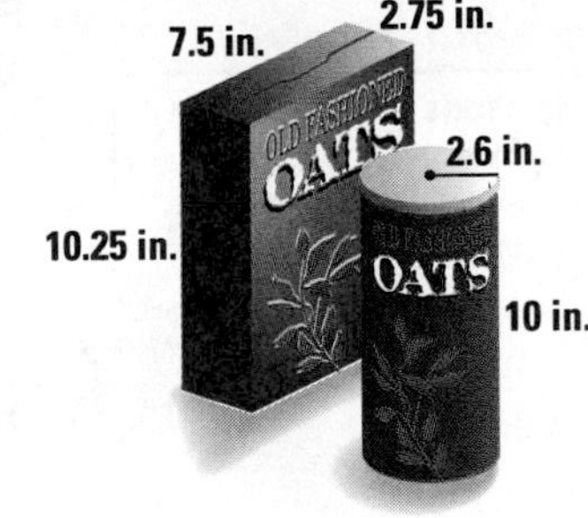

Solution

Start by finding the surface area of the box. The base area and base perimeter of the box are as follows:

$B = \ell \cdot w$	$P = 2\ell + 2w$	Write formula.
$= 7.5 \cdot 2.75$	$= 2(7.5) + 2(2.75)$	Substitute.
$= 20.625 \text{ in.}^2$	$= 20.5 \text{ in.}$	Simplify.

Use these values to find the surface area.

$S = 2B + Ph$	Write formula for surface area.
$= 2 \cdot 20.625 + 20.5 \cdot 10.25$	Substitute for *B*, *P*, and *h*.
$= 251.375$	Simplify.

ANSWER ▶ The surface area of the box is about 251 square inches. The cylindrical container has a smaller surface area. This means that it takes less material (assuming no waste) to manufacture the cylindrical container.

10.3 Exercises

Guided Practice

In Exercises 1–3, use the diagram of the right rectangular prism.

1. Find its base area. **45 ft²**

2. Find its base perimeter. **36 ft**

3. Find its surface area. **342 ft²**

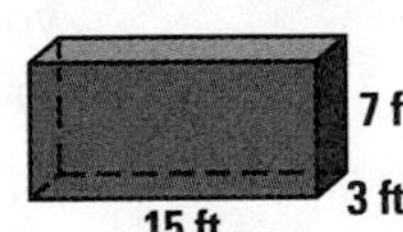

Find (a) the base perimeter (or base circumference) and (b) the base area of the right prism or right cylinder. (In Exercise 4, the prism has rectangular bases.)

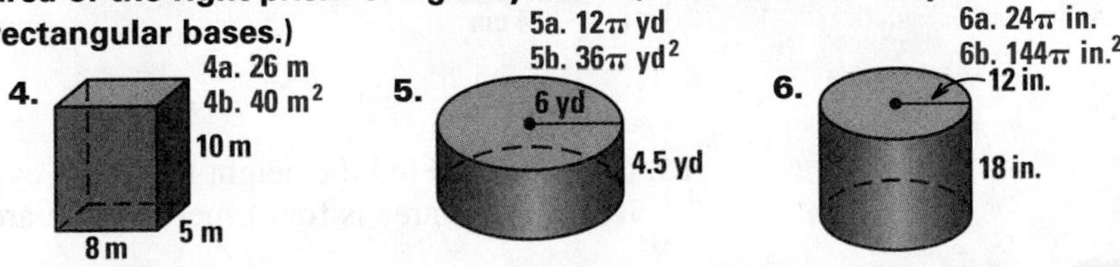

Extra Example 4

A company is considering changing the packaging of their product from a box that is a right rectangular prism to a right prism with a trapezoidal base as shown. The surface area of the trapezoidal prism is about 306.5 cm². What is the surface area of the current box? Which do you think would be cheaper to manufacture?

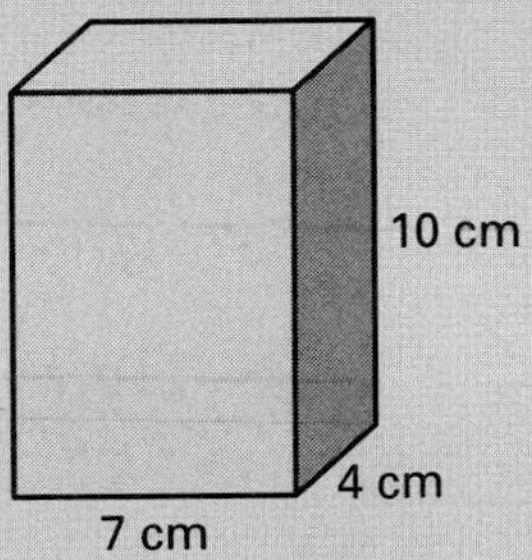

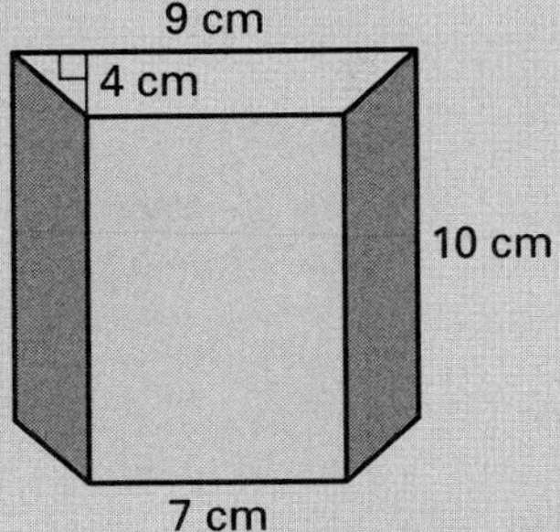

***S.A.* of current box is 276 cm². Since it uses less material, it would be cheaper to manufacture.**

Concept Check

Chuck calculates the surface area of a right rectangular prism by using the formula $S.A. = 2B + Ph$. Anne calculates the surface area of the same prism by finding the areas of each of the six sides and adding them together. Will they get the same answer? Explain your reasoning. **Assuming both Chuck and Anne follow their processes correctly, they will get the same answer. When Chuck uses *Ph* in this formula, he is using the distributive property as a faster way to find the sum of the areas of the four sides other than the bases.**

3 Apply

Assignment Guide

TRANSITIONAL
Day 1: pp. 526–527 Exs. 7–12, 25–32
Day 2: pp. 526–527 Exs. 13–16, 20–24
AVERAGE
Day 1: pp. 526–527 Exs. 7–12, 25–35
Day 2: pp. 526–527. Exs. 13–17, 20–24
ADVANCED
Day 1: pp. 526–527 Exs. 7–12, 25–35
Day 2: pp. 526–527 Exs. 13–17, 19*, 20–24
BLOCK SCHEDULE
pp. 526–527 Exs. 7–17, 20–35

Extra Practice

- Student Edition, pp. 708–709
- Chapter 10 Resource Book, p. 24

Homework Check

To quickly check student understanding of key concepts, go over the following exercises:

Transitional: 8, 9, 11, 16, 22
Average: 8, 9, 11, 14, 22
Advanced: 8, 9, 11, 14, 22

Math Reasoning

Take note of the fact that in Exercises 13–14 the surface area of the large cube is not the sum of the surface areas of the smaller cubes. However the volume of the large cube *is* the sum of the volumes of the small cubes.

15.

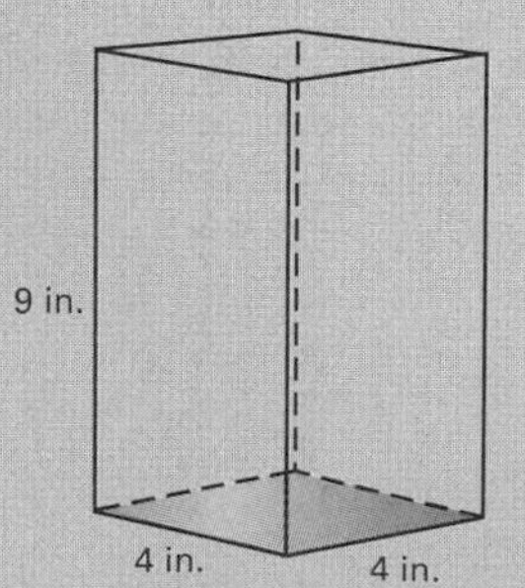

Practice and Problem Solving

Student Help

▶ **MORE PRACTICE**
Extra practice to help you master skills is on page 708.

Find the surface area of the right prism or right cylinder. (In Exercises 7 and 11, the prisms have rectangular bases.)

7. $664\ ft^2$

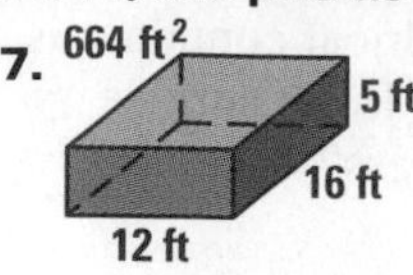

8. $1120\pi\ m^2$

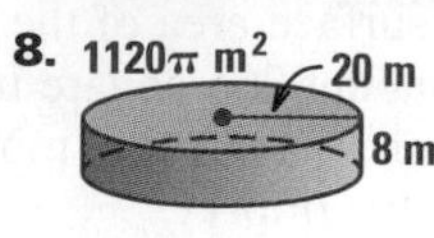

9. $144\ cm^2$

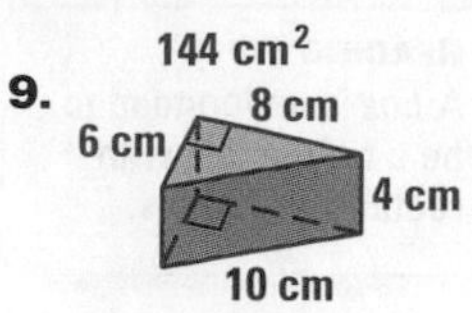

10. $800\pi\ mm^2$

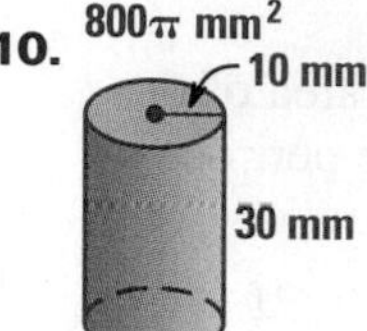

11. $40\ in.^2$

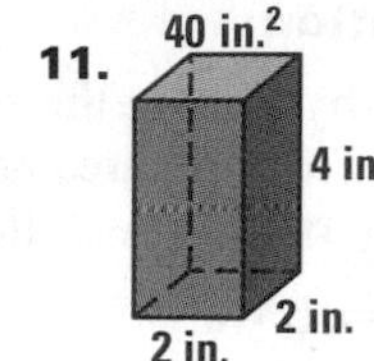

12. $486\pi\ yd^2$

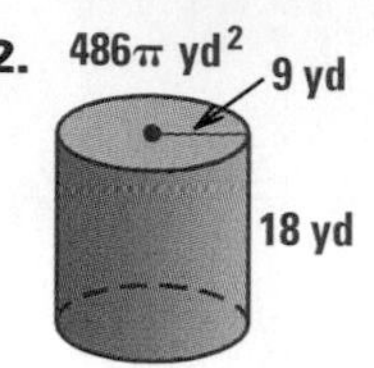

In Exercises 13 and 14, use the figure shown.

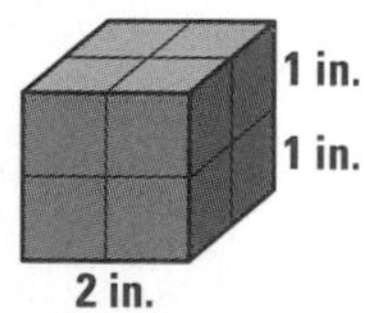

13. Find the surface area of the large cube. **$24\ in.^2$**

14. The large cube is cut into eight congruent smaller cubes. Find the surface area of each smaller cube. What is the total surface area of the eight cubes? **$6\ in.^2$; $48\ in.^2$**

15. Draw a right prism with square bases. Use dashed lines and shading to make the prism appear three-dimensional. Find the surface area of the prism when each base edge is 4 inches long and the height of the prism is 9 inches. **$176\ in.^2$; See margin.**

17. Surface area of shorter container is $24\pi\ in.^2$; Surface area of taller container is $26.32\pi\ in.^2$ The shorter container has the smaller surface area.

16. *Chapter Opener Link* Look back to page 507. Find the surface area of the tank using the formula for the surface area of a right prism. **$166\ ft^2$**

Student Help

▶ **HOMEWORK HELP**

Extra help with problem solving in Ex. 17 is available at www.mcdougallittell.com

17. MATHEMATICAL REASONING The two containers at the right hold about the same amount of liquid. Just by looking at them, guess which container has the smaller surface area. Find the surface area of both containers to check your answer. **See margin.**

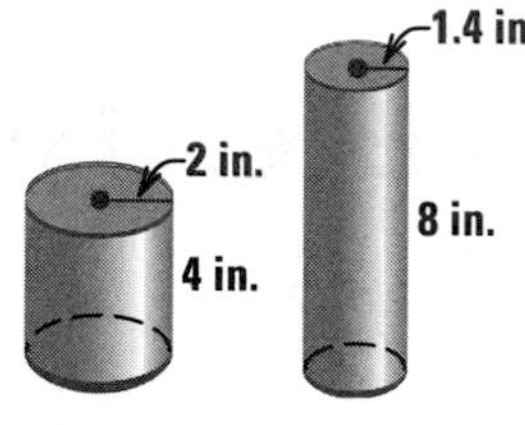

18. GIFT WRAPPING Determine which sheet of wrapping paper you should use to wrap a box that measures 45 centimeters by 27 centimeters by 6 centimeters. Explain your reasoning. **See margin.**

18. Surface area of box is $3294\ cm^2$. Wrap A is also $3294\ cm^2$ and could be used with no overlap. Wrap B is $3536\ cm^2$ and would be a better choice. Wrap C is too small.

A. 61 cm; 54 cm

B.

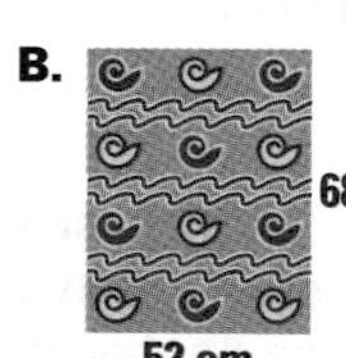

C.

19. CHALLENGE Find the height of a right cylinder with a radius of 6 feet if its surface area is four times its base area. **6 ft**

FARMING In Exercises 20–22, use the following information. Feed for animals can be stored in a tower silo or a bunker. The tower silo is a cylinder, and the bunker is a rectangular prism. Suppose a tower silo is 56 feet high and has a diameter of 36 feet, and a bunker is 50 feet wide, 95 feet long, and 12 feet high. Both the silo and the bunker described hold about the same amount of feed.

20. Find the surface area of the tower silo, excluding the area of its floor. **7351 ft^2**

21. Find the surface area of the bunker, excluding the area of its floor. **8230 ft^2**

22. Compare the two surface areas you found in Exercises 20 and 21. Give a reason why one storage container might be chosen over the other. Explain your reasoning. **The silo is better because it has a smaller footprint and takes less material to build.**

Multiple-Choice Practice

23. What is the surface area of the right prism? **A**

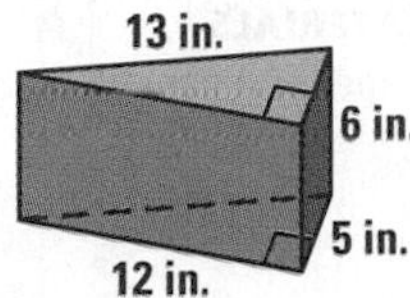

Ⓐ 240 in.^{2} Ⓑ 245 in.^{2}

Ⓒ 310 in.^{2} Ⓓ 324 in.^{2}

24. Which is the best estimate of the surface area of a 12 ounce beverage can with a radius of 1.25 inches and a height of 5 inches? **H**

Ⓕ 25 in.^{2} Ⓖ 35 in.^{2} Ⓗ 50 in.^{2} Ⓙ 100 in.^{2}

Mixed Review

Solve the proportion. Check your solution. *(7.2)*

25. $\frac{3}{4} = \frac{x}{32}$ **24** **26.** $\frac{18}{5} = \frac{3}{y}$ **$\frac{5}{6}$** **27.** $\frac{z}{6} = \frac{5}{9}$ **$\frac{10}{3}$** **28.** $\frac{24}{w} = \frac{3}{5}$ **40**

SIMPLE INTEREST In Exercises 29 and 30, use the following information. Your brother borrows $200 from you at 10% annual simple interest rate. *(7.8)*

29. Find the simple interest your brother owes you after six months. **$10**

30. Find the total amount your brother owes you after one year. **$220**

COMPOUND INTEREST In Exercises 31 and 32, use the following information. A bank advertises a 6% annual interest rate compounded monthly. *(7.9)*

31. How many times during the year is interest added to the account? **Twelve**

32. You deposit $150 in this account with no additions or withdrawals. Find the balance of the account at the end of one year. **$159.25**

33–35. See margin.

Solve the inequality. Then graph the solution. *(9.6, 9.7, 9.8)*

33. $-24 \le -2y$ **$y \le 12$** **34.** $13z + 26 > 0$ **$z > -2$** **35.** $7 - 6t > 4t$ **$t < \frac{7}{10}$**

4 Assess

Assessment Resources

- Assessment Book (Formal Assessment and Alternative Assessment)
- Test and Practice Generator

Mini-Quiz

1. Find the surface area of a right cylinder with radius 3 cm and height 8 cm. **about 207.35 cm^2**
2. Find the surface area of the right prism.

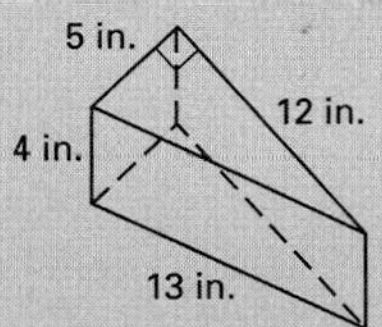

180 in.^{2}

3. Baby cereal comes in a cylindrical container with a diameter of 5 in. and a height of 6 in. The same cereal also comes in a box measuring 6 in. × 8 in. × 1.5 in. Find the surface area of each container. Which container requires the smaller amount of material to construct (assuming no waste)?
S.A. of cylinder is about 133.52 in.^{2}. S.A. of box is about 138 in.^{2}. The cylinder requires less material.

33.

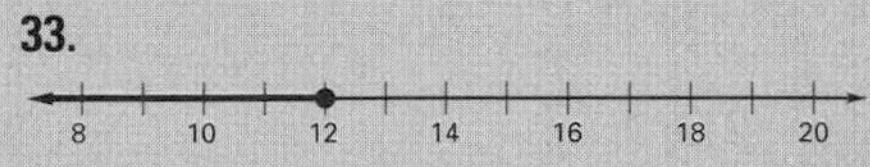

34.

−8 −6 −4 −2 0 2 4 6 8

35.

Planning the Activity

Purpose and Materials

See the margin of the student page. See also the Activity Support Master in the Chapter 10 Resource Book.

▶ LINK TO LESSON

In this activity students will develop the formula for finding the volume of a prism. This formula is applied in Example 1 of Lesson 10.4.

Math Reasoning

Students are

- Analyzing problems by observing patterns
- Formulating and justifying mathematical conjectures
- Applying strategies and results from simpler problems to more complex problems

California Standards and Assessment

CA Standards: MG 2.1, MR3.3

REASONING 10.4

DEVELOPING CONCEPTS
Volume of a Prism

For use with Lesson 10.4

California Standards

- ▶ Use formulas routinely for finding the volume of prisms. (MG 2.1)
- ▶ Develop generalizations of the results obtained and apply them to new problem situations. (MR 3.3)

MATERIALS

- Paper and pencil

The *volume* of a solid is a measure of how much space it occupies. Unit cubes can be used to find the volume of a right rectangular prism. A unit cube is shown at the right. It has a volume of 1 cubic unit.

Unit cube

SAMPLE 1 Finding the Volume of a Right Prism

Find the volume of the right rectangular prism.

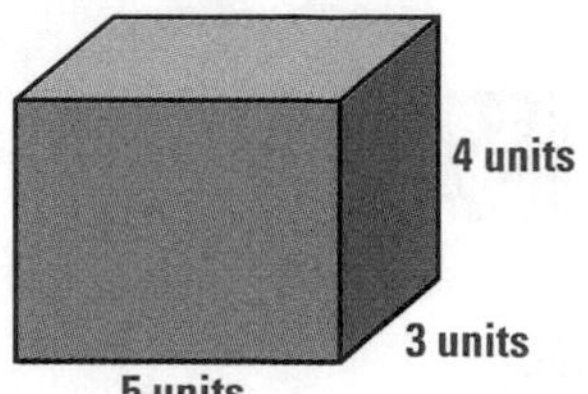

Here's How

Think of the prism as an empty box. The volume of the box is equal to the number of unit cubes that fit inside the box.

❶ It takes 15 cubes to cover the bottom of the box.

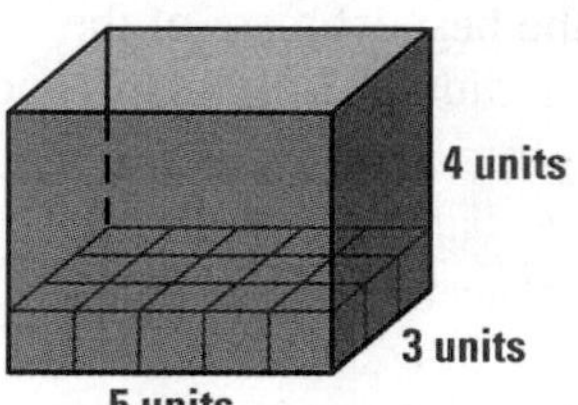

❷ It takes three more layers of 15 cubes to fill the box.

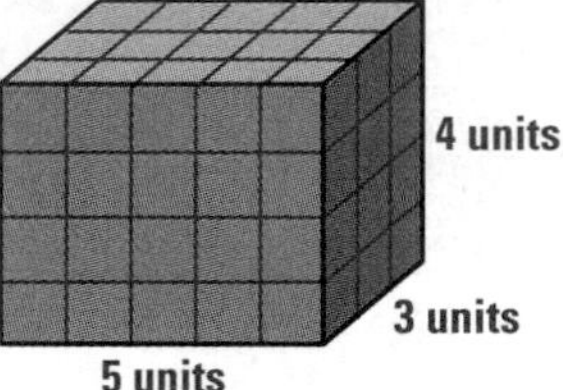

Because the box holds 4 layers of 15 cubes, it contains a total of $4 \cdot 15 = 60$ unit cubes. Each cube has a volume of 1 cubic unit, so the volume of the prism is 60 cubic units.

In Sample 1, notice that the number of layers of unit cubes is equal to the height of the prism, which is 4 units. Also, the number of unit cubes that cover a base is equal to the base area, which is $3 \cdot 5 = 15$ square units. So, the volume of the prism can be found as follows:

$$\text{Volume} = (\text{Base area}) \cdot (\text{Height})$$

This formula is true for any right prism.

Try These

1. Find the volume of the right prism shown. **544.5 ft^3**
2. **MATHEMATICAL REASONING** Write a formula for the volume of a right rectangular prism given its length ℓ, its width w, and its height h. $V = lwh$

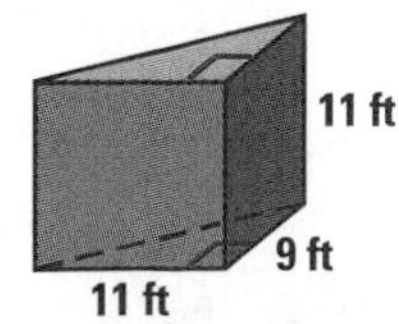

SAMPLE 2 Finding the Volume of an Oblique Prism

In an *oblique* prism, the edges connecting the bases are *not* perpendicular to the bases and its height is the perpendicular distance between its bases. By rearranging the pieces of an oblique rectangular prism, you can form a right rectangular prism with the same volume.

Here's How

1. Visualize the midpoints P, Q, R, and S of the edges connecting the bases.

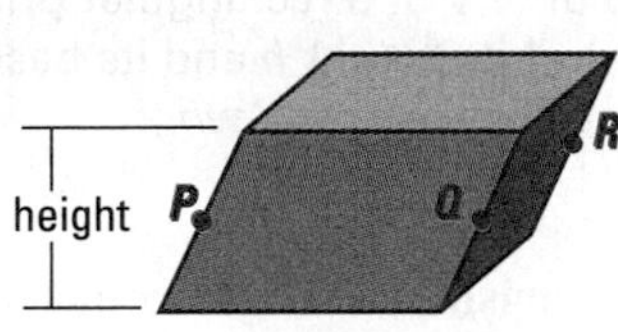

2. Slice the corners of the prism at the midpoints to form two congruent triangular prisms.

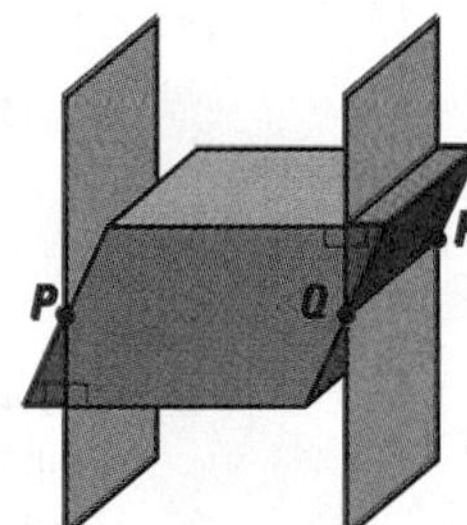

3. Rearrange the pieces to form a right rectangular prism.

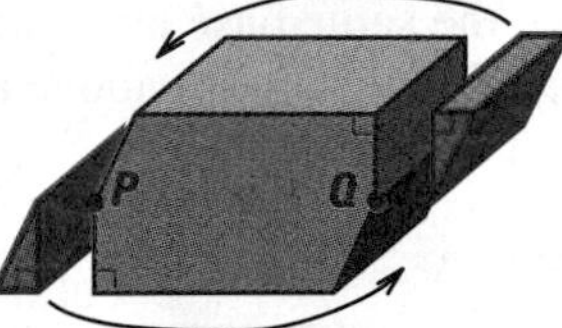

4. The right prism has the same base area and height as the oblique prism.

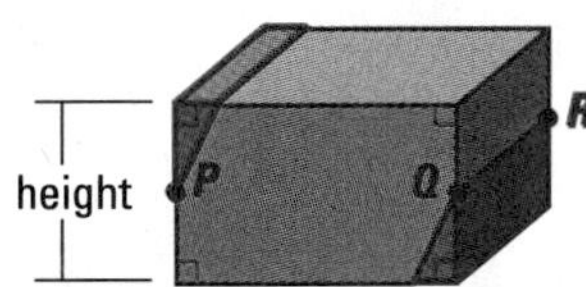

So, the right prism has the same volume as the oblique prism.

More elaborate forms of "cutting and gluing" can be used to show that the volume of an oblique prism is equal to the volume of a right prism with the same base area and height. So, the volume formula for a right prism applies to oblique prisms as well.

Try These

3. Find the volume of the oblique prism at the right. 24 m^3

   (Figure: 3 m, 4 m, 4 m, 5 m)

4. **MATHEMATICAL REASONING** An oblique prism has twice the base area and half the height of a right prism. What can you say about their volumes?

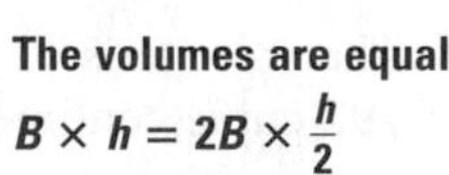
The volumes are equal.
$B \times h = 2B \times \frac{h}{2}$

2 Managing the Activity

Classroom Management

You can demonstrate that an oblique prism appears to have the same volume as a right prism with a deck of cards. As a deck, it is a right prism with a "volume" of 52 cards. Slide the cards until the lateral edges of the deck are at an angle. It is now an oblique prism, but its "volume" is still 52 cards.

3 Closing the Activity

★ **KEY DISCOVERY**

Volume of a prism = Bh where B is the area of the base and h is the height of the prism.

Activity Assessment

Use Exercise 4 to assess student understanding.

1 Plan

Pacing

Suggested Number of Days

Transitional: 2 days
Average: 2 days
Advanced: 2 days
Block Schedule: 1 block

Teaching Resources

Blacklines

(See page 506B.)

Transparencies

- Warm-Up Exercises
- Teacher Time-Savers
- English/Spanish Problem Solving
- Answers

Technology

- Electronic Teacher Tools
- Test and Practice Generator

2 Teach

Math Reasoning

For Mathematical Background Notes on mathematical reasoning related to this lesson, please refer to pages 506E and 506F in this Teacher's Edition.

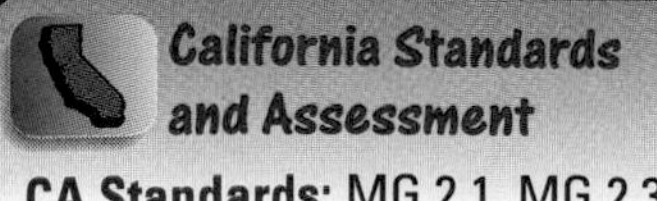

California Standards and Assessment

CA Standards: MG 2.1, MG 2.3

10.4 Volume of a Prism

California Standards

In this lesson you'll:

- Use formulas routinely for finding the volume of prisms. (MG 2.1)
- Compute the volume of a three-dimensional object built from rectangular solids. (MG 2.3)

Goal 1 FINDING THE VOLUME OF A PRISM

The **volume** of a solid is a measure of the amount of space the solid occupies. Volume is measured in *cubic units*, such as cubic inches. Cubic units can be converted into other measures of volume, such as liters, as discussed on page 536.

VOLUME OF A PRISM

1. The volume V of a prism is the product of its height h and its base area B. So, $V = Bh$.
2. The volume V of a rectangular prism is the product of its height h and its base area B. Because $B = \ell w$, $V = \ell wh$.

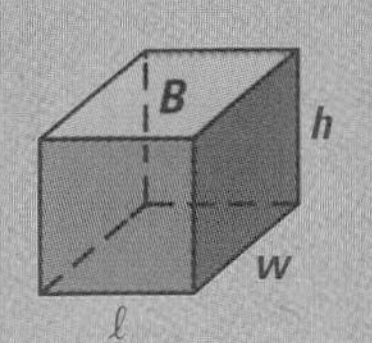

In an **oblique prism**, the edges connecting the bases are *not* perpendicular to the bases. The height of an oblique prism is the perpendicular distance between the bases. As you discovered in Developing Concepts 10.4, page 528, the volume of an oblique prism is equal to the volume of a right prism with the same base area and height. The first volume formula given above applies to both right and oblique prisms.

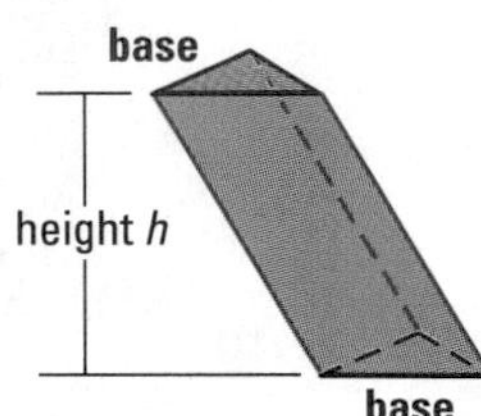

EXAMPLE 1 Finding the Volume of a Prism

Find the volume of the prism.

a.

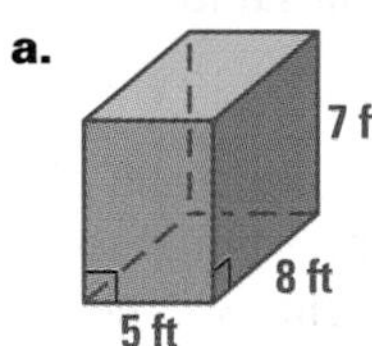

b. $B = 24$ cm^2

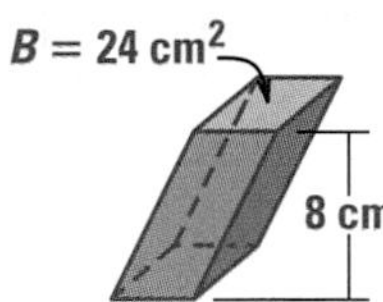

Solution

a. $V = \ell wh$

$= 5 \cdot 8 \cdot 7$

$= 280$

ANSWER ▶ The volume is 280 cubic feet.

b. $V = Bh$

$= 24 \cdot 8$

$= 192$

ANSWER ▶ The volume is 192 cubic centimeters.

Goal 2 USING VOLUME IN REAL LIFE

EXAMPLE 2 Finding the Width of a Prism

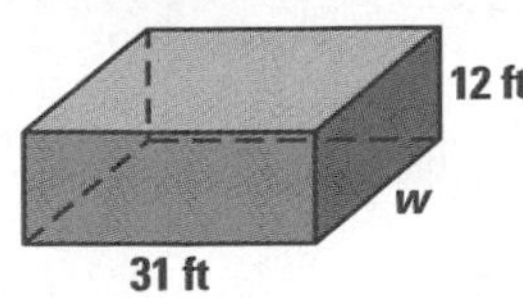

COMPUTER ROOM Your school is sectioning off part of a large room to create a computer room. The computer room should hold 35 people. The ventilation system requires that each person have 275 cubic feet of air space.

The wall in place is 31 feet long and 12 feet high. About how far from the existing wall should the new wall be built?

Solution

The computer room is to hold 35 people, each needing 275 cubic feet of air space. So, the room needs to be $35 \cdot 275 = 9625$ cubic feet in volume. Use the volume formula to find the width.

$V = \ell wh$	Write volume formula.
$9625 = 31 \cdot w \cdot 12$	Substitute for V, ℓ, and h.
$9625 = 372 \cdot w$	Simplify.
$25.87 \approx w$	Divide each side by 372.

ANSWER ▶ The computer room should be about 26 feet wide.

Some solids are made up of different prisms. To find the volume of such a solid, divide the solid into prisms that do not overlap, find the volume of each prism, and add the volumes together.

EXAMPLE 3 Finding the Volume of a Complex Solid

HISTORY LINK The first pyramids were step pyramids like the one shown. Find the volume of the step pyramid at the right. Each prism in the pyramid has square bases.

13 ft
13 ft
13 ft
36 ft
54 ft
72 ft

Solution

Find the volume of each prism.

$V_1 = \ell_1 w_1 h_1$ $= 72 \cdot 72 \cdot 13$ $= 67{,}392$

$V_2 = \ell_2 w_2 h_2$ $= 54 \cdot 54 \cdot 13$ $= 37{,}908$

$V_3 = \ell_3 w_3 h_3$ $= 36 \cdot 36 \cdot 13$ $= 16{,}848$

Add the volumes to find the volume of the entire pyramid.

$$V_1 + V_2 + V_3 = 67{,}392 + 37{,}908 + 16{,}848 = 122{,}148$$

ANSWER ▶ The volume of the pyramid is 122,148 cubic feet.

Link to History

MAYAN PYRAMIDS This pyramid is located in the ancient Mayan city of Chichén Itzá. Its base measures 180 feet on each side.

INTERNET More about ancient pyramids available at www.mcdougallittell.com

Extra Example 1

Find the volume of the prism.

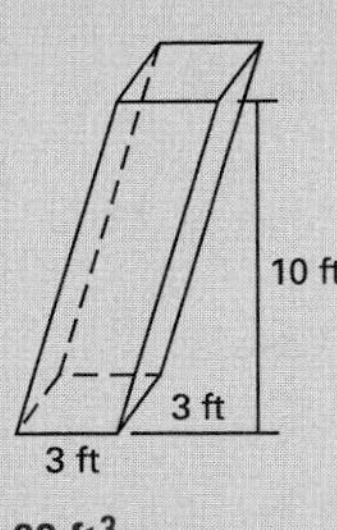

90 ft³

Extra Example 2

A cereal company is designing a rectangular prism package for a new cereal. The volume must be 176 cubic inches in order to hold the proper amount of cereal. The marketing department has set the width and height of the box to be 8 in. and 11 in., respectively. What must the depth of the box be to have the specified volume? **2 in.**

Extra Example 3

An office building is shaped like the letter "H" as shown. Find the total volume of the building.

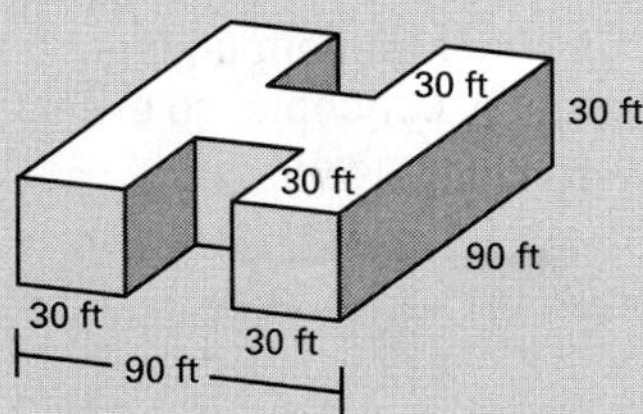

189,000 ft³

Concept Check

You are asked to find the volume of a right triangular prism, a right rectangular prism, and a right octagonal prism (base is an octagon). How are these three calculations similar and how are they different? **All three volumes can be found using the formula $V = Bh$ where B is the area of the base of the prism and h is the height of the prism. Since the three bases are all different shapes, the processes used to find their areas will be different.**

3 Apply

Assignment Guide

TRANSITIONAL
Day 1: pp. 532–533 Exs. 8–13, 20–21
Day 2: pp. 532–533 Exs.15–18, 27–28

AVERAGE
Day 1: pp. 532–533 Exs. 8–13, 20–21, 23–25
Day 2: pp. 532–533 Exs. 14–19, 22, 27–28

ADVANCED
Day 1: pp. 532–533 Exs. 8–13, 20–25
Day 2: pp. 532–533 Exs. 14–19, 26*, 27–28

BLOCK SCHEDULE
pp. 532–533 Exs. 8–25, 27–28

Extra Practice

- Student Edition, pp. 708–709
- Chapter 10 Resource Book, p. 33

Homework Check

To quickly check student understanding of key concepts, go over the following exercises:

Transitional: 8, 9,11, 12, 14, 18
Average: 8, 11, 12, 16, 18
Advanced: 8, 11, 12, 16, 18

10.4 Exercises

Guided Practice

In Exercises 1–3, use the diagram to find the indicated measurement of the right prism.

1. Height **2 cm**

2. Base area **6 cm²**

3. Volume **12 cm³**

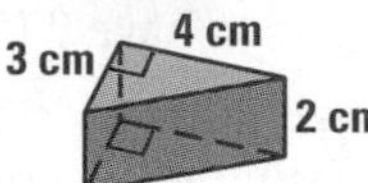

4. Describe the difference between a right prism and an oblique prism.

4. In a right prism, the edges connecting the bases are perpendicular to the bases; in an oblique prism, the edges are not perpendicular to the bases.

CONTAINERS **Find the volume of the right rectangular prism.**

5. **120 in.³**

6. **200 in.³**

4 in.
10 in.
5 in.

7. **343 cm³**

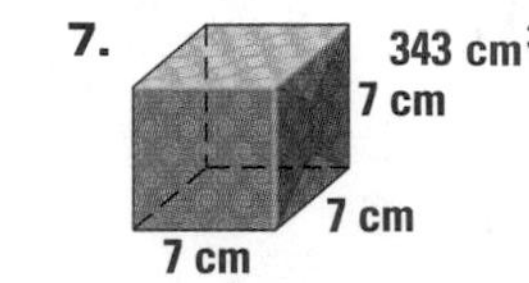

Practice and Problem Solving

Student Help

▶ MORE PRACTICE
Extra practice to help you master skills is on page 708.

Find the volume of the prism. (The solids in Exercises 8, 10, and 11 are right prisms.)

8. **336 cm³**

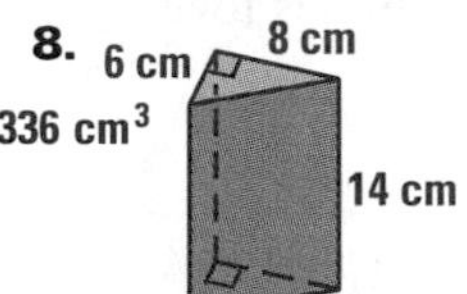

9. $B = 12$ yd² **84 yd³**

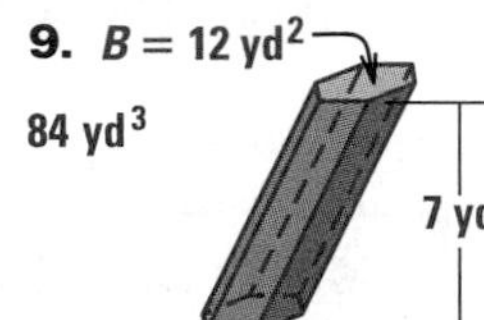

10. **519.6 in.³**

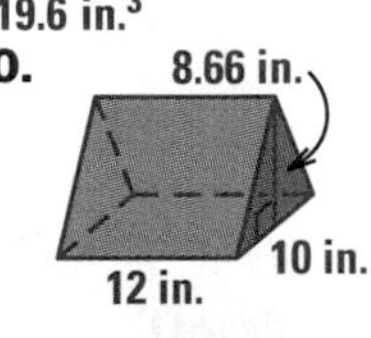

11. **49.5 ft³**

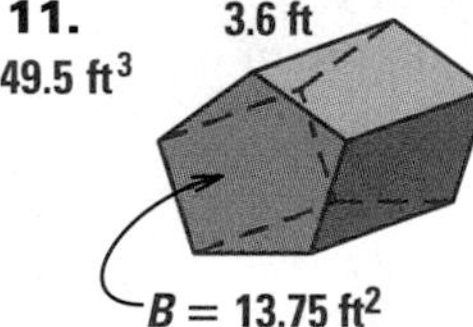

12. **792 m³**

12 m
11 m
6 m

13. **756 ft³**

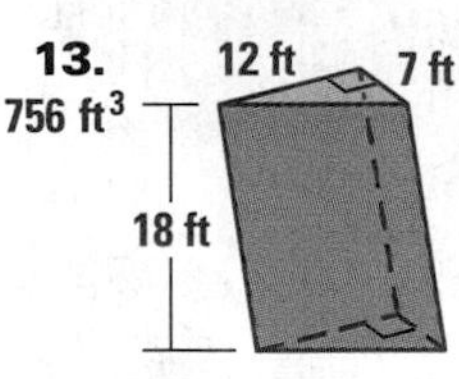

Student Help

▶ HOMEWORK HELP
Extra help with problem solving in Exs. 14–16 is available at www.mcdougallittell.com

Find the missing measure of the right prism given the volume *V*. (In Exercise 14, the prism has rectangular bases.)

14. $V = 16\text{ ft}^3$ **2 ft**

2 ft
4 ft
x

15. $V = 24\text{ in.}^3$ **3 in.**

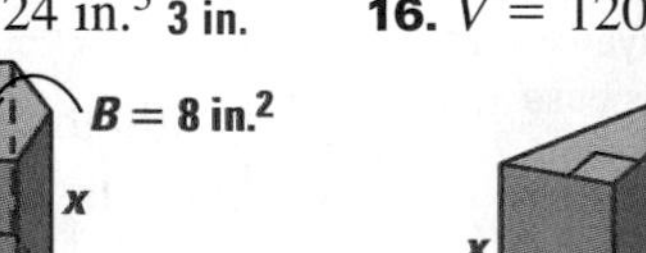

16. $V = 120\text{ m}^3$ **6 m**

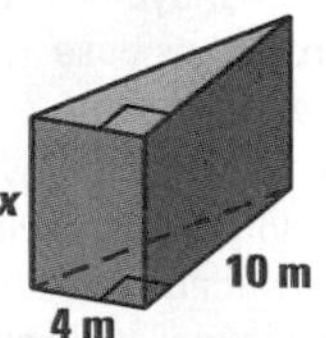

Find the volume of the solid. All the prisms are right and those with four-sided bases are rectangular.

17. 150 ft^3

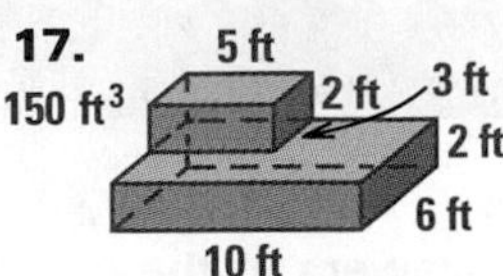

18. 3750 cm^3

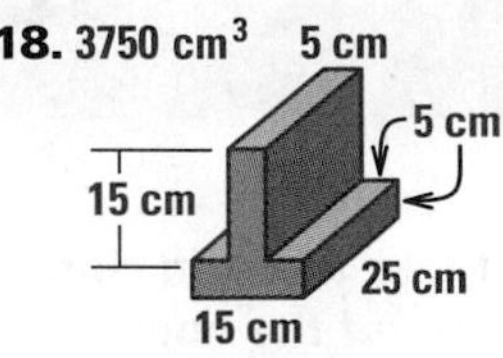

19. 360 m^3

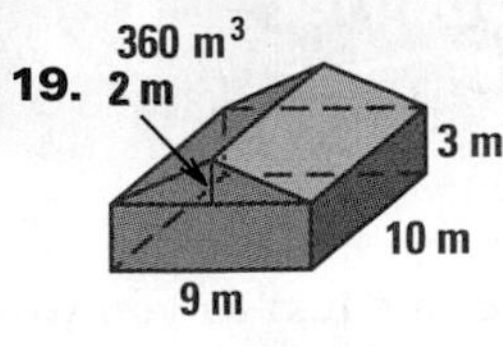

MOVING In Exercises 20 and 21, use the diagram of the moving van. The van's trailer is a right rectangular prism.

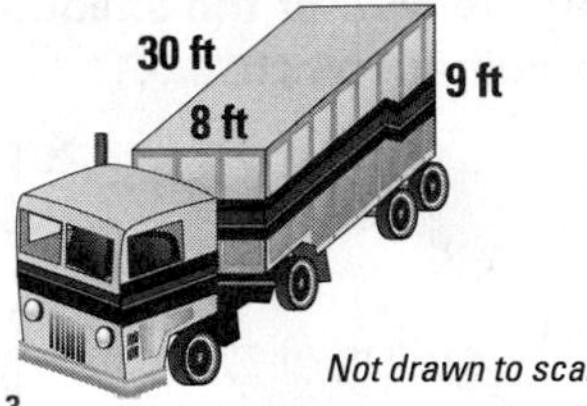

Not drawn to scale

20. Find the total volume of the trailer. **2160 ft^3**

21. Your belongings fill $\frac{2}{3}$ of the trailer. Find the volume of your belongings. **1440 ft^3**

22. MATHEMATICAL REASONING Draw a cube with side length x. Use your drawing to write a general formula for the volume of a cube. $V = x^3$

Science Link **In Exercises 23–25, use the following information.** You are studying the heat loss of four mammals. You use cubes of various sizes to model their relative surface areas and volumes. The edges of the cubes measure 1 centimeter, 2 centimeters, 3 centimeters, and 4 centimeters.

23–25. See margin.

23. Find the surface area and volume of each size of cube. List your results in a table.

24. For each cube, divide the surface area by the volume. Include the results in your table.

25. Mammals with a larger surface-area-to-volume ratio tend to lose body heat at a faster rate. Using your table, which mammal would lose heat faster, a small mammal or a large mammal? Explain your reasoning.

26. CHALLENGE Determine which two swimming pools hold about the same amount of water. **A and B**

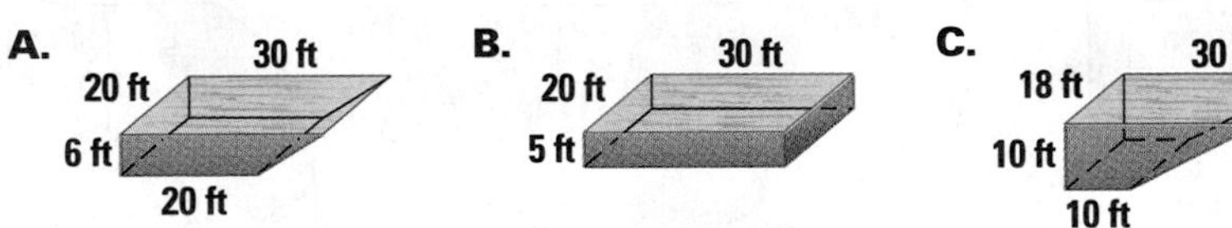

Link to Science

ARCTIC MAMMALS
Most polar bears live along the frozen shores of the Arctic Ocean. Their dense fur helps them retain their body heat.

More about arctic mammals available at www.mcdougallittell.com

25. Small mammal would lose heat faster since (surface area/volume) is greatest for cube of smallest edge size.

Multiple-Choice Practice

27. The volume of a box is 4608 cubic inches. The length of the box is 16 inches, and the width is 18 inches. What is the height of the box? **A**

Ⓐ 16 in. Ⓑ 18 in. Ⓒ 20 in. Ⓓ Not here

28. Each edge of a cube is 7 inches long. What is the volume of the cube? **H**

Ⓕ 21 in.^{3} Ⓖ 49 in.^{3} Ⓗ 343 in.^{3} Ⓙ Not here

4 Assess

Assessment Resources

- Assessment Book (Formal Assessment and Alternative Assessment)
- Test and Practice Generator

Mini-Quiz

1. Find the volume of the prism.

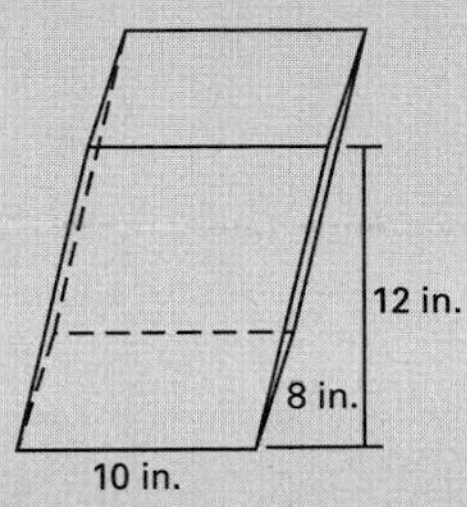

960 in.^{3}

2. A car maker advertises that its minivan has 20 cubic feet of cargo space behind the rear seat. You measure the car and find the width and depth of the cargo space are 5.5 feet and 1.5 feet, respectively. What height did the car maker use to calculate the advertised cargo volume? **about 2.42 ft**
3. A wedding cake is made by layering 3 sheet cakes in the form of right rectangular prisms. The bottom layer measures 24 in. × 18 in. × 3 in. The middle layer measures 18 in. × 12 in. × 3 in. The top layer measures 12 in. × 6 in. × 3 in. Find the total volume of the cake. **2160 in.^{3}**

23–24. See Additional Answers beginning on page AA1.

Additional Resources

A Mid-Chapter Test and a Mid-Chapter Partner Quiz are available in the *Assessment Book*, pp. 147–148 and p. 255.

Chapter 10 Mid-Chapter Test

Take this test as you would take a test in class. The answers to the exercises are given in the back of the book.

Find the area of the shaded region. Use 3.14 for π. Round your result to the nearest tenth.

1. 84.8 m²

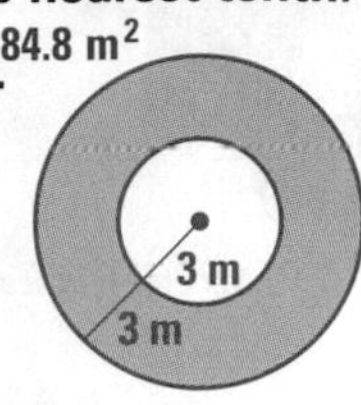

2. 13.8 ft²

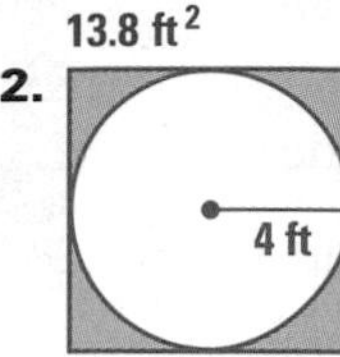

3. 55.0 cm²

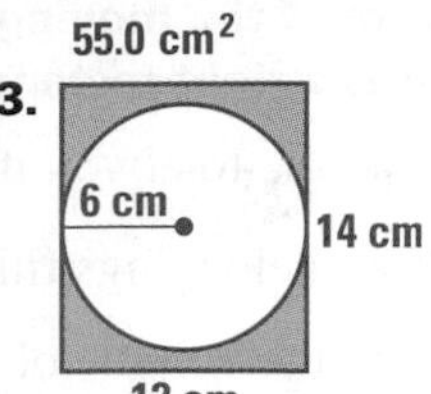

4. 30.5 yd²

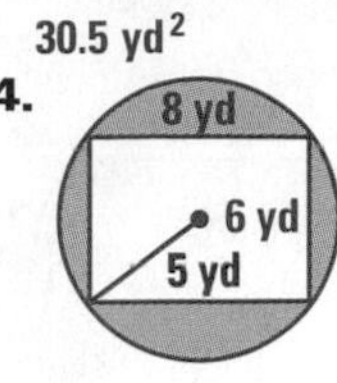

In Exercises 5–7, use the polyhedron at the right.

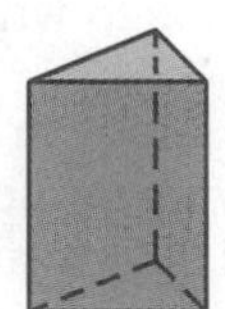

5. How many faces does the polyhedron have? 5

6. How many vertices does the polyhedron have? 6

7. How many edges does the polyhedron have? 9

Find the approximate surface area of the solid.

8. Diameter: 24 mm
Height: 2 mm
1056 mm²

9. Diameter: 14 mm
Length: 49 mm
2463 mm²

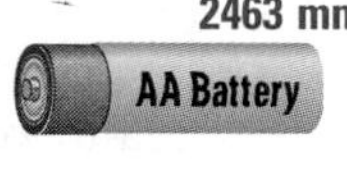

10. 32.5 cm²

0.5 cm
2.5 cm
5 cm

11. Width: $\frac{1}{8}$ in. 27.8 in.²

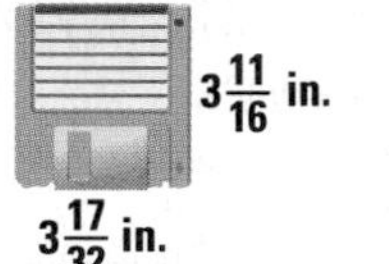

In Exercises 12–15, find the volume of the prism. The bases of the prisms are rectangles and right triangles.

12. 120 in.³

6 in.
4 in.
5 in.

13. 351 m³

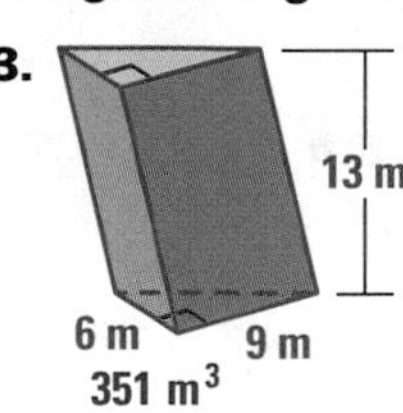

14. 2280 ft³

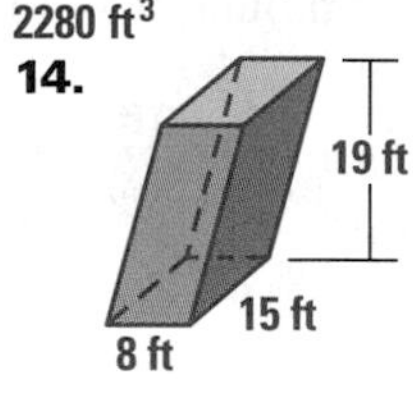

15. 260 cm³

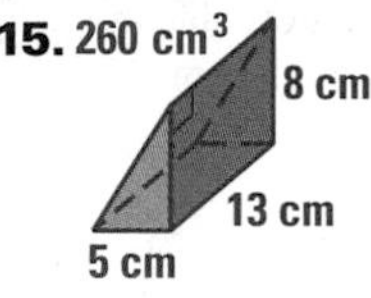

Science Link **In Exercises 16–18, use the following information.**
The Large Electron-Positron collider ring can accelerate sub-microscopic particles to nearly the speed of light. The collider ring is circular with a diameter of 5.41 miles as shown at the right.

FRANCE
5.41 mi
Collider ring
SWITZERLAND
1.91 ft

16. Find the circumference of the collider ring. 17 mi

17. Find the area of the land bounded by the collider ring. 23 mi²

18. Find the circumference of the cross section of the collider ring. 12 ft

10.5 Volume of a Cylinder

California Standards

In this lesson you'll:

- Compare capacities within and between measurement systems. (MG 1.1)
- Use formulas routinely for finding the volume of a cylinder. (MG 2.1)

Goal 1 FINDING THE VOLUME OF A CYLINDER

Finding the volume of a cylinder is like finding the volume of a prism: multiply the cylinder's height by its base area.

VOLUME OF A CYLINDER

The volume V of a cylinder is the product of its height h and its base area B.

$$V = Bh = \pi r^2 h$$

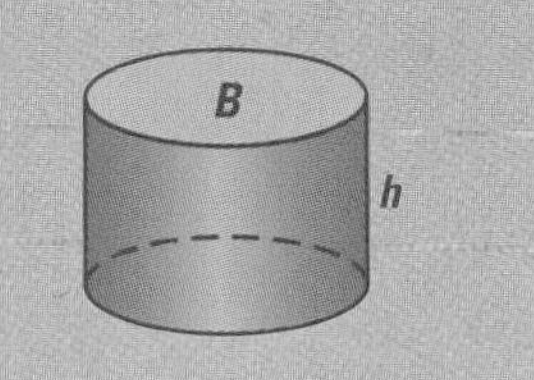

In an **oblique cylinder**, the segment joining the centers of the bases is *not* perpendicular to the bases. The height of an oblique cylinder is the perpendicular distance between the bases. As with prisms, the formula for finding the volume of a cylinder applies to both right and oblique cylinders.

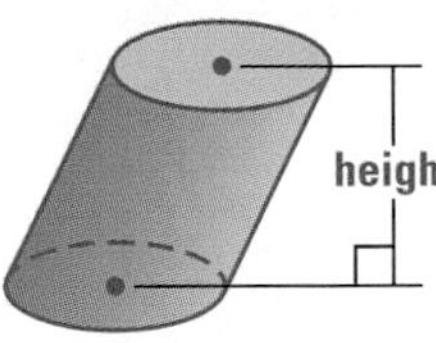

EXAMPLE 1 Finding Volumes of Cylinders

Find the volume of the cylinder.

a.

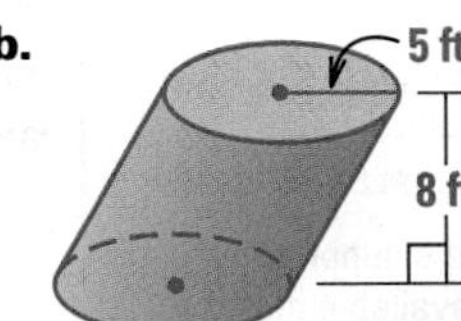

b.

Solution

a. First find the base area. Because the radius is 3 meters, the base area is πr^2, or $\pi \cdot 3^2 = 9\pi$ square meters.

$V = Bh$

$= 9\pi \cdot 5$

≈ 141.4

ANSWER ▶ The volume is about 141 cubic meters.

b. First find the base area. Because the radius is 5 feet, the base area is πr^2, or $\pi \cdot 5^2 = 25\pi$ square feet.

$V = Bh$

$= 25\pi \cdot 8$

≈ 628.3

ANSWER ▶ The volume is about 628 cubic feet.

1 Plan

Pacing

Suggested Number of Days

Transitional: 1 day
Average: 1 day
Advanced: 1 day
Block Schedule: 0.5 block with 10.6

Teaching Resources

Blacklines

(See page 506B.)

Transparencies

- Warm-Up Exercises
- Teacher Time-Savers
- English/Spanish Problem Solving
- Answers

Technology

- Electronic Teacher Tools
- Test and Practice Generator

2 Teach

Math Reasoning

For Mathematical Background Notes on mathematical reasoning related to this lesson, please refer to pages 506E and 506F in this Teacher's Edition.

Extra Example 1
See next page.

California Standards and Assessment

CA Standards: MG 1.1, MG 2.1

Math Reasoning

Cavalieri's principle shows that two cylinders, or two prisms, with the same height and the same base area have the same volume.

Extra Example 1

Find the volume of the cylinder.

a. a right cylinder with radius 4 inches and height 12 inches **about 603.19 in.^{3}**

b.

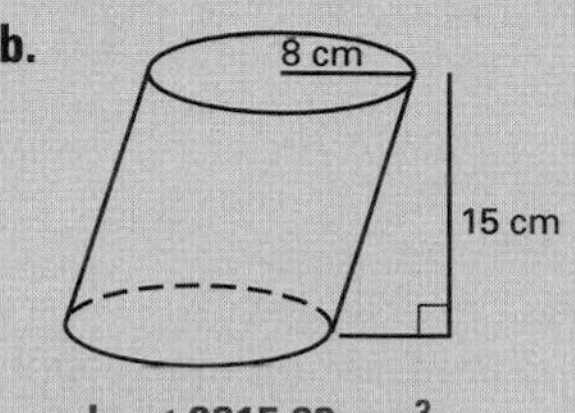

about 3015.93 cm^3

Extra Example 2

Find the height of the cylinder.

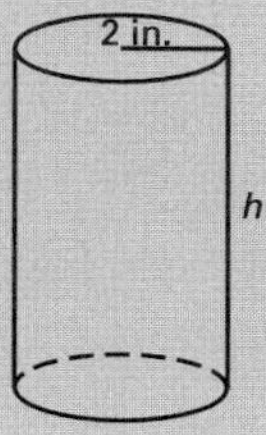

$V = 94.2$ in.^{3}

about 7.5 in.

Extra Example 3

Your grocery store sells milk in 1-liter bottles as well as 1-quart cartons. The liter bottle costs $1.42 while the quart carton costs $1.29. Which is the better buy? **The quart carton at $.040 per ounce is a better buy than the liter bottle at $.042 per ounce.**

Concept Check

A right triangular prism and a right cylinder have the same base area and the same height. How will their volumes compare? **Volumes are the same. Both volumes are calculated by multiplying the area of the base times the height.**

EXAMPLE 2 Finding the Height of a Cylinder

Find the height of the cylinder.

3 in.; h; $V = 37.7$ in.^{3}

Solution

$V = Bh$	Write volume formula.
$37.7 = \pi \cdot 3^2 \cdot h$	Substitute for V and B.
$\frac{37.7}{9\pi} = h$	Divide each side by 9π.
$1.3 \approx h$	Use a calculator.

ANSWER ▶ The cylinder has a height of about 1.3 inches.

Goal 2 Comparing Units of Volume

Volume is measured in cubic units. It is possible to convert cubic units into other more commonly used measures of volume, such as liters (L), gallons (gal), quarts (qt), and fluid ounces (fl oz). To compare volumes that are measured in different units, it helps to write both volumes with the same units. Here are some common conversions.

1 L ≈ 33.8 fl oz   1 gal = 4 qt   1 qt = 32 fl oz

EXAMPLE 3 Comparing Volumes

UNIT PRICING A two liter bottle of sparkling water costs $1.69, and a 6-pack of 12 ounce cans costs $1.99. Which is the better buy?

Solution

For comparison, convert the liters to ounces, and find the total volume of the 6-pack.

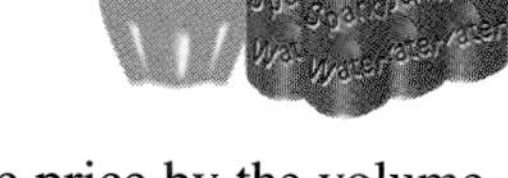

BOTTLE $V \approx 2\,\cancel{L} \cdot \frac{33.8 \text{ fl oz}}{\cancel{L}} = 67.6 \text{ fl oz}$

6-PACK $V = 6\,\cancel{\text{cans}} \cdot \frac{12 \text{ fl oz}}{\cancel{\text{can}}} = 72 \text{ fl oz}$

Now find the price per fluid ounce by dividing the price by the volume.

Container	Volume	Price	Price per fluid ounce
Bottle	67.6 fl oz	$1.69	$\frac{1.69}{67.6} = \$.025$
6-Pack	72 fl oz	$1.99	$\frac{1.99}{72.0} \approx \$.028$

ANSWER ▶ From the table you can see that the two liter bottle has a lower price per fluid ounce. So, the bottle is the better buy.

> **Student Help**
> ▶ **More Examples**
> More examples are available at www.mcdougallittell.com

10.5 Exercises

Guided Practice

In Exercises 1–3, use the right cylinder shown.

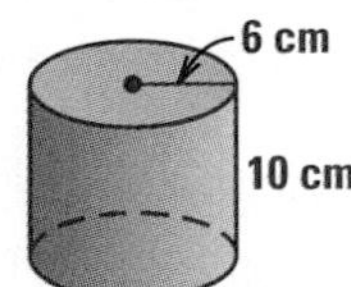

1. Find its base area. **113.1 cm^2**

2. What is the height of the cylinder? **10 cm**

3. Find the volume of the cylinder. **1131 cm^3**

HOCKEY In Exercises 4–6, a hockey puck is a right cylinder that has a diameter of 7.62 centimeters and a height of 2.54 centimeters.

4. Make a sketch of the hockey puck. **See margin.**

5. Find its base area. **45.6 cm^2**

6. Find the volume of the hockey puck. **115.8**

Practice and Problem Solving

Student Help

▶MORE PRACTICE Extra practice to help you master skills is on page 709.

INSTRUMENTS Find the volume of the drum.

7. **7539.8 $in.^3$**

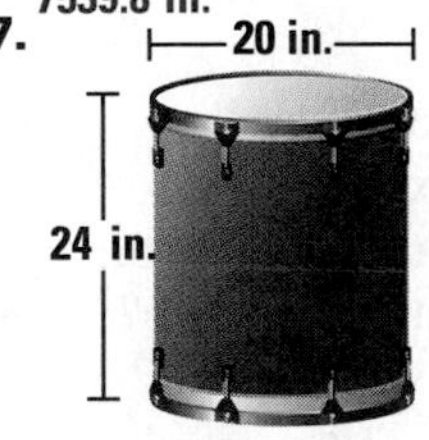

Surdo drum

8. **8620.5 $in.^3$**

14 in.

28 in.

Bass drum

9. **6107.3 $in.^3$**

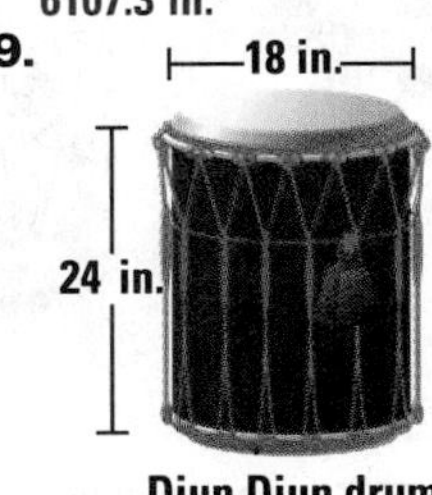

Djun Djun drum

Find the volume of the cylinder.

10. **47.1 m^3**

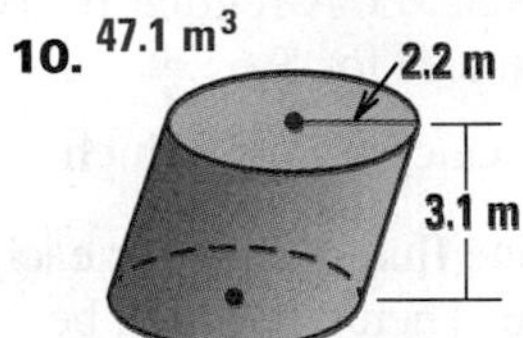

11. **1692.3 ft^3**

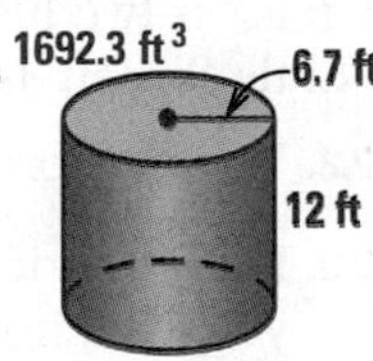

12. **4820.0 cm^3**

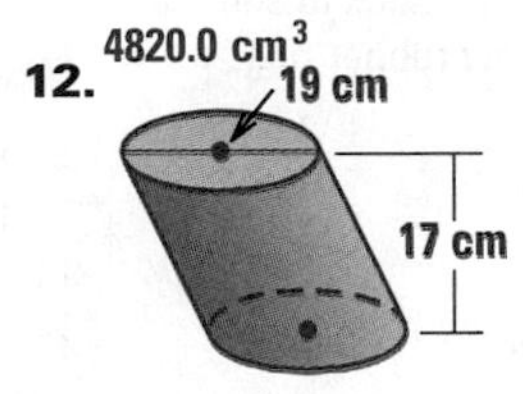

MATHEMATICAL REASONING In Exercises 13 and 14, use the following information. Right Cylinder A has a radius of 3 inches and a height of 4 inches. Right Cylinder B has a radius of 4 inches and a height of 6 inches.

13. Without doing any calculations, decide whether the volume of Cylinder A is greater than, less than, or equal to the volume of Cylinder B. Explain.

13. Cylinder A has less volume because its radius and height are less than those of Cylinder B.

14. To check your answer to Exercise 13, sketch both cylinders and find the volume of each.

14. Volume of A = 36π $in.^3$, Volume of B = 96π $in.^3$ See margin.

3 Apply

Assignment Guide

TRANSITIONAL
Day 1: pp. 537–538 Exs. 7–8, 11–16, 18–19, 23–25
AVERAGE
Day 1: pp. 537–538 Exs. 8–11, 13–16, 18–19, 22–25
ADVANCED
Day 1: pp. 537–538 Exs. 8–11, 16–19, 20*, 21–25
BLOCK SCHEDULE
pp. 537–538 Exs. 8–11, 13–16, 18–19, 22–25 (with 10.6)

Extra Practice

- Student Edition, pp. 708–709
- Chapter 10 Resource Book, p. 42

Homework Check

To quickly check student understanding of key concepts, go over the following exercises:

Transitional: 8, 12, 16, 19, 23
Average: 8, 10, 16, 19, 23
Advanced: 8, 10, 16, 19, 23

4.

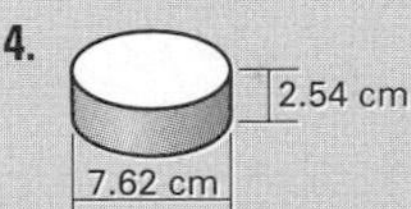

14.

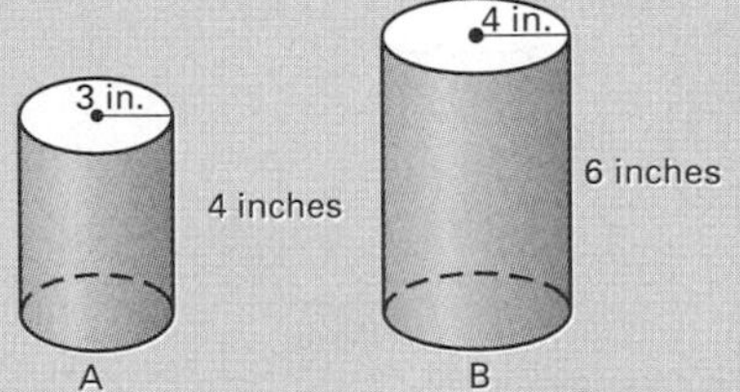

4 Assess

Assessment Resources

- Assessment Book (Formal Assessment and Alternative Assessment)
- Test and Practice Generator

Mini-Quiz

Find the volume of the cylinder.

1. a right cylinder with a radius of 7 inches and a height of 10 inches **about 1539.38 in.^{3}**

2.

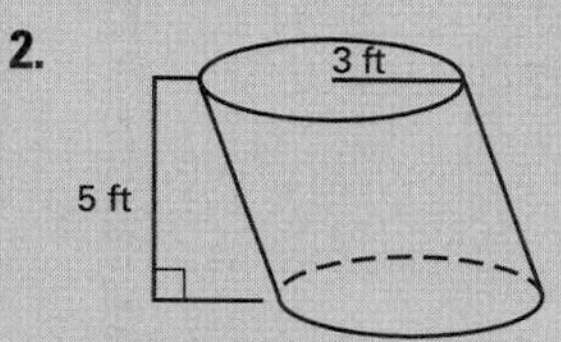

about 141.37 ft^3

3. A convenience store sells a 1-liter bottle of soda for \$.99 and a 32-ounce cup of soda for \$.85. Knowing that 1 liter equals approximately 33.8 fluid ounces, calculate which soda is the better buy. **At \$.027 per ounce, the 32-ounce cup is a better buy than the 1-liter bottle at \$.029 per ounce.**

4. Find the height of the cylinder.

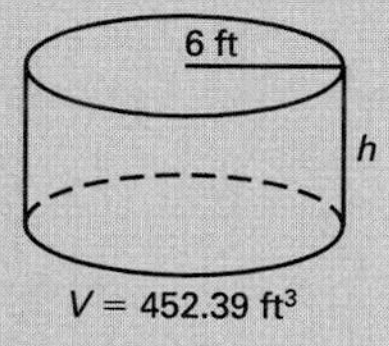

$V = 452.39$ ft^3

4 ft

23.

Drink	Volume	Price	Price per fl oz
Big Drink	67.6 fl oz	\$2.05	\$.030
Regular Drink	32 fl oz	\$.90	\$.028
Little Sipper	16 fl oz	\$.63	\$.039

The regular drink is the best buy.

Find the height of the right cylinder given its volume V. Round your answer to the nearest tenth.

15. $V = 37.7$ in.^{3}

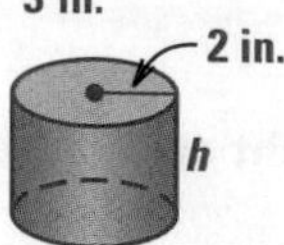

16. $V = 197.9$ m^3

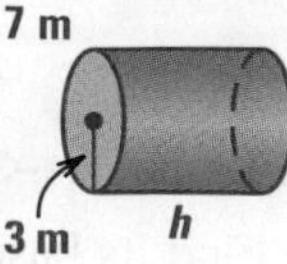

17. $V = 290.5$ cm^3

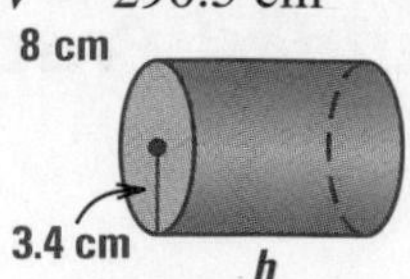

SEIKAN TUNNEL In Exercises 18 and 19, use the following information. The Seikan Tunnel in Japan is 33.5 miles long. Its shape can be approximated by a cylinder. A cross section of the tunnel is shown.

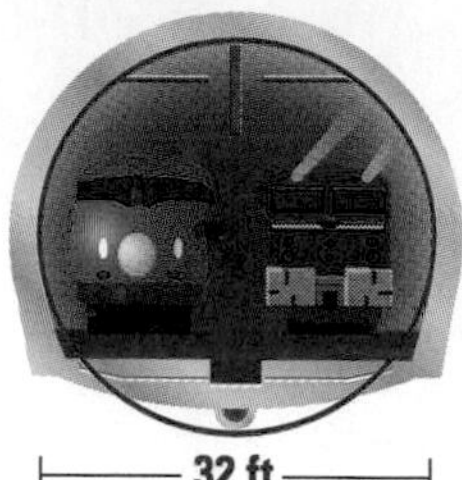

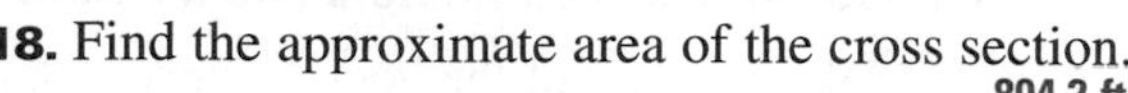

18. Find the approximate area of the cross section. **804.2 ft^2**

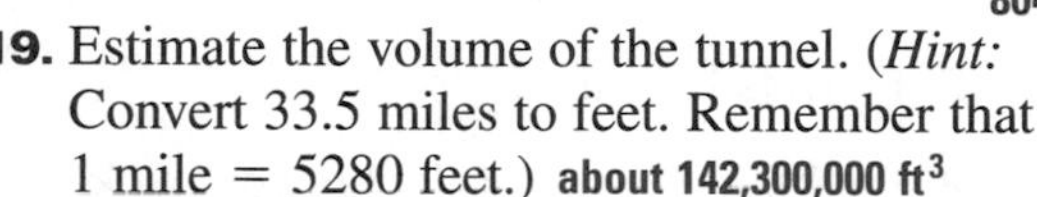

19. Estimate the volume of the tunnel. (*Hint:* Convert 33.5 miles to feet. Remember that 1 mile = 5280 feet.) **about 142,300,000 ft^3**

SPORTS In Exercises 20 and 21, use the following information. Ringette is a sport similar to ice hockey. Instead of using a puck, the players use a ring. A diagram of the ring is shown below.

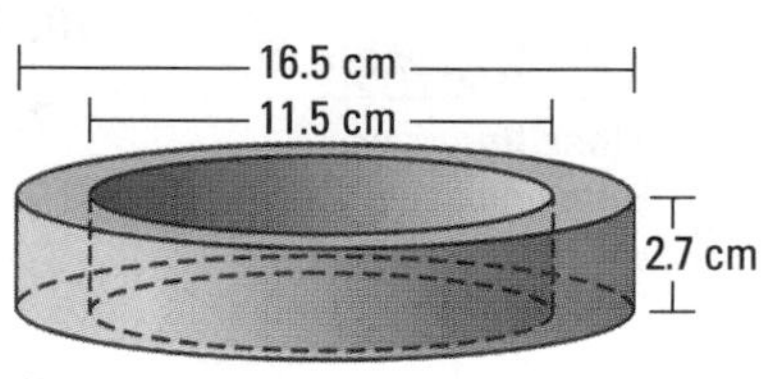

Not drawn to scale

20. CHALLENGE Find the volume of the ring. **about 296.9 cm^3**

21. Suppose the ring and the hockey puck described in Exercises 4–6 are made out of the same material. Which would cost more to make? Explain your reasoning.
The puck requires more material because its volume is greater.

22. **Regular drink; one liter is slightly bigger than one quart, but the "Big Drink" costs more than twice the price of one quart. The "Little Sipper" has half as many ounces as the regular but costs more than half as much.**

Link to Sports

RINGETTE was invented in Canada in 1963. Players use a straight stick to shoot a hollow rubber ring.

COMPARING VOLUMES In Exercises 22 and 23, use the following information. A convenience store has three sizes of beverages. The "Big Drink" is two liters for \$2.05. A regular drink is one quart for \$.90. The "Little Sipper" is 16 ounces for \$.63.

22. Without doing any calculations, which drink is the best buy? Explain. **See margin.**

23. Find the price of one fluid ounce for each beverage size. Organize your data in a table. Then tell which beverage size is the best buy. **See margin.**

Multiple-Choice Practice

Student Help

▶**TEST TIP**
When you are given a verbal description of a solid, make a sketch of the solid.

24. Which expression gives the volume of a right cylinder with radius r and height $2r$? **C**

Ⓐ $2\pi r^2$ Ⓑ $4\pi r^2$ Ⓒ $2\pi r^3$ Ⓓ πr^3

25. What is the volume of a right cylinder that has a diameter of 6 feet and a height of 10 feet? **H**

Ⓕ 30π ft^3 Ⓖ 60π ft^3 Ⓗ 90π ft^3 Ⓙ 360π ft^3

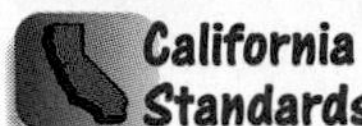

10.6 Volumes of Pyramids and Cones

California Standards

In this lesson you'll:

- Use formulas routinely for finding the volume of pyramids and cones. (MG 2.1)
- Estimate and compute the volume of complex three-dimensional figures by breaking the figures down into more basic figures. (MG 2.2)

Goal 1 Finding Volumes of Pyramids and Cones

A **pyramid** is a polyhedron in which the base is a polygon and the triangular faces meet at a point called the *vertex*. A **circular cone** has a circular base and a vertex that is not in the same plane as the base. All the cones in this book are circular. The height of a pyramid or a cone is the perpendicular distance between the base and the vertex.

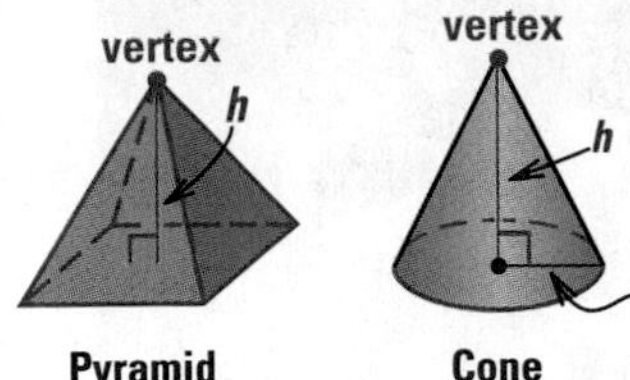

Pyramid Cone

You know that the volume of a prism is the product of the base area and the height. A pyramid with the same base area and height as a prism has one third the volume of the prism. This can be demonstrated with an experiment in which you fill the prism with three pyramids of sand, as shown. The same volume relationship is true of a cone and a cylinder.

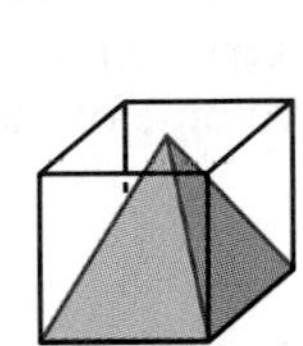
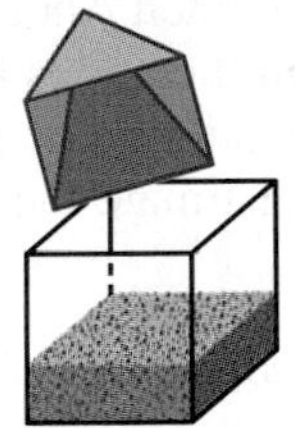
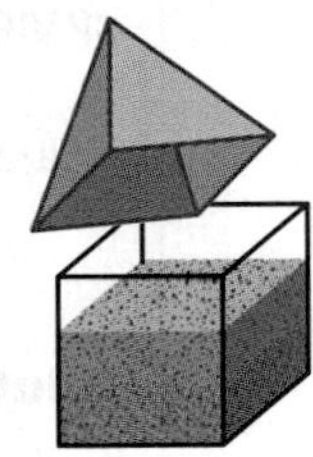
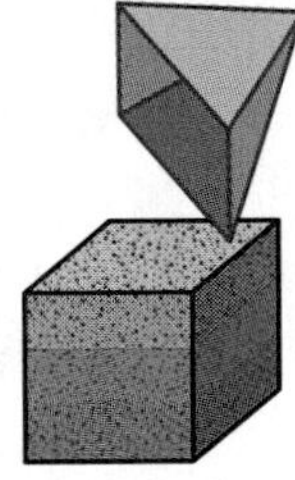

Volume of a Pyramid or a Cone

The volume V of a pyramid or a cone is one third the product of its height h and its base area B. That is, $V = \frac{1}{3}Bh$.

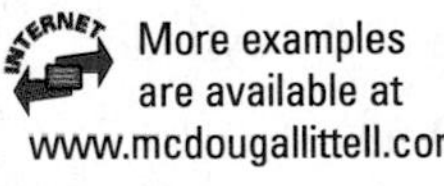

Student Help

More Examples

More examples are available at www.mcdougallittell.com

Example 1 Finding the Volume of a Pyramid

The volume of the pyramid shown can be found as follows.

$V = \frac{1}{3}Bh$ — Write formula.

$= \frac{1}{3} \cdot 36 \cdot 8$ — Substitute for B and h.

$= 96$ — Simplify.

Answer The volume of the pyramid is 96 cubic inches.

1 Plan

Pacing

Suggested Number of Days

Transitional: 1 day
Average: 1 day
Advanced: 1 day
Block Schedule: 0.5 block with 10.5

Teaching Resources

Blacklines

(See page 506B.)

Transparencies

- Warm-Up Exercises
- Teacher Time-Savers
- English/Spanish Problem Solving
- Answers

Technology

- Electronic Teacher Tools
- Test and Practice Generator

2 Teach

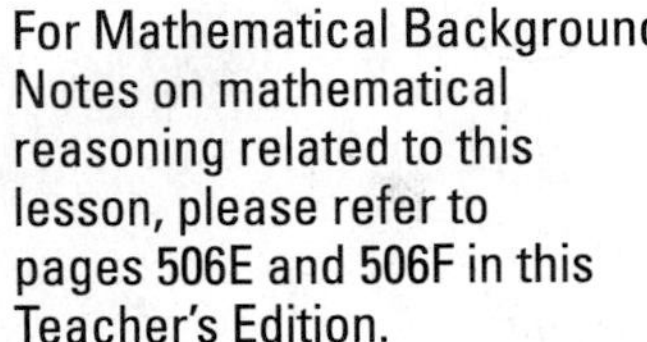

Math Reasoning

For Mathematical Background Notes on mathematical reasoning related to this lesson, please refer to pages 506E and 506F in this Teacher's Edition.

Extra Example 1
See next page.

California Standards and Assessment

CA Standards: MG 2.1, MG 2.2
CA Key Concepts Book: pp. S95–S96, S99

Extra Example 1

Find the volume of the pyramid shown.

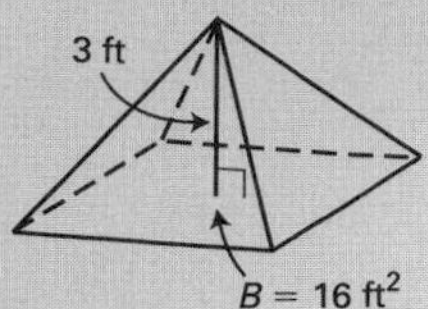

16 ft³

Extra Example 2

Find the volume of an ice cream cone with a radius of 1.5 inches and a height of 5 inches. **about 11.78 in.³**

Extra Example 3

A cylindrical silo with a cone-shaped roof can be filled to the top with grain. Estimate the total volume of this silo to the nearest cubic foot.

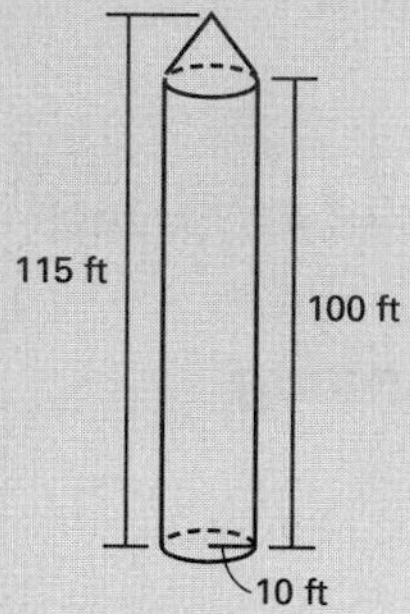

32,987 ft³

Teaching Tip

Height is measured along the perpendicular to the base, not along the surface of the solid.

Concept Check

A pyramid and a cone have the same height. What else must be true if their volumes are equal? **The areas of their bases are equal.**

540

Link to Agriculture

PILES OF GRAIN The angle that the grain makes with the ground is the *angle of repose.* The measure of this angle varies with the type of grain.

Goal 2 Finding Volumes in Real Life

EXAMPLE 2 Finding the Volume of a Cone

GRAIN Suppose a pile of grain is shaped like a cone, as shown in the diagram. What is the volume of the grain pile?

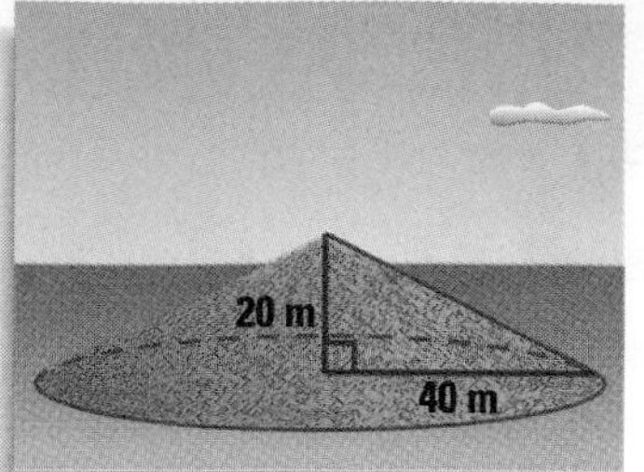

Solution

To find the volume of the cone, you need to know its base area. The area of the circular base is $\pi \cdot 40^2 = 1600\pi$ m².

$V = \frac{1}{3}Bh$ Write formula.

$= \frac{1}{3}(1600\pi)(20)$ Substitute for B and h.

$\approx 33{,}510.3$ Use a calculator.

ANSWER The volume of the grain pile is about 33,500 cubic meters.

EXAMPLE 3 Finding a Complicated Volume

SPACECRAFT Each Apollo spacecraft sent to the moon in the 1960s and 1970s consisted of a command module and a service module, as shown. Estimate the total volume of the spacecraft.

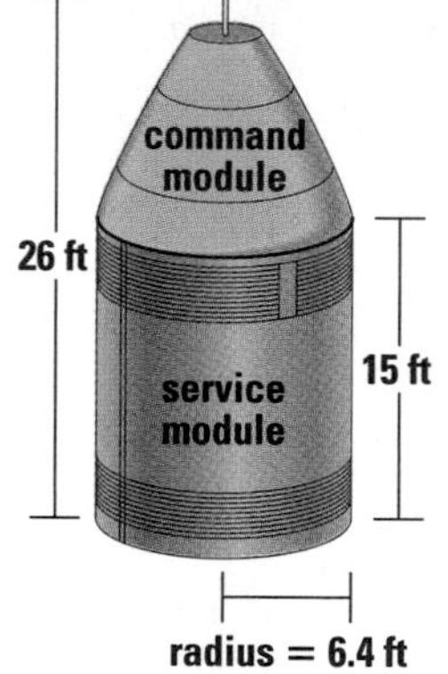

Solution

Think of the command module as a cone.

Height of cone: $26 - 15 = 11$ ft

Area of base: $\pi r^2 = \pi(6.4)^2 = 40.96\pi$ ft²

Use these values to find the volume of the cone.

Volume of cone: $V = \frac{1}{3}Bh = \frac{1}{3} \cdot 40.96\pi \cdot 11 \approx \mathbf{472}$ ft³

The volume of the command module is about 472 cubic feet.

Think of the service module as a cylinder. The base of the cylinder is the same as the base of the cone. Find the volume of the cylinder.

Volume of cylinder: $V = Bh = 40.96\pi \cdot 15 \approx \mathbf{1930}$ ft³

The volume of the service module is about 1930 cubic feet.

ANSWER The total volume of the spacecraft is the sum of the volumes of its parts. So, the estimated volume of the spacecraft is **472** + **1930** = 2402 cubic feet.

10.6 Exercises

Guided Practice

In Exercises 1 and 2, use the solids shown.

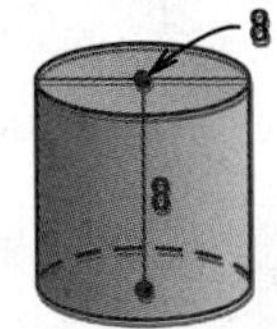

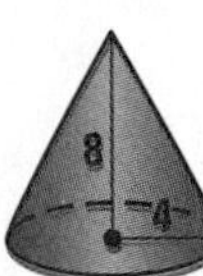

1. Base areas of both the cylinder and the cone are 16π.

2. The volume of the cone is $\frac{1}{3}$ the volume of the cylinder.

1. Compare the base areas of the solids.

2. Compare the volumes of the cylinder and the cone.

Find the volume of the solid. The pyramid in Exercise 5 has a rectangular base.

3. 3200 in.^{3}

10 in.
$B = 960$ in.^{2}

4. 100 cm^3

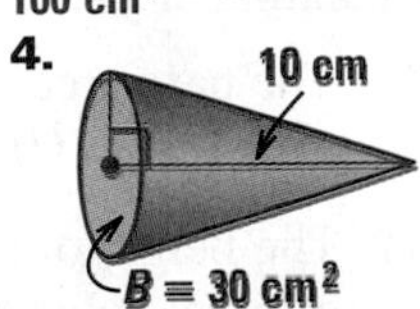

5. 200 m^3

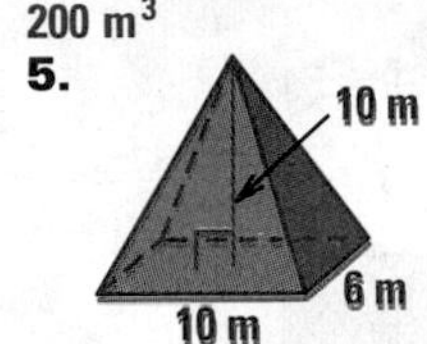

In Exercises 6–10, use the solid shown.

10 ft
8 ft
10 ft

6. Find the base area of the cone. 64π ft^2

7. Find the volume of the cone. 670 ft^3

8. Find the volume of the right cylinder. 2011 ft^3

9. Find the total volume of the solid. 2681 ft^3

10. Suppose the height of the cone is doubled. Find the new volume of the cone and of the entire solid. 1340 ft^3; 3351 ft^3

Practice and Problem Solving

> *Student Help*
>
> ▶ **MORE PRACTICE** Extra practice to help you master skills is on page 709.

In Exercises 11–16, find the volume of the solid.

11. Square base 8400 ft^3

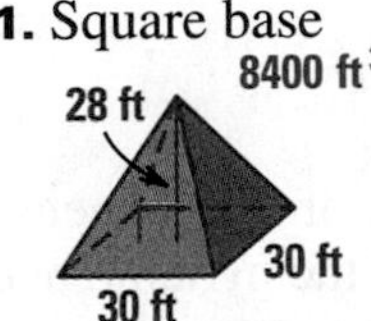

12. Rectangular base 1200 cm^3

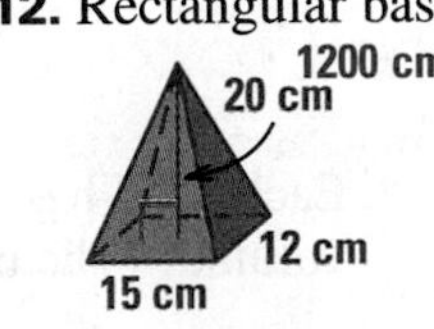

13. 10 in.^{3}

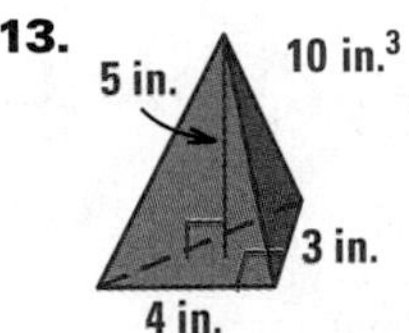

14. 2513 m^3

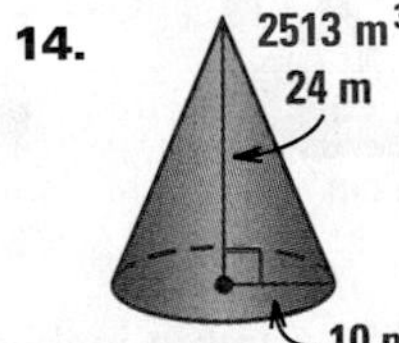

15. 1810 ft^3

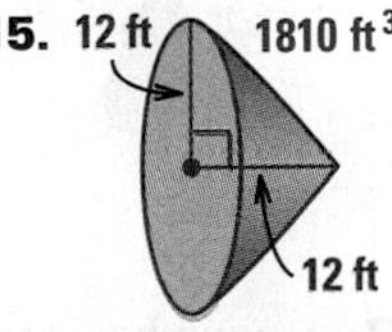

16. 5337 in.^{3}

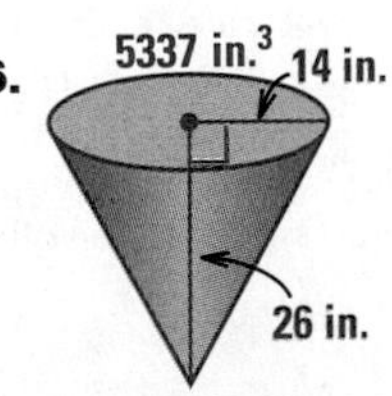

17. The pyramid whose base area is double would have a height of one-half of the other pyramid if the volumes are the same.

17. **MATHEMATICAL REASONING** Two pyramids have the same volume. The base area of one is double the base area of the other. How do the heights of the two pyramids compare? Explain.

3 Apply

> ### *Assignment Guide*
>
> **TRANSITIONAL**
> **Day 1:** pp. 541–542 Exs. 11–12, 14–15, 18–19, 21–22, 26–27
> **AVERAGE**
> **Day 1:** pp. 541–542 Exs. 12–13, 15–22, 26–27
> **ADVANCED**
> **Day 1:** pp. 541–542 Exs. 12–15, 19–23, 24*, 25–27
> **BLOCK SCHEDULE**
> pp. 541–542 Exs. 12–13, 15–22, 26–27 (with 10.5)

Extra Practice

- Student Edition, pp. 708–709
- Chapter 10 Resource Book, p. 51

Homework Check

To quickly check student understanding of key concepts, go over the following exercises:

Transitional: 12, 14, 18, 21, 22
Average: 12, 16, 20, 21, 22
Advanced: 12, 14, 20, 21, 22

> ### *Teaching Tip*
>
> In Exercises 11 and 12, the base has four sides, so it could be *any* parallelogram. This is why the base is described. In Exercise 13, the base has three sides, so it must be a triangle. Therefore, it does not need to be described.

4 Assess

Assessment Resources

- Assessment Book (Formal Assessment and Alternative Assessment)
- Test and Practice Generator

Mini-Quiz

1. Find the volume of the pyramid.

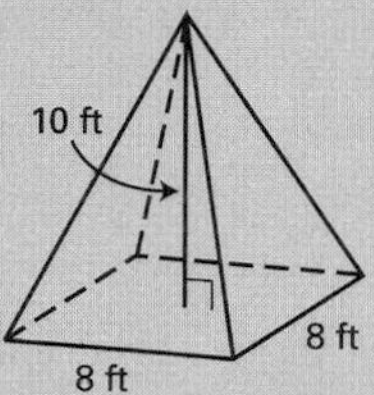

about 213.3 ft^3

2. Find the volume of the "snow cone" cup shown.

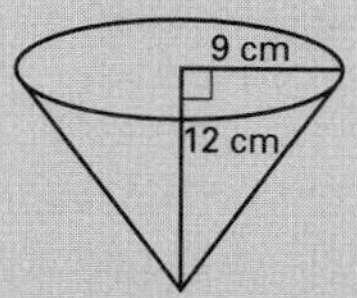

about 1018 cm^3

3. A crayon is shaped like a cylinder with a cone tip. Find the volume of the crayon shown to the nearest hundredth of a cubic centimeter.

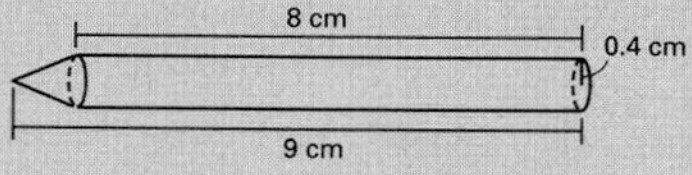

4.19 cm^3

Math Reasoning

It is a good exercise to decide whether the pyramid constructed from the net in Exercise 23 could serve as a scale model of the Khufu pyramid in Exercises 21–22.

542

Find the volume of the solid. The prism and pyramids have square bases.

18. **2160 in.^{3}**

9 in.; 12 in.; 12 in.; 12 in.

19. **8294 cm^3**

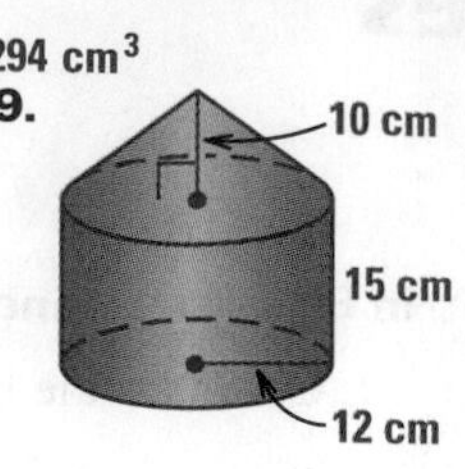

20. **16.7 cm^3**

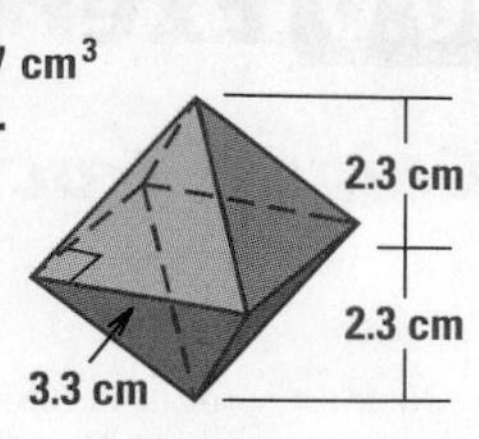

Link to History

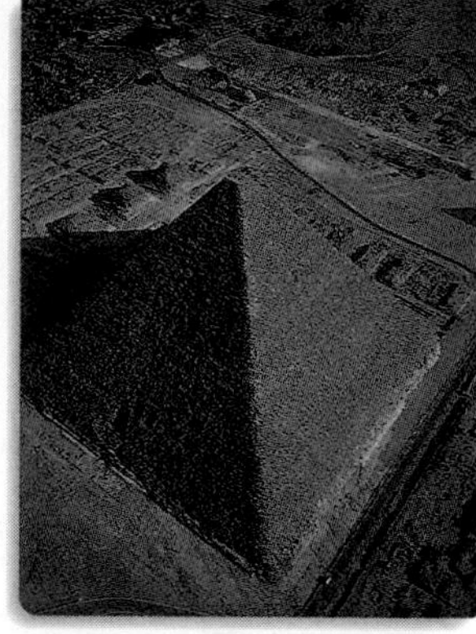

EGYPTIAN PYRAMIDS
The pyramid of Khufu contains more than two million stone blocks and was built without machinery or iron tools.

History Link **In Exercises 21 and 22, use the following information.** The largest Egyptian pyramid, located near Cairo, Egypt, is the pyramid of Khufu (2680 B.C.). This pyramid was built with a square base and four triangular sides.

21. The base area of the pyramid is 13 acres. Find the area of the base in square feet. (*Hint:* 1 acre = 43,560 square feet) **566,280 ft^2**

22. The height of the pyramid when it was built was 481 feet. Find the original volume of the pyramid using the area of the base that you found in Exercise 21. **90,793,560 ft^3**

In Exercises 23 and 24, use the net of the pyramid shown. The base is a square, and the other faces are congruent equilateral triangles.

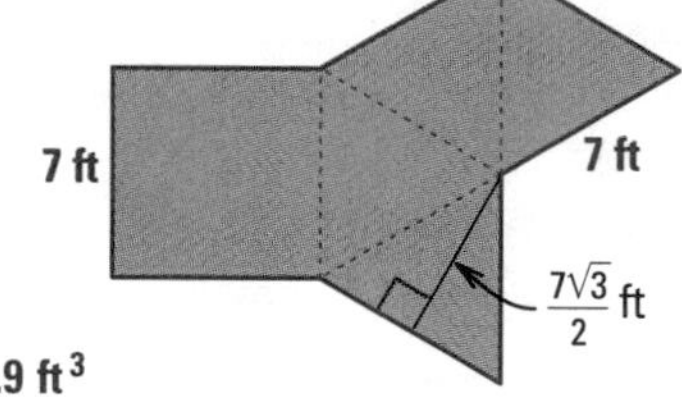

23. Sketch the pyramid. The height of the pyramid is about 4.95 feet. Find the approximate volume of the pyramid. **80.9 ft^3**

24. **CHALLENGE** Find the surface area of the pyramid. **133.9 ft^2**

25. **MATHEMATICAL REASONING** Which has a greater effect on the volume of a cone, doubling the radius or doubling the height? Give an example and explain your reasoning. **See margin.**

Multiple-Choice Practice

25. Doubling the radius has greater effect on the volume since the radius is squared. A cone of twice the height would have volume $\frac{2}{3}\pi r^2 h$ whereas a cone of twice the radius would have volume $\frac{4}{3}\pi r^2 h$.

26. Each solid has a height of 6 centimeters. Which solid has the greatest volume? (The bases of the pyramid and prism are square.) **D**

Ⓐ 

Ⓑ 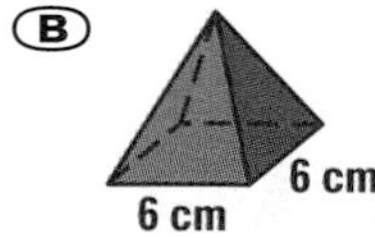

Ⓒ 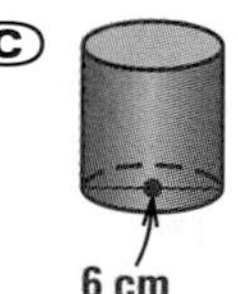

Ⓓ 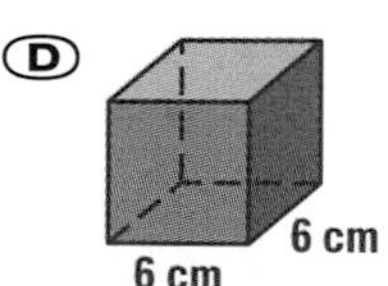

27. A cone has a volume of 56.5 cubic inches and a radius of 6 inches. What is the height of the cone? **F**

Ⓕ 1.5 inches Ⓖ 3 inches Ⓗ 5.5 inches Ⓙ 9 inches

10.7 Volume of a Sphere

California Standards

In this lesson you'll:

- Use formulas routinely for finding the volume of a sphere. (MG 2.1)
- Understand that when the dimensions of a solid are multiplied by a scale factor, the volume is multiplied by the cube of the scale factor. (MG 2.3)

Goal 1 FINDING VOLUMES OF SPHERES

A **sphere** is a set of all points in *space* that are a given distance from a point. The point is the **center** of the sphere. The **radius** of a sphere is the distance from the center to a point on the sphere. A half of a sphere is called a **hemisphere**.

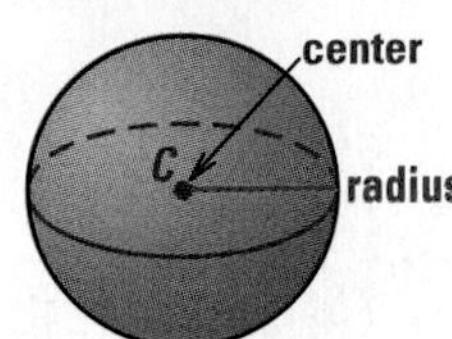

Imagine that a sphere is cut to form two hemispheres. Fit a cone into one of the hemispheres as shown below. If you were to fill the cone with sand and pour the sand into the hemisphere, you would find that the hemisphere is filled with exactly two cones of sand. So, it takes four cones of sand to fill a sphere.

The volume of the cone is $\frac{1}{3}Bh = \frac{1}{3}(\pi r^2)r = \frac{1}{3}\pi r^3$, so the volume of the sphere must be $4\left(\frac{1}{3}\pi r^3\right) = \frac{4}{3}\pi r^3$.

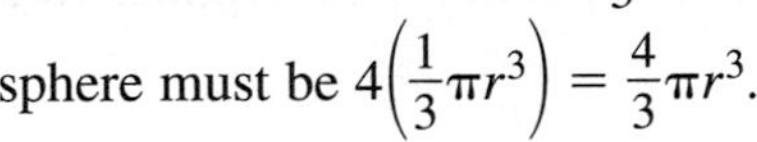

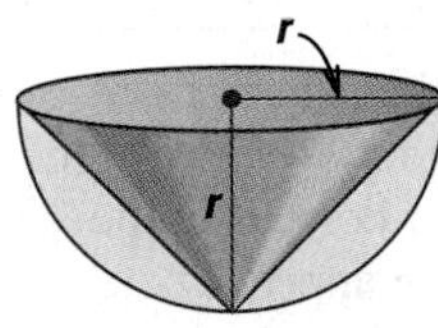

VOLUME OF A SPHERE

The volume V of a sphere is four thirds the product of π and the cube of its radius r. That is, $V = \frac{4}{3}\pi r^3$.

EXAMPLE 1 Finding the Volume of a Sphere

Find the volume of the sphere shown.

1.9 cm

Solution

$V = \frac{4}{3}\pi r^3$ Write volume formula.

$= \frac{4}{3} \cdot \pi \cdot (1.9)^3$ Substitute for r.

≈ 28.73 Use a calculator.

ANSWER ▶ The volume of the sphere is about 29 cubic centimeters.

1 Plan

Pacing

Suggested Number of Days

Transitional: 2 days
Average: 2 days
Advanced: 2 days
Block Schedule: 1 block

Teaching Resources

Blacklines
(See page 506B.)

Transparencies
- Warm-Up Exercises
- Teacher Time-Savers
- English/Spanish Problem Solving
- Answers

Technology
- Electronic Teacher Tools
- Test and Practice Generator

2 Teach

Math Reasoning

For Mathematical Background Notes on mathematical reasoning related to this lesson, please refer to pages 506E and 506F in this Teacher's Edition.

Extra Example 1
See next page.

California Standards and Assessment

CA Standards: MG 2.1, MG 2.3
CA Key Concepts Book: pp. S95–S96, S99

Math Reasoning

A sphere is a surface. When we speak of the volume of a sphere, we actually mean the volume of the solid ball whose boundary is the sphere.

Extra Example 1

Find the volume of a sphere with radius 3 feet.

about 113.10 ft^3

Extra Example 2

A physical therapist uses giant balls to improve her client's muscle strength and flexibility. The large ball has a radius of 18 inches and the medium ball has a radius of 13 inches. What is the difference in volume between the two balls? **about 15,226 in.^{3}**

Extra Example 3

An unpeeled orange is roughly spherical and its radius is 4 cm. If the peel is $\frac{1}{2}$ cm thick, find the volume of the orange peel. **about 88.49 cm^3**

Concept Check

Chris is using a calculator to find the volume of a sphere of radius 2. He calculates 4 ÷ 3, multiplies the answer by π, and then multiplies by 2. He then cubes the result to get his answer. Is his answer correct? **No. Only the radius should be cubed. Chris's calculation is $\left(\frac{4}{3}\pi r\right)^3$ instead of $\frac{4}{3}\pi r^3$.**

Goal 2 Using the Volume of a Sphere

EXAMPLE 2 Comparing Volumes

STORAGE TANK You are designing a spherical storage tank for natural gas. The radius of the tank is 18 feet. How much gas will it hold? If you double the radius will the tank hold twice as much?

Solution

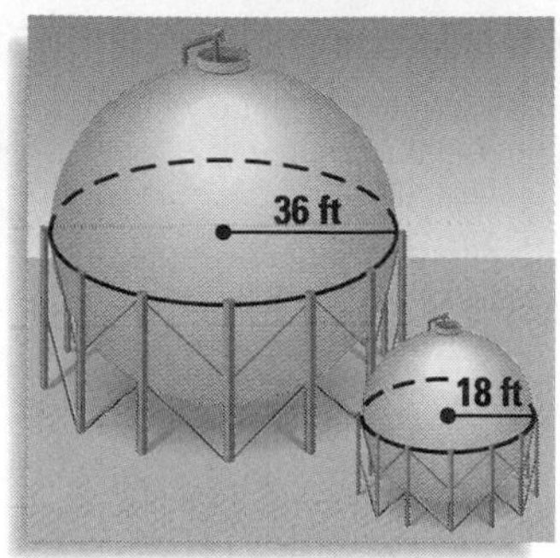

The volume of the tank is:

$$V = \frac{4}{3}\pi r^3 = \frac{4}{3} \cdot \pi \cdot 18^3$$
$$= 7776\pi \text{ ft}^3$$

Doubling the radius gives a volume of:

$$V = \frac{4}{3}\pi r^3 = \frac{4}{3} \cdot \pi \cdot 36^3$$
$$= 62{,}208\pi \text{ ft}^3$$

Notice that $62{,}208\pi \div 7776\pi = 8$. This means that the volume of the larger tank is eight times the original volume, not twice the volume.

Link to Science

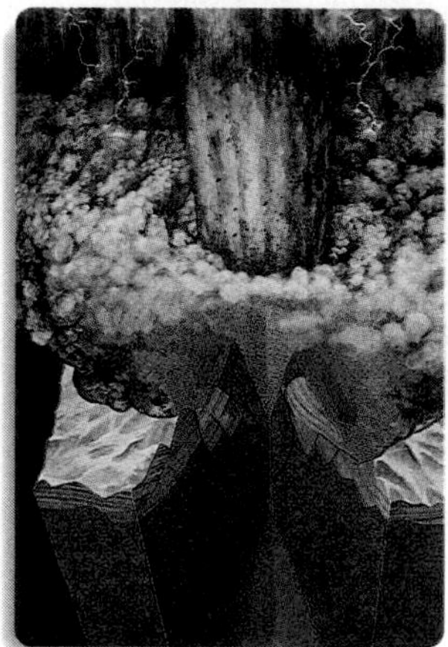

EARTH'S INTERIOR During the eruption of a volcano, pressure forces melted rock from the mantle to Earth's surface.

More about Earth available at www.mcdougallittell.com

EXAMPLE 3 Finding the Volume of a Shell

SCIENCE LINK Earth's interior consists of three parts: the mantle, the outer core, and the inner core. Use the diagram to find the approximate volume of the mantle.

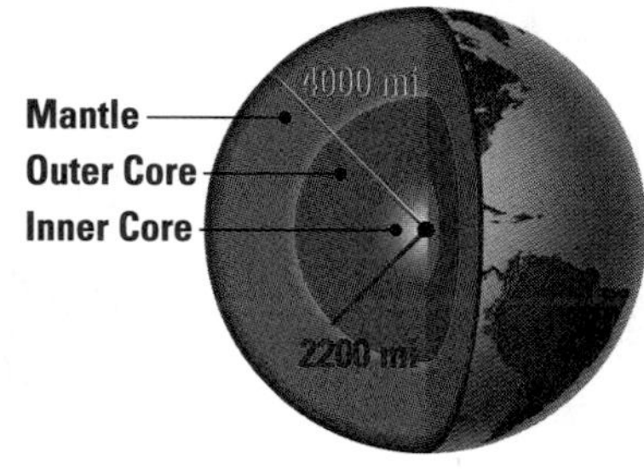

Solution

To find the volume of the mantle, subtract the volume of the sphere formed by the inner core and outer core from the volume of the sphere formed by the inner core, outer core, and mantle.

VOLUME OF LARGER SPHERE	VOLUME OF SMALLER SPHERE
$V = \frac{4}{3}\pi r^3$	$V = \frac{4}{3}\pi r^3$
$= \frac{4}{3} \cdot \pi \cdot (\mathbf{4000})^3$	$= \frac{4}{3} \cdot \pi \cdot (\mathbf{2200})^3$
$\approx 268{,}000{,}000{,}000 \text{ mi}^3$	$\approx 44{,}600{,}000{,}000 \text{ mi}^3$

ANSWER ▶ The approximate volume of the mantle is $268{,}000{,}000{,}000 - 44{,}600{,}000{,}000 = 223{,}400{,}000{,}000 \text{ mi}^3$.

10.7 Exercises

Guided Practice

In Exercises 1–3, use the sphere with center *A*.

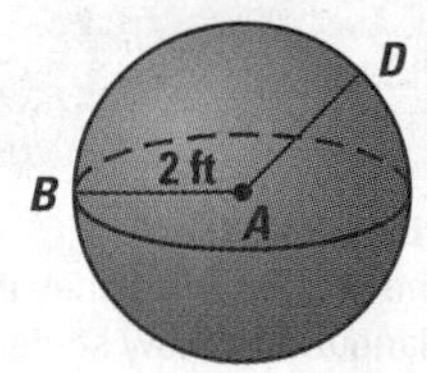

1. What is the radius of the sphere? **2 ft**

2. What is the length of $\overline{AD}$? Explain your answer.

2. $AD = 2$ ft. The radius is the distance from the center to any point on the surface.

3. Find the volume of the sphere. **33.5 ft³**

4. What is half of a sphere called? **hemisphere**

Practice and Problem Solving

Student Help

▶**MORE PRACTICE** Extra practice to help you master skills is on page 709.

SPORTS **Find the volume of the ball with the given radius *r*.**

5. $r = 12$ cm

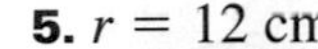

7238 cm³

6. $r = 10.5$ cm

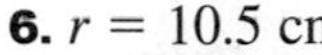

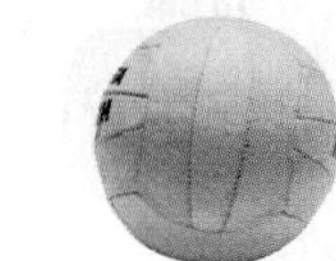

4849 cm³

7. $r = 11$ cm

5575 cm³

Find the volume of the sphere.

8.

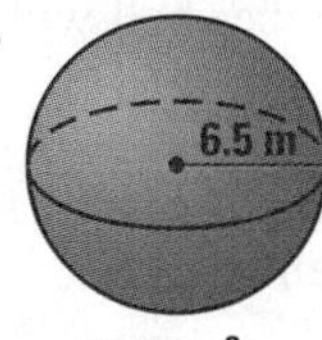

1150 m³

9.

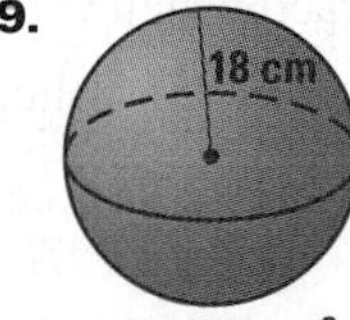

24,429 cm³

10.

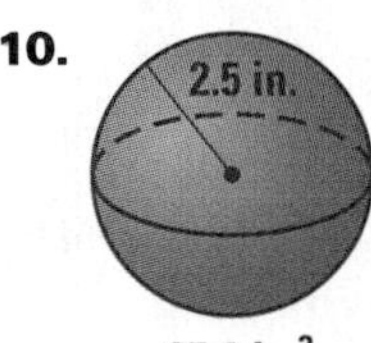

65.4 in.³

In Exercises 11–14, use the following information. A group of spheres have radii of 1, 2, and 3 units.

11. Find the volume of each sphere, leaving your answers in terms of π. Record your data in a table. **See margin.**

12. Describe what happens to the volume of a sphere when the radius doubles. **The volume is eight times larger when the radius is doubled.**

13. Describe what happens to the volume of a sphere when the radius triples. **The volume is twenty-seven times larger when the radius is tripled.**

14. Predict what will happen to the volume when the radius quadruples. Find the volume of a sphere with a radius of 4 units to test your prediction.

14. The volume is sixty-four times larger when the radius is quadrupled; $\frac{256\pi}{3}$.

15. ARCHITECTURE The Sunsphere, built for the 1982 World's Fair in Knoxville, Tennessee, is a 266 foot tower topped with a gold sphere. The radius of the sphere is about 36.5 feet. What is the volume of the sphere? **about 204,000 ft³**

3 Apply

Assignment Guide

TRANSITIONAL
Day 1: pp. 545–547 Exs. 5–6, 8–9, 15–17, 20–21, 40–43
Day 2: pp. 545–547 Exs. 11–14, 23–25, 31–39

AVERAGE
Day 1: pp. 545–547 Exs. 5–10, 15–17, 20–22, 40–43
Day 2: pp. 545–547 Exs. 11–14, 23–25, 30–39

ADVANCED
Day 1: pp. 545–547 Exs. 6–9, 15–17, 20–22, 40–43
Day 2: pp. 545–547 Exs. 11–14, 26–28, 29*, 30–39

BLOCK SCHEDULE
pp. 545–547 Exs. 5–17, 20–25, 30–43

Extra Practice

- Student Edition, pp. 708–709
- Chapter 10 Resource Book, p. 60

Homework Check

To quickly check student understanding of key concepts, go over the following exercises:

Transitional: 6, 12, 15, 20, 25
Average: 10, 12, 15, 20, 30
Advanced: 10, 14, 20, 26, 30

Math Reasoning

Regarding Exercises 11–14, the volume of a sphere of radius kr is k^3 times the volume of a sphere of radius r. Observe that a sphere of radius kr is similar to a sphere of radius r with scale factor k.

11.

Radius	1	2	3
Volume	$\frac{4\pi}{3}$	$\frac{32\pi}{3}$	$\frac{108\pi}{3}$

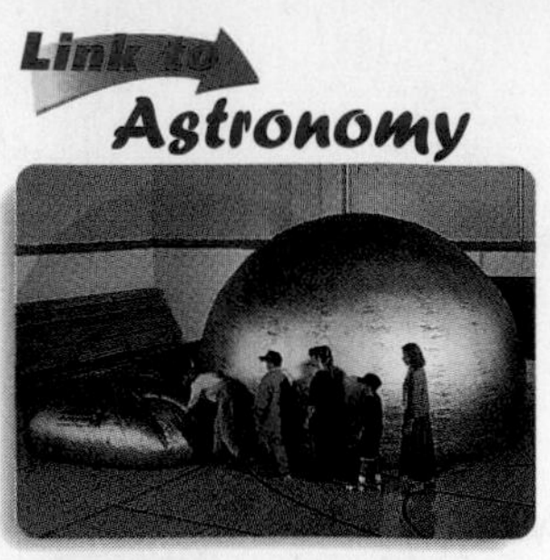

Link to Astronomy

PLANETARIUMS
The projection devices of a planetarium allow students to learn about astronomy and earth science. The planetarium shown can accommodate about 30 students.

17. 1072 ft^3; the volume of a hemisphere is one-half the volume of a sphere.

18. The volume of a sphere is $\frac{4}{3}\pi r^3$, not $\frac{1}{3}\pi r^3$. The radius is 3 meters if the diameter is 6 meters. Also, $\frac{1}{3}\pi(6)^3 = 72\pi$. The volume is 36π.

19. No. The volume is 8 times the original volume, because volume is proportional to r^3.

ASTRONOMY In Exercises 16 and 17, use the following information. The portable planetarium shown in the photo is a hemisphere with a radius of 8 feet.

16. If the lab were a complete sphere, what would its volume be? 2145 ft^3

17. Find the volume of the lab. Explain your reasoning. See margin.

In Exercises 18 and 19, a sphere has a diameter of 6 meters.

18. ERROR ANALYSIS Your friend is asked to find the volume of the sphere. Explain the error(s) in his work shown at the right, and find the correct volume. See margin.

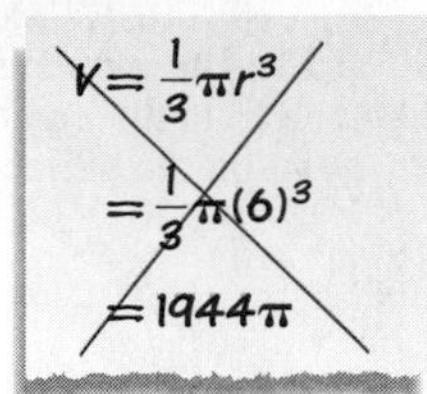

19. Double the radius of the sphere. Is the volume double the original volume? Explain. See margin.

Find the volume of the solid. The solids are composed of hemispheres, cones, right cylinders, and right rectangular prisms.

20. 18 cm, 10 cm
7749 cm^3

21.

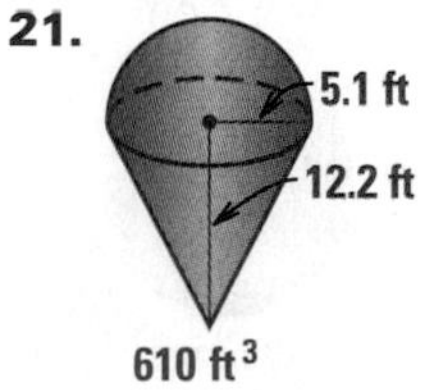

610 ft^3

22.

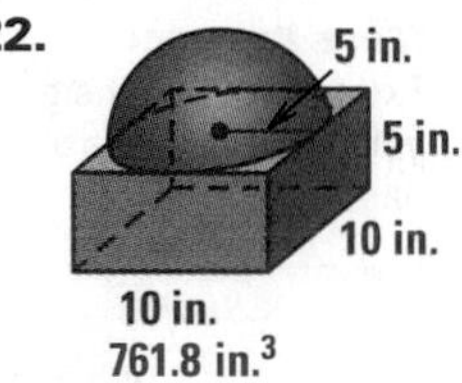

761.8 in.^{3}

RACQUETBALL In Exercises 23–25, use the following information. A racquetball is a hollow rubber ball with a radius of 1.3 inches.

23. Find the volume of a racquetball. 9.2 in.^{3}

24. The hollow center of a racquetball has a radius of 1 inch. Find the volume of the hollow center. 4.2 in.^{3}

25. Use the answers to Exercises 23 and 24 to find the volume of the rubber shell. 5.0 in.^{3}

▶ HOMEWORK HELP

Extra help with problem solving in Exs. 26–29 is available at www.mcdougallittell.com

In Exercises 26–29, use the solids below. Leave each answer in terms of π.

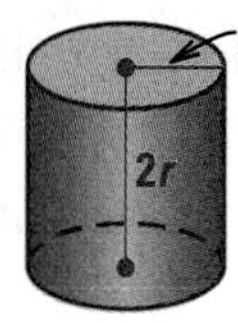

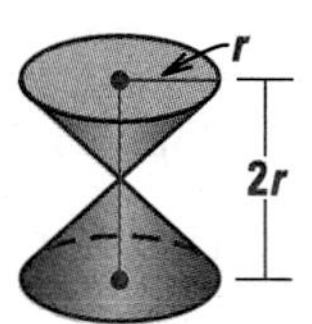

26. Write an expression for the volume of the right cylinder. $2\pi r^3$

27. Write an expression for the volume of the solid composed of the two cones. $\frac{2}{3}\pi r^3$

28. Write an expression for the volume of the sphere. $\frac{4}{3}\pi r^3$

29. CHALLENGE Write an equation relating the three volumes that you found in Exercises 26–28. *Sample answer:* V(right cylinder) = V(2 cones) + V(sphere)

30. COCONUT Inside a coconut there is a shell of edible white coconut meat and a non-edible husk, as shown in the diagram. The coconut is roughly a sphere with a radius of 3 inches. Assuming the husk is very thin, approximate the volume of the shell of coconut meat. **79.6 in.^{3}**

Multiple-Choice Practice

31. What is the volume of the sphere? **D**

Ⓐ 20.9 m^3 Ⓑ 65.4 m^3

Ⓒ 104.7 m^3 Ⓓ 523.3 m^3

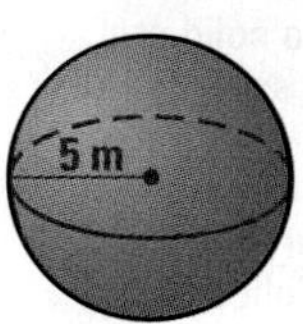

32. Which expression represents the volume of the object's shell? **H**

Ⓕ $\frac{4}{3}\pi(10)^3 + \frac{4}{3}\pi(8)^3$

Ⓖ $\frac{4}{3}\pi(2)^3$

Ⓗ $\frac{4}{3}\pi(10)^3 - \frac{4}{3}\pi(8)^3$

Ⓙ $\frac{4}{3}\pi(8)^3$

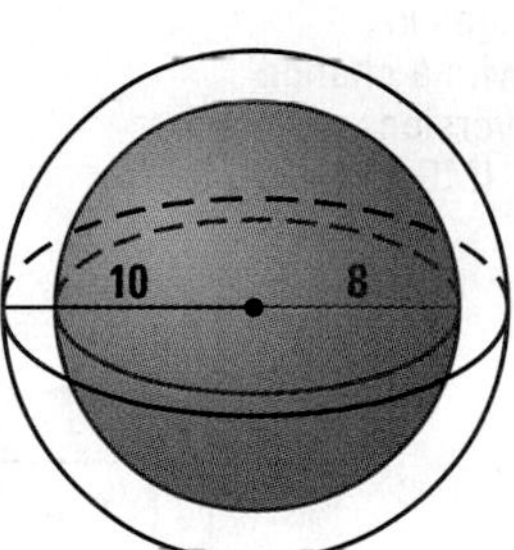

Mixed Review

In Exercises 33 and 34, use the diagram below. *(7.1)*

33. What is the ratio of blue squares to red squares? **5:2**

34. What is the ratio of red squares to yellow squares? **2:3**

In Exercises 35–39, use the diagram shown. *(8.1, 8.2)*

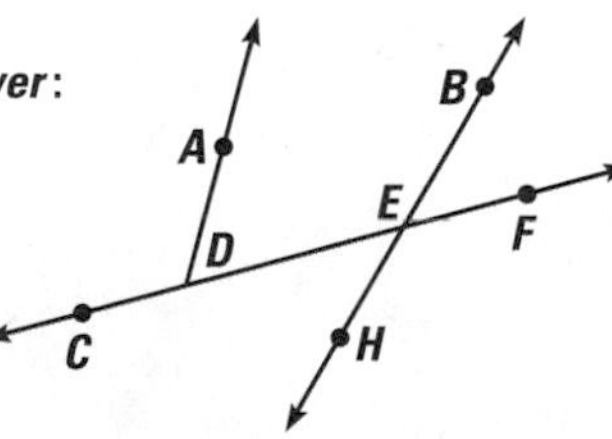

35. Is $\overrightarrow{DA}$ a segment, a ray, or a line? **Ray**

36. Give two other names for $\overleftrightarrow{BH}$. ***Sample answer*: $\overleftrightarrow{EB}$, $\overleftrightarrow{EH}$**

37. Give three other names for $\angle ADF$. **$\angle ADE$, $\angle EDA$, $\angle FDA$**

38. If $m\angle ADE = 60°$, find $m\angle CDA$. **120°**

39. If $m\angle BEF = 50°$, find $m\angle FEH$. **130°**

Solve the equation using mental math. *(9.1)*

40. $x^2 = 16$ **−4, 4** **41.** $169 = y^2$ **−13, 13** **42.** $m^2 = 400$ **−20, 20** **43.** $121 = p^2$ **−11, 11**

4 Assess

Assessment Resources

- Assessment Book (Formal Assessment and Alternative Assessment)
- Test and Practice Generator

Mini-Quiz

1. Find the volume of a sphere with radius 1.5 feet. **about 14.14 ft^3**
2. A grocery store sells large and small apples that are roughly spherical. The large apple has a radius of 2 inches and the small apple has a radius of 1.5 inches. What is the difference in volume between the 2 sizes? **about 19.37 in.^{3}**
3. A cherry and its pit are both roughly spherical. The cherry's radius is 1 cm and the pit's radius is 0.5 cm. What is the volume of the cherry without the pit? **about 3.67 cm^3**

1 Plan

Pacing

Suggested Number of Days

Transitional: 2 days
Average: 2 days
Advanced: 2 days
Block Schedule: 1 block

Teaching Resources

Blacklines
(See page 506B.)

Transparencies
- Warm-Up Exercises
- Teacher Time-Savers
- English/Spanish Problem Solving
- Answers

Technology
- Electronic Teacher Tools
- Test and Practice Generator

2 Teach

Math Reasoning

For Mathematical Background Notes on mathematical reasoning related to this lesson, please refer to pages 506E and 506F in this Teacher's Edition.

California Standards and Assessment

CA Standards: MG 2.3, MG 2.4

10.8 Similar Solids

California Standards

In this lesson you'll:

- Understand that when the dimensions of a solid are multiplied by a scale factor, the surface area is multiplied by the square of the scale factor and the volume is multiplied by the cube of the scale factor. (MG 2.3)
- Relate the changes in measurement with a change of scale to conversions between units. (MG 2.4)

Goal 1 Exploring Measures of Similar Solids

Two solids with equal ratios of all corresponding linear measures, such as heights or radii, are called **similar solids**. This common ratio is called the *scale factor*. Similar solids have the same shape, but their sizes may differ. Any two cubes are similar; so are any two spheres.

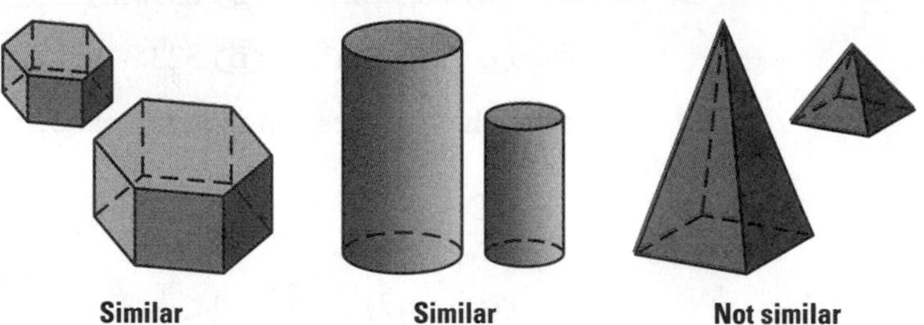

EXAMPLE 1 Comparing Ratios of Similar Solids

Find the surface area and volume of each cube. Then find the ratio of the surface area and volume of each cube to the corresponding measures of the smallest cube.

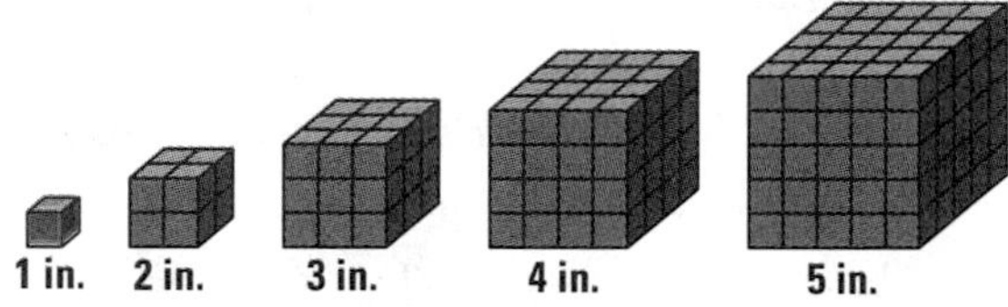

Solution

Edge length	Scale factor, k	Surface area (in in.^{2})	Ratio of surface areas	Volume (in in.^{3})	Ratio of volumes
1 in.	$\frac{1}{1} = 1$	6	$\frac{6}{6} = 1$	1	$\frac{1}{1} = 1$
2 in.	$\frac{2}{1} = 2$	24	$\frac{24}{6} = 4$	8	$\frac{8}{1} = 8$
3 in.	$\frac{3}{1} = 3$	54	$\frac{54}{6} = 9$	27	$\frac{27}{1} = 27$
4 in.	$\frac{4}{1} = 4$	96	$\frac{96}{6} = 16$	64	$\frac{64}{1} = 64$
5 in.	$\frac{5}{1} = 5$	150	$\frac{150}{6} = 25$	125	$\frac{125}{1} = 125$

Goal 2 COMPARING SIMILAR SOLIDS

The patterns in Example 1 suggest the following relationships.

RATIOS OF MEASURES OF SIMILAR SOLIDS

1. If two solids are similar with a scale factor of k, then the surface areas of the solids have a ratio of k^2.
2. If two solids are similar with a scale factor of k, then the volumes of the solids have a ratio of k^3.

Link to Models

SCALE MODELS At Tobu World Square, the world's most famous buildings and monuments are precisely reproduced on a smaller scale.

EXAMPLE 2 Comparing Surface Areas and Volumes

SCALE MODELS You are making a scale model of a building. In your model, a length of $\frac{1}{2}$ inch represents a length of 1 foot in the building.

a. What is the scale factor of the building to the model?

b. What is the ratio of the surface area of the building to the surface area of the model?

Solution

a. To find the scale factor, find the ratio of 1 foot to $\frac{1}{2}$ inch.

$$\frac{1 \text{ ft}}{\frac{1}{2} \text{ in.}} = \frac{12 \text{ in.}}{\frac{1}{2} \text{ in.}} = 12 \cdot \frac{2}{1} = 24$$

ANSWER ▶ The scale factor is 24.

b. With a scale factor of 24, the building's surface area is 24^2, or 576, times the model's surface area.

EXAMPLE 3 Comparing Similar Solids

The cylinders shown are similar. The ratio of their surface areas is 9 : 4. Find the ratio of their heights and the ratio of their volumes.

Solution

Let k be the scale factor.

$k^2 = \frac{9}{4}$ — Ratio of surface areas is the square of the scale factor.

$k = \frac{3}{2}$ — Take the positive square root of both sides.

ANSWER ▶ The ratio of the heights of the cylinders is $k = \frac{3}{2}$. The ratio of their volumes is $k^3 = \frac{27}{8}$.

Extra Example 1

One cube has an edge of 3 inches and another cube has an edge of 6 inches. Find the ratios of the edge lengths, surface areas, and volumes of the smaller cube to the larger cube. $\frac{1}{2}, \frac{1}{4}, \frac{1}{8}$

Extra Example 2

You are making a model of an Egyptian pyramid. In your model, 1 cm represents a length of 10 meters in the pyramid.

a. What is the scale factor of the pyramid to the model? **1000**

b. What is the ratio of the surface area of the pyramid to the model? **1,000,000 : 1**

Extra Example 3

Two right triangular prisms are similar. The ratio of their surface areas is 4 : 1. Find the ratio of their heights and volumes. **2 : 1; 8 : 1**

Math Reasoning

If two polyhedra are similar with scale factor k, then their corresponding faces are similar and the ratio of their areas is k^2. This can be used to explain property 1 of Goal 2. As for property 2, imagine a solid of some irregular shape built by gluing together unit cubes. If another solid is built in exactly the same way using cubes of edge length k, then the solids will be similar with scale factor k. It can be seen directly by counting cubes that the ratio of the volumes is k^3.

Concept Check

How can you tell if two pyramids are similar? **Check the ratios of corresponding base edges and heights. If the ratios are the same, the pyramids are similar.**

3 Apply

Assignment Guide

TRANSITIONAL
Day 1: pp. 550–551 Exs. 7–8, 11–17
Day 2: pp. 550–551 Exs. 9–10, 18–20, 22–23

AVERAGE
Day 1: pp. 550–551 Exs. 7–8, 11–17
Day 2: pp. 550–551 Exs. 9–10, 18–20, 22–23

ADVANCED
Day 1: pp. 550–551 Exs. 7–8, 11–17
Day 2: pp. 550–551 Exs. 9–10, 18–20, 21*, 22–23

BLOCK SCHEDULE
pp. 550–551 Exs. 7–20, 22–23

Extra Practice

- Student Edition, pp. 708–709
- Chapter 10 Resource Book, p. 69

Homework Check

To quickly check student understanding of key concepts, go over the following exercises:

Transitional: 8, 10, 12, 16, 18, 20
Average: 8, 10, 12, 16, 18, 20
Advanced: 8, 10, 12, 16, 18, 20

Problem Solving

Avoiding Common Errors
In Exercises 7 and 8, emphasize that students should not rely on eyesight alone. Encourage them to set up the appropriate proportions to check for similarity.

10.8 Exercises

Guided Practice

Determine whether the solids are similar. Explain your answer.

1. 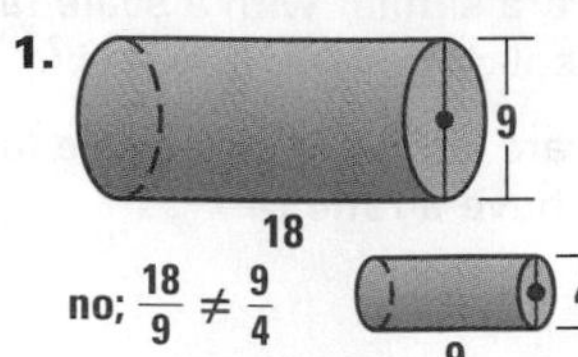

no; $\frac{18}{9} \neq \frac{9}{4}$

2. 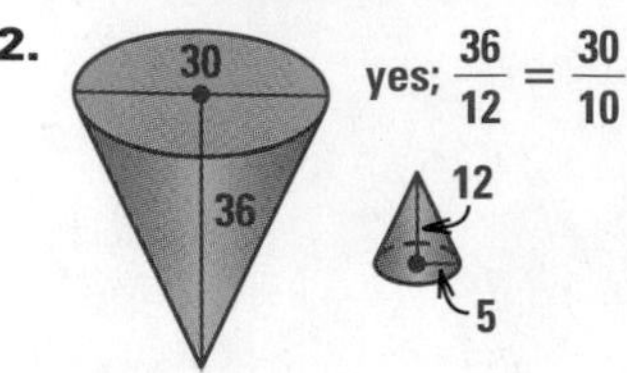

yes; $\frac{36}{12} = \frac{30}{10}$

In Exercises 3–6, use the similar right prisms shown.

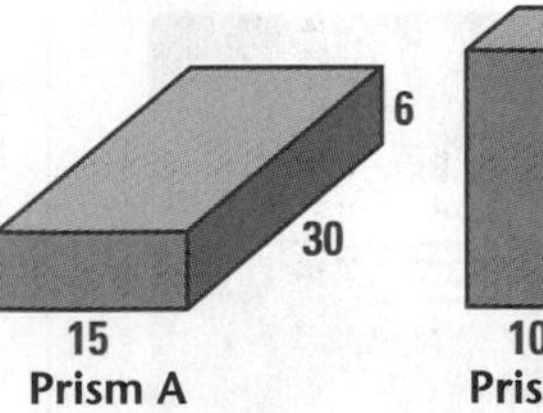

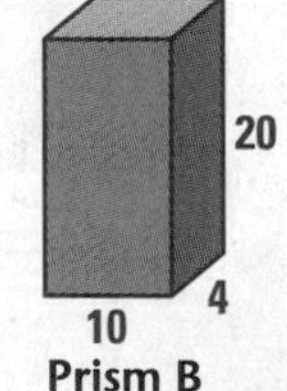

3. Find the scale factor of Prism A to Prism B. **1.5**

4. Find the surface area of Prism B. **640**

5. Use the scale factor and the surface area of Prism B to find the surface area of Prism A. **1440**

6. Describe how the volumes of the prisms are related.
Volume of A = $3\frac{3}{8}$ times volume of Prism B

Practice and Problem Solving

Student Help
▶ MORE PRACTICE
Extra practice to help you master skills is on page 709.

Match the solid with a similar solid.

7. 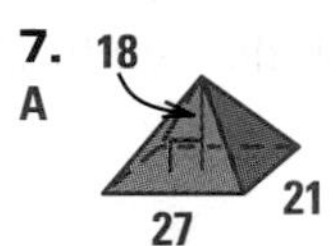

A

A. 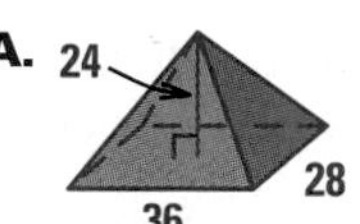

B. 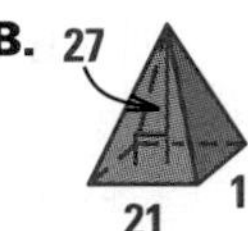

C. 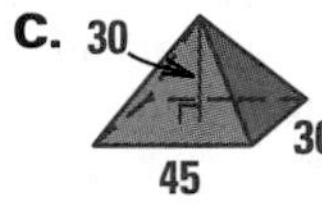

8. 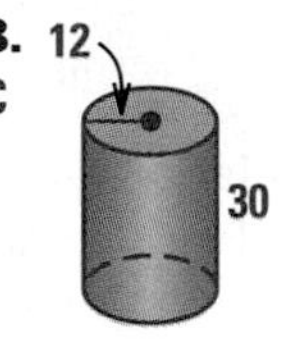

C

A. 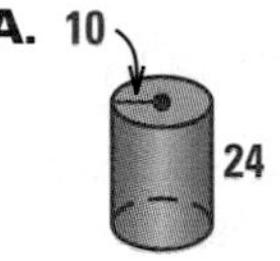

B. 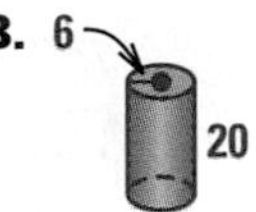

C. 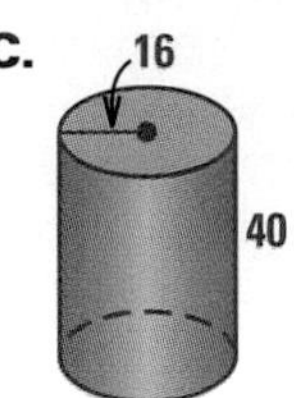

Student Help
▶ HOMEWORK HELP
Extra help with problem solving in Exs. 9–10 is available at www.mcdougallittell.com

The solids shown are similar. Use the given ratio of their surface areas to find the ratio of their volumes.

9. 25 : 4 **125:8**

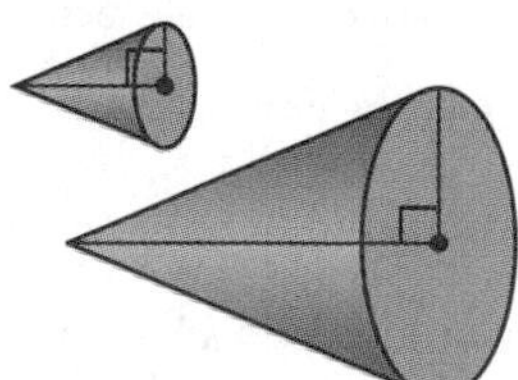

10. 16 : 9 **64:27**

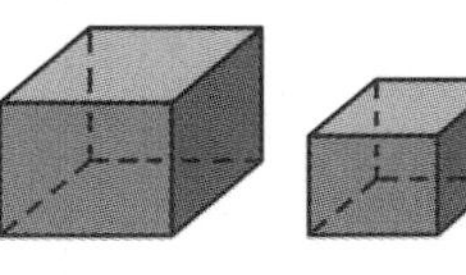

MATHEMATICAL REASONING **Complete the statement using *always*, *sometimes*, or *never*.**

11. Always
12. Sometimes
13. Sometimes
14. Always

11. Two spheres are __?__ similar. **12.** Two cones are __?__ similar.

13. Two cylinders are __?__ similar. **14.** A solid is __?__ similar to itself.

NESTING BOXES **In Exercises 15–17, use the following information.** You are building a set of three nesting boxes. The boxes are arranged so that each box opens to reveal a smaller box. All three boxes are cubes, whose edges measure 2 inches, 4 inches, and 6 inches.

15. Find the scale factor of the largest box to the smallest box and the scale factor of the mid-sized box to the smallest box. **3; 2**

16. Find the surface area of the smallest box. Use this surface area to find the surface areas of the other two boxes. **24 in.^{2}; 96 in.^{2}; 216 in.^{2}**

17. Find the volume of the smallest box. Use this volume to find the volumes of the other two boxes. **8 in.^{3}; 64 in.^{3}; 216 in.^{3}**

ARCHITECTURE **In Exercises 18–20, use the following information.** You are building a scale model of the Marina Towers in Chicago. Marina Towers consists of two towers that resemble right cylinders. Both towers are 588 feet high and have circular bases whose diameters measure 135 feet.

18. You decide that 150 feet of the actual building will correspond to 0.5 feet in your model. What is your scale factor? **300:1**

19. What is the ratio of the surface area of the actual towers to the surface area of the towers in your model? **90,000:1**

20. The ratio of the surface area of one of the towers to the surface area of a similar building is 36 : 1. Find the height of the similar building. **98 ft**

21. CHALLENGE One cube has edges of length x, and a second cube has edges of length kx. Find the ratio of their surface areas and the ratio of their volumes.

Link to Careers

ARCHITECT By creating scale models of their designs, architects are able to show their clients what the completed building will look like.

More about architects is available at www.mcdougallittell.com

Multiple-Choice Practice

21. Surface area of Cube 1 = $6x^2$; Surface area of Cube 2 = $6(kx)^2 = k^2(6x^2)$; ratio of surface areas is $1{:}k^2$. Volume of Cube 1 = x^3; volume of Cube 2 = $(kx)^3 = k^3x^3$; ratio of volumes is $1{:}k^3$.

22. What is the ratio of the volumes of the spheres? **D**

Ⓐ $\frac{\sqrt{2}}{\sqrt{5}}$ Ⓑ $\frac{2}{5}$

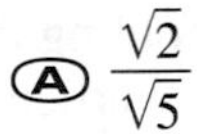

Ⓒ $\frac{4}{25}$ Ⓓ $\frac{8}{125}$

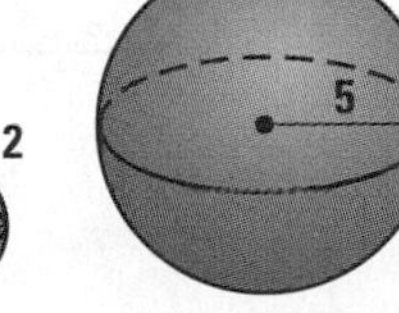

23. The dimensions of a prism are doubled. How many times larger is the volume of the new prism? **J**

Ⓕ $\frac{1}{2}$ Ⓖ 2 Ⓗ 4 Ⓙ 8

4 Assess

Assessment Resources

- Assessment Book (Formal Assessment and Alternative Assessment)
- Test and Practice Generator

Mini-Quiz

1. One cube has an edge of 3 cm and another one has an edge of 4 cm. Find the ratios of the surface areas and volumes of the smaller cube to the larger cube. **$\frac{9}{16}$, $\frac{27}{64}$**
2. An architect made a scale model of a building she is designing. In the model, a length of $\frac{1}{4}$ inch represents 1 foot in the building. What is the scale factor of the building to the model? What is the ratio of the surface area of the building to the surface area of the model? **48; 2304 : 1**
3. Two cylinders are similar. If the ratio of their surface areas is 25 : 16, find the ratio of their heights and the ratio of their volumes. **$\frac{5}{4}$, $\frac{125}{64}$**

Additional Resources

The following resources are available to help review the material in this chapter:

Technology

- Personal Student Tutor
- Test and Practice Generator

Chapter 10 Chapter Summary and Review

VOCABULARY

- **circle (center, radius, diameter, circumference),** *p. 511*
- **central angle,** *p. 513*
- **sector,** *p. 513*
- **chord,** *p. 516*
- **coplanar,** *p. 517*
- **skew lines,** *p. 517*
- **polyhedron (face, edge, vertex, net),** *p. 518*
- **prism,** *p. 523*
- **base,** *p. 523*
- **rectangular prism,** *p. 523*
- **circular cylinder,** *p. 523*
- **right prism,** *p. 523*
- **right cylinder,** *p. 523*
- **surface area,** *p. 523*
- **volume,** *p. 530*
- **oblique prism,** *p. 530*
- **oblique cylinder,** *p. 535*
- **pyramid,** *p. 539*
- **circular cone,** *p. 539*
- **sphere (center, radius),** *p. 543*
- **hemisphere,** *p. 543*
- **similar solids,** *p. 548*

10.1 CIRCUMFERENCE AND AREA OF A CIRCLE

Examples on pp. 511–513

EXAMPLE **Find the circumference and area of the circle shown.**

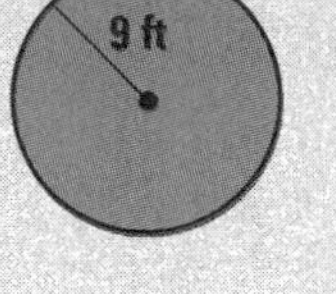

$C = 2\pi r$
$\approx 2(3.14)(9)$
$= 56.52$ ft

$A = \pi r^2$
$\approx 3.14(9^2)$
$= 254.34$ ft^2

1. Find the circumference and area of a circle with a diameter of 14 inches. **$C = 14\pi \approx 43.96$ in.; $A = 49\pi \approx 153.86$ in.^{2}**

2. Find the entire area of a circle given that a 60° sector of the circle has an area of 19 square meters. **114 m^2**

10.2 THREE-DIMENSIONAL FIGURES

Examples on pp. 517–519

EXAMPLE The polyhedron that results from folding the net on the left below is a prism with 6 faces, 12 edges, and 8 vertices.

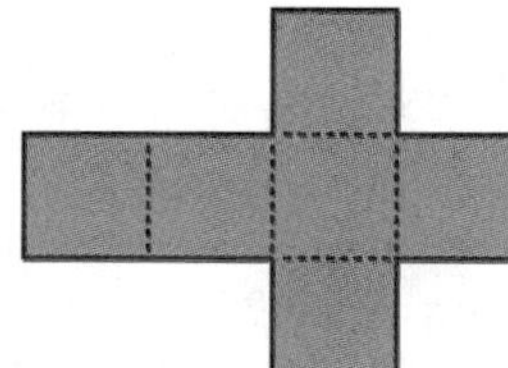

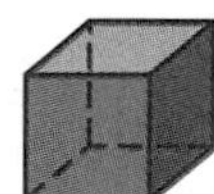

Identify the solid formed by folding the net. Find the number of faces, vertices, and edges of the solid.

3.

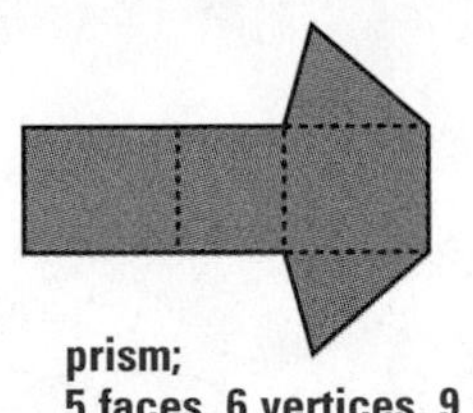

prism;
5 faces, 6 vertices, 9 edges

4.

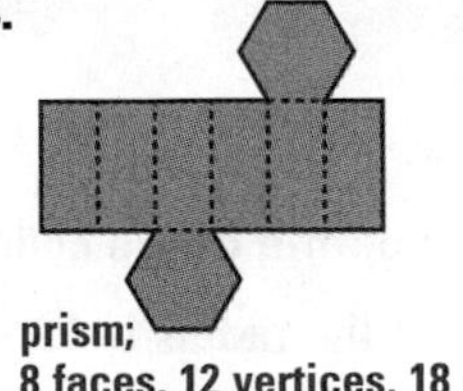

prism;
8 faces, 12 vertices, 18 edges

5.

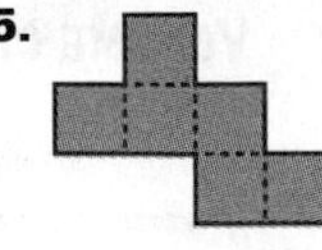

prism;
6 faces, 8 vertices, 12 edges

10.3 SURFACE AREAS OF PRISMS AND CYLINDERS

Examples on pp. 523–525

EXAMPLE **Find the surface area of the right prism.**

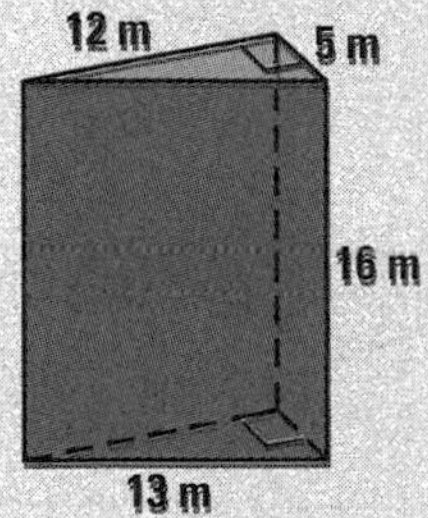

First find its base area and base perimeter.

$B = \frac{1}{2}bh = \frac{1}{2}(5)(12) = 30 \text{ m}^2 \qquad P = 13 + 12 + 5 = 30 \text{ m}$

$S = 2B + Ph = 2(30) + 30(16) = 540$

ANSWER ▶ The surface area is 540 square meters.

Find the surface area of the right prism or right cylinder.

6.

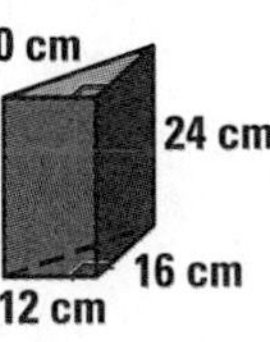

1344 cm^2

7.

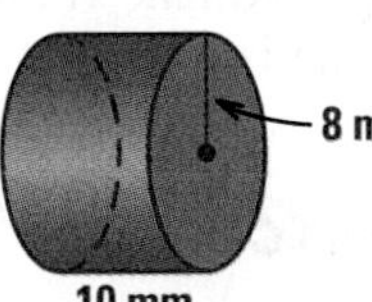

904.8 mm^2

8.

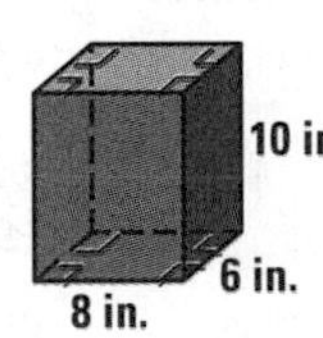

376 in.^{2}

10.4 VOLUME OF A PRISM

Examples on pp. 530–531

EXAMPLE **Find the volume of the rectangular prism.**

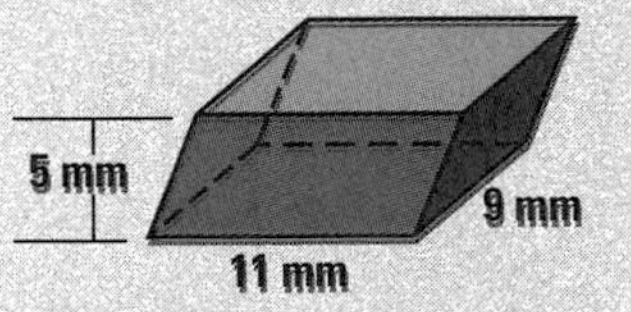

$V = \ell wh = 9(11)(5) = 495$

ANSWER ▶ The volume is 495 cubic millimeters.

Find the volume of the prism. (In Exercises 9 and 10, the prisms are right. In Exercise 10, the prism has rectangular bases.)

9.

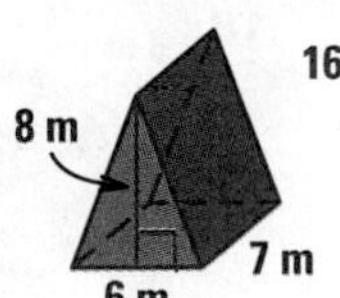

168 m^3

10.

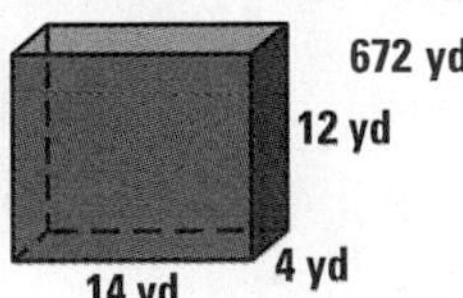

672 yd^3

11.

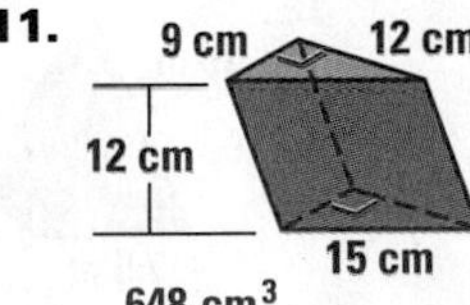

648 cm^3

10.5 VOLUME OF A CYLINDER

Examples on pp. 535–536

EXAMPLE **Find the volume of the cylinder.**

The diameter is 12 feet, so the radius is $12 \div 2 = 6$ feet.

The base area B is $\pi r^2 = 36\pi$ square feet.

$V = Bh$	Write formula for volume.
$= 36\pi \cdot 14$	Substitute for B and h.
≈ 1583.36	Use a calculator.

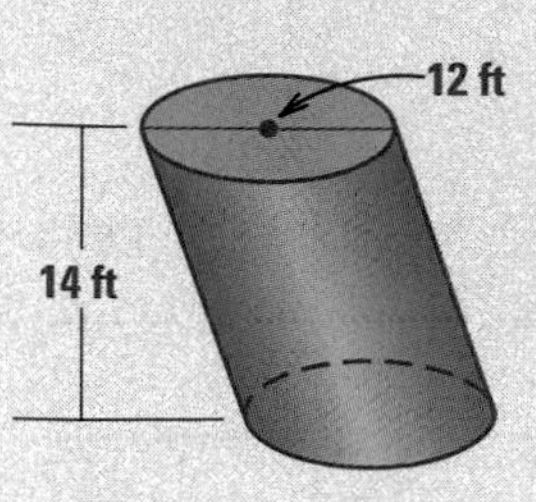

ANSWER ▶ The volume is about 1583 cubic feet.

In Exercises 12–14, find the volume of the cylinder.

12.

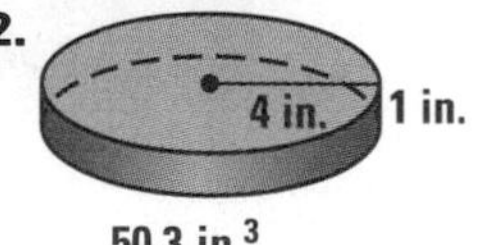

50.3 in.^{3}

13.

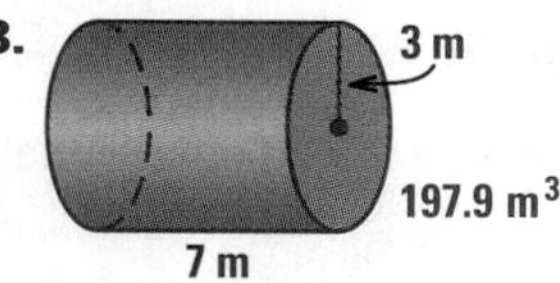

197.9 m^3

14.

3015.9 cm^3

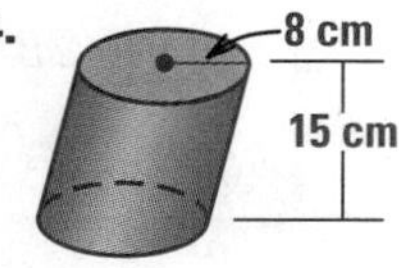

15. A right cylinder has an approximate volume of 1750 cubic meters and a diameter of 16 meters. What is its height? **8.7 m**

10.6 VOLUMES OF PYRAMIDS AND CONES

Examples on pp. 539–540

EXAMPLE **Find the volume of the pyramid.**

First find the base area B.

$$B = \frac{1}{2}bh = \frac{1}{2}(8)(12) = 48 \text{ m}^2$$

$$V = \frac{1}{3}Bh = \frac{1}{3}(48)(15) = 240$$

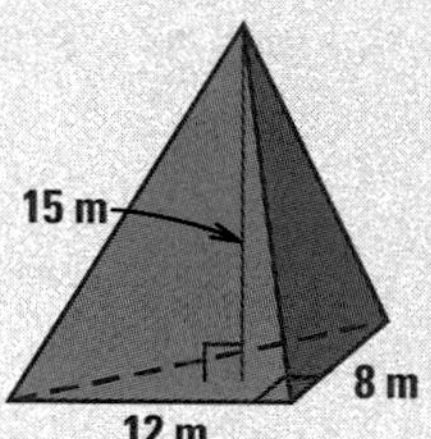

ANSWER ▶ The volume is 240 cubic meters.

Find the volume of the solid. The pyramids and prism have rectangular bases.

16.

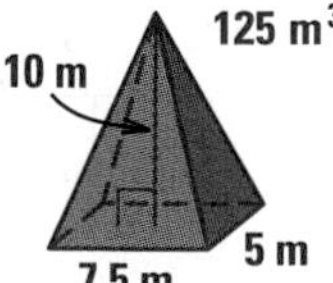

125 m^3

17.

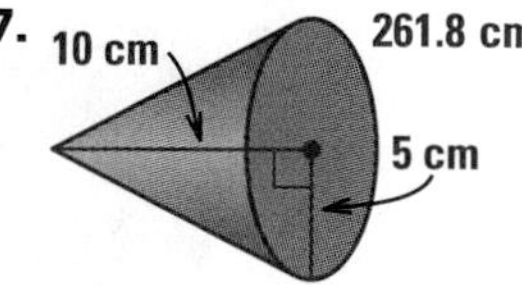

261.8 cm^3

18.

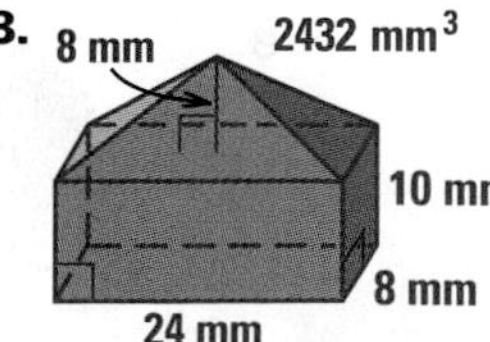

2432 mm^3

10.7 VOLUME OF A SPHERE

Examples on pp. 543–544

EXAMPLE **Find the volume of the sphere.**

$V = \frac{4}{3}\pi r^3$ Write formula for volume.

$= \frac{4}{3} \cdot \pi \cdot 40^3$ Substitute for r.

$\approx 268{,}083$ Use a calculator.

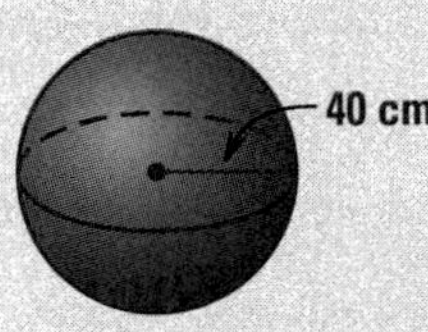

ANSWER ▶ The volume is about 268,083 cubic centimeters.

Find the volume of the sphere.

19.

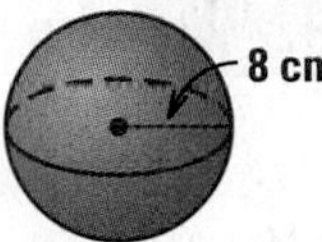

2145 cm^3

20.

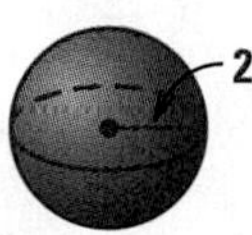

33.5 in.^{3}

21.

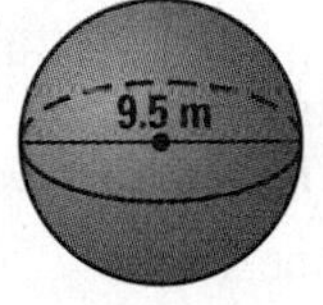

448.9 m^3

10.8 SIMILAR SOLIDS

Examples on pp. 548–549

EXAMPLE **Determine whether the solids are similar.**

The ratio of the heights is $\frac{45}{90} = \frac{1}{2}$, and the ratio of the radii is $\frac{20}{30} = \frac{2}{3}$. Because the ratios differ, the lengths are not proportional. So, the solids are not similar.

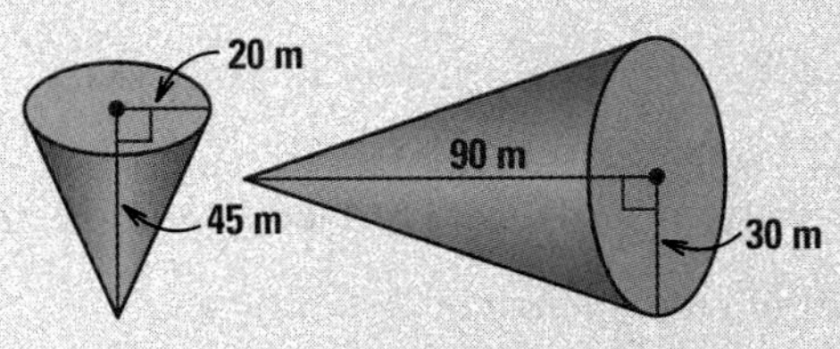

In Exercises 22 and 23, use the similar cylinders shown.

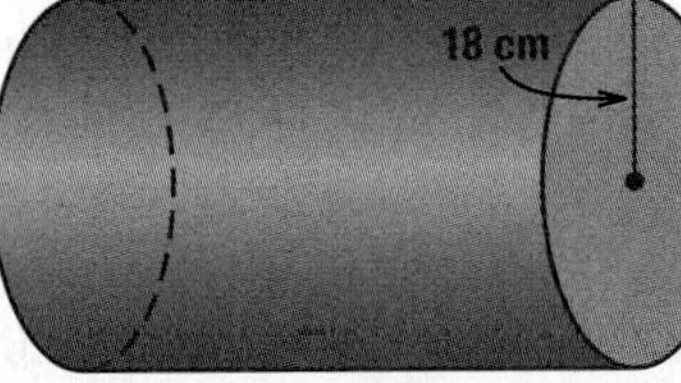

22. Find the scale factor of the large cylinder to the small cylinder. 6

23. Find the surface area of the large cylinder. Use your answer along with the scale factor to find the surface area of the small cylinder.

8143 cm^2; 226 cm^2

For Exercises 24 and 25, two prisms are similar with a scale factor of $\frac{3}{5}$.

24. What is the ratio of the volumes of the prisms? $\frac{27}{125}$

25. If the larger prism has a volume of 2875 cubic inches, what is the volume of the smaller prism? 621 in.^{3}

Additional Resources

Assessment Book

- Formal Assessment, pp. 151–159
- Alternative Assessment, pp. 193–207

Test and Practice Generator

Sample answer:

4. 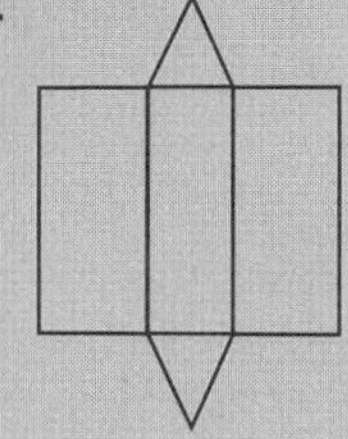

Chapter 10 Chapter Test

In Exercises 1–4, use the prism at the right.

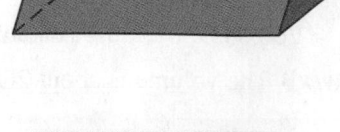

1. How many faces does the prism have? **5**
2. How many vertices does the prism have? **6**
3. How many edges does the prism have? **9**
4. Sketch a net for the prism. **See margin.**

In Exercises 5 and 6, use the right cylinder shown.

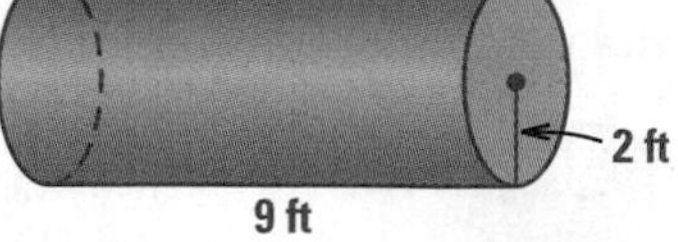

5. Find the surface area of the cylinder. **44π ft^2 or 138.2 ft^2**
6. Find the volume of the cylinder. **36π ft^3 or 113 ft^3**

Find the indicated measure of the solid.

7. Volume **16 cm^3**

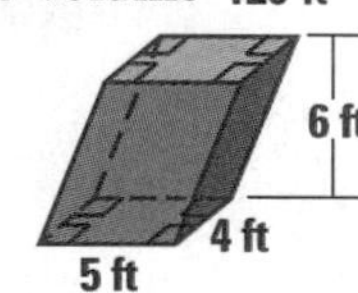

8. Volume **120 ft^3**

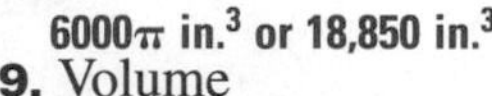
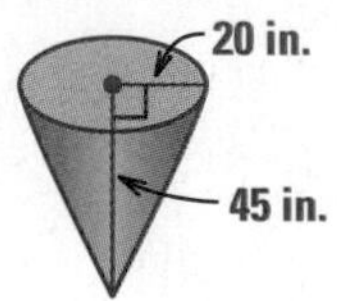

9. Volume **6000π in.^{3} or 18,850 in.^{3}**

10. Surface area **69.3 yd^2**

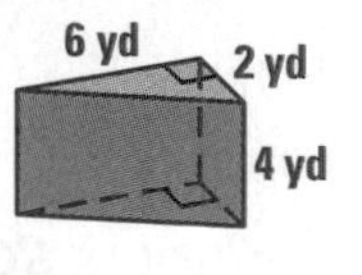

In Exercises 11–15, use the similar right prisms shown.

11. Find the scale factor of Prism A to Prism B. **3**
12. Find the surface area of Prism B. **84 m^2**
13. Use the scale factor and the surface area of Prism B to find the surface area of Prism A. **84 m^2 × 9 = 756 m^2**
14. Find the volume of Prism B. **36 m^3**
15. Use the scale factor and the volume of Prism B to find the volume of Prism A. **36 m^3 × 27 = 972 m^3**

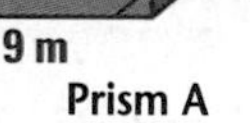
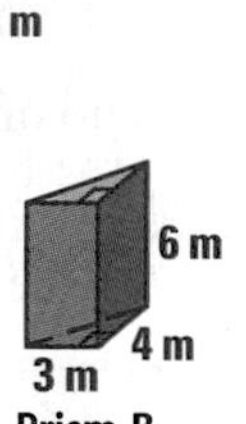

PIPES In Exercises 16–18, use the diagram at the right.

16. What is the surface area of the manhole cover? **9π ft^2 or 28.3 ft^2**
17. Find the volume of the manhole. **101 ft^3**
18. What is the volume of the 20-foot section of the drainage pipe? **320π ft^3 or 1005 ft^3**

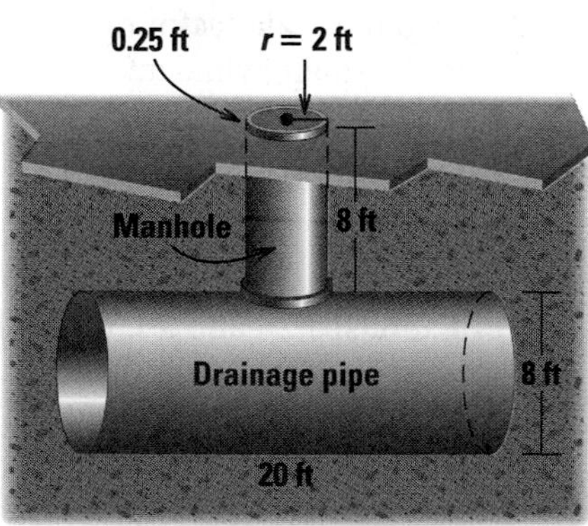

19. **ASTRONOMY** Earth's moon resembles a sphere with a diameter of 2160 miles. Find the approximate volume of the moon. **5,277,000,000 mi^3**

Multiple-Choice Practice

Test Tip Work at a pace that is right for you. Do not worry about how fast others are working.

1. The radius of a circle is 2.5 meters. What is the area of the circle? **D**

Ⓐ 6.25 m^2 Ⓑ $2.5\pi\text{ m}^2$

Ⓒ $5\pi\text{ m}^2$ Ⓓ $6.25\pi\text{ m}^2$

2. The diameter of a circle is 2.5 meters. What is the circumference of the circle? **G**

Ⓕ 6.25 m Ⓖ 2.5π m

Ⓗ 5π m Ⓙ 6.25π m

3. What solid is formed by folding the net? **B**

Ⓐ Prism

Ⓑ Pyramid

Ⓒ Cylinder

Ⓓ Cone

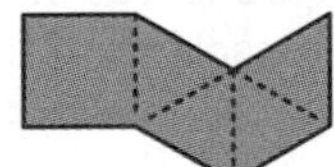

4. An oblique prism has the same height and base area as a right prism. Which statement about the prisms is true? **H**

Ⓕ The volume of the right prism is greater.

Ⓖ The prisms are similar.

Ⓗ The prisms have the same volume.

Ⓙ The volume of the oblique prism is one third the volume of the right prism.

5. What is the volume of the waffle cone shown? **A**

Ⓐ 14.1 in.^{3}

Ⓑ 18.8 in.^{3}

Ⓒ 42.2 in.^{3}

Ⓓ 56.5 in.^{3}

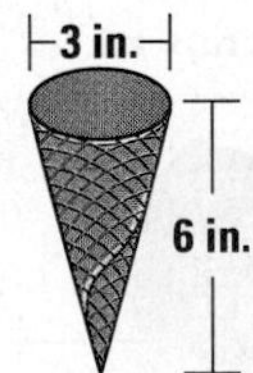

6. The two containers hold fruit juice. One container is a right rectangular prism, and the other is a right cylinder. Which statement about the containers is *false*? (The containers are not drawn to scale.) **G**

12 cm

8 cm

Ⓕ The containers have about the same volume.

Ⓖ The cylindrical container uses more packaging.

Ⓗ The containers hold about the same amount of juice.

Ⓙ The surface area of the rectangular container is greater than that of the cylindrical container.

7. What is the volume of a sphere with a radius of 6 feet? **C**

Ⓐ $36\pi\text{ ft}^3$ Ⓑ $72\pi\text{ ft}^3$

Ⓒ $288\pi\text{ ft}^3$ Ⓓ $2304\pi\text{ ft}^3$

8. The pyramids shown are similar. What is the value of x? **H**

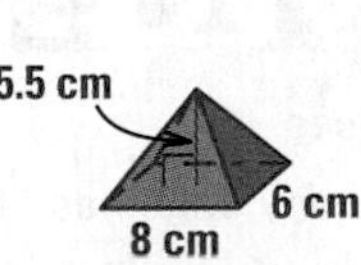

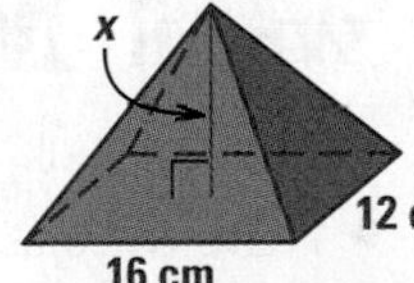

Ⓕ 2.75 cm Ⓖ 10 cm

Ⓗ 11 cm Ⓙ 30.25 cm

Teaching Tip

The Brain Games activity provides a motivating way to review selected content in the chapter. For a more comprehensive review, see the Chapter Summary and Review on pp. 552–555.

California Standards and Assessment

CA Standards: MG 2.1, MR 1.1

Brain games

California Standards

- Use formulas for finding the volume of prisms. (MG 2.1)
- Determine how to break a problem into simpler parts. (MR 1.3)

The Biggest Box

Materials

- **Rectangular piece of construction paper**
- **Metric ruler**
- **Scissors and tape**

Directions

Object of the Game

Teams earn points equal to the volume of their boxes. The team with the most points after a fixed number of rounds wins.

How to Play

STEP 1 Each team is given a piece of construction paper. Each team cuts a square from each corner of its piece of paper. Team members should be sure to cut the same size square from all four corners. Then each team forms a box as shown at the left.

STEP 2 Each team finds the length, width, and height of its box in centimeters and calculates the volume of its box. The points each team receives for the round is equal to the volume of its box.

STEP 3 For each round, repeat Steps 1 and 2 using different sizes of paper.

Another Way to Play

The team with the fewest points wins.

Brain Teaser

pyrite

Which MINERAL am I?

* I have eight vertices.
* I have twice as many edges as I have faces.
* I have at least two faces that are square.

The basic skills you'll review on this page will help prepare you for the next chapter.

Reviewing the Basics

EXAMPLE 1 Writing Expressions

On average, you do 12 hours of homework each week. How many hours of homework you do in w weeks?

Solution

To find the total number of homework hours, multiply the number of hours per week, 12, by the number of weeks, w.

ANSWER ▶ The total number of homework hours is $12w$.

Try These

1. Your age is three times that of your cousin. How old are you if your cousin is y years old? **$3y$**
2. You are buying tickets for a concert through a ticket agency. The agency charges $18 per ticket and a flat fee of $7.50 to process your order. How much will you have to pay for n tickets? **$18n + 7.5$**

EXAMPLE 2 Using the Coordinate Plane

Plot the points in the same coordinate plane.

$(-4, -1), (-2, 0), (0, 1), (2, 2)$

Solution

Draw a coordinate plane. Label the axes and the origin.

The first number of each ordered pair is the x-coordinate. The second number of each ordered pair is the y-coordinate.

To plot $(-4, -1)$, start at the origin. Move 4 units left. Then move 1 unit down. Similarly, plot the other points.

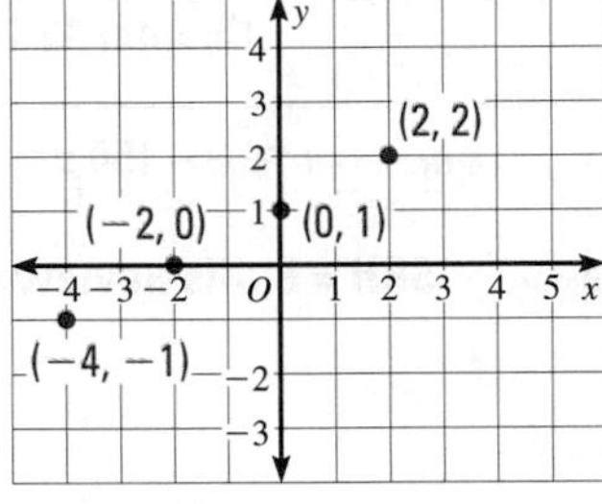

Try These

Plot each set of points in the same coordinate plane.

3. $(-4, 4), (-2, 3), (0, 2), (4, 0)$ **3–6. See margin.**
4. $(3, 4), (3, 2), (3, -1), (3, -3)$
5. $(-4, -2), (-1, -2), (0, -2), (3, -2)$
6. $(-3, -3), (1, 1), (2, 2), (4, 4)$

Student Help

▶ **MORE EXAMPLES**

INTERNET More examples and practice exercises available at www.mcdougallittell.com

Additional Resources

Technology

- Personal Student Tutor
- Test and Practice Generator

3.

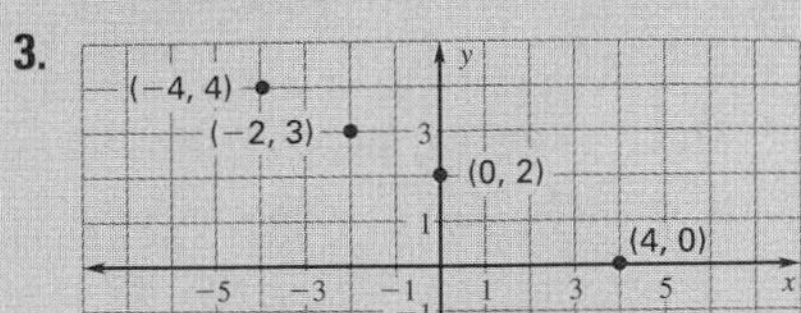

4.

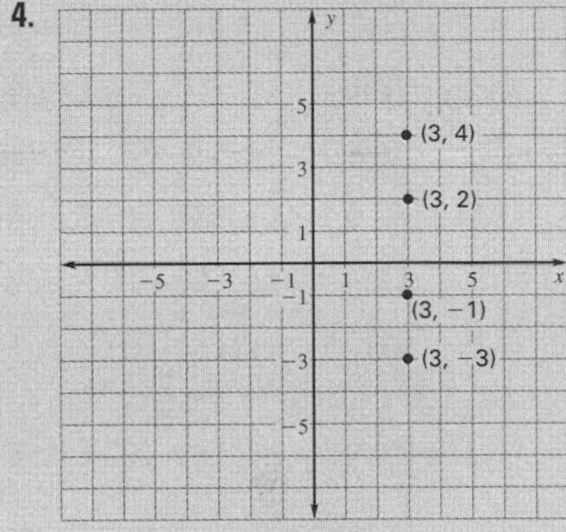

5.

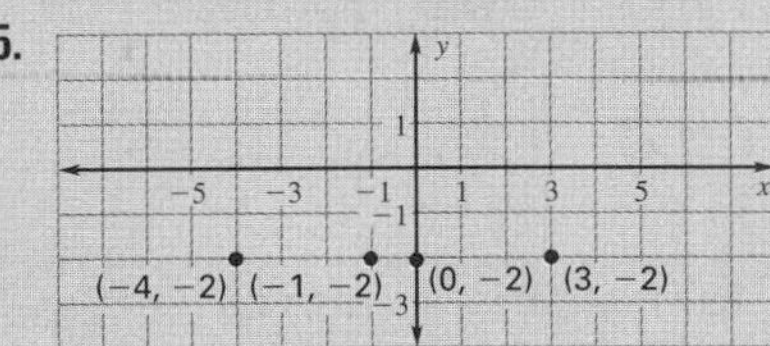

6.

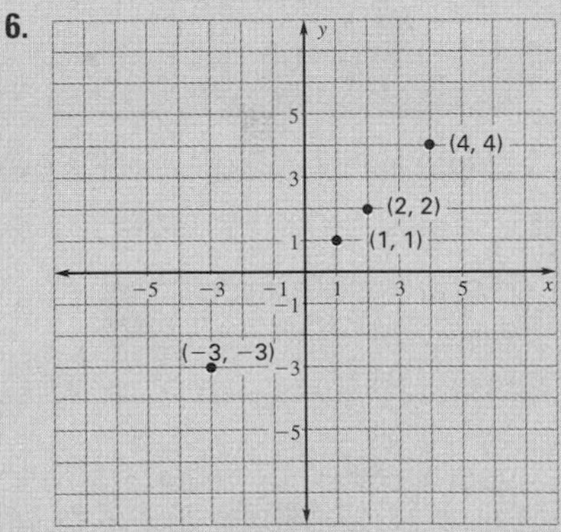

Pacing and Assignment Guide

Regular Schedule

Lesson	Les. Day	Transitional	Average	Advanced
11.1	Day 1	pp. 565–566 Exs. 7–13, 17, 21–22, 24–25	pp. 565–566 Exs. 9–13, 16–18, 21–22, 24–25	pp. 565–566 Exs. 9–16, 19–22, 23*, 24–25
11.2	Day 1	pp. 569–570 Exs. 16–17, 20–21, 24–26, 35–37, 44–45	pp. 569–570 Exs. 18–20, 27–37, 44–45	pp. 569–570 Exs. 18–19, 27–29, 35–41, 42–43*, 44–45
11.3	Day 1	pp. 573–575 Exs. 9–18, 21	pp. 573–575 Exs. 9–21	pp. 573–575 Exs. 9–21
	Day 2	pp. 573–575 Exs. 22–28, 33–34, 39–47	pp. 573–575 Exs. 22–25, 29–32, 35–37, 39–47	pp. 573–575 Exs. 26–32, 35–37, 38*, 39–47
11.4	Day 1	pp. 578–580 Exs. 9–14, 18–22	pp. 578–580 Exs. 9–22	pp. 578–580 Exs. 9–22
	Day 2	pp. 578–580 Exs. 23–28, 32–37, 46–48, 50–52	pp. 578–580 Exs. 26–33, 38–45, 50–52	pp. 578–580 Exs. 26–33, 42–48, 49*, 50–52
11.5	Day 1	pp. 586–587 Exs. 8–15, 28–43	pp. 586–587 Exs. 8–19, 28–43	pp. 586–587 Exs. 8–19, 28–43; EC: TE p. 560D*
	Day 2	pp. 586–587 Exs. 6–7, 20–23, 26–27	pp. 586–587 Exs. 6–7, 20–24, 26–27	pp. 586–587 Exs. 6–7, 20–24, 25*, 26–27
11.6	Day 1	pp. 591–592 Exs. 7–15, 19–24, 30–32, 35–36, 38–39	pp. 591–592 Exs. 7–15, 21–31, 33–34, 38–39	pp. 591–592 Exs. 7–15, 21–31, 33–34, 37*, 38–39
11.7	Day 1	pp. 596–597 Exs. 8–15, 17–19, 26–29	pp. 596–597 Exs. 8–19, 23–24, 28–29	pp. 596–597 Exs. 8–16, 20–24, 25*, 28–29, EC: TE p. 560D*
11.8	Day 1	pp. 600–601 Exs. 16–28, 32–33, 41–42	pp. 600–601 Exs. 18–22, 26–31, 34–37, 41–42	pp. 600–601 Exs. 18–22, 26–31, 38–40*, 41–42
11.9	Day 1	pp. 604–605 Exs. 9–12, 14–18, 22–25, 31–32	pp. 604–605 Exs. 9–10, 12–18, 24–28, 31–32	pp. 604–605 Exs. 9–10, 12–15, 19–21, 24–28, 20–30*, 31–32
Review	Day 1	pp. 606–609 Exs. 1–35	pp. 606–609 Exs. 1–35	pp. 606–609 Exs. 1–35
Assess	Day 1	Chapter 11 Test	Chapter 11 Test	Chapter 11 Test

Yearly Pacing *Chapter 11 Total* – 14 days *Chapters 1–11 Total* – 150 days *Remaining* – 10 days

* Challenge Exercises EP = Extra Practice SRH = Skills Review Handbook EC = Extra Challenge

Block Schedule

Day 1	Day 2	Day 3	Day 4	Day 5	Day 6	Day 7
11.1 pp. 565–566: Exs. 9–13, 16–18, 21–22, 24–25 **11.2** pp. 569–570: Exs. 18–20, 27–37, 44–45	**11.3** pp. 573–575: Exs. 9–25, 29–32, 35–37, 39–47	**11.4** pp. 578–580: Exs. 9–22, 26–33, 38–45, 50–52	**11.5** pp. 586–587: Exs. 6–24, 26–43	**11.6** pp. 591–592: Exs. 7–12, 16–18, 21–31, 33–34, 38–39 **11.7** pp. 596–597: Exs. 8–19, 23–24, 28–29	**11.8** pp. 600–601: Exs. 18–22, 26–31, 34–37, 41–42 **11.9** pp. 604–605: Exs. 9–10, 12–18, 24–28, 31–32	**Review** pp. 606–609: Exs. 1–35 **Assess** Chapter 11 Test

Yearly Pacing *Chapter 11 Total* – 7 days *Chapters 1–11 Total* – 75 days *Remaining* – 5 days

Support Materials

Chapter Resource Book

LESSON SUPPORT	11.1	11.2	11.3	11.4	11.5	11.6	11.7	11.8	11.9
Lesson Plans	p. 1	p. 10	p. 19	p. 28	p. 37	p. 46	p. 55	p. 64	p. 73
Lesson Plans for Block Scheduling	p. 2	p. 11	p. 20	p. 29	p. 38	p. 47	p. 56	p. 65	p. 74
Warm-Ups with Multiple-Choice Practice	p. 3	p. 12	p. 21	p. 30	p. 39	p. 48	p. 57	p. 66	p. 75
Problem of the Day	p. 4	p. 13	p. 22	p. 31	p. 40	p. 49	p. 58	p. 67	p. 76
Daily Cumulative Review	p. 5	p. 14	p. 23	p. 32	p. 41	p. 50	p. 59	p. 68	p. 77
Practice Masters	p. 6	p. 15	p. 24	p. 33	p. 42	p. 51	p. 60	p. 69	p. 78
Reteaching Masters	p. 7	p. 16	p. 25	p. 34	p. 43	p. 52	p. 61	p. 70	p. 79
Enrichment Masters	p. 9	p. 18	p. 27	p. 36	p. 45	p. 54	p. 63	p. 72	p. 81

Transparencies

	11.1	11.2	11.3	11.4	11.5	11.6	11.7	11.8	11.9
Warm-Ups with Multiple-Choice Practice	p. 86	p. 87	p. 88	p. 89	p. 90	p. 91	p. 92	p. 93	p. 94
Teacher Time-Saver Transparencies	✓	✓	✓	✓	✓	✓	✓	✓	✓
English/Spanish Problem Solving	p. 49	p. 50		p. 51		p. 52		p. 53	
Answer Transparencies	✓	✓	✓	✓	✓	✓	✓	✓	✓

Technology

- Personal Student Tutor
- Time-Saving Test and Practice Generator
- Electronic Teacher Tools
- Technology: Using Calculators and Computers

Additional Resources

- Math Log
- Assessment Book
- Worked-Out Solution Key
- Practice Workbook (English/Spanish)
- Home and School Connection
- California Standards: Key Concepts Book

Correlation to the California Curriculum

Correlations to the California Standards
CA Standards: AF 1.0, AF 1.1, AF 1.5, AF 3.0, AF 3.3, AF 3.4, AF 4.0, AF 4.2, MR 1.1, MR 1.2, MR 2.3, MR 3.3

California Curriculum Support

Key Concepts Book

- Pre-Course Review: Topic 1 Working with Decimals
  Topic 5 Measurement
- Key Standards: AF 3.3 Slope of a Line *(Lesson 11.5)*
  AF 3.3 Slope-Intercept Form *(Lesson 11.6)*
  AF 3.4 Graphing Linear Functions *(Lessons 11.5, 11.6)*
  AF 4.2 Direct Variation *(Lesson 11.7)*

California Standards Practice Workbook provides practice for each Standard that is covered in this chapter.

Strategies for Strategic Learners

PROVIDE CONCRETE EXAMPLES

The idea of direct variation is puzzling to many students. You can explain it in the following way. If there were a direct and positive relationship between age and height, you would grow the same amount each year, and you would not stop increasing in height until you died. In other words, you would grow by a *constant* amount for each unit of time. Imagine a creature that had 0 height when it was born and grew three inches each year. How tall would it be after 10 years? 20 years? 30 years? 40 years?

Since the relationship is a positive one (*i.e.*, as age increases, so does height) the slope of the line is positive. As students work more with functions they will understand that two variables x and y are directly proportional if their relationship can be expressed by $y = kx$, where k is called the constant of variation. Notice that for direct variation, there is nothing added to kx.

In fact, the actual relationship between a person's age and height is not a direct variation. A person's height increases very fast each year until the teenage years, when somewhere usually between the ages of 12 and 18, each person reaches his or her adult height, growth in height stops, and finally, as gravity causes the spine to compress, an older person's height decreases.

To investigate a relationship that does not vary directly, have students compare the areas of rectangles with their perimeters.

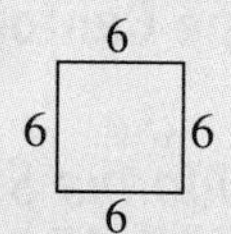

area = 36 units
perimeter = 24 units

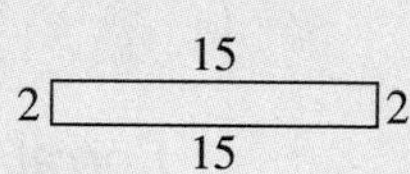

area = 30 units
perimeter = 34 units

Strategies for English Learners

VOCABULARY STUDY

The universal access suggestions for Chapter 4 suggested that students use the concept of opposites to learn and remember vocabulary words and to understand concepts in mathematics such as rational and irrational, logical and illogical, equal and unequal, input and output. If students seem comfortable with opposites, introduce the idea of analogies. An analogy expresses a similarity between otherwise dissimilar things. Put another way, it points to the similarity of two things that are not identical. Put this simple analogy on the board and ask students to think of others, using terms used in mathematics:

Addition is to sum as subtraction is to __?__.

This can be written in different ways, for example: addition : sum as subtraction : difference.

You could also express a relationship between these four things by highlighting the opposites in the following way:

Addition is to subtraction as sum is to difference.

Other possible examples:

Left is to negative as right is to positive.
Profit is to positive as loss is to negative.
Numerator is to denominator as dividend is to divisor.
Average is to outlier as mean is to extreme.
Rise is to run as vertical is to horizontal.
Similar is to congruent as proportional is to equal.

Have students make up their own analogies.

Note that these analogies, since they are focusing on the relationships between concepts, can be translated into any language and the concepts stay the same.

Students can try analogies with shapes that are rotated or flipped, such as:

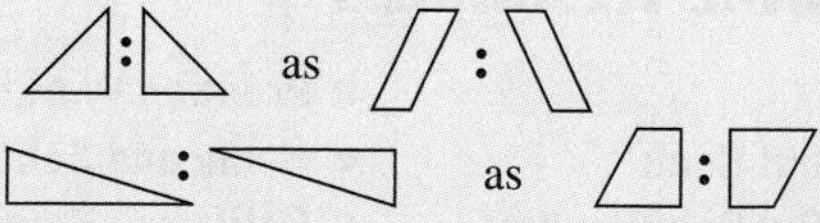

Strategies for Advanced Learners

SUBSTITUTE CHALLENGE PROBLEMS

Sometimes students can be challenged when a variable is introduced into a lesson. The following problems would add an extra challenge for those students who have already grasped the ideas of the chapter.

1. A line passes through the points $A(-2, 3)$, $B(2, 5)$, and $C(6, k)$. Find k. *(7)*

2. A line with x-intercept -4 passes through the points $Q(2, 6)$ and $R(p, 10)$. Find p. *(6)*

After solving these exercises, students could be challenged to make up similar problems for their classmates, using coordinates found in specified quadrants.

3. The vertices of a square are $A(2, 6)$, $B(10, 4)$, $C(8, -4)$, and $D(0, -2)$. Use the idea of slope to show that the point $E(5, 1)$ lies on the diagonal joining A and C, and on the diagonal joining B and D. *(The slopes of $\overline{AC}$ and $\overline{AE}$ are both $-\frac{5}{3}$, so E lies on $\overline{AC}$. The slopes of $\overline{DB}$ and $\overline{DE}$ are both $\frac{3}{5}$, so E lies on $\overline{DB}$.)*

4. The vertices of a right triangle are $A(-2, 1)$, $B(-2, -7)$, and $C(8, -7)$. Use the idea of slope to show that $D(3, -3)$ lies on one of the sides of the triangle. *(Make a sketch. It appears that $(3, -3)$ lies on $\overline{AC}$. To verify this, calculate the slope of $\overline{AD}$ and the slope of $\overline{AC}$. Since slope of $\overline{AD} = -\frac{4}{5} =$ slope of $\overline{AC}$, D lies on $\overline{AC}$.)*

Mathematical Background Notes

Lessons 11.1–11.2

FUNCTIONS Formally, a **function** is a rule that associates with each element x of a given set A a corresponding element y in a set B. The rule must be unambiguous, in the sense that with each element of A there is associated *exactly one* element of B. For example, if A and B are each taken to be the set of all real numbers and the rule is given verbally by "square the number," then the function associates with each real number x the value x^2.

A function machine can be useful for conveying the concept of function. In the above example we can visualize a machine that, for each *input* x, produces an *output* x^2.

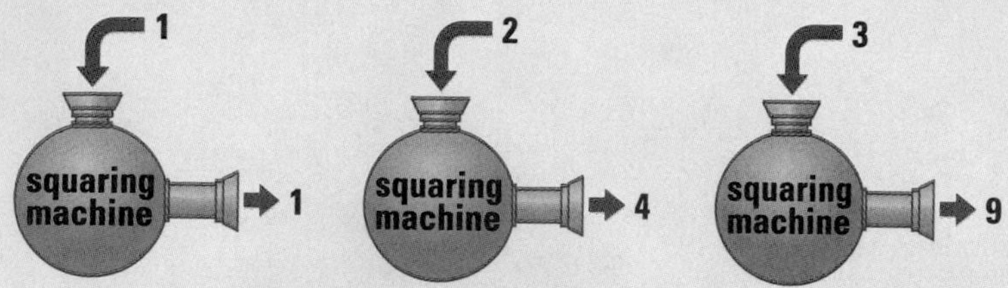

The set A of numbers to which the rule is to be applied is called the **domain** of the function. The set of all outputs generated by the numbers in the domain is called the **range** of the function. In the above example of the squaring function, the domain is the set of all real numbers while the range is the set of all numbers $y \geq 0$. Observe that in this example we chose B to be the set of all real numbers, but the range is not all of B.

If the domain A is a finite set, it may be feasible to describe the function by listing all **ordered pairs** (x, y) of inputs x and outputs $y = f(x)$. Such a listing is called an **input-output table** for the function. For example, if the domain is $A = \{1, 2, 3, 4, 5\}$ and the function is given verbally by the rule "square the number," the input-output table is as follows.

Input x	1	2	3	4	5
Output y	1	4	9	16	25

Here it is also possible to express the function symbolically in the form

$$y = x^2, \text{ where } x = 1, 2, 3, 4, 5.$$

This formulation specifies that the domain is $\{1, 2, 3, 4, 5\}$ and provides a basis for constructing the input-output table shown above.

On the other hand, the equation $y = x^2$ could also be used to represent a function whose domain is the set of *all* real numbers, with the simple amendment

$$y = x^2, \text{ where } x \text{ is any real number.}$$

Now that the domain has been specified as the set of all real numbers, the range turns out to be the set of all real numbers greater than or equal to 0. In this case it is not possible to exhibit a complete input-output table. However, a table with a sampling of inputs and the corresponding outputs can provide a basis for sketching a graph that conveys a visual representation of this function.

A **linear function** is one that associates with each input x an output of the form $Ax + B$, where A and B are fixed numbers. The function is given verbally by the rule "multiply by A and add B." For example, "multiply by 3 and add 1" corresponds to the function

$$y = 3x + 1, \text{ where } x \text{ is any real number.}$$

We can get a rough idea of the behavior of this function from an input-output table corresponding to the sample inputs $x = -3, -2, -1, 0, 1, 2, 3$.

x	−3	−2	−1	0	1	2	3
y	−8	−5	−2	1	4	7	10

Each ordered pair (x, y) in this table represents a solution of the equation $y = 3x + 1$, in the sense that $x = -1$ and $y = -2$ make the equation true.

An equation of the form $Ax + By = C$, where not both A and B are zero, is called a **linear equation.** If $B \neq 0$, the equation can be put in **function form** by finding an equivalent equation with y isolated on one side.

$$y = -\frac{A}{B}x + \frac{C}{B}$$

This form makes it convenient to construct a table of values and to sketch the graph of the equation, as discussed in Lesson 11.3.

Lessons 11.3–11.4

GRAPHS The **graph** of an equation $Ax + By = C$ consists of all points (x, y) in the coordinate plane such that (x, y) is a solution of the equation. As such, the graph consists of an infinite number of points in the coordinate plane. Because this equation is linear, its graph will turn out to be a straight line.

In sketching the graph of a function, the student can start by creating an input-output table for a few sample values of x. One way of creating an input-output table for an equation of the form $Ax + By = C$ $(B \neq 0)$ is to rewrite this equation as $y = -\left(\frac{A}{B}\right)x + \frac{C}{B}$ and then use the latter equation to make a table of values. However, the student can also make a table of values by choosing a specific value for x and then solving the resulting equation for y. For an equation such as $4y - 2x = 8$, this can be done in the following format.

x	Equation in y	y
-4	$4y - 2(-4) = 8$	0
-2	$4y - 2(-2) = 8$	1
0	$4y - 2(0) = 8$	2
2	$4y - 2(2) = 8$	3
4	$4y - 2(4) = 8$	4

This table provides a basis for plotting five points in the coordinate plane belonging to the graph of $4y - 2x = 8$.

By extending such a table to include more values of x, the student is likely to accept the assertion that *all* points (x, y) that satisfy $4y - 2x = 8$ lie on a straight line. It is this line (extended to include all real values of x) that constitutes the graph of the linear equation $4y - 2x = 8$.

Lesson 11.5

SLOPE In this lesson the intuitive notion of "steepness" of a line is given a mathematical formulation. Making use of the fact that "a line is determined by two points" and building on the characterization of steepness as *rise over run*, the **slope** of the line through points (x_1, y_1) and (x_2, y_2) is defined by

$$m = \frac{y_2 - y_1}{x_2 - x_1}.$$

When $y_2 > y_1$ and $x_2 > x_1$, this definition corresponds to rise over run. That is, both $y_2 - y_1$ and $x_2 - x_1$ are positive numbers. Negative slope can be given an intuitive interpretation by defining a "negative rise" corresponding to $y_2 - y_1 < 0$. Here it is important to maintain $x_2 - x_1 > 0$, corresponding to the notion that "run" is always positive. By taking care to label the points so that $x_2 > x_1$, even negative slopes can be given a "rise over run" interpretation (see Example 1). However, the above formula for m applies regardless of which point is denoted by the subscript 1 and which is denoted by the subscript 2.

If a graph is to give "rise over run" *geometric* meaning, it is essential that the same units of length be used on both axes. In this case, slope represents a unitless measure such as feet/feet.

However, slope is often calculated for graphs in which different units are used on the horizontal and vertical axes. An important example is when motion with constant velocity is modeled by a linear equation involving the variables distance d and time t (see Example 3). If the horizontal axis represents time (in seconds) and the vertical axis represents distance (in feet), then the slope is given by

$$m = \frac{d_2 - d_1}{t_2 - t_1} = \frac{\textbf{displacement}}{\textbf{elapsed time}}$$

and corresponds to the (constant) velocity in feet per second.

Lesson 11.6

SLOPE-INTERCEPT In Euclidean geometry, a line is typically determined by two points. After introducing the concept of slope, however, the Cartesian coordinate system also allows us to determine a line by specifying a single point on the line and the slope of the line. As shown in this lesson, when the line crosses the y-axis at $(0, b)$ and has slope m, the equation of the line is given by $y = mx + b$. An important advantage of this **slope-intercept form** of the equation of a line is that it enables us to read off the slope of the line without having to use the definition of slope to calculate its value.

Lesson 11.9

SYSTEMS Linear equations and linear inequalities can be used to model a wide range of phenomena that involve a single output. In many cases, however, real-world phenomena are based on **systems** that involve several inputs and several outputs. By enabling the student to solve *pairs* of linear equations and inequalities, this lesson represents an important step toward the modeling of systems.

The systems of linear equations studied in this lesson have the form

$$(*) \qquad \begin{aligned} ax + by &= e \\ cx + dy &= f \end{aligned}$$

where a, b, c, d, e, and f are real numbers. A solution of (*) is a pair of real numbers x and y that satisfies both equations.

Having learned to graph the individual equations that compose (*), students are now able to develop a geometric interpretation of the solution of such a system. When $b \neq 0$, the first equation corresponds to a line with slope $-\frac{a}{b}$ and y-intercept $\frac{e}{b}$. When $d \neq 0$, the second corresponds to a line with slope $-\frac{c}{d}$ and y-intercept $\frac{f}{d}$. Assuming $\frac{a}{b} \neq \frac{c}{d}$, these lines are not parallel and consequently they have a single point of intersection which can be denoted by (x_0, y_0). Because this point lies on *both* lines, the values $x = x_0$ and $y = y_0$ satisfy both equations. (When $b = 0$ or $d = 0$, one of the lines is vertical. In this case, similar geometric considerations apply.)

In Lesson 11.8 it was noted that a single linear inequality of the form $ax + by < e$ has as its graph a half-plane lying on one side of the line $ax + by = e$. This fact has important implications for systems of linear inequalities as well.

Recall that the solution of (*) corresponds to the intersection of two straight lines. This is because we interpret such a system as requiring that $x = x_0$ and $y = y_0$ satisfy $ax + by = e$ *and* $cx + dy = f$. A similar interpretation for

$$(**) \qquad \begin{aligned} ax + by &\geq e \quad && \textbf{Inequality 1} \\ cx + dy &< f \quad && \textbf{Inequality 2} \end{aligned}$$

leads to the requirement that a solution $x = x_0$ and $y = y_0$ belongs to the intersection of the half-planes defined by Inequality 1 and by Inequality 2. Because the first inequality is based on "≥" and the second on "<", care must be taken to include the points belonging to the graph of $ax + by = e$ while excluding points belonging to the graph of $cx + dy = f$. Whenever $ad \neq bc$, the solution will be an unbounded wedge-shaped region, such as that in Example 4.

Chapter Overview

Chapter Goals

In this chapter, students will use and evaluate functions and graph equations of linear functions using intercepts or the slope-intercept form of an equation of a line.
They will:

- Use problem solving techniques to solve real-life problem situations.
- Graph linear inequalities.
- Graph systems of linear equations and inequalities.

Career Note

Caterers provide food for weddings and other special events. They must plan menus, prepare the food, arrange for food servers or waiters, and clean up afterward.

Caterers must also be business managers and establish good customer relations. To prepare for a career in catering, students learn about cooking and management at technical schools and 2-year colleges, or earn a 4-year college degree in restaurant management or home economics.

Additional information about caterers is available at **www.mcdougallittell.com**

Graphing Linear Equations and Inequalities

Why is graphing linear equations and inequalities important?

Graphs can help you quickly see and understand relationships between variables. You will use graphs of linear equations and inequalities as you study future topics such as lines of best fit, systems of equations, and linear programming.

Many people use linear relationships in their careers, including caterers (page 561) and transportation engineers (page 577). For example, caterers use linear equations to determine prices.

Meeting the California Standards

The skills you'll learn in this chapter will help you meet state standards and prepare for standardized tests. In this chapter you'll:

- **Express quantitative relationships by using algebraic terminology, expressions, equations, inequalities, and graphs.** LESSONS 11.1–11.9
- **Write an equation, a system of equations, or an inequality that represents a verbal description.** LESSONS 11.1, 11.9
- **Graph and interpret linear functions.** LESSONS 11.1, 11.3, 11.4
- **Solve simple linear equations and inequalities.** LESSONS 11.2, 11.8
- **Graph quantitative relationships and interpret the graph.** LESSONS 11.3–11.9

Career Link **CATERER** A caterer uses linear equations and inequalities when:

- calculating how much to charge for an event.
- determining what to charge in order to make a profit.

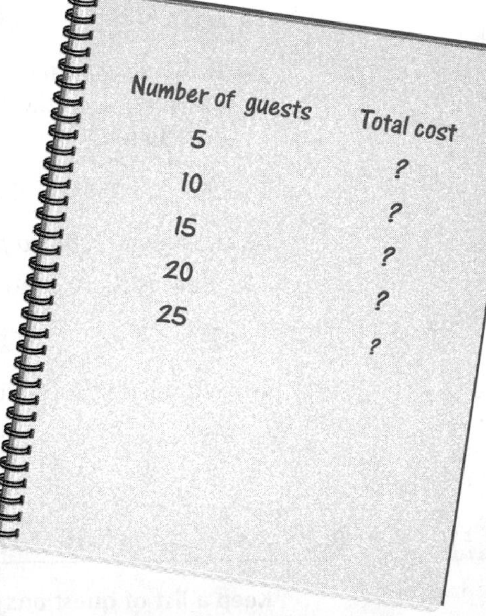

EXERCISES

To cater a three-hour event, a caterer charges $37.50 plus $18.25 per guest.

1. Copy and complete the table. **See margin.**
2. When the number of guests increases by 5, by what amount does the total cost increase? **$91.25**

In Lesson 11.7, you'll learn how to draw and use a graph of the data in the table.

Projects

A project covering Chapters 10–12 appears on pages 664–665 of the Student Edition. Additional projects for selected lessons in Chapter 11 are available in the *Assessment Book,* pp. 258–259.

Technology

Software

- Electronic Teacher Tools
- Online Lesson Planner
- Personal Student Tutor
- Test and Practice Generator

Internet Connections

- Application and Career Links 566, 574, 577, 601
- Student Help 568, 575, 580, 585, 590, 597, 603, 613

These Internet connections are available at **www.mcdougallittell.com**

1.

Number of Guests	Total Cost
5	$128.75
10	$220.00
15	$311.25
20	$402.50
25	$493.75

Prepare

Diagnostic Tools

The **chapter readiness quiz** can help you diagnose whether students have the following skills needed in Chapter 11:

- Identify the coordinate axes.
- Identify relationships between points on a graph.
- Solve linear equations.

Reteaching Materials

The following resources are available for students who need additional help with the skills on the chapter readiness quiz:

Chapter 11 Resource Book

- Reteaching with Practice (Lessons 3.8, 3.9, 4.1, 4.5)

Personal Student Tutor

Additional Resources

The following resources are provided to help you prepare for the upcoming chapter and customize review materials:

Chapter 11 Resource Book

- Lesson Plans, pp. 1, 10, 19, 28, 37, 46, 55, 64, 73
- Lesson Plans for Block Scheduling, pp. 2, 11, 20, 29, 38, 47, 56, 65, 74

Technology

- Electronic Teacher Tools with Lesson Planning Software
- Test and Practice Generator

Chapter 11 Getting Ready

PREVIEW

What's the chapter about?

- Writing, evaluating, and graphing **linear functions and equations**
- Graphing and finding solutions of **linear inequalities in two variables**
- Solving **systems of equations and inequalities in two variables**

WORDS TO KNOW

- **function,** *p. 563*
- **input,** *p. 563*
- **output,** *p. 563*
- **linear equation in two variables,** *p. 567*
- **slope,** *p. 583*
- **slope-intercept form,** *p. 589*
- **direct variation,** *p. 594*
- **linear inequality in two variables,** *p. 598*
- **half-planes,** *p. 598*
- **system of equations,** *p. 602*

PREPARE

Chapter Readiness Quiz

Take this quick quiz. If you are unsure of an answer, look back at the reference pages for help.

VOCABULARY CHECK *(refer to pp. 144, 149)*

1. The line on the coordinate plane for which the y-value of every point is zero is the __?__ . **B**

Ⓐ Origin Ⓑ x-axis Ⓒ y-axis Ⓓ y-coordinate

2. If the y-coordinates of the graph of a set of ordered pairs of data tend to decrease as the x-coordinates increase, then x and y have __?__ correlation. **H**

Ⓕ An inverse Ⓖ A positive Ⓗ A negative Ⓙ No obvious

SKILL CHECK *(refer to pp. 170, 189)*

3. What is the solution of the equation $4x + 3 = 11$? **B**

Ⓐ -1 Ⓑ 2 Ⓒ 3 Ⓓ 4

4. What is the solution of the equation $3x - 12 = 5x$? **F**

Ⓕ -6 Ⓖ -1 Ⓗ 1 Ⓙ 6

STUDY TIP

Keep a List of Questions

Keep a list of questions while you complete your assignments. Your list will remind you about what to ask your teacher the next day in class.

4/12 Questions about 11.1
1. What is the difference between input and output?
2. How can I tell if a rule is a function?

11.1 Functions

California Standards

In this lesson you'll:

- Use variables and appropriate operations to write an equation that represents a verbal description. (AF 1.1)
- Interpret linear functions. (AF 3.0)

Goal 1 EVALUATING FUNCTIONS

In mathematics, a **function** is a rule that assigns to each number in a given set a number in another set. Starting with a number called an **input**, the function associates with it exactly one number called an **output**.

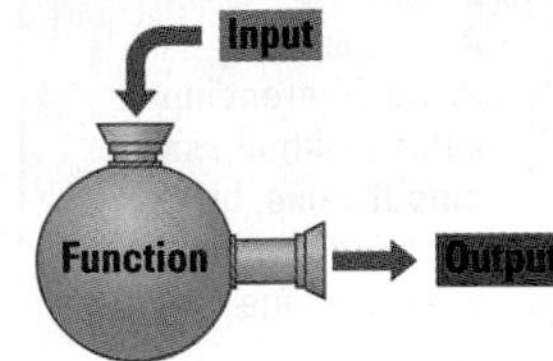

EXAMPLE 1 Evaluating a Function

THUNDERSTORMS Because light travels through air at a much faster speed than sound, you can estimate how many miles you are from a thunderstorm by counting the seconds between seeing the lightning and hearing the thunder.

The distance d from the storm is given by the equation

$$d = 0.20t.$$

This equation corresponds to the function that associates each nonnegative number t with the number $0.20t$. Use this function to find your distance from the storm when the time between the lightning and the thunder is 0, 1, 2, 3, and 4 seconds.

Solution

You can make a list to organize your work.

INPUT	EVALUATE FUNCTION.	OUTPUT
$t = 0$	$d = 0.20(0)$	$d = 0.0$
$t = 1$	$d = 0.20(1)$	$d = 0.2$
$t = 2$	$d = 0.20(2)$	$d = 0.4$
$t = 3$	$d = 0.20(3)$	$d = 0.6$
$t = 4$	$d = 0.20(4)$	$d = 0.8$

You can use an *input-output table* to summarize your results.

Input, t (in seconds)	0	1	2	3	4
Output, d (in miles)	0.0	0.2	0.4	0.6	0.8

Link to Thunderstorms

THUNDERSTORMS Lightning causes air to heat and expand rapidly. The heated air then collides violently with nearby cooler air, creating sound waves called thunder.

As you saw in Example 1, a function can be represented with words, an equation, or an input-output table. In Lesson 11.3 you will learn how to represent a function with a graph.

1 Plan

Pacing

Suggested Number of Days

Transitional: 1 day
Average: 1 day
Advanced: 1 day
Block Schedule: 0.5 block with 11.2

Teaching Resources

Blacklines
(See page 560B.)

Transparencies
- Warm-Up Exercises
- Teacher Time-Savers
- English/Spanish Problem Solving
- Answers

Technology
- Electronic Teacher Tools
- Test and Practice Generator

2 Teach

Math Reasoning

For Mathematical Background Notes on mathematical reasoning related to this lesson, please refer to pages 560E and 560F in this Teacher's Edition.

Extra Example 1
See next page.

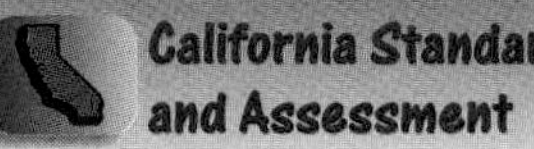

California Standards and Assessment

CA Standards: AF 1.1, AF 3.0

Extra Example 1

A mountain climber changes altitude by hiking up a mountain. The change in altitude, a, in feet, after climbing for t minutes, is expressed in the equation $a = 14t$. Use this function to find the change in altitude after 0, 1, 2, 3, and 4 minutes.

Input, t (in min)	0	1	2	3	4
Output, a (in ft)	0	14	28	42	56

Extra Example 2

Write a rule for a function to represent the following situation and identify the input and output variables:

You earn $5 for every hour you work.

Let M represent the amount of money you earn in dollars, and let t represent the time, in hours, you work. $M = 5t$. The input variable is t and the output variable is M.

Extra Example 3

Evaluate the function in Extra Example 2 when $t = 7$. What does this function value tell you? **$M = 5 \cdot 7 = 35$; The money earned for working 7 hours is $35.**

Extra Example 4

Some values of a function are shown in the table. Find a function rule that relates x and y.

Input, x	−2	−1	0	1	2
Output, y	−4	−3	−2	−1	0

$y = x - 2$

Concept Check

Can a function have two different output values for the same input value? Explain. ***Sample answer:* No. A function must have only one output for an input value.**

Goal 2 Writing a Function Rule

When you are given a function described in words or as an input-output table, you may be able to write a mathematical rule for the function.

Student Help

▶ Study Tip
A function may pair many different input values with the same output value, but for each input value there is exactly one output value.

EXAMPLE 2 Writing a Function Rule

a. Write a rule for a function to represent the following situation: You *earn $15 for every lawn you mow.*

b. Identify the input and output variables.

Solution

a. Let I represent the amount of money you earn mowing lawns, and let n represent the number of lawns mowed. The amount of money you earn depends on the number of lawns mowed. So, you can write:

$$I = 15n$$

b. The input variable is n and the output variable is I.

EXAMPLE 3 Evaluating a Function

Evaluate the function in Example 2 when the input is 3. What does this function value tell you?

Solution

When $n = 3$, the value of the function, or output is $I = 15(3) = 45$.

ANSWER ▶ This means that if you mow three lawns, you will earn $45.

Student Help

▶ Study Tip
In this text, x is understood to be the input for a function, and y is understood to be the output.

EXAMPLE 4 Writing a Function Rule

Some values of a function are shown in the table. Find a function rule that relates x and y.

Input, x	−2	−1	0	1	2	3
Output, y	1	2	3	4	5	6

Solution

Identify the pattern by looking at how the y-values relate to the x-values in the table. For every x-value, you can obtain the corresponding y-value by adding 3 to the x-value:

$-2 + 3 = 1,\quad -1 + 3 = 2,\quad 0 + 3 = 3,$

$1 + 3 = 4,\quad 2 + 3 = 5,\quad 3 + 3 = 6$

ANSWER ▶ A rule for this function is $y = x + 3$.

11.1 Exercises

Guided Practice

1. If I is the amount of money raised by the class, then I is equal to amount of money earned per subscription times number of subscriptions sold.

2. The input variable, m, represents the number of subscriptions sold. The output variable, I, represents the money raised from selling subscriptions.

FUND RAISING In Exercises 1–3, use the following information. Your class is hoping to sell 200 magazine subscriptions to raise money for new computer equipment. Your class earns $3.00 for every subscription sold.

1–3. See margin.

1. Explain why this situation is represented by the equation $I = 3.00m$.

2. Identify the input and output variables of the corresponding function. What does each represent?

3. Find how much money your class earns when 50, 100, 150, and 200 subscriptions are sold. Organize your data in an input-output table.

SPEED OF SOUND In Exercises 4 and 5 use the following information. The distance d that sound travels in sea water equals 0.9 mile per second times the number t of seconds.

4. Write an equation that describes the distance traveled in terms of the time elapsed. $d = 0.9t$

5. Regarding this equation as a rule for associating a distance d with a time t, evaluate the function when $t = 30$. What does this function value tell you? 27; the function value tells you that in 30 seconds sound travels 27 miles.

6. Some values of a function are shown in the table. Find a function rule that relates x and y. A rule for this function is $y = x - 4$.

Input, x	−2	−1	0	1	2
Output, y	−6	−5	−4	−3	−2

Practice and Problem Solving

Student Help

MORE PRACTICE
Extra practice to help you master skills is on page 710.

Copy and complete the table for each function. 7–10. See margin.

7. $y = 2x$

Input, x	0	2	4
Output, y	?	?	?

8. $y = x + 8$

Input, x	1	3	5
Output, y	?	?	?

9. $y = \frac{x}{7}$

Input, x	0	?	28
Output, y	?	2	?

10. $y = x - 5$

Input, x	?	?	11
Output, y	1	3	?

11. Find the output value of the function $y = 6x - 3$ when $x = -2$. −15

3 Apply

Assignment Guide

TRANSITIONAL
Day 1: pp. 565-566 Exs. 7–13, 17, 21–22, 24–25

AVERAGE
Day 1: pp. 565-566 Exs. 9–13, 16–18, 21–22, 24–25

ADVANCED
Day 1: pp. 565–566 Exs. 9–16, 19–22, 23*, 24–25

BLOCK SCHEDULE
pp. 565–566 Exs. 9–13, 16–18, 21–22, 24–25 (with 11.2)

Extra Practice

- Student Edition, pp. 710–711
- Chapter 11 Resource Book, p. 6

Homework Check

To quickly check student understanding of key concepts, go over the following exercises:

Transitional: 8, 10, 12, 13, 22
Average: 10, 12, 13, 16, 18, 22
Advanced: 10, 12, 13, 16, 18, 22

3.

Input, m	50	100	150	200
Output, I (in dollars)	150	300	450	600

7.

Input, x	0	2	4
Output, y	0	4	8

8.

Input, x	1	3	5
Output, y	9	11	13

9.

Input, x	0	14	28
Output, y	0	2	4

10.

Input, x	6	8	11
Output, y	1	3	6

4 Assess

Assessment Resources

- Assessment Book (Formal Assessment and Alternative Assessment)
- Test and Practice Generator

Mini-Quiz

Complete the table for each function.

1. $y = 5x$

Input, x	0	1	2	3
Output, y	?	?	?	?

0 5 10 15

2. $y = x - 6$

Input, x	0	5	10	15
Output, y	?	?	?	?

−6 −1 4 9

3. On a long trip, the distance d, in miles, that you drive after t hours is expressed by the equation $d = 55t$. Evaluate the function when $t = 3$. What does this function value tell you? **$d = 55 \cdot 3 = 165$; After driving for 3 hours, you have traveled 165 miles.**

15.

Input, x (in hours)	Output, y (in kilowatt-hours)
1	1.8
2	3.6
5	9
10	18
15	27

16. The input-output table does not represent a function because there are two output values for the input value 1. In a function, each input value has just one output value.

17.

Input, x	0	1	2	3	4
Output, y	0	3	6	9	12

18–20. See Additional Answers beginning on page AA1.

12. The input variable is t, the number of hours spent traveling. The output variable is d, the distance traveled. A rule for this function is $d = 45t$.

Write a rule for a function to represent the situation. Then identify the input and output variables. **12, 13. See margin.**

12. During a 10 hour train trip, the distance d you travel equals 45 miles per hour times the number t of hours spent traveling.

13. Your mother gives you \$15 for school lunches on Monday. The amount of money m you have left during the week equals \$15 minus \$2.50 times the number n of school lunches you have bought.

Link to Science

ENERGY GUIDE LABELS show a product's estimated yearly electricity consumption in kilowatt-hours on a scale for comparison among similar appliances. The more electricity that an appliance consumes on average, the higher the number on the label.

More about Energy Guide labels at www.mcdougallittell.com

13. The input variable is n, the number of school lunches bought. The output variable is m, the money left after buying school lunches. A rule for this function is $m = 15 - 2.5n$.

14. The input variable is x, the number of hours that electricity is used. The output variable is y, the number of kilowatt-hours of electricity used.

ENERGY In Exercises 14 and 15, use the following information. The function $y = 1.8x$ describes the number of kilowatt-hours of electricity used in x hours by a computer and a monitor. **14–16. See margin.**

14. Identify the input and output variables. What does each represent?

15. Find the number of kilowatt-hours of electricity used in 1, 2, 5, 10, and 15 hours. Organize your data in an input-output table.

16. MATHEMATICAL REASONING The input-output table below does not represent a function. Explain why not.

Input, x	−1	0	1	1	2
Output, y	1	0	−1	1	0

Make a table of values for the function. Use x-values of 0, 1, 2, 3, and 4. **17–20. See margin.**

17. $y = 3x$ **18.** $y = 5x + 2$ **19.** $y = \frac{1}{3}x + 6$ **20.** $y = x^2 - 1$

In Exercises 21 and 22, write a function rule that relates x and y.

21.

Input, x	1	2	3	4	5	6
Output, y	0.5	1	1.5	2	2.5	3

$y = \frac{x}{2}$

22.

Input, x	1	2	3	4	5	6
Output, y	4	8	12	16	20	24

$y = 4x$

23. CHALLENGE Describe a real-life situation that can be represented by the function $y = 2x + 8$. ***Sample answer:* A video club offers \$2 video rentals with a one time membership fee of \$8.**

Multiple-Choice Practice

24. Which function has an output value of 15 for an input value of 3? **D**

Ⓐ $y = 5x - 1$ Ⓑ $y = 4x + 5$ Ⓒ $y = 3x$ Ⓓ $y = 3x + 6$

25. What is the output value of the function $y = 6x - 9$ when $x = 3$? **H**

Ⓕ 1 Ⓖ 3 Ⓗ 9 Ⓙ 18

11.2 Linear Equations and Linear Functions

California Standards

In this lesson you'll:

- Solve simple linear equations over the rational numbers. (AF 4.0)
- Express quantitative relationships by using algebraic terminology, expressions, and equations. (AF 1.0)

Goal 1 FINDING SOLUTIONS OF LINEAR EQUATIONS

A **linear equation in two variables** is an equation in which the variables appear in separate terms, and each variable occurs only to the first power. For example, the following equations are linear.

$$y = 2x + 1 \qquad C = \pi d \qquad A = 1.06P$$

Equations such as $xy = 10$, $A = \pi r^2$, and $V = s^3$ are not linear.

In Lesson 3.8 you learned that (x, y) is a *solution* of an equation involving x and y if the equation is true when the values of x and y are substituted into the equation. Equations with two variables generally have more than one solution. For example, here are three solutions of $y = x + 3$.

EQUATION	SOLUTION	CHECK BY SUBSTITUTING.
$y = x + 3$	$(x, y) = (1, 4)$	$4 = 1 + 3$
$y = x + 3$	$(x, y) = (2, 5)$	$5 = 2 + 3$
$y = x + 3$	$(x, y) = (3, 6)$	$6 = 3 + 3$

To find a solution of an equation, choose a value for one of the variables, substitute it into the equation, and solve for the other variable.

EXAMPLE 1 Finding Solutions of Linear Equations

List several solutions of $2x + y = 10$.

Solution

Begin by choosing values of x. Substitute each value into the equation and solve for y.

X-VALUE	SUBSTITUTE FOR X.	SOLVE FOR Y.	SOLUTION
$x = 0$	$2(0) + y = 10$	$y = 10$	$(0, 10)$
$x = 1$	$2(1) + y = 10$	$y = 8$	$(1, 8)$
$x = 2$	$2(2) + y = 10$	$y = 6$	$(2, 6)$
$x = 3$	$2(3) + y = 10$	$y = 4$	$(3, 4)$
$x = 4$	$2(4) + y = 10$	$y = 2$	$(4, 2)$

You can organize your results in a table. The table shows the value of y for each chosen value of x.

x	0	1	2	3	4
y	10	8	6	4	2

1 Plan

Pacing

Suggested Number of Days

Transitional: 1 day
Average: 1 day
Advanced: 1 day
Block Schedule: 0.5 block with 11.1

Teaching Resources

Blacklines
(See page 560B.)

Transparencies
- Warm-Up Exercises
- Teacher Time-Savers
- English/Spanish Problem Solving
- Answers

Technology
- Electronic Teacher Tools
- Test and Practice Generator

2 Teach

Math Reasoning

For Mathematical Background Notes on mathematical reasoning related to this lesson, please refer to pages 560E and 560F in this Teacher's Edition.

Extra Example 1
See next page.

California Standards and Assessment

CA Standards: AF 1.0, AF 4.0

Math Reasoning

The input-output table in Example 1 indicates that there is a linear function associated with the given linear equation in two variables. Also, given a linear function, if you construct an input-output table with equally spaced inputs, you will find that the outputs are also equally spaced.

Extra Example 1

List several solutions of $x + 3y = 14$. ***Sample answers:*** **$(-4, 6)$, $(-1, 5)$, $(2, 4)$, $(5, 3)$, and $(8, 2)$**

Extra Example 2

Solve for y in the equation $-5x + y = 6$. **$y = 5x + 6$**

Extra Example 3

a. Write $12x - 4y = 8$ in function form. **$y = 3x - 2$**

b. Use the result to write a table of values for the equation.

x	-2	-1	0	1	2
y	-8	-5	-2	1	4

c. Describe the pattern in the table of values. **When x increases by 1 unit, y increases by 3 units.**

Concept Check

Is $y = x^2 - 4$ a linear equation? Why? ***Sample answer:*** **No. A linear equation must have each variable raised only to the first power.**

Goal 2 WRITING A LINEAR EQUATION AS A FUNCTION

In Example 1 you found solutions of the equation $2x + y = 10$ by substituting values of x and then solving for y. Another way to find solutions is to write the equation in *function form* first by solving the equation for y.

Student Help

MORE EXAMPLES

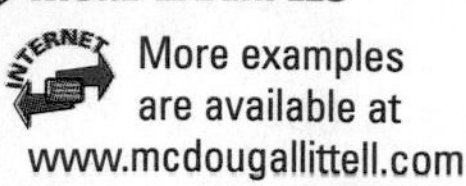

More examples are available at www.mcdougallittell.com

EXAMPLE 2 Writing an Equation in Function Form

Solve for y in the equation $2x + y = 10$.

Solution

$$2x + y = 10 \quad \text{Write original equation.}$$

$$-2x + 2x + y = -2x + 10 \quad \text{Add } -2x \text{ to each side.}$$

$$y = -2x + 10 \quad \text{Simplify.}$$

ANSWER ▶ In the form $y = -2x + 10$, the variable y is written as a function of x.

Every equation of the form $Ax + By = C$ where A, B, and C are constants and $B \neq 0$ can be written in function form by solving for y. The resulting equation corresponds to a *linear function.*

EXAMPLE 3 Writing a Table of Values

a. Write $-4x + 2y = 6$ in function form.

b. Use the result to write a table of values for the equation.

c. Describe the pattern in the table of values.

Solution

a.

$$-4x + 2y = 6 \quad \text{Write original equation.}$$

$$4x + (-4x) + 2y = 4x + 6 \quad \text{Add } 4x \text{ to each side.}$$

$$2y = 4x + 6 \quad \text{Simplify.}$$

$$\frac{1}{2}(2y) = \frac{1}{2}(4x + 6) \quad \text{Multiply each side by } \frac{1}{2}.$$

$$y = 2x + 3 \quad \text{Use distributive property.}$$

b. Choose some values of x. Substitute each x-value into the function form of the equation from part (a) and find y.

x	-2	-1	0	1	2
y	-1	1	3	5	7

c. From the table of values you can see that when x increases by 1 unit, y increases by 2 units.

Student Help

STUDY TIP

If you study Example 1 and Example 3, you will see that it is easier to make a table of values when the equation is written in function form.

11.2 Exercises

Guided Practice

5. no; The equation is not linear because the variable is to the third power.

6. yes; The equation is linear because both variables are only to the first power.

7. yes; The equation is linear because both variables are only to the first power.

8. no; The equation is not linear because one of the two variables is to the second power.

Tell whether the ordered pair is a solution of $2x + 3y = 7$. Explain.

1. $(1, 2)$ no, $2(1) + 3(2) = 8$ **2.** $(2, 1)$ yes, $2(2) + 3(1) = 7$ **3.** $(5, -1)$ yes, $2(5) + 3(-1) = 7$ **4.** $(4, -1)$ no, $2(4) + 3(-1) = 5$

Tell whether the equation is linear. Explain your answer. 5–8. See margin.

5. $V = \frac{4}{3}\pi r^3$ **6.** $r + \frac{1}{2}t = 30$ **7.** $100 - 6p = S$ **8.** $A = s^2$

Copy and complete the table of values below to show solutions of the given equation. 9–12. See margin.

x	−3	−2	−1	0	1	2	3
y	?	?	?	?	?	?	?

9. $y = x + 5$ **10.** $y = 5x + 6$ **11.** $3x - 3 = y$ **12.** $2x - y = 4$

Write the equation in function form. Then write a table of values.

13. $x + y = 3$ $y = 3 - x$; See margin. **14.** $2x - 5y = 7$ $y = \frac{2x - 7}{5}$; See margin. **15.** $\frac{1}{2}x + 3y = 0$ $y = -\frac{x}{6}$; See margin.

Practice and Problem Solving

19. yes, $7\left(\frac{1}{2}\right) - \left(-\frac{3}{2}\right) = 5$

Student Help

▶ **MORE PRACTICE** Extra practice to help you master skills is on page 710.

25. $y = \frac{13 - x}{2}$

Tell whether the ordered pair is a solution of $7x - y = 5$. Explain.

16. $(0, -5)$ yes, $7(0) - (-5) = 5$ **17.** $(2, 1)$ no, $7(2) - (1) = 13$ **18.** $(-1, 12)$ no, $7(-1) - (12) = -19$ **19.** $\left(\frac{1}{2}, -\frac{3}{2}\right)$ See margin.

Copy and complete the table of values below to show solutions of the given equation.

x	−3	−2	−1	0	1	2	3
y	?	?	?	?	?	?	?

20. $y = x - 8$ **21.** $y = 2x + 4$ **22.** $4x + y = 20$ **23.** $6x - y = 18$
20–23. See margin.

Write the equation in function form. Then write a table of values.

24. $x + y = 6$ $y = 6 - x$; See margin. **25.** $x + 2y = 13$ See margin. **26.** $6x + 2y = 24$ $y = 12 - 3x$; See margin.

27. $y - 3x = 10$ $y = 10 + 3x$; See margin. **28.** $-5y + 20x = 30$ $y = 4x - 6$; See margin. **29.** $3y + 9x = 0$ $y = -3x$; See margin.

Write an equation that represents the sentence. Then write the equation in function form. 30, 31. See margin.

30. $6x - 4y = 12$, $y = \frac{3x}{2} - 3$

31. $\frac{x}{2} + 2y = 54$, $y = 27 - \frac{x}{4}$

30. The difference of 6 times a number x and 4 times a number y is 12.

31. The sum of half a number x and twice another number y is 54.

3 Apply

Assignment Guide

TRANSITIONAL
Day 1: pp. 569–570 Exs. 16–17, 20–21, 24–26, 35–37, 44–45

AVERAGE
Day 1: pp. 569–570 Exs. 18–20, 27–37, 44–45

ADVANCED
Day 1: pp. 569–570 Exs. 18–19, 27–29, 35–41, 42–43*, 44–45

BLOCK SCHEDULE
pp. 569–570 Exs. 18–20, 27–37, 44–45 (with 11.1)

Extra Practice

- Student Edition, pp. 710–711
- Chapter 11 Resource Book, p. 15

Homework Check

To quickly check student understanding of key concepts, go over the following exercises:

Transitional: 20, 24, 26, 35, 36
Average: 20, 28, 32, 35, 36
Advanced: 28, 35, 36, 38, 40

9.

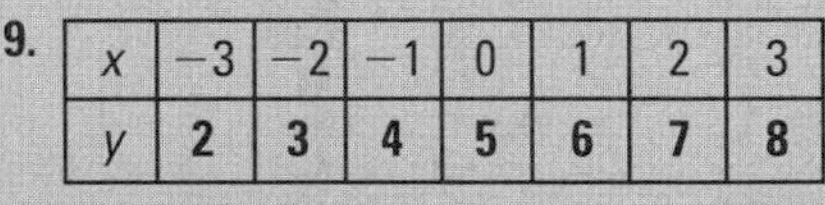

x	−3	−2	−1	0	1	2	3
y	2	3	4	5	6	7	8

10.

x	−3	−2	−1	0	1	2	3
y	−9	−4	1	6	11	16	21

11.

x	−3	−2	−1	0	1	2	3
y	−12	−9	−6	−3	0	3	6

12.

x	−3	−2	−1	0	1	2	3
y	−10	−8	−6	−4	−2	0	2

13.

x	−3	−2	−1	0	1	2	3
y	6	5	4	3	2	1	0

14.

x	−3	−2	−1	0	1	2	3
y	$-\frac{13}{5}$	$-\frac{11}{5}$	$-\frac{9}{5}$	$-\frac{7}{5}$	−1	$-\frac{3}{5}$	$-\frac{1}{5}$

15, 20–29. See Additional Answers beginning on page AA1.

Assess

Assessment Resources

- Assessment Book (Formal Assessment and Alternative Assessment)
- Test and Practice Generator

Mini-Quiz

1. Is the ordered pair $(-3, 2)$ a solution of the equation $x - 2y = -7$? Explain. **Yes; $-3 - 2(2) = -7$**
2. Make a table of values for $y = 3x - 6$ using the integers from -3 to 3 for x.

x	-3	-2	-1	0	1	2	3
y	-15	-12	-9	-6	-3	0	3

3. Solve $18x - 3y = -6$ for y. **$y = 6x + 2$**

32. $y = 150 - x$

x (in degrees)	10	30	60
y (in degrees)	**140**	**120**	**90**

33. $y = 180 - x$

x (in degrees)	10	30	60
y (in degrees)	**170**	**150**	**120**

34. $y = 90 - x$

x (in degrees)	10	30	60
y (in degrees)	**80**	**60**	**30**

40.

x (in pounds)	y (in ounces)
0	0
1	16
2	32
3	48
4	64
5	80
6	96
7	112
8	128
9	144
10	160

570

GEOMETRY **Match the linear equation with the figure. Write the linear equation in function form and list several solutions in a table of values.**

A.

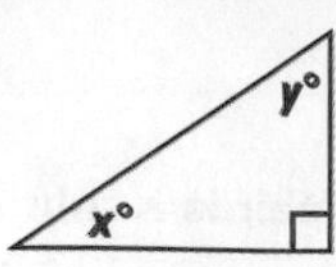

B.

x°
y°
30°

C.

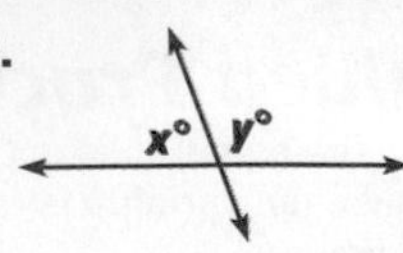

32. $x + y = 150$ **B; See margin.**

33. $x + y = 180$ **C; See margin.**

34. $x + y = 90$ **A; See margin.**

WEB PAGE DESIGN **In Exercises 35–37, use the following information.** You are working as a freelance Web page designer to save money for a new \$2500 computer. Your rates are \$250 for a basic page design and \$750 for a complex page design. The linear equation that models this situation is $750x + 250y = 2500$ where x is the number of complex pages that you design and y is the number of basic pages you design.

35. Write the linear equation in function form. **$y = 10 - 3x$**

36. How many basic pages must you design if you design only two complex pages? **4**

37. How many basic pages must you design if you design *only* basic pages? **10**

Student Help

▶**Skills Review**
For help with converting units of measure, see page 681.

UNIT CONVERSIONS **In Exercises 38–40, use the equation $y = 16x$, which relates a weight in ounces, y, to a weight in pounds, x.**

38. How much is 23 pounds in ounces? **368 oz**

39. How much is 112 ounces in pounds? **7 lb**

40. Use 0, 1, 2, . . . , 10 as values of x to write a table of values for converting between pounds and ounces. **See margin.**

41. MATHEMATICAL REASONING $Ax + By = C$ defines a function when $A = 0$, but *not* when $B = 0$. Give examples with tables of values to illustrate your answer. **See margin.**

41. When $A = 0$, the equation $Ax + By = C$ can be solved for y, in this case $y = \frac{C}{B} - \frac{A}{B}x$ for all values of x. If $B = 0$, the equation cannot be solved for y because the equation becomes $Ax = C$; in this case it cannot be written in function form.

CHALLENGE **For the following pairs of equations, tell which solutions of the first equation are also solutions of the second equation.**

42. $3x + 5y = 16$
$12x + 20y = 64$
See margin.

43. $9x - 2y = 18$
$18x - 4y = 30$
The two equations have no common solutions.

42. The two equations have the same solutions because they both can be written as the same function, $y = \frac{16 - 3x}{5}$.

Multiple-Choice Practice

44. Which ordered pair is *not* a solution of the equation $3x + 2y = 9$? **B**

Ⓐ (3, 0) Ⓑ (2, 3) Ⓒ (1, 3) Ⓓ (5, −3)

Test Tip Ⓐ Ⓑ Ⓒ Ⓓ

▶Read a difficult question twice before deciding how to solve the problem.

45. Which linear equation does *not* represent the following sentence? *The sum of twice a number x and four times a number y is 20.* **H**

Ⓕ $2x + 4y = 20$ Ⓖ $4y = -2x + 20$

Ⓗ $0 = -2x + 4y + 20$ Ⓙ $y = -0.5x + 5$

11.3 Graphs of Linear Functions

California Standards

In this lesson you'll:

- Graph and interpret linear functions. (AF 3.0)
- Represent quantitative relationships graphically and interpret the meaning of a specific part of the graph in the situation represented by the graph. (AF 1.5)

Goal 1 GRAPHING LINEAR FUNCTIONS

In Lesson 11.1 you learned how to represent functions with words, equations, and input-output tables. In this lesson you will learn to represent functions graphically.

EXAMPLE 1 Graphing a Linear Equation

The equation $y = 2x - 2$ defines a linear function whose inputs consist of all real numbers. Graph the function.

Solution

Find y-values for several x-values. It is convenient to organize your data in a table. Plot the xy-pairs in a coordinate plane.

x-value	y-value	xy-pairs
$x = -2$	$y = 2(-2) - 2 = \mathbf{-6}$	$(-2, \mathbf{-6})$
$x = -1$	$y = 2(-1) - 2 = \mathbf{-4}$	$(-1, \mathbf{-4})$
$x = 0$	$y = 2(0) - 2 = \mathbf{-2}$	$(0, \mathbf{-2})$
$x = 1$	$y = 2(1) - 2 = \mathbf{0}$	$(1, \mathbf{0})$
$x = 2$	$y = 2(2) - 2 = \mathbf{2}$	$(2, \mathbf{2})$

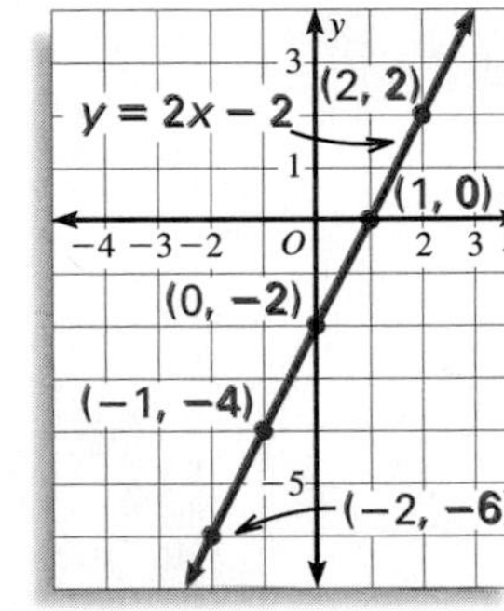

Notice that all the points lie on a line. As you continue to choose x-values, find corresponding y-values, and plot these xy-pairs, you will find that they also lie on the line. On this basis you can draw a line through the plotted points to represent the complete graph of the function.

In Example 1 the graph of the equation is a line. In general, the graphs of all linear equations are lines, which is why they are called *linear*.

Some linear equations, such as

$$x = 3 \text{ and } y = 1,$$

have just one variable. All solutions of $x = 3$ have the form $(3, y)$, and the graph of this equation is a *vertical line* that passes through $(3, 0)$. All solutions of $y = 1$ have the form $(x, 1)$, and the graph is a *horizontal line* that passes through $(0, 1)$.

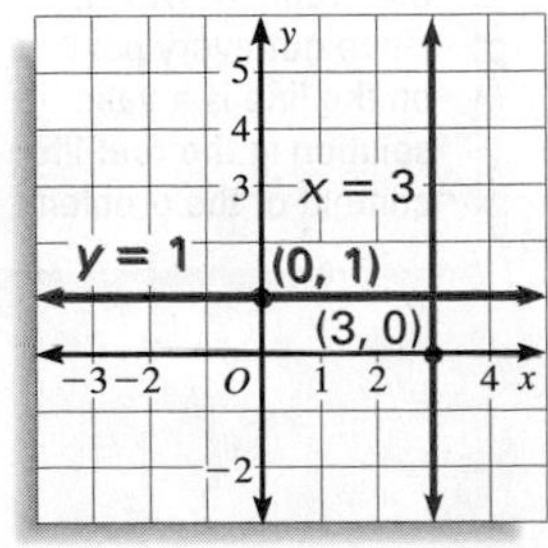

Student Help

STUDY TIP
The equation $x = 3$ does *not* represent a function. However, the equation $y = 1$ does represent a function, called a *constant function* because the function's output never changes.

1 Plan

Pacing

Suggested Number of Days

Transitional: 2 days
Average: 2 days
Advanced: 2 days
Block Schedule: 1 block

Teaching Resources

Blacklines
(See page 560B.)

Transparencies
- Warm-Up Exercises
- Teacher Time-Savers
- English/Spanish Problem Solving
- Answers

Technology
- Electronic Teacher Tools
- Test and Practice Generator

2 Teach

Math Reasoning

For Mathematical Background Notes on mathematical reasoning related to this lesson, please refer to pages 560E and 560F in this Teacher's Edition.

Extra Example 1
See next page.

California Standards and Assessment

CA Standards: AF 1.5, AF 3.0

Extra Example 1

Graph $y = 3x + 1$.

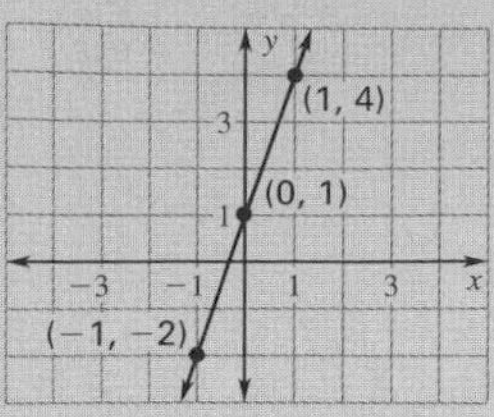

Extra Example 2

Graph the equation.

a. $y = -3$

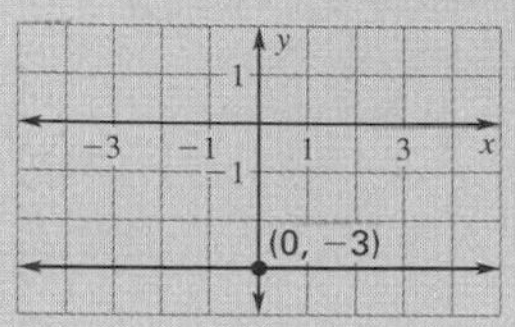

b. $x = 4$

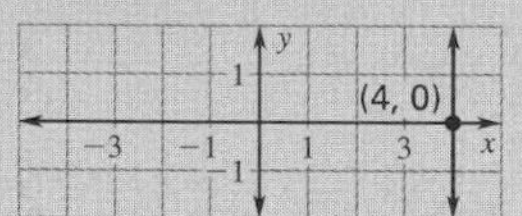

Extra Example 3

A car wash costs $4 for each car. A function that models the relationship between the number x of car washes and the total cost C is $C = 4x$. Graph the function.

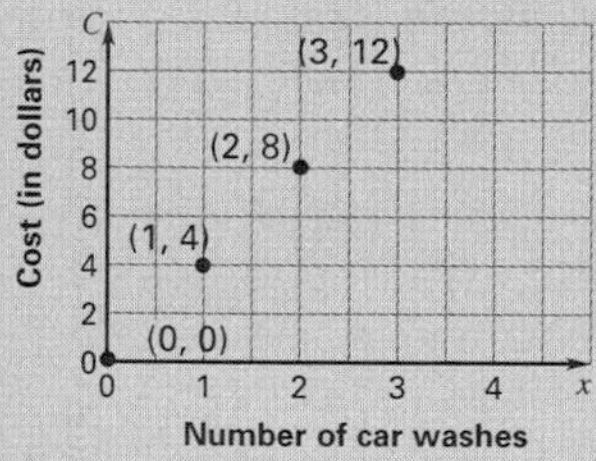

Concept Check

Explain how to determine from a linear equation whether its graph will be a horizontal line, a vertical line, or a slanted line. **If the linear equation has both an x- and y-variable, its graph will be a slanted line. If it has only an x-variable, its graph will be a vertical line. If it has only a y-variable, its graph will be a horizontal line.**

VERTICAL AND HORIZONTAL LINES

1. The graph of $x = a$ is a vertical line passing through $(a, 0)$.
2. The graph of $y = b$ is a horizontal line passing through $(0, b)$.

EXAMPLE 2 Graphing Horizontal and Vertical Lines

Graph the equation.

a. $x = -1$

The equation does not have y as a variable. So, for all values of y, the x-value is always -1. The graph of the equation is a vertical line through $(-1, 0)$.

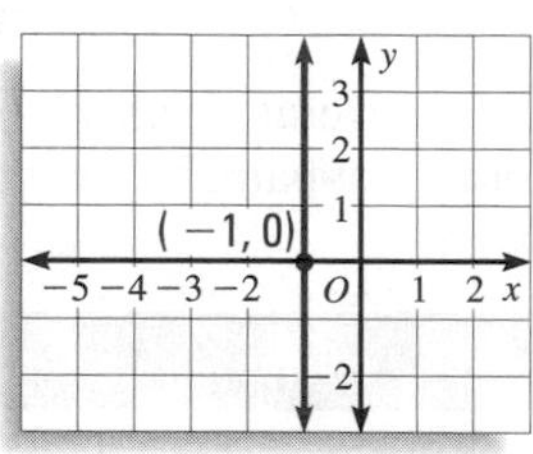

b. $y = 2$

The equation does not have x as a variable. So, for all values of x, the y-value is always 2. The graph of the equation is a horizontal line through $(0, 2)$.

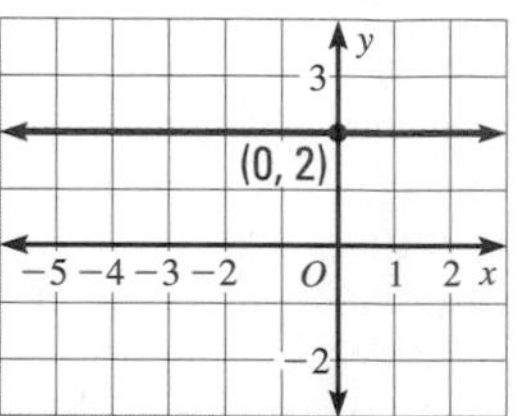

Goal 2 GRAPHING REAL-LIFE FUNCTIONS

When using functions as real-life models, you may need to restrict your input values to nonnegative numbers. So, graphs of such functions lie in the first and fourth quadrants of a coordinate plane. You may use variables other than x and y to identify variables in their real-life context.

EXAMPLE 3 Graphing a Real-Life Function

BAKE SALE One cookie at a bake sale costs $.50. A function that models the relationship between the number n of cookies purchased and the total cost C is $C = 0.50n$.

To graph the function, make a table of values, as shown below, and plot the ordered pairs, as shown at the right.

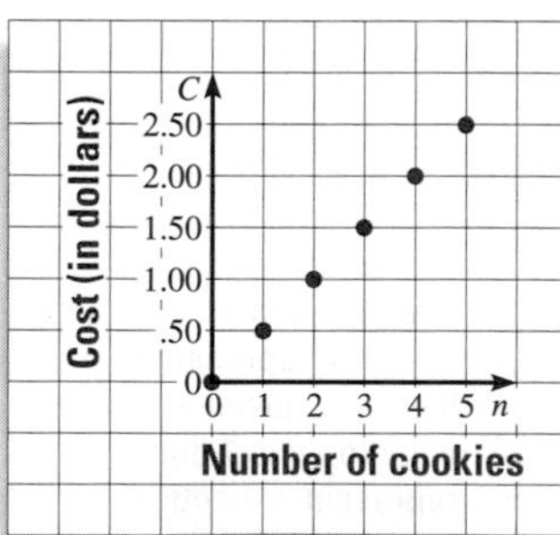

n	0	1	2	3	4	5
C	0	0.50	1.00	1.50	2.00	2.50

Student Help

STUDY TIP
The function in Example 3 is linear. You would not draw a line through the points on the graph, however, since not every point on the line is a valid solution in the real-life context of the problem.

Sometimes it is convenient to draw a line that connects the points that are solutions to a real-life problem even when the line includes points that are not valid solutions.

For example, consider the graph of $C = 0.8875752g + 8.13$, which represents the cost C of using g therms of natural gas for residential heating. The graph includes such points as (28.4, 33.33713568) and (64.5, 65.3786004), even though the gas company measures gas usage in whole numbers of therms and rounds charges to the nearest penny.

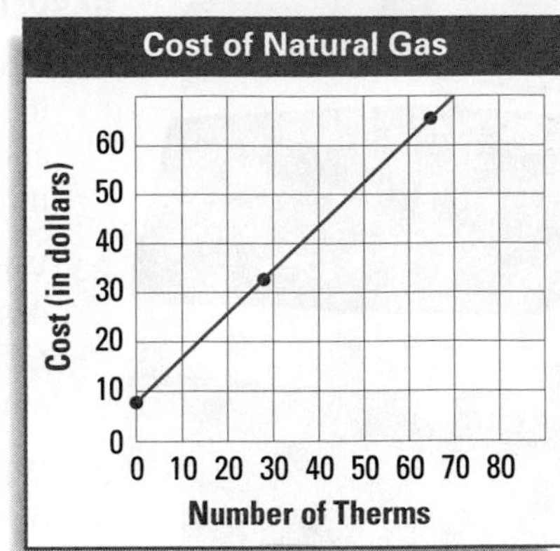

11.3 Exercises

Guided Practice

1. *Sample answer:* Find *y*-values for several *x*-values and organize the values in a table. Plot the *xy*-pairs in a coordinate plane. Draw a line through the plotted points.

1. Describe how to graph a linear equation. **See margin.**

In Exercises 2–4, match the equation with the description of its graph.

A. Horizontal line **B.** Vertical line **C.** Slanted line

2. $2x + 3y = 8$ **C** **3.** $y = 4$ **A** **4.** $x = -2$ **B**

Graph the equation. **5–8. See margin.**

5. $y = 5$ **6.** $x = -4$ **7.** $y = 3x - 1$ **8.** $x + y = 8$

Practice and Problem Solving

Student Help

▶ More Practice
Extra practice to help you master skills is on page 710.

In Exercises 9–11, match the equation with its graph.

A.

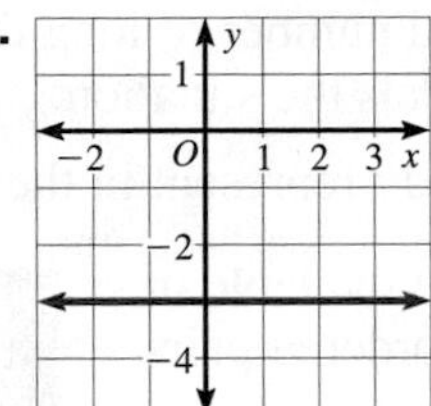

B.

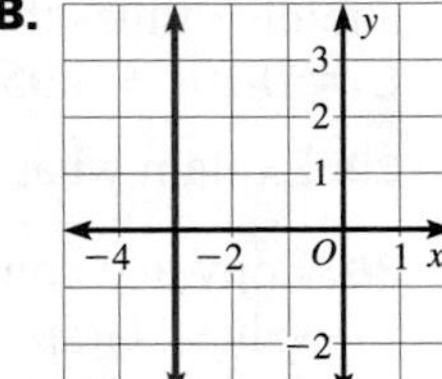

C.

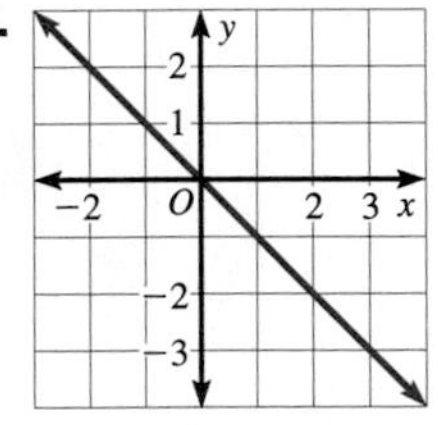

9. $y = -x$ **C** **10.** $y = -3$ **A** **11.** $x = -3$ **B**

Graph the equation. **12–20. See margin.**

12. $y = x + 4$ **13.** $y = 2x - 6$ **14.** $y = -1$

15. $y = 3x - 2$ **16.** $y = -x + 2$ **17.** $y = 5x$

18. $x = \frac{3}{2}$ **19.** $y = \frac{x}{3}$ **20.** $y = \frac{3}{2}x - 5$

3 Apply

Assignment Guide

Transitional
Day 1: pp. 573–575 Exs. 9–18, 21
Day 2: pp. 573–575 Exs. 22–28, 33–34, 39–47

Average
Day 1: pp. 573–575 Exs. 9–21
Day 2: pp. 573–575 Exs. 22–25, 29–32, 35–37, 39–47

Advanced
Day 1: pp. 573–575 Exs. 9–21
Day 2: pp. 573–575 Exs. 26–32, 35–37, 38*, 39–47

Block Schedule
pp. 573–575 Exs. 9–25, 29–32, 35–37, 39–47

Extra Practice

- Student Edition, pp. 710–711
- Chapter 11 Resource Book, p. 24

Homework Check

To quickly check student understanding of key concepts, go over the following exercises:

Transitional: 12, 14, 16, 18, 28
Average: 12, 14, 18, 20, 32
Advanced: 12, 14, 18, 20, 38

5.

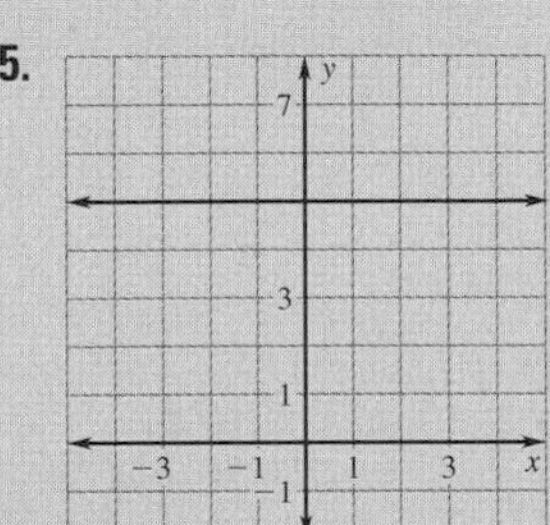

6.

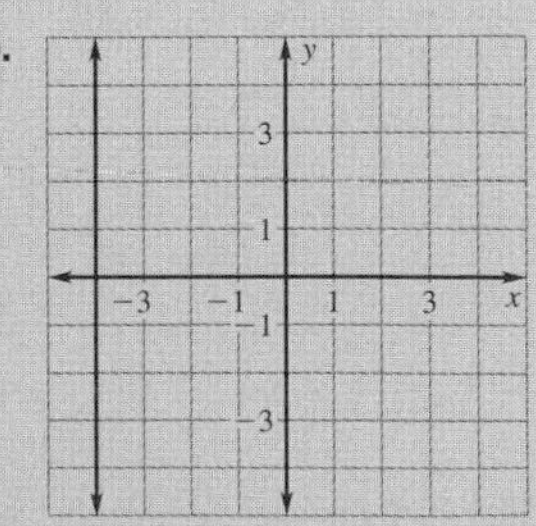

7–8, 12–20. See Additional Answers beginning on page AA1.

Math Reasoning

The graph of the function defined in Exercise 31 is a *step function,* consisting of horizontal steps that are each 1 unit long and which rise at the rate of $\frac{1}{10}$ of a unit per step. In Exercise 32 the steps of the graph would rise at the rate of 0.07 units per unit step if each fraction of a minute is treated as a whole minute.

22. ***Sample answer***:

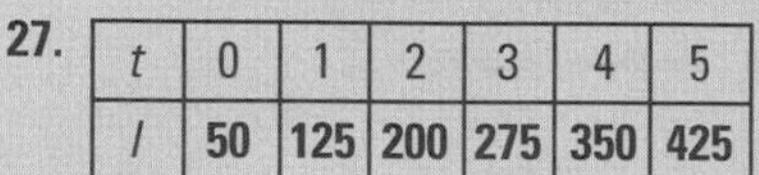

a (in gallons)	2	4	6	8
C (in dollars)	2.40	4.80	7.20	9.60

27.

t	0	1	2	3	4	5
I	50	125	200	275	350	425

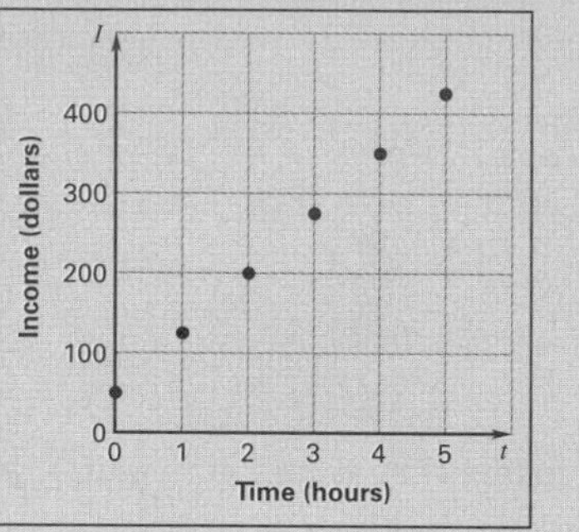

30.

t	0	10	20	30	40	50
C	4.95	5.95	6.95	7.95	8.95	9.95

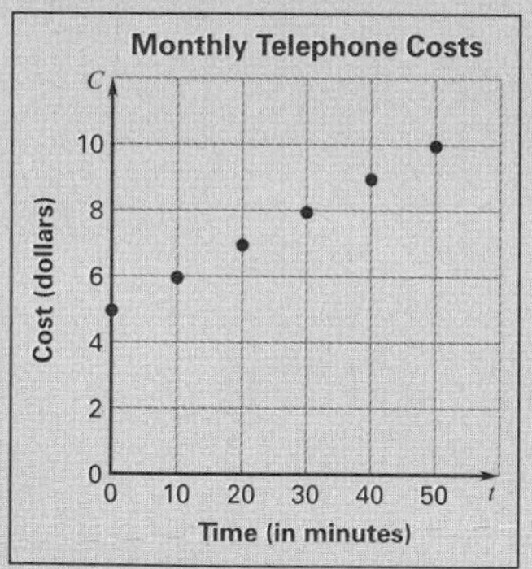

Link to Science

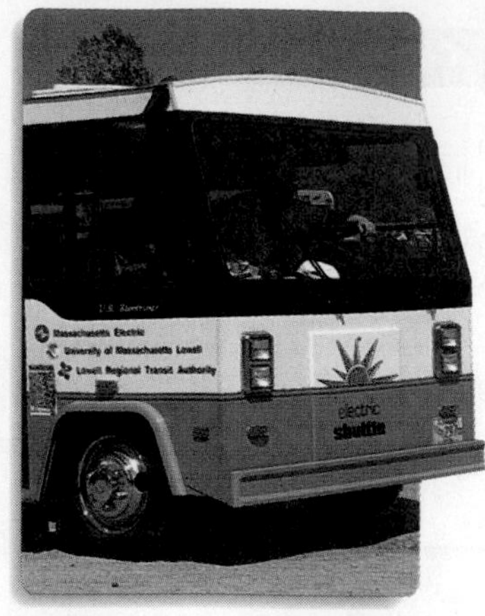

ELECTRIC VEHICLES are helping to reduce air pollution. Electric drive engines don't create pollution and are 100% more energy efficient than gasoline engines.

More about electric vehicles available at www.mcdougallittell.com

25. Yes, it makes sense to draw a line through the points because you can buy fractions of a gallon of gas.

21. In a coordinate plane, the graphs of $x = 0$ and $y = 0$ have special names. What are these names?
The graphs of $x = 0$ and $y = 0$ are the *y*-axis and *x*-axis, respectively.

GASOLINE In Exercises 22–25, use the graph of the function shown.

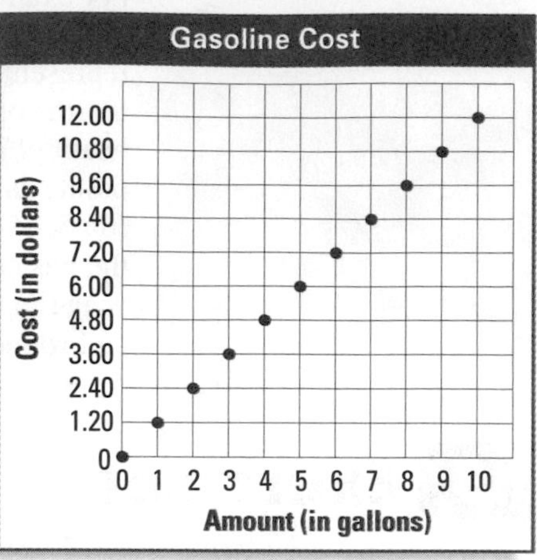

22. Use the plotted points to identify 4 pairs of input and output values. Make an input-output table. **See margin.**

23. Write a function rule to describe the graph using C for total cost and a for amount in gallons.
$C = 1.20a$

24. What is the total cost if you buy 12 gallons of gas?
$14.40

25. Does it make sense to draw a line through the plotted points? Explain. **See margin.**

PLUMBING In Exercises 26–28, use the following information.
A plumber charges $50 to make a house call plus $75 per hour for the number of hours worked on a job. The function $I = 75t + 50$ models the situation.

26. Explain what I and t represent in the function. ***I* represents the income from a job and *t* represents the number of hours worked on the job.**

27. Copy and complete the table of values. Graph the ordered pairs from the table. **See margin.**

t	0	1	2	3	4	5
I	?	?	?	?	?	?

28. Find the value of I when $t = 7.5$. Is this value of the function valid? Explain. **$612.50, yes; this value represents the income earned on a job that took 7.5 hours to complete.**

CALLING PLAN In Exercises 29–32, use the following information.
The monthly charge for a long distance calling plan is $4.95 plus $.10 a minute times the total number of long distance minutes. The function $C = 0.10t + 4.95$ models the situation.

29. Explain what C and t represent in the function. ***C* represents the monthly telephone charge and *t* represents the total number of long distance minutes.**

30. Copy and complete the table of values. Graph the ordered pairs from the table. **See margin.**

t	0	10	20	30	40	50
C	?	?	?	?	?	?

31. If the long distance provider treats a fraction of a minute as another whole minute does the given equation model the situation? That is, does it make sense to draw a line through the points you plotted in Exercise 30? Explain. **no; The real plot would look like stairs.**

32. MATHEMATICAL REASONING If the long distance provider keeps the monthly fee at $4.95 but lowers the per-minute charge for long distance calls from $.10 to $.07, how would the graph change? **See margin.**

32. The slant of the straight line through the points would decrease if the points were plotted in the same manner.

▶HOMEWORK HELP Extra help with problem solving in Exs. 33–34 is available at www.mcdougallittell.com

ON-LINE SHOPPING In Exercises 33 and 34, use the table, which shows the shipping charges for 1 to 6 items purchased on the Internet.

Number of items	1	2	3	4	5	6
Shipping charge	\$2.19	\$4.38	\$6.57	\$8.76	\$10.95	\$13.14

33. Plot the data from the table on a coordinate plane. **See margin.**

34. What is the rule the shipper seems to be using? Use your answer to calculate the shipping charge when 8 items are purchased.
$y = 2.19x$; \$17.52

In Exercises 35–38, use the following information. To ride the bus, you pay \$1.25 per ride.

35. Copy and complete the table. **See margin.**

Number of rides	5	10	15	20	25	30	35
Cost	\$6.25	?	?	?	?	?	?

36. Plot the data from the table on a coordinate plane. **See margin.**

37. Does it make sense to draw a line through the plotted points? Explain.
No. You can't buy a fraction of a ride.

38. CHALLENGE A monthly bus pass costs \$25.00. Use your graph to determine how many rides you need to take per month for the monthly bus pass to be a better buy. **more than twenty rides**

39. What is the graph of the equation $y = 5$? **A**

Ⓐ A horizontal line Ⓑ A vertical line

Ⓒ A slanted line Ⓓ Not a line

40. If the point $(2, b)$ lies on the graph of $y = 2x + 1$, what is b? **J**

Ⓕ $-\frac{1}{2}$ Ⓖ $\frac{3}{2}$ Ⓗ 2 Ⓙ 5

Mixed Review

Tell whether the number is *rational* or *irrational*. Explain. *(9.2)*
41–44. See margin.

41. $\frac{2}{3}$ **42.** $\sqrt{7}$ **43.** 3.47 **44.** $\sqrt{64}$

41. The number, $\frac{2}{3}$, is rational because its decimal representation repeats.

42. The number, $\sqrt{7}$, is irrational because its decimal representation never terminates or repeats.

43. The number, 3.47, is rational because its decimal representation terminates.

44. The number, $\sqrt{64}$, is rational because it is an integer.

Use the Pythagorean theorem to solve for the missing side length. Round your answer to the nearest hundredth. *(9.3)*

45. 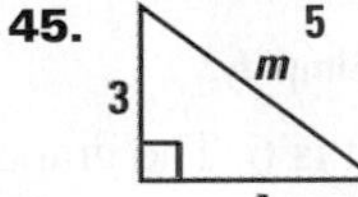

46. 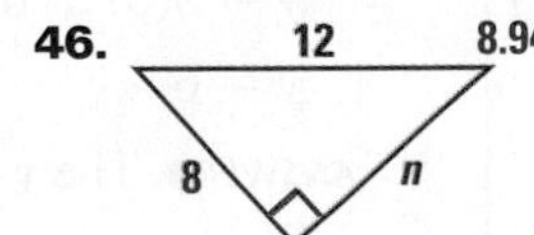

8.94

47. 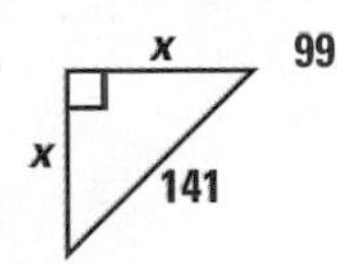

99.70

4 Assess

Assessment Resources

- Assessment Book (Formal Assessment and Alternative Assessment)
- Test and Practice Generator

Mini-Quiz

Sketch the graph of the equation. Tell whether each line is *horizontal*, *vertical*, or *slanted*.

1. $y = 1$ **horizontal**

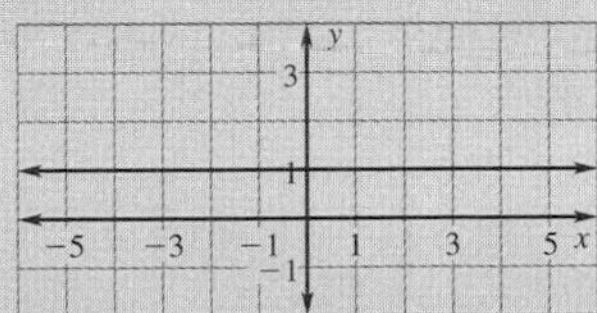

2. $x + y = 4$ **slanted**

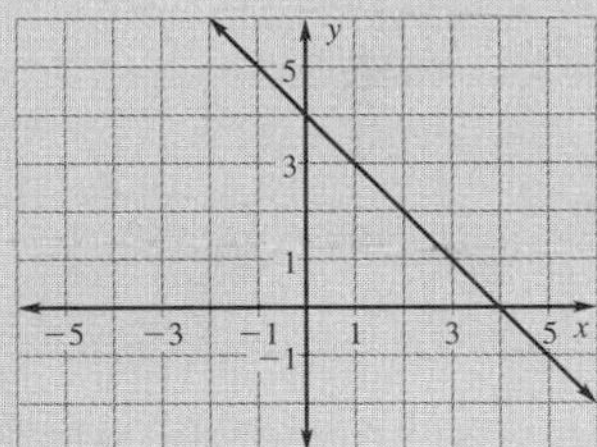

3. $x = 2$ **vertical**

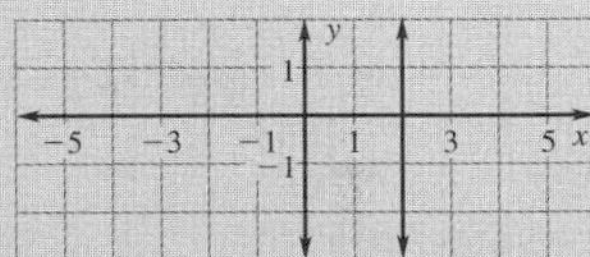

4. The table shows the speed of a car as it moves up an entrance ramp onto a highway. Plot the points in a coordinate plane. Is the relationship linear?

Time (s)	0	1	2	3	4
Speed (mi/h)	30	33	38	46	56

Check students' work; the relationship is not linear since the points do not lie on a straight line.

33, 35–36. See Additional Answers beginning on page AA1.

1 Plan

Pacing

Suggested Number of Days

Transitional: 2 days
Average: 2 days
Advanced: 2 days
Block Schedule: 1 block

Teaching Resources

Blacklines
(See page 560B.)

Transparencies
- Warm-Up Exercises
- Teacher Time-Savers
- English/Spanish Problem Solving
- Answers

Technology
- Electronic Teacher Tools
- Test and Practice Generator

2 Teach

Math Reasoning

For Mathematical Background Notes on mathematical reasoning related to this lesson, please refer to pages 560E and 560F in this Teacher's Edition.

CA Standards: AF 1.5, AG 3.0

11.4 Intercepts of Graphs

California Standards

In this lesson you'll:
- Represent quantitative relationships graphically and interpret the meaning of a specific part of the graph. (AF 1.5)
- Graph and interpret linear functions. (AF 3.0)

Goal 1 Finding Intercepts of Lines

The ***x*-intercept** of a graph is the *x*-coordinate of a point where the graph crosses the *x*-axis. The *y*-coordinate of this point is 0. In the graph at the right, the *x*-intercept is **4**.

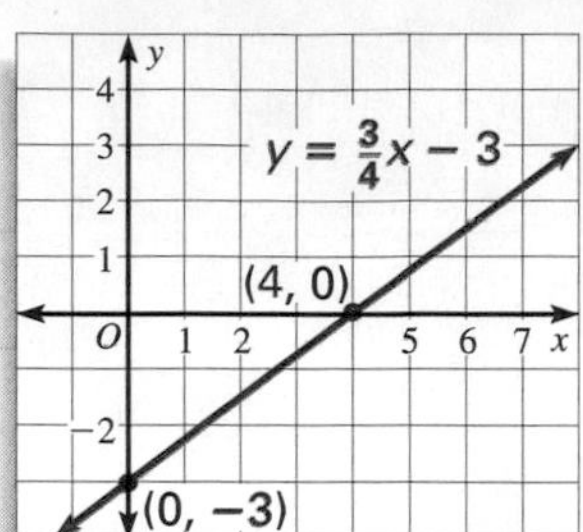

The ***y*-intercept** of a graph is the *y*-coordinate of a point where the graph crosses the *y*-axis. The *x*-coordinate of this point is 0. In the graph at the right, the *y*-intercept is **−3**.

You can use an equation of a line to find the *x*- and *y*-intercepts of the line.

Finding the Intercepts of Lines

1. To find the *x*-intercept of a line, substitute $y = 0$ into the equation and solve for *x*.
2. To find the *y*-intercept of a line, substitute $x = 0$ into the equation and solve for *y*.

Example 1 Finding Intercepts of a Line

a. Find the *x*-intercept of the graph of the equation $y = 3x + 6$.

$y = 3x + 6$	Write original equation.
$0 = 3x + 6$	Substitute 0 for *y*.
$-6 = 3x$	Add −6 to each side.
$-2 = x$	Multiply each side by $\frac{1}{3}$.

ANSWER ▶ The *x*-intercept is −2. The graph contains the point (−2, 0).

b. Find the *y*-intercept of the graph of the equation $y = 3x + 6$.

$y = 3x + 6$	Write original equation.
$y = 3(0) + 6$	Substitute 0 for *x*.
$y = 6$	Simplify.

ANSWER ▶ The *y*-intercept is 6. The graph contains the point (0, 6).

Goal 2 SKETCHING QUICK GRAPHS

An accepted fact from geometry is that two points determine a line. So, to graph a linear equation, you need to know the coordinates of only two points belonging to its graph.

SKETCHING A QUICK GRAPH OF A LINE

To sketch a quick graph of a linear equation, graph two solutions of the equation and draw a line through the points. You can use any two solutions, but the intercepts are often convenient.

EXAMPLE 2 Sketching a Quick Graph

SUBWAYS You are designing a subway car. It has a total of 408 square feet for passengers. A standing passenger requires 4 square feet of space, and a seated passenger requires 6 square feet of space.

The combined number of standing passengers x and seated passengers y is given by the equation $4x + 6y = 408$. Sketch the graph of this equation and interpret the intercepts.

Solution

Find the intercepts of the graph of the equation.

To find the x-intercept, let $y = 0$ and solve for x.	To find the y-intercept, let $x = 0$ and solve for y.
$4x + 6y = 408$	$4x + 6y = 408$
$4x + 6(0) = 408$	$4(0) + 6y = 408$
$4x = 408$	$6y = 408$
$x = 102$	$y = 68$
The x-intercept is 102, so the point (102, 0) is on the graph.	The y-intercept is 68, so the point (0, 68) is on the graph.

Plot the intercepts and draw a line through them.

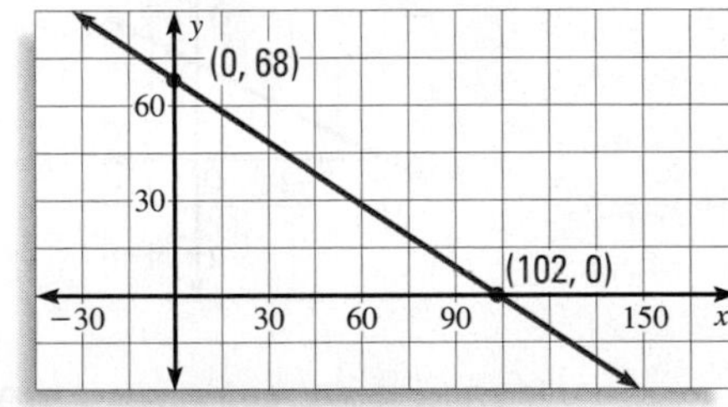

The x-intercept 102 means that there is room for 102 standing passengers with no sitting room. The y-intercept 68 means that there is room for 68 seated passengers with no standing room.

Link to Careers

TRANSPORTATION ENGINEERS design and supervise the construction of systems for the safe and efficient movement of people and goods.

INTERNET More about transportation engineers available at www.mcdougallittell.com

Student Help

▶**STUDY TIP**
In Example 2 note that only the part of the graph that lies in the first quadrant applies to the real-life situation of designing a subway car because you can't have a negative number of passengers.

Extra Example 1

a. Find the x-intercept of the graph of $x - 3y = 3$. **3**

b. Find the y-intercept of the graph of $x - 3y = 3$. **−1**

Extra Example 2

You are riding the school bus home. After x min, the number of miles from home, y, is given by $3x + 4y = 24$. Sketch the graph of the equation and interpret the intercepts.

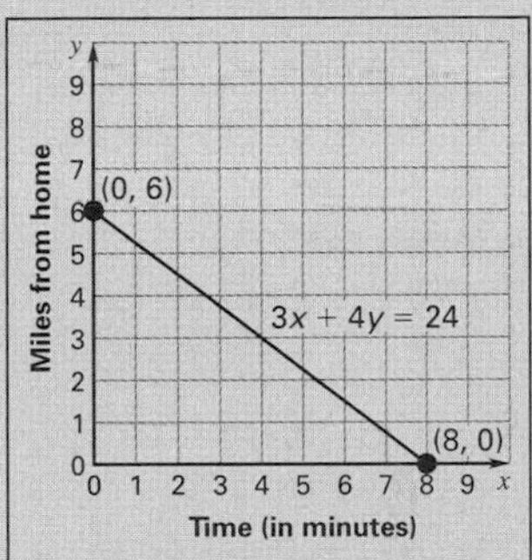

The x-intercept, 8, means that it takes 8 min to get home. The y-intercept, 6, means that you start the trip 6 mi from home.

Teaching Tip

In the graph for Extra Example 2, point out that even though the line extends forever in both directions, the portions of the line below the x-axis and to the left of the y-axis have no meaning in the context of the real-life problem. That is, the situation does not involve a negative number of minutes or a negative number of miles from home.

Concept Check

Explain how to find the intercepts of the graph of a line when you are given its equation. **To find the x-intercept, replace y with 0 in the equation and solve for x. To find the y-intercept, replace x with 0 and solve for y.**

3 Apply

Assignment Guide

TRANSITIONAL

Day 1: pp. 578–580 Exs. 9–14, 18–22

Day 2: pp. 578–580 Exs. 23–28, 32–37, 46–48, 50–52

AVERAGE

Day 1: pp. 578–580 Exs. 9–22

Day 2: pp. 578–580 Exs. 26–33, 38–45, 50–52

ADVANCED

Day 1: pp. 578–580 Exs. 9–22

Day 2: pp. 578–580 Exs. 26–33, 42–48, 49*, 50–52

BLOCK SCHEDULE

pp. 578–580 Exs. 9–22, 26–33, 38–45, 50–52

Extra Practice

- Student Edition, pp. 710–711
- Chapter 11 Resource Book, p. 33

Homework Check

To quickly check student understanding of key concepts, go over the following exercises:

Transitional: 10, 14, 24, 28, 36
Average: 10, 16, 28, 30, 39, 40
Advanced: 10, 16, 28, 30, 47, 48

6. *x*-intercept: 5, *y*-intercept: 5,

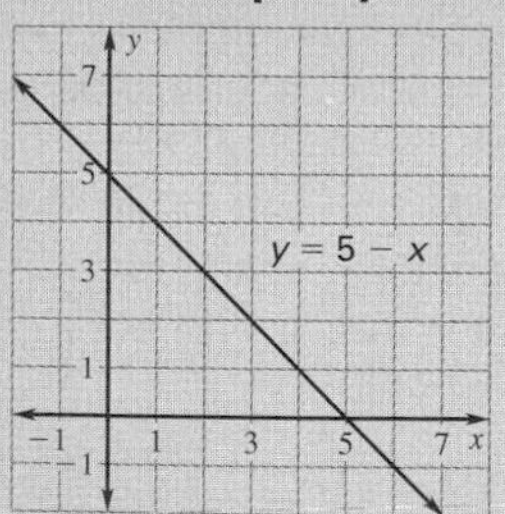

7–8. See Additional Answers beginning on page AA1.

11.4 Exercises

Guided Practice

1. *x*-intercept: 4, *y*-intercept: 2
2. *x*-intercept: 2, *y*-intercept: −1
3. *x*-intercept: −2, *y*-intercept: −2

Identify the intercepts of the graph. 1–3. See margin.

1. 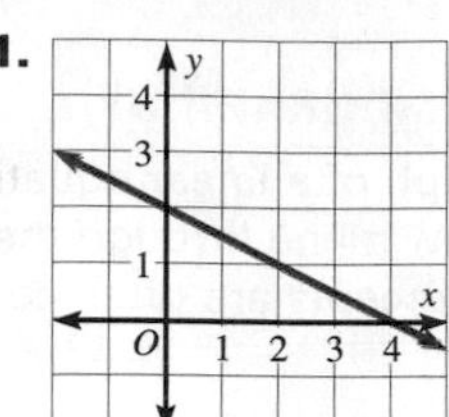

2. 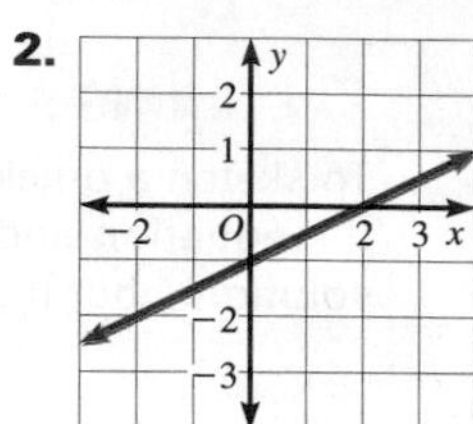

3. 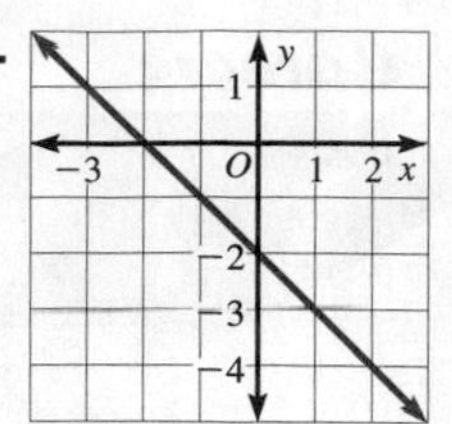

Describe each step you would take to find the specified intercept of the graph of the given equation.

4. Find the x-intercept of the graph of $y = 2x - 1$. Let $y = 0$ in the equation $y = 2x - 1$ and solve the remaining equation, $0 = 2x - 1$, for x.

5. Find the y-intercept of the graph of $5x + 3y = 9$. Let $x = 0$ in the equation $5x + 3y = 9$ and solve remaining equation, $3y = 9$, for y.

Find the intercepts of the graph of the equation. Sketch a quick graph.

6. $x + y = 5$ *x*-intercept: 5, *y*-intercept: 5; See margin.

7. $x - y = 5$ *x*-intercept: 5, *y*-intercept: −5; See margin.

8. $y = \frac{5}{4}x + 3$ *x*-intercept: $\frac{-12}{5}$, *y*-intercept: 3; See margin.

Practice and Problem Solving

Student Help

▶**MORE PRACTICE**
Extra practice to help you master skills is on page 710.

9. *x*-intercept: −1, *y*-intercept: 4
10. *x*-intercept: 2, *y*-intercept: 6
11. *x*-intercept: 2, *y*-intercept: −8
12. *x*-intercept: −5, *y*-intercept: −2
13. *x*-intercept: 4, *y*-intercept: −5
14. *x*-intercept: 1, *y*-intercept: −1
15. *x*-intercept: 3, *y*-intercept: −7
16. *x*-intercept: 60, *y*-intercept: 100
17. *x*-intercept: −1.8, *y*-intercept: 4.5
21. The line slants upward from left to right. If the *x*-intercept is positive, then the line crosses the positive *x*-axis. If the *y*-intercept is negative the line crosses the negative *y*-axis. Such a line is slanted upward from left to right.

Find the intercepts of the graph of the equation. 9–17. See margin.

9. $y = 4x + 4$ **10.** $y = -3x + 6$ **11.** $y = 4x - 8$

12. $y = -\frac{2}{5}x - 2$ **13.** $y = \frac{5}{4}x - 5$ **14.** $x - y = 1$

15. $-7x + 3y = -21$ **16.** $5x + 3y = 300$ **17.** $4y - 10x = 18$

In Exercises 18–20, match the equation with its graph. (Finding the intercepts of the graph may be helpful.)

A. 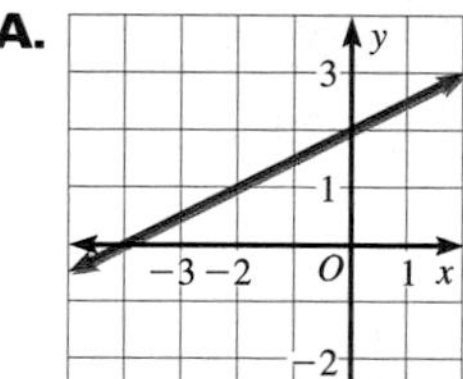

B. 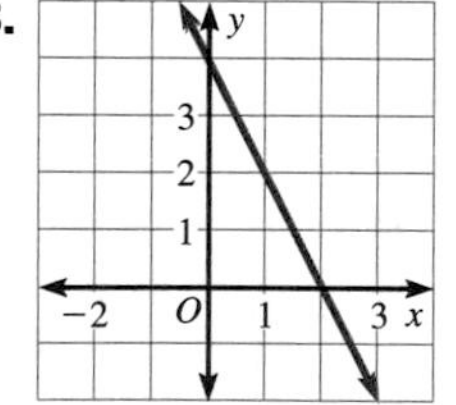

C. 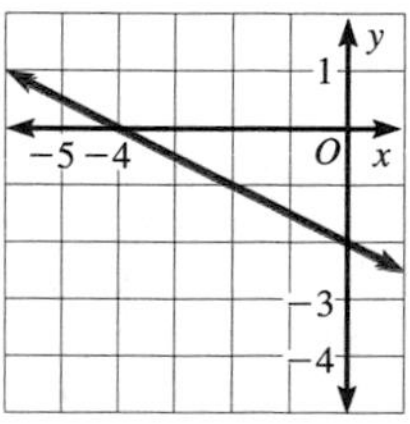

18. $y = \frac{1}{2}x + 2$ A **19.** $y = -\frac{1}{2}x - 2$ C **20.** $2x + y = 4$ B

21. MATHEMATICAL REASONING If the x-intercept of a line is positive and the y-intercept is negative, does the line slant upward or downward from left to right? Explain your reasoning. See margin.

22. The x-intercept by definition is the x-coordinate of the point where the graph crosses x-axis. The coordinates of this point for the equation $y = x + 5$ are $(-5, 0)$. The x-intercept is -5.

34. 6; The x-intercept is the number of cars that can be washed in sixty minutes if no sport utility vehicles, minivans or trucks are washed.

35. 4; The y-intercept is the number of sport utility vehicles, minivans or trucks that can be washed in sixty minutes if no cars are washed.

38. Each car has four brakes and each brake wears out in about three days. The rate at which a car's brakes will wear out is $\frac{4 \text{ brakes}}{3 \text{ days}}$, which is $\frac{4}{3}$ brakes per day.

Cable Cars

CABLE CARS In 1873 Andrew S. Hallidie invented the cable car and helped install the first one in San Francisco. Cable cars made it easier for people to travel up and down the hills of San Francisco.

22. ERROR ANALYSIS A student says that the x-intercept of the graph of $y = x + 5$ is the point $(0, 5)$. Why is the student incorrect? **See margin.**

Find the intercepts of the graph of the equation and use them to sketch a quick graph. Check your graph by finding and plotting a third solution. **23–31. See margin.**

23. $y = \frac{4}{3}x + 6$ **24.** $y = -6 - 3x$ **25.** $y = -\frac{3}{2}x + 4$

26. $x + y = 8$ **27.** $x + y = -3$ **28.** $x + 5y = 5$

29. $2x - 3y = 9$ **30.** $3x - 4y = 24$ **31.** $6x - 7y = 42$

CALCULATOR Use a calculator to find the intercepts of the line. Round your results to the nearest hundredth.

32. $y = -3.64x + 2.18$
x-intercept: 0.60, y-intercept: 2.18

33. $y = 1.85x - 14.302$
x-intercept: 7.73, y-intercept: −14.30

CAR WASH In Exercises 34–37, use the following information. You and your friends hold a car wash to raise money for a local charity. It takes 10 minutes to wash a car and 15 minutes to wash a sport utility vehicle, minivan, or truck. The number of vehicles that you and your friends can wash in one hour (60 minutes) is given by the equation $10x + 15y = 60$ where x is the number of cars washed and y is the number of sport utility vehicles, minivans, and trucks washed.

34. Find the x-intercept of the equation and interpret its meaning. **See margin.**

35. Find the y-intercept of the equation and interpret its meaning. **See margin.**

36. Sketch a graph of the equation. **See margin.**

37. At the beginning of one hour you and your friends wash 3 cars. Use your graph from Exercise 36 to find the number of sport utility vehicles, minivans, and trucks you and your friends can wash in what is left of the hour. **2**

CABLE CARS In Exercises 38–41, use the following information.
In San Francisco, California, 40 historic cable cars are used to transport passengers along city streets. Because the four track brakes on each cable car are made of soft wood, they wear out quickly and have to be replaced after about three days of use. You can use the equation $y = \frac{4}{3}x$ to estimate the number of track brakes y that a cable car needs for x days of operation.

38. Explain how the equation $y = \frac{4}{3}x$ models the situation described. **See margin.**

39. Make a table of values and graph the equation $y = \frac{4}{3}x$. Are there any intercepts? Explain.
x-intercept: 0, y-intercept: 0; no; See margin.

40. Use your graph from Exercise 39 to find the number of track brakes that a cable car needs for 9 days of operation. **12**

41. Use the graph from Exercise 39 to find how many days it will take for the cable car to use 20 brakes. **15**

Problem Solving

Exercise 38
Students may better understand why $y = \frac{4}{3}x$ models the situation if they make a table. Ask them to write down the number of brake pads used after each 3-day period.

23.
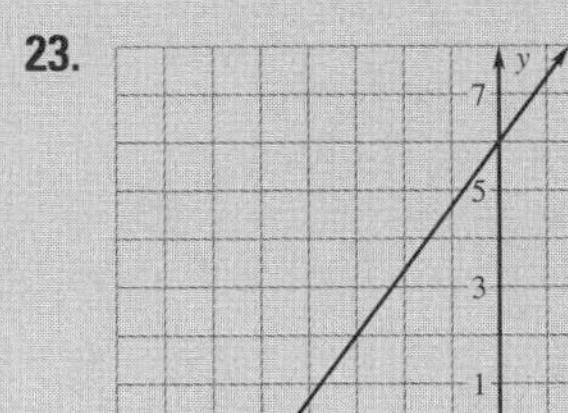

24.
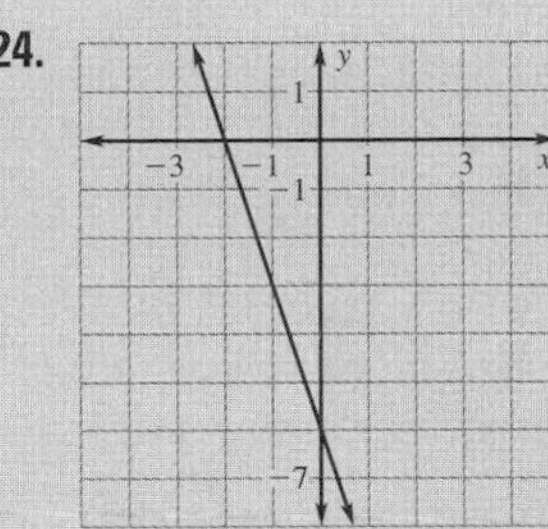

25.
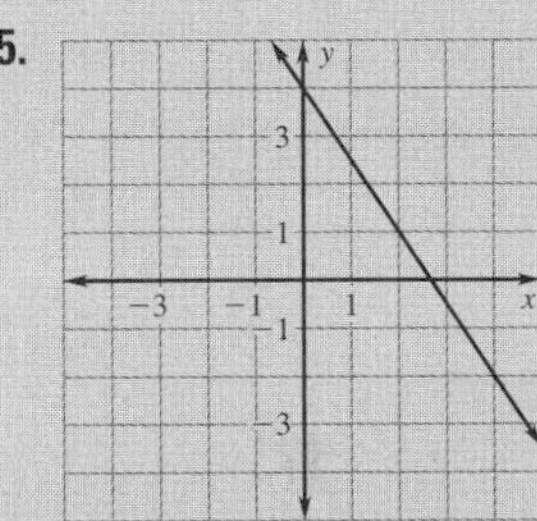

26.
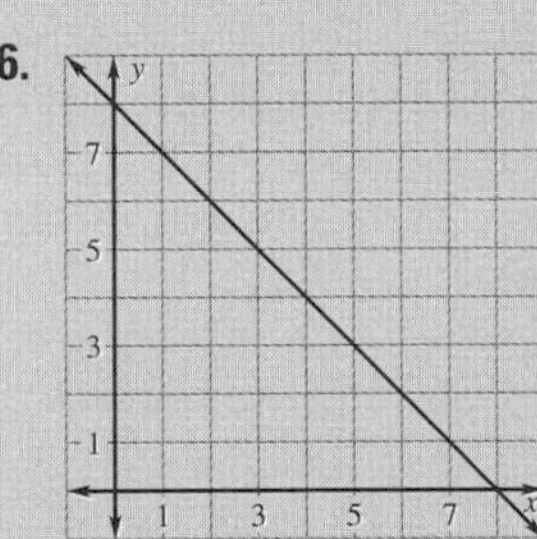

27–31, 36, 39. See Additional Answers beginning on page AA1.

4 Assess

Assessment Resources

- Assessment Book (Formal Assessment and Alternative Assessment)
- Test and Practice Generator

Mini-Quiz

Find the intercepts of the line.

1. $3x + 5y = 30$ **x-intercept: 10; y-intercept: 6**
2. $y = -4x + 8$ **x-intercept: 2; y-intercept: 8**
3. For a fund-raiser, you plan to sell hot dogs for $1 each and hamburgers for $2 each. You want the sales of hot dogs and hamburgers to total $100. The number of hot dogs, x, and hamburgers, y, that you must sell is given by the equation $x + 2y = 100$. Sketch the graph of this equation and interpret the intercepts.

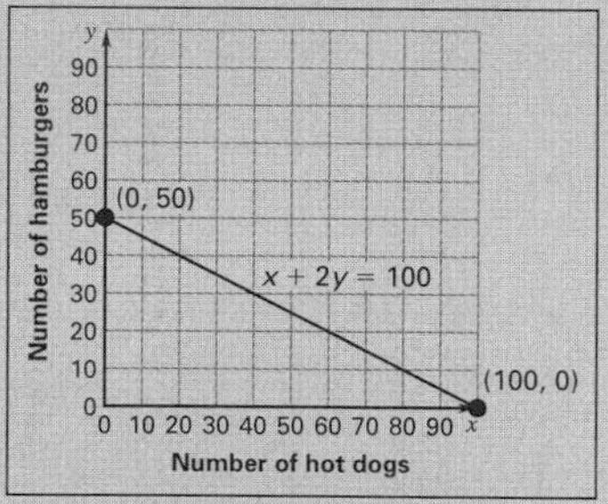

The x-intercept indicates that if no hamburgers are sold, then you must sell 100 hot dogs. The y-intercept indicates that if no hot dogs are sold, then you must sell 50 hamburgers.

43.

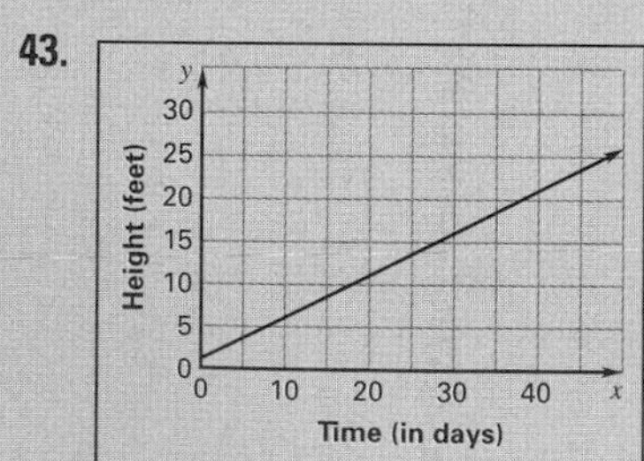

47, 49. See Additional Answers beginning on page AA1.

Student Help

▶ HOMEWORK HELP

Extra help with problem solving in Exs. 42–44 is available at www.mcdougallittell.com

42. The x-intercept is −2, which represents the number of days before day zero that it took the plant to grow to a height of 1 foot. The y-intercept is 1, which represents the height of the plant (in feet) on day zero.

46. The x-intercept is 15, which represents the number of pizzas that can be bought if no chicken wings are bought. The y-intercept is 24, which represents the number of pounds of chicken wings that can be bought if no pizzas are bought.

GARDENING In Exercises 42–45, use the following information. You plant a fast-growing bamboo plant that is 1 foot high. The equation $y = \frac{1}{2}x + 1$ can be used to predict the growth of your variety of bamboo. In the equation, x represents the time in days and y represents the height of the bamboo in feet.

42. Find the intercepts of the graph of the equation $y = \frac{1}{2}x + 1$. Interpret the meaning of the intercepts. **See margin.**

43. Sketch the graph of the equation. **See margin.**

44. Use your graph from Exercise 43 to estimate how long it will take the bamboo to reach a height of 25 feet. **about 48 days**

45. After about 120 days, the bamboo stops growing. Describe how this portion of the graph from Exercise 43 would appear. **For x larger than 120, the graph would be horizontal.**

CATERING In Exercises 46–48, use the following information. You want to have a party for a group of friends. You have $120 to spend on catered food. Each pizza costs $8. A pound of chicken wings costs $5. The equation $8x + 5y = 120$ describes the number x of pizzas and the number y of pounds of chicken wings that you can buy.

46. Find the intercepts of the graph of the equation $8x + 5y = 120$. Interpret the meaning of the intercepts. **See margin.**

47. Sketch the graph of the equation. **See margin.**

48. You decide to order 5 pizzas. Use your graph from Exercise 46 to determine the number of pounds of chicken wings you can order. **16 lb**

49. CHALLENGE Use the information in Exercises 46–48. Suppose the caterer offers to charge you only $4 per pizza if you order at least 20 pizzas. Write an equation describing the number x of pizzas and the number y of pounds of chicken wings you can buy. Sketch a quick graph. Then identify the portion of the graph that represents the possible choices you can make. Explain your reasoning.
$4x + 5y = 120$; $x \geq 20$; Points (20, 8), (25, 4), (30, 0) are meaningful choices. Other points on the graph yield fractions of pizzas and/or fractions of pounds of chicken. See margin.

Multiple-Choice Practice

50. At which point does the graph of the equation $y = 2x - 4$ cross the x-axis? **C**

Ⓐ (0, −4) Ⓑ (0, 2) Ⓒ (2, 0) Ⓓ (−4, 0)

51. What is the y-intercept of the graph of the equation $y = 3x - 6$? **J**

Ⓕ −2 Ⓖ 2 Ⓗ 6 Ⓙ Not here

52. Which equation has a graph whose y-intercept is −5? **C**

Ⓐ $y = -5x + 3$ Ⓑ $y = 3x + 5$

Ⓒ $y = -5 + 3x$ Ⓓ $y - 5 = 3x$

Chapter 11 Mid-Chapter Test

Take this test as you would take a test in class. The answers to the exercises are given in the back of the book.

Make a table of values for the function. Use *x*-values of 0, 1, 2, 3, and 4. **1–4 See margin.**

1. $y = 3 - x$ **2.** $y = \frac{2}{3}x$ **3.** $y = 2x + 5$ **4.** $y = 4x - 7$

Write a function rule that relates *x* and *y*.

5.

Input, x	0	1	2	3	4
Output, y	0	3	6	9	12

A rule for this function is $y = 3x$.

6.

Input, x	1	2	3	4	5
Output, y	6	7	8	9	10

A rule for this function is $y = x + 5$.

Tell whether the ordered pair is a solution of the equation $3x + 4y = 28$.

7. (0, 7) **yes** **8.** (8, 1) **yes** **9.** (−4, 4) **no** **10.** (−12, −2) **no**

UNIT CONVERSIONS **In Exercises 11–13, use the equation $i = 36y$. The equation relates yards, *y*, and inches, *i*.**

11. A student is 2 yards tall. Find the student's height in inches. **72 in.**

12. A rope is 252 inches long. Find its length in yards. **7 yd**

13. A designer has $16\frac{1}{2}$ yards of fabric. A small pillow uses 18 inches of fabric. Is there enough fabric to make 34 small pillows? Explain your answer. **Thirty-four pillows cannot be made. *Sample answer:* If each pillow requires 0.5 yards (18 inches), then 34 pillows will require 17 yards. Since there are only 16.5 yards of fabric, only 33 pillows can be made.**

In Exercises 14 and 15, use the equation $2x + 5y = 42$.
14–15. See margin.

14. Copy and complete the table at the right.

15. Use your table from Exercise 14 to graph $2x + 5y = 42$.

x	1	6	11	16
y	?	?	?	?

Find the intercepts of the graph of the equation.

16. $8x + 2y = 32$ **x-intercept: 4, y-intercept: 16**

17. $4x + 5y = 20$ **x-intercept: 5, y-intercept: 4**

18. $12x + 8y = 24$ **x-intercept: 2, y-intercept: 3**

19. $y = -3x + 7$ **x-intercept: $\frac{7}{3}$, y-intercept: 7**

In Exercises 20–22, match the equation with its graph.

A. 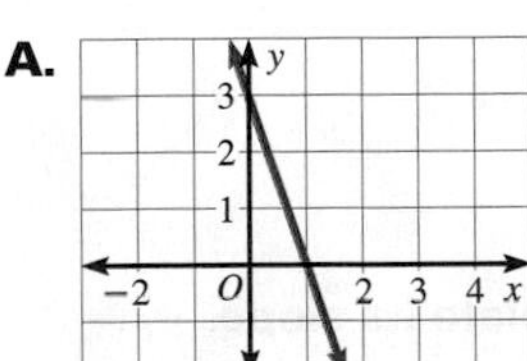

B. 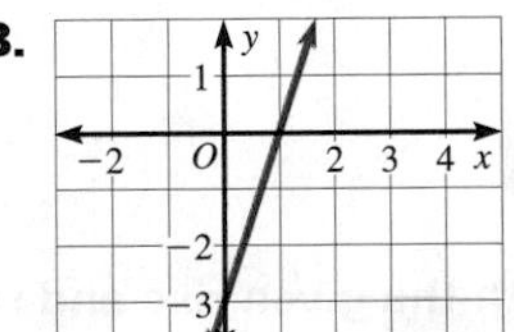

C. 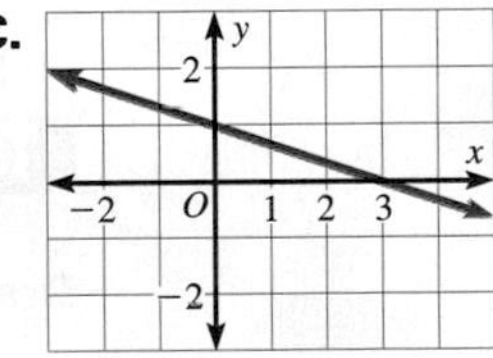

20. $y = 3x - 3$ **B** **21.** $3x + y = 3$ **A** **22.** $y = -\frac{1}{3}x + 1$ **C**

Additional Resources

A Mid-Chapter Test and a Mid-Chapter Partner Quiz are available in the *Assessment Book*, pp. 162–163 and 260.

1.

Input, x	0	1	2	3	4
Output, y	3	2	1	0	−1

2.

Input, x	0	1	2	3	4
Output, y	0	$\frac{2}{3}$	$\frac{4}{3}$	2	$\frac{8}{3}$

3.

Input, x	0	1	2	3	4
Output, y	5	7	9	11	13

4.

Input, x	0	1	2	3	4
Output, y	−7	−3	1	5	9

14.

x	1	6	11	16
y	8	6	4	2

15. 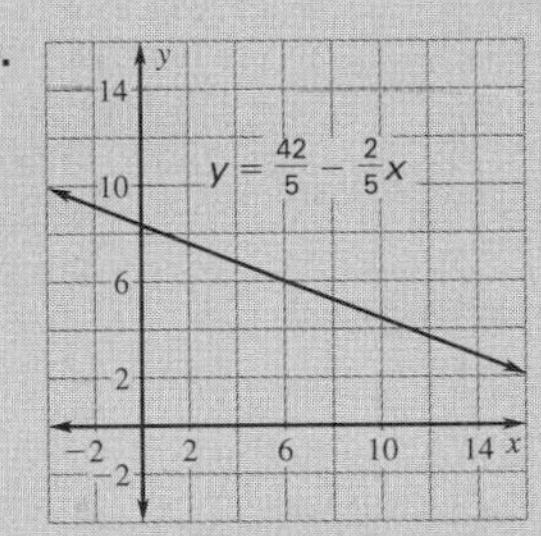

1 Planning the Activity

Purpose and Materials

See the margin of the student page.

▶ LINK TO LESSON
Students apply the results of the activity to the Examples in Lesson 11.5.

Math Reasoning

Students use deductive reasoning to prove that the slopes are constant. They develop generalizations of the results to apply to new situations.

2 Managing the Activity

Classroom Management

You may wish to use an overhead to demonstrate the proof.

3 Closing the Activity

★ KEY DISCOVERY
The slope of a line is given by the ratio of rise to run, and for a line the slope is constant.

Activity Assessment

Use Exercises 1–3 to assess student understanding.

1–3. See Additional Answers beginning on page AA1.

California Standards and Assessment

CA Standards: AF 3.3, MR 1.2
CA Key Concepts Book: pp. S54–S56

REASONING 11.5

DEVELOPING CONCEPTS
Slope of a Line

For use with Lesson 11.5

California Standards

- ▶ Formulate and justify mathematical conjectures. (MR 1.2)
- ▶ Note that the vertical change per unit of horizontal change is always the same for a line. (AF 3.3)

MATERIALS:
- Pencil and paper

You can describe the *slope* of a line by comparing its vertical *rise* to its horizontal *run* in a ratio.

$$\text{slope} = \frac{\textbf{rise}}{\textbf{run}}$$

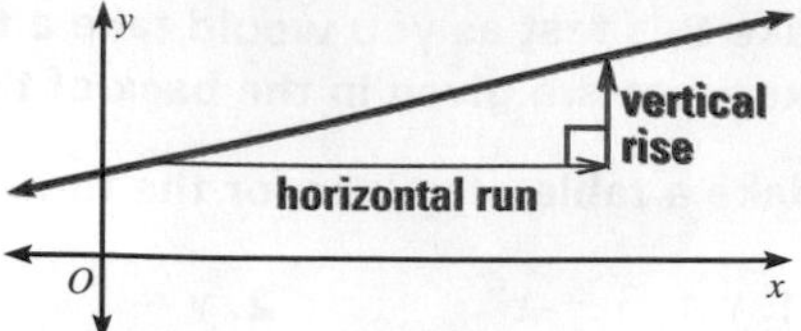

SAMPLE 1 Showing Slopes Are the Same

Points A, B, C, and D lie on a line. Show that the slope is the same whether you use points A and B or points C and D.

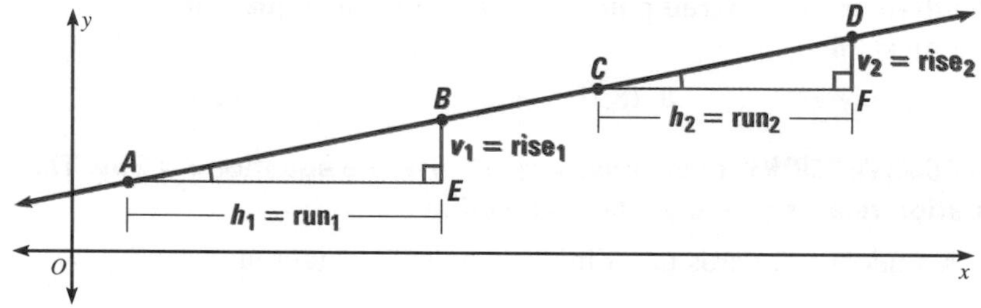

Here's How

$\triangle ABE \sim \triangle CDF$	**Angle-angle similarity postulate**
$\frac{v_1}{v_2} = \frac{h_1}{h_2}$	**Definition of similar triangles**
$v_1 \cdot h_2 = h_1 \cdot v_2$	**Use cross products property.**
$\frac{v_1 \cdot h_2}{h_1 \cdot h_2} = \frac{h_1 \cdot v_2}{h_1 \cdot h_2}$	**Divide each side by $h_1 \cdot h_2$.**
$\frac{\boldsymbol{v_1}}{\boldsymbol{h_1}} = \frac{\boldsymbol{v_2}}{\boldsymbol{h_2}}$	**Simplify.**

Since $\frac{\text{rise}_1}{\text{run}_1} = \frac{\text{rise}_2}{\text{run}_2}$, you can use any two points on the line to calculate its slope.

Student Help

▶ STUDY TIP
In the diagram from Sample 1, notice that $\overline{AE}$ and $\overline{CF}$ are horizontal, so they're parallel. $\angle A$ and $\angle C$ are corresponding angles so $\angle A \cong \angle C$. In addition, $\angle E \cong \angle F$ because they're both right angles. So, $\triangle ABE \sim \triangle CDF$ by AA similarity.

Try These

Draw a line with the given rise and run and calculate its slope.
1–4. See margin.

1. rise = 2; run = 4 **2.** rise = 5; run = 5 **3.** rise = 1; run = 3

4. If a line slopes *downward*, what can you say about the rise and run?

4. They have opposite signs.

11.5 The Slope of a Line

In this lesson you'll:

- Graph linear functions, noting that the vertical change per unit of horizontal change is always the same and is called the slope of a line. (AF 3.3)
- Fit a line to a plot and understand that the slope of the line equals the ratio of the quantities. (AF 3.4)

Goal 1 FINDING THE SLOPE OF A LINE

As you saw in Developing Concepts 11.5, page 582, the **slope** of a nonvertical line is the ratio of the *rise* (change in *y*) to the *run* (change in *x*) between any two points on the line.

SLOPE OF A LINE

The slope *m* of the nonvertical line passing through the points (x_1, y_1) and (x_2, y_2) is:

$$m = \frac{\text{rise}}{\text{run}} = \frac{y_2 - y_1}{x_2 - x_1}$$

The slope of a line does not depend on which two points from the line are used in the formula.

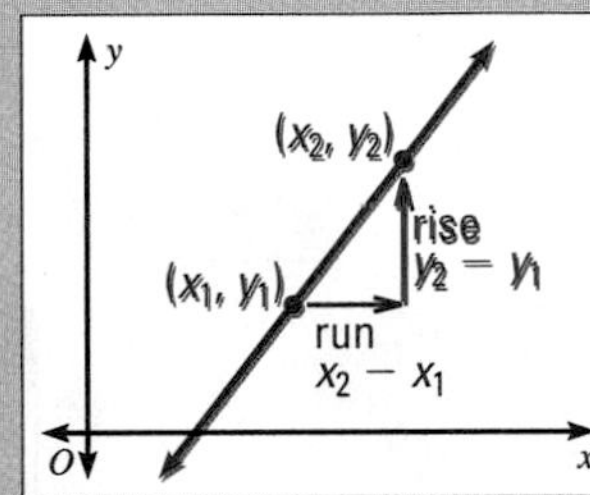

Student Help

STUDY TIP
When you are using the formula for slope, it doesn't matter which point you treat as (x_1, y_1). For instance, in part (a) of Example 1, you can let (3, 5) be (x_1, y_1) and (1, 2) be (x_2, y_2). Then you can write:
$m = \frac{2-5}{1-3} = \frac{-3}{-2} = \frac{3}{2}$

EXAMPLE 1 Finding the Slope of a Line

a. To find the slope of the line through (1, 2) and (3, 5), let (1, 2) be (x_1, y_1), and let (3, 5) be (x_2, y_2). Then the slope is:

$$m = \frac{\text{rise}}{\text{run}} = \frac{y_2 - y_1}{x_2 - x_1} = \frac{5-2}{3-1} = \frac{3}{2}$$

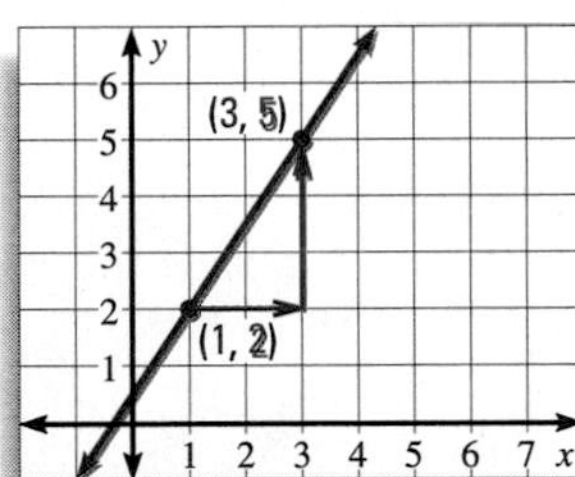

b. To find the slope of the line through (−6, 5) and (−3, 1), let (−6, 5) be (x_1, y_1), and let (−3, 1) be (x_2, y_2). Then the slope is:

$$m = \frac{\text{rise}}{\text{run}} = \frac{y_2 - y_1}{x_2 - x_1} = \frac{1-5}{-3-(-6)} = \frac{-4}{3}, \text{ or } -\frac{4}{3}$$

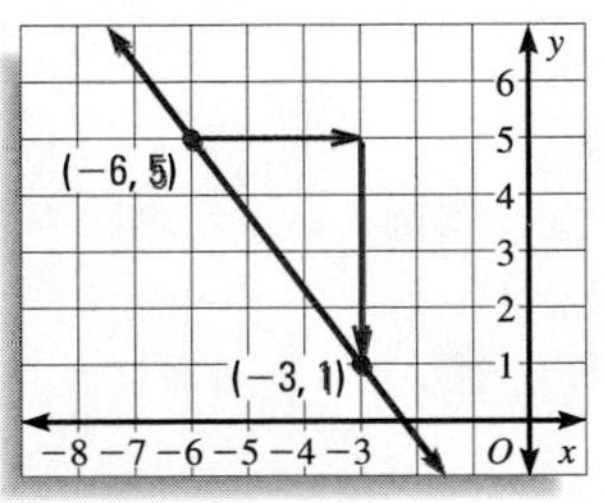

1 Plan

Pacing

Suggested Number of Days

Transitional: 2 days
Average: 2 days
Advanced: 2 days
Block Schedule: 1 block

Teaching Resources

Blacklines
(See page 560B.)

Transparencies
- Warm-Up Exercises
- Teacher Time-Savers
- English/Spanish Problem Solving
- Answers

Technology
- Electronic Teacher Tools
- Test and Practice Generator

2 Teach

Math Reasoning

For Mathematical Background Notes on mathematical reasoning related to this lesson, please refer to pages 560E and 560F in this Teacher's Edition.

Extra Example 1
See next page.

California Standards and Assessment

CA Standards: AF 3.3, AF 3.4
CA Key Concepts Book: pp. S54–S56, S61–S63

Extra Example 1

a. Find the slope of a line through (3, −4) and (−2, 1). $m = -1$

b. Find the slope of a line through (2, 5) and (0, −1). $m = 3$

Extra Example 2

Which is steeper: a graph with a slope of $\frac{1}{2}$ or a graph with a slope of $\frac{1}{3}$? **The graph with a slope of $\frac{1}{2}$ is steeper, since $\frac{1}{2} > \frac{1}{3}$.**

Extra Example 3

Two cars are traveling along a highway. The graph shows the distance d that each car travels in t hours. Calculate the slope of each line to find the average rate at which each car is traveling.

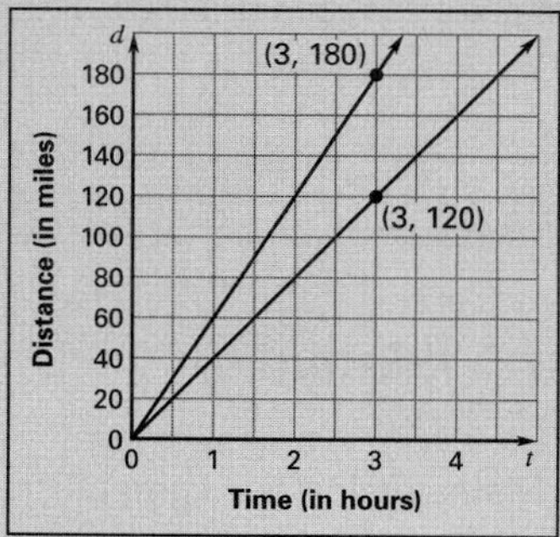

60 mi/h and 40 mi/h

Math Reasoning

Note that in *comparing* rates, as in Example 3, the choice of scale on the axis is not significant. But a change of scale on one axis might change the visual perception of the magnitude of each rate.

Teaching Tip

Emphasize that the subscripts used in the variables x_1, x_2, y_1, and y_2 are there to indicate the coordinates of two specific points.

Imagine that you are walking *to the right* on a line. A positive slope means that you are walking uphill, a negative slope means that you are walking downhill, and a zero slope means that you are walking on level ground. In Exercise 24, you will show that the slope of a vertical line is *undefined*.

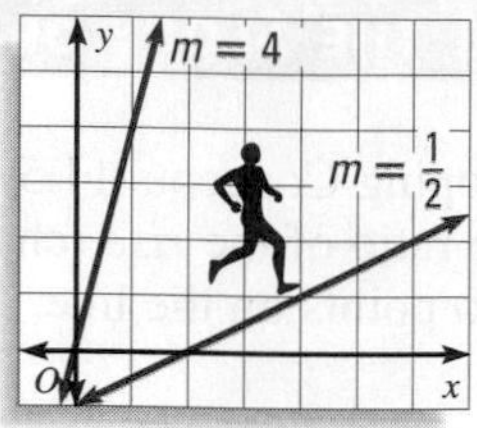

Positive slope

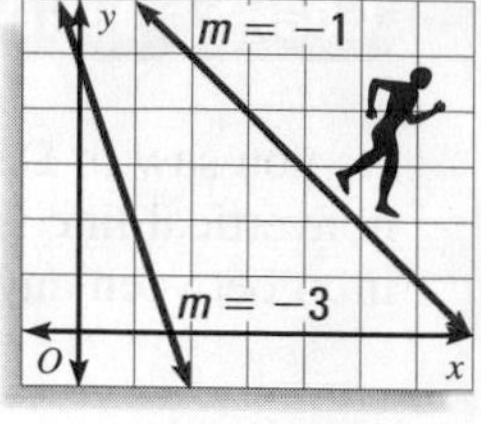

Negative slope

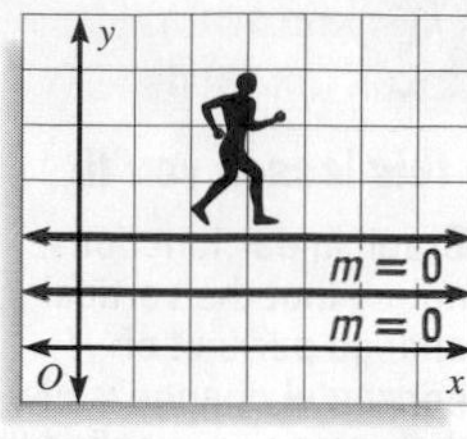

Zero slope

Goal 2 COMPARING SLOPES

EXAMPLE 2 Comparing Slopes

Compare the slopes of the lines in each of the first two graphs at the top of the page.

In the first graph, a line with a slope of **4** is steeper, or closer to vertical, than a line with a slope of $\mathbf{\frac{1}{2}}$.

Similarly, as shown in the second graph, a line with a slope of **−3** is steeper than a line with a slope of **−1**.

In real-life situations, the slope of a graph can represent a rate.

EXAMPLE 3 Interpreting Slope as a Rate

You are walking at a steady rate. Your friend is jogging at a steady rate. The graph shows the distance that each of you travels in t seconds.

Calculate the slope of each line to find the rate at which each of you is traveling.

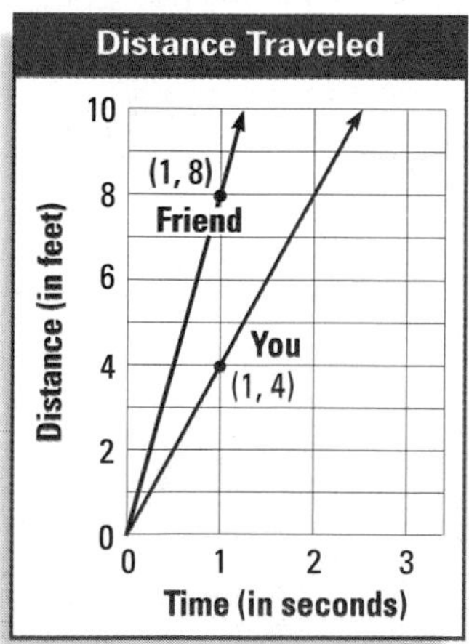

Solution

$$\text{Your rate} = \frac{4 \text{ ft} - 0 \text{ ft}}{1 \text{ sec} - 0 \text{ sec}} = 4 \text{ ft/sec}$$

$$\text{Friend's rate} = \frac{8 \text{ ft} - 0 \text{ ft}}{1 \text{ sec} - 0 \text{ sec}} = 8 \text{ ft/sec}$$

Student Help

▶ MORE EXAMPLES

More examples are available at www.mcdougallittell.com

EXAMPLE 4 Interpreting a Graph

Water is poured at a constant rate into each of the beakers shown. Tell which graph represents which beaker. Explain your reasoning. (Assume the time and height scales on the two graphs are the same.)

Graph I

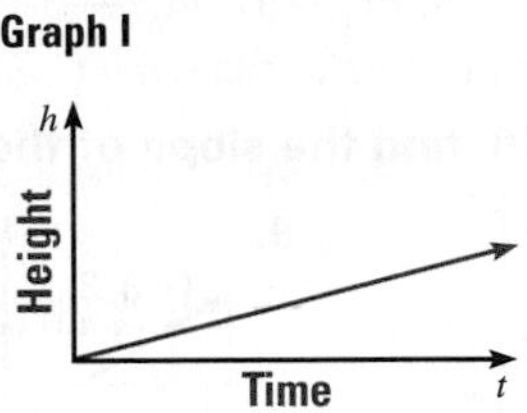

Graph II

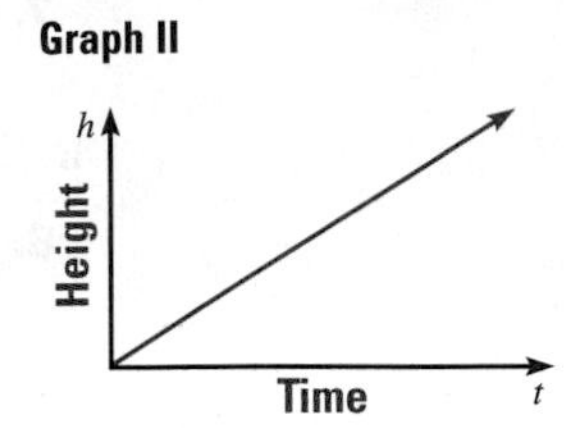

Solution

The rate at which the water height in each beaker rises is represented by the expression $\frac{h}{t}$ where h is the water height after t seconds. For Graph I and Graph II, this expression is also the slope of the graph.

The radius of Beaker A is less than the radius of Beaker B, so the water rises faster in Beaker A than in Beaker B.

Because Graph II is steeper than Graph I, the slope of Graph II is greater than the slope of Graph I. So, Graph II represents Beaker A. Graph I represents Beaker B.

11.5 Exercises

Guided Practice

In Exercises 1–3, find the slope of the line.

1. 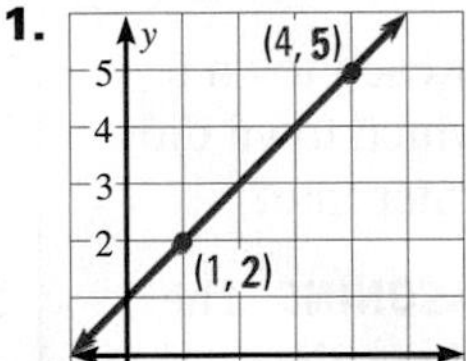

1

2. 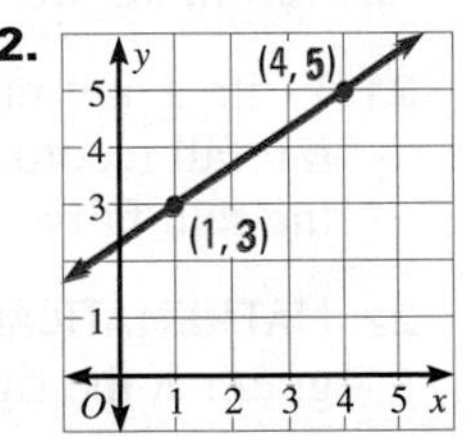

$\frac{2}{3}$

3. 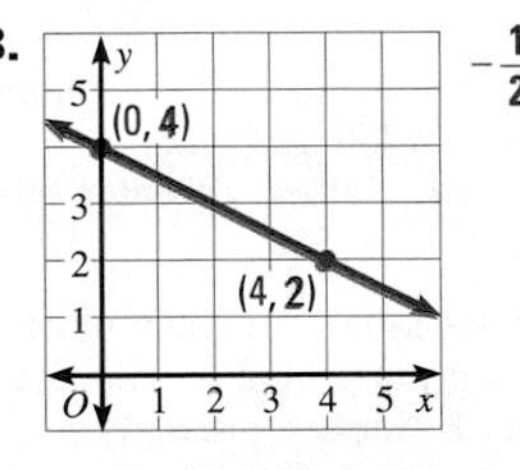

$-\frac{1}{2}$

4. The slope of line a is 3, and the slope of line b is 4. Which line is steeper? Explain. **See margin.**

5. You are walking at a steady rate. You are given a graph that shows the distance you travel in t seconds. Describe how to use the graph to find the rate at which you are walking. **See margin.**

4. ***b*; a line with a slope of 4 has a rise of 4 to a run of 1. A line with a slope of 3 has a rise of 3 to a run of 1. The line that has the greater rise for the same run is steeper.**

5. The rate is the slope of the line. To compute it, select two points on the line. Find the ratio of the difference of the two *y*-values and the difference of the two *x*-values.

Extra Example 4

Two women are out hiking in the mountains. The first woman hikes faster than the second, so that her change in elevation is greater than the second woman's. Tell which graph represents which hiker.

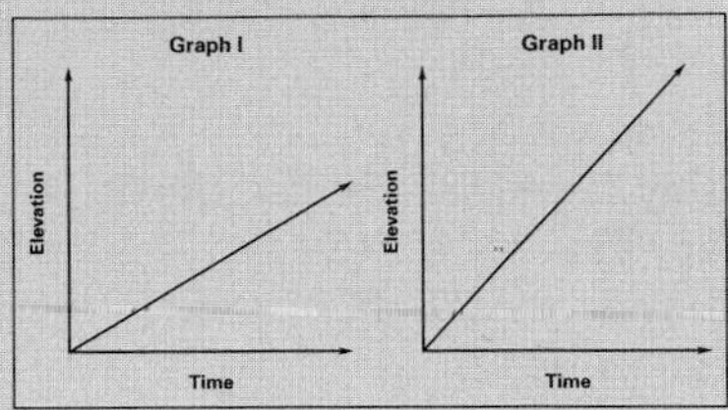

Because the slope of Graph II is greater than the slope of Graph I, Graph II represents the first, faster hiker. Graph I represents the second hiker.

Math Reasoning

Have students discuss why it is essential in Example 4 that the time and height scales on the two graphs be the same.

Concept Check

Explain what happens if you try to find the slope of a vertical line. **The run is zero, so the denominator in the slope formula is zero. Since division by zero is not defined, neither is the slope of a vertical line.**

3 Apply

Assignment Guide

TRANSITIONAL

Day 1: pp. 586–587 Exs. 8–15, 28–43

Day 2: pp. 586–587 Exs. 6–7, 20–23, 26–27

AVERAGE

Day 1: pp. 586–587 Exs. 8–19, 28–43

Day 2: pp. 586–587 Exs. 6–7, 20–24, 26–27

ADVANCED

Day 1: pp. 586–587 Exs. 8–19, 28–43; EC: TE p. 560D*

Day 2: pp. 586–587 Exs. 6–7, 20–24, 25*, 26–27

BLOCK SCHEDULE

pp. 586–587 Exs. 6–24, 26–43

Extra Practice

- Student Edition, pp. 710–711
- Chapter 11 Resource Book, p. 42

Homework Check

To quickly check student understanding of key concepts, go over the following exercises:

Transitional: 8, 10, 14, 20, 22
Average: 10, 12, 16, 20, 22
Advanced: 10, 16, 18, 20, 22

11.

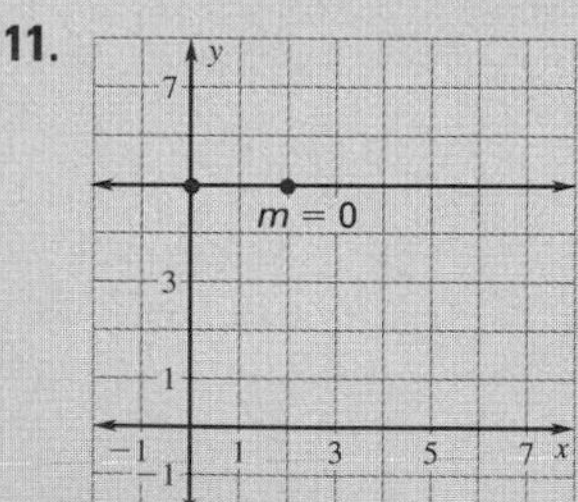

12–19. See Additional Answers beginning on page AA1.

Practice and Problem Solving

Student Help

▶**MORE PRACTICE** Extra practice to help you master skills is on page 711.

In Exercises 6 and 7, the slopes of four lines are listed. Determine which of the lines is the steepest. Justify your answer.

6. $m_1 = -1, m_2 = -6, m_3 = -4, m_4 = -\frac{17}{4}$

m_2; it has a greater rise for the same run than the other slopes.

7. $m_1 = \frac{5}{2}, m_2 = 3, m_3 = 0, m_4 = 5$

m_4; it has a greater rise for the same run than the other slopes.

In Exercises 8–10, find the slope of the line.

8.

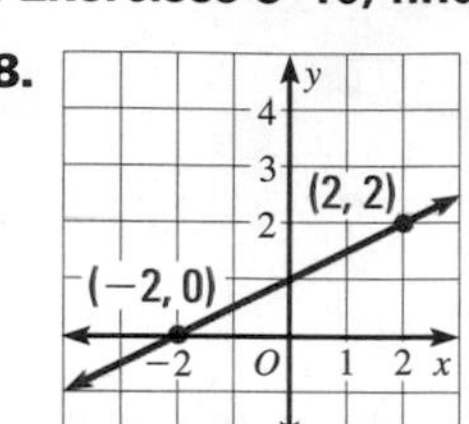

$\frac{1}{2}$

9.

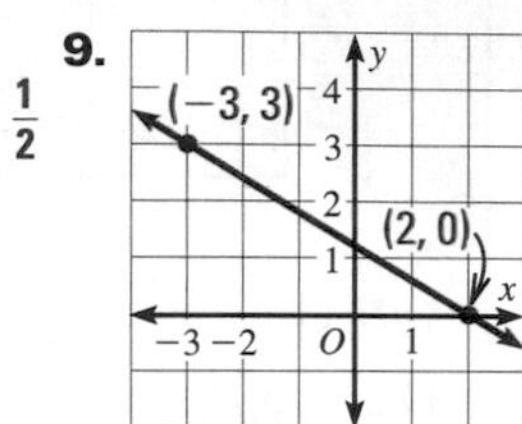

$-\frac{3}{5}$

10.

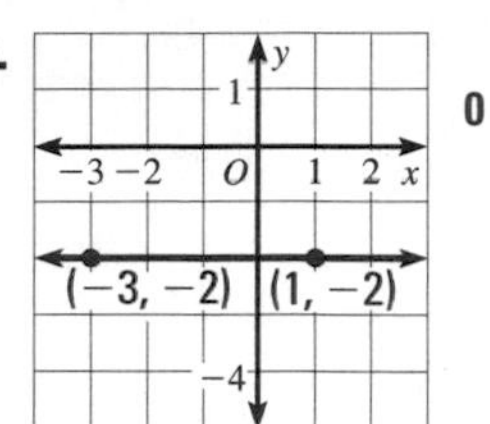

0

In Exercises 11–19, plot the points. Then find the slope of the line through the points. 11–19. See margin.

11. (2, 5), (0, 5)
12. (3, 4), (4, 3)
13. (0, −2), (3, 7)
14. (0, 0), (−5, 0)
15. (4, −2), (−1, −5)
16. (6, 3), (−3, 4)
17. (1, −2), (−1, −6)
18. (0, −1), (1, −7)
19. (2, 3), (−2, 1)

20. ROADS A road rises 15 feet vertically for every 70 feet it runs horizontally. A second road rises 12 feet for every 60 feet it runs horizontally. Which road is steeper? Explain. See margin.

20. The road with the rise of 15 feet for a run of 70 feet is steeper than the road with the rise of 12 feet for a run of 60 feet. The first road has a slope of 0.21. The second road has a slope of 0.20. Because 0.21 is larger than 0.2, the first road is steeper.

RECORD RAINFALL In Exercises 21 and 22, use the following information. On July 4, 1956, 3.1 centimeters of rain fell in 1 minute in the town of Unionville, Maryland. On June 22, 1947, 30.5 centimeters of rain fell in 42 minutes in Holt, Missouri. 21–22. See margin.

21. Write a unit rate for each town's rainfall record. In which town did the rain fall at a greater rate?

22. MATHEMATICAL REASONING The graph at the right shows the amount of rain that would have fallen if the rain had continued to fall for an hour in each town. Which line represents which town? Explain your reasoning.

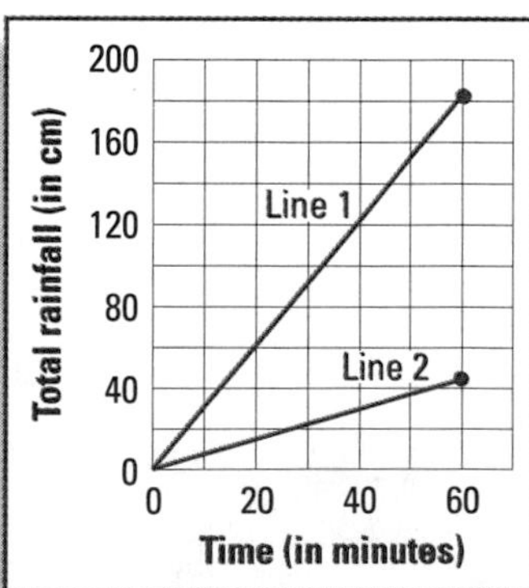

21. Unionville, MD: 3.1 cm/min; Holt, MO: 0.7 cm/min; The rain fell at a greater rate in Unionville, MD.

22. Because the slope of line 1 is greater than the slope of line 2, line 1 represents a greater rate. So, line 1 represents Unionville, MD.

23. **WATER FLOW RATES** Suppose water flows into the barrel shown at each of the three rates given below. For each rate, sketch a graph showing the volume V of the water in the barrel after t minutes. Draw the three graphs in the same coordinate plane. **See margin.**

a. 3 gallons per minute

b. 5 gallons per minute

c. 10 gallons per minute

24. **MATHEMATICAL REASONING** Draw a vertical line through the point (1, 3) on a coordinate plane. Identify another point on the line and find the ratio of the rise to the run. Use your results to explain why the slope of a vertical line is undefined. **See margin.**

25. **CHALLENGE** Determine whether the points $(0, -1)$, $\left(\frac{4}{3}, 3\right)$, and $\left(-\frac{1}{3}, -\frac{5}{3}\right)$ lie on a line. Explain your reasoning. **See margin.**

24. ***Sample answer*: (1, 2). The x-coordinates of the two points are both one. So the slope of the line will be a value divided by zero, which is undefined.**

25. No: the line that passes through (0, −1) and $\left(\frac{4}{3}, 3\right)$ has slope 3. Since the line passes through (0, −1) and $\left(-\frac{1}{3}, -\frac{5}{3}\right)$ has slope 2, the three points do not lie on the same line.

Multiple-Choice Practice

26. What is the slope of the line shown? **A**

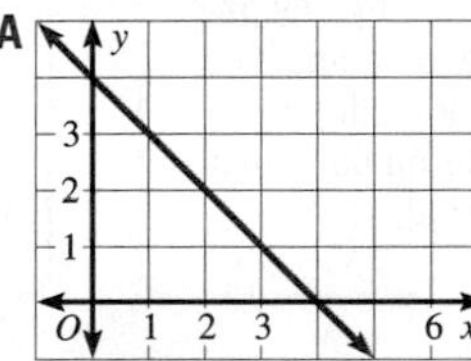

Ⓐ −1　　Ⓑ 1

Ⓒ 2　　Ⓓ 4

27. What is the slope of the line through the points (−3, 4) and (2, −3)? **F**

Ⓕ $-\frac{7}{5}$　　Ⓖ −1　　Ⓗ $-\frac{5}{7}$　　Ⓙ $\frac{1}{5}$

Mixed Review

Rewrite the decimal as a simplified fraction. *(5.5)*

28. 0.8 $\frac{4}{5}$　　**29.** 0.35 $\frac{7}{20}$　　**30.** $0.\overline{3}$ $\frac{1}{3}$　　**31.** $0.\overline{4}$ $\frac{4}{9}$

Rewrite the fraction as a decimal. *(5.5)*

32. $\frac{1}{5}$ 0.2　　**33.** $\frac{3}{8}$ 0.375　　**34.** $\frac{7}{9}$ $0.\overline{7}$　　**35.** $\frac{5}{11}$ $0.\overline{45}$

Perform the indicated operation. *(6.1–6.5)*

36. $\frac{1}{5} + \frac{2}{5}$ $\frac{3}{5}$　　**37.** $\frac{4}{9} + \frac{1}{3}$ $\frac{7}{9}$　　**38.** $\frac{4}{9} - \frac{2}{9}$ $\frac{2}{9}$　　**39.** $\frac{4}{5} - \frac{3}{4}$ $\frac{1}{20}$

40. $\frac{3}{8} \times \frac{1}{2}$ $\frac{3}{16}$　　**41.** $\frac{4}{7} \times \frac{2}{3}$ $\frac{8}{21}$　　**42.** $\frac{3}{10} \div \frac{9}{2}$ $\frac{1}{15}$　　**43.** $\frac{7}{3} \div \frac{3}{7}$ $\frac{49}{9}$

4 Assess

Assessment Resources

- Assessment Book (Formal Assessment and Alternative Assessment)
- Test and Practice Generator

Mini-Quiz

Find the slope of the line through the points. If you were walking from left to right along this line, would you be walking *uphill, downhill,* or *on level ground*?

1. (3, −4), (−1, 2) **$-\frac{3}{2}$; downhill**
2. (4, −3), (6, −3) **0; on level ground**
3. One hiker rises 100 feet in elevation for every 8 minutes she hikes. Another hiker rises 120 feet in elevation for every 10 minutes she hikes. Sketch a graph showing each hiker's elevation E after t minutes.

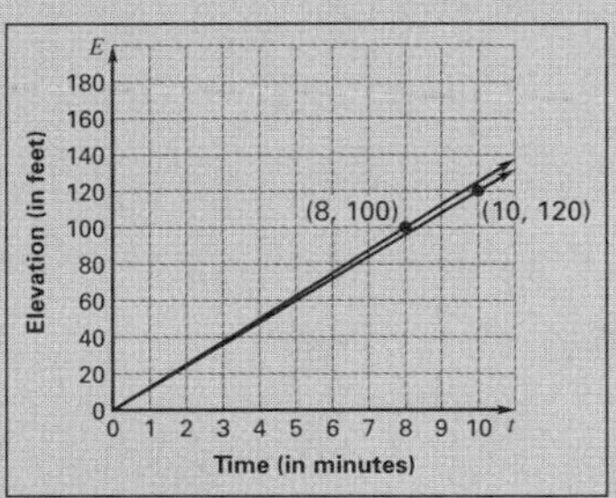

4. Which hiker in Question 3 hikes at a faster rate? **the hiker who climbs 100 ft in 8 min**

23.

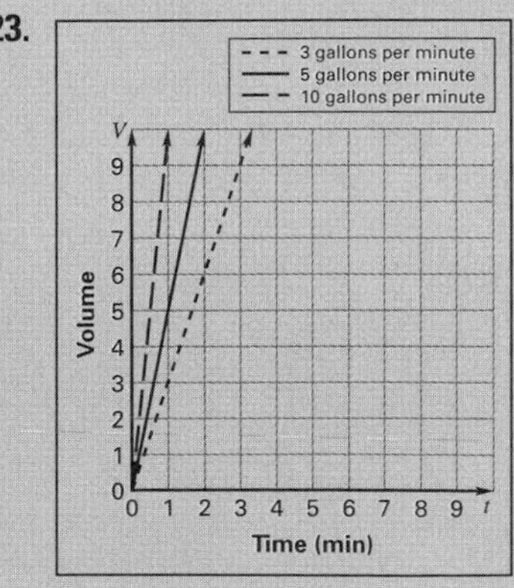

1 Planning the Activity

Purpose and Materials

See the margin of the student page.

▶ LINK TO LESSON

Students apply the results of this activity to Examples 1–4 of Lesson 11.6.

Math Reasoning

Students analyze problems by observing patterns and develop generalizations based on their observations.

2 Managing the Activity

Classroom Management

Students should work with a partner or in a group so that they can compare their results.

3 Closing the Activity

★ KEY DISCOVERY

If an equation is written in the form $y = mx + b$, the slope of the line, m, can be read directly from the equation.

Activity Assessment

Use Exercises 1–6 to assess student understanding.

1–8. See Additional Answers beginning on page AA1.

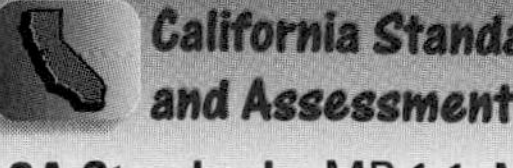

California Standards and Assessment

CA Standards: MR 1.1, MR 3.3

CA Key Concepts Book: pp. S57–S60

REASONING 11.6

DEVELOPING CONCEPTS

The Equation $y = mx + b$

For use with Lesson 11.6

California Standards

- Analyze problems by observing patterns. (MR 1.1)
- Develop generalizations of the results obtained. (MR 3.3)

MATERIALS:

- Pencil and paper

You can calculate the slope of several lines to find out how slope relates to the equation of a line.

SAMPLE 1 Comparing Slopes of Lines

Make a table of values and calculate the slope of each line. Then compare the slope with the equation of the line. Describe the pattern.

a. $y = 2x + 3$ **b.** $y = -3x + 1$ **c.** $y = \frac{1}{2}x - 5$

Here's How

a. $y = 2x + 3$

x	y
0	3
1	5

slope $= \frac{5-3}{1-0} = 2$

b. $y = -3x + 1$

x	y
0	1
1	−2

slope $= \frac{-2-1}{1-0} = -3$

c. $y = \frac{1}{2}x - 5$

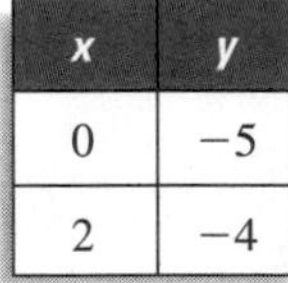

x	y
0	−5
2	−4

slope $= \frac{-4-(-5)}{2-0} = \frac{1}{2}$

In each case, the slope is the same as the coefficient of x in the equation of the line.

Student Help

▶ STUDY TIP
Because slope is determined by any pair of points on a line, you need to include only two ordered pairs in a table of values.

Sample 1 suggests that when an equation is written in the form $y = mx + b$, the value of m is the slope of the line.

Try These

In Exercises 1–6, make a table of values and calculate the slope of the line whose equation is given. Compare the slope with the equation of the line. **1–8. See margin.**

1. $y = x + 2$ **2.** $y = 3x - 5$ **3.** $y = -2x + 7$

4. $y = \frac{1}{3}x - 1$ **5.** $y = -x + \frac{3}{4}$ **6.** $y = \frac{5}{8}x - \frac{1}{2}$

7. Repeat Exercises 1–6, this time finding the y-intercept of the line and comparing it with the equation of the line. What do you notice?

8. MATHEMATICAL REASONING Complete the statement below and then use it to find both the slope and y-intercept of the line with equation $y = mx + b$. What do your results show?

The line with equation $y = mx + b$ passes through the points $(0, \underline{?})$ and $(1, \underline{?})$.

11.6 The Slope-Intercept Form

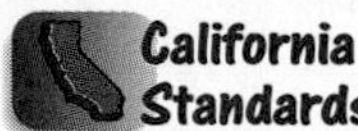

California Standards

In this lesson you'll:

- Represent quantitative relationships graphically and interpret the meaning of a specific part of a graph in the situation represented by the graph. (AF 1.5)
- Graph linear functions, noting that the vertical change per unit of horizontal change is always the same and know that the ratio is called the slope of a graph. (AF 3.3)

Goal 1 Using the Slope-Intercept Form

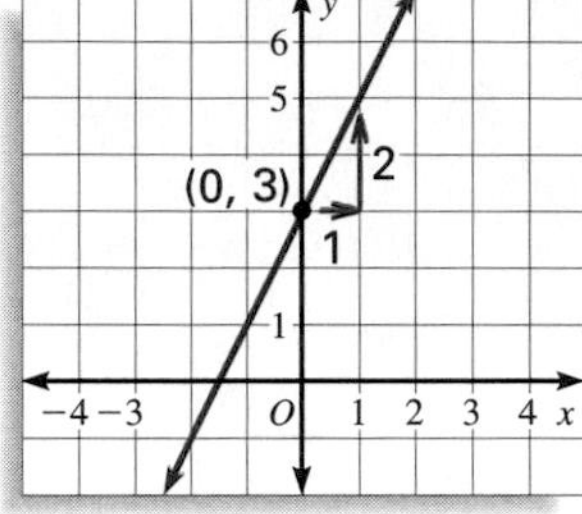

As you learned in Developing Concepts 11.6, page 588, there is a quick way to find the slope of a line and its y-intercept provided that its equation is in the proper form. The line given by $y = 2x + 3$, shown at the right, has a slope of 2 and a y-intercept of 3.

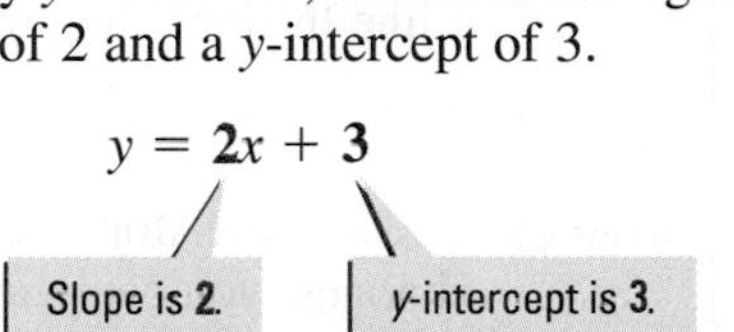

In general, a linear equation $y = mx + b$ is said to be in **slope-intercept form** because m is the slope of the line and b is the y-intercept.

EXAMPLE 1 Using the Slope-Intercept Form

Find the slope and y-intercept of the graph of $y = x - 4$, shown at the right.

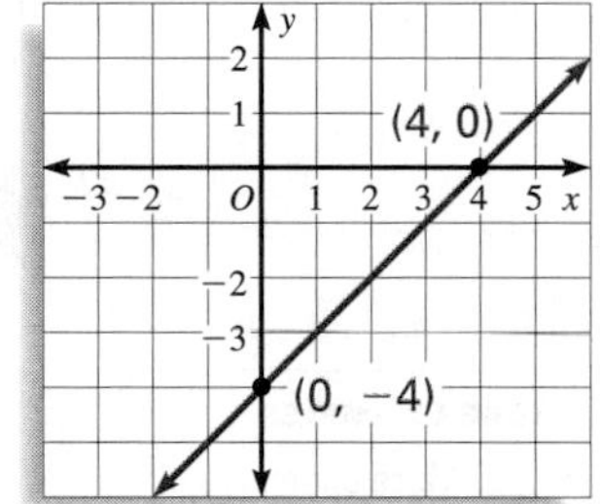

Solution

The equation $y = x - 4$ can be rewritten as $y = \mathbf{1}x + (\mathbf{-4})$.

ANSWER ▶ The line has a slope of **1** and a y-intercept of **−4**.

CHECK ✓ The line crosses the y-axis at $(0, -4)$, so the y-intercept is -4. Use the two points labeled on the graph to check the slope.

$$m = \frac{0 - (-4)}{4 - 0} = \frac{4}{4} = 1 \checkmark$$

Student Help

▶ **STUDY TIP**
Remember that the identity property of multiplication states that $1 \cdot a = a$.

EXAMPLE 2 Writing Equations in Slope-Intercept Form

	EQUATION	SLOPE-INTERCEPT FORM	SLOPE	Y-INTERCEPT
a.	$y = -x + 2$	$y = (-1)x + 2$	$m = -1$	2
b.	$y = \frac{x + 5}{2}$	$y = \frac{1}{2}x + \frac{5}{2}$	$m = \frac{1}{2}$	$\frac{5}{2}$
c.	$y = 7$	$y = 0x + 7$	$m = 0$	7

1 Plan

Pacing

Suggested Number of Days

Transitional: 1 day
Average: 1 day
Advanced: 1 day
Block Schedule: 0.5 block with 11.7

Teaching Resources

Blacklines
(See page 560B.)

Transparencies
- Warm-Up Exercises
- Teacher Time-Savers
- English/Spanish Problem Solving
- Answers

Technology
- Electronic Teacher Tools
- Test and Practice Generator

2 Teach

Math Reasoning

For Mathematical Background Notes on mathematical reasoning related to this lesson, please refer to pages 560E and 560F in this Teacher's Edition.

Extra Examples 1 and 2
See next page.

California Standards and Assessment

CA Standards: AF 1.5, AF 3.3
CA Key Concepts Book: pp. S57–S60, S61–S63

Extra Example 1

Find the slope and y-intercept of the graph of $y = 2x + 3$, shown below.

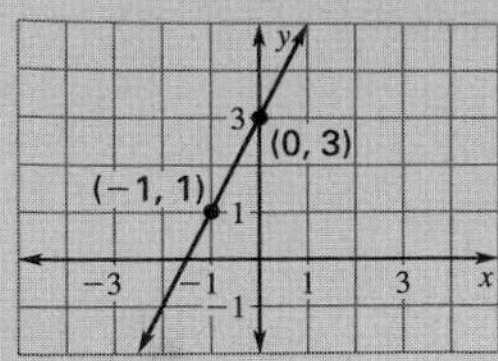

slope: 2; y-intercept: 3

Extra Example 2

Find the slope and y-intercept.

a. $y = -4x + 7$ **The slope is −4 and the y-intercept is 7.**

b. $y = 5x$ **The slope is 5 and the y-intercept is 0.**

Extra Example 3

Sketch a quick graph of $y = -\frac{1}{3}x + 4$. **The slope is $-\frac{1}{3}$ and the y-intercept is 4.**

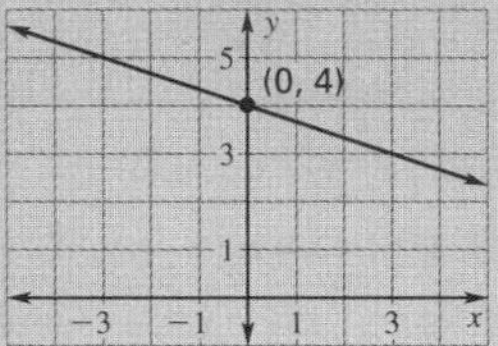

Extra Example 4

Sketch a quick graph of $x + 2y = 6$. **The slope-intercept form of the equation is $y = -\frac{1}{2}x + 3$, so the slope is $-\frac{1}{2}$ and the y-intercept is 3.**

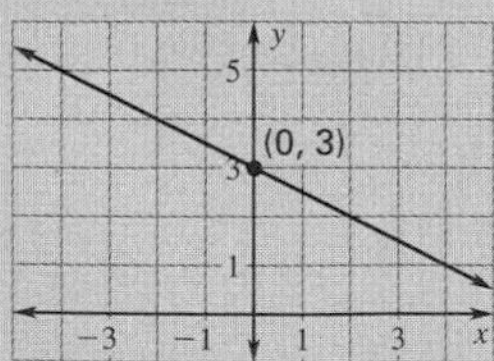

Concept Check

Explain how you would do a quick sketch of the graph of a linear equation. ***Sample answer:*** **Rewrite the equation in slope-intercept form and identify the slope and y-intercept. Plot the intercept and then plot another point by using the rise and run indicated by the slope. Draw a line through the two points.**

Goal 2 Sketching Quick Graphs

EXAMPLE 3 Sketching a Quick Graph

To sketch a quick graph of $y = \frac{1}{2}x + 2$, follow these steps.

STEP 1 The y-intercept is 2, so plot the point (0, 2).

STEP 2 The slope is $\frac{1}{2}$, so plot a second point by moving to the **right 2 units** and **up 1 unit**. Draw a line through the points.

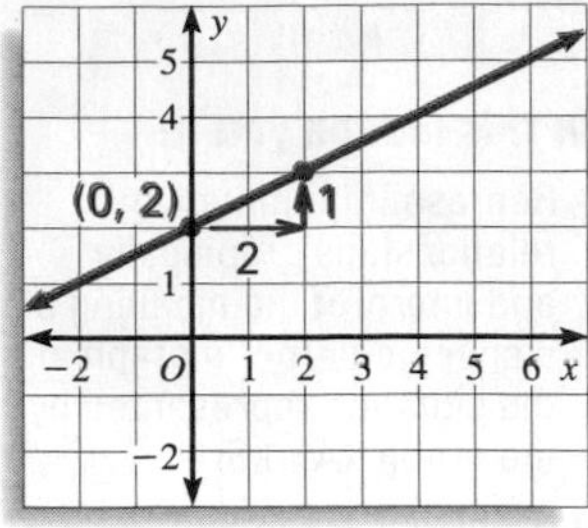

STEP 3 Because the slope of a line never changes, you can continue to plot points to check the accuracy of your graph. To plot each new point, move **right 2 units** and **up 1 unit**.

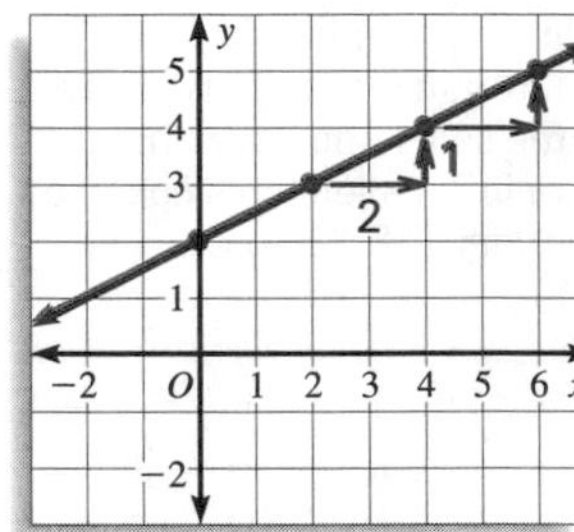

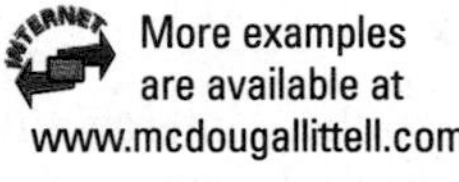

Student Help
MORE EXAMPLES
More examples are available at www.mcdougallittell.com

EXAMPLE 4 Sketching a Quick Graph

Sketch a quick graph of $2x + y = 4$.

Solution

To sketch a quick graph of $2x + y = 4$, write the equation in slope-intercept form. Begin by solving the equation for y.

$2x + y = 4$	Write original equation.
$y = 4 - 2x$	Subtract $2x$ from each side.
$y = -2x + 4$	Rewrite in slope-intercept form.

With the equation in slope-intercept form, you can see that the slope is −2 and the y-intercept is 4.

Since the y-intercept is 4, plot the point (0, 4). The slope is −2, which equals $\frac{-2}{1}$. Plot a second point by moving to the **right 1 unit** and **down 2 units**. Draw a line through the points. You can check your line by plotting another point, as shown.

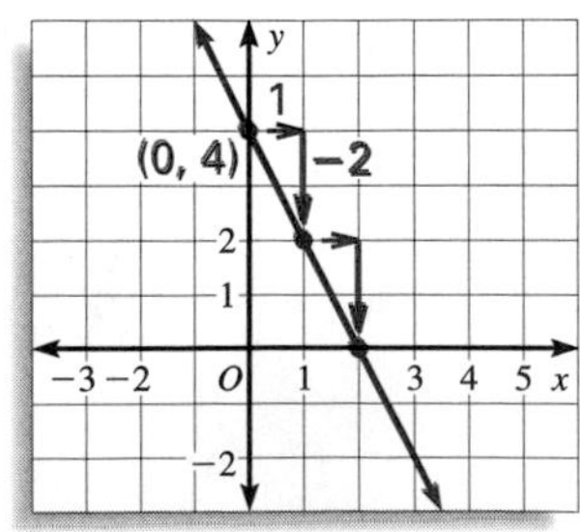

11.6 Exercises

Guided Practice

1. The equation $y = mx + b$, is called the slope-intercept form of the equation because the slope of the line is m, the coefficient of x, and the y-intercept is b, the constant.

1. Explain why the equation $y = mx + b$ is called the slope-intercept form of the equation of a line. **See margin.**

2. Show how to write the equation $3x + y = 5$ in slope-intercept form.
$y = (-3)x + 5$

3. Determine which equation listed below is an equation of the line shown at the right. **C**

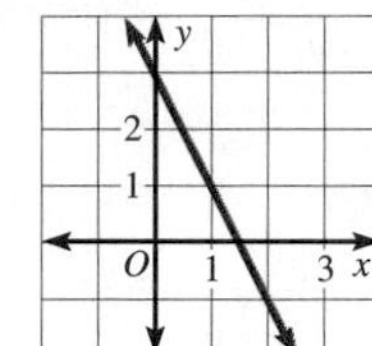

A. $y = 2x + 3$ **B.** $y = 2x - 3$

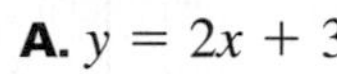

C. $y = -2x + 3$ **D.** $y = -2x - 3$

Find the slope and y-intercept of the line whose equation is given.

4. $y = -4x + 5$ **−4, 5** **5.** $y = \frac{1}{4}x - 1$ **$\frac{1}{4}$, −1** **6.** $-3x + y = 2$ **3, 2**

Practice and Problem Solving

In Exercises 7–9, match the equation with its graph.

A.

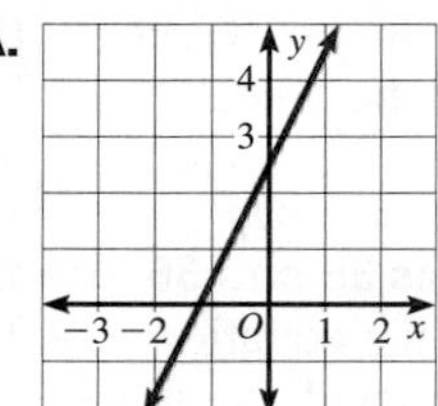

B.

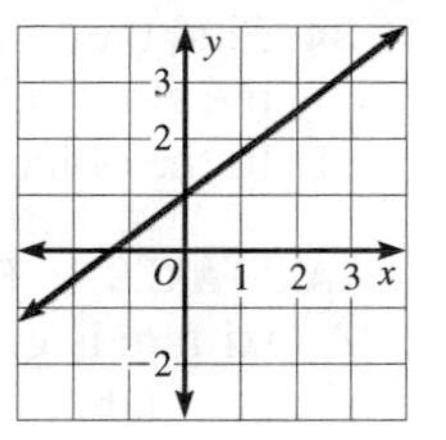

C.

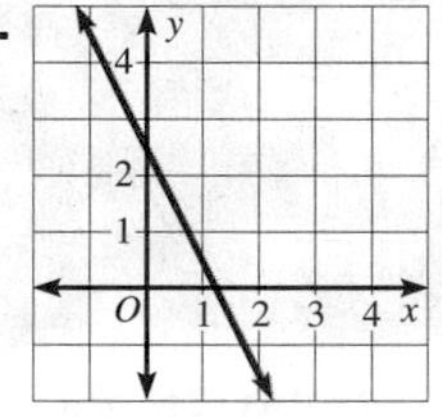

7. $y = -2x + \frac{5}{2}$ **C** **8.** $y = 2x + \frac{5}{2}$ **A** **9.** $y = \frac{3}{4}x + 1$ **B**

Student Help

▶MORE PRACTICE
Extra practice to help you master skills is on page 711.

Find the slope and y-intercept of the line whose equation is given.

10. $y = 7x + 9$ **7, 9** **11.** $\frac{x + 8}{4} = y$ **$\frac{1}{4}$, 2** **12.** $5x + y = 10$ **−5, 10**

13. $y = -6x$ **−6, 0** **14.** $x = 3y - 2$ **$\frac{1}{3}$, $\frac{2}{3}$** **15.** $y = 17$ **0, 17**

16. $x + y = 7$ **−1, 7** **17.** $x = 5$ **undefined, none** **18.** $y = 0 - 4x$ **−4, 0**

Sketch a quick graph of the line whose equation is given.
19–27. See margin.

19. $y = x - 3$ **20.** $y = -x + 3$ **21.** $y = -\frac{2}{3}x + 2$

22. $y = 3x$ **23.** $y - 4x = 5$ **24.** $y = -2$

25. $2x + y = 1$ **26.** $\frac{1}{5}y + x = -3$ **27.** $-2x + y = 3$

3 Apply

Assignment Guide

TRANSITIONAL
Day 1: pp. 591–592 Exs. 7–15, 19–24, 30–32, 35–36, 38–39

AVERAGE
Day 1: pp. 591–592 Exs. 7–15, 21–31, 33–34, 38–39

ADVANCED
Day 1: pp. 591–592 Exs. 7–15, 21–31, 33–34, 37*, 38–39

BLOCK SCHEDULE
pp. 591–592 Exs. 7–12, 16–18, 21–31, 33–34, 38–39 (with 11.7)

Extra Practice

- Student Edition, pp. 710–711
- Chapter 11 Resource Book, p. 51

Homework Check

To quickly check student understanding of key concepts, go over the following exercises:

Transitional: 10, 12, 20, 24, 36
Average: 10, 14, 26, 30, 34
Advanced: 10, 12, 26, 30, 34

Problem Solving

Exercises 10–27
Remind students that the equation should be written in slope-intercept form before identifying the slope and y-intercept.

19.

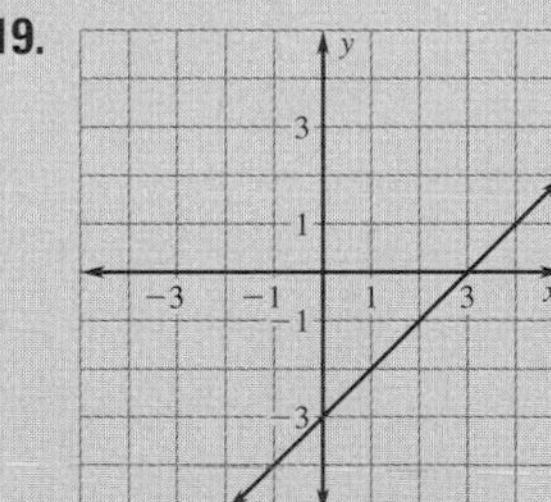

20–27. See Additional Answers beginning on page AA1.

Assess

Assessment Resources

- Assessment Book (Formal Assessment and Alternative Assessment)
- Test and Practice Generator

Mini-Quiz

Find the slope and y-intercept of the line.

1. $y = -2x + 3$ **slope: −2; y-intercept: 3**
2. $4x + y = -5$ **slope: −4; y-intercept: −5**
3. Explain how you would sketch a quick graph of $y = \frac{2}{3}x - 2$. **Since −2 is the y-intercept, plot the point (0, −2). Using the slope $\frac{2}{3}$, plot a second point by moving up 2 units and then right 3 units from the point (0, −2). Draw a line through the two points.**

Math Reasoning

Exercises 33–34 are based on the fact that the speed s of a falling object is governed by the equation $s = gt + s_0$, where t represents the time elapsed, s_0 is the initial speed, and g is the acceleration due to gravity.

33.

time, x (in seconds)	speed, y (in meters per second)
0	7.0
1	16.8
2	26.6
3	36.4
4	46.2

35. See Additional Answers beginning on page AA1.

30. $y = \left(\frac{-2}{3}\right)x + 1$

31. $y = \left(\frac{-5}{2}\right)x + 2$

32. $y = \left(\frac{2}{5}\right)x - 2$

Link to Science

ACCELERATION of a falling object is due to the force of gravity between the object and Earth. If air resistance is ignored, for every second an object is in free fall, its speed is increasing by 32 feet per second.

MATHEMATICAL REASONING Tell whether the statement is *true* or *false*. If false, tell what change would make it true.

28. The graph of $y - 2x = 5$ has a slope of -2 and a y-intercept of 5. **false; Change the value of −2 to 2 in the statement.**

29. The graph of $\frac{1}{4}x + y = 5$ has a slope of $-\frac{1}{4}$ and a y-intercept of 5. **true**

Write the equation of the line in slope-intercept form. **30–32. See margin.**

30.

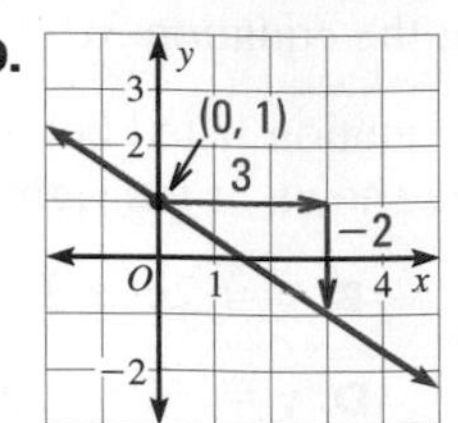

31.

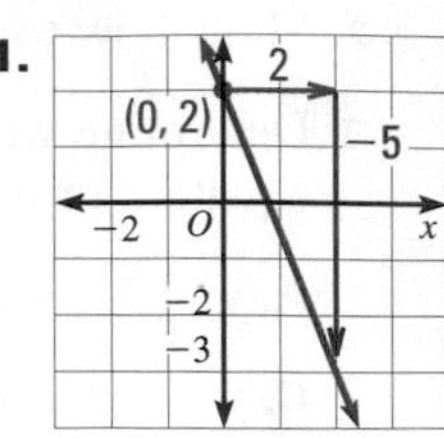

32.

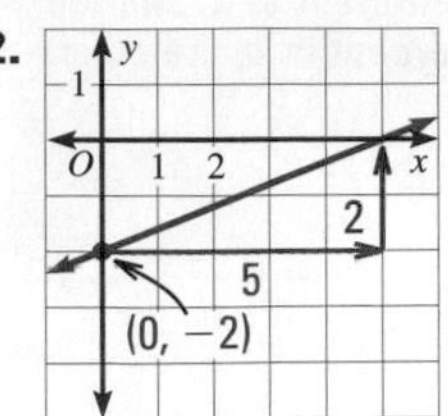

Science Link **In Exercises 33 and 34, use the following information.** An object is thrown straight down with an initial speed of 7 meters per second. The speed of the object is given by the equation $y = 9.8x + 7$ where y represents the speed (in meters per second) and x represents the time (in seconds) after the object is released.

33. Make a table showing the object's speed after 0, 1, 2, 3, and 4 seconds. How much does the speed increase every second? **See margin; The speed increases by 9.8 meters per second each second.**

34. Find the slope and the y-intercept of the line $y = 9.8x + 7$. How is the slope related to the object's speed? How is the y-intercept related to the object's speed? **$m = 9.8$; $b = 7$; The slope of the line is the increase in the speed of the object each second and the y-intercept is the initial speed of the object.**

TAXI FARES In Exercises 35 and 36, use the following information. A taxi fare is given by the equation $y = 2.5x + 1.25$ where y represents the total fare (in dollars) and x represents the distance traveled (in miles).

35. Make a table of values showing the fare after you ride 0, 1, 2, 3, 4, 5, and 6 miles. Plot the ordered pairs in the same coordinate plane. **See margin.**

36. Use your graph to find the slope and the y-intercept of the line through the plotted points. How are the slope and the y-intercept related to the taxi fare? **$m = 2.5$, $b = 1.25$; The slope of the line is the charge per mile and the y-intercept is the initial fare.**

37. CHALLENGE Two points on the line $y = mx + b$ are $(x_1, y_1) = (x_1, mx_1 + b)$ and $(x_2, y_2) = (x_2, mx_2 + b)$. Show that the slope of the line is m. **slope $= \frac{y_2 - y_1}{x_2 - x_1} = \frac{mx_2 + b - (mx_1 + b)}{x_2 - x_1} = \frac{mx_2 - mx_1}{x_2 - x_1} = \frac{m(x_2 - x_1)}{(x_2 - x_1)} = m$**

Multiple-Choice Practice

38. What is the y-intercept of the graph $8x - y = 5$? **B**

(A) −8 (B) −5 (C) 5 (D) 8

39. What is the slope of the graph of $-2x + y = 6$? **H**

(F) −2 (G) 1 (H) 2 (J) 6

11.7 Problem Solving with Linear Equations

California Standards

In this lesson you'll:

- Solve multistep problems involving rate or direct variation. (AF 4.2)
- Estimate unknown quantities graphically and solve for them by using algebraic techniques. (MR 2.3)

Goal 1 DEVELOPING LINEAR MODELS

In real-life situations modeled by the equation $y = mx + b$, the value of m can be a rate of change and the value of b can be an initial amount.

EXAMPLE 1 Writing Linear Models

You have raised \$20 for a shelter. You ask friends for pledges of \$5.

a. Write a linear equation that models the relationship between the number of pledges and the total amount you raise.

b. Find the total amount of money you will raise with 12 pledges.

Solution

a. Let x represent the number of pledges and let y represent the total amount raised. When $x = 0$, $y = 20$, so the value of b in $y = mx + b$ is 20. The money raised increases by \$5 for each additional pledge, so the value of m is 5. The relationship can be modeled by the equation $y = 5x + 20$.

b. Substitute 12 for x in the equation $y = 5x + 20$. So, $y = 5(12) + 20$ or $y = 80$. You will raise \$80 with 12 pledges.

Student Help

STUDY TIP
In Example 2, x stands for the number of years since 1990. Also, y stands for the population in thousands, so $y = 590$ represents 590,000.

EXAMPLE 2 Using a Scatter Plot

In the scatter plot, a line has been drawn to show the trend in the population data for Vermont. Estimate the population in 1996.

Vermont Population

Solution

First find the equation of the line. As shown in the graph, the y-intercept is 563. To find the slope, use the points (0, 563) and (4, 581).

$$m = \frac{581 - 563}{4 - 0} = \frac{18}{4} = 4.5$$

The equation of the line is $y = 4.5x + 563$. To estimate the population in 1996, substitute 6 for x.

$$y = 4.5(6) + 563 = 590$$

ANSWER ▶ The population of Vermont in 1996 was about 590,000.

1 Plan

Pacing

Suggested Number of Days

Transitional: 1 day
Average: 1 day
Advanced: 1 day
Block Schedule: 0.5 block with 11.6

Teaching Resources

Blacklines
(See page 560B.)

Transparencies
- Warm-Up Exercises
- Teacher Time-Savers
- English/Spanish Problem Solving
- Answers

Technology
- Electronic Teacher Tools
- Test and Practice Generator

2 Teach

Math Reasoning

For Mathematical Background Notes on mathematical reasoning related to this lesson, please refer to pages 560E and 560F in this Teacher's Edition.

Extra Examples 1 and 2
See next page.

California Standards and Assessment

CA Standards: AF 4.2, MR 2.3
CA Key Concepts Book: pp. S74–S76

Extra Example 1

A city has a population of 20,000 and is growing by 500 people every year.

a. Write a linear equation that models the relationship between the city's population and the number of years it continues to grow. **$y = 500x + 20{,}000$, where y is the population and x is the number of years.**

b. Find the total population after 6 years' growth. **23,000 people**

Extra Example 2

Refer to the scatter plot in Example 2. About what year did the population of Vermont reach 570,000? **1992**

Extra Example 3

Suppose y varies directly as x, and $y = 5$ when $x = -3$.

a. Write an equation relating y and x. **$y = -\frac{5}{3}x$**

b. Graph the equation.

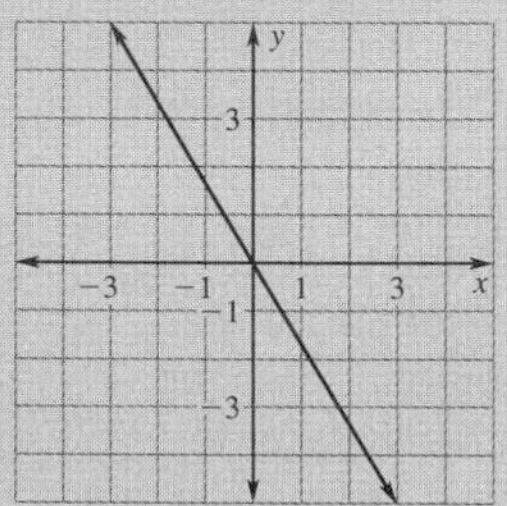

The graph passes through the origin and has a slope of $-\frac{5}{3}$.

c. Find the value of y when $x = 9$. **−15**

Math Reasoning

A line with y-intercept 0 passes through the origin. The equation $y = kx$ is in slope-intercept form, corresponding to a line with slope k passing through (0, 0). See Exercise 16 on page 596.

Goal 2 USING DIRECT VARIATION

A linear equation of the form $y = kx$, where k is a nonzero number, is called **direct variation**, and we say *y varies directly with x*. The number k is called the **constant of variation**.

PROPERTIES OF GRAPHS OF DIRECT VARIATIONS

- The graph of $y = kx$ is a line through the origin.
- The slope of the graph of $y = kx$ is k.

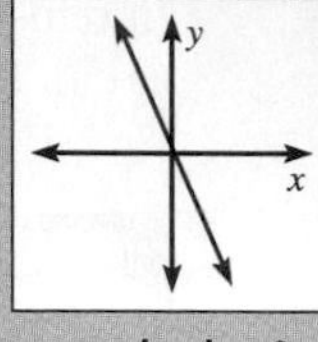

$y = kx,\ k < 0$

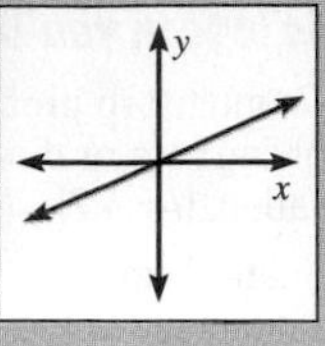

$y = kx,\ k > 0$

EXAMPLE 3 Writing a Direct Variation Equation

Suppose y varies directly with x, and $y = -2$ when $x = 4$.

a. Write an equation relating x and y.

b. Graph the equation.

c. Find the value of y when $x = -2$.

Solution

a. Because x and y vary directly, the equation that relates them has the form $y = kx$. Solve $y = kx$ for k.

$y = kx$ **Write model for direct variation.**

$-2 = k(4)$ **Substitute 4 for x and −2 for y.**

$-\frac{1}{2} = k$ **Divide each side by 4.**

An equation that relates x and y is $y = -\frac{1}{2}x$.

b. The graph passes through the origin. The slope of the graph is $-\frac{1}{2}$.

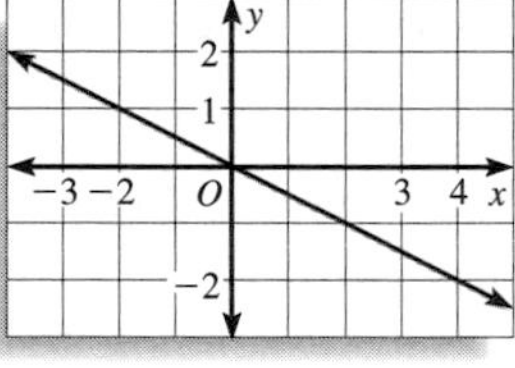

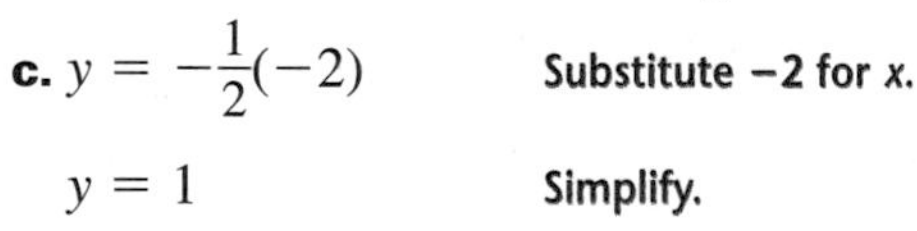

c. $y = -\frac{1}{2}(-2)$ **Substitute −2 for x.**

$y = 1$ **Simplify.**

When $x = -2$, $y = 1$.

The direct variation model $y = kx$ is equivalent to the equation $k = \frac{y}{x}$. This tells you that if y varies directly with x, the ratio of y to x is the same for any pair of corresponding x- and y-values.

Link to Science

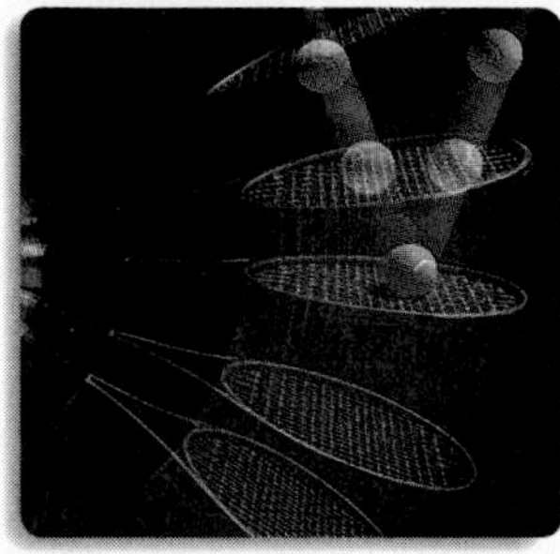

BOUNCING BALLS Balls that bounce high are good storers of energy. Conditions that affect bounce height include bounce surface, air temperature, and air pressure inside the ball.

EXAMPLE 4 Modeling Direct Variation

When a ball is dropped and hits the ground, it bounces up but not as high as the distance it fell. The results of dropping a ball from various heights are shown in the table.

Drop height, x (in inches)	20	30	40	50	60
Bounce height, y (in inches)	15	24	32.5	41	48.5

a. Write a model relating the drop height and the bounce height.

b. Estimate the bounce height if the drop height is 45 inches.

Solution

a. First find the ratio of y to x for each drop.

Drop height, x (in inches)	20	30	40	50	60
Bounce height, y (in inches)	15	24	32.5	41	48.5
Ratio, $\frac{y}{x}$	0.75	0.8	0.81	0.82	0.81

Because the ratio is about 0.8 for each drop, it is reasonable to use a direct variation model with the constant of variation 0.8. So an equation relating x and y is $y = 0.8x$.

b. You can use the direct variation equation to find the bounce height, y, when the drop height, x, is 45 inches.

$y = 0.8x$ — Write model for direct variation.

$y = 0.8(45)$ — Substitute 45 for x.

$y = 36$ — Simplify.

ANSWER ▶ If the ball is dropped from a height of 45 inches, the bounce height will be about 36 inches.

Student Help

▶**STUDY TIP**
The answer in part (b) is reasonable when you compare it with the data in the table. Since the drop height of 45 in. is between 40 in. and 50 in., you would expect the bounce height of 36 in. to be between 32.5 in. and 41 in.

Extra Example 4

When a weight is attached to a spring, the spring stretches. The results of attaching various weights to a spring are shown in the table.

Weight, x (grams)	Length of spring, y (centimeters)
100	2.4
200	4.2
300	5.7
400	9.2
500	9.5

a. Write a model relating the length of the spring and the weight.

Ratio, $\frac{y}{x}$	0.024	0.021	0.019	0.023	0.019

$y = 0.02x$

b. Estimate the length of the spring if the weight attached to it is 350 grams. **7 cm**

Concept Check

What is the relationship between a general linear equation and a direct variation equation? **The direct variation equation is a linear equation whose y-intercept is always zero.**

11.7 Exercises

Guided Practice

Identify the values of m and b in the linear equation $y = mx + b$ that models the situation. Then write the equation. 1–2. See margin.

1. A kudzu plant is 5 feet long and is expected to grow 1 foot per day. Relate the number x of days of growth and the plant's length y in feet.

2. A long-distance phone service charges $4.90 per month plus $.10 per minute. Relate the number x of minutes and the total monthly cost y.

1. $m = 1$ ft/day; $b = 5$ feet; $y = 1x + 5 = x + 5$

2. $m = \$.10$ /min; $b = \$4.90$; $y = 0.10x + 4.90$

3 Apply

Assignment Guide

TRANSITIONAL
Day 1: pp. 596–597 Exs. 8–15, 17–19, 26–29

AVERAGE
Day 1: pp. 596–597 Exs. 8–19, 23–24, 28–29

ADVANCED
Day 1: pp. 596–597 Exs. 8–16, 20–24, 25*, 28–29; EC: TE p. 560D*

BLOCK SCHEDULE
pp. 596–597 Exs. 8–19, 23–24, 28–29 (with 11.6)

Extra Practice

- Student Edition, pp. 710–711
- Chapter 11 Resource Book, p. 60

Homework Check

To quickly check student understanding of key concepts, go over the following exercises:

Transitional: 8, 10, 14, 18, 26
Average: 8, 10, 14, 18, 24
Advanced: 8, 10, 14, 20, 24

Teaching Tip

In Exercises 13–15, students may wonder how to get the equation of the line for the scatter plot. Explain to them that finding the equation is difficult and requires mathematics (linear regression) which they may not study for several years.

8, 10. See Additional Answers beginning on page AA1.

3. direct variation; The graph passes through the origin.

4. direct variation; The graph passes through the origin.

5. not a direct variation; The graph does not pass through the origin.

Tell whether the graph of the line is direct variation. Explain.
3–5. See margin.

3.

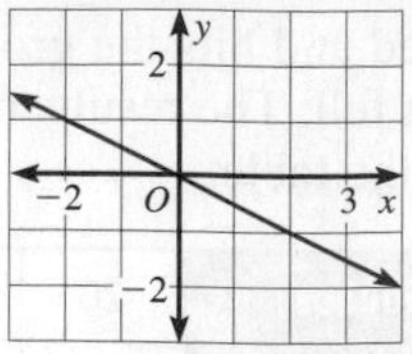

4.

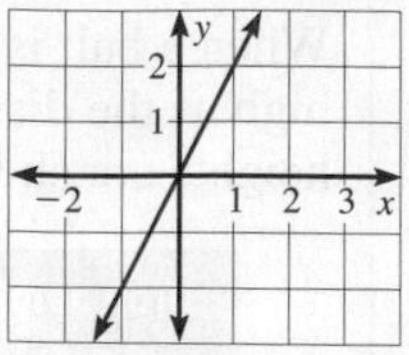

5.

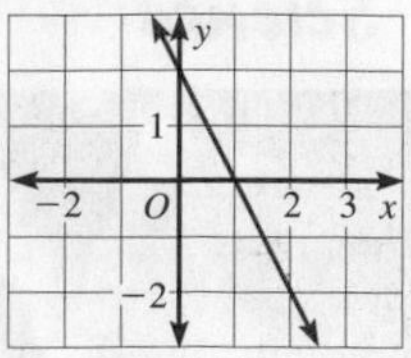

In Exercises 6 and 7, *y* varies directly with *x*.

6. When $x = 12$, $y = 54$. Find the constant of variation, and write the direct variation equation. $k = 4.5$; $y = 4.5x$

7. Find the value of y when $x = 8$. 36

Practice and Problem Solving

Student Help

▶ **MORE PRACTICE** Extra practice to help you master skills is on page 711.

BANKING In Exercises 8 and 9, use the following information. You have \$350 in a savings account. You plan to make regular monthly deposits of \$10.

8. Write and graph a linear equation that models the relationship between x, the number of deposits, and y, the amount in the account. $y = 10x + 350$; See margin.

9. Find the amount in your account after 12 deposits. \$470

Chapter Opener Link **In Exercises 10–12, use the information on page 561.**

10. Write and graph a linear equation that models the relationship between x, the number of people who attend a catered event, and y, the fee the caterer charges for the event. $y = 18.25x + 37.50$; See margin.

11. How much does the caterer charge to cater an event with 22 people? \$439

12. If the number of people who attend a catered event is doubled, are the caterer's charges doubled? Explain your answer. No. This not direct variation.

POPULATION GROWTH In Exercises 13–15, use the scatter plot. The graph shows the population of Wyoming from 1990 to 1995. A line has been drawn to show the trend in the data.

13. The slope is approximately 5 and the *y*-intercept is 454.

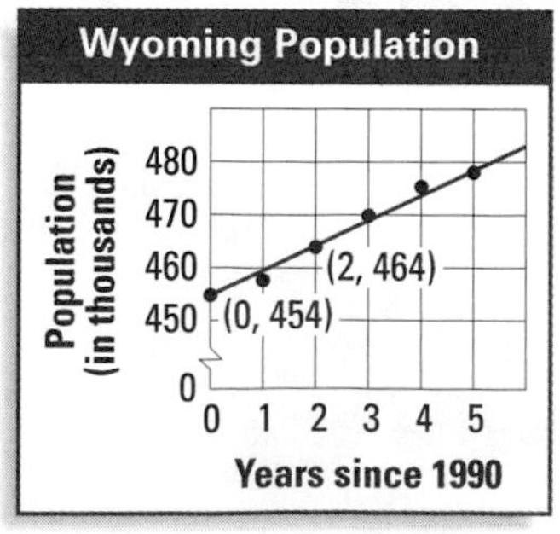

13. Use the points on the graph to estimate the line's slope and y-intercept. See margin.

14. Let x represent the number of years since 1990 and let y represent the population in thousands. Write a linear equation that models the data. $y = 454 + 5x$

15. Use the model to estimate the population of Wyoming in 1996. 484 thousand

16. Because a direct variation is in the form $y = kx$, no matter what the value of k is, y will be zero when $x = 0$. So, one of the coordinate pairs of the equation of any direct variation will be (0, 0), the origin. So, the graph of any direct variation will pass through the origin.

16. MATHEMATICAL REASONING Explain why the graph of a direct variation must pass through the origin. See margin.

17. $y = -3x$; -6

18. $y = \left(\frac{1}{2}\right)x$; 1

19. $y = \left(\frac{3}{2}\right)x$; 3

20. $y = -\left(\frac{1}{2}\right)x$; -1

21. $y = -\left(\frac{1}{5}\right)x$; $-\frac{2}{5}$

22. $y = \left(\frac{1}{3}\right)x$, $\frac{2}{3}$

Suppose y varies directly with x. Use the given values to write and graph an equation that relates x and y. Find the value of y when $x = 2$.
17–22. See margin.

17. $x = -2, y = 6$ **18.** $x = 10, y = 5$ **19.** $x = 6, y = 9$

20. $x = 12, y = -6$ **21.** $x = 5, y = -1$ **22.** $x = 9, y = 3$

In Exercises 23 and 24, the relationship between the variables can be modeled by direct variation.

23. A distance of 50 miles is approximately 80.45 kilometers. Write a direct variation model relating distance x in kilometers and distance y in miles. The distance from Cleveland, Ohio, to Los Angeles, California, is about 3900 kilometers. Find the distance in miles.
$y = 0.622x$, 2426 miles

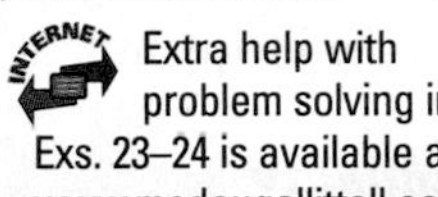

Student Help

▶HOMEWORK HELP
Extra help with problem solving in Exs. 23–24 is available at www.mcdougallittell.com

24. When a weight is attached to a spring, the spring stretches. A weight of 10 pounds causes a given spring to stretch 5 inches. Write a direct variation model relating the weight x in pounds and the amount of stretch y in inches. Determine the amount the spring stretches if a weight of 5 pounds is attached. **$y = \frac{1}{2}x$, 2.5 in.**

25. CHALLENGE In the direct variation $y = kx$, what happens to y when x is doubled? Is this true for a linear function of the form $y = mx + b$?
See margin.

25. In a direct variation, if x is doubled, then y is doubled. No; this is not true for a linear function which doesn't pass through the origin.

Determine whether the variables can reasonably be modeled by direct variation. If so, write the direct variation model and graph the equation.

26.

Sales Commissions

Amount of sales, x (in dollars)	398	712	999	1299	1479
Commission, y (in dollars)	20	36	50	65	74

$y = 0.050x$; See margin.

27.

Slope of Rain Gutters

Length of rain gutter, x (in feet)	38	45	52	57	65
Drop from end to end, y (in inches)	3.8	4.5	5.2	5.7	6.5

$y = 0.1x$; See margin.

Multiple-Choice Practice

28. Your club is planning an outing. You have \$250 in your treasury and you will cover the rest of the cost by selling tickets at \$5 per ticket. Let x represent the number of tickets sold, and let y represent the amount of money available. Which equation models the situation? **B**

Ⓐ $y = 250 - 5x$ Ⓑ $y = 5x + 250$

Ⓒ $5y = 250x$ Ⓓ Not here

29. An object's weight on Mars and its weight on Earth vary directly. A 150 pound person would weigh 57 pounds on Mars. About how many pounds would a 175 pound person weigh on Mars? **G**

Ⓕ 22 Ⓖ 67 Ⓗ 82 Ⓙ 461

4 Assess

Assessment Resources

- Assessment Book (Formal Assessment and Alternative Assessment)
- Test and Practice Generator

Mini-Quiz

A boy has \$35 and plans to save his weekly allowance of \$7.

1. Write a linear equation that models the relationship between the amount of money he has saved, S, and the number of weeks, w. **$S = 7w + 35$**
2. How much money will he have after 12 weeks? **\$119**
3. Suppose y varies directly as x, and $y = 3$ when $x = -4$. Write an equation relating y and x. **$y = -\frac{3}{4}x$**

17.

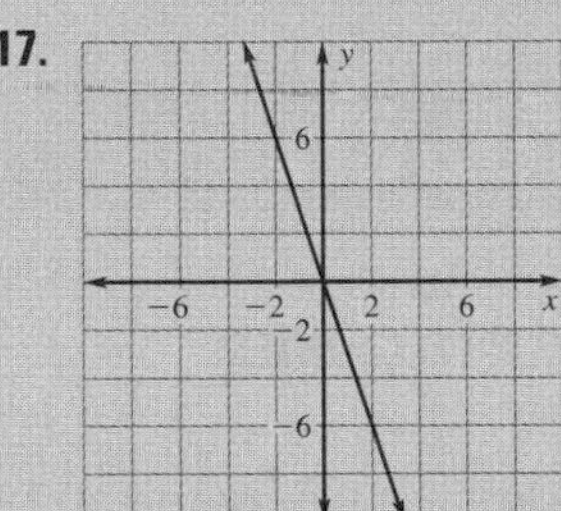

18.

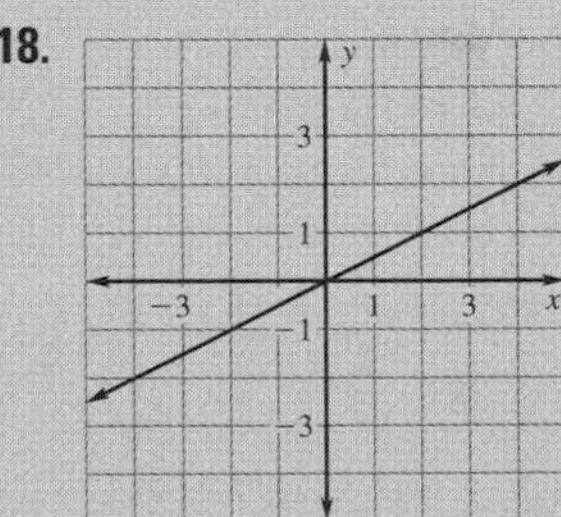

19.

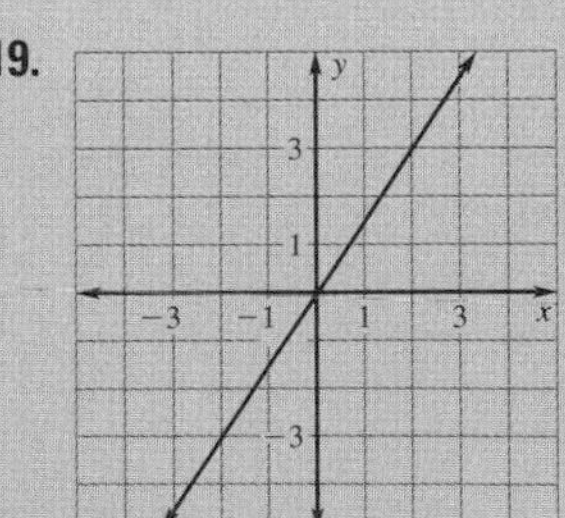

20–22, 26–27. See Additional Answers beginning on page AA1.

1 Plan

Pacing

Suggested Number of Days

Transitional: 1 day
Average: 1 day
Advanced: 1 day
Block Schedule: 0.5 block with 11.9

Teaching Resources

Blacklines
(See page 560B.)

Transparencies
- Warm-Up Exercises
- Teacher Time-Savers
- English/Spanish Problem Solving
- Answers

Technology
- Electronic Teacher Tools
- Test and Practice Generator

2 Teach

Math Reasoning

For Mathematical Background Notes on mathematical reasoning related to this lesson, please refer to pages 560E and 560F in this Teacher's Edition.

California Standards and Assessment

CA Standards: AF 1.5, AF 4.0

11.8 Graphs of Linear Inequalities

In this lesson you'll:
- Solve inequalities over the rational numbers. (AF 4.0)
- Represent quantitative relationships graphically and interpret the meaning of a specific part of a graph in the situation represented by the graph. (AF 1.5)

Goal 1 Finding Solutions of Linear Inequalities

A **linear inequality in two variables** x and y is an inequality that can be written in one of the following forms (where a, b, and c are constants and a and b are not both zero.):

$$ax + by < c \qquad ax + by \leq c \qquad ax + by > c \qquad ax + by \geq c$$

An ordered pair (x, y) is a **solution** of a linear inequality if the inequality is true when the values of x and y are substituted into the inequality.

EXAMPLE 1 Checking Solutions of an Inequality

Graph the line $y = x - 2$ using a dashed line. Plot two points above the line and two points below the line. Test each point and identify the ones that are solutions of the inequality $y > x - 2$. What do you observe?

Solution

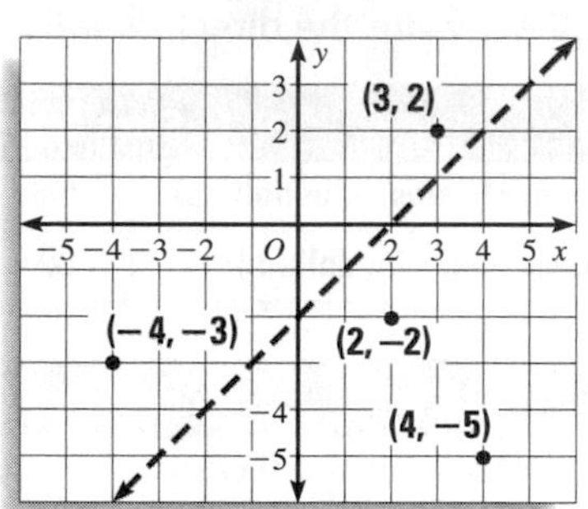

- $(3, 2)$ is a solution because $2 > 3 - 2$.
- $(-4, -3)$ is a solution because $-3 > -4 - 2$.
- $(2, -2)$ is not a solution because $-2 \not> 2 - 2$.
- $(4, -5)$ is not a solution because $-5 \not> 4 - 2$.

Each point that lies above the line is a solution of $y > x - 2$. Each point that lies below the line is *not* a solution of $y > x - 2$.

A line divides a coordinate plane into two **half-planes**. As Example 1 suggests, the graph of a linear inequality is a half-plane, bounded by a line. A dashed line indicates that points on the line are *not* solutions. A solid line indicates that points on the line *are* solutions.

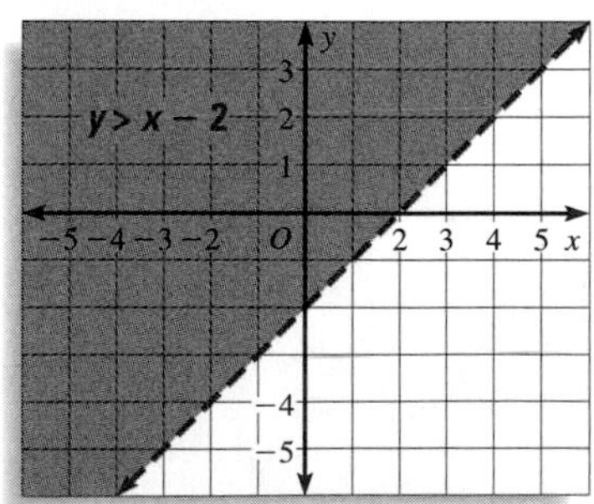

The set of solutions of an inequality is indicated by shading. The graph of $y > x - 2$ is shown at the right.

Goal 2 GRAPHING LINEAR INEQUALITIES

GRAPHING A LINEAR INEQUALITY

To graph a linear inequality, follow these steps:

1. Replace the inequality symbol with "=" and graph the equation. Decide whether the line should be dashed (>, <) or solid (≥, ≤).
2. Test a point in one of the half-planes to find whether it is a solution of the inequality.
3. If the test point is a solution, shade the half-plane it is in. If not, shade the other half-plane.

EXAMPLE 2 Graphing a Linear Inequality

The perimeter of a rectangle is less than or equal to 16 inches. That is, if ℓ is the length of the rectangle and w is the width, then $2\ell + 2w \le 16$. Graph $2\ell + 2w \le 16$.

Solution

1. Find the intercepts of the graph of the equation $2\ell + 2w = 16$.

$$2\ell + 2(0) = 16 \qquad 2(0) + 2w = 16$$
$$2\ell = 16 \qquad 2w = 16$$
$$\ell = 8 \qquad w = 8$$

The ℓ-intercept is 8 and the w-intercept is 8, so plot the points (0, 8) and (8, 0).

Because the inequality uses the symbol ≤, draw a solid line.

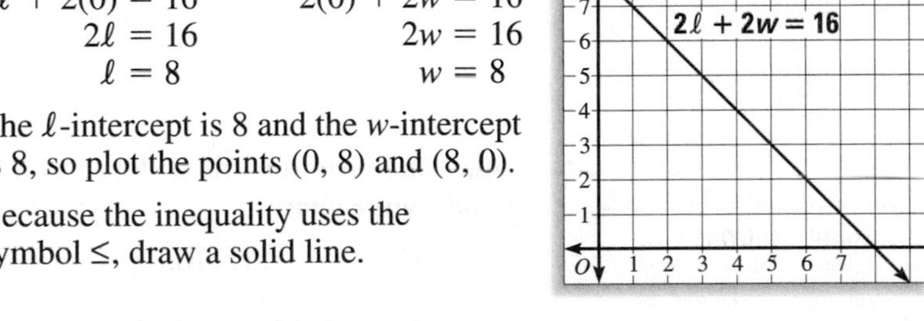

2. Choose a point, say (5, 6), above the line. (5, 6) is *not* a solution because

$$2(6) + 2(5) = 22 \text{ and } 22 \not\le 16.$$

Choose a point, say (0, 0), below the line. (0, 0) is a solution because

$$2(0) + 2(0) = 0 \text{ and } 0 \le 16.$$

Every point on or below the line represents a solution, so shade the half-plane below the line.

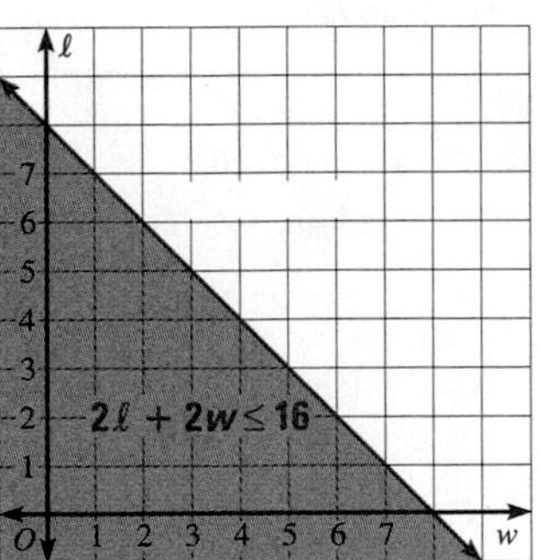

All points in the shaded region are solutions of the inequality. However, note that only points in the first quadrant represent the length and width of a rectangle because length and width are always positive.

Student Help

▶**STUDY TIP**
You can use any point that is not on the line as a test point. It is convenient to use the origin (0, 0) whenever possible because it is easy to substitute 0 for each variable.

Extra Example 1

Graph the inequality $y > x - 4$. Which points are solutions?

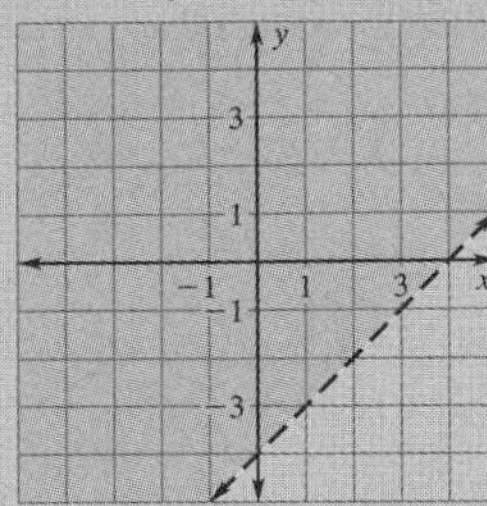

All points above $y = x - 4$ are solutions.

Extra Example 2

You can sell $6 adult tickets and $3 child tickets to earn at least $1500 for a fund-raiser. That is, if x is the number of adult tickets sold and y is the number of child tickets sold, then $6x + 3y \ge 1500$. Graph $6x + 3y \ge 1500$.

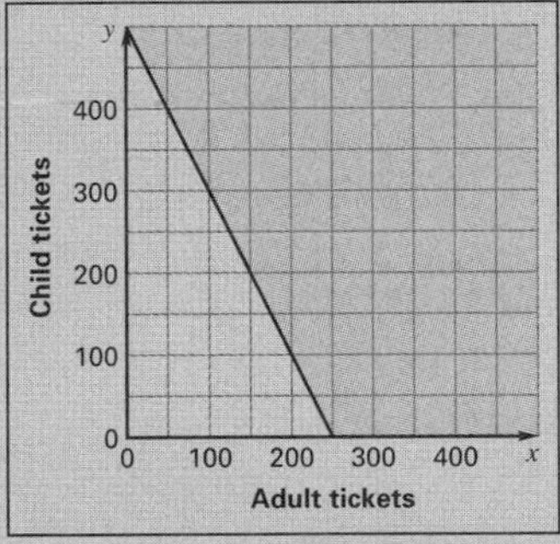

Teaching Tip

Point out that just as there is an infinite number of solutions to a single-variable inequality, the shaded half-plane shows that there is an infinite number of ordered pair solutions (x, y) to a linear inequality in two variables.

Concept Check

How do you decide which half-plane to shade when graphing a linear inequality in two variables? **Graph the boundary line (dashed or solid) and then test points on each side of the line. Shade the half-plane that contains the points that make the inequality a true statement.**

3 Apply

Assignment Guide

TRANSITIONAL
Day 1: pp. 600–601 Exs. 16–28, 32–33, 41–42

AVERAGE
Day 1: pp. 600–601 Exs. 18–22, 26–31, 34–37, 41–42

ADVANCED
Day 1: pp. 600–601 Exs. 18–22, 26–31, 38–40*, 41–42

BLOCK SCHEDULE
pp. 600–601 Exs. 18–22, 26–31, 34–37, 41–42 (with 11.9)

Extra Practice

- Student Edition, pp. 710–711
- Chapter 11 Resource Book, p. 69

Homework Check

To quickly check student understanding of key concepts, go over the following exercises:

Transitional: 16, 24, 26, 28, 32, 33
Average: 18, 28, 30, 34, 36
Advanced: 18, 28, 30, 38, 40

Problem Solving

Exercises 23–31
Remind students to write the equation that represents the inequality in slope-intercept form to graph the line.

12.

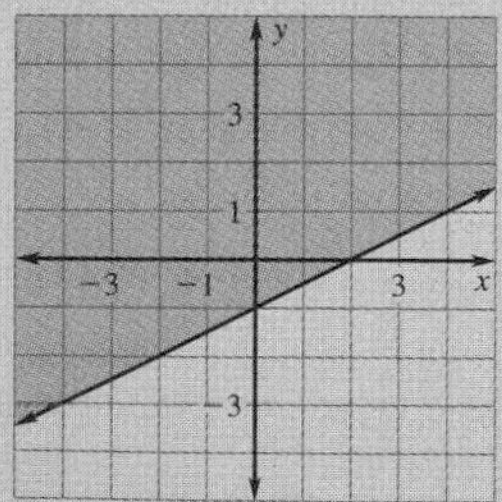

13–15, 23–31. See Additional Answers beginning on page AA1.

11.8 Exercises

Guided Practice

In Exercises 1–3, use the graph of $y > 2x - 4$ shown.

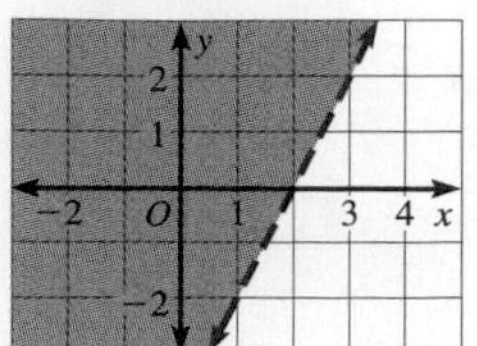

1. Is (2, 3) a solution of the inequality? **yes**

2. Is (3, 2) a solution of the inequality? **no**

3. Name three other solutions of the inequality.
Sample answer: **(0, 0), (−2, −2), (1, 1)**

Tell whether the graph of the inequality includes a solid line or a dashed line.

4. $x + y \geq 10$ **solid** **5.** $3x + y > 42$ **dashed** **6.** $x - y < 4$ **dashed** **7.** $x + 2y \leq -10$ **solid**

Determine whether (0, 0) is a solution of the inequality.

8. $y < -2x - 3$ **no** **9.** $x - 2y \leq 5$ **yes** **10.** $x + 3y > 0$ **no** **11.** $x + y < 1$ **yes**

Graph the inequality. **12–15. See margin.**

12. $y \geq \frac{1}{2}x - 1$ **13.** $x - y > 2$ **14.** $3x - y > 9$ **15.** $x > -2$

16. no; 4(5) + 6(5) = 50, which is not less than or equal to 48.

17. yes; 4(10) + 6(−2) = 28, which is less than or equal to 48.

18. no; 4(−2) + 6(10) = 52, which is not less than or equal to 48.

19. yes; 4(6) + 6(4) = 48, which is less than or equal to 48.

23. See margin; *Sample answer:* (0, 0), (1, 1), (−1, −1)

Practice and Problem Solving

Student Help
▶MORE PRACTICE
Extra practice to help you master skills is on page 711.

Determine whether the ordered pair is a solution of $4x + 6y \leq 48$. Explain your answer. **16–19. See margin.**

16. (5, 5) **17.** (10, −2) **18.** (−2, 10) **19.** (6, 4)

In Exercises 20–22, match the inequality with its graph.

A.

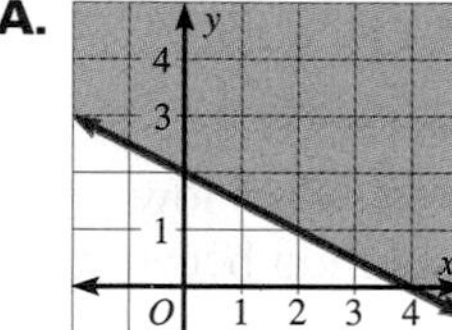

B.

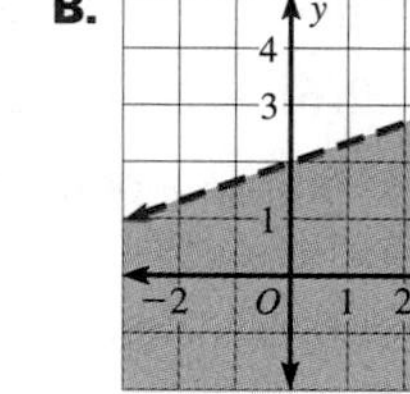

C.

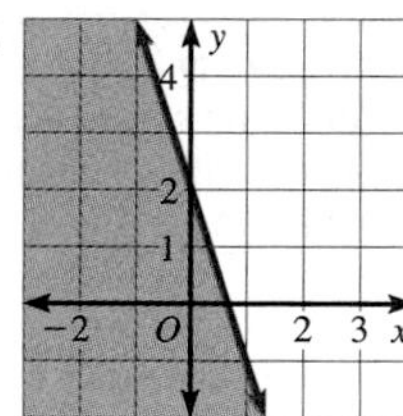

20. $y < \frac{1}{3}x + 2$ **B** **21.** $-3x - y \geq -2$ **C** **22.** $x + 2y \geq 4$ **A**

Graph the inequality. Then list several solutions. **23–31. See margin.**

23. $y \leq \frac{1}{4} + 1$ **24.** $y > -2x - 2$ **25.** $x + y < 25$

26. $y \geq x + 3$ **27.** $3x \leq y + 8$ **28.** $5y + 5x \geq 10$

29. $4x + 3y \geq 9$ **30.** $2x + y \leq 4$ **31.** $\frac{1}{4}y + \frac{1}{2}x \geq 1$

24. See margin; *Sample answer:* (0, 0), (1, 1), (−1, 1)

25. See margin; *Sample answer:* (0, 0), (1, 1), (−1, −1)

26. See margin; *Sample answer:* (0, 4), (1, 5), (−2, 2)

27. See margin; *Sample answer:* (0, 0), (1, 1), (−1, −1)

28. See margin; *Sample answer:* (0, 4), (1, 2), (−1, 4)

29. See margin; *Sample answer:* (0, 4), (1, 2), (−1, 5)

30. See margin; *Sample answer:* (0, 0), (1,−2), (−1, 5)

31. See margin; *Sample answer:* (0, 5), (1, 3), (−1, 7)

In Exercises 32 and 33, use the following statement. The sum of twice one number and five times another number is less than 30.

32. Which of the following inequalities represents the sentence? **D**

A. $7y < 30$ **B.** $2x + 5y > 30$ **C.** $3x < 30$ **D.** $2x + 5y < 30$

33. Graph the inequality you chose in Exercise 32. List several solutions. **See margin; *Sample answer:* (0, 0), (−5, 6), (5, 2)**

ROAD RACE In Exercises 34–36, use the following information. You are running in a 10 kilometer (10K) road race. Being a novice, you may need to walk part of the way to finish the race. Let x represent the number of kilometers you run, and let y represent the number of kilometers you walk.

34. You are not sure that you can finish the race. Determine which of the following inequalities best describes your situation. Explain your answer. **C; You will travel 10 km or less.**

A. $x + y > 10$ **B.** $x + y \geq 10$ **C.** $x + y \leq 10$ **D.** $x + y < 10$

35. Graph the correct inequality from Exercise 34. **See margin.**

36. You are sure that you cannot finish the race. Which of the inequalities from Exercise 34 best describes this situation? How does the graph of the inequality differ from the graph in Exercise 35? **D; The half-plane does not contain the line $x + y = 10$.**

37. MATHEMATICAL REASONING Graph $y < mx + b$ and $y > mx + b$ for various values of m and b. Use your graph to explain how you can tell which half-plane to shade given an inequality such as $y < 2x + 1$ or $y > -3x + 4$. **See margin.**

CHALLENGE In Exercises 38–40, use the following information. Your math club is selling popcorn. The profit is \$4 on each bucket of buttered popcorn and \$6 on each bucket of caramel popcorn. The club wants to raise at least \$600. Let x represent the number of buckets of buttered popcorn, and let y represent the number of buckets of caramel popcorn.

38. Write an inequality to represent this situation. **$4x + 6y \geq 600$**

39. Graph your inequality. **See margin.**

40. Use your graph to find four solutions of your inequality. **See margin.**

History

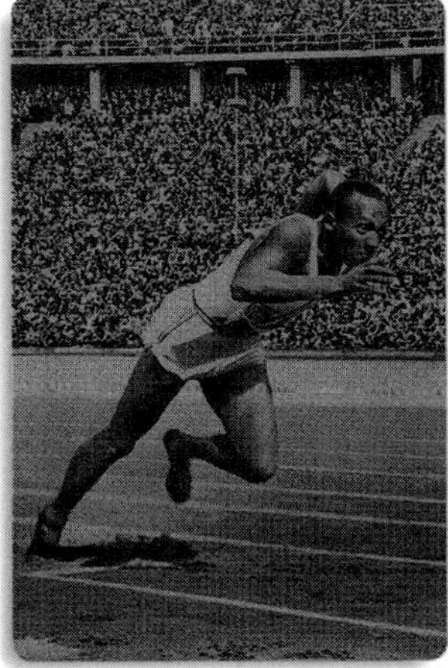

OLYMPICS The first recorded Olympic contest was an 180 meter footrace that took place in 776 B.C. Shown here is Jesse Owens who won the gold medal for the 100 meter and 200 meter races in the 1936 Summer Olympic Games.

More about the Olympics available at www.mcdougallittell.com

37. The half-plane lying below the boundary line should be shaded for solutions to the "less than" inequality. The half-plane lying above the boundary line should be shaded for solutions to the "greater than" inequality.

40. *Sample answer:* 100 buckets of caramel corn; or 50 buckets of buttered popcorn and 75 buckets of caramel corn; or 150 buckets of buttered popcorn; or 25 buckets of buttered popcorn and 100 buckets of caramel popcorn

Multiple-Choice Practice

In Exercises 41 and 42, use the graph shown.

41. Which inequality matches the graph? **D**

Ⓐ $2x + y \geq 2$ Ⓑ $2x - y \leq 2$

Ⓒ $-2x - y \geq 2$ Ⓓ $-2x + y \geq 2$

42. Which point is *not* a solution of the inequality? **G**

Ⓕ $(-1, 0)$ Ⓖ $(3, -3)$ Ⓗ $(-3, 3)$ Ⓙ $(0, 2)$

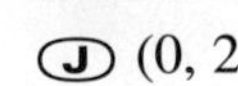

4 Assess

Assessment Resources

- Assessment Book (Formal Assessment and Alternative Assessment)
- Test and Practice Generator

Mini-Quiz

1. Name three solutions to $y \geq 2x + 5$. ***Sample answers:* (3, 14), (2, 10), (−1, 4)**
2. You have \$60 to spend on summer clothes. Shorts are \$15 each and T-shirts are \$12 each. Let x be the number of shorts and y be the number of T-shirts. Then $15x + 12y \leq 60$ represents the situation. Graph $15x + 12y \leq 60$.

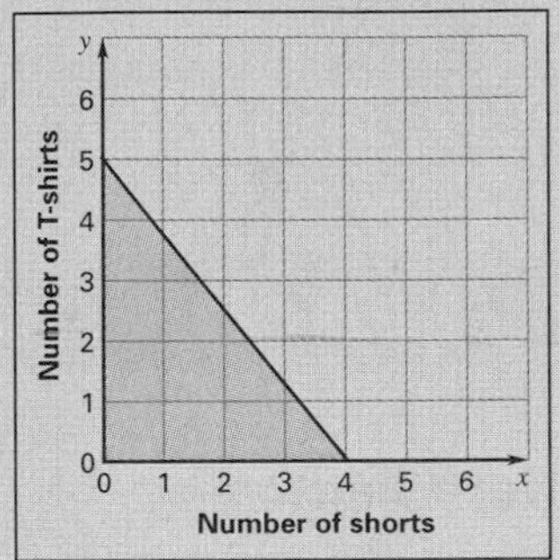

33.

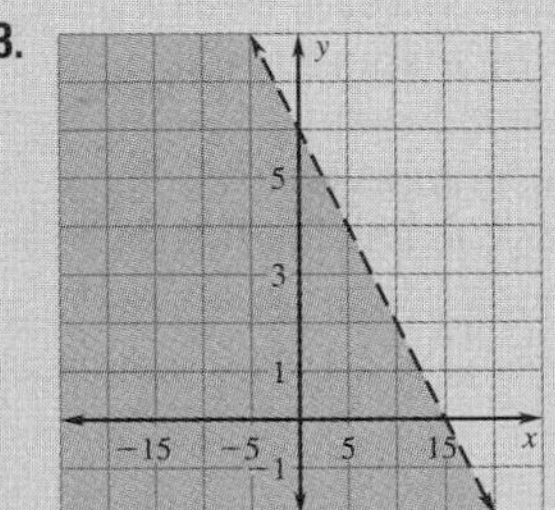

35.

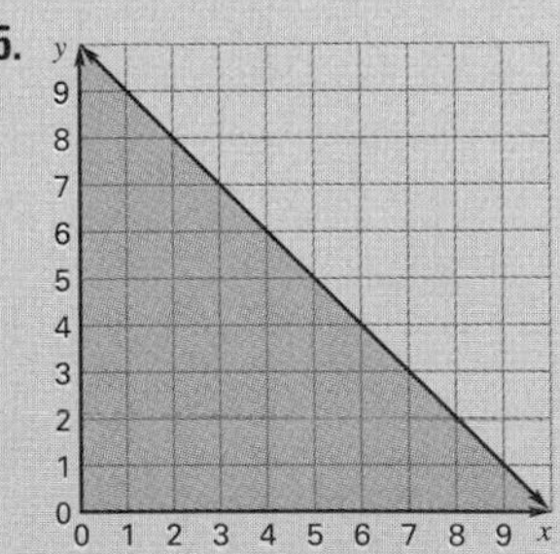

37, 39. See Additional Answers beginning on page AA1.

1 Plan

Pacing

Suggested Number of Days

Transitional: 1 day
Average: 1 day
Advanced: 1 day
Block Schedule: 0.5 block with 11.8

Teaching Resources

(See page 560B.)

Transparencies

- Warm-Up Exercises
- Teacher Time-Savers
- English/Spanish Problem Solving
- Answers

Technology

- Electronic Teacher Tools
- Test and Practice Generator

2 Teach

Math Reasoning

For Mathematical Background Notes on mathematical reasoning related to this lesson, please refer to pages 560E and 560F in this Teacher's Edition.

CA Standards: AF 1.1, AF 1.5

602

11.9 Systems of Equations and Inequalities

California Standards

In this lesson you'll:

- Use variables and appropriate operations to write a system of equations or inequalities that represents a verbal description. (AF 1.1)
- Interpret the meaning of a specific part of a graph in the situation represented by the graph. (AF 1.5)

Goal 1 Systems of Linear Equations

A set of two or more equations in the same variables is a **system of equations**. Similarly, a **system of inequalities** contains two or more inequalities in the same variables.

EXAMPLE 1 Writing a System of Linear Equations

Write a system of linear equations that represents the following:

The sum of two numbers x and y is 6, *and* y is twice x.

Solution

Write an equation that models each part of the verbal statement.

VERBAL MODEL	ALGEBRAIC MODEL
The sum of x and y is 6.	$x + y = 6$
y is twice x.	$y = 2x$

A **solution of a system of linear equations** is an ordered pair (x, y) that is a solution of each equation in the system. To represent a system of linear equations graphically, graph both equations in the same coordinate plane. If the lines intersect in a point, that point represents the solution of the system.

Student Help

▶ Study Tip
Because you are reading the solution of a system of equations from a graph, it's important to draw the lines carefully and to check the coordinates of the point of intersection in both equations.

EXAMPLE 2 Graphing and Solving a System of Equations

Solve the system in Example 1: $x + y = 6$ **Equation 1**

$y = 2x$ **Equation 2**

First write each equation in function form. Then graph both equations.

$y = -x + 6$ **Equation 1**

$y = 2x$ **Equation 2**

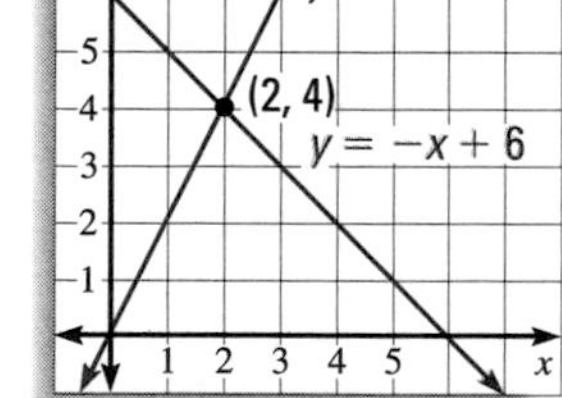

The lines intersect at the point (2, 4). The solution of the system is (2, 4).

CHECK ✓ Substitute 2 for x and 4 for y in each original equation.

Equation 1: $2 + 4 = 6$ **Equation 2:** $4 = 2(2)$

Since both equations are satisfied, (2, 4) is the solution of the system.

Goal 2 SYSTEMS OF LINEAR INEQUALITIES

EXAMPLE 3 Writing a System of Linear Inequalities

Write a system of linear inequalities that represents the following:

The sum of two numbers x and y is less than 6, *and* y is less than twice x.

Solution

Write an inequality that models each part of the verbal statement.

VERBAL MODEL	ALGEBRAIC MODEL
The sum of x and y is less than 6.	$x + y < 6$
y is less than twice x.	$y < 2x$

A **solution of a system of linear inequalities** is an ordered pair (x, y) that is a solution of each of the inequalities in the system.

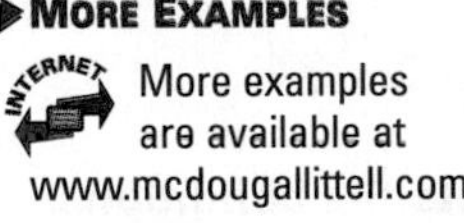

Student Help

▶ **MORE EXAMPLES**

More examples are available at www.mcdougallittell.com

EXAMPLE 4 Graphing and Solving a System of Inequalities

Graph the system of linear inequalities in Example 3. Identify several solutions of the system.

$x + y < 6$ **Inequality 1**

$y < 2x$ **Inequality 2**

Solution

Graph both inequalities in the same coordinate plane. First graph the related equations $x + y = 6$ (or $y = -x + 6$) and $y = 2x$.

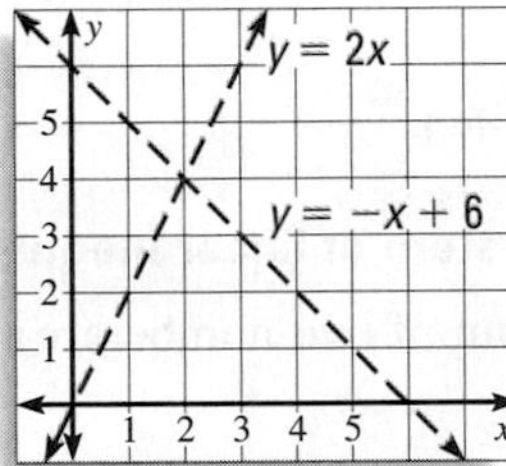

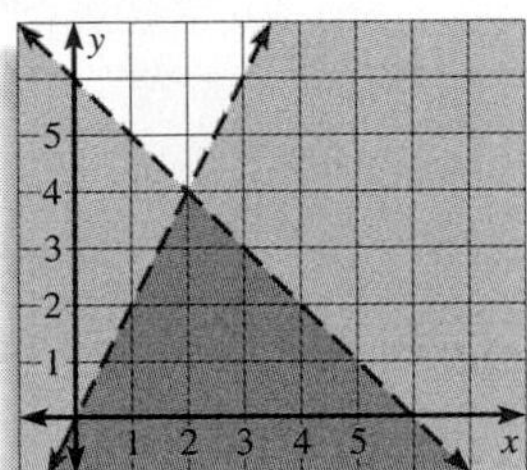

All the points that lie in the wedge-shaped region shaded twice are solutions of the system. For example, notice that (3, 1) is in the doubly shaded region. To test this solution, substitute 3 for x and 1 for y in each inequality.

Inequality 1: $3 + 1 < 6$ **Inequality 2:** $1 < 2(3)$

Since (3, 1) satisfies both inequalities, (3, 1) is a solution of the system. Some other solutions are (1, 0), (2, 3), and (1, 1).

Extra Example 1

Write a system of linear equations that represents the following:

The difference of two numbers y and x is 2, *and* y is half x.

$y - x = 2$ and $y = \frac{1}{2}x$

Extra Example 2

Solve the system in Extra Example 1:

$y - x = 2$

$y = \frac{1}{2}x$

(−4, −2)

Extra Example 3

Write a system of linear inequalities that represents the following:

The difference of two numbers y and x is less than 2, *and* y is more than half x.

$y - x < 2$ and $y > \frac{1}{2}x$

Extra Example 4

Graph the system of linear inequalities in Extra Example 3. Identify several solutions of the system.

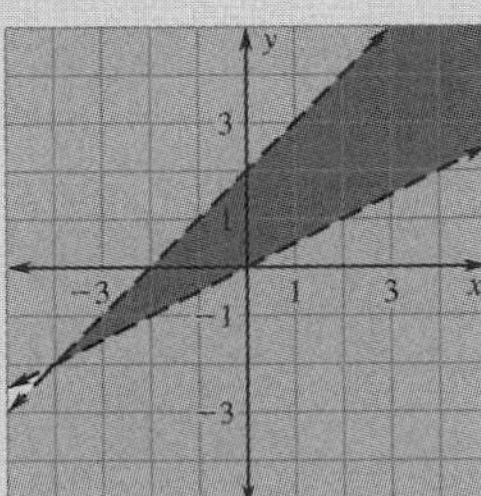

Some solutions of the system are (1, 2), (−1, 0), (2, 3).

Concept Check

How does the graph of solutions of a system of linear inequalities differ from the solution of one linear inequality? ***Sample answer:*** **The graph of a system of linear inequalities shows the solutions of each linear inequality. The area where the solutions of the individual inequalities overlap is the area of solutions to the system.**

3 Apply

Assignment Guide

TRANSITIONAL
Day 1: pp. 604–605 Exs. 9–12, 14–18, 22–25, 31–32

AVERAGE
Day 1: pp. 604–605 Exs. 9–10, 12–18, 24–28, 31–32

ADVANCED
Day 1: pp. 604–605 Exs. 9–10, 12–15, 19–21, 24–28, 29–30*, 31–32

BLOCK SCHEDULE
pp. 604–605 Exs. 9–10, 12–18, 24–28, 31–32 (with 11.8)

Extra Practice

- Student Edition, pp. 710–711
- Chapter 11 Resource Book, p. 78

Homework Check

To quickly check student understanding of key concepts, go over the following exercises:

Transitional: 12, 14, 16, 22, 24
Average: 12, 14, 18, 24, 26
Advanced: 12, 14, 20, 24, 26

3.
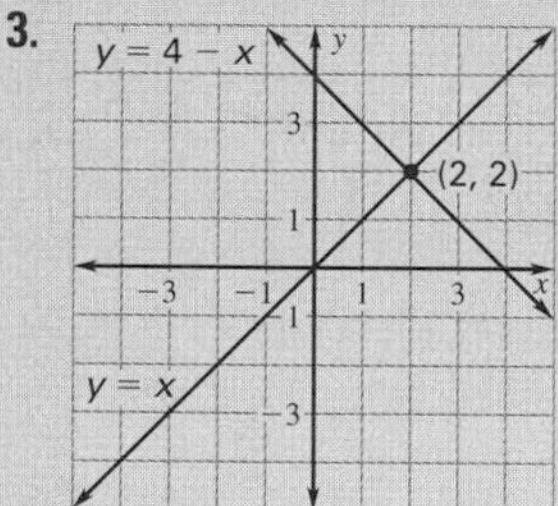

4.
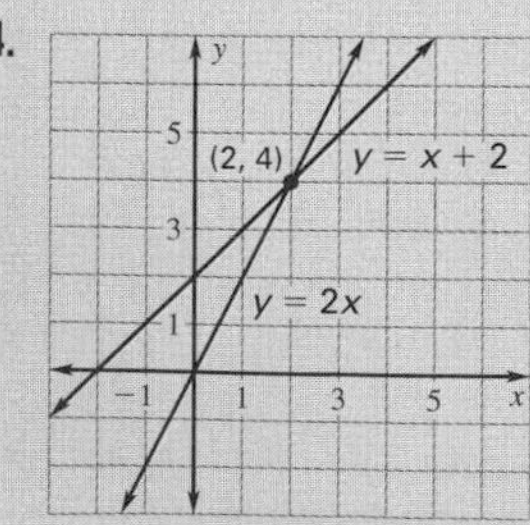

5–8, 11–13, 16–21. See Additional Answers beginning on page AA1.

11.9 Exercises

Guided Practice

1. Write a system of linear equations that represents the following: **$x - y = 3$, $2x = y$**
The difference of two numbers x and y is 3, *and* the product of 2 and x is y.

2. Write a system of linear inequalities that represents the following:
The sum of two numbers x and y is less than or equal to 5, *and* y is greater than x. **$x + y \le 5$, $y > x$**

Graph the system of linear equations. Then find the solution.

3. $y = 4 - x$
$x = y$
See margin; (2, 2)

4. $y = 2x$
$x - y = -2$
See margin; (2, 4)

5. $y = 3x - 5$
$3x + y = 7$
See margin; (2, 1)

Graph the system of linear inequalities. Then identify three solutions.
6–8. See margin.

6. $y \ge x$
$4y < x$

7. $x - \frac{1}{2} < y$
$y < x + 5$

8. $y \le 2x + 4$
$y + 2x \le 4$

6. See margin; *Sample answer:* (−1, −1), (−2, −2), (−3, −3)
7. See margin; *Sample answer:* (−1, −1), (0, 0), (1, 1)
8. See margin; *Sample answer:* (−1, −2), (0, 0), (1, 2)

Practice and Problem Solving

Student Help
▶MORE PRACTICE
Extra practice to help you master skills is on page 711.

Write a system of linear equations that represents the conditions.

9. The sum of two numbers x and y is 1, *and* y is equal to 3 times x.
$x + y = 1$, $y = 3x$

10. The sum of a number x and twice another number y is 9, *and* y is one half of x. **$x + 2y = 9$, $y = \left(\frac{1}{2}\right)x$**

Graph the system of equations. Then find the solution.

11. $x = 3$
$y = x + 1$
See margin; (3, 4)

12. $x = 3y$
$y = x - 4$
See margin; (6, 2)

13. $2x = 3 + y$
$x = y$
See margin; (3, 3)

Write a system of linear inequalities that represents the conditions.

14. The sum of two numbers x and y is greater than 14, *and* y is greater than x. **$x + y > 14$, $y > x$**

15. The sum of a number x and twice another number y is greater than 5, *and* y is less than twice x. **$x + 2y > 5$, $y < 2x$**

Graph the system of inequalities. Then identify three solutions.
16–21. See margin.

16. $y \ge 2 + x$
$x < 3$

17. $y \ge -x$
$y \ge x - 2$

18. $x - y > 1$
$y + 3 \ge x$

19. $y - x \le 4$
$3y + x \le 8$

20. $y + 3 \ge x$
$y \le 5 - x$

21. $x \le 9 - y$
$y < x + 3$

16. *Sample answer:* (−1, 1), (0, 3), (1, 8)
17. *Sample answer:* (−1, 1), (0, 0), (1, 1)
18. *Sample answer:* (−1, −3), (0, −2), (1, −1)
19. *Sample answer:* (−1, −1), (0, 0), (1, 1)
20. *Sample answer:* (−1, −1), (0, 0), (1, 1)
21. *Sample answer:* (−1, 0), (0, 2), (1, 1)

Write a system of linear equations. Then graph the system and find the solution.

22. The sum of 6 and a number y is twice another number x, *and* the difference of 6 and y is x. **$6 + y = 2x$, $6 - y = x$; see margin; (4, 2)**

23. The sum of two numbers x and y is 25, *and* y is 1 more than twice x. **$x + y = 25$, $y = 2x + 1$; see margin; (8, 17)**

Write a system of linear inequalities. Then graph the system and identify three solutions. **24–25. See margin.**

24. The sum of two times a number x and another number y is greater than 5, *and* twice x is less than y. **$2x + y > 5$, $2x < y$; See margin; *Sample answer:* (−1, 8), (0, 6), (1, 5)**

25. The difference of two numbers x and y is less than 8, *and* the sum of y and twice x is greater than 1. **$x - y < 8$, $y + 2x > 1$; See margin; *Sample answer:* (−1, 4), (0, 2), (1, 1)**

27. The school has raised only \$400 but has to pay the band \$700; so it has lost money.

28. The school has to sell more than 100 tickets. At 100 tickets, the school has collected \$800 dollars, but has to pay the band \$600 + \$200; so, the school has not made any money. If the school sells 101, the school has collected \$808, but has to pay the band \$600 + \$202. Now the school has made \$6.00. So the school has to sell at least 101 tickets to make money.

29. The system of equations has no solution. The graphs of the equations are parallel because they have the same slope and different intercepts. Because the lines are parallel they do not intersect.

30. The system of equations can be simplified into the same equation and therefore both equations in the system have the same solutions, namely all the pairs (x, y) on the line.

FUNDRAISING In Exercises 26–28, use the following information. Your school is hosting a concert to raise money. The charge is \$8 for a ticket. The band is paid \$600 plus \$2 for every ticket sold. The situation can be modeled by a system of linear equations. Let x represent the number of tickets sold. Let y represent the number of dollars. Then: **26–28. See margin.**

Equation 1 (money collected): $y = 8x$

Equation 2 (money paid to band): $y = 2x + 600$

26. Graph the system of linear equations. Since both variables must be positive, draw only the part of the graph in the first quadrant.

27. MATHEMATICAL REASONING Suppose you sell 50 tickets. Does your school make or lose money? Explain.

28. MATHEMATICAL REASONING Use the graph in Exercise 26 to determine the number of tickets that need to be sold before your school starts making money. Explain your reasoning.

CHALLENGE Graph each system of equations. What can you determine about the solution of each system? **29, 30. See margin.**

29. $y = x + 2$
$y = x - 2$

30. $2x + y = 3$
$4x + 2y = 6$

Multiple-Choice Practice

Test Tip (A)(B)(C)(D)

▶ If any ordered pair fails to solve one equation or inequality, don't bother checking whether it solves the other (it can't be a solution to the system).

31. Which ordered pair is the solution of the system of linear equations $y = 2x + 2$ *and* $2y - 4 = x$? **C**

(A) (0, 0) (B) (1, 4) (C) (0, 2) (D) (2, 3)

32. Which ordered pair is *not* a solution of the system of linear inequalities $y > 2x - 5$ *and* $x + y > 4$? **H**

(F) (1, 4) (G) (5, 6) (H) (3, 1) (J) (4, 4)

4 Assess

Assessment Resources

- Assessment Book (Formal Assessment and Alternative Assessment)
- Test and Practice Generator

Mini-Quiz

1. Write a system of linear inequalities that represents the conditions:

   The sum of a number x and 5 is more than another number y, *and* the sum of a number x and another number y is more than 2.

   $x + 5 > y$ and $x + y > 2$

2. Graph the system of inequalities in Question 1.

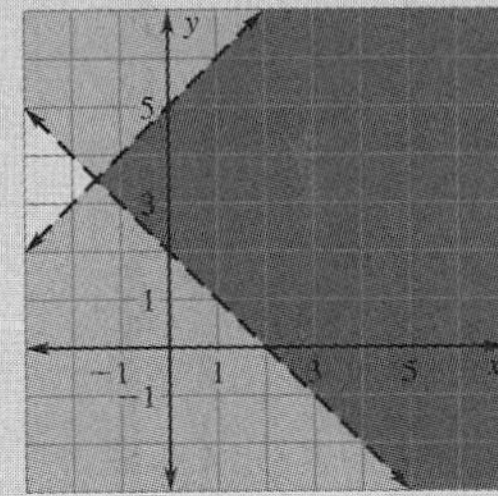

22.

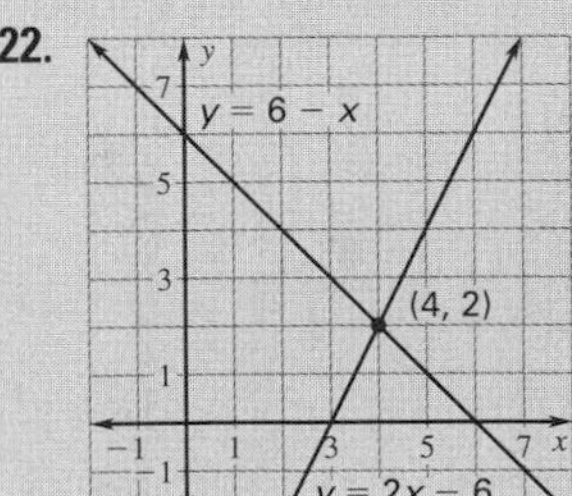

23.

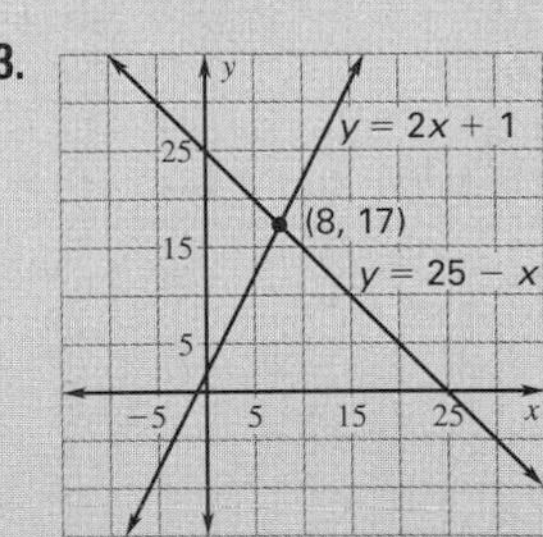

24–26. See Additional Answers beginning on page AA1.

Additional Resources

The following resources are available to help review the material in this chapter:

Technology
- Personal Student Tutor
- Test and Practice Generator

1.

x	−2	0	2	4
y	4	0	−4	−8

2.

x	−2	0	2	4
y	−14	−6	2	10

3.

x	−2	0	2	4
y	6	5	4	3

4.

x	−2	0	2	4
y	2.5	2	1.5	1

6. $y = 6 - 4x$

x	−1	0	1	2
y	10	6	2	−2

7. $y = 16 - 6x$

x	−1	0	1	2
y	22	16	10	4

8. $y = 3x - 8$

x	−1	0	1	2
y	−11	−8	−5	−2

9. $y = 5x - 7$

x	−1	0	1	2
y	−12	−7	−2	3

10.

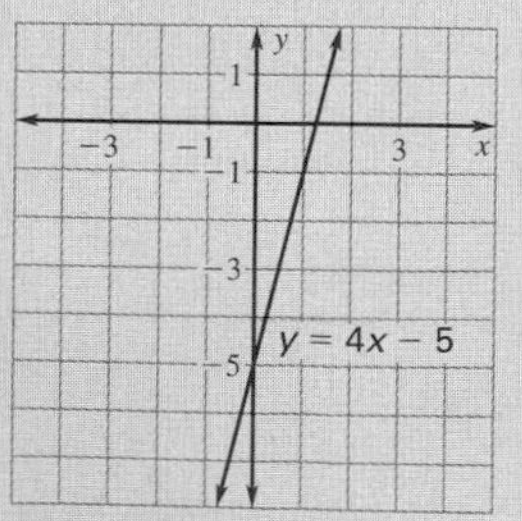

Chapter 11 Chapter Summary and Review

VOCABULARY

- **function,** *p. 563*
- **input,** *p. 563*
- **output,** *p. 563*
- **linear equation in two variables,** *p. 567*
- ***x*-intercept,** *p. 576*
- ***y*-intercept,** *p. 576*
- **slope,** *p. 583*
- **slope-intercept form,** *p. 589*
- **direct variation,** *p. 594*
- **constant of variation,** *p. 594*
- **linear inequality in two variables,** *p. 598*
- **solution of a linear inequality,** *p. 598*
- **half-planes,** *p. 598*
- **system of equations,** *p. 602*
- **system of inequalities,** *p. 602*
- **solution of a system of linear equations,** *p. 602*
- **solution of a system of linear inequalities,** *p. 603*

11.1 FUNCTIONS

Examples on pp. 563–564

EXAMPLE The time t in hours it takes for a 240 mile trip depends on your speed r. The time is the distance, 240, divided by the speed: $t = \frac{240}{r}$. Make a table of values for the function.

Input, *r* (in miles per hour)	40	48	50	60	64
Output, *t* (in hours)	6	5	4.8	4	3.75

In Exercises 1–4, find y when $x = -2$, 0, 2, and 4. Organize your data in an input-output table. 1–4. See margin.

1. $y = -2x$ **2.** $y = 4x - 6$ **3.** $y = -\frac{1}{2}x + 5$ **4.** $y = 2 - \frac{x}{4}$

5. Write a function rule that relates x and y for the ordered pairs $(-9, 6)$, $(-6, 4)$, $(-3, 2)$, $(0, 0)$, $(3, -2)$, and $(6, -4)$. **A rule for this function is $y = \left(-\frac{2}{3}\right)x$.**

11.2 LINEAR EQUATIONS AND LINEAR FUNCTIONS

Examples on pp. 567–568

EXAMPLE **Write $2x - y = 3$ in function form, and then make a table of values.**

To write the equation in function form, subtract $2x$ from both sides to get $-y = -2x + 3$. Then divide both sides by -1 to get $y = 2x - 3$.

x	−2	0	1	2
y	−5	−3	−1	1

In Exercises 6–9, write the equation in function form. Then make a table of values. **6–9. See margin.**

6. $4x + y = 6$ **7.** $6x + y = 16$ **8.** $3x - y = 8$ **9.** $-5x + y = -7$

11.3 GRAPHS OF LINEAR FUNCTIONS

Examples on pp. 571–573

EXAMPLE **Graph the linear function $y = 3x - 4$.**

First make a table of values.

Then plot the ordered pairs and draw a line through the points.

x	y	Solution
0	−4	(0, −4)
1	−1	(1, −1)
2	2	(2, 2)

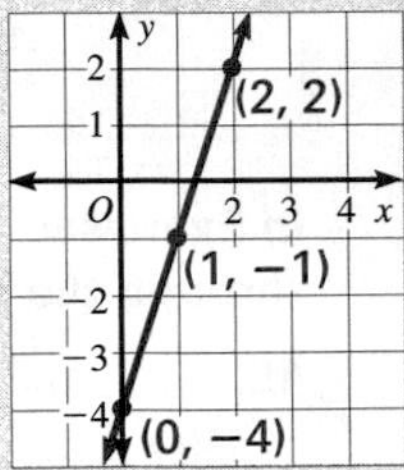

In Exercises 10–13, graph the equation. **10–13. See margin.**

10. $y = 4x - 5$ **11.** $3x - y = 10$ **12.** $x = 2$ **13.** $y = -3$

14. VALET PARKING For parking cars, your sister earns $40 per night plus a $2 tip for each car she parks. The equation $y = 2x + 40$ models her income y in dollars when she parks x cars in a night. Make a table that shows her income for parking from 5 to 10 cars. Graph the ordered pairs from the table. **See margin.**

11.4 INTERCEPTS OF GRAPHS

Examples on pp. 576–577

EXAMPLE **Find the x- and y-intercepts of the line $3x + 4y = 24$.**

x-intercept: Let $y = 0$ and solve for x.

$$3x + 4y = 24$$
$$3x + 4(0) = 24$$
$$3x = 24$$
$$x = 8$$

y-intercept: Let $x = 0$ and solve for y.

$$3x + 4y = 24$$
$$3(0) + 4y = 24$$
$$4y = 24$$
$$y = 6$$

The x-intercept is 8, and the y-intercept is 6, so the points (8, 0) and (0,6) are on the graph.

Find the intercepts of the graph of the equation and use them to sketch a quick graph. **15–18. See margin.**

15. $5x - y = 10$ **16.** $y = -8x + 2$ **17.** $y = 4 + 3x$ **18.** $6x - 7 = -y$

11.

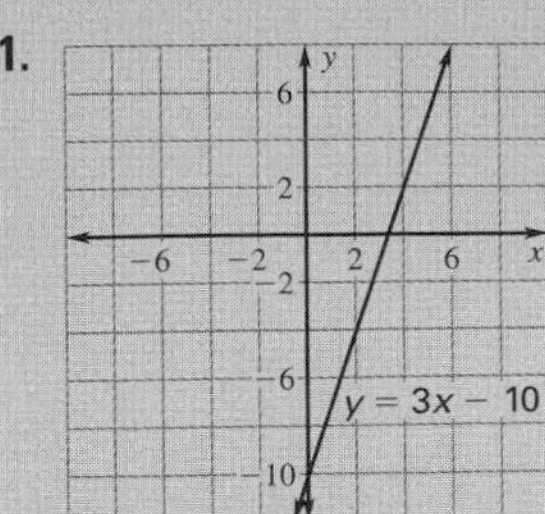

12.

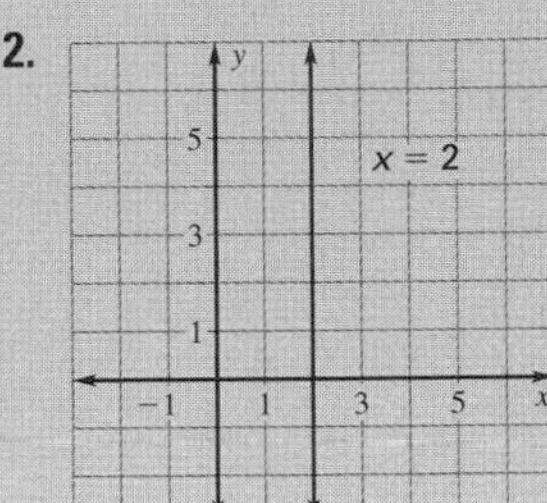

13.

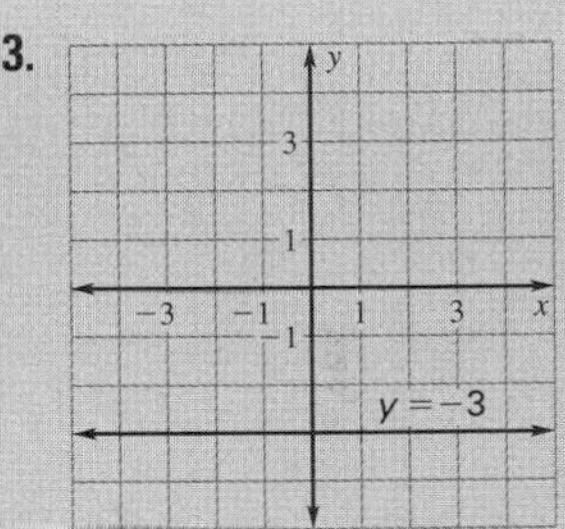

14.

Cars parked, x	Income, y (in dollars)
5	50
6	52
7	54
8	56
9	58
10	60

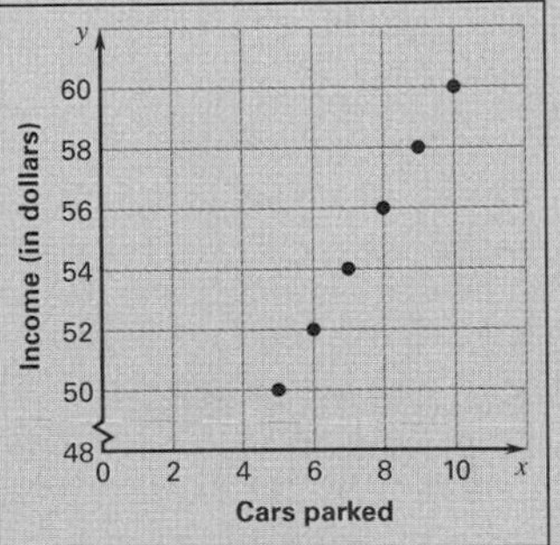

15–18. See Additional Answers beginning on page AA1.

19.

$m = -3$

20.

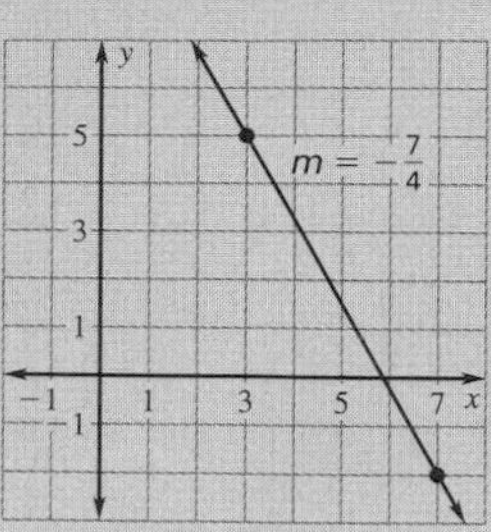

21.

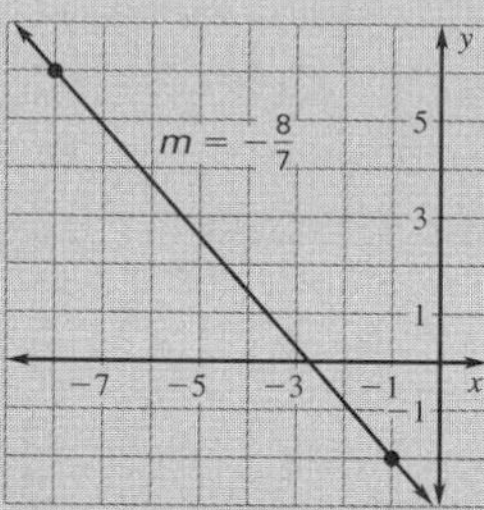

22.

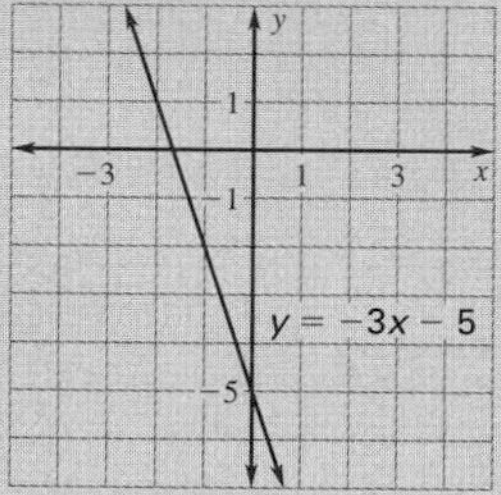

23.

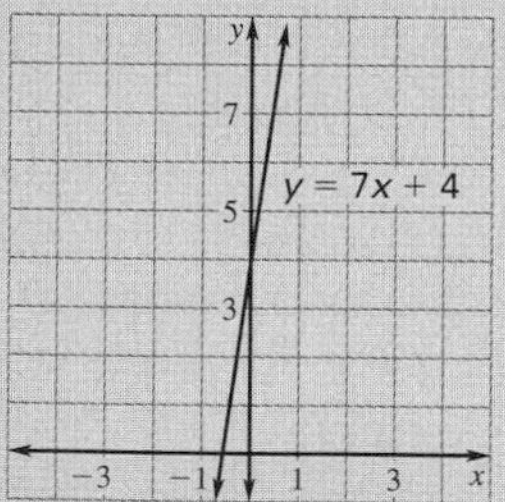

24–25. See Additional Answers beginning on page AA1.

11.5 THE SLOPE OF A LINE

Examples on pp. 583–585

EXAMPLE **Find the slope of the line through the points (0, 1) and (5, 4).**

Let (0, 1) be (x_1, y_1) and let (5, 4) be (x_2, y_2).

$$\text{Slope} = \frac{\text{rise}}{\text{run}} = \frac{y_2 - y_1}{x_2 - x_1} = \frac{4-1}{5-0} = \frac{3}{5}$$

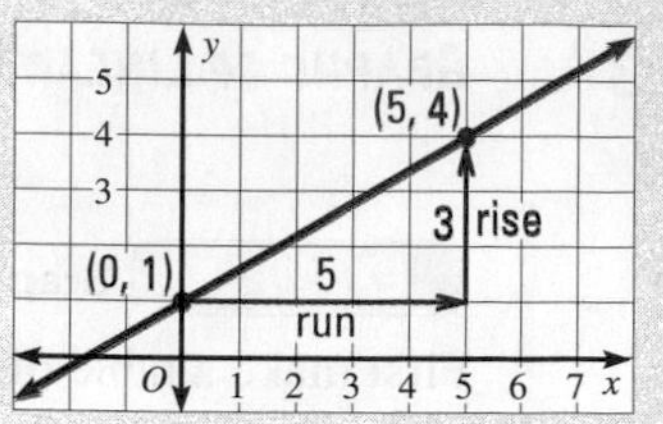

In Exercises 19–21, plot the points. Then find the slope of the line through the points.

19. (4, 9) and (6, 3)
See margin; $m = -3$

20. (3, 5) and (7, −2)
See margin; $m = -\frac{7}{4}$

21. (−8, 6) and (−1, −2)
See margin; $m = -\frac{8}{7}$

11.6 THE SLOPE-INTERCEPT FORM

Examples on pp. 589–590

EXAMPLE **Sketch a quick graph of the line $y = \frac{2}{5}x + 1$.**

The y-intercept is 1, so plot the point (0, 1).

The slope is $\frac{2}{5}$, so plot a second point by moving right 5 units and up 2 units. Draw a line through the two points.

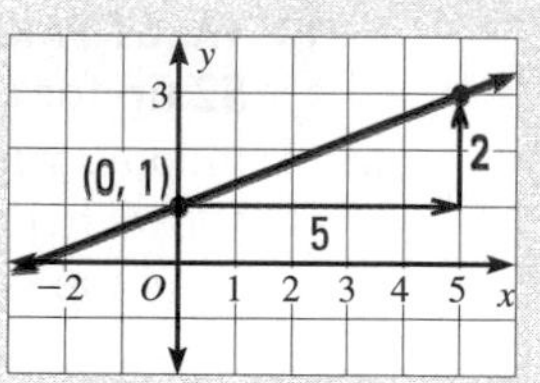

Find the slope and *y*-intercept of the line whose equation is given. Sketch a quick graph.

22. $y = -3x - 5$
$m = -3$, $b = -5$; See margin.

23. $y = 4 + 7x$
$m = 7$, $b = 4$; See margin.

24 $9x + 3 = y$
$m = 9$, $b = 3$; See margin.

25. $4x + y = 3$
$m = -4$, $b = 3$; See margin.

11.7 PROBLEM SOLVING WITH LINEAR EQUATIONS

Examples on pp. 593–595

EXAMPLE You pay a $25 fee to join a shopping club and spend a monthly average of $125 at the club. Let x represent the number of months and y the total amount you have spent. Write a linear equation that models the relationship between x and y and determine if y varies directly with x.

When $x = 0$, $y = 25$, so the y-intercept of the graph is 25. The rate of change is 125, so the relationship can be modeled by $y = 125x + 25$. The relationship is not direct variation. If there were no fee, the equation would be $y = 125x$, which is direct variation.

26. You have 280 stamps in your collection. You add 25 stamps to your collection each month. Write and graph a linear equation that models the relationship between y, the number of stamps in your collection, and x, the number of months. **$y = 280 + 25x$; See margin.**

Given that y varies directly with x, use the values to write and graph an equation that relates x and y. Find the value of y when $x = 4$.

27. $x = 3, y = -9$
$y = -3x$; See margin; -12

28. $x = 15, y = 9$
$y = \left(\frac{3}{5}\right)x$; See margin; $\frac{12}{5}$

29. $x = 36, y = -4$
$y = \left(-\frac{1}{9}\right)x$; See margin; $-\frac{4}{9}$

11.8 GRAPHS OF LINEAR INEQUALITIES

Examples on pp. 598–599

EXAMPLE **Graph the inequality $y < 3x$.**

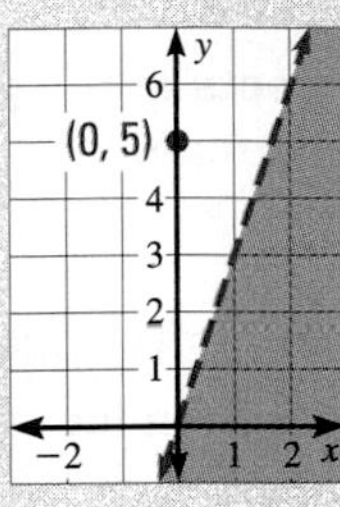

First graph the line $y = 3x$. Because the inequality is $<$, use a dashed line.

Since $5 \nless 3(0)$, the point (0, 5) is not a solution of $y < 3x$. Shade the half-plane that does not include (0, 5).

Graph the inequality. Then list several solutions.

30. $y < 8x - 12$
See margin; *Sample answer:* (−1, −21), (0, −13), (1, −5)

31. $2x - y \geq -16$
See margin; *Sample answer:* (−1, −1), (0, 0), (1, 1)

32. $2y + 6x \leq -4$
See margin; *Sample answer:* (−1, 1), (0, −4), (1, −7)

11.9 SYSTEMS OF EQUATIONS AND INEQUALITIES

Examples on pp. 602–603

EXAMPLE Write a system of linear inequalities that represents the following: The difference of 4 and x is less than y, *and* the product of 3 and x is greater than y.

VERBAL MODEL	ALGEBRAIC MODEL
The difference of 4 and x is less than y.	$4 - x < y$, or $y > -x + 4$
The product of 3 and x is greater than y.	$3x > y$, or $y < 3x$

Graph the inequalities in the same coordinate plane by graphing the related equations $y = -x + 4$ and $y = 3x$. Then shade the appropriate half-plane for each inequality.

A solution of the system must be a solution of each inequality. Some solutions are (2, 3), (5, 0), and (4, 5).

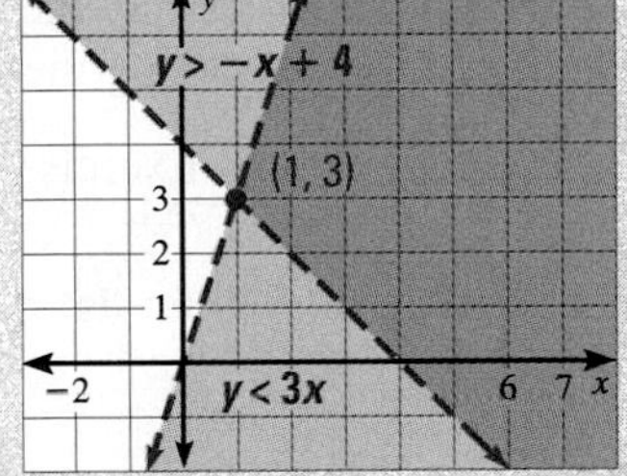

Graph the system of inequalities. Then identify three solutions.

33. $x \geq 2$
$y \geq x + 1$
See margin; *Sample answer:* (2, 3), (3, 5), (4, 6)

34. $x > y - 2$
$y > x - 2$
See margin; *Sample answer:* (−1, −1), (0, 0), (1, 1)

35. $x + 2y \leq 3$
$2x - y \geq -3$
See margin; *Sample answer:* (−1, −1), (0, 0), (1, 1)

26.

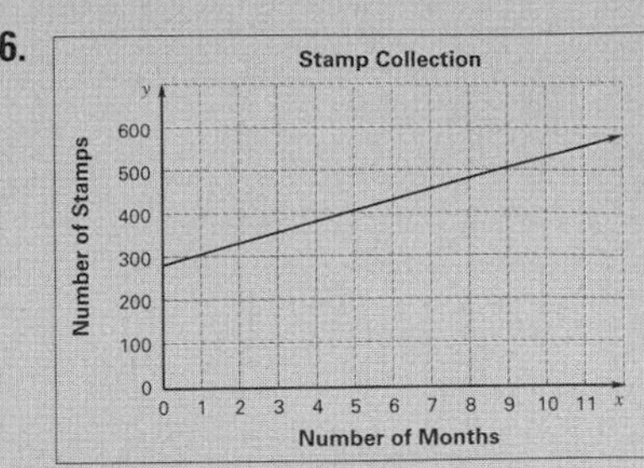

27.

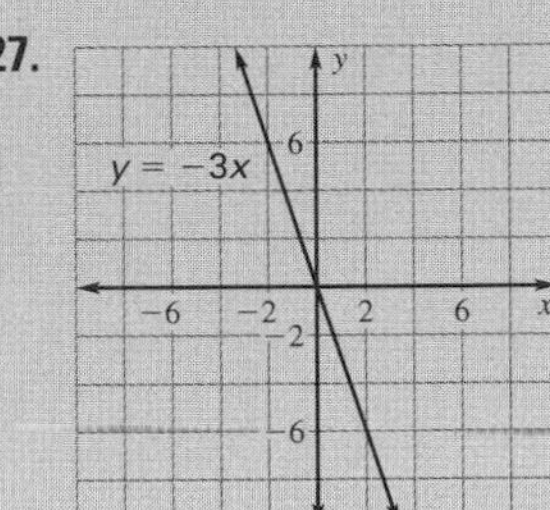

28.

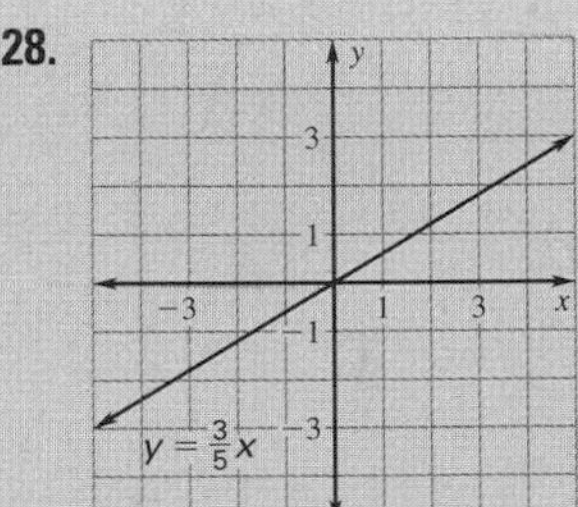

29.

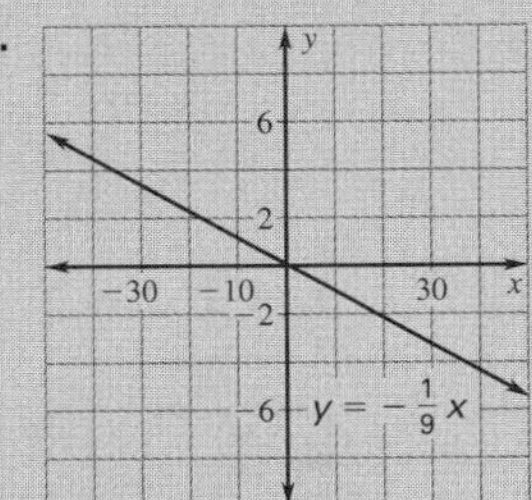

30.

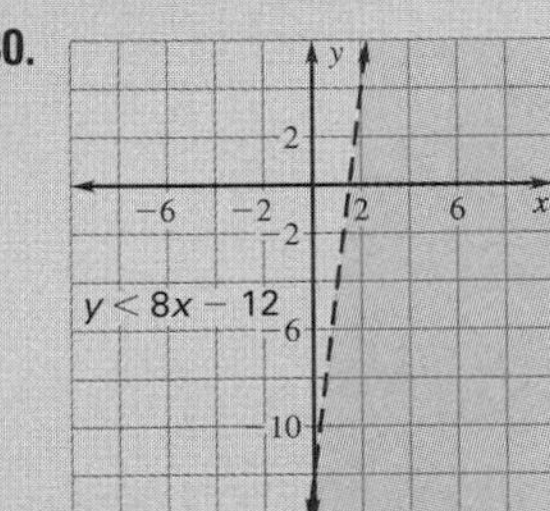

31.

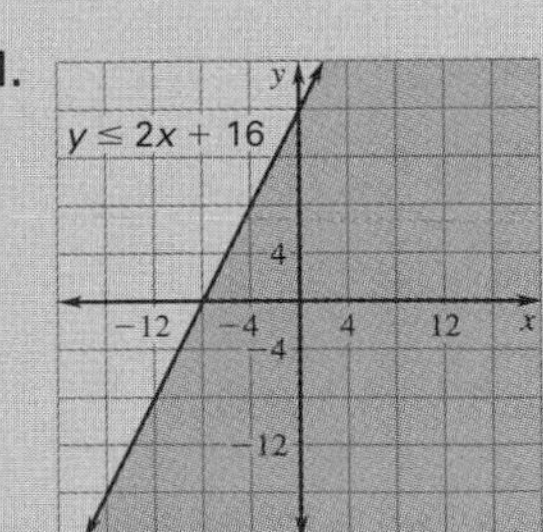

32–35. See Additional Answers beginning on page AA1.

Additional Resources

Assessment Book

- Formal Assessment, pp. 166–174
- Alternative Assessment, pp. 193–207

Test and Practice Generator

5.

x	−3	−2	−1	0	1	2	3
y	12	10	8	6	4	2	0

6.

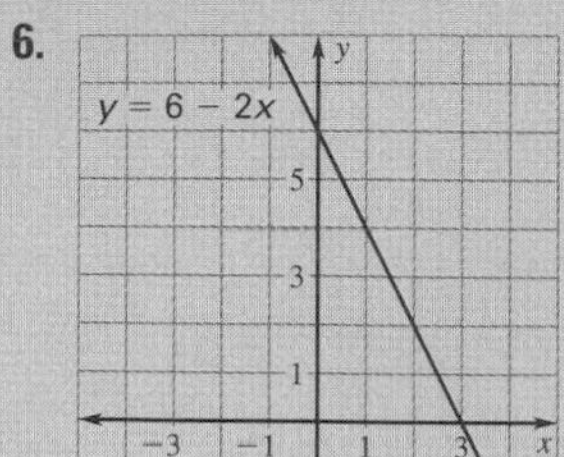

7.

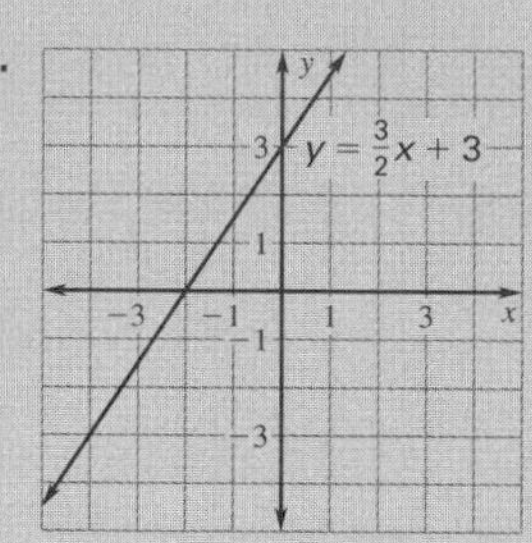

8.

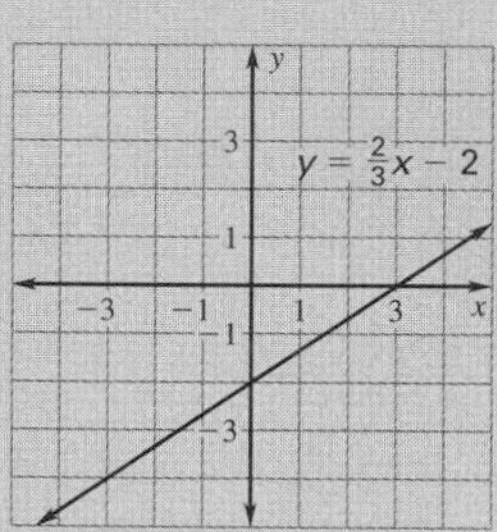

9.

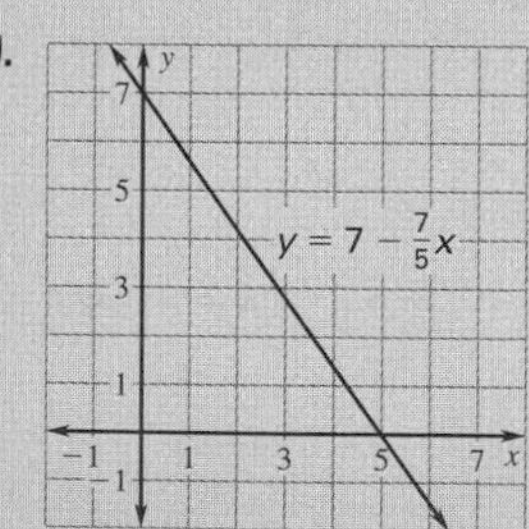

10.

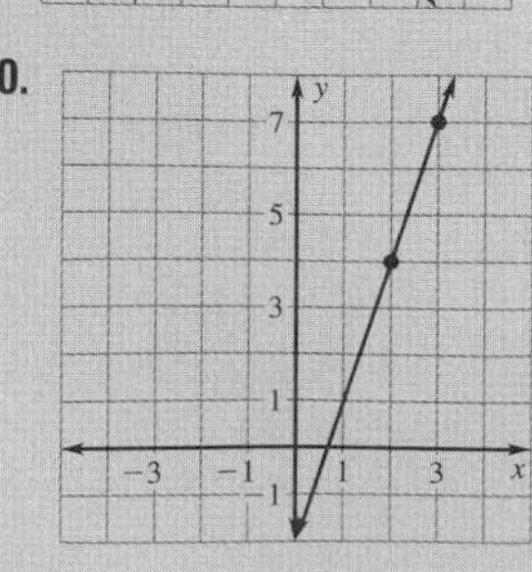

Chapter 11 Chapter Test

Tell whether the ordered pair is a solution of $x + 3y = 16$.

1. (8, 3) **no** **2.** (1, 5) **yes** **3.** (−2, 6) **yes** **4.** (5, 3) **no**

In Exercises 5 and 6, use the equation $2x + y = 6$. **5, 6. See margin.**

5. Complete the table of values.

6. Sketch a quick graph of the line.

x	−3	−2	−1	0	1	2	3
y	?	?	?	?	?	?	?

Find the intercepts of the graph of the equation and use them to sketch a quick graph.

7. $y = \frac{3}{2}x + 3$ **x-intercept: −2; y-intercept: 3; See margin.**

8. $-2x + 3y = -6$ **x-intercept: 3; y-intercept: −2; See margin.**

9. $7x + 5y = 35$ **x-intercept: 5; y-intercept: 7; See margin.**

Plot the points. Then find the slope of the line through the points.

10. (3, 7) and (2, 4) **See margin; $m = 3$**

11. (4, 6) and (3, −2) **See margin; $m = 8$**

12. (1, 2) and (−5, 3) **See margin; $m = -\frac{1}{6}$**

Write the equation of the line in slope-intercept form.

13.

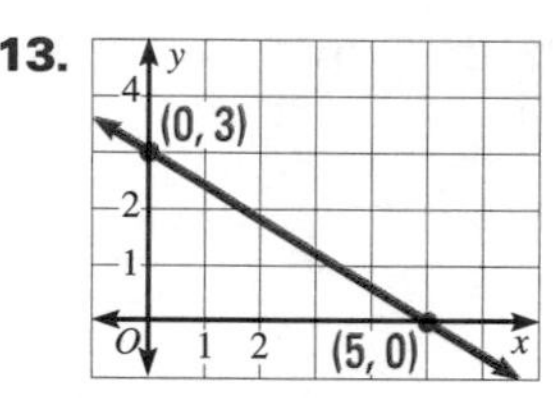

$y = -\left(\frac{3}{5}\right)x + 3$

14.

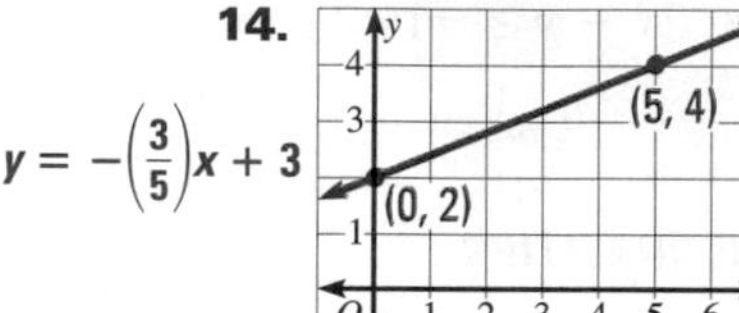

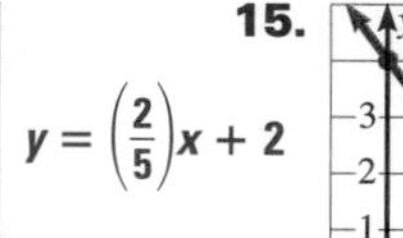

$y = \left(\frac{2}{5}\right)x + 2$

15.

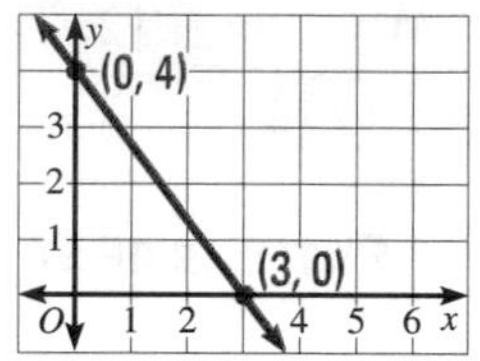

$y = -\left(\frac{4}{3}\right)x + 4$

CARS **In Exercises 16–18, use the graph which shows the speed of a car that accelerates from rest at a constant rate.**

16. Let x represent the time (in seconds) and let y represent the speed (in miles per hour). Write an equation for the speed as a function of time. **$y = 4x$**

17. Use the graph to estimate the speed of the car after 8 seconds. Check your answer using the equation from Exercise 16. **32 mi/h**

18. Is the equation from Exercise 16 direct variation? Explain. **yes; The equation is in the form $y = kx$, which is the form of a direct variation.**

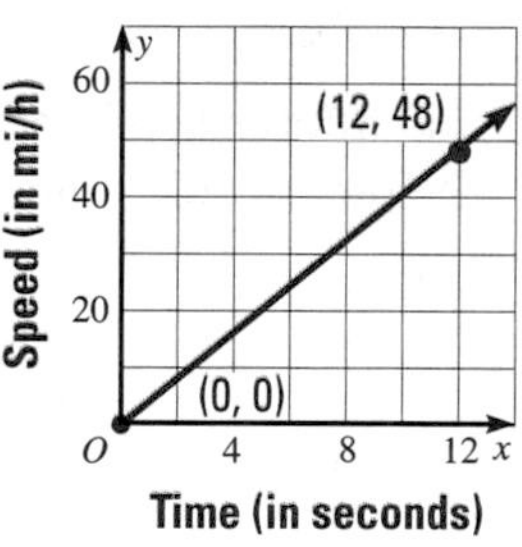

Graph the inequality. Then list three solutions.

19. $y < 7x$ **See margin. *Sample answer:* (−1, −8), (0, −1), (1, 6)**

20. $y \geq 2x + 2$ **See margin. *Sample answer:* (−1, 0), (0, 2), (1, 5)**

21. $y > 5x - 7$ **See margin. *Sample answer:* (−1, −1), (0, 0), (1, 1)**

Graph the system to find the solution or solutions.

22. $x = y - 4$, $y = -3x$ **See margin; (−1, 3)**

23. $x \geq y$, $3y \geq x$ **See margin.**

24. $x > y - 5$, $x < y + 5$ **See margin.**

Multiple-Choice Practice

Test Tip When checking your work, try to use a method other than the one you originally used to find your answer.

1. Which function rule relates x and y for the ordered pairs $(0, -2)$, $(2, 2)$, $(3, 4)$, and $(5, 8)$? **C**

Ⓐ $y = x^2 - 2$ Ⓑ $y = x - 2$

Ⓒ $y = 2x - 2$ Ⓓ $y = 3x - 5$

2. From 1990 through 1994, the U.S. skim milk consumption C (in gallons) per person can be modeled by the linear equation $C = 0.17t + 2.6$ where $t = 0$ represents 1990, $t = 1$ represents 1991, and so on. Which ordered pair is *not* described by the equation? **F**

Ⓕ (0, 2.77) Ⓖ (2, 2.94)

Ⓗ (3, 3.11) Ⓙ (4, 3.28)

3. The table shows the number of hits you had playing softball for each season from 1995 through 1999, where $t = 5$ represents 1995. Which linear equation represents the data? **C**

t	5	6	7	8	9
N	21	25	29	33	37

Ⓐ $N = 2t + 11$ Ⓑ $N = 3t + 6$

Ⓒ $N = 4t + 1$ Ⓓ $N = 5t - 4$

4. Which statement about the graph of the equation $y = -\frac{1}{2}x + 3$ is *false*? **F**

Ⓕ The line's x-intercept is 3.

Ⓖ The line has a negative slope.

Ⓗ The line's y-intercept is 3.

Ⓙ The line has a slope of $-\frac{1}{2}$.

5. What are the slope and y-intercept of the graph of the linear equation $3x + 2y = -4$? **D**

Ⓐ 3; −4 Ⓑ −3; −2

Ⓒ 1.5; −2 Ⓓ −1.5; −2

6. Which inequality represents the sentence? *The difference of 6 times a number and twice another number is greater than 19.* **J**

Ⓕ $4y > 19$ Ⓖ $2x - 6y \geq 19$

Ⓗ $2x - 6y > 19$ Ⓙ $6x - 2y > 19$

7. Which line is the graph of direct variation? **C**

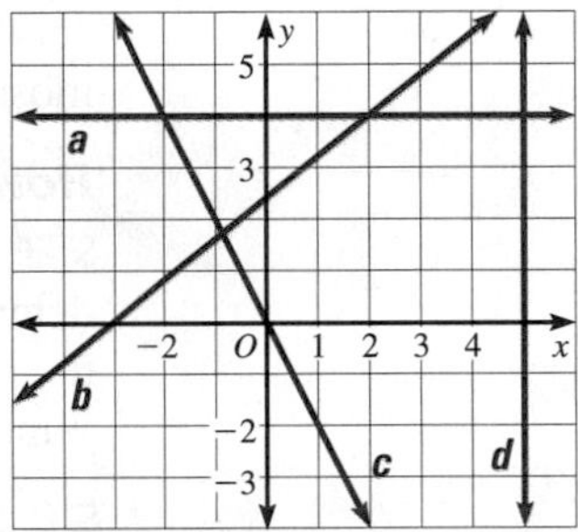

Ⓐ Line a Ⓑ Line b

Ⓒ Line c Ⓓ Line d

8. Which ordered pair is *not* a solution of the system? **J**

$$y \leq 3x$$
$$x \geq 2y$$

Ⓕ (0, 0) Ⓖ (1, 0)

Ⓗ (3, 1) Ⓙ (2, 3)

11.

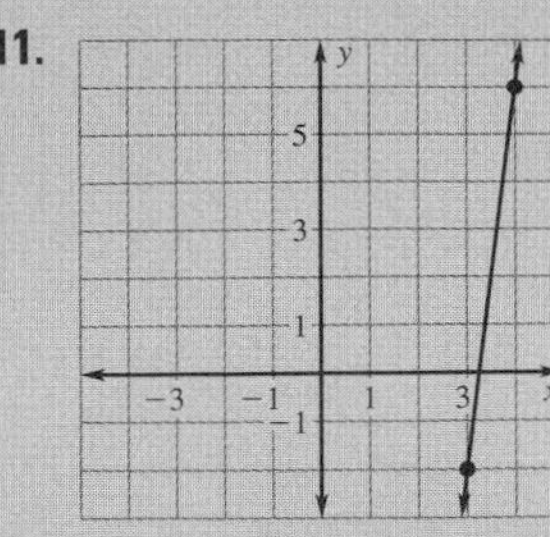

12.

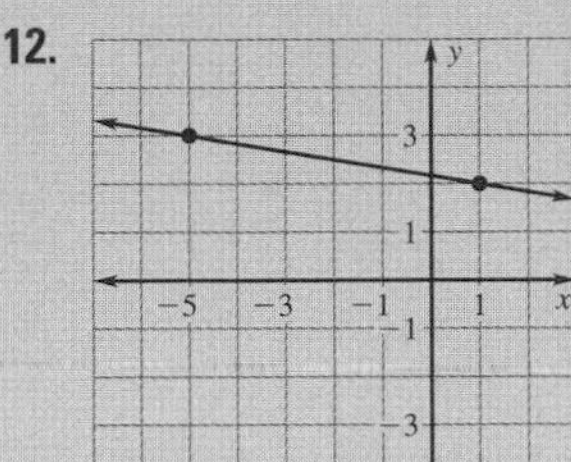

19.

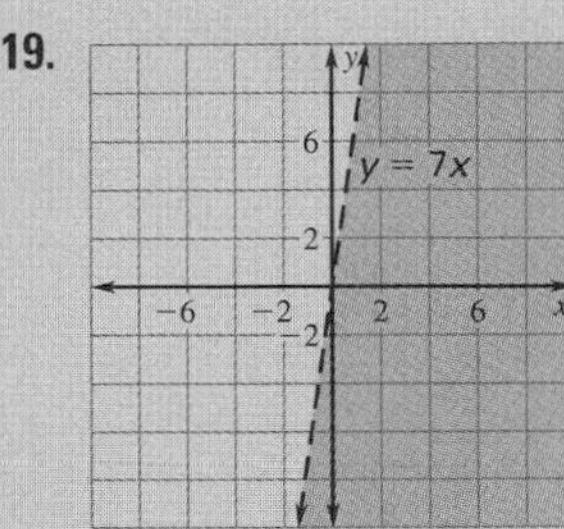

20.

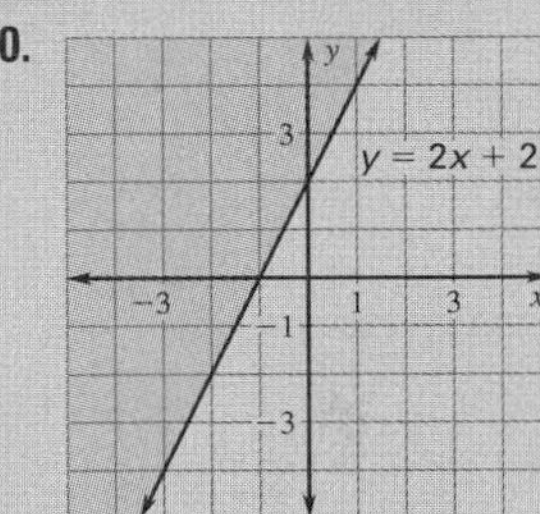

21.

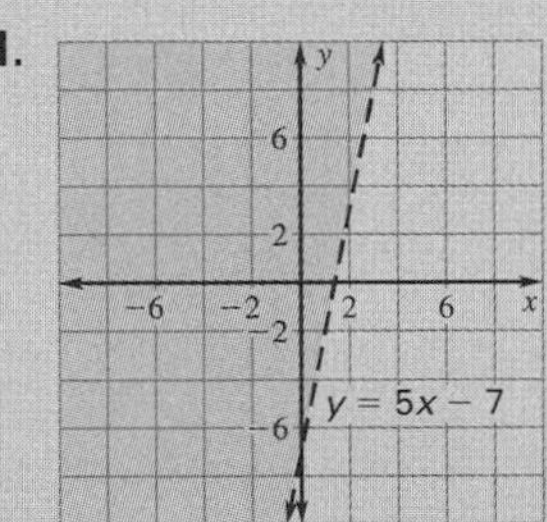

22.

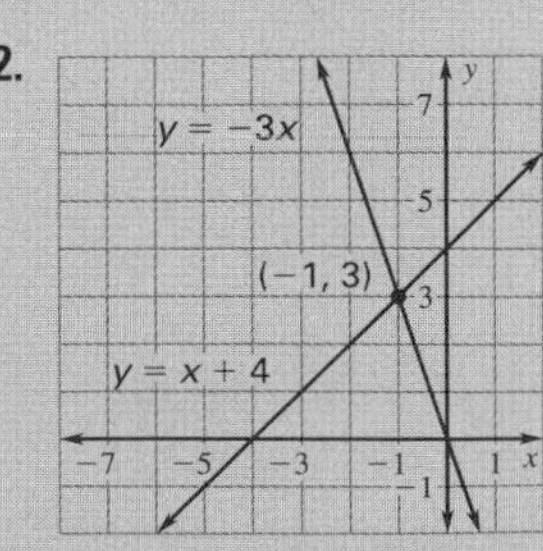

23–24. See Additional Answers beginning on page AA1.

Teaching Tip

The Brain Games activity provides a motivating way to review selected content in the chapter. For a more comprehensive review, see the Chapter Summary and Review on pp. 606–609.

Brain games

California Standards

- Graph and interpret linear functions. (AF 3.0)
- Analyze problems by observing patterns. (MR 1.1)

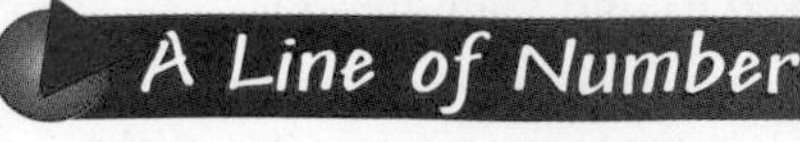

A Line of Numbers

Materials

- **2 coordinate planes**
- **2 pieces of transparency film with a line drawn on each**
- **A slope spinner with sections labeled 1, 3, $-\frac{1}{4}$, $\frac{2}{3}$, −0.5, and 4**
- **A *y*-intercept spinner with sections labeled 0, −1, 2, 3, −4, and 6**

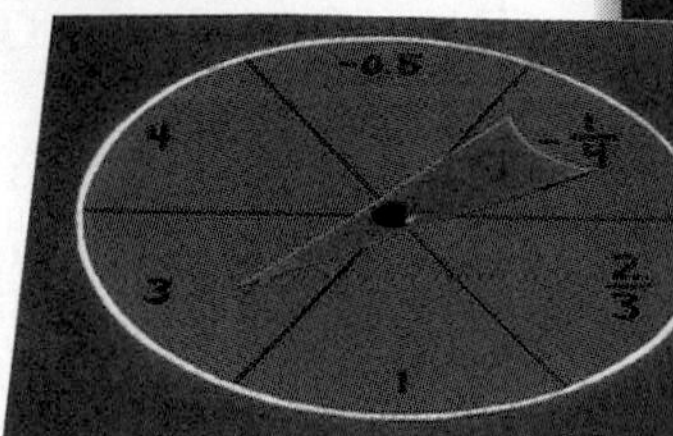

SLOPE

Y-INTERCEPT

Directions

Object of the Game

Play in groups of five. Form two teams of two players and choose a referee. Teams earn one point for writing the correct equation and two points for correctly placing the line on the coordinate plane. The winner of the game is the team with the most points after a set number of rounds.

How to Play

STEP 1 One team spins the slope spinner to determine the slope. The other team spins the *y*-intercept spinner to determine the *y*-intercept. The referee records the results.

STEP 2 Each team writes an equation of the line using the recorded slope and *y*-intercept. Then each team uses the line on the transparency film to show the placement of the line on the coordinate plane. The referee determines the correct answers and records the score for each team.

Another Way to Play

Use the *y*-intercept spinner as an *x*-intercept spinner.

Brain Teaser

$y = -x + 7$

What Linear Function am I?

• When my input is 4 my output is 3.

• When my input is 3 my output is 4.

California Standards and Assessment

CA Standards: AF 3.0, MR 1.1

The basic skills you'll review on this page will help prepare you for the next chapter.

Reviewing the Basics

EXAMPLE 1 Combining Like Terms

Simplify the expression $y + 2x - 3y + x^2$ by combining like terms. Then evaluate the expression when $x = 2$ and $y = 4$.

Solution

$y + 2x - 3y + x^2 = y - 3y + 2x + x^2$ Commutative property

$= (1 - 3)y + 2x + x^2$ Distributive property

$= -2y + 2x + x^2$ Simplify.

When $x = 2$ and $y = 4$,
$-2y + 2x + x^2 = -2(4) + 2(2) + 2^2 = 0.$

Try These

Simplify the expression. Then evaluate the expression when $x = 3$ and $y = 2$.

1. $8x + 8y + 8x + 8$ **$16x + 8y + 8$; 72**
2. $13x - 3y - 8x$ **$5x - 3y$; 9**
3. $7 + y - x - 9y$ **$7 - x - 8y$; -12**
4. $10x + 2x + 5 - y$ **$12x + 5 - y$; 39**
5. $3x + 5x + 2x - 16x$ **$-6x$; -18**
6. $2x + y^2 + 2y^2$ **$2x + 3y^2$; 18**

EXAMPLE 2 Simplifying Variable Expressions

Simplify the expression $\frac{4ab^2c}{2bc}$.

Solution

$$\frac{4ab^2c}{2bc} = \frac{\overset{1}{\cancel{2}} \cdot 2 \cdot a \cdot \overset{1}{\cancel{b}} \cdot b \cdot \overset{1}{\cancel{c}}}{\underset{1}{\cancel{2}} \cdot \underset{1}{\cancel{b}} \cdot \underset{1}{\cancel{c}}} = \frac{2ab}{1} = 2ab$$

Try These

Simplify the expression.

7. $\frac{10xy}{5x}$ **$2y$**
8. $\frac{3x^2}{2x}$ **$\frac{3x}{2}$**
9. $\frac{15x^2y^2z^3}{5x^2y^2z}$ **$3z^2$**
10. $\frac{20a^2b}{10ac}$ **$\frac{2ab}{c}$**
11. $\frac{3x^2z}{15xy}$ **$\frac{xz}{5y}$**
12. $\frac{25mn^2}{100mnp^2}$ **$\frac{n}{4p^2}$**
13. $\frac{49b^3c}{14b}$ **$\frac{7b^2c}{2}$**
14. $\frac{4def^2}{72de}$ **$\frac{f^2}{18}$**
15. $\frac{54a^5bc^2}{12a^2bc}$ **$\frac{9a^3c}{2}$**

Student Help

▶ **MORE EXAMPLES**

INTERNET More examples and practice exercises available at www.mcdougallittell.com

Additional Resources

Technology

- Personal Student Tutor
- Test and Practice Generator

Pacing and Assignment Guide

Regular Schedule

Lesson	Les. Day	Transitional	Average	Advanced
12.1	Day 1	EP p. 701 Exs. 88–93; pp. 620–621 Exs. 21–24, 33–36, 47–50, 56–59, 68–70, 78–79, 87–88	pp. 620–621 Exs. 25–28, 37–40, 46–50, 60–63, 71–73, 80–81, 87–88	pp. 620–621 Exs. 29–32, 41–45, 51–55, 64–67, 74–76, 77*, 82–83, 87–88; EC: TE p. 614D*
12.2	Day 1	pp. 624–625 Exs. 15–17, 21–24, 31–36, 42–43, 52–53	pp. 624–625 Exs. 15–17, 23–26, 33–38, 42–45, 52–53	pp. 624–625 Exs. 15–17, 27–30, 35–40, 41*, 42–43, 48–49, 52–53
12.3	Day 1	pp. 628–629 Exs. 5–12, 16–19, 25–26	pp. 628–629 Exs. 5–15, 18–19, 23*, 25–26	pp. 628–629 Exs. 5–12, 18–22, 23–24*, 25–26
12.4	Day 1	EP p. 705 Exs. 31–33; pp. 632–634 Exs. 10–18, 22–25, 27–31, 45–51	pp. 632–634 Exs. 13–25, 27–31, 39–40, 45–51	pp. 632–634 Exs. 13–23, 25–31, 36–38, 42–44*, 45–51
12.5	Day 1	pp. 640–641 Exs. 11–15, 19–24, 32–33, 35–38, 54–55	pp. 640–641 Exs. 12–15, 22–27, 32–33, 39–42, 51–52, 54–55	pp. 640–641 Exs. 16–18, 25–31, 33–34, 43–48, 52, 53*, 54–55; EC: TE p. 614D*
12.6	Day 1	pp. 645–647 Exs. 6–12, 14–16, 18–20, 33–34	pp. 645–647 Exs. 6–9, 11–16, 23–28, 33–34	pp. 645–647 Exs. 6–9, 11–16, 22*, 23–28, 29–32*, 33–34
12.7	Day 1	pp. 651–653 Exs. 21–32, 62–63, 87–89, 93–96, 98–100	pp. 651–653 Exs. 25–36, 62–63, 87–89, 93–96, 98–100	pp. 651–653 Exs. 25–36, 62–63, 87–89, 93–96, 98–100
	Day 2	pp. 651–653 Exs. 37–45, 55–56, 59–60, 68–71, 75–78, 85–86	pp. 651–653 Exs. 40–48, 55–56, 64–65, 68–70, 83–86	pp. 651–653 Exs. 46–54, 57–58, 60–61, 65–67, 73–74, 79, 80–82*, 83–86
Review	Day 1	pp. 654–657 Exs. 1–71	pp. 654–657 Exs. 1–71	pp. 654–657 Exs. 1–71
Assess	Day 1	Chapter 12 Test	Chapter 12 Test	Chapter 12 Test

Yearly Pacing *Chapter 12 Total* – **10 days** *Chapters 1–12 Total* – **160 days** *Remaining* – **0 days**

* Challenge Exercises EP = Extra Practice SRH = Skills Review Handbook EC = Extra Challenge

Block Schedule

Day 1	Day 2	Day 3	Day 4	Day 5
12.1 pp. 620–621: Exs. 25–28, 37–40, 46–50, 60–63, 71–73, 80–81, 87–88 **12.2** pp. 624–625: Exs. 15–17, 23–26, 33–38, 42–43, 44–45, 52–53	**12.3** pp. 628–629: Exs. 5–15, 18–19, 23*, 25–26 **12.4** pp. 632–634: Exs. 13–25, 27–31, 39–40, 45–51	**12.5** pp. 640–641: Exs. 12–15, 22–27, 32–33, 39–42, 51–52, 54–55 **12.6** pp. 645–647: Exs. 6–9, 11–16, 22–28, 33–34	**12.7** pp. 651–653: Exs. 25–36, 40–48, 55–56, 62–65, 68–70, 83–89, 93–96, 98–100	**Review** pp. 654–657: Exs. 1–71 **Assess** Chapter 12 Test

Yearly Pacing *Chapter 12 Total* – **5 days** *Chapters 1–12 Total* – **80 days** *Remaining* – **0 days**

Support Materials

Chapter Resource Book

LESSON SUPPORT	12.1	12.2	12.3	12.4	12.5	12.6	12.7
Lesson Plans	p. 1	p. 10	p. 19	p. 28	p. 37	p. 46	p. 55
Lesson Plans for Block Scheduling	p. 2	p. 11	p. 20	p. 29	p. 38	p. 47	p. 56
Warm-Ups with Multiple-Choice Practice	p. 3	p. 12	p. 21	p. 30	p. 39	p. 48	p. 57
Problem of the Day	p. 4	p. 13	p. 22	p. 31	p. 40	p. 49	p. 58
Daily Cumulative Review	p. 5	p. 14	p. 23	p. 32	p. 41	p. 50	p. 59
Practice Masters	p. 6	p. 15	p. 24	p. 33	p. 42	p. 51	p. 60
Reteaching Masters	p. 7	p. 16	p. 25	p. 34	p. 43	p. 52	p. 61
Enrichment Masters	p. 9	p. 18	p. 27	p. 36	p. 45	p. 54	p. 63

Transparencies

	12.1	12.2	12.3	12.4	12.5	12.6	12.7
Warm-Ups with Multiple-Choice Practice	p. 95	p. 96	p. 97	p. 98	p. 99	p. 100	p. 101
Teacher Time-Saver Transparencies	✓	✓	✓	✓	✓	✓	✓
English/Spanish Problem Solving			p. 54		p. 55	p. 56	p. 57
Answer Transparencies	✓	✓	✓	✓	✓	✓	✓

Technology

- Personal Student Tutor
- Time-Saving Test and Practice Generator
- Electronic Teacher Tools
- Technology: Using Calculators and Computers

Additional Resources

- Math Log
- Assessment Book
- Worked-Out Solution Key
- Practice Workbook (English/Spanish)
- Home and School Connection
- California Standards: Key Concepts Book

Correlation to the California Curriculum

Correlations to the California Standards
CA Standards: NS 2.3, AF 1.3, AF 1.4, AF 1.5, AF 2.1, AF 2.2, AF 3.1, AF 3.2, MR 2.2, MR 2.5

California Curriculum Support

Key Concepts Book
- Pre-Course Review: Topic 1 Working with Decimals
  Topic 5 Measurement

California Standards Practice Workbook provides practice for each Standard that is covered in this chapter.

Providing Universal Access

Strategies for Strategic Learners

EXPLICITLY TEACH PATTERNS

In solving polynomials, students should watch for three recurring themes:

$$(a + b)(a + b) = a^2 + 2ab + b^2$$

$$(a - b)(a - b) = a^2 - 2ab + b^2$$

$$(a - b)(a + b) = a^2 - b^2$$

These basic patterns recur repeatedly when multiplying polynomials; recognizing them in different forms is a big help in problem solving.

DIFFERENTIATE INSTRUCTION IN TERMS OF PACING

In spite of all the hard work of students, teachers, and parents, some students will not be able to master the concepts in this course. Typically, the next course is algebra or an integrated course involving algebra. If students are struggling at this point, it is probably because they do not really understand the key concepts that have been covered thus far. Nothing is to be gained by rushing these students. A better strategy is to slow the pace down for these students and analyze which key concepts are not well understood. The teacher can use the online test generator to help diagnose weak areas.

EXTEND INSTRUCTIONAL TIME Students who are falling behind need more mathematics instructional time. Work with the student and his or her parents, with the school principal, and with the district office to see if struggling students can extend the instructional time through summer school. If not, students who will complete the course with a C or lower should be strongly encouraged to repeat the course. Repeating a course is something adults are very comfortable with. Many of us take a computer course over or repeat a course we took some time ago because we have forgotten the material. But for a student, repeating a course is usually seen as a failure. Encouraging students to retake a math course as a way to ensure the proper foundation for future study should be presented as a viable option for students. Students may find that the course is much easier the second time because they are building on those concepts and skills they did learn. This can provide a welcome relief in a difficult class schedule for many students. Repeating a course can demonstrate to students that persistence pays off. And most of all, research has shown that self-esteem grows when students tackle a challenge and succeed.

Strategies for English Learners

FOCUS ON MATHEMATICAL SYMBOLS

In spite of the fact that the English used in the text is becoming increasingly abstract, part of students' developing competence in mathematics is being able to learn the language of the discipline. Some of the new phrases are:

power of a product rule (p. 617)
second-degree polynomial (p. 626)
extracting positive square roots (p. 648)

For English learners, however, you may want to express the concepts in mathematical symbols first and follow with a discussion of the verbal description. *Concepts and Skills* instruction follows a dual format: verbal descriptions in English are accompanied by mathematical symbols, phrases, and formulas. For example, when teaching the power of a product property, teachers may want to start by putting this expression from page 617 on the board:

$$(ab)^m = a^m b^m$$

Next, substitute numbers for variables, so that students can see that the rule works. Then discuss the explanation in English on that same page.

Students should be reassured that even though they are working with mathematical expressions and equations that are more complex, logical mathematical reasoning underlies all of mathematics. Everything can be explained, although some explanations have to be taken at face value at this point, because students are still learning the mathematics they need to be able to understand the proofs. The same basic rules, including the associative property, the distributive property, and the commutative property, still apply. The same basic strategies for evaluating polynomials, such as combining like terms and removing factors of one, still apply.

Strategies for Advanced Learners

SUBSTITUTE CHALLENGE PROBLEMS

Advanced students may benefit from substituting more challenging problems for some of the problems in the textbook.

Problem: Which is greater, $(3^3)^3$ or $3^{(3^3)}$? How many times greater is it?

Solution: $3^{(3^3)}$; 3^{18} times

Problem: Show that $16^x \cdot (4^x)^2 = (2^x)^8$.

Solution: $16^x \cdot (4^x)^2 = 16^x \cdot 4^{2x} = (2^4)^x \cdot (2^2)^{2x}$
$= 2^{4x} \cdot 2^{4x} = 2^{8x} = (2^x)^8$

Advanced students could also be challenged by exercises involving both positive and negative signs.

Find the product.

1. $(x + 2)(x - 4)$ $(x^2 - 2x - 8)$
2. $(-x - 1)(-x + 3)$ $(x^2 - 2x - 3)$
3. $(3x - 1)(2x - 2)$ $(6x^2 - 8x + 2)$
4. $(-2x - 5)(x + 8)$ $(-2x^2 - 21x - 40)$
5. $(-2x + 1)(x + 3)$ $(-2x^2 - 5x + 3)$
6. $(-6x + 2)(x - 4)$ $(-6x^2 + 26x - 8)$

After using the distributive property to multiply several of these types of problems with positive and negative signs, students may see a number of patterns emerging. Ask students to consider what happens in the following situations using variables (where a, b, c, and d are all positive):

$(a + b)(c + d) = \underline{\ ?\ }$ $(ac + ad + bc + bd)$
$(a - b)(c - d) = \underline{\ ?\ }$ $(ac - ad - bc + bd)$
$(a + b)(c - d) = \underline{\ ?\ }$ $(ac - ad + bc - bd)$

Students should be able to see that in the first case, all the terms in the resulting expression will be positive.

In the second case, the first term $(a)(c)$ will be positive, and the last term $(-b)(-d)$ will be positive.

In the third case, the first term $(a)(c)$ will be positive, but the last term $(b)(-d)$ will be negative.

This information will be vital to students when they factor more complicated equations.

CHAPTER 12

Mathematical Background Notes

In earlier chapters, the basic rules for arithmetic were extended from real numbers to variables. In the present chapter they are extended to polynomials.

In many ways, the algebraic properties of polynomials are like those of real numbers. The sum and product of two polynomials is again a polynomial, and the CAD laws are satisfied for polynomials as they are for real numbers. This is not surprising, since we are dealing with polynomials whose variables represent real numbers.

Lessons 12.2–12.5

ADDING AND SUBTRACTING As was the case with numbers, the commutative and associative properties are central to the addition of polynomials. Since

$$(3x^2 + x) + 5 = 3x^2 + (x + 5),$$

we can simply omit the parentheses and write $3x^2 + x + 5$. These properties also allow us to regroup and rearrange terms when adding polynomials, as in

$$\begin{aligned}(3x^2 + x + 5) + (x^2 + 2x + 1) &= 3x^2 + x^2 + x + 2x + 5 + 1\\ &= 4x^2 + 3x + 6.\end{aligned}$$

The "opposite" of a polynomial $Q(x)$ results from multiplication by -1. Using the distributive property, the opposite of $Q(x) = x^2 - 2x + 5$ is

$$\begin{aligned}(-1)Q(x) = (-1)(x^2 - 2x + 5) &= (-1)(x^2 + (-2)x + 5)\\ &= (-1)x^2 + (-1)(-2)x + (-1)5\\ &= -x^2 + 2x - 5.\end{aligned}$$

As with numbers, subtracting $Q(x)$ from a polynomial $P(x)$ is the same as adding the opposite of $Q(x)$ to $P(x)$.

$$\begin{aligned}(3x^2 + x + 5) - (x^2 - 2x + 5) &= (3x^2 + x + 5) + (-x^2 + 2x - 5)\\ &= 3x^2 - x^2 + x + 2x + 5 - 5\\ &= 2x^2 + 3x\end{aligned}$$

MULTIPLYING Multiplication of polynomials depends heavily on the distributive property. The student should begin by calculating the products of polynomials and monomials, such as

$$\begin{aligned}(3x^2)(2x^3 - 4x^2 + 3x + 1) &= (3x^2)(2x^3) - (3x^2)(4x^2) + (3x^2)(3x) + 3x^2\\ &= 6x^5 - 12x^4 + 9x^3 + 3x^2.\end{aligned}$$

In simplifying products of monomials, the associative and commutative properties of multiplication are used.

$$(3x^2)(2x^3) = (3) \cdot (2) \cdot (x \cdot x) \cdot (x \cdot x \cdot x) = 6 \cdot x \cdot x \cdot x \cdot x \cdot x = 6x^5$$

The steps detailed in the last line correspond to the general rule

$$(ax^m)(bx^n) = abx^{m+n}$$

for numbers a and b and integers m and n.

Having learned to apply the rule $(ax^m)(bx^n) = abx^{m+n}$, the student has the essential tools for the multiplication of polynomials. In this chapter, these skills are only applied to the product of simple binomials. For example,

$$\begin{aligned}(2x + 4)(3x + 5) &= (2x)(3x) + (2x)(5) + (4)(3x) + (4)(5)\\ &= 6x^2 + 10x + 12x + 20\\ &= 6x^2 + 22x + 20\end{aligned}$$

where "FOIL" can be used to make the process more efficient. The FOIL rule for multiplication corresponds to two applications of the distributive property.

$$(a + b)(c + d) = a(c + d) + b(c + d) = \underset{\text{First}}{ac} + \underset{\text{Outer}}{ad} + \underset{\text{Inner}}{bc} + \underset{\text{Last}}{bd}$$

This can be applied whether a, b, c, and d are numbers or polynomials.

In later courses the student will encounter polynomials with more than two terms and a more general rule resulting from the distributive property. Applying the distributive property to the product of three terms gives

$$\begin{aligned}(a + b + c)(d + e + f) &= a(d + e + f) + b(d + e + f) + c(d + e + f)\\ &= ad + ae + af + bd + be + bf + cd + ce + cf\end{aligned}$$

and illustrates the fact that the product of *any* two sums is the product of terms taken two at a time.

VISUAL REPRESENTATIONS Such identities also have geometric interpretations corresponding to the picture for $(a + b)(a + b)$ at the top of page 639. For example, if a, b, c, d, e, and f are positive numbers, we can dissect a rectangle of base $= (a + b + c)$ and height $= (d + e + f)$ into smaller rectangles, as below.

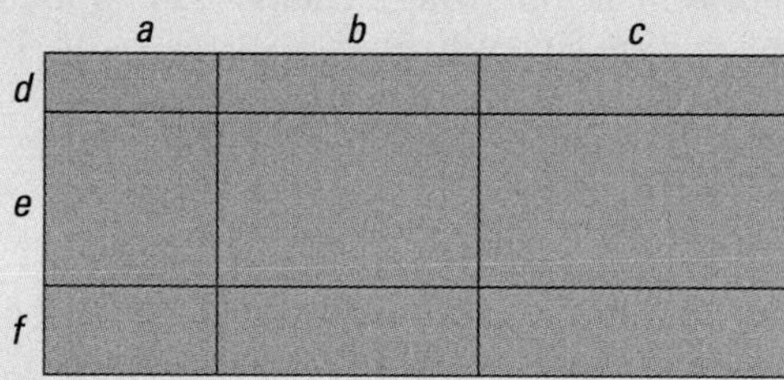

The product formula for $(a + b + c)(d + e + f)$ expresses the fact that the area of the big rectangle is the sum of the areas of the nine little rectangles.

Pictorial representations of algebraic identities are often intriguing and can be used for enrichment as well as reinforcing abstract concepts. For $a > b > 0$, the picture below contains a geometric representation of the important identity

$$a^2 - b^2 = (a - b)(a + b).$$

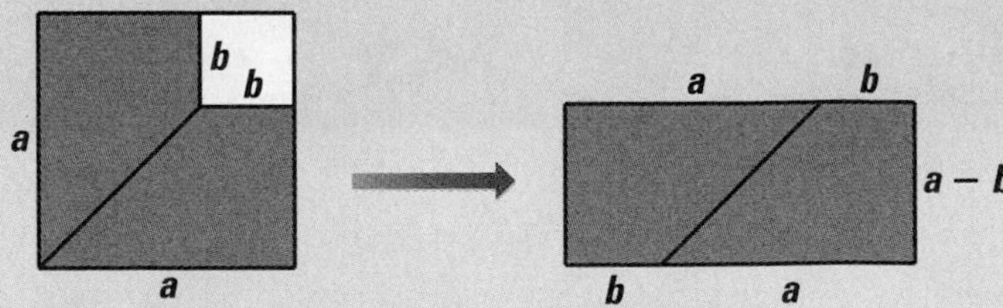

Such examples illustrate the important fact that if a plane figure is cut into smaller pieces, then the area of the figure is the sum of the areas of the pieces. In the picture above, the L-shaped figure and the rectangle have each been cut into two congruent trapezoids of equal areas.

Lessons 12.6–12.7

SOLVING ALGEBRAICALLY These lessons discuss the solution of the simple quadratic equation $ax^2 = b$ in both algebraic and graphical forms.

In dealing algebraically with $ax^2 = b$, where $a \neq 0$, the first step is to transform the equation into the equivalent form

$$x^2 = \frac{b}{a}$$

by "dividing both sides by a." If $\frac{b}{a} < 0$, this equation has no solution, since x^2 cannot be negative. But assuming $\frac{b}{a} \geq 0$, the solution calls for "taking the square root of both sides" to obtain

$$\sqrt{x^2} = \sqrt{\frac{b}{a}}.$$

Since $\sqrt{x^2} = |x|$, this gives $|x| = \sqrt{\frac{b}{a}}$ which implies that $x = \sqrt{\frac{b}{a}}$ or $x = -\sqrt{\frac{b}{a}}$. In this way we are led to the solution

$$x = \pm\sqrt{\frac{b}{a}}.$$

At a later stage, one encounters the question of whether these are the *only* solutions of $x^2 = \frac{b}{a}$. This turns out to be the same as asking whether the only solutions of

$$x^2 = c^2 \quad \text{or} \quad x^2 - c^2 = 0$$

are $x = \pm c$.

The answer to the second question can be addressed by noting that $x^2 - c^2 = 0$ is equivalent to

$$(x + c)(x - c) = 0.$$

The *zero product property* of arithmetic asserts that for real numbers A and B, we have $AB = 0$ if and only if $A = 0$ or $B = 0$ (or both). Therefore, the equation $(x + c)(x - c) = 0$ is satisfied if and only if

$$x + c = 0 \text{ or } x - c = 0.$$

These equations are equivalent to $x = -c$ and $x = c$, respectively.

SOLVING GRAPHICALLY A graphical treatment of the equation

$$ax^2 = b$$

gives students some practice in graphing and links geometry to the solution of equations. In Example 6 on page 650, the equation

$$\frac{1}{3}x^2 = 12$$

is studied by first drawing the graph of $y = \frac{1}{3}x^2$. The curve so obtained is a parabola that opens upward. Next the graph of $y = 12$ is drawn. This is a horizontal line 12 units above the x-axis. A point (x_1, y_1) that marks the intersection between the line and the parabola lies on both graphs and, therefore, must satisfy both

$$y_1 = \frac{1}{3}x_1{}^2 \quad \text{and} \quad y_1 = 12.$$

Since $\frac{1}{3}x_1{}^2 = y_1 = 12$, it follows that x_1 satisfies the equation $\frac{1}{3}x^2 = 12$.

In examining these graphs, we see that the line intersects the parabola in two points whose coordinates appear to be $(-6, 12)$ and $(6, 12)$. On this basis we may guess that $x = \pm 6$ are the solutions of $\frac{1}{3}x^2 = 12$, a result that can now be confirmed algebraically.

It must be kept in mind that such graphical methods of solution can only be relied upon to provide *approximations* to the actual solution. Algebraic methods are required to determine whether or not such approximations are in fact solutions.

Chapter Overview

Chapter Goals

In this chapter, students will learn more properties of exponents and will recognize monomials and polynomials. They will:

- Add, subtract, and multiply polynomials.
- Graph $y = ax^2$ and $y = ax^3$.
- Solve polynomial equations.

Career Note

Part of the job of state police officers is to investigate accidents on state highways. When responding to an accident, they often must give first aid, call for emergency vehicles, and direct traffic around the site of the accident. They must interview drivers and witnesses, and take measurements at the scene in order to write a report to help determine the cause of the accident. Training for state troopers varies by state, but they often have to pass a written exam and meet certain physical requirements.

Additional information about state police officers and accident investigation is available at **www.mcdougallittell.com**

Polynomials

Why are polynomials important?

The expressions $4s$ for the perimeter of a square, s^2 for the area of a square, and s^3 for the volume of a cube are all examples of monomials, the building blocks of polynomials. Polynomials are not only useful in expressing geometric measurements but also may be used to model real-life data.

Polynomials are used in many careers, including accident investigation (page 615) and human resources (page 639). For example, accident investigators can use a polynomial equation to tell how fast a car was going before it began to skid.

Meeting the California Standards

The skills you'll learn in this chapter will help you meet state standards and prepare for standardized tests. In this chapter you'll:

- **Multiply and divide monomials. Take powers of and extract roots of monomials.** LESSONS 12.1, 12.4, 12.5, 12.7
- **Use algebraic terminology, such as coefficient and term.** LESSON 12.2
- **Simplify numerical expressions.** LESSONS 12.2–12.5, 12.7
- **Graph and use functions of the form $y = nx^2$ and $y = nx^3$.** LESSON 12.6
- **Plot the values of volumes of three-dimensional shapes for various values of the edge lengths.** LESSON 12.6

Career Link **ACCIDENT INVESTIGATOR** An accident investigator uses polynomials when:

- determining the speed of a car before it began to skid.
- predicting a car's stopping distance.

EXERCISES

When a car skids to a stop, an accident investigator can use the length of the skid d (in feet) to find the speed s (in miles per hour) of the car before it began to skid. In the equation below, the coefficient of friction f is determined by the road surface and weather. In dry weather $f = 0.8$.

$$d = \frac{1}{30f}s^2$$

1. Copy and complete the table. **See margin.**

2. If one vehicle's skid mark at an accident site is twice as long as another vehicle's skid mark, does that mean the first vehicle was traveling twice as fast as the second vehicle? Explain. Use the data in your table. **See margin.**

3. Compare the stopping distance at 50 miles per hour to distances you are familiar with, such as the length of your classroom. **Answers will vary.**

In Lesson 12.7, you will learn how to find the speed of a car that left skid marks on a wet road.

Stopping Distance in Dry Weather	
Speed (in miles per hour)	Stopping distance (in feet)
10	?
20	?
30	?
40	?
50	?
60	?

Projects

A project covering Chapters 10–12 appears on pages 664–665 of the Student Edition. Additional projects for selected lessons in Chapter 12 are available in the *Assessment Book,* pp. 263–264.

Technology

Software

- Electronic Teacher Tools
- Online Lesson Planner
- Personal Student Tutor
- Test and Practice Generator

Internet Connections

- Application and Career Links 619, 623, 625, 629, 639, 652
- Student Help 618, 633, 638, 644, 646, 649, 661

These Internet connections are available at **www.mcdougallittell.com**

1.

Stopping Distance in Dry Weather	
Speed (in miles per hour)	Stopping distance (in feet)
10	4
20	17
30	38
40	67
50	104
60	150

2. ***Sample answer:*** **No; a vehicle traveling at 30 miles per hour would make a skid mark about 38 feet long, while a vehicle traveling at 60 miles per hour would make a skid mark about 150 feet long.**

Prepare

Diagnostic Tools

The **chapter readiness quiz** can help you diagnose whether students have the following skills needed in Chapter 12:

- Solve linear equations.
- Compute square roots.
- Simplify algebraic expressions.
- Evaluate algebraic expressions.

Reteaching Materials

The following resources are available for students who need additional help with the skills on the chapter readiness quiz:

Chapter 12 Resource Book

- Reteaching with Practice (Lessons 1.8, 3.4, 3.5, 4.2, 9.1)

Personal Student Tutor

Additional Resources

The following resources are provided to help you prepare for the upcoming chapter and customize review materials:

Chapter 12 Resource Book

- Lesson Plans, pp. 1, 10, 19, 28, 37, 46, 55
- Lesson Plans for Block Scheduling, pp. 2, 11, 20, 29, 38, 47, 56

Technology

- Electronic Teacher Tools with Lesson Planning Software
- Test and Practice Generator

Chapter 12 Getting Ready

PREVIEW

What's the chapter about?

- Adding, subtracting, and multiplying **polynomials**
- Graphing **nonlinear functions** and solving nonlinear polynomial equations

WORDS TO KNOW

- **monomial,** *p. 617*
- **polynomial,** *p. 622*
- **binomial,** *p. 622*
- **trinomial,** *p. 622*
- **standard form,** *p. 622*
- **degree of a polynomial,** *p. 626*
- **FOIL method,** *p. 638*

PREPARE

Chapter Readiness Quiz

VOCABULARY CHECK *(refer to pp. 174, 449)*

1. What is the solution of the equation $3x + 2x - 10 = 5$? **C**

Ⓐ -3 Ⓑ -2 Ⓒ 3 Ⓓ 15

2. What are the two square roots of 4000? **J**

Ⓕ 20 and -20 Ⓖ 40 and -40 Ⓗ 40 and 100 Ⓙ Not here

SKILL CHECK *(refer to pp. 38, 124, 130)*

3. Which of these expressions is equivalent to $3(x + 6)$? **D**

Ⓐ $3x + 6$ Ⓑ $3x + 6x$ Ⓒ $3x + 9$ Ⓓ $3x + 18$

4. Simplify $3y - (-5y) - 2$. **G**

Ⓕ $8y + 2$ Ⓖ $8y - 2$ Ⓗ $6y$ Ⓙ $-2y - 2$

5. What is the value of $-a^2b^3$ when $a = 3$ and $b = -5$? **D**

Ⓐ -1125 Ⓑ -90 Ⓒ 90 Ⓓ 1125

STUDY TIP

Review Your Notes

Review your notes before you take a quiz or a test. This review will help you remember the important concepts you have studied.

Reviewing My Notes

- Look through all notes I took that apply to the test or quiz.
- Be sure I understand what I wrote.
- Look in my book for more information.

12.1 Monomials and Powers

California Standards

In this lesson you'll:

- Multiply, divide, and simplify rational numbers by using exponent rules. (NS 2.3)
- Extend the process of taking powers to monomials. (AF 2.2)

Goal 1 Powers of Products and Quotients

In Lesson 6.7 you learned two properties of exponents, the product of powers rule and the quotient of powers rule. In this lesson you will learn several other properties of exponents. First, consider what happens when you raise a product to a positive power.

$$(ab)^m = \underbrace{ab \cdot ab \cdot \cdots \cdot ab}_{m \text{ factors of } ab} = \underbrace{(a \cdot a \cdot \cdots \cdot a)}_{m \text{ factors of } a}\underbrace{(b \cdot b \cdot \cdots \cdot b)}_{m \text{ factors of } b} = a^m b^m$$

This result is known as the *power of a product* rule. In Exercise 77, you will show that this rule also holds when m is a negative integer.

Student Help

READING TIP
The expression $(ab)^m$ is read as "the *quantity* ab raised to the mth power." In general, it is *not* the same as $ab^m = a \cdot b^m$.

Raising a Product to a Power

Let m be an integer, and let a and b be nonzero numbers.

In Words	To raise a product to a power, raise each factor to that power.
In Algebra	$(ab)^m = a^m b^m$
In Arithmetic	$(2 \cdot 3)^2 = 2^2 \cdot 3^2$ because $(2 \cdot 3)^2 = 6^2 = 36$ and $2^2 \cdot 3^2 = 4 \cdot 9 = 36$.

A **monomial** is a number, a variable, or the product of a number and one or more variables raised to whole number powers, such as $3x^2$ and $-2xy^3$. When you raise a monomial to a power, you can use the power of a product rule.

EXAMPLE 1 Raising a Product to a Power

Simplify the expression.

a. $(2x)^4$ **b.** $(-x)^3$ **c.** $(-3xy)^2$

Solution

a. $(2x)^4 = 2^4x^4 = 16x^4$

b. Use the multiplicative property of -1 to rewrite $-x$ as $(-1)x$.

$(-x)^3 = [(-1)x]^3 = (-1)^3x^3 = -1x^3 = -x^3$

c. $(-3xy)^2 = (-3)^2(xy)^2 = (-3)^2x^2y^2 = 9x^2y^2$

As you will see in Exercise 45, you can extend the power of a product rule to a product of three or more factors.

1 Plan

Pacing

Suggested Number of Days

Transitional: 1 day
Average: 1 day
Advanced: 1 day
Block Schedule: 0.5 block with 12.2

Teaching Resources

Blacklines
(See page 614B.)

Transparencies
- Warm-Up Exercises
- Teacher Time-Savers
- English/Spanish Problem Solving
- Answers

Technology
- Electronic Teacher Tools
- Test and Practice Generator

2 Teach

Math Reasoning

For Mathematical Background Notes on mathematical reasoning related to this lesson, please refer to pages 614E and 614F in this Teacher's Edition.

Extra Example 1
See next page.

California Standards and Assessment

CA Standards: NS 2.3, AF 2.2

Extra Example 1

Simplify the expression.

a. $(3x)^3$ $27x^3$

b. $(-2x)^5$ $-32x^5$

c. $(-8xy)^2$ $64x^2y^2$

Extra Example 2

Simplify the expression.

a. $\left(\frac{x}{3}\right)^4$ $\frac{x^4}{81}$

b. $\left(\frac{2a}{5b}\right)^2$ $\frac{4a^2}{25b^2}$

Math Reasoning

The formula $(ab)^m = a^mb^m$ is the result of repeated applications of the commutative and associative laws of multiplication. The formula $\left(\frac{a}{b}\right)^m = \frac{a^m}{b^m}$ makes use of the fact that fractions satisfy the associative law of multiplication and that their products are calculated by the rule $\frac{a}{b} \times \frac{c}{d} = \frac{ac}{bd}$.

Teaching Tip

Remind students that whole numbers are the nonnegative integers 0, 1, 2, 3, and so on. Variable expressions that use negative integers as powers are not considered monomials. This will be important for students when they identify and classify polynomials in Lesson 12.2.

Now consider what happens when you raise a quotient to a power.

$$\left(\frac{a}{b}\right)^m = \underbrace{\left(\frac{a}{b}\right)\left(\frac{a}{b}\right) \cdot \cdots \cdot \left(\frac{a}{b}\right)}_{m \text{ factors}} = \frac{a \cdot a \cdot \cdots \cdot a}{b \cdot b \cdot \cdots \cdot b} = \frac{a^m}{b^m}$$

This result is known as the *power of a quotient* rule.

RAISING A QUOTIENT TO A POWER

Let m be an integer, and let a and b be nonzero numbers.

In Words To raise a quotient to a power, raise the numerator to that power and raise the denominator to that power.

In Algebra $\left(\frac{a}{b}\right)^m = \frac{a^m}{b^m}$

In Arithmetic $\left(\frac{2}{3}\right)^2 = \frac{2^2}{3^2}$ because $\left(\frac{2}{3}\right)^2 = \frac{2}{3} \cdot \frac{2}{3} = \frac{4}{9}$ and $\frac{2^2}{3^2} = \frac{4}{9}$.

Student Help

▶MORE EXAMPLES

More examples are available at www.mcdougallittell.com

EXAMPLE 2 Raising a Quotient to a Power

Simplify the expression.

a. $\left(\frac{x}{4}\right)^3$

b. $\left(\frac{5x}{y}\right)^2$

Solution

a. $\left(\frac{x}{4}\right)^3 = \frac{x^3}{4^3} = \frac{x^3}{64}$

b. Use the power of a quotient and the power of a product rules.

$$\left(\frac{5x}{y}\right)^2 = \frac{(5x)^2}{y^2} = \frac{5^2x^2}{y^2} = \frac{25x^2}{y^2}$$

Goal 2 RAISING A POWER TO A POWER

One more property of exponents involves raising a power to a power. It is a consequence of the product of powers rule from Lesson 6.7.

$$(a^m)^n = \underbrace{a^m \cdot a^m \cdot \cdots \cdot a^m}_{n \text{ factors}} \qquad \text{Use } a^m \text{ as a factor } n \text{ times.}$$

$$= a^{\overbrace{}^{}\underbrace{m + m + \cdots + m}_{n \text{ terms}}} \qquad \text{Product of powers rule}$$

$$= a^{mn} \qquad \text{Simplify exponent.}$$

This result is known as the *power of a power* rule.

RAISING A POWER TO A POWER

Let m and n be integers, and let a be a nonzero number.

In Words To raise a power to a power, multiply the exponents.

In Algebra $(a^m)^n = a^{mn}$

In Arithmetic $(4^3)^2 = 4^6$ because $(4^3)^2 = 64^2 = 4096$ and $4^6 = 4096$.

EXAMPLE 3 Raising a Power to a Power

Simplify the expression.

a. $(x^3)^5$ **b.** $(y^5)^2$

Solution

a. $(x^3)^5 = x^{3 \cdot 5} = x^{15}$ **b.** $(y^5)^2 = y^{5 \cdot 2} = y^{10}$

EXAMPLE 4 Using Several Properties of Exponents

Simplify the expression $(-3y^2)^3$.

Solution

$(-3y^2)^3 = (-3)^3(y^2)^3$ Use power of a product rule.

$= -27(y^2)^3$ Simplify.

$= -27y^{2 \cdot 3}$ Use power of a power rule.

$= -27y^6$ Simplify.

Link to Astronomy

SUN The surface of the sun is called the *photosphere*. A region called the *corona* extends millions of kilometers beyond the photosphere and is visible during eclipses.

More about the sun available at www.mcdougallittell.com

EXAMPLE 5 Using Properties of Exponents

SUN The radius of the sun is about 7.0×10^5 kilometers. What is the sun's approximate volume? Express the answer in scientific notation.

Solution

$V = \frac{4}{3}\pi r^3$ Write formula for volume of a sphere.

$= \frac{4}{3}\pi(7.0 \times 10^5)^3$ Substitute 7.0×10^5 for r.

$= \frac{4}{3}\pi(7.0)^3(10^5)^3$ Use power of a product rule.

$= \frac{4}{3}\pi(343)(10^{15})$ Use power of a power rule and simplify.

$\approx (1437)(10^{15})$ Use a calculator.

$\approx 1.4 \times 10^{18}$ Express result in scientific notation.

ANSWER ▶ The volume of the sun is about 1.4×10^{18} cubic kilometers.

Extra Example 3

Simplify the expression.

a. $(m^2)^4$ m^8

b. $(n^3)^6$ n^{18}

Extra Example 4

Simplify the expression $(-5a^3)^2$. $25a^6$

Extra Example 5

The radius of Earth is about 2.1×10^7 feet. What is Earth's approximate volume? Express the answer in scientific notation. **about 3.9×10^{22} ft^3**

Math Reasoning

In carrying out computations involving π, students should be encouraged to simplify expressions before substituting an approximate value for π.

Concept Check

How do you simplify an expression that has a product raised to a power? that has a quotient raised to a power? that has a power raised to a power? ***Sample answer:*** **Raise each of the factors in the product to the power and then simplify each. Raise both the numerator and the denominator to the power and simplify each. Multiply the powers.**

3 Apply

Assignment Guide

Transitional
Day 1: pp. 620–621 Exs. 21–24, 33–36, 47–50, 56–59, 68–70, 78–79, 87–88

Average
Day 1: pp. 620–621 Exs. 25–28, 37–40, 46–50, 60–63, 71–73, 80–81, 87–88

Advanced
Day 1: pp. 620–621 Exs. 29–32, 41–45, 51–55, 64–67, 74–76, 77*, 82–83, 87–88; EC: TE p. 614D*

Block Schedule
pp. 620–621 Exs. 25–28, 37–40, 46–50, 60–63, 71–73, 80–81, 87–88 (with 12.2)

Extra Practice

- Student Edition, pp. 712–713
- Chapter 12 Resource Book, p. 6

Homework Check

To quickly check student understanding of key concepts, go over the following exercises:

Transitional: 22, 34, 48, 56, 68, 78,
Average: 26, 38, 48, 60, 72, 80
Advanced: 30, 42, 52, 64, 74, 82

12.1 Exercises

Guided Practice

Simplify the expression.

1. $(2x)^3$ $8x^3$ **2.** $(3y)^4$ $81y^4$ **3.** $(-2z)^5$ $-32z^5$ **4.** $(-3w)^6$ $729w^6$

5. $(xy)^3$ x^3y^3 **6.** $(ab)^4$ a^4b^4 **7.** $\left(\frac{e}{2}\right)^2$ $\frac{e^2}{4}$ **8.** $\left(\frac{m}{4}\right)^3$ $\frac{m^3}{64}$

9. $\left(\frac{2r}{5}\right)^2$ $\frac{4r^2}{25}$ **10.** $\left(\frac{3s}{2}\right)^3$ $\frac{27s^3}{8}$ **11.** $\left(\frac{1}{x}\right)^4$ $\frac{1}{x^4}$ **12.** $\left(\frac{2}{z}\right)^5$ $\frac{32}{z^5}$

Simplify the expression.

13. $(x^3)^2$ x^6 **14.** $(y^4)^2$ y^8 **15.** $(z^5)^3$ z^{15} **16.** $(w^0)^{17}$ 1

Evaluate the power. Write your answer in scientific notation.

17. $(1 \times 10^4)^2$ 1×10^8 **18.** $(2 \times 10^2)^3$ 8×10^6 **19.** $(3 \times 10^7)^4$ 8.1×10^{29}

20. MOON Ganymede, the largest moon of Jupiter, has a radius of about 2.6×10^3 kilometers. Find the approximate volume of Ganymede. 7.4×10^{10} km^3

Practice and Problem Solving

Student Help

▶More Practice
Extra practice to help you master skills is on page 712.

Simplify the expression.

21. $(5x)^3$ $125x^3$ **22.** $(4y)^4$ $256y^4$ **23.** $(3z)^2$ $9z^2$ **24.** $(2w)^5$ $32w^5$

25. $(-2p)^6$ $64p^6$ **26.** $(-4q)^3$ $-64q^3$ **27.** $(-5r)^2$ $25r^2$ **28.** $(-s)^7$ $-s^7$

29. $(ab)^2$ a^2b^2 **30.** $(pq)^3$ p^3q^3 **31.** $-(mn)^4$ $-m^4n^4$ **32.** $-(xy)^5$ $-x^5y^5$

In Exercises 33–44, simplify the expression.

33. $(4ab)^2$ $16a^2b^2$ **34.** $4(ab)^2$ $4a^2b^2$ **35.** $(3xy)^3$ $27x^3y^3$ **36.** $3(xy)^3$ $3x^3y^3$

37. $(2mn)^4$ $16m^4n^4$ **38.** $2(mn)^4$ $2m^4n^4$ **39.** $(6pqr)^2$ $36p^2q^2r^2$ **40.** $12(bcd)^0$ 12

41. $(-3mn)^2$ $9m^2n^2$ **42.** $-(3mn)^2$ $-9m^2n^2$ **43.** $(-2pq)^3$ $-8p^3q^3$ **44.** $-(2pq)^3$ $-8p^3q^3$

45. MATHEMATICAL REASONING Generalize the power of a product rule to products of three or more factors. In particular, show that $(abc)^m = a^mb^mc^m$. See margin.

45. $(abc)^m = (abc \cdot abc \cdot abc \cdot \ldots \cdot abc) = (ab \cdot ab \cdot \ldots \cdot ab)(c \cdot c \cdot \ldots \cdot c) = (a \cdot a \cdot \ldots \cdot a)(b \cdot b \cdot \ldots \cdot b)(c \cdot c \cdot \ldots \cdot c) = a^mb^mc^m$

46. GEOMETRY A sphere has a radius of $2x$. Find its volume in terms of x. $\frac{32\pi x^3}{3}$

In Exercises 47–54, simplify the expression.

47. $\left(\frac{m}{4}\right)^2$ $\frac{m^2}{16}$ **48.** $\left(\frac{n}{2}\right)^3$ $\frac{n^3}{8}$ **49.** $\left(\frac{5}{u}\right)^4$ $\frac{625}{u^4}$ **50.** $\left(\frac{1}{v}\right)^5$ $\frac{1}{v^5}$

51. $\left(\frac{3r}{4}\right)^2$ $\frac{9r^2}{16}$ **52.** $\left(\frac{4s}{3}\right)^3$ $\frac{64s^3}{27}$ **53.** $\left(\frac{2w}{x}\right)^4$ $\frac{16w^4}{x^4}$ **54.** $\left(\frac{-3ab}{c}\right)^2$ $\frac{9a^2b^2}{c^2}$

55. GEOMETRY A cube has edges of length $\frac{x}{2}$. Find both its surface area and its volume in terms of x. **$\frac{3x^2}{2}$, $\frac{x^3}{8}$**

In Exercises 56–67, simplify the expression.

56. $(x^2)^3$ **x^6** **57.** $(y^3)^2$ **y^6** **58.** $(z^4)^4$ **z^{16}** **59.** $(w^5)^0$ **1**

60. $(2p^4)^2$ **$4p^8$** **61.** $(7q^3)^3$ **$343q^9$** **62.** $(-3r^2)^4$ **$81r^8$** **63.** $(-p^5)^2$ **p^{10}**

64. $(ab^2)^3$ **a^3b^6** **65.** $(c^3d^4)^5$ **$c^{15}d^{20}$** **66.** $(-fg^5)^2$ **f^2g^{10}** **67.** $(k^2l^2m^2)^3$ **$k^6l^6m^6$**

Evaluate the power. Write your answer in scientific notation.

68. $(3 \times 10^5)^2$ **9×10^{10}** **69.** $(2 \times 10^4)^3$ **8×10^{12}** **70.** $(2 \times 10^0)^4$ **1.6×10^1**

71. $(5 \times 10^7)^2$ **2.5×10^{15}** **72.** $(6 \times 10^9)^3$ **2.16×10^{29}** **73.** $(4 \times 10^3)^4$ **2.56×10^{14}**

74. $(1.2 \times 10^3)^2$ **1.44×10^6** **75.** $(2.2 \times 10^5)^3$ **1.0648×10^{16}** **76.** $(5.1 \times 10^6)^4$ **6.77×10^{26}**

77. CHALLENGE Show that if m is a whole number, then $(ab)^{-m} = a^{-m}b^{-m}$.

77. $(ab)^{-m} = \frac{1}{(ab)^m} = \frac{1}{a^m b^m} = \frac{1}{a^m} \cdot \frac{1}{b^m} = a^{-m}b^{-m}$

PLANETS In Exercises 78–86, use the radius of the planet given in the table to find the approximate volume of the planet. Express the answer in scientific notation. **78–86. See margin.**

	Planet	Radius (kilometers)	Volume (cubic kilometers)
78.	Mercury	2.4×10^3	?
79.	Venus	6.1×10^3	?
80.	Earth	6.4×10^3	?
81.	Mars	3.4×10^3	?
82.	Jupiter	7.1×10^4	?
83.	Saturn	6.0×10^4	?
84.	Uranus	2.6×10^4	?
85.	Neptune	2.5×10^4	?
86.	Pluto	1.1×10^3	?

Student Help

▶LOOK BACK For help with scientific notation, see page 309.

78. 5.8×10^{10}
79. 9.5×10^{11}
80. 1.1×10^{12}
81. 1.6×10^{11}
82. 1.5×10^{15}
83. 9.0×10^{14}
84. 7.4×10^{13}
85. 6.5×10^{13}
86. 5.6×10^9

Multiple-Choice Practice

87. Which expression is equal to $\left(\frac{ab^2}{c^3}\right)^3$? **B**

Ⓐ $\frac{ab^6}{c^9}$ Ⓑ $\frac{a^3b^6}{c^9}$ Ⓒ $\frac{a^4b^5}{c^6}$ Ⓓ Not here

88. Which expression is equal to $-x^4y^6$? **J**

Ⓕ $(-x^2y^3)^2$ Ⓖ $-(x^2y^4)^2$ Ⓗ $(-x)^4(y^2)^3$ Ⓙ Not here

4 Assess

Assessment Resources

- Assessment Book (Formal Assessment and Alternative Assessment)
- Test and Practice Generator

Mini-Quiz

Simplify each expression.

1. $(4x)^3$ **$64x^3$**
2. $\left(\frac{a}{2}\right)^4$ **$\frac{a^4}{16}$**
3. $(5ab)^2$ **$25a^2b^2$**
4. $(-4x^2)^4$ **$256x^8$**
5. A sphere has radius 6×10^5. Find its volume. Write your answer in scientific notation. **about 9.0×10^{17}**

Math Reasoning

In solving Exercise 77, students should make use of the definition of a^{-m} as $\frac{1}{a^m}$ to conclude that $(ab)^{-m} = \frac{1}{(ab)^m}$.

1 Plan

Pacing

Suggested Number of Days

Transitional: 1 day
Average: 1 day
Advanced: 1 day
Block Schedule: 0.5 block with 12.1

Teaching Resources

Blacklines
(See page 614B.)

- Warm-Up Exercises
- Teacher Time-Savers
- English/Spanish Problem Solving
- Answers

Technology

- Electronic Teacher Tools
- Test and Practice Generator

2 Teach

Math Reasoning

For Mathematical Background Notes on mathematical reasoning related to this lesson, please refer to pages 614E and 614F in this Teacher's Edition.

CA Standards: AF 1.3, AF 1.4

12.2 Polynomials in One Variable

In this lesson you'll:

- Simplify expressions by applying properties of rational numbers. (AF 1.3)
- Use algebraic terminology, such as coefficient and term, correctly. (AF 1.4)

Goal 1 Identifying and Simplifying Polynomials

A **polynomial** is a monomial or an expression that can be written as a sum of monomials. Polynomials are identified by the number of terms they contain.

Type of polynomial	Number of terms	Example
Monomial	One	$3x^2$
Binomial	Two	$y + 4$
Trinomial	Three	$2z^2 + 4z - 5$

EXAMPLE 1 Identifying Polynomials

Determine whether the expression is a polynomial. If it is, state whether it is a *monomial*, a *binomial*, or a *trinomial*.

a. $5p^5 - 6p$ **b.** $3x^{-2} + 7x$ **c.** $17s^2$

Solution

a. Binomial **b.** Not a polynomial **c.** Monomial

In part (b), the term $3x^{-2}$ is not a monomial, because the exponent is not a whole number. So, the expression is not a polynomial.

A polynomial in one variable is written in **standard form** if the powers of the variable decrease from left to right.

Original Polynomial	Standard Form
$3m + 4m^3 - 2m^2 + 5$	$4m^3 - 2m^2 + 3m + 5$

You can use the commutative property to write a polynomial in standard form.

Student Help

Vocabulary Tip
If you rewrite a polynomial as a sum, then the addends are the *terms*. The terms of $-4x^3 + x^2 + 3x - 9$ are $-4x^3$, x^2, $3x$, and -9.

EXAMPLE 2 Writing a Polynomial in Standard Form

Write the polynomial $3x - 4x^3 + x^2 - 9$ in standard form.

Solution

$3x - 4x^3 + x^2 - 9 = 3x + (-4x^3) + x^2 - 9$ **Rule for subtraction**

$= -4x^3 + 3x + x^2 - 9$ **Commutative property**

$= -4x^3 + x^2 + 3x - 9$ **Commutative property**

If two or more terms have identical variable parts, they are called *like terms*. To *simplify* a polynomial, you should combine like terms by using the commutative and distributive properties.

EXAMPLE 3 Simplifying a Polynomial

Simplify $2x^5 - 7x^7 + 5x^7$ and write the result in standard form.

Solution

$2x^5 - 7x^7 + 5x^7 = 2x^5 + (-7x^7) + 5x^7$	Rule for subtraction
$= -7x^7 + 5x^7 + 2x^5$	Commutative property
$= (-7 + 5)x^7 + 2x^5$	Distributive property
$= -2x^7 + 2x^5$	Simplify.

Goal 2 USING POLYNOMIALS

When an object is dropped, a polynomial equation can be used to model the object's height as a function of time. This equation takes gravity into account but ignores air resistance and other factors that may influence the fall.

Link to History

INCLINED PLANE Galileo measured the distances traveled by balls rolling down a ramp for various lengths of time. He found that the distance varies with the square of the time and is independent of the mass of the ball.

More about Galileo's plane experiment at www.mcdougallittell.com

EXAMPLE 4 Using a Polynomial

FALLING ROCK A rock is dropped from a height of 200 feet. During its fall, the rock's height h (in feet) is given by

$$h = -16t^2 + 200$$

where t is the time in seconds. Find the height when $t = 0, 1, 2, 3,$ and 3.5 seconds. When does the rock hit the ground?

Solution

Time (in seconds)	Substitution	Height (in feet)
0	$-16(0)^2 + 200 = 0 + 200$	200
1	$-16(1)^2 + 200 = -16 + 200$	184
2	$-16(2)^2 + 200 = -64 + 200$	136
3	$-16(3)^2 + 200 = -144 + 200$	56
3.5	$-16(3.5)^2 + 200 = -196 + 200$	4

ANSWER ▶ Notice that the height is close to 0 when $t = 3.5$.

So, the rock hits the ground after falling a little more than 3.5 seconds.

Extra Example 1

Determine whether the expression is a polynomial. If it is, state whether it is a *monomial*, a *binomial*, or a *trinomial*.

a. $8x^2 + 4y^2 - 1$ **trinomial**

b. $-3x^5$ **monomial**

c. $7 + 5m^{-2}$ **not a polynomial**

Extra Example 2

Write the polynomial $4y^2 - y^3 - 6 + y$ in standard form. $-y^3 + 4y^2 + y - 6$

Extra Example 3

Simplify $4x + 5x^2 - 6x - x^2$ and write the result in standard form. $4x^2 - 2x$

Extra Example 4

You observe a toy rocket being shot into the air. It goes up a height of 130 feet. Then it burns out and drops to the ground. Its height h (in feet) t seconds after burnout is given by $h = -16t^2 + 130$. Find its height when $t = 0, 1, 2, 2.5,$ and 2.75 s. How long does the drop last? **130 ft, 114 ft, 66 ft, 30 ft, and 9 ft; The drop lasts a little more than 2.75 s.**

Math Reasoning

The formula in Example 4 could also be written $h = -\frac{1}{2}gt^2 + 200$, where g is a physical constant representing acceleration due to gravity. Near Earth's surface, $g \approx 32.2$ feet per second per second, and the number 16 is often used as an approximation for $\frac{1}{2}g$.

Concept Check

Explain how you can determine whether an expression is a polynomial. ***Sample answer:*** **Each term in the expression should have the variable raised to a whole number power.**

3 Apply

Assignment Guide

TRANSITIONAL
Day 1: pp. 624–625 Exs. 15–17, 21–24, 31–36, 42–43, 52–53

AVERAGE
Day 1: pp. 624–625 Exs. 15–17, 23–26, 33–38, 42–45, 52–53

ADVANCED
Day 1: pp. 624–625 Exs. 15–17, 27–30, 35–40, 41*, 42–43, 48–49, 52–53

BLOCK SCHEDULE
pp. 624–625 Exs. 15–17, 23–26, 33–38, 42–45, 52–53 (with 12.1)

Extra Practice

- Student Edition, pp. 712–713
- Chapter 12 Resource Book, p. 15

Homework Check

To quickly check student understanding of key concepts, go over the following exercises:

Transitional: 16, 22, 32, 36, 42
Average: 16, 24, 34, 36, 42
Advanced: 16, 28, 36, 40, 42

Problem Solving

Exercises 31–40
When simplifying polynomials, students may forget which terms they have already simplified. Have them underline like terms with, say, three underlines for cubic terms, two underlines for squared terms, etc. They may wish to strike through the terms once they have them simplified.

12.2 Exercises

Guided Practice

Determine whether the expression is a polynomial. If it is, state whether it is a *monomial,* a *binomial,* or a *trinomial.*

1. $y + 1$ **polynomial; binomial**
2. $3t^{-3}$ **not a polynomial**
3. $4n^{-2} - 7$ **not a polynomial**
4. 5 **polynomial; monomial**
5. $3x^2 + x^{-1}$ **not a polynomial**
6. $4s^3 - 8s + 2$ **polynomial; trinomial**
7. $\sqrt{5}\,r^2 - \frac{1}{2}$ **polynomial; binomial**
8. $2m^4 + m$ **polynomial; binomial**

Write the polynomial in standard form. Then list its terms.

9. $4x - 2 + 3x^2$ **$3x^2 + 4x - 2$; $3x^2, 4x, -2$**
10. $3p - 16p^2 + p^3$ **$p^3 - 16p^2 + 3p$; $p^3, -16p^2, 3p$**
11. $10 - 5r^3 + 4r$ **$-5r^3 + 4r + 10$; $-5r^3, 4r, 10$**

Simplify the polynomial and write the result in standard form.

12. $t^2 + t - 5t + 2t^2$ **$3t^2 - 4t$**
13. $2 - 6x^3 + 5x^3 - 7$ **$-x^3 - 5$**
14. $2n + 1 + 12n - 8$ **$14n - 7$**

Practice and Problem Solving

> **Student Help**
> ▶**MORE PRACTICE**
> Extra practice to help you master skills is on page 712.

Determine whether the expression is a polynomial. If it is, state whether it is a *monomial,* a *binomial,* or a *trinomial.*

15. $\frac{1}{2}t^2 - 5t + 3$ **polynomial; trinomial**
16. $9n - \sqrt{2}\,n^3$ **polynomial; binomial**
17. $\frac{6}{x^2} - 3x^3$ **not a polynomial**
18. $6.2y^4$ **polynomial; monomial**
19. $q - 1$ **polynomial; binomial**
20. $2w^{-1}$ **not a polynomial**

Write the polynomial in standard form. Then list its terms. **21–30. See margin.**

21. $3p^2 + 5p^5$
22. $q^3 + 2q + 3q^4$
23. $8x^2 + 2x^4 + 7x^3$
24. $y + 6y^4 + 2y^5$
25. $14m - 10m^2 + 5m^3$
26. $6x^3 - x - 2x^2$
27. $5 - 11y - 8y^3$
28. $9z^2 - 7z + 3 - z^3$
29. $2 - t^4 + t^2 + t$
30. $w + 4w^2 - 3 + 15w^3$

21. $5p^5 + 3p^2$; $5p^5, 3p^2$
22. $3q^4 + q^3 + 2q$; $3q^4, q^3, 2q$
23. $2x^4 + 7x^3 + 8x^2$, $2x^4, 7x^3, 8x^2$
24. $2y^5 + 6y^4 + y$; $2y^5, 6y^4, y$
25. $5m^3 - 10m^2 + 14m$; $5m^3, -10m^2, 14m$
26. $6x^3 - 2x^2 - x$; $6x^3, -2x^2, -x$
27. $-8y^3 - 11y + 5$; $-8y^3, -11y, 5$
28. $-z^3 + 9z^2 - 7z + 3$; $-z^3, 9z^2, -7z, 3$
29. $-t^4 + t^2 + t + 2$; $-t^4, t^2, t, 2$
30. $15w^3 + 4w^2 + w - 3$; $15w^3, 4w^2, w, -3$

Simplify the polynomial and write the result in standard form.

31. $y + 2y^2 - 3y$ **$2y^2 - 2y$**
32. $x^3 - 3x + 5x - x^3$ **$2x$**
33. $8 - 4x^2 + 10x^2 - 11$ **$6x^2 - 3$**
34. $x^2 + 7x + 10 + x^2 + 2x$ **$2x^2 + 9x + 10$**
35. $2x^2 + 5x + 3 + 5x + 4$ **$2x^2 + 10x + 7$**
36. $x^2 + 2x + 4 + 2x^2 + 4x + 6$ **$3x^2 + 6x + 10$**
37. $15 + 7s^3 - 21 - 3s^2 + s^3$ **$8s^3 - 3s^2 - 6$**
38. $-7 + 8z - 7 - 8z$ **-14**
39. $1.1r^2 - 2.9r + 1.8r^2 + 3.3r$ **$2.9r^2 + 0.4r$**
40. $5.2q + 3.2q^3 - 5q^3 - 7.8q$ **$-1.8q^3 - 2.6q$**

41. CHALLENGE Simplify the polynomial. **$-3xy^2 - xy + 4x^2y$**

$$3x^2y - xy^2 + 4xy + x^2y - 5xy - 2xy^2$$

EROSION Gorges are formed by rivers eroding rock. The Arkansas River has dug out the Royal Gorge at a rate of about one foot per 2500 years.

More about river erosion available at www.mcdougallittell.com

43. 8 seconds; Use time intervals of $\frac{1}{10}$, $\frac{1}{100}$, etc.

Science Link **In Exercises 42 and 43, use the following information.** The Royal Gorge Bridge in Colorado is 1053 feet above the Arkansas River. You are on the bridge and accidentally drop your camera. The camera's height h (in feet above the river) after t seconds is modeled by $h = -16t^2 + 1053$.

42. Copy and complete the table. **See margin.**

t (in seconds)	0	1	2	3	4	5	6	7	8	9
h (in feet)	?	?	?	?	?	?	?	?	?	?

43. MATHEMATICAL REASONING Find to the nearest second when the camera hits the water. How can you get a more precise answer? **See margin.**

In Exercises 44–47, use what you know about powers of products to write the expression as a polynomial in standard form.

EXAMPLE

$(3x)^3 + (5x)^2 = 3^3 \cdot x^3 + 5^2 \cdot x^2$ Use power of a product rule.

$= 27x^3 + 25x^2$ Simplify.

44. $(3x)^2 + (5x)^3$ **$125x^3 + 9x^2$**

45. $(3x)^3 + (5x)^3$ **$152x^3$**

46. $(-3x)^3 + (-5x)^2$ **$-27x^3 + 25x^2$**

47. $(-3x)^2 + (-5x)^2$ **$34x^2$**

In Exercises 48–51, use what you know about powers of powers to write the expression as a polynomial in standard form.

EXAMPLE

$(4x^2)^3 + (7x^3)^2 = 4^3 \cdot (x^2)^3 + 7^2 \cdot (x^3)^2$ Use power of a product rule.

$= 64x^6 + 49x^6$ Use power of a power rule.

$= 113x^6$ Combine like terms.

48. $(3x^2)^2 + 5x^4$ **$14x^4$**

49. $(-x^3)^2 + (7x^2)^2 - 9x^4$ **$x^6 + 40x^4$**

50. $(2x^2)^3 + (-x)^6 + 3x^5$ **$9x^6 + 3x^5$**

51. $(3x^2)^3 + (-3x^2)^3$ **0**

Multiple-Choice Practice

52. Write the polynomial $4 + 5x^2 - 3x - 10x^3$ in standard form. **D**

Ⓐ $4 - 3x + 5x^2 - 10x^3$ Ⓑ $-10x^3 + 5x^2 + 4 - 3x$

Ⓒ $-3x + 4 + 5x^2 - 10x^3$ Ⓓ $-10x^3 + 5x^2 - 3x + 4$

53. Simplify the polynomial $x^2 - 4x^3 + 5 - x + x^3 - 2x^2$. **G**

Ⓕ $-3x^3 + x^2 - x + 5$ Ⓖ $-3x^3 - x^2 - x + 5$

Ⓗ $3x^3 + x^2 + x + 5$ Ⓙ $3x^3 - x^2 - x + 5$

4 Assess

Assessment Resources

- Assessment Book (Formal Assessment and Alternative Assessment)
- Test and Practice Generator

Mini-Quiz

1. Simplify the polynomial $-3x + 4x^3 - 7x - 6 + x^2 - 12$ and write it in standard form. **$4x^3 + x^2 - 10x - 18$**
2. A penny is dropped from a 300 ft tall building. Its height h, in feet, after t seconds is given by $h = -16t^2 + 300$.
   a. Find the height of the penny after 1 s, 2 s, 3 s, 4 s, and 4.25 s. **284 ft, 236 ft, 156 ft, 44 ft, 11 ft**
   b. When does the penny reach the ground? **a little more than 4.25 s after being dropped**

42.

t	h
0	1053
1	1037
2	989
3	909
4	797
5	653
6	477
7	269
8	29
9	−243

1 Plan

Pacing

Suggested Number of Days

Transitional: 1 day
Average: 1 day
Advanced: 1 day
Block Schedule: 0.5 block with 12.4

Teaching Resources

Blacklines
(See page 614B.)

Transparencies
- Warm-Up Exercises
- Teacher Time-Savers
- English/Spanish Problem Solving
- Answers

Technology
- Electronic Teacher Tools
- Test and Practice Generator

2 Teach

Math Reasoning

For Mathematical Background Notes on mathematical reasoning related to this lesson, please refer to pages 614E and 614F in this Teacher's Edition.

California Standards and Assessment

CA Standards: AF 1.3, AF 2.1

12.3 Adding and Subtracting Polynomials

California Standards

In this lesson you'll:

- Simplify expressions by applying properties of rational numbers. (AF 1.3)
- Simplify and evaluate expressions that include exponents. (AF 2.1)

Goal 1 Adding Polynomials

You can add polynomials by combining like terms.

EXAMPLE 1 Adding Polynomials

Add $2x^2 + 3x + 3$ and $x^2 + x + 2$.

Solution

Method 1 Use a horizontal format. The commutative, associative, and distributive properties allow you to rearrange, regroup, and combine like terms.

$$\begin{aligned}(2x^2 + 3x + 3) + (x^2 + x + 2) &= 2x^2 + 3x + 3 + x^2 + x + 2\\ &= 2x^2 + x^2 + 3x + x + 3 + 2\\ &= 3x^2 + 4x + 5\end{aligned}$$

Method 2 Use a vertical format. Line up like terms and combine.

$$\begin{array}{rl} 2x^2 + 3x + 3 & \text{Write each polynomial in standard form.}\\ +\ \underline{(x^2 + x + 2)} & \text{Line up like terms.}\\ 3x^2 + 4x + 5 & \text{Add coefficients of like terms.}\end{array}$$

The **degree** of a simplified polynomial in one variable is the greatest exponent of the variable.

Second-Degree Polynomial	Third-Degree Polynomial
$2n^2 - 5n + 3$	$-n^3 - 4n^2 + 7$

EXAMPLE 2 Adding Polynomials

Add the polynomials. State the degree of the sum.

a. $(-n^3 + 2n^2 - n + 4) + (2n^3 + 3n + 6)$

b. $(x^3 + 5x^2 - 2x + 3) + (2x^2 + 4x - 5)$

Solution

You can use either a horizontal or vertical format. The vertical format is shown below. The first step is to line up like terms.

a.
$$\begin{array}{r} -n^3 + 2n^2 - n + 4\\ +\ \underline{(2n^3 + 3n + 6)}\\ n^3 + 2n^2 + 2n + 10\end{array}$$

b.
$$\begin{array}{r} x^3 + 5x^2 - 2x + 3\\ +\ \underline{ (2x^2 + 4x - 5)}\\ x^3 + 7x^2 + 2x - 2\end{array}$$

Both sums are third-degree polynomials.

Student Help

STUDY TIP
In Example 2, the polynomial $2n^3 + 3n + 6$ is written with a blank space because there is no n^2 term.

Goal 2 SUBTRACTING POLYNOMIALS

To subtract polynomials, you can add the opposite of the polynomial being subtracted.

EXAMPLE 3 Taking the Opposite of a Polynomial

Write the opposite of $2x^2 - x + 5$.

Solution

$-(2x^2 - x + 5) = (-1)(2x^2 - x + 5)$	$-a = (-1)a$
$= (-1)(2x^2) - (-1)(x) + (-1)(5)$	Distributive prop.
$= -2x^2 - (-x) + (-5)$	$(-1)a = -a$
$= -2x^2 + x - 5$	Rule for subtraction

EXAMPLE 4 Subtracting Polynomials

Subtract $2x^2 - x + 5$ from $3x^2 - x + 7$. State the degree of the difference.

Solution

To subtract, add the opposite. Use the result from Example 3.

$$\begin{aligned}(3x^2 - x + 7) - (2x^2 - x + 5) &= (3x^2 - x + 7) + [-(2x^2 - x + 5)] \\ &= (3x^2 - x + 7) + (-2x^2 + x - 5) \\ &= 3x^2 + (-2x^2) - x + x + 7 - 5 \\ &= x^2 + 2\end{aligned}$$

The difference is a second-degree polynomial.

Student Help

▶STUDY TIP
Subtracting polynomials uses the same rule for subtraction as subtracting real numbers:
$a - b = a + (-b)$

EXAMPLE 5 Subtracting Polynomials

Find an expression that represents the area of the blue region formed by the rectangles.

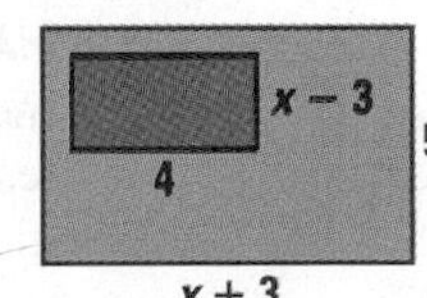

Solution

The area of the larger rectangle is $5(x + 3) = 5x + 15$. The area of the smaller rectangle is $4(x - 3) = 4x - 12$. You can use a vertical format to subtract the areas.

$$\begin{array}{r} 5x + 15 \\ -\ \underline{(4x - 12)} \end{array} \quad \text{Take the opposite.} \quad \begin{array}{r} 5x + 15 \\ +\ \underline{(-4x + 12)} \\ x + 27 \end{array} \quad \text{Then add.}$$

ANSWER ▶ The area of the blue region is $x + 27$.

Extra Example 1

Add $5x^2 + 3x - 1$ and $2x^2 - 4x + 6$. $7x^2 - x + 5$

Extra Example 2

Add the polynomials. State the degree of the sum.

a. $(n^3 - 3n^2 + 4n - 6) + (n^3 + n^2 + 5)$ $2n^3 - 2n^2 + 4n - 1$; degree 3

b. $(-x^3 + 6x^2 - 3x) + (5x^3 + 3x - 4)$ $4x^3 + 6x^2 - 4$; degree 3

Extra Example 3

Write the opposite of $-3x^2 + 4x - 5$. $3x^2 - 4x + 5$

Extra Example 4

Subtract $-3x^2 + 4x - 5$ from $5x^2 - 2x + 6$. State the degree of the difference. $8x^2 - 6x + 11$; degree 2

Extra Example 5

Find an expression that represents the area of the shaded region. $7a$

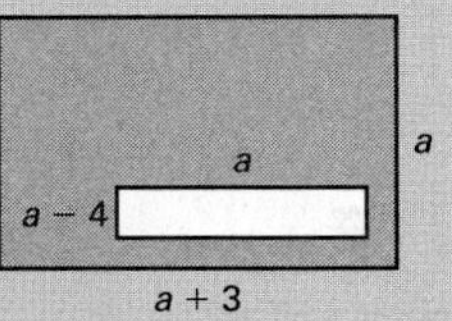

Teaching Tip

You may wish to encourage students to write missing terms with 0 as their coefficient to act as placeholders when using the vertical format. This will help students line up like terms.

Concept Check

Describe the procedure for adding polynomials using the vertical format. ***Sample answer:*** **Write each polynomial in standard form and line up the like terms. Then add like terms.**

3 Apply

Assignment Guide

TRANSITIONAL
Day 1: pp. 628–629 Exs. 5–12, 16–19, 25–26

AVERAGE
Day 1: pp. 628–629 Exs. 5–15, 18–19, 23*, 25–26

ADVANCED
Day 1: pp. 628–629 Exs. 5–12, 18–22, 23–24*, 25–26

BLOCK SCHEDULE
pp. 628–629 Exs. 5–15, 18–19, 23*, 25–26 (with 12.4)

Extra Practice

- Student Edition, pp. 712–713
- Chapter 12 Resource Book, p. 24

Homework Check

To quickly check student understanding of key concepts, go over the following exercises:

Transitional: 6, 8, 10, 12, 16, 18
Average: 6, 8, 10, 12, 14, 18
Advanced: 6, 8, 10, 12, 18, 24

13. *Sample answer:* **It is possible for the degree of the sum of two polynomials of the same degree to be less than the degree of the polynomials being added if the coefficients of the terms with the highest power are additive inverses. Example: $(2x^3 + x^2 + 1) + (-2x^3 + 2) = x^2 + 3$**
It is also possible for the degree of the difference of two polynomials of the same degree to be less than the degree of the polynomials being subtracted if the coefficients of the terms with the highest power are equal. Example: $(2x^3 + x^2 + 1) - (2x^3 + 2) = x^2 - 1$

12.3 Exercises

Guided Practice

Use a horizontal format to find the sum or difference. State the degree of the result.

1. $(3x^2 - 7x + 5) + (3x^2 - 10)$ **$6x^2 - 7x - 5$; 2**

2. $(n^2 + 8n - 7) - (-n^2 + 8n)$ **$2n^2 - 7$; 2**

Use a vertical format to find the sum or difference. State the degree of the result.

3. $\begin{array}{r} 2y^3 + y^2 - 4y + 3 \\ -\ (y^3 - 5y^2 + 2y - 6) \\ \hline \end{array}$ **$y^3 + 6y^2 - 6y + 9$; 3**

4. $\begin{array}{r} 2y^3 + y^2 - 4y + 3 \\ +\ (y^3 - 5y^2 + 2y - 6) \\ \hline \end{array}$ **$3y^3 - 4y^2 - 2y - 3$; 3**

Practice and Problem Solving

Student Help
▶MORE PRACTICE
Extra practice to help you master skills is on page 712.

Add or subtract the polynomials using a horizontal format. State the degree of the result.

5. $(-x^2 + 9x - 5) + (6x^2 - 2x + 16)$ **$5x^2 + 7x + 11$; 2**

6. $(-8a^3 + a^2 + 17) + (6a^2 - 3a + 9)$ **$-8a^3 + 7a^2 - 3a + 26$; 3**

7. $(-b^3 + 4b^2 - 1) - (7b^3 + 4b^2 + 3)$ **$-8b^3 - 4$; 3**

8. $(-5x^3 - 13x + 4) - (-3x^3 + x^2 + 10x - 9)$ **$-2x^3 - x^2 - 23x + 13$; 3**

Add or subtract the polynomials using a vertical format. State the degree of the result.

9. $\begin{array}{r} x^3 + 4x^2 - 9x + 2 \\ +\ (-2x^3 + 5x^2 + x - 6) \\ \hline \end{array}$ **$-x^3 + 9x^2 - 8x - 4$; 3**

10. $\begin{array}{r} 2n^4 + 2n^3 - n^2 - 4n + 6 \\ +\ (n^4 + 3n^3 - 3n^2 - 5n + 2) \\ \hline \end{array}$ **$3n^4 + 5n^3 - 4n^2 - 9n + 8$; 4**

11. $\begin{array}{r} 3t^3 + 4t^2 + t - 5 \\ -\ (t^3 + 2t^2 - 9t + 1) \\ \hline \end{array}$ **$2t^3 + 2t^2 + 10t - 6$; 3**

12. $\begin{array}{r} x^4 + 3x^3 + x^2 + 2x + 5 \\ -\ (x^4 + 2x^3 + 3x^2 + 4x - 4) \\ \hline \end{array}$ **$x^3 - 2x^2 - 2x + 9$; 3**

13. MATHEMATICAL REASONING When you add or subtract polynomials of the same degree, is it possible for the result to have a degree that is less than the degree of either polynomial? Explain your reasoning and give examples. **See margin.**

GEOMETRY Express the total area of the blue region formed by rectangles as a polynomial in x. Then evaluate the area when $x = 2$.

14. **$2x^2 + 5x + 2$, 20**

$x^2 + 3x + 2$

$x^2 + 2x$

15. **$3x^2 + 5x + 2$, 24**

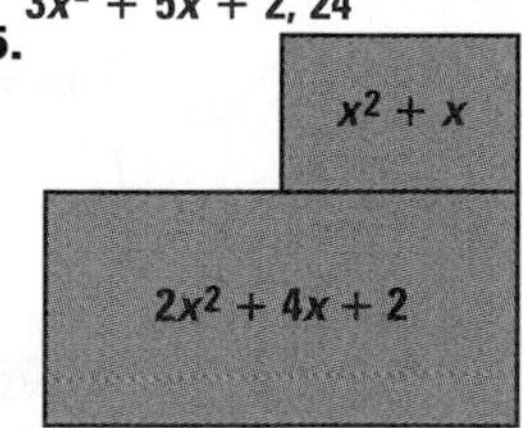

Careers

WEB DESIGN On the World Wide Web, color is made by adding red, green, and blue light. With 256 tints of each of these colors, you can make $256^3 = 16{,}777{,}216$ colors.

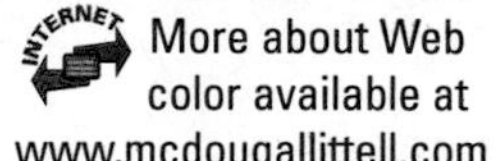

More about Web color available at www.mcdougallittell.com

16. ***Sample answer:*** The student is adding z^2 and $6z$, which is incorrect because they are not like terms. Also, $-4z^3 + 3z^3 = -z^3$, not $-z^6$.

$$\begin{array}{r} -4z^3 + z^2 \quad + 7 \\ + 3z^3 \quad - 6z - 5 \\ \hline -z^3 + z^2 - 6z + 2 \end{array}$$

17. ***Sample answer:*** The student is not adding the opposite of $2x^3 + x^2 + 2x + 1$.

$$\begin{array}{r} 4x^3 + 3x^2 + 4x + 3 \\ + (-2x^3 - x^2 - 2x - 1) \\ \hline 2x^3 + 2x^2 + 2x + 2 \end{array}$$

ERROR ANALYSIS Describe and correct the errors. **16–17. See margin.**

16.

$$\begin{array}{r} -4z^3 + \quad z^2 + 7 \\ + 3z^3 - 6z \quad - 5 \\ \hline -z^6 - 5z^3 + 2 \end{array}$$

17.

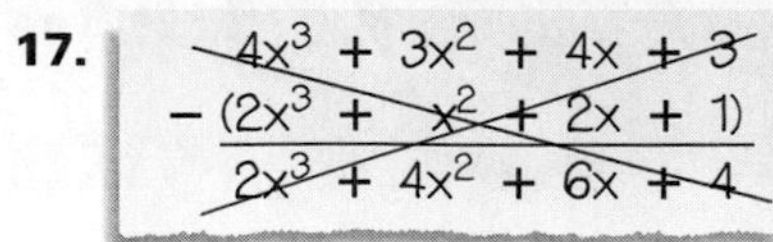

$$\begin{array}{r} 4x^3 + 3x^2 + 4x + 3 \\ -(2x^3 + \quad x^2 + 2x + 1) \\ \hline 2x^3 + 4x^2 + 6x + 4 \end{array}$$

GEOMETRY Find an expression that represents the area of the blue region formed by the rectangles. Then evaluate the area when $x = 6$.

18. **$2x + 11$, 23**

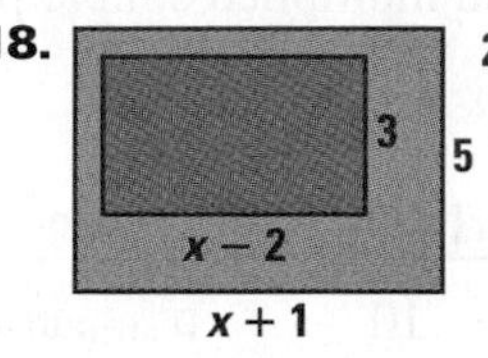

19. **$7x - 3$, 39**

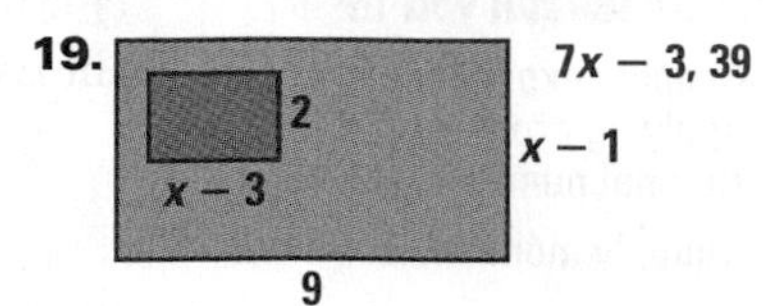

HEXADECIMAL In Exercises 20–22, use the following information about adding or subtracting base 16 numbers. Check your answer using base 10. On the World Wide Web, colors are specified as combinations of red, green, and blue light using *hexadecimal* (base 16) notation. There are 16 digits in hexadecimal—0, 1, 2, 3, 4, 5, 6, 7, 8, 9, A, B, C, D, E, and F—corresponding to the numbers 0 through 15 in base 10.

In base 16	Expansion in base 10	Check
003399	$0(16)^5 + 0(16)^4 + 3(16)^3 + 3(16)^2 + 9(16) + 9$	13,209
+ 66CC33	$+ 6(16)^5 + 6(16)^4 + 12(16)^3 + 12(16)^2 + 3(16) + 3$	+ 6,736,947
66FFCC	$6(16)^5 + 6(16)^4 + 15(16)^3 + 15(16)^2 + 12(16) + 12$	6,750,156

20.
CC 00 33
+ 00 66 00
?? ?? ??
CC 66 33

21.
00 33 FF
+ FF CC 00
?? ?? ??
FF FF FF

22.
33 99 CC
− 00 66 99
?? ?? ??
33 33 33

CHALLENGE Perform the indicated operations.

23. $(2x^2 + 9x - 4) + (-8x^2 + 3x + 6) + (x^2 - 5x - 7)$ **$-5x^2 + 7x - 5$**

24. $(4x^2 + x - 17) - (x^2 - 15x + 7) - (-7x^2 + x + 6)$ **$10x^2 + 15x - 30$**

Multiple-Choice Practice

25. What is the degree of the polynomial $3x^2 - x^2 + 4x + 10$? **B**

Ⓐ 1 Ⓑ 2 Ⓒ 3 Ⓓ 4

26. What is the difference of $2x^3 + 3x + 7$ and $3x^3 - 2x^2 + 4x - 3$? **J**

Ⓕ $-x^3 - 2x^2 - x - 4$ Ⓖ $5x^3 - 2x^2 - 7x + 10$

Ⓗ $-x^3 + 2x^2 - x - 4$ Ⓙ $-x^3 + 2x^2 - x + 10$

4 Assess

Assessment Resources

- Assessment Book (Formal Assessment and Alternative Assessment)
- Test and Practice Generator

Mini-Quiz

Add or subtract the polynomials.

1. $(2x^2 - 3x + 4) + (x^3 + x^2 - 10)$ **$x^3 + 3x^2 - 3x - 6$**
2. $(x^3 - x + 12) - (2x^2 - 5x + 8)$ **$x^3 - 2x^2 + 4x + 4$**
3. Find an expression that represents the area of the shaded region formed by the rectangles. Then evaluate the area when $x = 4$.

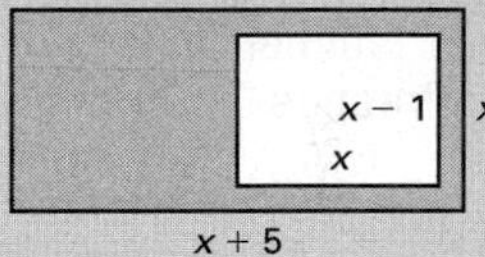

area: $6x$; 24

Math Reasoning

In Exercises 21 and 22, alert your students to the fact that working in base 16 will require learning some new addition facts, such as "3 + C = F", "8 + 9 = 11" and "A + D = 17."

1 Plan

Pacing

Suggested Number of Days

Transitional: 1 day
Average: 1 day
Advanced: 1 day
Block Schedule: 0.5 block with 12.3

Teaching Resources

 ***Blacklines***
(See page 614B.)

Transparencies
- Warm-Up Exercises
- Teacher Time-Savers
- English/Spanish Problem Solving
- Answers

Technology
- Electronic Teacher Tools
- Test and Practice Generator

2 Teach

Math Reasoning

For Mathematical Background Notes on mathematical reasoning related to this lesson, please refer to pages 614E and 614F in this Teacher's Edition.

California Standards and Assessment

CA Standards: AF 1.3, AF 2.2

12.4 Multiplying a Monomial and a Polynomial

California Standards

In this lesson you'll:
- Simplify expressions by applying properties of rational numbers. (AF 1.3)
- Multiply monomials. (AF 2.2)

Goal 1 USING THE DISTRIBUTIVE PROPERTY

Earlier in this book you multiplied simple polynomials, as shown in Example 1.

EXAMPLE 1 Multiplying Monomials and Polynomials

a. $2(3x + 5) = 6x + 10$ — Distributive property (Lesson 1.8)

b. $(y^2)(y^3) = y^5$ — Product of powers rule (Lesson 6.7)

In this lesson you will combine the product of powers rule with the distributive property to multiply a monomial and a polynomial. The general rule for finding this type of product is stated below.

MULTIPLYING A MONOMIAL AND A POLYNOMIAL

To multiply a monomial and a polynomial, write the polynomial as a sum, multiply each term by the monomial, and add the results.

You may find it helpful to use the rule for subtraction to express a polynomial as a sum before applying the distributive property.

EXAMPLE 2 Multiplying a Monomial and a Polynomial

a. $3x(x^2 + 2x + 5) = 3x(x^2) + 3x(2x) + 3x(5)$ — Distributive property

$= 3x^3 + 6x^2 + 15x$ — Simplify.

b. $n^2(2n^3 - 4n) = n^2[2n^3 + (-4n)]$ — Rule for subtraction

$= n^2(2n^3) + n^2(-4n)$ — Distributive property

$= 2n^5 + (-4n^3)$ — Simplify.

$= 2n^5 - 4n^3$ — Rule for subtraction

c. $-5y(3y^2 + y - 7) = -5y[3y^2 + y + (-7)]$

$= -5y(3y^2) + [-5y(y)] + [-5y(-7)]$

$= -15y^3 + (-5y^2) + 35y$

$= -15y^3 - 5y^2 + 35y$

Student Help

STUDY TIP
A common error is to forget to multiply a monomial by *all* the terms of the polynomial.

Incorrect

$3x(2x^2 + 4x - 1)$
$= 6x^3 + 4x - 1$

Correct

$3x(2x^2 + 4x - 1)$
$= 6x^3 + 12x^2 - 3x$

EXAMPLE 3 Using Polynomial Multiplication

GEOMETRY The rectangle shown is divided into five regions.

a. Write an expression for the area of each region. Find the total area.

b. Use the length and width of the entire rectangle to write an expression for the total area.

c. Compare the area expressions from parts (a) and (b). Evaluate the expressions when $x = 3$.

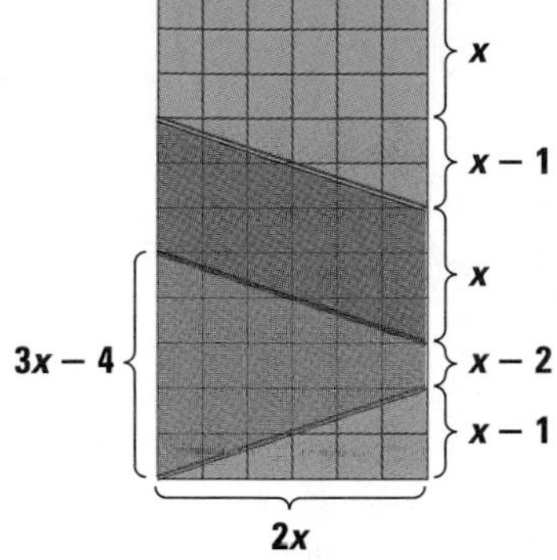

Student Help

▶ LOOK BACK
For help with area of parallelograms and trapezoids, see page 419.

Solution

a. You can make a table to organize the information about the area of each region.

Polygon	Formula	Area	Simplified
Rectangle	bh	$2x(x)$	$2x^2$
Triangle	$\frac{1}{2}bh$	$\frac{1}{2}(2x)(x-1)$	$x^2 - x$
Parallelogram	bh	$2x(x)$	$2x^2$
Trapezoid	$\frac{1}{2}(b_1 + b_2)h$	$\frac{1}{2}(2x)[(3x-4)+(x-2)]$	$4x^2 - 6x$
Triangle	$\frac{1}{2}bh$	$\frac{1}{2}(2x)(x-1)$	$x^2 - x$

Add the expressions to find the total area:

$$(2x^2) + (x^2 - x) + (2x^2) + (4x^2 - 6x) + (x^2 - x) = 10x^2 - 8x$$

b. The width of the entire rectangle is $2x$, and the length is $5x - 4$. So, the area of the entire rectangle is $2x(5x - 4) = 10x^2 - 8x$.

c. The expressions are the same. Evaluate the expression when $x = 3$.

$10x^2 - 8x = 10(3)^2 - 8(3)$ **Substitute 3 for *x*.**

$= 10(9) - 8(3)$ **Evaluate power.**

$= 90 - 24$ **Multiply.**

$= 66$ **Subtract.**

ANSWER ▶ When $x = 3$, the area of the rectangle is 66 square units.

Extra Example 1

Multiply.

a. $7(6n + 11)$ **$42n + 77$**

b. $(w^3)(w^4)$ **w^7**

Extra Example 2

Multiply.

a. $4x(x^2 - x + 2)$ **$4x^3 - 4x^2 + 8x$**

b. $a^2(3a + 6)$ **$3a^3 + 6a^2$**

c. $-7m^2(3m^3 - 2m^2 - 5m + 1)$ **$-21m^5 + 14m^4 + 35m^3 - 7m^2$**

Extra Example 3

The rectangle below is divided into four regions.

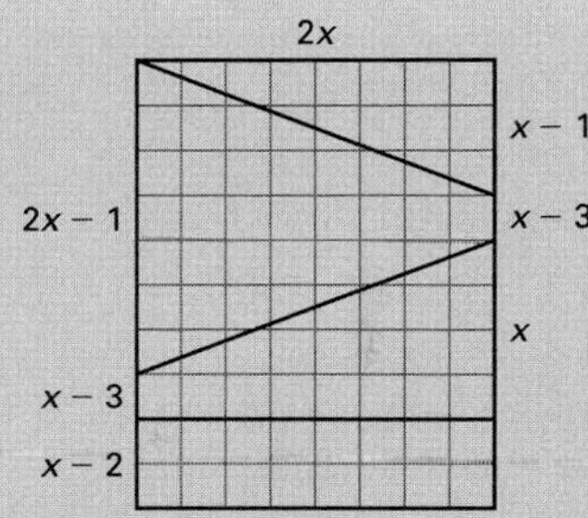

a. Write an expression for the area of each region. Find the total area. **right triangle: $x^2 - x$; isosceles trapezoid: $3x^2 - 4x$; right trapezoid: $2x^2 - 3x$; rectangle: $2x^2 - 4x$; total area: $8x^2 - 12x$**

b. Use the length and width of the entire rectangle to write an expression for the total area. **$(4x - 6) \cdot 2x = 8x^2 - 12x$**

c. Compare the area expressions from parts (a) and (b). Evaluate the expressions when $x = 4$. **The expressions are the same. When $x = 4$, the area is 80 square units.**

Concept Check

Describe the procedure for multiplying a monomial by a polynomial. ***Sample answer:*** **Write the polynomial as a sum. Multiply each term of the polynomial by the monomial and add the products. Simplify the result, if necessary.**

3 Apply

Assignment Guide

TRANSITIONAL
Day 1: EP p. 705 Exs. 31–33; pp. 632–634 Exs. 10–18, 22–25, 27–31, 45–51

AVERAGE
Day 1: pp. 632–634 Exs. 13–25, 27–31, 39–40, 45–51

ADVANCED
Day 1: pp. 632–634 Exs. 13–23, 25–31, 36–38, 42–44*, 45–51

BLOCK SCHEDULE
pp. 632–634 Exs. 13–25, 27–31, 39–40, 45–51 (with 12.3)

Extra Practice

- Student Edition, pp. 712–713
- Chapter 12 Resource Book, p. 33

Homework Check

To quickly check student understanding of key concepts, go over the following exercises:

Transitional: 10, 14, 18, 24, 28, 30
Average: 14, 18, 20, 24, 28, 30
Advanced: 14, 18, 20, 26, 28, 30

12.4 Exercises

Guided Practice

Find the product.

1. $3x(7x^2 + x)$ **$21x^3 + 3x^2$**

2. $8y^2(6y + 2)$ **$48y^3 + 16y^2$**

3. $2z^3(8z^2 + 3)$ **$16z^5 + 6z^3$**

4. $4m(2m^2 - 3m)$ **$8m^3 - 12m^2$**

5. $3n^2(n^2 + 2n - 5)$ **$3n^4 + 6n^3 - 15n^2$**

6. $-p(p^2 - 4)$ **$-p^3 + 4p$**

In Exercises 7–9, use the figure shown.

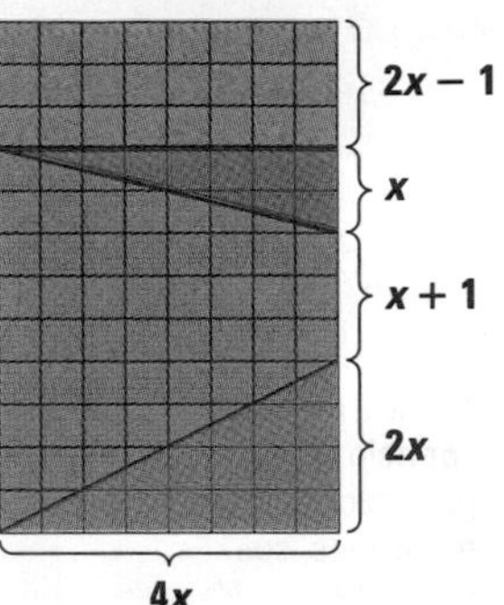

7. Write an expression for the area of each region. Find the total area. **See margin.**

8. Use the length and width of the entire rectangle to write an expression for the total area. **$24x^2$**

9. Compare the area expressions from Exercises 7 and 8. Evaluate the expressions when $x = 2$. **The expressions are equal. 96**

7. Area of each region (from top to bottom): $8x^2 - 4x$, $2x^2$, $10x^2 + 4x$, $4x^2$; $24x^2$

Practice and Problem Solving

Student Help

▶**MORE PRACTICE**
Extra practice to help you master skills is on page 713.

Find the product.

10. $2x(x^2 + 1)$ **$2x^3 + 2x$**

11. $4y(3y^2 + 2y + 1)$ **$12y^3 + 8y^2 + 4y$**

12. $z^3(z^2 + 6z)$ **$z^5 + 6z^4$**

13. $3a^3(2a - 7)$ **$6a^4 - 21a^3$**

14. $8b^2(-b^2 + 2)$ **$-8b^4 + 16b^2$**

15. $c^5(c^2 - 3c + 2)$ **$c^7 - 3c^6 + 2c^5$**

16. $p^4(1 - p)$ **$p^4 - p^5$**

17. $s^7(8s^2 + 10s - 1)$ **$8s^9 + 10s^8 - s^7$**

18. $2q(-4q^2 + 6q - 2)$ **$-8q^3 + 12q^2 - 4q$**

19. $-r(r^2 + r + 1)$ **$-r^3 - r^2 - r$**

20. $-n(n^3 + n^2 - n)$ **$-n^4 - n^3 + n^2$**

21. $-6w(2w^5 - w^3)$ **$-12w^6 + 6w^4$**

Translate the verbal phrase to a variable expression. Then multiply.

22. The product of a number and one more than that number **$x(x + 1)$, $x^2 + x$**

23. The cube of a number times the difference of the number and 2 **$x^3(x - 2)$, $x^4 - 2x^3$**

In Exercises 24–26, write a polynomial for the area of the figure.

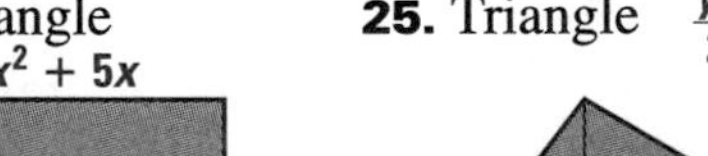

24. Rectangle **$25x^2 + 5x$**

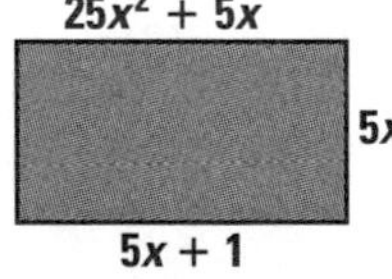

25. Triangle **$\frac{y^2}{2} + \frac{3y}{2}$**

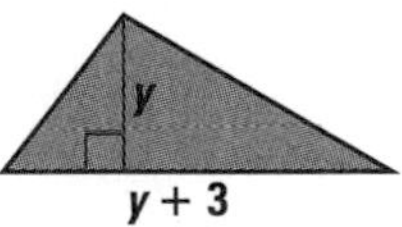

26. Parallelogram **$6z^2 - 4z$**

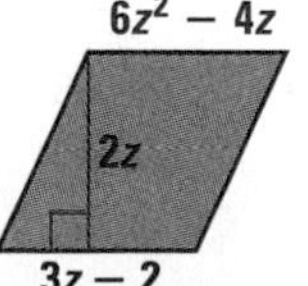

27. **GARDENS** Write a variable expression for the area of a rectangular garden that is twice as long as it is wide. **$A = 2w^2$**

Student Help

▶ **HOMEWORK HELP** Extra help with problem solving in Exs. 28–31 is available at www.mcdougallittell.com

GEOMETRY In Exercises 28–31, use the figure shown.

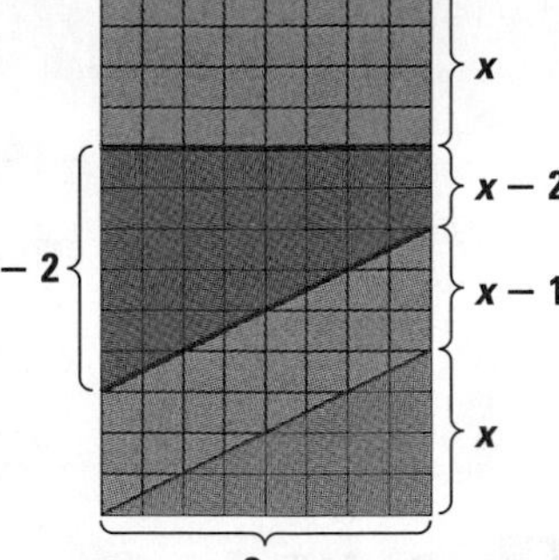

28. Write an expression for the area of each region. **Area of each region (from top to bottom): $2x^2$, $3x^2 - 4x$, $2x^2 - 2x$, x^2**

29. Use the results from Exercise 28 to write an expression for the total area. **$8x^2 - 6x$**

30. Use the length and width of the entire rectangle to write an expression for the total area. **$8x^2 - 6x$**

31. Compare the expressions from Exercises 29 and 30. Evaluate the expressions when $x = 4$. **The two expressions are equal. 104**

GEOMETRY In Exercises 32–35, use the right rectangular prism shown.

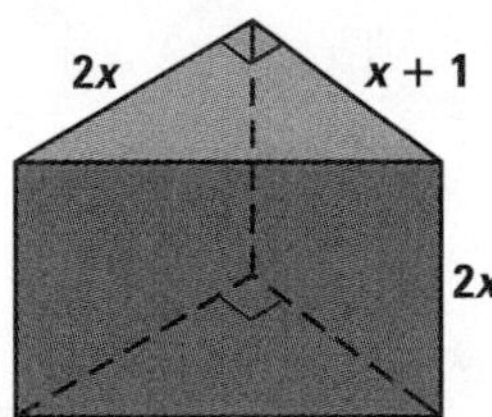

32. Write an expression for the base area of the prism. **$3x^2 + x$**

33. Write an expression for the volume of the prism. **$6x^3 + 2x^2$**

34. Write an expression for the surface area of the prism. **$22x^2 + 6x$**

35. The surface area of the prism is 216 square units. Confirm that $x = 3$ and find the volume of the prism. **180**

GEOMETRY In Exercises 36–38, use the right prism shown.

$2x$ $x + 1$ $2x$

36. Write an expression for the base area. Simplify your expression. **$x^2 + x$**

37. Write an expression for the volume of the prism. **$2x^3 + 2x^2$**

38. Find the surface area of the prism when $x = 2$. **48**

ERROR ANALYSIS Describe and correct the error. **39–40. See margin.**

39.

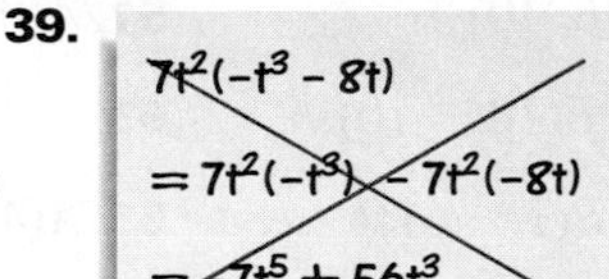

40.

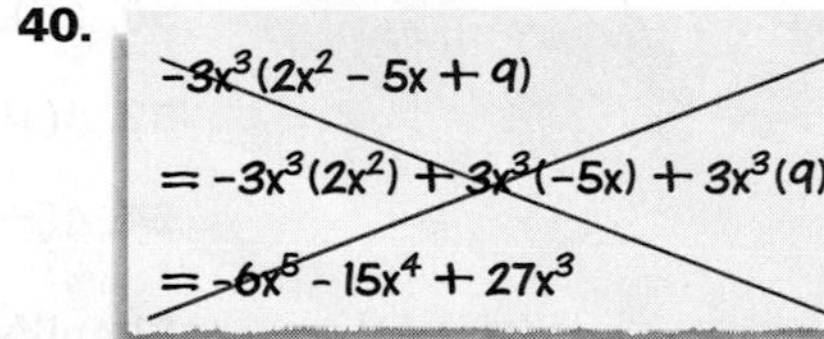

39. ***Sample answer:*** **In the first line of the solution the student incorrectly applied the distributive property. The first line should be: $= 7t^2(-t^3) + 7t^2(-8t)$. $= -7t^5 - 56t^3$.**

40. ***Sample answer:*** **In the first line of the solution the student incorrectly applied the distributive property. The first line should be: $= -3x^3(2x^2) - 3x^3(-5x) - 3x^3(9)$. $= -6x^5 + 15x^4 - 27x^3$**

41. MATHEMATICAL REASONING When you multiply a monomial and a polynomial, how is the degree of the product related to the degrees of the monomial and polynomial?
Sample answer: **The degree of the product of a monomial and a polynomial is the sum of the degrees of the monomial and polynomial.**

4 Assess

Assessment Resources

- Assessment Book (Formal Assessment and Alternative Assessment)
- Test and Practice Generator

Mini-Quiz

Multiply.

1. a. $-8(x^3 + 3x - 10)$ **$-8x^3 - 24x + 80$**
   b. $3x(2x^2 - 5x + 8)$ **$6x^3 - 15x^2 + 24x$**
2. Use the figure below.

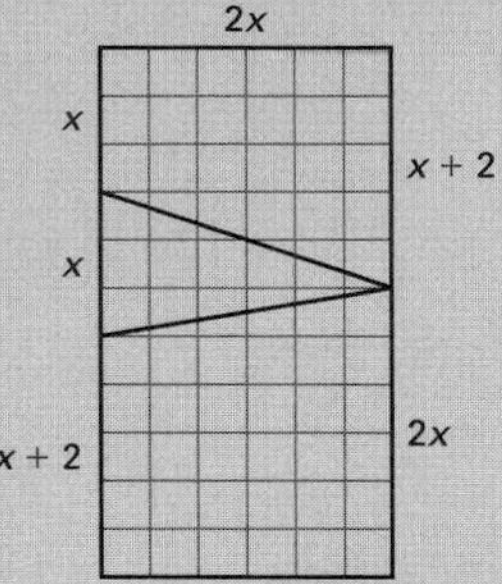

a. Write an expression for the area of each region. **smaller trapezoid: $2x^2 + 2x$; triangle: x^2; larger trapezoid: $3x^2 + 2x$**

b. Use the results of part (a) to write an expression for the area of the entire region. **$6x^2 + 4x$**

CHALLENGE In Exercises 42–44, use the pattern shown below.

$$a(a + 1) + 1(a + 1) = a^2 + a + a + 1 = a^2 + 2a + 1$$

$$a(a + 2) + 2(a + 2) = a^2 + 2a + 2a + 4 = a^2 + 4a + 4$$

$$a(a + 3) + 3(a + 3) = a^2 + 3a + 3a + 9 = a^2 + 6a + 9$$

42. Simplify $a(a + 4) + 4(a + 4)$. **$a^2 + 8a + 16$**

43. Simplify $a(a + 5) + 5(a + 5)$. **$a^2 + 10a + 25$**

44. Generalize: $a(a + b) + b(a + b) =$ ___?___. **$a^2 + 2ab + b^2$**

Multiple-Choice Practice

Student Help

▶TEST TIP In Exercise 46, use what you know about products of integers to predict the *signs* of the terms in the answer.

45. What is the product of $5z$ and $(6 - 2z^2)$? **C**

Ⓐ $30z - 2z^2$ Ⓑ $30z - 10z^2$

Ⓒ $30z - 10z^3$ Ⓓ $30z + 10z^3$

46. What is the product of $-t$ and $(4t^2 - 2t - 1)$? **J**

Ⓕ $-4t^2 + 2t + t$ Ⓖ $-5t^3 - 3t^2 + t$

Ⓗ $4t^3 - 2t^2 - t$ Ⓙ $-4t^3 + 2t^2 + t$

Mixed Review

In Exercises 47–49, use the similar triangles shown. *(8.9)*

47. Write and solve a proportion to find x. **$\frac{6}{9} = \frac{x}{6}$; $x = 4$**

48. What is the ratio of the perimeters of the triangles? **$\frac{2}{3}$**

49. What is the ratio of the areas of the triangles? **$\frac{4}{9}$**

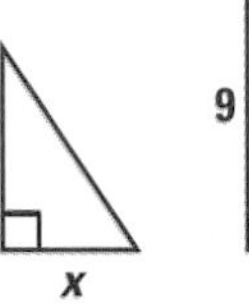

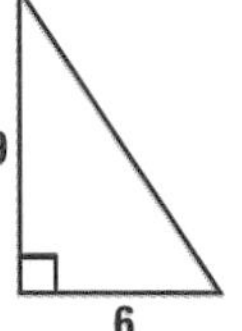

Find the length and the midpoint of $\overline{AB}$ given the coordinates of A and B. *(9.5)*

50. $A(0, 0)$ and $B(6, 10)$ **11.7, (3, 5)**

51. $A(0, 0)$ and $B(-4, -4)$ **5.7, (−2, −2)**

52. $A(10, 10)$ and $B(10, -10)$ **20, (10, 0)**

53. $A(2, 4)$ and $B(6, 8)$ **5.7, (4, 6)**

54. $A(-1, 0)$ and $B(7, -6)$ **10, (3, −3)**

55. $A(4, 3)$ and $B(-6, 3)$ **10, (−1, 3)**

Simplify the expression. *(12.1)*

56. $(7x)^2$ **$49x^2$**

57. $(2y)^4$ **$16y^4$**

58. $(-q)^9$ **$-q^9$**

59. $(ab)^5$ **a^5b^5**

60. $\left(\frac{m}{5}\right)^2$ **$\frac{m^2}{25}$**

61. $\left(\frac{3}{n}\right)^4$ **$\frac{81}{n^4}$**

62. $\left(\frac{5z}{2}\right)^3$ **$\frac{125z^3}{8}$**

63. $\left(\frac{10w}{3}\right)^6$ **See margin.**

64. $(g^7)^3$ **g^{21}**

65. $(h^0)^{10}$ **1**

66. $(c^2d^3)^4$ **c^8d^{12}**

67. $(-7p^4)^2$ **$49p^8$**

63. $\frac{1{,}000{,}000w^6}{729}$

Chapter 12 Mid-Chapter Test

Take this test as you would take a test in class. The answers to the exercises are given in the back of the book.

Simplify the expression.

1. $(2x)^6$ $64x^6$
2. $(4y)^3$ $64y^3$
3. $(-2z)^5$ $-32z^5$
4. $(-w)^8$ w^8
5. $\left(\frac{p}{3}\right)^4$ $\frac{p^4}{81}$
6. $\left(\frac{1}{q}\right)^7$ $\frac{1}{q^7}$
7. $\left(\frac{2r}{5}\right)^2$ $\frac{4r^2}{25}$
8. $\left(\frac{st}{w}\right)^3$ $\frac{s^3t^3}{w^3}$
9. $(m^2)^3$ m^6
10. $(2n^3)^4$ $16n^{12}$
11. $(-3pq^2)^2$ $9p^2q^4$
12. $(xyz^2)^5$ $x^5y^5z^{10}$

Simplify the polynomial and write the result in standard form.

13. $8x + 4 - 3x + 2$ $5x + 6$
14. $x^2 - 3x + 2x^2 + 4$ $3x^2 - 3x + 4$
15. $3x^3 - x^2 - x - x^3 + x$ $2x^3 - x^2$
16. $5x + 7 + 4x - x^2 + 9$ $-x^2 + 9x + 16$

Add or subtract the polynomials. State the degree of the result.

17. $(3x + 9) + (2x^2 - x + 3)$
    $2x^2 + 2x + 12$, second-degree polynomial
18. $(4x^3 + x + 2) - (x^2 + 3x - 4)$
    $4x^3 - x^2 - 2x + 6$, third-degree polynomial
19. $(x^2 - 3x + 4) - (2x^2 + x - 8)$
    $-x^2 - 4x + 12$, second-degree polynomial
20. $(2x^2 - x + 3) + (x^2 - x - 4)$
    $3x^2 - 2x - 1$, second-degree polynomial

Find the product.

21. $5x(3x^2 + 5x)$ $15x^3 + 25x^2$
22. $7x(8x^2 + x + 2)$ $56x^3 + 7x^2 + 14x$
23. $2x(4x^2 - 3x + 5)$ $8x^3 - 6x^2 + 10x$
24. $3x^2(7x - 10)$ $21x^3 - 30x^2$
25. $4x^2(3x^2 + x - 14)$ $12x^4 + 4x^3 - 56x^2$
26. $-x^2(3x^2 - 4x + 12)$ $-3x^4 + 4x^3 - 12x^2$
27. $-3x^2(4x^4 - 6x^2 + 3x - 1)$
    $-12x^6 + 18x^4 - 9x^3 + 3x^2$
28. $6x(2x^4 - 5x^3 + x^2 - 4x - 2)$
    $12x^5 - 30x^4 + 6x^3 - 24x^2 - 12x$

Write a polynomial for the area of the figure.

29. Rectangle $3x^2 - 6x$

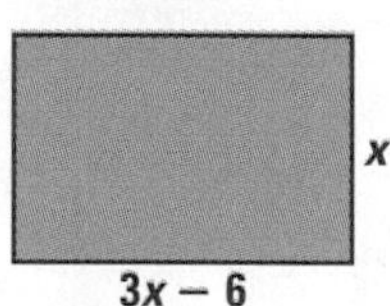

30. Triangle 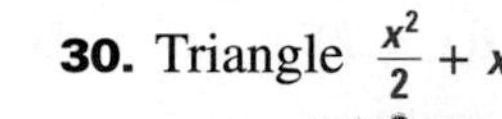 $\frac{x^2}{2} + x$

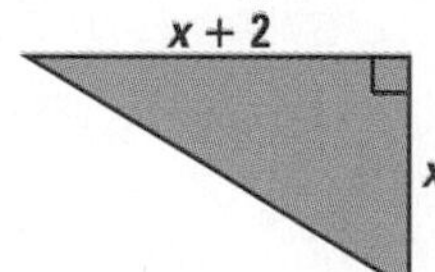

31. Parallelogram $9x - x^2$

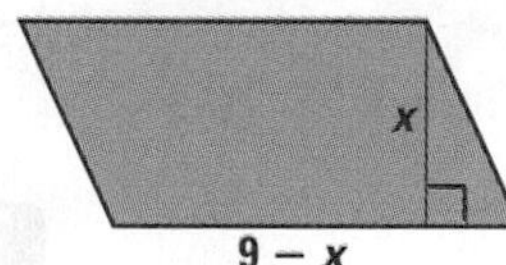

GEOMETRY **In Exercises 32–34, use the figure shown, which is made of rectangles.**

32. Find the area of the larger rectangle. $6x^2 + 2x$
33. Find the area of the smaller rectangle. $2x^2 - x$
34. Write an expression for the area of the blue region as a polynomial in standard form. $4x^2 + 3x$

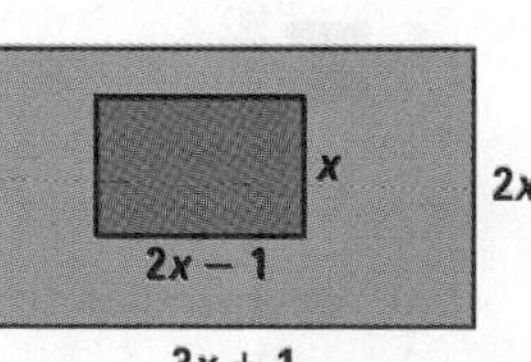

Additional Resources

A Mid-Chapter Test and a Mid-Chapter Partner Quiz are available in the *Assessment Book*, pp. 177–178 and p. 265.

Planning the Activity

Purpose and Materials

See the margin of the student page.

Link to Lesson

Since students will have used algebra tiles to model binomial multiplication, they should be ready to use the symbolic methods presented in Lesson 12.5. If students still need a concrete representation, you may wish to have them use algebra tiles to model Examples 1 and 2.

Math Reasoning

Students use symbols, diagrams, and models to explain mathematical reasoning and apply the results in new situations.

4. $2x + 6$

5. $8x + 4$

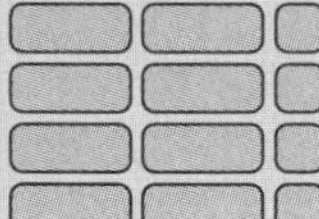

6. $x^2 + 4x$

7. $6x^2 + 6x$

California Standards and Assessment

CA Standards: AF 1.3, MR 2.5

Developing Concepts: Polynomial Multiplication

For use with Lesson 12.5

California Standards

- Simplify numerical expressions by applying properties of rational numbers. (AF 1.3)
- Use a variety of methods, such as symbols, diagrams, and models, to explain mathematical reasoning. (MR 2.5)

Materials:

- Algebra tiles

You can use algebra tiles to represent polynomials.

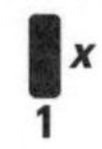

The large square tile has an area of $x \cdot x = x^2$, the rectangular tile has an area of $x \cdot 1 = x$, and the small square tile has an area of $1 \cdot 1 = 1$.

You can refer to these as x^2*-tiles*, x*-tiles*, and *1-tiles*.

SAMPLE 1 Multiplying a Monomial and a Binomial

Use algebra tiles to represent the product. Write the product as a polynomial in standard form.

a. $3(x + 5)$ **b.** $2x(x + 2)$

Here's How

a. Think of the product $3(x + 5)$ as the area of a rectangle with width 3 and length $(x + 5)$.

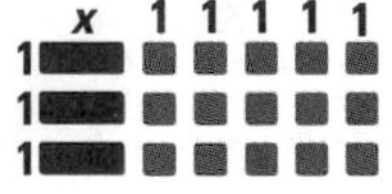

You need 3 x-tiles and 15 1-tiles to build such a rectangle.

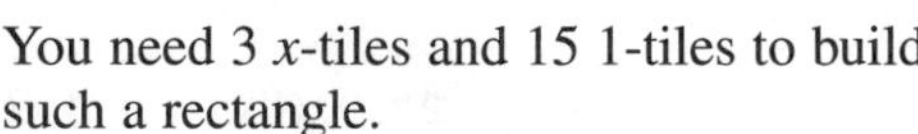

ANSWER ▶ So, $3(x + 5) = 3x + 15$.

b. Think of the product $2x(x + 2)$ as the area of a rectangle with width $2x$ and length $(x + 2)$.

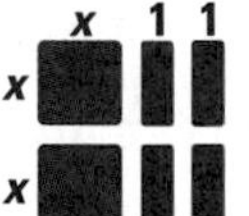

You need 2 x^2-tiles and 4 x-tiles to build such a rectangle.

ANSWER ▶ So, $2x(x + 2) = 2x^2 + 4x$.

Try These

Write the product represented by the algebra tiles as a polynomial in standard form.

1. $2(x + 3) = 2x + 6$

2. $x(x + 5) = x^2 + 5x$

3. $2x(x + 4) = 2x^2 + 8x$

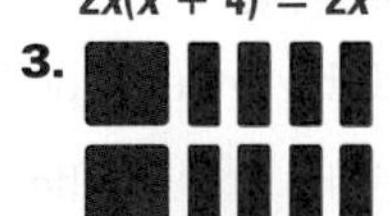

4–7. See margin.

Use algebra tiles to find the product. Show a sketch of your result.

4. $2(x + 3)$ **5.** $4(2x + 1)$ **6.** $x(x + 4)$ **7.** $3x(2x + 2)$

SAMPLE 2 Multiplying Two Binomials

Use algebra tiles to represent the product $(x + 3)(2x + 1)$. Write the product as a polynomial in standard form.

Here's How

Think of the product $(x + 3)(2x + 1)$ as the area of a rectangle with width $(x + 3)$ and length $(2x + 1)$.

You need 2 x^2-tiles, 7 x-tiles, and 3 1-tiles to build such a rectangle. You can write the result as follows:

$$(x + 3)(2x + 1) = 2x^2 + 7x + 3$$

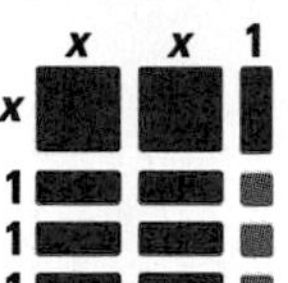

In Sample 2 notice that the result matches what happens if you use the distributive property several times to simplify the product.

$(x + 3)(2x + 1) = (x + 3)(2x) + (x + 3)(1)$	Distributive property
$= x(2x) + 3(2x) + x(1) + 3(1)$	Distributive property
$= 2x^2 + 6x + 1x + 3$	Multiply monomials.
$= 2x^2 + 7x + 3$	Combine like terms.

Try These

Write the product represented by the algebra tiles as a polynomial in standard form.

8. $(x + 1)(2x + 3) = 2x^2 + 5x + 3$

9. 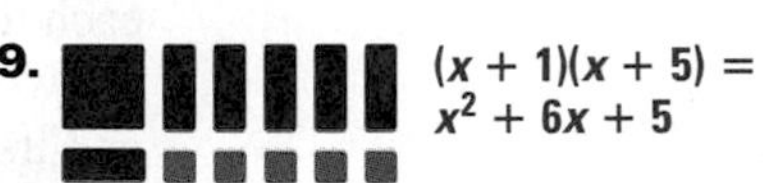 $(x + 1)(x + 5) = x^2 + 6x + 5$

10.  $(x + 2)(3x + 2) = 3x^2 + 8x + 4$

11. 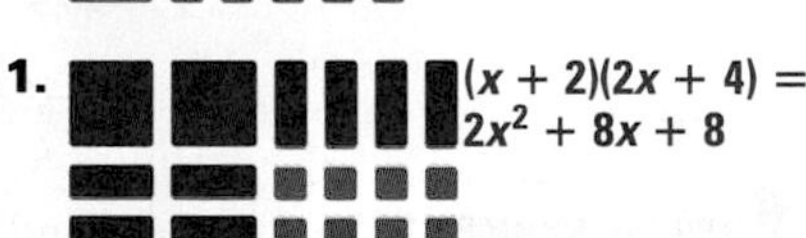 $(x + 2)(2x + 4) = 2x^2 + 8x + 8$

Use algebra tiles to find the product. Sketch your result. 12–15. See margin.

12. $(x + 1)(x + 3)$

13. $(x + 2)(2x + 1)$

14. $(x + 1)(3x + 4)$

15. $(2x + 2)(2x + 3)$

16. MATHEMATICAL REASONING Use algebra tiles to represent $(x + 1)^2$, $(x + 2)^2$, $(x + 3)^2$, and so on. Explain why it is *incorrect* to claim that $(x + n)^2 = x^2 + n^2$ when n is a positive integer. See margin.

16. $x^2 + 2x + 1$; $x^2 + 4x + 4$, $x^2 + 6x + 9$; Sample answer: It is incorrect to say that $(x + n)^2 = x^2 + n^2$ when n is a positive integer because $(x + n)^2$ differs from $x^2 + n^2$ by $2nx$.

2 Managing the Activity

Classroom Management

Store enough algebra tiles in resealable bags so that each student is able to complete the problems given. Use algebra tiles at the overhead to enable student volunteers to share their results.

3 Closing the Activity

★ Key Discovery

An area model can be used to multiply two binomials. The model shows that the distributive property is used twice when multiplying two binomials.

Activity Assessment

Use Exercises 5, 6, 14, and 15 to assess student understanding.

12. $x^2 + 4x + 3$

13. $2x^2 + 5x + 2$

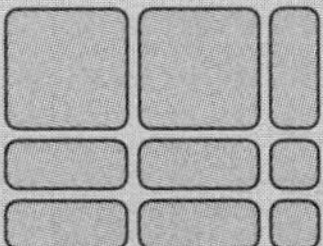

14. $3x^2 + 7x + 4$

15. $4x^2 + 10x + 6$

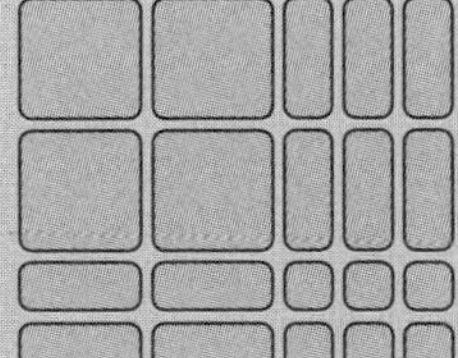

1 Plan

Pacing

Suggested Number of Days

Transitional: 1 day
Average: 1 day
Advanced: 1 day
Block Schedule: 0.5 block with 12.6

Teaching Resources

Blacklines
(See page 614B.)

Transparencies

- Warm-Up Exercises
- Teacher Time-Savers
- English/Spanish Problem Solving
- Answers

Technology

- Electronic Teacher Tools
- Test and Practice Generator

2 Teach

Math Reasoning

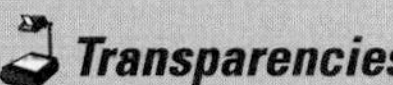

For Mathematical Background Notes on mathematical reasoning related to this lesson, please refer to pages 614E and 614F in this Teacher's Edition.

California Standards and Assessment

CA Standards: AF 1.3, AF 2.2

12.5 Multiplying Polynomials

California Standards

In this lesson you'll:

- Simplify expressions by applying properties of rational numbers. (AF 1.3)
- Multiply monomials. (AF 2.2)

Goal 1 MULTIPLYING TWO BINOMIALS

As you saw in Developing Concepts 12.5, page 636, you can use the distributive property to multiply two binomials.

EXAMPLE 1 Using the Distributive Property

Find the product $(x + 1)(2x + 3)$.

Solution

Method 1 Use a vertical format.

$x + 1$	Write first binomial.
$2x + 3$	Write second binomial.
$3x + 3$	Multiply 3 and $(x + 1)$.
$2x^2 + 2x$	Multiply $2x$ and $(x + 1)$.
$2x^2 + 5x + 3$	Add $(3x + 3)$ and $(2x^2 + 2x)$.

Method 2 Use a horizontal format.

$(x + 1)(2x + 3) = (x + 1)(2x) + (x + 1)(3)$	Distribute $(x + 1)$.
$= x(2x) + 1(2x) + x(3) + 1(3)$	Distribute $2x$ and 3.
$= 2x^2 + 2x + 3x + 3$	Multiply monomials.
$= 2x^2 + 5x + 3$	Combine like terms.

Example 1 shows that each term of one binomial must be multiplied with each term of the other binomial. One way to remember this is to think of the word **FOIL**, because the products of each pair of terms can be labeled as **F**irst, **O**uter, **I**nner, and **L**ast, as Example 2 shows.

Student Help

MORE EXAMPLES

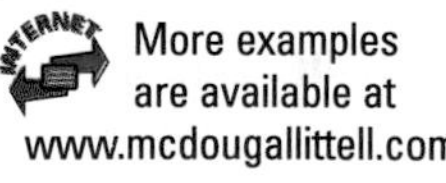

More examples are available at www.mcdougallittell.com

EXAMPLE 2 Using the FOIL Method

Find the product $(3x + 5)(2x + 1)$.

Solution

First, Outer, Inner, Last

$$(3x + 5)(2x + 1) = \mathbf{3x \cdot 2x + 3x \cdot 1 + 5 \cdot 2x + 5 \cdot 1}$$
$$= 6x^2 + 3x + 10x + 5$$
$$= 6x^2 + 13x + 5$$

Goal 2 SQUARING BINOMIALS

Shown below is a pattern that results when you square a binomial. Notice how the pattern is used in the following examples.

Student Help

▶**STUDY TIP**
The pattern for squaring a binomial can be represented using areas. The area of the large square is the sum of the areas of the two rectangles and the two smaller squares.

Squaring a Binomial

$$(a + b)^2 = (a + b)(a + b)$$
$$= (a + b)(a) + (a + b)(b)$$
$$= a \cdot a + b \cdot a + a \cdot b + b \cdot b$$
$$= a^2 + 2ab + b^2$$

	a	b
a	a^2	ab
b	ba	b^2

EXAMPLE 3 Squaring a First-Degree Binomial

Write as a polynomial in standard form.

a. $(x + 7)^2$ **b.** $(3y + 5)^2$

Solution

a. $(x + 7)^2 = x^2 + 2(x)(7) + 7^2$
$= x^2 + 14x + 49$

b. $(3y + 5)^2 = (3y)^2 + 2(3y)(5) + 5^2$
$= 3^2y^2 + 30y + 25$
$= 9y^2 + 30y + 25$

EXAMPLE 4 Squaring a Second-Degree Binomial

Write $(z^2 + 8)^2$ as a polynomial in standard form.

Solution

$(z^2 + 8)^2 = (z^2)^2 + 2(z^2)(8) + 8^2$ Apply $(a + b)^2 = a^2 + 2ab + b^2$.
$= z^4 + 16z^2 + 64$ Use power of a power rule.

Link to Careers

HUMAN RESOURCES specialists include managers who develop and explain pay rates and benefits to a company's employees.

More about human resources available at www.mcdougallittell.com

EXAMPLE 5 Using Binomial Multiplication

PAY RAISE You start a job with an annual salary of $20,000 and receive a fixed percent of increase p (expressed as a decimal) each year. Write an expression for your salary after 2 years.

Solution

Salary in Year 1: 20,000
Salary in Year 2: $20{,}000(1 + p)$
Salary in Year 3: $20{,}000(1 + p)(1 + p) = 20{,}000(1 + 2p + p^2)$

Extra Example 1

Find the product $(2x - 5)(x + 3)$. $2x^2 + x - 15$

Extra Example 2

Find the product $(4x - 1)(3x + 2)$. $12x^2 + 5x - 2$

Extra Example 3

Write as a polynomial in standard form.

a. $(x + 4)^2$ $x^2 + 8x + 16$
b. $(2y + 3)^2$ $4y^2 + 12y + 9$

Extra Example 4

Write $(a^2 + 5)^2$ as a polynomial in standard form. $a^4 + 10a^2 + 25$

Extra Example 5

A flock of geese starts with 20 geese and increases each year by a fixed percent p (expressed as a decimal). Write an expression for the number of geese after 2 years. $20(1 + 2p + p^2)$

Teaching Tip

Point out the similarities between multiplying two binomials using a vertical format and multiplying a pair of two-digit whole numbers.

Concept Check

Explain how to use the FOIL method to multiply two binomials. ***Sample answer:*** **FOIL stands for First, Outer, Inner, Last. Multiply the first terms of each binomial, then the outer terms of the two binomials, next the inner terms, and finally the last terms of each. Add the products and combine like terms to simplify.**

3 Apply

Assignment Guide

TRANSITIONAL
Day 1: pp. 640–641 Exs. 11–15, 19–24, 32–33, 35–38, 54–55

AVERAGE
Day 1: pp. 640–641 Exs. 12–15, 22–27, 32–33, 39–42, 51–52, 54–55

ADVANCED
Day 1: pp. 640–641 Exs. 16–18, 25–31, 33–34, 43–48, 52, 53*, 54–55; EC: TE p. 614D*

BLOCK SCHEDULE
pp. 640–641 Exs. 12–15, 22–27, 32–33, 39–42, 51–52, 54–55 (with 12.6)

Extra Practice

- Student Edition, pp. 712–713
- Chapter 12 Resource Book, p. 42

Homework Check

To quickly check student understanding of key concepts, go over the following exercises:

Transitional: 14, 20, 24, 32, 36
Average: 14, 22, 26, 32, 42
Advanced: 16, 26, 30, 34, 44

Problem Solving

Exercise 31
Have students multiply the first two polynomials together using the distributive property and then multiply this product by the third polynomial using either the vertical format or the FOIL method.

31. $2x^3 + 22x^2 + 56x$; *Sample answer:* the degree of the product is the sum of the degrees of the polynomials that are factors.

1. $(x + 2)(x + 7)$
$= (x + 2)(x) + (x + 2)(7)$
Distribute $(x + 2)$.
$= x(x) + 2(x) + x(7) + 2(7)$
Distribute x and 7.
$= x^2 + 2x + 7x + 14$
Multiply monomials.
$= x^2 + 9x + 14$
Combine like terms.

2. $(x + 3)(3x + 2)$
$= (x + 3)(3x) + (x + 3)(2)$
Distribute $(x + 3)$.
$= x(3x) + 3(3x) + x(2) + 3(2)$
Distribute $3x$ and 2.
$= 3x^2 + 9x + 2x + 6$
Multiply monomials.
$= 3x^2 + 11x + 6$
Combine like terms.

3. $(2x + 1)(4x + 5)$
$= (2x + 1)(4x) + (2x + 1)(5)$
Distribute $(2x + 1)$.
$= 2x(4x) + 1(4x) + 2x(5) + 1(5)$
Distribute $4x$ and 5.
$= 8x^2 + 4x + 10x + 5$
Multiply monomials.
$= 8x^2 + 14x + 5$
Combine like terms.

11. In first line of solution, the student did not distribute $(x + 6)$.
$(x + 6)(2x + 5)$
$= (x + 6)(2x) + (x + 6)(5)$
$= x(2x) + 6(2x) + x(5) + 6(5)$
$= 2x^2 + 17x + 30$

12. In third line of solution, $4x$ was not distributed onto $3x$ and 3 was not distributed onto $3x$.
$(3x + 4)(4x + 3)$
$= (3x + 4)(4x) + (3x + 4)(3)$
$= 3x(4x) + 4(4x) + 3x(3) + 4(3)$
$= 12x^2 + 16x + 9x + 12$
$= 12x^2 + 25x + 12$

12.5 Exercises

Guided Practice

Use the distributive property to find the product. Justify each step. 1–3. See margin.

1. $(x + 2)(x + 7)$ **2.** $(x + 3)(3x + 2)$ **3.** $(2x + 1)(4x + 5)$

Match the product with its equivalent expression.

4. $(4x + 3)(3x + 2)$	D	**A.** $12x^2 + 15x + 3$	
5. $(2x + 8)(6x + 2)$	B	**B.** $12x^2 + 52x + 16$	
6. $(12x + 3)(x + 1)$	A	**C.** $12x^2 + 32x + 16$	
7. $(6x + 4)(2x + 4)$	C	**D.** $12x^2 + 17x + 6$	

Write as a polynomial in standard form.

8. $(x + 4)^2$ $x^2 + 8x + 16$
9. $(x + 10)^2$ $x^2 + 20x + 100$
10. $(4x + 5)^2$ $16x^2 + 40x + 25$

Practice and Problem Solving

Student Help

▶MORE PRACTICE
Extra practice to help you master skills is on page 713.

ERROR ANALYSIS Describe and correct the error. 11–12. See margin.

11.

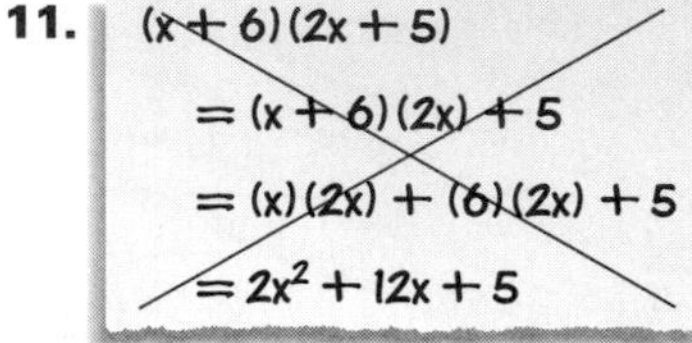

12.
$(3x + 4)(4x + 3)$
$= (3x + 4)(4x) + (3x + 4)(3)$
$= (3x) + (4)(4x) + (3x) + (4)(3)$
$= 3x + 16x + 3x + 12$
$= 22x + 12$

Multiply the binomials using a vertical format. Then check the result by using a horizontal format.

13. $3x + 2$ / $6x + 8$ — $18x^2 + 36x + 16$
14. $9x + 6$ / $3x + 1$ — $27x^2 + 27x + 6$
15. $x + 10$ / $4x + 15$ — $4x^2 + 55x + 150$
16. $5x + 1$ / $x + 7$ — $5x^2 + 36x + 7$
17. $6x + 1$ / $6x + 1$ — $36x^2 + 12x + 1$
18. $3x + 10$ / $10x + 3$ — $30x^2 + 109x + 30$

In Exercises 19–30, find the product.

19. $(x + 3)(x + 8)$ $x^2 + 11x + 24$
20. $(x + 6)(x + 12)$ $x^2 + 18x + 72$
21. $(2x + 3)(x + 5)$ $2x^2 + 13x + 15$
22. $(x + 3)(8x + 12)$ $8x^2 + 36x + 36$
23. $(5x + 6)(x + 2)$ $5x^2 + 16x + 12$
24. $(2x + 1)(9x + 7)$ $18x^2 + 23x + 7$
25. $(4x + 5)(5x + 4)$ $20x^2 + 41x + 20$
26. $(10x + 10)(2x + 2)$ $20x^2 + 40x + 20$
27. $(3x + 8)(3x + 2)$ $9x^2 + 30x + 16$
28. $(2x + 3)(4x + 1)$ $8x^2 + 14x + 3$
29. $(2x + 4)(7x + 9)$ $14x^2 + 46x + 36$
30. $(6x + 5)(3x + 5)$ $18x^2 + 45x + 25$

31. Find the product $(2x)(x + 4)(x + 7)$. How is the degree of the product related to the degrees of the polynomials that are factors? See margin.

GEOMETRY **Write the area of the figure as a polynomial in standard form.**

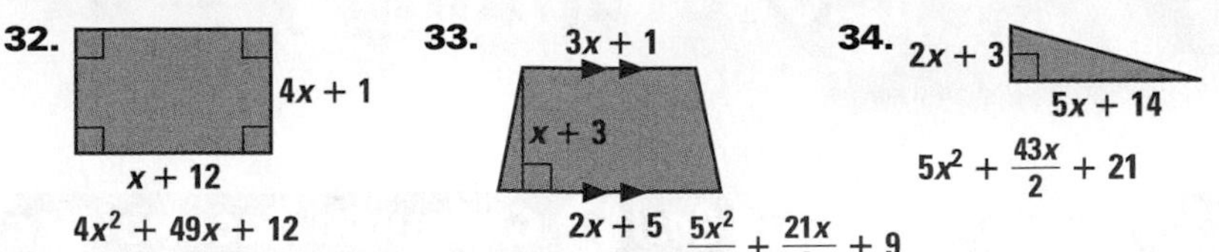

32. $4x^2 + 49x + 12$
33. $\frac{5x^2}{2} + \frac{21x}{2} + 9$
34. $5x^2 + \frac{43x}{2} + 21$

In Exercises 35–50, write as a polynomial in standard form.

35. $(x + 3)^2$ $x^2 + 6x + 9$
36. $(y + 10)^2$ $y^2 + 20y + 100$
37. $(z + 2)^2$ $z^2 + 4z + 4$
38. $(w + 9)^2$ $w^2 + 18w + 81$
39. $(m + 5)^2$ $m^2 + 10m + 25$
40. $(n + 1)^2$ $n^2 + 2n + 1$
41. $(p + 7)^2$ $p^2 + 14p + 49$
42. $(q + 11)^2$ $q^2 + 22q + 121$
43. $(2a + 1)^2$ $4a^2 + 4a + 1$
44. $(3b + 2)^2$ $9b^2 + 12b + 4$
45. $(6c + 4)^2$ $36c^2 + 48c + 16$
46. $(5d + 3)^2$ $25d^2 + 30d + 9$
47. $(e^2 + 6)^2$ $e^4 + 12e^2 + 36$
48. $(g^2 + 1)^2$ $g^4 + 2g^2 + 1$
49. $(j^2 + 8)^2$ $j^4 + 16j^2 + 64$
50. $(5k^2 + 1)^2$ $25k^4 + 10k^2 + 1$

51. $(a - b)(a - b)$
$= a(a - b) - b(a - b)$ Dist. Prop.
$= a^2 - ab - ab + b^2$ Dist. Prop.
$= a^2 - 2ab + b^2$ Combine like terms.
$4x^2 - 12x + 9$

51. MATHEMATICAL REASONING Write $(a - b)^2$ as a polynomial in standard form. Justify each step. Then use the pattern to rewrite $(2x - 3)^2$. **See margin.**

52. MATHEMATICAL REASONING Write $(a + b)^3$ as a polynomial in standard form. (*Hint:* Use the fact that $(a + b)^3 = (a + b)^2(a + b)$.) Then use the pattern to rewrite $(3x + 2)^3$.
$a^3 + 3a^2b + 3ab^2 + b^3$; $27x^3 + 54x^2 + 36x + 8$

53. CHALLENGE Suppose you receive a certain percent pay raise one year, then that same percent as a pay cut the next year, as shown.

Salary in Year 1	\$20,000
Salary in Year 2	\$20,000(1 + *p*)
Salary in Year 3	\$20,000(1 + *p*)(1 − *p*)

No, your salary in year 3 will not be the same as in year 1. year 3 salary: (\$20,000)$(1 - p^2)$ which is less than year 1 salary: \$20,000.

Will your salary in Year 3 be the same as it was in Year 1? Find the product in Year 3 and use it to justify your answer.

Multiple-Choice Practice

54. Which polynomial represents the area of the parallelogram? D

Ⓐ $7x + 4$
Ⓑ $10x^2 + 3$
Ⓒ $7x^2 + 11x + 4$
Ⓓ $10x^2 + 11x + 3$

2x + 1
5x + 3

55. Write $(x + 10)^2$ as a polynomial in standard form. H

Ⓕ $2x + 20$
Ⓖ $x^2 + 20$
Ⓗ $x^2 + 20x + 100$
Ⓙ $x^2 + 100x + 100$

4 Assess

Assessment Resources
- Assessment Book (Formal Assessment and Alternative Assessment)
- Test and Practice Generator

Mini-Quiz
1. Multiply $(3x + 10)$ and $(x + 7)$ using the distributive property. $3x^2 + 31x + 70$
2. Multiply $(5x + 4)$ and $(9x + 2)$ using the FOIL method. $45x^2 + 46x + 8$

Write as a polynomial in standard form.

3. $(m + 8)^2$ $m^2 + 16m + 64$
4. $(x^2 + 3)^2$ $x^4 + 6x^2 + 9$
5. $(3a + 5)^2$ $9a^2 + 30a + 25$

Math Reasoning
Unlike what happens under a doubling of scale, the parallelogram obtained by setting $x = 2$ in Problem 54 does *not* have twice the perimeter or four times the area of the parallelogram obtained when $x = 1$. Here it may be instructive to ask students to sketch these two geometric figures.

1 Plan

Pacing

Suggested Number of Days

Transitional: 1 day
Average: 1 day
Advanced: 1 day
Block Schedule: 0.5 block with 12.5

Teaching Resources

Blacklines
(See page 614B.)

Transparencies
- Warm-Up Exercises
- Teacher Time-Savers
- English/Spanish Problem Solving
- Answers

Technology
- Electronic Teacher Tools
- Test and Practice Generator

2 Teach

Math Reasoning

For Mathematical Background Notes on mathematical reasoning related to this lesson, please refer to pages 614E and 614F in this Teacher's Edition.

California Standards and Assessment

CA Standards: AF 3.1, AF 3.2

12.6 Graphing $y = ax^2$ and $y = ax^3$

California Standards

In this lesson you'll:
- Graph functions of the form $y = nx^2$ and $y = nx^3$ and use in solving problems. (AF 3.1)
- Plot the values of volumes of three-dimensional shapes for various values of the edge lengths. (AF 3.2)

Student Help

STUDY TIP
If you plot *xy*-pairs other than those in the table, you will find that they all lie along a smooth curve.

Goal 1 GRAPHING SECOND-DEGREE FUNCTIONS

In Chapter 11 you learned that the graph of a linear function is a line. In this lesson you will study the graphs of two types of *nonlinear* functions.

EXAMPLE 1 Graphing a Second-Degree Function

Graph the function $y = x^2$.

Solution

Make a table of values for the function. Plot the *xy*-pairs and connect the points with a smooth curve, as shown.

x	y
-2	$(-2)^2 = 4$
-1	$(-1)^2 = 1$
0	$0^2 = 0$
1	$1^2 = 1$
2	$2^2 = 4$

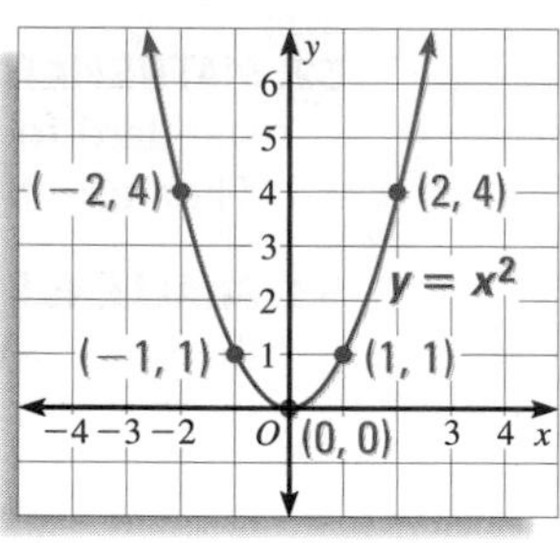

EXAMPLE 2 Graphing a Second-Degree Function

Graph the function $y = 0.25x^2$.

Solution

Make a table of values for the function. Plot the *xy*-pairs and connect the points with a smooth curve, as shown.

x	y
-4	$(0.25)(-4)^2 = (0.25)(16) = 4$
-2	$(0.25)(-2)^2 = (0.25)(4) = 1$
0	$(0.25)(0)^2 = (0.25)(0) = 0$
2	$(0.25)(2)^2 = (0.25)(4) = 1$
4	$(0.25)(4)^2 = (0.25)(16) = 4$

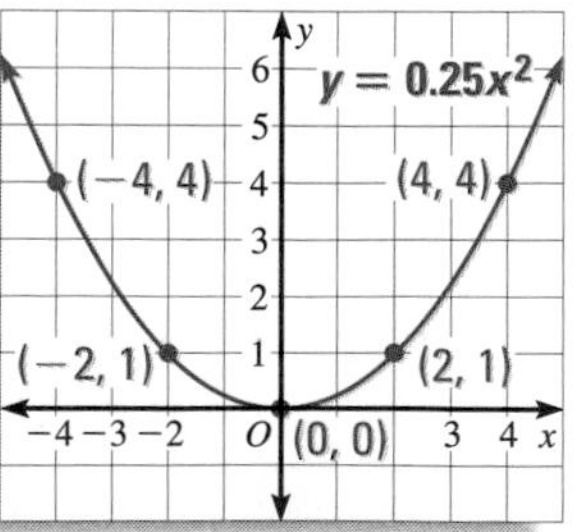

EXAMPLE 3 Graphing a Second-Degree Function

Graph the function $y = -2x^2$.

Solution

Make a table of values for the function. Plot the xy-pairs and connect the points with a smooth curve, as shown.

x	y
−2	$-2(-2)^2 = -2(4) = -8$
−1	$-2(-1)^2 = -2(1) = -2$
0	$-2(0)^2 = 0$
1	$-2(1)^2 = -2(1) = -2$
2	$-2(2)^2 = -2(4) = -8$

Student Help

▶ **STUDY TIP**
The graph of $y = ax^2$ is a U-shaped curve that looks like a *smile* when a is *positive.* It looks like a *frown* when a is *negative.*

EXAMPLE 4 Problem Solving with a Second-Degree Function

Consider a rectangle whose length is twice its width. Write an equation that represents its area as a function of its width. Graph the function.

Solution

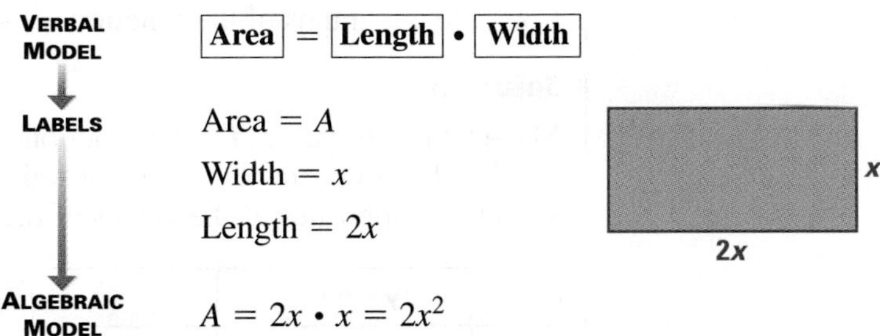

Begin by making a table of values. Only nonnegative values of x make sense in this situation. Plot the ordered pairs from the table. Connect the points with a smooth curve, as shown.

x	A
0	$2(0)^2 = 2(0) = 0$
0.5	$2(0.5)^2 = 2(0.25) = 0.5$
1	$2(1)^2 = 2(1) = 2$
1.5	$2(1.5)^2 = 2(2.25) = 4.5$
2	$2(2)^2 = 2(4) = 8$

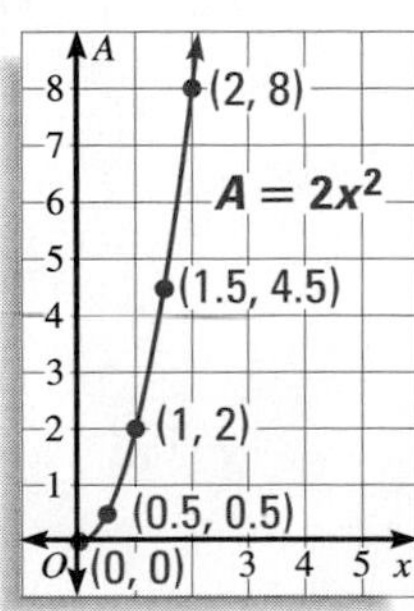

Extra Example 1

Graph the function $y = 2x^2$.

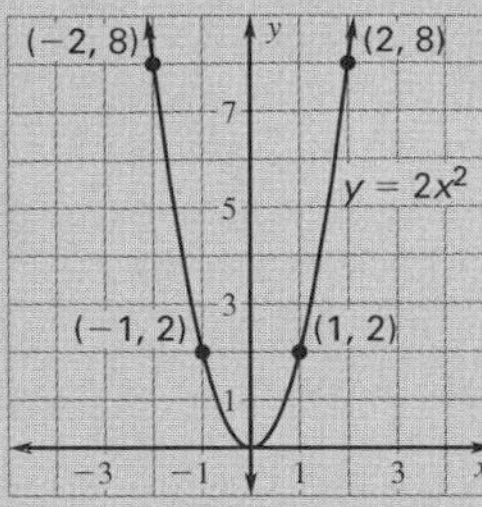

Extra Example 2

Graph the function $y = 0.75x^2$.

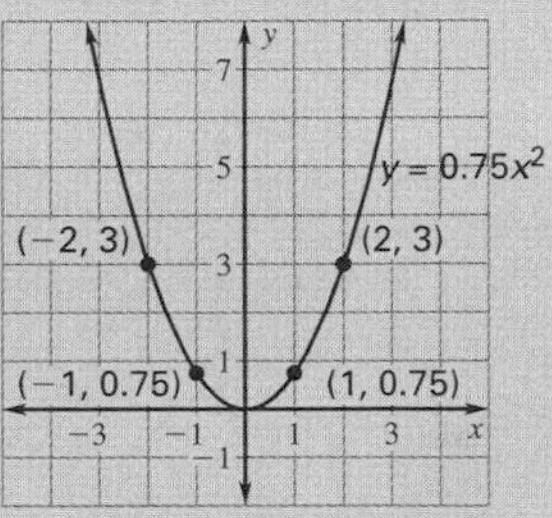

Extra Example 3

Graph the function $y = -x^2$.

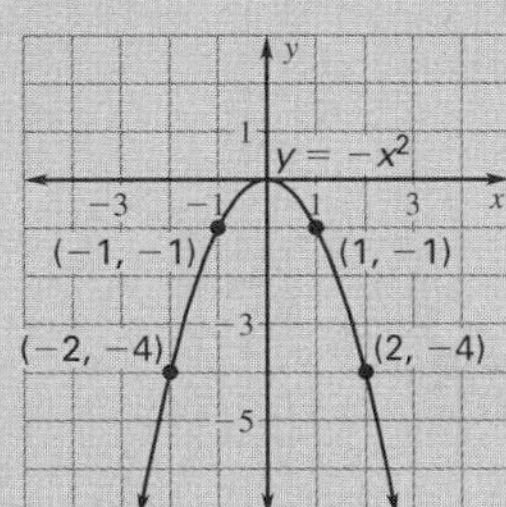

Extra Example 4

Consider a rectangle whose length is three times its width. Write an equation that represents its area as a function of its width. Graph the function. $A = 3x^2$

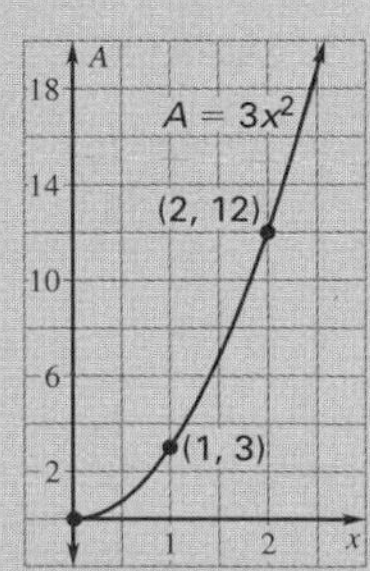

Teaching Tip

Common Error When students are evaluating a function of the form $y = ax^2$, they often multiply the coefficient and the x value together before squaring. Remind them that the exponent goes only with the number or variable directly preceding it, unless parentheses are used.

Extra Example 5

Graph the function $y = 2x^3$.

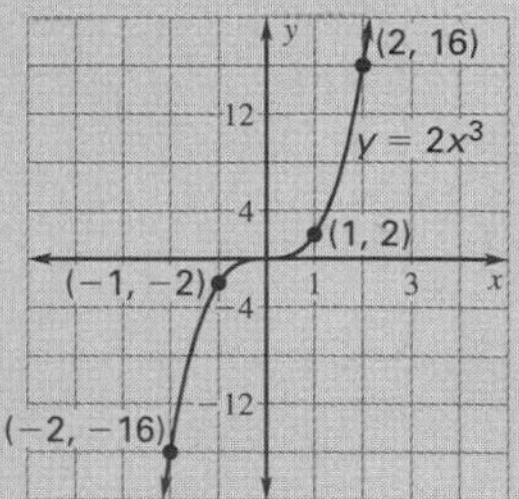

Extra Example 6

Compare the graphs of the functions $y = 0.5x^3$ and $y = -0.5x^3$.

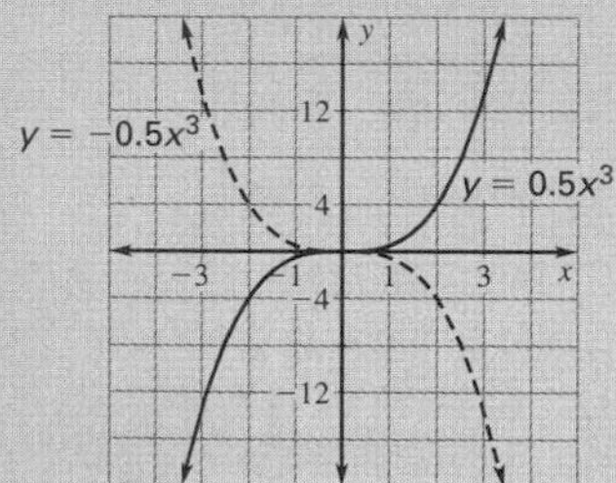

The graphs are reflections of each other in the *x*-axis.

Concept Check

Explain how to graph a function of the form $y = ax^2$ or $y = ax^3$. ***Sample answer:*** **Make a table of values and plot the points; then connect the points with a smooth curve.**

Goal 2 GRAPHING THIRD-DEGREE FUNCTIONS

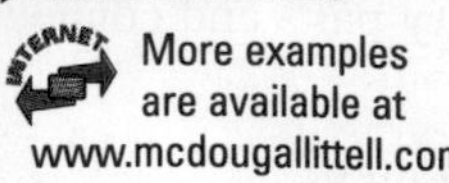

Student Help

▶**MORE EXAMPLES**
More examples are available at www.mcdougallittell.com

EXAMPLE 5 Graphing a Third-Degree Function

Graph the function $y = x^3$.

Solution

Make a table of values for the function.

x	y
-2	$(-2)^3 = -8$
-1	$(-1)^3 = -1$
0	$0^3 = 0$
1	$1^3 = 1$
2	$2^3 = 8$

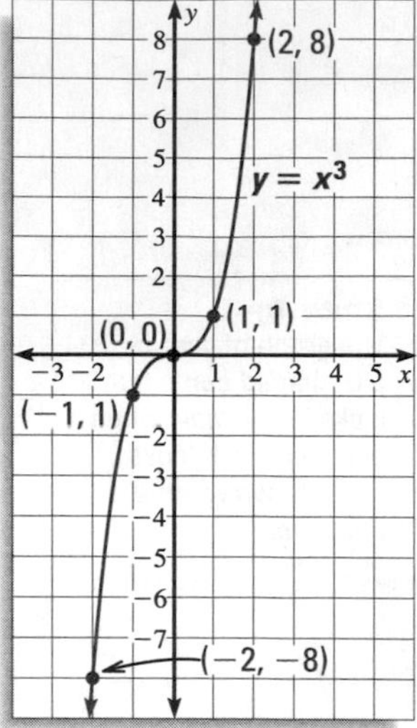

Plot the xy-pairs and connect the points with a smooth curve, as shown.

EXAMPLE 6 Comparing Third-Degree Functions

Compare the graphs of the functions $y = 0.1x^3$ and $y = -0.1x^3$.

Solution

Make a table of values for the functions. Because the coefficients of $0.1x^3$ and $-0.1x^3$ are opposites, the values of the second function are simply the opposites of the values of the first function.

x	$y = 0.1x^3$	$y = -0.1x^3$
-3	$0.1(-3)^3 = -2.7$	2.7
-2	$0.1(-2)^3 = -0.8$	0.8
-1	$0.1(-1)^3 = -0.1$	0.1
0	$0.1(0)^3 = 0$	0
1	$0.1(1)^3 = 0.1$	-0.1
2	$0.1(2)^3 = 0.8$	-0.8
3	$0.1(3)^3 = 2.7$	-2.7

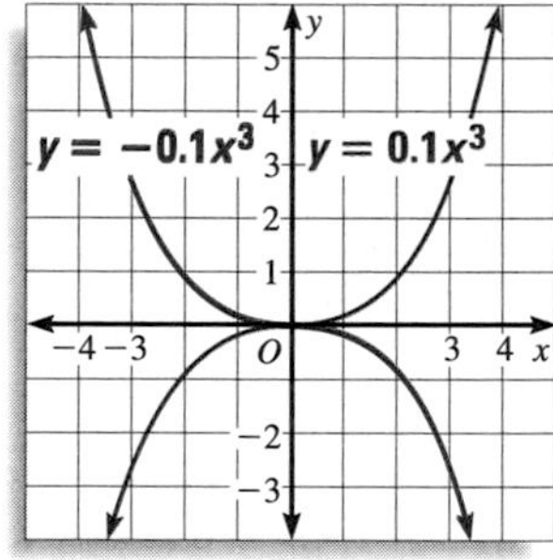

Plot the xy-pairs for each function and connect the points with smooth curves, as shown.

The graphs of the functions are reflections of each other in the x-axis.

12.6 Exercises

Guided Practice

In Exercises 1 and 2, complete the table for the function. Plot the *xy*-pairs and draw a smooth curve through the points to graph the function. **1–2. See margin.**

1. $y = \frac{1}{2}x^2$

x	−3	−2	−1	0	1	2	3
y	?	?	?	?	?	?	?

2. $y = \frac{1}{2}x^3$

x	−3	−2	−1	0	1	2	3
y	?	?	?	?	?	?	?

GEOMETRY In Exercises 3–5, use the right pyramid shown. The base of the pyramid is a square.

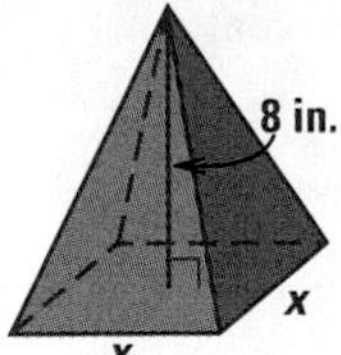

3. Write the volume of the pyramid as a function of its base edge length. $V = \frac{8x^2}{3}$

4. Find the volume of the pyramid when $x = 0, 0.5, 1, 1.5, 2, 2.5$, and 3. Organize your data in a table. **See margin.**

5. Graph the ordered pairs from your table of values. Then connect the points with a smooth curve. **See margin.**

Practice and Problem Solving

Student Help

▶MORE PRACTICE Extra practice to help you master skills is on page 713.

In Exercises 6–9, match the equation with its graph.

A.

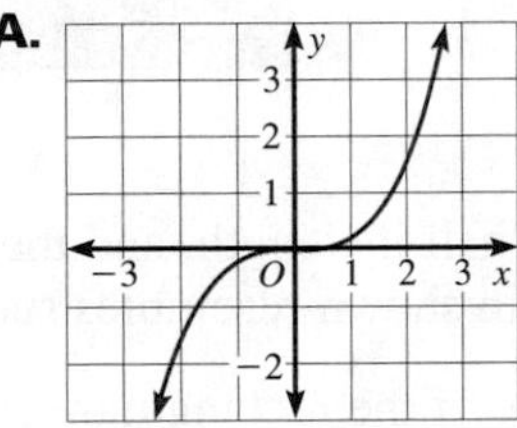

B.

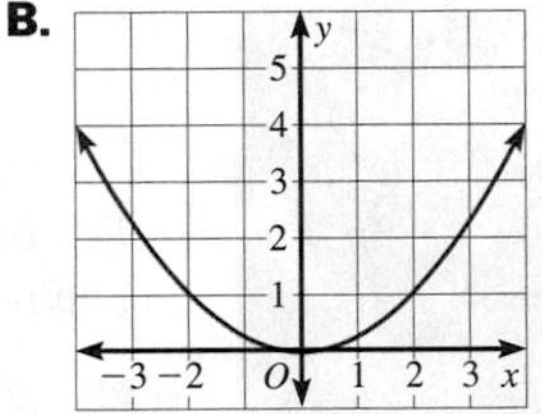

C.

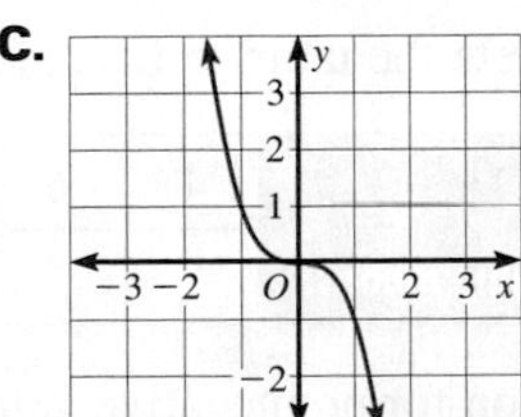

D.

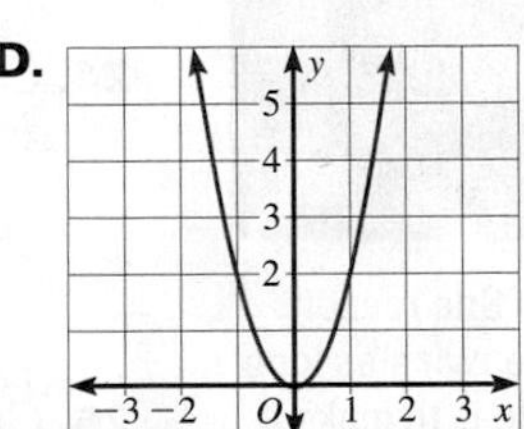

6. $y = 2x^2$ **D** **7.** $y = \frac{1}{4}x^2$ **B** **8.** $y = \frac{1}{5}x^3$ **A** **9.** $y = -x^3$ **C**

3 Apply

Assignment Guide

TRANSITIONAL
Day 1: pp. 645–647 Exs. 6–12, 14–16, 18–20, 33–34

AVERAGE
Day 1: pp. 645–647 Exs. 6–9, 11–16, 23–28, 33–34

ADVANCED
Day 1: pp. 645–647 Exs. 6–9, 11–16, 22*, 23–28, 29–32*, 33–34

BLOCK SCHEDULE
pp. 645–647 Exs. 6–9, 11–16, 22–28, 33–34 (with 12.5)

Extra Practice

- Student Edition, pp. 712–713
- Chapter 12 Resource Book, p. 51

Homework Check

To quickly check student understanding of key concepts, go over the following exercises:

Transitional: 10, 12, 16, 18, 20
Average: 12, 14, 16, 24, 26
Advanced: 12, 14, 16, 24, 30

1–2, 4. See Additional Answers beginning on AA1.

5.

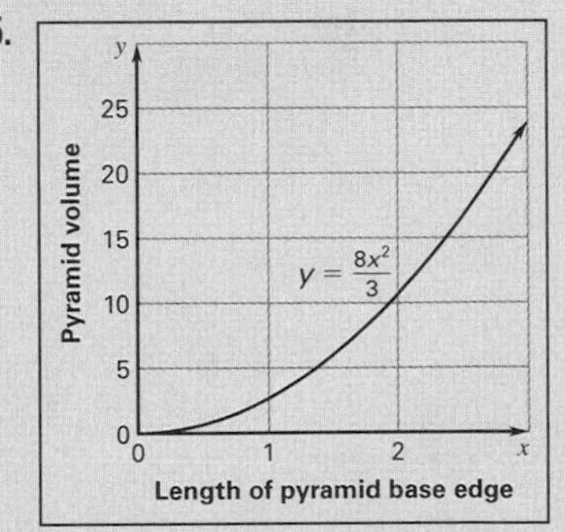

10.

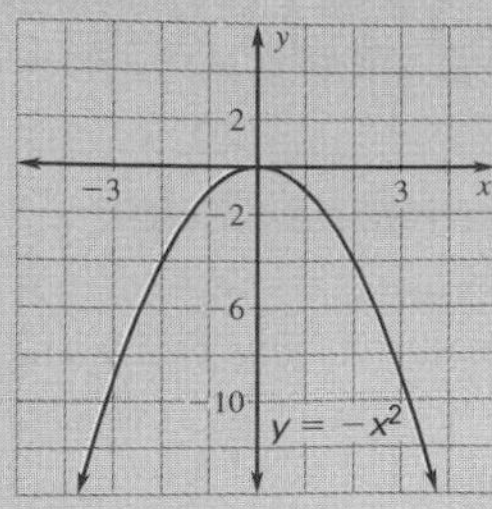

11.

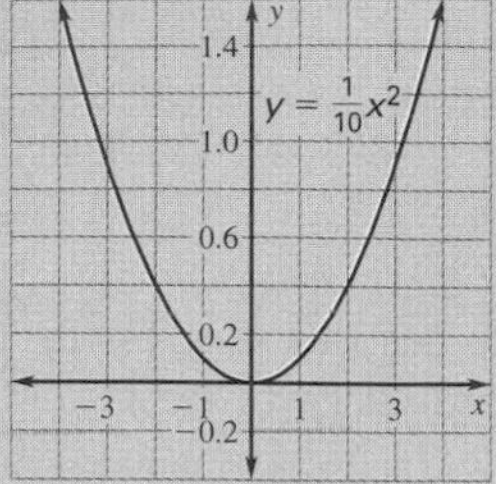

12.

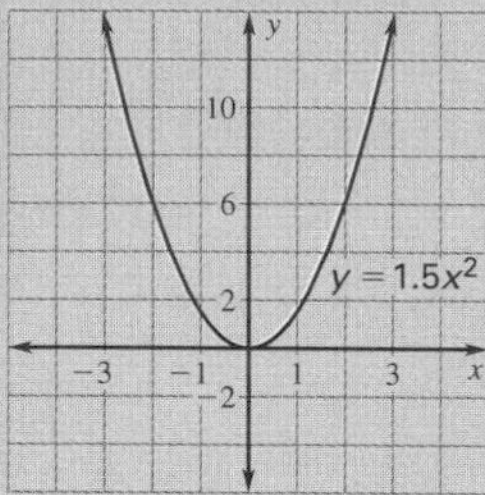

13.

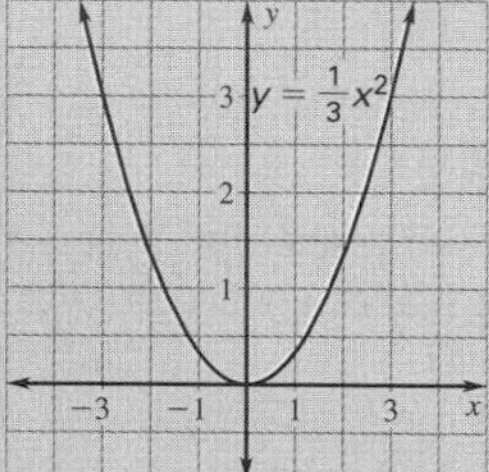

14.

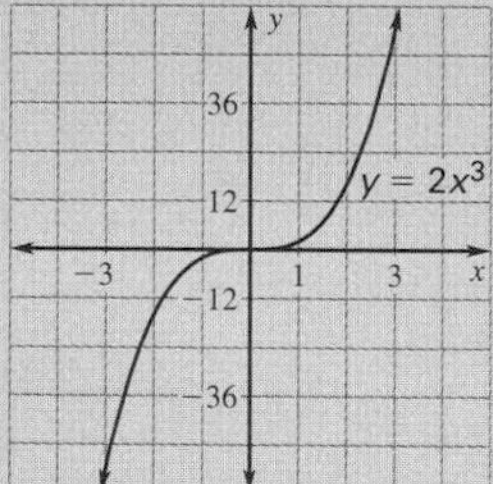

15.

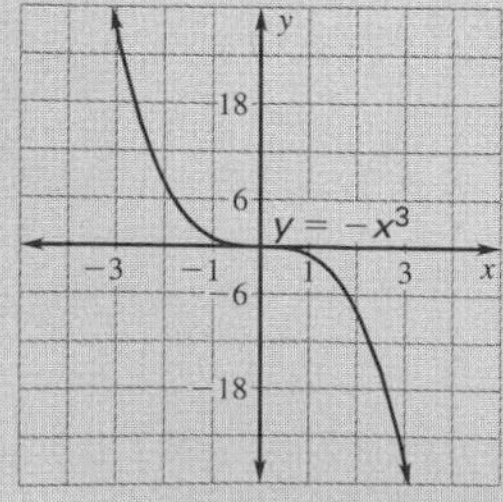

16–17, 19–20, 22, 24–25. See Additional Answers beginning on page AA1.

Student Help

▶ HOMEWORK HELP

Extra help with problem solving in Exs. 10–17 is available at www.mcdougallittell.com

Make a table of values for the function. Plot the *xy*-pairs and draw a smooth curve through the points. **10–17. See margin.**

10. $y = -x^2$ **11.** $y = \frac{1}{10}x^2$ **12.** $y = 1.5x^2$ **13.** $y = \frac{1}{3}x^2$

14. $y = 2x^3$ **15.** $y = -x^3$ **16.** $y = -\frac{1}{2}x^3$ **17.** $y = 3x^3$

GEOMETRY In Exercises 18–21, use the cube shown. All edges of the cube have a length of *x*.

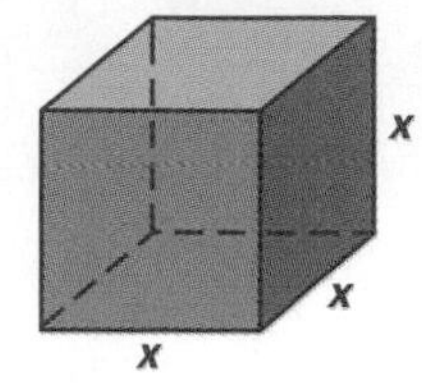

18. Write an equation that represents the surface area of the cube as a function of x. **$A = 6x^2$**

19. Calculate the surface area of the cube when the edges are of length 1, 2, 3, and 4. Organize your data in a table. **See margin.**

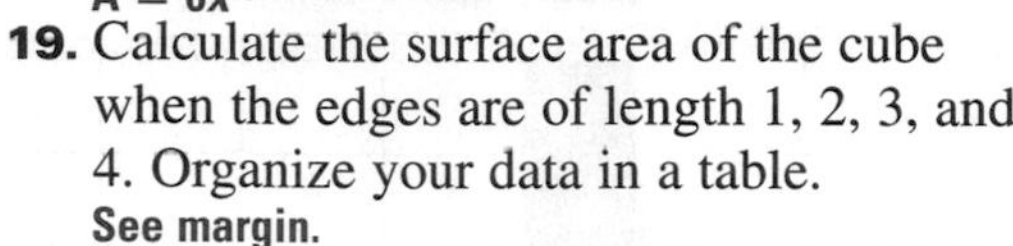

20. Graph the equation from Exercise 18 for nonnegative values of x. **See margin.**

21. MATHEMATICAL REASONING What happens to the surface area of a cube when you double every edge length? Explain the result using your graph from Exercise 20 or algebraic reasoning.

21. The surface area increases by a factor of 4. For example, for $x = 1$, $A = 6$; for $x = 2$, $A = 24$, which is four times the former area.

22. CHALLENGE A triangular prism with an equilateral base has a height of 4 units. The volume of the prism is given by the function $y = \sqrt{3} \cdot x^2$ where x is the length of any side of the triangular base. List at least four ordered pairs that are solutions of this equation. Then graph the equation for nonnegative values of x. **See margin.**

BRICKWORK In Exercises 23–26, use the following information. Bricks are often made using dimensions in this extended ratio:

length : width : height

$1 : \frac{1}{2} : \frac{1}{4}$

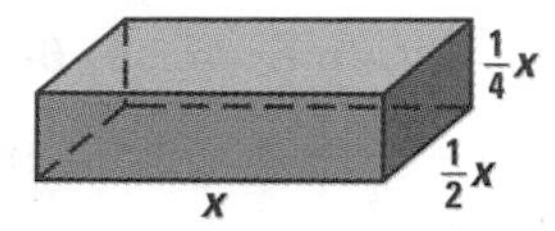

The brick's width is half its length, and the brick's height is half its width. The rectangular prism shown resembles such a brick.

23. Write the volume of the rectangular prism as a function of x. **$\frac{x^3}{8}$**

24. Copy and complete the table to find the volume of the prism. **See margin.**

x (in inches)	4	6	8	10	12
Volume (in cubic inches)	?	?	?	?	?

25. Graph the function for nonnegative values of x. **See margin.**

26. MATHEMATICAL REASONING What happens to the volume when the edge lengths of a brick are doubled? **See margin.**

26. By comparing the values of V for $x = 4$ and $x = 8$ and for $x = 6$ and $x = 12$, the table shows that the volume increases by a factor of 8 when the edges of a brick are doubled.

Link to Construction

BRICKWORK One reason bricks are made twice as long as they are wide is to make it easier to build corners wherever needed with no special sizes.

In Exercises 27 and 28, complete the statements.

27. The graph of $y = ax^2$ for $a > 0$ contains (0, 0) and otherwise lies in Quadrants __?__ and __?__. The graph of $y = ax^2$ for $a < 0$ contains (0, 0) and otherwise lies in Quadrants __?__ and __?__. **1, 2; 3, 4**

28. The graph of $y = ax^3$ for $a > 0$ contains (0, 0) and otherwise lies in Quadrants __?__ and __?__. The graph of $y = ax^3$ for $a < 0$ contains (0, 0) and otherwise lies in Quadrants __?__ and __?__. **1, 3; 2, 4**

CHALLENGE In Exercises 29–32, use the sphere shown.

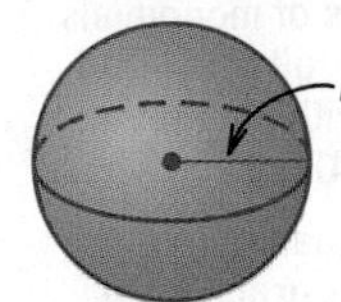

29. Write the volume of the sphere as a function of its radius. $V = \frac{4\pi r^3}{3}$

30. Find the volume of the sphere when the radius is 0.2, 0.4, 0.6, 0.8, 1.0, 1.2, and 1.4 units. Organize your data in a table. **See margin.**

31. Graph the ordered pairs from your table. Connect the points with a smooth curve. **See margin.**

32. What happens to the volume of a sphere if you double the length of its radius? Explain. **See margin.**

Multiple-Choice Practice

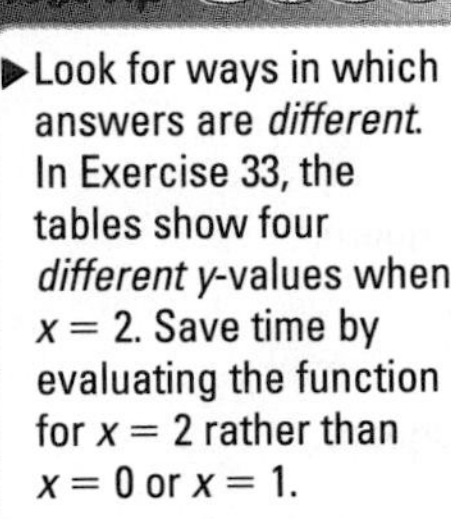

Test Tip Ⓐ Ⓑ Ⓒ Ⓓ

▶ Look for ways in which answers are *different*. In Exercise 33, the tables show four *different* y-values when $x = 2$. Save time by evaluating the function for $x = 2$ rather than $x = 0$ or $x = 1$.

33. Which of the following is a table of values for the equation $y = 0.1x^3$? **C**

Ⓐ

x	0	1	2	3
y	0	0.3	0.6	0.9

Ⓑ

x	0	1	2	3
y	0	0.1	0.9	2.7

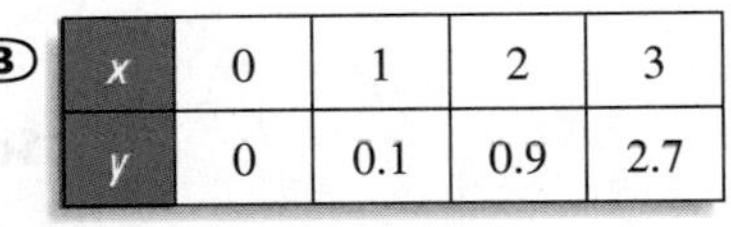

Ⓒ

x	0	1	2	3
y	0	0.1	0.8	2.7

Ⓓ

x	0	1	2	3
y	0.3	0.4	0.5	0.6

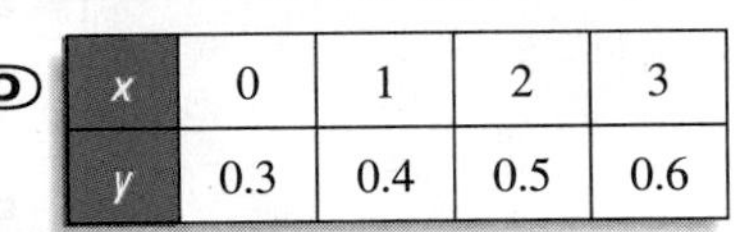

34. Which of the following is the graph of the equation $y = 0.1x^3$? **F**

Ⓕ
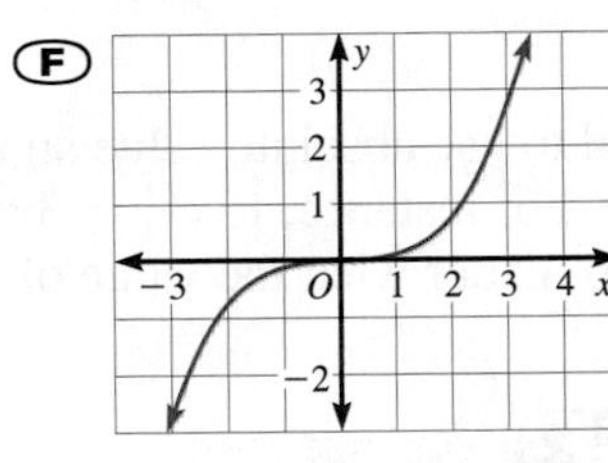

Ⓖ
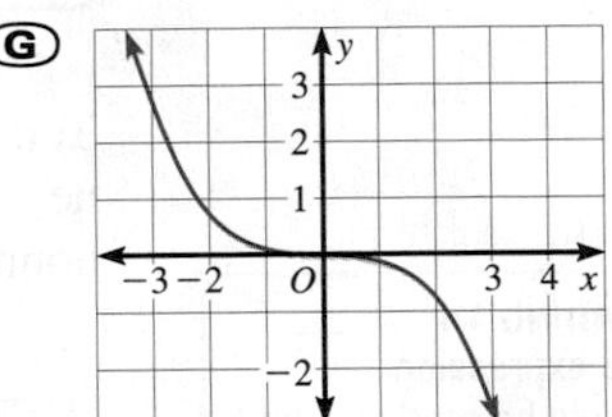

Ⓗ
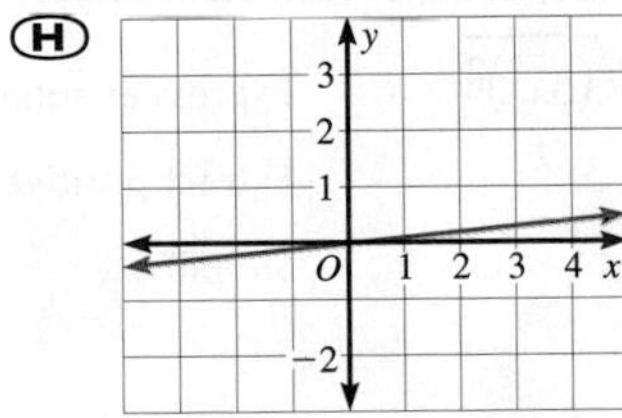

Ⓙ
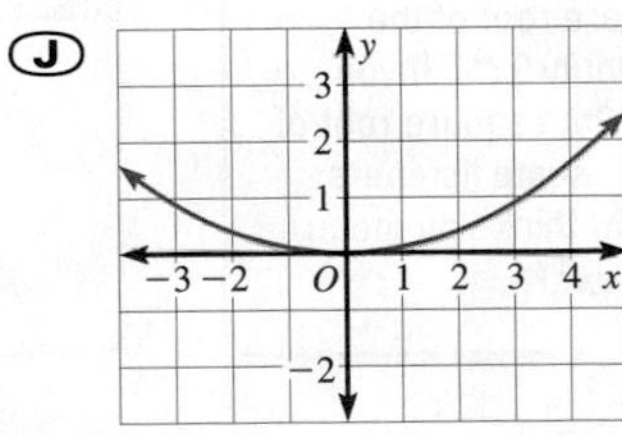

4 Assess

Assessment Resources

- Assessment Book (Formal Assessment and Alternative Assessment)
- Test and Practice Generator

Mini-Quiz

Make a table of values for each of the functions. Use integer values of *x* between −2 and 2. Then graph the function.

1. $y = -3x^2$

x	−2	−1	0	1	2
y	−12	−3	0	−3	−12

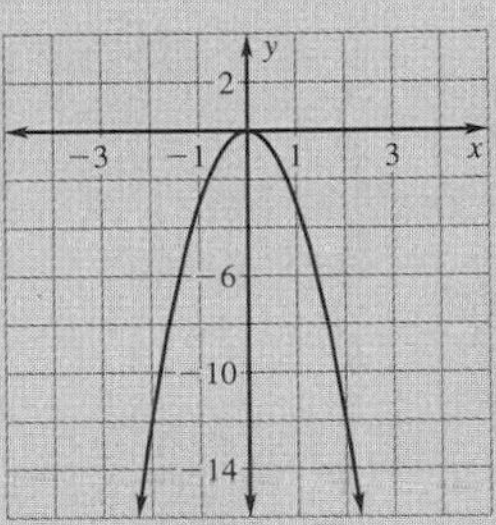

2. $y = 2x^3$

x	−2	−1	0	1	2
y	−16	−2	0	2	16

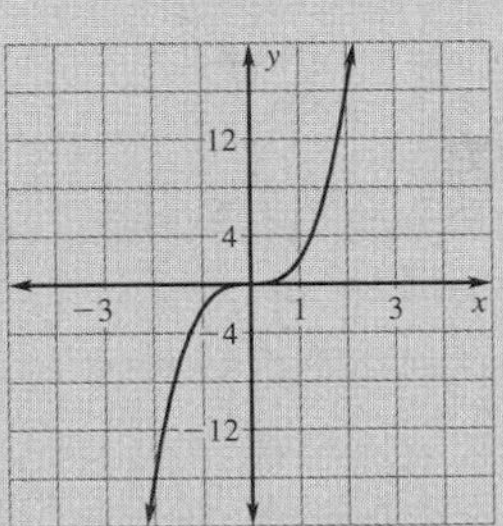

3. A cube with sides of length *x* has a volume of $V = x^3$. What happens to the volume if each side of the cube is doubled? **The volume will be 8 times greater.**

30–32. See Additional Answers beginning on page AA1.

1 Plan

Pacing

Suggested Number of Days

Transitional: 2 days
Average: 2 days
Advanced: 2 days
Block Schedule: 1 block

Teaching Resources

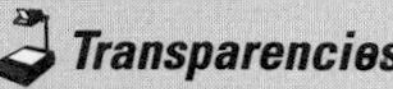

(See page 614B.)

Transparencies

- Warm-Up Exercises
- Teacher Time-Savers
- English/Spanish Problem Solving
- Answers

Technology

- Electronic Teacher Tools
- Test and Practice Generator

2 Teach

Math Reasoning

For Mathematical Background Notes on mathematical reasoning related to this lesson, please refer to pages 614E and 614F in this Teacher's Edition.

CA Standards: AF 1.5, AF 2.2

12.7 Solving Polynomial Equations

California Standards

In this lesson you'll:

- Extract roots of monomials when the result is a monomial with an integer exponent. (AF 2.2)
- Represent quantitative relationships graphically and interpret the meaning of a specific part of a graph. (AF 1.5)

Goal 1 EXTRACTING SQUARE ROOTS

In Lesson 9.1 you learned that the square root symbol $\sqrt{}$ always refers to the *positive square root*. So, when you simplify an expression such as $\sqrt{a^2}$, you need to indicate that the answer is nonnegative. One way of doing this is to use absolute value.

EXTRACTING POSITIVE SQUARE ROOTS OF SQUARES

In Words	The positive square root of a^2 is the absolute value of a.
In Algebra	$\sqrt{a^2} = \lvert a \rvert$
In Arithmetic	$\sqrt{5^2} = \lvert 5 \rvert = 5$ and $\sqrt{(-5)^2} = \lvert -5 \rvert = 5$

EXAMPLE 1 Extracting a Positive Square Root

Simplify the expression.

a. $\sqrt{4x^2}$ **b.** $\sqrt{y^6}$

Solution

a. $\sqrt{4x^2} = \sqrt{(2x)^2}$ Express as square root of a square.

$= \lvert 2x \rvert$ Extract positive square root.

b. $\sqrt{y^6} = \sqrt{(y^3)^2}$ Express as square root of a square.

$= \lvert y^3 \rvert$ Extract positive square root.

Student Help

READING TIP
The expression $\sqrt{9x^4}$ should be read as "the square root of the *quantity* $9x^4$." If you say "the square root of $9x^4$," some listeners might think you mean $\sqrt{9} \cdot x^4$.

You don't need to use absolute value signs around an expression that is never negative. For instance, $\lvert 3x^2 \rvert = 3x^2$ because 3 is positive and x^2 is nonnegative no matter what the value of x is.

EXAMPLE 2 Extracting a Positive Square Root

$\sqrt{9x^4} = \sqrt{(3x^2)^2}$ Express as square root of a square.

$= \lvert 3x^2 \rvert$ Extract positive square root.

$= 3x^2$ Simplify.

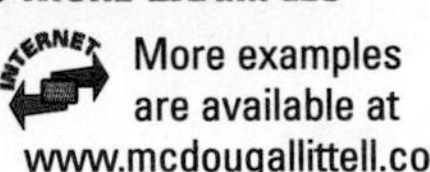

▶MORE EXAMPLES

More examples are available at www.mcdougallittell.com

Goal 2 SOLVING A SECOND-DEGREE EQUATION

To solve a second-degree equation of the form $x^2 = a^2$, you can extract the square root of each side. Doing this produces $|x| = |a|$, which has two solutions, a and $-a$. These two solutions can be written as $\pm a$, which is read as "plus or minus a."

EXAMPLE 3 Solving a Second-Degree Equation

Solve the equation $x^2 = 4$.

Solution

$x^2 = 4$	Write original equation.
$\sqrt{x^2} = \sqrt{4}$	Take square root of each side.
$\|x\| = 2$	Simplify square root of a square.
$x = \pm 2$	$\|2\| = 2$ and $\|-2\| = 2$

The solutions are 2 and -2. Check these in the original equation:

$2^2 = 4$ ✓ and $(-2)^2 = 4$ ✓

Student Help

▶STUDY TIP

In Example 4, the step $|n| = 3$ is not shown between the steps $n^2 = 9$ and $n = \pm 3$. In general, you do not need to show $|x| = |a|$ as long as you remember that $x^2 = a^2$ leads to $x = \pm a$.

EXAMPLE 4 Solving a Second-Degree Equation

Solve the equation $n^2 + 5 = 14$.

Solution

$n^2 + 5 = 14$	Write original equation.
$n^2 + 5 - 5 = 14 - 5$	Subtract 5 from each side.
$n^2 = 9$	Simplify.
$n = \pm 3$	Extract positive and negative square roots.

The solutions are 3 and -3. Check these in the original equation.

EXAMPLE 5 Solving a Second-Degree Equation

Solve the equation $3m^2 = 75$.

Solution

$3m^2 = 75$	Write original equation.
$\frac{3m^2}{3} = \frac{75}{3}$	Divide each side by 3.
$m^2 = 25$	Simplify.
$m = \pm 5$	Extract positive and negative square roots.

The solutions are 5 and -5. Check these in the original equation.

Extra Example 1

Simplify the expression.

a. $\sqrt{81n^2}$ $|9n|$

b. $\sqrt{4y^6}$ $|2y^3|$

Extra Example 2

Simplify the expression $\sqrt{36a^8}$. $6a^4$

Extra Example 3

Solve the equation $x^2 = 49$. 7 and -7

Extra Example 4

Solve the equation $n^2 - 6 = 3$. 3 and -3

Extra Example 5

Solve the equation $2m^2 = 72$. 6 and -6

Teaching Tip

Multiple Representations

Numerically, the equation $x^2 = a^2$ can be interpreted to mean: *What number(s) can I square to get a^2?* Since, for example, $7^2 = 49$ and $(-7)^2 = 49$, there will be two solutions. Graphically, the equation $x^2 = a^2$ can be interpreted to mean: *What x value gives a y value of a^2 on the graph of $y = x^2$?* Since, for example, the y value of 49 occurs for $x = 7$ and $x = -7$ on $y = x^2$, both are solutions to $x^2 = 49$.

Extra Example 6

Solve the equation $\frac{1}{3}x^2 = 27$ using a graph.

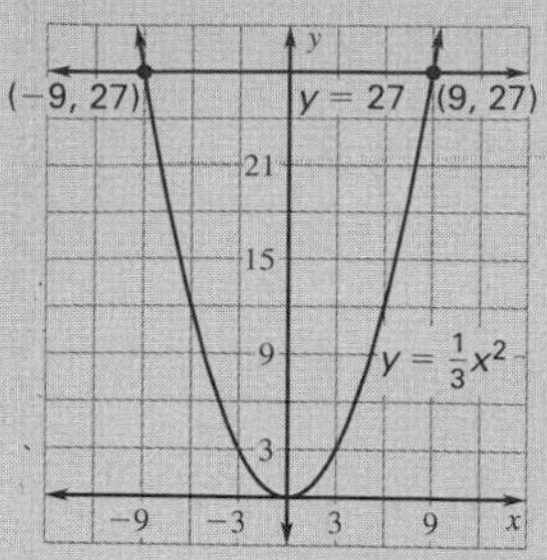

The solutions are −9 and 9.

Concept Check

How can you solve an equation of the form $x^2 = a^2$? ***Sample answer:*** **Extract the square root of each side to get two solutions $x = a$ or $x = -a$.**

Student Help

▶ STUDY TIP
When you solve an equation in one variable by graphing functions with two variables, you want to find the points where the graphs intersect. The *x*-coordinates of these points are solutions of the equation.

EXAMPLE 6 Solving Using a Graph

Solve the equation $\frac{1}{3}x^2 = 12$ using a graph.

Solution

Treat each side of the equation as a function:

$$y = \frac{1}{3}x^2 \text{ and } y = 12$$

Graph the functions. The graphs appear to intersect at (6, 12) and (−6, 12).

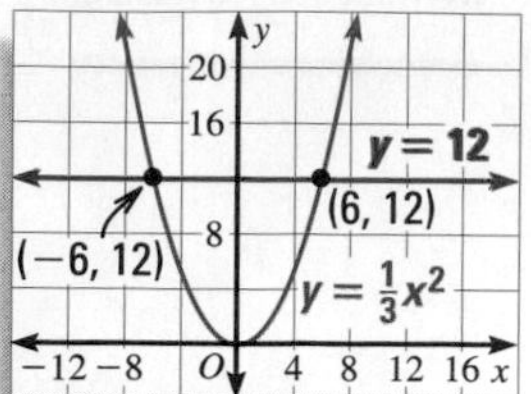

Check the *x*-coordinates of these points in the equation.

$\frac{1}{3}(6)^2 = \frac{1}{3}(36) = 12$ ✓

$\frac{1}{3}(-6)^2 = \frac{1}{3}(36) = 12$ ✓

ANSWER ▶ The solutions are 6 and −6.

12.7 Exercises

Guided Practice

Simplify the expression.

1. $\sqrt{25}$ **5** **2.** $\sqrt{100}$ **10** **3.** $\sqrt{x^2}$ $|x|$ **4.** $\sqrt{y^{14}}$ $|y^7|$

5. $\sqrt{4y^2}$ $|2y|$ **6.** $\sqrt{16z^4}$ $4z^2$ **7.** $\sqrt{m^2n^2}$ $|mn|$ **8.** $\sqrt{9p^4q^4}$ $3p^2q^2$

Solve the equation.

9. $x^2 = 9$ **±3** **10.** $y^2 = 25$ **±5** **11.** $z^2 + 9 = 10$ **±1**

12. $x^2 - 26 = 23$ **±7** **13.** $2y^2 = 8$ **±2** **14.** $5z^2 = 500$ **±10**

15. $3x^2 = 108$ **±6** **16.** $7y^2 - 13 = 162$ **±5** **17.** $2z^2 - 16 = z^2$ **±4**

FREE-FALL In Exercises 18–20, use the following information.
A tennis ball is dropped from the top of a 400 foot cliff. The ball's height above the ground can be modeled by the equation

$$h = -16t^2 + 400$$

where *h* represents the height (in feet) and *t* represents the time (in seconds).

18. Find *t* when $h = 256$. **3 sec** **19.** Find *t* when $h = 0$. **5 sec**

20. What is the significance of the answer in Exercise 19?

20. The value is the time it takes the tennis ball to reach the ground if it is dropped from a height of 400 feet.

Practice and Problem Solving

Student Help

▶ MORE PRACTICE
Extra practice to help you master skills is on page 713.

Simplify the expression.

21. $\sqrt{36}$ **6** **22.** $\sqrt{81}$ **9** **23.** $\sqrt{400}$ **20** **24.** $\sqrt{2500}$ **50**

25. $\sqrt{z^2}$ **$|z|$** **26.** $\sqrt{y^4}$ **y^2** **27.** $\sqrt{x^{10}}$ **$|x^5|$** **28.** $\sqrt{w^{16}}$ **w^8**

29. $\sqrt{4p^4}$ **$2p^2$** **30.** $\sqrt{49q^2}$ **$|7q|$** **31.** $\sqrt{64r^6}$ **$|8r^3|$** **32.** $\sqrt{100s^{12}}$ **$10s^6$**

33. $\sqrt{a^2b^6}$ **$|ab^3|$** **34.** $\sqrt{25x^2y^2}$ **$|5xy|$** **35.** $\sqrt{81x^2y^4z^2}$ **$|9xy^2z|$** **36.** $\sqrt{121w^0}$ **11**

Solve the equation.

37. $x^2 = 10{,}000$ **±100** **38.** $y^2 = 900$ **±30** **39.** $z^2 = 3600$ **±60**

40. $a^2 + 2 = 27$ **±5** **41.** $b^2 + 15 = 51$ **±6** **42.** $c^2 + 40 = 184$ **±12**

43. $d^2 - 10 = 26$ **±6** **44.** $e^2 - 1 = 0$ **±1** **45.** $g^2 - 19 = -15$ **±2**

46. $2m^2 = 18$ **±3** **47.** $3n^2 = 300$ **±10** **48.** $\frac{1}{2}p^2 = 200$ **±20**

49. $2u^2 - 50 = 0$ **±5** **50.** $4v^2 + 21 = 57$ **±3** **51.** $7w^2 + 7 = 350$ **±7**

52. $2x^2 + 49 = 3x^2$ **±7** **53.** $5y^2 - 432 = 2y^2$ **±12** **54.** $3z^2 - 45 = -2z^2$ **±3**

Find the length and width of the rectangle using the given area.

55. Area = 98 in.^{2}
l = 14 in.; w = 7 in.

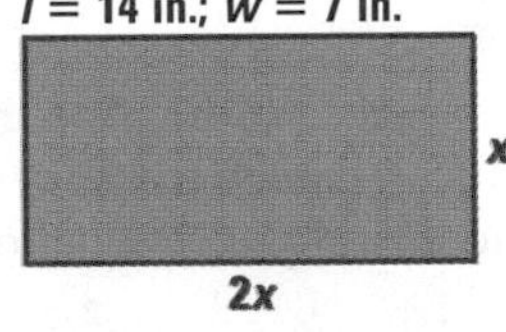

x
2x

56. Area = 54 ft^2
l = 9 ft; w = 6 ft

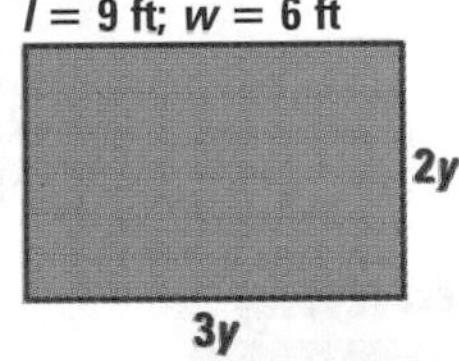

2y
3y

57. Area = 1500 m^2
l = 50 m; w = 30 m

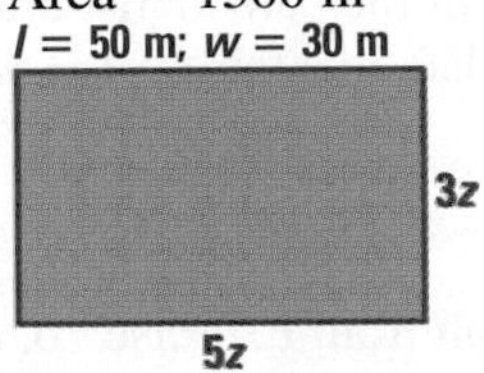

3z
5z

58. Area = 1000 cm^2
l = 40 cm; w = 25 cm

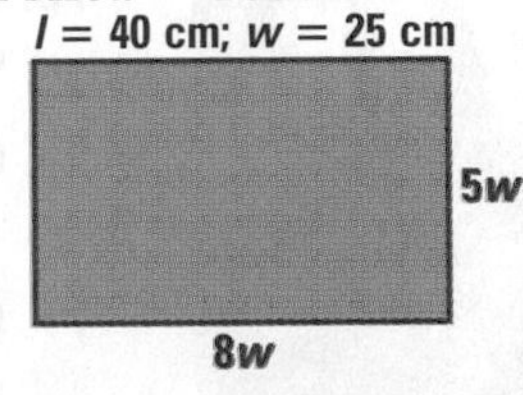

5w
8w

CALCULATOR **Estimate the solutions of the equation. Then use a calculator to solve the equation. Round your answers to the nearest hundredth.**

59. $x^2 = 39$ **±6.24** **60.** $2y^2 = 100$ **±7.07** **61.** $3z^2 = 26$ **±2.94**

ERROR ANALYSIS **Describe and correct the error.**

62.

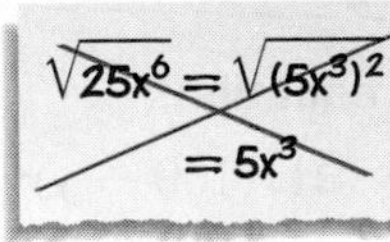

See margin.

63.

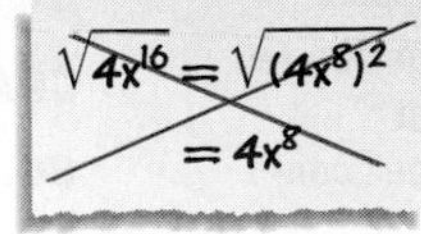

See margin.

62. The second line of the solution should be $|5x^3|$.

Student Help

▶ HOMEWORK HELP
A table of squares and square roots is on page 717.

63. In the first line of the solution, the student has $\sqrt{4x^{16}}$ equaling $\sqrt{(4x^8)^2}$. The term should equal $\sqrt{(2x^8)^2}$. The final line should be $2x^8$.

3 Apply

Assignment Guide

TRANSITIONAL
Day 1: pp. 651–653 Exs. 21–32, 62–63, 87–89, 93–96, 98–100
Day 2: pp. 651–653 Exs. 37–45, 55–56, 59–60, 68–71, 75–78, 85–86

AVERAGE
Day 1: pp. 651–653 Exs. 25–36, 62–63, 87–89, 93–96, 98–100
Day 2: pp. 651–653 Exs. 40–48, 55–56, 64–65, 68–70, 83–86

ADVANCED
Day 1: pp. 651–653 Exs. 25–36, 62–63, 87–89, 93–96, 98–100
Day 2: pp. 651–653 Exs. 46–54, 57–58, 60–61, 65–67, 73–74, 79, 80–82*, 83–86

BLOCK SCHEDULE
pp. 651–653 Exs. 25–36, 40–48, 55–56, 62–65, 68–70, 83–89, 93–96, 98–100

Extra Practice
- Student Edition, pp. 712–713
- Chapter 12 Resource Book, p. 60

Homework Check
To quickly check student understanding of key concepts, go over the following exercises:

Transitional: 30, 40, 56, 70, 76
Average: 32, 44, 64, 70, 84
Advanced: 32, 48, 66, 74, 84

Problem Solving
Exercises 55–58
Point out to students that the equations to be solved can be done by extracting square roots, but the negative solutions can be thrown out since a side of a rectangle cannot have a negative length.

Teaching Tip

In Exercise 83, students may notice that the stopping distances under wet conditions (when $f = 0.4$) are twice as long as the stopping distances under dry conditions (when $f = 0.8$) that they may have calculated for the table on page 615. This makes sense, because f is in the denominator of the equation for stopping distance. The value of f under wet conditions is *half* of what it is under dry conditions, so the stopping distance is *twice* as long.

75.

time (s)	height (ft)
0	10,000
5	9600
10	8400
15	6400

76.

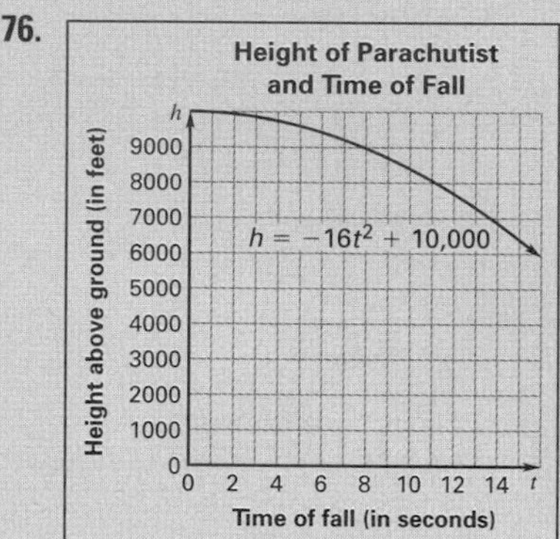

83.

s	d
10	8.3
20	33
30	75
40	133
50	208
60	300

Student Help

▶ **LOOK BACK** For help with the Pythagorean theorem, see page 460.

GEOMETRY **Use the Pythagorean theorem to write an equation relating the lengths of the three sides of the right triangle. Solve for the unknown side length.**

64.

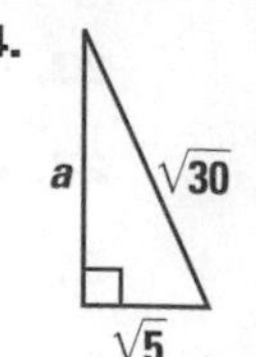

$a^2 + 5 = 30, 5$

65.

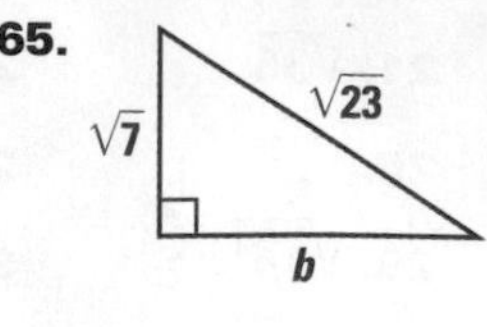

$b^2 + 7 = 23, 4$

66.

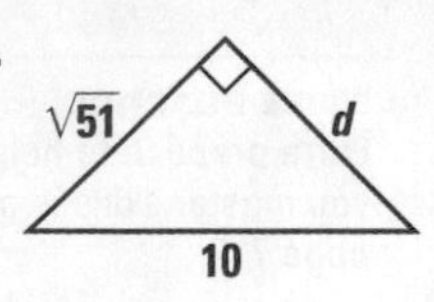

$d^2 + 51 = 100, 7$

Write an equation that can be solved using the graph. Find the solutions and check them. 67–68. See margin.

67. $\frac{x^2}{4} = 4$; ± 4

68. $\frac{-x^2}{2} = -8$; ± 4

67.

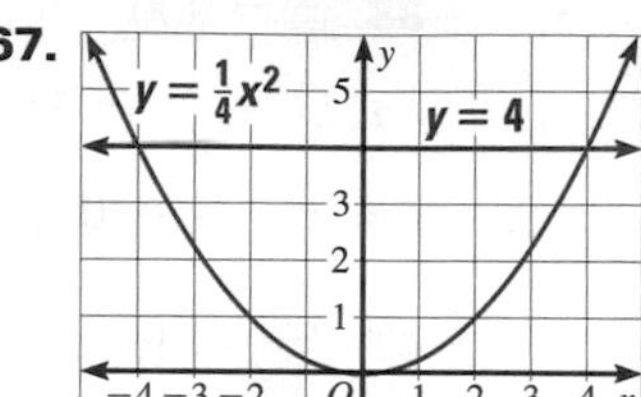

68.

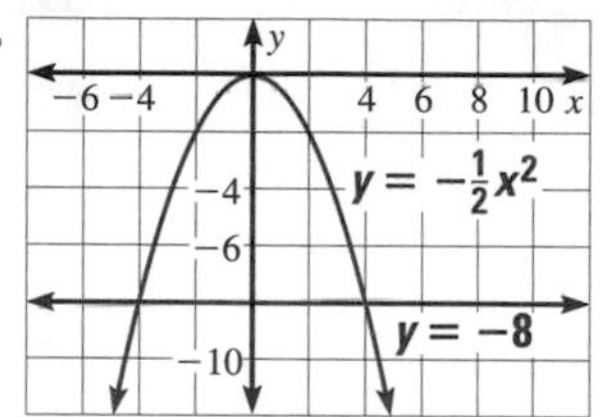

Solve the equation by graphing.

69. $x^2 = 1$ ± 1

70. $\frac{1}{4}x^2 = 1$ ± 2

71. $-\frac{1}{2}x^2 = -18$ ± 6

72. $2x^2 = 200$ ± 10

73. $\frac{1}{2}x^2 = 72$ ± 12

74. $x^2 = x$ 0, 1

PARACHUTING **In Exercises 75–78, use the following information.** Before deploying a parachute, a parachutist's height h (in feet above the ground) after t seconds is modeled by this equation:

$$h = -16t^2 + 10{,}000$$

75. Find the height of the parachutist after 0, 5, 10, and 15 seconds. Organize your data in a table. See margin.

76. Graph the ordered pairs from your table. Connect the points with a smooth curve. See margin.

77. Using your graph from Exercise 76, estimate when the parachutist will be at 8000 feet. about 11 sec

78. Solve the equation $8000 = -16t^2 + 10{,}000$. Compare your answer with your estimate in Exercise 77. about 11.2 sec; this solution is more exact.

Link to Parachuting

FREE-FALL Actual free-fall times during parachuting are affected by air density, the jumper's weight and build, and drag from the jumpsuit.

More about free-fall available at www.mcdougallittell.com

79. MATHEMATICAL REASONING If n is a whole number, for what values of n does $\sqrt{x^{2n}} = |x^n|$ regardless of the value of x? For what values of n does $\sqrt{x^{2n}} = x^n$ regardless of the value of x?

$\sqrt{x^{2n}} = |x^n|$ for all n; $\sqrt{x^{2n}} = x^n$ for even n.

CHALLENGE **Solve the equation.**

80. $(x - 3)^2 = 225$ 18, −12

81. $(100 - y)^2 = 400$ 120, 80

82. $3(z + 2)^2 = 27$ 1, −5

Chapter Opener Link **In Exercises 83 and 84, use the following information.** When a car skids to a stop, the length of the skid d (in feet) for a car traveling at speed s (in miles per hour) is given by

$$d = \frac{1}{30f}s^2$$

where f is the coefficient of friction determined by the road surface and weather.

83. Under wet conditions, $f = 0.4$. Make a table of values, like the one on page 615, showing skid lengths for various speeds under wet conditions. **See margin.**

84. If you have only 120 feet to stop safely, what is the maximum speed you should be driving under dry conditions, when $f = 0.8$? How does your answer change under wet conditions, when $f = 0.4$?
53 mi/h, 37 mi/h

Multiple-Choice Practice

85. What is the simplified form of the expression $\sqrt{16x^2}$? **D**

Ⓐ $16x^2$ Ⓑ $|8x|$ Ⓒ $4x^2$ Ⓓ $|4x|$

86. What are the solutions of the equation $3x^2 - 5 = 7$? **F**

Ⓕ 2 and −2 Ⓖ 4 and −4 Ⓗ 5 and −5 Ⓙ 0

Mixed Review

In Exercises 87–92, solve the inequality. *(9.8)*

87. $3x - 4 > 8$ **$x > 4$**
88. $2y + 5 < 9$ **$y < 2$**
89. $-1 + 3z \geq 11$ **$z \geq 4$**
90. $7 + 14w \leq 35$ **$w \leq 2$**
91. $-4p + 2 > 10$ **$p < -2$**
92. $-q - 7 < 0$ **$q > -7$**

93. Find the volume of a can of tuna that has a radius of 4.2 centimeters and a height of 3.5 centimeters. *(10.5)* **193.96 cm³**

94. Find the volume of a beach ball that has a diameter of 2 feet. *(10.7)* **4.19 ft³**

Find the slope of the line. *(11.5)*

95.

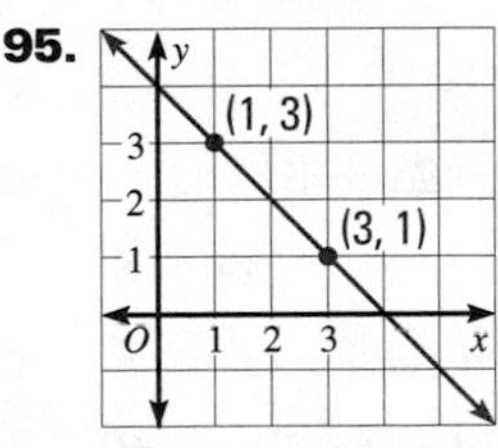

−1

96.

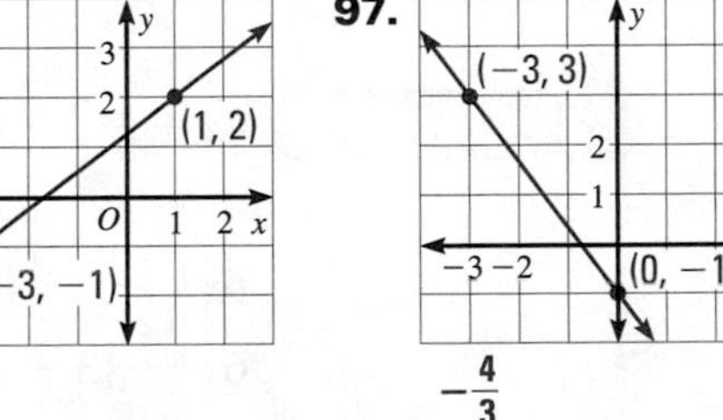

$\frac{3}{4}$

97. (−3, 3), (0, −1)

$-\frac{4}{3}$

Find the product. *(12.4)*

98. $2(3x + 4)$ **$6x + 8$**
99. $5y(y + 7)$ **$5y^2 + 35y$**
100. $3z^2(z - 4)$ **$3z^3 - 12z^2$**
101. $4w(3w^2 + 5w)$ **$12w^3 + 20w^2$**
102. $p^5(p^3 - p)$ **$p^8 - p^6$**
103. $-2q^3(-q + 2)$ **$2q^4 - 4q^3$**

4 Assess

Assessment Resources

- Assessment Book (Formal Assessment and Alternative Assessment)
- Test and Practice Generator

Mini-Quiz

Simplify each expression.

1. $\sqrt{16a^2}$ **$|4a|$**
2. $\sqrt{25m^4}$ **$5m^2$**

Solve each equation.

3. $x^2 = 64$ **8 and −8**
4. $n^2 - 5 = 11$ **4 and −4**
5. $8m^2 = 32$ **2 and −2**

Math Reasoning

Stopping a car of mass m moving with speed s requires work equivalent to the car's kinetic energy $\frac{1}{2}ms^2$. The work done in braking the car is given by "force times distance" or $mgfd$, where mg is the weight of the car, mgf is the braking force, and d is the stopping distance. When the same units are used throughout (for example, s is measured in feet/second and $g \approx 32$ feet/second², and d is measured in feet) the equation $\frac{1}{2}ms^2$ leads to $d = \frac{1}{64f}s^2$. Note, however, that these exercises are based on the speed being given in miles per hour, and this is the reason that d is given by $\frac{1}{30f}s^2$. (Note that 1 mile/hour $= \frac{5280}{3600}$ feet/second.)

Additional Resources

The following resources are available to help review the material in this chapter:

Technology

- Personal Student Tutor
- Test and Practice Generator

Chapter 12 Chapter Summary and Review

VOCABULARY

- **monomial,** *p. 617*
- **polynomial,** *p. 622*
- **binomial,** *p. 622*
- **trinomial,** *p. 622*
- **standard form,** *p. 622*
- **degree of a polynomial,** *p. 626*
- **FOIL method,** *p. 638*

12.1 MONOMIALS AND POWERS

Examples on pp. 617–619

Summary: $(ab)^m = a^m b^m$ $\quad \left(\frac{a}{b}\right)^m = \frac{a^m}{b^m}$ $\quad (a^m)^n = a^{mn}$

EXAMPLES

a. $(-x)^3 = (-1)^3x^3$
$= -1x^3$
$= -x^3$

b. $\left(\frac{2y}{z}\right)^5 = \frac{2^5y^5}{z^5}$
$= \frac{32y^5}{z^5}$

c. $-(3w^2)^4 = -(3^4)(w^2)^4$
$= -81w^8$

Simplify the expression.

1. $(2p)^6$ **$64p^6$** **2.** $(4q)^2$ **$16q^2$** **3.** $(-3r)^3$ **$-27r^3$** **4.** $(-st)^2$ **s^2t^2**

5. $\left(\frac{a}{2}\right)^3$ **$\frac{a^3}{8}$** **6.** $\left(\frac{-1}{b}\right)^5$ **$\frac{-1}{b^5}$** **7.** $\left(\frac{3c}{5}\right)^2$ **$\frac{9c^2}{25}$** **8.** $\left(\frac{d}{3e}\right)^4$ **$\frac{d^4}{81e^4}$**

9. $(w^3)^5$ **w^{15}** **10.** $(2x^4)^4$ **$16x^{16}$** **11.** $-(4y^3)^3$ **$-64y^9$** **12.** $(-3z^5)^2$ **$9z^{10}$**

12.2 POLYNOMIALS IN ONE VARIABLE

Examples on pp. 622–623

EXAMPLE

$4x + 3x^2 + 6x^3 - 4x^2 - 2x + 8$	Given polynomial
$4x + 3x^2 + 6x^3 + (-4x^2) + (-2x) + 8$	Rule for subtraction
$6x^3 + 3x^2 + (-4x^2) + 4x + (-2x) + 8$	Commutative property
$6x^3 + [3 + (-4)]x^2 + [4 + (-2)]x + 8$	Distributive property
$6x^3 + (-1)x^2 + 2x + 8$	Simplify.
$6x^3 - x^2 + 2x + 8$	Rule for subtraction

Simplify the polynomial and write the result in standard form.

13. $10x - 7 - 3x + 8$ **$7x + 1$**

14. $5y^2 + 4y^2 - 3y^2$ **$6y^2$**

15. $3z^4 - 8z^3 + 2z^2 + 5z^3$ **$3z^4 - 3z^3 + 2z^2$**

16. $9 + 15r^3 - 7r^3 + 10$ **$8r^3 + 19$**

17. $3s^2 - 4s + 2s^2 + 2s - 9$ **$5s^2 - 2s - 9$**

18. $4t^2 - 6t + t^2 + 9t$ **$5t^2 + 3t$**

19. $-9a + 5a^2 + 14a + 14$ **$5a^2 + 5a + 14$**

20. $b^4 - 3b - 2b^4 + 12$ **$-b^4 - 3b + 12$**

21. $(3c^2)^3 + 8c^5 + 3c^6$ **$30c^6 + 8c^5$**

12.3 ADDING AND SUBTRACTING POLYNOMIALS

Examples on pp. 626–627

EXAMPLE **Simplify $(n^2 + 5n + 4) - (3n^2 - 4n + 3)$.**

$(n^2 + 5n + 4) - (3n^2 - 4n + 3)$	Write original expression.
$(n^2 + 5n + 4) + [-(3n^2 - 4n + 3)]$	Rule for subtraction
$n^2 + 5n + 4 + (-3n^2) + 4n + (-3)$	Distributive property
$n^2 + (-3n^2) + 5n + 4n + 4 + (-3)$	Commutative property
$-2n^2 + 9n + 1$	Simplify.

Perform the indicated operation.

22. $(6m^2 + 3m) + (m^2 - m)$ **$7m^2 + 2m$**

23. $(7n^2 + 3n) - (n^2 + n)$ **$6n^2 + 2n$**

24. $(6p^2 + 3p - 7) - (p^2 - 9)$ **$5p^2 + 3p + 2$**

25. $(5q^2 - 2q + 9) + (8q^2 + 3q - 2)$ **$13q^2 + q + 7$**

26. $(6r^2 + 3r - 1) + (-2r^2 - r - 9)$ **$4r^2 + 2r - 10$**

27. $(-4s^2 + 3s - 3) - (s^2 - 7s + 8)$ **$-5s^2 + 10s - 11$**

28. $(2w^3 - 4w^2 + w - 1) - (-7w^2 + w)$ **$2w^3 + 3w^2 - 1$**

29. $(4x^3 - 2x^2 - 5) + (-3x^3 + x^2 - 7)$ **$x^3 - x^2 - 12$**

12.4 MULTIPLYING A MONOMIAL AND A POLYNOMIAL

Examples on pp. 630–631

EXAMPLE **Simplify $m(m^2 + 2m - 4)$.**

$m(m^2 + 2m - 4)$	Write original expression.
$m[m^2 + 2m + (-4)]$	Rule for subtraction
$m(m^2) + m(2m) + m(-4)$	Distributive property
$m^3 + 2m^2 + (-4m)$	Product of powers rule
$m^3 + 2m^2 - 4m$	Rule for subtraction

Find the product.

30. $x(x^2 + x)$ **$x^3 + x^2$**

31. $y(y^3 + 4)$ **$y^4 + 4y$**

32. $z(z^4 + 3z^3 + 7z^2)$ **$z^5 + 3z^4 + 7z^3$**

33. $b^2(b^3 + 5b)$ **$b^5 + 5b^3$**

34. $c^2(3c - 7)$ **$3c^3 - 7c^2$**

35. $d^3(d^2 - 6d)$ **$d^5 - 6d^4$**

36. $2p^3(5p^2 + 5p - 3)$ **$10p^5 + 10p^4 - 6p^3$**

37. $-q^2(q^3 - q + 3)$ **$-q^5 + q^3 - 3q^2$**

38. $r(-r^2 - 3r + 8)$ **$-r^3 - 3r^2 + 8r$**

48.

49.

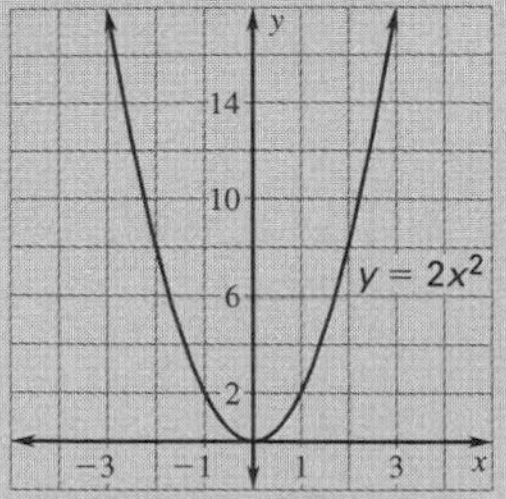

50.

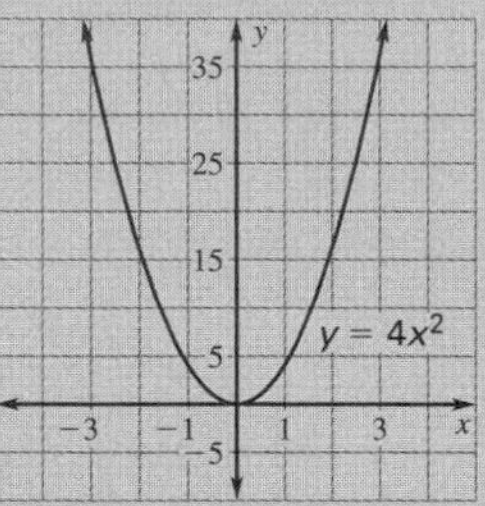

51.

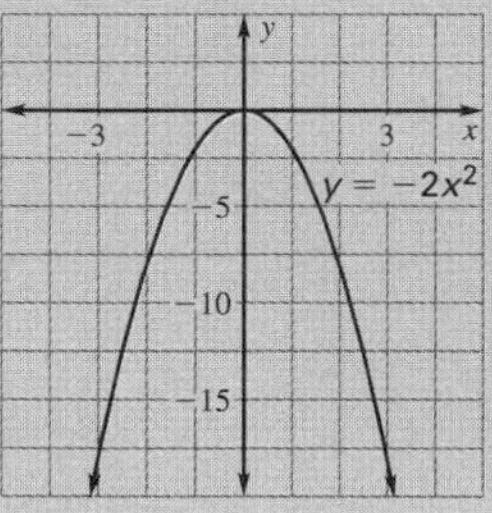

12.5 MULTIPLYING POLYNOMIALS

Examples on pp. 638–639

You can use two methods to multiply two binomials.

EXAMPLE

Distributive Property		First Outside Inside Last (FOIL)
$(x + 1)(x + 3)$	Write expression.	$(x + 1)(x + 3)$
$(x + 1)(x) + (x + 1)(3)$	Distribute or use FOIL.	$(x)(x) + (x)(3) + (1)(x) + (1)(3)$
$(x)(x) + (1)(x) + (x)(3) + (1)(3)$	Distribute again.	
$x^2 + x + 3x + 3$	Simplify.	$x^2 + 3x + x + 3$
$x^2 + 4x + 3$	Combine like terms.	$x^2 + 4x + 3$

Write as a polynomial in standard form.

39. $(x + 2)(x + 5)$ **$x^2 + 7x + 10$**
40. $(x + 4)(x + 9)$ **$x^2 + 13x + 36$**
41. $(x + 1)(x + 7)$ **$x^2 + 8x + 7$**
42. $(2b + 1)(6b + 5)$ **$12b^2 + 16b + 5$**
43. $(4c + 3)(4c + 3)$ **$16c^2 + 24c + 9$**
44. $(3d + 5)(d + 4)$ **$3d^2 + 17d + 20$**
45. $(x + 4)^2$ **$x^2 + 8x + 16$**
46. $(y + 12)^2$ **$y^2 + 24y + 144$**
47. $(6z + 5)^2$ **$36z^2 + 60z + 25$**

12.6 GRAPHING $y = ax^2$ AND $y = ax^3$

Examples on pp. 642–644

EXAMPLE **Graph the function $y = \frac{1}{8}x^2$.**

Make a table of values for the function. Plot the *xy*-pairs and connect the points with a smooth curve, as shown.

x	*y*
−2	$\frac{1}{8}(-2)^2 = \frac{1}{2}$
−1	$\frac{1}{8}(-1)^2 = \frac{1}{8}$
0	$\frac{1}{8}(0)^2 = 0$
1	$\frac{1}{8}(1)^2 = \frac{1}{8}$
2	$\frac{1}{8}(2)^2 = \frac{1}{2}$

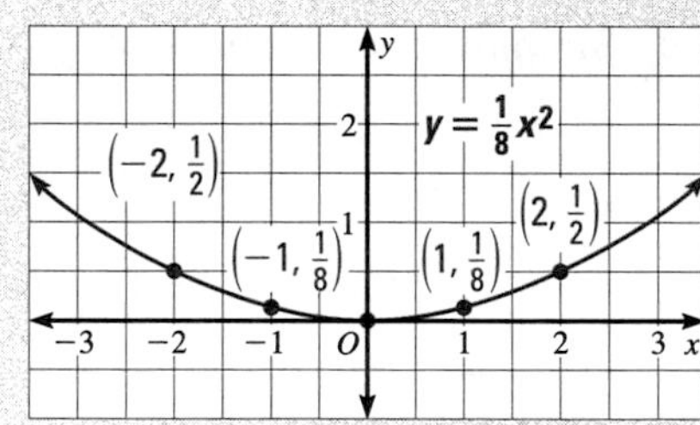

Make a table of values for the function. Then graph the function.
48–51. See margin.

48. $y = \frac{1}{2}x^2$
49. $y = 2x^2$
50. $y = 4x^2$
51. $y = -2x^2$

EXAMPLE **Graph the function $y = -x^3$.**

Make a table of values for the function. Plot the *xy*-pairs and connect the points with a smooth curve, as shown.

x	y
-2	$-(-2)^3 = -(-8) = 8$
-1	$-(-1)^3 = -(-1) = 1$
0	$-(0)^3 = -0 = 0$
1	$-(1)^3 = -(1) = -1$
2	$-(2)^3 = -(8) = -8$

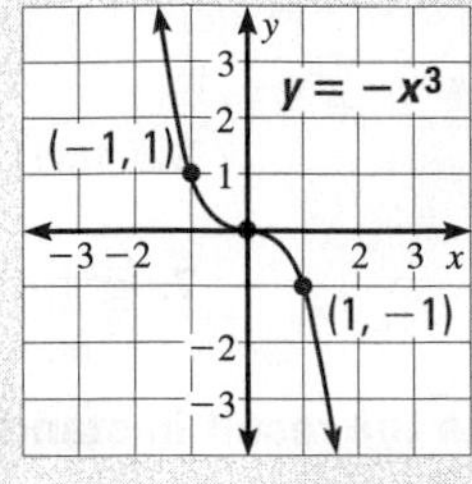

Make a table of values for the function. Then graph the function. **52–55. See margin.**

52. $y = x^3$ **53.** $y = 2x^3$ **54.** $y = -2x^3$ **55.** $y = \frac{1}{4}x^3$

12.7 SOLVING POLYNOMIAL EQUATIONS

Examples on pp. 648–650

EXAMPLES **Simplify $\sqrt{25x^2y^6}$.**

$\sqrt{25x^2y^6} = \sqrt{(5xy^3)^2}$ Express as square root of a square.

$= |5xy^3|$ Use $\sqrt{a^2} = |a|$.

Solve the equation $x^2 + 5 = 30$.

$x^2 + 5 = 30$ Write original equation.

$x^2 + 5 - 5 = 30 - 5$ Subtract 5 from each side.

$x^2 = 25$ Simplify.

$x = \pm 5$ Extract positive and negative square roots.

Simplify the expression.

56. $\sqrt{x^2}$ **$|x|$** **57.** $\sqrt{4m^2}$ **$|2m|$** **58.** $\sqrt{9n^6}$ **$|3n^3|$** **59.** $\sqrt{16x^4}$ **$4x^2$**

60. $\sqrt{a^2b^2}$ **$|ab|$** **61.** $\sqrt{9x^2y^2}$ **$|3xy|$** **62.** $\sqrt{c^4d^4}$ **c^2d^2** **63.** $\sqrt{36x^2y^4z^6}$ **$|6xy^2z^3|$**

Solve the equation.

64. $3x^2 = 27$ **± 3** **65.** $\frac{1}{3}x^2 = 27$ **± 9** **66.** $4x^2 = 4$ **± 1** **67.** $x^2 + 4 = 8$ **± 2**

68. $x^2 - 28 = 72$ **± 10** **69.** $z^2 + 16 = 41$ **± 5** **70.** $2y^2 + 5 = 37$ **± 4** **71.** $3x^2 - 54 = 54$ **± 6**

52.

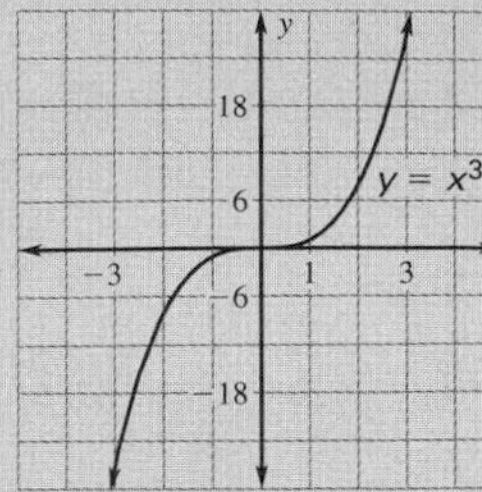

53.

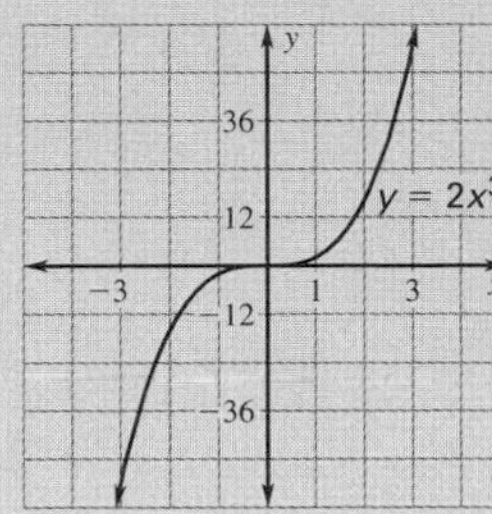

54.

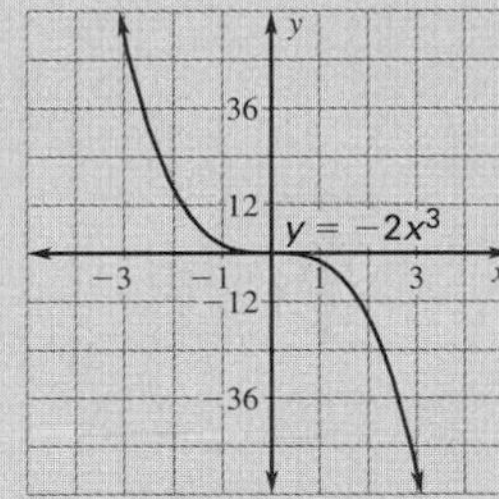

55.

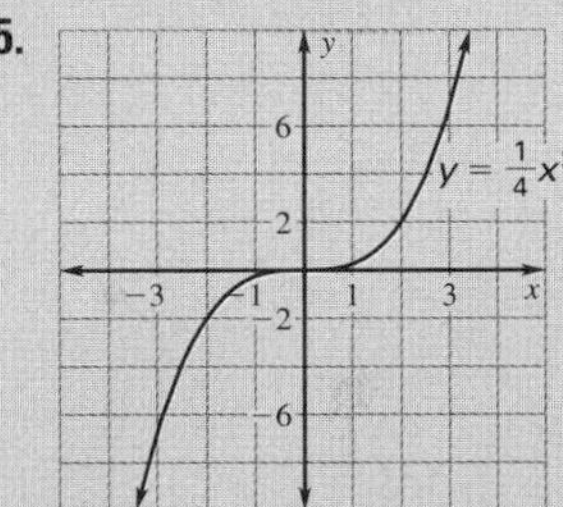

Additional Resources

Assessment Book

- Formal Assessment, pp. 180–188
- Alternative Assessment, pp. 193–207

Test and Practice Generator

27.

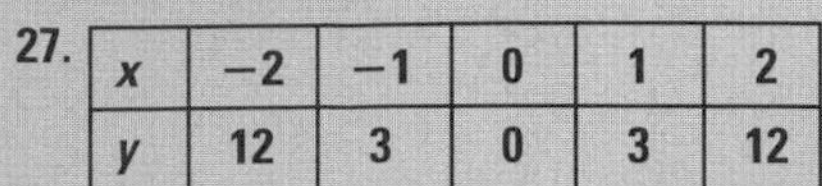

x	−2	−1	0	1	2
y	12	3	0	3	12

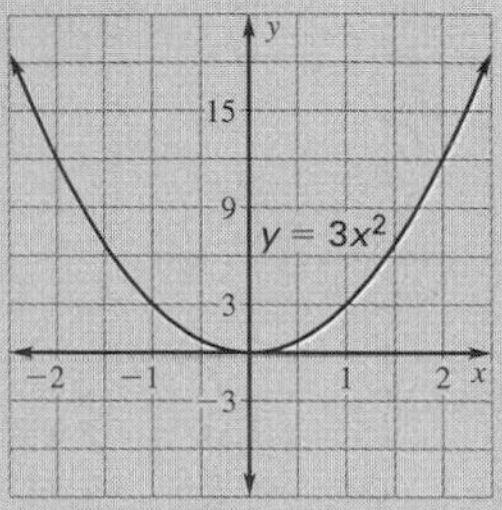

28.

x	−3	−1	0	1	3
y	−9	$-\frac{1}{3}$	0	$\frac{1}{3}$	9

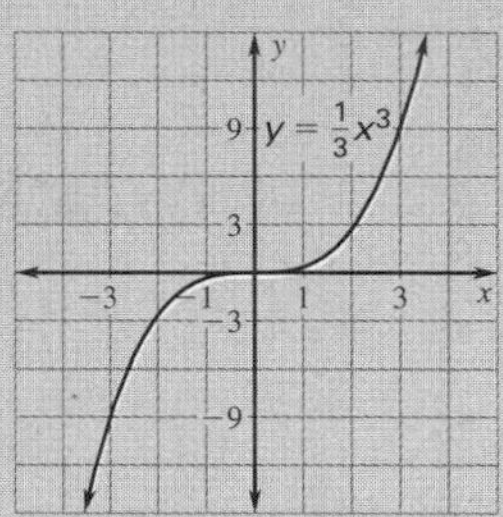

29.

x	−2	−1	0	1	2
y	−4	−1	0	−1	−4

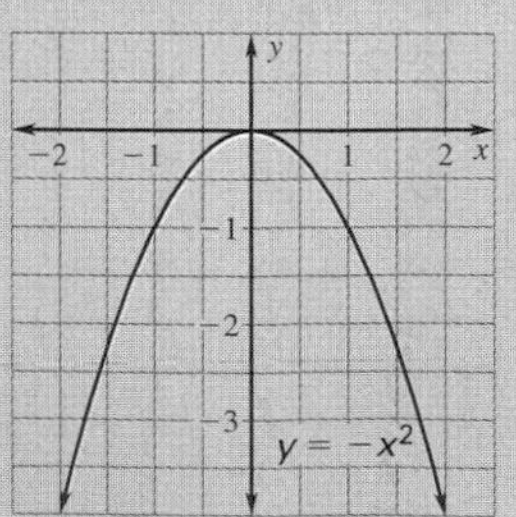

Chapter 12 Chapter Test

Simplify the expression.

1. $(5p)^2$ $\mathbf{25p^2}$

2. $(-2q)^3$ $\mathbf{-8q^3}$

3. $(3rs)^4$ $\mathbf{81r^4s^4}$

4. $-(7t)^2$ $\mathbf{-49t^2}$

5. $\left(\frac{x}{3}\right)^4$ $\mathbf{\frac{x^4}{81}}$

6. $\left(\frac{-1}{5y}\right)^2$ $\mathbf{\frac{1}{25y^2}}$

7. $(z^3)^7$ $\mathbf{z^{21}}$

8. $(4w^5)^3$ $\mathbf{64w^{15}}$

Simplify the polynomial and write the result in standard form.

9. $2p^2 - p^3 + p + 2p^3$ $\mathbf{p^3 + 2p^2 + p}$

10. $3n^3 + 4 - n^2 - n^3$ $\mathbf{2n^3 - n^2 + 4}$

11. $m^2 + 8m^2 - 5m^2 - 7m^2$ $\mathbf{-3m^2}$

12. $4q^2 + 2q^3 + 4 - q^2 + 8 - q^2$ $\mathbf{2q^3 + 2q^2 + 12}$

Perform the indicated operation.

13. $(3x^2 + 2x + 5) + (7x^2 - 4x + 2)$ $\mathbf{10x^2 - 2x + 7}$

14. $(4p^3 + 6p - 4) - (p^3 - p^2 + 6p - 5)$ $\mathbf{3p^3 + p^2 + 1}$

15 $(y^3 + 4y^2 - y) - (-4y^2 - 2y)$ $\mathbf{y^3 + 8y^2 + y}$

16. $(3s^2 - 4s + 9) + (3s^3 + 4s + 9)$ $\mathbf{3s^3 + 3s^2 + 18}$

Write as a polynomial in standard form.

17. $2y(3y^2 + 2y + 1)$ $\mathbf{6y^3 + 4y^2 + 2y}$

18. $3p(2p^3 - 2p^2 - p)$ $\mathbf{6p^4 - 6p^3 - 3p^2}$

19. $-4x(5x^2 - 3x + 8)$ $\mathbf{-20x^3 + 12x^2 - 32x}$

20. $-z^2(4z^2 + 2z - 5)$ $\mathbf{-4z^4 - 2z^3 + 5z^2}$

Find the product.

21. $(x + 3)(x + 4)$ $\mathbf{x^2 + 7x + 12}$

22. $(y + 2)(y + 5)$ $\mathbf{y^2 + 7y + 10}$

23. $(z + 10)(z + 1)$ $\mathbf{z^2 + 11z + 10}$

24. $(2w + 7)(w + 2)$ $\mathbf{2w^2 + 11w + 14}$

25. $(p + 2)^2$ $\mathbf{p^2 + 4p + 4}$

26. $(5q + 7)^2$ $\mathbf{25q^2 + 70q + 49}$

Make a table of values for the function. Then graph the function. **27–29. See margin.**

27. $y = 3x^2$

28. $y = \frac{1}{3}x^3$

29. $y = -x^2$

Simplify the expression.

30. $\sqrt{25x^2}$ $\mathbf{|5x|}$

31. $\sqrt{a^4b^4}$ $\mathbf{a^2b^2}$

32. $\sqrt{144m^8n^{10}}$ $\mathbf{|12m^4n^5|}$

Solve the equation.

33. $x^2 = 36$ **±6**

34. $4x^2 = 36$ **±3**

35. $\frac{1}{2}x^2 = 8$ **±4**

36. $x^2 + 11 = 60$ **±7**

37. $2x^2 + 150 = 350$ **±10**

38. $5x^2 - 25 = 100$ **±5**

39. FREE-FALL Suppose you drop your sunglasses off the Golden Gate Bridge and they fall to the water 220 feet below. The equation

$$h = -16t^2 + 220$$

represents the height of the glasses as a function of time. Find approximately how many seconds the sunglasses take to reach the water. **about 4 sec**

Multiple-Choice Practice

Test Tip Go back and check as many of your answers as you can.

1. Simplify the expression $(2xy^2)^3$. B

Ⓐ $6x^3y^6$ Ⓑ $8x^3y^6$

Ⓒ $8x^4y^5$ Ⓓ $2xy^6$

2. Simplify $4n^2 - 3 + 4n + n^2 - 7n + 9$. G

Ⓕ $4n^2 - 3n + 6$

Ⓖ $5n^2 - 3n + 6$

Ⓗ $4n^2 - 11n + 12$

Ⓙ $5n^2 + 3n + 6$

3. What is $(5x^2 + 3x) - (2x^2 - 3x)$? D

Ⓐ $3x^2$ Ⓑ $3x^3$

Ⓒ $10x^4 - 9x^2$ Ⓓ $3x^2 + 6x$

4. Which expression represents the blue area formed by the rectangles? G

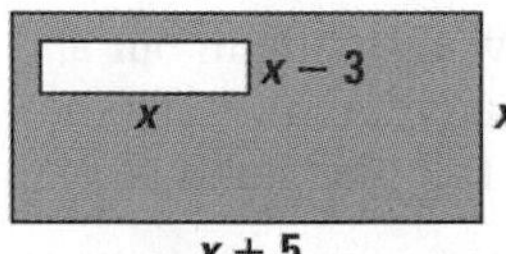

Ⓕ $2x$ Ⓖ $8x$

Ⓗ $2x^2 + 2x$ Ⓙ $2x^2 + 8x$

5. What is the product of $3x^2$ and $2x^2 - 4x + 3$? C

Ⓐ $6x^2 + 12x + 9$

Ⓑ $6x^4 + 12x^3 + 9x^2$

Ⓒ $6x^4 - 12x^3 + 9x^2$

Ⓓ $6x^4 - 12x^2 + 9x^2$

6. Which polynomial is equivalent to $(5n + 3)^2$? H

Ⓕ $25n^2 + 9$

Ⓖ $10n^2 + 30n + 6$

Ⓗ $25n^2 + 30n + 9$

Ⓙ Not here

7. Which equation is represented by the graph shown below? D

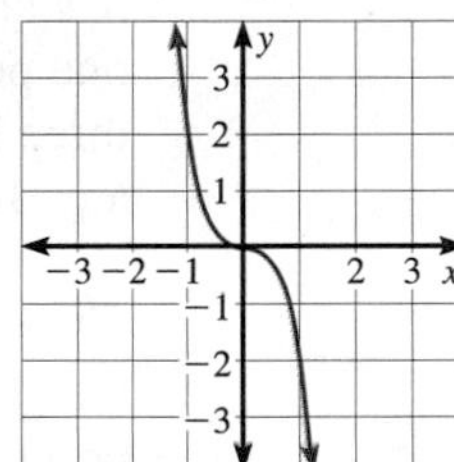

Ⓐ $y = 2x^2$ Ⓑ $y = -x^2$

Ⓒ $y = -x^3$ Ⓓ $y = -2x^3$

8. Simplify the expression $\sqrt{16x^4}$. G

Ⓕ $|4x|$ Ⓖ $4x^2$

Ⓗ $8x^2$ Ⓙ $16x^4$

9. What are the solutions of the equation? C

$$2x^2 - 8 = 24$$

Ⓐ 0

Ⓑ 2 and −2

Ⓒ 4 and −4

Ⓓ 16 and −16

Teaching Tip

The Brain Games activity provides a motivating way to review selected content in the chapter. For a more comprehensive review, see the Chapter Summary and Review on pp. 654–657.

Brain games

California Standards

- Simplify expressions by applying properties of rational numbers. (AF 1.3)
- Multiply monomials. (AF 2.2)
- Apply strategies and results from simpler problems to more complex problems. (MR 2.2)

Polynomial Tic-Tac-Toe

Materials

- Graph paper
- Paper and pencil

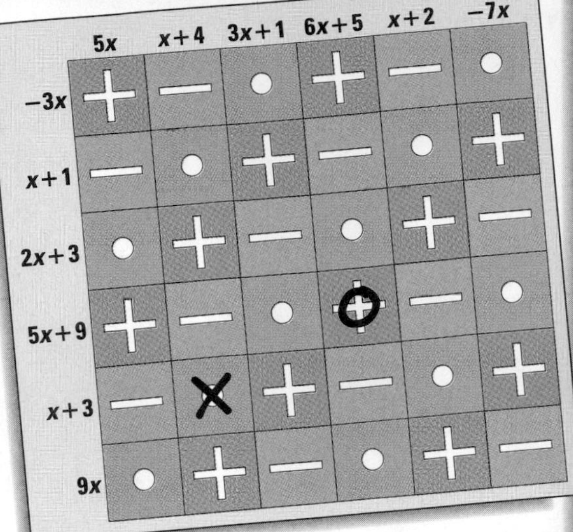

Directions

Object of the Game

Perform operations on polynomials to fill the table with X's and O's, scoring one point for every three in a row in any direction.

How to Play

STEP 1 Choose a square. Add, subtract, or multiply the polynomials to the left and above that square, as indicated.

STEP 2 You win a square if you are correct. Your opponent wins if you are wrong and he or she shows the right answer.

STEP 3 If you win three squares in a row, cross them out and score a point. You cannot use those squares again. When no more points are possible or the table is full, the game is over.

Another Way to Play

Build your own table, of any size, with different polynomials.

Brain Teaser

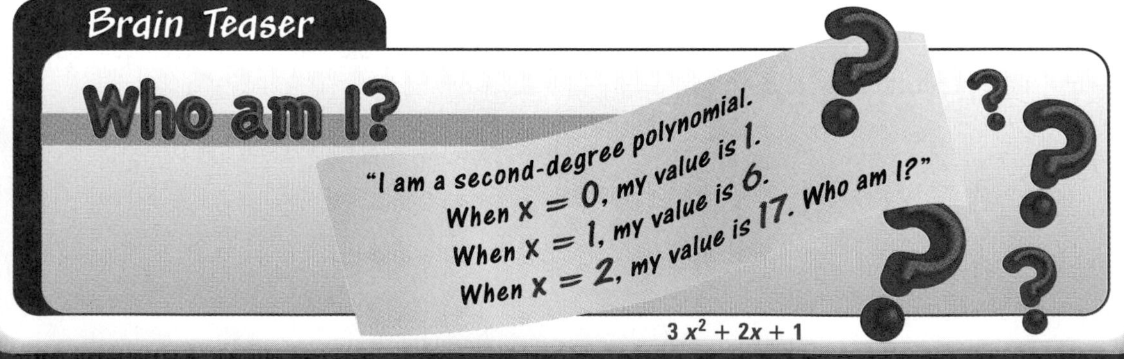

Who am I?
"I am a second-degree polynomial.
When x = 0, my value is 1.
When x = 1, my value is 6.
When x = 2, my value is 17. Who am I?"

$3x^2 + 2x + 1$

California Standards and Assessment

CA Standards: AF 1.3, AF 2.2, MR 2.2

The basic skills you'll review on this page will help prepare you for your next course.

Reviewing the Basics

When simplifying an expression, use the following order:

1. Evaluate expressions inside grouping symbols.
2. Evaluate powers.
3. Multiply and divide from left to right.
4. Add and subtract from left to right.

EXAMPLE 1 Order of Operations

Evaluate the expression $2(x^2 + y) - 9$ when $x = 2$ and $y = 3$.

Solution

$2(x^2 + y) - 9 = 2(2^2 + 3) - 9$ Substitute 2 for x and 3 for y.

$= 2(7) - 9$ Do operations in parentheses.

$= 14 - 9$ Multiply.

$= 5$ Subtract.

Try These

Evaluate the expression when $x = 7$ and $y = 4$.

1. $5x - 7y$ **7** **2.** $4 + (x + 1) \div y$ **6** **3.** $8(x - y)$ **24**

4. $x^2 + y^3$ **113** **5.** $3(2x - y^2)$ **−6** **6.** $2x - 3y \div 2$ **8**

EXAMPLE 2 Slope

Find the slope of the line through (0, 4) and (2, 2).

Solution

Let (0, 4) be (x_1, y_1) and let (2, 2) be (x_2, y_2).

$$m = \frac{y_2 - y_1}{x_2 - x_1} = \frac{2 - 4}{2 - 0} = \frac{-2}{2} = -1$$

Student Help

▶ **MORE EXAMPLES**

More examples and practice exercises available at www.mcdougallittell.com

Try These

Find the slope of the line through the points.

7. (0, 7) and (5, 7) **0** **8.** (0, 0) and (4, 4) **1** **9.** (0, 0) and (2, −4) **−2**

10. (1, 1) and (1, −1) **undefined** **11.** (−3, 2) and (3, 5) $\frac{1}{2}$ **12.** (3, 0) and (0, 3) **−1**

Additional Resources

Technology

- Personal Student Tutor
- Test and Practice Generator

Additional Resources

A Cumulative Test for Chapters 10–12 is available in the *Assessment Book*, pp. 189–192.

37. The 18 ounce box of cereal is a better buy because its unit price of 0.177 dollar per ounce is less than the unit price of 0.189 dollar per ounce for the 10 ounce box.

38. The fifteen 1 liter bottles are a better buy because their unit price of 1.07 dollars per liter is less than the unit price of 1.17 dollars per liter for the twenty-four 0.5 liter bottles.

42.

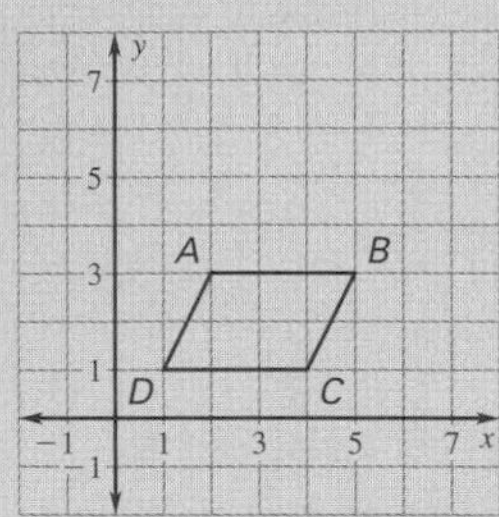

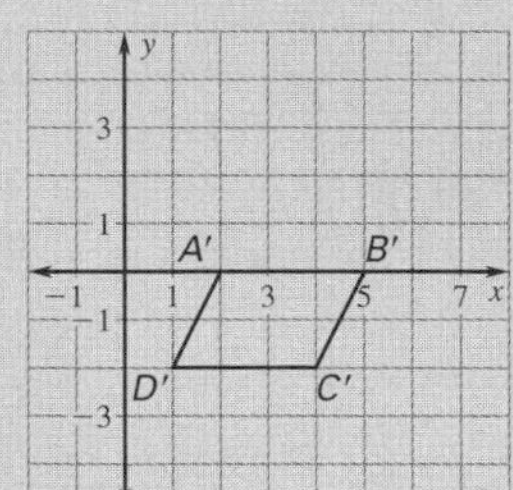

43.

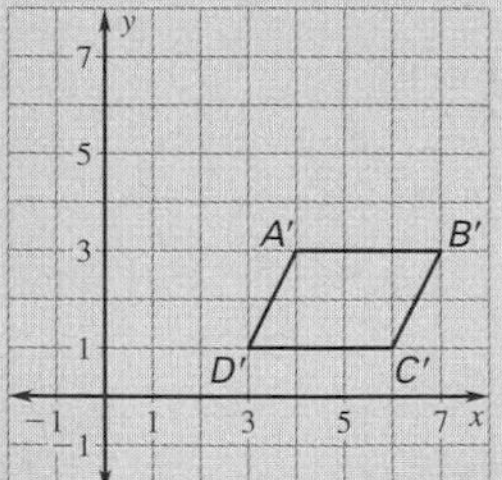

44.

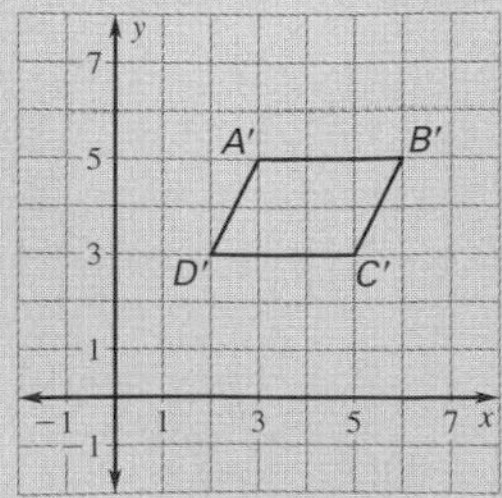

Chapters 1-12 Cumulative Practice

Name the property that justifies the equality. (1.7)

1. $(3 \cdot 4) \cdot 7 = 3 \cdot (4 \cdot 7)$ **associative property of multiplication**
2. $(5 + 7) \cdot 4 = (7 + 5) \cdot 4$ **commutative property of addition**
3. $6 + (5 + 11) = (6 + 5) + 11$ **associative property of addition**
4. $5 \div (6 \cdot 8) = 5 \div (8 \cdot 6)$ **commutative property of multiplication**

Solve the equation. Justify your steps and check your solution. (2.5)

5. $m + 5 = 98$ **93**
6. $140 + n = 187$ **47**
7. $p - 34 = 78$ **112**
8. $96 = q - 4$ **100**
9. $r - 35.5 = 90$ **125.5**
10. $200 = s + 17$ **183**

Simplify the expression. Then evaluate the expression when $x = 7$. (3.3)

11. $-3x + 5 + 9x$ **6x + 5, 47**
12. $5x + (-3x) + 2x$ **4x, 28**
13. $5x + (-7) + 2x$ **7x − 7, 42**
14. $5x + 7 + (-2x) + (-5)$ **3x + 2, 23**

Solve the equation. (4.3)

15. $-3p + 7 = 34$ **−9**
16. $5 - q = -4$ **9**
17. $-6r + 16 = 10$ **1**
18. $20 = 10 - x$ **−10**
19. $-y + 7 = -8$ **15**
20. $7z - 9 - 3z = 15$ **6**

Write the fraction as a percent. (5.7)

21. $\frac{3}{5}$ **60%**
22. $\frac{2}{3}$ **$66.\overline{6}$%**
23. $\frac{7}{10}$ **70%**
24. $\frac{45}{30}$ **150%**
25. $\frac{12}{4}$ **300%**
26. $\frac{50}{250}$ **20%**
27. $\frac{9}{12}$ **75%**
28. $\frac{7}{8}$ **87.5%**

Add or subtract. Then simplify, if possible. (6.1)

29. $\frac{2}{7} + \frac{3}{7}$ **$\frac{5}{7}$**
30. $\frac{14}{15} - \frac{8}{15}$ **$\frac{2}{5}$**
31. $\frac{3}{5} - \frac{1}{3}$ **$\frac{4}{15}$**
32. $\frac{5}{9} + \frac{2}{11}$ **$\frac{73}{99}$**
33. $\frac{3}{4} + \frac{3}{10}$ **$\frac{21}{20}$**
34. $\frac{21}{32} - \frac{1}{8}$ **$\frac{17}{32}$**
35. $5\frac{1}{6} - 2\frac{2}{9}$ **$\frac{53}{18}$**
36. $1\frac{3}{7} + \frac{1}{8}$ **$\frac{87}{56}$**

UNIT PRICING In Exercises 37 and 38, determine which is a better buy. Explain your reasoning. (7.1)

37. A 10 ounce box of cereal for \$1.89 or an 18 ounce box for \$3.19 **See margin.**
38. Twenty-four 0.5 liter bottles of spring water for \$14.00 or fifteen 1 liter bottles for \$16.00. **See margin.**

Find the perimeter and the area of the polygon. (8.6)

39. **36, 72**

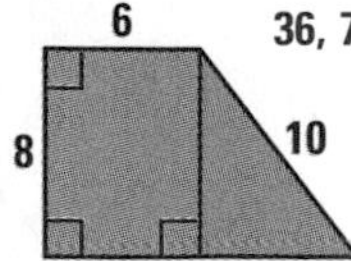

40. **24, 28**

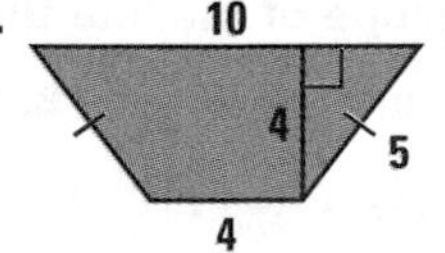

41. **66, 224**

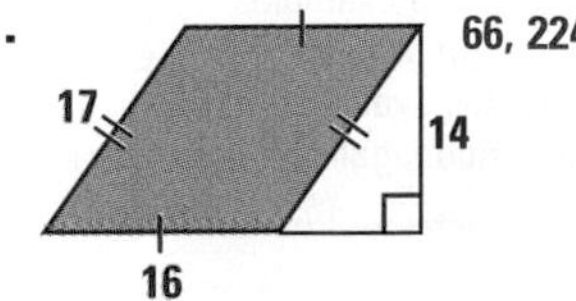

You are given that parallelogram *ABCD* has vertices at *A*(2, 3), *B*(5, 3), *C*(4, 1), and *D*(1, 1). Draw parallelogram *ABCD*. Then perform the indicated translation. **(8.8)** 42–44. See margin.

42. $(x, y) \rightarrow (x, y - 3)$ **43.** $(x, y) \rightarrow (x + 2, y)$ **44.** $(x, y) \rightarrow (x + 1, y + 2)$

Copy and complete the table. Determine whether a triangle with side lengths *a*, *b*, and *c* is a *right triangle*, an *acute triangle*, or an *obtuse triangle*. (9.4)

	a	b	c	$a^2 + b^2$	c^2	Type of triangle	
45.	5	5	7	?	?	?	50, 49, acute triangle
46.	3	8	$\sqrt{77}$	?	?	?	73, 77, obtuse triangle
47.	$\sqrt{5}$	3	$\sqrt{14}$	?	?	?	14, 14, right triangle

Find the surface area of the solid. Round your result to the nearest hundredth. (10.3)

48.

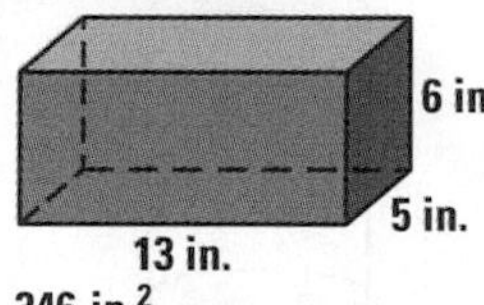

346 in.^{2}

49.

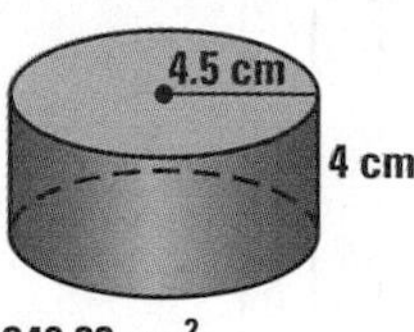

240.33 cm^2

50.

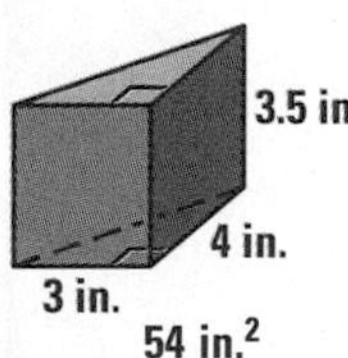

54 in.^{2}

Find the volume of the solid. Round your result to the nearest hundredth. (10.6, 10.7)

51.

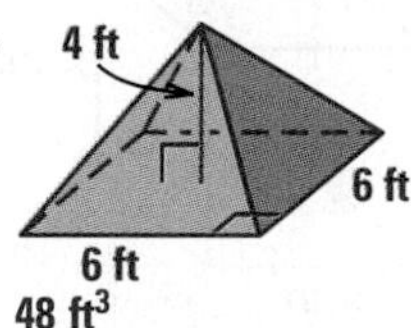

48 ft^3

52.

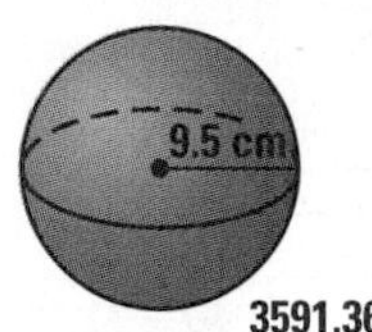

3591.36 cm^3

53.

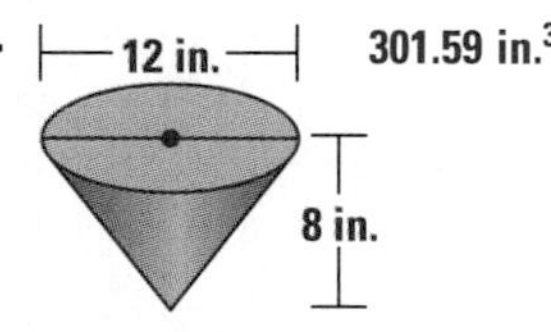

301.59 in.^{3}

Plot the points and find the slope of the line through the points. Then write an equation of the line in slope-intercept form. (11.5, 11.6) 54–56. See margin.

54. (0, 0), (2, 6) **55.** (0, 2), (4, 4) **56.** $(-1, 3), (0, -3)$

Graph the inequality. Then list several solutions. (11.8) 57–59. See margin.

57. $y < -2x$ **58.** $x + y > 3$ **59.** $2x + 3y \geq 6$

Perform the operation. Write the result in standard form. (12.3, 12.4)

60. $(x^3 + 3x^2 - 4) + (2x^2 - 2x)$ $x^3 + 5x^2 - 2x - 4$

61. $(3x^2 + 2x + 1) - (3x^2 - 2x + 4)$ $4x - 3$

62. $(4x - 3) - (-3x^2 + 3x + 3)$ $3x^2 + x - 6$

63. $(x^4 - 3x^3 - x^2 + 5) + (4x^3 - 2x^2 - 3x + 7)$ $x^4 + x^3 - 3x^2 - 3x + 12$

64. $x^2(3x^3 + 4x^2 - 6x + 8)$ $3x^5 + 4x^4 - 6x^3 + 8x^2$

65. $3x(2x^3 - 4x^2 + 10x + 4)$ $6x^4 - 12x^3 + 30x^2 + 12x$

Solve the equation. (12.7)

66. $x^2 - 4 = 12$ ± 4 **67.** $2y^2 = 18$ ± 3

68. $4z^2 + 4 = 20$ ± 2 **69.** $3q^2 - 62 = 46$ ± 6

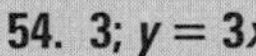

54. 3; $y = 3x$

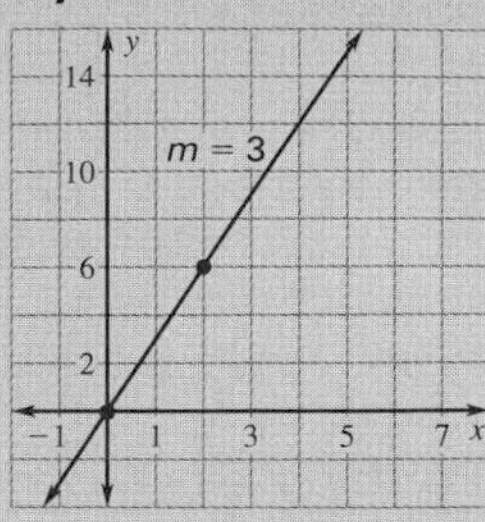

55. $\frac{1}{2}$; $y = \frac{1}{2}x + 2$

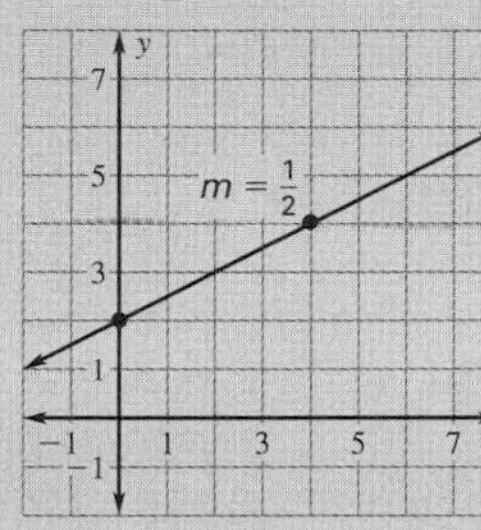

56. -6; $y = -6x - 3$

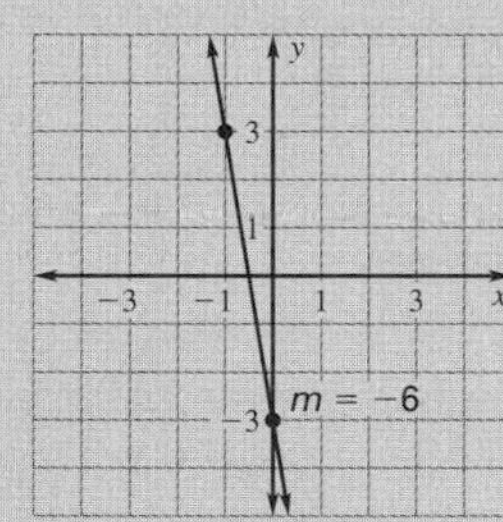

57. *Sample answer:* $(-1, -1), (0, -2), (1, -3)$

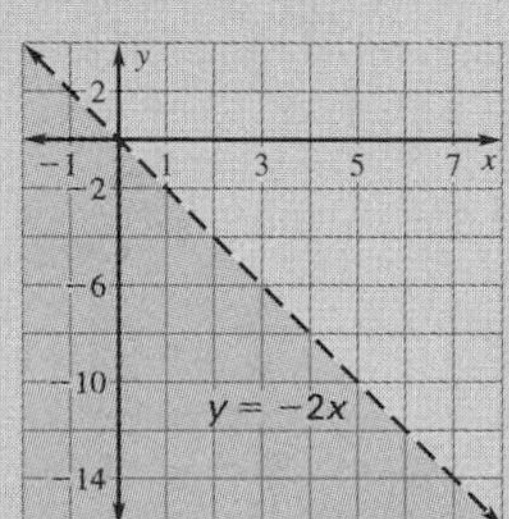

58–59. See Additional Answers beginning on page AA1.

Project Overview

Mathematical Goals

- Calculate the surface area and volume of a 3-dimensional solid.
- Recognize that solids with the same volume can have different surface areas.
- Determine the total cost of an item.
- Order decimals from least to greatest.

Managing the Project

Classroom Management
Students can work individually or in small groups. The group members should distribute designs A–F to each person. Have each student find the missing dimension for their package(s), then calculate the surface area and cost for each. Group members should check the work of others in their group. All group members can work together to order the costs of the containers. All group members should contribute to writing the report.

Guiding Students' Work
Students may have difficulty calculating the surface area of the containers. You may wish to have them review Lesson 10.3. If they have difficulty computing the cost of the containers, remind them that the cost per square inch is $\frac{\$0.02}{10 \text{ in.}^2}$ or \$0.002 per square inch.

California Standards and Assessment

CA Standards: AF 3.1, MG 2.1

Chapters 10-12 Project

California Standards

- Use formulas routinely for finding the surface area and volume of basic three-dimensional figures. (MG 2.1)
- Use functions of the form $y = nx^2$ and $y = nx^3$ in solving problems. (AF 3.1)

Materials

- Calculator
- Pencil
- Paper

Designing Packaging

OBJECTIVE Design a cost-efficient container.

Investigation

1. You are designing a container that can hold 240 cubic inches. Some possible right cylinders and right prisms are shown below. For each shape, find the value of x. Round your answers to the nearest tenth of an inch.

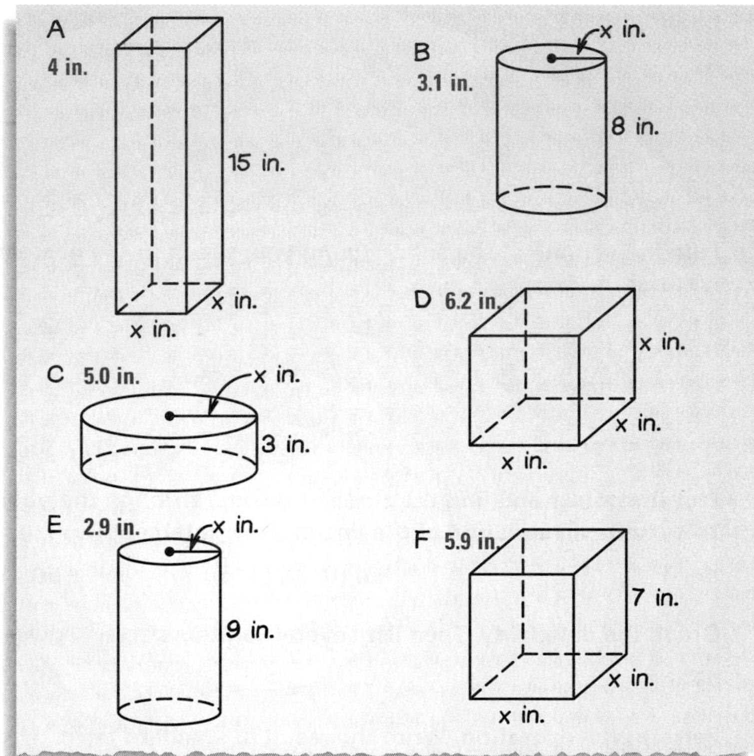

2. Calculate the surface area of each container.
A: 272 in.^{2}, B: 216.2 in.^{2}, C: 251.3 in.^{2}, D: 230.6 in.^{2}, E: 216.8 in.^{2}, F: 234.8 in.^{2}

3. The material you will use to make the containers costs \$.02 for 10 square inches. Use your surface area calculations to find the cost of the material for each container.
A: \$.54, B: \$.43, C: \$.50, D: \$.46, E: \$.43, F: \$.47

4. Which container is most expensive? Which is least expensive? Use your answer to Exercise 3.
Container A; Container B and Container E both cost about \$.43; Container B is slightly less expensive than Container E.

5. Draw another container that can hold 240 cubic inches. Label the measurements of the container on your drawing. What is the surface area? How much does the material cost to make the container?
Answers will vary.

Present Your Results

What shape and dimensions do you recommend for the container? Write a report to present and support your recommendation.

- Include a discussion of various container shapes and their cost efficiency.
- Include your answers to Exercises 1–5. Be sure to show how you got your answers.
- You've analyzed the cost of materials. What other factors are important in choosing a shape for a container?
- You may want to include models of the shapes you analyzed.

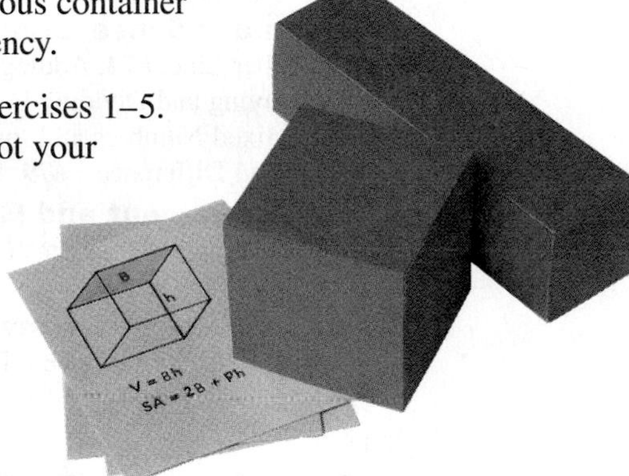

Extension

You decide to add large and small containers to your product line.

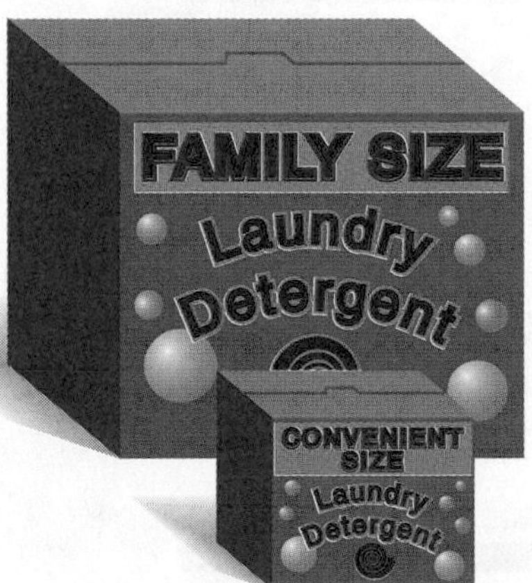

6. Family-size containers have a volume of 960 cubic inches. Choose a cost-efficient shape for your container. Sketch the container and label its measurements. Since the container is larger than the standard size, the material used to make it must be thicker and more expensive. The material costs $.05 for 10 square inches. Calculate the cost of the material for the container. **Answers will vary.**

7. Convenient-size containers have a volume of 120 cubic inches. Choose a cost-efficient shape for your container. Sketch the container and label its measurements. The material costs $.01 for 10 square inches. Calculate the cost of the material for the container. **Answers will vary.**

Concluding the Project
Students should present their reports to the class by having group members report how they calculated the surface area of each package. One member of the group should address any other important factors in choosing the shape of the container. You can use questions like the following for class discussion:

- Would a fragile item need a larger or smaller container than an item of the same size which is not fragile? Why?
- Would a container made to hold something light, like popcorn, need to be made the same as a container made to hold something heavier, like a liquid?

Grading the Project

A well-written project will have the following characteristics:

- Complete and correct solutions to Exercises 1–5.
- A thorough and well-written report which answers all questions about the project.
- An extension to the project in which students answer all parts of the questions in the extension.

Contents of Student Resources

Skills Review Handbook

Mathematical Reasoning

PROBLEM SOLVING: IDENTIFYING AND EXTENDING PATTERNS GRADE 6, MR 1.1

EXAMPLE **Describe the pattern. Then list the next three numbers you expect to find in the sequence.**

3, 9, 27, 81, 243, ?, ?, ?, . . .

SOLUTION Look for a relationship between consecutive numbers in the sequence to help you see the pattern. Division shows that each number after the first is 3 times the previous number.

To find the next three numbers, continue multiplying by 3.

$243 \times 3 = 729$ $729 \times 3 = 2187$ $2187 \times 3 = 6561$

The next three numbers are 729, 2187, and 6561.

EXAMPLE **Describe the pattern in the products. Then predict the value of the product 100,000,001 × 100,000,001.**

$101 \times 101 = 10{,}201$

$1001 \times 1001 = 1{,}002{,}001$

$10{,}001 \times 10{,}001 = 100{,}020{,}001$

SOLUTION In each product, a power of ten plus 1 is multiplied by itself. The result has a 1 at each end and a 2 in the middle. Zeros separate these digits. Notice that the number of zeros in the product matches the total number of zeros in the original numbers.

Using this pattern, you can predict that

$100{,}000{,}001 \times 100{,}000{,}001 = 10{,}000{,}000{,}200{,}000{,}001$.

Practice

Describe the pattern. Then list the next three numbers you expect to find in the sequence. 1–6. See margin.

1. 16, 20, 24, 28, ?, ?, ?, . . .

2. 2, 10, 50, 250, ?, ?, ?, . . .

3. 10, 7, 4, 1, ?, ?, ?, . . .

4. 12, 121, 1212, 12121, ?, ?, ?, . . .

5. 80, 40, 20, 10, ?, ?, ?, . . .

6. $\frac{1}{2}, \frac{2}{3}, \frac{3}{4}, \frac{4}{5}$, ?, ?, ?, . . .

Describe the pattern in the products. Then list the next three products you expect to find in the sequence. 7–9. See margin.

7. $2 \times 99 = 198$
$3 \times 99 = 297$
$4 \times 99 = 396$

8. $1 \times 1 = 1$
$11 \times 11 = 121$
$111 \times 111 = 12{,}321$

9. $5 \times 3 = 15$
$5 \times 15 = 75$
$5 \times 75 = 375$

SKILLS REVIEW

1. Each number is 4 more than the previous number; 32, 36, 40
2. Each number is 5 times the previous number; 1250; 6250; 31,250
3. Each number is 3 less than the previous number; −2, −5, −8
4. To find the next number alternate attaching a 1 or a 2 to the end of the previous number; 121212, 1212121, 12121212
5. Each number is the previous number divided by 2; 5, 2.5, 1.25
6. To find the next number increase both the numerator and the denominator by 1; $\frac{5}{6}, \frac{6}{7}, \frac{7}{8}$
7. The first digit in the product increases by 1, the second digit remains 9, and the third digit decreases by 1; 495, 594, 693
8. The middle digit in the product increases by 1 and the digits to the left and right of the middle digit count down to 1 which is always the first and last digit in the product; 1,234,321; 123,454,321; 12,345,654,321
9. The next product is 5 times the previous product; 1875, 9375, 46875

California Standards and Assessment

CA Standard: Grade 6, MR 1.1

4.

Karen	Laurie
5	1
4	2
3	3
2	4
1	5

6.

	Pancakes	Waffles	Biscuits
Baking Mix (in cups)	2	2	$2\frac{1}{4}$
Milk (in cups)	1	$1\frac{1}{3}$	$\frac{2}{3}$
Eggs	2	1	0
Oil (in table-spoons)	0	2	0

CA Standard: Grade 6, MR 2.4

Mathematical Reasoning

PROBLEM SOLVING: USING A TABLE, GRAPH, OR DIAGRAM

GRADE 6, MR 2.4

A set of data is easier to understand when it is organized in a table or displayed in a graph. A table lists the data, while a graph is used to give the data a visual meaning.

EXAMPLE **Use a table to find how many different ways you can combine quarters, dimes, and nickels to make $.40.**

SOLUTION

Quarters	Dimes	Nickels
1	1	1
1	0	3
0	4	0
0	3	2
0	2	4
0	1	6
0	0	8

These combinations use a quarter.

These combinations do not use a quarter. They are listed according to the number of dimes.

ANSWER ▶ There are seven ways of getting $.40 using only quarters, dimes, and nickels.

Practice

In Exercises 1–5, use a table to organize your answer.

1. How many ways can you make $1.00 using quarters and dimes? **3 ways**
2. How many ways can you make $.75 using quarters and nickels? **4 ways**
3. How many ways can you make $.35 using quarters, dimes, and nickels? **6 ways**
4. Your soccer team won its last game with a score of 6 to 4. All of the 6 goals were scored by two people, Karen and Laurie. How many goals could each person have scored? **See margin.**
5. You can have one or two toppings on your pizza. The toppings that are available are pepperoni, mushroom, onion, and extra cheese. List all the possible types of pizza you can have.
6. Organize the following ingredients in a table: **See margin.**
   - The ingredients for pancakes are 2 cups baking mix, 1 cup milk, and 2 eggs.
   - The ingredients for waffles are 2 cups baking mix, $1\frac{1}{3}$ cups milk, 1 egg, and 2 tablespoons oil.
   - The ingredients for biscuits are $2\frac{1}{4}$ cups baking mix and $\frac{2}{3}$ cup milk.

5. pepperoni, pepperoni and mushroom, pepperoni and onion, pepperoni and extra cheese, mushroom, mushroom and onion, mushroom and extra cheese, onion, onion and extra cheese, extra cheese

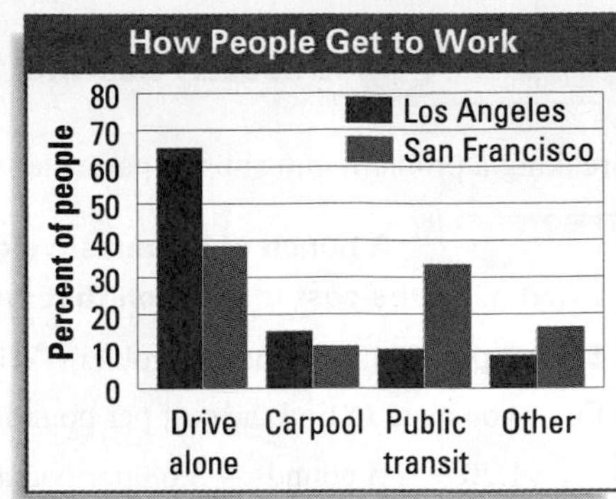

EXAMPLE **Use the bar graph to estimate the percent of people in Los Angeles who use each kind of transportation to get to work.**

SOLUTION Compare the labels on the graph with the words in the problem. Find the facts you need from the graph.

The vertical scale tells you that each row represents 10% of the working population.

ANSWER ▶ About 65% of the people in Los Angeles drive alone, about 15% carpool to work, about 10% use public transit, and about 10% use some other kind of transportation.

EXAMPLE **The length and width of a rectangle are whole numbers. The area of the rectangle is 24 square units. Of the possible rectangles, which has the smallest perimeter?**

SOLUTION Picture the situation described. Draw all the possible rectangles.

P = 50 (24 by 1)

P = 28

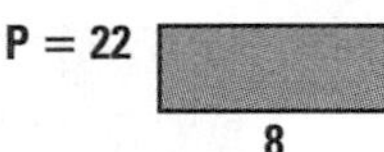

12 by 2

P = 22

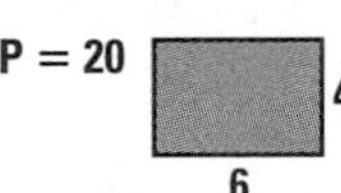

8 by 3

P = 20 (6 by 4)

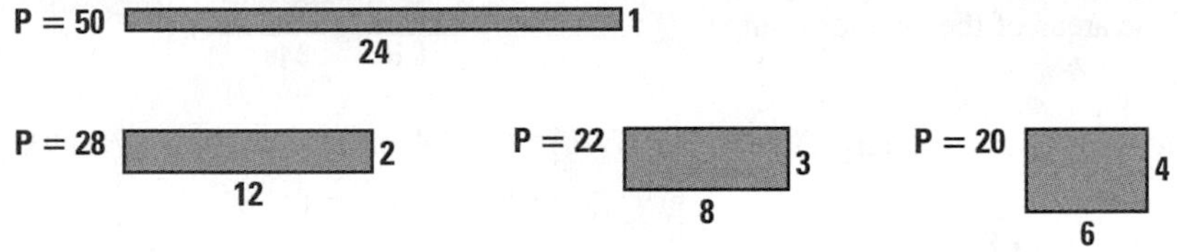

ANSWER ▶ The rectangle with the smallest perimeter is 4 units by 6 units.

Practice

In Exercises 7 and 8, use the bar graph at the top of the page.

7. Estimate the percent of people in San Francisco who use each kind of transportation to get to work. ***Sample answer:*** **About 38% drive alone, about 12% carpool, about 33% use public transit, and about 17% use some other kind of transportation.**

8. Which methods of getting to work are more popular in San Francisco than in Los Angeles? **public transit and other**

In Exercises 9–12, draw a diagram to find the answer.

9. The length and width of a rectangle are whole numbers. The area is 36 square centimeters. Find the rectangle with the smallest perimeter. **6 cm by 6 cm**

10. The length and width of a rectangle are whole numbers. The perimeter is 20 meters. Find the rectangle with the largest area. **5 m by 5 m**

11. Four students are playing tennis. They want to make sure that everyone gets to play everyone else. How many games do they need to play? **6 games**

12. In a city with square city blocks, you walk 2 blocks east, 3 blocks north, 4 blocks west, then 5 blocks south. Describe all the shortest paths back to where you started from. **See margin.**

12. walk 2 blocks north and 2 blocks east; walk 1 block north, 1 block east, 1 block north, and 1 block east; walk 1 block north, 2 blocks east, and 1 block north; walk 1 block east, 2 blocks north, and 1 block east; walk 1 block east, 1 block north, 1 block east, and 1 block north; walk 2 blocks east and 2 blocks north

SKILLS REVIEW

SKILLS REVIEW

Breaking a problem into simpler parts may make the problem easier to solve.

EXAMPLE **A bunch of bananas weighs 2.5 pounds and costs $1.70. Find the cost of a bunch that weighs 3.5 pounds.**

SOLUTION Think about the problem. What do you need to do first? next?

First, you need to find the cost per pound.

$1.70 ÷ 2.5 pounds = $.68 per pound

Next, multiply the cost per pound by 3.5 pounds.

$.68 per pound × 3.5 pounds = $2.38

ANSWER A bunch of bananas that weighs 3.5 pounds would cost $2.38.

EXAMPLE **Find the area of the figure shown.**

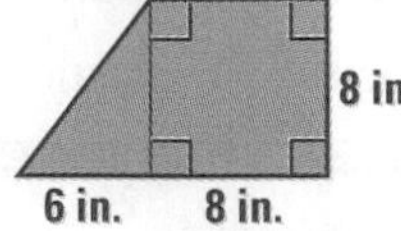

SOLUTION Divide the figure into two smaller figures. The total area is the sum of the areas of the smaller figures.

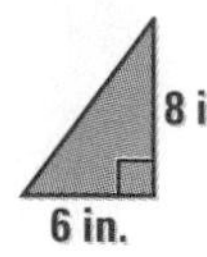

$\text{Area} = \frac{1}{2} \cdot (\text{Base}) \cdot (\text{Height})$

$= \frac{1}{2} \cdot 6 \cdot 8$

$= 24$ square inches

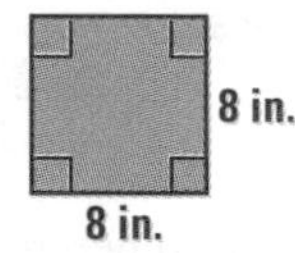

$\text{Area} = (\text{Length}) \cdot (\text{Width})$

$= 8 \cdot 8$

$= 64$ square inches

Total area = 24 square inches + 64 square inches = 88 square inches

Practice

1. A square garden is enclosed by 28 meters of fencing. What is the area of the garden? **49 m^2**

2. An electrician charges a basic service fee plus a labor charge for each hour of service. A 2 hour job costs $74, and a 3 hour job costs $96. Find the electrician's basic service fee. **$30**

3. In hockey, a team earns 2 points for a win, 1 point for a tie, and 0 points for a loss. Out of 82 games played, a hockey team won 46 games and lost 31 games. How many points did the team earn for the 82 games? **97 points**

Find the area of the figure.

4. 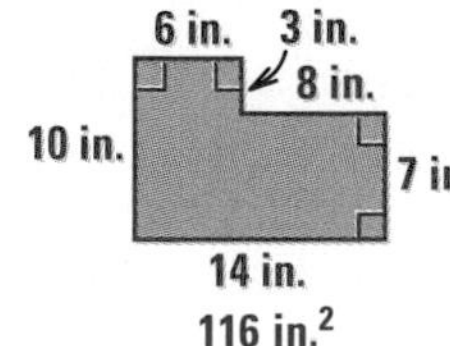

116 in.^{2}

5. 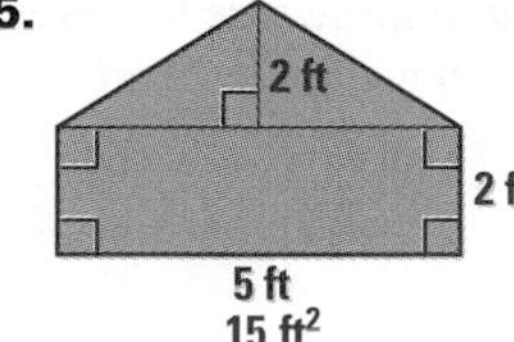

15 ft^2

6. 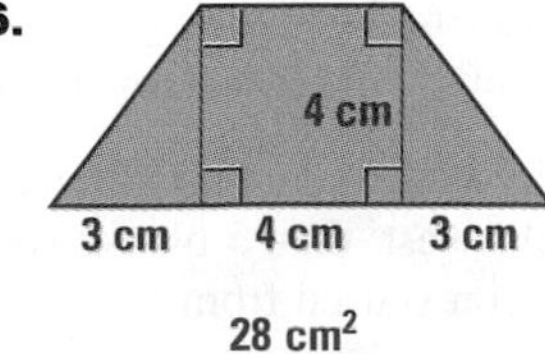

28 cm^2

California Standards and Assessment
CA Standard: Grade 6, MR 1.3

PROBLEM SOLVING: CHECKING REASONABLENESS

Check your answer to a problem by deciding if your answer is reasonable.

EXAMPLE **A coat costs $225 and is on sale for half off. The sales clerk tells you the sale price of the coat is $175. Is this statement reasonable?**

SOLUTION The original cost of the coat is $225. Use mental math: because $225 is a little more than $200, half of $225 should be a little more than $100.

ANSWER The price the sales clerk told you is too high.

EXAMPLE **There are 33 students taking a class trip to the zoo. A van can hold 12 students. How many vans are needed?**

SOLUTION Divide 33 by 12: $33 \div 12 = 2.75$.

Sometimes the answer you get in computation is not the answer to the problem. You calculate that 2.75 vans are needed to take the students on their trip. Because the number of vans must be a whole number, you need to round the calculated number up.

ANSWER You will need 3 vans for 33 students.

EXAMPLE **Use the following information.**

You earn $5.60 per hour working at the library. Last week you worked 12 hours. You round both numbers down and estimate that you have earned about $5 • 10 = $50. Is this amount reasonable?

SOLUTION Rounding both values down produces a low estimate. By rounding only one value, the estimate will be closer to the exact amount.

$5 per hour • 12 hours = $60

ANSWER A more reasonable estimate would be $60.

Practice

Use mental math or estimation to choose the answer that is reasonable.

1. Three roommates split their monthly rent evenly. If the rent is $768 per month, how much is each person's share? **C**

   A. $2304 **B.** $768 **C.** $256

2. You have $42 to spend on compact discs. How many can you buy if each compact disc costs $12.88? **A**

   A. 3 **B.** 4 **C.** 5

3. A restaurant sold 264 beverages on Friday. If each cup holds 8 ounces, about how many ounces did the restaurant sell that day? **B**

   A. 4200 ounces **B.** 2100 ounces **C.** 30 ounces

SKILLS REVIEW

CA Standard: Grade 6, MR 3.1

1. $1 \times 1000 + 2 \times 100 + 5 \times 10 + 4 \times 1$
2. $6 \times 1{,}000{,}000 + 7 \times 100 + 5 \times 10$
3. $3 \times 100 + 8 \times 10 + 2 \times \frac{1}{10}$
4. $1 \times 10 + 2 \times 1 + 4 \times \frac{1}{100} + 5 \times \frac{1}{1000}$
5. $1 \times 10{,}000 + 9 \times 100 + 4 \times 10 + 6 \times 1$
6. $9 \times 100{,}000 + 1 \times 1$
7. $1 \times 100 + 1 \times \frac{1}{100}$
8. $1 \times 1000 + 4 \times 100 + 8 \times 10 + 7 \times 1 + 2 \times \frac{1}{10} + 8 \times \frac{1}{100}$

California Standards and Assessment

CA Standard: Grade 5, NS 1.1

Number Sense

PLACE VALUE AND ROUNDING

The base-ten number system is a place-value system where the value of each digit depends on its place in the number. For example, in the number 59.2, the 5 has a value of $5 \times 10 = 50$ because it is in the tens place.

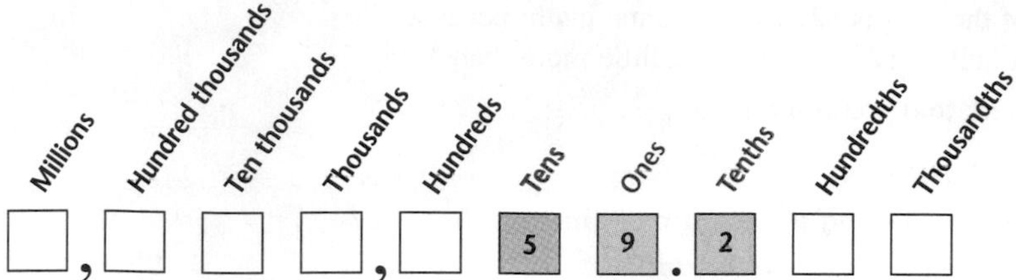

EXAMPLE **Write the number 432.7 in expanded form.**

SOLUTION

$432.7 = \mathbf{400} + \mathbf{30} + 2 + \mathbf{0.7}$

$= \mathbf{4 \times 100 + 3 \times 10 + 2 \times 1 + 7 \times \frac{1}{10}}$

EXAMPLE **Write the number in standard decimal form.**

a. Three million, four hundred thousand, fifty

b. Seven and 19 hundredths

SOLUTION

a. Write 3 in the millions place, 4 in the hundred thousands place, and 5 in the tens place. Use zeros as placeholders for the other places. The answer is 3,400,050.

b. Write 7 in the ones place, 1 in the tenths place, and 9 in the hundredths place. The answer is 7.19.

Practice

Write the number in expanded form. **1–8. See margin.**

1. 1254 **2.** 6,000,750 **3.** 380.2 **4.** 12.045

5. 10,946 **6.** 900,001 **7.** 100.01 **8.** 1,487.28

Write the number in standard decimal form.

9. $6 \times 10{,}000 + 4 \times 1000 + 8 \times 10 + 7 \times 1$ **64,087**

10. $5 \times 100 + 4 \times 1 + 3 \times \frac{1}{10} + 7 \times \frac{1}{100}$ **504.37**

11. $7 \times 10 + 9 \times 1 + 2 \times \frac{1}{10} + 2 \times \frac{1}{100}$ **79.22**

12. $1 \times 100{,}000 + 5 \times 10{,}000 + 3 \times 1$ **150,003**

13. Fifty-three thousand, eight hundred **53,800**

14. Four hundred seven and sixteen hundredths **407.16**

15. Sixty-four and seven tenths **64.7**

16. Nine and fifty-three thousandths **9.053**

To round a number to a given decimal place, look at the digit to its right.

If the digit is a 4 or less, round down.

If the digit is a 5 or more, round up.

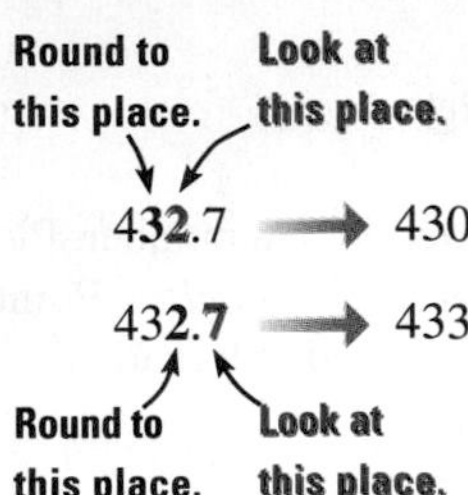
Round to this place.
Look at this place.
432.7 → 430
432.7 → 433
Round to this place.
Look at this place.

EXAMPLE

	Round to nearest	Number	Up or down?	Answer
a.	Ten	983	Round down	980
b.	Hundred	6058	Round up	6100
c.	Thousand	74,598	Round up	75,000
d.	Thousandth	7.7256	Round up	7.726
e.	Hundredth	6.452	Round down	6.45
f.	Tenth	256.231	Round down	256.2
g.	One	738.4	Round down	738
h.	One	0.998	Round up	1

Practice

Copy and complete the table.

	Round to nearest	Number	Up or down?	Answer
17.	Ten	9758	Round up	? **9760**
18.	Thousand	1,231,498	?	?
19.	One	6.592	?	?
20.	Thousandth	15.2842	?	?
21.	Hundred	189,098	?	?
22.	Tenth	172.893	?	?
23.	Hundredth	0.342	?	?
24.	?	9.111	?	9.11
25.	?	98,132	?	98,000
26.	?	1.58	?	2
27.	?	147.7	?	148

18–27. See margin.

18. Round down; 1,231,000
19. Round up; 7
20. Round down; 15.284
21. Round up; 189,100
22. Round up; 172.9
23. Round down; 0.34
24. Hundredth; round down
25. Thousand; round down
26. One; round up
27. One; round up

9. 0.2, 1.2, 3.2, 3.5, 4.2

10. 6.6, 6.7, 6.8, 7.6, 8.6

11. 0.2, 0.8, 2.3, 3.2, 4.3

12. 3.7, 3.8, 3.9, 4.0, 4.8

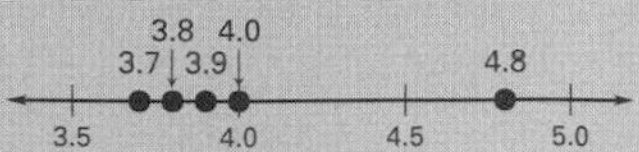

13. 7.9, 8.7, 8.9, 9.8, 9.9

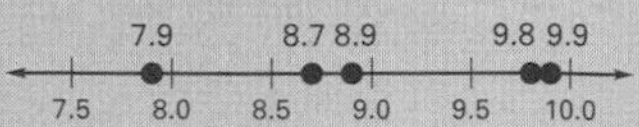

14. 2.05, 2.35, 2.39, 2.53

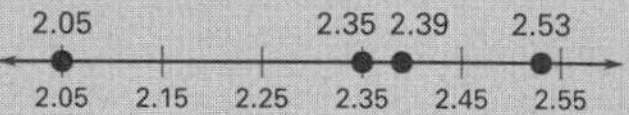

15. 0.09, 0.13, 0.85, 1.25

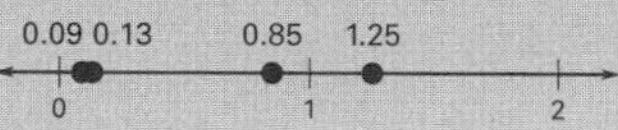

16. 5.56, 5.65, 6.56, 6.65

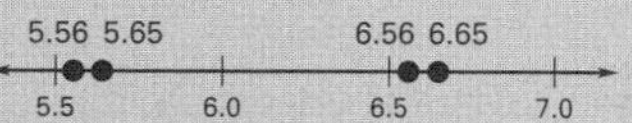

17. 4.05, 4.4, 4.45, 4.5

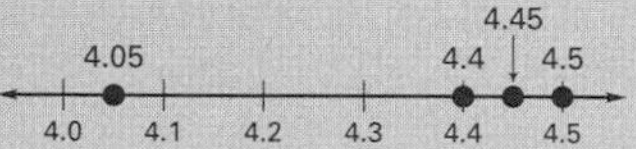

California Standards and Assessment

CA Standard: Grade 6, NS 1.1

Number Sense

USING A NUMBER LINE

GRADE 6, NS 1.1

Every point on a number line is associated with a number. Plotting the point that corresponds to a number is called *graphing the number*. Points that correspond to whole numbers are labeled with evenly spaced tick marks.

EXAMPLE **Graph 2.6 on a number line.**

SOLUTION Begin by drawing a number line. Locate the points for 2 and 3. To show tenths, draw nine equally spaced tick marks between 2 and 3. Plot the point that corresponds to 2.6.

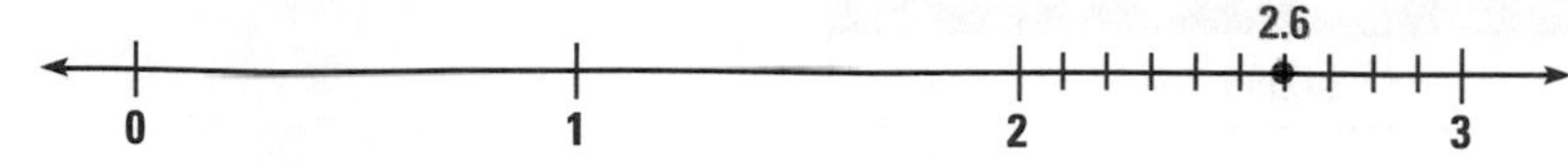

EXAMPLE **Use a number line to compare 1.7 and 1.6.**

SOLUTION Begin by graphing 1.7 and 1.6 on the same number line.

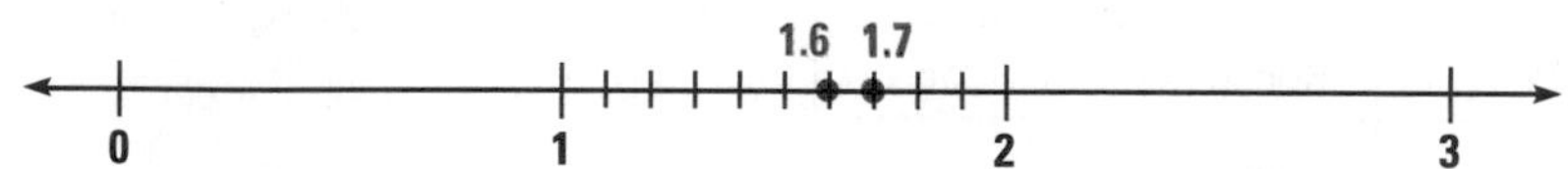

ANSWER Remember: “<” means *is less than* and “>” means *is greater than.* Because 1.6 is to the left of 1.7, you can write 1.6 < 1.7 or 1.7 > 1.6.

EXAMPLE **Order 2.3, 2.09, 2.32, 2.27, and 2.37 from least to greatest.**

SOLUTION Begin by graphing all five numbers on the same number line.

ANSWER In order, the numbers are 2.09, 2.27, 2.3, 2.32, and 2.37.

Practice

Use a number line to compare the numbers.

1. 0.9 and 1.9 **0.9 < 1.9**
2. 1.2 and 0.8 **1.2 > 0.8**
3. 3.2 and 2.3 **3.2 > 2.3**
4. 2.35 and 2.31 **2.35 > 2.31**
5. 3.56 and 3.50 **3.56 > 3.50**
6. 0.19 and 0.20 **0.19 < 0.20**
7. 1.26 and 1.62 **1.26 < 1.62**
8. 7.08 and 7.03 **7.08 > 7.03**

Graph the numbers on the same number line. Then order the numbers from least to greatest. **9–17. See margin.**

9. 1.2, 3.2, 4.2, 0.2, 3.5
10. 6.7, 6.6, 8.6, 6.8, 7.6
11. 2.3, 3.2, 0.2, 4.3, 0.8
12. 3.9, 3.7, 4.0, 4.8, 3.8
13. 9.8, 8.9, 7.9, 9.9, 8.7
14. 2.35, 2.53, 2.05, 2.39
15. 0.09, 0.85, 0.13, 1.25
16. 6.56, 5.65, 6.65, 5.56
17. 4.45, 4.4, 4.05, 4.5

ADDING AND SUBTRACTING DECIMALS

GRADE 5, NS 2.1

Adding and subtracting decimals is like adding and subtracting whole numbers. Remember to line up the decimal places.

EXAMPLE **Add or subtract.** **a.** 2.4 + 0.86 + 6 **b.** 11.8 − 3.54

SOLUTION Write each problem in a vertical format, using zeros as placeholders. Add or subtract. Regroup when needed. Don't forget the decimal point in the answer.

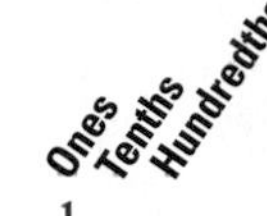

a.
```
   1
   2.40   ← Use zeros as placeholders.
   0.86
 + 6.00   ←
 ------
   9.26
```

Tens Ones Tenths Hundredths

b.
```
  0 1  7 1
  1 1 . 8 0
 −   3 . 5 4
 -----------
     8 . 2 6
```

CHECK ✓ Round decimals to whole numbers and add: 2 + 1 + 6 = 9. The answer is reasonable.

CHECK ✓ Add 8.26 and 3.54 to see if you get 11.8. It checks: 8.26 + 3.54 = 11.8.

Practice

Add or subtract.

1. 2.8 + 3.1 **5.9** **2.** 12 + 5.5 **17.5** **3.** 1.01 + 4.3 **5.31** **4.** 0.66 + 0.04 **0.7**

5. 5.6 − 1.4 **4.2** **6.** 9.25 − 3.72 **5.53** **7.** 10.4 − 0.57 **9.83** **8.** 16 − 1.2 **14.8**

9. 3.28 + 612 **615.28** **10.** 35.012 + 6.32 **41.332** **11.** 9.999 + 0.001 **10** **12.** 0.105 + 1.02 **1.125**

13. 8.8 − 2.02 **6.78** **14.** 10 − 1.8 **8.2** **15.** 102.5 − 30.6 **71.9** **16.** 36.85 − 32.06 **4.79**

Simplify.

17. 15.3 + 0.65 − 10.4 **5.55** **18.** 96 + 10.2 − 75.4 **30.8** **19.** 0.65 + 3.20 − 1.09 **2.76**

20. 42.06 − 32.1 + 0.68 **10.64** **21.** 32.14 − 6.23 + 4.07 **29.98** **22.** 89.123 − 64.07 − 15.7 **9.353**

Solve the problem.

23. To pay for milk that costs \$3.62, you hand the clerk a \$5 bill. How much change should you receive? **\$1.38**

24. You buy a pair of soccer shorts for \$5.95 and a team shirt for \$8.50. How much do you spend? **\$14.45**

25. Normal body temperature is about 98.6° Fahrenheit. A nurse finds that a patient's temperature is 101° Fahrenheit. By how many degrees is the patient's temperature above normal? **2.4° Fahrenheit**

California Standards and Assessment
CA Standard: Grade 5, NS 2.1

Multiplying and Dividing Decimals

SKILLS REVIEW

When you multiply two decimals, remember that the number of decimal places in the product is equal to the sum of the number of decimal places in the factors.

EXAMPLE **Multiply.** **a.** 4.25 × 1.4 **b.** 1.24 × 0.06

SOLUTION Multiply as with whole numbers. Be sure to write the decimal point in the answer.

a.

```
   4.25   Two decimal places
 × 1.4    One decimal place
   1700
   425
  5.950   Three decimal places
```

b.

```
   1.24   Two decimal places
 × 0.06   Two decimal places
 0.0744   Four decimal places
```

To divide by a decimal, convert the division problem to a related one with a whole number divisor that has the same answer.

EXAMPLE **Divide 0.086 ÷ 0.2.**

SOLUTION Write the problem in long-division form.

0.2)0.086

Move the decimal points in the divisor and dividend the same number of places until the divisor is a whole number. Then divide.

0.2)0.086

Move decimal points one place to the right.

```
    0.43
 2)0.86
    8
     6
     6
     0
```

Line up decimal place in quotient with decimal place in dividend.

ANSWER ▶ 0.086 ÷ 0.2 = 0.43

Practice

In Exercises 1–8, multiply.

1. 8.5 × 2.5 **21.25**
2. 2.5 × 0.04 **0.1**
3. 6.2 × 4.5 **27.9**
4. 3.05 × 2.7 **8.235**
5. 9.33 × 0.1 **0.933**
6. 0.04 × 260 **10.4**
7. 500 × 0.0003 **0.15**
8. 0.00002 × 16 **0.00032**

In Exercises 9–16, divide.

9. 600 ÷ 0.3 **2000**
10. 36.36 ÷ 1.2 **30.3**
11. 6.024 ÷ 0.04 **150.6**
12. 6.71 ÷ 2.2 **3.05**
13. 95 ÷ 0.05 **1900**
14. 59.18 ÷ 0.011 **5380**
15. 31.28 ÷ 9.2 **3.4**
16. 2.75 ÷ 0.005 **550**

17. To find the approximate number of kilometers in a given number of miles, multiply the number of miles by 1.6. About how many kilometers is 26.2 miles? **about 41.92 kilometers**

California Standards and Assessment

CA Standard: Grade 5, NS 2.1

Number Sense

FRACTIONS AND PERCENTS

GRADE 5, NS 1.2

A *fraction* can used to describe one or more equal parts of a whole. The rectangle at the right represents the fraction $\frac{5}{6}$. The denominator of the fraction $\frac{5}{6}$ tells you that the rectangle is divided into 6 equal parts. The numerator of the fraction tells you that 5 parts are shaded.

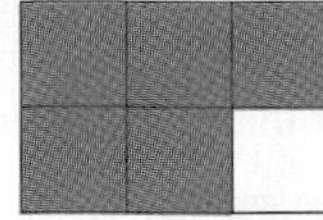

EXAMPLE **Tell what fraction the model represents. Then write two equivalent fractions.**

SOLUTION The total number of equal parts is 12. Eight of these parts are shaded. The model represents the fraction $\frac{8}{12}$.

To write an equivalent fraction, you can multiply or divide the numerator and denominator by the same nonzero number.

$$\frac{8}{12} = \frac{8 \cdot \mathbf{2}}{12 \cdot \mathbf{2}} = \frac{16}{24} \qquad \frac{8}{12} = \frac{8 \div \mathbf{4}}{12 \div \mathbf{4}} = \frac{2}{3}$$

When a whole is divided into 100 equal parts, you can write a *percent* using the symbol %. Since *percent* means "per hundred," the number 1% means $\frac{1}{100}$.

EXAMPLE **What percent of the square is shaded?**

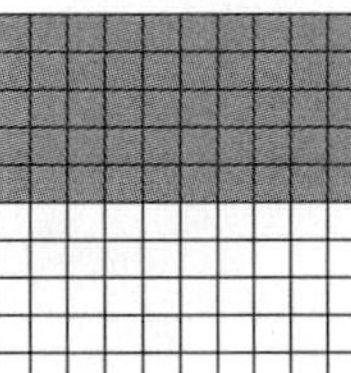

SOLUTION The square is divided into 100 equal parts. Fifty parts are shaded. The fraction of the square that is shaded is $\frac{50}{100}$.

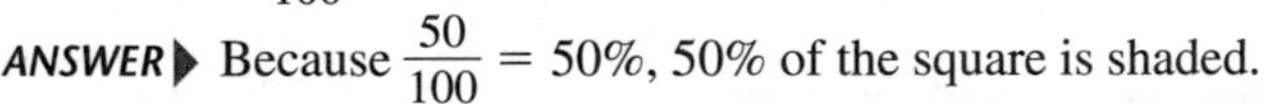

ANSWER Because $\frac{50}{100} = 50\%$, 50% of the square is shaded.

Practice

Tell what fraction the model represents. Then write two equivalent fractions. **1–4. See margin.**

1.

2. 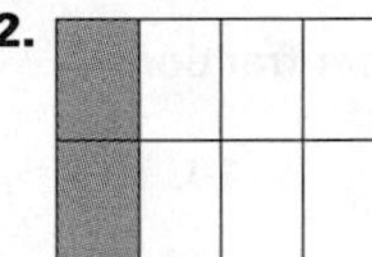

3. 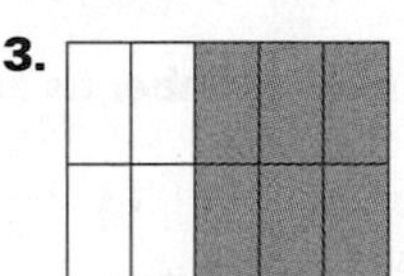

4. 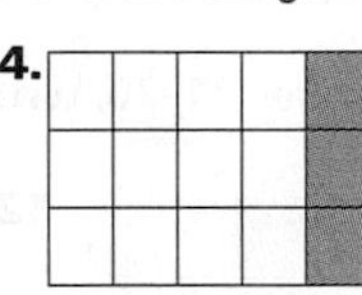

Tell what fraction the model represents. Then write the fraction as a percent. **5–8. See margin.**

5. 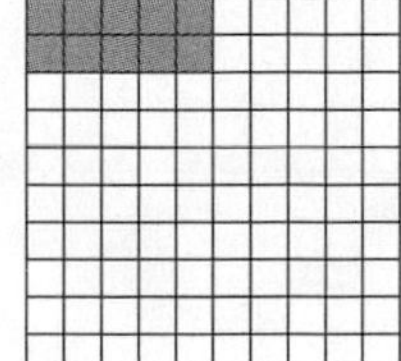

6. 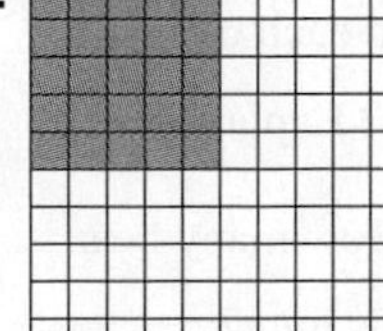

7. 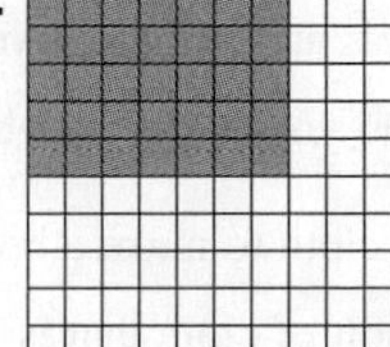

8. 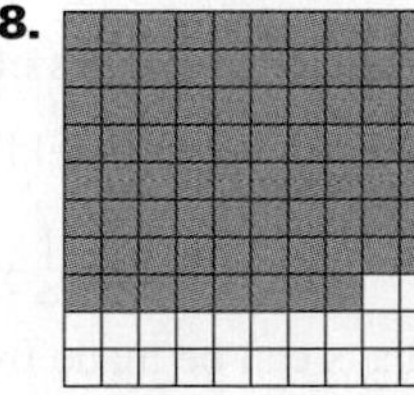

SKILLS REVIEW

1. $\frac{6}{9}$; *Sample answer:* $\frac{2}{3}, \frac{12}{18}$
2. $\frac{2}{8}$; *Sample answer:* $\frac{1}{4}, \frac{4}{16}$
3. $\frac{6}{10}$; *Sample answer:* $\frac{3}{5}, \frac{12}{20}$
4. $\frac{3}{15}$; *Sample answer:* $\frac{1}{5}, \frac{6}{30}$
5. $\frac{10}{100}$; 10%
6. $\frac{25}{100}$; 25%
7. $\frac{35}{100}$; 35%
8. $\frac{78}{100}$; 78%

California Standards and Assessment

CA Standard: Grade 5, NS 1.2

MIXED NUMBERS AND IMPROPER FRACTIONS

A positive number that can be written as the sum of a whole number equal to or greater than 1 and a fraction is a *mixed number*. A fraction that is equal to or greater than 1 is an *improper fraction*.

EXAMPLE **Write the improper fraction $\frac{23}{6}$ as a mixed number.**

SOLUTION You can use division to write an improper fraction as a mixed number. Because $\frac{23}{6}$ means "23 divided by 6," divide 23 by 6. The remainder will be the numerator of the mixed number's fraction.

$$\frac{23}{6} \longrightarrow 6\overline{)23}\ \text{3 R5} \longrightarrow 3\frac{5}{6}$$

EXAMPLE **Write the mixed number $3\frac{5}{6}$ as an improper fraction.**

SOLUTION There are two methods you can use to write a mixed number as a fraction.

Method 1: Write the whole number as an equivalent fraction. Then add.

$$3\frac{5}{6} = 3 + \frac{5}{6} = \frac{3 \times 6}{1 \times 6} + \frac{5}{6}$$

$$= \frac{18}{6} + \frac{5}{6} = \frac{18 + 5}{6} = \frac{23}{6}$$

Method 2: Multiply the whole number by the denominator of the fraction. Then add.

$$3\frac{5}{6} = \frac{(3 \times 6) + 5}{6}$$

$$= \frac{18 + 5}{6} = \frac{23}{6}$$

Practice

In Exercises 1–10, write the improper fraction as a mixed number.

1. $\frac{10}{3}$ **$3\frac{1}{3}$** **2.** $\frac{11}{7}$ **$1\frac{4}{7}$** **3.** $\frac{15}{2}$ **$7\frac{1}{2}$** **4.** $\frac{11}{10}$ **$1\frac{1}{10}$** **5.** $\frac{17}{12}$ **$1\frac{5}{12}$**

6. $\frac{12}{5}$ **$2\frac{2}{5}$** **7.** $\frac{29}{4}$ **$7\frac{1}{4}$** **8.** $\frac{33}{20}$ **$1\frac{13}{20}$** **9.** $\frac{64}{25}$ **$2\frac{14}{25}$** **10.** $\frac{7}{6}$ **$1\frac{1}{6}$**

In Exercises 11–20, write the mixed number as an improper fraction.

11. $7\frac{1}{2}$ **$\frac{15}{2}$** **12.** $4\frac{7}{8}$ **$\frac{39}{8}$** **13.** $1\frac{7}{50}$ **$\frac{57}{50}$** **14.** $10\frac{2}{7}$ **$\frac{72}{7}$** **15.** $2\frac{3}{5}$ **$\frac{13}{5}$**

16. $8\frac{3}{10}$ **$\frac{83}{10}$** **17.** $5\frac{18}{25}$ **$\frac{143}{25}$** **18.** $15\frac{1}{3}$ **$\frac{46}{3}$** **19.** $17\frac{5}{6}$ **$\frac{107}{6}$** **20.** $3\frac{11}{16}$ **$\frac{59}{16}$**

21. You have $3\frac{3}{4}$ bags of pretzels and want to give $\frac{1}{4}$ bag to each of 20 people on a field trip. Do you have enough pretzels? Explain. **No; *Sample answer:* You would need 5 bags to have enough pretzels for everyone on the trip.**

22. A company uses $\frac{1}{4}$ yard of cloth to make a bean bag. How many bean bags can be made from a bolt of cloth that is $12\frac{3}{4}$ yards long? **51 bean bags**

California Standards and Assessment

CA Standard: Grade 6, NS 1.0

Number Sense

Estimating Sums and Differences

Grade 5, NS 2.2

Estimation is a useful skill that provides a quick answer to a problem. When you estimate a sum or difference, look at the front-end digits in the problem.

EXAMPLE **Estimate the difference 37.143 − 12.657.**

SOLUTION ***Round*** each decimal to the nearest whole number.

$$\begin{array}{r} 37 \\ -\ 13 \\ \hline 24 \end{array}$$

Subtract the rounded numbers.

ANSWER ▶ The difference 37.143 − 12.657 is about 24.

EXAMPLE **Estimate the sum 695 + 273 + 1004.**

SOLUTION

Add the front-end digits.

$$\begin{array}{r} 695 \\ 273 \\ +\ 1004 \\ \hline 1800 \end{array}$$

Round the remaining parts of the numbers and add.

95 } about 100
73, 4 } about 100
200

Add this sum to your first result.

The estimate is 1800 + 200 = 2000.

ANSWER ▶ The sum 695 + 273 + 1004 is about 2000.

Practice

In Exercises 1–12, estimate the sum or difference. **1–13. Estimates may vary.**

1. 573.3 + 272.6 + 410.2 **1300**

2. 272.3 − 24.85 **247**

3. 29.95 + 61.61 + 55.10 **147**

4. 651 + 270.509 **922**

5. 539 + 226 + 912 **1680**

6. 76.832 − 39.595 **37**

7. 4.456 + 7.201 + 37.81 **49**

8. 43,507 + 65,880 + 34,231 **140,000**

9. 77,806 − 22,051 **56,000**

10. 48.89 + 90.05 + 21.27 **160**

11. 348 + 477 + 312 **1140**

12. 597.276 − 113.904 **483**

13. A few years ago when a family purchased a used car, the odometer reading was 55,707 miles. Now the odometer reading is 88,851. Estimate the number of miles the family has driven the car. **30,000 mi**

14. At a hobby shop, you buy model train kits that cost \$6.38, \$5.25, and \$8.45, and a locomotive that costs \$15.50. Estimate if \$40 is enough if you must pay a sales tax of \$2.15 on your purchases. Explain your reasoning.
yes; the difference is about \$3.

SKILLS REVIEW

California Standards and Assessment

CA Standard: Grade 5, NS 2.2

Number Sense

ESTIMATING PRODUCTS AND QUOTIENTS

GRADE 5, NS 2.2

SKILLS REVIEW

When you estimate products and quotients, you can use rounding or you can use *compatible numbers*, that is, numbers that are easy to compute mentally.

EXAMPLE **Use rounding to estimate the product or quotient.**

a. 4.5×12.37 **b.** $64.2 \div 3.8$

SOLUTION

Round each decimal to the nearest whole number.

Multiply (or ***divide***) the rounded numbers.

a. $12.37 \times 4.5 \longrightarrow 12 \times 5 = 60$

ANSWER ▶ The product 4.5×12.37 is about 60.

b. $3.8\overline{)64.2} \longrightarrow 4\overline{)64} = 16$

ANSWER ▶ The quotient $64.2 \div 3.8$ is about 16.

EXAMPLE **Use compatible numbers to estimate the product or quotient.**

a. 74.1×2.3 **b.** $1486 \div 14.7$

SOLUTION

Find numbers that are easy to compute mentally.

Multiply (or ***divide***) the compatible numbers.

a. $74.1 \times 2.3 \longrightarrow 75 \times 2 = 150$

ANSWER ▶ The product 74.1×2.3 is about 150.

b. $14.7\overline{)1486} \longrightarrow 14\overline{)1400} = 100$

ANSWER ▶ The quotient $1486 \div 14.7$ is about 100.

Practice

Estimate the product. Tell which method you used. **1–18. Estimates and methods may vary.**

1. 39×21 **800; rounding**
2. 82×45 **4000; rounding**
3. 12×79 **800; compatible numbers**
4. 7×563 **4200; rounding**
5. 39.5×4.8 **200; rounding**
6. 23.47×6 **120; compatible numbers**
7. 230.49×9 **2300; compatible numbers**
8. 785.23×18 **16,000; rounding**

In Exercises 9–16, estimate the quotient. Tell which method you used.

9. $24\overline{)185}$ **9; compatible numbers**
10. $1.6\overline{)53.7}$ **27; rounding**
11. $34\overline{)24,516}$ **800; compatible numbers**
12. $4817 \div 75$ **60; compatible numbers**
13. $3893.9 \div 9.1$ **400; compatible numbers**
14. $25.95 \div 1.6$ **13; rounding**
15. $12.35 \div 7$ **2; compatible numbers**
16. $9023.97 \div 48.8$ **180; compatible numbers**

17. You go to a restaurant with seven friends. The bill for the meal comes to \$51.50. Estimate each person's share of the bill if everyone agrees to pay an equal amount. **\$7.00**

18. The area of a rectangle is the product of its length and width. Estimate the area of the rectangle at the right. **1800 in.^{2}**

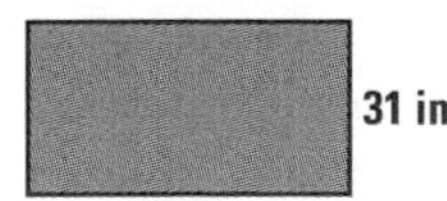

California Standards and Assessment

CA Standard: Grade 5, NS 2.2

CONVERTING UNITS OF MEASUREMENT

To convert from one unit of measurement to another, multiply the given unit by an appropriate conversion fraction equal to 1.

EXAMPLE **Write a conversion fraction for 1 yard = 36 inches and use it to convert 6 yards to inches.**

SOLUTION 1 yard = 36 inches — Write original equation.

$\frac{1 \not{\text{yard}}}{1 \not{\text{yard}}} = \frac{36 \text{ inches}}{1 \text{ yard}}$ — Divide each side by 1 yard.

$1 = \frac{36 \text{ inches}}{1 \text{ yard}}$ — Fraction equal to 1

Because the fraction $\frac{36 \text{ inches}}{1 \text{ yard}}$ is equal to 1, you can multiply by this fraction without changing the given measurement.

$$6 \not{\text{yards}} \cdot \frac{36 \text{ inches}}{1 \not{\text{yard}}} = 6 \cdot 36 \text{ inches} = 216 \text{ inches}$$

ANSWER ▶ So, 6 yards is equal to 216 inches.

EXAMPLE **Write a conversion fraction for 1 foot = 12 inches and use it to convert 3 feet to inches.**

SOLUTION 1 foot = 12 inches — Write original equation.

$\frac{1 \not{\text{foot}}}{1 \not{\text{foot}}} = \frac{12 \text{ inches}}{1 \text{ foot}}$ — Divide each side by 1 foot.

$1 = \frac{12 \text{ inches}}{1 \text{ foot}}$ — Fraction equal to 1

Use the fraction to convert 3 feet to inches.

$$3 \not{\text{feet}} \cdot \frac{12 \text{ inches}}{1 \not{\text{foot}}} = 3 \cdot 12 \text{ inches} = 36 \text{ inches}$$

ANSWER ▶ So, 3 feet is equal to 36 inches.

Practice

1. a. Write a conversion fraction for converting inches to feet. $\frac{1 \text{ foot}}{12 \text{ inches}}$

b. Use the conversion fraction from part (a) to find the number of feet in 108 inches. **9 ft**

2. a. Write a conversion fraction for converting inches to yards. $\frac{1 \text{ yard}}{36 \text{ inches}}$

b. Use the conversion fraction from part (a) to find the number of yards in 180 inches. **5 yd**

3. Use the fact that 1 cup = 8 fluid ounces to find the number of fluid ounces in 9 cups. **72 fluid oz**

4. Use the fact that 1 meter ≈ 3.28 feet to find the number of feet in a 100 meter sprint. **≈ 328 ft**

California Standards and Assessment

CA Standard: Grade 5, MG 1.4

PERIMETER, AREA, AND VOLUME

Measurement involves a comparison with a unit that is considered a standard. The most common standard units involve length, area, and volume.

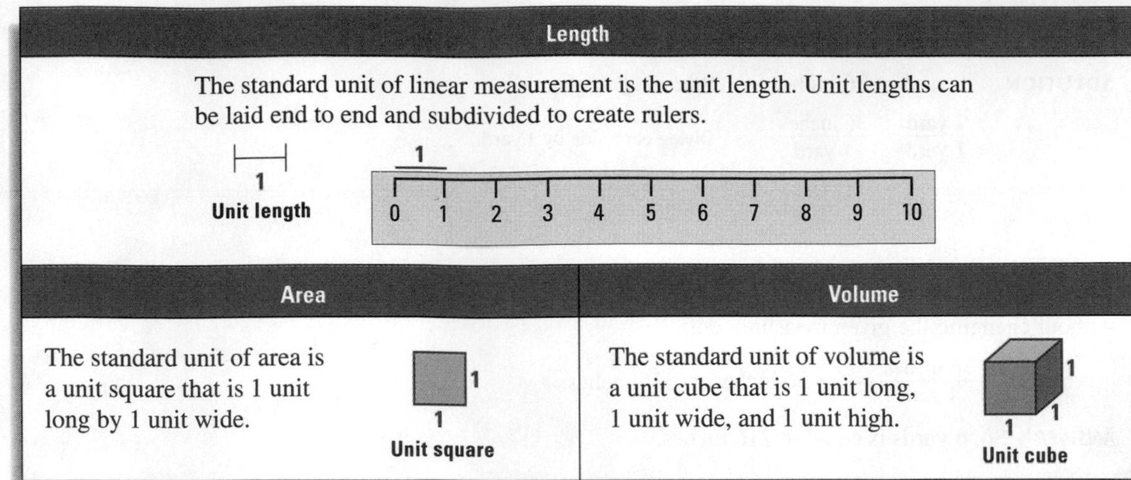

Length
The standard unit of linear measurement is the unit length. Unit lengths can be laid end to end and subdivided to create rulers.
1
Unit length
1
0 1 2 3 4 5 6 7 8 9 10
Area
The standard unit of area is a unit square that is 1 unit long by 1 unit wide.
1
1
Unit square
Volume
The standard unit of volume is a unit cube that is 1 unit long, 1 unit wide, and 1 unit high.
1
1
1
Unit cube

Perimeter and Area

The distance around a figure is its *perimeter.* Perimeter is measured in linear units such as inches (in.) or centimeters (cm). The *area* of a figure is measured by the number of unit squares needed to cover the figure (where some squares might have to be cut to fit). Area is measured in square units such as square inches (in.^{2}) or square centimeters (cm^2).

Recall that a *rectangle* is a four-sided figure having opposite sides of equal length and four right angles.

EXAMPLE **Find the perimeter and area of the rectangle.**

SOLUTION The perimeter is the distance around the rectangle.

$5 + 4 + 5 + 4 = 18$ units

By definition, the area of the rectangle is the number of unit squares required to cover the rectangle. By counting, you see that the rectangle is covered by 20 unit squares. So, the rectangle has an area of 20 square units.

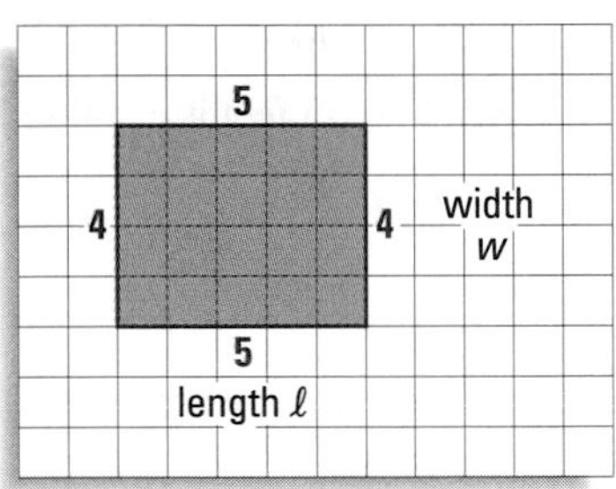

Notice in the example above that to find the perimeter of the rectangle, you added $5 + 4$, the sum of the length and width, twice. This process holds in general. That is, the perimeter of any rectangle is given by the formula

$$\text{Perimeter} = 2(\ell + w) = 2\ell + 2w$$

where ℓ and w are the length and width of the rectangle.

California Standards and Assessment

CA Standards: Grade 5, MG 1.1, MG1.4

Notice also in the example on the previous page that the number of unit squares covering the rectangle is 5 • 4, the product of the length and width of the rectangle. This process holds in general. That is, the area of any rectangle is given by the formula

Area $= \ell \cdot w$

where ℓ and w are the length and width of the rectangle.

Recall that a *triangle* is a geometric figure with three sides.

EXAMPLE **Find the area of the shaded triangle shown.**

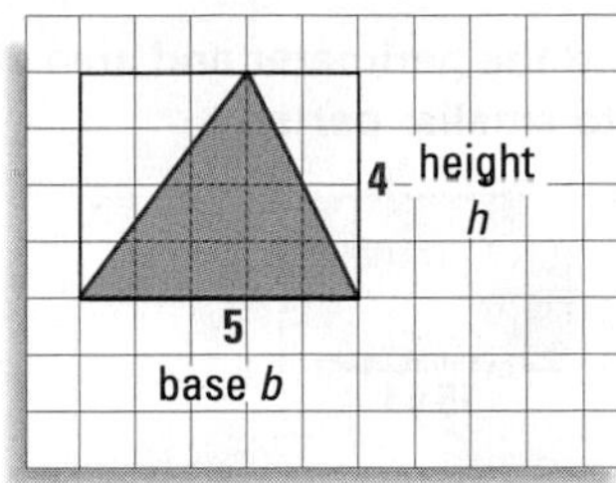

SOLUTION The *base* of the triangle is the same as the length of the rectangle that encloses it. The *height* of the triangle is the same as the width of the rectangle. The triangle has half the area of the rectangle. (To see this, copy the diagram, cut out the unshaded regions, and rearrange them to form a triangle that matches the shaded one.)

$$\text{Area of triangle} = \frac{1}{2}(\text{Area of rectangle})$$

$$= \frac{1}{2} \cdot (\text{Base}) \cdot (\text{Height})$$

$$= \frac{1}{2} \cdot 5 \cdot 4$$

$$= 10 \text{ square units}$$

You can check this result by seeing how 10 unit squares can be used to cover the triangle (after some unit squares are cut up to fit).

Volume

Volume is a measure of how many unit cubes are needed to fill an object. Volume is measured in cubic units such as cubic inches (in.^{3}) or cubic centimeters (cm^3).

EXAMPLE **Find the volume of the box shown.**

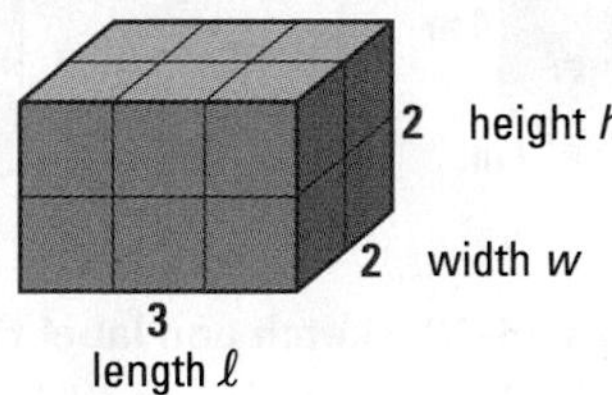

SOLUTION The volume of the box is measured by how many unit cubes are needed to fill it. Counting the cubes in the diagram gives 12 unit cubes.

ANSWER ▶ The volume of the box is 12 cubic units.

Notice in the example above that the number of unit cubes is 3 • 2 • 2, the product of the length, width, and height of the edges of the box. This process holds in general. That is, the volume of any box is given by the formula

Volume $= \ell \cdot w \cdot h$

where ℓ, w, and h are the length, width, and height of the box.

10.

18 mm

20 mm

11.

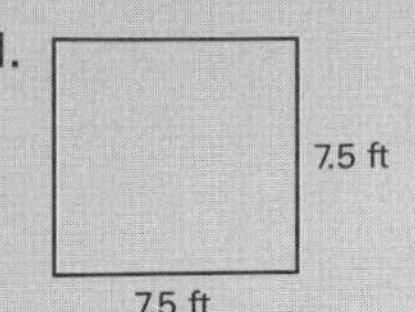

12.

26 m

10 m

24 m

16.

2.5 cm

2.5 cm

2.5 cm

17.

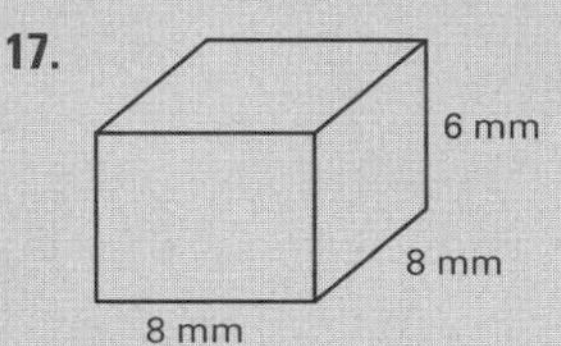

18.

3 ft

12 ft

4 ft

SKILLS REVIEW

Practice

In Exercises 1–3, use the fact that a *square* is a rectangle with four sides of equal length.

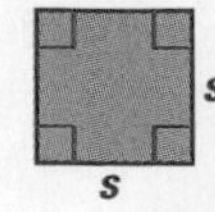

1. Write a formula for the perimeter of a square in terms of its side length s. $P = 4s$

2. Write a formula for the area of a square in terms of its side length s. $A = s^2$

3. The faces of a *cube* are all squares. Write a formula for the volume of a cube in terms of its edge length s. $V = s^3$

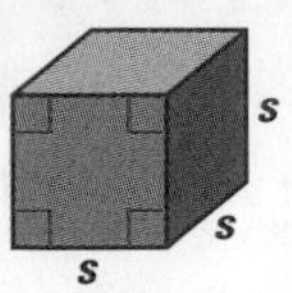

Find the perimeter and area of the figure. (You may need to break the figure into smaller parts.)

4. 48 yd; 135 yd^2

9 yd

15 yd

5. 12 mm; 9 mm^2

3 mm

3 mm

6. 12 in.; 6 in.^{2}

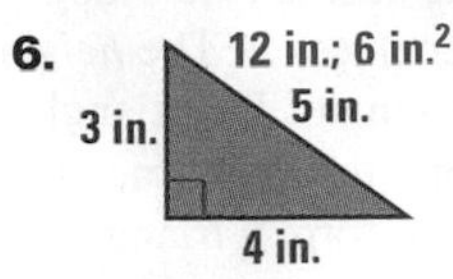

7. 48 ft; 84 ft^2

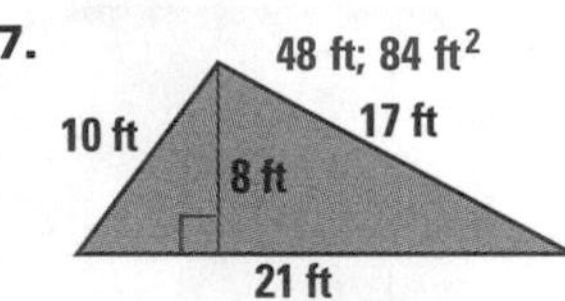

8. 60 cm; 210 cm^2

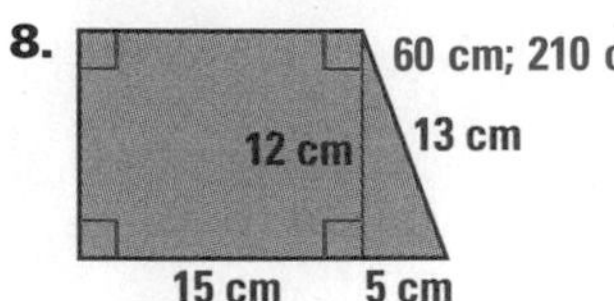

9. 22 m; 18 m^2

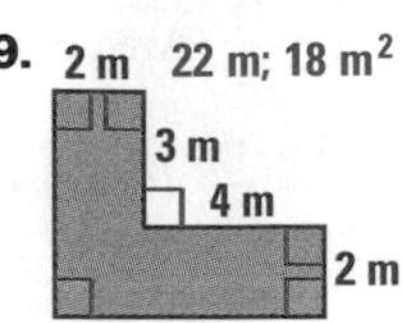

Sketch and label the figure described. Then find the perimeter and area of the figure.

10. A rectangle with a length of 20 millimeters and a width of 18 millimeters **76 mm; 360 mm^2; See margin.**

11. A square with sides of length 7.5 feet **30 ft; 56.25 ft^2; See margin.**

12. A right triangle with sides of length 10 meters, 24 meters, and 26 meters **60 m; 120 m^2; See margin.**

Find the volume of the box.

13. 64 m^3

4 m

4 m

4 m

14. 72 in.^{3}

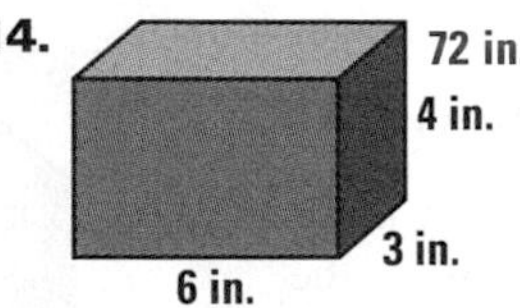

15. 40 cm^3

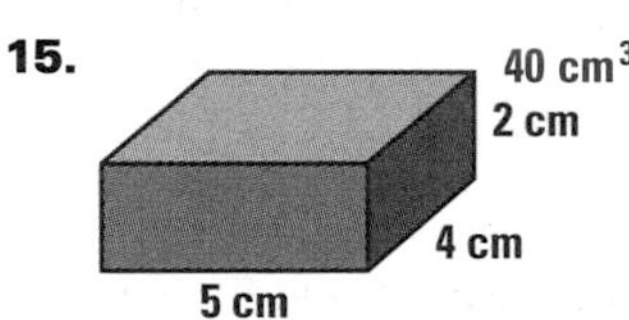

In Exercises 16–18, sketch and label the figure described. Then find the volume.

16. A cube with edges of length 2.5 centimeters **15.625 cm^3; See margin.**

17. A box with a length of 8 millimeters, a width of 8 millimeters, and a height of 6 millimeters **384 mm^3; See margin.**

18. A box with a length of 12 feet, a width of 4 feet, and a height of 3 feet **144 ft^3; See margin.**

19. A gallon is about 231 cubic inches. Could you pour a gallon of milk into a cube with an edge length of 6 inches without having any milk left over? Explain. **No; the cube has a volume of only 216 cubic inches.**

CONSTRUCTIONS

A *construction* is a geometric drawing made by using a compass and a straightedge (a ruler without numbers). A compass is an instrument used to draw circles or parts of circles (*arcs*) and to copy distances. Practice using your compass to construct circles.

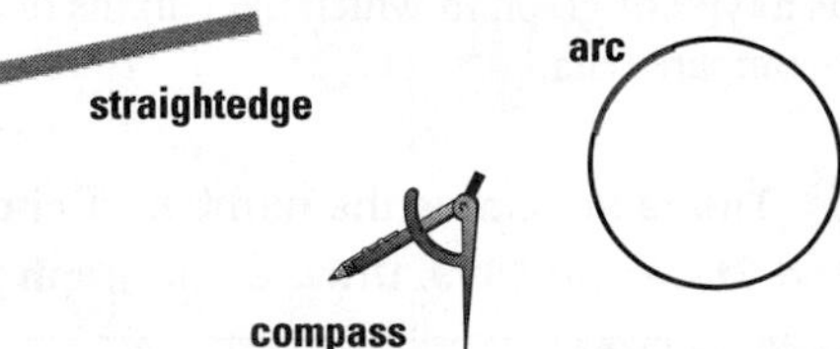

EXAMPLE

Use a compass and straightedge to draw and label an arc on a circle. The distance between the endpoints of the arc should equal the radius of the circle.

SOLUTION

1. Draw and label point *A*.
2. Open your compass. Place the compass point on point *A*. Use your compass to draw a circle with center *A*. (The distance between *A* and any point on the circle is called the *radius* of the circle.)
3. Choose a point *B* on the circle. Then, keeping the same compass setting used in Step 2, place the compass point on *B*. Draw an arc that intersects the circle at point *C*. Arc *BC* is the desired arc.

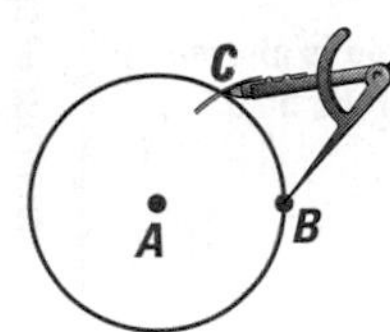

Practice

1. Repeat the construction in the example above. Use the same compass setting to construct arcs *CD*, *DE*, and so on around the circle. (You should end up at point *B*.) Connect points on the circle to draw a figure. How many sides does the figure have? What can you say about the side lengths of the figure?
6 sides; The sides are congruent; See margin.

In Exercises 2–4, use a compass and straightedge.

2. Complete the following steps. **See margin.**

1. Use a straightedge to draw a line segment.
2. Draw a point above the line segment. Label the point *P*.
3. Place your compass point on point *P*. Keeping your compass setting fixed, draw two arcs that cross the line segment in two different places. Label these points *A* and *B*.

3. What can you conclude about the distances between points *A* and *P* and between points *B* and *P* in your construction? **The distances are the same.**

4. Use your compass to determine whether the distance between *A* and *B* in your construction is *greater than*, *equal to*, or *less than* the distance between *A* and *P*. Describe the steps you take and explain your reasoning.

4. *Sample answer:* Greater than; using my same compass setting I anchored my compass at point *A*. Since my compass does not reach point *B* I know *AB* is greater than my compass setting which equals *AP*.

1.

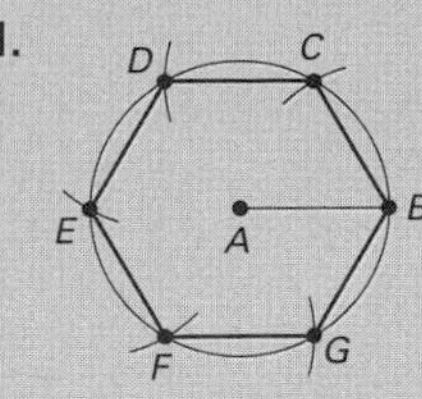

2.

California Standards and Assessment

CA Standard: Grade 5, MG 2.1

3.

Animal Speeds

Speed (mi/h)

70 60 50 40 30 20 10 0

Black mamba snake, Cheetah, Elephant, Giraffe, Greyhound

Animal

4.

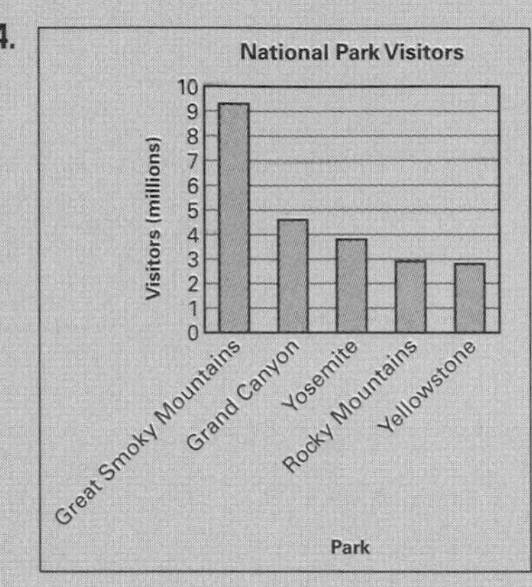

Statistics, Data Analysis, & Probability

READING AND DRAWING A BAR GRAPH

GRADE 5, SDP 1.2

SKILLS REVIEW

A *bar graph* is a type of graph in which the lengths of the bars are used to represent and compare data.

EXAMPLE **The table shows the number of endangered animal species in the United States for 1999. Draw a bar graph to display the data.**

Animal group	Mammals	Birds	Reptiles	Fishes	Insects
Number of species	61	74	14	69	28

SOLUTION

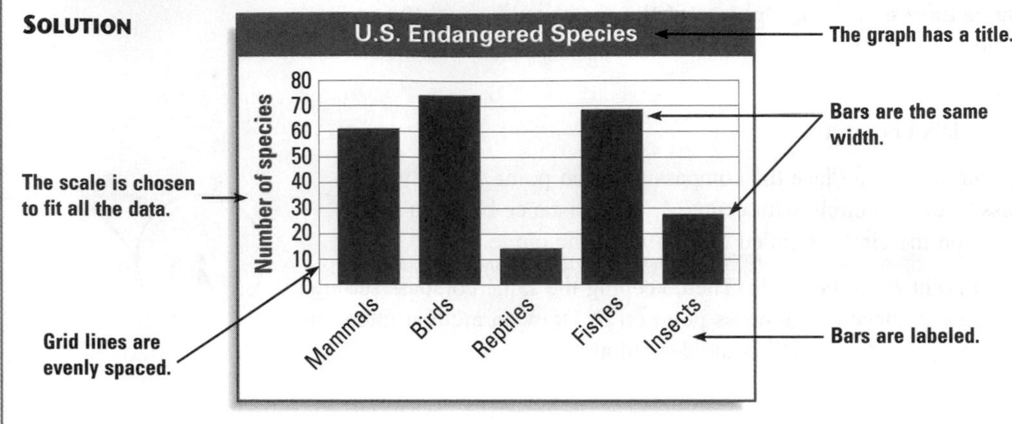

Practice

1. In the bar graph above, which animal group has the least number of endangered species? the most? **reptiles; birds**

2. Describe the scale you would use for a bar graph with the following data: 22, 11, 8, 41, 45, 58, 16. ***Sample answer:*** **0–60 increasing by tens**

In Exercises 3 and 4, draw a bar graph to display the data. **3, 4. See margin.**

3.

Animal	Speed (in mi/h)
Black mamba snake	20
Cheetah	70
Elephant	25
Giraffe	30
Greyhound	39

4.

National park	Visitors (in millions)
Great Smoky Mountains	9.3
Grand Canyon	4.6
Yosemite	3.8
Rocky Mountains	2.9
Yellowstone	2.8

California Standards and Assessment

CA Standard: Grade 5, SDP 1.2

Statistics, Data Analysis, & Probability

READING AND DRAWING A LINE GRAPH

GRADE 5, SDP 1.4

A *line graph* is a type of graph that uses points connected by line segments.

EXAMPLE **The table shows the number of passenger cars manufactured in the United States from 1970 to 1995. Draw a line graph of the data.**

Year	1970	1975	1980	1985	1990	1995
Millions of cars	6.6	6.7	6.4	8.2	6.1	6.4

SOLUTION

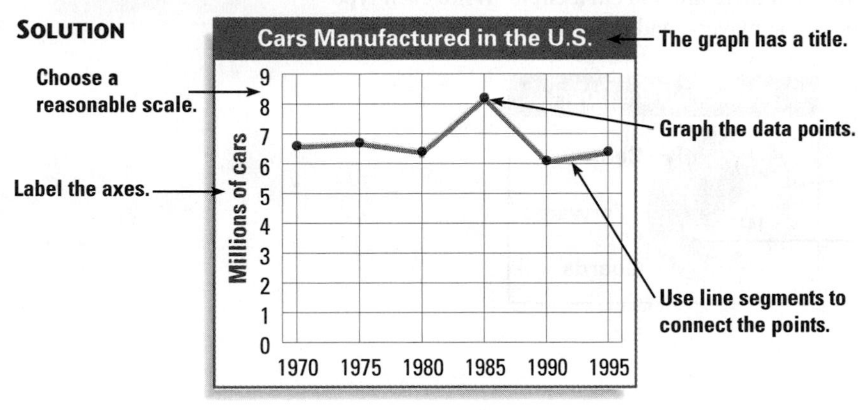

Practice

In Exercises 1 and 2, refer to the line graph in the example above.

1. Between 1970 and 1995, when was the greatest increase in the manufacture of passenger cars? the greatest decrease? **1980–1985; 1985–1990**
2. Describe the overall trend in the manufacture of cars from 1970 to 1995.

2. ***Sample answer:*** **The number of cars manufactured remained about the same from 1970 to 1995.**

In Exercises 3–5, refer to the line graph showing annual profits for a business.

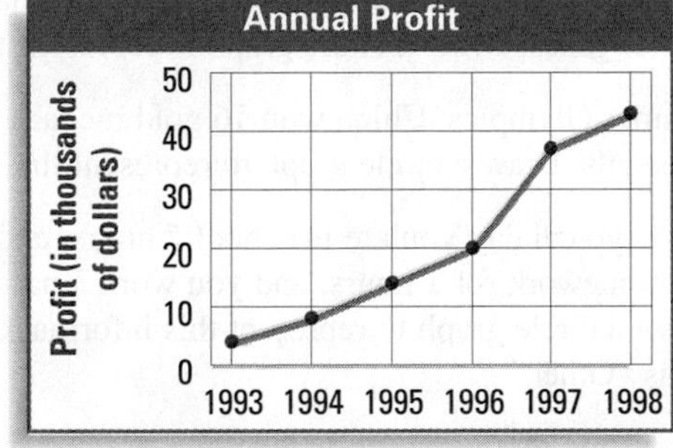

3. In what year were the profits over \$10,000 for the first time? **1995**
4. Did profits increase every year? How can you tell from the line graph?
5. Estimate the 1999 profit. ***Sample answer:*** **\$45,000**

4. Yes; ***Sample answer:*** **Each line segment slopes upward from left to right.**

6. The table shows the value of a car. Draw a line graph of the data. **See margin.**

Age (years)	0	1	2	3	4	5
Value	\$25,000	\$17,500	\$12,000	\$8500	\$6000	\$4000

SKILLS REVIEW

6. **Value of a Car**

Value (dollars): 24,000; 20,000; 16,000; 12,000; 8000; 4000; 0
Age (years): 0 1 2 3 4

California Standards and Assessment

CA Standard: Grade 5, SDP 1.4

3.

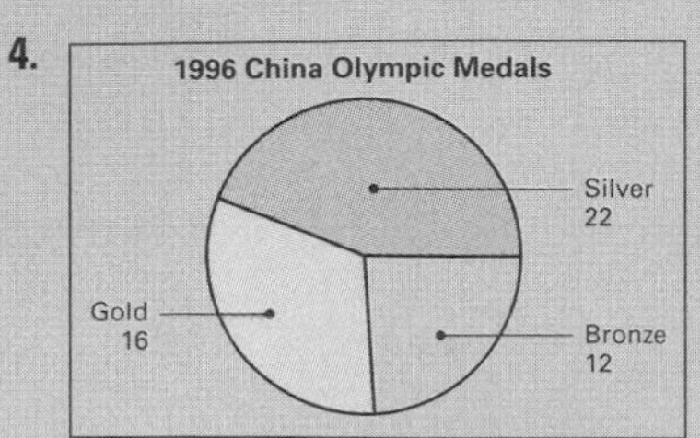

4.

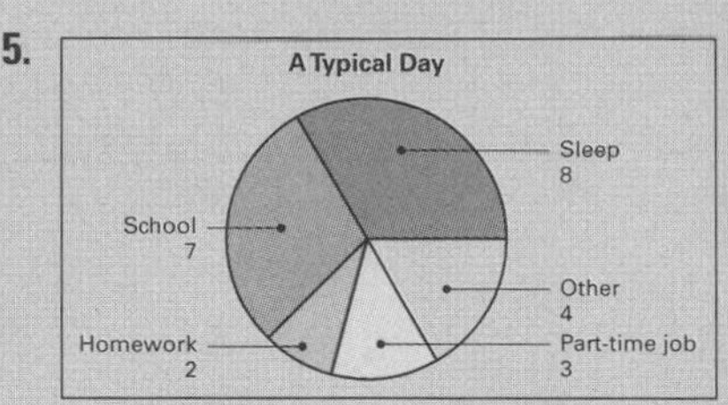

5.

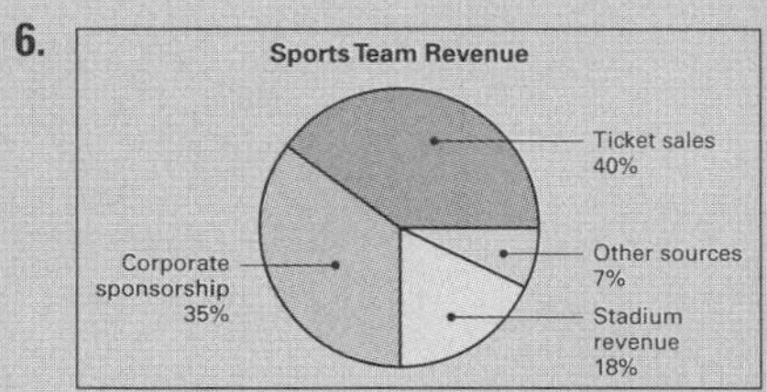

6.

Sports Team Revenue

Ticket sales 40%

Corporate sponsorship 35%

Other sources 7%

Stadium revenue 18%

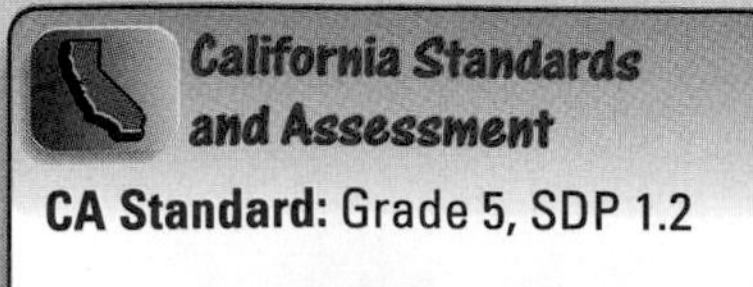

CA Standard: Grade 5, SDP 1.2

READING AND DRAWING A CIRCLE GRAPH

A *circle graph* is a graph that represents data as parts of a circle. Each wedge represents a fraction or percent of the circle. The entire circle represents the whole, so the percents (or fractions) assigned to the wedges must add up to 100% (or 1).

EXAMPLE **During a basketball game there are 10 players on a court; 2 centers, 4 forwards, and 4 guards. Draw a circle graph to show the data.**

SOLUTION To find the measure of the angle for each wedge in the circle graph, you can use the fact that there are 360° in a circle. Write each type of player as a fraction of all the players, and multiply this fraction by 360°.

$\frac{2}{10} \times 360° = 72°$

$\frac{4}{10} \times 360° = 144°$

$\frac{4}{10} \times 360° = 144°$

$72° + 144° + 144° = 360°$

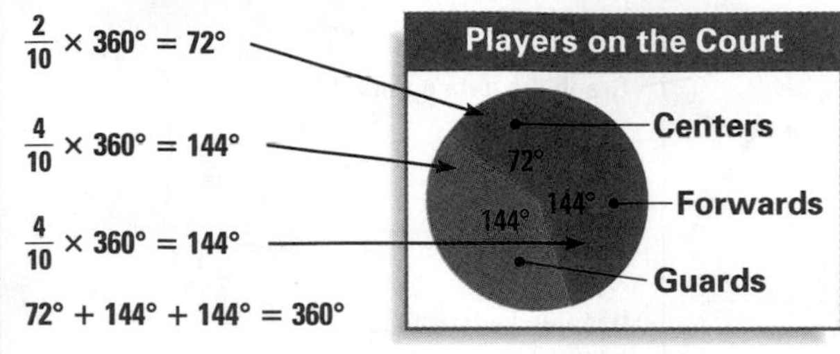

Practice

In Exercises 1 and 2, use the circle graph at the right. The graph shows the result of an election for class president.

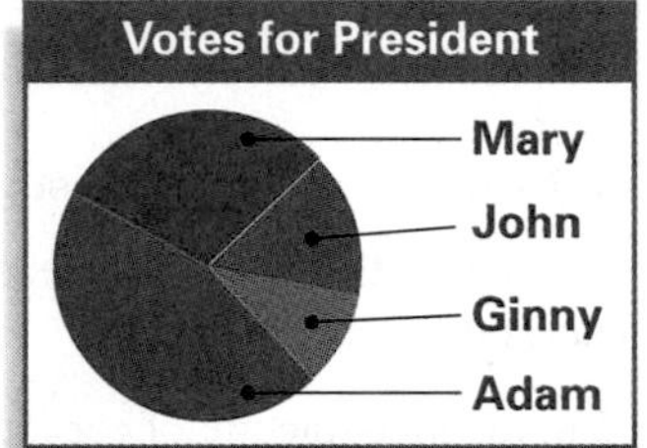

1. Who received the most votes? **Adam**
2. Did the person who received the most votes receive more than half of the votes? Explain your reasoning.

2. No; *Sample answer:* Adam's wedge of the circle graph is less than half of the circle so he received less than half of the votes.

3. Air is about 78% nitrogen and about 21% oxygen. The remaining percentage is made up of other gases. Draw a circle graph to represent the data. **3–6. See margin.**
4. In the 1996 Summer Olympics, China won 16 gold medals, 22 silver medals, and 12 bronze medals. Draw a circle graph to represent the data.
5. Suppose that on a typical day you are in school 7 hours, and you sleep for 8 hours. You do homework for 2 hours, and you work a part-time job for 3 hours. Draw a circle graph to represent this information. Mark any remaining time as "Other."
6. The sources of revenue of a local sports team are as follows: ticket sales, 40%; corporate sponsorship, 35%; stadium revenue, 18%; other sources, 7%. Draw a circle graph to represent the data.

READING AND DRAWING A LINE PLOT

A *line plot* is a number line diagram that shows the frequency of data. A line plot is useful because it lets you see how the data are distributed.

EXAMPLE **Use a line plot to organize the numbers of soccer goals scored by your team in the last 15 games. What do you observe?**

Game	1	2	3	4	5	6	7	8	9	10	11	12	13	14	15
Goals	6	3	6	3	5	7	4	6	5	3	4	4	5	1	0

SOLUTION To draw a line plot of soccer goals, first draw a number line that includes all the numbers in the data set. Place an x above the appropriate number.

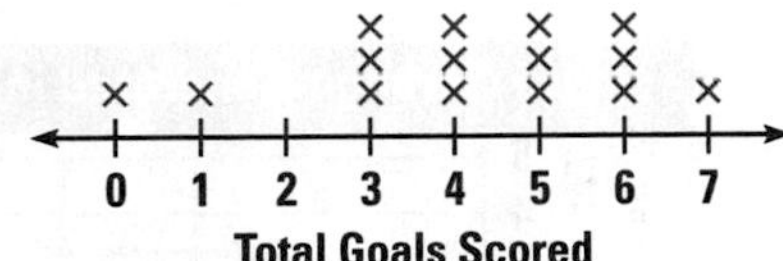

Total Goals Scored

ANSWER ▶ Your team scored between 0 and 7 goals in the last 15 games. Your team usually scores between 3 and 6 goals.

Practice

In Exercises 1–3, match the description with the line plot.

1. Includes 10 numbers **C**

2. Has gap at 6 **A**

3. 3 is most frequent response **B**

A.

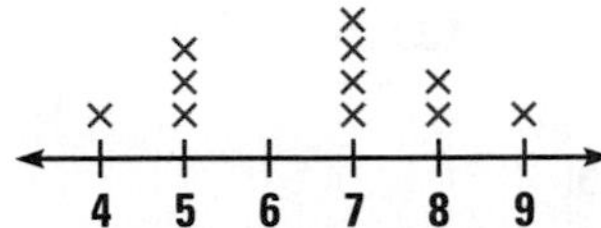

B.

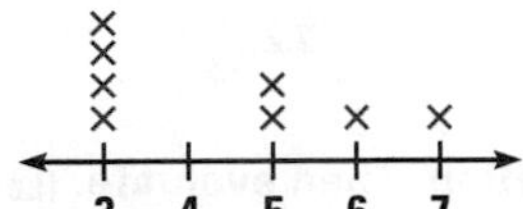

C.

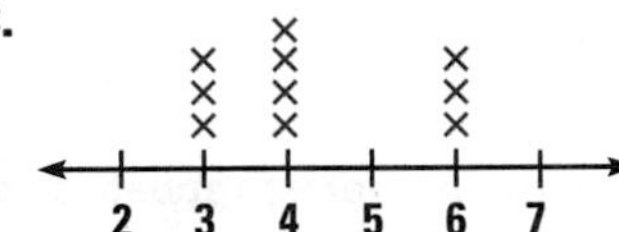

In Exercises 4–6, use the following information. You toss a pair of number cubes 40 times. Here are the totals: 10, 6, 12, 6, 6, 5, 11, 7, 5, 4, 8, 8, 6, 5, 11, 10, 5, 8, 9, 8, 8, 7, 6, 8, 4, 4, 5, 5, 6, 4, 6, 7, 6, 6, 11, 10, 5, 7, 2, 7.

4. Use a line plot to display the totals. **See margin.**

5. What is the difference between the greatest total and the least total? **10**

6. Which total appeared most frequently? **6**

In Exercises 7 and 8, use the following information. In a survey, 25 people were asked how many television sets their family owned. Their responses were: 3, 1, 2, 3, 0, 1, 5, 2, 2, 2, 3, 1, 0, 1, 1, 1, 1, 2, 1, 3, 1, 0, 2, 2, 1.

7. Use a line plot to display the results. **See margin.**

8. Describe how the data are distributed. ***Sample answer:*** **The people questioned own 0–5 television sets, and most families own 1 or 2 televisions.**

4.

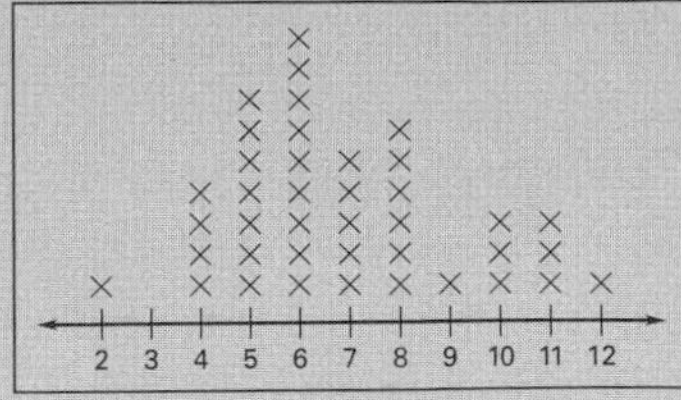

Number Cube Totals

7.

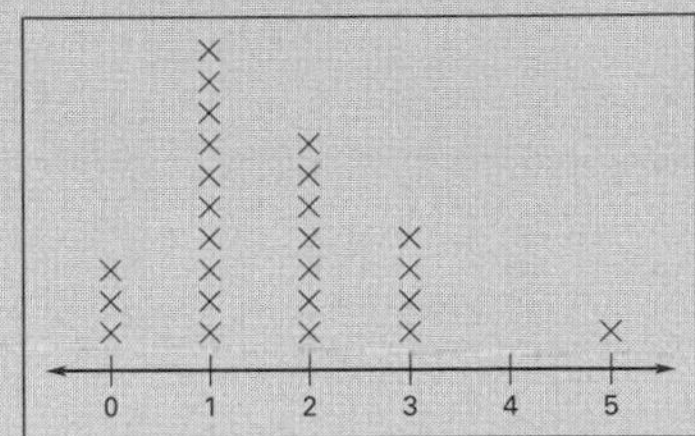

Number of Television Sets

California Standards and Assessment

CA Standard: Grade 5, SDP 1.2

6. 130; The product of 13 and 10 is 130.

7. 12; The difference of 42 and 30 is 12.

8. 25; The sum of 16 and 9 is 25.

9. 30; The quotient of 450 and 15 is 30.

Extra Practice

EXTRA PRACTICE

Chapter 1

In Exercises 1–3, use the table. It shows the enrollments in the social studies classes at a high school. **(Lesson 1.1)**

Class Enrollments (per year)			
Class	**1998**	**1999**	**2000**
Psychology	70	62	72
World History	82	80	55
U.S. History	98	93	88

1. In what year(s) was the total enrollment in social studies classes greater than 220? **1998, 1999**

2. Which class had the highest enrollment in each year? **U.S. History**

3. Describe any pattern in enrollments in World History classes over the three years. ***Sample answer*: The enrollment in World History declined each year over the three-year period.**

In Exercises 4 and 5, use the line graph. It shows the amount of garbage generated in the U.S. **(Lesson 1.1)**

Garbage Generated in the U.S.

Pounds per person per day

5
4
3
2
1
0

1960 1965 1970 1975 1980 1985 1990

4. Did the number of pounds of garbage per person per day *increase* or *decrease* over the period shown in the graph? **increase**

5. How did the number of pounds of garbage per person change from 1970 to 1975? ***Sample answer*: It remained the same.**

Evaluate the expression. Then write the result in words. **(Lesson 1.2)** **6–9. See margin.**

6. 13×10 **7.** $42 - 30$ **8.** $16 + 9$ **9.** $450 \div 15$

Evaluate the variable expression when $n = 6$. **(Lesson 1.2)**

10. $11n$ **66** **11.** $9 + n$ **15** **12.** $\frac{n}{3}$ **2** **13.** $25 - n$ **19**

Rewrite the power as repeated multiplication. Then evaluate. **(Lesson 1.3)**

14. 3^4 **$3 \cdot 3 \cdot 3 \cdot 3$; 81** **15.** 8^2 **$8 \cdot 8$; 64** **16.** 2^5 **$2 \cdot 2 \cdot 2 \cdot 2 \cdot 2$; 32** **17.** 1^6 **$1 \cdot 1 \cdot 1 \cdot 1 \cdot 1 \cdot 1$; 1**

In Exercises 18–21, evaluate the expression when $k = 2$. **(Lesson 1.3)**

18. k^4 **16** **19.** $k^3 + 1$ **9** **20.** $(6 - k)^2$ **16** **21.** $(k + 3)^2$ **25**

22. A box in the shape of a cube measures 20 inches by 20 inches by 20 inches. Find the area of the top of the box and the volume of the box. **(Lesson 1.3)** **400 in.^{2}; 8000 in.^{3}**

Evaluate the expression. **(Lesson 1.4)**

23. $3 + 14 \div 7$ **5** **24.** $15 + 3 \times 5$ **30** **25.** $3^2 - 10 \div 5$ **7** **26.** $18 \div (2 \cdot 9) \cdot 12$ **12**

27. $26 - (4 \cdot 4) + 8$ **18** **28.** $2[12 - (4 + 2) \div 3]$ **20** **29.** $25 - 3^2 + 4 \cdot 5$ **36** **30.** $(8 + 2) \div 5 \cdot 10$ **20**

Evaluate the expression when $c = 3$ and $d = 5$. **(Lesson 1.4)**

31. $4c + 2d - 1$ **21** **32.** $3(d - c) + 10$ **16** **33.** $cd - 2$ **13** **34.** $c^2 + d^2$ **34**

In Exercises 35–37, find the perimeter and area of the figure. (Lesson 1.5)

35. 20 ft; 18 ft^2

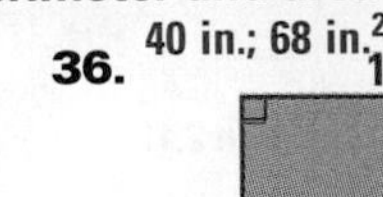
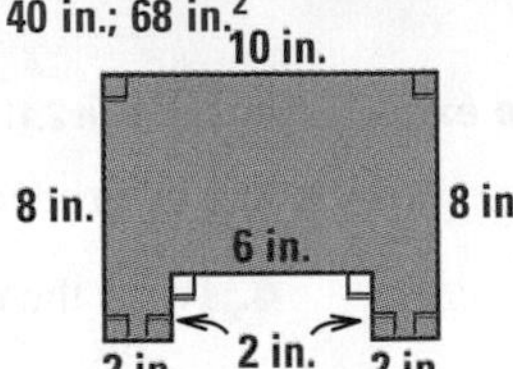

36. 40 in.; 68 in.^{2}

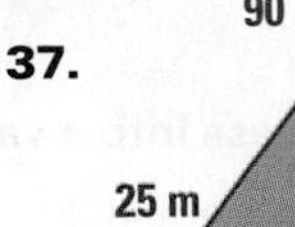
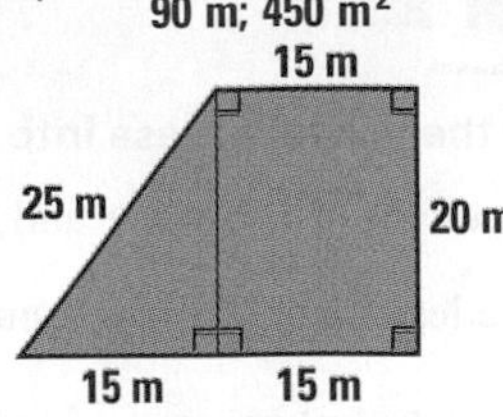

37. 90 m; 450 m^2

15 m, 25 m, 20 m, 15 m, 15 m

38. Use the formula $d = r \cdot t$. Find the speed at which you traveled if you traveled 400 miles in 8 hours. **(Lesson 1.5) 50 mi/h**

39. The length of a side of a square is 5 centimeters. What are the perimeter and area of the square? **(Lesson 1.5) 20 cm; 25 cm^2**

Identify the irrelevant information. Describe additional information, if any, needed to solve the problem. Solve the problem, if possible. (Lesson 1.6)

40. A car averages 26 miles per gallon of gas. The car's gas tank holds 18 gallons. How far can the car be driven before the tank is refilled if the car is driven at a speed of 52 miles per hour? **The car is driven at a speed of 52 mi/h; 468 mi**

41. A one year membership in a health club costs \$335 for an individual and \$750 for a family. How much can the Henderson family save by buying a one year family membership rather than individual single memberships? **How many people are in the Henderson family?**

42. A study group divides a list of topics equally among themselves. Each of the twelve students chooses three topics and agrees to write a two page report on each topic. How many pages must each student write? **A study group divides a list of topics equally among themselves and the study group has 12 students; 6 pages**

Describe the pattern. List the next three numbers you expect to find in the sequence. (Lesson 1.6)

43. 90, 82, 74, 66, ?, ?, ? **subtract 8; 58, 50, 42**

44. 20, 23, 27, 32, ?, ?, ? **add 3, then 4, then 5, etc.; 38, 45, 53**

45. 4, 16, 64, 256, ?, ?, ? **multiply by 4; 1024, 4096, 16,384**

46. 500, 50, 5, 0.5, ?, ?, ? **divide by 10; 0.05, 0.005, 0.0005**

In Exercises 47–50, name the property illustrated. (Lesson 1.7)

47. $27 + (35 + 19) = (27 + 35) + 19$ **associative property of addition**

48. $4(7)(5) = 4(5)(7)$ **commutative property of multiplication**

49. $(5 + 7)34 = (7 + 5)34$ **commutative property of addition**

50. $(15 \cdot 12) \cdot 9 = 15 \cdot (12 \cdot 9)$ **associative property of multiplication**

51. Give a counterexample to show that subtraction is not commutative. **(Lesson 1.7)** ***Sample answer:*** **$3 - 2 = 1$ but $2 - 3 = -1$**

52. Use mental math to evaluate $52 + 16 + 48 + 84$. Justify each step. **(Lesson 1.7) 200; See margin.**

Use the distributive property to write an equivalent numerical expression. Then show that the two expressions have the same value. (Lesson 1.8) 53–56. See margin.

53. $17(8 + 11)$ **54.** $42(7) + 42(91)$ **55.** $8(24 - 9)$ **56.** $9(3 + 12 + 5)$

Use the distributive property to write an equivalent variable expression. Then simplify when possible. (Lesson 1.8)

57. $3(g + 2)$ **$3(g) + 3(2) = 3g + 6$**

58. $19(k) + 19(2)$ **$19(k + 2)$**

59. $2(n - 21)$ **$2(n) - 2(21) = 2n - 42$**

60. $62(8) - 62(z)$ **$62(8 - z)$**

61. $18(x + y)$ **$18(x) + 18(y) = 18x + 18y$**

62. $(15 - 8)t$ **$(15)t - (8)t = 7t$**

63. $2(4v + 1)$ **$2(4v) + 2(1) = 8v + 2$**

64. $w(y - z)$ **$w(y) - w(z) = wy - wz$**

EXTRA PRACTICE

52. ***Sample answers:***
$52 + 16 + 48 + 84$
$= 52 + 48 + 16 + 84$
(Commutative prop. of addition)
$= (52 + 48) + (16 + 84)$
(Associative prop. of addition)
$= 100 + 100$ **(Add.)**
$= 200$ **(Add.)**

53. $17(8) + 17(11)$; $17(19) = 323 = 136 + 187$

54. $42(7 + 91)$; $294 + 3822 = 4116 = 42(98)$

55. $8(24) - 8(9)$; $8(15) = 120 = 192 - 72$

56. $9(3) + 9(12) + 9(5)$; $9(20) = 180 = 27 + 108 + 45$

9. *Sample answer:* The quotient of 42 and a number

10. *Sample answer:* The sum of a number and 35

11. *Sample answer:* Three less than 18 times a number

12. *Sample answer:* Fifteen times the difference of a number and 9

33. What number plus 2 equals 10?; 8

34. Six times what number equals 54?; 9

35. What number minus 15 equals 14?; 29

36. What number divided by 12 equals 4?; 48

37. Seventy-five divided by what number equals 25?; 3

38. Fourteen plus what number equals 20?; 6

39. What number minus 10 equals 40?; 50

40. Six times what number equals 78?; 13

45. $\frac{x}{15} = 225$

EXTRA PRACTICE

Chapter 2

Translate the verbal phrase into a variable expression. (Lesson 2.1)

1. The quotient of a number and 20 $\frac{x}{20}$

2. The product of a number and 17 $x \cdot 17$ or $17x$

3. Twelve less than 15 times a number $15x - 12$

4. Twice the difference of 9 and a number $2(9 - x)$

Write the verbal phrase as a variable expression. Tell what the variable represents. (Lesson 2.1)

5. Two seconds more than the winning time $x + 2$; the winning time

6. Eight points lower than your last score $x - 8$; your last score

7. Three times your age plus 1 year $3x + 1$; your age

8. Ten dollars more than twice your savings $2x + 10$; your savings

Write the variable expression as a word phrase. (Lesson 2.1) 9–12. See margin.

9. $\frac{42}{b}$

10. $z + 35$

11. $18k - 3$

12. $15(n - 9)$

Tell whether the expression can be simplified. Explain. (Lesson 2.2)

13. $2m + 2$ no; no like terms

14. $k^2 + 5k^3$ no; no like terms

15. $4a + 4$ no; no like terms

16. $6 + 10y + 9$ yes; $6 + 10y + 9 = 15 + 10y$

Simplify the expression by combining like terms. (Lesson 2.2)

17. $4x + x$ $5x$

18. $5b + 7b + 1$ $12b + 1$

19. $3x + 7y + 4x$ $7x + 7y$

20. $2z^2 - z^2$ z^2

21. $2z + 6z + 9$ $8z + 9$

22. $2a + 7b + 9a$ $11a + 7b$

23. $4(a + 5) + 6a$ $10a + 20$

24. $3s + 3r + s$ $4s + 3r$

25. $2p + 5 + 8 + p$ $3p + 13$

26. $n^2 + n + 5n$ $n^2 + 6n$

27. $5(x + 3) + x + 9$ $6x + 24$

28. $3(a - b) + 7b$ $3a + 4b$

Decide whether the given values of *x* are solutions of the equation. (Lesson 2.3)

29. $x - 7 = 4$; $x = 10, 11, 12$ no; yes; no

30. $x + 5 = 10$, $x = 2, 3, 4$ no; no; no

31. $6x + 1 = 25$; $x = 2, 3, 4$ no; no; yes

32. $12 - 3x = 3$; $x = 1, 2, 3$ no; no; yes

Write the equation as a question. Then solve the equation. (Lesson 2.3) 33–40. See margin.

33. $x + 2 = 10$

34. $6y = 54$

35. $h - 15 = 14$

36. $\frac{n}{12} = 4$

37. $75 \div k = 25$

38. $14 + z = 20$

39. $m - 10 = 40$

40. $6d = 78$

Match the sentence with the equation. (Lesson 2.4)

A. $18 = n + 6$

B. $18 - n = 6$

C. $\frac{n}{6} = 18$

D. $6n = 18$

41. The difference of 18 and *n* is 6. B

42. The quotient of *n* and 6 is 18. C

43. The product of *n* and 6 is 18. D

44. 18 is the sum of *n* and 6. A

Write an equation that represents the verbal sentence. (Lesson 2.4)

45. The quotient of a number and 15 is 225. See margin.

46. The sum of 19 and a number is 133. $19 + x = 133$

47. Five less than 4 times a number is 11. $4x - 5 = 11$

48. The product of 8 and twice a number is 3. $8(2x) = 3$

Use the subtraction property of equality to solve the equation. Then check your solution. (Lesson 2.5)

49. $x + 9 = 47$ **38**
50. $n + 25 = 55$ **30**
51. $24 = y + 16$ **8**
52. $m + 23 = 43$ **20**
53. $17 + z = 94$ **77**
54. $410 = s + 208$ **202**
55. $6.52 = w + 3.08$ **3.44**
56. $t + 3.7 = 11.2$ **7.5**

Use the addition property of equality to solve the equation. Then check your solution. (Lesson 2.5)

57. $m - 5 = 38$ **43**
58. $20 = j - 11$ **31**
59. $d - 20 = 100$ **120**
60. $b - 0.5 = 12.5$ **13**
61. $x - 12.5 = 17$ **29.5**
62. $1.6 = z - 0.2$ **1.8**
63. $f - 3.8 = 5.4$ **9.2**
64. $6.52 = w - 3.08$ **9.6**

Use the division property of equality to solve the equation. Then check your solution. (Lesson 2.6)

65. $3x = 15$ **5**
66. $10y = 120$ **12**
67. $81 = 9z$ **9**
68. $7a = 42$ **6**
69. $6p = 13.2$ **2.2**
70. $9q = 23.4$ **2.6**
71. $5d = 51.5$ **10.3**
72. $12n = 14.4$ **1.2**

Use the multiplication property of equality to solve the equation. Then check your solution. (Lesson 2.6)

73. $\frac{b}{9} = 8$ **72**
74. $5 = \frac{c}{3}$ **15**
75. $\frac{d}{7} = 4$ **28**
76. $\frac{m}{5} = 10$ **50**
77. $\frac{n}{1.6} = 8$ **12.8**
78. $\frac{k}{16} = 4.5$ **72**
79. $\frac{y}{15} = 3.2$ **48**
80. $\frac{v}{3.2} = 3$ **9.6**

Write a verbal model and assign labels to each part. (Lesson 2.7) **81, 82. See margin.**

81. You have 120 minutes to complete 48 test questions. Explain how to find the number of minutes you should plan to spend on each question.

82. You have hiked 1.9 miles of a 2.7 mile hike. Explain how to find the number of miles you have left to hike.

In Exercises 83–85, use the following information. A CD player costs $135 including tax. You save $15 per week toward the purchase of the CD player. (Lesson 2.7)

83. Write a verbal model that relates the amount of money you save per week to the number of weeks it takes to save $135. Assign labels to each part of the verbal model. **See margin.**

84. Write and solve an algebraic model using the verbal model and labels from Exercise 83. **$15x = 135$; 9 weeks**

85. Check your solution from Exercise 84 for reasonableness. **15(9) = 135, the answer is reasonable.**

Solve the inequality. Justify each step of the solution. (Lesson 2.8) **86–97. See margin.**

86. $x + 5 < 18$
87. $y - 3 \geq 12$
88. $4z < 16$
89. $15 > c + 3$
90. $a - 7 > 10$
91. $\frac{k}{5} \leq 10$
92. $12 \geq 10 + f$
93. $8.1d \leq 24.3$
94. $19 < b - 4$
95. $32 \leq 8t$
96. $\frac{n}{2} > 200$
97. $\frac{w}{3.2} < 6.4$

EXTRA PRACTICE

81–83. See Additional Answers beginning on page AA1.

86. $x < 13$; Subtract 5 from both sides.
87. $y \geq 15$; Add 3 to both sides.
88. $z < 4$; Divide both sides by 4.
89. $12 > c$; Subtract 3 from both sides.
90. $a > 17$; Add 7 to both sides.
91. $k \leq 50$; Multiply both sides by 5.
92. $2 \geq f$; Subtract 10 from both sides.
93. $d \leq 3$; Divide both sides by 8.1.
94. $23 < b$; Add 4 to both sides.
95. $4 \leq t$; Divide both sides by 8.
96. $n > 400$; Multiply both sides by 2.
97. $w < 20.48$; Multiply both sides by 3.2.

Chapter 3

Complete each statement using $<$ or $>$. (Lesson 3.1)

1. -2 ? 0 $<$ **2.** -2 ? -4 $>$ **3.** 3 ? -4 $>$

4. $|-2|$? -3 $>$ **5.** $|-5|$? $|-4|$ $>$ **6.** 0 ? $|-5|$ $<$

Order the integers from least to greatest. (Lesson 3.1)

7. $-6, 5, 3, -2, 0, -1$ **−6, −2, −1, 0, 3, 5**

8. $-11, 7, 0, 6, -3, -5$ **−11, −5, −3, 0, 6, 7**

9. $-10, 7, -13, 4, -2, 5$ **−13, −10, −2, 4, 5, 7**

10. $6, -9, -7, 7, 10, -3$ **−9, −7, −3, 6, 7, 10**

11. $-7, -3, 4, 9, -2, -4$ **−7, −4, −3, −2, 4, 9**

12. $13, -11, -10, -8, 2, -4$ **−11, −10, −8, −4, 2, 13**

In Exercises 13–20, use a number line to find the sum. (Lesson 3.2)

13. $3 + 10$ **13** **14.** $-5 + (-4)$ **−9** **15.** $-11 + (-11)$ **−22** **16.** $-5 + 5$ **0**

17. $12 + (-18)$ **−6** **18.** $-19 + 12$ **−7** **19.** $22 + (-22)$ **0** **20.** $12 + 0$ **12**

21. At 6 A.M., the temperature is -4°F. By 3 P.M., it has increased by 18°F. What is the temperature at 3 P.M.? (Lesson 3.2) **14°F**

Find the sum. (Lesson 3.3)

22. $5 + (-8)$ **−3** **23.** $(-2) + (-9)$ **−11** **24.** $-7 + (-8)$ **−15**

25. $-16 + 14 + (-3)$ **−5** **26.** $-10 + 10 + (-2)$ **−2** **27.** $-10 + 6 + (-9)$ **−13**

28. $-10 + (-7) + (-15)$ **−32** **29.** $6 + (-6) + (-4)$ **−4** **30.** $10 + (-2) + 12$ **20**

Simplify the expression. Then evaluate the expression when $x = 2$. (Lesson 3.3)

31. $-7x + 15 + 3x$ **$-4x + 15$; 7** **32.** $4x + 9x + 8x$ **$21x$; 42** **33.** $10x + 5x + (-7x)$ **$8x$; 16**

34. $-6x + 11x + (-2x)$ **$3x$; 6** **35.** $-12x + (-11) + 2x + 2$ **$-10x - 9$; −29** **36.** $-3x + 8 + 2x + (-3)$ **$-x + 5$; 3**

Find the difference. (Lesson 3.4)

37. $3 - 7$ **−4** **38.** $-4 - (-3)$ **−1** **39.** $6 - (-8)$ **14** **40.** $10 - (-2)$ **12**

41. $-23 - 2$ **−25** **42.** $12 - (-8)$ **20** **43.** $14 - (-3)$ **17** **44.** $16 - (-16)$ **32**

Evaluate the expression. (Lesson 3.4)

45. $14 - 3 - 1$ **10** **46.** $-7 + 9 - 3$ **−1** **47.** $-8 - 6 - (-12)$ **−2** **48.** $20 - (-3) - 7$ **16**

Simplify the expression. Then evaluate the expression when $x = 2$. (Lesson 3.4)

49. $6x - 3 - 2x$ **$4x - 3$; 5** **50.** $11x + (-5x) - 3x$ **$3x$; 6** **51.** $9x - (-10x) + 3x$ **$22x$; 44** **52.** $-13x + 15x - 6$ **$2x - 6$; −2**

Find the product. (Lesson 3.5)

53. $6(-8)$ **−48** **54.** $-8(12)$ **−96** **55.** $-3(-4)$ **12** **56.** $-15(3)$ **−45**

57. $10(-7)$ **−70** **58.** $7(-6)$ **−42** **59.** $-3(-8)$ **24** **60.** $0(-20)$ **0**

Evaluate the expression when $a = -3$. (Lesson 3.5)

61. a^2 **9** **62.** $-a^4$ **−81** **63.** $a^2 - a$ **12** **64.** $a^2 - a^3$ **36**

Find the quotient. If the quotient is undefined, explain why. (Lesson 3.6)

65. $\frac{96}{3}$ **32** **66.** $\frac{180}{4}$ **45** **67.** $\frac{-512}{16}$ **−32** **68.** $-208 \div (-8)$ **26**

69. $288 \div (-16)$ **−18** **70.** $\frac{0}{-19}$ **0** **71.** $\frac{-2 \cdot 8}{0}$ **undefined; division by zero is undefined.** **72.** $-1008 \div 14$ **−72**

Evaluate the expression. Follow the order of operations. (Lesson 3.6)

73. $24 - 16 \div 2$ **16** **74.** $\frac{20 - 2 \cdot 3}{-7}$ **−2** **75.** $3(-6) - 5$ **−23** **76.** $-5 - (-2)^2 \div 2$ **−7**

Find the average of the numbers. (Lesson 3.6)

77. −13, 19, 9, −13, −7 **−1** **78.** 11, −13, −9, −7, 3, 3 **−2** **79.** −7, 19, −3, 12, 5, −4, 6 **4**

In Exercises 80–91, solve the equation. Check your solution. (Lesson 3.7)

80. $a + 5 = 2$ **−3** **81.** $y - 6 = -3$ **3** **82.** $x - 5 = 12$ **17** **83.** $-20 = b - 8$ **−12**

84. $c + 5 = -4$ **−9** **85.** $z - 4 = -12$ **−8** **86.** $-36 = 9d$ **−4** **87.** $-5f = -75$ **15**

88. $\frac{m}{-3} = -15$ **45** **89.** $-24 = -8n$ **3** **90.** $8p = -64$ **−8** **91.** $\frac{x}{2} = -14$ **−28**

92. Your class is selling tickets to a dance for $3 each. You spend $42 on decorations and $86 on refreshments. Write an equation for the profit your class will make. Then find the profit if 150 tickets are sold. **(Lesson 3.7)** ***P* = 3*x* − 128; $322**

Plot all the points in the same coordinate plane. Name the quadrant (if any) that contains each point. (Lesson 3.8) **93–100. See margin.**

93. $A(2, 1)$ **Quadrant 1** **94.** $B(-2, 3)$ **Quadrant 2** **95.** $C(0, 3)$ **None** **96.** $D(-1, -5)$ **Quadrant 3**

97. $E(-3, -2)$ **Quadrant 3** **98.** $F(0, 7)$ **None** **99.** $G(4, -4)$ **Quadrant 4** **100.** $H(-6, 1)$ **Quadrant 2**

Make a table of values that shows four solutions of the equation. Then plot the solutions. Draw a line through the points to represent all the solutions of the equation. (Lesson 3.8) **101–103. See margin.**

101. $y = x + 1$ **102.** $y = -2x - 1$ **103.** $x + y = 5$

In Exercises 104–106, use the following information. The table shows the number of swimmers at a town beach on each of six days and the daily high temperature for the day. **(Lesson 3.9)**

Daily high temperature (°F)	84	88	80	81	91	94
Number of swimmers	120	135	115	120	133	150

104. Use the data to make a scatter plot. Put highest daily temperature on the horizontal axis and the number of swimmers on the vertical axis. **See margin.**

105. Use your scatter plot to describe the correlation shown by the data. Draw a line that shows the trend in the data. **As the daily high temperature increases, the number of swimmers also increases; *Sample answer;* See margin.**

106. Use the line to predict the number of swimmers on a day when the high temperature is 100°F. ***Sample answer:* 160 swimmers**

93–100.

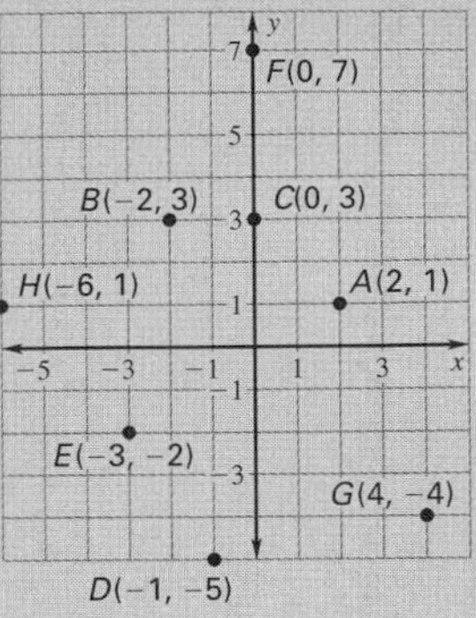

101. *Sample answer:*

x	−1	0	1	2
y	0	1	2	3

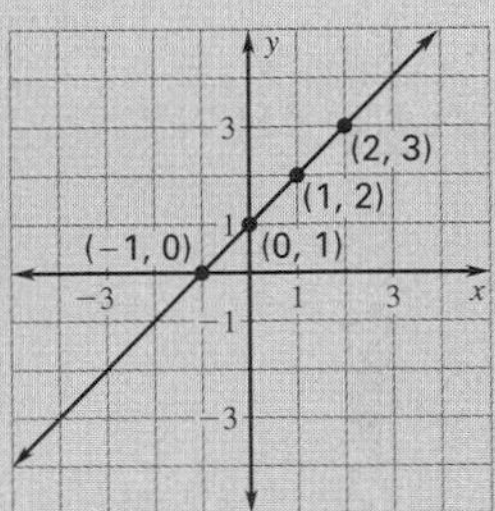

102. *Sample answer:*

x	−2	−1	0	1
y	3	1	−1	−3

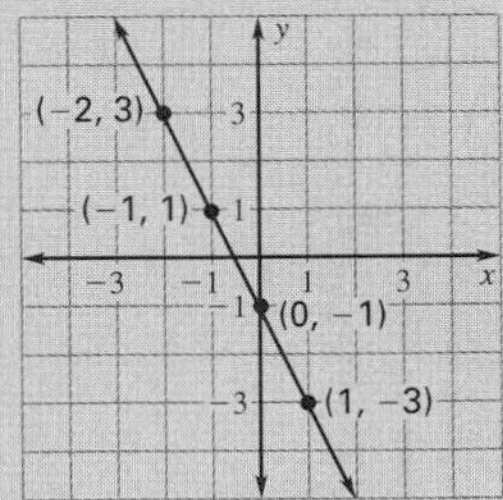

103. *Sample answer:*

x	−1	0	1	2
y	6	5	4	3

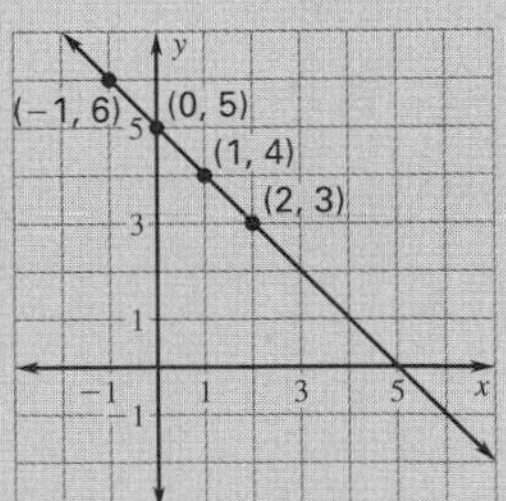

104–105. See Additional Answers beginning on page AA1.

21. See Additional Answers beginning on page AA1.

Chapter 4

Solve the equation. Then check your solution. (Lesson 4.1)

1. $9x - 3 = 78$ **9**

2. $12p + 8 = 44$ **3**

3. $52 = 7k - 4$ **8**

4. $3m + 4 = 76$ **24**

5. $13 = 5n - 47$ **12**

6. $7x - 4 = 101$ **15**

7. $-2 = 3x + 1$ **−1**

8. $\frac{m}{2} + 4 = 10$ **12**

9. $\frac{x}{3} - 4 = -7$ **−9**

Write and solve an equation to answer the question. (Lesson 4.1)

10. You have already read 85 pages of a 245 page novel. You plan to read 20 pages per day. How many days will it take you to finish the novel? **$20x + 85 = 245$; 8 days**

11. Your neighbors are paying you to organize their child's birthday party. You plan to charge a flat fee of \$25 plus \$2.00 per child. How many children can the parents have at the party if they have budgeted \$75? **$75 = 25 + 2.00x$; 25 children**

In Exercises 12–20, solve the equation. Then check your solution. (Lesson 4.2)

12. $4x + 5x = 18$ **2**

13. $3y + 2y - y = 20$ **5**

14. $32 = 7a - 2a + 3a$ **4**

15. $5z - 4z - 8 = 2$ **10**

16. $6b - 2b + 12 = -4$ **−4**

17. $7n - n + 6 = 36$ **5**

18. $12m - 3m + 6 = 42$ **4**

19. $10x - 4x - 8 = 4$ **2**

20. $11m - 5m - 6 = 60$ **11**

21. At the end of the year, your club plans to use the \$465 left in its treasury for a field trip to a museum. Admission to the museum is \$5 per person and lunch is \$3 per person. Renting a bus will cost \$225. Write a verbal model and assign labels to find the number of members you can afford to send. Then write and solve an algebraic model. **(Lesson 4.2)** **See margin.**

In Exercises 22–29, solve the equation. Then check your solution. (Lesson 4.3)

22. $-3m - 4 = 2$ **−2**

23. $-6 - 18y = 30$ **−2**

24. $-13t + 10 = -16$ **2**

25. $-4t + 6 = -10$ **4**

26. $11 - 2x = 29$ **−9**

27. $-3z + 9 = 24$ **−5**

28. $-63 = 12 - 5k$ **15**

29. $n - 7n + 3 = 51$ **−8**

30. Your parents agree to lend you the money to buy a \$225 bicycle. You have \$45 saved and plan to pay your parents the remaining amount at the rate of \$5 per week. Write and solve an equation to find the number of weeks it will take to repay the loan. **(Lesson 4.3)** **$5x + 45 = 225$; 36 weeks**

In Exercises 31–39, solve the equation. Then check your solution. (Lesson 4.4)

31. $3y + 2(y - 1) = 8$ **2**

32. $6 = 3z + 3(z - 6)$ **4**

33. $3(2 - s) = -9$ **5**

34. $16(q + 1) + 6q = -28$ **−2**

35. $9(r - 4) + 18 = 0$ **2**

36. $12(x - 4) + 6x = 6$ **3**

37. $2(x + 7) = -26$ **−20**

38. $7(y - 11) = 63$ **20**

39. $54 = 3(p + 2)$ **16**

40. Two friends shared the driving on a 460 mile trip. Each driver drove for 4 hours. The first driver's speed was 5 miles per hour faster than the second driver's speed. What were the two drivers' speeds? **(Lesson 4.4)** **55 mi/h, 60 mi/h**

In Exercises 41–49, solve the equation. Then check your solution. **(Lesson 4.5)**

41. $6x + 10 = 4x$ **−5** **42.** $8y + 12 = 4y - 4$ **−4** **43.** $-3z + 2 = -7z - 22$ **−6**

44. $-5x + 12 = -3x$ **6** **45.** $4(n - 1) = n + 11$ **5** **46.** $-8x + 2 = -6x + 10$ **−4**

47. $-16 - 8t = 7(t + 2)$ **−2** **48.** $5(x + 3) = 4(x - 4)$ **−31** **49.** $10(3m + 1) = 2(10m - 5)$ **−2**

In Exercises 50 and 51, you may wish to draw a diagram to model the problem. **(Lesson 4.5)**

50. The sides of a triangle have length $x + 9$, $x + 9$, and $2x + 3$. Find the value of x so that the triangle is equilateral. **6**

51. A rectangle has length $5x - 2$ and width $x + 3$. Find the value of x so that the perimeter of the rectangle is 50. **4**

In Exercises 52–55, use the following information. Membership in a figure skating club costs \$45 per year. Members pay \$5 per hour for ice time. Nonmembers pay \$10 per hour. **(Lesson 4.6)**

52. Write expressions for the costs of ice time for members and nonmembers. **Members: 45 + 5*x*, Nonmembers: 10*x***

53. Copy and complete the table. **See margin.**

Number of hours	1	2	3	4	5	6	7	8	9	10
Member cost (in dollars)	?	?	?	?	?	?	?	?	?	?
Nonmember cost (in dollars)	?	?	?	?	?	?	?	?	?	?

54. Use your table from Exercise 53 to find the number of hours of ice time in a year for which the cost is the same for members and nonmembers. **9 h**

55. Use an equation to solve the problem in Exercise 54. **45 + 5*x* = 10*x*; 9 h**

In Exercises 56–64, solve the equation. You may use a calculator if you wish. Round your answer to the nearest tenth. **(Lesson 4.7)**

56. $4n - 7 = 15.3$ **5.6** **57.** $11x + 15 = 27.5$ **1.1** **58.** $45.7 - 7y = 68$ **−3.2**

59. $3.1k - 6 = 25.5$ **10.2** **60.** $23y + 8.5 = 27.2$ **0.8** **61.** $5.6m - 3.2 = 20.7$ **4.3**

62. $2.4t + 42.6 = -9.2$ **−21.6** **63.** $0.25d - 11.6 = 2.45d$ **−5.3** **64.** $3.21(4.2y - 5.1) = 18.92$ **2.6**

65. You go to the store with \$5 to buy a gallon of milk. The milk costs \$2.49 and you notice that your favorite yogurt is on sale for \$.59 per container. How many containers can you buy? **(Lesson 4.7)** **4 containers**

In Exercises 66–71, find the mean, median, and mode of the data. **(Lesson 4.8)**

66. 11, 8, 7, 5, 5, 3, 12, 15, 6 **8; 7, 5** **67.** 124, 110, 150, 142, 124 **130, 124, 124**

68. 20, 22, 21, 24, 20, 19 **21, 20.5, 20** **69.** 12, 8, 9, 11, 9, 8, 9, 8, 6, 12, 10, 8, 7 **9, 9, 8**

70. 46, 46, 48, 51, 51, 48, 43, 48, 42 **47, 48, 48** **71.** 17.5, 18.8, 16.5, 19.3, 18, 18.2, 17 **17.9, 18, none**

72. Your goal is to maintain an average of 90 in your math class. On the first 5 tests, you have scores of 82, 91, 98, 86, and 88. What score do you need on your next test to meet your goal? **(Lesson 4.8)** **95 or better**

EXTRA PRACTICE

53.

Number of hours	Member cost (in dollars)	Nonmember cost (in dollars)
1	50	10
2	55	20
3	60	30
4	65	40
5	70	50
6	75	60
7	80	70
8	85	80
9	90	90
10	95	100

19. 1, 2, 4, 11, 22, 44, x, $2x$, $4x$, $11x$, $22x$, $44x$

20. 1, 3, 5, 15, 25, 75, n, $3n$, $5n$, $15n$, $25n$, $75n$, n^2, $3n^2$, $5n^2$, $15n^2$, $25n^2$, $75n^2$, n^3, $3n^3$, $5n^3$, $15n^3$, $25n^3$, $75n^3$

21. 1, 3, 13, 39, a, $3a$, $13a$, $39a$, b, $3b$, $13b$, $39b$, a^2, $3a^2$, $13a^2$, $39a^2$, ab, $3ab$, $13ab$, $39ab$, a^2b, $3a^2b$, $13a^2b$, $39a^2b$

22. 1, 2, 4, 17, 34, 68, w, $2w$, $4w$, $17w$, $34w$, $68w$, w^2, $2w^2$, $4w^2$, $17w^2$, $34w^2$, $68w^2$, w^3, $2w^3$, $4w^3$, $17w^3$, $34w^3$, $68w^3$

62.
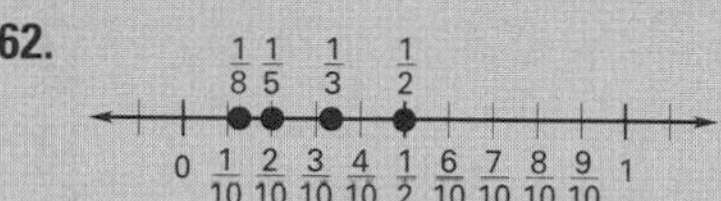

63.
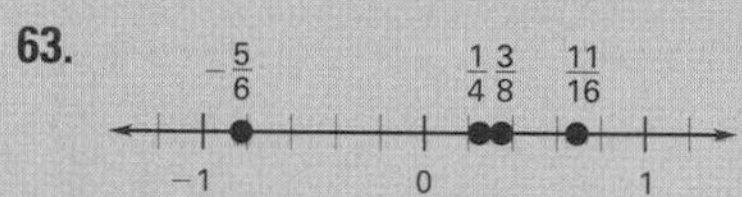

64.

65.
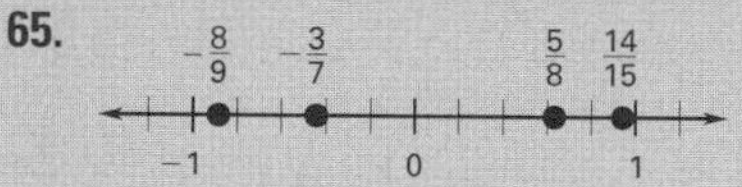

EXTRA PRACTICE

Chapter 5

Write the prime factorization of the number. Use exponents for repeated factors. (Lesson 5.1)

1. 63 $3^2 \cdot 7$ **2.** 100 $2^2 \cdot 5^2$ **3.** 64 2^6 **4.** 84 $2^2 \cdot 3 \cdot 7$ **5.** 245 $5 \cdot 7^2$

6. 420 $2^2 \cdot 3 \cdot 5 \cdot 7$ **7.** 165 $3 \cdot 5 \cdot 11$ **8.** 330 $2 \cdot 3 \cdot 5 \cdot 11$ **9.** 231 $3 \cdot 7 \cdot 11$ **10.** 1008 $2^4 \cdot 3^2 \cdot 7$

Factor the variable expression completely. (Lesson 5.1)

11. $25x^3y$ $5 \cdot 5 \cdot x \cdot x \cdot x \cdot y$ **12.** $-39m^2n^2$ $(-1) \cdot 3 \cdot 13 \cdot m \cdot m \cdot n \cdot n$ **13.** $20y^5z^3$ $2 \cdot 2 \cdot 5 \cdot y \cdot y \cdot y \cdot y \cdot y \cdot z \cdot z \cdot z$ **14.** $-35a^4b^2$ $(-1) \cdot 5 \cdot 7 \cdot a \cdot a \cdot a \cdot a \cdot b \cdot b$

Find all the factors of the number. (Lesson 5.1)

15. 49 1, 7, 49 **16.** 22 1, 2, 11, 22 **17.** 70 1, 2, 5, 7, 10, 14, 35, 70 **18.** 118 1, 2, 59, 118

Find all the factors of the variable expression. (Lesson 5.1) 19–22. See margin.

19. $44x$ **20.** $75n^3$ **21.** $39a^2b$ **22.** $68w^3$

Find the GCF of the numbers. (Lesson 5.2)

23. 12, 20 4 **24.** 60, 130 10 **25.** 48, 96 48 **26.** 100, 45 5

27. 108, 198 18 **28.** 1004, 1040 4 **29.** 660, 1155 165 **30.** 30, 24, 56 2

Find the GCF of the variable expressions. (Lesson 5.2)

31. a^5b^2, ab^3 ab^2 **32.** $3b^2$, $15bc^2$ $3b$ **33.** $20x^2y^3z^4$, $45x^3y^3$ $5x^2y^3$ **34.** $55bcd^5$, $44b^4c^5$ $11bc$

Find the LCM of the numbers. (Lesson 5.3)

35. 5, 9 45 **36.** 8, 9 72 **37.** 9, 15 45 **38.** 10, 12 60

39. 12, 15 60 **40.** 12, 36 36 **41.** 75, 180 900 **42.** 216, 240 2160

Find the LCM of the variable expressions. (Lesson 5.3)

43. $7y$, $21y^3$ $21y^3$ **44.** $8m^2n$, $64mn^2$ $64m^2n^2$ **45.** $9a^3b^5$, $11a^2b^3$ $99a^3b^5$ **46.** $6st^2$, $15s^4t^2w$ $30s^4t^2w$

Simplify the fraction. (Lesson 5.4)

47. $\frac{15}{45}$ $\frac{1}{3}$ **48.** $\frac{14}{21}$ $\frac{2}{3}$ **49.** $\frac{5}{65}$ $\frac{1}{13}$ **50.** $\frac{12}{28}$ $\frac{3}{7}$ **51.** $\frac{27}{48}$ $\frac{9}{16}$

52. $\frac{10}{24}$ $\frac{5}{12}$ **53.** $\frac{9}{21}$ $\frac{3}{7}$ **54.** $\frac{18}{54}$ $\frac{1}{3}$ **55.** $\frac{6}{39}$ $\frac{2}{13}$ **56.** $\frac{33}{132}$ $\frac{1}{4}$

Simplify the variable expression. (Lesson 5.4)

57. $\frac{3xy}{12x^2y}$ $\frac{1}{4x}$ **58.** $\frac{5a^2b^3}{75a^4b^2}$ $\frac{b}{15a^2}$ **59.** $\frac{33m^2n}{44mn^4}$ $\frac{3m}{4n^3}$ **60.** $\frac{7yz^3}{21y^2}$ $\frac{z^3}{3y}$ **61.** $\frac{14p^2q^2}{35pq^5}$ $\frac{2p}{5q^3}$

Graph the fractions on a number line. Then order the fractions from least to greatest. (Lesson 5.4)

62. $\frac{1}{2}, \frac{1}{3}, \frac{1}{5}, \frac{1}{8}$ $\frac{1}{8}, \frac{1}{5}, \frac{1}{3}, \frac{1}{2}$; See margin. **63.** $\frac{3}{8}, \frac{1}{4}, \frac{11}{16}, -\frac{5}{6}$ $-\frac{5}{6}, \frac{1}{4}, \frac{3}{8}, \frac{11}{16}$; See margin. **64.** $\frac{5}{12}, \frac{3}{8}, \frac{1}{16}, \frac{9}{10}$ $\frac{1}{16}, \frac{3}{8}, \frac{5}{12}, \frac{9}{10}$; See margin. **65.** $-\frac{8}{9}, -\frac{3}{7}, \frac{5}{8}, \frac{14}{15}$ $-\frac{8}{9}, -\frac{3}{7}, \frac{5}{8}, \frac{14}{15}$; See margin.

Tell whether the number is a member of the given set. (Lesson 5.5)

66. $0.\overline{8}$; rational numbers **yes** **67.** -14; natural numbers **no** **68.** -205; integers **yes**

Write the fraction as a decimal. (Lesson 5.5)

69. $\frac{4}{5}$ **0.8** **70.** $\frac{17}{20}$ **0.85** **71.** $\frac{5}{12}$ **$0.41\overline{6}$** **72.** $\frac{1}{9}$ **$0.\overline{1}$** **73.** $\frac{8}{11}$ **$0.\overline{72}$**

Write the decimal as a fraction. Simplify if possible. (Lesson 5.5)

74. 0.9 $\frac{9}{10}$ **75.** 0.24 $\frac{6}{25}$ **76.** 1.55 $\frac{31}{20}$ **77.** $0.\overline{06}$ $\frac{2}{33}$ **78.** $5.\overline{6}$ $\frac{17}{3}$

Write the fraction as a percent. (Lesson 5.6)

79. $\frac{5}{20}$ **25%** **80.** $\frac{2}{40}$ **5%** **81.** $\frac{4}{50}$ **8%** **82.** $\frac{13}{25}$ **52%** **83.** $\frac{196}{400}$ **49%**

Find the percent of the letters in the word that are the letter O. (Lesson 5.6)

84. PHOTOGRAPH **20%** **85.** POEM **25%** **86.** LOOPHOLE **37.5%** **87.** SPOOKY **$33\frac{1}{3}$%**

Write the percent as a decimal. (Lesson 5.7)

88. 44% **0.44** **89.** 15% **0.15** **90.** 1.5% **0.015** **91.** 25% **0.25** **92.** 0.75% **0.0075**

Write the decimal or fraction as a percent. Round to the nearest tenth if necessary. (Lesson 5.7)

93. 0.5 **50%** **94.** 0.74 **74%** **95.** 0.3 **30%** **96.** 1.5 **150%** **97.** 0.008 **0.8%**

98. $\frac{28}{32}$ **87.5%** **99.** $\frac{1}{400}$ **0.3%** **100.** $\frac{120}{32}$ **375%** **101.** $\frac{180}{60}$ **300%** **102.** $\frac{20}{30}$ **66.7%**

Write the percent as a fraction. Simplify if possible. (Lesson 5.7)

103. 47% $\frac{47}{100}$ **104.** 50% $\frac{1}{2}$ **105.** 65% $\frac{13}{20}$ **106.** 4% $\frac{1}{25}$ **107.** 250% $\frac{5}{2}$

In Exercises 108 and 109, use the stem-and-leaf plot at the right.

Stem	Leaves
3	5
4	7 8 8
5	2 3 3 4 6 8
6	0 1 4 7

Key: 6 | 0 represents 60.

108. Find the least and greatest numbers in the data set. **35; 67**

109. Order the data from least to greatest. **35, 47, 48, 48, 52, 53, 53, 54, 56, 58, 60, 61, 64, 67**

In Exercises 110 and 111, use the following information. The lists below give the number of girls and boys enrolled in a middle school soccer league for the years 1981–2000. (Lesson 5.8)

Girl's League: 39, 46, 45, 41, 22, 39, 39, 43, 40, 40, 49, 42, 36, 51, 44, 43, 46, 40, 50, 52

Boy's League: 52, 40, 48, 48, 31, 37, 40, 36, 37, 37, 49, 39, 47, 40, 38, 35, 46, 43, 40, 47

110. Make a back-to-back stem-and-leaf plot comparing the data for each league.

110.

Girl's League		Boy's League
2	2	
9996	3	15677789
966543321000	4	00003677889
210	5	2

111. Write a conclusion based on the stem-and-leaf plot. Explain how the stem-and-leaf plot supports your conclusion. ***Sample answer:*** **The number of both boys and girls enrolled is most often in the 40s; The row containing the 40s is the longest for both boys and girls.**

Chapter 6

EXTRA PRACTICE

Add or subtract. Then simplify, if possible. (Lesson 6.1)

1. $\frac{2}{5} + \frac{3}{5}$ **1**

2. $-\frac{2}{5} - \frac{3}{5}$ **−1**

3. $1\frac{2}{5} + 3\frac{3}{5}$ **5**

4. $\frac{7}{12} - \frac{5}{12}$ $\mathbf{\frac{1}{6}}$

5. $\frac{7}{10} - \frac{2}{5}$ $\mathbf{\frac{3}{10}}$

6. $\frac{1}{10} + \frac{4}{15}$ $\mathbf{\frac{11}{30}}$

7. $-\frac{1}{4} - \frac{5}{12}$ $\mathbf{-\frac{2}{3}}$

8. $\frac{2}{15} + \frac{3}{5}$ $\mathbf{\frac{11}{15}}$

9. $4\frac{2}{3} - 2\frac{1}{3}$ $\mathbf{2\frac{1}{3}}$

10. $3\frac{1}{5} + 5\frac{3}{4}$ $\mathbf{8\frac{19}{20}}$

11. $7\frac{1}{3} + 6\frac{4}{7}$ $\mathbf{13\frac{19}{21}}$

12. $12\frac{4}{9} - 8\frac{7}{10}$ $\mathbf{3\frac{67}{90}}$

13. $\frac{1}{3x} - \frac{2}{3x}$ $\mathbf{-\frac{1}{3x}}$

14. $\frac{2}{5x} - \frac{1}{5x}$ $\mathbf{\frac{1}{5x}}$

15. $\frac{a}{5} + \frac{a}{10}$ $\mathbf{\frac{3a}{10}}$

16. $\frac{-2}{z} + \frac{3}{2z}$ $\mathbf{-\frac{1}{2z}}$

Add or subtract. Then simplify, if possible. (Lesson 6.2)

17. $\frac{3}{8} + \frac{2}{3}$ $\mathbf{1\frac{1}{24}}$

18. $\frac{4}{9} - \left(-\frac{1}{3}\right)$ $\mathbf{\frac{7}{9}}$

19. $\frac{3}{5} + \left(-\frac{1}{4}\right)$ $\mathbf{\frac{7}{20}}$

20. $\frac{5}{6} + \frac{1}{2}$ $\mathbf{1\frac{1}{3}}$

21. $-\frac{7}{8} + \frac{2}{5}$ $\mathbf{-\frac{19}{40}}$

22. $-\frac{7}{9} + \frac{3}{4}$ $\mathbf{-\frac{1}{36}}$

23. $-\frac{3}{8} + \frac{2}{3}$ $\mathbf{\frac{7}{24}}$

24. $7\frac{1}{2} - 1\frac{5}{6}$ $\mathbf{5\frac{2}{3}}$

25. $-3\frac{1}{8} + 10\frac{1}{4}$ $\mathbf{7\frac{1}{8}}$

26. $12\frac{5}{6} - \left(2\frac{3}{5}\right)$ $\mathbf{10\frac{7}{30}}$

27. $-\frac{7}{12} + \frac{1}{4} - \frac{1}{3}$ $\mathbf{-\frac{2}{3}}$

28. $4\frac{5}{8} - \frac{3}{4} - \frac{2}{3}$ $\mathbf{3\frac{5}{24}}$

Multiply. Then simplify, if possible. (Lesson 6.3)

29. $\frac{1}{2} \cdot \frac{2}{5}$ $\mathbf{\frac{1}{5}}$

30. $\frac{1}{3} \cdot \left(\frac{-6}{7}\right)$ $\mathbf{-\frac{2}{7}}$

31. $\frac{-2}{9} \cdot \frac{3}{4}$ $\mathbf{-\frac{1}{6}}$

32. $1\frac{7}{10} \cdot \frac{2}{5}$ $\mathbf{\frac{17}{25}}$

33. $-2\frac{1}{5} \cdot \frac{7}{15}$ $\mathbf{-1\frac{2}{75}}$

34. $\frac{-1}{4} \cdot \frac{1}{4} \cdot \frac{1}{2}$ $\mathbf{-\frac{1}{32}}$

35. $\frac{x}{10} \cdot \left(-\frac{2}{5}\right)$ $\mathbf{-\frac{x}{25}}$

36. $2 \cdot \frac{5}{12}$ $\mathbf{\frac{5}{6}}$

37. $8 \cdot \frac{3}{16}$ $\mathbf{1\frac{1}{2}}$

38. $\frac{-5}{8} \cdot \left(\frac{4}{-15}\right)$ $\mathbf{\frac{1}{6}}$

39. $1\frac{1}{5} \cdot 4\frac{1}{3}$ $\mathbf{5\frac{1}{5}}$

40. $\frac{3z}{4} \cdot \frac{5}{6}$ $\mathbf{\frac{5z}{8}}$

Find the multiplicative inverse. Justify your answer. (Lesson 6.3)

41. $-\frac{4}{13}$ $\mathbf{-\frac{13}{4};\ -\frac{4}{13} \cdot \left(-\frac{13}{4}\right) = 1}$

42. 25 $\mathbf{\frac{1}{25};\ 25 \cdot \frac{1}{25} = 1}$

43. $3\frac{4}{11}$ $\mathbf{\frac{11}{37};\ 3\frac{4}{11} \cdot \frac{11}{37} = 1}$

44. $-\frac{13}{5}$ $\mathbf{-\frac{5}{13};\ -\frac{13}{5} \cdot \left(-\frac{5}{13}\right) = 1}$

Write the percent as a decimal or a fraction. Then multiply to find the percent of a number. (Lesson 6.4)

45. 10% of 200 **0.1 or $\frac{1}{10}$; 20**

46. 23% of 250 **0.23 or $\frac{23}{100}$; 57.5 or $57\frac{1}{2}$**

47. 75% of 40 **0.75 or $\frac{3}{4}$; 30**

48. 150% of 6 **1.5 or $1\frac{1}{2}$; 9**

49. 25% of 96 **0.25 or $\frac{1}{4}$; 24**

50. 47% of 500 **0.47 or $\frac{47}{100}$; 235**

51. 90% of 120 **0.9 or $\frac{9}{10}$; 108**

52. 12% of 15 **0.12 or $\frac{3}{25}$; 1.8 or $1\frac{4}{5}$**

53. 110% of 50 **1.1 or $1\frac{1}{10}$; 55**

54. 200% of 26 **2; 52**

55. 0.5% of 300 **0.005 or $\frac{1}{200}$; 1.5 or $1\frac{1}{2}$**

56. 2.5% of 80 **0.025 or $\frac{1}{40}$; 2**

Find each amount. (Lesson 6.4)

57. A commission of 5% on a $225,000 sale **$11,250**

58. A 20% tip on a restaurant bill of $18.42 **$3.68**

59. The total cost of a $1299 computer system if the sales tax is 5% **$1363.95**

In Exercises 60–71, divide. Then simplify, if possible. (Lesson 6.5)

60. $\frac{5}{2} \div \frac{1}{2}$ **5** **61.** $\frac{1}{3} \div \left(\frac{-1}{2}\right)$ $-\frac{2}{3}$ **62.** $\frac{-4}{9} \div \frac{2}{3}$ $-\frac{2}{3}$ **63.** $\frac{1}{2} \div 5$ $\frac{1}{10}$

64. $2 \div \left(\frac{-7}{6}\right)$ $-1\frac{5}{7}$ **65.** $\frac{-1}{3} \div \left(\frac{-1}{4}\right)$ $1\frac{1}{3}$ **66.** $2\frac{1}{2} \div \frac{2}{5}$ $6\frac{1}{4}$ **67.** $\frac{6}{7} \div 1\frac{1}{3}$ $\frac{9}{14}$

68. $\frac{-2}{x} \div \frac{3}{x}$ $-\frac{2}{3}$ **69.** $\frac{n}{2} \div \frac{3}{4}$ $\frac{2n}{3}$ **70.** $2\frac{1}{3} \div y$ $\frac{7}{3y}$ **71.** $\frac{15}{z} \div \frac{3}{z}$ **5**

72. You were billed \$175 in labor charges for car repairs that took $3\frac{1}{2}$ hours to complete. Find the labor charge per hour. **(Lesson 6.5) \$50**

73. A crafter uses $1\frac{3}{4}$ yards of ribbon to trim a place mat. How many place mats can be trimmed with $10\frac{2}{3}$ yards of ribbon? **(Lesson 6.5) 6 place mats**

Solve the equation. Check the solution. (Lesson 6.6)

74. $z - \frac{2}{3} = \frac{1}{2}$ $1\frac{1}{6}$ **75.** $k + \frac{5}{6} = \frac{1}{3}$ $-\frac{1}{2}$ **76.** $t - 2 = \frac{1}{5}$ $2\frac{1}{5}$ **77.** $\frac{2}{5}m = 4$ **10**

78. $\frac{3}{8}n = \frac{2}{3}$ $1\frac{7}{9}$ **79.** $3t = \frac{6}{7}$ $\frac{2}{7}$ **80.** $b + \frac{3}{8} = 1\frac{1}{2}$ $1\frac{1}{8}$ **81.** $x - 2\frac{1}{4} = \frac{5}{6}$ $3\frac{1}{12}$

82. $\frac{1}{2} - b = \frac{7}{10}$ $-\frac{1}{5}$ **83.** $2w - \frac{5}{8} = \frac{1}{2}$ $\frac{9}{16}$ **84.** $\frac{4}{5}c - 2 = 1\frac{1}{4}$ $4\frac{1}{16}$ **85.** $\frac{7}{16}y + \frac{1}{8} = \frac{3}{4}$ $1\frac{3}{7}$

Simplify the expression. (Lesson 6.7)

86. $3^2 \cdot 3^4$ 3^6 **87.** $5^3 \cdot 5^3$ 5^6 **88.** $(-9)^2 \cdot (-9)^3$ $(-9)^5$ **89.** $z^9 \cdot z^{10}$ z^{19} **90.** $4n^6 \cdot 2n^5$ $8n^{11}$

91. $\left(\frac{1}{2}\right)^4 \cdot \left(\frac{1}{2}\right)^3$ $\left(\frac{1}{2}\right)^7$ **92.** $\frac{3^{10}}{3^4}$ 3^6 **93.** $\frac{(-7)^5}{(-7)^2}$ $(-7)^3$ **94.** $\frac{(-n)^{10}}{(-n)^8}$ n^2 **95.** $\frac{42x^{15}}{6x^9}$ $7x^6$

Simplify the expression. (Lesson 6.8)

96. 2^{-3} $\frac{1}{8}$ **97.** -4^{-2} $-\frac{1}{16}$ **98.** 24^0 **1** **99.** x^{-3} $\frac{1}{x^3}$ **100.** $5a^{-2}$ $\frac{5}{a^2}$

101. $6n^{-4}$ $\frac{6}{n^4}$ **102.** $\left(\frac{1}{8}\right)^{-4}$ **4096** **103.** $\left(\frac{4}{9}\right)^0$ **1** **104.** $-7y^{-5}$ $\frac{-7}{y^5}$ **105.** $2ab^{-8}$ $\frac{2a}{b^8}$

Rewrite the expression using a negative exponent. (Lesson 6.8)

106. $\frac{1}{n^8}$ n^{-8} **107.** $\frac{-1}{x^{12}}$ $-x^{-12}$ **108.** $\frac{10}{b^7}$ $10b^{-7}$ **109.** $\frac{w}{y^3}$ wy^{-3} **110.** $\frac{15}{-z^6}$ $-15z^{-6}$

Write the number in decimal form. (Lesson 6.9)

111. 9.2×10^3 **9200** **112.** 4.3×10^5 **430,000** **113.** 6.70×10^{-4} **0.00067** **114.** 7.2×10^6 **7,200,000** **115.** 5.5×10^{-8} **0.000000055**

Write the number in scientific notation. (Lesson 6.9)

116. 4000 4×10^3 **117.** 253,000 2.53×10^5 **118.** 0.28 2.8×10^{-1} **119.** 21,465,000 2.1465×10^7 **120.** 0.00927 9.27×10^{-3}

23.

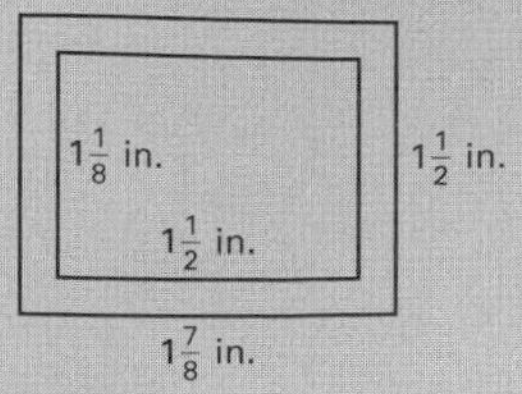

EXTRA PRACTICE

Chapter 7

Write the ratio as a fraction $\frac{a}{b}$ in simplest form. (Lesson 7.1)

1. 19 out of 95 students **$\frac{1}{5}$**

2. 14 field goals out of 21 attempts **$\frac{2}{3}$**

3. 84 correct responses in 100 tries **$\frac{21}{25}$**

4. 42 wins out of 168 games **$\frac{1}{4}$**

Express both quantities in a common unit of measure, then write the ratio as a fraction $\frac{a}{b}$ in simplest form. (Lesson 7.1)

5. $\frac{9 \text{ feet}}{18 \text{ yards}}$ ***Sample answer:*** **$\frac{9 \text{ feet}}{54 \text{ feet}}$; $\frac{1}{6}$**

6. $\frac{12 \text{ minutes}}{1 \text{ hour}}$ ***Sample answer:*** **$\frac{12 \text{ minutes}}{60 \text{ minutes}}$; $\frac{1}{5}$**

7. $\frac{75 \text{ centimeters}}{1 \text{ meter}}$ ***Sample answer:*** **$\frac{75 \text{ centimeters}}{100 \text{ centimeters}}$; $\frac{3}{4}$**

8. $\frac{12 \text{ days}}{3 \text{ weeks}}$ ***Sample answer:*** **$\frac{12 \text{ days}}{21 \text{ days}}$; $\frac{4}{7}$**

Find the unit price. (Lesson 7.1)

9. \$12.95 for 5 pounds **\$2.59/lb**

10. \$374.85 for 15 square yards **\$24.99/yd^2**

11. \$2.79 for 64 ounces **≈ \$.04/oz**

In Exercises 12–19, solve the proportion. Check your solution. (Lesson 7.2)

12. $\frac{x}{5} = \frac{14}{35}$ **2**

13. $\frac{z}{12} = \frac{3}{9}$ **4**

14. $\frac{5}{15} = \frac{y}{20}$ **$6\frac{2}{3}$**

15. $\frac{6}{11} = \frac{n}{22}$ **12**

16. $\frac{2}{p} = \frac{3}{9}$ **6**

17. $\frac{5}{q} = \frac{12}{20}$ **$8\frac{1}{3}$**

18. $\frac{8}{7} = \frac{64}{m}$ **56**

19. $\frac{9}{15} = \frac{12}{y}$ **20**

20. A portable color printer printed a 4 page report in 10 minutes. How long will it take the printer to print a 10 page report? **(Lesson 7.2)** **25 min**

In Exercises 21 and 22, use the following information. An artist sketches the layout of an apartment using a scale of $\frac{1}{2}$ inch = 2 feet. (Lesson 7.3)

21. In the sketch, the living room is 4 inches wide and 5 inches long. Find the actual measurements of the room. **16 ft wide and 20 ft long**

22. Find the scale factor. **1:48**

23. You plan to put a carpet that is 9 feet wide and 12 feet long in a room that is 12 feet wide and 15 feet long. Make a scale drawing showing the carpet and the floor, using a scale of $\frac{1}{4}$ inch = 2 feet. **(Lesson 7.3)** **See margin.**

In Exercises 24–27, the spinner at the right is divided into 8 equal sections. Find the theoretical probability that the spinner will land on the color. (Lesson 7.4)

24. Blue **0.25**

25. Red **0.50**

26. Green **0.125**

27. Yellow **0.125**

28. A 6-sided number cube is tossed 50 times. The cube lands with an even number facing up 23 times and an odd number facing up 27 times. Find the experimental probability of tossing an even number. **(Lesson 7.4)** **$\frac{23}{50}$ or 0.46**

Write and solve a proportion to answer the question (Lesson 7.5) **29–37. See margin.**

29. 56 is what percent of 175? **30.** 14 is 2% of what number? **31.** What is 15% of 240?

32. 72 is what percent of 54? **33.** What is 140% of 65? **34.** 33 is what percent of 55?

35. 17 is 85% of what number? **36.** What is 225% of 64? **37.** 8 is 4% of what number?

Find the amount of markup or the amount of discount. Round your answer to the nearest hundredth. (Lesson 7.6)

38. \$115 coat; 20% discount **\$23**

39. \$229.99 CD player; 225% markup **\$517.48**

40. \$14.99 book; 40% discount **\$6.00**

41. \$13.99 telephone; 275% markup **\$38.47**

Find the cost of the item after the markup or discount described. Round your answer to the nearest hundredth. (Lesson 7.6)

42. \$16 shirt; 200% markup **\$48**

43. \$650 sofa; 30% discount **\$455**

44. \$.33 juice drink; 180% markup **\$.92**

45. \$15.99 CD; 20% discount **\$12.79**

Find the percent of change. (Lesson 7.7)

46. Before: 15
After: 18
20% increase

47. Before: 12
After: 15
25% increase

48. Before: 116
After: 87
25% decrease

49. Before: 1260
After: 1890
50% increase

Determine whether the change is an *increase* or a *decrease* and find the percent of change. (Lesson 7.7)

50. Beginning balance: \$740
Ending balance: \$999
increase; 35%

51. Regular price: \$18.20
Sale price: \$16.80
decrease; 8%

52. Opening price: \$30.10
Closing price: \$31.20
increase; 4%

Find the simple interest and the balance of the account. Assume the interest rate is annual. (Lesson 7.8)

53. \$500 at 4% for 6 months **\$10; \$510**

54. \$1200 at 6% for 9 months **\$54; \$1254**

55. \$2000 at 10% for 3 months **\$50; \$2050**

56. \$1800 at 6.5% for 1 year **\$117; \$1917**

Find the annual simple interest rate. (Lesson 7.8)

57. \$162 interest on \$1800 for 9 months **12%**

58. \$85 interest on \$2000 for 6 months **8.5%**

59. \$87.50 interest on \$7000 for 3 months **5%**

60. \$1500 interest on \$15,000 for 1 year **10%**

Use the information to find the balance in an account when \$5000 is invested for one year. (Lesson 7.9)

61. 10% interest compounded monthly **\$5523.57**

62. 6.5% interest compounded annually **\$5325**

63. 5% interest compounded semiannually **\$5253.13**

64. 8% interest compounded quarterly **\$5412.16**

Use the information to find the amount in the account after the given number of years. (Lesson 7.9)

65. Principal: \$10,000; annual interest rate: 9% compounded monthly for 1 year **\$10,938.07**

66. Principal: \$1000; annual interest rate: 8% compounded annually for 3 years **\$1259.71**

67. Principal: \$800; annual interest rate: 5%; compounded quarterly for 2 years **\$883.59**

29. $\frac{56}{175} = \frac{x}{100}$; 32

30. $\frac{14}{x} = \frac{2}{100}$; 700

31. $\frac{x}{240} = \frac{15}{100}$; 36

32. $\frac{72}{54} = \frac{x}{100}$; $133.\overline{3}$

33. $\frac{x}{65} = \frac{140}{100}$; 91

34. $\frac{33}{55} = \frac{x}{100}$; 60

35. $\frac{17}{x} = \frac{85}{100}$; 20

36. $\frac{x}{64} = \frac{225}{100}$; 144

37. $\frac{8}{x} = \frac{4}{100}$; 200

EXTRA PRACTICE

7.

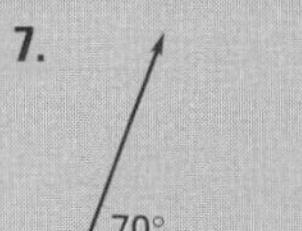

8.

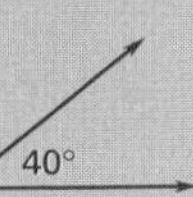

9. 105°

10. 25°

11. 150°

12. acute: ∠V, ∠X, ∠VZW, ∠WZY, ∠VWZ, ∠ZWY, ∠YWX; obtuse: ∠VWY, ∠ZWX

27. △PQR ≅ △STU, ∠P ≅ ∠S, ∠Q ≅ ∠T, ∠R ≅ ∠U, $\overline{PQ} \cong \overline{ST}$, $\overline{QR} \cong \overline{TU}$, $\overline{RP} \cong \overline{US}$

28. quadrilateral JKLM ≅ quadrilateral ABCD, ∠J ≅ ∠A, ∠K ≅ ∠B, ∠L ≅ ∠C, ∠M ≅ ∠D, $\overline{JK} \cong \overline{AB}$, $\overline{KL} \cong \overline{BC}$, $\overline{LM} \cong \overline{CD}$, $\overline{MJ} \cong \overline{DA}$

34.

line of reflection: the y-axis

35.

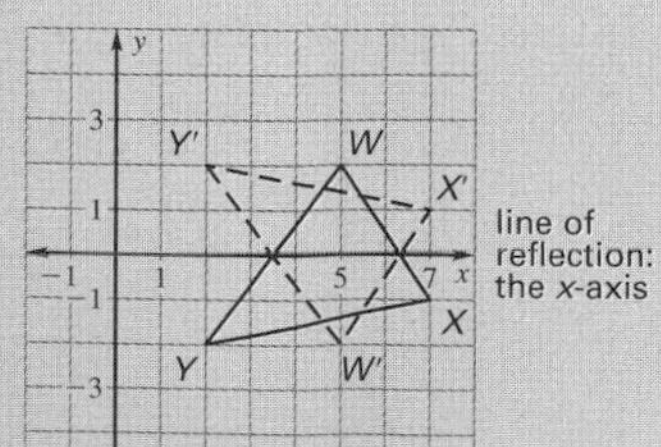

line of reflection: the x-axis

Chapter 8

Use the diagram at the right. (Lesson 8.1)

1. Write three other names for $\overleftrightarrow{ZY}$. ***Sample answers:*** $\overleftrightarrow{ZB}$, $\overleftrightarrow{BY}$, $\overleftrightarrow{BZ}$

2. Name three different line segments that lie on $\overleftrightarrow{ZY}$. $\overline{ZB}$, $\overline{BY}$, $\overline{ZY}$

3. Name four rays with endpoint Z. $\overrightarrow{ZB}$, $\overrightarrow{ZY}$, $\overrightarrow{ZV}$, $\overrightarrow{ZW}$

4. Assume that $\overline{SV} \cong \overline{WZ}$. Find the length of $\overline{SV}$. **12**

5. Which segments intersect $\overline{TU}$? Which segments appear to be parallel to $\overline{TU}$? $\overline{ST}$, $\overline{XT}$, $\overline{VU}$, $\overline{YU}$; $\overline{SV}$, $\overline{XY}$, $\overline{WZ}$

6. $\overline{ST}$ is parallel to $\overline{UV}$ and $\overline{ZY}$ is parallel to $\overline{UV}$. What can you conclude about $\overline{ST}$ and $\overline{ZY}$? Explain. **They are parallel. Two lines that are parallel to a third line are parallel to each other.**

Use a protractor to draw an angle with the given measure. (Lesson 8.2) 7–11. See margin.

7. 70° **8.** 40° **9.** 105° **10.** 25° **11.** 150°

Use the diagram at the right. (Lesson 8.2)

12. Name the angles that appear to be acute. Name the angles that appear to be obtuse. **See margin.**

13. Find $m\angle ZYW$ given that $\angle ZYW$ and $\angle XYW$ are supplementary angles. **90°**

14. Name the right angles in the diagram. **∠VZY, ∠ZYW, ∠XYW**

In Exercises 15–19, use the figure at the right. (Lesson 8.3)

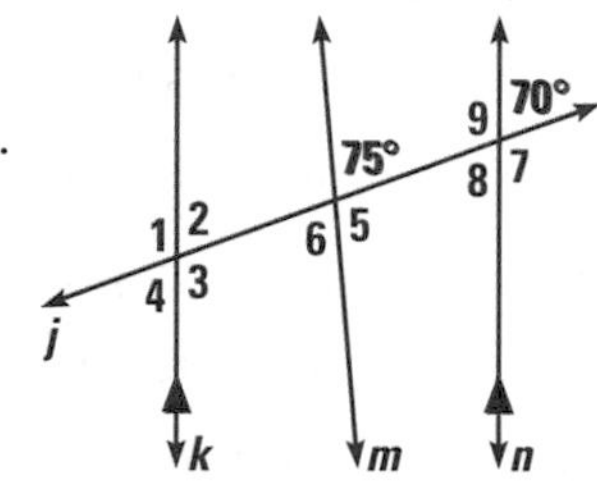

15. Explain why ∠4 is not congruent to ∠6. ***k* is not parallel to *m*.**

16. Name two pairs of corresponding angles that have different measures. ***Sample answer:*** **∠4 and ∠6, ∠3 and ∠5**

17. Name two corresponding angles that have the same measure. ***Sample answer:*** **∠4 and ∠8**

18. Name each angle whose measure is 70°. **∠2, ∠4, ∠8**

19. Name each angle whose measure is 110°. **∠1, ∠3, ∠7, ∠9**

Classify the triangle by its angles and by its sides. (Lesson 8.4)

20. 75°, 30°, 75° **acute isosceles**

21.

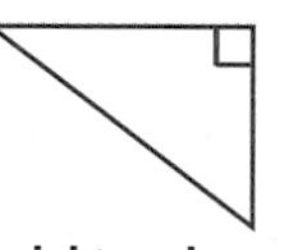

right scalene

22.

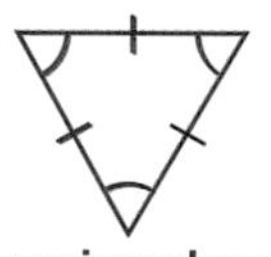

equiangular, equilateral

23.

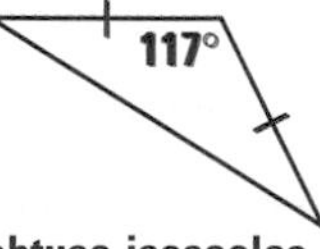

obtuse isosceles

Use the given markings to classify the quadrilateral. (Lesson 8.4)

24. **square**

25. **rectangle**

26.

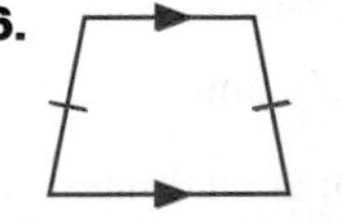

isosceles trapezoid

Determine whether the figures are congruent. If they are, write a congruence statement. Then list the corresponding angles and the corresponding sides. (Lesson 8.5) 27, 28. See margin.

27.

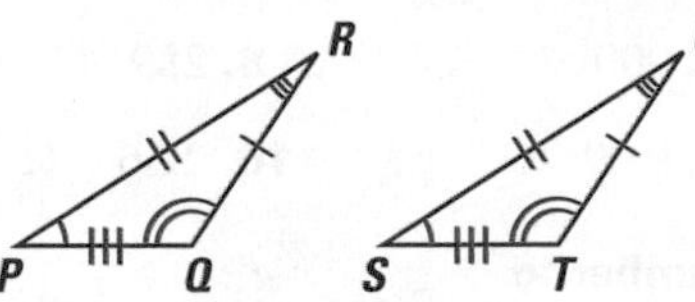

28.

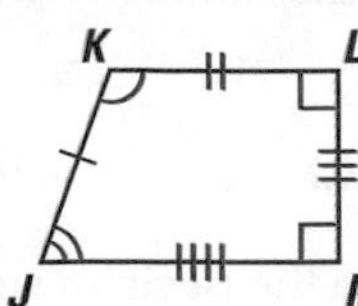

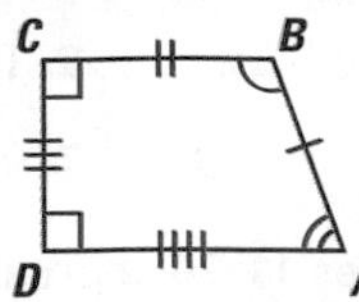

Find the indicated angle measures and side lengths. (Lesson 8.5)

29. $\triangle JKL \cong \triangle WYX$ $JL = 7$, $m\angle W = 60°$

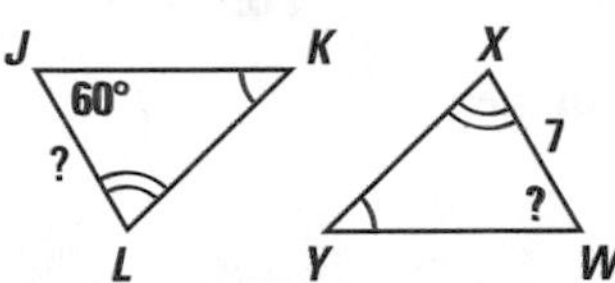

30. $\triangle DEF \cong \triangle GHJ$
$m\angle F = 70°$, $m\angle H = 65°$, $m\angle G = 45°$

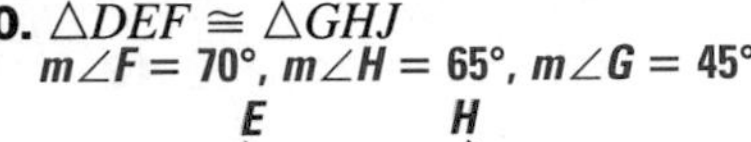

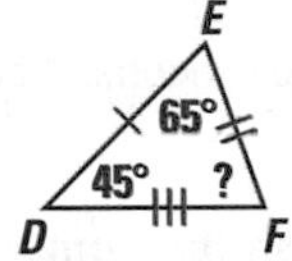

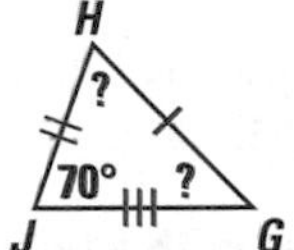

Find the area of the polygon. (Lesson 8.6)

31. 70

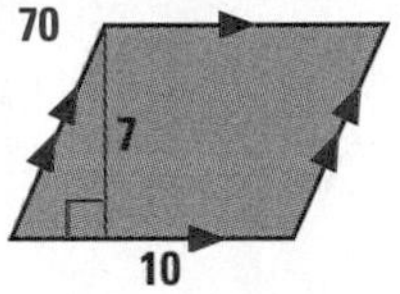

32. 57

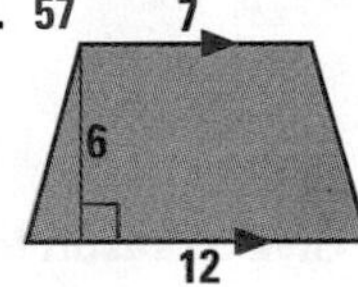

33. 96

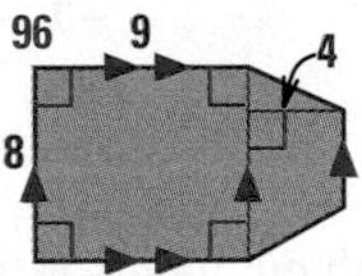

In Exercises 34 and 35, plot the given points and connect them to form a polygon. Then draw the image of the polygon after the indicated reflection. Identify the line of reflection. (Lesson 8.7) 34, 35. See margin.

34. $J(1, 1)$, $K(5, 1)$, $L(5, 4)$, $M(1, 4)$; reflection: $(x, y) \to (-x, y)$

35. $W(5, 2)$, $X(7, -1)$, $Y(2, -2)$; reflection: $(x, y) \to (x, -y)$

In Exercises 36 and 37, draw $\triangle ABC$ with vertices $A(0, 2)$, $B(3, 5)$, and $C(4, -1)$ in a coordinate plane. Then draw its image after the indicated translation. Use coordinate notation to describe the translation. (Lesson 8.8)

36. Translate 2 units right and 3 units up. $(x, y) \to (x + 2, y + 3)$; See margin.

37. Translate 3 units left and 1 unit down. $(x, y) \to (x - 3, y - 1)$; See margin.

38. $\triangle DEF$ has vertices $D(3, 3)$, $E(5, -2)$, and $F(0, 0)$. Draw $\triangle DEF$. Then draw the image of the triangle after the following translation: $(x, y) \to (x + 6, y - 2)$. (Lesson 8.8) See margin.

Quadrilateral *ABCD* ~ quadrilateral *PQRS*. (Lesson 8.9)

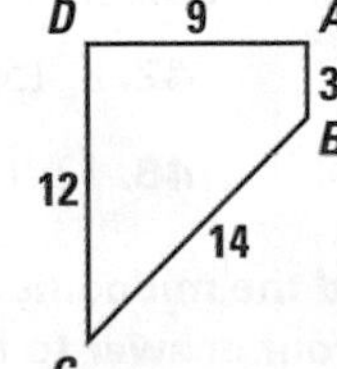

39. Write statements describing the relationships between the corresponding sides and between the corresponding angles of quadrilaterals *ABCD* and *PQRS*. See margin.

40. Find *PQ*, *QR*, and *PS*. $PQ = 2$, $QR = \frac{28}{3}$, $PS = 6$

41. Find the ratio of the perimeter of quadrilateral *ABCD* to the perimeter of quadrilateral *PQRS*. Find the ratio of the area of quadrilateral *ABCD* to the area of quadrilateral *PQRS*. $\frac{3}{2}, \frac{9}{4}$

EXTRA PRACTICE

36.

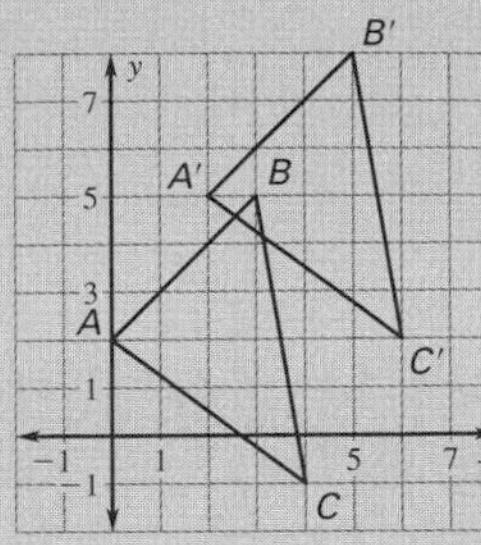

37.

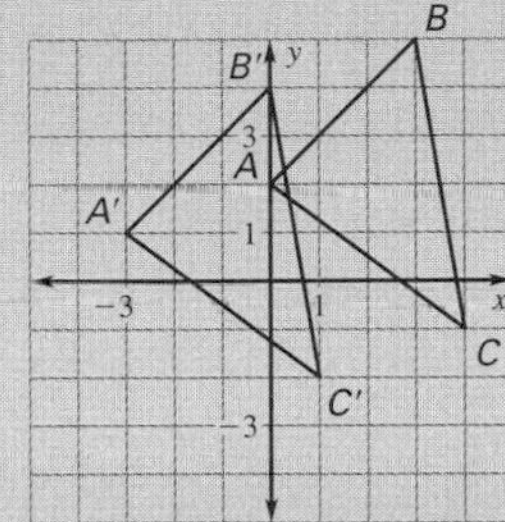

38.

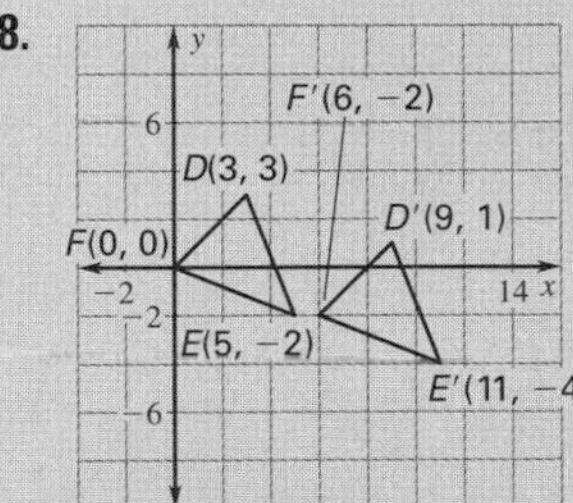

39. $\frac{AB}{PQ} = \frac{BC}{QR} = \frac{CD}{RS} = \frac{DA}{SP}$, $m\angle A = m\angle P$, $m\angle B = m\angle Q$, $m\angle C = m\angle R$, $m\angle D = m\angle S$

26. rational; it is of the form $\frac{a}{b}$ where a and b are integers.

27. rational; it is of the form $\frac{a}{b}$ where a and b are integers.

28. irrational; it cannot be written in the form $\frac{a}{b}$ for any integers a and b.

29. rational; $-\sqrt{25} = -5 = -\frac{5}{1}$

30. irrational; it cannot be written in the form $\frac{a}{b}$ for any integers a and b.

55. $x \le 10$, $10 \ge x$

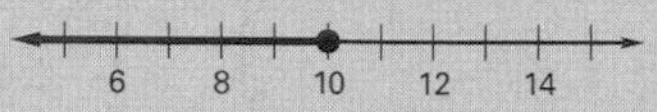

56. $x > -7$, $-7 < x$

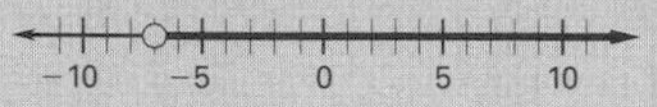

57. $x \ge -3$, $-3 \le x$

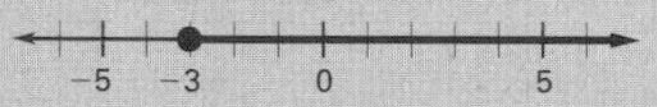

58. $x < 8$, $8 > x$

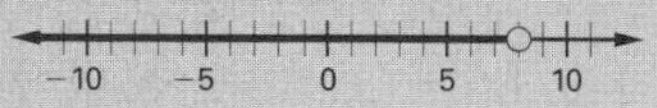

59.

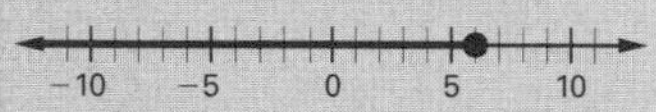

60.

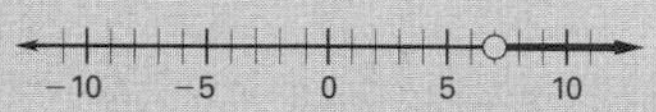

61.

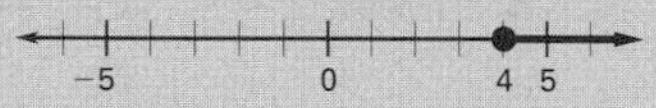

62.

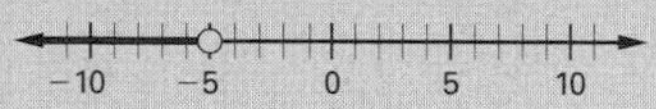

63.

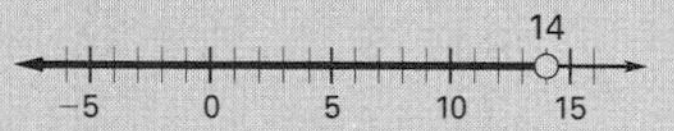

64.

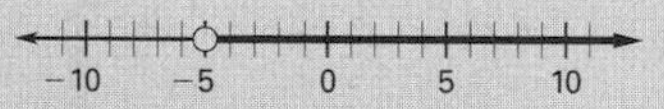

65.

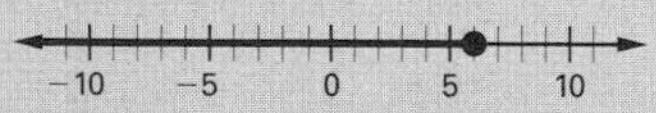

66.

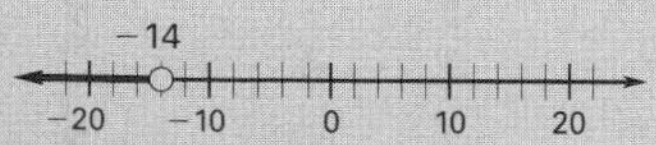

67.

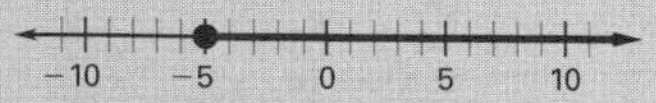

68.

706

EXTRA PRACTICE

Chapter 9

Write the two square roots of the number. (Lesson 9.1)

1. 9 **3, −3** **2.** 196 **14, −14** **3.** 441 **21, −21** **4.** 900 **30, −30** **5.** 289 **17, −17**

6. 0.01 **0.1, −0.1** **7.** 0.49 **0.7, −0.7** **8.** 0.64 **0.8, −0.8** **9.** 0.09 **0.3, −0.3** **10.** 2.56 **1.6, −1.6**

In Exercises 11–20 approximate the positive square root of the number to the nearest whole number and the nearest tenth. (Lesson 9.1)

11. $\sqrt{8}$ **3; 2.8** **12.** $\sqrt{30}$ **5; 5.5** **13.** $\sqrt{20}$ **4; 4.5** **14.** $\sqrt{94}$ **10; 9.7** **15.** $\sqrt{108}$ **10; 10.4**

16. $\sqrt{38}$ **6; 6.2** **17.** $\sqrt{55}$ **7; 7.4** **18.** $\sqrt{83}$ **9; 9.1** **19.** $\sqrt{50}$ **7; 7.1** **20.** $\sqrt{130}$ **11; 11.4**

21. The area of a square is 120 square meters. About how long is one side of the square? **(Lesson 9.1)** **about 11 m**

Match each number with a point on the number line. (Lesson 9.2)

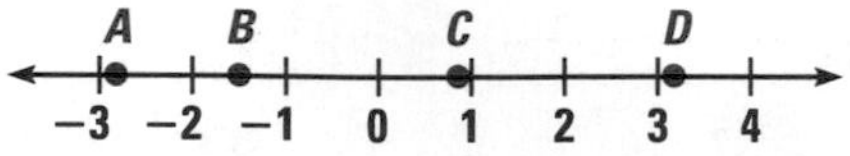

A B C D

−3 −2 −1 0 1 2 3 4

22. $\sqrt{10}$ **D** **23.** $-\sqrt{8}$ **A** **24.** $\sqrt{0.81}$ **C** **25.** $-\sqrt{\frac{9}{4}}$ **B**

Tell whether each number is *rational* or *irrational*. Give a reason for your answer. (Lesson 9.2) **26–30. See margin.**

26. $\frac{13}{3}$ **27.** $\frac{-31}{17}$ **28.** $\sqrt{12}$ **29.** $-\sqrt{25}$ **30.** $-\sqrt{\frac{5}{2}}$

Let *a* and *b* be the lengths of the legs of a right triangle. Let *c* be the length of the hypotenuse. Use the Pythagorean theorem to find the missing length. Round your answer to the nearest tenth. (Lesson 9.3)

31. $a = 10, b = 24, c = ?$ **26** **32.** $a = 9, b = 15, c = ?$ **17.5** **33.** $a = 6, b = 12, c = ?$ **13.4**

34. $a = 6, b = ?, c = 10$ **8** **35.** $a = ?, b = 24, c = 25$ **7** **36.** $a = 8, b = 8, c = ?$ **11.3**

Determine whether a triangle with the given side lengths is a right triangle. (Lesson 9.4)

37. 20, 21, 29 **yes** **38.** 7, 8, $\sqrt{113}$ **yes** **39.** 5, 8, $\sqrt{85}$ **no** **40.** 4, 10, $\sqrt{116}$ **yes**

Determine whether a triangle with the given side lengths is a *right triangle*, an *acute triangle*, or an *obtuse triangle*. (Lesson 9.4)

41. 12, 18, 28 **obtuse triangle** **42.** 8, 15, 17 **right triangle** **43.** 7, 7, 9 **acute triangle** **44.** 2, 2, $\sqrt{5}$ **acute triangle**

45. 16, 16, $16\sqrt{2}$ **right triangle** **46.** 12, 15, 19 **acute triangle** **47.** 9, 40, 41 **right triangle** **48.** 5, 10, 11 **acute triangle**

Find the length and the midpoint of $\overline{AB}$ given the coordinates of *A* and *B*. If necessary, round your answer to the nearest tenth. (Lesson 9.5)

49. $A(0, 0)$ and $B(3, 4)$ **5; (1.5, 2)** **50.** $A(2, 0)$ and $B(7, 12)$ **13; (4.5, 6)** **51.** $A(3, 6)$ and $B(7, 8)$ **$2\sqrt{5}$; (5, 7)**

52. $A(-2, 1)$ and $B(6, 5)$ **$4\sqrt{5}$; (2, 3)** **53.** $A(-2, -4)$ and $B(6, 10)$ **$2\sqrt{65}$; (2, 3)** **54.** $A(1, -4)$ and $B(-3, -10)$ **$2\sqrt{13}$; (−1, −7)**

Write two inequalities for the phrase. Then graph the inequalities. (Lesson 9.6) **55–58. See margin.**

55. All real numbers less than or equal to 10

56. All real numbers greater than -7

57. All real numbers greater than or equal to -3

58. All real numbers less than 8

Solve the inequality. Then graph the solution. (Lesson 9.6) **59–70. See margin for graphs.**

59. $x + 3 \le 9$ $x \le 6$

60. $y - 7 > 0$ $y > 7$

61. $m + 1 \ge 5$ $m \ge 4$

62. $w + 3 < -2$ $w < -5$

63. $b - 10 < 4$ $b < 14$

64. $n + 3 > -2$ $n > -5$

65. $a - 9 \le -3$ $a \le 6$

66. $s - 1 < -15$ $s < -14$

67. $0 \le 5 + t$ $-5 \le t$

68. $-8 \ge k - 5$ $-3 \ge k$

69. $15 \le 18 + d$ $-3 \le d$

70. $f + 1.8 > 3.5$ $f > 1.7$

Solve the inequality. Then graph the solution. (Lesson 9.7) **71–82. See margin for graphs.**

71. $2x < 3$ $x < 1\frac{1}{2}$

72. $5y \ge 12$ $y \ge 2\frac{2}{5}$

73. $-4x > 4$ $x < -1$

74. $-6a < -30$ $a > 5$

75. $9 \le \frac{x}{3}$ $27 \le x$

76. $-\frac{1}{3}p > 12$ $p < -36$

77. $10 < \frac{n}{5}$ $50 < n$

78. $\frac{2}{5}m \le -8$ $m \le -20$

79. $-\frac{2}{3} < -\frac{1}{6}x$ $4 > x$

80. $-0.8d \ge -5.6$ $d \le 7$

81. $\frac{1}{2}z < -\frac{3}{4}$ $z < -1\frac{1}{2}$

82. $\frac{5}{8} \ge -\frac{1}{4}n$ $-2\frac{1}{2} \le n$

Solve the inequality. Then graph the solution. (Lesson 9.8) **83–94. See margin for graphs.**

83. $0.5x + 3 > -4$ $x > -14$

84. $4z - 2 \le 18$ $z \le 5$

85. $8 \ge 5x + 10$ $-\frac{2}{5} \ge x$

86. $5 - 3w < 29$ $w > -8$

87. $\frac{2}{3}a - 1 < \frac{1}{3}$ $a < 2$

88. $\frac{f}{3} + \frac{1}{2} \ge 2$ $f \ge 4\frac{1}{2}$

89. $\frac{1}{3}n - 8 \ge -6$ $n \ge 6$

90. $6x - 24 \le 3$ $x \le 4\frac{1}{2}$

91. $25 + 2a > 7 + a$ $a > -18$

92. $-2(x + 5) > 6$ $x < -8$

93. $18 \le 4(x + 2)$ $2\frac{1}{2} \le x$

94. $10 - x < 7x - 2$ $x > 1\frac{1}{2}$

In Exercises 95–102, use the box-and-whisker plot, which shows the number of videos rented in one year by people responding to a survey. (Lesson 9.9)

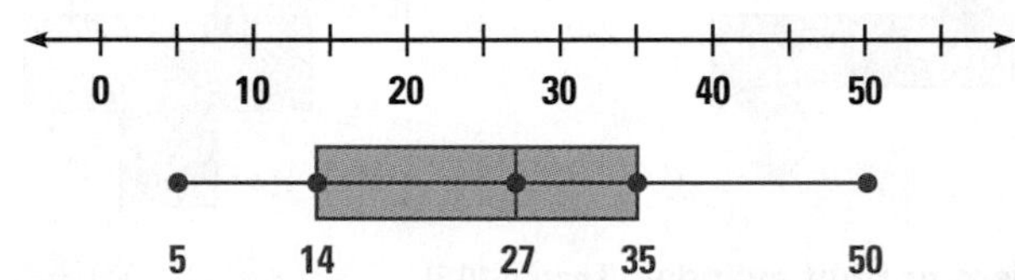

95. Minimum number **5**

96. Maximum number **50**

97. Median **27**

98. Lower quartile **14**

99. Upper quartile **35**

100. Range **45**

101. Interquartile range **21**

102. Percent of numbers between 5 and 27 **50%**

Draw a box-and-whisker plot for the set of data. Describe the variation. (Lesson 9.9) **103, 104. See margin.**

103. Average daily high temperatures in January (in degrees Fahrenheit) for 25 popular overseas tourist destinations: 78, 34, 77, 68, 84, 36, 65, 42, 35, 54, 64, 80, 54, 55, 47, 88, 40, 81, 78, 47, 44, 43, 21, 75, 37

104. Number of days 20 gym members worked out at the gym last month: 16, 4, 8, 12, 10, 30, 22, 5, 1, 20, 7, 8, 9, 6, 10, 12, 10, 3, 2, 5

69.
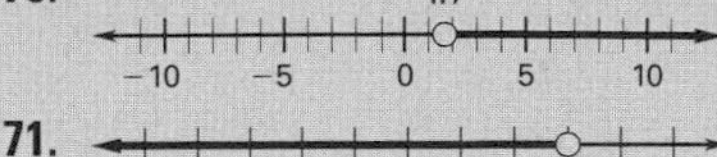

70.
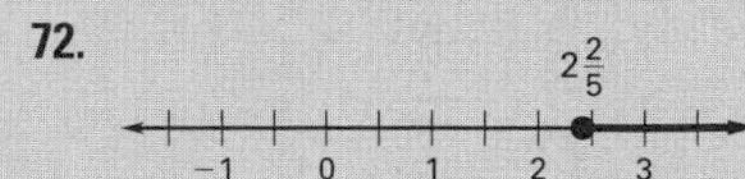

71.
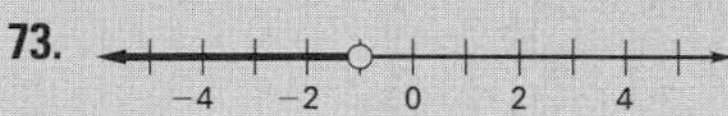

72. $2\frac{2}{5}$

73.

74.

75.

76.

77.

78.

79.

80.

81.

82.
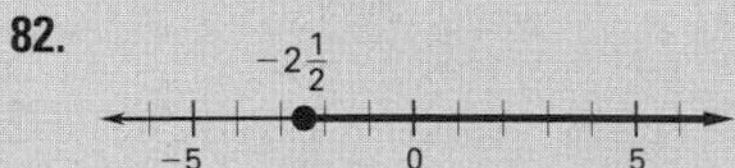

83. -14

84.

85.
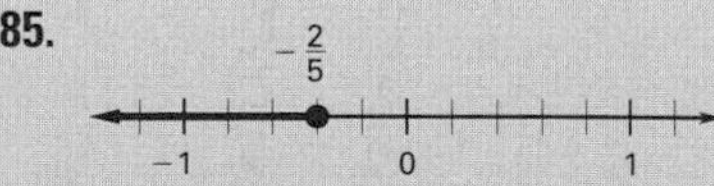

86.

87.

88.
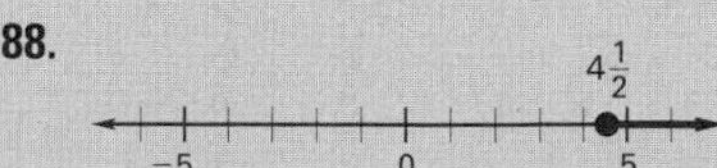

89–94, 103–104. See Additional Answers beginning on page AA1.

21.

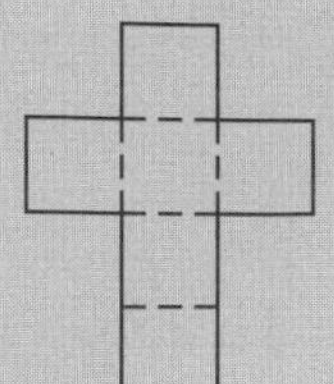

Chapter 10

EXTRA PRACTICE

Find the circumference and area of a circle with the given radius *r* or diameter *d*. Use 3.14 for π. Round your result to the nearest tenth. (Lesson 10.1)

1. $r = 7.5$ in. **47.1 in.; 176.6 in.^{2}**
2. $r = 2.2$ yd **13.8 yd; 15.2 yd^2**
3. $d = 40$ cm **125.6 cm; 1256 cm^2**
4. $r = 6.2$ cm **38.9 cm; 120.7 cm^2**
5. $d = 1$ ft **3.1 ft; 0.8 ft^2**
6. $d = 0.5$ mm **1.6 mm; 0.2 mm^2**
7. $r = 9.3$ m **58.4 m; 271.6 m^2**
8. $d = 11$ in. **34.5 in.; 95.0 in.^{2}**

Find the radius and diameter of a circle with the given circumference *C* or area *A*. Use 3.14 for π. Round your result to the nearest tenth. (Lesson 10.1)

9. $A = 35$ in.^{2} **3.3 in.; 6.7 in.**
10. $A = 77$ cm^2 **5 cm; 9.9 cm**
11. $A = 1000$ ft^2 **17.8 ft; 35.7 ft**
12. $C = 57.8$ cm **9.2 cm; 18.4 cm**
13. $C = 17.3$ ft **2.8 ft; 5.5 ft**
14. $A = 5$ m^2 **1.3 m; 2.5 m**
15. $C = 33.3$ yd **5.3 yd; 10.6 yd**
16. $C = 3.14$ in. **$\frac{1}{2}$ in.; 1 in.**

17. The measure of the central angle of a sector of circle is 45°. If the area of the sector is 12 square feet, find the area of the circle. (Lesson 10.1) **96 ft^2**

In Exercises 18–21, use the solid shown. (Lesson 10.2)

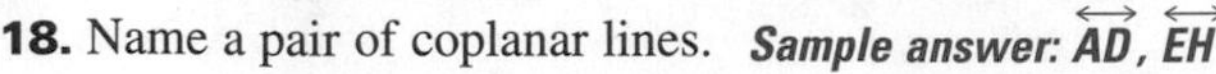

18. Name a pair of coplanar lines. ***Sample answer:* $\overleftrightarrow{AD}$, $\overleftrightarrow{EH}$**

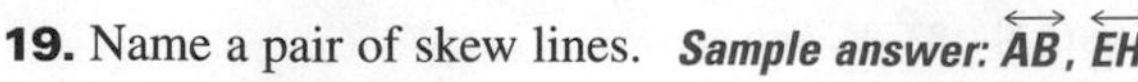

19. Name a pair of skew lines. ***Sample answer:* $\overleftrightarrow{AB}$, $\overleftrightarrow{EH}$**

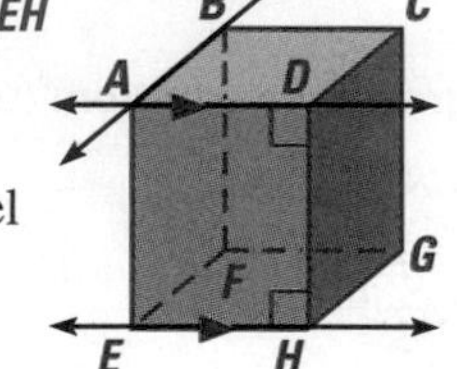

20. Is the plane containing points *A*, *B*, *C*, and *D* parallel to the plane containing points *A*, *D*, *H*, and *E*? **no**

21. Sketch a net for the solid. **See margin.**

Identify the solid formed by folding the net. (Lesson 10.2)

22.

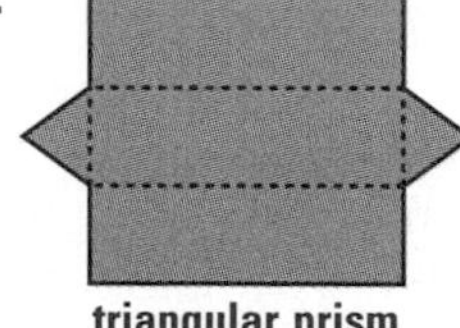

triangular prism

23.

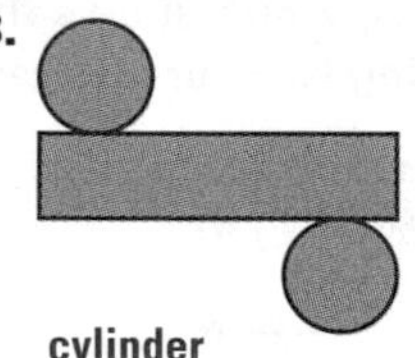

cylinder

24.

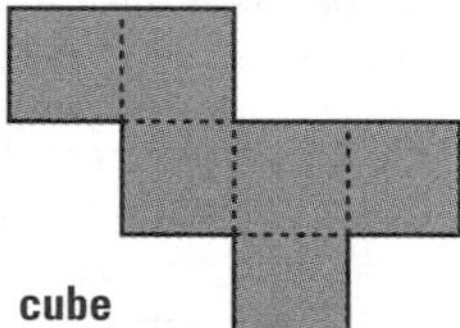

cube

Find the surface area of the right prism or right cylinder. (Lesson 10.3)

25. **562 ft^2**

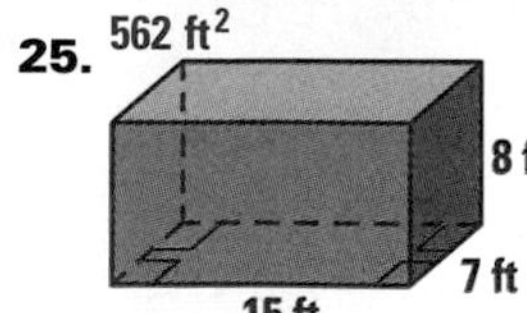

26. **108 m^2**

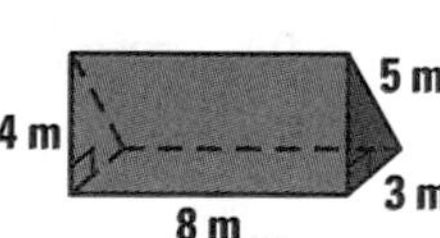

27. **216π cm^2**

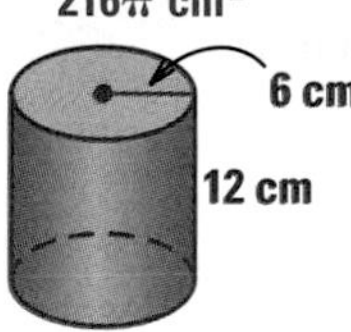

Find the volume of the prism. (In Exercises 28 and 29, the solids are right. In Exercise 30, the solid has rectangular bases.) (Lesson 10.4)

28. **960 ft^3**

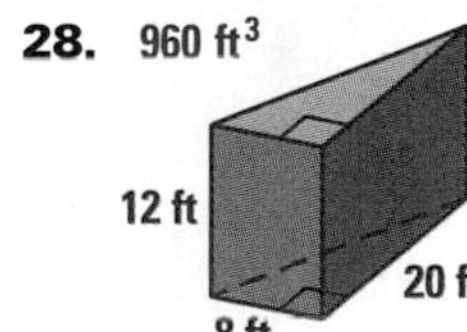

29. $B = 31.8$ cm^2 **318 cm^3**

10 cm

30. **648 m^3**

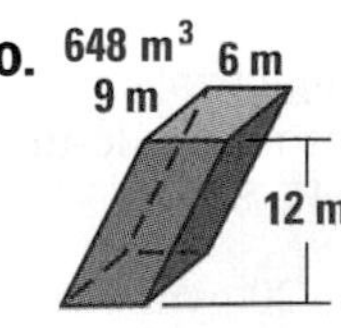

Find the volume of the cylinder. (Lesson 10.5)

31. 4 cm, 6 cm, 96π cm^3

32. 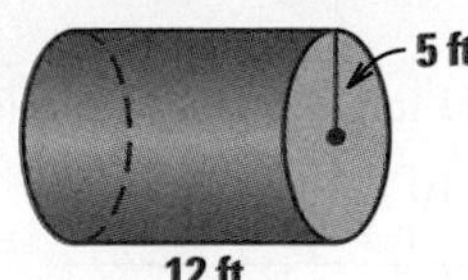

300π ft^3

33. 1600π m^3 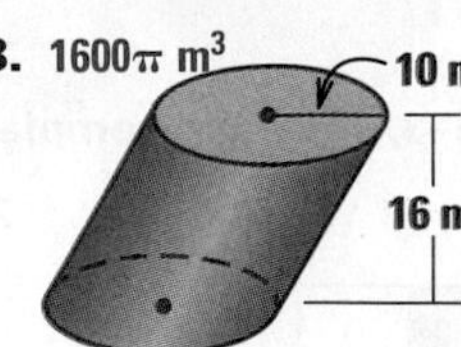

The volume V and radius r of a cylinder are given. Find the height of the cylinder. Round your answer to the nearest tenth. (Lesson 10.5)

34. $V = 145.5$ in.^{3}; $r = 5$ in. 1.9 in.

35. $V = 88.6$ cm^3; $r = 4$ cm 1.8 cm

36. $V = 300$ ft^3; $r = 12$ ft 0.7 ft

Find the volume of the pyramid or cone. (In Exercises 37 and 40, the solids have square bases.) (Lesson 10.6)

37. 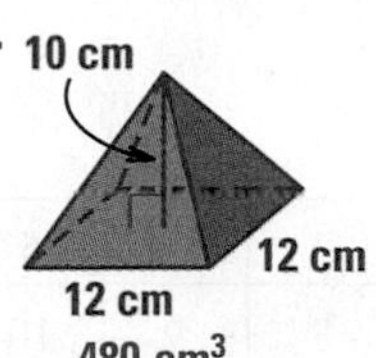

480 cm^3

38. 1125π m^3 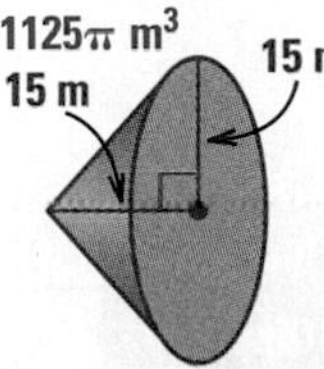

39. 15π ft^3 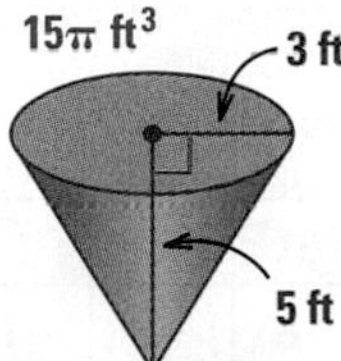

40. 48 in.^{3} 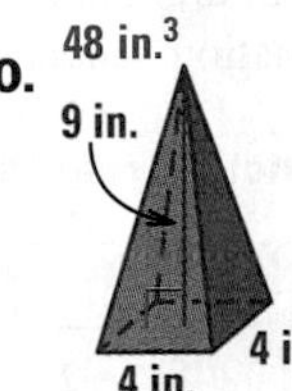

Find the volume of the solid. (In Exercise 42, the pyramid and prism have square bases and the prism is right.) (Lesson 10.6)

41. $\frac{980\pi}{3}$ 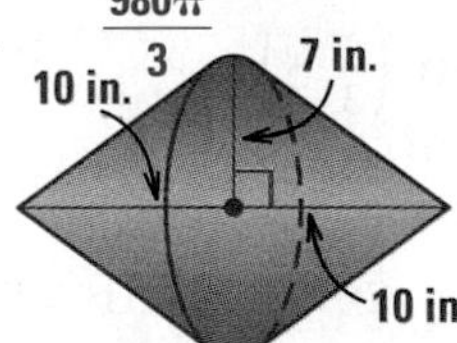

42. $2025\frac{1}{3}$ cm^3 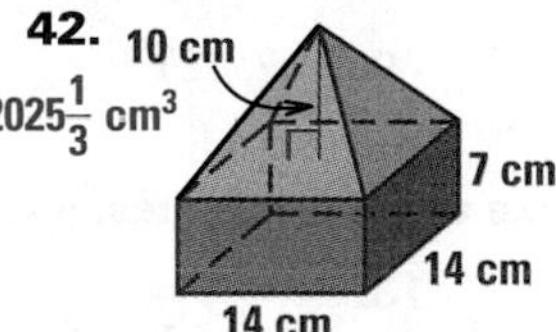

43. $18{,}240\pi$ ft^3 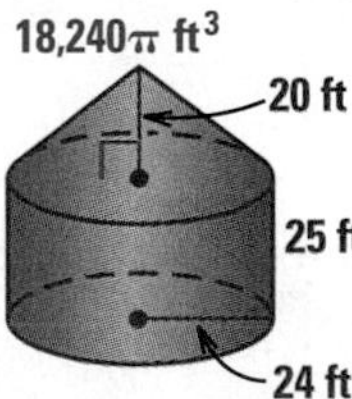

Find the volume of a sphere with the given radius. (Lesson 10.7)

44. 15 centimeters 4500π cm^3

45. 23 inches $\frac{48{,}668\pi}{3}$ in.^{3}

46. 6.3 feet 333.396π ft^3

47. 1.8 meters 7.776π m^3

Determine whether the solids are similar. Explain your answer. (Lesson 10.8)

48. yes 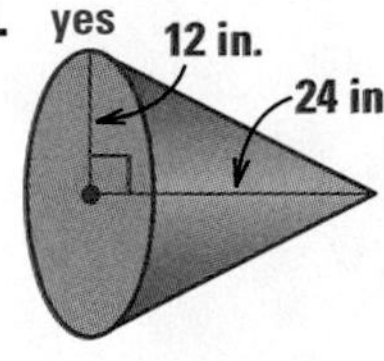

49. no 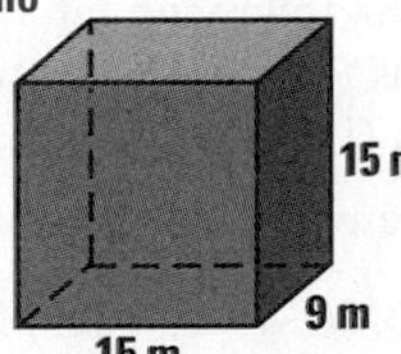

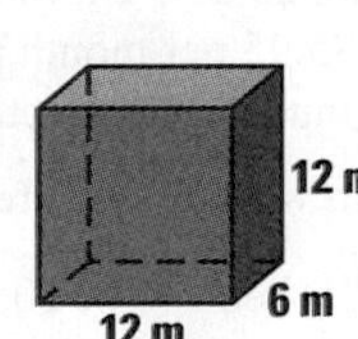

The solids shown are similar. Use the ratio of their surface areas to find the ratio of their volumes. (Lesson 10.8)

50. 25 : 9 125 : 27

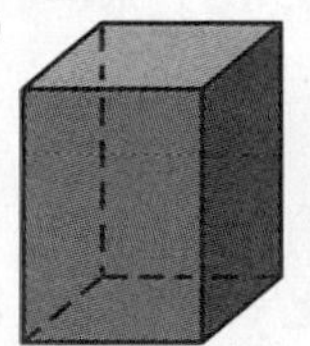
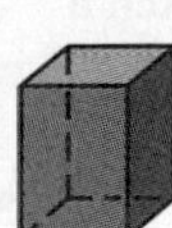

51. 4 : 1 8 : 1

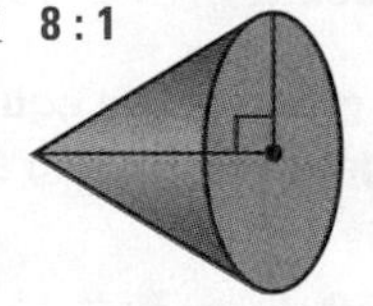

EXTRA PRACTICE

1.

Input, x	0	1	2
Output, y	0	6	12

2.

Input, x	−3	0	3
Output, y	7	10	13

3.

Input, x	2	−1	10
Output, y	−1	−4	7

11. $y = x$; *Sample answer:*

x	−2	−1	0	1	2
y	−2	−1	0	1	2

12. $y = 10x + 5$; *Sample answer:*

x	−2	−1	0	1	2
y	−15	−5	5	15	25

13. $y = -2x + 8$; *Sample answer:*

x	−2	−1	0	1	2
y	12	10	8	6	4

14. $y = -\frac{2}{3}x + 17$; *Sample answer:*

x	−6	−3	0	3	6
y	21	19	17	15	13

15. $y = -3x + 4$; *Sample answer:*

x	−2	−1	0	1	2
y	10	7	4	1	−2

16. $y = -2x - 7$; *Sample answer:*

x	−2	−1	0	1	2
y	−3	−5	−7	−9	−11

17. $y = -3x + \frac{1}{4}$; *Sample answer:*

x	−2	−1	0	1	2
y	$6\frac{1}{4}$	$3\frac{1}{4}$	$\frac{1}{4}$	$-2\frac{3}{4}$	$-5\frac{3}{4}$

18. $y = \frac{5}{3}x + 10$; *Sample answer:*

x	−6	−3	0	3	6
y	0	5	10	15	20

19–22, 24–32. See Additional Answers beginning on page AA1.

Chapter 11

In Exercises 1–3, copy and complete the table for each function. (Lesson 11.1) **1–3. See margin.**

1. $y = 6x$

Input, x	0	1	2
Output, y	?	?	?

2. $y = x + 10$

Input, x	−3	0	3
Output, y	?	?	?

3. $y = x - 3$

Input, x	2	?	?
Output, y	?	−4	7

4. You are preparing a turkey dinner. You need a turkey with weight w (in pounds) equal to $\frac{3}{4}$ times the number n of people you are serving. Identify the input and output variables. Then write a rule for a function to represent the situation. (Lesson 11.1) **input = n; output = w; $w = \frac{3}{4}n$**

Write a function rule that relates x and y. (Lesson 11.1)

5. **$y = -2x$**

Input, x	1	2	3	4	5
Output, y	−2	−4	−6	−8	−10

6. **$y = x + 5$**

Input, x	1	2	3	4	5
Output, y	6	7	8	9	10

Determine whether the ordered pair is a solution of $3x - y = 6$. Explain. (Lesson 11.2)

7. $(0, -6)$ **yes; $3(0) - (-6) = 0 + 6 = 6$**

8. $(2, 0)$ **yes; $3(2) - (0) = 6 - 0 = 6$**

9. $(-2, 12)$ **no; $3(-2) - (12) = -6 - 12 = -18$**

10. $\left(\frac{1}{3}, 5\right)$

Write the equation in function form. Then make a table of values. (Lesson 11.2) **11–18. See margin.**

11. $x - y = 0$
12. $y - 10x = 5$
13. $2x + y = 8$
14. $2x + 3y = 51$
15. $9x + 3y = 12$
16. $-4x - 2y = 14$
17. $8y + 24x = 2$
18. $3y - 5x = 30$

Graph the equation. (Lesson 11.3) **19–22. See margin.**

19. $x = 3$
20. $y = -5$
21. $y = x - 4$
22. $y = 3x + 1$

In Exercises 23 and 24, use the following information. A long distance calling plan costs \$5.95 per month plus \$.07 per minute times the total number of long distance minutes. The function $C = 0.07t + 5.95$ models the situation. (Lesson 11.3)

23. Explain what C and t represent in the function. **C = total monthly cost of long distance service; t = total number of long distance minutes in a month**

24. Find C when $t = 0, 10, 20, 30, 40,$ and 50. Make a table of values. Graph the ordered pairs from the table. **See margin.**

Find the intercepts of the graph of the equation. (Lesson 11.4) **25–28. See margin.**

25. $y = 2x + 2$
26. $3x + 5y = 15$
27. $4x - 7y = 28$
28. $6x + 7y = 21$

Find the intercepts of the graph of the equation and use them to sketch a quick graph. Check your graph by finding and plotting a third solution. (Lesson 11.4) **29–32. See margin.**

29. $x + y = 4$
30. $5x - 3y = 15$
31. $3x - 2y = 12$
32. $y = -\frac{3}{4}x - 6$

In Exercises 33–40, plot the points. Then find the slope of the line through the points. **(Lesson 11.5) 33–40. See margin.**

33. (7, 1), (−2,1) **34.** (4, 0), (5, 1) **35.** (0, 3), (3, 1) **36.** (2, 5), (5, 2)

37. (2, −1), (−3, 4) **38.** (0, −2), (3, −1) **39.** (−1, 0), (2, −2) **40.** (−3, 0), (0, 3)

41. One line has slope −2 and another has slope −5. Which line is steeper? **(Lesson 11.5) The line with slope −5.**

Find the slope and *y*-intercept of the line whose equation is given. (Lesson 11.6)

42. $y = -2x - 2$ **−2; −2** **43.** $y - 5x = 10$ **5; 10** **44.** $y = 2x + 5$ **2; 5** **45.** $y = -3x - 3$ **−3; −3**

46. $y = 9x - 4$ **9; −4** **47.** $y = -7x + 15$ **−7; 15** **48.** $x + 8y = 24$ $-\frac{1}{8}$**; 3** **49.** $6x - 5y = 30$ $\frac{6}{5}$**; −6**

In Exercises 50–53, sketch a quick graph of the line whose equation is given. (Lesson 11.6) 50–53. See margin.

50. $y = -2 + 3x$ **51.** $2y = -8x + 14$ **52.** $3x + 5y = 15$ **53.** $7x + 14y = 49$

54. A restaurant offers children's birthday parties at a cost of \$35 plus \$3 per child. Write and graph a linear equation that models the relationship between *x*, the number of children and *y*, the cost of the party. Then find the cost of a party for 15 children. **(Lesson 11.6)** $y = 3x + 35$**; See margin; \$80**

Suppose *y* varies directly with *x*. Use the given values to write and graph an equation that relates *x* and *y*. Find the value of *y* when *x* = 4. (Lesson 11.7)

55. $x = 3, y = -24$ $y = -8x$**; See margin; −32**

56. $x = -4, y = -9$ $y = \frac{9}{4}x$**; See margin; 9**

57. $x = -\frac{1}{2}, y = 3$ $y = -6x$**; See margin; −24**

58. $x = 20, y = -5$ $y = -\frac{1}{4}x$**; See margin; −1**

Determine whether the ordered pair is a solution of 2*x* − 3*y* > 12. Explain your answer. (Lesson 11.8)

59. (0, 1) **no; 2(0) − 3(1) = −3 < 12**

60. (8, 2) **no; 2(8) − 3(2) = 10 < 12**

61. (2, −4) **yes; 2(2) − 3(−4) = 16 > 12**

62. (12, 2) **yes; 2(12) − 3(2) = 18 > 12**

In Exercises 63–66, graph the inequality. Then list several solutions. (Lesson 11.8) 63–66. See margin.

63. $y > -x - 3$ **64.** $y \le 4x$ **65.** $y - 2x < 6$ **66.** $x - y > 10$

67. The difference of two numbers *x* and *y* is 14 *and* *y* is 4 less than one half of *x*. Write a system of linear equations that represents the conditions. **(Lesson 11.9)** $x - y = 14,\ y = \frac{1}{2}x - 4$

68. The sum of two numbers *x* and *y* is less than or equal to 30 *and* *y* is greater than 3 times *x*. Write a system of linear inequalities that represents the conditions. **(Lesson 11.9)** $x + y \le 30,\ y > 3x$

Graph the system of equations. Then find the solution. (Lesson 11.9)

69. $y = 4x$; $y - x = 9$ **(3, 12); See margin.**

70. $x = -1$; $x + y = 1$ **(−1, 2); See margin.**

71. $y = x + 6$; $y = 2x$ **(6, 12); See margin.**

72. $y = -x - 8$; $x = y$ **(−4, −4); See margin.**

Graph the system of inequalities. Then identify three solutions. (Lesson 11.9) 73–76. See margin.

73. $x < 1$; $y > 3$ **74.** $y < x$; $y \ge -x - 1$ **75.** $x + y \ge 2$; $y < 2$ **76.** $y > -x - 3$; $y < x - 1$

EXTRA PRACTICE

33. 0

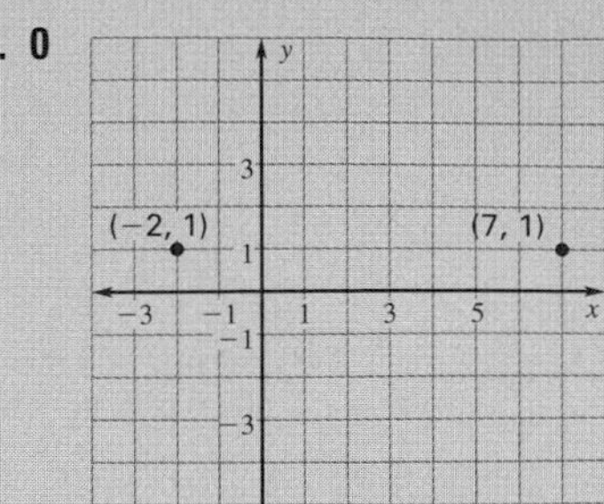

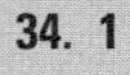

34. 1

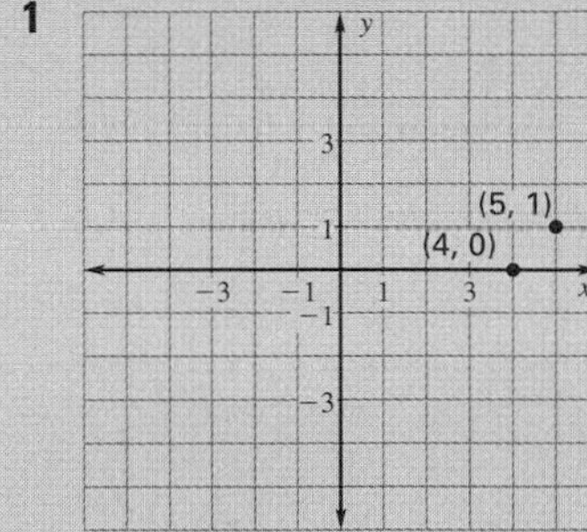

35. $-\frac{2}{3}$

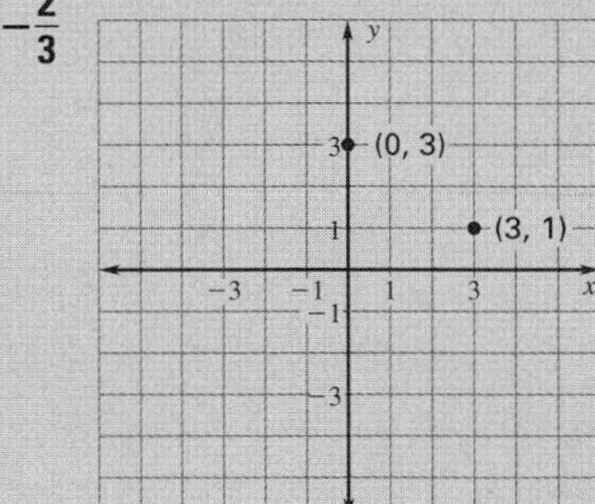

36. −1

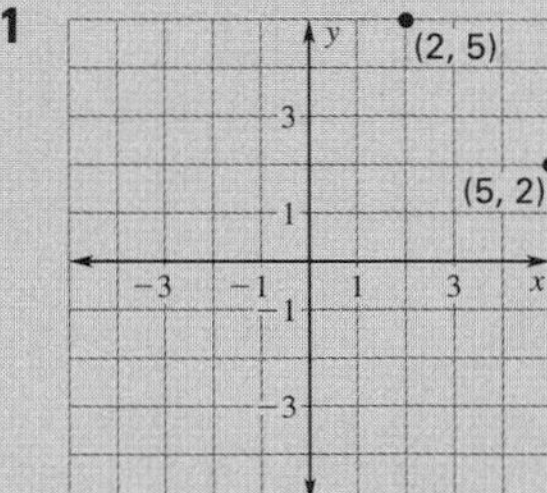

37. −1

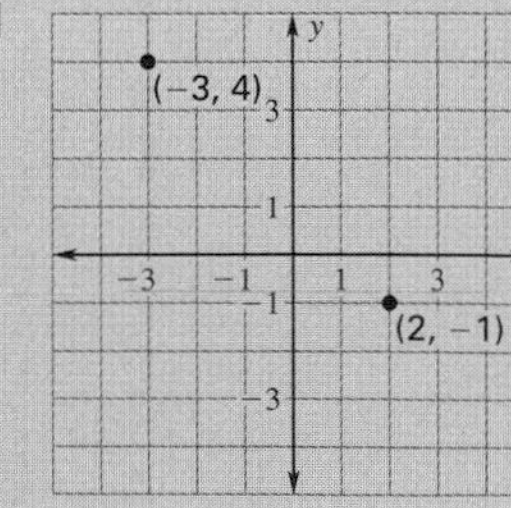

38–40, 50–58, 63–66, 69–76. See Additional Answers beginning on page AA1.

42. $11n^4 - 10n^3 - n^2 + 4n - 5$; 4

43. $k^4 - 14k^3 + 2k^2 - 8k + 11$; 4

EXTRA PRACTICE

Chapter 12

Simplify the expression. (Lesson 12.1)

1. $(12z)^2$ $144z^2$ **2.** $(10m)^3$ $1000m^3$ **3.** $(3ab)^3$ $27a^3b^3$ **4.** $(4n)^2$ $16n^2$

5. $(-2xz)^5$ $-32x^5z^5$ **6.** $5(pq)^5$ $5p^5q^5$ **7.** $-(5x)^3$ $-125x^3$ **8.** $(-2mn)^6$ $64m^6n^6$

9. $\left(\frac{y}{5}\right)^2$ $\frac{y^2}{25}$ **10.** $\left(\frac{5}{k}\right)^3$ $\frac{125}{k^3}$ **11.** $\left(\frac{2x}{3}\right)^4$ $\frac{16x^4}{81}$ **12.** $\left(\frac{-3}{4t}\right)^3$ $-\frac{27}{64t^3}$

13. $(y^3)^6$ y^{18} **14.** $(m^{10})^2$ m^{20} **15.** $(wz^6)^6$ w^6z^{36} **16.** $(a^5b^3)^4$ $a^{20}b^{12}$

Evaluate the power. Write your answer in scientific notation. (Lesson 12.1)

17. $(2 \times 10^4)^5$ 3.2×10^{21} **18.** $(3 \times 10^{12})^2$ 9×10^{24} **19.** $(5 \times 10^8)^3$ 1.25×10^{26} **20.** $(1.5 \times 10^7)^2$ 2.25×10^{14}

Write the polynomial in standard form. Then list its terms. (Lesson 12.2)

21. $2x - 3x^2 + 5$ $-3x^2 + 2x + 5$; $-3x^2$, $2x$, 5 **22.** $2y^2 - y^3 + 3y$ $-y^3 + 2y^2 + 3y$; $-y^3$, $2y^2$, $3y$ **23.** $9 - 3z^2 + 6z$ $-3z^2 + 6z + 9$; $-3z^2$, $6z$, 9

Determine whether the expression is a polynomial. If it is, state whether it is a *monomial*, a *binomial*, or a *trinomial*. (Lesson 12.2)

24. $14x^3 - x^4 + 1.25x$ yes; trinomial **25.** $\frac{1}{2}y - \frac{7}{8}y^2$ yes; binomial **26.** $15n^{-3}$ no **27.** $\frac{5}{k} - 2k + k^2$ no

Simplify the polynomial and write the result in standard form. (Lesson 12.2)

28. $b + 4b^2 - 7b + 1$ $4b^2 - 6b + 1$ **29.** $m^2 + 3m - 4 + 2m^2 - 5m + 5$ $3m^2 - 2m + 1$

30. $n + 2n^2 - 2n + 5 - n^2$ $n^2 - n + 5$ **31.** $3 - 2p + 3p^3 - p^2 + 5p - 6$ $3p^3 - p^2 + 3p - 3$

32. $2.2x^2 - 3.5x + 2.5x^2 + 2.3x$ $4.7x^2 - 1.2x$ **33.** $\frac{4}{5}y + 6 - \frac{2}{5}y - 7$ $\frac{2}{5}y - 1$

Add or subtract the polynomials using a horizontal format. State the degree of the result. (Lesson 12.3)

34. $(8a^2 - 3a - 3) + (-3a^2 + 4a - 7)$ $5a^2 + a - 10$; 2

35. $(3b^2 - 4b - 11) - (-b^2 - 2b + 1)$ $4b^2 - 2b - 12$; 2

36. $(m^3 - 3m^2 + 8m - 11) + (3m^3 + 2m^2 - 10m - 7)$ $4m^3 - m^2 - 2m - 18$; 3

37. $(3n^4 - 3n^3 + 2n^2 - 16n - 11) + (-5n^4 + 2n^3 - 11n^2 + 10n - 7)$ $-2n^4 - n^3 - 9n^2 - 6n - 18$; 4

38. $(3x^3 - 2x^2 + 5x - 11) - (-3x^3 + 11x^2 - 7x - 6)$ $6x^3 - 13x^2 + 12x - 5$; 3

39. $(2y^4 - 11y^3 - 2y^2 + 5y - 11) - (-y^4 + 6y^3 + 11y^2 - 7y + 10)$ $3y^4 - 17y^3 - 13y^2 + 12y - 21$; 4

Add or subtract the polynomials using a vertical format. State the degree of the result. (Lesson 12.3)

40.
$$\begin{array}{r} x^3 + 5x^2 - 3x + 2 \\ +\ \underline{(x^3 - 3x^2 + 10x - 8)} \end{array}$$
$2x^3 + 2x^2 + 7x - 6$; 3

41.
$$\begin{array}{r} 5w^4 - 6w^3 - w^2 + 10w - 7 \\ +\ \underline{(-2w^4 + 2w^3 + 9w^2 - w + 3)} \end{array}$$
$3w^4 - 4w^3 + 8w^2 + 9w - 4$; 4

42.
$$\begin{array}{r} 12n^4 - 5n^3 + n^2 + 3n - 1 \\ -\ \underline{(n^4 + 5n^3 + 2n^2 - n + 4)} \end{array}$$

42, 43. See margin.

43.
$$\begin{array}{r} 11k^4 - 7k^3 + k^2 - 2k + 3 \\ -\ \underline{(10k^4 + 7k^3 - k^2 + 6k - 8)} \end{array}$$

Find the product. (Lesson 12.4)

44. $3x(x^2 - 1)$ $3x^3 - 3x$

45. $2a(a^2 + 3a + 2)$ $2a^3 + 6a^2 + 4a$

46. $-3(4x^2 + 7x - 2)$ $-12x^2 - 21x + 6$

47. $3b^2(-5b - 8)$ $-15b^3 - 24b^2$

48. $-y^3(2y^2 - 5y + 12)$ $-2y^5 + 5y^4 - 12y^3$

49. $4n(-2n^2 + 2n - 3)$ $-8n^3 + 8n^2 - 12n$

50. $m(-2m^3 - 7m + 15)$ $-2m^4 - 7m^2 + 15m$

51. $-5z(3z^4 - 2z^2 + 6)$ $-15z^5 + 10z^3 - 30z$

52. $a^4(-a^3 + a^2 - a + 1)$ $-a^7 + a^6 - a^5 + a^4$

Exercises 53–55 refer to a right rectangular prism with height $5d$ and a base that has length d and width $2d - 1$. (Lesson 12.4)

53. Write an expression for the base area of the prism. $2d^2 - d$

54. Write an expression for the volume of the prism. $10d^3 - 5d^2$

55. Write an expression for the surface area of the prism. $34d^2 - 12d$

Find the product. (Lesson 12.5)

56. $(x + 2)(3x + 5)$ $3x^2 + 11x + 10$

57. $(5x + 6)(x + 3)$ $5x^2 + 21x + 18$

58. $(3x + 1)(2x + 3)$ $6x^2 + 11x + 3$

59. $(2x + 5)(5x + 2)$ $10x^2 + 29x + 10$

60. $(7x + 7)(3x + 3)$ $21x^2 + 42x + 21$

61. $(4x + 3)(4x + 2)$ $16x^2 + 20x + 6$

62. $(3x + 6)(4x + 7)$ $12x^2 + 45x + 42$

63. $(2x + 5)(3x + 1)$ $6x^2 + 17x + 5$

64. $(5x + 7)(3x + 9)$ $15x^2 + 66x + 63$

Write as a polynomial in standard form. (Lesson 12.5)

65. $(x + 12)^2$ $x^2 + 24x + 144$

66. $(z + 6)^2$ $z^2 + 12z + 36$

67. $(k + 8)^2$ $k^2 + 16k + 64$

68. $(b + 11)^2$ $b^2 + 22b + 121$

69. $(5 + n)^2$ $n^2 + 10n + 25$

70. $(3 + t)^2$ $t^2 + 6t + 9$

71. $(2x + 3)^2$ $4x^2 + 12x + 9$

72. $(3y + 1)^2$ $9y^2 + 6y + 1$

73. $(a^2 + 3)^2$ $a^4 + 6a^2 + 9$

74. $(n^2 + 4)^2$ $n^4 + 8n^2 + 16$

75. $(w^2 + 7)^2$ $w^4 + 14w^2 + 49$

76. $(2m^2 + 1)^2$ $4m^4 + 4m^2 + 1$

Make a table of values for the function. Plot the xy-pairs and draw a smooth curve through the points. (Lesson 12.6) 77–84. See margin.

77. $y = 0.8x^2$

78. $y = -2x^2$

79. $y = \frac{3}{4}x^2$

80. $y = -\frac{1}{2}x^2$

81. $y = 1.25x^2$

82. $y = \frac{3}{2}x^2$

83. $y = 1.5x^3$

84. $y = -2x^3$

Simplify the expression. (Lesson 12.7)

85. $\sqrt{49}$ 7

86. $\sqrt{64}$ 8

87. $\sqrt{k^{12}}$ k^6

88. $\sqrt{t^6}$ $|t^3|$

89. $\sqrt{16n^4}$ $4n^2$

90. $\sqrt{x^2y^{12}}$ $|xy^6|$

91. $\sqrt{a^4b^2}$ $|a^2b|$

92. $\sqrt{121m^6y^8}$ $|11m^3y^4|$

Solve the equation. (Lesson 12.7)

93. $b^2 = 121$ $-11, 11$

94. $k^2 = 400$ $-20, 20$

95. $x^2 - 2 = 47$ $-7, 7$

96. $5z^2 = 80$ $-4, 4$

97. $2d^2 + 17 = 35$ $-3, 3$

98. $4w^2 - 31 = 545$ $-12, 12$

Solve by graphing. (Lesson 12.7) 99–104. See margin for graphs.

99. $\frac{1}{2}x^2 = 8$ $-4, 4$

100. $\frac{1}{2}x^3 = 4$ 2

101. $-\frac{1}{3}x^2 = -3$ $-3, 3$

102. $x^3 = x^2$ 0, 1

103. $x^2 = -x$ $-1, 0$

104. $x^3 = x$ $-1, 0, 1$

77. Sample answer:

x	-2	-1	0	1	2
y	3.2	0.8	0	0.8	3.2

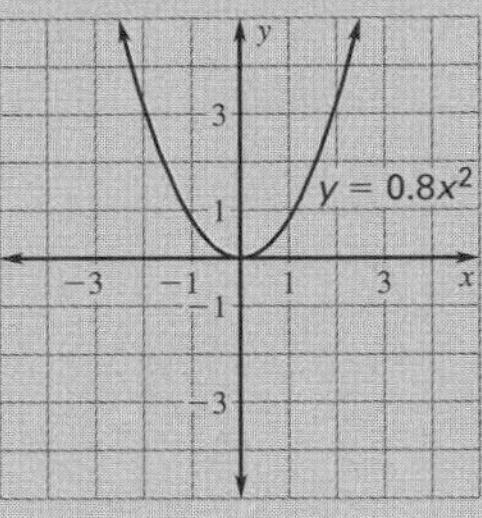

78. Sample answer:

x	-2	-1	0	1	2
y	-8	-2	0	-2	-8

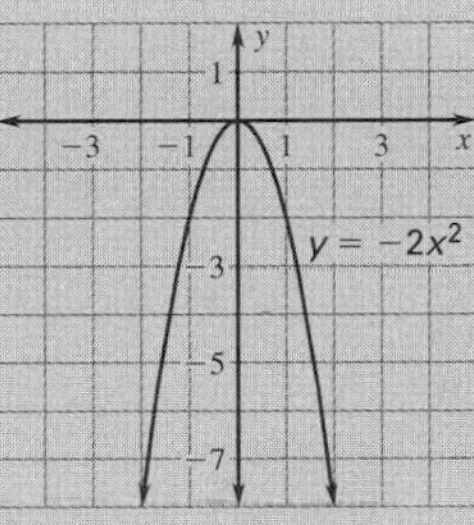

79. Sample answer:

x	-2	-1	0	1	2
y	3	$\frac{3}{4}$	0	$\frac{3}{4}$	3

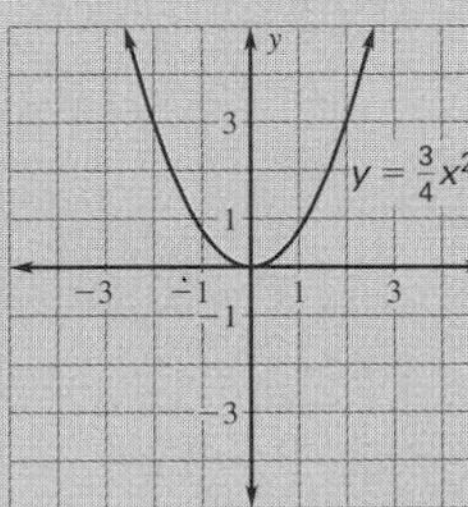

80. Sample answer:

x	-2	-1	0	1	2
y	-2	$-\frac{1}{2}$	0	$-\frac{1}{2}$	-2

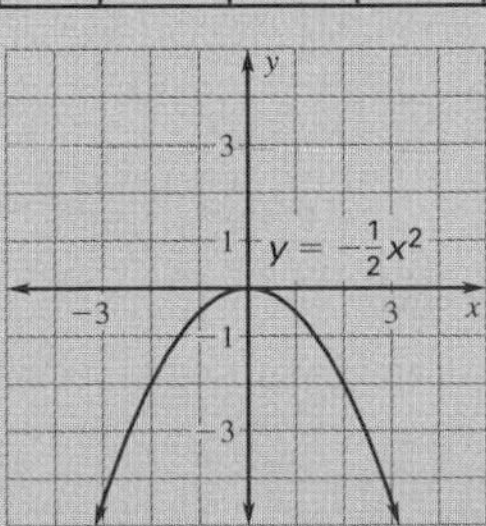

81–84, 99–104. See Additional Answers beginning on page AA1.

End-of-Course Test

RATIONAL NUMBERS

NS 1.2, 1.3, 1.4, 1.5, 2.2

Perform the indicated operation.

1. $-5 + 8$ **3**

2. $6 - (-3)$ **9**

3. $(-4)(-7)$ **28**

4. $\frac{-24}{12}$ **−2**

Write the prime factorization of each number. Use exponents for repeated factors.

5. 720 $2^4 \cdot 3^2 \cdot 5$

6. 91 $7 \cdot 13$

7. 1445 $5 \cdot 17^2$

8. 415 $5 \cdot 83$

Perform the indicated operation. Then simplify, if possible.

9. $\frac{11}{15} - \left(\frac{-5}{18}\right)$ $\frac{91}{90}$

10. $\frac{-7}{18} + \frac{1}{36}$ $-\frac{13}{36}$

11. $\left(\frac{-12}{35}\right)\left(\frac{49}{50}\right)$ $-\frac{42}{125}$

12. $\frac{-14}{45} \div \left(\frac{-42}{125}\right)$ $\frac{25}{27}$

Tell whether the number is *rational* or *irrational*. Explain.

13. 0.107 **rational; it is a terminating decimal.**

14. $\sqrt{\frac{25}{9}}$ **rational;** $\sqrt{\frac{25}{9}} = \frac{5}{3}$

15. 0.121121112. . . **irrational; it is a nonterminating, nonrepeating decimal.**

16. $\sqrt{7}$ **irrational; 7 is not a perfect square so** $\sqrt{7}$ **is equivalent to a nonterminating, nonrepeating decimal.**

Write the decimal as a fraction. Simplify if possible.

17. 0.37 $\frac{37}{100}$

18. 0.64 $\frac{16}{25}$

19. 0.564 $\frac{141}{250}$

20. 1.0025 $\frac{401}{400}$

Write the fraction as a decimal. Tell whether the decimal is a *terminating decimal* or a *repeating decimal*.

21. $\frac{13}{12}$ $1.08\overline{3}$**; repeating**

22. $\frac{7}{40}$ **0.175; terminating**

23. $\frac{3}{8}$ **0.375; terminating**

24. $\frac{5}{7}$ $0.\overline{714285}$**; repeating**

PERCENTS IN PROBLEM SOLVING

NS 1.7

25. As a real estate agent, you earn a 6% commission on the sale of a house. If a house sells for $150,000, what commission do you earn? **$9000**

26. A $25 book is on sale for $18. Find the amount of discount and the percent of discount. **$7; 28%**

27. The wholesale price of a shirt is $12. The percent of markup is 120%. Find the retail price of the shirt and the profit on each shirt. **$26.40; $14.40**

28. You deposit $600 in a savings account. The annual interest rate is 6.5%. How much simple interest will you earn in 8 months? **$26**

29. You deposit $1500 in an account at 8% annual interest compounded quarterly. Find the balance in the account after three years. **$1902.36**

END-OF-COURSE TEST

EXPONENTS AND ABSOLUTE VALUE
NS 1.2, 2.3, 2.5

Simplify the expression.

30. $\left(\frac{1}{4}\right)^2 \cdot \left(\frac{1}{4}\right)^3$ $\left(\frac{1}{4}\right)^5 = \frac{1}{1024}$ **31.** $\frac{2^{11}}{2^8}$ $2^3 = 8$ **32.** $\left(\frac{2}{3}\right)^5 \div \left(\frac{2}{3}\right)^3$ $\left(\frac{2}{3}\right)^2 = \frac{4}{9}$ **33.** $\left(\frac{3}{5}\right)^4$ $\frac{3^4}{5^4} = \frac{81}{625}$

In Exercises 34–37, evaluate the expression.

34. $|-16|$ **16** **35.** $|0|$ **0** **36.** $|-3-7|$ **10** **37.** $|-3|-|7|$ **−4**

PROPERTIES
AF 1.3

Name the property illustrated.

38. $2(x + y) = 2x + 2y$ **distributive property**
39. $2(x + y) = (x + y)2$ **commutative property of multiplication**
40. $2(x + y) = 2(y + x)$ **commutative property of addition**

41. $\left(\frac{2}{3}\right)\left(\frac{3}{2}x\right) = \left[\left(\frac{2}{3}\right)\left(\frac{3}{2}\right)\right]x$ **See margin.** **42.** $\left[\left(\frac{2}{3}\right)\left(\frac{3}{2}\right)\right]x = 1 \cdot x$ **See margin.** **43.** $1 \cdot x = x$ **identity property of multiplication**

44. Show and justify the steps you take to simplify $3n + 1 + (-2n)$. **See margin.**

GRAPHING LINEAR FUNCTIONS
AF 3.3, 3.4

In Exercises 45 and 46, use the following information. You are returning home from a trip. The equation $y = 225 - 50x$ represents your distance y (in miles) from home after traveling x hours.

45. Graph the equation for $x \geq 0$ in the coordinate plane. **See margin.**

46. What are the slope and y-intercept of the graph? Explain what the slope and y-intercept mean in terms of the situation. **The slope of −50 means you get 50 miles closer to home each hour; The *y*-intercept of 225 means you start 225 miles from home.**

In Exercises 47 and 48, use the table, which shows the cost of riding a subway.

47. Graph the data from the table in a coordinate plane Draw a line that shows any trend in the data. **See margin.**

Number of rides	2	4	6	8
Cost (dollars)	3	6	9	12

48. What is the slope of the line you drew in Exercise 47? Explain how the slope is related to the cost of a subway ride. **1.5; The slope shows that each ride costs $1.50.**

LINEAR EQUATIONS AND INEQUALITIES
AF 4.0, 4.1

In Exercises 49–56, solve the equation or inequality.

49. $6x + 5 = -1$ **−1** **50.** $2 - 12y = 20$ **−1.5** **51.** $-8x + 3 = 7$ $-\frac{1}{2}$ **52.** $p - 2 = 2p$ **−2**

53. $27 - 4t > 3$ $t < 6$ **54.** $5x - 14 \leq 11$ $x \leq 5$ **55.** $3n + 7 \geq 1$ $n \geq -2$ **56.** $2x + 1 < x$ $x < -1$

41. associative property of multiplication

42. inverse property of multiplication

44. $3n + 1 + (-2n) = 3n + (-2n) + 1$ **Commutative property of addition**
$= [3n + (-2n)] + 1$ **Associative property of addition**
$= [3 + (-2)]n + 1$ **Distributive property**
$= 1 \cdot n + 1$ **Addition**
$= n + 1$ **Identity property of multiplication**

45.

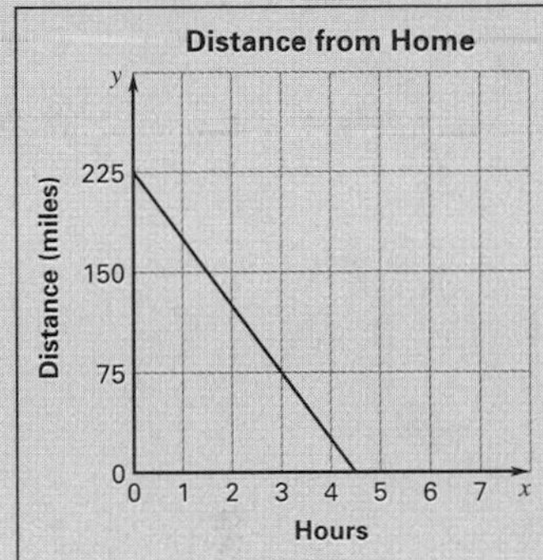

47.

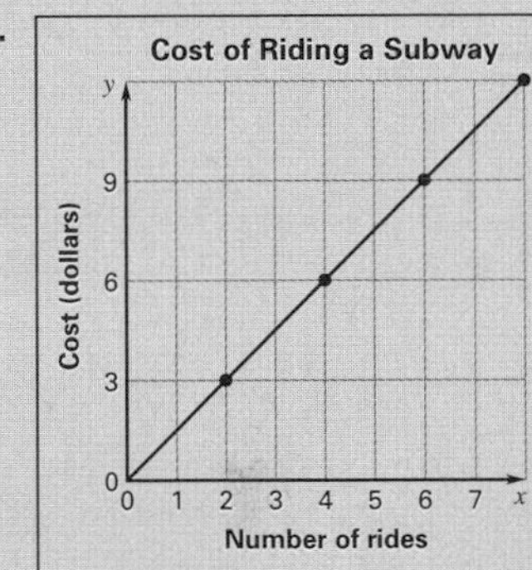

END-OF-COURSE TEST

66.

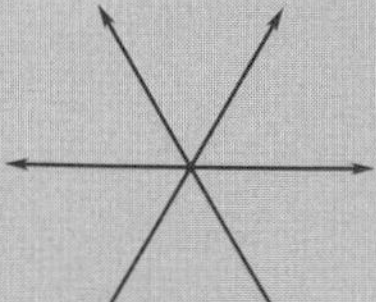

67.

68.

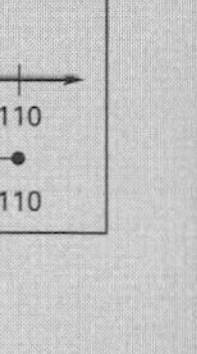

57. You have \$50 and plan to save \$20 each week. Write and solve an equation to find the number of weeks you need to save before you can buy a CD player that costs \$210. Check that your answer is reasonable. **$50 + 20x = 210$; 8 weeks**

UNITS OF MEASURE IN PROBLEM SOLVING

AF 4.2, MG 1.3

58. A running track is $\frac{1}{4}$ mile long. You run around the track 10 times in 25 minutes. Find your average speed in miles per hour. Check your answer using unit analysis. **6 miles per hour**

59. A *person-hour* is a unit of measure representing the work done by one person in one hour. A carpenter estimates that it will take 32 person-hours to install new carpeting. If there are four people installing the carpet, how many hours will the job take? Check your answer using unit analysis. **8 hours**

GEOMETRY CONCEPTS

MG 3.3, 3.4, 3.6

60. The lengths of the legs of a right triangle are 16 centimeters and 63 centimeters. Find the length of the hypotenuse. **65 centimeters**

61. The lengths of the sides of a triangle are 13, 80, and 81. Is the triangle a right triangle? Explain. **No; $13^2 + 80^2 \neq 81^2$**

In Exercises 62 and 63, use the diagram.

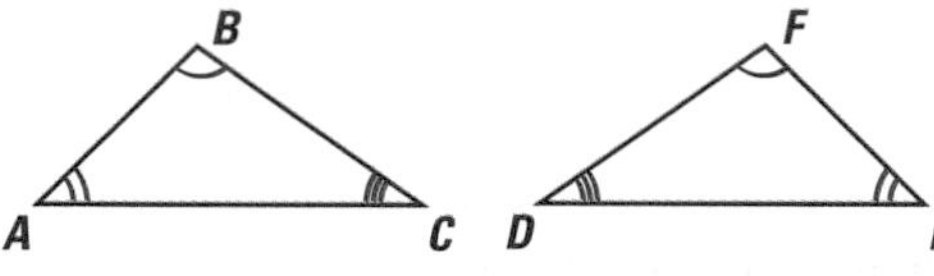

62. Complete the congruence statement: $\triangle ABC \cong \triangle$ __?__. ***EFD***

63. If $m\angle A = 45°$ and $m\angle B = 100°$, find the measures of $\angle D$, $\angle E$, and $\angle F$. **$m\angle D = 35°$; $m\angle E = 45°$; $m\angle F = 100°$**

In Exercises 64 and 65, use the diagram.

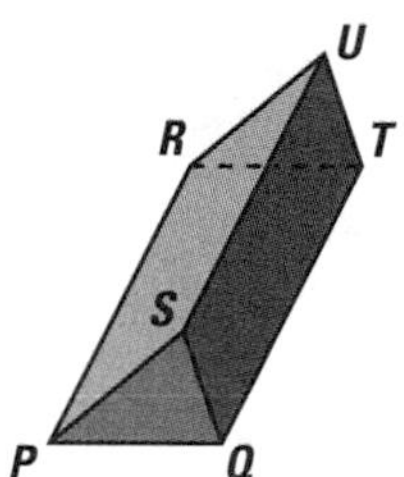

64. Name two parallel lines, two intersecting lines, and two skew lines. ***Sample answers:* line *PR*, line *SU*; line *PR*, line *PQ*; line *PQ*, line *SU***

65. Name two parallel planes and two intersecting planes. ***Sample answers:* plane *SPQ*, plane *URT*; plane *SPQ*, plane *USQT***

66. Is it possible for three lines to intersect in exactly one point? Draw a diagram to support your answer. **Yes; See margin.**

67. Is it possible for three planes to intersect in exactly one line? Make a sketch to support your answer. **Yes; See margin.**

ANALYZING DATA SETS

SDP 1.3

68. The number of shutouts that 10 baseball pitchers had in their careers are as follows: 63, 80, 69, 61, 60, 58, 90, 110, 76, 61. Identify the minimum, lower quartile, the median, the upper quartile, and the maximum of the data. Then draw a box-and-whisker plot of the data. **58; 61; 66; 80; 110; See margin.**

Table of Measures

Time	
60 seconds (sec) = 1 minute (min)	365 days, 52 weeks (approx.), 12 months = 1 year
60 minutes = 1 hour (h)	10 years = 1 decade
24 hours = 1 day	100 years = 1 century
7 days = 1 week	
4 weeks (approx.) = 1 month	

Metric	United States Customary
Length	**Length**
10 millimeters (mm) = 1 centimeter (cm)	12 inches (in.) = 1 foot (ft)
100 cm, 1000 mm = 1 meter (m)	36 in., 3 ft = 1 yard (yd)
1000 m = 1 kilometer (km)	5280 ft, 1760 yd = 1 mile (mi)
Area	**Area**
100 square millimeters (mm^2) = 1 square centimeter (cm^2)	144 square inches ($in.^2$) = 1 square foot (ft^2)
10,000 cm^2 = 1 square meter (m^2)	9 ft^2 = 1 square yard (yd^2)
10,000 m^2 = 1 hectare (ha)	43,560 ft^2, 4840 yd^2 = 1 acre (A)
Volume	**Volume**
1000 cubic millimeters (mm^3) = 1 cubic centimeter (cm^3)	1728 cubic inches ($in.^3$) = 1 cubic foot (ft^3)
1,000,000 cm^3 = 1 cubic meter (m^3)	27 ft^3 = 1 cubic yard (yd^3)
Liquid Capacity	**Liquid Capacity**
1000 milliliters (mL) = 1 liter (L)	8 fluid ounces (fl oz) = 1 cup (c)
1000 L = 1 kiloliter (kL)	2 c = 1 pint (pt)
	2 pt = 1 quart (qt)
	4 qt = 1 gallon (gal)
Mass	**Weight**
1000 milligrams (mg) = 1 gram (g)	16 ounces (oz) = 1 pound (lb)
1000 g = 1 kilogram (kg)	2000 lb = 1 ton (t)
1000 kg = 1 metric ton (t)	
Temperature Degrees Celsius (°C)	**Temperature** Degrees Fahrenheit (°F)
0°C = freezing point of water	32°F = freezing point of water
37°C = normal body temperature	98.6°F = normal body temperature
100°C = boiling point of water	212°F = boiling point of water

TABLES

Finding Squares and Square Roots

TABLES

EXAMPLE 1

Find 54^2.

Solution

Find 54 in the column labeled *No.* (an abbreviation for *Number*). Read across that line to the column labeled *Square*. So, $54^2 = 2916$.

No.	Square	Sq. Root
51	2601	7.141
52	2704	7.211
53	2809	7.280
54	2916	7.348
55	3025	7.416

EXAMPLE 2

Find a decimal approximation of $\sqrt{54}$.

Solution

Find 54 in the column labeled *No.* Read across that line to the column labeled *Sq. Root.* So, an approximation rounded to the nearest thousandth of $\sqrt{54}$ is 7.348.

No.	Square	Sq. Root
51	2601	7.141
52	2704	7.211
53	2809	7.280
54	2916	7.348
55	3025	7.416

EXAMPLE 3

Find a decimal approximation of $\sqrt{3000}$.

Solution

Find the two numbers in the *Square* column that 3000 is between. Read across these two lines to the column labeled *No.*; $\sqrt{3000}$ is between 54 and 55, but closer to 55. So, $\sqrt{3000} \approx 55$. A more accurate approximation can be found using a calculator: 54.772256.

No.	Square	Sq. Root
51	2601	7.141
52	2704	7.211
53	2809	7.280
54	2916	7.348
55	3025	7.416

Table of Squares and Square Roots

No.	Square	Sq. Root	No.	Square	Sq. Root	No.	Square	Sq. Root
1	1	1.000	51	2601	7.141	101	10,201	10.050
2	4	1.414	52	2704	7.211	102	10,404	10.100
3	9	1.732	53	2809	7.280	103	10,609	10.149
4	16	2.000	54	2916	7.348	104	10,816	10.198
5	25	2.236	55	3025	7.416	105	11,025	10.247
6	36	2.449	56	3136	7.483	106	11,236	10.296
7	49	2.646	57	3249	7.550	107	11,449	10.344
8	64	2.828	58	3364	7.616	108	11,664	10.392
9	81	3.000	59	3481	7.681	109	11,881	10.440
10	100	3.162	60	3600	7.746	110	12,100	10.488
11	121	3.317	61	3721	7.810	111	12,321	10.536
12	144	3.464	62	3844	7.874	112	12,544	10.583
13	169	3.606	63	3969	7.937	113	12,769	10.630
14	196	3.742	64	4096	8.000	114	12,996	10.677
15	225	3.873	65	4225	8.062	115	13,225	10.724
16	256	4.000	66	4356	8.124	116	13,456	10.770
17	289	4.123	67	4489	8.185	117	13,689	10.817
18	324	4.243	68	4624	8.246	118	13,924	10.863
19	361	4.359	69	4761	8.307	119	14,161	10.909
20	400	4.472	70	4900	8.367	120	14,400	10.954
21	441	4.583	71	5041	8.426	121	14,641	11.000
22	484	4.690	72	5184	8.485	122	14,884	11.045
23	529	4.796	73	5329	8.544	123	15,129	11.091
24	576	4.899	74	5476	8.602	124	15,376	11.136
25	625	5.000	75	5625	8.660	125	15,625	11.180
26	676	5.099	76	5776	8.718	126	15,876	11.225
27	729	5.196	77	5929	8.775	127	16,129	11.269
28	784	5.292	78	6084	8.832	128	16,384	11.314
29	841	5.385	79	6241	8.888	129	16,641	11.358
30	900	5.477	80	6400	8.944	130	16,900	11.402
31	961	5.568	81	6561	9.000	131	17,161	11.446
32	1024	5.657	82	6724	9.055	132	17,424	11.489
33	1089	5.745	83	6889	9.110	133	17,689	11.533
34	1156	5.831	84	7056	9.165	134	17,956	11.576
35	1225	5.916	85	7225	9.220	135	18,225	11.619
36	1296	6.000	86	7396	9.274	136	18,496	11.662
37	1369	6.083	87	7569	9.327	137	18,769	11.705
38	1444	6.164	88	7744	9.381	138	19,044	11.747
39	1521	6.245	89	7921	9.434	139	19,321	11.790
40	1600	6.325	90	8100	9.487	140	19,600	11.832
41	1681	6.403	91	8281	9.539	141	19,881	11.874
42	1764	6.481	92	8464	9.592	142	20,164	11.916
43	1849	6.557	93	8649	9.644	143	20,449	11.958
44	1936	6.633	94	8836	9.695	144	20,736	12.000
45	2025	6.708	95	9025	9.747	145	21,025	12.042
46	2116	6.782	96	9216	9.798	146	21,316	12.083
47	2209	6.856	97	9409	9.849	147	21,609	12.124
48	2304	6.928	98	9604	9.899	148	21,904	12.166
49	2401	7.000	99	9801	9.950	149	22,201	12.207
50	2500	7.071	100	10,000	10.000	150	22,500	12.247

Table of Symbols

Symbol		Page
$=$	is equal to	3
$\times$, $\cdot$, $(a)(b)$	multiplied by or times	7
$\div$	divided by	7
$\frac{a}{b}$	a divided by b	7
a^m	mth power of a	12
$(\ )$	parentheses	17
$[\ ]$	brackets	17
$\stackrel{?}{=}$	is equal to?	61
$\neq$	is not equal to	61
$>$	is greater than	90
$<$	is less than	90
$\geq$	is greater than or equal to	90
$\leq$	is less than or equal to	90
$\lvert a \rvert$	absolute value of a	106
$-a$	the opposite of a	106
(x, y)	ordered pair	144
$\approx$	is approximately equal to	198
$0.\overline{27}$	repeating decimal, $0.\overline{27} = 0.272727\ldots$	240

Symbol		Page
$\%$	percent	244
$\frac{1}{a}$	reciprocal of a, $a \neq 0$	279
$\frac{a}{b}$	ratio of a to b, or $a : b$	329
$\overleftrightarrow{AB}$	line AB	385
$\overrightarrow{AB}$	ray AB	385
$\overline{AB}$	segment AB	385
AB	the length of segment AB	385
$\cong$	is congruent to	385
$\angle A$	angle A	390
$m\angle A$	measure of angle A	390
$^\circ$	degree(s)	390
$\sim$	is similar to	432
$\sqrt{a}$	the positive square root of a number a when $a > 0$	449
π	pi, a number approximately equal to 3.14	509
m	slope	583
b	y-intercept	589
$\pm$	plus or minus	649

TABLES

Table of Formulas

Geometric Formulas	
Perimeter of a rectangle, p. 22	$P = 2\ell + 2w$ where ℓ = length and w = width
Perimeter of a square, p. 22	$P = 4s$ where s = side length
Area of a square, p. 13	$A = s^2$ where s = side length
Area of a triangle, p. 22	$A = \frac{1}{2}bh$ where b = base and h = height
Area of a rectangle, p. 22	$A = \ell w$ where ℓ = length and w = width
Area of a parallelogram, p. 419	$A = bh$ where b = base and h = height
Area of a trapezoid, p. 419	$A = \frac{1}{2}(b_1 + b_2)h$ where b_1, b_2 = bases and h = height
Circumference of a circle, p. 511	$C = 2\pi r$ where r = radius, or $C = \pi d$ where d = diameter
Area of a circle, p. 512	$A = \pi r^2$ where r = radius
Surface area of a right prism, p. 523	$S = 2B + Ph$ where B = base area, P = base perimeter, and h = height
Surface area of a right cylinder, p. 523	$S = 2B + Ch$ where B = base area, C = base circumference, and h = height
Volume of a cube, p. 13	$V = s^3$ where s = edge length
Volume of a prism, p. 530	$V = Bh$ where B = base area and h = height
Volume of a rectangular prism, p. 530	$V = \ell wh$ where ℓ = length, w = width, and h = height
Volume of a cylinder, p. 535	$V = \pi r^2$ where r = radius and h = height
Volume of a pyramid, p. 539	$V = \frac{1}{3}Bh$ where B = base area and h = height
Volume of a cone, p. 539	$V = \frac{1}{3}\pi r^2 h$ where r = radius and h = height
Volume of a sphere, p. 543	$V = \frac{4}{3}\pi r^3$ where r = radius

Algebraic Formulas	
Distance formula, p. 470	The distance between (x_1, y_1) and (x_2, y_2) is $\sqrt{(x_2 - x_1)^2 + (y_2 - y_1)^2}$.
Midpoint formula, p. 471	The midpoint between (x_1, y_1) and (x_2, y_2) is $\left(\frac{x_1 + x_2}{2}, \frac{y_1 + y_2}{2}\right)$.
Slope formula, p. 583	$m = \frac{y_2 - y_1}{x_2 - x_1}$ where m = slope and (x_1, y_1) and (x_2, y_2) are two points

Table of Properties

Basic Properties	Addition	Multiplication
Commutative, p. 32	$a + b = b + a$	$ab = ba$
Associative, p. 32	$(a + b) + c = a + (b + c)$	$(ab)c = a(bc)$
Identity, p. 57	$a + 0 = a, 0 + a = a$	$a(1) = a, 1(a) = a$
Inverse, pp. 117, 279	$a + (-a) = 0$	$\frac{a}{b} \cdot \frac{b}{a} = 1, a \neq 0, b \neq 0$
Property of -1, p. 129		$(-1)a = -a$ or $a(-1) = -a$
Distributive, p. 38	$a(b + c) = ab + ac$ or $(b + c)a = ba + ca$	

Properties of Equality	
Addition, p. 75	If $x - a = b$, then $x - a + a = b + a$.
Subtraction, p. 74	If $x + a = b$, then $x + a - a = b - a$.
Multiplication, p. 81	If $\frac{x}{a} = b$ and $a \neq 0$, then $a \cdot \frac{x}{a} = a \cdot b$.
Division, p. 80	If $ax = b$ and $a \neq 0$, then $\frac{ax}{a} = \frac{b}{a}$.

Properties of Exponents			
Product of Powers, p. 299	$a^m \cdot a^n = a^{m+n}$	Power of a Product, p. 617	$(ab)^m = a^m b^m$
Quotient of Powers, p. 300	$\frac{a^m}{a^n} = a^{m-n}, a \neq 0$	Power of a Quotient, p. 618	$\left(\frac{a}{b}\right)^m = \frac{a^m}{b^m}, b \neq 0$
Zero Exponent, p. 305	$a^0 = 1, a \neq 0$	Power of a Power, p. 619	$(a^m)^n = a^{mn}$
Negative Exponent, p. 305	$a^{-n} = \frac{1}{a^n}, a \neq 0$		

Property of Proportions	
Cross Products, p. 333	If $\frac{a}{b} = \frac{c}{d}$ where $b \neq 0$ and $d \neq 0$, then $ad = bc$.

Special Products and Their Factors	
Square of a Binomial Pattern, p. 639	$(a + b)^2 = a^2 + 2ab + b^2$
FOIL, p. 638	$(a + b)(c + d) = a \cdot c + a \cdot d + b \cdot c + b \cdot d$ (First, Outer, Inner, Last)

Properties of Rational Numbers	
Addition, pp. 269, 270	$\frac{a}{c} + \frac{b}{c} = \frac{a + b}{c}, \frac{a}{b} + \frac{c}{d} = \frac{ad + bc}{bd}$
Subtraction, pp. 269, 270	$\frac{a}{c} - \frac{b}{c} = \frac{a - b}{c}, \frac{a}{b} - \frac{c}{d} = \frac{ad - bc}{bd}$
Multiplication, p. 278	$\frac{a}{b} \cdot \frac{c}{d} = \frac{ac}{bd}$
Division, p. 289	$\frac{a}{b} \div \frac{c}{d} = \frac{a}{b} \cdot \frac{d}{c} = \frac{ad}{bc}$

Glossary

A

absolute value **(p. 106)** The absolute value of a number is the distance between the number and 0 on a number line.

acute angle **(p. 391)** An angle with a measure between 0° and 90°.

acute triangle **(p. 404)** A triangle with three acute angles.

additive identity **(p. 57)** The number 0 is the additive identity since the result of adding 0 to a number is the original number. For any real number a, $a + 0 = a$.

additive inverses **(p. 117)** A number and its opposite. For example, 5 and -5 are additive inverses. The sum of a number and its additive inverse is 0. For example, $5 + (-5) = 0$.

adjacent angles **(p. 392)** Two angles in the same plane that share a vertex and a common side and do not overlap.

altitude of a triangle **(p. 410)** A perpendicular segment from a vertex of a triangle to the line containing the opposite side.

angle **(p. 390)** A figure formed by two rays with a common endpoint called the vertex. The rays are the sides of the angle.

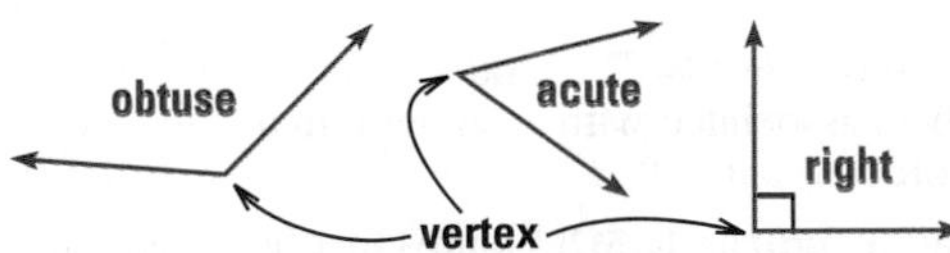

angle bisector **(pp. 391, 395)** A ray, line, or line segment that divides an angle into two congruent angles.

area **(pp. 13, 22)** A measure of how much surface is covered by a figure. Area is measured in square units.

associative property of addition **(p. 32)** Changing the grouping of terms will not change the sum. For all real numbers a, b, and c, $(a + b) + c = a + (b + c)$.

associative property of multiplication **(p. 32)** Changing the grouping of factors will not change the product. For all real numbers a, b, and c, $(ab)c = a(bc)$.

average **(pp. 136, 203)** The sum of the numbers in a set of data divided by the number of items in the set. The average is also called the *mean*.

axes **(p. 144)** *See* coordinate plane.

B

balance **(p. 366)** The result of adding interest to the principal.

bar graph **(p. 4)** A type of graph in which the lengths of bars are used to represent and compare data.

base of a parallelogram **(p. 417)** Any side of a parallelogram can be used as the base. *See also* parallelogram.

base of a power **(p. 12)** The number or expression that is used as a factor in a repeated multiplication. For example, in the power 5^2, the base is 5.

binomial **(p. 622)** A polynomial with two terms.

box-and-whisker plot **(p. 489)** A display that divides a data set into four parts using the median and quartiles.

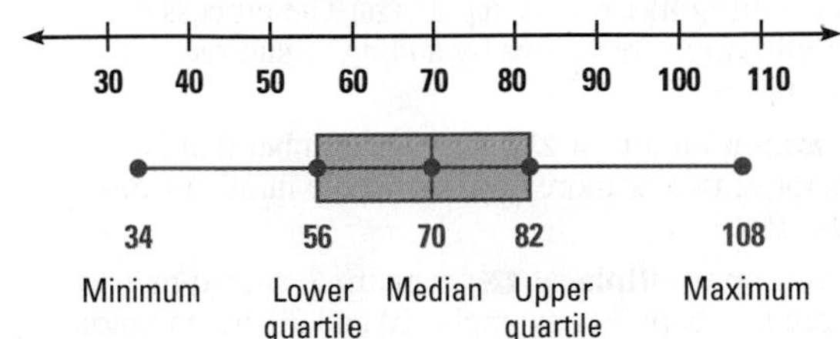

C

center of a circle **(p. 511)** The point inside a circle that is the same distance from all points on the circle. *See also* circle.

central angle **(p. 513)** An angle whose vertex is the center of a circle and whose sides are radii of the circle.

chord **(p. 516)** A line segment whose endpoints lie on a circle.

circle **(p. 511)** The set of all points in a plane that are an equal distance from a given point, the center.

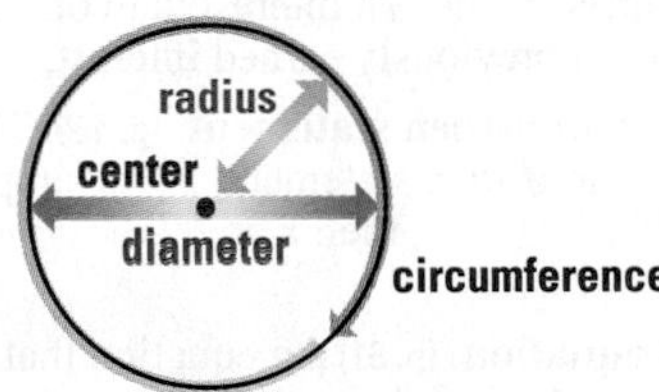

circular cone **(p. 539)** A solid with a circular base and a vertex that is not in the same plane as the base. The height of a cone is the perpendicular distance between the base and the vertex.

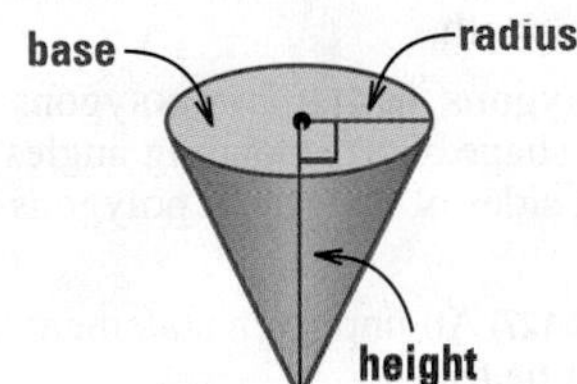

circular cylinder (p. 523) A solid with congruent circular bases that lie in parallel planes. The height of a cylinder is the perpendicular distance between the bases.

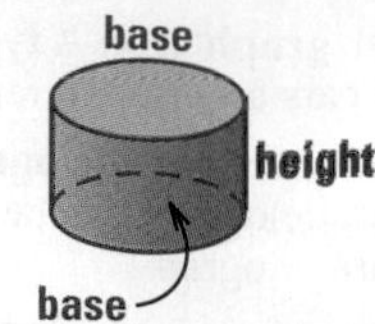

circumference of a circle (p. 511) The distance around a circle. Circumference is measured in linear units. *See also* circle.

coefficient (p. 57) The numerical part of a variable term. For example, in the term $3x^2$, the coefficient of x^2 is 3.

combining like terms (pp. 57, 626) The process of simplifying expressions by adding or subtracting like terms.

common factor (p. 225) A whole number that is a factor of two or more nonzero whole numbers. *See also* factor.

common multiple (p. 229) A multiple shared by two or more numbers. For example, 10 and 20 are common multiples of 2 and 5.

commutative property of addition (p. 32) In a sum, you can add terms in any order. For all real numbers a and b, $a + b = b + a$.

commutative property of multiplication (p. 32) In a product, you can multiply factors in any order. For all real numbers a and b, $ab = ba$.

complementary angles (p. 391) Two angles whose measures have a sum of 90°.

composite number (p. 220) A whole number greater than 1 that has factors other than 1 and itself.

compound interest (p. 369) Interest paid on the principal and on previously earned interest.

conclusion of an if-then statement (p. 465) The "then" part of an *if-then* statement. For example, in the statement "If $x + 1 = 3$, then $x = 2$," the conclusion is "$x = 2$."

conditional equation (p. 61) An equation that is true for only some values of the variables contained in the equation.

congruent angles (p. 391) Angles that have the same measure.

congruent line segments (p. 385) Line segments that have the same length.

congruent polygons (p. 412) Two polygons with the same size and shape. Corresponding angles and corresponding sides of congruent polygons are congruent.

conjecture (p. 127) An unproven statement that is believed might be true.

constant function (p. 571) A function whose output never changes, for example, $y = 2$ when x is any real number.

constant term (p. 57) A term that is a number.

constant of variation (p. 594) In a direct variation, the nonzero constant k for which $y = kx$.

converse (p. 465) The statement formed by reversing the hypothesis and the conclusion of an *if-then* statement. For example, the converse of "If $x + 1 = 3$, then $x = 2$" is "If $x = 2$, then $x + 1 = 3$."

convex quadrilateral (p. 405) A quadrilateral is convex if for every pair of interior points, the segment joining them lies completely within the quadrilateral.

coordinate plane (p. 144) A coordinate system formed by a horizontal number line called the x-axis and a vertical number line called the y-axis. The axes divide a coordinate plane into four regions called *quadrants*. A coordinate plane is used to plot ordered pairs.

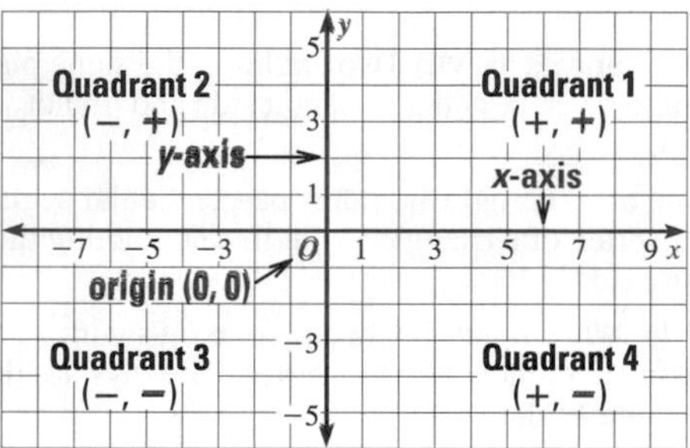

coordinates (p. 144) The unique ordered pair of real numbers associated with each point in a plane. *See also* ordered pair.

coplanar figures (p. 517) Figures that lie in the same plane, including intersecting lines and parallel lines.

corresponding angles (p. 399) Two angles that are formed by two lines and a transversal and occupy corresponding positions. In the diagram below, ∠1 and ∠2 are corresponding angles, as are ∠3 and ∠4.

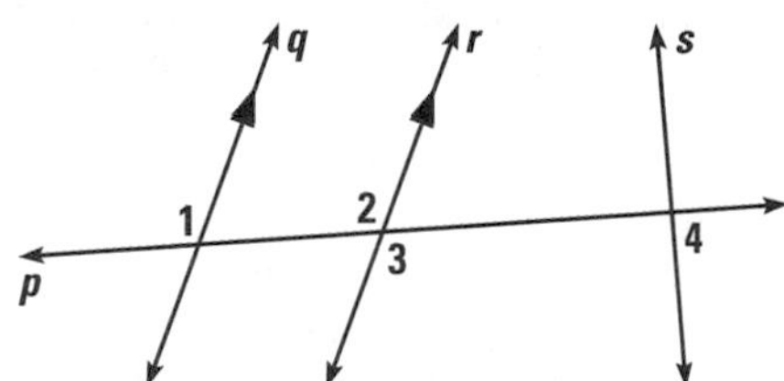

counterexample (p. 33) An example that shows that a statement is not always true.

cross multiplying (p. 333) The process of forming the cross products of a proportion.

cross products (p. 333) The cross products of the proportion $\frac{a}{b} = \frac{c}{d}$ are ad and bc.

GLOSSARY

cube **(p. 386)** A three-dimensional figure bounded by six squares called *faces* of the cube.

cube of a number **(p. 12)** The third power of a number.

cylinder **(p. 523)** *See* circular cylinder.

data **(p. 3)** Numbers or facts that describe something.

degree of a polynomial **(p. 626)** The degree of a simplified polynomial in one variable is the greatest exponent of the variable.

diagonal **(p. 414)** A segment joining two nonconsecutive vertices of a polygon.

diameter of a circle **(p. 511)** The distance across a circle through its center; twice the radius. Also, a line segment that passes through the center and has endpoints on the circle. *See also* circle.

direct variation **(p. 594)** A linear equation of the form $y = kx$ where k is a nonzero number. In this case, y varies directly with x.

discount **(p. 357)** The difference between a regular price and a sale price.

distributive property **(pp. 38, 39)** For all real numbers a, b, and c, $a(b + c) = ab + ac$. For example, $4(3 + 8) = 4(3) + 4(8)$. Also, for all real numbers a, b, c, and d, $a(b + c + d) = ab + ac + ad$ and $a(b - c) = ab - ac$.

divisible **(p. 220)** A nonzero whole number is divisible by another nonzero whole number if the second number is a factor of the first. For example, $2 \cdot 3 = 6$, so 6 is divisible by 2 and by 3.

divisor **(p. 220)** A nonzero whole number that divides another nonzero whole number evenly. *See also* factor.

double bar graph **(p. 4)** A type of graph in which the lengths of bars are used to represent and compare two sets of data.

edge of a polyhedron **(p. 518)** A segment where two faces of a polyhedron meet. *See also* polyhedron.

endpoint **(p. 385)** *See* line segment *and* ray.

equation **(p. 61)** A statement that two expressions are equal.

equiangular triangle **(p. 404)** A triangle in which all three angles have the same measure.

equilateral triangle **(pp. 190, 404)** A triangle in which all three sides have the same length.

equivalent equations **(p. 74)** Equations with the same solutions.

equivalent fractions **(p. 233)** Fractions that have the same simplest form.

equivalent inequalities **(p. 90)** Inequalities with all the same solutions.

equivalent numerical expressions **(p. 38)** Numerical expressions that have the same value.

equivalent variable expressions **(p. 38)** Variable expressions that always have the same values when numbers are substituted for the variables.

evaluating a numerical expression **(p. 7)** Finding the value of the expression.

evaluating a variable expression **(p. 8)** Finding the value of the expression by substituting a number for each variable and finding the value of the resulting numerical expression.

event **(p. 345)** A collection of outcomes of an experiment.

experimental probability **(p. 346)** A probability based on repeated trials of an experiment. The experimental probability of an event is given by the ratio $\frac{\text{Number of successes}}{\text{Number of trials}}$.

exponent **(p. 12)** A number or variable that represents the number of times a base is used as a factor in a repeated multiplication. For example, in the power 5^2, the exponent is 2.

face of a polyhedron **(p. 518)** A polygon that is part of the boundary of a polyhedron. *See also* polyhedron.

factor **(p. 7)** When two nonzero whole numbers are multiplied together, each number is a factor of the product. Since $2 \times 3 = 6$, 2 and 3 are factors of 6. *See also* divisor.

factor tree **(p. 220)** A diagram that can be used to show the prime factorization of a number.

favorable outcomes **(p. 345)** Outcomes corresponding to an event. For example, if you toss a number cube, then there are 3 favorable outcomes for getting an even number: 2, 4, and 6.

formula **(p. 22)** An algebraic equation that relates two or more variables.

frequency **(p. 343)** The number of times a data item occurs.

function **(p. 563)** A rule that assigns to each number in a given set a number in another set. Starting with a number called an *input*, the function associates with it exactly one number called an *output*.

function form of an equation **(p. 568)** The equation obtained by solving an equation in two variables, x and y, for y.

greatest common divisor, GCD **(p. 225)** The largest common divisor of two or more nonzero whole numbers. It is also called the *greatest common factor, GCF*.

greatest common factor, GCF **(p. 225)** The largest common factor of two or more nonzero whole numbers. It is also called the *greatest common divisor, GCD*. *See also* common factor.

grouping symbols **(p. 17)** Symbols such as parentheses ( ) and brackets [ ] that are used to indicate the order of operations or to make an expression clearer.

half-plane **(p. 598)** Either of the two regions into which a plane is divided by a line.

height of a parallelogram **(p. 417)** The perpendicular distance between the base of a parallelogram and the opposite side. *See also* parallelogram *and* base.

height of a trapezoid **(p. 418)** The perpendicular distance between the parallel sides of a trapezoid. *See also* trapezoid.

hemisphere **(p. 543)** Half of a sphere.

hexagon **(p. 413)** A polygon with six sides.

hypotenuse **(p. 460)** The side of a right triangle that is opposite the right angle; the longest side of a right triangle. *See also* right triangle.

hypothesis of an if-then statement **(p. 465)** The "if" part of an *if-then* statement. For example, in the statement "If $x + 1 = 3$, then $x = 2$," the hypothesis is "$x + 1 = 3$."

identity **(p. 61)** An equation that is true for all values of the variables contained in the equation.

image **(pp. 423, 428)** The new figure resulting from the transformation of a figure.

inequality **(p. 90)** A mathematical sentence formed by separating two expressions by one of the inequality symbols ($>$, $<$, $\geq$, $\leq$).

input **(p. 563)** A number on which a function operates.

integers **(pp. 105, 239)** The numbers . . . , -4, -3, -2, -1, 0, 1, 2, 3, 4, . . . , consisting of the negative integers, zero, and the positive integers.

interest **(p. 365)** Money paid for the use of money.

interest rate **(p. 365)** The percent of increase in the principal per unit of time.

interquartile range **(p. 489)** The difference between the upper quartile and lower quartile in a data set.

intersection of geometric figures **(p. 386)** The set of points that two or more geometric figures have in common.

inverse operation **(pp. 74, 170)** An operation that "undoes" another operation. Addition and subtraction are inverse operations, as are multiplication and division.

irrational numbers **(p. 453)** Real numbers that cannot be written as the quotient of two integers.

isosceles right triangle **(p. 461)** A right triangle whose legs have the same length.

isosceles trapezoid **(p. 405)** A trapezoid whose nonparallel sides are congruent.

isosceles triangle **(p. 404)** A triangle with at least two sides of the same length.

justifying a step **(p. 33)** Using a known property to explain why a step is valid.

kite **(p. 405)** A quadrilateral with two pairs of congruent sides, but with opposite sides not congruent.

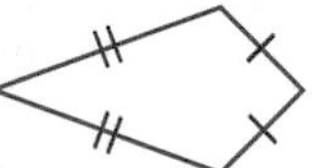

least common denominator, LCD **(p. 273)** The least common multiple of the denominators of two or more fractions.

least common multiple, LCM **(p. 229)** The smallest common multiple of two or more numbers. *See also* common multiple.

legs of a right triangle **(p. 460)** The sides of a right triangle that form the right angle. *See also* right triangle.

like terms **(pp. 57, 623)** Two or more terms in an expression that have identical variable parts.

linear equation in two variables **(p. 567)** An equation in which the variables appear in separate terms, and each variable occurs only to the first power. For example, the equation $2x + y = 5$ is a linear equation in two variables.

linear function **(p. 568)** A function of the form $y = mx + b$.

linear inequality in two variables **(p. 598)** An inequality that can be written in one of the following forms: $ax + by < c$, $ax + by \leq c$, $ax + by > c$, or $ax + by \geq c$, where a, b, and c are constants.

line graph **(p. 4)** A type of graph that uses points connected by line segments.

line of reflection **(p. 423)** A line that is perpendicular to and bisects each segment that joins a point and its image in a reflection.

line plot **(p. 203)** A number line diagram that shows the frequency of data.

line segment **(p. 385)** A part of a line consisting of two endpoints and all the points between them.

line symmetry (p. 424) A figure has line symmetry if you can draw a line through the figure such that the part of the figure on one side of the line is the reflection of the part on the other side.

lower quartile (p. 489) The median of the lower half of a set of data. *See also* box-and-whisker plot.

markup (p. 356) The difference between the retail and the wholesale prices of an item.

mean (pp. 136, 203) The sum of the numbers in a set of data divided by the number of items in the set. The mean is also called the *average*.

measure of an angle (p. 390) An angle's size, which can be expressed in degrees.

measure of central tendency (p. 203) A single number that is "typical" of the numbers in a set of data. The *mean*, *median*, and *mode* are common measures of central tendency.

median (pp. 203, 489) The middle number of a group of numbers when you order the numbers from least to greatest; for an even number of items, the median is the *mean* of the two middle numbers.

midpoint (p. 403) The point that divides a segment into two congruent segments.

mode (p. 203) The number that occurs most often in a set of numbers.

monomial (p. 617) A number, a variable, or the product of a number and one or more variables raised to whole number powers; a polynomial with one term.

multiple of a number (p. 229) A multiple of a number is the product of the number and any nonzero whole number.

multiplicative identity (p. 57) The number 1 is the multiplicative identity. The result of multiplying a number by 1 is the original number.

multiplicative inverses (p. 279) Two numbers whose product is 1. Multiplicative inverses are also called *reciprocals*.

natural numbers (p. 239) The numbers 1, 2, 3, ... They are also called *counting numbers*.

negative correlation (p. 149) In a collection of ordered pairs (x, y) of numerical data, if the y-coordinates tend to decrease as the x-coordinates increase, then x and y have a negative correlation.

net (p. 518) A two-dimensional figure that can be folded to form a solid.

no obvious correlation (p. 149) If no pattern exists between the x-coordinates and the y-coordinates of a collection of ordered pairs (x, y) of numerical data, then x and y have no obvious correlation.

nonlinear function (p. 642) A function whose graph is not a line.

numerical expression (p. 7) An expression that represents a particular number. The expression consists of numbers and arithmetic operations to be performed.

oblique circular cylinder (p. 535) In an oblique circular cylinder, the segment joining the centers of the bases is not perpendicular to the bases. The height of an oblique cylinder is the perpendicular distance between the bases.

oblique prism (p. 530) In an oblique prism, the edges connecting the bases are not perpendicular to the bases. The height of an oblique prism is the perpendicular distance between the bases.

obtuse angle (p. 391) An angle with a measure between 90° and 180°.

obtuse triangle (p. 404) A triangle with an obtuse angle.

opposites (pp. 106, 117) Two numbers that have the same absolute value but have different signs. For example, -7 and 7 are opposites. The opposite of a number is also called the *additive inverse* of the number.

ordered pair (p. 144) A pair of numbers that can be used to locate a point in a coordinate plane. The first number is the x-coordinate, and the second is the y-coordinate.

order of operations (p. 16) A procedure for evaluating an expression involving more than one operation.

1. Evaluate expressions inside grouping symbols.
2. Evaluate powers.
3. Multiply and divide from left to right.
4. Add and subtract from left to right.

origin (p. 144) The point (0, 0) where the x-axis and the y-axis intersect in a coordinate plane. *See also* coordinate plane.

outcomes (p. 345) The possible results when an experiment is performed. For example, heads and tails are the possible outcomes of tossing a coin.

outlier (p. 204) A number in a data set that is much greater than or much less than most of the other numbers in the set.

output (p. 563) A number produced by evaluating a function using a given input.

parallel lines (p. 386) Lines that lie in the same plane and do not intersect. (Identical lines are sometimes considered to be parallel.) In the diagram, arrowheads are used to indicate that the lines are parallel.

parallelogram (pp. 405, 419) A quadrilateral whose opposite sides are parallel.

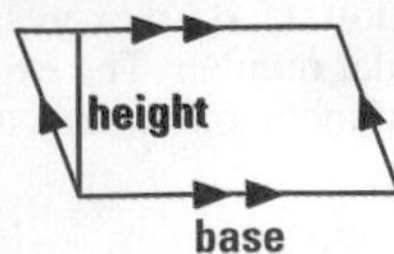

pentagon (p. 413) A polygon with five sides.

percent (pp. 244, 248) A comparison of a number to 100; per hundred.

percent of change (p. 361) A measure of how much a quantity has increased or decreased relative to the original amount; a percent of increase or decrease.

perfect square (p. 449) The square of an integer.

perimeter (p. 22) The distance around a figure; for a polygon, the sum of the lengths of the sides. Perimeter is measured in linear units.

perpendicular bisector (p. 403) A line, segment, or ray perpendicular to a line segment at its midpoint.

perpendicular lines (p. 398) Two lines that intersect to form a right angle.

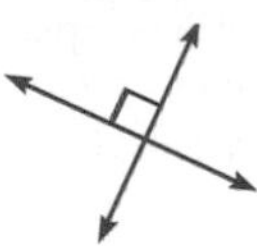

pi (π) (p. 511) The ratio of the circumference of a circle to its diameter. This ratio is irrational and approximately equal to 3.14.

plane (p. 385) A plane can be thought of as a flat surface that extends indefinitely in all directions.

point (p. 385) A point represents a location in a plane or in space.

polygon (p. 412) A closed plane figure bounded by line segments called the *sides* of the polygon. Triangles and quadrilaterals are examples of polygons.

polyhedron (p. 518) A closed solid that is bounded by polygons called the *faces* of the polyhedron. Adjacent faces meet at the *edges* of the polyhedron. A *vertex* of a polyhedron is a point where edges meet.

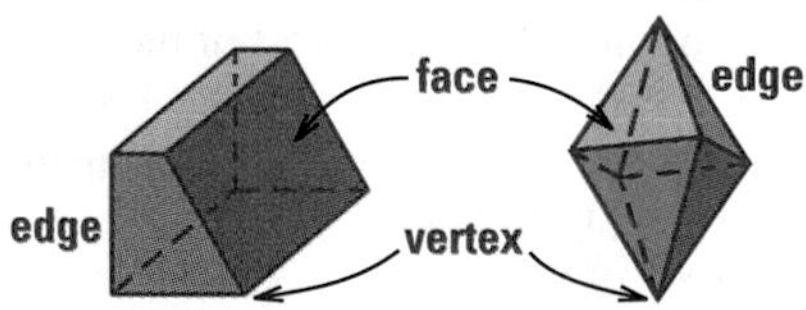

polynomial (p. 622) A monomial or an expression that can be written as a sum of monomials.

positive correlation (p. 149) In a collection of ordered pairs (x, y) of numerical data, if the y-coordinates tend to increase as the x-coordinates increase, then x and y have a positive correlation.

postulate (p. 399) A statement that is not proved but used as a basis for proving other statements.

power (p. 12) An expression such as 5^2 that has a *base*, 5, and an *exponent*, 2. The expression represents a repeated multiplication.

prime factorization (p. 220) Writing a number as the product of prime numbers.

prime number (p. 220) A whole number greater than 1 whose only whole number factors are 1 and itself.

principal (p. 365) An amount of money that is deposited or borrowed.

prism (p. 523) A polyhedron with two congruent bases that lie in parallel planes. The height of a prism is the perpendicular distance between its bases.

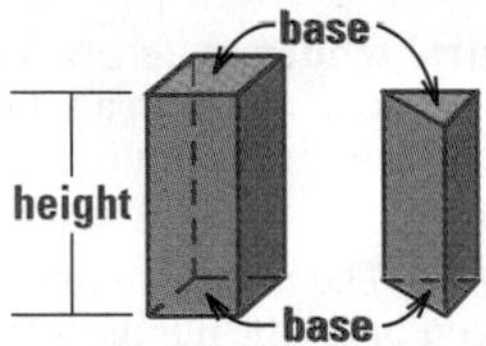

probability of an event (p. 345) A measure of the likelihood that the event will occur. It is a number between 0 and 1 that can be expressed as a fraction, decimal, or percent.

profit (p. 141) The difference between total income and total expenses.

proportion (p. 333) An equation that states that two ratios are equal. A proportion has the form $\frac{a}{b} = \frac{c}{d}$.

pyramid (p. 539) A polyhedron in which the base is a polygon and the triangular faces meet at a point called the *vertex*. The height of a pyramid is the perpendicular distance between the base and the vertex.

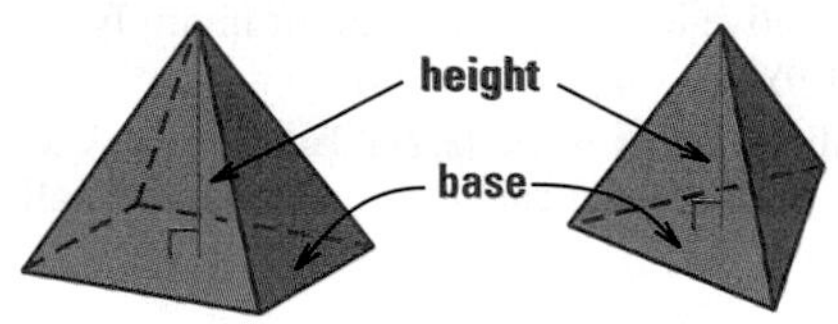

Q

quadrants (p. 144) Four regions into which a coordinate plane is divided by the x-axis and the y-axis. *See also* coordinate plane.

quadrilateral (p. 405) A closed figure with four sides that are line segments joined at their endpoints.

R

radical sign (p. 449) The symbol $\sqrt{\ }$ used to represent the positive square root.

radius of a circle (p. 511) The distance between the center and a point on a circle. Also, a line segment whose endpoints are the center of the circle and a point on the circle. *See also* circle.

range (in statistics) (p. 489) The difference between the maximum and minimum values in a data set.

rate (p. 330) A type of ratio that compares two quantities a and b that have different units of measure.

ratio (p. 329) A comparison of a number a and a nonzero number b using division.

rational number (p. 239) A number that can be written as the quotient $\frac{a}{b}$ of two integers a and b where $b \neq 0$.

ray (p. 385) A part of a line that has one endpoint and extends indefinitely in one direction.

real numbers (p. 453) The set of all rational numbers and irrational numbers. (The real numbers can also be thought of as the set of all decimals, finite or infinite in length.)

reciprocals (p. 279) Two numbers whose product is 1. Reciprocals are also called *multiplicative inverses*.

rectangle (pp. 22, 405) A parallelogram with four right angles.

rectangular prism (p. 523) A prism whose bases are rectangles.

reflection (p. 423) An operation that maps every point P in a figure to its image point P' so that (1) if P is not on the line of reflection, then the line of reflection is the perpendicular bisector of $\overline{PP'}$; and (2) if P is on the line of reflection, then $P = P'$.

regular polygon (p. 413) A polygon whose sides all have the same length and whose angles all have the same measure.

repeating decimal (p. 240) A fraction $\frac{a}{b}$ $(b \neq 0)$ can be written in decimal form by using long division to divide a by b. If the division process does not stop, then it leads to a digit or a group of digits that repeats over and over. In this case, the decimal form of the fraction is a repeating decimal.

rhombus (p. 405) A parallelogram with all sides congruent.

right angle (pp. 22, 391) An angle with a measure of 90°.

right circular cylinder (p. 523) In a right circular cylinder, the segment joining the centers of the bases is perpendicular to the bases.

right prism (p. 523) In a right prism, the edges connecting the bases are perpendicular to the bases.

right triangle (pp. 404, 460) A triangle with a right angle.

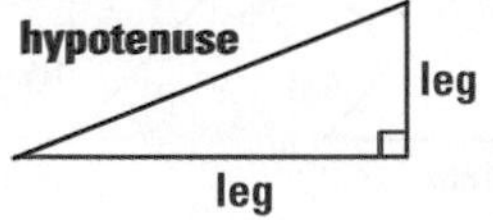

scale (p. 338) In a scale drawing, the scale gives the relationship between the drawing's measurements and the actual measurements. For example, the scale 1 in. = 2 ft means that 1 in. in the drawing represents an actual distance of 2 ft.

scale drawing (p. 338) A diagram of an object in which the length and width are proportional to the actual length and width of the object.

scale factor (pp. 433, 548) The scale factor of two similar polygons or two similar solids is the ratio of corresponding linear measures, such as side lengths or radii.

scale factor in a scale drawing (p. 338) The ratio of the length and width in the drawing to the corresponding actual length and width.

scalene triangle (p. 404) A triangle whose three sides all have different lengths.

scatter plot (p. 149) The graph of a collection of ordered pairs (x, y).

scientific notation (p. 309) A number written in the form $c \times 10^n$, where c is greater than or equal to 1 and less than 10, and n is an integer.

sector of a circle (p. 513) A part of a circle determined by two radii.

segment (p. 385) *See* line segment.

sequence (p. 28) An ordered list of numbers.

similar figures (p. 432) Two figures with the same shape but not necessarily the same size. Corresponding angles of similar figures are congruent and the ratios of the lengths of the corresponding sides are equal. For example, $\triangle ABC \sim \triangle DEF$.

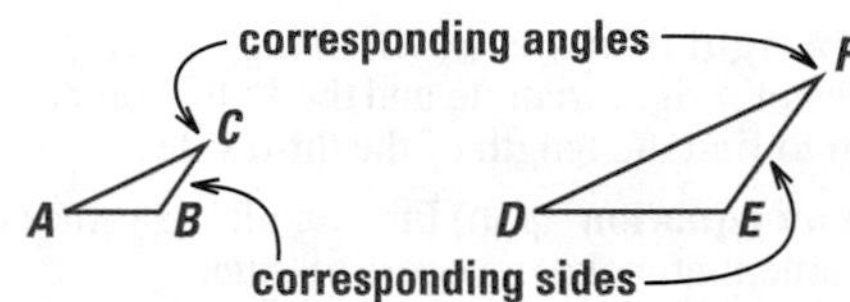

similar solids (p. 548) Two solids with the same shape but not necessarily the same size. Corresponding linear measures, such as heights or radii, have the same ratio. The common ratio is called the *scale factor*.

simple interest (p. 365) Interest that is paid only on the principal; the product of the principal, the annual interest rate, and the time in years. $I = Prt$

simplest form of a fraction (p. 233) A fraction is in simplest form if the only common factor of the numerator and denominator is 1.

skew lines (p. 517) Lines in space that do not intersect and are not parallel. Skew lines do not lie in the same plane.

slide (p. 428) *See* translation.

slope **(p. 583)** The slope of a nonvertical line is the ratio of the *rise* (change in *y*) to the *run* (change in *x*) between any two points on the line. In the diagram below, *m* is the slope.

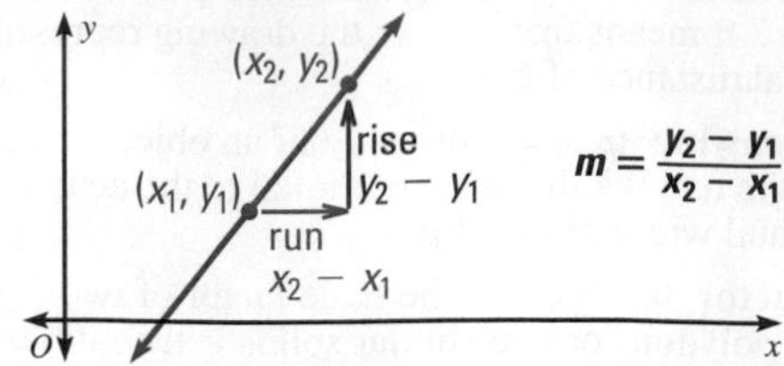

slope-intercept form **(p. 589)** A linear equation in the form $y = mx + b$ where *m* is the slope and *b* is the *y*-intercept.

solution of an equation in one variable **(p. 61)** A value of the variable that makes the equation true when substituted in the equation.

solution of an equation in two variables **(pp. 145, 567)** An ordered pair (x, y) that produces a true statement when substituted for the variables in the equation.

solution of an inequality in one variable **(p. 90)** A number that produces a true statement when it is substituted for the variable in the inequality.

solution of an inequality in two variables **(p. 598)** An ordered pair (x, y) that produces a true statement when substituted for the variables in the inequality.

solution of a system of equations **(p. 602)** An ordered pair (x, y) that is a solution of each equation in the system.

solution of a system of inequalities **(p. 603)** An ordered pair (x, y) that is a solution of each inequality in the system.

solving a right triangle **(p. 461)** Using the lengths of two sides of a right triangle and the Pythagorean theorem to find the length of the third side.

solving an equation **(p. 61)** Finding all the values of the variable that make the equation true.

solving an inequality **(p. 90)** Finding all the values of the variable that make the inequality true.

sphere **(p. 543)** A set of points in space that are a given distance from a point called the *center* of the sphere. The *radius* of a sphere is the distance from the center to a point on the sphere.

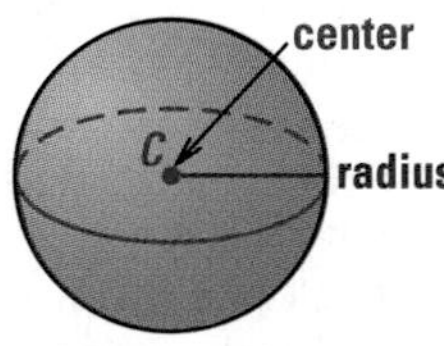

square **(pp. 22, 405)** A rectangle with all sides congruent.

square of a number **(p. 12)** The second power of a number.

square root **(p. 449)** A square root of a number is a number which, when multiplied by itself, produces the given number. For example, 6 and -6 are both square roots of 36 because $6^2 = 36$ and $(-6)^2 = 36$.

standard form of a polynomial **(p. 622)** A polynomial written so that the powers of the variable decrease from left to right.

stem-and-leaf plot **(p. 253)** A display of data that allows you to see the way the data are distributed. It can be used to arrange the data in increasing or decreasing order.

straight angle **(p. 391)** An angle with a measure of 180°.

supplementary angles **(p. 391)** Two angles whose measures have a sum of 180°.

surface area of a solid **(p. 523)** The sum of the areas of all the surfaces that bound the solid.

system of equations **(p. 602)** A set of two or more equations in the same variables.

system of inequalities **(p. 602)** A set of two or more inequalities in the same variables.

terminating decimal **(p. 240)** A fraction $\frac{a}{b}$ $(b \neq 0)$ can be written in decimal form by using long division to divide *a* by *b*. If the division stops because a remainder is zero, then the decimal form of the fraction is a terminating decimal.

terms of a sum **(p. 7)** In a sum, the numbers or expressions that are added.

theoretical probability **(p. 346)** A probability that is found by mathematical reasoning. If the outcomes of an experiment are equally likely, then the theoretical probability of an event is given by the ratio $\frac{\text{Number of favorable outcomes}}{\text{Total number of outcomes}}$.

transformation **(p. 428)** An operation that makes a figure correspond to another figure, called the *image*. Reflections and translations are transformations.

translation **(p. 428)** A transformation that slides each point of a figure the same distance in the same direction; also called a *slide*.

transversal **(p. 399)** A line that intersects two other lines.

trapezoid **(p. 405)** A quadrilateral with exactly one pair of parallel sides.

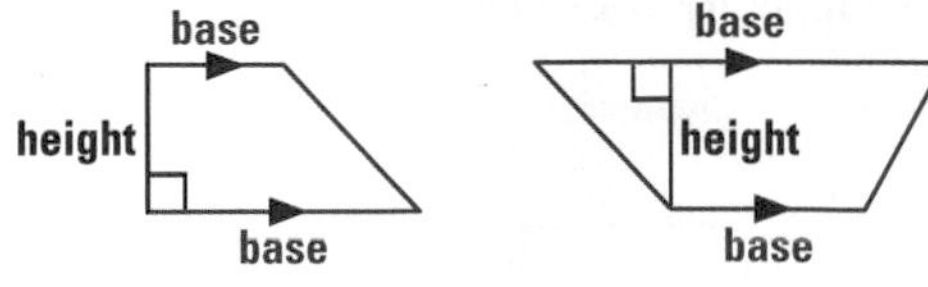

GLOSSARY

triangle (p. 22) A polygon with three sides. *See also* polygon.

trinomial (p. 622) A polynomial with three terms.

unit rate (p. 330) A rate with a denominator of 1 unit. For example, $23 per foot is a unit rate.

upper quartile (p. 489) The median of the upper half of a set of data. *See also* box-and-whisker plot.

value(s) of a variable (p. 8) The number(s) represented by the variable.

variable (p. 8) A letter that represents one or more numbers.

variable expression (p. 8) An expression that consists of numbers and variables and operations to be performed.

variation (p. 489) A measure of spread for the values in a data set.

Venn diagram (p. 239) A drawing that uses geometric shapes to show relationships among sets.

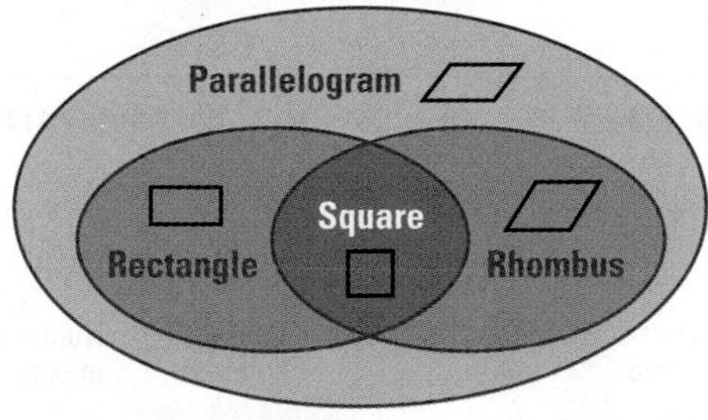

vertex of an angle (p. 390) The common endpoint of the rays that form the sides of the angle. *See also* angle.

vertex of a polygon (p. 412) A point where two sides of a polygon meet. *See also* polygon.

vertex of a polyhedron (p. 518) A point where three or more edges of a polyhedron meet. *See also* polyhedron.

vertical angles (p. 398) Two pairs of nonadjacent angles formed by intersecting lines; vertical angles are congruent. In the diagram below, $\angle 1$ and $\angle 3$ are vertical angles, as are $\angle 2$ and $\angle 4$.

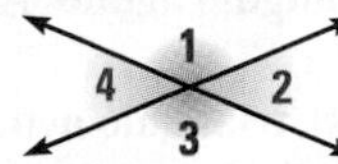

volume (pp. 13, 530) The volume of a solid is a measure of the amount of space the solid occupies. Volume is measured in cubic units.

***x*-axis** (p. 144) The horizontal axis in a coordinate plane. *See also* coordinate plane.

***x*-coordinate** (p. 144) The first number of the coordinates of a point, which gives the position of the point relative to the x-axis. *See also* ordered pair.

***x*-intercept** (p. 576) The x-coordinate of a point where a graph crosses the x-axis; the value of x when $y = 0$.

***y*-axis** (p. 144) The vertical axis in a coordinate plane. *See also* coordinate plane.

***y*-coordinate** (p. 144) The second number of the coordinates of a point, which gives the position of the point relative to the y-axis. *See also* ordered pair.

***y*-intercept** (p. 576) The y-coordinate of a point where a graph crosses the y-axis; the value of y when $x = 0$.

English-to-Spanish Glossary

absolute value (p. 106) **valor absoluto** El valor absoluto de un número es la distancia existente entre ese número y 0 en una recta numérica.

acute angle (p. 391) **ángulo agudo** Ángulo que mide entre 0° y 90°.

acute triangle (p. 404) **triángulo acutángulo** Triángulo que tiene tres ángulos agudos.

additive identity (p. 57) **elemento neutro de la suma** El número 0 es el elemento neutro de la suma ya que, al sumar 0 a un número, resulta el número original. Para cualquier número real a, $a + 0 = a$.

additive inverses (p. 117) **inversos aditivos** Un número y su opuesto. Por ejemplo, 5 y –5 son inversos aditivos. La suma de un número y su inverso aditivo es 0 como, por ejemplo, $5 + (-5) = 0$.

adjacent angles (p. 392) **ángulos adyacentes** Dos ángulos del mismo plano que comparten un vértice y un lado común sin superponerse.

altitude of a triangle (p. 410) **altura de un triángulo** Segmento perpendicular que va desde un vértice del triángulo a la recta que contiene el lado opuesto.

angle (p. 390) **ángulo** Figura formada por dos semirrectas que tienen un extremo común llamado vértice. Las semirrectas son los lados del ángulo.

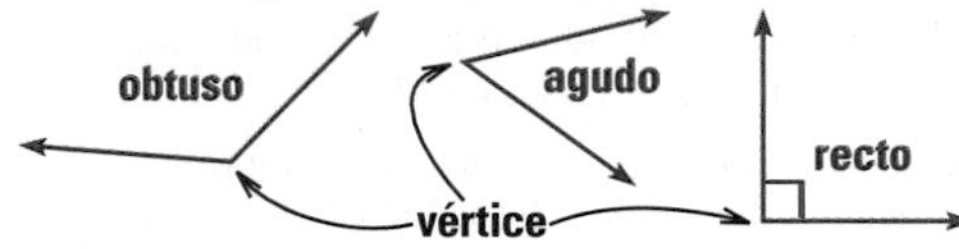

angle bisector (pp. 391, 395) **bisectriz de un ángulo** Semirrecta, recta o segmento de recta que divide al ángulo en dos ángulos congruentes.

area (pp. 13, 22) **área** Medida de la superficie que cubre una figura. El área se mide en unidades cuadradas.

associative property of addition (p. 32) **propiedad asociativa de la suma** Al cambiar la agrupación de los términos, no cambia la suma. Para todos los números reales a, b y c, $(a + b) + c = a + (b + c)$.

associative property of multiplication (p. 32) **propiedad asociativa de la multiplicación** Al cambiar la agrupación de los factores, no cambia el producto. Para todos los números reales a, b y c, $(ab)c = a(bc)$.

average (pp. 136, 203) **promedio** Suma de los números de un conjunto de datos dividida entre la cantidad de elementos del conjunto. El promedio se llama también *media.*

axes (p. 144) **ejes** *Ver* plano de coordenadas.

balance (p. 366) **balance** Resultado obtenido al sumar el interés al capital.

bar graph (p. 4) **gráfica de barras** Tipo de gráficas en el que aparecen barras cuya longitud sirve para representar y comparar datos.

base of a parallelogram (p. 417) **base de un paralelogramo** Cualquier lado de un paralelogramo puede servir de base. *Ver también* paralelogramo.

base of a power (p. 12) **base de una potencia** Número o expresión que se repite como factor en una multiplicación. Por ejemplo, en la potencia 5^2, la base es 5.

binomial (p. 622) **binomio** Polinomio de dos términos.

box-and-whisker plot (p. 489) **gráfica de frecuencias acumuladas** Representación que mediante la mediana y los cuartiles divide a un conjunto de datos en cuatro partes.

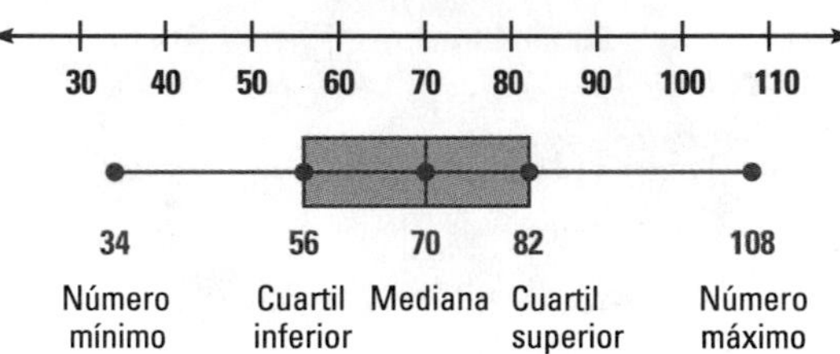

center of a circle (p. 511) **centro de un círculo** Punto del interior de un círculo que está a igual distancia de todos los puntos del círculo. *Ver también* círculo.

central angle (p. 513) **ángulo central** Ángulo cuyo vértice es el centro de un círculo y cuyos lados son radios del círculo.

chord (p. 516) **cuerda** Segmento de recta cuyos extremos se encuentran en un círculo.

circle (p. 511) **círculo** Conjunto de todos los puntos de un plano que están a igual distancia de un punto dado, el centro.

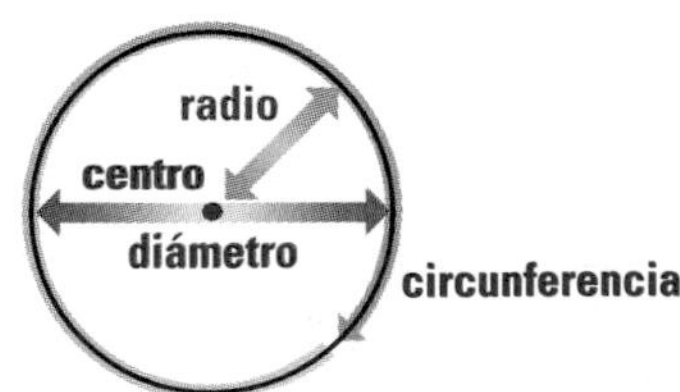

circular cone (p. 539) **cono circular** Sólido con una base circular y un vértice que se encuentran en planos diferentes. La altura de un cono es la distancia perpendicular entre la base y el vértice.

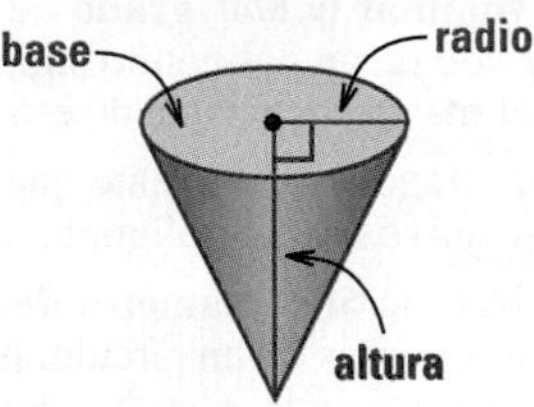

circular cylinder (p. 523) **cilindro circular** Sólido con bases circulares congruentes que se encuentran en planos paralelos. La altura de un cilindro es la distancia perpendicular entre las bases.

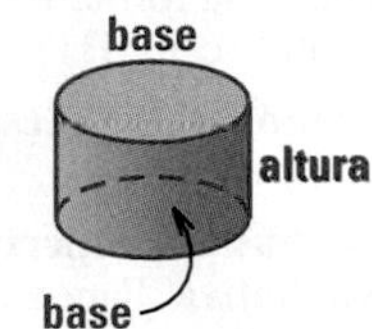

circumference of a circle (p. 511) **circunferencia de un círculo** Longitud del contorno de un círculo. La circunferencia se mide en unidades lineales. *Ver también* círculo.

coefficient (p. 57) **coeficiente** Parte numérica de un término algebraico. Por ejemplo, en el término $3x^2$, el coeficiente de x^2 es 3.

combining like terms (pp. 57, 626) **combinar términos semejantes** Proceso de simplificar expresiones mediante la suma o la resta de términos semejantes.

common factor (p. 225) **factor común** Número entero que es factor de dos o más números enteros distintos a cero. *Ver también* factor.

common multiple (p. 229) **múltiplo común** Múltiplo compartido por dos o más números. Por ejemplo, 10 y 20 son múltiplos comunes de 2 y 5.

commutative property of addition (p. 32) **propiedad conmutativa de la suma** En una suma, no importa el orden de los términos. Para todos los números reales a y b, $a + b = b + a$.

commutative property of multiplication (p. 32) **propiedad conmutativa de la multiplicación** En un producto, no importa el orden de los factores. Para todos los números reales a y b, $ab = ba$.

complementary angles (p. 391) **ángulos complementarios** Dos ángulos cuyas medidas suman 90°.

composite number (p. 220) **número compuesto** Número entero mayor que 1 que tiene otros factores además de 1 y de él mismo.

compound interest (p. 369) **interés compuesto** Interés pagado sobre el capital y sobre el interés previamente ganado.

conclusion of an if-then statement (p. 465) **conclusión de un enunciado de si-entonces** La parte del "entonces" en un enunciado de *si-entonces*. Por ejemplo, en el enunciado "Si $x + 1 = 3$, entonces $x = 2$", la conclusión es "$x = 2$".

conditional equation (p. 61) **ecuación condicional** Ecuación que es verdadera sólo para algunos valores de las variables contenidas en la misma.

congruent angles (p. 391) **ángulos congruentes** Ángulos de igual medida.

congruent line segments (p. 385) **segmentos de recta congruentes** Segmentos de recta que tienen la misma longitud.

congruent polygons (p. 412) **polígonos congruentes** Dos polígonos de igual tamaño y forma. Los ángulos correspondientes y los lados correspondientes de polígonos congruentes son congruentes.

conjecture (p. 127) **conjetura** Enunciado sin demostrar que se considera probable.

constant function (p. 571) **función constante** Función que tiene una salida fija como, por ejemplo, $y = 2$ cuando x es un número real cualquiera.

constant term (p. 57) **término constante** Término que es un número.

constant of variation (p. 594) **constante de variación** En una variación directa, la constante k distinta a cero tal que $y = kx$.

converse (p. 465) **recíproco** Afirmación que se forma al intercambiar la hipótesis y la conclusión de un enunciado de *si-entonces.* Por ejemplo, el recíproco de "Si $x + 1 = 3$, entonces $x = 2$" es "Si $x = 2$, entonces $x + 1 = 3$".

convex quadrilateral (p. 405) **cuadrilátero convexo** Un cuadrilátero es convexo si, para todo par de puntos interiores, el segmento que los une se encuentra íntegramente dentro del cuadrilátero.

ENGLISH-TO-SPANISH GLOSSARY

coordinate plane (p. 144) **plano de coordenadas** Sistema de coordenadas formado por una recta numérica horizontal llamada eje de las x y una recta numérica vertical denominada eje de las y. Los ejes dividen al plano de coordenadas en cuatro regiones llamadas *cuadrantes*. El plano de coordenadas sirve para marcar pares ordenados.

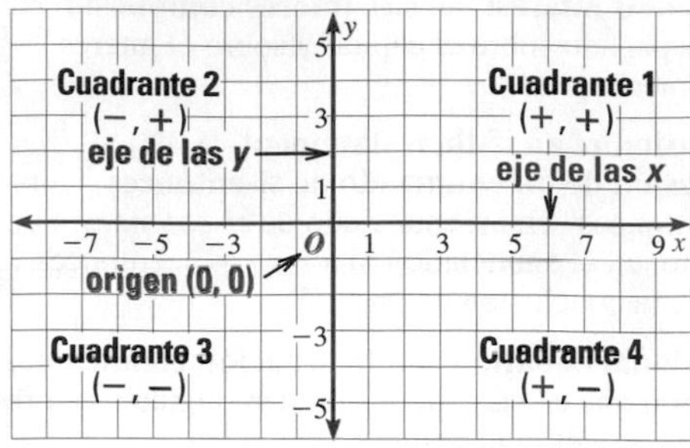

coordinates (p. 144) **coordenadas** El único par ordenado de números reales asociados con un punto en un plano. *Ver también* par ordenado.

coplanar figures (p. 517) **figuras coplanarias** Figuras, incluyendo rectas secantes y rectas paralelas, que se encuentran en el mismo plano.

corresponding angles (p. 399) **ángulos correspondientes** Dos ángulos que ocupan posiciones correspondientes y están formados por dos rectas y una transversal. En el diagrama abajo, $\angle 1$ y $\angle 2$ son ángulos correspondientes y también lo son $\angle 3$ y $\angle 4$.

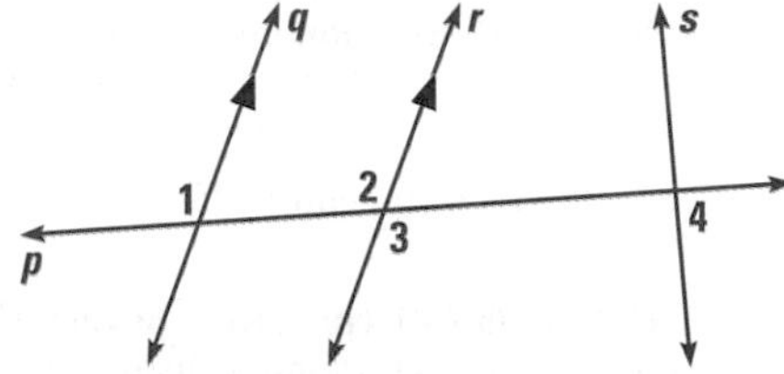

counterexample (p. 33) **contraejemplo** Ejemplo que muestra que un enunciado no es siempre verdadero.

cross multiplying (p. 333) **multiplicar en cruz** Proceso de formar los productos cruzados de una proporción.

cross products (p. 333) **productos cruzados** Los productos cruzados de la proporción $\frac{a}{b} = \frac{c}{d}$ son ad y bc.

cube (p. 386) **cubo** Figura tridimensional limitada por seis cuadrados llamados *caras* del cubo.

cube of a number (p. 12) **cubo de un número** Tercera potencia de un número.

cylinder (p. 523) **cilindro** *Ver* cilindro circular.

D

data (p. 3) **datos** Números o hechos que describen algo.

degree of a polynomial (p. 626) **grado de un polinomio** El grado de un polinomio simplificado con una variable es el mayor exponente de esa variable.

diagonal (p. 414) **diagonal** Segmento que une dos vértices no consecutivos de un polígono.

diameter of a circle (p. 511) **diámetro de un círculo** Distancia entre dos puntos de un círculo, pasando por su centro; es igual a dos veces el radio. Además, es un segmento de recta que, pasando por el centro del círculo, tiene sus extremos en el mismo. *Ver también* círculo.

direct variation (p. 594) **variación directa** Ecuación lineal de la forma $y = kx$ donde k es un número distinto a cero. En este caso, y varía directamente a x.

discount (p. 357) **descuento** Diferencia entre el precio usual y el rebajado.

distributive property (pp. 38, 39) **propiedad distributiva** Para todos los números reales a, b y c, $a(b + c) = ab + ac$. Por ejemplo, $4(3 + 8) = 4(3) + 4(8)$. Además, para todos los números reales a, b, c y d, $a(b + c + d) = ab + ac + ad$ y $a(b - c) = ab - ac$.

divisible (p. 220) **divisible** Un número entero distinto a cero es divisible por otro número entero distinto a cero si el segundo es factor del primero. Por ejemplo, $2 \cdot 3 = 6$, por lo que 6 es divisible por 2 y 3.

divisor (p. 220) **divisor** Número entero distinto a cero que divide exactamente a otro número entero distinto a cero. *Ver también* factor.

double bar graph (p. 4) **gráfica de doble barra** Tipo de gráficas en el que aparecen barras cuya longitud sirve para representar y comparar dos conjuntos de datos.

edge of a polyhedron (p. 518) **arista de un poliedro** Segmento donde se unen dos caras de un poliedro. *Ver también* poliedro.

endpoint (p. 385) **extremo** *Ver* segmento de recta y semirrecta.

equation (p. 61) **ecuación** Enunciado que indica la igualdad de dos expresiones.

equiangular triangle (p. 404) **triángulo equiángulo** Triángulo que tiene los tres ángulos de igual medida.

equilateral triangle (pp. 190, 404) **triángulo equilátero** Triángulo que tiene los tres lados de igual longitud.

equivalent equations (p. 74) **ecuaciones equivalentes** Ecuaciones que tienen las mismas soluciones.

equivalent fractions (p. 233) **fracciones equivalentes** Fracciones que al quedar reducidas a su mínima expresión son iguales.

equivalent inequalities (p. 90) **desigualdades equivalentes** Desigualdades que tienen todos los mismos soluciones.

equivalent numerical expressions (p. 38) **expresiones numéricas equivalentes** Expresiones numéricas que tienen el mismo valor.

equivalent variable expressions (p. 38) **expresiones algebraicas equivalentes** Expresiones algebraicas que siempre tienen los mismos valores al sustituir las variables por números.

evaluating a numerical expression (p. 7) **evaluar una expresión numérica** Hallar el valor de la expresión.

evaluating a variable expression (p. 8) **evaluar una expresión algebraica** Hallar el valor de la expresión mediante la sustitución de cada variable por un número y posteriormente hallar el valor de la expresión numérica resultante.

event (p. 345) **suceso** Conjunto de casos de un experimento.

experimental probability (p. 346) **probabilidad experimental** Probabilidad basada en la realización de las pruebas de un experimento repetidas veces. La probabilidad experimental de un suceso viene dada por la razón $\frac{\text{Número de éxitos}}{\text{Número de pruebas}}$.

exponent (p. 12) **exponente** Número o variable que representa las veces que la base se repite como factor en una multiplicación. Por ejemplo, en la potencia 5^2, el exponente es 2.

face of a polyhedron (p. 518) **cara de un poliedro** Polígono que forma parte del límite de un poliedro. *Ver también* poliedro.

factor (p. 7) **factor** Al multiplicar dos números enteros distintos a cero, cada uno de ellos es factor del producto. Como $2 \times 3 = 6$, 2 y 3 son factores de 6. *Ver también* divisor.

factor tree (p. 220) **árbol de factorización** Diagrama que sirve para mostrar la descomposición de un número en sus factores primos.

favorable outcomes (p. 345) **casos favorables** Resultados correspondientes a un suceso. Por ejemplo, al lanzar un dado hay 3 casos favorables a obtener un número par: 2, 4 y 6.

formula (p. 22) **fórmula** Ecuación algebraica que relaciona dos o más variables.

frequency (p. 343) **frecuencia** Número de veces que aparece un dato.

function (p. 563) **función** Regla que asigna a cada número de un conjunto dado un número de otro conjunto. La función parte de un número llamado *entrada* y lo asocia a un solo número llamado *salida.*

function form of an equation (p. 568) **forma de función de una ecuación** Ecuación obtenida al resolver para *y* una ecuación con dos variables *x* e *y*.

greatest common divisor, GCD (p. 225) **máximo común divisor, MCD** Mayor divisor común de dos o más números enteros distintos a cero. Se llama también *máximo común factor, MCF.*

greatest common factor, GCF (p. 225) **máximo común factor, MCF** Mayor factor común de dos o más números enteros distintos a cero. Se llama también *máximo común divisor, MCD. Ver también* factor común.

grouping symbols (p. 17) **signos de agrupación** Signos como los paréntesis ( ) y los corchetes [ ] que se utilizan para indicar el orden de las operaciones o para señalar claramente una expresión.

half-plane (p. 598) **semiplano** Cualquiera de las dos regiones en las que queda dividido un plano por una recta.

height of a parallelogram (p. 417) **altura de un paralelogramo** Distancia perpendicular entre la base de un paralelogramo y el lado opuesto. *Ver también* paralelogramo *y* base.

height of a trapezoid (p. 418) **altura de un trapecio** Distancia perpendicular entre los lados paralelos de un trapecio. *Ver también* trapecio.

hemisphere (p. 543) **hemisferio** Media esfera.

hexagon (p. 413) **hexágono** Polígono de seis lados.

hypotenuse (p. 460) **hipotenusa** Lado opuesto al ángulo recto en un triángulo rectángulo; es el lado más largo del triángulo rectángulo. *Ver también* triángulo rectángulo.

hypothesis of an if-then statement (p. 465) **hipótesis de un enunciado de si-entonces** La parte del "si" en un enunciado de *si-entonces*. Por ejemplo, en el enunciado "Si $x + 1 = 3$, entonces $x = 2$", la hipótesis es "$x + 1 = 3$".

identity (p. 61) **identidad** Ecuación que es cierta para todos los valores de las variables de la ecuación.

image (pp. 423, 428) **imagen** Nueva figura obtenida al transformar otra.

ENGLISH-TO-SPANISH GLOSSARY

inequality (p. 90) **desigualdad** Enunciado matemático formado por dos expresiones separadas entre sí mediante uno de los signos de desigual (>, <, ≥, ≤).

input (p. 563) **entrada** Número sobre el que opera una función.

integers (pp. 105, 239) **números enteros** Los números . . . , −4, −3, −2, −1, 0, 1, 2, 3, 4, . . . , los cuales consisten en los números enteros negativos, los positivos y cero.

interest (p. 365) **interés** Dinero pagado a cambio del uso de otro dinero.

interest rate (p. 365) **tipo de interés** Porcentaje de aumento del capital por unidad de tiempo.

interquartile range (p. 489) **recorrido intercuartílico** Diferencia entre los cuartiles superior e inferior de un conjunto de datos.

intersection of geometric figures (p. 386) **intersección de figuras geométricas** Conjunto de puntos que dos o más figuras geométricas tienen en común.

inverse operation (pp. 74, 170) **operación inversa** Operación que "anula" a otra. La suma y la resta son operaciones inversas y también lo son la multiplicación y la división.

irrational numbers (p. 453) **números irracionales** Números reales que no pueden escribirse como cociente de dos números enteros.

isosceles right triangle (p. 461) **triángulo rectángulo isósceles** Triángulo rectángulo cuyos catetos tienen la misma longitud.

isosceles trapezoid (p. 405) **trapecio isósceles** Trapecio cuyos lados no paralelos son congruentes.

isosceles triangle (p. 404) **triángulo isósceles** Triángulo que tiene al menos dos lados de igual longitud.

justifying a step (p. 33) **justificar un paso** Aplicar una propiedad establecida para explicar la validez de un paso.

kite (p. 405) **cometa** Cuadrilátero que tiene dos pares de lados congruentes, pero en el que los lados opuestos no son congruentes.

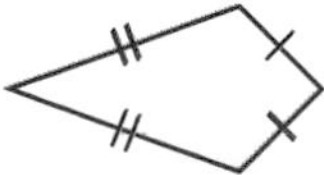

least common denominator, LCD (p. 273) **mínimo común denominador, mcd** Menor múltiplo común de los denominadores de dos o más fracciones.

least common multiple, LCM (p. 229) **mínimo común múltiplo, mcm** Menor múltiplo común de dos o más números. *Ver también* múltiplo común.

legs of a right triangle (p. 460) **catetos de un triángulo rectángulo** Lados de un triángulo rectángulo que forman el ángulo recto. *Ver también* triángulo rectángulo.

like terms (pp. 57, 623) **términos semejantes** En una expresión, dos o más términos en los que las partes que llevan las variables son iguales.

linear equation in two variables (p. 567) **ecuación lineal de dos variables** Ecuación cuyas variables aparecen en términos diferentes y están elevadas sólo a la primera potencia. Por ejemplo, la ecuación $2x + y = 5$ es una ecuación lineal de dos variables.

linear function (p. 568) **función lineal** Función de la forma $y = mx + b$.

linear inequality in two variables (p. 598) **desigualdad lineal de dos variables** Desigualdad que puede escribirse en una de las siguientes formas: $ax + by < c$, $ax + by \leq c$, $ax + by > c$ ó $ax + by \geq c$, donde a, b y c son constantes.

line graph (p. 4) **gráfica lineal** Tipo de gráficas en el que aparecen puntos unidos mediante segmentos de recta.

line of reflection (p. 423) **eje de reflexión** Recta que en una reflexión biseca y es perpendicular a cada segmento que une un punto y su imagen.

line plot (p. 203) **diagrama de puntos** Diagrama con rectas numéricas que muestra la frecuencia de datos.

line segment (p. 385) **segmento de recta** Parte de una recta que consiste en dos extremos y en todos los puntos comprendidos entre ellos.

line symmetry (p. 424) **simetría axial** Una figura tiene simetría axial cuando, al ser atravesada por una recta, la parte de la figura situada a un lado de la recta es una reflexión de la parte situada al otro lado.

lower quartile (p. 489) **cuartil inferior** Mediana de la mitad inferior de un conjunto de datos. *Ver también* gráfica de frecuencias acumuladas.

markup (p. 356) **margen de beneficio** Diferencia entre el precio de venta y el de costo de un ítem.

mean **(pp. 136, 203)** **media** Suma de los números de un conjunto de datos dividida entre la cantidad de elementos del conjunto. La media se llama también *promedio.*

measure of an angle **(p. 390)** **medida de un ángulo** Tamaño de un ángulo, el cual puede expresarse en grados.

measure of central tendency **(p. 203)** **medida de tendencia central** Un solo número que es "típico" de los números de un conjunto de datos. La *media*, la *mediana* y la *moda* son medidas de tendencia central comunes.

median **(pp. 203, 489)** **mediana** Número central de un grupo de números cuando éstos están ordenados de menor a mayor; en el caso de un número par de elementos, la mediana es la *media* de los dos números centrales.

midpoint **(p. 403)** **punto medio** Punto que divide a un segmento en dos segmentos congruentes.

mode **(p. 203)** **moda** Número que aparece más veces en un conjunto de números.

monomial **(p. 617)** **monomio** Número, variable o producto de un número y una o más variables elevadas a potencias enteras; es un polinomio de un término.

multiple of a number **(p. 229)** **múltiplo de un número** Un múltiplo de un número es el producto de ese número y cualquier número entero distinto a cero.

multiplicative identity **(p. 57)** **elemento neutro de la multiplicación** El número 1 es el elemento neutro de la multiplicación. Al multiplicar un número por 1, resulta el número original.

multiplicative inverses **(p. 279)** **inversos multiplicativos** Dos números cuyo producto es 1. Los inversos multiplicativos se llaman también *recíprocos.*

natural numbers **(p. 239)** **números naturales** Los números 1, 2, 3, … . Son también los números que se usan para *contar.*

negative correlation **(p. 149)** **correlación negativa** En un conjunto de pares ordenados (x, y) de datos numéricos, si las coordenadas y tienden a disminuir al aumentar las coordenadas x, entonces la correlación entre x e y es negativa.

net **(p. 518)** **patrón** Figura bidimensional que al doblarse forma un sólido.

no obvious correlation **(p. 149)** **ninguna correlación evidente** En un conjunto de pares ordenados (x, y) de datos numéricos, si las coordenadas x e y no siguen un patrón, entonces no hay ninguna correlación evidente entre x e y.

nonlinear function **(p. 642)** **función no lineal** Función cuya gráfica no es una recta.

numerical expression **(p. 7)** **expresión numérica** Expresión que representa un número determinado. Además, consiste en números y operaciones aritméticas que deben realizarse.

oblique circular cylinder **(p. 535)** **cilindro circular oblicuo** En un cilindro circular oblicuo, el segmento que une los centros de las bases no es perpendicular a ellas. La altura de este tipo de cilindros es la distancia perpendicular entre las bases.

oblique prism **(p. 530)** **prisma oblicuo** En un prisma oblicuo, las aristas que unen las bases no son perpendiculares a ellas. La altura de un prisma oblicuo es la distancia perpendicular entre las bases.

obtuse angle **(p. 391)** **ángulo obtuso** Ángulo que mide entre 90° y 180°.

obtuse triangle **(p. 404)** **triángulo obtusángulo** Triángulo que tiene un ángulo obtuso.

opposites **(pp. 106, 117)** **opuestos** Dos números que tienen el mismo valor absoluto, pero signo diferente. Por ejemplo, -7 y 7 son opuestos. El opuesto de un número se llama también *inverso aditivo* de ese número.

ordered pair **(p. 144)** **par ordenado** Par de números que sirven para localizar un punto en un plano de coordenadas. El primer número es la coordenada x y el segundo la coordenada y.

order of operations **(p. 16)** **orden de las operaciones** Proceso para evaluar una expresión relacionada con más de una operación.

1. Evaluar las expresiones de los signos de agrupación.
2. Evaluar las potencias.
3. Multiplicar y dividir de izquierda a derecha.
4. Sumar y restar de izquierda a derecha.

origin **(p. 144)** **origen** El punto (0, 0) donde el eje de las x y el de las y se cortan en un plano de coordenadas. *Ver también* plano de coordenadas.

outcomes **(p. 345)** **casos** Resultados posibles al realizar un experimento. Por ejemplo, cara y cruz son los casos posibles al lanzar al aire una moneda.

outlier **(p. 204)** **valor extremo** Número de un conjunto de datos que es mucho mayor o mucho menor que la mayoría de los otros números del conjunto.

output **(p. 563)** **salida** Número obtenido al evaluar una función a partir de una entrada dada.

parallel lines (p. 386) **rectas paralelas** Rectas del mismo plano que no se cortan. A veces se consideran paralelas las rectas idénticas. En el diagrama, se utilizan flechas para indicar que las rectas son paralelas.

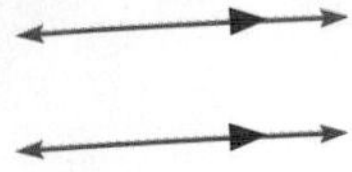

parallelogram (pp. 405, 419) **paralelogramo** Cuadrilátero cuyos lados opuestos son paralelos.

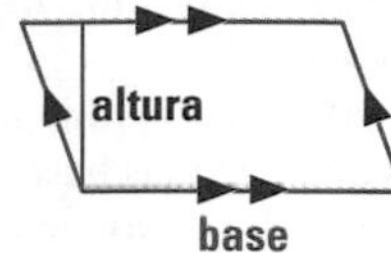

pentagon (p. 413) **pentágono** Polígono de cinco lados.

percent (pp. 244, 248) **porcentaje** Comparación que relaciona un número con 100; por ciento.

percent of change (p. 361) **porcentaje de cambio** Medida del aumento o de la disminución que ha sufrido una cantidad con respecto a la original; es un porcentaje de aumento o de disminución.

perfect square (p. 449) **cuadrado perfecto** Cuadrado de un número entero.

perimeter (p. 22) **perímetro** Longitud del contorno de una figura; en el caso de un polígono, es la suma de las longitudes de los lados. El perímetro se mide en unidades lineales.

perpendicular bisector (p. 403) **mediatriz** Recta, segmento o rayo que es perpendicular a un segmento de recta en su punto medio.

perpendicular lines (p. 398) **rectas perpendiculares** Dos rectas que se cortan, formando un ángulo recto.

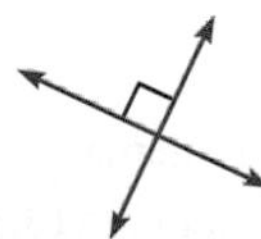

pi (π) (p. 511) **pi (π)** Razón de la circunferencia de un círculo a su diámetro. Esta razón es irracional y equivale aproximadamente a 3.14.

plane (p. 385) **plano** Un plano puede considerarse como una superficie plana que se prolonga indefinidamente en todas las direcciones.

point (p. 385) **punto** Un punto representa una posición en un plano o en el espacio.

polygon (p. 412) **polígono** Figura plana cerrada limitada por segmentos de recta llamados *lados* del polígono. Los triángulos y los cuadriláteros son ejemplos de polígonos.

polyhedron (p. 518) **poliedro** Sólido cerrado limitado por polígonos llamados *caras* del poliedro. Las caras adyacentes se unen en las *aristas* del poliedro. El punto donde se unen las aristas es un *vértice* del poliedro.

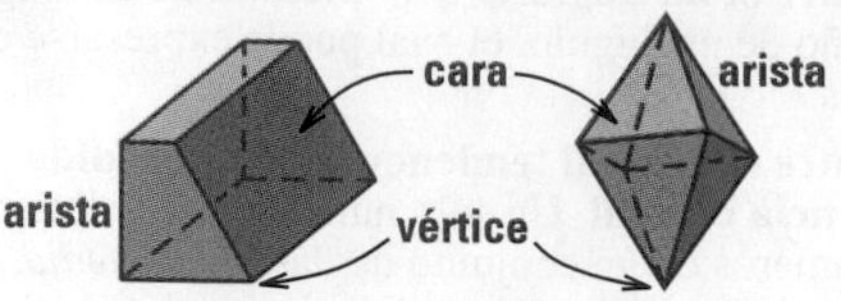

polynomial (p. 622) **polinomio** Monomio o expresión que puede escribirse como suma de monomios.

positive correlation (p. 149) **correlación positiva** En un conjunto de pares ordenados (x, y) de datos numéricos, si las coordenadas y tienden a aumentar al aumentar las coordenadas x, entonces la correlación entre x e y es positiva.

postulate (p. 399) **postulado** Enunciado no demostrado que sirve de base para demostrar otros enunciados.

power (p. 12) **potencia** Expresión como 5^2 que tiene una *base*, 5, y un *exponente*, 2. La expresión representa una multiplicación en la que el factor se repite.

prime factorization (p. 220) **descomposición en factores primos** Proceso de escribir un número como producto de números primos.

prime number (p. 220) **número primo** Número entero mayor que 1 cuyos factores enteros son sólo 1 y él mismo.

principal (p. 365) **capital** Cantidad de dinero depositada o tomada a préstamo.

prism (p. 523) **prisma** Poliedro con dos bases congruentes que se encuentran en planos paralelos. La altura de un prisma es la distancia perpendicular entre sus bases.

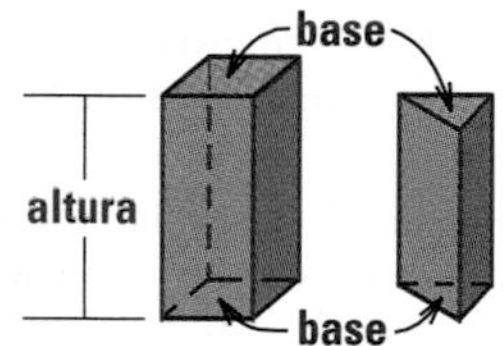

probability of an event (p. 345) **probabilidad de un suceso** Medida de las posibilidades de que ocurra un suceso. Es un número comprendido entre 0 y 1 que puede expresarse en forma de fracción, decimal o porcentaje.

profit (p. 141) **ganancia** Diferencia entre el total de ingresos y de gastos.

proportion (p. 333) **proporción** Ecuación que afirma la igualdad de dos razones. Una proporción tiene la forma $\frac{a}{b} = \frac{c}{d}$.

pyramid (p. 539) **pirámide** Poliedro en el que la base es un polígono y las caras triangulares se unen en un punto llamado *vértice.* La altura de una pirámide es la distancia perpendicular entre la base y el vértice.

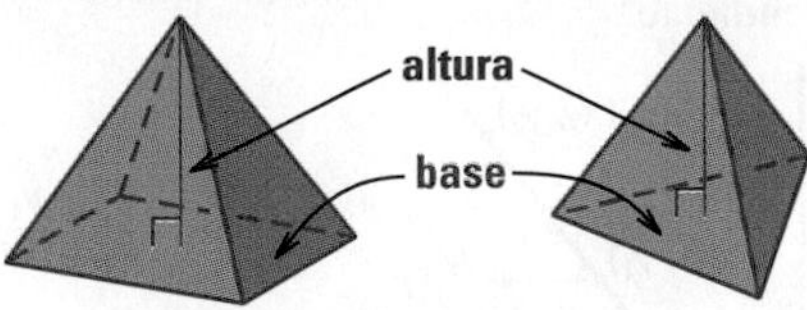

quadrants (p. 144) **cuadrantes** Las cuatro regiones en que el eje de las x y el de las y dividen a un plano de coordenadas. *Ver también* plano de coordenadas.

quadrilateral (p. 405) **cuadrilátero** Figura cerrada de cuatro lados que son segmentos de recta unidos en sus extremas.

radical sign (p. 449) **signo radical** El signo $\sqrt{\ }$, utilizado para representar la raíz cuadrada positiva.

radius of a circle (p. 511) **radio de un círculo** Distancia entre el centro del círculo y uno de sus puntos. Es además un segmento de recta que tiene por extremos el centro del círculo y un punto del mismo. *Ver también* círculo.

range (in statistics) (p. 489) **recorrido (en estadística)** Diferencia entre los valores máximo y mínimo de un conjunto de datos.

rate (p. 330) **relación** Tipo de razones en el que se comparan dos cantidades a y b expresadas en distintas unidades de medida.

ratio (p. 329) **razón** Comparación de un número a y un número b distinto a cero por medio de la división.

rational number (p. 239) **número racional** Número que puede escribirse como cociente $\frac{a}{b}$ de dos números enteros a y b donde $b \neq 0$.

ray (p. 385) **semirrecta, rayo** Parte de una recta que en una dirección tiene un extremo y en la otra se prolonga indefinidamente.

real numbers (p. 453) **números reales** Conjunto formado por todos los números racionales y los irracionales. (Se puede considerar que los números reales son el conjunto de todos los decimales finitos o infinitos.)

reciprocals (p. 279) **recíprocos** Dos números cuyo producto es 1. Los recíprocos se llaman también *inversos multiplicativos.*

rectangle (pp. 22, 405) **rectángulo** Paralelogramo de cuatro ángulos rectos.

rectangular prism (p. 523) **prisma rectangular** Prisma que tiene por bases rectángulos.

reflection (p. 423) **reflexión** Operación que hace corresponder a cada punto P de una figura con su punto imagen P', de manera que (1) si P no está en el eje de reflexión, entonces ese eje es la mediatriz de $\overline{PP'}$; y (2) si P está en el eje de reflexión, entonces $P = P'$.

regular polygon (p. 413) **polígono regular** Polígono cuyos lados son todos de igual longitud y cuyos ángulos son todos de igual medida.

repeating decimal (p. 240) **decimal periódico** Para escribir en forma decimal una fracción $\frac{a}{b}$ $(b \neq 0)$, se divide a entre b mediante la división desarrollada. Cuando el proceso de división no concluye, entonces se llega a un dígito o a un grupo de dígitos que se repite indefinidamente. En ese caso, la fracción puede expresarse en forma de decimal periódico.

rhombus (p. 405) **rombo** Paralelogramo que tiene todos sus lados congruentes.

right angle (pp. 22, 391) **ángulo recto** Ángulo que mide 90°.

right circular cylinder (p. 523) **cilindro circular recto** En un cilindro circular recto, el segmento que une los centros de las bases es perpendicular a ellas.

right prism (p. 523) **prisma recto** En un prisma recto, las aristas que unen las bases son perpendiculares a ellas.

right triangle (pp. 404, 460) **triángulo rectángulo** Triángulo que tiene un ángulo recto.

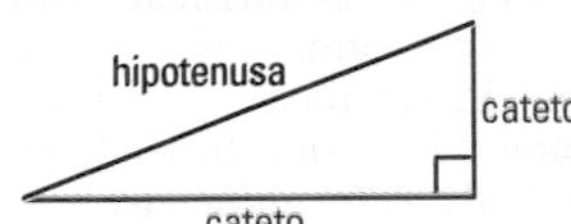

scale (p. 338) **escala** En un dibujo a escala, la escala da la relación entre las medidas del dibujo y las reales. Por ejemplo, la escala 1 pulg = 2 pies significa que 1 pulg del dibujo representa una distancia real de 2 pies.

scale drawing (p. 338) **dibujo a escala** Diagrama de un objeto en el que la longitud y la anchura son proporcionales a la longitud y a la anchura reales del objeto.

scale factor (pp. 433, 548) **factor de escala** El factor de escala de dos polígonos semejantes o de dos sólidos semejantes es la razón entre las medidas lineales correspondientes como, por ejemplo, las longitudes de los lados y los radios.

scale factor in a scale drawing (p. 338) **factor de escala de un dibujo a escala** Razón entre la longitud y la anchura del dibujo y la longitud y la anchura reales correspondientes.

scalene triangle (p. 404) **triángulo escaleno** Triángulo que tiene sus tres lados de distinta longitud.

scatter plot (p. 149) **diagrama de dispersión** Gráfica de un conjunto de pares ordenados (x, y).

scientific notation (p. 309) **notación científica** Número escrito en la forma $c \times 10^n$, donde c es mayor o igual a 1 y menor que 10, y n es un número entero.

sector of a circle (p. 513) **sector circular** Parte de un círculo determinada por dos radios.

segment (p. 385) **segmento** *Ver* segmento de recta.

sequence (p. 28) **sucesión** Lista ordenada de números.

similar figures (p. 432) **figuras semejantes** Dos figuras que tienen la misma forma, pero no necesariamente el mismo tamaño. Los ángulos correspondientes de las figuras semejantes son congruentes y las razones entre las longitudes de los lados correspondientes son iguales. Por ejemplo, $\triangle ABC \sim \triangle DEF$.

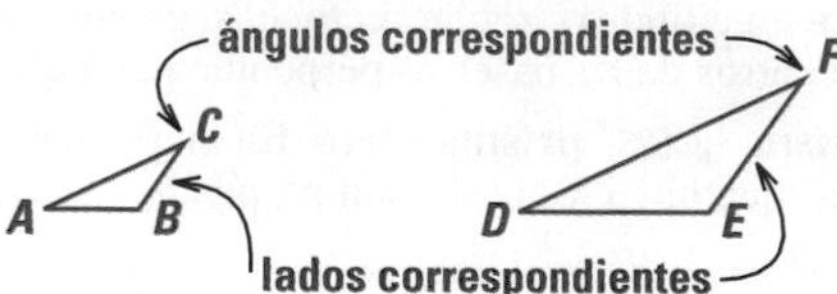

similar solids (p. 548) **sólidos semejantes** Dos sólidos que tienen la misma forma, pero no necesariamente el mismo tamaño. Las medidas lineales correspondientes como las alturas o los radios tienen la misma razón. La razón común se llama *factor de escala.*

simple interest (p. 365) **interés simple** Interés pagado sólo sobre el capital; es el producto obtenido al multiplicar el capital, el tipo de interés anual y el tiempo en años. $I = Prt$

simplest form of a fraction (p. 233) **mínima expresión de una fracción** Una fracción está en su mínima expresión cuando el único factor común del numerador y del denominador es 1.

skew lines (p. 517) **rectas alabeadas** Rectas del espacio que no se cortan, y no son paralelas. Las rectas alabeadas no se encuentran en el mismo plano.

slide (p. 428) **deslizamiento** *Ver* traslación.

slope (p. 583) **pendiente** La pendiente de una recta no vertical es la razón de la *distancia vertical* (cambio de y) a la *distancia horizontal* (cambio de x) entre dos puntos cualesquiera de la recta. En el diagrama abajo, m es la pendiente.

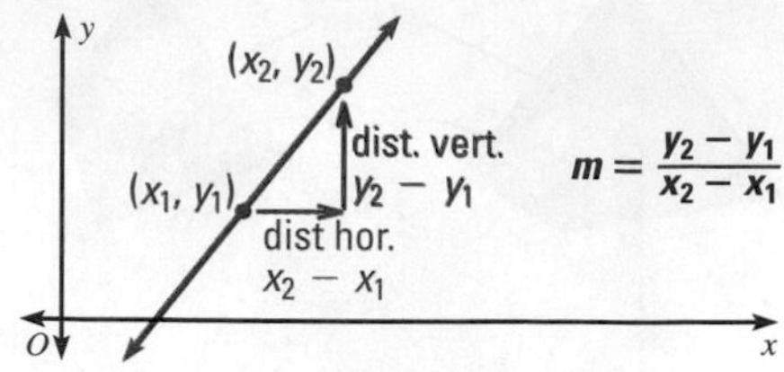

slope-intercept form (p. 589) **ecuación pendiente intercepción de una recta** Ecuación lineal de la forma $y = mx + b$ donde m es la pendiente y b la intercepción en y.

solution of an equation in one variable (p. 61) **solución de una ecuación de una variable** Valor que satisface la ecuación al sustituir a la variable de la misma.

solution of an equation in two variables (pp. 145, 567) **solución de una ecuación de dos variables** Par ordenado (x, y) que cumple la ecuación al sustituir a las variables de la misma.

solution of an inequality in one variable (p. 90) **solución de una desigualdad de una variable** Número que satisface la desigualdad al sustituir a la variable de la misma.

solution of an inequality in two variables (p. 598) **solución de una desigualdad de dos variables** Par ordenado (x, y) que cumple la desigualdad al sustituir a las variables de la misma.

solution of a system of equations (p. 602) **solución de un sistema de ecuaciones** Par ordenado (x, y) que es una solución de cada ecuación del sistema.

solution of a system of inequalities (p. 603) **solución de un sistema de desigualdades** Par ordenado (x, y) que es una solución de cada desigualdad del sistema.

solving a right triangle (p. 461) **resolver un triángulo rectángulo** Usar las longitudes de dos lados de un triángulo rectángulo, además del teorema de Pitágoras, para hallar la longitud del tercer lado.

solving an equation (p. 61) **resolver una ecuación** Hallar todos los valores de la variable que satisfacen la ecuación.

solving an inequality (p. 90) **resolver una desigualdad** Hallar todos los valores de la variable que satisfacen la desigualdad.

sphere (p. 543) **esfera** Conjunto de puntos del espacio que están a una distancia dada de un punto llamado *centro* de la esfera. El *radio* de una esfera es la distancia del centro a un punto de la esfera.

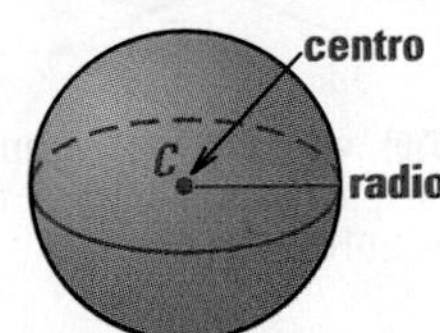

square (pp. 22, 405) **cuadrado** Rectángulo que tiene todos los lados congruentes.

square of a number (p. 12) **cuadrado de un número** Segunda potencia de un número.

square root (p. 449) **raíz cuadrada** Una raíz cuadrada de un número es otro número tal que, al multiplicarse por sí mismo, da el número original. Por ejemplo, 6 y -6 son ambos raíces cuadradas de 36 ya que $6^2 = 36$ y $(-6)^2 = 36$.

standard form of a polynomial (p. 622) **forma usual de un polinomio** Polinomio escrito de tal manera que las potencias de la variable disminuyen de izquierda a derecha.

stem-and-leaf plot (p. 253) **tabla arborescente** Representación de datos que permite observar la distribución de los datos. Es de utilidad para colocar los datos en orden ascendente o descendente.

straight angle (p. 391) **ángulo llano** Ángulo que mide 180°.

supplementary angles (p. 391) **ángulos suplementarios** Dos ángulos cuyas medidas suman 180°.

surface area of a solid (p. 523) **área superficial de un sólido** Suma de las áreas de todas las superficies que limitan al sólido.

system of equations (p. 602) **sistema de ecuaciones** Conjunto de dos o más ecuaciones con las mismas variables.

system of inequalities (p. 602) **sistema de desigualdades** Conjunto de dos o más desigualdades con las mismas variables.

terminating decimal (p. 240) **decimal exacto** Para escribir en forma decimal una fracción $\frac{a}{b}$ $(b \neq 0)$, se divide a entre b mediante la división desarrollada. Cuando el proceso de división concluye con un residuo de cero, entonces la fracción puede expresarse en forma de decimal exacto.

terms of a sum (p. 7) **términos de una suma** Números o expresiones que se suman.

theoretical probability (p. 346) **probabilidad teórica** Probabilidad que se halla mediante el razonamiento matemático. Si los casos de un experimento son igualmente probables, entonces la probabilidad teórica del suceso viene dada por la razón $\frac{\text{Número de casos favorables}}{\text{Número total de casos}}$.

transformation (p. 428) **transformación** Operación que hace corresponder a una figura con otra llamada *imagen.* Las reflexiones y las traslaciones son transformaciones.

translation (p. 428) **traslación** Transformación en la que se desliza cada uno de los puntos de una figura, conservando la distancia y la dirección; también se llama *deslizamiento.*

transversal (p. 399) **transversal** Recta que corta a otras dos rectas.

trapezoid (p. 405) **trapecio** Cuadrilátero que tiene un solo par de lados paralelos.

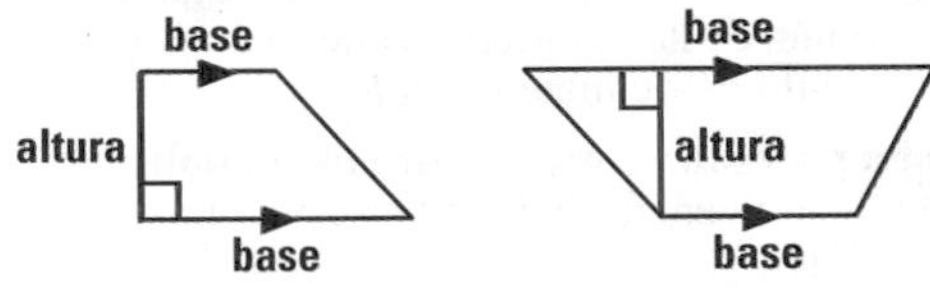

triangle (p. 22) **triángulo** Polígono de tres lados. *Ver también* polígono.

trinomial (p. 622) **trinomio** Polinomio de tres términos.

unit rate (p. 330) **relación unitaria** Relación cuyo denominador es 1 unidad. Por ejemplo, $23 por pie es una relación unitaria.

ENGLISH-TO-SPANISH GLOSSARY

upper quartile (p. 489) **cuartil superior** Mediana de la mitad superior de un conjunto de datos. *Ver también* gráfica de frecuencias acumuladas.

value(s) of a variable (p. 8) **valor(es) de una variable** Número o números que representa una variable.

variable (p. 8) **variable** Letra que representa uno o más números.

variable expression (p. 8) **expresión algebraica** Expresión que consiste en números, variables y operaciones que deben realizarse.

variation (p. 489) **variación** Medida de la gama de valores que hay en un conjunto de datos.

Venn diagram (p. 239) **diagrama de Venn** Dibujo que emplea figuras geométricas para mostrar las relaciones existentes entre los conjuntos.

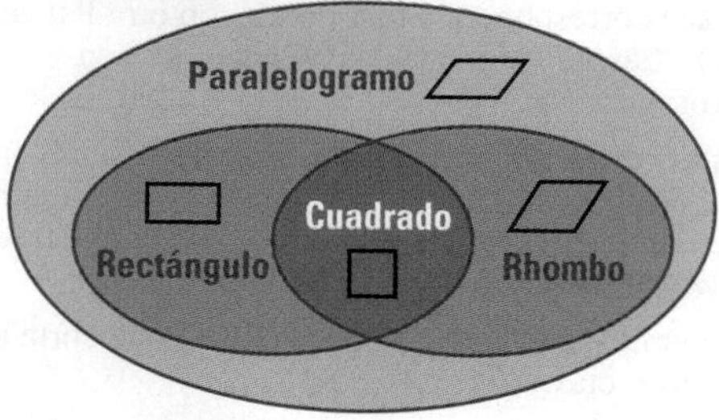

vertex of an angle (p. 390) **vértice de un ángulo** Extremo común de las semirrectas que forman los lados del ángulo. Ver también *ángulo.*

vertex of a polygon (p. 412) **vértice de un polígono** Punto donde se unen dos lados de un polígono. *Ver también* polígono.

vertex of a polyhedron (p. 518) **vértice de un poliedro** Punto donde se unen tres o más aristas de un poliedro. *Ver también* poliedro.

vertical angles (p. 398) **ángulos opuestos por el vértice** Dos pares de ángulos no adyacentes formados por rectas secantes; los ángulos opuestos por el vértice son congruentes. En el diagrama abajo, tanto $\angle 1$ y $\angle 3$ como $\angle 2$ y $\angle 4$ son ángulos opuestos por el vértice.

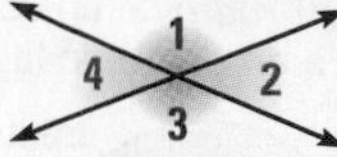

volume (pp. 13, 530) **volumen** El volumen de un sólido es la medida del espacio que ocupa. El volumen se mide en unidades cúbicas.

x*-axis** (p. 144) **eje de las *x Eje horizontal de un plano de coordenadas. *Ver también* plano de coordenadas.

x*-coordinate** (p. 144) **coordenada *x Primer número de las coordenadas de un punto, el cual indica la posición del punto con respecto al eje de las *x*. *Ver también* par ordenado.

x*-intercept** (p. 576) **intercepción en *x Coordenada *x* de un punto donde una gráfica corta al eje de las *x*; es el valor de *x* cuando $y = 0$.

y*-axis** (p. 144) **eje de las *y Eje vertical de un plano de coordenadas. *Ver también* plano de coordenadas.

y*-coordinate** (p. 144) **coordenada *y Segundo número de las coordenadas de un punto, el cual indica la posición del punto con respecto al eje de las *y*. *Ver también* par ordenado.

y*-intercept** (p. 576) **intercepción en *y Coordenada *y* de un punto donde una gráfica corta al eje de las *y*; es el valor de *y* cuando $x = 0$.

Credits

Cover Photography

Ralph Mercer

Photography

i Ralph Mercer; **iii** RMIP/Richard Haynes; **1** Ariel Skelley/The Stock Market (tl); Roy Morsch/The Stock Market (tr); Conly L. Rieder/BPS/Tony Stone Images (b); **5** Donavan Reese/Tony Stone Images; **6** David Madison/The Image Bank; **8** Loren McIntrye/Woodfin Camp and Associates; **15** Corbis/Bettmann; **25** Courtesy of NASA/JPL/Caltech; **27** Gerd Ludwig/Woodfin Camp and Associates; **28** Renee Lynn/Tony Stone Images; **30** Conly L. Rieder/BPS/Tony Stone Images; **48** PhotoDisc (all); **51** Stephen Derr/Image Bank (tl); **51** David Young-Wolff/Tony Stone Images (tr); **54** Clint Crowley/Images West Photography; Artville; PhotoDisc (montage); **56** Alan Schein/The Stock Market; **60** W. Perry Conway/Corbis; **64** RMIP/Richard Haynes; **67** Rich Iwasaki/Tony Stone Images; **69** Robert Holmes/Corbis; **70** Peter Beck/The Stock Market; **77** James Martin; **83** Neil Crosby-Neil Studios/Women's Basketball Hall of Fame; **88** Jeffrey Dunn; **93** Karl Weatherly/Tony Stone Images; **103** Otto Greule/AllSport (tl); Kevin R. Morris/Corbis (tr); **106** Carl Roessler/FPG International; **111** Museo della Scienza/Art Resource; **119** Francois Gohier/Photo Researchers, Inc.; **124** Steven Peters/Tony Stone Images; **126** Liaison International; **131** Alan Bean/The Greenwich Workshop; **133** Tony Page/Tony Stone Images; **138** Mike Powell/Allsport; **148** Courtesy of Levi Strauss and Co. Archives, San Francisco; **152** Jeff Foott/Jeff Foott Productions; **164** A. Witte/C. Mahaney/Tony Stone Images; **165** Lori Adamski Peek/Tony Stone Images; **167** Roger Ball/The Stock Market (tl); Paula Lerner/Woodfin Camp and Associates (tr); **171** Superstock; **173** Barbara Filet/Tony Stone Images; **175** Ted Horowitz/The Stock Market; **177** Courtesy of Consolidated Edison, New York; **180** Jim A. Simek/NumisGraphic Enterprises (both); **182** Charlie Ott/Photo Researchers, Inc.; **184** Leonard de Selva/Corbis; **186** The Granger Collection, New York; **188** Tony Perrottet/Omni Photo Communications; **192** Donald Daily/Daily & Daily; **194** Richard Olsenius/National Geographic Image Collection; **202** The Granger Collection, New York; **207** Toni AngerMayer/Photo Researchers, Inc.; **217** Spencer Grant/Monkmeyer Press (tr); Eric Futran/Liaison Inc. (tl); **223** The Granger Collection, New York; **226** Chuck Savage/The Stock Market; **228** Billie Ruth Sudduth, "Nature's Sequence", 17"H × 18"W × 18"D. 1994. Photo credit: Melva Calder. Collection of the Renwick Gallery, National Museum of American Art, Smithsonian Institution; **232** The Granger Collection, New York (tl); Japack/Leo de Wys (tr); **237** Reuters Newmedia Inc./Corbis; **244** Brown Brothers (bl, inset); **245** Giraudon/Art Resource; **247** Bob Daemmrich/Tony Stone Images; **254** Peggy and Ronald Barnett/The Stock Market; **264** Artville, LLC. (tc); School Division, Houghton Mifflin Company (tr); PhotoDisc, Inc. (bl); **267** Roger Tully/Tony Stone Images (tl); David W. Crow/Photo Edit (tr); Corbis (cr); Richardson West/Corbis (c, inset); **271** John Betty/Tony Stone Images; **272** RMIP/Richard Haynes; **276** Richard T. Nowitz/Corbis; **281** Nicholas Pinturas/Tony Stone Images; **287** Michael Newman/PhotoEdit; **295** Bettmann/Corbis; **307** Ted Horowitz/The Stock Market; **308** Hulton Getty/Tony Stone Images; **312** Richard T. Nowitz/Corbis; **320** Ken O'Donoghue; **325** Michael Newman/PhotoEdit; **327** Steve Leonard/Black Star (tl); Tim Brown/Tony Stone Images (tr); **330** Don Smetzer/Tony Stone Images; **332** Kit Houghton/Corbis; **334** Ralph A. Clevenger/Corbis; **336** Chris Johns/National Geographic Image Collection; **339** Peter Vanderwarker/Peter Vanderwarker Photo; **341** Joel W. Rodgers/Corbis (cl); Russell R. Grundke (cr); **342** Mehau Kulyk/Science Photo Library; **353** Michael Newman/PhotoEdit; **359** Chris Jones/The Stock Market; **364** Lester Lefkowitz/The Stock Market; **373** BachMann/Photo Researchers, Inc.; **383** Paul Barton/The Stock Market (tl); Bruce Ayres/Tony Stone Images (tr); RMIP/Richard Haynes (br); **388** Digital Art/Corbis; **393** Clive Freeman/BIOSYM Technologies/Photo Researchers; **400** Bettman/Corbis; **406** John Lei/Omni Photo Communications (all); **409** Kermani/Liaison International; **411** School Division, Houghton Mifflin Company; **416** Artist: Erica Licea-Kane, Spring 1982, Untitled, Photo: Thomas Vati, Technique: Double Weave Pick-up, Loom: 8 Harness Maconber, Materials: 100% Cotton Thread, Size: 4" × 5" (tl, tr); **422** Courtesy of NASA; **429** Omni Photo Communications; **436** Christie's Images/Superstock; **447** Robert Azzi/Woodfin Camp and Associates (tl); Jeff Greenberg/PhotoEdit (tr); **452** Tom Sheppard/Tony Stone Images; **453** Bob Daemmrich Photography; **461** Gianni Dagi Orti/Corbis; **471** Elena Rooraid/PhotoEdit; **477** Jim West/Jim West Photography; **479** Jean Y. Rusniewski/Tony Stone Images; **483** James P. Blair/National Geographic Image Collection; **487** Susan Middleton/Corbis (cl); Dan Guravich/Corbis (inset); **492** Corbis; **504** Hulton Getty/Tony Stone Images; **505** Loren McIntrye/Woodfin Camp and Associates; **507** Andy Ryan/Massachusetts Turnpike Authority (tl);

Teacher's Edition Credits

Cover Photography Ralph Mercer

Photography

T1, T2, T5 Ralph Mercer; **T3** RMIP/ Richard Haynes; **T10** Michael Goss.

Illustrations

School Division, Houghton Mifflin Company and McDougal Littell.

Kaluzny/Thatcher/Tony Stone Images (tr); **512** Chuck Place; **514** PhotoDisc, Inc. (all); **515** The Granger Collection, New York; **531** Michael Howell/Envision; **533** Norbert Rosing/National Geographic Image Collection; **538** John Lypian/Spectrum Stock Inc.; **540** Jim Foster/The Stock Market; **542** Will & Deni McIntyre/Tony Stone Images; **544** William Bond/National Geographic Image Collection (bl); **545** PhotoDisc, Inc. (all); **546** Learning Technologies, Inc.; **549** Richard Nowitz; **551** Rob Lewine/The Stock Market; **558** Jerome Wycoff/Visuals Unlimited (l); Charles D. Winters/Photo Researchers, Inc. (cl, c); Brian Parker/Tom Stack & Associates (cr); Betty Crowell/Faraway Places (r); **561** Stewart Cohen/Tony Stone Images (tl); Bernard Gotfryd/Woodfin Camp and Associates (tr); **563** Wm. L. Wantland/Tom Stack & Associates; **566** Grace Davies/Envision; **574** Jean-Claude LeJeune/Stock Boston; **577** Zigy Kaluzny/Tony Stone Images; **579** David Weintraub/Photo Researchers, Inc.; **592** Jim Sugar Photography/Corbis; **595** Pick/Weber/Stock Boston; **601** Hulton Getty/Tony Stone Images; **612** Ken O'Donoghue (both); **615** Brian G. Miller/Illinois State Police. Courtesy of Nathan S. Shigemura (both); **619** Roger Ressmeyer/Corbis; **623** Scala/Art Resource, New York; **625** Vince Streano/Corbis; **629** Bob Daemmrich Photography; **639** Bob Daemmrich Photography; **646** Tom Pantages; **652** Joe McBride/Tony Stone Images; **665** Ken O'Donoghue.

Illustration

School Division, Houghton Mifflin Company and McDougal Littell.

CREDITS

Selected Answers

Pre-Course Practice

Number Sense (p. xxii)
1. $2 \times 1000 + 3 \times 100 + 6 \times 10 + 5 \times 1$
3. $4 \times 100 + 9 \times 10 + 1 \times 1 + 3 \times 0.1$ **5.** 55,098
7. 508.17 **9.** thousandths; 0.769 **11.** tenths; 8.7
13. $0.8 < 2.8$ **15.** $8.08 < 8.09$
17. 0.3, 2.2, 4.2, 4.5, 5.2 **19.** 0.3, 0.9, 3.3, 4.3, 5.4

21. 19.6 **23.** 0.82 **25.** 80.1 **27.** 17.3 **29.** 0.1775
31. 300 **33.** 0.868 **35.** 0.015 **37.** \$4.35/yd **39.** $\frac{3}{4}$,
Sample answer: $\frac{6}{8}$; $\frac{12}{16}$ **41.** $\frac{3}{8}$, *Sample answer:* $\frac{6}{16}$; $\frac{12}{32}$
43. $\frac{35}{100}$, 35% **45.** $2\frac{3}{4}$ **47.** $5\frac{1}{3}$ **49.** $2\frac{1}{3}$ **51.** $2\frac{8}{15}$
53. $\frac{26}{3}$ **55.** $\frac{37}{25}$ **57.** $\frac{85}{9}$ **59.** $\frac{31}{2}$
In 61–73, estimates may vary. **61.** 160 **63.** 236,000
65. 25,000 **67.** *Sample answer:* yes; An estimate might be \$11.00, but this would not be enough money because the real answer is \$11.21. **69.** 6500, using rounding
71. 27, using rounding **73.** 55, using compatible numbers

Measurement and Geometry (p. xxiv) **75.** $204.\overline{6}$ yd
77. 35 ft **79.** 92.3 cm **81.** 60 ft; 225 ft^2
83. 80 m; 300 m^2
85. 108 mm; 704 mm^2

22 mm
32 mm

87. 125 mm^3 **89.** 1260 in.^{3}
91. 46.656 cm^3

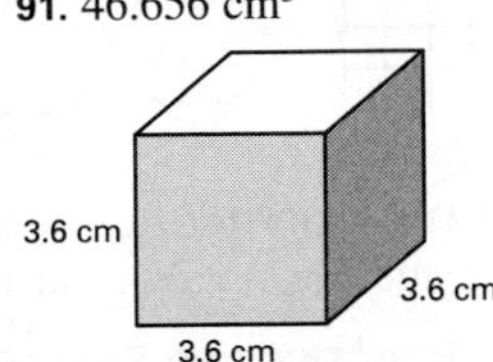

Statistics, Data Analysis, & Probability (p. xxv)
93.

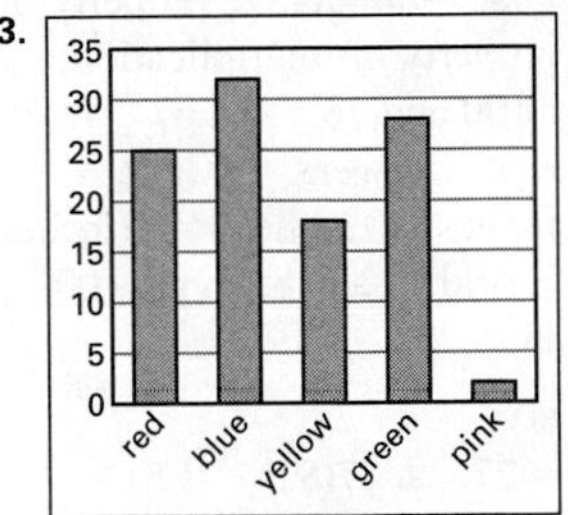

95. 5 and 10 mi/h **97.** about 1.5°F

99.

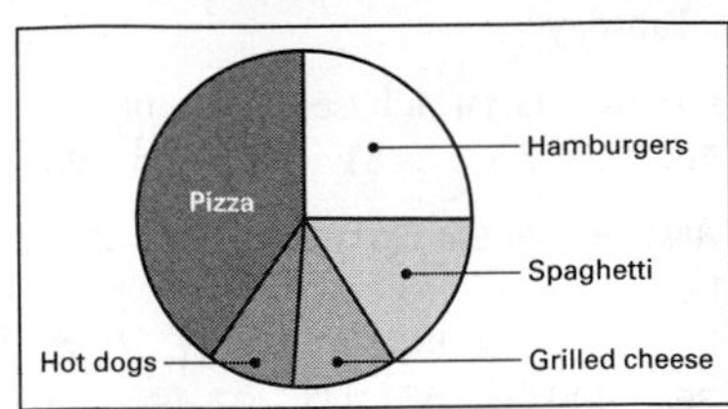

101. *Sample answer:* Most families had either 2, 3, or 4 telephones.

Chapter 1

Getting Ready (p. 2) **1.** C **2.** G **3.** C **4.** J

1.1 Guided Practice (p. 5) **1.** It depends on the number of letters to be engraved. Company A is less expensive for 4 or fewer letters and Company B is less expensive for 6 letters.

1.1 Practice and Problem Solving (pp. 5–6)
3.

# of times you use swimming pool in month	0	1	2	3	4	5	6	7	8
Charge	10	12	14	16	18	20	22	24	26

The charge increases \$2.00 each time the pool is used.
5. The volume of gas increases. **7.** 240 feet **9.** *Sample answer:* You could tell that the greatest men's distance was in 1992, the greatest women's distance was in 1988, and the men's distances were greater than the women's distances. **11.** United States **13.** Russia

1.2 Guided Practice (p. 9) **1.** factors **3.** 68; the sum of 28 and 40 is 68. **5.** 13; the difference of 40 and 27 is 13. **7.** 83; the difference of 90 and 7 is 83. **9.** 78; the product of 13 and 6 is 78. **11.** $15 + 33 = 48$
13. $18 - 9 = 9$ **15.** 9 **17.** 1 **19.** 3 **21.** 6

1.2 Practice and Problem Solving (pp. 9–11)
23. 48; the product of 6 and 8 is 48. **25.** 47; the sum of 33 and 14 is 47. **27.** 55; the difference of 111 and 56 is 55. **29.** 20; the sum of 10, 6, and 4 is 20. **31.** 60; the product of 5 and 12 is 60. **33.** 9.7; the sum of 5.4 and 4.3 is 9.7. **39.** $56 + 89 = 145$ **41.** $\frac{50}{10} = 5$
43. $6 \cdot 5 = 30$ **45.** $200 - 36 = 164$ **47.** *Sample answer:* $66 + 33 = 99$; $198 \div 2 = 99$; $100 - 1 = 99$ **49.** 2.2
51. 1 **53.** 40 **55.** 5 **57.** 8 **59.** 70 **61.** 9 **63.** 18
65. \$48 **67.** $4.95 + 4(2.95) = 4.95 + 11.80 = \$16.75$
75. 2, 4, 6, 8, 10, 12, 14, 16, 18, 20
When $s = 2$, the pattern results in the even numbers.
77. $5a$, where a = your age **79.** $a \div 2$, where a = your age **81.** 3 **87–91.** Estimates may vary. **87.** 7000

89. 8000 **91.** 25 **93.** The doubling pattern increases by large amounts. No; by day 7 exercise time will be $5\frac{1}{3}$ hours, probably more time than you can spend exercising. **95.** Tuesday

1.3 GUIDED PRACTICE (p. 14) **1.** base; exponent **3.** $4 \cdot 4 = 16$ **5.** $3 \cdot 3 \cdot 3 \cdot 3 = 81$ **7.** 196 ft^2 **9.** 512

1.3 PRACTICE AND PROBLEM SOLVING (pp. 14–15)
11. $5 \cdot 5 \cdot 5 = 125$ **13.** $3 \cdot 3 \cdot 3 = 27$ **15.** 3^7 **17.** 10^4 **19.** 1^5 **21.** $2^5 = 32$ **23.** $12^2 = 144$ **25.** 27 **27.** 27 **29.** 243 **31.** = **33.** > **35.** 1,000,000; 531,441 **37.** 4900; 4624 **39.** 3 **41.** 5 **43.** 160 minutes or 2 hours forty minutes

45.

Power	10^6	10^5	10^4	10^3	10^2	10^1
Number	1,000,000	100,000	10,000	1,000	100	10

The exponent is the number of zeros; 10,000,000,000.

1.4 GUIDED PRACTICE (p. 18) **1.** 6 **3.** 9 **5.** 15 **13.** 6 **15.** 19 **17.** 45 **19.** Multiply first, then add. $2 + 3 \cdot 4 + 5 = 2 + 12 + 5 = 19$

1.4 PRACTICE AND PROBLEM SOLVING (pp. 18–20)
21. 0 **23.** 21 **25.** 10 **27.** 25 **29.** 22 **31.** 42 **33.** The quotient of 16 and 4, subtracted from 20, is 16. **35.** The difference of 20 and 16, divided by 4, is 1. **37.** The difference of 10 and 3, multiplied by 12, is 84. **39.** $4 \cdot 15 + \frac{1}{2}(6) + 6 = \$69$, assuming that the coupon can be used only once **41.** 42 **43.** 4 **45.** 25 **47.** 0 **49.** 5 **53.** 35 **55.** 50 **57.** 110 **59.** 113 **61.** 18 **63.** $(7 + 2) \div (7 - 4) = 3$ **65.** correct **67.** $(8 + 16) \div (2 \cdot 2) = 6$ **69.** 2(2,000,000,000 + 4,000,000,000) = \$12,000,000,000

MID-CHAPTER TEST (p. 21) **1.** Union **2.** about 98,000 **3.** about 50,000 **4.** 57; the product of 19 and 3 is 57. **5.** 59; the sum of 27 and 32 is 59. **6.** 37; the difference between 59 and 22 is 37. **7.** 4; the quotient of 60 and 15 is 4. **8.** 9 **9.** 6 **10.** 4 **11.** 15 **12.** $8 \cdot 8 = 64$ **13.** $2 \cdot 2 \cdot 2 \cdot 2 = 16$ **14.** $3 \cdot 3 \cdot 3 = 27$ **15.** $1 \cdot 1 \cdot 1 \cdot 1 \cdot 1 \cdot 1 \cdot 1 \cdot 1 = 1$ **16.** 2 **17.** 32 **18.** 25 **19.** 6 **20.** 441 ft^2 **21.** 147 **22.** 8 **23.** 18 **24.** 25 **25.** 18 **26.** 2 **27.** 11 **28.** 8 **29.** 56 **30.** 3 **31.** $(21 - 10) \times 2 = 22$ **32.** correct **33.** $24 - 20 \div (4 + 6) = 22$ **34.** correct **35.** $2^2 \cdot (5 + 6) \div 2 = 22$ **36.** $3^3 - (15 \div 5 + 2) = 22$

1.5 GUIDED PRACTICE (p. 24)
1. perimeter: 40 ft; area: 88 ft^2 **3.** 2400 ft

1.5 PRACTICE AND PROBLEM SOLVING (pp. 24–26)
5. perimeter: 40 mi; area: 46 mi^2 **7.** perimeter: 24 cm; area: 28 cm^2

9.

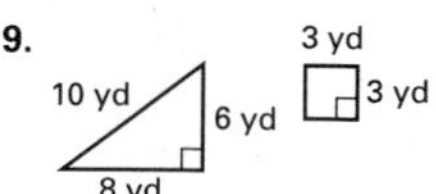

Sample answer: I divided the figures into a 6, 8, 10 right triangle and a 3 yd square, found the area of each and summed the areas.

11. 14 boxes of fertilizer **13.** 11.36 mi **15.** 34,146,000 mi **17.** perimeter: 20 in.; area: 25 $in.^2$ **19.** perimeter: 60 in.; area: 225 $in.^2$ **21.** 4; because the area is s^2 and the perimeter is $4s$, so s must equal 4.

27.

Distance traveled	20	40	60	80	100	120
Cost in dollars	49	53	57	61	65	69

Each time the distance increases 20 mi, the cost increases \$4.

29. 8 **31.** 16 **33.** 25 **35.** 216 $in.^3$ **37.** 24 **39.** 4 **41.** 6

1.6 GUIDED PRACTICE (p. 29) **1.** The price of lemons is irrelevant. **3.** The number of pens purchased and the number of pens remaining are irrelevant. **5.** Add 1 (20 + 1 = 21), add 2 (21 + 2 = 23), add 3 (23 + 3 = 26), and so on; 35, 41, 48. **7.** Each number is $\frac{1}{10}$ the number before it; 0.01, 0.001, 0.0001. **9.** The weight of a bottle of mustard is needed.

1.6 PRACTICE AND PROBLEM SOLVING (pp. 29–31)
11. The cost of the cabinets and of the plumbing; \$3.00 **13.** The amount of gasoline is irrelevant; need information about how fast or how far the family traveled each day after the first day. **15.** Subtract 5 from the preceding number; 60, 55, 50. **17.** Add 9 to the preceding number; 99, 108, 117. **19.** Add 1 to the numerator and the denominator of the preceding term; $\frac{5}{6}, \frac{6}{7}, \frac{7}{8}$. **21.** Each term is the square of one less than the square root of the preceding term; 36, 25, 16. **23.** 1, 2, 4, 8, 16, 32, . . . **25.** 16,384; I doubled 8192. **27.** Subtract miles driven from total distance.

31. **33.**

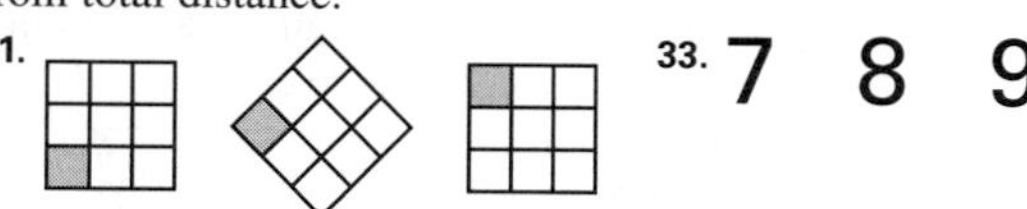

1.7 GUIDED PRACTICE (p. 34) **1.** associative property of multiplication **3.** commutative property of addition

1.7 PRACTICE AND PROBLEM SOLVING (pp. 34–35)
9. commutative property of addition **11.** commutative property of multiplication **13.** commutative property of multiplication; associative property of multiplication; multiply 25 and 4; multiply 100 and 78. **15.** 67 **17.** 5 **19.** 89 **21.** 200 in. **23.** *Sample answers:* 20 inches × 40 inches; 30 inches × 30 inches; 10 inches × 50 inches **25.** Add 46 and 54 to get 100; Add 15 and 85 to get 100; So: 46 + 15 + 37 + 54 + 85 = 237.

1.8 GUIDED PRACTICE (p. 40)
1. $3(2 + 7) = 3 \cdot 2 + 3 \cdot 7 = 27$ **3.** $17(8.5 - 1.5) = 17(8.5) - 17(1.5) = 119$ **5.** incorrect; $2(3 + 5) = 2(3) + 2(5)$ **7.** incorrect; $6(4x) + 6(1) = 24x + 6$ **9.** $4 \cdot x + 4 \cdot 9 = 4x + 36$ **11.** $8 \cdot 4 - 8q = 32 - 8q$ **13.** $(32 + 8)a = 40a$ **15.** $a \cdot b + a \cdot 4 + a \cdot c = ab + 4a + ac$ **17.** $8 \cdot 10 + 8 \cdot 20 = 240$ ft^2; $8(10 + 20) = 240$ ft^2 **19.** 70

SELECTED ANSWERS

1.8 Practice and Problem Solving (pp. 40–41) **21.** $6(4 + 3) = 6 \cdot 4 + 6 \cdot 3 = 42$ **23.** $53 \cdot 6 + 53 \cdot 8 = 53(6 + 8) = 742$ **25.** $3 \cdot 4k - 3 \cdot 9 = 12k - 27$ **27.** $7(c + 3) = 7c + 21$ **29.** $mn + mp$ **31.** $50x$ **33.** n **37.** $12(1800 + 1500 + 1300)$ or $12 \cdot 1800 + 12 \cdot 1500 + 12 \cdot 1300$ **39.** 3 added to, rather than multiplied by 2; $3(5 + 2x) = 15 + 6x$ **41.** $8 \times \$10 + 8 \times \$.50 = \$84$ **43.** $12(6) - 12\left(\frac{1}{4}\right) = 69$ m

Chapter Summary and Review (pp. 42–45) **1.** AZ, MD, WA **3.** WA **5.** 65; the sum of 52 and 13 is 65. **7.** 77; the difference of 127 and 50 is 77. **9.** 9 **11.** 12 **13.** $3 \cdot 12 + 2 \cdot 9 + 7 = \$61$ **15.** 10 **17.** 1 **19.** 105 **21.** 648 cm^3 **23.** 12 **25.** 103 **27.** 260 mi **29.** Add 4, then 5, then 6, and so on; 23, 31, 40 **31.** The missing information is your walking speed on the third day. **33.** 38,000 **35.** $4x - 8$ **37.** $14(17 + 3)$

Reviewing the Basics (p. 49) **1.** 9.5 **3.** 4.1 **5.** 13.99 **7.** 7.15 **9.** 15.09 **11–21.** Estimates may vary. **11.** 1000 **13.** 150 **15.** 3000 **17.** 20 **19.** 30 **21.** 500

Chapter 2

Getting Ready (p. 52) **1.** C **2.** E **3.** A **4.** B **5.** D **6.** D

2.1 Guided Practice (p. 55) **7.** $t + 20$; t is the current temperature. **9.** $10t + 5$; t is the number of tickets.

2.1 Practice and Problem Solving (pp. 55–56) **11.** $10x + 9$ **13.** $8 - 2x$ **15.** $\frac{x}{y + 2}$ **17.** $x - 2$; x is the number of runs the other team scored. **19.** $\frac{d}{7} + w$; number of days $= d$, number of weeks $= w$ **21.** The product of three and a number **23.** Seven more than twice a number **25.** $15t + 12$ **27.** *Sample answer:* It depends on how long it takes to make each centerpiece. The flat rate is more profitable if the centerpiece takes less than about $2\frac{1}{2}$ hours to make. **29.** $\frac{7 + 3h}{4}$

2.2 Guided Practice (p. 59) **1.** $4x$ **3.** $2x + 4y + 4$ **5.** $7r^2$ **7.** $2x + 2x + (2x + 3)$; $6x + 3$; 15 **9.** $r + 3r$ or $4r$ where r is the time taken to do research

2.2 Practice and Problem Solving (pp. 59–60) **11.** Can be simplified; like terms **13.** Can be simplified; constants may be added. **15.** Cannot be simplified; unlike terms **17.** $12b + 10$ **19.** $2x + 4y + 20z$ **21.** $3a + 3b + 2c$ **23.** $2x^2$ **25.** $6a + 6b$ **27.** $(3x + 2) + (2x + 2) + (x + 1)$; $6x + 5$; 23

29.

$2x + 3 + 5x = 2x + 5x + 3$	Commutative property of addition
$= (2 + 5)x + 3$	Distributive property
$= 7x + 3$	Simplify.

31. $5x + 4y$; 30 **33.** $11x + 4y$; 42 **35.** $6y + 2x^2$; 38 **37.** $8x$; perimeter increases by 8 as x increases by 1.

x	1	2	3	4	5
Perimeter	8	16	24	32	40

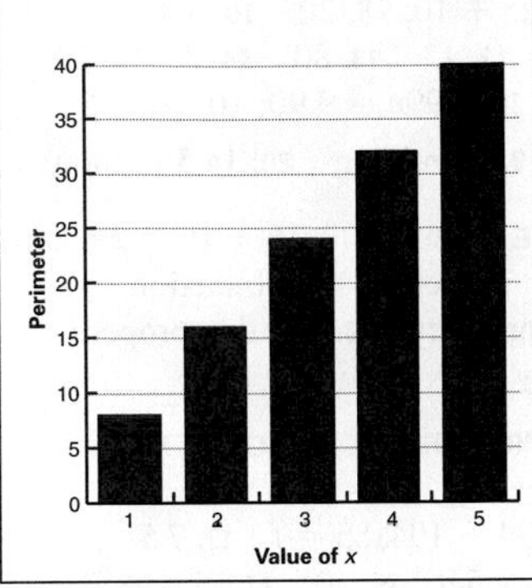

39. $27d$; \$270

2.3 Guided Practice (p. 63) **1.** An identity is an equation that is true for all values of the variables it contains; *example:* $2(x + 4) = 2x + 8$. A conditional equation is true only for some values of the variables it contains; *example:* $3x = 15$ is true only for $x = 5$ and is not true for any other value of x. **5.** 10 **7.** 24 **9.** 14 **11.** 10

2.3 Practice and Problem Solving (pp. 63–65) **13.** Not an identity; the equation is only true for $x = \frac{9}{8}$. **15.** Identity; the equation is true for all values of b. **17.** Not an identity; the equation is only true for $c = 10$. **23.** 3 is a solution; substituting 3 for x makes the equation true. **25.** 9 is a solution; substituting 9 for x makes the equation true. **27.** none of the values is a solution; substituting any of them for x does not make the equation true. **29.** 3 is a solution; substituting 3 for x makes the equation true. **31.** What number can you multiply by 7 to get 42?; 6 **33.** What number can 9 be divided by to get 3?; 3 **35.** From what number can you subtract 13 to get 5?; 18 **37.** What number can you multiply by 4 to get 0?; 0 **39.** 9 **41.** 7 **43.** yes **45.** no; 3 **47.** no; 2 **49.** 3 **51.** 15 **53.** 5 **55.** 36 **57.** 15 **59.** yes; commutative property of addition **61.** no; $\frac{x}{12} \neq \frac{12}{x}$ **63.** $105 + x = 134$ **65.** Substitute 29 into the equation. **69.** $106 + x = 990$; 884 lb **79.** $3y + 4$; 16 **81.** $3y + xy + x^2$; 33 **83.** $5x + 5y$; 35

2.4 Guided Practice (p. 68) **1.** equation; 16 **3.** equation; 9 **5.** $x - 20 = 64$ **7.** $\frac{x}{24} = 3$ **9.** $13 = p - 5$

2.4 Practice and Problem Solving (pp. 68–70) **17.** $18 + 2x = 30$ **19.** $10 - \frac{x}{2} = 3$ **21.** $x + 9 = 20$ **23.** $3x = 90.75$ **25.** $11.99x = 35.97$ **29.** \$550

31. 19 miles per hour **33.** 6.4 million **35.** 6.3 million **37.** $x - 3 = 23$; \$26

MID-CHAPTER TEST (p. 71) **1.** $9x - 8$ **2.** $2x + 2y$ **3.** $\frac{x}{7 + y}$ **4.** $12a$ **5.** $3x + 8$ **6.** $9y + 21$ **7.** $40b$ **8.** $7x + 8$; 36, 57 **9.** $2z + 10$; 18, 20 **10.** not an identity **11.** identity **12.** 13 **13.** 80 **14.** 3 **15.** 20 **16.** $x - 12 = 20$; 32 **17.** $0.99n = 9.90$; 10 **18.** $\frac{x}{60} = 2$; 120 mi **19.** 11 million **20.** 14.5 million

2.5 GUIDED PRACTICE (p. 76) **1.** $q - 16 + 16 = 29 + 16$; $q = 45$ **3.** subtraction property **5.** subtraction property **7.** addition property **9.** addition property **11.** subtraction property

2.5 PRACTICE AND PROBLEM SOLVING (pp. 76–77) **13.** $76 + 29 = y - 29 + 29$; $105 = y$ **15.** $279 - 194 = t + 194 - 194$; $85 = t$ **17.** 7.5 **19.** 13.25 **21.** 31.75 **23.** 5.8 **25.** 10 **27.** 21 **29.** 23 **31.** 11 **33.** 30.1 **35.** 40.5 **37.** 330.5 **39.** 50.3 **41.** 14.6 **43.** $x + 45 = 65$; 20 **45.** $723 - x = 317$; 406 **49.** 532.32 **51.** 17.86 **53.** 3116 **55.** $y - 6500 = 1100$; 7600 ft

2.6 GUIDED PRACTICE (p. 82) **1.** $\frac{3a}{3} = \frac{21}{3}$; $a = 7$ **3.** division property **5.** multiplication property **7.** multiplication property

2.6 PRACTICE AND PROBLEM SOLVING (pp. 82–84) **9.** $14 \cdot \frac{m}{14} = 14 \cdot 5$; $m = 70$ **11.** 4 **13.** 8 **15.** 24 **17.** 100 **19.** 40 **21.** 25.6 **23.** 8 **25.** 1.3 **27.** 6.3 **29.** 524 **31.** 63 **33.** 2 **35.** 55 **37.** 6 **39.** 4992 **41.** 15 mi/h **43.** $9s = 27$; 3 cm **45.** $6w = 48$; 8 km **47.** 94 ft **49.** $b = \frac{2A}{h}$ **53.** increasing; graph is rising. **55.** $4r + 2$; 18 **57.** $r + 3s$; 19 **59.** $3.1 + z = 15.2$

2.7 GUIDED PRACTICE (p. 87) **1.** D, A, F, B, C, E

2.7 PRACTICE AND PROBLEM SOLVING (pp. 88–89) **3.** Min exercised + Min needed = Goal for five days; Min exercised = 35 + 60 + 20 + 55 = 170, Min needed = m, Goal for five days = 225; $170 + m = 225$; $m = 55$ min; You need to exercise 55 min on the fifth day; 170 + 55 = 225 **5.** Rate × Time = Distance; Rate = 9, Time = t, Distance = 26.2 **7.** $8.25x = 165$; 20 h **9.** Distance for two days + Distance on third day = Total Distance; Distance for two days = 8.1 + 5.8 = 13.9, Distance on third day = x, Total distance = 18.5 **11.** 8 + 6 + 5 = 19 and 19 ≈ 18.5. **13.** $4x = 22$; 5.5 h **15.** This is not reasonable since Washington, DC and Portland, Oregon are more than 3000 miles apart. **17.** 21.4 h

2.8 GUIDED PRACTICE (p. 92) **1.** < less than; > greater than; ≤ less than or equal to; ≥ greater than or equal to **3.** False; *Sample answer:* Both inequalities, $2 < 3$ and $3 > 2$ are true. **5.** No. 11 = 11 **7.** No. 25 > 11 **9.** Divide both sides of the inequality by 3.

2.8 PRACTICE AND PROBLEM SOLVING (pp. 92–93) **11.** $2x < 42$; $x < 21$ **13.** $20 \geq \frac{m}{6}$; $120 \geq m$ **15.** *Sample answer:* 10, 8 **17.** *Sample answer:* 100, 80 **19.** *Sample answer:* 3.1, $7\frac{1}{2}$ **21.** *Sample answer:* 0.1, 0 **23.** $x < 6$ **25.** $y \leq 6$ **27.** $n \leq 50$ **29.** $0 \leq b$ **31.** $4 < r$ **33.** $j < 19.1$ **35.** $p > 11.9$ **37.** $14 < t$ **39.** $w \leq 104$ **41.** An inequality is still true if the same number is added to both sides. **43.** Cyclist A: 6 h 30 min + x < 10 h 40 min; x < 4 h 10 min; Cyclist B: 6 h 36 min + y < 10 h 40 min; y < 4 h 4 min; Cyclist C: 6 h 39 min + z < 10 h 40 min; z < 4 h 1 min **45.** $\frac{18}{6} \neq 6$; The last line should be $d \leq 3$. **47.** $37 + x \geq 50$; $x \geq 13$; at least \$13 more

CHAPTER SUMMARY AND REVIEW (pp. 94–97) **1.** $s - 30$; s is your salary **3.** $60 + 27.5p$; p is the number of monthly payments **5.** $4x + 4$ **7.** $8b + 25$ **9.** $3x + 5t + y$ **11.** $2(3x + 1) + 6x + 6$; $12x + 8$; 32 **13.** What number can you add to 9 to get 10? 1 **15.** From what number can you subtract 6 to get 12? 18 **17.** By what number can you divide 15 to get 5? 3 **19.** What number can you multiply by 9 to get 36? 4 **21.** $\frac{x}{7} = 10$ **23.** 10 **25.** 126 **27.** $x + 17 = 45$; 28 **29.** $z - 32 = 61$; 93 **31.** 48 **33.** 6 **35.** $5x = 30$; 6 in. **37.** $6y = 54$; 9 ft

39.

Amount of allowance saved per week	×	Number of weeks	=	Cost of camera

Amount of allowance saved per week = \$7.50
Number of weeks = n
Cost of camera = \$67.50

$7.50 \cdot n = 67.50$

$7.50 \cdot \frac{n}{7.50} = \frac{67.50}{7.50}$

$n = 9$ weeks

41. $z \leq 3$ **43.** $g < 3$ **45.** $14.7 < w$ **47.** $1.77 < v$

REVIEWING THE BASICS (p. 101) **1.** 768 **3.** 38,608 **5.** 327 **7.** 81

9. 0 5 10 15 20 25 30

11. 0 5 10 15 20 25 30

13. 0 5 10 15 20 25 30

15. 0 5 10 15 20 25 30

17. 0 5 10 15 20 25 30

SELECTED ANSWERS

19. 

Chapter 3

GETTING READY (p. 104) **1.** A **2.** J **3.** B **4.** H

3.1 GUIDED PRACTICE (p. 107) **1.** −4, −3, −2, −1, 0, 1, 2, 3, 4 **3.** 1 **5.** 0 **7.** 12 **9.** 0 **11.** 4 **13.** −3

3.1 PRACTICE AND PROBLEM SOLVING (pp. 107–109)

15. 

17. 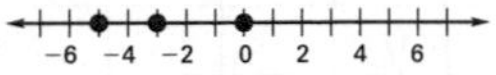

19. 

21. −6, −3, 0, 4, 5 **23.** −4, −2, −1, 0, 2 **25.** −5, −4, −2, 4, 6 **27.** −250 **29.** 25 **31.** −17 **33.** −15 **35.** 11 **37.** 2 **39.** −20 **41.** 100 **43.** −5 or 5 **45.** −4 **47.** < **49.** > **51.** >

53. 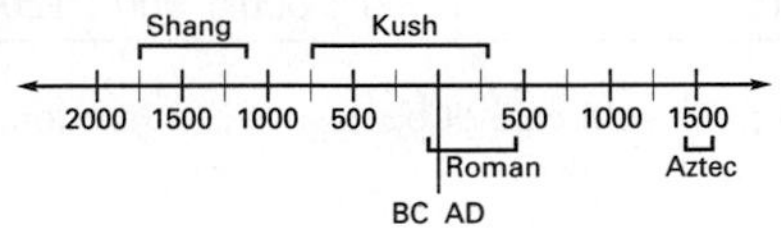

55. Aztec Empire **57.** 55°F **59.** 18°F **61.** 19°F **63.** 68°F **65.** 83°F **67.** true **69.** false **75.** 5 **77.** 16 **79.** 69 **81.** 55 **83.** $9m + 12m + 16m$ **85.** 16 **87.** 20 **89.** 18

3.2 GUIDED PRACTICE (p. 112) **1.** C **3.** 0 **5.** −12 **7.** 1 **9.** gain; 33 yd line

3.2 PRACTICE AND PROBLEM SOLVING (pp. 112–113) **11.** 1 **13.** 0 **15.** 4 **17.** −1 **19.** −14 **21.** −12 **23.** 9th **25.** 13 ft **27.** players 2 and 3

3.3 GUIDED PRACTICE (p. 118) **1.** 15 **3.** 6 **5.** 0 **7.** −10 **9.** *Sample answer:* Student 1 is rearranging the terms in order to use the inverse property of addition. Student 2 is rearranging the terms to group positive terms and negative terms. **11.** $3x + 7$; 19 **13.** $2x$; 8

3.3 PRACTICE AND PROBLEM SOLVING (pp. 119–120) **15.** −10 **17.** 0 **19.** −6 **21.** 13 **23.** −5 **25.** −126 **27.** 23 **29.** 7 **31.** −46 **33.** 3 **35.** $-7x$ **37.** $-10x$ **39.** $15x$; 45 **41.** $10x + 8$; 38 **43.** $2x - 5$; 1 **45.** −208 + 142; −66; Cretaceous Period **53.** 18 **55.** 51 **57.** 21 **59.** The difference between successive terms is 13; 451, 438, 425. **61.** $16n$ **63.** $x - 16$

3.4 GUIDED PRACTICE (p. 125) **1.** 3 + 5; 8 **3.** 5 + (−3); 2 **5.** −6 + 2; −4 **7.** 7 + 3; 10 **9.** $3x + 5$; 14 **11.** $7x + 4$; 25 **13.** 3 − 6 = 3 + (−6) = −3

3.4 PRACTICE AND PROBLEM SOLVING (pp. 125–126) **15.** −4 **17.** 6 **19.** 0 **21.** −10 **23.** −30 **25.** 6 **27.** −4 **29.** 4, −6 **31.** −1, −11 **33.** 3, 7 **35.** 0, 10 **39.** $7x + (-9x) + (-5)$; $7x$, $-9x$, −5; $-2x - 5$ **41.** $4 + (-2n) + 4m$; 4, $-2n$, $4m$ **43.** $-11f + 3g + 9$; $-11f$, $3g$, 9 **45.** $6x$; 30 **47.** $3x - 17$; −2 **49.** $x + 5$; 10 **51.** true for all values of x **53.** true only for positive values of x **55.** 91°F **57.** 1 in.

3.5 GUIDED PRACTICE (p. 131) **1.** 20 **3.** −20 **5.** −48 **7.** $-3n + 5$; −7 **9.** $-3n - 12$; −24 **11.** −18, 18 **13.** 16, 16 **15.** 8, 14

3.5 PRACTICE AND PROBLEM SOLVING (pp. 132–133) **17.** 20 **19.** −48 **21.** 10 **23.** 20 **25.** 24 **27.** 4 **29.** 231 **31.** −36 **33.** −75 **35.** −512

37.

x	−3	−2	−1	0	1	2	3
$4x$	−12	−8	−4	0	4	8	12

As x increases by 1, $4x$ increases by 4. As x decreases by 1, $4x$ decreases by 4.
45. 7 **47.** $-5x + 13$ **49.** $-3x + 5$ **51.** $-8n + 8$; 32 **53.** $-7n + 6$; 27 **55.** $-9n + 4$; 31 **57.** positive **59.** negative **61.** positive; (−2)(−1)(−3)(−1) = 6 **63.** $35 - 5x$ **65.** $40 - 8x$ **67.** 32 **69.** −512

MID-CHAPTER TEST (p. 134)

1. 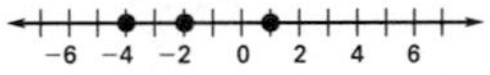

2. 

3. 

4. 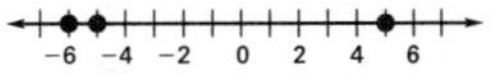

5. −7; 7 **6.** 5; 5 **7.** −42; 42 **8.** 132; 132 **9.** −11, −9, 6, 9 **10.** −5, −1, 0, 1 **11.** −3, −2, 1, 3 **12.** −6, −2, 4, 5 **13.** 2 **14.** 5 **15.** −10 **16.** −1 **17.** −2 **18.** −9 **19.** 2 **20.** 10 **21.** lose; $194; *Sample answer:* The sum of the profits for January through June is a negative number, indicating a loss. **22.** $-15x + 2$ **23.** $-13x - 6$ **24.** $4x$ **25.** $6a - 6$; 30 **26.** $4a - 2$; 22 **27.** $11 - 7a$; −31 **28.** true; −1 + (−3) = −4 **29.** true; $|-4| = 4$ **30.** false; −7 − (−8) = 1 **31.** 21 **32.** −36 **33.** −10 **34.** −60

3.6 GUIDED PRACTICE (p. 137) **1.** positive; 24 **3.** negative; −8 **5.** Multiply −2 by 3. **7.** positive; both a and b are negative, and the quotient of two negative numbers is positive. **9.** zero, a is 0, and 0 divided by any nonzero number is zero.

3.6 PRACTICE AND PROBLEM SOLVING (pp. 137–139) **11.** 27 **13.** 0 **15.** −6 **17.** −3 **19.** 9 **21.** undefined **23.** 8; −2 **25.** −3; 12 **27.** 0; 0 **29.** −4, 1 **31.** −1 **33.** 16 **35.** 2 **37.** 12 **39.** 128 **41.** −2 **43.** 7 **45.** −1 **47.** 3 **49.** 21 **51.** −2 **53.** $-\frac{21}{8}$ **55.** −3°F

57. *Sample answer:* The skater's time in that trial was less than the team average. **59.** 44.65 sec; yes; *Sample answer:* 45 sec − 0.35 sec = 44.65 sec. **65.** Start with 2 and multiply by −2; 32, −64, 128. **67.** 86 **69.** 70 **71.** 17

3.7 Guided Practice (p. 142) **7.** addition property; −4 **9.** multiplication property; −35 **11.** $P = 5n - 55$; $945

3.7 Practice and Problem Solving (pp. 142–143)
13. yes **15.** yes **17.** no; 48 **19.** no; −4 **21.** 9 **23.** −4 **25.** 12 **27.** 55 **29.** 33 **31.** −3 **33.** negative **35.** negative **37.** positive **39.** $-10 = y + 25$; −35 **41.** $51 = -3a$; −17 **43.** A; 25,370 ft
45.

Tickets Sold	100	150	200	250	300	350
Profit($)	−600	−350	−100	150	400	650

3.8 Guided Practice (p. 146) **1.** $A(1, 2)$ Quadrant 1; $B(-4, 3)$ Quadrant 2; $C(1, -3)$ Quadrant 4; $D(-3, 0)$; $E(5, 2)$ Quadrant 1; $F(-2, -4)$ Quadrant 3; $G(5, -3)$ Quadrant 4; $H(-5, 5)$ Quadrant 2 **3.** 4

3.8 Practice and Problem Solving (pp. 147–148)
5. *J*; Quadrant 4 **7.** *K* **9.** *N*
11–19.

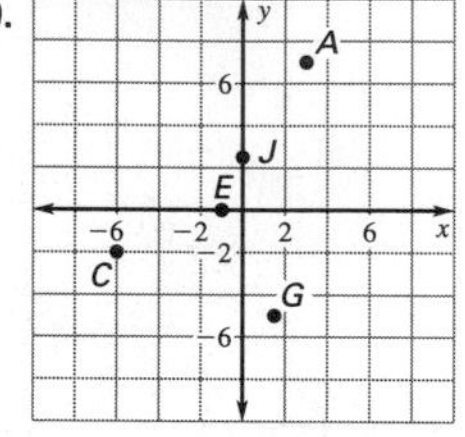

11. Quadrant 1 **13.** Quadrant 3 **17.** Quadrant 4 **21.** (3, 4), (3, −5); 9 **23.** (1, 2), (1, −3); 5 **25.** *RSVT*: perimeter = 20, area = 25; *MNPQ*: perimeter = 22, area = 18 **27.** solution; *Sample answers:* (3, 11), (0, 8), (−2, 6) **29.** solution; *Sample answers:* (2, 4), (−2, 8), (1, 5) **31.** solution; *Sample answers:* (0, 0); (−3, −6), (2, 4) **33.** solution; *Sample answers:* (1, 3); (−1, −9), (2, 9)
35. *Sample answer:*

x	0	1	2	3
y	4	3	2	1

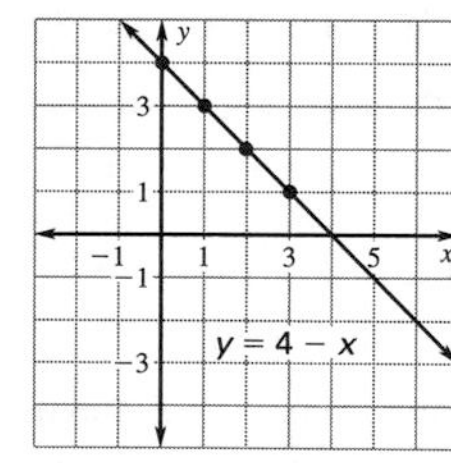

37. *Sample answer:*

x	−1	0	1	2
y	−3	−1	1	3

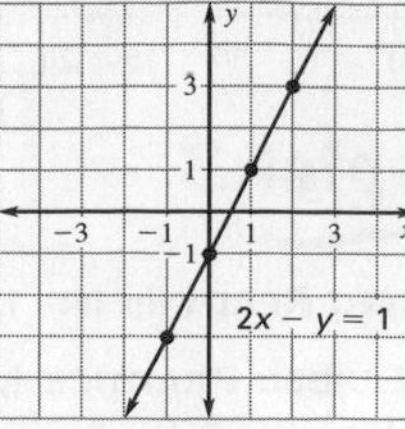

39. *Sample answer:*

x	−2	−1	0	1
y	0	−1	−2	−3

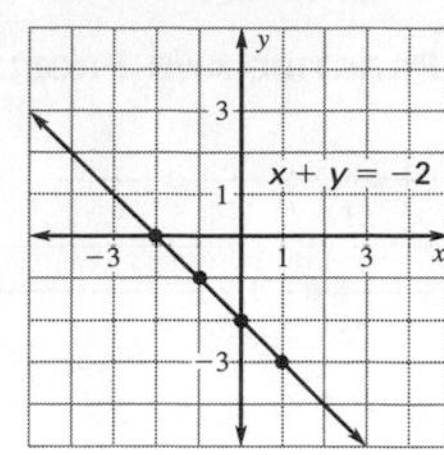

41.

Number of pairs of jeans	10	20	30	40
Revenue ($)	300	600	900	1200

43. Number of pairs sold cannot be negative, a fraction, or a decimal.

3.9 Guided Practice (p. 151) **1.** negative correlation **3.** no obvious correlation **5.** No; the number sold will reach zero before 2010.

3.9 Practice and Problem Solving (pp. 151–153)
7. negative correlation **9.** Positive correlation; the higher the temperature, the more air conditioners that will be used. **11.** No correlation; taller students do not necessarily get better grades. **13.** Positive correlation; the greater the number of pages, the thicker the book will be. **15.** positive correlation **17.** positive correlation

19.

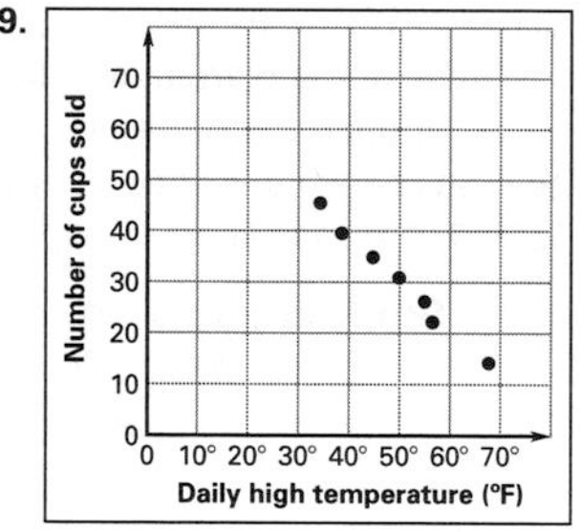

21. *Sample answer:* 6 cups

SELECTED ANSWERS

23.

Possible Lengths and Widths for a Rectangle Whose Perimeter is 12 Units					
Length, x	1	2	3	4	5
Width, y	5	4	3	2	1
Perimeter	12	12	12	12	12

25. 2.5 units

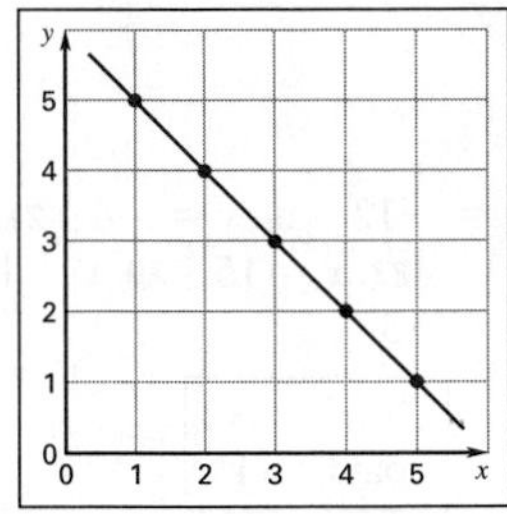

29. 9 **31.** -57 **33.** 4 **35.** -16 **37.** -130 **39.** 1

CHAPTER SUMMARY AND REVIEW (pp. 154–157) **1.** $-9, -5, -1, 0, 3, 4, 5$ **3.** -9 **5.** 2 **7.** -7 **9.** 6 **11.** $x + 2$; 7 **13.** -41 **15.** 5 **17.** $3y - 10$ **19.** -12 **21.** 375 **23.** $-8z + 6$; 30 **25.** $-6z - 7$; 11 **27.** -4 **29.** 0 **31.** -8 **33.** -17 **35.** $\frac{m}{-15} = 3$; -45 **37.** Quadrant 4

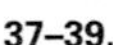

37–39.

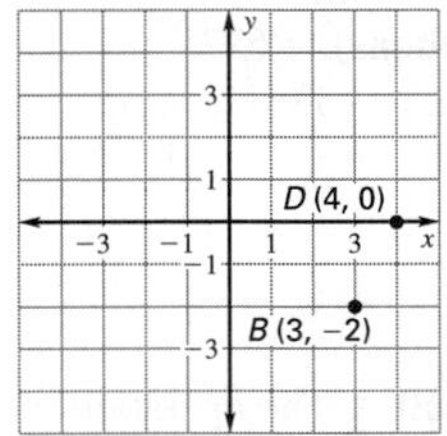

41. not a solution **43.** \$57

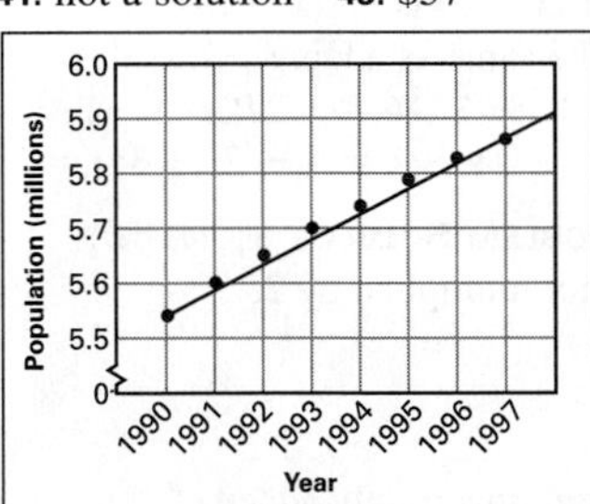

positive correlation

REVIEWING THE BASICS (p. 161) **1.** $3x + 24$ **3.** $-18 + 9b$ **5.** $40m + 15$ **7.** $(-13 + 12)x = -x$ **9.** $(-6 - 11)t = -17t$ **11.** -26 **13.** -37 **15.** -90 **17.** 10

CUMULATIVE PRACTICE (pp. 162–163) **1.** 64 **3.** 729 **5.** 20 **7.** 1029 **9.** 280 **11.** 60 cm; 135 cm^2 **13.** 42 m; 66 m^2 **15.** decrease by two; 12, 10, 8 **17.** Numerator is sequence of odd numbers and denominator is sequence of even numbers; $\frac{9}{10}, \frac{11}{12}, \frac{13}{14}$. **19.** commutative property of addition **21.** associative property of multiplication **23.** $x + 9 = 33$; 24 **25.** $7x > 91$; $x > 13$

27. **29.**

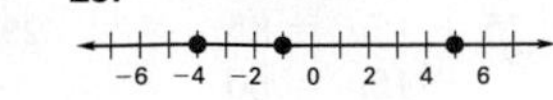

31. 3 **33.** -15 **35.** -110 **37.** 24 **39.** 23 **41.** $-21 + 3x$; -33 **43.** $9 - 9x$; 45 **45.** $-10t + 6$; -14 **47.** -12 **49.** -12 **51.** -11 **53.** 21 **55.** -4 **57.** 64 **59.** $p > 8$ **61.** $y \le 20$ **63.** $2 > t$ **65.** $360 \le s$

67–69.

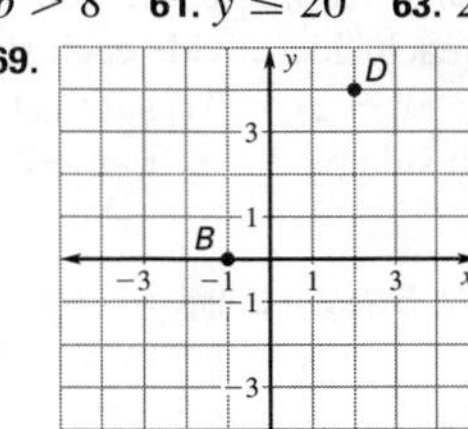

67. no quadrant **69.** Quadrant 1 **71.** solution; *Sample answer:* (0, 0), (1, 7), (2, 14)

73.

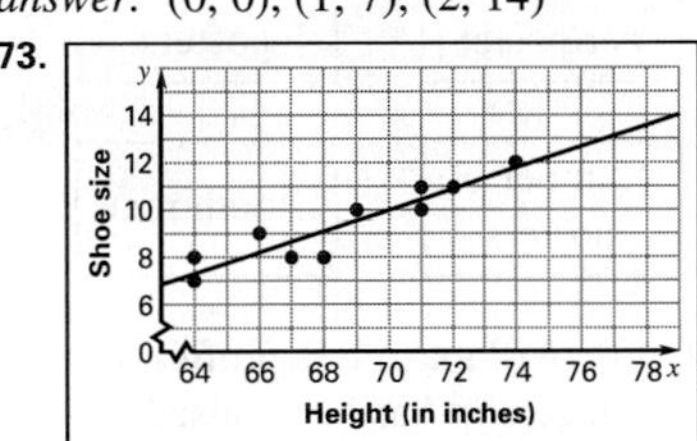

75. 12 or 13

Chapter 4

GETTING READY (p. 168) **1.** B **2.** D **3.** A **4.** C **5.** C **6.** J

4.1 GUIDED PRACTICE (p. 172) **1.** Add 4 to each side of the equation. **3.** Subtract 2 from each side of the equation.

5. "15" was added to the left side of the equation but should have been added to the right side instead of subtracted.

$$5x - 15 = 25$$
$$5x - 15 + 15 = 25 + 15$$
$$5x = 40$$
$$\frac{x}{5} = \frac{40}{5}$$
$$x = 8$$

4.1 PRACTICE AND PROBLEM SOLVING (pp. 172–173)

7. $3x - 13 + 13 = 14 + 13$ Add 13 to each side.
$3x = 27$ Simplify.
$\frac{3x}{3} = \frac{27}{3}$ Divide each side by 3.
$x = 9$ Simplify.

9. $x = 3$ **11.** $p = 2$ **13.** $r = 13$ **15.** $x = 1$ **17.** $x = 9$

SELECTED ANSWERS

19. $z = 8$ **21.** $3x + 17 = 38; x = 7$ **23.** $3x + 7 = 34; x = 9$ **25.** $\frac{x}{4} - 2 = 5; x = 28$

27.
$$25 + 15m = 85$$
$$15m = 60$$
$$m = 4 \text{ min}$$
5 min total

29.
$$x + (x + 1) = 49$$
$$2x = 48$$
$$x = 24$$
Numbers are 24 and 25.

Alternate methods may vary.

4.2 GUIDED PRACTICE (p. 176) **1.** Combine like terms: $3x - x = 2x$, subtract 8 from each side, divide each side by 2. **3.** Combine like terms: $5x - 2x = 3x$, subtract 11 from each side, divide each side by 3. **5.** $x = -2$ **7.** $x = -4$ **9.** $x = 1$

4.2 PRACTICE AND PROBLEM SOLVING (pp. 176–178)
11. $t = 5$ **13.** $y = 7$ **15.** $x = 1$ **17.** $s = 7$ **19.** $x = 1$ **21.** $a = 5$ **23.** $x = -2$ **25.** $y = 9$ **27.** $x = 3$ **29.** $x = 0$ **31.** $2x + (-4) = 0; x = 2$ **33.** $3x + 2x + 7x + 6 = 42; x = 3$ **35.** $4x + x - 14 = 1; x = 3$

37. [Profit] = [Price per poster] · [Number of posters] − [Cost per poster] · [Number of posters] − [Booth rent]

39. $300 = 5x - [3x + 30]$; Will make less profit for same number of posters since cost has been raised.
$$300 = 2x - 30$$
$$330 = 2x$$
$$165 = x\text{, number of posters}$$

41.
$$129 = 2x - x - 15$$
$$129 = x - 15$$
$$144 = x\text{, number of bottles}$$

43. \$5.00; \$.078760/kW · h

45.
$$\text{Total charges} = 5.00 + (500)(0.078760)$$
$$= 5.00 + 39.38$$
$$= 44.38; \$44.38$$

51.

x	−2	−1	0	1	2
Value	12	9	6	3	0

Value decreases by 3 as x increases by 1.

53. $n = 36$ **55.** $q = -6$ **57.** $s = 28$ **59.** $u = 12$ **61.** 1 **63.** none **65.** 2

67.
$$17 = 5 + 2x$$
$$12 = 2x$$
$$6 = x\text{; 6 errands}$$

4.3 GUIDED PRACTICE (p. 181)

1.
$$7 - x = -8$$
$$7 + (-1)x = -8$$
$$7 + (-1)x - 7 = -8 - 7$$
$$\frac{-1x}{-1} = \frac{-15}{-1}$$
$$x = 15$$

3. Add 6 or $3x$ to both sides. **5.** Subtract 39 from both sides or add n to both sides. **7.** $m = -7$ **9.** $m = 3$ **11.** $z = -6$

4.3 PRACTICE AND PROBLEM SOLVING (pp. 181–182)

13.
$$-31 = -4y + 9$$
$$-31 - 9 = -4y + 9 - 9$$
$$-40 = -4y$$
$$\frac{-40}{-4} = \frac{-4y}{-4}$$
$$10 = y$$

15. $x = -4$ **17.** $m = -12$ **19.** $y = -6$ **21.** $z = -1$ **23.** $t = 2$ **25.** $t = 37$ **27.** $x = 15$ **29.** $x = 10$ **31.** $w = -2$ **33.** $y = -3$

35. [Balance left to pay] = [Total to be paid back] − [Amount paid per week] · [Number of weeks paid]
$$0 = 125 - 5 \cdot x$$
$$125 = 5x$$
$$25 = x\text{, weeks to replace money}$$

37. You can see that your balance is 0 after 25 weeks.

39. Oil produced (in millions) = 429
Oil produced in 1992 (in millions) = 627
Change each year (in millions) = 33
Number of years since 1992 = N
$$429 = 627 - 33N$$
$$33N = 198$$
$$N = 6\text{; in 1998}$$

4.4 GUIDED PRACTICE (p. 185) **1.** The operation of subtraction is the same as adding the opposite of a quantity. The opposite of $(x - 2)$ is $-1(x - 2)$. Subtracting 2 from x is the same as adding -2 to x. **3.** $5x - 35 = 5; x = 8$ **5.** $8x - 16 = -24; x = -1$ **7.** $m + 4m + 4 = 9; m = 1$ **9.** $-1 = 4 - 2t - 3; t = 1$

4.4 PRACTICE AND PROBLEM SOLVING (pp. 185–187)

11. The negative 2 was not multiplied by 2.
$$2(x - 2) = 4$$
$$2x - 4 = 4$$
$$x = 4$$

13. The $-5x$ and $-7x$ were incorrectly added.
$$-5x - 7x + 5 = 29$$
$$-12x = 29 - 5$$
$$x = -2$$

15. $y = 7$ **17.** $s = -2$ **19.** $x = 0$ **21.** $q = 16$ **23.** $n = -5$ **25.** $n = 6$ **27.** $x = -6$

29.
$$48 = 12(x - 5)$$
$$x = 9 \text{ m}$$

31.
$$16 = 4(3x + 1)$$
$$x = 1 \text{ yd}$$

33.
$$10(n + 3) = 20$$
$$10n + 30 = 20$$
$$10n = -10$$
$$n = -1$$

35.
$$9(4 - y) = -27$$
$$36 - 9y = -27$$
$$63 = 9y$$
$$7 = y$$

37. Total earned each week = \$142
Total weekday hours = 10
Total Saturday hours = 8
Saturday wage/h = $x + 2$
Weekday wage/h = x

39. $142 \text{ dollars} = 10 \text{ h} \cdot 7 \frac{\text{dollars}}{\text{h}} + 8 \text{ h} \cdot (7 + 2) \frac{\text{dollars}}{\text{h}}$

$142 \text{ dollars} = 70 \text{ dollars} + 72 \text{ dollars}$

45. -6 **47.** -9 **49.** 15 **51.** $8x - 12$ **53.** $14 - 7z$ **55.** $12 + 6x - 6y$ **57.** $x < 5$ **59.** $x > 2$ **61.** $x < 30$ **63.** $y = 7$ **65.** $r = 2$ **67.** $m = 18$ **69.** 45

MID-CHAPTER TEST (p. 188) **1.** $y = 7$ **2.** $t = -4$ **3.** $b = 3$ **4.** $x = 6$ **5.** $r = 4$ **6.** $m = -1$ **7.** $p = 2$ **8.** $n = -10$ **9.** 10 **10.** $s = 8$ **11.** $t = 6$ **12.** $x = -9$ **13.** $x = -3$ **14.** $p = 4$ **15.** $b = -2$ **16.** $n = 5$ **17.** $x = 0$ **18.** $d = -7$ **19.** $2x + 3 = 21; x = 9$

20. $\frac{x}{4} - 3 = 1; x = 16$

21. $2x + x + 5 = 17$
$3x = 12$
$x = 4$

22. $5x + 2 = 17; x = 3$ **23.** 126 km **24.** 8792 km **25.** 9270 km **26.** 7540 km

4.5 GUIDED PRACTICE (p. 191)

1.

$2x - 4 = x$	Write original equation.
$2x - 4 - 2x = x - 2x$	Subtract $2x$ from each side.
$-4 = -x$	Simplify.
$-4(-1) = -x(-1)$	Multiply each side by -1.
$4 = x$	Simplify. x is by itself.

3. Right side, to keep coefficient positive
$x + 14 = 2x + 12$
$2 = x$

4.5 PRACTICE AND PROBLEM SOLVING (pp. 191–192)

5. $x = 2$ **7.** $x = 2$ **9.** $x = 3$ **11.** $x = 0$ **13.** $x = 2$ **15.** $x = 3$ **17.** $3x - 1 = x + 19$
$2x = 20$
$x = 10$

19. $x = 5$ **21.** $x = 5, 24$

23. $7y = 360 + 4y$
$y = 120$

25. $0.75 + 0.08 \cdot 0.075x = 25 + 0.08 \cdot 0.02x$
$0.75 + 0.006x = 25 + 0.0016x$
$0.0044x = 24.25$
$x \approx 5511.4$

4.6 GUIDED PRACTICE (p. 195)

1. Height of cornstalk now = 5 in.
Stalk's rate of growth = 2 in./wk
Height of weed now = 11 in.
Weed's rate of growth = 1 in./wk

3. 6 weeks from then

4.6 PRACTICE AND PROBLEM SOLVING (pp. 195–197)

5. Club: $50 + 10c$; Store: $15c$ **7.** 10 CDs

9. [Height of one candle] − [Burn rate] · [Number of hours] = [Height of other candle] − [Burn rate] · [Number of hours]

11. $12 \text{ cm} - \frac{3 \text{ cm}}{\cancel{\text{h}}} \cdot 2 \cancel{\text{h}} \stackrel{?}{=} 10 \text{ cm} - \frac{2 \text{ cm}}{\cancel{\text{h}}} \cdot 2 \cancel{\text{h}}$
$6 \text{ cm} = 6 \text{ cm}$

13. $6h = 30 + 4h$
$2h = 30$
$h = 15$; 15 h of lessons

15. Use Studio B if you will be taking more than 15 hours of lessons in a year.

17.

Number of shirts	Revenue	Costs	Profit (loss)
25	850	1950	(1100)
50	1700	2400	(700)
75	2550	2850	(300)
94	3196	3192	4
100	3400	3300	100
200	6800	5100	1700

According to the table, the number of shirts needed to break even must be between 75 and 94 shirts.

23. $\frac{4}{x + 9}$ **25.** $y < 4$ **27.** $c < 7$ **29.** $p \leq 14$ **31.** 0 **33.** -4 **35.** 2 **37.** -1 **39.** 3 **41.** -2 **43.** -4

4.7 GUIDED PRACTICE (p. 200) **1.** $x = 2.5$ means "x is exactly 2.5"; $x \approx 2.5$ means "x is approximately 2.5" **3.** 22.8 **5.** $-15.63 = -2.9x; x \approx 5.4$ **7.** 11.16 gal

4.7 PRACTICE AND PROBLEM SOLVING (pp. 201–202)

9. $0.58x - 0.82 = 10.6$
$0.58x = 11.42$
$x \approx 19.7$

11. -0.4 **13.** -8.4 **15.** -3.6 **17.** -4.4 **19.** 6.37 **21.** 4.77 **23.** 63°F **25.** 144; 75°F **27.** $2 = 0.33 + 0.22x$; 8 oz package can be sent

29.

Number of hours	Cost: Provider A	Cost: Provider B
1	24.95	29.95
2	24.95	29.95
3	24.95	29.95
4	24.95	29.95
5	24.95	29.95
6	29.90	33.90
7	34.85	37.85
8	39.80	41.80

Number of hours	Cost: Provider A	Cost: Provider B
9	44.75	45.75
10	49.70	49.70
11	54.65	53.65
12	59.60	57.60
13	64.55	61.55
14	69.50	65.50
15	74.45	69.45

31. if you use more than 10 hours per month of Internet service

4.8 GUIDED PRACTICE (p. 205) **1.** Median **3.** Mean **5.** Mean $\approx$ 4.9; median = 5; mode = 5; mean is the average, median is the middle, mode is the number of baskets scored most often.

4.8 PRACTICE AND PROBLEM SOLVING (pp. 206–207) **7.** Mean = 89; median = 90; mode = 90 **9.** Mean = 71; median = 77; no mode **11.** Mean $\approx$ 8.6; median $\approx$ 8.6; no mode **13.** 5 **15.** *Sample answer*: Mean, since there are no outliers in this set. **17.** 149 **19.** (Thousands) 30, 30, 30, 30, 30, 30, 30, 30, 30, 40, 40, 40, 60, 100 **21.** *Sample answer*: Mode or median, most employees earn $30,000. **23.** 6th day; pH level jumped from 6.3 to 6.9. **25.** All three measures are the same. **27.** The mean is much higher than the median or the mode. The outliers are 35 and 40, and they raise the mean.

CHAPTER SUMMARY AND REVIEW (pp. 208–211) **1.** 5 **3.** 3 **5.** 16 **7.** $4 - (-12) = -8, x = -80$ **9.** 3 **11.** −1 **13.** 15 **15.** −1 **17.** 3 **19.** 20 **21.** 11 **23.** 4 **25.** −3 **27.** 6

29.

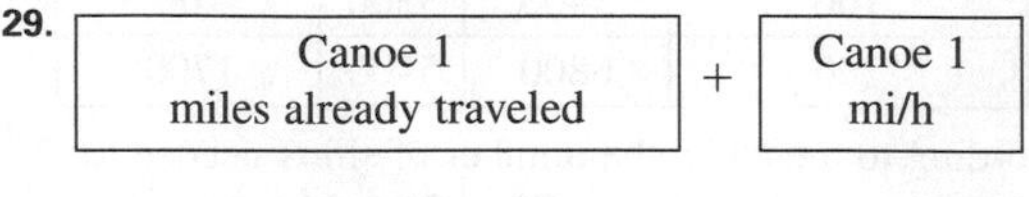

Number of hours = Canoe 2 mi/h · Number of hours

Canoe 1 miles already traveled = 4
Canoe 1 mi/h = 4
Canoe 2 mi/h = 5
Number of hours = n

31. 4.69 **33.** 2.50 **35.** mean $\approx$ 5.21, median = 5, mode = 5 **37.** mean = 44.3, median = 44.5, mode = 41

REVIEWING THE BASICS (p. 215) **1.** $24.39 **3.** 2^4 **5.** 4^2 **7.** b^2

Chapter 5

GETTING READY (p. 218) **1.** B **2.** H **3.** C **4.** G

5.1 GUIDED PRACTICE (p. 222) **1.** true; 39 is composite since $39 = 3 \cdot 13$. **3.** false; 8 can be factored into 2^3, so the prime factorization of 56 is $7 \cdot 2^3$. **5.** false; 1 is neither prime nor composite. **7.** $2 \cdot 3 \cdot 11$ **9.** $2 \cdot 5 \cdot 11$ **11.** $2^3 \cdot 3$ **13.** $2^2 \cdot 3^2 \cdot 5$ **15.** 1, 2, 3, 6, 9, 18, 27, 54 **17.** 1, 2, 5, 10, 13, 26, 65, 130 **19.** $3 \cdot 3 \cdot 5 \cdot y \cdot y \cdot y \cdot y$ **21.** $2 \cdot 2 \cdot 2 \cdot 5 \cdot n \cdot n \cdot n$ **23.** 1, 2, 4, 11, 22, 44, w, $2w$, $4w$, $11w$, $22w$, $44w$, w^2, $2w^2$, $4w^2$, $11w^2$, $22w^2$, $44w^2$ **25.** 1, 5, 25, w, $5w$, $25w$, y, $5y$, $25y$, w^2, $5w^2$, $25w^2$, wy, $5wy$, $25wy$, w^2y, $5w^2y$, $25w^2y$

5.1 PRACTICE AND PROBLEM SOLVING (pp. 223–224) **27.** composite; 9 can be factored into $3 \cdot 3$. **29.** composite; 27 can be factored into $3 \cdot 3 \cdot 3$. **31.** composite; 52 can be factored into $2 \cdot 2 \cdot 13$. **33.** prime; the only factors are 1 and 73. **35.** $2 \cdot 3 \cdot 11$ **37.** $2^4 \cdot 3^2$ **39.** $2 \cdot 3^3 \cdot 5$ **41.** $2^4 \cdot 5 \cdot 11$ **43.** $2 \cdot 89$ **45.** $2 \cdot 7 \cdot 19$ **47.** 1, 2, 5, 10, 25, 50 **49.** 1, 3, 9, 11, 33, 99 **51.** 1, 3, 7, 9, 21, 63 **53.** 1, 11, 17, 187 **55.** $2 \cdot 2 \cdot 3 \cdot p \cdot p \cdot p \cdot p \cdot q$ **57.** $(-1) \cdot 2 \cdot 5 \cdot 5 \cdot s \cdot s \cdot t \cdot t \cdot t \cdot t \cdot t$ **59.** $3 \cdot 19 \cdot w \cdot w \cdot w \cdot z \cdot z \cdot z \cdot z$ **61.** $3 \cdot 19 \cdot p \cdot p \cdot q \cdot q$ **63.** 1, 2, 5, 10, 25, 50, y, $2y$, $5y$, $10y$, $25y$, $50y$ **65.** 1, 3, 29, 87, b, $3b$, $29b$, $87b$, b^2, $3b^2$, $29b^2$, $87b^2$ **67.** 1, 2, 4, 7, 14, 28, z, $2z$, $4z$, $7z$, $14z$, $28z$, z^2, $2z^2$, $4z^2$, $7z^2$, $14z^2$, $28z^2$, z^3, $2z^3$, $4z^3$, $7z^3$, $14z^3$, $28z^3$ **69.** 1, 71, x, $71x$, y, $71y$, xy, $71xy$, x^2, $71x^2$, y^2, $71y^2$, x^2y, $71x^2y$, xy^2, $71xy^2$, x^2y^2, $71x^2y^2$, y^3, $71y^3$, xy^3, $71xy^3$, x^2y^3, $71x^2y^3$ **71.** *Sample answers:* 196, 294 **73.** *Sample answers:* $2x$, $10x^2$, $20xy$ **75.** 30 = 13 + 17 or 11 + 19; 32 = 13 + 19; 34 = 11 + 23 or 17 + 17; 36 = 13 + 23 or 17 + 19; 38 = 19 + 19; 40 = 11 + 29 or 17 + 23 **77.** Yes; every even number after 2 is divisible by 2, so each cannot be prime. **79.** 17 and 19, 29 and 31, 41 and 43, 59 and 61, 71 and 73 **85.** $-3 + (-2)$; −5 **87.** −20 **89.** −43 **91.** 28

5.2 GUIDED PRACTICE (p. 227) **1.** 1, 2, 3, 6; 6 **3.** 1, 5; 5 **5.** 6 **7.** 10 **9.** $7m$ **11.** $5xy$ **13.** $4xy$

5.2 PRACTICE AND PROBLEM SOLVING (pp. 227–228) **15.** 4 **17.** 5 **19.** 1 **21.** 70 **23.** 30 **25.** 68 **27.** 1 **29.** 18 **31.** xy **33.** $2yz$ **35.** $3x^2y$ **37.** 100 **39.** $14s^3t^3$ **41.** relatively prime **43.** relatively prime **45.** not relatively prime **47.** relatively prime **49.** True; 5 divides each of the three numbers evenly. **51.** False; it is $8x^2yz$. **53.** No; The greatest common factor is a factor of each number, so it must be less than or equal to each number. *Sample example:* Out of 10 and 120, the greatest common factor is 10 and any other factor of 120 could not possibly divide 10 evenly. **55.** 8 students per row; 6 rows for the color guard and 7 rows for the band

5.3 GUIDED PRACTICE (p. 231) **1.** 12, 24, 36, 48, 60, 72 **3.** 32, 64, 96, 128, 160, 192 **5.** 96 **7.** 160 **9.** $2 \cdot 3 \cdot 11$ **11.** $3 \cdot 5 \cdot 11$ **13.** 330 **15.** 990 **17.** $36m^2n^2$ **19.** 5 packages of hot dogs and 9 packages of rolls

5.3 PRACTICE AND PROBLEM SOLVING (pp. 231–232) **21.** 36 **23.** 9 **25.** 30 **27.** 44 **29.** 56 **31.** 500 **33.** 4320 **35.** 8100 **37.** $35ab^2$ **39.** $49s^2t^2$ **41.** $21m^6n^4$ **43.** The greater number; The greater number is a multiple of the second number and it is a multiple (× 1) of itself. *Sample examples:* 3 and 15, 8 and 24; *Sample answer:* LCM of 3 and 15 is 15. **45.** *Sample answers:* 4 and 16, 8 and 16 **47.** 60 pens **49.** 14 tiles; These can be placed 7 across and 2 deep to form a 28 in. by 28 in. square. **51.** *Sample answer:* List the multiples of each number and compare.

5.4 Guided Practice (p. 235) **1. a.** $\frac{1}{3}$ **b.** $\frac{1}{4}$ **3.** $-\frac{1}{3}$ **5.** $\frac{1}{5}$ **7.** $-\frac{3rs}{4x^2}$ **9.** $\frac{z}{4w}$ **11.** $\frac{5}{20}, \frac{4}{20}; \frac{1}{4}$ **13.** $\frac{14}{35}, \frac{15}{35}; \frac{3}{7}$

5.4 Practice and Problem Solving (pp. 236–237)
15. $\frac{7}{10}$ **17.** $\frac{3}{14}$ **19.** $\frac{1}{13}$ **21.** $\frac{1}{6}$ **23.** $\frac{3}{10g^2}$ **25.** $\frac{3y}{2x}$ **27.** $\frac{x^2}{3}$ **29.** $\frac{2}{5t}$ **31.** $-\frac{5}{9}, \frac{1}{4}, \frac{8}{10}, \frac{9}{10}$

33. $-\frac{1}{3}, -\frac{1}{4}, \frac{1}{10}, \frac{1}{7}$

35. $-\frac{7}{8}, -\frac{5}{9}, -\frac{3}{10}, \frac{1}{5}$ **37.** $<$ **39.** $=$ **41.** $>$ **43.** false; *Sample answer:* $-\frac{1}{2}$ is graphed halfway between 0 and -1, which is to the left of 0. **45.** false; *Sample answer:* $\frac{4}{5} < 1$ **47.** Friend; $\frac{5}{14} > \frac{3}{11}$ **49.** $\frac{1}{125}; \frac{1}{125} > \frac{1}{250}$, so the speed will be slower. **51.** $\frac{1}{7}$ **53.** Yes; the graph gives $\frac{4}{21} + \frac{3}{21} = \frac{7}{21} = \frac{1}{3}$.

Mid-Chapter Test (p. 238) **1.** $2^4 \cdot 5$ **2.** $2^2 \cdot 11$ **3.** $3 \cdot 5 \cdot 7$ **4.** $2^2 \cdot 3 \cdot 11$ **5.** $7 \cdot 23$ **6.** $2 \cdot 97$ **7.** $2 \cdot 5^2 \cdot 7$ **8.** $5^2 \cdot 37$ **9.** 1, 2, 4, 7, 8, 14, 28, 56 **10.** 1, 2, 3, 4, 5, 6, 10, 12, 15, 20, 30, 60 **11.** 1, 2, 89, 178 **12.** 1, 3, 5, 11, 15, 33, 55, 165 **13.** 1, 2, 5, 10, x, $2x$, $5x$, $10x$, x^2, $2x^2$, $5x^2$, $10x^2$ **14.** 1, 3, a, b, c, $3a$, $3b$, $3c$, ab, bc, ac, $3ab$, $3ac$, $3bc$, abc, $3abc$ **15.** 1, 19, x, $19x$, y, $19y$, xy, $19xy$, x^2y, $19x^2y$, x^2, $19x^2$ **16.** 1, 3, 7, 21, a, $3a$, $7a$, $21a$, b, $3b$, $7b$, $21b$, ab, $3ab$, $7ab$, $21ab$, b^2, $3b^2$, $7b^2$, $21b^2$, ab^2, $3ab^2$, $7ab^2$, $21ab^2$ **17.** 12 **18.** 3 **19.** 33 **20.** 5 **21.** $3b$ **22.** $6y$ **23.** $8a^2b$ **24.** $9xy$ **25.** 65 **26.** 42 **27.** 495 **28.** 130 **29.** $18x^2$ **30.** $35ab$ **31.** $64mn^2$ **32.** $54x^3y^2$ **33.** $\frac{1}{5}$ **34.** $\frac{5}{34}$ **35.** $\frac{y}{3}$ **36.** $\frac{3m}{10n}$ **37.** 15 tiles; place 5 across by 3 deep to form 30 by 30 square. **38.** 42 tiles; place 6 across by 7 deep to form 42 by 42 square. **39.** 18 tiles; place 2 across by 9 deep to form 36 by 36 square. **40.** 7 of the 6 inch boxes, 3 of the 14 inch boxes **41.** least common multiple

5.5 Guided Practice (p. 241) **1.** integer, rational; $\frac{-3}{1}$ **3.** natural, whole, integer, rational; $\frac{7}{1}$ **5.** rational; $\frac{97}{20}$ **7.** rational; $\frac{17}{2}$ **9.** *Sample answer:* You can show that the number can be written in the form $\frac{a}{b}$, where a is an integer and b is an integer not equal to 0. $3 = \frac{3}{1}$, $0.8 = \frac{4}{5}$, $1\frac{1}{2} = \frac{3}{2}$ **11.** $0.8\overline{3}$ **13.** 1.25 **15.** $1.\overline{3}$ **17.** $0.08\overline{3}$ **19.** $\frac{4}{5}$ **21.** $\frac{3}{8}$ **23.** $\frac{23}{99}$ **25.** $\frac{1}{15}$

5.5 Practice and Problem Solving (pp. 242–243)
27. yes **29.** yes **31.** no **33.** always **35.** 0.35 **37.** 3.12 **39.** $1.\overline{7}$ **41.** $0.91\overline{6}$ **43.** $\frac{3}{5}$ **45.** $-\frac{21}{25}$ **47.** $\frac{517}{1{,}000}$ **49.** $\frac{7}{3}$ **51.** terminating **53.** repeating **55.** repeating **57.** terminating **59.** $\frac{43}{125}$ **61.** $\frac{61}{200}$ **63.** 1.2 in., 0.6 in., 1.2 in., 0.6 in., $3\frac{3}{5}$ in.; 3.6 in. **65.** 0.125 in., 0.25 in., 0.3125 in., 0.3125 in., 0.25 in; 1.25 in., $1\frac{1}{4}$ in. **67.** banana **73.** 16 **75.** $x < 27$ **77.** $y \le 15$ **79.** -7 **81.** $0.08(x - 1) + 0.35 = 0.75$; 6 min

5.6 Guided Practice (p. 246) **1.** 35% **3.** 80% **5.** 25% **7.** 5% **9.** 50% **11.** Estimates may vary. *Sample:* 50%

5.6 Practice and Problem Solving (pp. 246–247)
13. 95% **15.** 55% **17.** 76% **19.** 75% **21.** 29% **23.** 19% **25.** 20% **27.** 33% **29.** $55.\overline{5}\%$ **33.** 40% **35.** No; 42% of Group A thought the product was affordable and 60% of Group B thought the product was affordable. **37.** about 66% **39.** *Sample answer:* Converted the fractions to percents.

5.7 Guided Practice (p. 250) **1.** 0.65 **3.** 1.31 **5.** 38% **7.** 201% **9.** 85% **11.** 37.5% **13.** $\frac{13}{20}$ **15.** $\frac{7}{2}$ **17.** The fraction equivalent will be greater than 1 if the percent is greater than 100%. The percent equivalent will be greater than 100% if the numerator is greater than the denominator of the fraction.

5.7 Practice and Problem Solving (pp. 251–252)
19. 0.2 **21.** 1.15 **23.** 2.29 **25.** 0.003 **27.** 25% **29.** 70% **31.** 1% **33.** 0.9% **35.** 60% **37.** 18.8% **39.** 66.7% **41.** 400% **43.** $\frac{13}{25}$ **45.** $\frac{3}{50}$ **47.** $\frac{11}{10}$ **49.** $\frac{4}{25}$ **51.** 31.25% **53.** $78.\overline{78}\%$ **55.** $\frac{23}{95}$ **57.** 0.2759 **59.** 375% **61.** 0.09 **63.** 83% **65.** $\frac{77}{500}$ **71.** 16 **73.** $4n$ **75.** $6x + 6y$ **77.** $x - 13 = 24$

5.8 Guided Practice (p. 255) **1.** 2, 2, 8, 10, 11, 15, 15, 16, 19, 20, 23, 25, 27, 31, 32, 34, 34, 36

3.

1	9
2	5 7
3	0 0 2 4 4 4 4 5 5 6 6 7 7 7 9 9 9
4	0 1 1 2 2 3 4 4 5 5 8

2 | 5 represents 25°.

5. 19°; 48°

5.8 Practice and Problem Solving (pp. 255–257)
7. 20, 68; 20, 21, 21, 23, 35, 37, 39, 41, 48, 50, 52, 53, 64, 66, 66, 68 **9.** 13.5, 17.8; 13.5, 13.6, 14.3, 14.5, 14.9, 15.1, 15.9, 15.9, 16.1, 16.2, 16.3, 16.7, 17.2, 17.3, 17.4, 17.6, 17.8 **11.** *Sample answer:* The lowest test score was 52%. The highest test score was 100%. The greatest number of students scored between 80% and 89%.

13.

1980		2000
6	3	
5	4	9
3 3	5	4
6 2	6	4 4 7
6 2	7	1 9
	8	0

2 | 7 | 1 represents 72 (1980) and 71 (2000).

15.

East		West
9 9 9 9 9 9 9 9 8 8 8 8	1	
8 8 8 8 8 8 8 7 7 7 7 7	1	8 8 9 9 9 9 9 9 9
0	2	0 0 0 0 0 0 0 0 0 0 1 1 1 1 3 4

7 | 1 | 8 represents 17% (East) and 18% (West).

17.

0	7 8 9 9
1	0 1 2 3 4 5 6 6 8
2	1 1 5 7
3	1 2 9

3 | 2 represents 32.

19. The shape of the histogram is the same as the stem-and-leaf plot, only placed on its side. The frequency became vertical in the histogram instead of horizontal as in the stem-and-leaf plot.

CHAPTER SUMMARY AND REVIEW (pp. 258–261) **1.** $2^3 \cdot 3^2$ **3.** $2 \cdot 3 \cdot 5^2$ **5.** $2 \cdot 2 \cdot 3 \cdot 3 \cdot a \cdot a \cdot a$ **7.** $37 \cdot x \cdot y \cdot y \cdot y$ **9.** 1, 2, 4, 19, 38, 76; 1, 2, 3, 4, 6, 8, 9, 12, 18, 24, 36, 72, y, z, z^2, $2y$, $3y$, $4y$, $6y$, $8y$, $9y$, $12y$, $18y$, $24y$, $36y$, $72y$, $2z$, $3z$, $4z$, $6z$, $8z$, $9z$, $12z$, $18z$, $24z$, $36z$, $72z$, $2z^2$, $3z^2$, $4z^2$, $6z^2$, $8z^2$, $9z^2$, $12z^2$, $18z^2$, $24z^2$, $36z^2$, $72z^2$, yz, $2yz$, $3yz$, $4yz$, $6yz$, $8yz$, $9yz$, $12yz$, $18yz$, $24yz$, $36yz$, $72yz$, yz^2, $2yz^2$, $3yz^2$, $4yz^2$, $6yz^2$, $8yz^2$, $9yz^2$, $12yz^2$, $18yz^2$, $24yz^2$, $36yz^2$, $72yz^2$ **11.** 4 **13.** 5 **15.** $6z^2$ **17.** $9m^2n^2$ **19.** 900 **21.** 68 **23.** $84xy^3$ **25.** $144x^3y^4$ **27.** $\frac{16}{3}$ **29.** $\frac{100x}{7}$ **31.** $\frac{11}{18}, \frac{5}{8}, \frac{2}{3}$ **33.** 0.275 **35.** $2.\overline{09}$ **37.** $\frac{14}{25}$ **39.** $\frac{4}{33}$ **41.** 25% **43.** 75% **45.** 25% **47.** 20% **49.** 0.32; $\frac{8}{25}$ **51.** 0.705; $\frac{141}{200}$ **53.** 57.5% **55.** 315% **57.** 123, 135, 147, 158, 165, 166, 182

REVIEWING THE BASICS (p. 265) **1.** 22 **3.** 22 **5.** −75 **7.** −85 **9.** −99 **11.** 60 **13.** 16, −8

Chapter 6

GETTING READY (p. 268) **1.** C **2.** H **3.** C **4.** J

6.1 GUIDED PRACTICE (p. 271) **1.** $\frac{2}{4} + \frac{1}{4} = \frac{3}{4}$ **3.** $\frac{4}{5}$ **5.** $-\frac{1}{3}$ **7.** $\frac{1}{21}$ **9.** *Sample answer:* When the denominators are the same, add or subtract the numerators using the rules for adding or subtracting positive and negative numbers. Write the answer over the common denominator. $\frac{1}{9} + \frac{7}{9} = \frac{8}{9}, \frac{5}{11} - \frac{2}{11} = \frac{3}{11}$

6.1 PRACTICE AND PROBLEM SOLVING (pp. 271–272) **11.** $\frac{2}{5}$ **13.** $\frac{4}{5}$ **15.** $\frac{1}{2}$ **17.** $-\frac{7}{40}$ **19.** $3\frac{1}{6}$ **21.** $5\frac{17}{18}$ **23.** $\frac{13m}{12}$ **27.** $4\frac{1}{4}$ mi **29.** Yes; $1\frac{1}{4} + 2\frac{3}{8} = 3\frac{5}{8}$ ft, which is less than the total length of $4\frac{1}{2}$ ft. **31.** $17\frac{1}{8}$ or $17.125 **33.** $\frac{5}{2}$

6.2 GUIDED PRACTICE (p. 275) **1.** $\frac{1}{2} + \frac{1}{6} = \frac{4}{6}$ **3.** $\frac{13}{24}$ **5.** $\frac{9}{8}$ or $1\frac{1}{8}$ **7.** $-\frac{1}{9}$ **9.** $\frac{1}{6}$ **11.** $\frac{17}{18}$ **13.** $\frac{7}{18}$

6.2 PRACTICE AND PROBLEM SOLVING (pp. 275–277) **15.** $\frac{7}{12} + \frac{5}{9}$; $\frac{41}{36}$ or $1\frac{5}{36}$ **17.** $\frac{17}{30}$ **19.** $-\frac{5}{12}$ **21.** $-1\frac{1}{12}$ **23.** $-\frac{4}{15}$ **25.** $\frac{29}{30}$ **27.** $\frac{31}{40}$ **29.** $\frac{3}{8}$ **31.** $\frac{5}{18}$ **33.** $\frac{5}{24}$ **35.** $\frac{3}{20}$ **37.** $\frac{33}{20}$ or $1\frac{13}{20}$ **39.** $10\frac{13}{24}$ in. **41.** longer; $\frac{1}{32}$ in. **43.** parents and teachers, and science fiction TV series; NASA **45.** $\frac{1}{25}$ **47.** $4\frac{1}{4}$ ft in my team's direction **49.** $\frac{305}{304}$ **51.** $\frac{29}{414}$ **53.** $\frac{391}{435}$

6.3 GUIDED PRACTICE (p. 280) **1.** $\frac{2}{5} \cdot \frac{1}{3}$; $\frac{2}{15}$ **3.** $\frac{5}{6} \cdot \frac{1}{4}$; $\frac{5}{24}$ **5.** 4 **7.** 4 **9.** 10 **11.** $6x$ **13.** associative property of multiplication **15.** distributive property **17.** $\frac{2}{7}$ **19.** $\frac{3}{8}$

6.3 PRACTICE AND PROBLEM SOLVING (pp. 281–282) **21.** $-\frac{16}{27}$ **23.** $\frac{16}{5}$ or $3\frac{1}{5}$ **25.** $\frac{23}{2}$ or $11\frac{1}{2}$ **27.** $\frac{1}{6}$ **29.** $\frac{56y}{3}$ **31.** $\frac{a}{3}$ **33.** $\frac{9}{25}$ **35.** $2\frac{7}{9}$ **37.** $\frac{8}{27}$ **39.** $15\frac{5}{8}$ **41, 43.** *Sample answers given.* **41.** $\frac{3}{4} \cdot \left(\frac{1}{2} \cdot \frac{2}{3}\right) = \left(\frac{3}{4} \cdot \frac{1}{2}\right) \cdot \frac{2}{3}$ **43.** $\frac{2}{3} \cdot \frac{3}{2} = 1$ **45.** $\frac{1}{4}$ **47.** $\frac{2}{15}$ **51.** 1237.5 cal **53.** false; $\frac{162}{376} = \frac{81}{188} \neq \frac{3}{7}$ **55.** false; $-2\frac{3}{5} = -\frac{13}{5}$; which is not the reciprocal of $-\frac{15}{13}$ **57.** 72 coins **61.** mean 98.6, median 98.7, mode 98.7 **63.** *Sample answer:* The fewest number of candy bars sold was 3, and the most sold was 80. Half of the students sold in the 30–59 range.

6.4 GUIDED PRACTICE (p. 285) **1.** 4.8 **3.** 32 **5.** 171 **7.** $330.15 **9.** about $7.50

6.4 PRACTICE AND PROBLEM SOLVING (pp. 285–287) **11.** 228 **13.** 17 **15.** 115 **17.** 52 **19.** 0.3 **21.** 0.1 **27.** 4 **29.** 9 **31.** 2.5 **33.** 120 **35–39.** *Sample answers.* **35.** 20; 20.8 **37.** 46; 44.16 **39.** 154; 152.6 **41.** 736 people **43.** 71%; about 140 million square miles **45.** $.29 **47.** $14 **49.** $28.21 **51.** $362.50 **55.** $15.00; round $102.30 down to $100, then multiply by 15%. **57.** $0.075x$; $5000 + 0.045x$

MID-CHAPTER TEST (p. 288) **1.** $\frac{4}{11}$ **2.** $\frac{2}{3}$ **3.** $6\frac{2}{5}$ **4.** $-\frac{x}{2}$ **5.** $\frac{27}{50}$ **6.** $\frac{2}{5}$ **7.** $\frac{1}{4}$ **8.** $-\frac{1}{15}$ **9.** $-\frac{1}{2}$ **10.** $\frac{2}{5}$ **11.** $1\frac{2}{5}$ **12.** $-\frac{12}{25}$ **13.** 0 **14.** $-\frac{35}{6}$ **15.** $\frac{3}{10}$ **16.** $-\frac{15}{4}$ **17.** $\frac{7}{6}$ **18.** -4 **19.** $-\frac{1}{12}$ **20.** $\frac{5}{18}$ **21.** 54 **22.** 55 **23.** 78 **24.** 0.056 **25.** $15\frac{7}{15}$ in., $12\frac{4}{5}$ in.^{2} **26.** 6 ft, $1\frac{5}{16}$ ft^2 **27.** $47\frac{1}{4}$ ft, $113\frac{29}{32}$ ft^2 **28.** \$10, \$20 **29.** \$15, \$15 **30.** \$202.23 **31.** about \$3.00

6.5 GUIDED PRACTICE (p. 291) **1.** $\frac{3}{5}$ **3.** 30 **5.** $\frac{2n}{9}$ **7.** $\frac{10y}{3}$ **9.** $6\frac{2}{3}$ mi/h

6.5 PRACTICE AND PROBLEM SOLVING (pp. 292–293) **13.** $\frac{5}{8}$ **15.** $\frac{5}{3}$ or $1\frac{2}{3}$ **17.** $-\frac{18}{5}$ or $-3\frac{3}{5}$ **19.** -7 **21.** $\frac{14}{3}$ **23.** $-\frac{x}{15}$ **25.** $\frac{4n}{5}$ **27.** $\frac{5}{6}$ **29.** The person did not multiply the denominators; $-\frac{8}{9}$. **31.** $\frac{15}{4}$ mi or $3\frac{3}{4}$ mi **33.** 42 ft **35.** 7 yd **41.** $7(x + 4) = 49$; 3 in. **43.** $2 \cdot 13$ **45.** $3 \cdot 5 \cdot 7$ **47.** 6 **49.** $5xy$ **51.** $-\frac{7}{3}$ **53.** $-\frac{9}{10}$

6.6 GUIDED PRACTICE (p. 297) **1.** $5\frac{1}{4}$ **3.** $\frac{15}{8}$ or $1\frac{7}{8}$ **5.** $\frac{13}{20}$ **7.** $\frac{2}{3}x = 10{,}000$, \$15,000

6.6 PRACTICE AND PROBLEM SOLVING (pp. 297–298) **9.** $\frac{5}{16}$ **11.** $1\frac{1}{8}$ **13.** $\frac{7}{3}$ or $2\frac{1}{3}$ **15.** $\frac{32}{5}$ or $6\frac{2}{5}$ **17.** $\frac{13}{2}$ or $6\frac{1}{2}$ **19.** $\frac{7}{3}$ or $2\frac{1}{3}$ **21.** 2 **23.** $x \cdot 3\frac{1}{2} = \frac{63}{4}$; $4\frac{1}{2}$ units **25.** $x \cdot \frac{2}{5} = \frac{7}{15}$; $1\frac{1}{6}$ units **27.** $\frac{x}{2} + 13 = 30$, 34 **29.** $86 + \frac{x}{5} = -24$, -550 **31.** 82°C **33.** 32°C **35.** -22°C **37.** 13°C **39.** 1 h 52 min

6.7 GUIDED PRACTICE (p. 301) **1.** 4^8 **3.** $(-a)^7$ **5.** 3^2 **7.** $(-a)^3$

6.7 PRACTICE AND PROBLEM SOLVING (pp. 301–302) **11.** 6^5 **13.** $(-2)^6$ **15.** $\left(-\frac{3}{5}\right)^4$ **17.** $6n^9$ **19.** 3 **21.** $-5y^2$ **23.** $5y$ **25.** $\frac{1}{20}x$ **27.** $6 \cdot 6^3$; 6^4 **29.** $\frac{3^5}{3^2}$; 3^3 **31.** The base was not preserved after subtracting the exponents. 2^2 **33.** true **35.** false; 6^2 **37.** true **39.** 10^4 **41.** $\left(\frac{1}{3}\right)^2$; $\frac{1}{9}$ **43.** $\left(-\frac{3}{2}\right)^3$; $-\frac{27}{8}$ **47.** $\frac{10^6}{10^4}$, 10^2 or 100 times more PINs with the new system

6.8 GUIDED PRACTICE (p. 307) **1.** $\frac{1}{49}$ **3.** 32 **5.** $\frac{1}{x^2}$ **7.** $-\frac{2}{y^2}$ **11.** $2^{-2} \cdot 3^{-2}$ **13.** $-2^{-2} \cdot 5^{-2}$

6.8 PRACTICE AND PROBLEM SOLVING (pp. 307–308) **15.** $-\frac{1}{1000}$ **17.** 81 **19.** 1 **21.** 1 **23.** $\frac{2}{x^3}$ **25.** 1 **27.** $-\frac{3}{x^2}$ **29.** $\frac{x}{y^3}$ **31.** -5^{-3} **33.** 2^{-10} **35.** -11^{-2} **37.** -3^{-4} **39.** x^{-5} **41.** $-x^{-10}$ **43.** $5x^{-5}$ **45.** 2^2x^{-2} **47.** $\frac{1}{1{,}000{,}000}$, 10^{-6} **49.** $\frac{15 \text{ lb}}{\text{ft}} \cdot 24$ ft, 360 lb **51.** $\frac{3600 \text{ sec}}{\text{h}} \cdot 2.5$ h, 9000 sec **53.** 1,000,000 times greater **55.** 1,000,000,000 times greater

6.9 GUIDED PRACTICE (p. 311) **1.A.** no; $12.3 > 10$ **B.** Yes; the number is between 1 and 10, times a power of 10. **C.** no; $0.123 < 1$ **3.** -3 **5.** 0.0000087 **7.** 8.7×10^5 **9.** 9.375×10^{-3}

6.9 PRACTICE AND PROBLEM SOLVING (pp. 311–313) **11.** 1×10^5 **13.** 4.1×10^{-4} **15.** 3.261×10^7 **17.** 1.2×10^{-8} **19.** 6.987×10^{-3} **21.** 2×10^0 **23.** 0.0057 **25.** 25,000 **27.** 630,000,000 **29.** 516,000 **31.** 9860 **33.** 7.6 **35.** yes **37.** no; 2.56×10^9 **39.** yes **41.** no; 1×10^4 **43.** no; 7.6×10^{11} **45.** 1.53×10^3, 1530 **47.** 3.2766×10^{-7}, 0.00000032766 **49.** 5.4404×10^2; 544.04 **51.** $\frac{(9.7 \times 10^4)(2.4 \times 10^2)}{2.5 \times 10^{-1}}$; 9.312×10^7; 93,120,000 **53.** $(5.2 \times 10^2)(8.67 \times 10^{-4})$; 4.5084×10^{-1}; 0.45084 **55.** $\frac{(1 \times 10^{-3})(6.7 \times 10^{-4})}{(8.4 \times 10^{-3})(9 \times 10^{-4})}$; 8.86×10^{-2}; 0.0886 **57.** 1×10^{14} **59.** 4.6×10^4, 4.56×10^5, 4.65×10^5, 4.5×10^6 **61.** 82,000,000; 45,000,000; 15,000,000; 12,000,000; 12,000,000 **63.** 1.09×10^2 **65.** 2.04×10^4 dollars; \$20,400 **71.** $>$ **73.** $<$ **75.** $>$ **77, 79.**

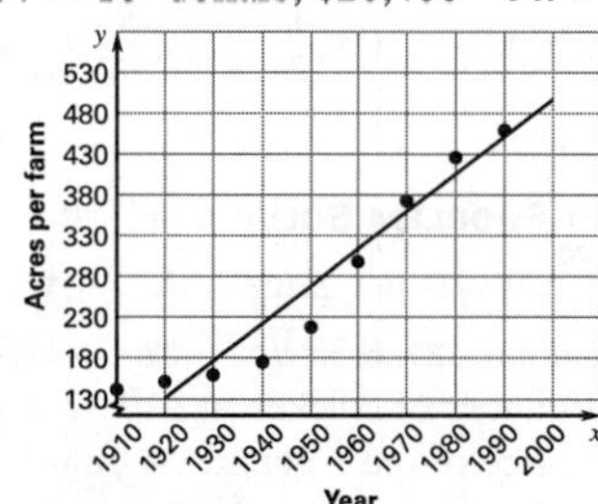

79. about 500 acres per farm **81.** $\frac{14}{27}$ **83.** $\frac{51}{100}$ **85.** x **87.** $3x$

CHAPTER SUMMARY AND REVIEW (pp. 314–317) **1.** $\frac{43}{25}$ or $1\frac{18}{25}$ **3.** $\frac{2y}{7}$ **5.** $\frac{37}{30}$ or $1\frac{7}{30}$ **7.** $-\frac{185}{168}$ or $-1\frac{17}{168}$ **9.** $\frac{11}{18}$ **11.** $\frac{3}{4}$ **13.** $\frac{65}{42}$ or $1\frac{23}{42}$ **15.** $\frac{11}{24}$ **17.** $-\frac{1}{12}$ **19.** $12x$ **21.** $\frac{55}{12}$ m^2 or $4\frac{7}{12}$ m^2 **23.** 7.2 **25.** 112.2 **27.** $\frac{3n}{10}$ **29.** $-\frac{4}{3}$ or $-1\frac{1}{3}$ **31.** $-\frac{1}{8}$ **33.** $\frac{49}{40}$ or $1\frac{9}{40}$ **35.** $\left(\frac{2}{3}\right)^5$ **37.** x^6 **39.** $\frac{7^4}{7^3} = 7$ **41.** $\frac{1}{64}$ **43.** $\frac{1}{x^5}$ **45.** $-\frac{5}{x^3}$ **47.** 3 **49.** 1.45302×10^6 **51.** 8.7×10^1 **53.** 1.2×10^{-4} **55.** 4.07×10^{-2}

REVIEWING THE BASICS (p. 321) **1.** $\frac{5}{9}$ **3.** $\frac{27}{14}$ or $1\frac{13}{14}$ **5.** $2x$ **7.** a^2c^2 **9.** 2 **11.** 5 **13.** 14 **15.** 6 **17.** -1

CUMULATIVE PRACTICE (pp. 322–323) **1.** 72 **3.** 65 **5.** $n + 5 = 21$; 16 **7.** Let n = the number of tubes of paint. $2.70n = 40.50$ **9.** $z - 9 < -5$; $z < 4$ **11.** 4; yes **13.** $-2y - 6x + 3z$; 19 **15.** $4z - y$; 16 **17.** 4 **19.** 1 **21.** mean 2, median 2, mode 2 **23.** $2 \cdot 7$, 7^2; 98 **25.** $2 \cdot 3 \cdot x^2 \cdot y$, $2^3 \cdot x \cdot y^3$; $24x^2y^3$ **27.** 6; $\frac{1}{8}$ **29.** 5; $\frac{2}{3}$ **31.** 1.6, $\frac{8}{5}$ **33.** $0.\overline{3}$, $33\frac{1}{3}\%$

35.

18	0 8
19	5 6
20	4 6 9
21	1 6 6 9
22	1 5
23	1
24	3 8

Key: 24 | 3 represents 243.

37. $\frac{2}{5}$ **39.** $8\frac{1}{2}$ m, $3\frac{3}{16}$ m^2 **41.** $\frac{1}{a^4}$ **43.** 1000 **45.** x^{17} **47.** $\frac{4a^2b}{5}$ **49.** 2.6473×10^4 **51.** 1.5×10^8

Chapter 7

GETTING READY (p. 328) **1.** B **2.** J

7.1 GUIDED PRACTICE (p. 331) **1.** $\frac{1}{2}$ **3.** $\frac{4}{9}$, $\frac{5}{9}$, 4 : 5, 5 : 4, 9 to 5, 9 to 4 **5.** $\frac{1}{3}$ **7.** $\frac{4}{1}$

7.1 PRACTICE AND PROBLEM SOLVING (pp. 331–332) **9.** $\frac{1}{4}$ **11.** $\frac{19}{25}$ **13.** $\frac{89}{412}$ losses per game **15.** $\frac{4}{3}$ **17.** $\frac{2}{5}$ **19.** 1500 tickets per hour **21.** \$.359/oz **23.** \$1.125/gal **25.** The 5 pounds, 2 ounces of chicken at \$10.92 is the better buy. The unit price of the 2 pounds, 4 ounces at \$6.50 is \$.18/ounce; the unit price of the 5 pounds, 2 ounces of chicken at \$10.92 is \$.13/ounce. **29.** The dog has a faster heartbeat. The horse's heartbeat is $\frac{1}{2}$ beat per second. The dog's heartbeat is $\frac{5}{3}$ beats per second. So, the dog's heart is beating more rapidly.

31.

$\frac{\text{Perimeter of green region}}{\text{Perimeter of yellow region}}$	$\frac{\text{Area of green region}}{\text{Area of yellow region}}$
$\frac{10}{9}$	$\frac{3}{2}$

Sample answer: The ratio of the area of the green region to the area of the yellow region is greater than the ratio of the perimeter of the green region to the perimeter of the yellow region because $\frac{3}{2}$ is greater than $\frac{10}{9}$.

7.2 GUIDED PRACTICE (p. 335) **1.** 1 **3.** 24 **5.** *Sample answer:* The student is setting two ratios equal that are not in proportion. $\frac{35}{5} = \frac{d}{17}$; \$119

7.2 PRACTICE AND PROBLEM SOLVING (pp. 336–337) **7.** $\frac{x}{6} = \frac{8}{9}$, $\frac{16}{3}$ **9.** $\frac{3}{8} = \frac{m}{24}$, 9 **11.** $\frac{4}{3}$ **13.** $\frac{10}{7}$ **15.** 20 **17.** 18 **19.** *Sample answer:* $\frac{840}{30} \stackrel{?}{=} \frac{1008}{36}$ **21.** 10 loaves **23.** 4 loaves **25.** \$2.00 **27.** about 894 million lb **33.** 60 in. **35.** 72 **37.** 17.5 **39.** 3.96 **41.** 0.081 **43.** 1.1025

7.3 GUIDED PRACTICE (p. 340) **1.** *Sample answer:* $\frac{2.25 \text{ ft}}{0.75 \text{ in.}} = \frac{x}{1 \text{ in.}}$ (x meas. in ft) **3.** No; the enlarged photograph has twice the perimeter and four times the area of the wallet-sized photograph. Perimeter of wallet-sized photograph: $2(2) + 2(3) = 10$ in.; perimeter of enlarged photograph: $2(4) + 2(6) = 20$ in.; The enlarged photograph has twice the perimeter of the wallet-sized photograph; Area of wallet-sized photograph: $2(3) = 6$ in.^{2}; area of enlarged photograph: $4(6) = 24$ in.^{2}; The area of the enlarged photograph is four times the area of the wallet-sized photograph.

7.3 PRACTICE AND PROBLEM SOLVING (pp. 341–342) **5.** $\frac{1}{90} = \frac{520 \text{ mm}}{l}$, $\frac{1}{90} = \frac{615 \text{ mm}}{h}$ **7.** length: 46.8 m, height: 55.35 m **9.** The sizes of the deck in the drawing should be $4\frac{1}{2}$ inches in length and 3 inches in width. The drawing must indicate that the scale is $\frac{1}{2}$ inch = 2 feet. **11.** Accept reasonable scale drawings that include appropriate scales. **13.** 500 mi **15.** 80 mi **17.** 140 mi

7.4 GUIDED PRACTICE (p. 347) **1.** C **3.** A **5.** E

7.4 PRACTICE AND PROBLEM SOLVING (pp. 348–349) **7.** $\frac{1}{4}$ or 25% **9.** $\frac{1}{12}$ or about 8% **11.** *Sample data:* $\frac{18}{30}$ or 60% **13.** M: $\frac{1}{7}$ or about 14%, A: $\frac{4}{7}$ or about 57%, B: $\frac{1}{7}$ or about 14%; L: $\frac{1}{7}$ or about 14% **15.** *Sample answer:*

Letter	Experimental probability	Theoretical probability
A	60%	about 57%
B	about 13%	about 14%
L	10%	about 14%
M	about 17%	about 14%

The experimental probabilities were fairly close to the theoretical probabilities.

17. $\frac{1}{50}$ or 2% **19.** 1900 **21.** 33, 36, 39, 63, 66, 69, 93, 96, and 99; the probability is $\frac{1}{9} \approx 0.11$ or 11%. **23.** *Sample data:* 39: $\frac{6}{50}$ or 12% **25.** No; the street may not be representative of the community. It would be better for the analyst to say that Candidate A will win 60% of the votes on that street than 60% of the votes cast citywide.

7.5 GUIDED PRACTICE (p. 352) **1.** 52%, the percent that 13 is of 25 **3.** 5, the number of which 3 is 60 percent **5.** $\frac{a}{50} = \frac{16}{100}$, 8 **7.** $\frac{30}{150} = \frac{p}{100}$, 20%

7.5 PRACTICE AND PROBLEM SOLVING (pp. 352–354)
9. 50 **11.** $33\frac{1}{3}\%$ **13.** 33 **15.** Student is writing proportion that asks the question, "150 is what percent of 45?" not "45 is what percent of 150?" $\frac{45}{150} = \frac{p}{100}$, 30% **17.** $\frac{21}{30} = \frac{p}{100}$, 70% **19.** $\frac{66}{b} = \frac{120}{100}$, 55 **21.** $\frac{6.06}{b} = \frac{20.2}{100}$, 30 **23.** $\frac{1}{50} = \frac{p}{100}$, 2% **25.** $\frac{23}{b} = \frac{25}{100}$, 92 **27.** $p = \frac{a}{b} \times 100$; to change the ratio in the form of a fraction to a percent, the fraction is multiplied by 100. **29.** 4 students **31.** 18 students **33.** \$560 **35.** 39% **37.** about 9.7% **39.** 18% **41.** She will receive the bonus.

MID-CHAPTER TEST (p. 355) **1.** $\frac{50}{9}$ m/sec **2.** 3 lures per fisherman **3.** $\frac{7}{8}$ **4.** $\frac{5}{7}$ **5.** 1 **6.** $\frac{8}{3}$ **7.** \$.28/apple **8.** \$2.60/lb **9.** \$1.12/gal **10.** 16 **11.** $\frac{27}{7}$ **12.** $\frac{648}{25}$ or 25.92 **13.** 15 **14.** 185 min (3 h and 5 min) **15.** 5 mi **16.** No; the perimeter of the enlarged photograph is five times the perimeter of the original photograph; the area is 25 times the area of the original photograph. **17.** 128 ft^2 **18.** $\frac{1}{2}$ **19.** $\frac{5}{26}$ **20.** $\frac{2}{3}$ **21.** $\frac{15}{b} = \frac{125}{100}$, 12 **22.** $\frac{a}{18} = \frac{35}{100}$, 6.3 **23.** $\frac{36}{150} = \frac{p}{100}$, 24 percent **24.** $\frac{25}{250} = \frac{p}{100}$, 10 percent

7.6 GUIDED PRACTICE (p. 358) **1.** 14.3% discount
3. 16.7% discount
5. sale price = original price − discount
sale price = original price −
(percent of discount) • (original price)
$29.99 = x - 0.25x$
$29.99 = 0.75x$
$x = 39.99$, original price is \$39.99
7. 160%

7.6 PRACTICE AND PROBLEM SOLVING (pp. 359–360)
9. \$17.60 **11.** \$26.40 **13.** \$1.88 **15.** \$76.50 **17.** \$39.38 **19.** \$96.77 **21.** \$1.32 **23.** 56% **25.** 15% **27.** \$77.00

29. The percent of discount for the entire purchase is about 18.9%, but the average of the individual percents of discount is 20%. **33.** \$1138.50 **35.** \$1232.43 **39.** 7 **41.** 5 **43.** 27 **45.** −9 **47.** 0.21 **49.** $\frac{1}{2}$ **51.** 0.83, $\frac{83}{100}$ **53.** 2.06, $\frac{206}{100}$ **55.** 0.178, $\frac{178}{1000}$ **57.** 0.0004, $\frac{4}{10{,}000}$ **59.** 25 **61.** 6 **63.** $\frac{3}{10}$ **65.** $\frac{12}{5}$

7.7 GUIDED PRACTICE (p. 363) **1.** increase, 50% **3.** decrease, −12% **5.** increase, 145.81%

7.7 PRACTICE AND PROBLEM SOLVING (pp. 363–364)
7. −14.3% **9.** +122.2% **11.** +40% **13.** 100% **15.** +100%; 16, 32, 64 **17.** The cost of a bag of groceries increased from \$2.39 in 1949 to \$7.08 in 1999, which represents a 196.23% increase. **19.** Florida **21.** Wyoming

7.8 GUIDED PRACTICE (p. 367) **1.** \$24 **3.** \$83.33 **5.** \$512.50 **7.** \$1425

7.8 PRACTICE AND PROBLEM SOLVING (pp. 367–368)
9. \$25, \$1275 **11.** \$15, \$815 **13.** \$47.50, \$547.50 **15.** 20% **17.** 7% **19.** \$11,200 **21.** The value of *t* is incorrect. Instead of 0.5, it should be 0.25 for 3 months. \$51.00 **23.** \$3248 **25.** \$3500, \$2500

7.9 GUIDED PRACTICE (p. 371) **1.** *Sample answers:* Simple interest is interest paid only on the principal; compound interest is interest paid on the principal and on previously earned interest. Example: six percent compounded quarterly

3.

Number of compoundings	Balance
1	\$1020.00
2	\$1040.40
3	\$1061.21
4	\$1082.43

5. \$1000, 5%, 6 months, 12 **7.** \$1200, 9%, 1 month, 24

7.9 PRACTICE AND PROBLEM SOLVING (pp. 371–373)
9. 12, 4, 2, 1 **11.** \$1126.83 **13.** \$1055.00 **15.** \$108.31 **17.** \$2709.17 **19.** 15 years **21.** 12 years **23.** \$100

25.

Year	Compound interest balance
0	\$5,000.00
1	\$5,450.00
2	\$5,940.50
3	\$6,475.15
4	\$7,057.91
5	\$7,693.12

27. The difference becomes greater as the compound interest grows faster.

CHAPTER SUMMARY AND REVIEW (pp. 374–377) **1.** $\frac{4}{48} = \frac{1}{12}$ **3.** $\frac{5}{2}$ **5.** $\frac{9}{4}$ **7.** 49.2 ft tall **9.** $\frac{1}{12}$ **11.** $\frac{5}{12}$ **13.** 0.35 or 35% **15.** 200 **17.** Discount of 25% **19.** Markup of 40% **21.** −6.8% **23.** 11.1% **25.** \$75; \$1575 **27.** \$2,831.04

REVIEWING THE BASICS (p. 381) **1.** 12 **3.** −30 **5.** 300 **7.** $P = 40$ m; $A = 60$ m^2 **9.** $P = 44$ ft, $A = 121$ ft^2

Chapter 8

GETTING READY (p. 384) **1.** C **2.** J **3.** A

8.1 GUIDED PRACTICE (p. 387) **1.** C **3.** B **5.** *Sample answer*: One pair of parallel lines is represented by the top and bottom of a window. A pair of intersecting lines is represented by one side of the window and the top. The plane that contains these lines can be represented by the window.

8.1 PRACTICE AND PROBLEM SOLVING (pp. 387–389) **7.** $\overline{AC}$, $\overline{AG}$ and $\overline{CG}$ **9.** $\overleftrightarrow{AG}$ and $\overleftrightarrow{CF}$, $\overleftrightarrow{BE}$ and $\overleftrightarrow{CF}$ **11.** no; They have different starting points and continue in opposite directions. **13.** yes; A line continues indefinitely in both directions.

15.

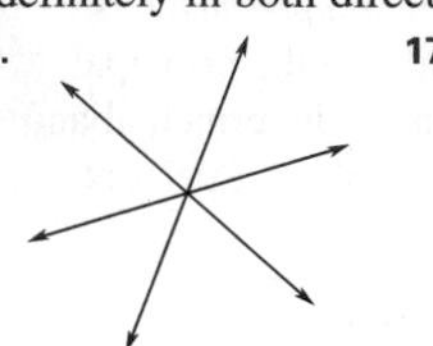

17.

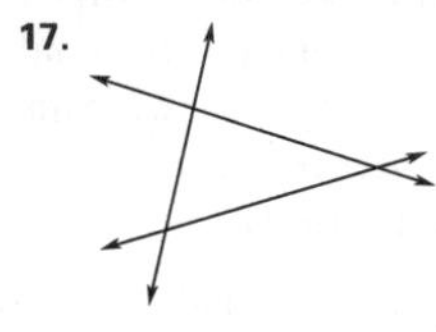

19. 6 **21.** $\overline{PT}$, $\overline{PS}$, $\overline{QU}$ and $\overline{QR}$; $\overline{SR}$, $\overline{VW}$ and $\overline{TU}$ **23.** no; The plane containing P, Q, and R contains the whole top face of the cube, and point V is not in that same plane. **25.** $x + 2x = 27$, $x = 9$ **27.** $x - 3 + x + x - 3 = 9$, $x = 5$ **29.** 53 ft **31.** 44%

8.1 CONSTRUCTION (p. 389) **1–2.** Check drawings.

8.2 GUIDED PRACTICE (p. 392) **1.** X **3.** $\angle WXY$, $\angle YXW$, $\angle ZXW$, $\angle X$ **5.** 70°; acute **7.** $\angle MNP$, $\angle PNO$; complementary

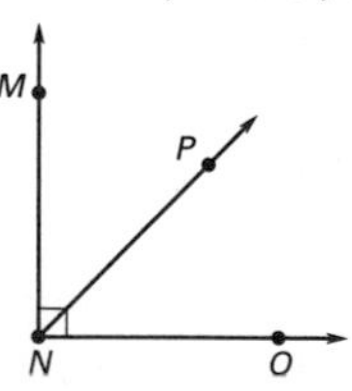

8.2 PRACTICE AND PROBLEM SOLVING (pp. 393–394) **9.** 160°; obtuse

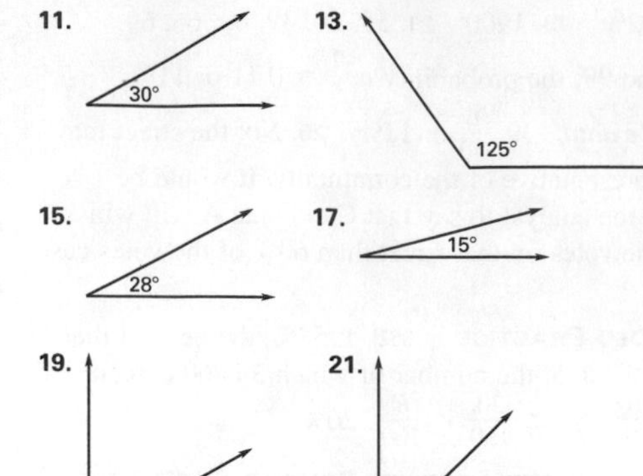

19. 60° 30° **21.** 45°

23. 90° **25.** The vertex is D; the sides are $\overrightarrow{DC}$ and $\overrightarrow{DE}$. D is the vertex of many different angles. **27.** 180° **29.** 110° **31.** They are supplementary angles. **33.** 66° **35.** 1° **37.** 90° **39.** 2° **41.** $m\angle B = 70°$, $m\angle A = 110°$ **43.** True. An acute angle measures less than 90° so there exist angles whose measures may be added to the measure of any acute angle so that they sum to 90° or to 180°. **45.** False. The supplement of an acute angle must be an obtuse angle.

8.2 CONSTRUCTION (p. 395) **1–3.** Check drawings. **4.** No. An obtuse angle is an angle measuring between 90° and 180°. Since twice an obtuse angle will be more than 180°, it is not possible to bisect an obtuse angle to form two congruent obtuse angles.

8.3 GUIDED PRACTICE (p. 400) **1.** m and n are parallel, t is a transversal. **3.** $\angle 1$ and $\angle 5$, $\angle 2$ and $\angle 6$, $\angle 3$ and $\angle 7$, $\angle 4$ and $\angle 8$

8.3 PRACTICE AND PROBLEM SOLVING (pp. 400–402) **7.** $\angle 5$, $\angle 8$, $\angle 6$, and $\angle 7$; $\angle 8$ is given to be a right angle; $\angle 5$ and $\angle 8$ are vertical angles and therefore congruent; $\angle 6$ and $\angle 7$ are both supplementary to $\angle 8$ and therefore are right angles also. **9.** Line m is not parallel to line k. **11.** *Sample answer*: $\angle 2$ and $\angle 10$ **13.** $\angle 5$ and $\angle 8$ **15.** $\angle 6$ and $\angle 7$ **17.** $\angle 1 \cong \angle 2$ because they are corresponding angles, $\angle 2 \cong \angle 3$ because they are corresponding angles and $\angle 3 \cong \angle 4$ because they are vertical angles. Therefore, $\angle 1 \cong \angle 2 \cong \angle 3 \cong \angle 4$ or $\angle 1 \cong \angle 4$. **19.** 13 **21.** 25 **23.** When two lines intersect, each pair of nonstraight angles are either vertical or supplementary angles. Vertical angles are congruent. Hence $\angle 1 \cong \angle 3$ and $\angle 2 \cong \angle 4$. Since $\angle 1$ is acute; $\angle 3$ is also acute. A supplement of an acute angle must be obtuse, so $\angle 2$ and $\angle 4$ are obtuse. **25.** They are vertical angles and are congruent. **27.** 115° **33.** −4 **35.** $l = 20$, $w = 10$; $P = 60$, $A = 200$ **37.** $\frac{4}{6} = \frac{2}{3}$ **39.** $-\frac{14}{15}$ **41.** $\frac{2x}{6} = \frac{x}{3}$ **43.** $\frac{3y - 10}{6}$

8.3 CONSTRUCTION (p. 403) 1–2. Check drawings.

8.4 GUIDED PRACTICE (p. 407) 1. C, G **3.** C, G **5.** C, F **7.** Parallelogram, rectangle, square, rhombus **9.** Rhombus, square **11.** Kite

8.4 PRACTICE AND PROBLEM SOLVING (pp. 407–409)
13. Acute, isosceles **15.** Obtuse, scalene **17.** Obtuse, isosceles
19.

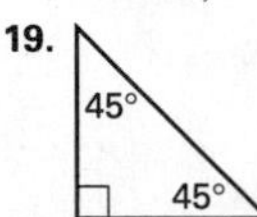

21. Corresponding angles; vertical angles **25.** 34° **27.** Trapezoid **29.** Square **31.** Rectangle **39.** no; yes **41.** sometimes **43.** sometimes **45.** sometimes

8.4 CONSTRUCTION (p. 410) 1. Check drawings. **2.** Check drawings; All altitudes intersect in a point. **3.** Check drawings; An obtuse triangle has two altitudes that lie outside the triangle. **4.** 1 because $\overline{AC}$ is an altitude to $\overline{BC}$ and $\overline{BC}$ is an altitude to $\overline{AC}$.

MID-CHAPTER TEST (p. 411) 1. Q **2.** $\overleftrightarrow{PQ}$ and $\overleftrightarrow{KL}$ **3.** *Sample answer*: $\overrightarrow{RS}$ and $\overrightarrow{RL}$ **4.** P **5.** $\angle AFC$, $\angle CFE$ **6.** $\angle AFB$, $\angle BFC$, $\angle CFD$ and $\angle DFE$ **7.** $\angle AFD$, $\angle BFD$ and $\angle BFE$ **8.** $\angle AFE$ **9.** $\angle AFB$ and $\angle CFB$ or $\angle CFD$ and $\angle DFE$ **10.** *Sample answer*: $\angle AFB$ and $\angle BFE$ **11.** vertical **12.** corresponding **13.** corresponding **14.** $m\angle 1 = m\angle 7 = m\angle 3 = m\angle 5 = 118°$; $m\angle 2 = m\angle 8 = m\angle 4 = m\angle 6 = 62°$ **15.** Obtuse, scalene **16.** Equiangular, equilateral **17.** Right, scalene **18.** Acute, isosceles **19.** sometimes **20.** never **21.** always **22.** always **23.** 10

8.5 GUIDED PRACTICE (p. 414) 1. $\triangle RTS$; $\angle M \cong \angle R$, $\angle N \cong \angle T$ and $\angle P \cong \angle S$, $\overline{MN} \cong \overline{RT}$, $\overline{MP} \cong \overline{RS}$ and $\overline{NP} \cong \overline{TS}$ **3.** 95°; $m\angle R = 56°$, $m\angle T = 29°$, $m\angle S = 95°$ **5.** The two triangles formed are congruent because of SSS or SAS. (Either is correct.)

8.5 PRACTICE AND PROBLEM SOLVING (pp. 415–416)
7. No. They are not congruent. **9.** No. They are not congruent. **11.** $m\angle K = 102°$, $m\angle M = 92°$, $PN = 8$ **13.** $m\angle D = 84°$, $AD = BC$ and $AB = 9$ **15.** Regular hexagon **17.** 18 **19.** *Sample answer: CELK ≅ CEHB; CDJK ≅ CDAB; EDJL ≅ EDAH*
23. SSS

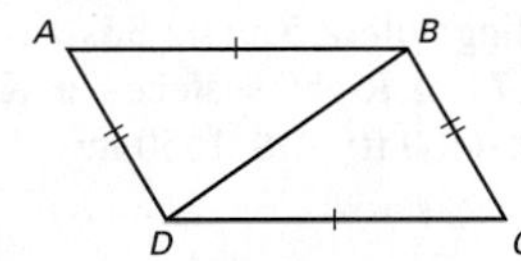

8.6 GUIDED PRACTICE (p. 421) 1. C, D; 9 units^2 **3.** C; 21.7 units^2 **5.** B; 139.5 units^2

8.6 PRACTICE AND PROBLEM SOLVING (pp. 421–422)
7. 63 units^2 **9.** 33.6 units^2 **11.** 32 units^2 **13.** Trapezoid, rectangle and triangle; $8 + 10 + 5 = 23$ units^2 **15.** Square, rectangle and trapezoid; $4 + 3 + 8 + 6 = 21$ units^2
17.

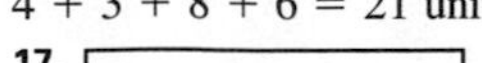

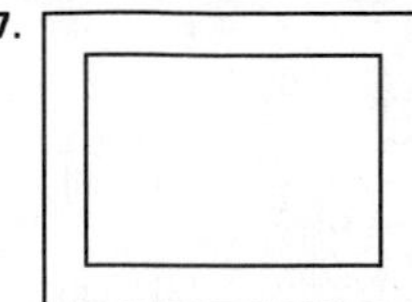

19. 391.68 in.^{2}
21. $A = bh$

8.7 GUIDED PRACTICE (p. 425) 1. $(x, y) \rightarrow (-x, y)$; The line of reflection is the y-axis.

8.7 PRACTICE AND PROBLEM SOLVING (pp. 425–427)
3. No **5.** Yes

7.

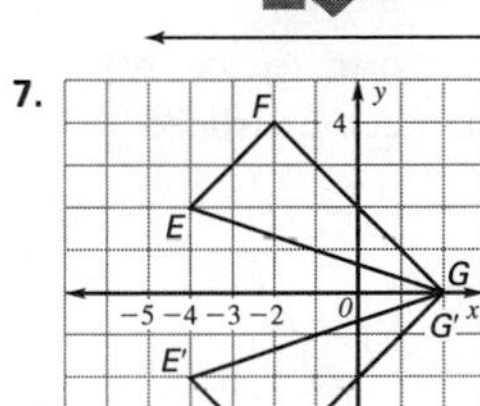

9. You come back to the original figure; $(x, y) \rightarrow (-x, y) \rightarrow (x, y)$, $(x, y) \rightarrow (x, -y) \rightarrow (x, y)$. **11.** No, it is the reflection in the x-axis. **13.** True. $(x, y) \rightarrow (x, -y)$ for a reflection in the x-axis.
15. Line of reflection = x-axis

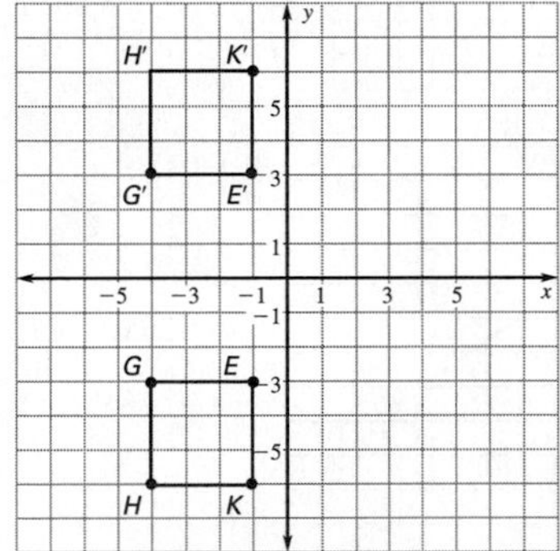

SELECTED ANSWERS

17. Line of reflection = x-axis

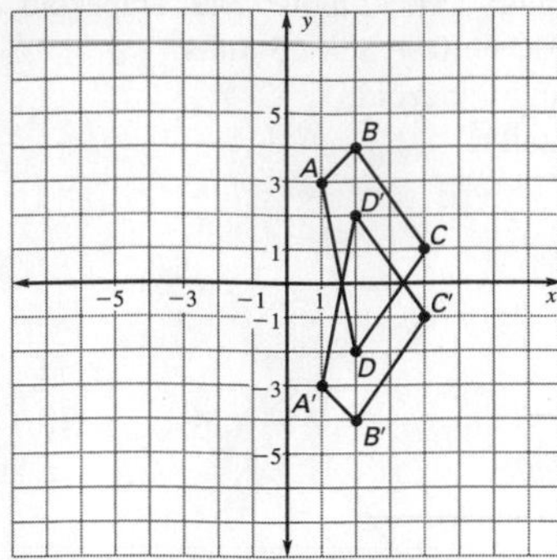

23. $b = \frac{1}{2}$ **25.** $a = 6.02$ **27.** $m = 2$ **29.** $t = \frac{26}{15}$
31. 2.1×10^3 **33.** 1.6×10^7 **35.** 1.793×10^3
37. decrease; −4.6% **39.** decrease; −14.3%

8.8 GUIDED PRACTICE (p. 430) **1.** Translation; Each point on the blue figure has been translated 5 units to the right and 4 units down. **3.** Reflection; Each point on the red figure is a reflection of the blue figure in the y-axis. **5 A.** 4 **5 B.** 3 **5 C.** 1 **5 D.** 2

8.8 PRACTICE AND PROBLEM SOLVING (pp. 430–431)
7. Each point on the blue figure has been translated 2 units to the left and 4 units up.
9. $(x, y) \rightarrow (x, y + 5)$

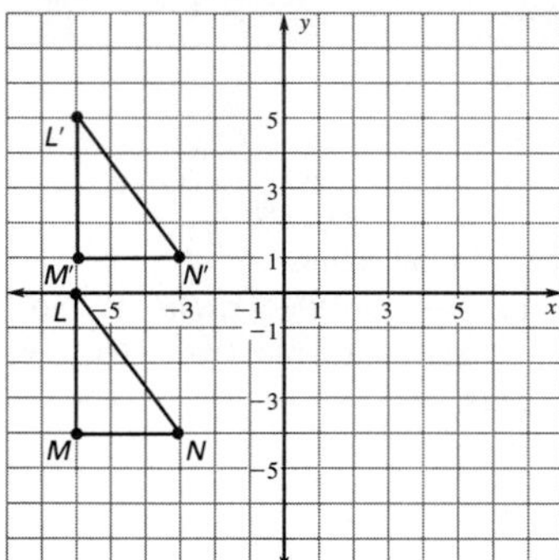

11.

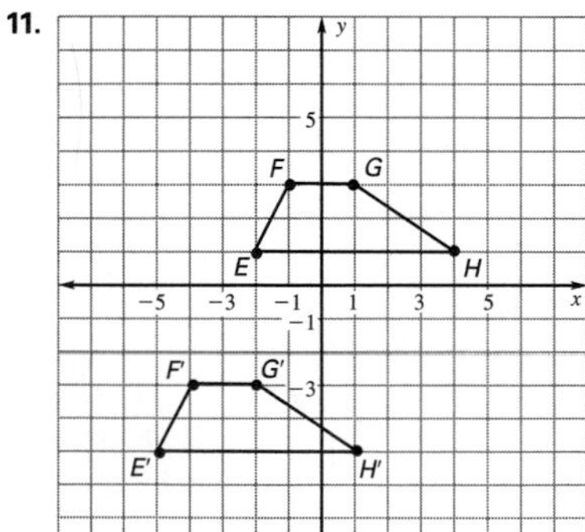

13.

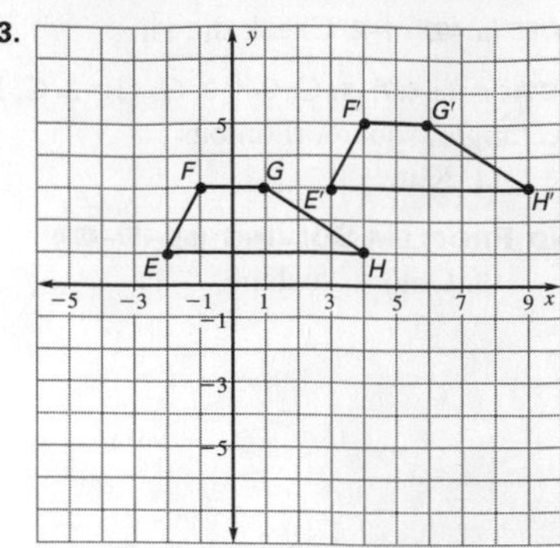

15. Trapezoid $EFGH$ is translated 3 units to the left and 6 units down; Trapezoid $EFGH$ is translated 4 units to the right and 3 units down; Trapezoid $EFGH$ is translated 5 units to the right and 2 units up; Trapezoid $EFGH$ is translated 4 units up. **17.** Caleb's Bay **19.** One set of vertices for a square is (−5, 4), (−2, 4), (−2, 1), and (−5, 1). If the square is transformed to its image in the fourth quadrant the new coordinates would be (5, −4), (2, −4), (5, −1) and (2, −1). If the square is translated according to $(x, y) \rightarrow (x, + 7, y - 5)$, the image vertices are (2, −1), (5, −1), (5, −4) and (2, −4). To translate back to the original square, use $(x, y) \rightarrow (x, - 7, y + 5)$. The coordinate notations use inverse operations such as add 7 and subtract 7.

8.9 GUIDED PRACTICE (p. 435) **1.** The AA Similarity Postulate. **3.** $\frac{GH}{MK} = \frac{HJ}{KL} = \frac{JG}{LM}$ **5.** 6.5; 12

8.9 PRACTICE AND PROBLEM SOLVING (pp. 435–437)
7. The corresponding angles are congruent. **9.** $QT = 15$, $ST = 14$, $XY = 3.6$ **11.** $x = 8$ **13.** $x = 2.4$
15. sometimes **17.** always **19.** 1 in. high and 2 in. wide
21. The ratio is $\frac{1}{6}$; the same as the scale factor.
23. about 3.7 **25.** The painting's perimeter is about 3.7 times the perimeter of the reproduction and the area is about 13.4 times the area of the reproduction. **27.** 400 ft
31. The perimeter is 24. **33.** 0.1 **35.** −7.4 **37.** −9.5

CHAPTER SUMMARY AND REVIEW (pp. 438–441) **1.** $\overrightarrow{FD}$ and $\overrightarrow{FC}$ **3.** $\angle AEC$, $\angle BED$ **5.** $m\angle 7 = 120°$, $\angle 5$, $\angle 1$ and $\angle 3$ are all congruent with $\angle 7$. $\angle 5$ is vertical with $\angle 7$, $\angle 1$ is corresponding with $\angle 5$ and $\angle 3$ is corresponding with $\angle 7$. **7.** Right, scalene **9.** Kite
11. Parallelogram **13.** 4500 ft^2 **15.** 1550 m^2

17. Line of reflection is x-axis.

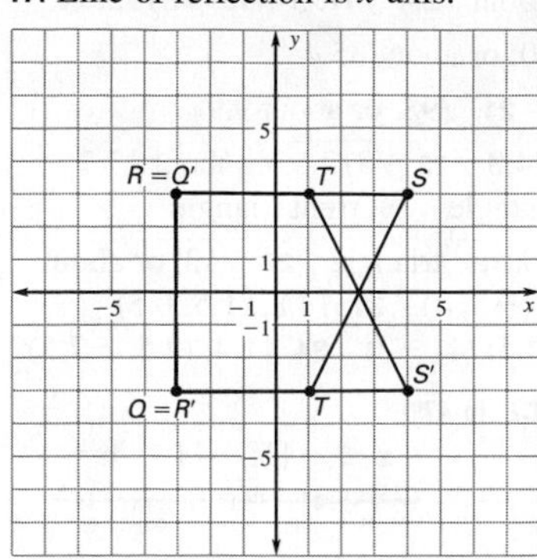

19. One unit to the left and three units down **21.** $\frac{3}{1}$ **23.** 7

REVIEWING THE BASICS (p. 445) **1.** $10x - 2$; -32 **3.** $-2x + 2y$; -20 **5.** $-2m + m^2$, 80 **7.** -10 **9.** -7 **11.** -5

Chapter 9

GETTING READY (p. 448) **1.** C **2.** J **3.** C

9.1 GUIDED PRACTICE (p. 451) **1.** 5, -5 **3.** 10, -10 **5.** 2.2, -2.2 **7.** 4.4, -4.4 **9.** 4; 3.9 **11.** 17; 17.3 **13.** about 8.4 m

9.1 PRACTICE AND PROBLEM SOLVING (pp. 451–452) **15.** 13, -13 **17.** 20, -20 **19.** 0.2, -0.2 **21.** 1.1, -1.1 **23.** 8.5 **25.** 14.1 **27.** 0.9 **29.** 89.7 **31.** 7.5 units **33.** 3; 2.8 **35.** 6; 6.5 **37.** 6.3 in. **39.** 8.4 ft **41.** 4, -4 **43.** 25, -25 **45.** 6, -6 **47.** 5, -5 **49.** $\frac{1}{2}$, $-\frac{1}{2}$ **51.** $\frac{2}{3}$, $-\frac{2}{3}$ **53.** 6,370,152.139 **55.** increase by 0.01 m **57.** 6.7 mi

9.2 GUIDED PRACTICE (p. 455) **1.** *Sample answer:* The decimal form of a rational number either terminates or is a repeating decimal. Examples are 2.4 and $5.\overline{7}$. The decimal form of an irrational number neither terminates nor does it repeat. An example is $\pi \approx 3.14159$. **3.** irrational; decimal form neither terminates nor repeats **5.** irrational; decimal form neither terminates nor repeats **7.** rational; terminating decimal **9.** rational; terminating decimal **11.** 3, $-\sqrt{8}$

9.2 PRACTICE AND PROBLEM SOLVING (pp. 455–457) **17.** integer, rational, real **19.** irrational, real **21.** rational, real **23.** rational, real **25.** irrational; decimal form neither terminates nor repeats **27.** irrational; decimal form neither terminates nor repeats **29.** rational; 25 is a perfect square. **31.** Always; all irrational numbers are real numbers. **33.** Sometimes; the square root of a perfect-square number is rational. **35.** $<$ **37.** $=$ **39.** $<$ **41.** $>$ **43.** $=$

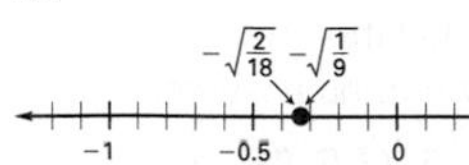

45. $-4, -3.75, \frac{5}{2}, \sqrt{8}$ **47.** $-2, 1.02, \sqrt{1.25}, \sqrt{2.5}$ **49.** $\frac{10}{9}, 1.8, \sqrt{7.2}, \sqrt{10}$ **51.** 1, 4, 9, 16, 25, 36, 49, 64, 81, 100; 10% **53.** *Sample answer:* 0.04004000400004 . . . **61.** \$100; $2.50 \cdot 200 - 400 = 100$ **63.** 3 **65.** $2y$ **67.** about 1,194,000 Americans

9.3 GUIDED PRACTICE (p. 462) **1.** 17 **3.** 9 **5.** 7.5 **7.** about 4.2 ft

9.3 PRACTICE AND PROBLEM SOLVING (pp. 462–464) **9.** 25 **11.** 35.4 **13.** 18.0 **15.** 12 **17.** 28 **19.** 25 **21.** 4, 20 **23.** about 9.2 **25.** always (assuming that you know whether the missing side is the hypotenuse) **27.** about 8.9 ft **29.** about 5.7 ft **31.** The person used the length of the hypotenuse as the length of one leg; $\sqrt{28}$, or about 5.3. **33.** about 38.7 ft; about 35.7 ft

9.3 CONSTRUCTION (p. 464)

1. $\sqrt{53} \approx 7.3$

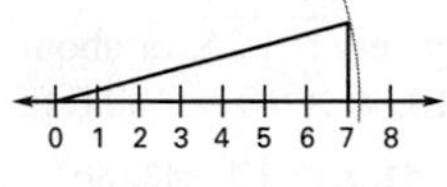

2. $\sqrt{34} \approx 5.8$

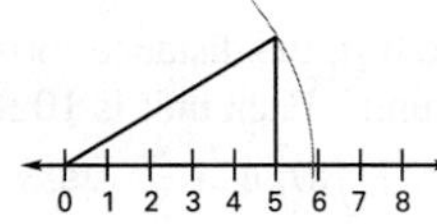

3. $\sqrt{61} \approx 7.8$

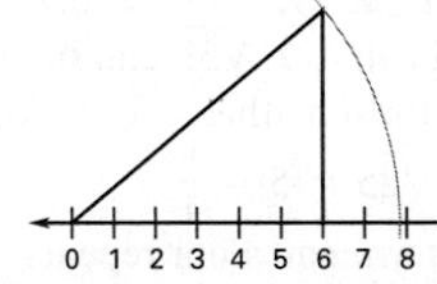

4. $\sqrt{2} \approx 1.4$

SELECTED ANSWERS

5.

9.4 GUIDED PRACTICE (p. 467) **1.** *Sample answer:* With the Pythagorean theorem, you know that a triangle is a right triangle, and can use this fact to find the length of a side. With the converse of the Pythagorean theorem, you know the lengths of all of the sides, and can use this to find out if the triangle is a right triangle. **3.** no **5.** acute triangle

9.4 PRACTICE AND PROBLEM SOLVING (pp. 467–468) **7.** yes **9.** no **11.** 25; 25; right triangle **13.** 18; 16; acute triangle **15.** 6; 4; acute triangle **19.a.** Pythagorean theorem **b.** transitive property or substitution **c.** Taking the square root of each side of an equation retains the equality, because c and d are known to be positive.

9.5 GUIDED PRACTICE (p. 472) **1.** 5; (3.5, 2) **3.** 4.5; (0, 4) **5.** $A(-2, 3)$; $B(4, 3)$; $C(4, -1)$; $D(-2, -1)$ **7.** (1, 1); (1, 1)

9.5 PRACTICE AND PROBLEM SOLVING (pp. 472–474) **9.** (5, 6) and (3, 1) **11.** 8.9; (10, 7) **13.** 7.2; (−7, 14) **15.** 25.0; (14.5, 7.5) **17.** 7.8 **19.** 5.8 **21.** (3, 1) and (4, −5)

23. $\sqrt{(14-2)^2+(3-8)^2} = 13$, $\sqrt{(2-2)^2+(8-3)^2} = 5$, $\sqrt{(14-2)^2+(3-3)^2} = 12$; $5^2 + 12^2 = 13^2$

27.

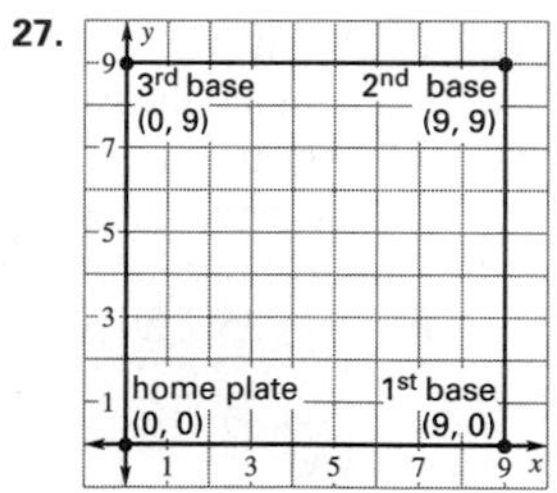

29. 100.6 ft; the distance formula gave $\sqrt{101.25}$, or about 10.06 units. Each unit is 10 ft, so $10.06 \times 10 = 100.6$ ft. **35.** $p < 7$ **37.** $n > \frac{8}{5}$ **39.** $s < 7$ **41.** $r > 10$ **43.** $8n^9$ **45.** $\frac{4}{s^{10}}$

MID-CHAPTER TEST (p. 475) **1.** 4, −4 **2.** 11, −11 **3.** 0.7, −0.7 **4.** 0.6, −0.6 **5.** 10 in. **6.** 11 in. **7.** $\sqrt{33}$ cm, or about 5.7 cm **8.** irrational; decimal form neither terminates nor repeats **9.** rational; $\sqrt{25} = 5 = \frac{5}{1}$ **10.** irrational; decimal form neither terminates nor repeats **11.** rational; $\sqrt{0.25} = 0.5 = \frac{1}{2}$ **12.** < **13.** < **14.** < **15.** < **16.** $\sqrt{153}$, or about 12.4 **17.** 5 **18.** $\sqrt{8192}$, or about 90.5 **19.** $\sqrt{1250}$, or about 35.4 **20.** $\sqrt{18}$, or about 4.2 **21.** $\sqrt{98}$, or about 9.9 **22.** $\sqrt{220.5}$, or about 14.8 **23.** $\sqrt{312.5}$, or about 17.7 **24.** 1, 4 **25.** obtuse triangle **26.** right triangle **27.** right triangle **28.** acute triangle **29.** $\sqrt{13}$, or about 3.6; (2.5, 2) **30.** 2.8; (−3, 4) **31.** 14.8; (1.5, 0.5) **32.** 2; (−5, −1) **33.** 4.5; (1, −2) **34.** 11.4; (2.5, −7.5)

9.6 GUIDED PRACTICE (p. 478)

5. $x < 15$; $15 > x$

7. $x \le -11$; $-11 \ge x$

9. $x \ge 3$

11. $x + 3 > 40$; $x > 37$; the apples weigh more than 37 pounds.

9.6 PRACTICE AND PROBLEM SOLVING (pp. 478–479)

13. $x \le -1$ **15.** $x \ge 2$

17. $x \le -2$; $-2 \ge x$ **19.** $x < 10$; $10 > x$

21. **23.**

25. **27.**

29. $w < 9$ **31.** $y \le 3$

33. $6 \ge t$ **35.** $x \ge -2$

37. $-4 > a$ **39.** $d \ge -8$

41. $17 \ge k$ **43.** $2 < q$

45. $19 + x > 50$; the larger fish weighed more than 31 pounds. **47.** B; the number of students must be an integer.

9.7 GUIDED PRACTICE (p. 482) **1.** yes **3.** no **5.** > **7.** ≤ **9.** $b > 6$ **11.** $-72 \le f$ **13.** Your total purchase is at least $40 before sales tax is included.

9.7 PRACTICE AND PROBLEM SOLVING (pp. 482–483) **15.** The inequality sign should not have been reversed; $z \le -36$. **17.** > **19.** ≥ **25.** $8x > 216$; The width is more than 27 inches.

27. $n \ge \frac{5}{2}$

29. $y > 32$

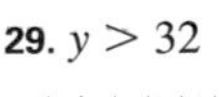

SELECTED ANSWERS

SA20

31. $a < -\frac{1}{4}$ **33.** $p \le -10$

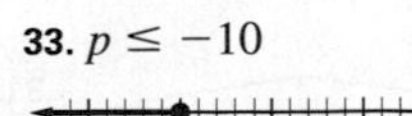

35. $y \ge -12$ **37.** $a \ge 2$

39. $15t > 12$; ride more than 0.8 hour (48 minutes). **41.** less than or equal to 20 feet **43.** 9; this is the greatest integer that is less than 10.

9.8 Guided Practice (p. 486)

1. $x < 5$ **3.** $y > -\frac{1}{2}$

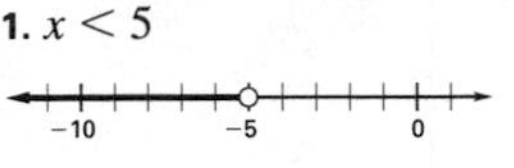

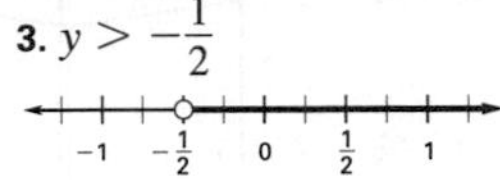

5. $y > 10$

7. Reverse the sign when multiplying or dividing both sides of the inequality by a negative number. Examples will vary.

9.8 Practice and Problem Solving (pp. 486–488)

9. When dividing both sides of an inequality by a negative number the direction of the inequality must be reversed; $x \le 3$.

15. $x > 3$ **17.** $a \ge -3$

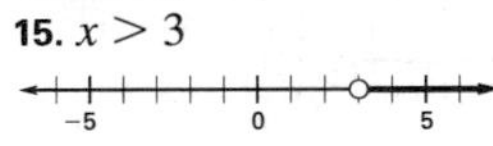

19. $c \ge 9$ **21.** $y \le -20$

23. $x < -3$ **25.** $p \le -7$

27. $k > -\frac{13}{5}$ **29.** $x \le \frac{3}{2}$

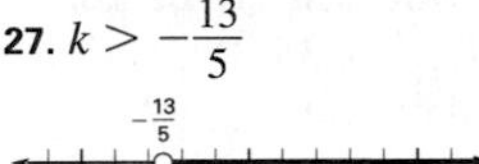

31. $-2, -1, 0, 1, 2$ **33.** 2 **35.** -2 **37.** $n + n + 1 \ge 7$; $n \ge 3$ **39.** $n + n + 1 < 20$; $n < \frac{19}{2}$ **41.** 1995 **43.** $x \ge 3$ (and $x < 5.5$ since side lengths are positive) **45.** $10 + 0.25t \le 20$; you can buy at most 40 tickets. **51.** $5 \cdot 29$ **53.** $5 \cdot 41$ **55.** $3^2 \cdot 41$ **57.** $2^3 \cdot 5 \cdot 11$ **59.** $-0.1\overline{3}$ **61.** $-2.\overline{8}$ **63.** \$41.57 **65.** irrational **67.** rational **69.** rational **71.** 8.9 **73.** 12 **75.** 6.9

9.9 Guided Practice (p. 491)

1. 6 **3.** 34 **5.** 44 **7.** 25%

9.

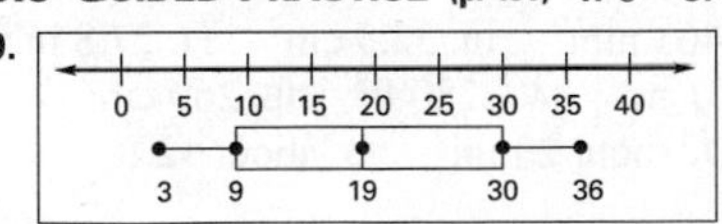

9.9 Practice and Problem Solving (pp. 491–493)

11. 96 **13.** 40 **15.** 82 **17.** 50%

19.

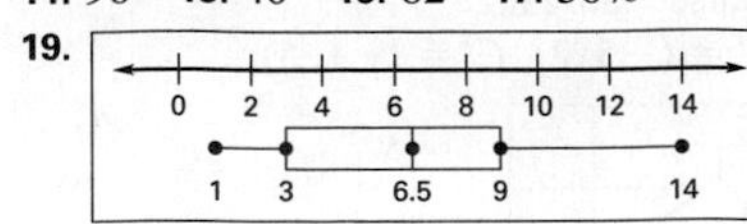

The range is 13. The interquartile range is 6. **21.** B; most of the viewers are children and therefore more likely to watch cartoons. **23.** *Sample answer:* The median of City B is colder than the median of City A. 25% of the temperatures are between 5 and 40 degrees in City B, whereas in City A practically all of the temperatures are above that. Although they both have interquartile ranges of 20 degrees, City B has 50% between 40 and 60 degrees, while City A has 50% between 55 and 75 degrees. Since City B is colder, it is more likely to be farther north. **25.** *Sample answer:* The maximum age for the Democrats is almost the upper quartile age for the Republicans. The median age for the Democrats is nearly the lower quartile for the Republicans. The range of the Republicans is more than the range of the Democrats. In general, Republican presidents are older. Half of the Democrats are between 46 and 56, while half of the Republicans are between 51 and 62.

Chapter Summary and Review (pp. 494–497)

1. $7, -7$ **3.** $11, -11$ **5.** $6.4, -6.4$ **7.** $9.6, -9.6$ **9.** 6.7 ft

11. $>$ **13.** $<$

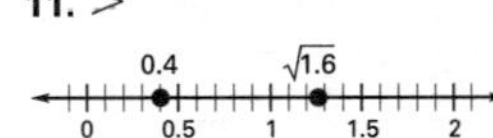

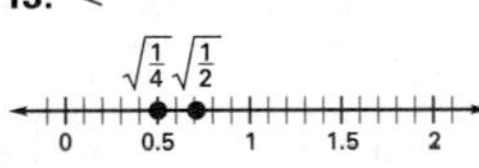

15. 9.2 **17.** 7.2 **19.** acute **21.** obtuse **23.** 9.5; $(-0.5, 4.5)$

25. $x > 9$ **27.** $b \le -5$

29. $x \le -4$ **31.** $x > -6$

33. $0.08x < 8.05$; you can talk up to about 100.6 minutes.

35. $z > 11$ **37.** $x > \frac{7}{4}$

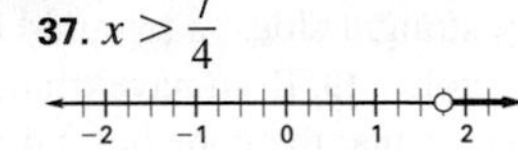

39.

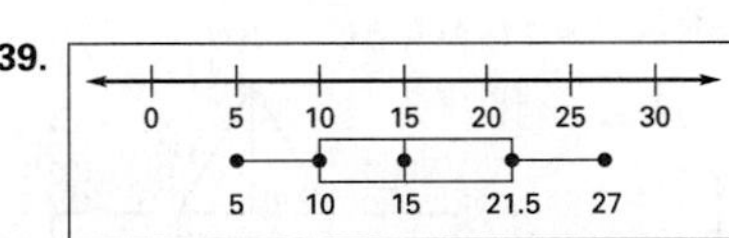

Reviewing the Basics (p. 501)

1. 48 in.^{2} **3.** 121 cm^2 **5.** 6 **7.** 7 **9.** 30 **11.** 4

Cumulative Practice (pp. 502–503)

1. 9 **3.** 3 **5.** 12 days **7.** 2 **9.** $\frac{1}{4}$ **11.** 83 (prime) **13.** $2^4 \cdot 3^2$

23. \$2800 **25.** 34 **27.** 70 **29.** about -35%
31. \$4488.28 **33.** false **35.** false
37. $A' = (-2, 1)$, $B' = (-5, 2)$, $C' = (-1, 5)$

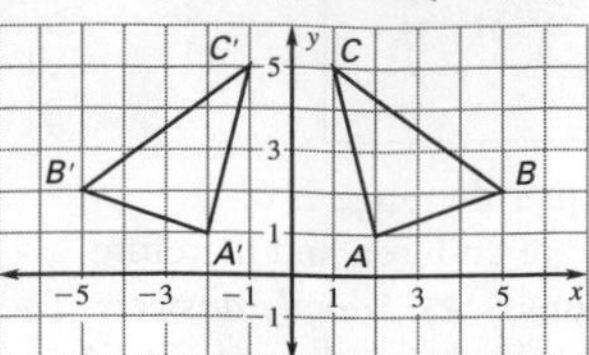

39. 11 **41.** $\sqrt{69}$, or about 8.3 **43.** $\sqrt{52}$, or about 7.2; (1, 2)
45. $a < -5$ **47.** $m \le \frac{3}{2}$

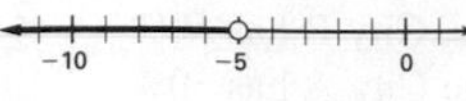

$\frac{3}{2}$
-5 0 5

Chapter 10

GETTING READY (p. 508) **1.** D **2.** G **3.** C

10.1 GUIDED PRACTICE (p. 513) **1.** $\overline{AB}$ or $\overline{AC}$
3. 14π cm **5.** The wheel with radius 14 inches has circumference 28π inches, which is greater than the circumference of the wheel with radius 13 inches which is 26π inches.

10.1 PRACTICE AND PROBLEM SOLVING (pp. 514–515)
7. $C \approx 18.8$ cm; $A \approx 28.3$ cm^2 **9.** 9.4 ft^2 **11.** 4.6 m^2
13. $r \approx 6$ cm; $d \approx 12$ cm **15.** 38 m^2 **17.** 90 cm^2
19.

radius	1	2	3	4	5	6
area	π	4π	9π	16π	25π	36π

21. $A = \frac{\pi d^2}{4}$ **23.** about 18.8 in.^{2} **25.** about 10 mi
27. about 314 mi^2

10.2 GUIDED PRACTICE (p. 519) **1.** True; parallel lines lie in the same plane. **7.** 5

10.2 PRACTICE AND PROBLEM SOLVING (pp. 520–521)
9. $\overleftrightarrow{NR}$ and $\overleftrightarrow{RM}$, or $\overleftrightarrow{NR}$ and $\overleftrightarrow{KL}$ **11.** no **13.** $\overline{NR}$, $\overline{KL}$, $\overline{JM}$, or $\overline{PQ}$ **15.** no **17.** *Sample answer:* Both nets have only straight sides; a pyramid has triangles while a prism may not. **19.** Both have triangular or triangle-like components; the cone has a circular base while the base of a pyramid is a polygon. **21.** $\overline{AG}$, $\overline{EC}$ or $\overline{BH}$

23.

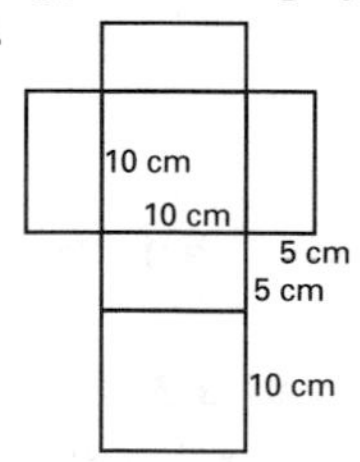

25.

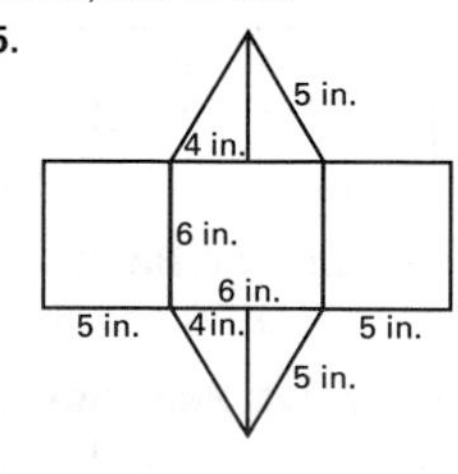

27. Cone
29.

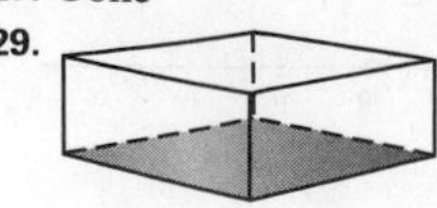

31.

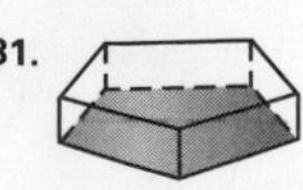

33. No; if you try to fold it into a cube, two of the faces will overlap.

10.3 GUIDED PRACTICE (p. 525) **1.** 45 ft^2 **3.** 342 ft^2
5.a. 12π yd **b.** 36π yd^2

10.3 PRACTICE AND PROBLEM SOLVING (pp. 526–527)
7. 664 ft^2 **9.** 144 cm^2 **11.** 40 in.^{2} **13.** 24 in.^{2}
15. 176 in.^{2}

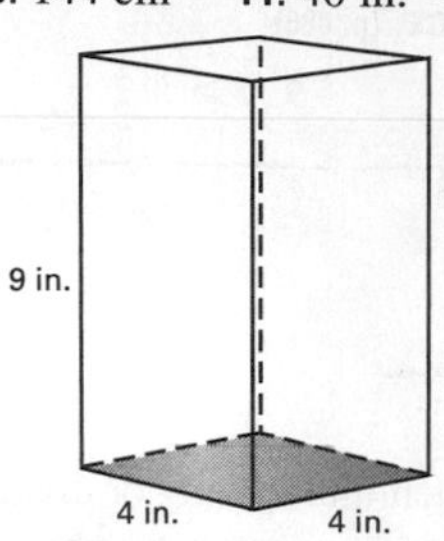

17. Surface area of shorter container is 24π in.^{2}; Surface area of taller container is 26.32π in.^{2} The shorter container has the smaller surface area. **21.** 8230 ft^2
25. 24 **27.** $\frac{10}{3}$ **29.** \$10 **31.** Twelve
33. $y \le 12$

-2 0 2 4 6 8 10 12 14

35. $t < \frac{7}{10}$

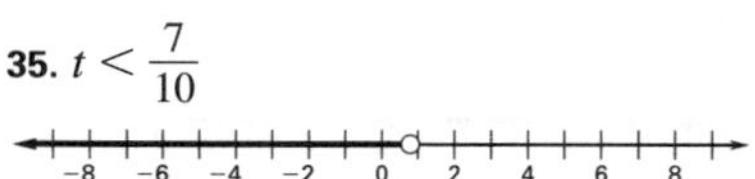

10.4 GUIDED PRACTICE (p. 532) **1.** 2 cm **3.** 12 cm^3
5. 120 in.^{3} **7.** 343 cm^3

10.4 PRACTICE AND PROBLEM SOLVING (pp. 532–533)
9. 84 yd^3 **11.** 49.5 ft^3 **13.** 756 ft^3 **15.** 3 in.
17. 150 ft^3 **19.** 360 m^3 **21.** 1440 ft^3
23.

Edge	1 cm	2 cm	3 cm	4 cm
Surface Area	6 cm^2	24 cm^2	54 cm^2	96 cm^2
Volume	1 cm^3	8 cm^3	27 cm^3	64 cm^3

25. Small mammal would lose heat faster since $\frac{\text{surface area}}{\text{volume}}$ is greatest for cube of smallest edge size.

MID-CHAPTER TEST (p. 534) **1.** 84.8 m^2 **2.** 13.8 ft^2
3. 55.0 cm^2 **4.** 30.5 yd^2 **5.** 5 **6.** 6 **7.** 9
8. 1056 mm^2 **9.** 2463 mm^2 **10.** 32.5 cm^2 **11.** 27.8 in.^{2}
12. 120 in.^{3} **13.** 351 m^3 **14.** 2280 ft^3 **15.** 260 cm^3
16. about 17 mi **17.** about 23 mi^2 **18.** about 12 ft

10.5 GUIDED PRACTICE (p. 537) **1.** ≈ 113.1 cm^2 **3.** ≈ 1131 cm^3 **5.** ≈ 45.6 cm^2

10.5 PRACTICE AND PROBLEM SOLVING (pp. 537–538) **7.** ≈ 7539.8 in.^{3} **9.** ≈ 6107.3 in.^{3} **11.** ≈ 1692.3 ft^3 **13.** Cylinder A has less volume because its radius and height are less than those of Cylinder B. **15.** 3 in. **17.** 8 cm **19.** about 142,300,000 ft^3 **21.** The puck would cost more, because its volume is greater.
23.

Drink	Volume	Price	Price per fl oz
Big Drink	67.6 fl oz	$2.05	$.030
Regular Drink	32 fl oz	$.90	$.028
Little Sipper	16 fl oz	$.63	$.039

The regular drink is the best buy.

10.6 GUIDED PRACTICE (p. 541) **1.** Base areas of both the cylinder and the cone are 16π. **3.** 3200 in.^{3} **5.** 200 m^3 **7.** ≈ 670 ft^3 **9.** ≈ 2681 ft^3

10.6 PRACTICE AND PROBLEM SOLVING (pp. 541–542) **11.** 8400 ft^3 **13.** 10 in.^{3} **15.** ≈ 1810 ft^3 **17.** The pyramid whose base area is double would have a height of one-half of the other pyramid. **19.** ≈ 8294 cm^3 **21.** 566,280 ft^2 **23.** ≈ 80.9 ft^3 **25.** Doubling the radius has greater effect on the volume since the radius is squared in the volume formula.

10.7 GUIDED PRACTICE (p. 545) **1.** 2 ft **3.** ≈ 33.5 ft^3

10.7 PRACTICE AND PROBLEM SOLVING (pp. 545–547) **5.** ≈ 7238 cm^3 **7.** ≈ 5575 cm^3 **9.** $\approx 24{,}429$ cm^3
11.

Radius	1	2	3
Volume	$\frac{4\pi}{3}$	$\frac{32\pi}{3}$	$\frac{108\pi}{3}$

13. The volume is twenty-seven times larger when the radius is tripled. **15.** about 204,000 ft^3 **17.** ≈ 1072 ft^3; the volume of a hemisphere is one-half the volume of a sphere. **19.** No; the volume is 8 times the original volume, because volume is proportional to r^3. **21.** 610 ft^3 **23.** 9.2 in.^{3} **25.** 5.0 in.^{3} **27.** $\frac{2}{3}\pi r^3$ **33.** 5 : 2 **35.** Ray **37.** $\angle ADE$, $\angle EDA$, $\angle FDA$ **39.** 130° **41.** -13, 13 **43.** -11, 11

10.8 GUIDED PRACTICE (p. 550) **1.** no; $\frac{18}{9} \neq \frac{9}{4}$ **3.** 1.5 **5.** 1440

10.8 PRACTICE AND PROBLEM SOLVING (pp. 550–551) **9.** 125 : 8 **11.** always **13.** sometimes **15.** 3; 2 **17.** 8 in.^{3}; 64 in.^{3}; 216 in.^{3} **19.** 90,000 : 1

CHAPTER SUMMARY AND REVIEW (pp. 552–555) **1.** $C \approx 43.96$ in.; $A = 153.86$ in.^{2} **3.** prism; 5 faces, 6 vertices, 9 edges **5.** prism; 6 faces, 8 vertices, 12 edges **7.** ≈ 904.8 mm^2 **9.** 168 m^3 **11.** 648 cm^3 **13.** ≈ 197.9 m^3 **15.** ≈ 8.7 m **17.** ≈ 261.8 cm^3 **19.** ≈ 2145 cm^3 **21.** ≈ 448.9 m^3 **23.** ≈ 8143 cm^2; ≈ 226 cm^2 **25.** 621 in.^{3}

REVIEWING THE BASICS (p. 559) **1.** $3y$
3.
(−4, 4)
(−2, 3)
(0, 2)
(4, 0)

5.
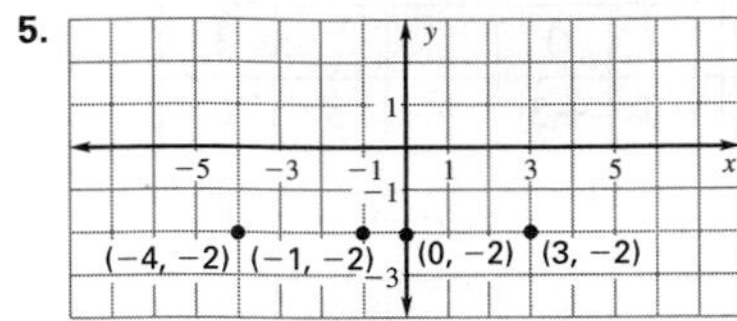

Chapter 11

GETTING READY (p. 562) **1.** B **2.** H **3.** B **4.** F

11.1 GUIDED PRACTICE (p. 565) **1.** If I is the amount of money raised by the class, then I is equal to amount of money earned per subscription times number of subscriptions sold.
3.

Input, m	50	100	150	200
Output, I (in dollars)	150	300	450	600

5. 27; the function value tells you that in 30 seconds sound travels 27 miles.

11.1 PRACTICE AND PROBLEM SOLVING (pp. 565–566)
7.

Input, x	0	2	4
Output, y	**0**	**4**	**8**

9.

Input, x	0	**14**	28
Output, y	**0**	2	**4**

11. -15 **13.** The input variable is n, the number of school lunches bought. The output variable is m, the money left after buying school lunches. A rule for this function is $m = 15 - 2.5n$.
15.

Input, x (in hours)	1	2	5	10	15
Output, y (in kilowatt-hours)	**1.8**	**3.6**	**9**	**18**	**27**

17.

Input, x	0	1	2	3	4
Output, y	**0**	**3**	**6**	**9**	**12**

19.

Input, x	0	1	2	3	4
Output, y	**6**	$6\frac{1}{3}$	$6\frac{2}{3}$	**7**	$7\frac{1}{3}$

21. $y = \frac{x}{2}$

11.2 GUIDED PRACTICE (p. 569) **1.** no, $2(1) + 3(2) = 8$ **3.** yes, $2(5) + 3(-1) = 7$ **5.** no; The equation is not linear because the variable is to the third power. **7.** yes; The equation is linear because both variables are only to the first power.

9.

x	−3	−2	−1	0	1	2	3
y	**2**	**3**	**4**	**5**	**6**	**7**	**8**

11.

x	−3	−2	−1	0	1	2	3
y	**−12**	**−9**	**−6**	**−3**	**0**	**3**	**6**

13. $y = 3 - x$

x	−3	−2	−1	0	1	2	3
y	**6**	**5**	**4**	**3**	**2**	**1**	**0**

15. $y = -\frac{x}{6}$

x	−3	−2	−1	0	1	2	3
y	$\frac{1}{2}$	$\frac{1}{3}$	$\frac{1}{6}$	**0**	$-\frac{1}{6}$	$-\frac{1}{3}$	$-\frac{1}{2}$

11.2 PRACTICE AND PROBLEM SOLVING (pp. 569–570)

17. no, $7(2) - (1) = 13$ **19.** yes, $7\left(\frac{1}{2}\right) - \left(-\frac{3}{2}\right) = 5$

21.

x	−3	−2	−1	0	1	2	3
y	**−2**	**0**	**2**	**4**	**6**	**8**	**10**

23.

x	−3	−2	−1	0	1	2	3
y	**−36**	**−30**	**−24**	**−18**	**−12**	**−6**	**0**

25. $y = \frac{13 - x}{2}$

x	−2	−1	0	1	2
y	$\frac{15}{2}$	**7**	$\frac{13}{2}$	**6**	$\frac{11}{2}$

27. $y = 10 + 3x$

x	−2	−1	0	1	2
y	**4**	**7**	**10**	**13**	**16**

29. $y = -3x$

x	−2	−1	0	1	2
y	**6**	**3**	**0**	**−3**	**−6**

31. $\frac{x}{2} + 2y = 54$, $y = 27 - \frac{x}{4}$

33. C; $y = 180 - x$

x (in degrees)	10	30	60
y (in degrees)	**170**	**150**	**120**

35. $y = 10 - 3x$ **37.** 10 **39.** 7 lb **41.** When $A = 0$, the equation $Ax + By = C$ can be solved for y, in this case $y = \frac{C}{B} - \frac{A}{B}x$ for all values of x. If $B = 0$, the equation cannot be solved for y because the equation becomes $Ax = C$; in this case it cannot be written in function form.

11.3 GUIDED PRACTICE (p. 573) **1.** *Sample answer:* Find y-values for several x-values and organize the values in a table. Plot the xy-pairs in a coordinate plane. Draw a line through the plotted points. **3.** A

5.

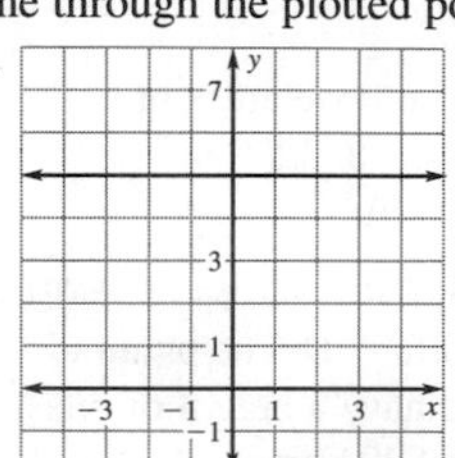

7.

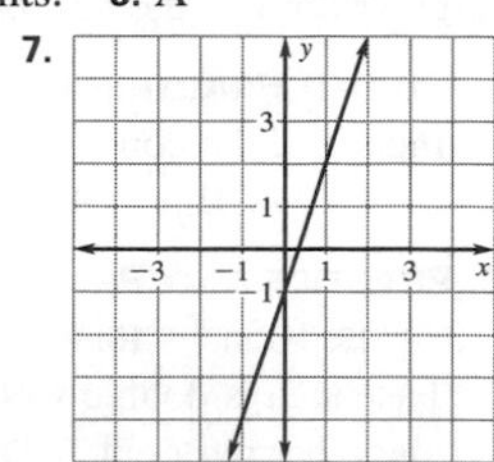

11.3 PRACTICE AND PROBLEM SOLVING (pp. 573–575)

13.

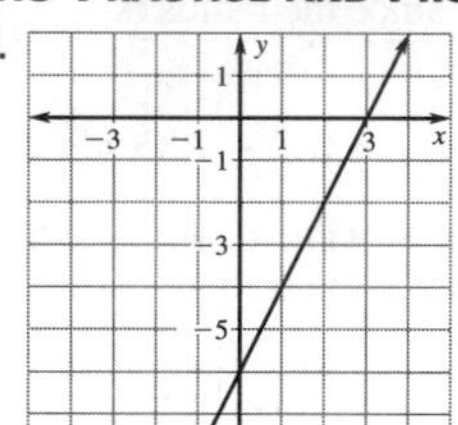

15.

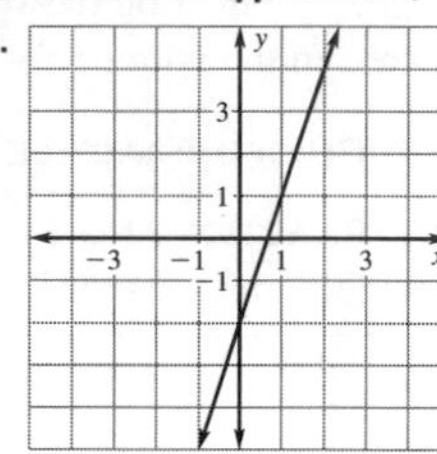

17.

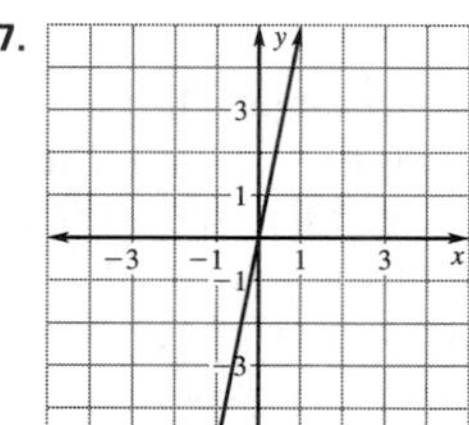

19.

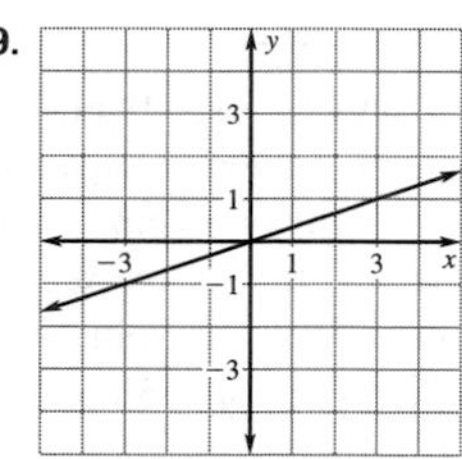

21. The graphs of $x = 0$ and $y = 0$ are the y-axis and x-axis, respectively. **23.** $C = 1.20a$ **25.** Yes, it makes sense to draw a line through the points because you can buy fractions of a gallon of gas.

27.

t	0	1	2	3	4	5
I	50	125	200	275	350	425

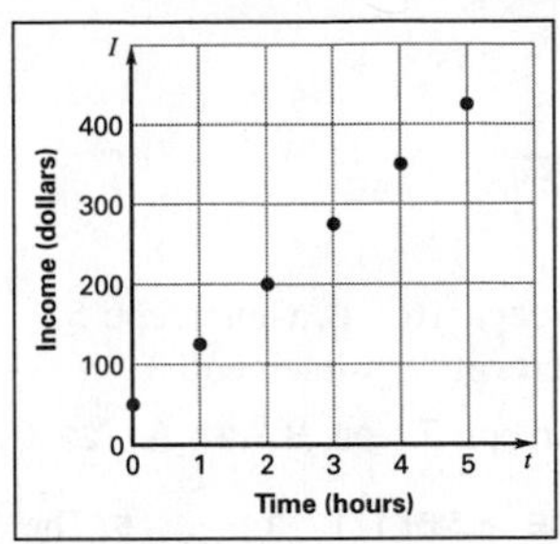

29. C represents the monthly telephone charge and t represents the total number of long distance minutes.
31. no; The real plot would look like stairs.

33. Shipping Charges

Shipping charge (in dollars)

Number of items shipped

35.

Number of rides	5	10	15	20	25	30	35
Cost	$6.25	$12.50	$18.75	$25.00	$31.25	$37.50	$43.75

37. No; you can't buy a fraction of a ride. 41. The number, $\frac{2}{3}$, is rational because its decimal representation repeats. 43. The number, 3.47, is rational because its decimal representation terminates. 45. 5 47. 99.70

11.4 Guided Practice (p. 578) 1. x-intercept: 4, y-intercept: 2 3. x-intercept: -2, y-intercept: -2
5. Let $x = 0$ in the equation $5x + 3y = 9$ and solve remaining equation, $3y = 9$, for y.
7. x-intercept: 5, y-intercept: -5

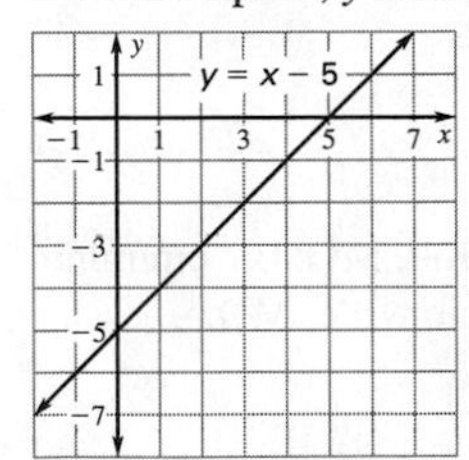

11.4 Practice and Problem Solving (pp. 578–580)
9. x-intercept: -1, y-intercept: 4 11. x-intercept: 2, y-intercept: -8 13. x-intercept: 4, y-intercept: -5
15. x-intercept: 3, y-intercept: -7 17. x-intercept: -1.8, y-intercept: 4.5 21. The line slants upward from left to right. If the x-intercept is positive, then the line crosses the positive x-axis. If the y-intercept is negative, the line crosses the negative y-axis. Such a line is slanted upward from left to right.

23. 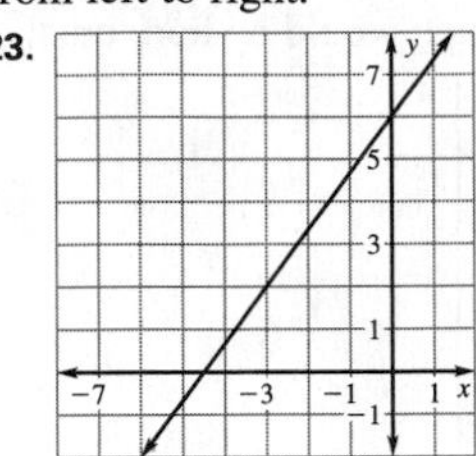

25. 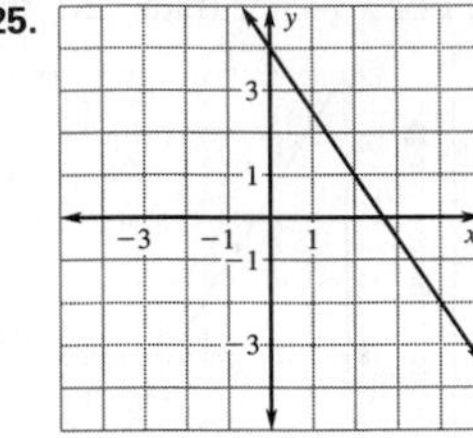

27. 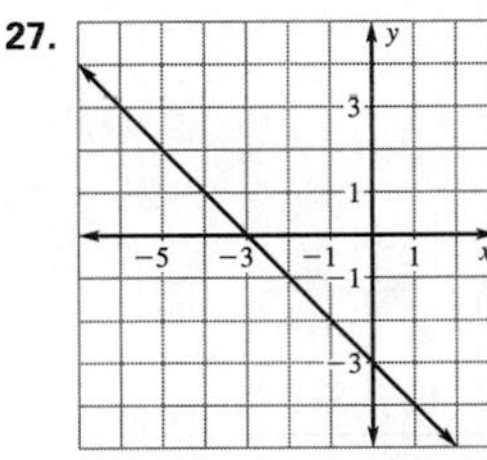

29. 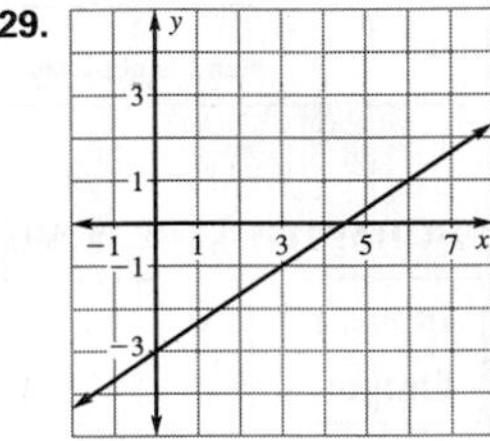

31. 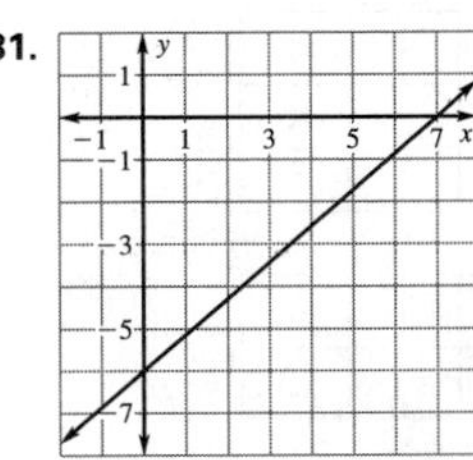

33. x-intercept: 7.73, y-intercept: -14.30
35. 4; The y-intercept is the number of sport utility vehicles, minivans or trucks that can be washed in sixty minutes if no cars are washed. 37. 2
39. x-intercept: 0, y-intercept: 0; The graph goes through the origin, since when $x = 0$, $y = 0$.

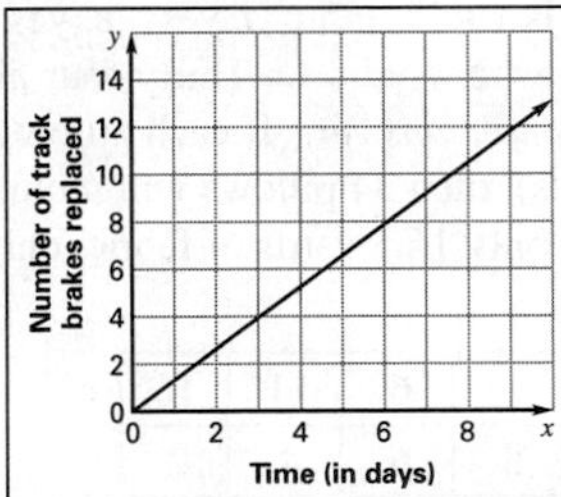

SELECTED ANSWERS

41. 15 **43.**

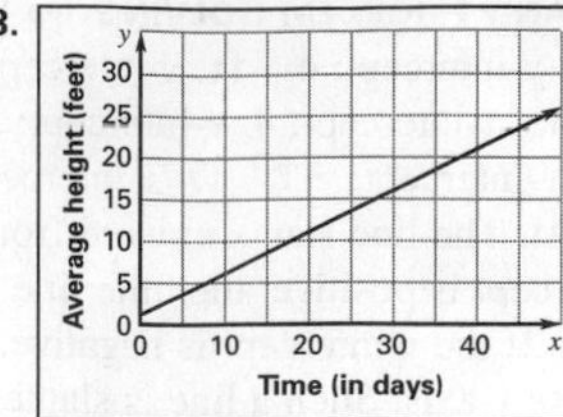

45. For x larger than 120, the graph would be horizontal.

47.

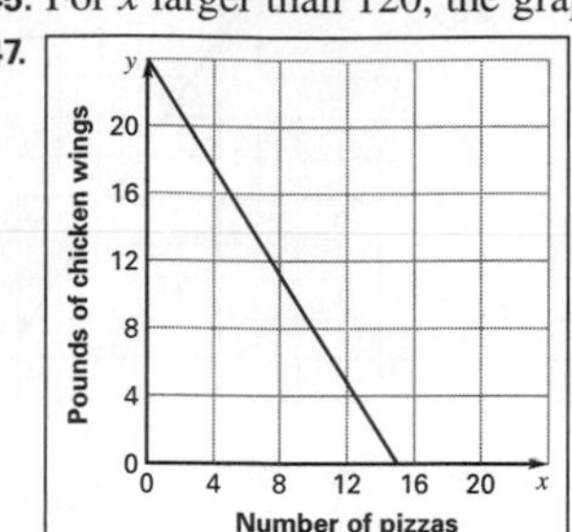

MID-CHAPTER TEST (p. 581)

1.

Input, x	0	1	2	3	4
Output, y	**3**	**2**	**1**	**0**	**−1**

2.

Input, x	0	1	2	3	4
Output, y	**0**	$\frac{2}{3}$	$\frac{4}{3}$	**2**	$\frac{8}{3}$

3.

Input, x	0	1	2	3	4
Output, y	**5**	**7**	**9**	**11**	**13**

4.

Input, x	0	1	2	3	4
Output, y	**−7**	**−3**	**1**	**5**	**9**

5. A rule for this function is $y = 3x$. **6.** A rule for this function is $y = x + 5$. **7.** yes **8.** yes **9.** no **10.** no **11.** 72 in. **12.** 7 yd **13.** Thirty-four pillows cannot be made. *Sample answer:* If each pillow requires 0.5 yards (18 inches), then 34 pillows will require 17 yards. Since there are only 16.5 yards of fabric, only 33 pillows can be made.

14.

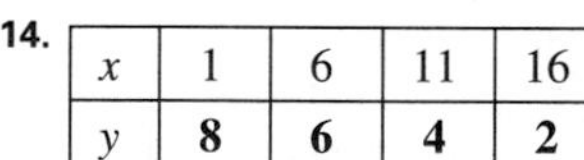

x	1	6	11	16
y	**8**	**6**	**4**	**2**

15.

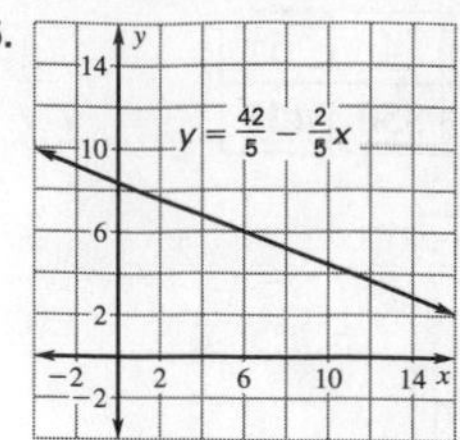

16. x-intercept: 4, y-intercept: 16 **17.** x-intercept: 5, y-intercept: 4 **18.** x-intercept: 2, y-intercept: 3 **19.** x-intercept: $\frac{7}{3}$, y-intercept: 7 **20.** B **21.** A **22.** C

11.5 GUIDED PRACTICE (p. 585) **1.** 1 **3.** $-\frac{1}{2}$ **5.** The rate is the slope of the line. To compute it, select two points on the line. Find the ratio of the difference of the two y-values and the difference of the two x-values.

11.5 PRACTICE AND PROBLEM SOLVING (pp. 586–587)

7. m_4; it has a greater rise for the same run than the other slopes. **9.** $-\frac{3}{5}$

11.

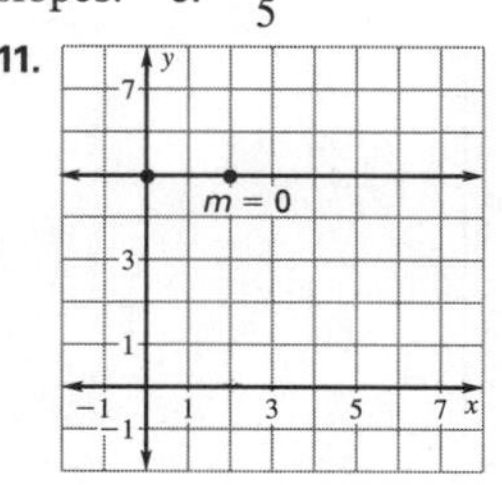

13.

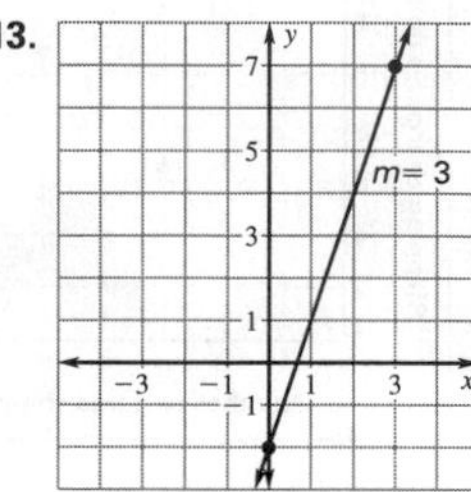

15.

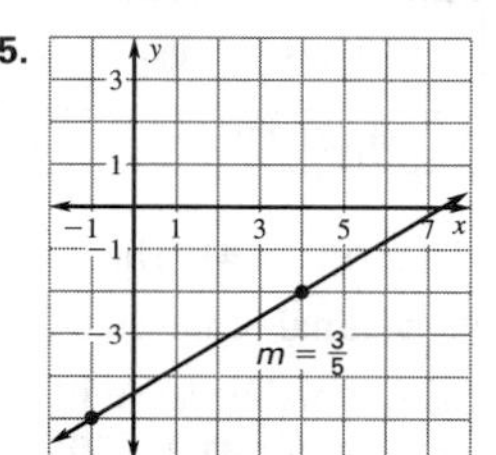

17.

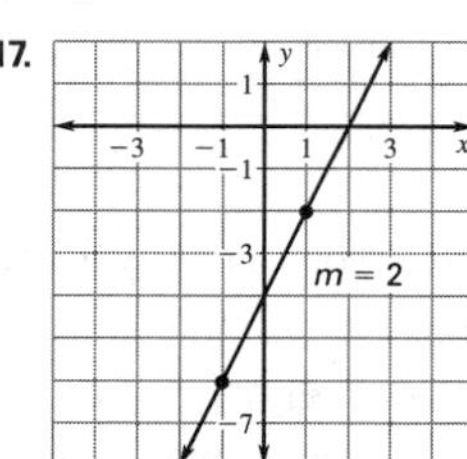

19.

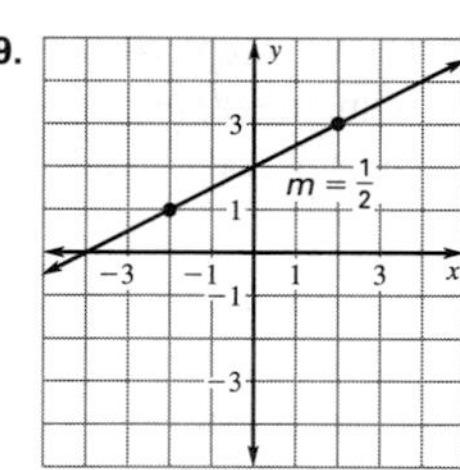

21. Unionville, MD: 3.1 cm/min; Holt, MO: 0.7 cm/min; The rain fell at a greater rate in Unionville, MD.

SELECTED ANSWERS

23.

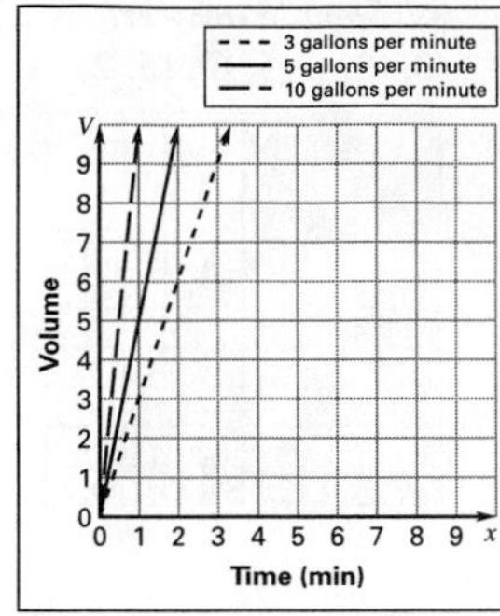

29. $\frac{7}{20}$ 31. $\frac{4}{9}$ 33. 0.375 35. $0.4\overline{5}$ 37. $\frac{7}{9}$ 39. $\frac{1}{20}$
41. $\frac{8}{21}$ 43. $\frac{49}{9}$

11.6 GUIDED PRACTICE (p. 591) **1.** The equation $y = mx + b$ is called the slope-intercept form of the equation because the slope of the line is m, the coefficient of x, and the y-intercept is b, the constant.
3. C **5.** $\frac{1}{4}$, -1

11.6 PRACTICE AND PROBLEM SOLVING (pp. 591–592)
11. $\frac{1}{4}$, 2 **13.** -6, 0 **15.** 0, 17 **17.** undefined, none

19.

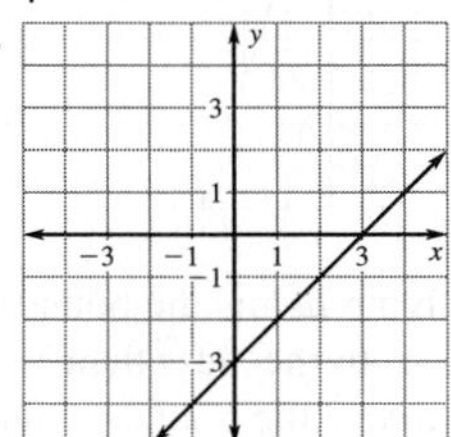

21.

23.

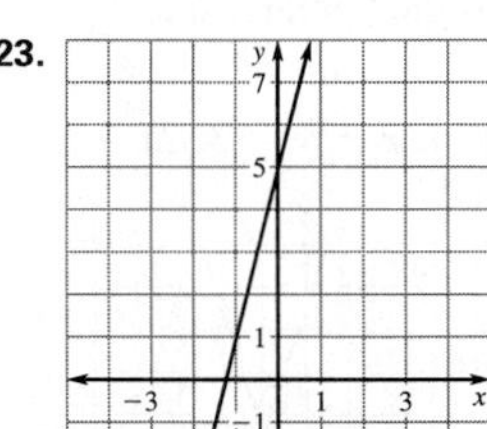

25.

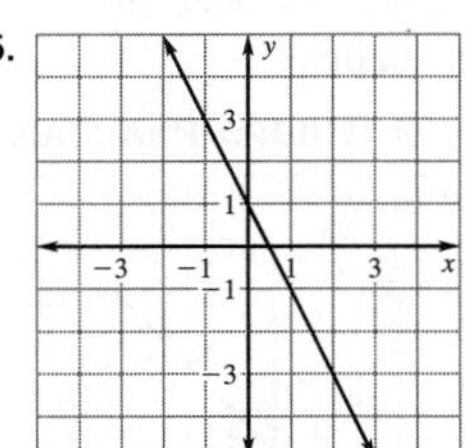

27.

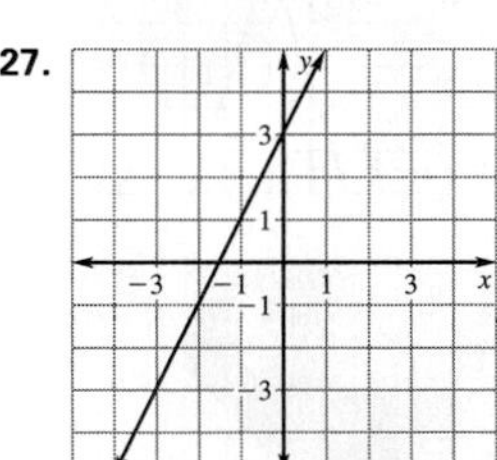

29. True **31.** $y = \left(-\frac{5}{2}\right)x + 2$

33.

time, x, (in seconds)	0	1	2	3	4
speed, y, (in meters per second)	7.0	16.8	26.6	36.4	46.2

The speed increases by 9.8 meters per second each second.

35.

Distance traveled, x, (in miles)	0	1	2	3	4	5	6
Total fare, y, (in dollars)	1.25	3.75	6.25	8.75	11.25	13.75	16.25

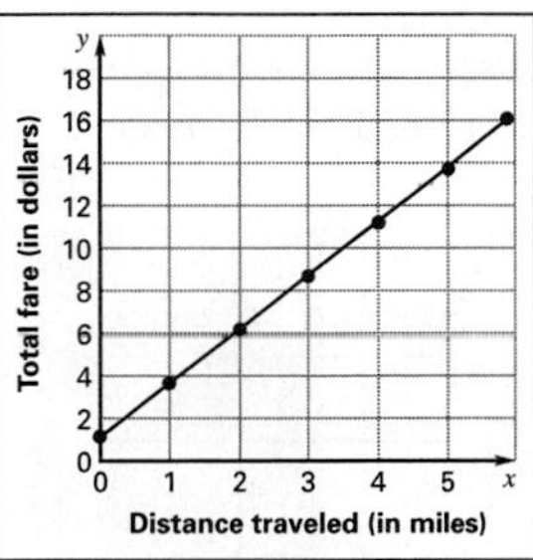

11.7 GUIDED PRACTICE (pp. 595–596) **1.** $m = 1$ ft/day; $b = 5$ feet; $y = 1x + 5 = x + 5$ **3.** direct variation; The graph passes through the origin. **5.** not a direct variation; The graph does not pass through the origin. **7.** 36

11.7 PRACTICE AND PROBLEM SOLVING (pp. 596–597)
9. \$470 **11.** \$439 **13.** The slope is approximately 5 and the y-intercept is 454. **15.** 484 thousand

17. $y = -3x$, -6

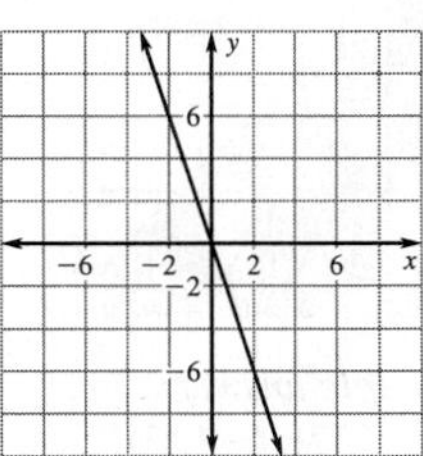

19. $y = \left(\frac{3}{2}\right)x$, 3

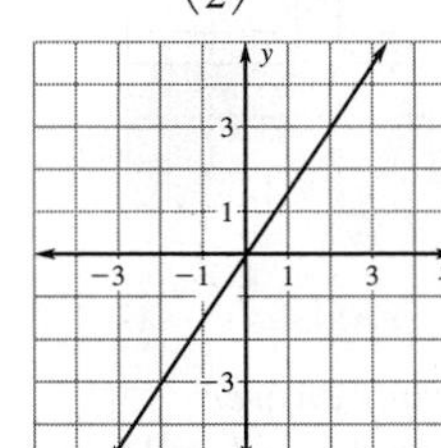

21. $y = -\left(\frac{1}{5}\right)x$, $-\frac{2}{5}$

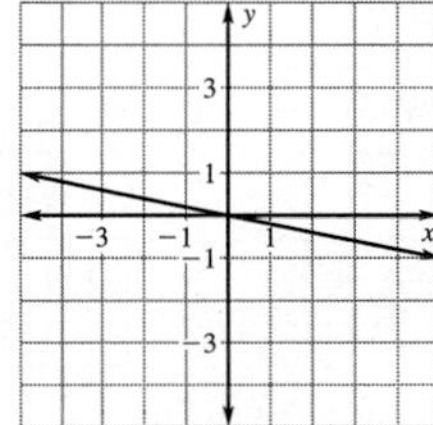

23. $y = 0.622x$, 2426 miles

27. $y = 0.1x$

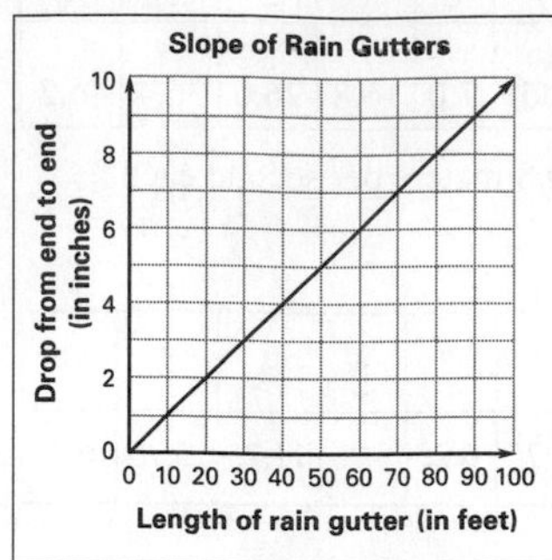

11.8 GUIDED PRACTICE (p. 600) 1. yes 3. *Sample answer:* (0, 0), (−2, −2), (1, 1) 5. dashed 7. solid 9. yes 11. yes

13. 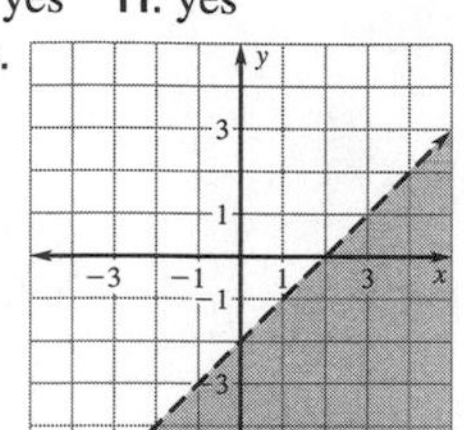

15. 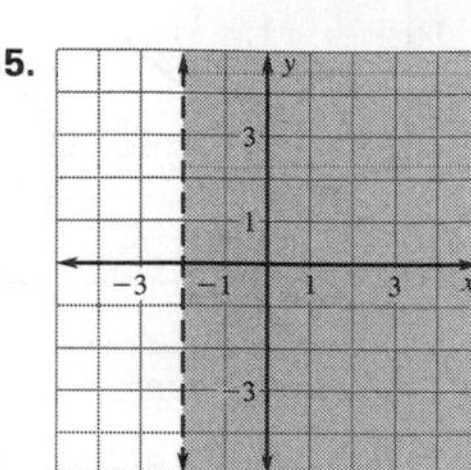

11.8 PRACTICE AND PROBLEM SOLVING (pp. 600–601)
17. yes; 4(10) + 6(−2) = 28, which is less than or equal to 48. 19. yes; 4(6) + 6(4) = 48, which is less than or equal to 48.

23. *Sample answer:* (0, 0), (1, 1), (−1, −1)

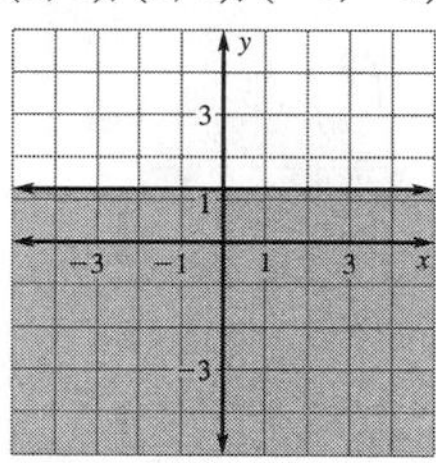

25. *Sample answer:* (0, 0), (1, 1), (−1, −1)

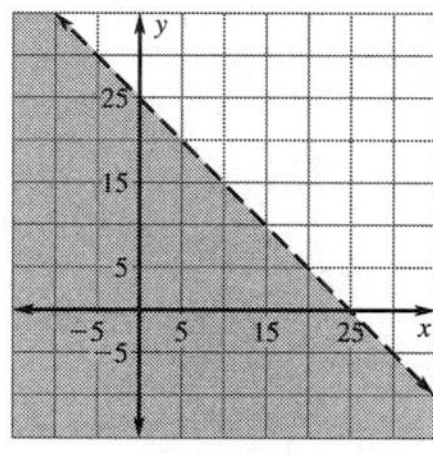

27. *Sample answer:* (0, 0), (1, 1), (−1, −1)

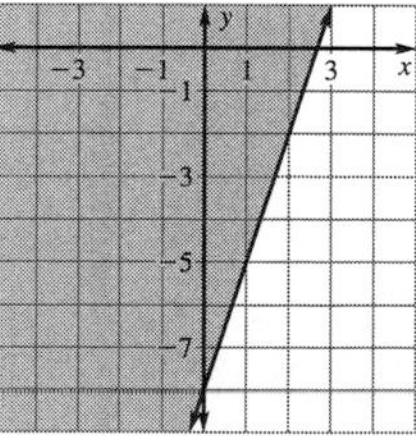

29. *Sample answer:* (0, 4), (1, 2), (−1, 5)

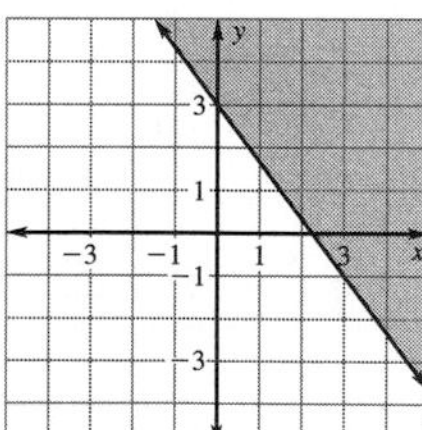

31. *Sample answer:* (0, 5), (1, 3), (−1, 7)

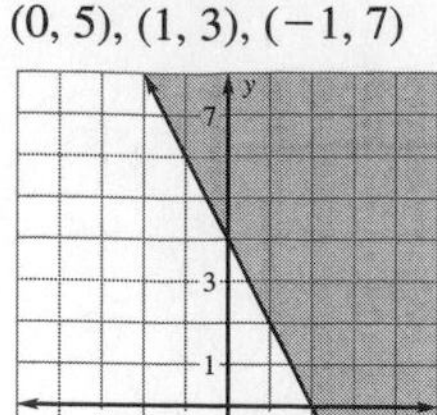

33. *Sample answer:* (0, 0), (−5, 6), (5, 2)

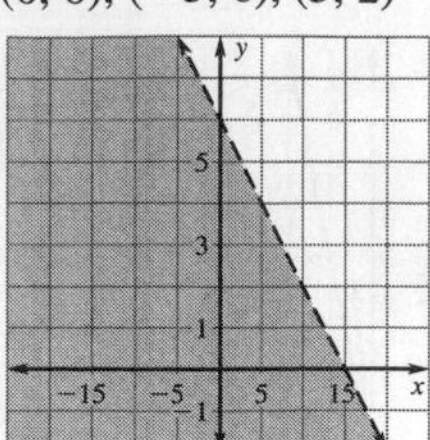

35. 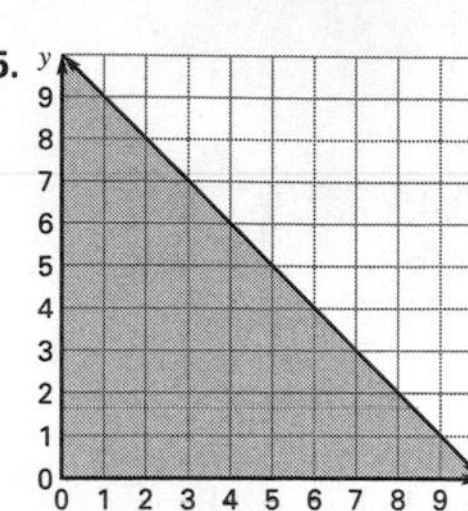

37. *Sample answer:*

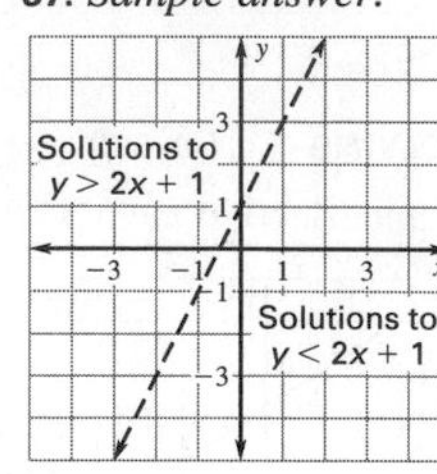

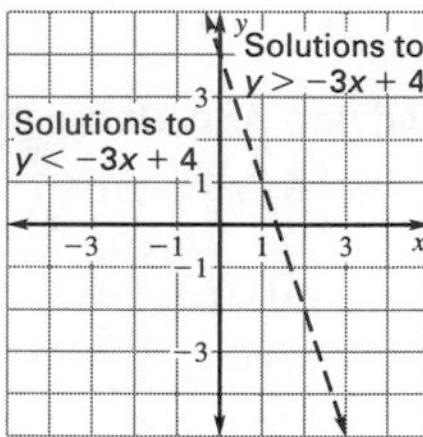

Sample answer: The half-plane lying *below* the boundary line should be shaded for solutions to the "less than" inequality. The half-plane lying *above* the boundary line should be shaded for solutions to the "greater than" inequality.

11.9 GUIDED PRACTICE (p. 604) 1. $x - y = 3$, $2x = y$

3. (2, 2)

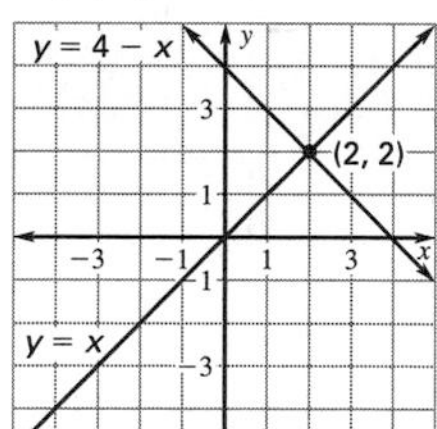

5. (2, 1)

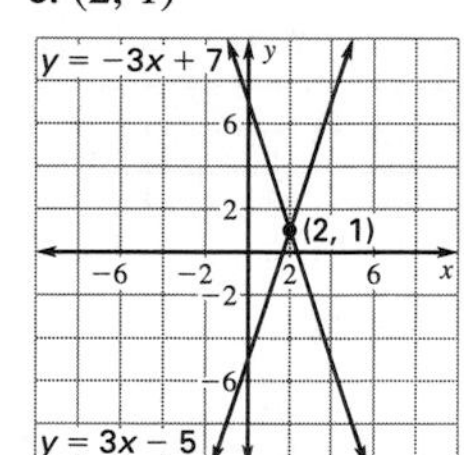

7. *Sample answer:* (−1, −1), (0, 0), (1, 1)

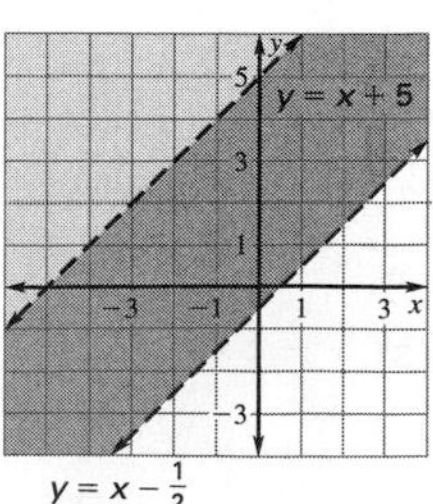

$y = x - \frac{1}{2}$

SELECTED ANSWERS

11.9 PRACTICE AND PROBLEM SOLVING (pp. 604–605)

9. $x + y = 1, y = 3x$

11. (3, 4)

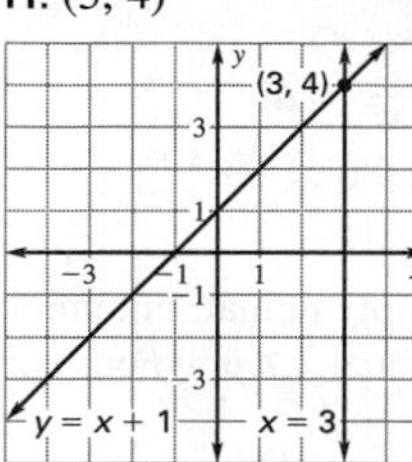

13. (3, 3)

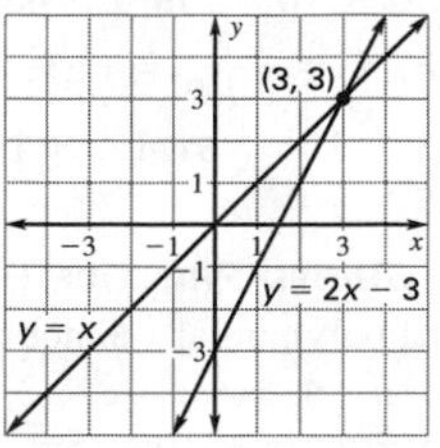

15. $x + 2y > 5, y < 2x$

17. *Sample answer:* (−1, 1), (0, 0), (1, 1)

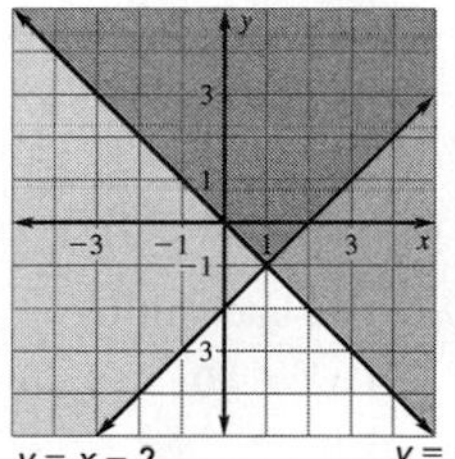

19. *Sample answer:* (−1, −1), (0, 0), (1, 1)

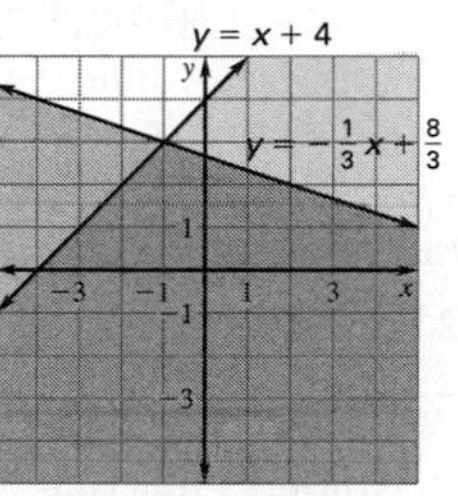
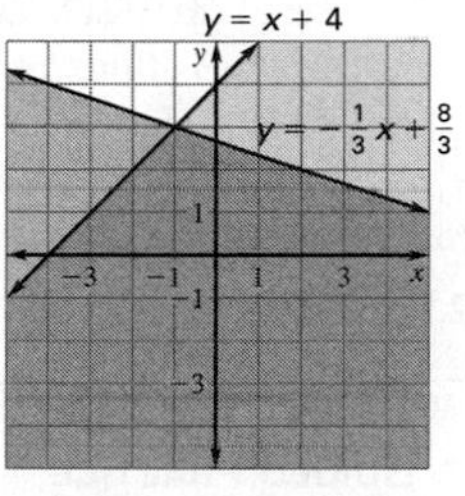

21. *Sample answer:* (−1, 0), (0, 2), (1, 1)

23. $x + y = 25, y = 2x + 1$ (8, 17)

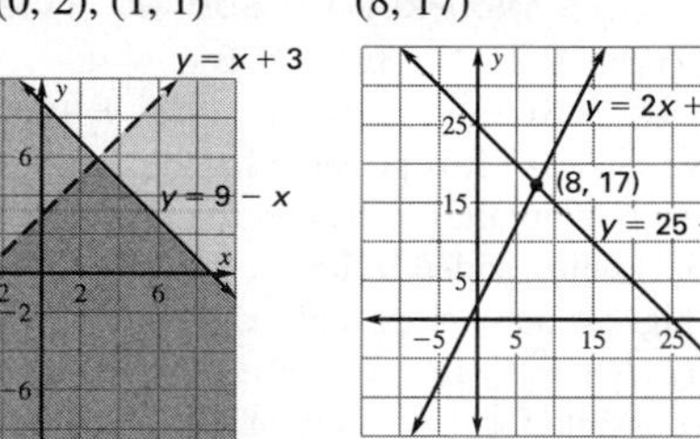

25. $x - y < 8, y + 2x > 1$

Sample answer: (−1, 4), (0, 2), (1, 1)

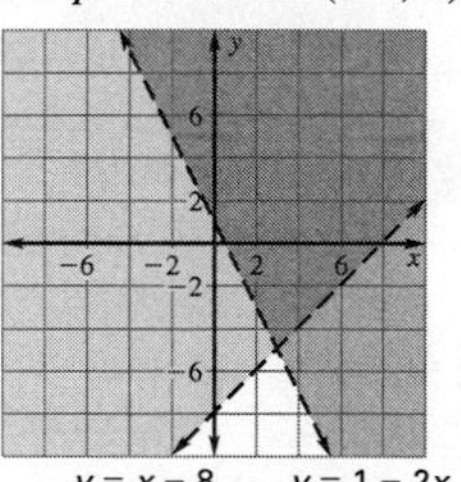

27. The school has raised only \$400 but has to pay the band \$700, so it has lost money.

CHAPTER SUMMARY AND REVIEW (pp. 606–609)

1.

x	−2	0	2	4
y	4	0	−4	−8

3.

x	−2	0	2	4
y	6	5	4	3

5. A rule for this function is $y = \left(-\frac{2}{3}\right)x$.

7. $y = 16 - 6x$

x	−1	0	1	2
y	22	16	10	4

9. $y = 5x - 7$

x	−1	0	1	2
y	−12	−7	−2	3

11.

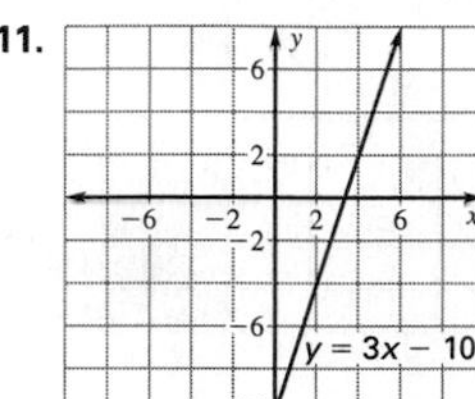

13.

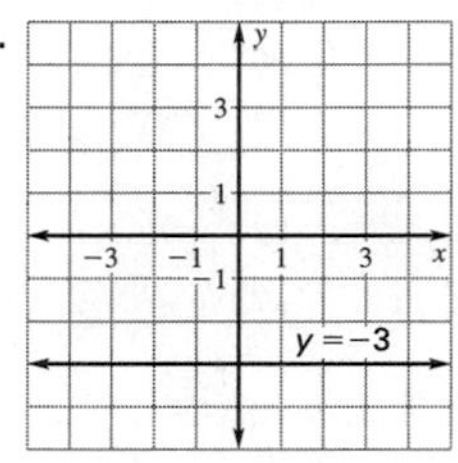

15. 2, −10

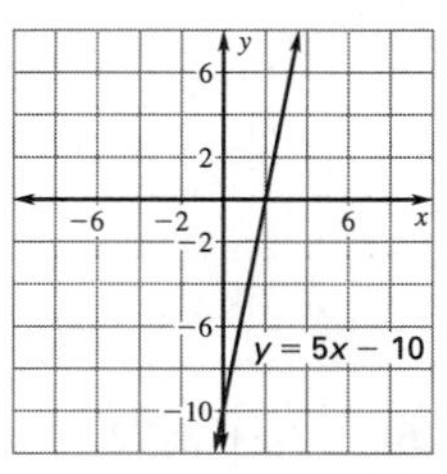

17. $-\frac{4}{3}$, 4

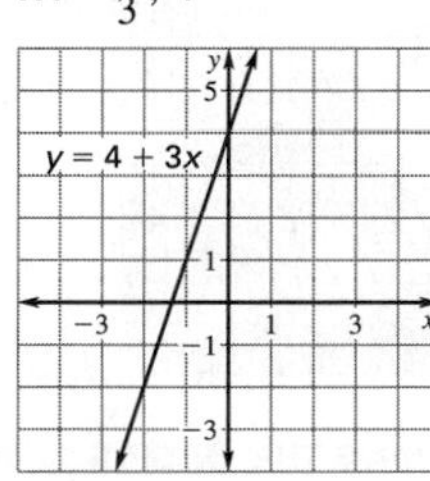

19. $m = -3$

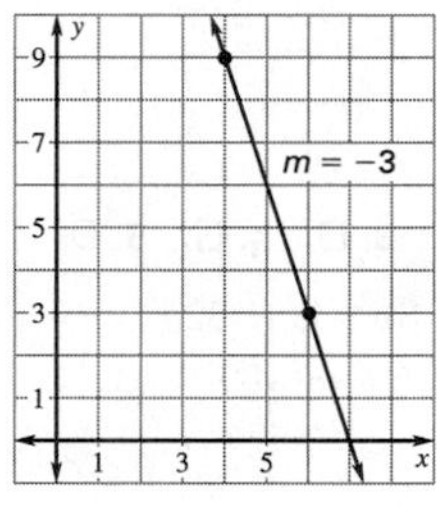

21. $m = -\frac{8}{7}$

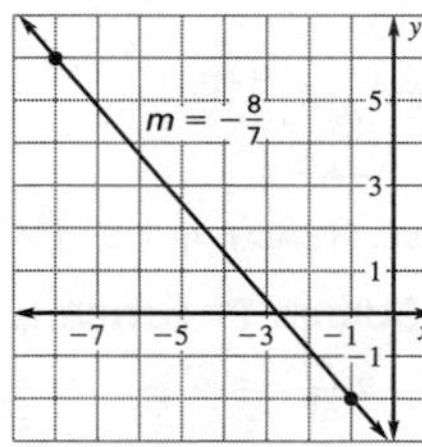

23. $m = 7, b = 4$

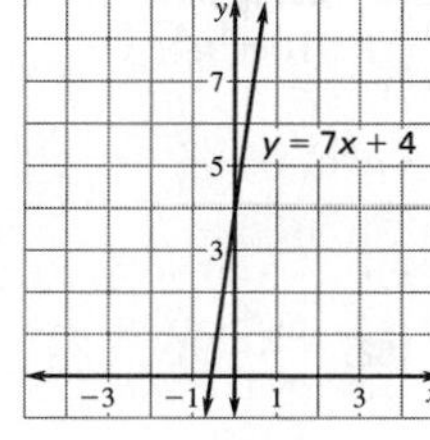

25. $m = -4, b = 3$

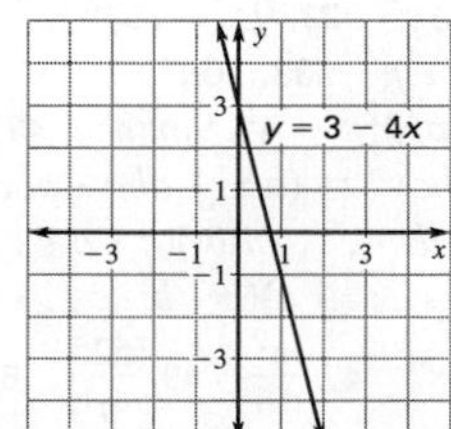

SELECTED ANSWERS

27. $y = -3x$; -12

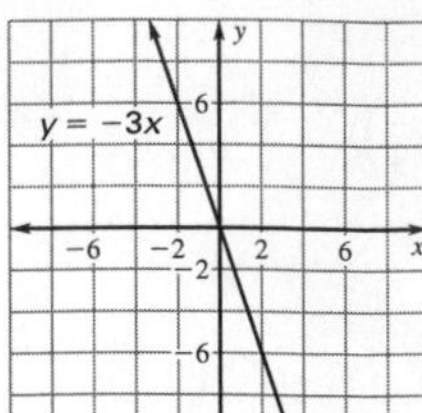

29. $y = \left(-\frac{1}{9}\right)x$; $-\frac{4}{9}$

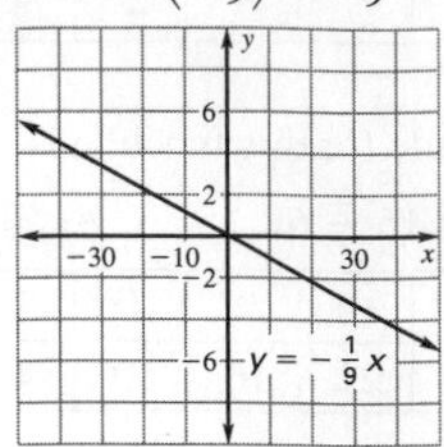

31. *Sample answer:* $(-1, -1)$, $(0, 0)$, $(1, 1)$

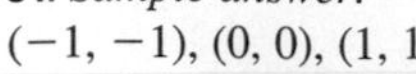

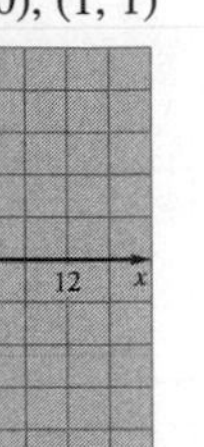

33. *Sample answer:* $(2, 3)$, $(3, 5)$, $(4, 6)$

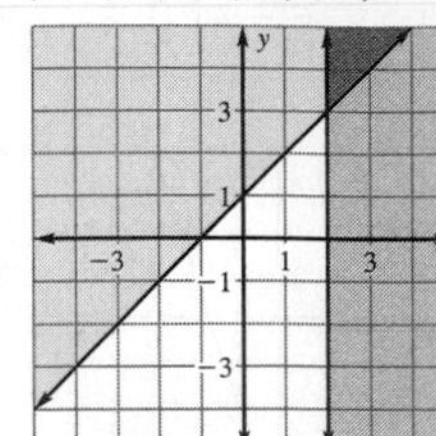

35. *Sample answer:* $(-1, -1)$, $(0, 0)$, $(1, 1)$

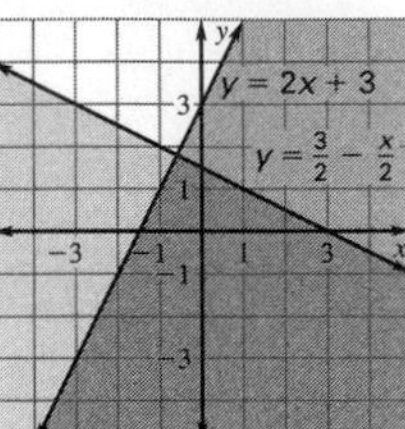

REVIEWING THE BASICS (p. 613) 1. $16x + 8y + 8$; 72 3. $7 - x - 8y$; -12 5. $-6x$; -18 7. $2y$ 9. $3z^2$ 11. $\frac{xz}{5y}$ 13. $\frac{7b^2c}{2}$ 15. $\frac{9a^3c}{2}$

Chapter 12

GETTING READY (p. 616) 1. C 2. J 3. D 4. G 5. D

12.1 GUIDED PRACTICE (p. 620) 1. $8x^3$ 3. $-32z^5$ 5. x^3y^3 7. $\frac{e^2}{4}$ 9. $\frac{4r^2}{25}$ 11. $\frac{1}{x^4}$ 13. x^6 15. z^{15} 17. 1×10^8 19. 8.1×10^{29}

12.1 PRACTICE AND PROBLEM SOLVING (pp. 620–621) 21. $125x^3$ 23. $9z^2$ 25. $64p^6$ 27. $25r^2$ 29. a^2b^2 31. $-m^4n^4$ 33. $16a^2b^2$ 35. $27x^3y^3$ 37. $16m^4n^4$ 39. $36p^2q^2r^2$ 41. $9m^2n^2$ 43. $-8p^3q^3$ 45. $(abc)^m = (abc \cdot abc \cdot abc \cdot \ldots \cdot abc) =$ $(ab \cdot ab \cdot \ldots \cdot ab)(c \cdot c \cdot \ldots \cdot c) =$ $(a \cdot a \cdot \ldots \cdot a)(b \cdot b \cdot \ldots \cdot b)(c \cdot c \cdot \ldots \cdot c) =$ $a^mb^mc^m$ 47. $\frac{m^2}{16}$ 49. $\frac{625}{u^4}$ 51. $\frac{9r^2}{16}$ 53. $\frac{16w^4}{x^4}$

55. $\frac{3x^2}{2}, \frac{x^3}{8}$ 57. y^6 59. 1 61. $343q^9$ 63. p^{10} 65. $c^{15}d^{20}$ 67. $k^6l^6m^6$ 69. 8×10^{12} 71. 2.5×10^{15} 73. 2.56×10^{14} 75. 1.0648×10^{16} 77. $(ab)^{-m} = \frac{1}{(ab)^m} = \frac{1}{a^mb^m} = \frac{1}{a^m} \cdot \frac{1}{b^m} = a^{-m}b^{-m}$ 79. 9.5×10^{11} 81. 1.6×10^{11} 83. 9.0×10^{14} 85. 6.5×10^{13}

12.2 GUIDED PRACTICE (p. 624) 1. polynomial; binomial 3. not a polynomial 5. not a polynomial 7. polynomial; binomial 9. $3x^2 + 4x - 2$; $3x^2, 4x, -2$ 11. $-5r^3 + 4r + 10$; $-5r^3, 4r, 10$ 13. $-x^3 - 5$

12.2 PRACTICE AND PROBLEM SOLVING (pp. 624–625) 15. polynomial; trinomial 17. not a polynomial 19. polynomial; binomial 21. $5p^5 + 3p^2$; $5p^5, 3p^2$ 23. $2x^4 + 7x^3 + 8x^2$, $2x^4, 7x^3, 8x^2$ 25. $5m^3 - 10m^2 + 14m$; $5m^3, -10m^2, 14m$ 27. $-8y^3 - 11y + 5$; $-8y^3, -11y, 5$ 29. $-t^4 + t^2 + t + 2$; $-t^4, t^2, t, 2$ 31. $2y^2 - 2y$ 33. $6x^2 - 3$ 35. $2x^2 + 10x + 7$ 37. $8s^3 - 3s^2 - 6$ 39. $2.9r^2 + 0.4r$ 43. 8 seconds; Use time intervals of $\frac{1}{10}, \frac{1}{100}$, etc. 45. $152x^3$ 47. $34x^2$ 49. $x^6 + 40x^4$ 51. 0

12.3 GUIDED PRACTICE (p. 628) 1. $6x^2 - 7x - 5$; 2 3. $y^3 + 6y^2 - 6y + 9$; 3

12.3 PRACTICE AND PROBLEM SOLVING (pp. 628–629) 5. $5x^2 + 7x + 11$; 2 7. $-8b^3 - 4$; 3 9. $-x^3 + 9x^2 - 8x - 4$; 3 11. $2t^3 + 2t^2 + 10t - 6$; 3 13. *Sample answer:* It is possible for the degree of the sum of two polynomials to be less than the degree of the polynomials being added if the coefficients of the terms with the highest powers are additive inverses. Example:

$$(2x^3 + x^2 + 1) + (-2x^3 + 2) = x^2 + 3$$

It is also possible for the degree of the difference of two polynomials of the same degree to be less than the degree of the polynomials being subtracted if the coefficients of the terms with the highest powers are equal. Example:

$$(2x^3 + x^2 + 1) - (2x^3 + 2) = x^2 - 1$$

15. $3x^2 + 5x + 2$, 24

17. *Sample answer:* The student is not adding the opposite of $2x^3 + x^2 + 2x + 1$.

$$\begin{array}{r} 4x^3 + 3x^2 + 4x + 3 \\ +\ (-2x^3 - x^2 - 2x - 1) \\ \hline 2x^3 + 2x^2 + 2x + 2 \end{array}$$

19. $7x - 3$, 39 21. FF FF FF

12.4 GUIDED PRACTICE (p. 632) 1. $21x^3 + 3x^2$ 3. $16z^5 + 6z^3$ 5. $3n^4 + 6n^3 - 15n^2$ 7. Area of each region (from top to bottom): $8x^2 - 4x$, $2x^2$, $10x^2 + 4x$, $4x^2$; $24x^2$ 9. The expressions are equal. 96

12.4 PRACTICE AND PROBLEM SOLVING (pp. 632–634) 11. $12y^3 + 8y^2 + 4y$ 13. $6a^4 - 21a^3$ 15. $c^7 - 3c^6 + 2c^5$ 17. $8s^9 + 10s^8 - s^7$

SELECTED ANSWERS

19. $-r^3 - r^2 - r$ **21.** $-12w^6 + 6w^4$ **23.** $x^3(x - 2)$, $x^4 - 2x^3$ **25.** $\frac{y^2}{2} + \frac{3y}{2}$ **27.** $A = 2w^2$ **29.** $8x^2 - 6x$ **31.** The two expressions are equal. 104 **33.** $6x^3 + 2x^2$ **35.** 180 **37.** $2x^3 + 2x^2$ **39.** *Sample answer:* In the second line of the solution the student incorrectly applied the distributive property. The second line should be $= 7t^2(-t^3) + 7t^2(-8t)$. $-7t^5 - 56t^3$. **41.** *Sample answer:* The degree of the product of a monomial and a polynomial is the sum of the degrees of the monomial and polynomial. **47.** $\frac{6}{9} = \frac{x}{6}$; $x = 4$ **49.** $\frac{4}{9}$ **51.** 5.7, $(-2, -2)$ **53.** 5.7, (4, 6) **55.** 10, $(-1, 3)$ **57.** $16y^4$ **59.** a^5b^5 **61.** $\frac{81}{n^4}$ **63.** $\frac{1{,}000{,}000w^6}{729}$ **65.** 1 **67.** $49p^8$

MID-CHAPTER TEST (p. 635) **1.** $64x^6$ **2.** $64y^3$ **3.** $-32z^5$ **4.** w^8 **5.** $\frac{p^4}{81}$ **6.** $\frac{1}{q^7}$ **7.** $\frac{4r^2}{25}$ **8.** $\frac{s^3t^3}{w^3}$ **9.** m^6 **10.** $16n^{12}$ **11.** $9p^2q^4$ **12.** $x^5y^5z^{10}$ **13.** $5x + 6$ **14.** $3x^2 - 3x + 4$ **15.** $2x^3 - x^2$ **16.** $-x^2 + 9x + 16$ **17.** $2x^2 + 2x + 12$, second-degree polynomial **18.** $4x^3 - x^2 - 2x + 6$, third-degree polynomial **19.** $-x^2 - 4x + 12$, second-degree polynomial **20.** $3x^2 - 2x - 1$, second-degree polynomial **21.** $15x^3 + 25x^2$ **22.** $56x^3 + 7x^2 + 14x$ **23.** $8x^3 - 6x^2 + 10x$ **24.** $21x^3 - 30x^2$ **25.** $12x^4 + 4x^3 - 56x^2$ **26.** $-3x^4 + 4x^3 - 12x^2$ **27.** $-12x^6 + 18x^4 - 9x^3 + 3x^2$ **28.** $12x^5 - 30x^4 + 6x^3 - 24x^2 - 12x$ **29.** $3x^2 - 6x$ **30.** $\frac{x^2}{2} + x$ **31.** $9x - x^2$ **32.** $6x^2 + 2x$ **33.** $2x^2 - x$ **34.** $4x^2 + 3x$

12.5 GUIDED PRACTICE (p. 640)

1. $(x + 2)(x + 7)$

$= (x + 2)(x) + (x + 2)(7)$	Distribute $(x + 2)$.
$= x(x) + 2(x) + x(7) + 2(7)$	Distribute x and 7.
$= x^2 + 2x + 7x + 14$	Multiply monomials.
$= x^2 + 9x + 14$	Combine like terms.

3. $(2x + 1)(4x + 5)$

$= (2x + 1)(4x) + (2x + 1)(5)$	Distribute $(2x + 1)$.
$= 2x(4x) + 1(4x) + 2x(5) + 1(5)$	Distribute $4x$ and 5.
$= 8x^2 + 4x + 10x + 5$	Multiply monomials.
$= 8x^2 + 14x + 5$	Combine like terms.

5. B **7.** C **9.** $x^2 + 20x + 100$

12.5 PRACTICE AND PROBLEM SOLVING (pp. 640–641)

11. In first line of solution, the student did not distribute $(x + 6)$.
$(x + 6)(2x + 5) =$
$= (x + 6)(2x) + (x + 6)(5)$
$= x(2x) + 6(2x) + x(5) + 6(5)$
$= 2x^2 + 17x + 30$
13. $18x^2 + 36x + 16$ **15.** $4x^2 + 55x + 150$ **17.** $36x^2 + 12x + 1$ **19.** $x^2 + 11x + 24$ **21.** $2x^2 + 13x + 15$ **23.** $5x^2 + 16x + 12$ **25.** $20x^2 + 41x + 20$ **27.** $9x^2 + 30x + 16$

29. $14x^2 + 46x + 36$ **31.** $2x^3 + 22x^2 + 56x$; *Sample answer:* The degree of the product is the sum of the degrees of the polynomials that are factors. **33.** $\frac{5x^2}{2} + \frac{21x}{2} + 9$ **35.** $x^2 + 6x + 9$ **37.** $z^2 + 4z + 4$ **39.** $m^2 + 10m + 25$ **41.** $p^2 + 14p + 49$ **43.** $4a^2 + 4a + 1$ **45.** $36c^2 + 48c + 16$ **47.** $e^4 + 12e^2 + 36$ **49.** $j^4 + 16j^2 + 64$

51. $(a - b)(a - b)$

$= a(a - b) - b(a - b)$	Distributive Property
$= a^2 - ab - ab + b^2$	Distributive Property
$= a^2 - 2ab + b^2$	Combine like terms.

$(2x - 3)^2 = 4x^2 - 12x + 9$

12.6 GUIDED PRACTICE (p. 645)

1.

x	-3	-2	-1	0	1	2	3
y	4.5	2.0	0.5	0	0.5	2.0	4.5

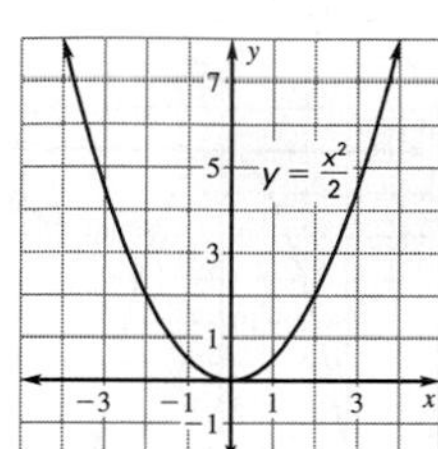

3. $V = \frac{8x^2}{3}$

12.6 PRACTICE AND PROBLEM SOLVING (pp. 645–647)

19.

x	1	2	3	4
Surface area	6	24	54	96

21. The surface area increases by a factor of 4. For example, for $x = 1$, $A = 6$; for $x = 2$, $A = 24$, which is four times the former area. **23.** $\frac{x^3}{8}$ **27.** 1, 2, 3, 4 **29.** $V = \frac{4\pi r^3}{3}$

12.7 GUIDED PRACTICE (p. 650) **1.** 5 **3.** $|x|$ **5.** $|2y|$ **7.** $|mn|$ **9.** ± 3 **11.** ± 1 **13.** ± 2 **15.** ± 6 **17.** ± 4 **19.** 5 sec

12.7 PRACTICE AND PROBLEM SOLVING (pp. 651–653)

21. 6 **23.** 20 **25.** $|z|$ **27.** $|x^5|$ **29.** $2p^2$ **31.** $|8r^3|$ **33.** $|ab^3|$ **35.** $|9xy^2z|$ **37.** ± 100 **39.** ± 60 **41.** ± 6 **43.** ± 6 **45.** ± 2 **47.** ± 10 **49.** ± 5 **51.** ± 7 **53.** ± 12 **55.** $\ell = 14$ in.; $w = 7$ in. **57.** $\ell = 50$ m; $w = 30$ m **59.** ± 6.24 **61.** ± 2.94 **63.** In the first line of the solution, the student has $\sqrt{4x^{16}}$ equaling $\sqrt{(4x^8)^2}$. The term should equal $\sqrt{(2x^8)^2}$. The final line should be $2x^8$. **65.** $b^2 + 7 = 23$, 4 **67.** $\frac{x^2}{4} = 4$; ± 4 **69.** ± 1 **71.** ± 6 **73.** ± 12

75.

t	0	5	10	15
h	10,000	9600	8400	6400

SELECTED ANSWERS

77. 11 sec **79.** $\sqrt{x^{2n}} = |x^n|$ for all n; $\sqrt{x^{2n}} = x^n$ for even n.

83.

s	10	20	30	40	50	60	70
d	8.3	33	75	133	208	300	408

87. $x > 4$ **89.** $z \geq 4$ **91.** $p < -2$ **93.** 193.96 cm^3 **95.** -1 **97.** $-\frac{4}{3}$ **99.** $5y^2 + 35y$ **101.** $12w^3 + 20w^2$ **103.** $2q^4 - 4q^3$

CHAPTER SUMMARY AND REVIEW (pp. 654–657) **1.** $64p^6$ **3.** $-27r^3$ **5.** $\frac{a^3}{8}$ **7.** $\frac{9c^2}{25}$ **9.** w^{15} **11.** $-64y^9$ **13.** $7x + 1$ **15.** $3z^4 - 3z^3 + 2z^2$ **17.** $5s^2 - 2s - 9$ **19.** $5a^2 + 5a + 14$ **21.** $30c^6 + 8c^5$ **23.** $6n^2 + 2n$ **25.** $13q^2 + q + 7$ **27.** $-5s^2 + 10s - 11$ **29.** $x^3 - x^2 - 12$ **31.** $y^4 + 4y$ **33.** $b^5 + 5b^3$ **35.** $d^5 - 6d^4$ **37.** $-q^5 + q^3 - 3q^2$ **39.** $x^2 + 7x + 10$ **41.** $x^2 + 8x + 7$ **43.** $16c^2 + 24c + 9$ **45.** $x^2 + 8x + 16$ **47.** $36z^2 + 60z + 25$

49.

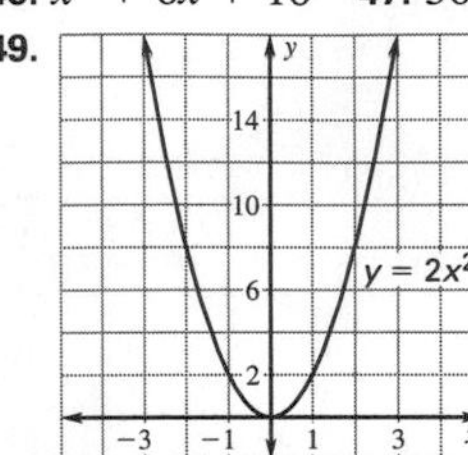

51.

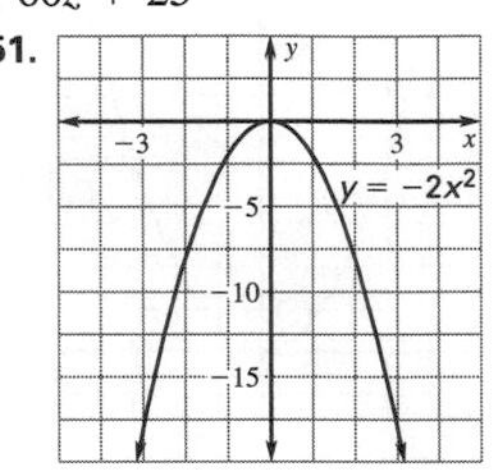

53.

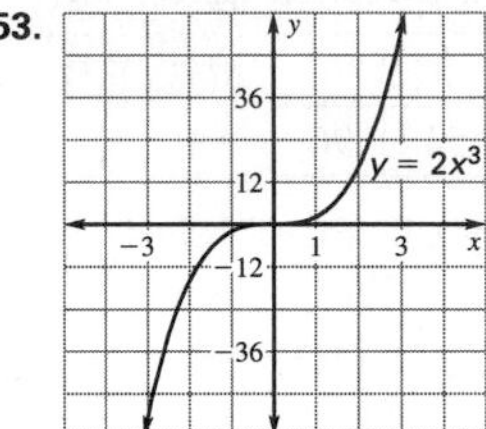

55.

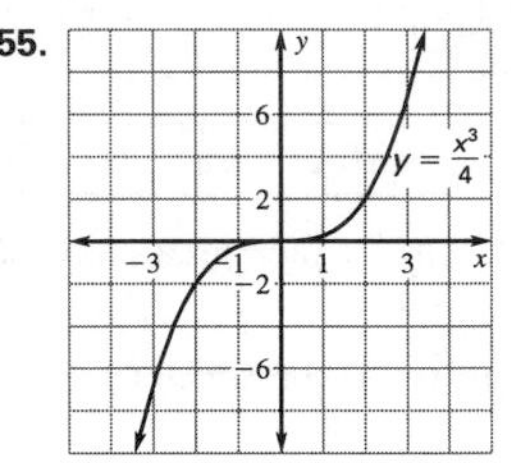

57. $|2m|$ **59.** $4x^2$ **61.** $|3xy|$ **63.** $|6xy^2z^3|$ **65.** ± 9 **67.** ± 2 **69.** ± 5 **71.** ± 6

REVIEWING THE BASICS (p. 661) **1.** 7 **3.** 24 **5.** -6 **7.** 0 **9.** -2 **11.** $\frac{1}{2}$

CUMULATIVE PRACTICE (pp. 662–663) **1.** associative property of multiplication **3.** associative property of addition **5.** 93 **7.** 112 **9.** 125.5 **11.** $6x + 5$, 47 **13.** $7x - 7$, 42 **15.** -9 **17.** 1 **19.** 15 **21.** 60% **23.** 70% **25.** 300% **27.** 75% **29.** $\frac{5}{7}$ **31.** $\frac{4}{15}$ **33.** $\frac{21}{20}$ **35.** $\frac{53}{18}$ **37.** The 18 ounce box of cereal is a better buy because its unit price of 0.177 dollar per ounce is less than the unit price of 0.189 dollar per ounce for the 10 ounce box. **39.** 36, 72 **41.** 66, 224 **45.** 50, 49, acute triangle **47.** 14, 14, right triangle **49.** 240.33 cm^2 **51.** 48 ft^3 **53.** 301.59 $in.^3$ **55.** $y = \frac{x}{2} + 2$ **57.** *Sample answer:* $(-1, -1)$, $(0, -2)$, $(1, -3)$

59. *Sample answer:* $(-1, 4)$, $(0, 3)$, $\left(\frac{9}{2}, 0\right)$ **61.** $4x - 3$ **63.** $x^4 + x^3 - 3x^2 - 3x + 12$ **65.** $6x^4 - 12x^3 + 30x^2 + 12x$ **67.** ± 3 **69.** ± 6

Selected answers for the Skills Review Handbook begin on page SA37.

Extra Practice

CHAPTER 1 (p. 690) **1.** 1998, 1999 **3.** *Sample answer:* The enrollment in World History declined each year over the three-year period. **5.** *Sample answer:* It remained the same. **7.** 12; The difference of 42 and 30 is 12. **9.** 30; The quotient of 450 and 15 is 30. **11.** 15 **13.** 19 **15.** $8 \cdot 8$; 64 **17.** $1 \cdot 1 \cdot 1 \cdot 1 \cdot 1 \cdot 1$; 1 **19.** 9 **21.** 25 **23.** 5 **25.** 7 **27.** 18 **29.** 36 **31.** 21 **33.** 13 **35.** 20 ft; 18 ft^2 **37.** 90 m; 450 m^2 **39.** 20 cm; 25 cm^2 **41.** How many people are in the Henderson family? **43.** subtract 8; 58, 50, 42 **45.** multiply by 4; 1024, 4096, 16,384 **47.** associative property of addition **49.** commutative property of addition **51.** *Sample answer:* $3 - 2 = 1$ but $2 - 3 = -1$ **53.** $17(8) + 17(11)$; $17(19) = 323 = 136 + 187$ **55.** $8(24) - 8(9)$; $8(15) = 120 = 192 - 72$ **57.** $3(g) + 3(2) = 3g + 6$ **59.** $2(n) - 2(21) = 2n - 42$ **61.** $18(x) + 18(y) = 18x + 18y$ **63.** $2(4v) + 2(1) = 8v + 2$

CHAPTER 2 (p. 692) **1.** $\frac{x}{20}$ **3.** $15x - 12$ **5.** $x + 2$; the winning time **7.** $3x + 1$; your age **9.** *Sample answer:* The quotient of 42 and a number. **11.** *Sample answer:* Three less than 18 times a number. **13.** no; no like terms **15.** no; no like terms **17.** $5x$ **19.** $7x + 7y$ **21.** $8z + 9$ **23.** $10a + 20$ **25.** $3p + 13$ **27.** $6x + 24$ **29.** no; yes; no **31.** no; no; yes **33.** What number plus 2 equals 10?; 8 **35.** What number minus 15 equals 14?; 29 **37.** Seventy-five divided by what number equals 25?; 3 **39.** What number minus 10 equals 40?; 50 **41.** B **43.** D **45.** $\frac{x}{15} = 225$ **47.** $4x - 5 = 11$ **49.** 38 **51.** 8 **53.** 77 **55.** 3.44 **57.** 43 **59.** 120 **61.** 29.5 **63.** 9.2 **65.** 5 **67.** 9 **69.** 2.2 **71.** 10.3 **73.** 72 **75.** 28 **77.** 12.8 **79.** 48

81.

Number of questions	·	Number of minutes per question	=	Total number of minutes

Number of questions = 48, Number of minutes per question = x; Total number of minutes = 120; divide 120 by 48.

83.

Amount saved per week	·	Number of weeks	=	Total amount saved

Amount saved per week = 15, Number of weeks = x, Total amount saved = 135

SELECTED ANSWERS

85. $15(9) = 135$ **87.** $y \geq 15$; Add 3 to both sides. **89.** $12 > c$; Subtract 3 from both sides. **91.** $k \leq 50$; multiply both sides by 5. **93.** $d \leq 3$; Divide both sides by 8.1. **95.** $4 \leq t$; Divide both sides by 8. **97.** $w < 20.48$; Multiply both sides by 3.2.

CHAPTER 3 (p. 694) **1.** < **3.** > **5.** > **7.** −6, −2, −1, 0, 3, 5 **9.** −13, −10, −2, 4, 5, 7 **11.** −7, −4, −3, −2, 4, 9 **13.** 13 **15.** −22 **17.** −6 **19.** 0 **21.** 14°F **23.** −11 **25.** −5 **27.** −13 **29.** −4 **31.** $-4x + 15$; 7 **33.** $8x$; 16 **35.** $-10x - 9$; −29 **37.** −4 **39.** 14 **41.** −25 **43.** 17 **45.** 10 **47.** −2 **49.** $4x - 3$; 5 **51.** $22x$; 44 **53.** −48 **55.** 12 **57.** −70 **59.** 24 **61.** 9 **63.** 12 **65.** 32 **67.** −32 **69.** −18 **71.** undefined; division by zero is undefined. **73.** 16 **75.** −23 **77.** −1 **79.** 4 **81.** 3 **83.** −12 **85.** −8 **87.** 15 **89.** 3 **91.** −28

93. Quadrant 1
95. None
97. Quadrant 3
99. Quadrant 4

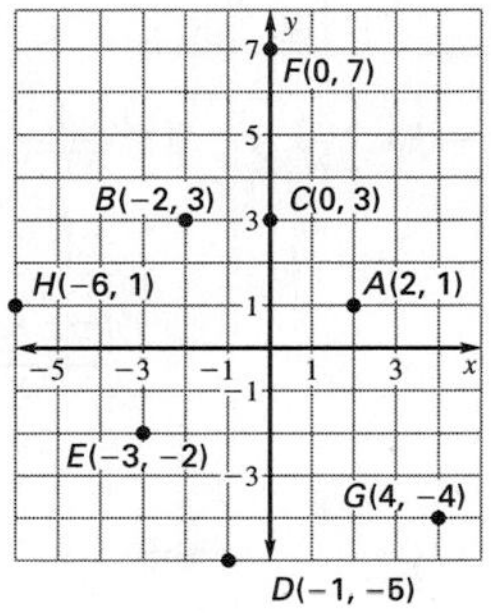

101. *Sample answer:*

x	−1	0	1	2
y	0	1	2	3

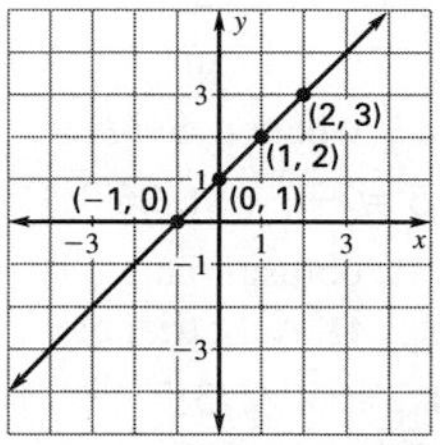

103. *Sample answer:*

x	−1	0	1	2
y	6	5	4	3

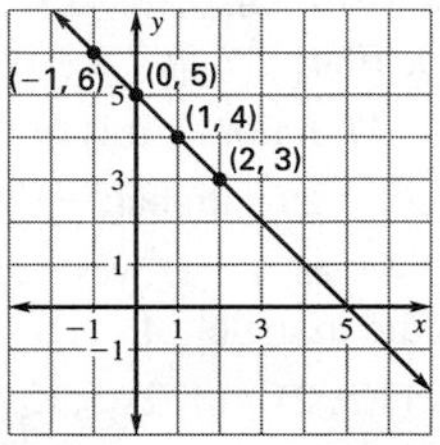

105. As the highest daily temperature increases, the number of swimmers also increases; *Sample answer:*

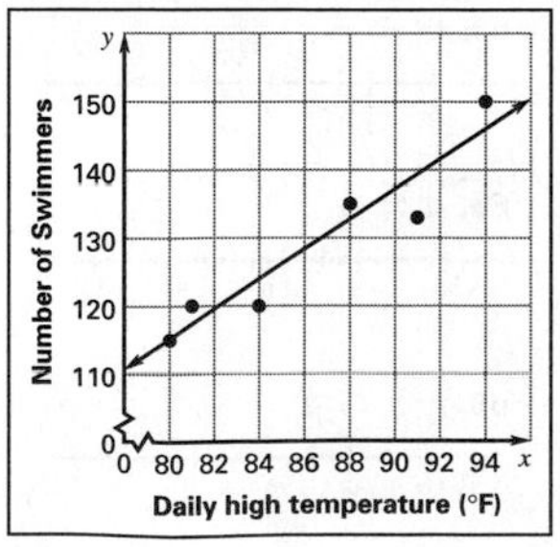

CHAPTER 4 (p. 696) **1.** 9 **3.** 8 **5.** 12 **7.** −1 **9.** −9 **11.** $75 = 25 + 2.00x$; 25 **13.** 5 **15.** 10 **17.** 5 **19.** 2 **21.**

[Cost of admission] · [Number of members] + [Cost of lunch] · [Number of members] + [Cost of bus] = [Total cost]

Cost of admission = 5, Number of members = x, Cost of lunch = 3, Cost of bus = 225, Total cost = 465; $5x + 3x + 225 = 465$; 30 members **23.** −2 **25.** 4 **27.** −5 **29.** −8 **31.** 2 **33.** 5 **35.** 2 **37.** −20 **39.** 16 **41.** −5 **43.** −6 **45.** 5 **47.** −2 **49.** −2 **51.** 4

53.

Number of hours	Member cost (in dollars)	Nonmember cost (in dollars)
1	50	10
2	55	20
3	60	30
4	65	40
5	70	50
6	75	60
7	80	70
8	85	80
9	90	90
10	95	100

55. $45 + 5x = 10x$; 9 h **57.** 1.1 **59.** 10.2 **61.** 4.3 **63.** −5.3 **65.** 4 containers **67.** 130, 124, 124 **69.** 9, 9, 8 **71.** 17.9, 18, none

CHAPTER 5 (p. 698) **1.** $3^2 \cdot 7$ **3.** 2^6 **5.** $5 \cdot 7^2$ **7.** $3 \cdot 5 \cdot 11$ **9.** $3 \cdot 7 \cdot 11$ **11.** $5 \cdot 5 \cdot x \cdot x \cdot x \cdot y$ **13.** $2 \cdot 2 \cdot 5 \cdot y \cdot y \cdot y \cdot y \cdot y \cdot z \cdot z \cdot z$ **15.** 1, 7, 49 **17.** 1, 2, 5, 7, 10, 14, 35, 70 **19.** 1, 2, 4, 11, 22, 44, x, $2x$, $4x$, $11x$, $22x$, $44x$ **21.** 1, 3, 13, 39, a, $3a$, $13a$, $39a$, a^2, $3a^2$, $13a^2$, $39a^2$, b, $3b$, $13b$, $39b$, ab, $3ab$, $13ab$, $39ab$, a^2b, $3a^2b$, $13a^2b$, $39a^2b$ **23.** 4 **25.** 48 **27.** 18 **29.** 165 **31.** ab^2 **33.** $5x^2y^3$ **35.** 45 **37.** 45 **39.** 60 **41.** 900 **43.** $21y^3$ **45.** $99a^3b^5$ **47.** $\frac{1}{3}$ **49.** $\frac{1}{13}$ **51.** $\frac{9}{16}$ **53.** $\frac{3}{7}$ **55.** $\frac{2}{13}$ **57.** $\frac{1}{4x}$ **59.** $\frac{3m}{4n^3}$ **61.** $\frac{2p}{5q^3}$

63. $-\frac{5}{6}, \frac{1}{4}, \frac{3}{8}, \frac{11}{16}$

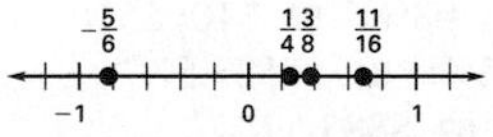

65. $-\frac{8}{9}, -\frac{3}{7}, \frac{5}{8}, \frac{14}{15}$

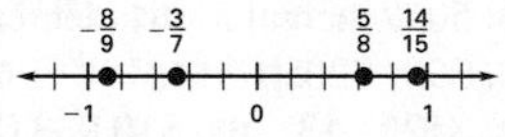

67. no **69.** 0.8 **71.** $0.41\overline{6}$ **73.** $0.\overline{72}$ **75.** $\frac{6}{25}$ **77.** $\frac{2}{33}$ **79.** 25% **81.** 8% **83.** 49% **85.** 25% **87.** $33\frac{1}{3}$%

SELECTED ANSWERS

89. 0.15 **91.** 0.25 **93.** 50% **95.** 30% **97.** 0.8% **99.** 0.3% **101.** 300% **103.** $\frac{47}{100}$ **105.** $\frac{13}{20}$ **107.** $\frac{5}{2}$
109. 35, 47, 48, 48, 52, 53, 53, 54, 56, 58, 60, 61, 64, 67
111. *Sample answer:* The number of both boys and girls enrolled is most often in the 40s; The row containing the 40s is the longest for both boys and girls.

CHAPTER 6 (p. 700) **1.** 1 **3.** 5 **5.** $\frac{3}{10}$ **7.** $-\frac{2}{3}$ **9.** $2\frac{1}{3}$ **11.** $13\frac{19}{21}$ **13.** $-\frac{1}{3x}$ **15.** $\frac{3a}{10}$ **17.** $1\frac{1}{24}$ **19.** $\frac{7}{20}$ **21.** $-\frac{19}{40}$ **23.** $\frac{7}{24}$ **25.** $7\frac{1}{8}$ **27.** $-\frac{2}{3}$ **29.** $\frac{1}{5}$ **31.** $-\frac{1}{6}$ **33.** $-1\frac{2}{75}$ **35.** $-\frac{x}{25}$ **37.** $1\frac{1}{2}$ **39.** $5\frac{1}{5}$ **41.** $-\frac{13}{4}$; $-\frac{4}{13} \cdot \left(-\frac{13}{4}\right) = 1$ **43.** $\frac{11}{37}$; $3\frac{4}{11} \cdot \frac{11}{37} = 1$ **45.** 0.1 or $\frac{1}{10}$; 20 **47.** 0.75 or $\frac{3}{4}$; 30 **49.** 0.25 or $\frac{1}{4}$; 24 **51.** 0.9 or $\frac{9}{10}$; 108 **53.** 1.1 or $1\frac{1}{10}$; 55 **55.** 0.005 or $\frac{1}{200}$; 1.5 or $1\frac{1}{2}$ **57.** \$11,250 **59.** \$1363.95 **61.** $-\frac{2}{3}$ **63.** $\frac{1}{10}$ **65.** $1\frac{1}{3}$ **67.** $\frac{9}{14}$ **69.** $\frac{2n}{3}$ **71.** 5 **73.** 6 place mats **75.** $-\frac{1}{2}$ **77.** 10 **79.** $\frac{2}{7}$ **81.** $3\frac{1}{12}$ **83.** $\frac{9}{16}$ **85.** $1\frac{3}{7}$ **87.** 5^6 **89.** z^{19} **91.** $\left(\frac{1}{2}\right)^7$ **93.** $(-7)^3$ **95.** $7x^6$ **97.** $-\frac{1}{16}$ **99.** $\frac{1}{x^3}$ **101.** $\frac{6}{n^4}$ **103.** 1 **105.** $\frac{2a}{b^8}$ **107.** $-x^{-12}$ **109.** wy^{-3} **111.** 9200 **113.** 0.00067 **115.** 0.000000055 **117.** 2.53×10^5 **119.** 2.1465×10^7

CHAPTER 7 (p. 702) **1.** $\frac{1}{5}$ **3.** $\frac{21}{25}$ **5.** *Sample answer:* $\frac{9 \text{ feet}}{54 \text{ feet}}$; $\frac{1}{6}$ **7.** *Sample answer:* $\frac{75 \text{ centimeters}}{100 \text{ centimeters}}$; $\frac{3}{4}$ **9.** \$2.59/lb **11.** ≈\$.04/oz **13.** 4 **15.** 12 **17.** $8\frac{1}{3}$ **19.** 20 **21.** 16 ft wide and 20 ft long
23.

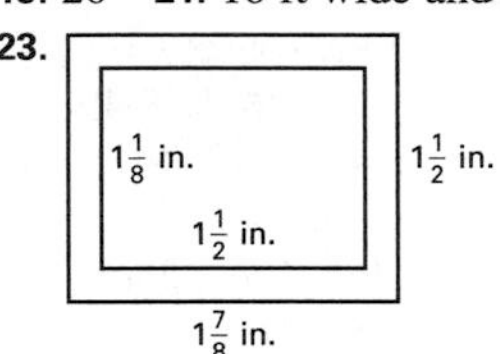

25. 0.50 **27.** 0.125 **29.** $\frac{56}{175} = \frac{x}{100}$; 32 **31.** $\frac{x}{240} = \frac{15}{100}$; 36 **33.** $\frac{x}{65} = \frac{140}{100}$; 91 **35.** $\frac{17}{x} = \frac{85}{100}$; 20 **37.** $\frac{8}{x} = \frac{4}{100}$; 200 **39.** \$517.48 **41.** \$38.47 **43.** \$455 **45.** \$12.79 **47.** 25% increase **49.** 50% increase **51.** decrease; ≈8% **53.** \$10; \$510 **55.** \$50; \$2050 **57.** 12% **59.** 5% **61.** \$5523.57 **63.** \$5253.13 **65.** \$10,938.07 **67.** \$883.59

CHAPTER 8 (p. 704) **1.** *Sample answers:* $\overleftrightarrow{ZB}$, $\overleftrightarrow{BY}$, $\overleftrightarrow{BZ}$ **3.** $\overline{ZB}$, $\overline{ZY}$, $\overline{ZV}$, $\overline{ZW}$ **5.** $\overline{ST}$, $\overline{XT}$, $\overline{VU}$, $\overline{YU}$; $\overline{SV}$, $\overline{XY}$, $\overline{WZ}$

7. 70° **9.** 105° **11.** 150°

15. Because k is not parallel to m **17.** *Sample answer:* ∠4 and ∠8 **19.** ∠1, ∠3, ∠7, ∠9 **21.** right scalene **23.** obtuse isosceles **25.** rectangle **27.** $\triangle PQR \cong \triangle STU$, $\angle P \cong \angle S$, $\angle Q \cong \angle T$, $\angle R \cong \angle U$, $\overline{PQ} \cong \overline{ST}$, $\overline{QR} \cong \overline{TU}$, $\overline{RP} \cong \overline{US}$ **29.** $JL = 7$, $m\angle W = 60°$ **31.** 70 **33.** 96
35.

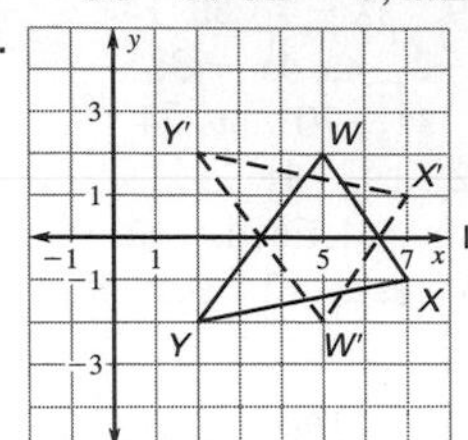

37. $(x, y) \rightarrow (x - 3, y - 1)$

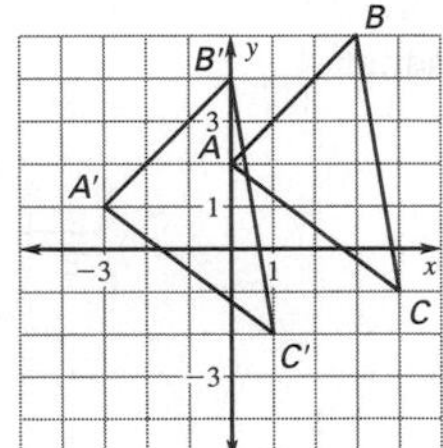

39. $\frac{AB}{PQ} = \frac{BC}{QR} = \frac{CD}{RS} = \frac{DA}{SP}$, $m\angle A = m\angle P$, $m\angle B = m\angle Q$, $m\angle C = m\angle R$, $m\angle D = m\angle S$ **41.** $\frac{3}{2}$; $\frac{9}{4}$

CHAPTER 9 (p. 706) **1.** 3, −3 **3.** 21, −21 **5.** 17, −17 **7.** 0.7, −0.7 **9.** 0.3, −0.3 **11.** 3; 2.8 **13.** 4; 4.5 **15.** 10; 10.4 **17.** 7; 7.4 **19.** 7; 7.1 **21.** ≈11 m **23.** A **25.** B **27.** rational; it is of the form $\frac{a}{b}$ where a and b are integers. **29.** rational; $-\sqrt{25} = -5 = -\frac{5}{1}$ **31.** 26 **33.** 13.4 **35.** 7 **37.** yes **39.** no **41.** obtuse triangle **43.** acute triangle **45.** right triangle **47.** right triangle **49.** 5; (1.5, 2) **51.** $2\sqrt{5}$; (5, 7) **53.** $2\sqrt{65}$; (2, 3)
55. $x \le 10$, $10 \ge x$

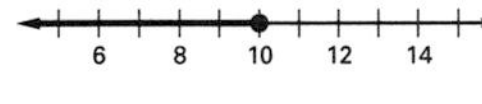

57. $x \ge -3$, $-3 \le x$

59. $x \le 6$

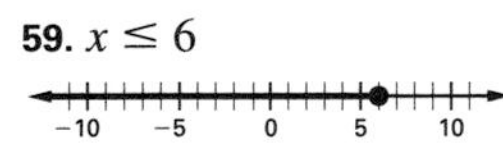

61. $m \ge 4$

63. $b < 14$

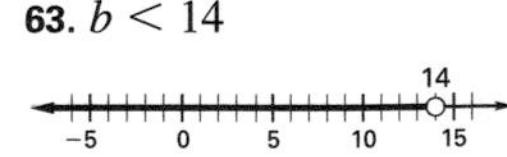

65. $a \le 6$

67. $-5 \le t$

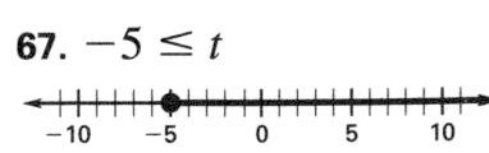

69. $-3 \le d$

SA34

71. $x < 1\frac{1}{2}$ **73.** $x < -1$

75. $27 \le x$ **77.** $50 < n$

79. $4 > x$ **81.** $z < -1\frac{1}{2}$

83. $x > -14$ **85.** $-\frac{2}{5} \ge x$

87. $a < 2$ **89.** $n \ge 6$

91. $a > -18$ **93.** $2\frac{1}{2} \le x$

95. 5 **97.** 27 **99.** 35 **101.** 21

103.

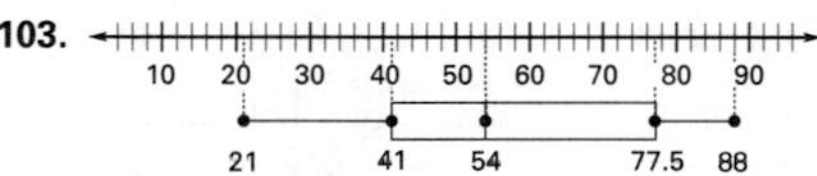

The range is 67 and the interquartile range is 36.5.

Chapter 10 (p. 708) **1.** 47.1 in.; 176.6 in.^{2} **3.** 125.6 cm; 1256 cm^2 **5.** 3.1 ft; 0.8 ft^2 **7.** 58.4 m; 271.6 m^2 **9.** 3.3 in.; 6.7 in. **11.** 17.8 ft; 35.7 ft **13.** 2.8 ft; 5.5 ft **15.** 5.3 yd; 10.6 yd **17.** 96 ft^2 **19.** $\overleftrightarrow{AB}$, $\overleftrightarrow{EH}$

21. *Sample answer*:

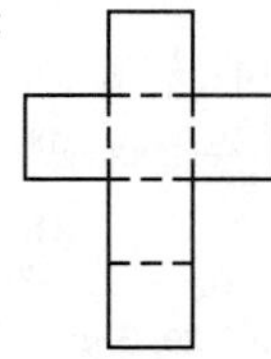

23. cylinder **25.** 562 ft^2 **27.** 216π cm^2 **29.** 318 cm^3 **31.** 96π cm^3 **33.** 1600π m^3 **35.** 1.8 cm **37.** 480 cm^3 **39.** 15π ft^3 **41.** $\frac{980\pi}{3}$ in.^{3} **43.** $18{,}240\pi$ ft^3 **45.** $\frac{48{,}668\pi}{3}$ in.^{3} **47.** 7.776π m^3 **49.** no **51.** 8 : 1

Chapter 11 (p. 710)

1.

Input, x	0	1	2
Output, y	0	6	12

3.

Input, x	2	-1	10
Output, y	-1	-4	7

5. $y = -2x$ **7.** yes; $3(0) - (-6) = 0 + 6 = 6$ **9.** no; $3(-2) - (12) = -6 - 12 = -18$ **11.** $y = x$; *Sample answer:*

x	-2	-1	0	1	2
y	-2	-1	0	1	2

13. $y = -2x + 8$; *Sample answer:*

x	-2	-1	0	1	2
y	12	10	8	6	4

15. $y = -3x + 4$; *Sample answer:*

x	-2	-1	0	1	2
y	10	7	4	1	-2

17. $y = -3x + \frac{1}{4}$; *Sample answer:*

x	-2	-1	0	1	2
y	$6\frac{1}{4}$	$3\frac{1}{4}$	$\frac{1}{4}$	$-2\frac{3}{4}$	$-5\frac{3}{4}$

19.

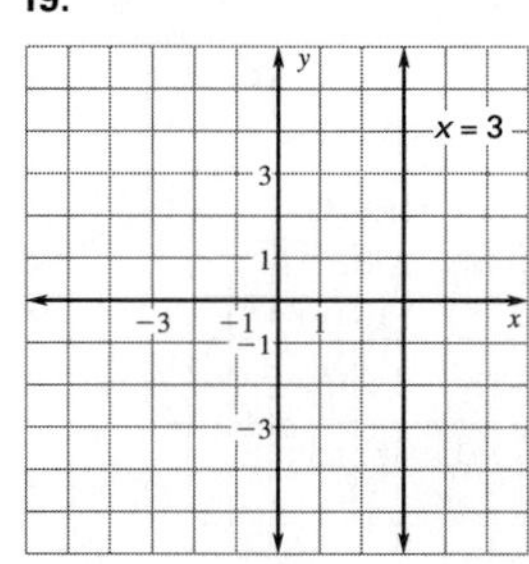

21.

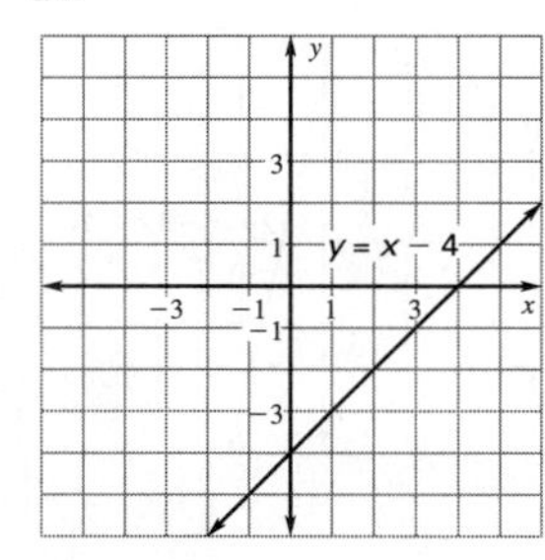

23. C = total monthly cost of long distance service; t = total number of long distance minutes in a month **25.** x-intercept $= -1$; y-intercept $= 2$ **27.** x-intercept $= 7$; y-intercept $= -4$ **29.** x-intercept $= 4$; y-intercept $= 4$; *Sample answer:* (1, 3)

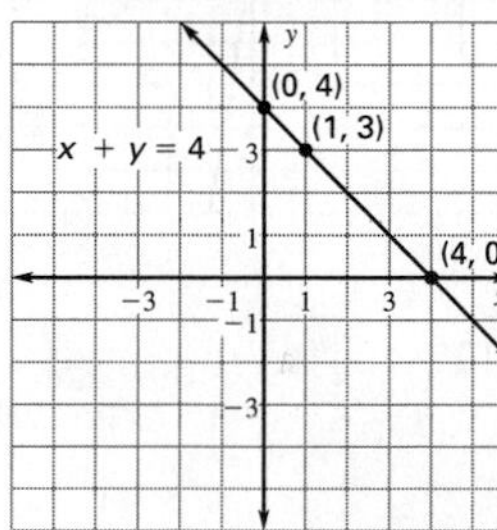

31. x-intercept $= 4$; y-intercept $= -6$ *Sample answer:* (8, 6)

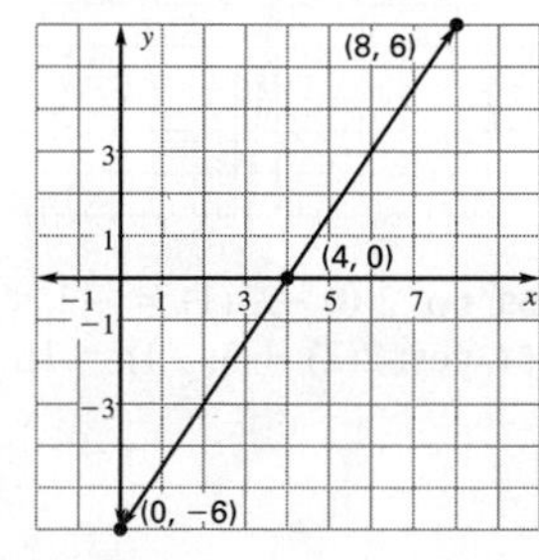

SELECTED ANSWERS

33. 0

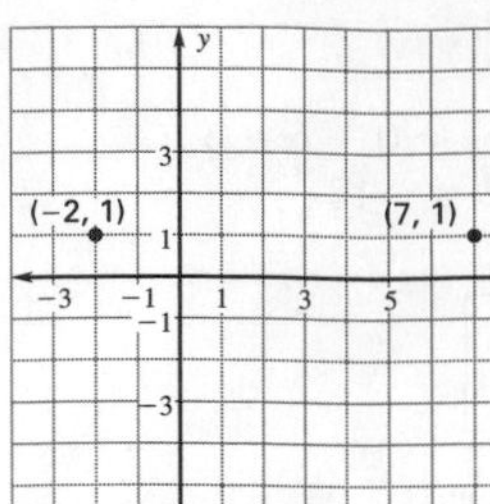

35. $-\frac{2}{3}$

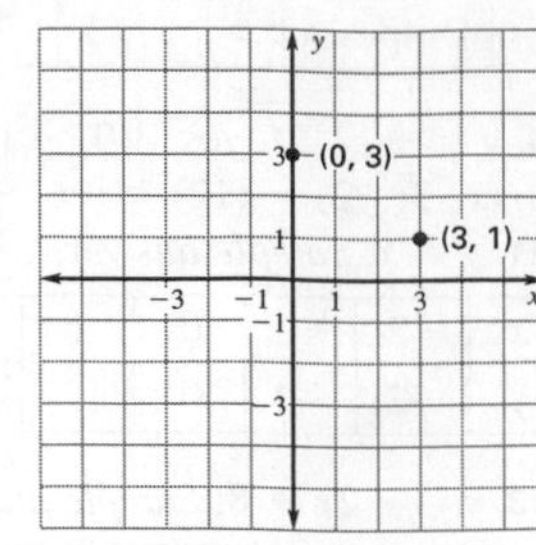

37. −1

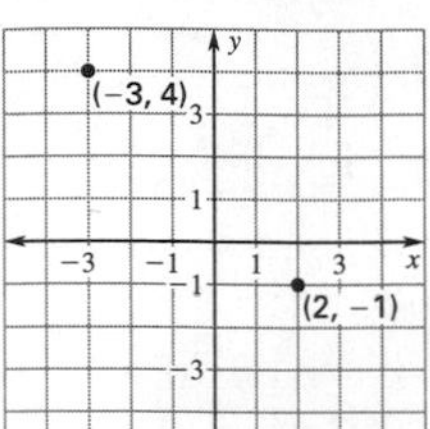

39. $-\frac{2}{3}$

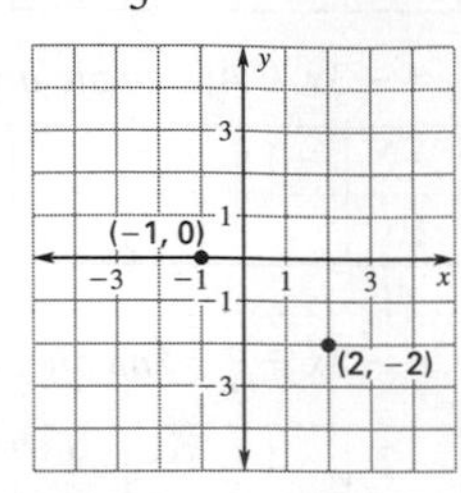

41. The line with slope −5 **43.** 5; 10 **45.** −3; −3
47. −7; 15 **49.** $\frac{6}{5}$; −6

51.

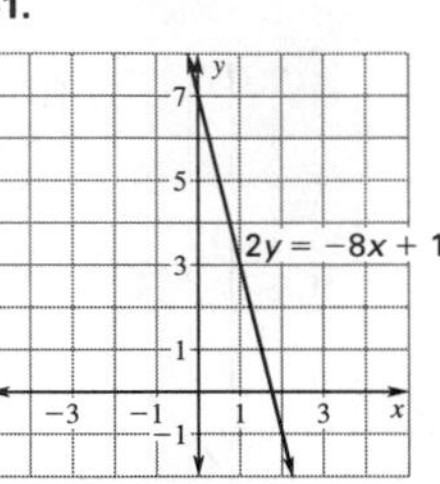

53.

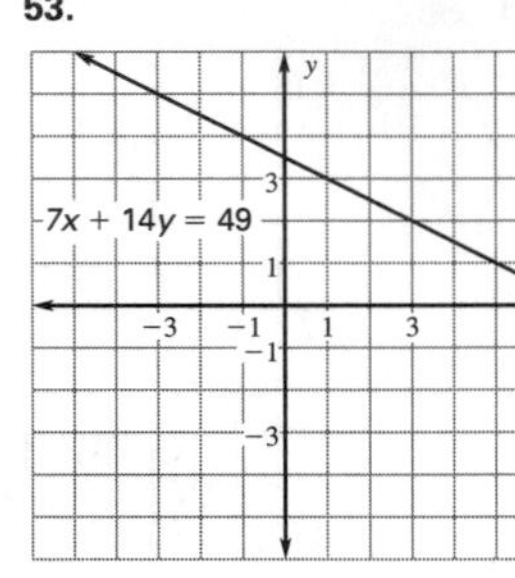

55. $y = -8x$; −32

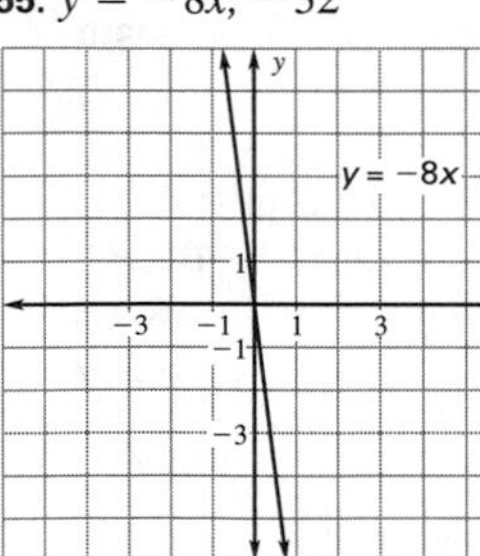

57. $y = -6x$; −24

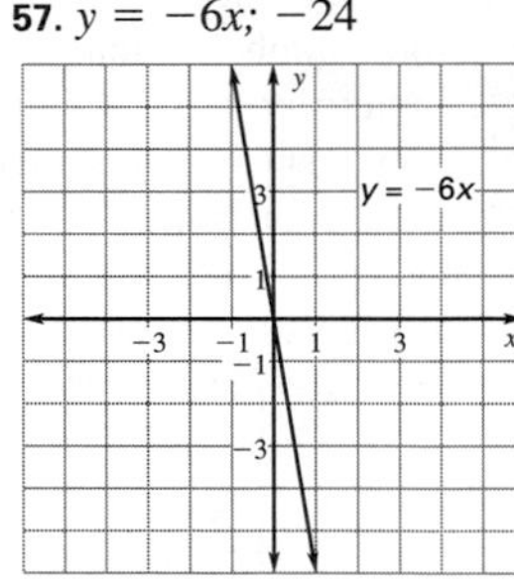

59. no; $2(0) - 3(1) = -3 < 12$
61. yes; $2(2) - 3(-4) = 16 > 12$

63. *Sample answer:* (0, 0), (3, 0), (0, 3)

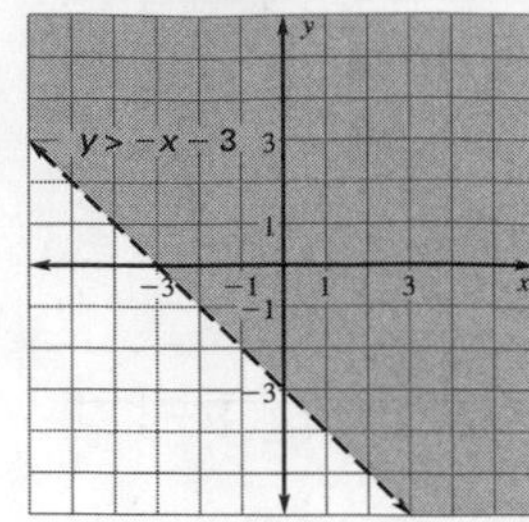

65. *Sample answer:* (0, 0), (6, 6), (6, −6)

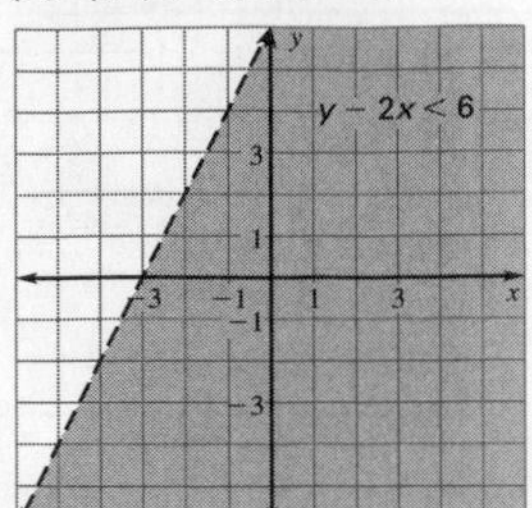

67. $x - y = 14$; $y = \frac{1}{2}x - 4$
69. (3, 12)

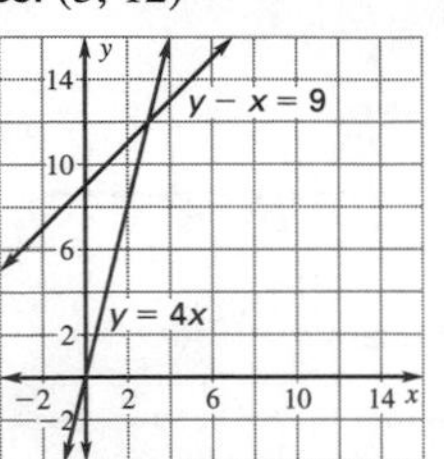

71. (6, 12)

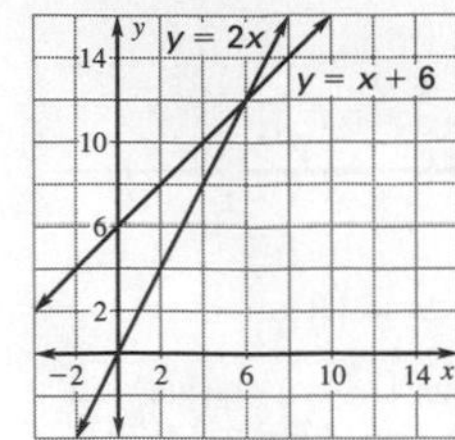

73. *Sample answer:* (−4, 4), (−3, 4), (−2, 4)

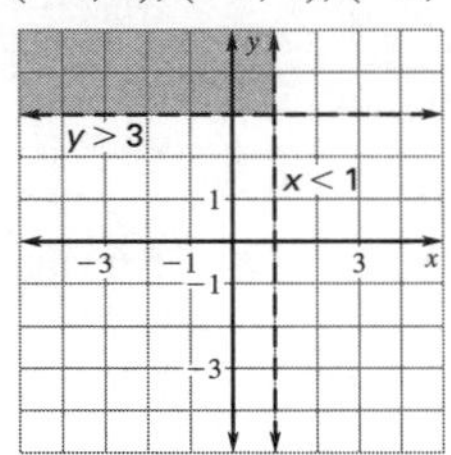

75. *Sample answer:* (3, 1), (4, 0), (4, −1)

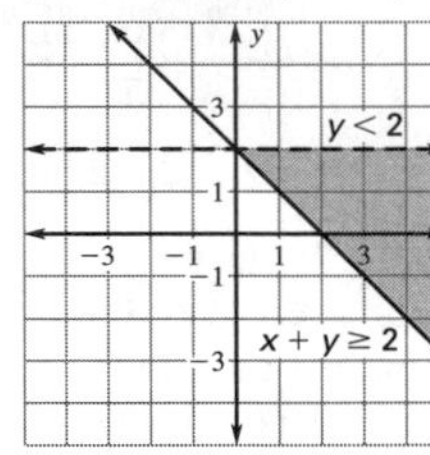

CHAPTER 12 (p. 712) **1.** $144z^2$ **3.** $27a^3b^3$ **5.** $-32x^5z^5$
7. $-125x^3$ **9.** $\frac{y^2}{25}$ **11.** $\frac{16x^4}{81}$ **13.** y^{18} **15.** w^6z^{36}
17. 3.2×10^{21} **19.** 1.25×10^{26} **21.** $-3x^2 + 2x + 5$; $-3x^2, 2x, 5$ **23.** $-3z^2 + 6z + 9$; $-3z^2, 6z, 9$
25. yes; binomial **27.** no **29.** $3m^2 - 2m + 1$
31. $3p^3 - p^2 + 3p - 3$ **33.** $\frac{2}{5}y - 1$
35. $4b^2 - 2b - 12$; 2 **37.** $-2n^4 - n^3 - 9n^2 - 6n - 18$; 4
39. $3y^4 - 17y^3 - 13y^2 + 12y - 21$; 4
41. $3w^4 - 4w^3 + 8w^2 + 9w - 4$; 4
43. $k^4 - 14k^3 + 2k^2 - 8k + 11$; 4 **45.** $2a^3 + 6a^2 + 4a$
47. $-15b^3 - 24b^2$ **49.** $-8n^3 + 8n^2 - 12n$
51. $-15z^5 + 10z^3 - 30z$ **53.** $2d^2 - d$ **55.** $34d^2 - 12d$
57. $5x^2 + 21x + 18$ **59.** $10x^2 + 29x + 10$
61. $16x^2 + 20x + 6$ **63.** $6x^2 + 17x + 5$
65. $x^2 + 24x + 144$ **67.** $k^2 + 16k + 64$
69. $n^2 + 10n + 25$ **71.** $4x^2 + 12x + 9$
73. $a^4 + 6a^2 + 9$ **75.** $w^4 + 14w^2 + 49$

77. *Sample answer:*

x	-2	-1	0	1	2
y	3.2	0.8	0	0.8	3.2

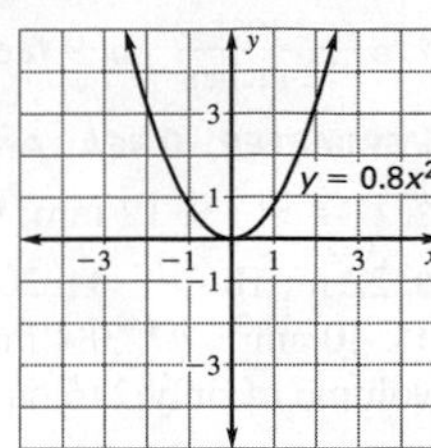

103. $-1, 0$

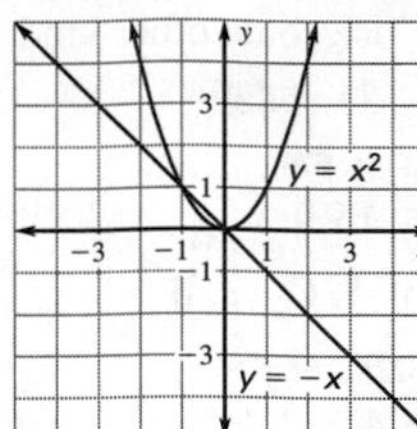

79. *Sample answer:*

x	-2	-1	0	1	2
y	3	$\frac{3}{4}$	0	$\frac{3}{4}$	3

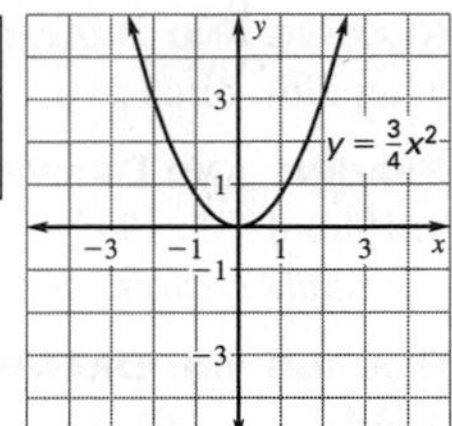

81. *Sample answer:*

x	-2	-1	0	1	2
y	5	1.25	0	1.25	5

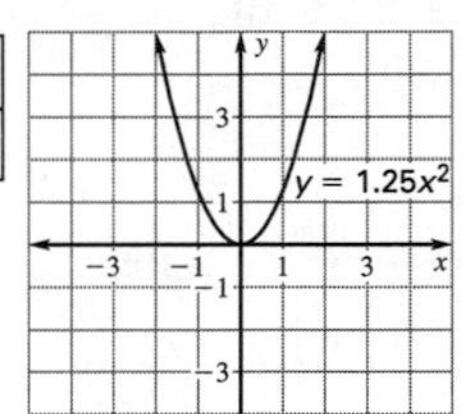

83. *Sample answer:*

x	-2	-1	0	1	2
y	-12	-1.5	0	1.5	12

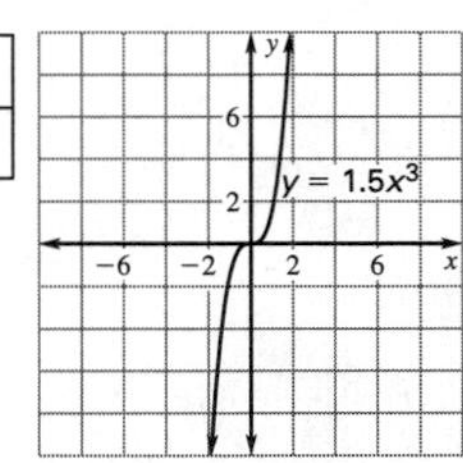

85. 7 **87.** k^6 **89.** $4n^2$ **91.** $a^2|b|$ **93.** $-11, 11$
95. $-7, 7$ **97.** $-3, 3$
99. $-4, 4$ **101.** $-3, 3$

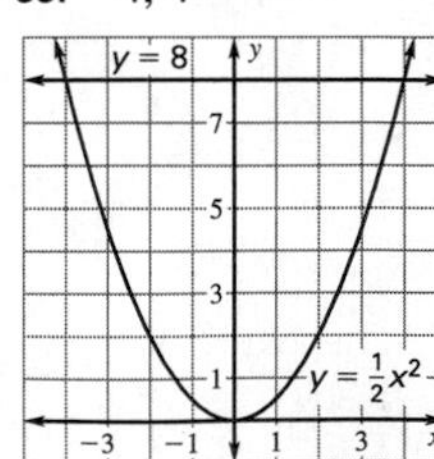

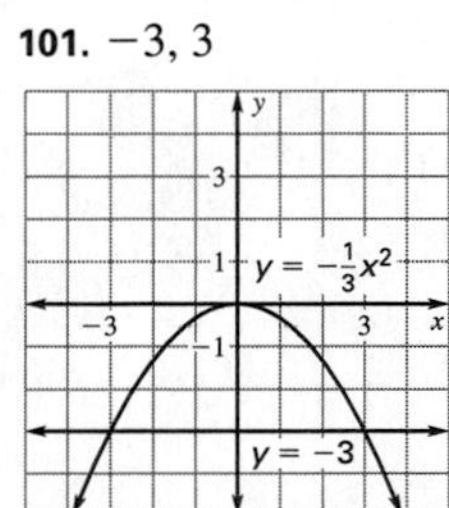

Skills Review Handbook

Identifying and Extending Patterns (p. 667)

1. Each number is 4 more than the previous number; 32, 36, 40 **3.** Each number is 3 less than the previous number; $-2, -5, -8$ **5.** Each number is the previous number divided by 2; 5, 2.5, 1.25 **7.** The first number in the product increases by 1, the second number remains 9, and the third number decreases by 1; 495, 594, 693
9. The next product is 5 times the previous product; 1875, 9375, 46,875

Using a Table, Graph, or Diagram (p. 668)

1. 3 ways

Quarters	Dimes
4	0
2	5
0	10

3. 6 ways

Quarters	Dimes	Nickels
1	1	0
1	0	2
0	3	1
0	2	3
0	1	5
0	0	7

5. pepperoni, pepperoni and mushroom, pepperoni and onion, pepperoni and extra cheese, mushroom, mushroom and onion, mushroom and extra cheese, onion, onion and extra cheese, extra cheese

Pepperoni	Mushroom	Onion	Extra cheese
✓			
✓	✓		
✓		✓	
✓			✓
	✓		
	✓	✓	
	✓		✓
		✓	
		✓	✓
			✓

7. *Sample answer:* ≈38% drive alone, ≈12% carpool, ≈33% use public transit, and ≈17% use some other kind of transportation. 9. 6 cm by 6 cm 11. 6 games

BREAKING A PROBLEM INTO PARTS (p. 670)
1. 49 square meters 3. 97 points 5. 15 ft^2

CHECKING REASONABLENESS (p. 671) 1. C 3. B

PLACE VALUE AND ROUNDING (p. 672)
1. $1 \times 1000 + 2 \times 100 + 5 \times 10 + 4 \times 1$
3. $3 \times 100 + 8 \times 10 + 2 \times \frac{1}{10}$
5. $1 \times 10{,}000 + 9 \times 100 + 4 \times 10 + 6 \times 1$
7. $1 \times 100 + 1 \times \frac{1}{100}$ 9. 64,087 11. 79.22
13. 53,800 15. 64.7 17. 9760 19. Round up; 7
21. Round up; 189,100 23. Round down; 0.34
25. Thousand; Round down 27. One; Round up

USING A NUMBER LINE (p. 674) 1. $0.9 < 1.9$ 3. $3.2 > 2.3$
5. $3.56 > 3.50$ 7. $1.26 < 1.62$ 9. 0.2, 1.2, 3.2, 3.5, 4.2
11. 0.2, 0.8, 2.3, 3.2, 4.3 13. 7.9, 8.7, 8.9, 9.8, 9.9
15. 0.09, 0.13, 0.85, 1.25 17. 4.05, 4.4, 4.45, 4.5

ADDING AND SUBTRACTING DECIMALS (p. 675) 1. 5.9
3. 5.31 5. 4.2 7. 9.83 9. 615.28 11. 10 13. 6.78
15. 71.9 17. 5.55 19. 2.76 21. 29.98 23. $1.38
25. 2.4° Fahrenheit

MULTIPLYING AND DIVIDING DECIMALS (p. 676) 1. 21.25
3. 27.9 5. 0.933 7. 0.15 9. 2000 11. 150.6
13. 1900 15. 3.4 17. ≈41.92 kilometers

FRACTIONS AND PERCENTS (p. 677) 1. $\frac{6}{9}$; *Sample answer:* $\frac{2}{3}, \frac{12}{18}$ 3. $\frac{6}{10}$; *Sample answer:* $\frac{3}{5}, \frac{12}{20}$
5. $\frac{10}{100}$; 10% 7. $\frac{35}{100}$; 35%

MIXED NUMBERS AND IMPROPER FRACTIONS (p. 678)
1. $3\frac{1}{3}$ 3. $7\frac{1}{2}$ 5. $1\frac{5}{12}$ 7. $7\frac{1}{4}$ 9. $2\frac{14}{25}$ 11. $\frac{15}{2}$ 13. $\frac{57}{50}$
15. $\frac{13}{5}$ 17. $\frac{143}{25}$ 19. $\frac{107}{6}$ 21. No; *Sample answer:* $3\frac{3}{4}$ bags $= \frac{15}{4}$ bags, but you need $\frac{20}{4}$ bags to have enough pretzels for everyone on the trip.

ESTIMATING SUMS AND DIFFERENCES (p. 679)
1. *Sample answer:* ≈1300 3. *Sample answer:* ≈147
5. *Sample answer:* ≈1700 7. *Sample answer:* ≈49
9. *Sample answer:* ≈56,000 11. *Sample answer:* ≈1100 13. *Sample answer:* ≈30,000 miles

ESTIMATING PRODUCTS AND QUOTIENTS (p. 680)
1. *Sample answer:* ≈800; rounding 3. *Sample answer:* ≈800; compatible numbers 5. *Sample answer:* ≈200; rounding 7. *Sample answer:* ≈2300; compatible numbers 9. *Sample answer:* ≈9; compatible numbers
11. *Sample answer:* ≈800; compatible numbers
13. *Sample answer:* ≈400; compatible numbers
15. *Sample answer:* ≈2; compatible numbers
17. *Sample answer:* ≈$7.00

CONVERTING UNITS OF MEASUREMENT (p. 681)
1. a. $\frac{1 \text{ foot}}{12 \text{ inches}}$ b. 9 feet 3. 72 fluid ounces

PERIMETER, AREA, AND VOLUME (p. 684) 1. $P = 4s$
3. $V = s^3$ 5. 12 mm; 9 mm^2 7. 48 ft; 84 ft^2
9. 22 m; 18 m^2 11. 30 ft; 56.25 ft^2 13. 64 m^3
15. 40 cm^3 17. 384 mm^3 19. No; the cube has a volume of only 216 cubic inches.

CONSTRUCTIONS (p. 685) 1. 6 sides; The sides are congruent. 3. The distances are the same.

READING AND DRAWING A BAR GRAPH (p. 686)
1. reptiles; birds

READING AND DRAWING A LINE GRAPH (p. 687)
1. 1980–1985; 1985–1990 3. 1995
5. *Sample answer:* $45,000

READING AND DRAWING A CIRCLE GRAPH (p. 688)
1. Adam

READING AND DRAWING A LINE PLOT (p. 689) 1. C
3. B 5. 10

TEACHER'S EDITION INDEX

Student Edition entries in black.
Teacher's Edition entries in blue.

A

Continued

TEACHER'S EDITION INDEX

B

TEACHER'S EDITION INDEX

D

TEACHER'S EDITION INDEX

J

K

L

M

TEACHER'S EDITION INDEX

N

O

P

Q

S

TEACHER'S EDITION INDEX

T

Continued

Additional Answers

Chapter 2

2.1 Practice and Problem Solving (pp. 55–56)

31.

U.S. dollars	$1.00	$2.00	$5.00	$10.00	$6.00	$8.00
Canadian dollars	$1.50	$3.00	$7.50	$15.00	$9.00	$12.00

2.2 Practice and Problem Solving (pp. 59–60)

37. $8x$

x	1	2	3	4	5
Perimeter	8	16	24	32	40

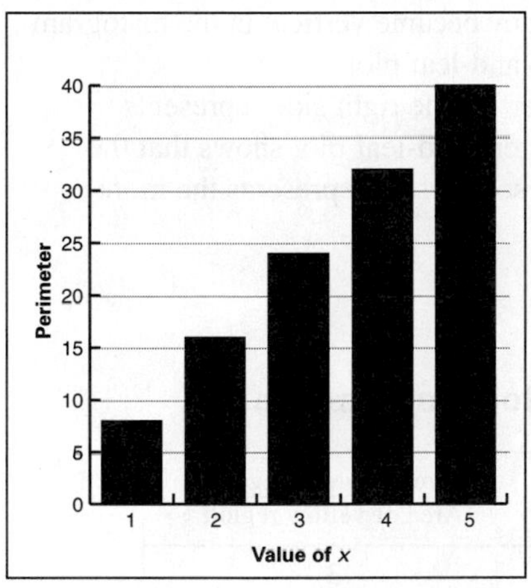

Chapter Test (p. 98)

19. Weekly cost of operating Store 1 + Weekly cost of operating Store 2 = Weekly cost of operating both stores

38.

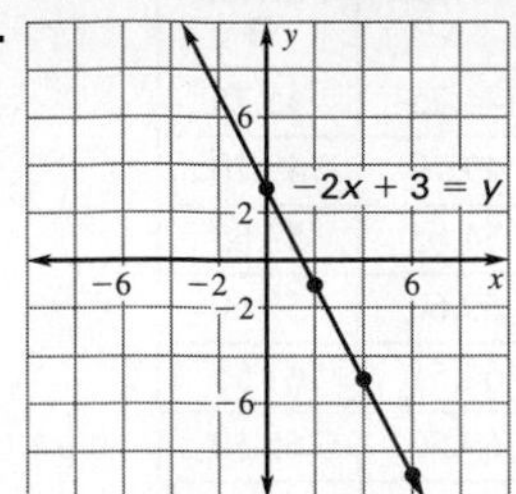

39.

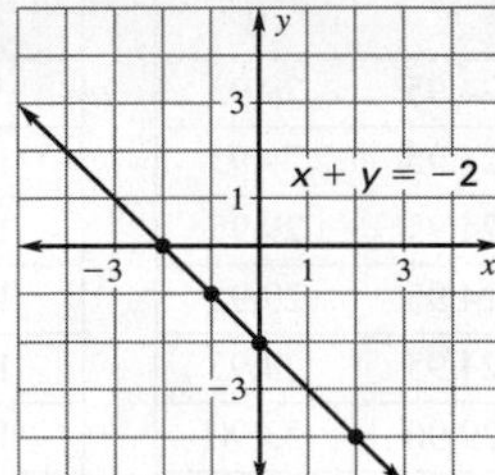

40.

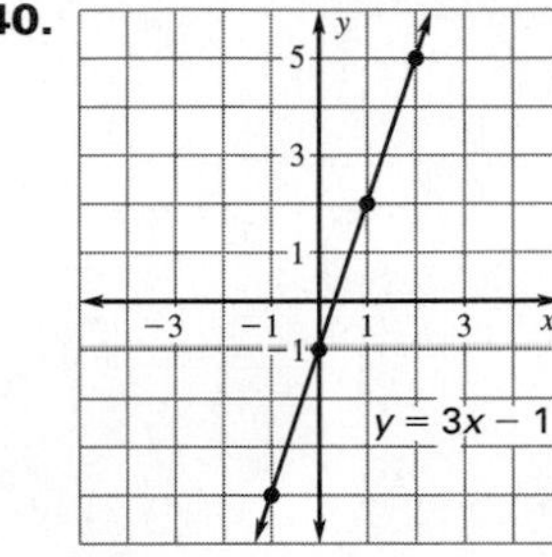

41.

Number of pairs of jeans	10	20	30	40
Revenue ($)	300	600	900	1200

44. $A = 24$

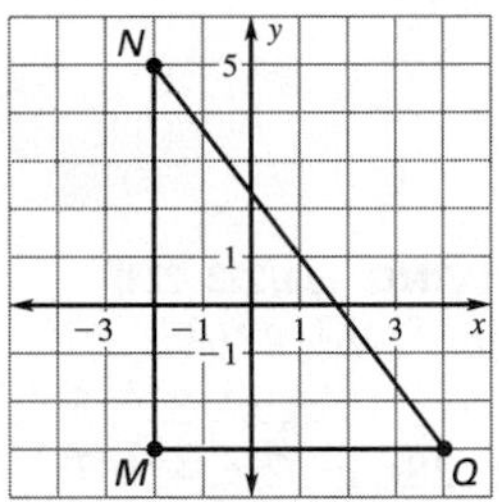

Chapter 3

3.8 Practice and Problem Solving (pp. 147–148)

36.

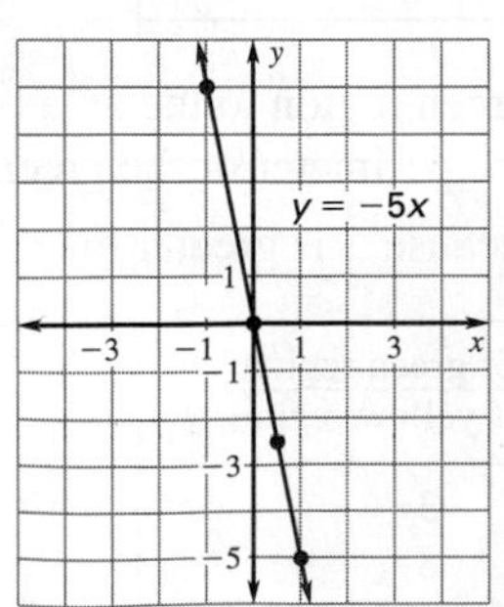

37.

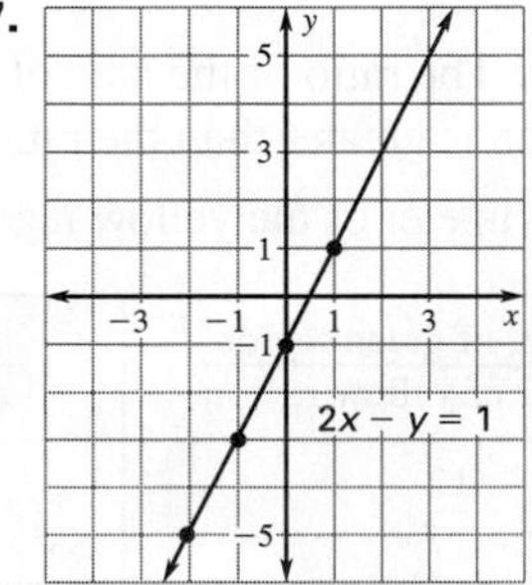

Chapter 4

4.1 Guided Practice (p. 172)

6. $5x - 7 = 13$

$5x = 20$ — Add 7 to each side.

$x = 4$ — Divide each side by 5.

4.1 Practice and Problem Solving (pp. 172–173)

7. $3x - 13 + 13 = 14 + 13$ — Add 13 to each side.

$3x = 27$ — Simplify.

$\frac{3x}{3} = \frac{27}{3}$ — Divide each side by 3.

$x = 9$ — Simplify.

8. $7x + 15 - 15 = 36 - 15$ — Subtract 15 from each side.

$7x = 21$ — Simplify.

$\frac{7x}{7} = \frac{21}{7}$ — Divide each side by 7.

$x = 3$ — Simplify.

4.7 Practice and Problem Solving (pp. 201–202)

29.

Number of hours	Cost: Provider A	Cost: Provider B
1	24.95	29.95
2	24.95	29.95
3	24.95	29.95
4	24.95	29.95
5	24.95	29.95
6	29.90	33.90
7	34.85	37.85
8	39.80	41.80

Number of hours	Cost: Provider A	Cost: Provider B
9	44.75	45.75
10	49.70	49.70
11	54.65	53.65
12	59.60	57.60
13	64.55	61.55
14	69.50	65.50
15	74.45	69.45

32.

Cost ($)
80
70
60
50
40
30
20
(13, 64.55)
(10, 49.70)
(13, 61.55)
B
A
1 3 5 7 9 11 13 15
Number of hours

Chapter 5

5.1 Practice and Problem Solving (pp. 223–224)

65. 1, 3, 29, 87, b, $3b$, $29b$, $87b$, b^2, $3b^2$, $29b^2$, $87b^2$
66. 1, 3, 5, 15, x, $3x$, $5x$, $15x$, x^2, $3x^2$, $5x^2$, $15x^2$, x^3, $3x^3$, $5x^3$, $15x^3$
67. 1, 2, 4, 7, 14, 28, z, $2z$, $4z$, $7z$, $14z$, $28z$, z^2, $2z^2$, $4z^2$, $7z^2$, $14z^2$, $28z^2$, z^3, $2z^3$, $4z^3$, $7z^3$, $14z^3$, $28z^3$
68. 1, 5, 25, w, $5w$, $25w$, w^2, $5w^2$, $25w^2$, y, $5y$, $25y$, wy, $5wy$, $25wy$, w^2y, $5w^2y$, $25w^2y$
69. 1, 71, x, $71x$, y, $71y$, xy, $71xy$, x^2, $71x^2$, y^2, $71y^2$, x^2y, $71x^2y$, xy^2, $71xy^2$, x^2y^2, $71x^2y^2$, y^3, $71y^3$, xy^3, $71xy^3$, x^2y^3, $71x^2y^3$
75. *Sample answer:* $30 = 13 + 17$; $32 = 13 + 19$; $34 = 11 + 23$; $36 = 13 + 23$; $38 = 7 + 31$; $40 = 11 + 29$
76. 6; 1 ft by 96 ft, 2 ft by 48 ft, 3 ft by 32 ft, 4 ft by 24 ft, 6 ft by 16 ft, 8 ft by 12 ft
77. Yes; every even number after 2 is divisible by 2, so each cannot be prime.

5.8 Practice and Problem Solving (pp. 255–257)

15.

East		West
9999999988888888888877777	1	889999999
0	2	0000000000111134

Key: 9 | 1 | 8 represents 19% in an Eastern state and 18% in a Western state.

18.

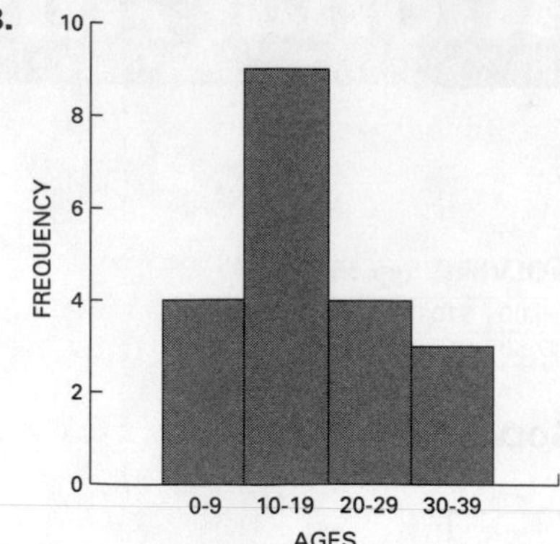

19. The shape of the histogram is the same as the stem-and-leaf plot, only placed on its side. The frequency became vertical in the histogram instead of horizontal as in the stem-and-leaf plot.
20. The left side represents fertilizer B. The right side represents fertilizer A. *Sample answer:* The stem-and-leaf plot shows that the plants on the right side grew taller, so this side represents the more effective fertilizer.

Chapter 7

7.1 Practice and Problem Solving (pp. 331–332)

30.

$\frac{\text{Perimeter of green region}}{\text{Perimeter of yellow region}}$	$\frac{\text{Area of green region}}{\text{Area of yellow region}}$
$\frac{16}{9}$	$\frac{3}{4}$

Sample answer: The ratio of the perimeter of the green region to the perimeter of the yellow region is greater than the ratio of the area of the green region to the area of the yellow region because $\frac{16}{9}$ is greater than $\frac{3}{4}$.

31.

$\frac{\text{Perimeter of green region}}{\text{Perimeter of yellow region}}$	$\frac{\text{Area of green region}}{\text{Area of yellow region}}$
$\frac{10}{9}$	$\frac{3}{2}$

Sample answer: The ratio of the area of the green region to the area of the yellow region is greater than the ratio of the perimeter of the green region to the perimeter of the yellow region because $\frac{3}{2}$ is greater than $\frac{10}{9}$.

32.

$\frac{\text{Perimeter of green region}}{\text{Perimeter of yellow region}}$	$\frac{\text{Area of green region}}{\text{Area of yellow region}}$
$\frac{12}{17}$	$\frac{3}{8}$

Sample answer: The ratio of the perimeter of the green region to the perimeter of the yellow region is greater than the ratio of the area of the green region to the area of the yellow region because $\frac{12}{17}$ is greater than $\frac{3}{8}$.

7.3 Practice and Problem Solving (pp. 341–342)

12. No; the new office space has only nine-sixteenths the area of the old office, but three-fourths the perimeter of the old office.
Area of old office: $60(40) = 2400 \text{ ft}^2$;
area of new office: $45(30) = 1350 \text{ ft}^2$.
The ratio of the area of the new office to the area of the old office is $\frac{1350 \text{ feet}}{2400 \text{ feet}}$, which is nine-sixteenths.
Perimeter of old office: $2(60) + 2(40) = 200$ ft;
perimeter of new office: $2(45) + 2(30) = 150$ ft.
The ratio of the perimeter of the new office to the perimeter of the old office is $\frac{150 \text{ feet}}{200 \text{ feet}}$, which is three-quarters.

7.6 Practice and Problem Solving (pp. 359–360)

31. No, the sale price is not \$200, but \$250.

regular price = wholesale price + markup
= wholesale price + (percent of markup) • (wholesale price)
$= 200 + 1.5 \cdot 200$
$= 500$

The regular price is \$500.00.

sale price = regular price − discount
= regular price − (percent of discount) • (regular price)
$= 500 - 0.50 \cdot 500$
$= 250$

sale price = \$250.00

Chapter 8

8.1 Practice and Problem Solving (pp. 387–389)

18.

8.2 Practice and Problem Solving (pp. 393–394)

14.
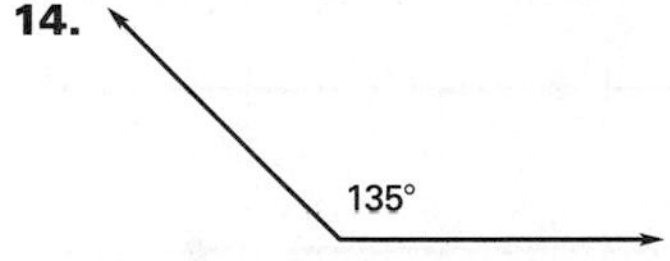

15.

28°

16.
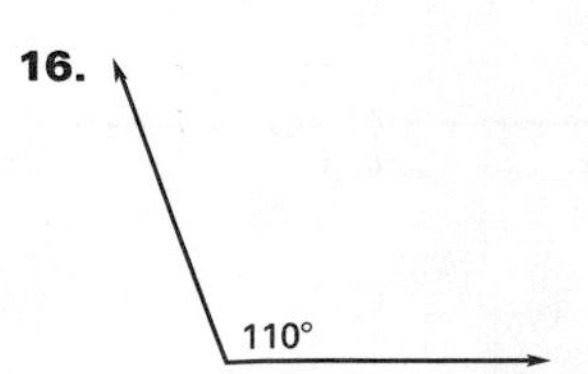

17.
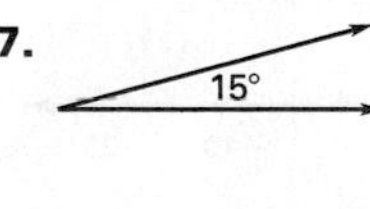

18.

19. *Sample answer*:

20. *Sample answer*:
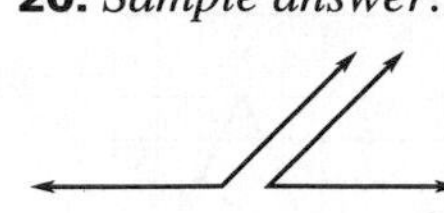

21.
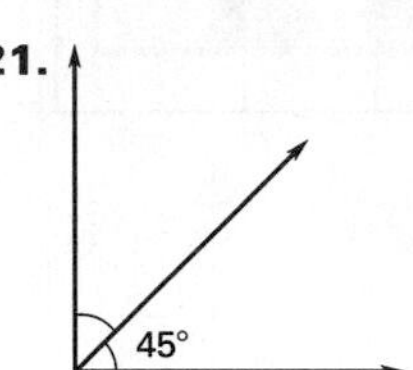

8.3 Practice and Problem Solving (pp. 400–402)

28. $b = 50$ and $a = 130$; $b = 2b - 50$ because $b°$ and $(2b - 50)°$ are measures of corresponding angles. From here find $b = 50$. $a + 2b - 50 = 180$, or $a = 130$ because $a°$ and $(2b - 50)°$ are measures of supplementary angles.

8.5 Practice and Problem Solving (pp. 415–416)

23. $\triangle DAB \cong \triangle BCD$ by the SSS postulate.

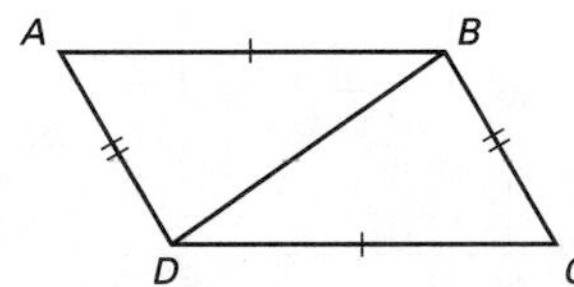

24. $\triangle ABC \cong \triangle AED$. They are congruent according to the side-angle-side congruence postulate.

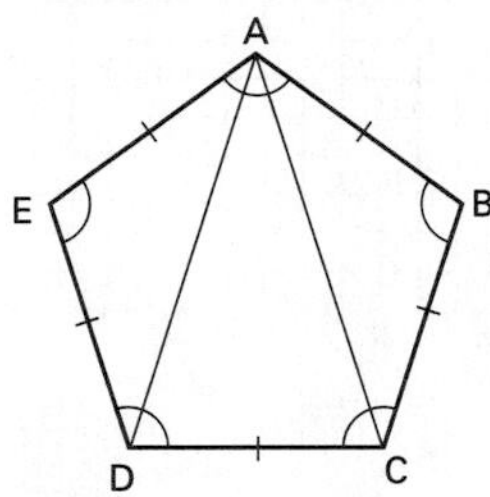

25. The similar triangles created by drawing diagonals of the hexagon are all congruent according to the side-angle-side congruence postulate. Therefore, the triangle formed in the center of the hexagon has three sides of equal length and so is an equilateral triangle.

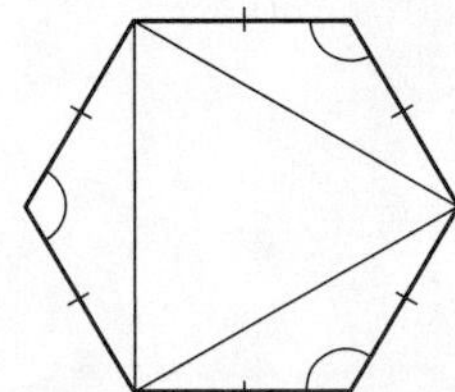

ADDITIONAL ANSWERS

8.7 Practice and Problem Solving (pp. 425–427)

18.

k

1 VEST FRONT

2 VEST BACK

19. *Sample answer:*

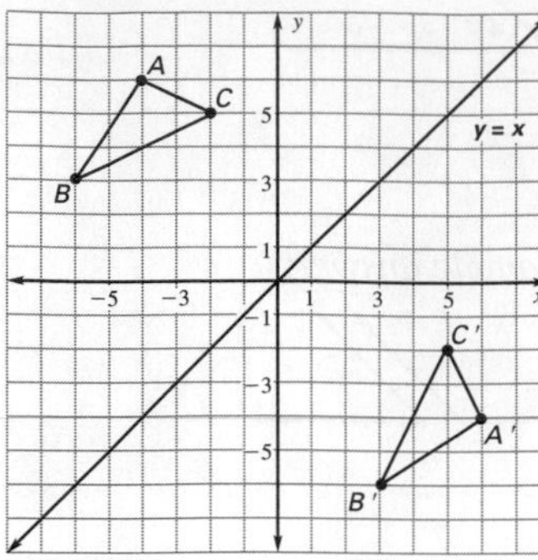

8.8 Practice and Problem Solving (pp. 430–431)

8.

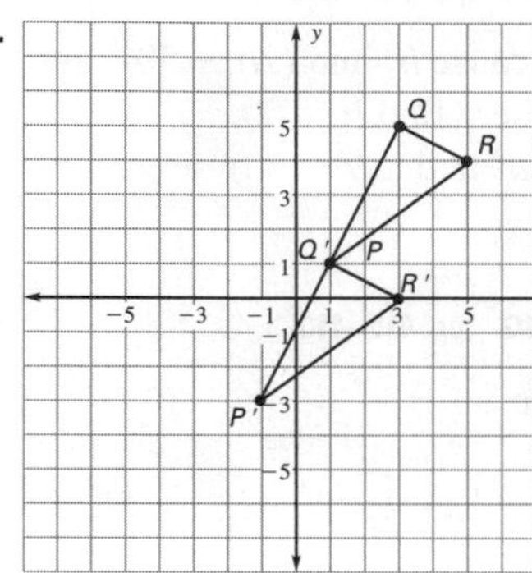

9.

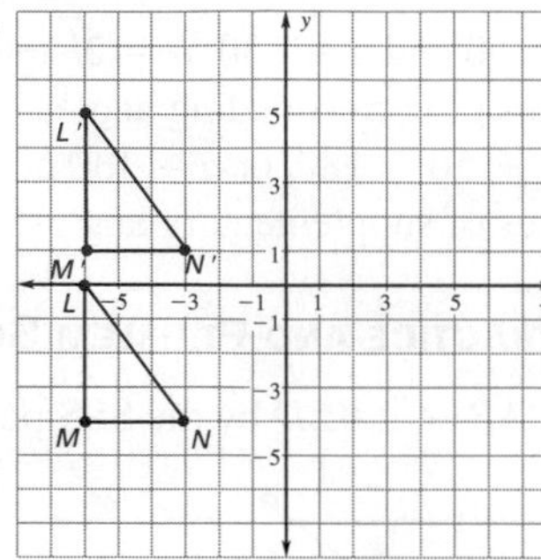

10.

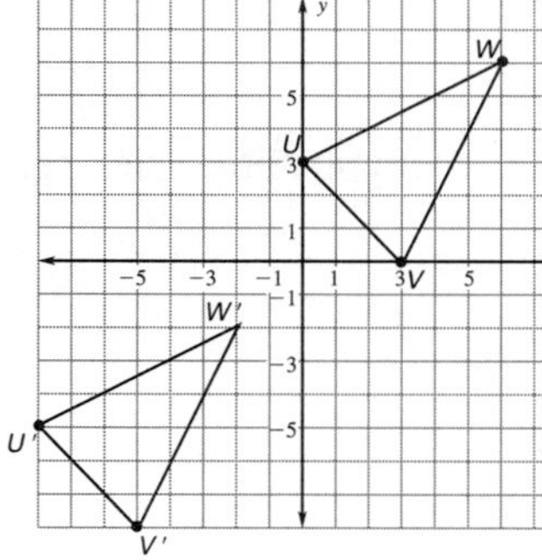

13.

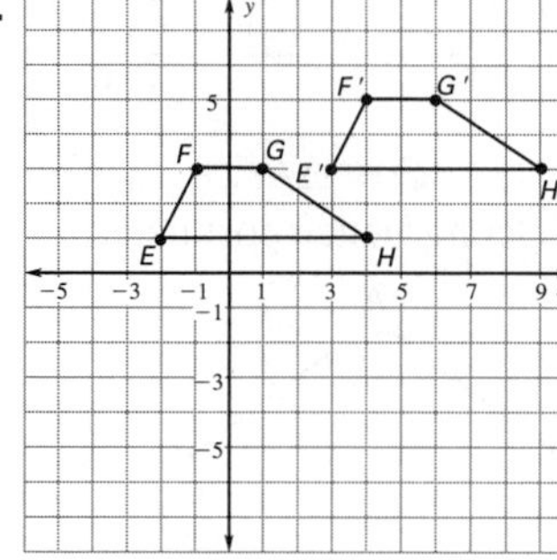

14.

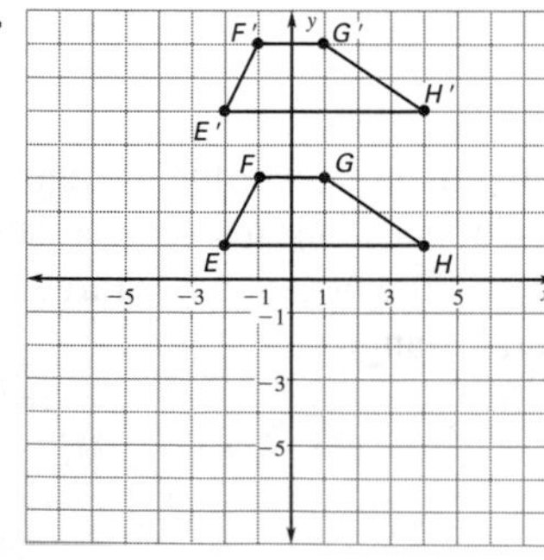

Chapter Summary and Review (pp. 438–441)

20.

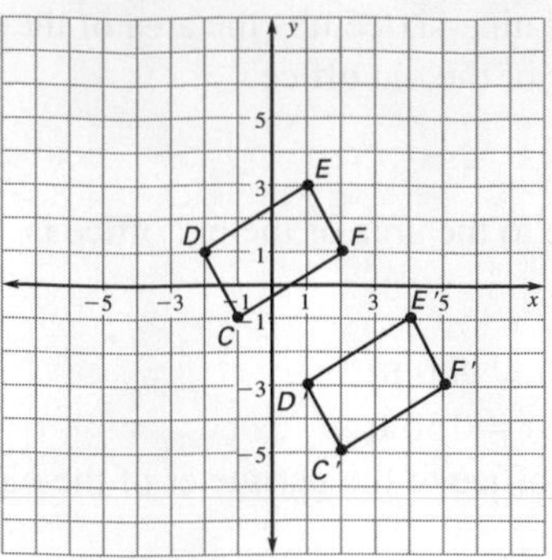

Chapter 9

9.6 Practice and Problem Solving (pp. 478–479)

16. −5 0 5

17.

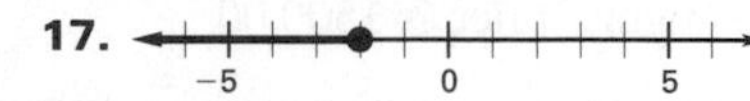

18. −10 −5 0 5 10

19.

20. −5 0 5

27.

28. −10 −5 0 5 10

29.

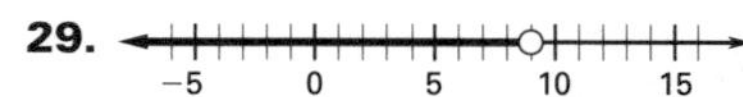

30. −10 −5 0 5 10

31.

32. −10 −5 0 5 10

33.

34. −20 −10 0 10 20

35. −5 0 5

36. −10 −5 0 5 10

37. −5 0 5

38. −10 −5 0 5 10

39.

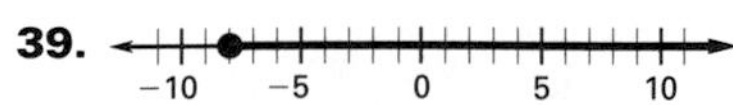

40. −5 0 5

41. 0 5 10 15 20

42. −20 −10 0 10 20

43.

9.7 Practice and Problem Solving (pp. 482–483)

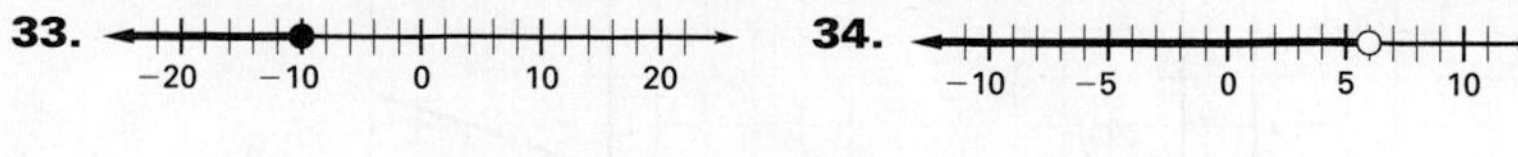

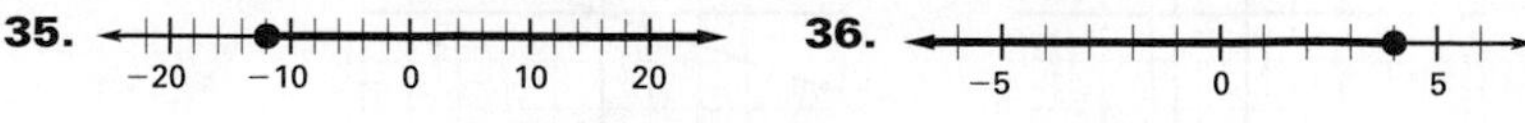

37. −5 0 5

Chapter 10

10.2 Practice and Problem Solving (pp. 520–521)

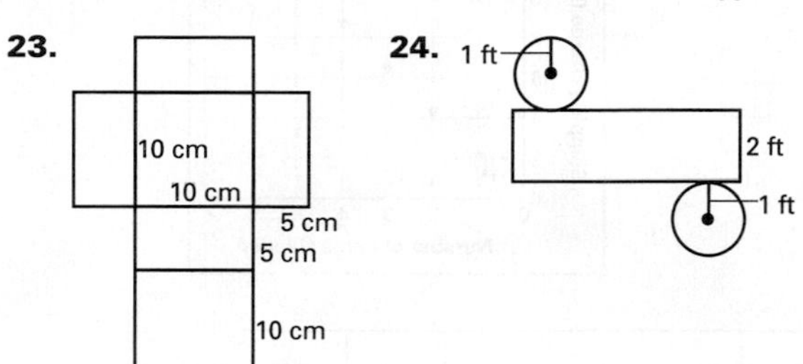

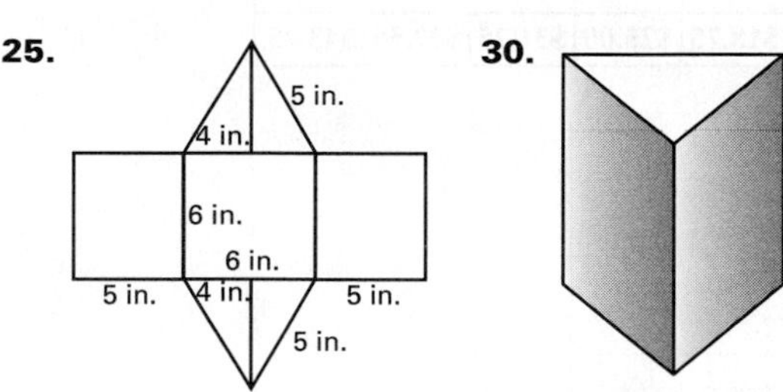

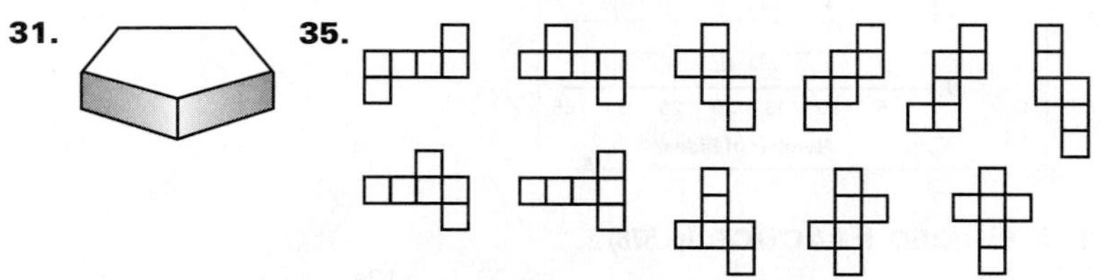

10.4 Practice and Problem Solving (pp. 532–533)

23–24.

Edge	Surface Area	Volume	Surface Area ÷ Volume
1 cm	6 cm^2	1 cm^3	6 cm^{-1}
2 cm	24 cm^2	8 cm^3	3 cm^{-1}
3 cm	54 cm^2	27 cm^3	2 cm^{-1}
4 cm	96 cm^2	64 cm^3	1.5 cm^{-1}

Chapter 11

11.1 Practice and Problem Solving (pp. 565–566)

18.

Input, x	0	1	2	3	4
Output, y	**2**	**7**	**12**	**17**	**22**

19.

Input, x	0	1	2	3	4
Output, y	**6**	$6\frac{1}{3}$	$6\frac{2}{3}$	**7**	$7\frac{1}{3}$

20.

Input, x	0	1	2	3	4
Output, y	**−1**	**0**	**3**	**8**	**15**

11.2 Guided Practice (p. 569)

15.

x	−3	−2	−1	0	1	2	3
y	$\frac{1}{2}$	$\frac{1}{3}$	$\frac{1}{6}$	**0**	$-\frac{1}{6}$	$-\frac{1}{3}$	$-\frac{1}{2}$

11.2 Practice and Problem Solving (pp. 569–570)

20.

x	−3	−2	−1	0	1	2	3
y	**−11**	**−10**	**−9**	**−8**	**−7**	**−6**	**−5**

21.

x	−3	−2	−1	0	1	2	3
y	**−2**	**0**	**2**	**4**	**6**	**8**	**10**

22.

x	−3	−2	−1	0	1	2	3
y	**32**	**28**	**24**	**20**	**16**	**12**	**8**

23.

x	−3	−2	−1	0	1	2	3
y	**−36**	**−30**	**−24**	**−18**	**−12**	**−6**	**0**

24.

x	−2	−1	0	1	2
y	**8**	**7**	**6**	**5**	**4**

25.

x	−2	−1	0	1	2
y	$\frac{15}{2}$	**7**	$\frac{13}{2}$	**6**	$\frac{11}{2}$

26.

x	−2	−1	0	1	2
y	**18**	**15**	**12**	**9**	**6**

27.

x	−2	−1	0	1	2
y	**4**	**7**	**10**	**13**	**16**

28.

x	−2	−1	0	1	2
y	**−14**	**−10**	**−6**	**−2**	**2**

29.

x	−2	−1	0	1	2
y	**6**	**3**	**0**	**−3**	**−6**

11.3 Guided Practice (p. 573)

7.

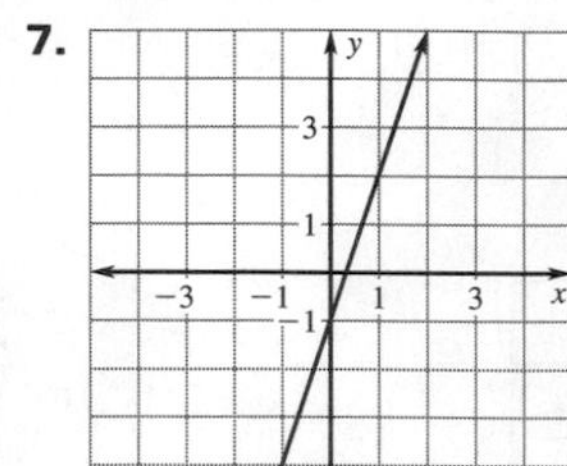

8.

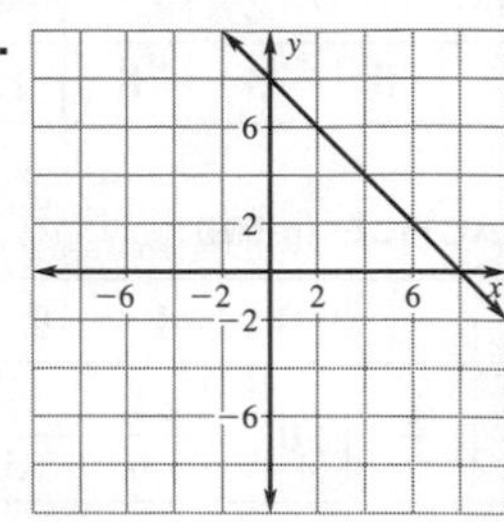

11.3 Practice and Problem Solving (pp. 573–575)

12.

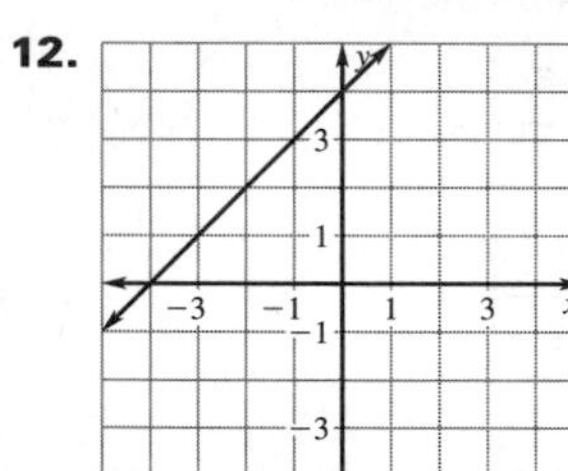

13.

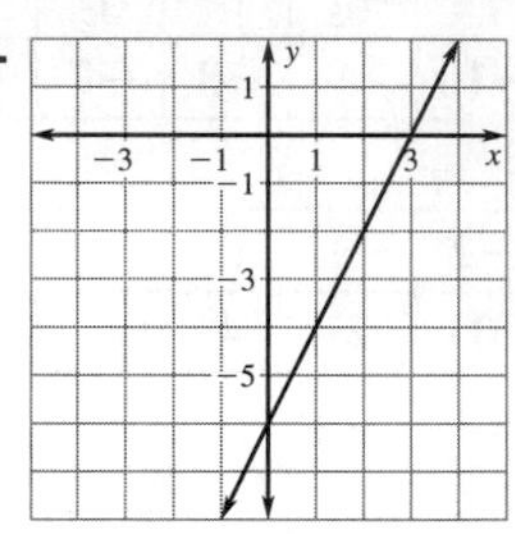

14.

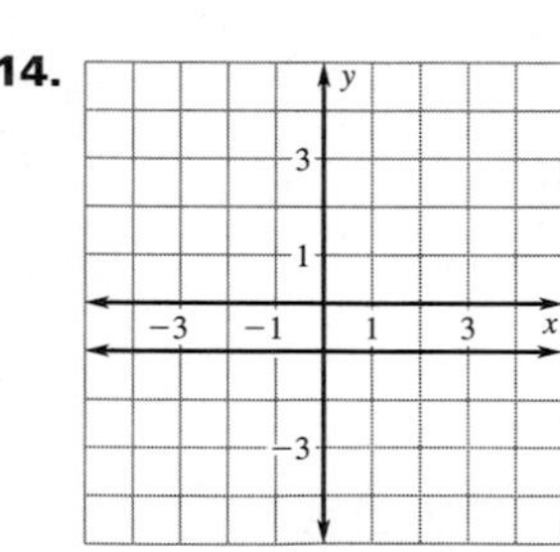

15.

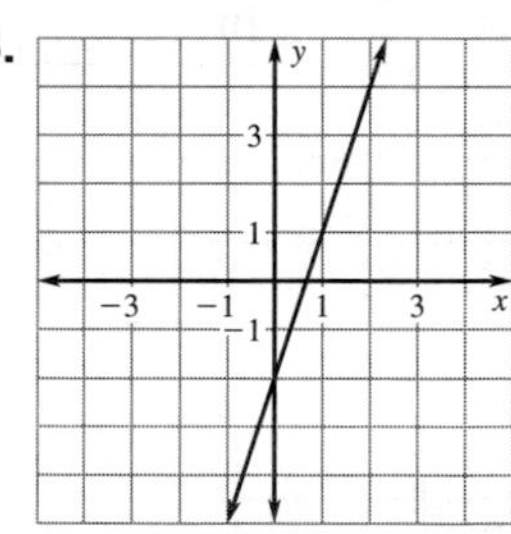

16.

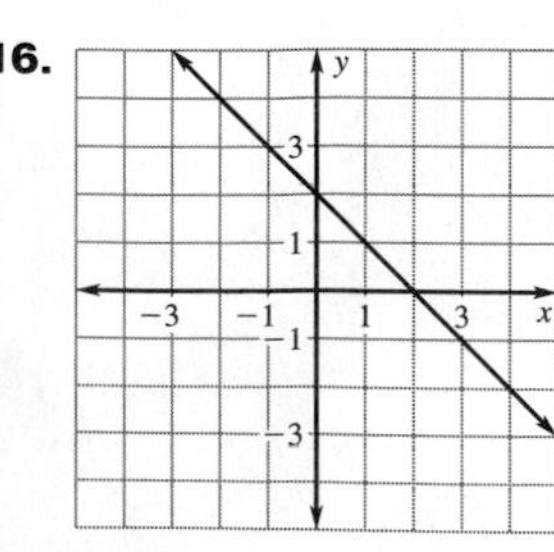

17.

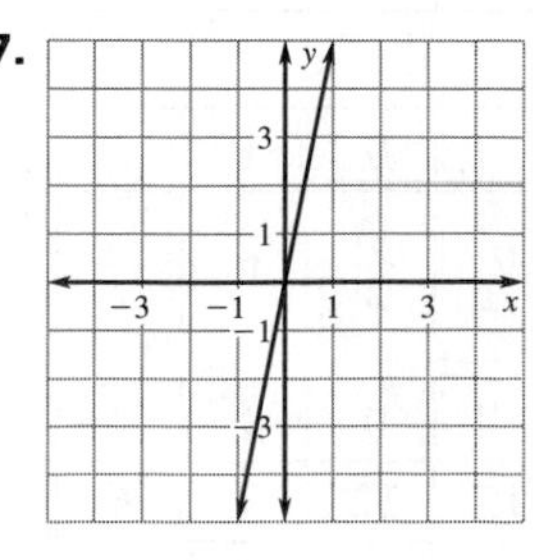

18.

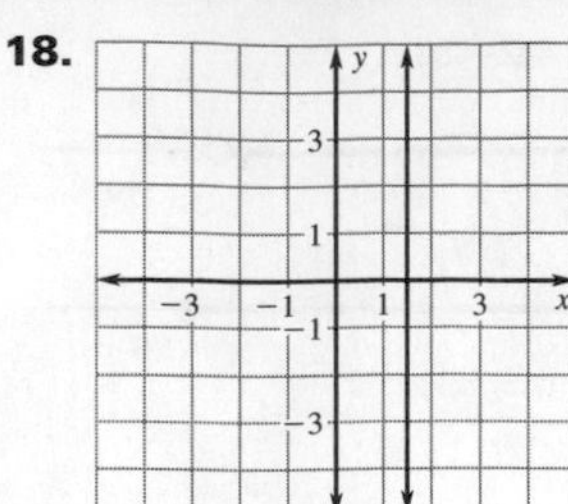

19.

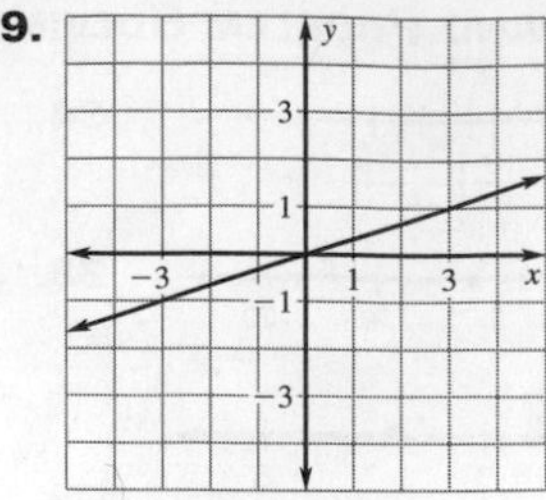

20.

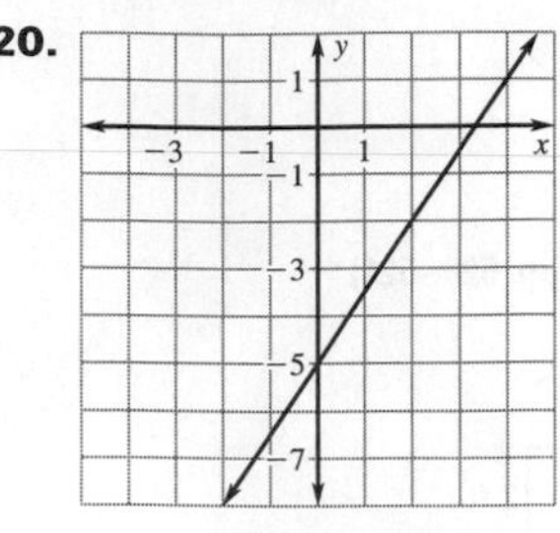

33.

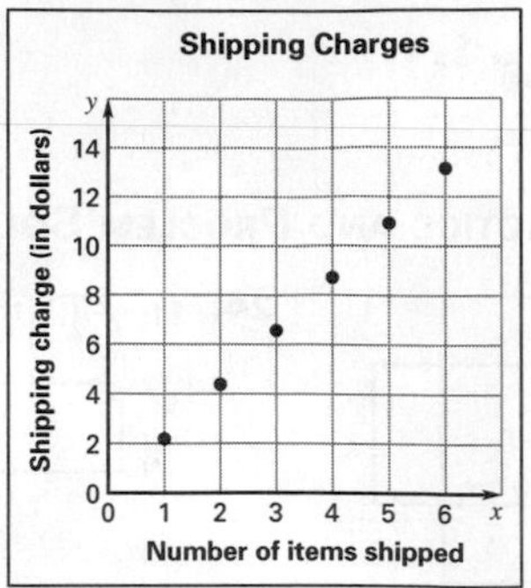

35.

Number of rides	5	10	15	20	25	30	35
Cost	**$6.25**	**$12.50**	**$18.75**	**$25.00**	**$31.25**	**$37.50**	**$43.75**

36.

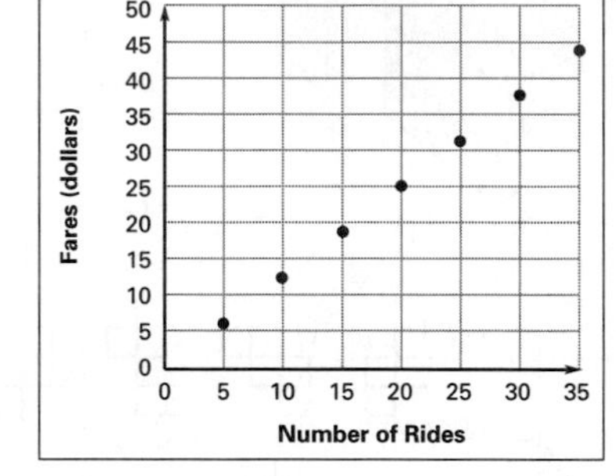

11.4 Guided Practice (p. 578)

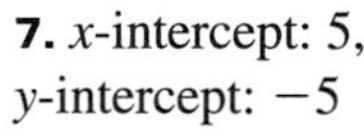

7. x-intercept: 5, y-intercept: -5

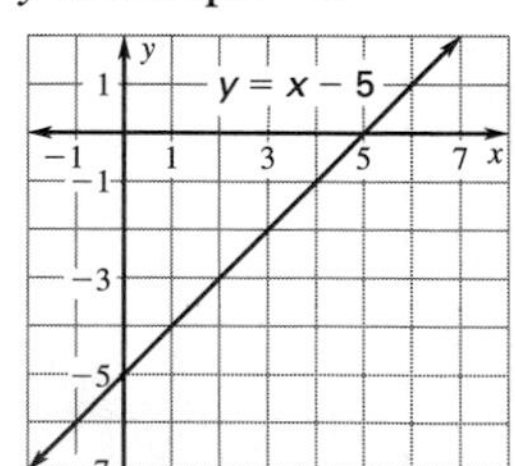

8. x-intercept: $-\frac{12}{5}$, y-intercept: 3

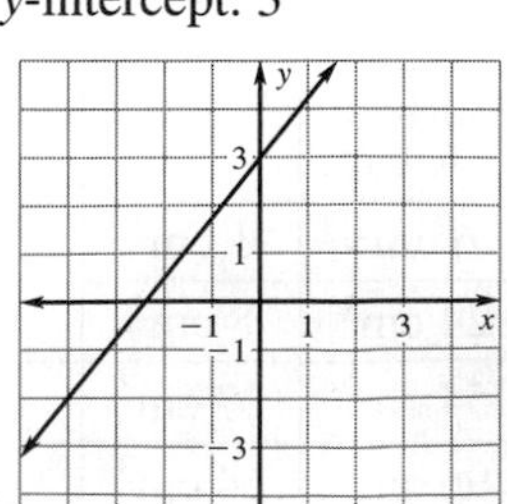

11.4 Practice and Problem Solving (pp. 579–580)

27.

28.

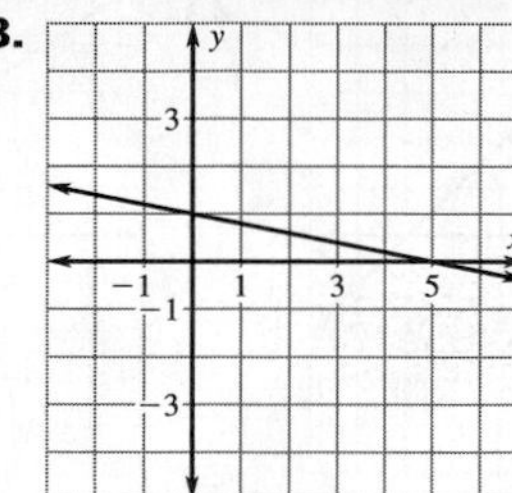

29.

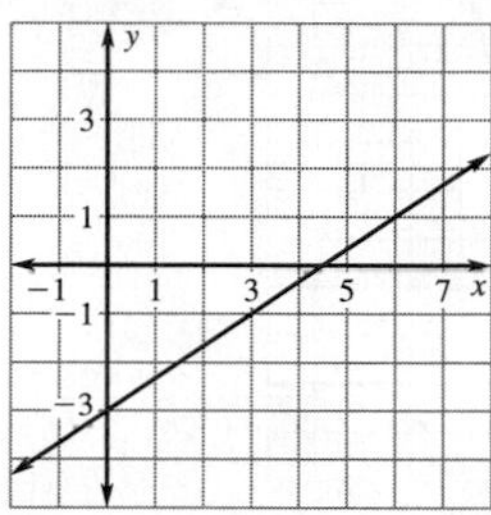

30.

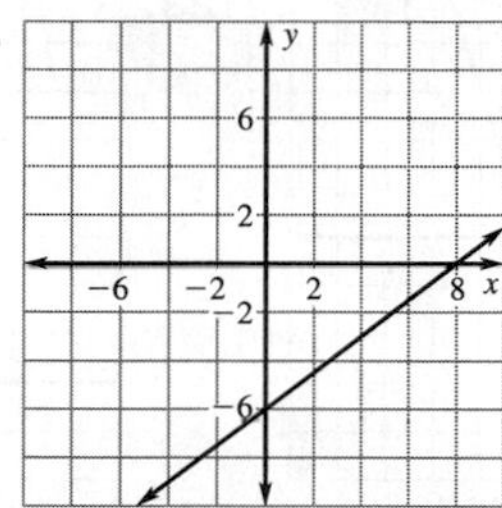

31.

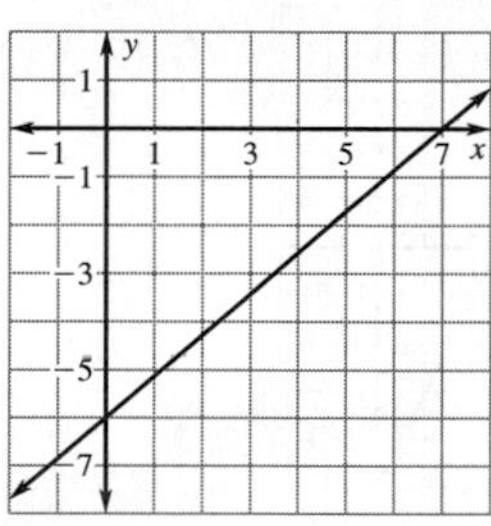

36.

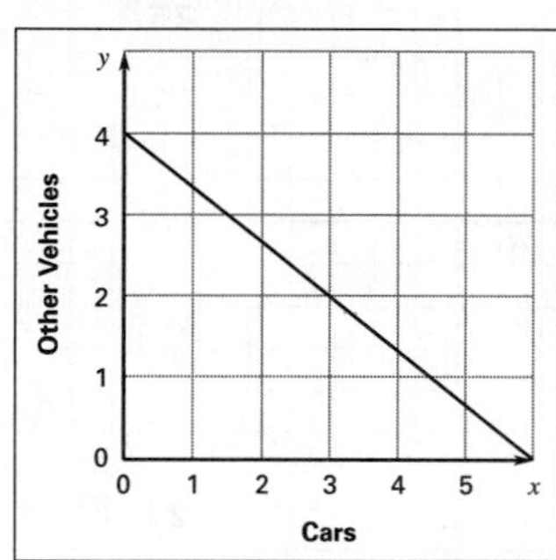

39.

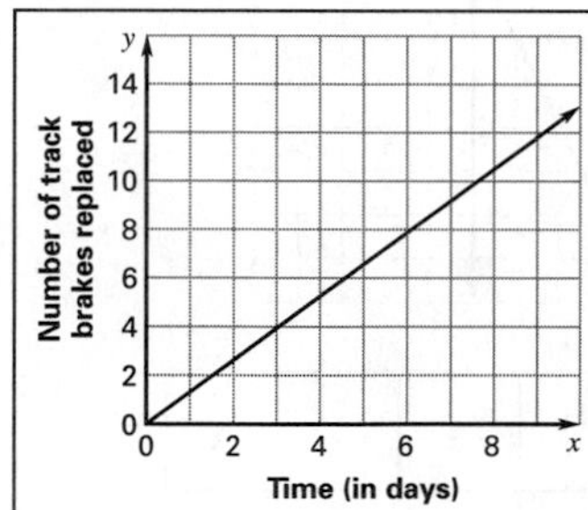

47.

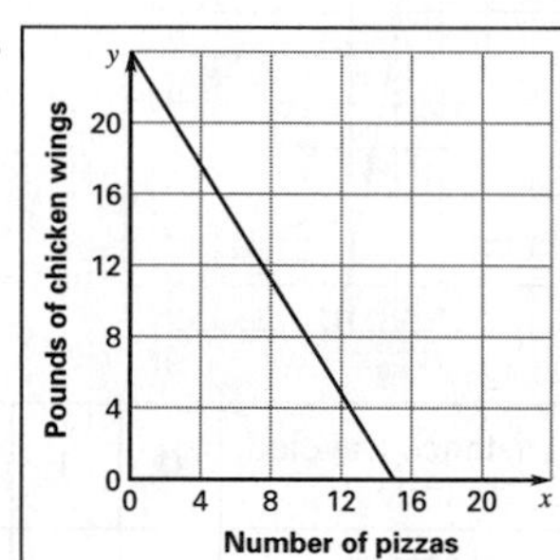

49.

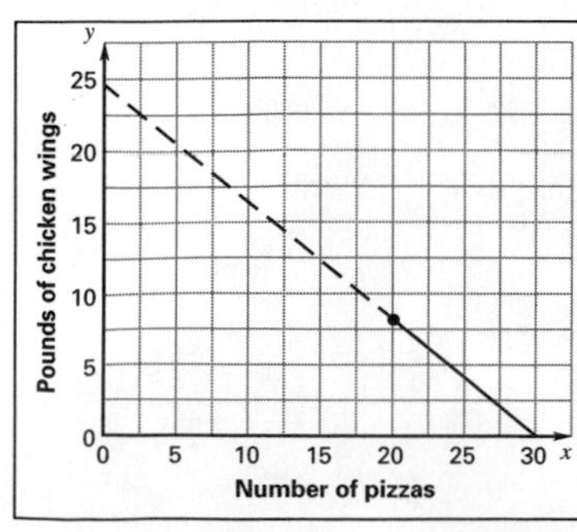

11.5 Developing Concepts (p. 582)

1.

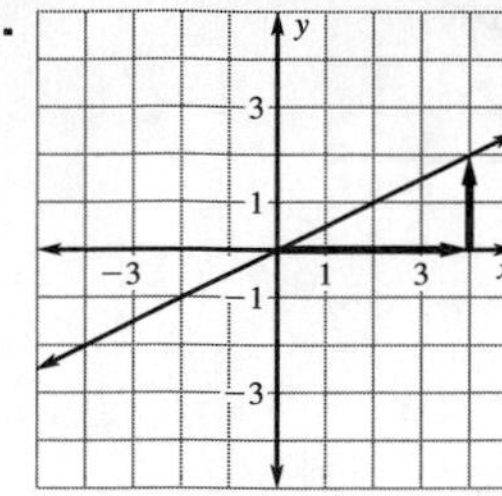

Slope = $\frac{1}{2}$

2.

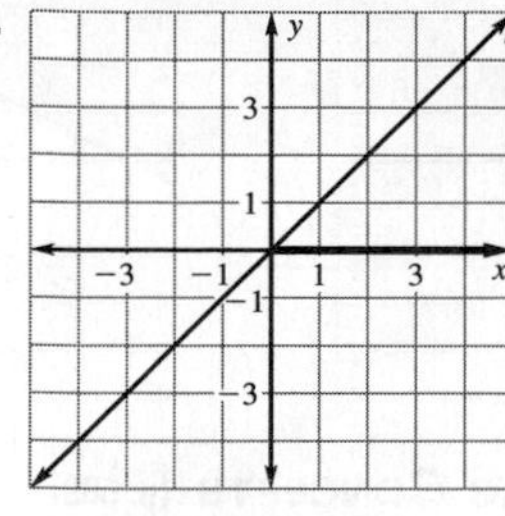

Slope = 1

3.

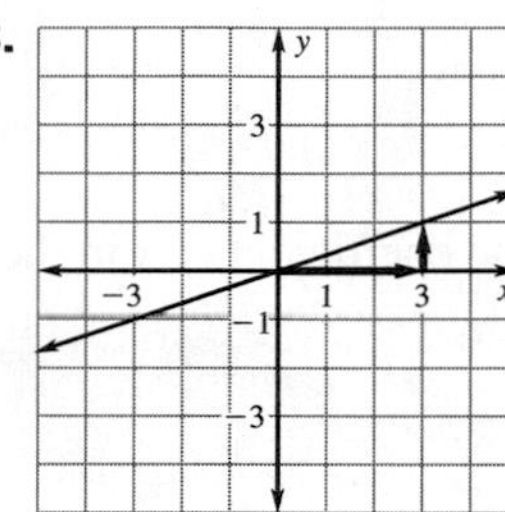

Slope = $\frac{1}{3}$

11.5 Practice and Problem Solving (pp. 586–587)

12.

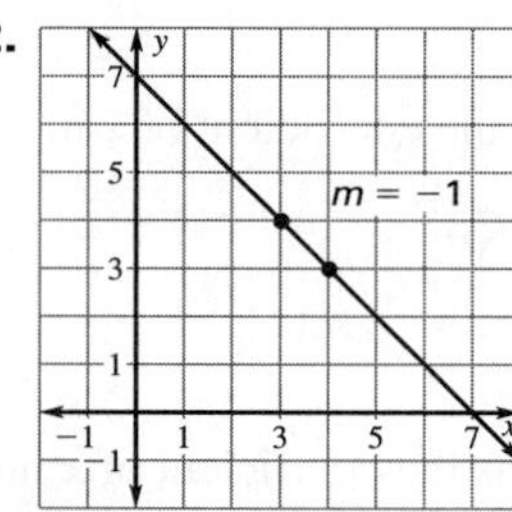

13.

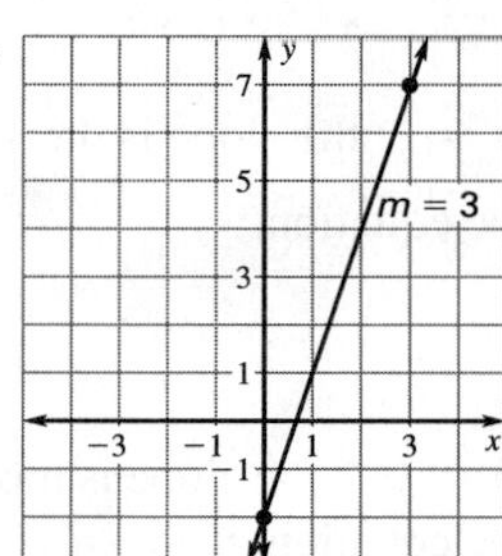

14.

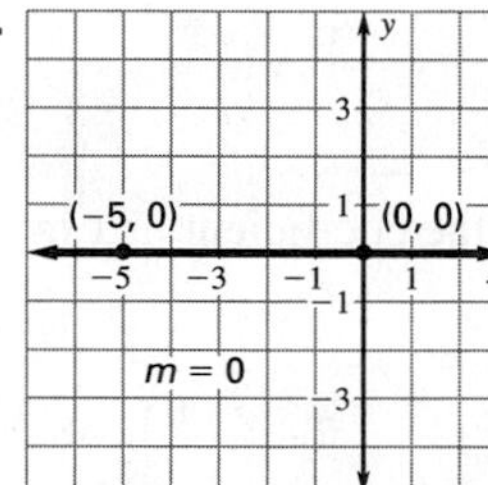

15.

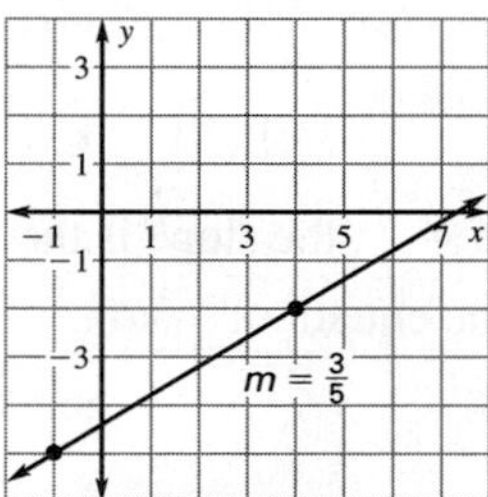

16.

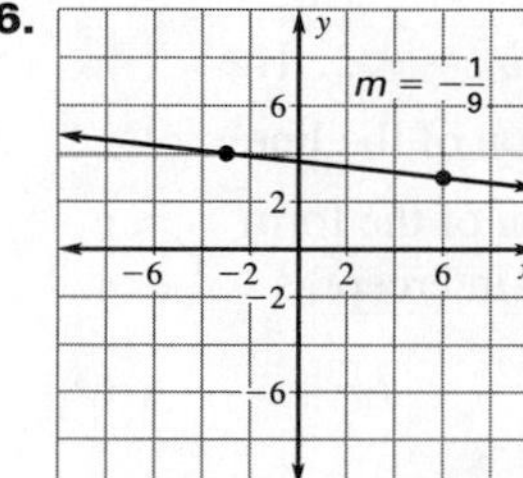

17.

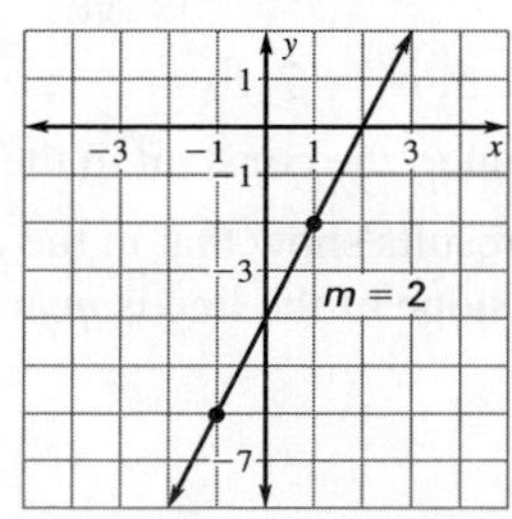

18.

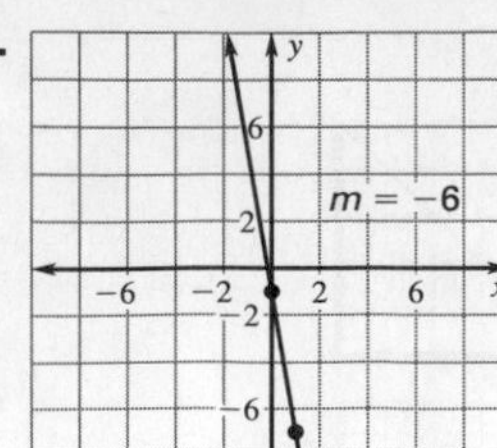

19.

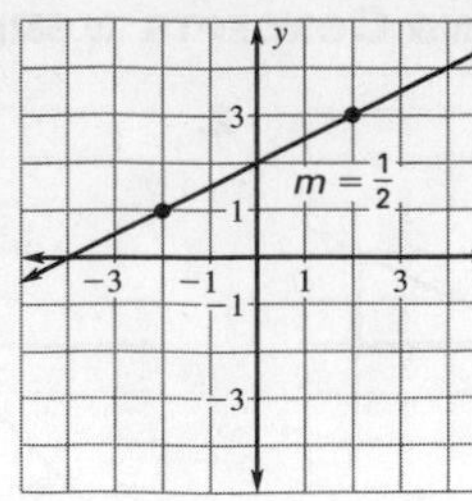

11.6 Developing Concepts (p. 588)

1.

x	y
0	2
1	3

$m = 1$; the slope is the same as the coefficient of x in the equation.

2.

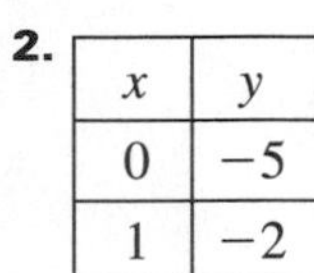

x	y
0	−5
1	−2

$m = 3$; the slope is the same as the coefficient of x in the equation.

3.

x	y
0	7
1	5

$m = -2$; the slope is the same as the coefficient of x in the equation.

4.

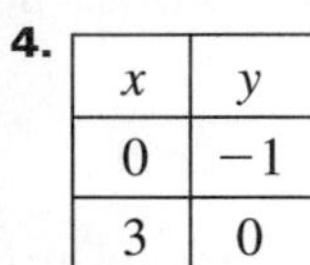

x	y
0	−1
3	0

$m = \frac{1}{3}$; the slope is the same as the coefficient of x in the equation.

5.

x	y
0	$\frac{3}{4}$
1	$-\frac{1}{4}$

$m = -1$; the slope is the same as the coefficient of x in the equation.

6.

x	y
0	$-\frac{1}{2}$
8	$\frac{9}{2}$

$m = \frac{5}{8}$; the slope is the same as the coefficient of x in the equation.

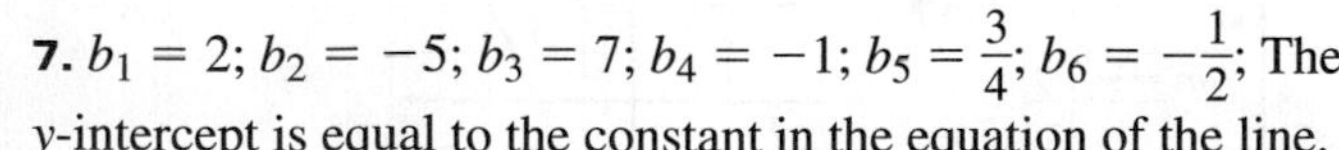

7. $b_1 = 2$; $b_2 = -5$; $b_3 = 7$; $b_4 = -1$; $b_5 = \frac{3}{4}$; $b_6 = -\frac{1}{2}$; The y-intercept is equal to the constant in the equation of the line.

8. b, $m + b$; the results show that in the equation of the form $y = mx + b$, the slope of the line is m and the y-intercept is b.

11.6 Practice and Problem Solving (pp. 591–592)

20.

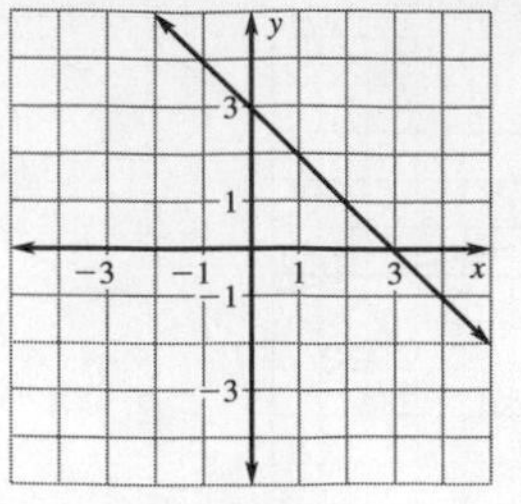

21.

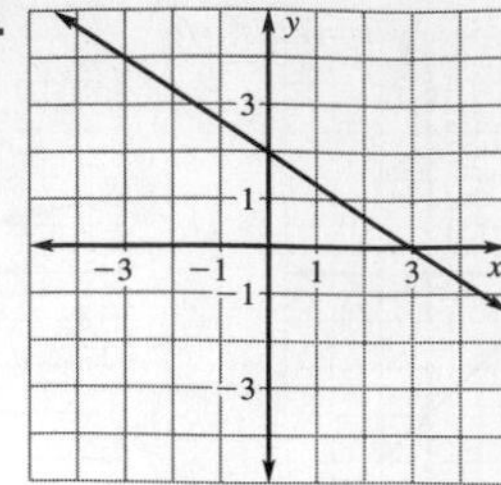

22.

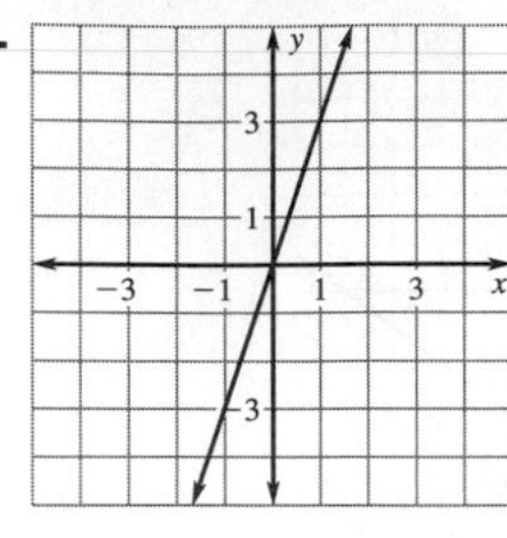

23.

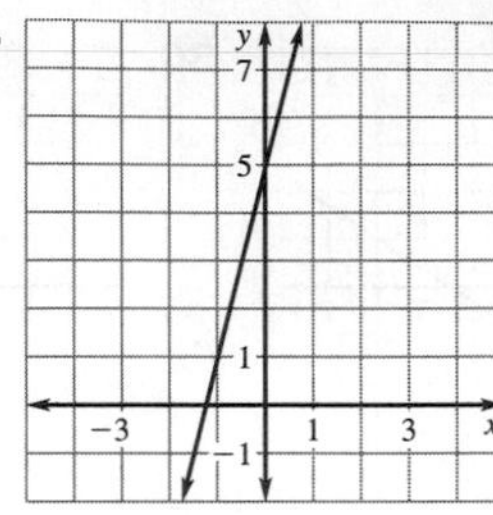

24.

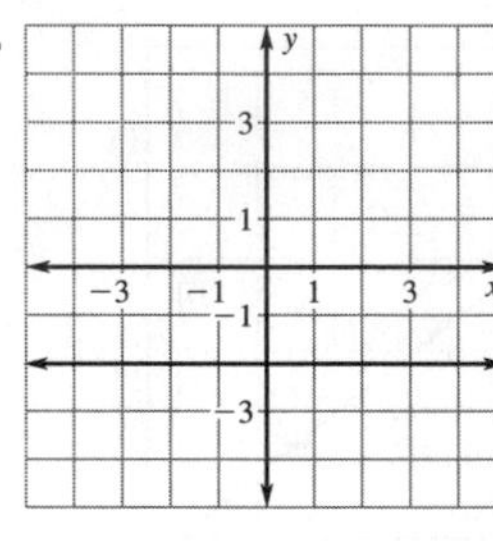

25.

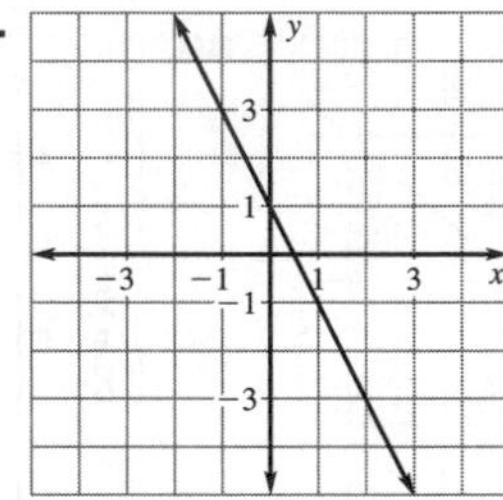

26.

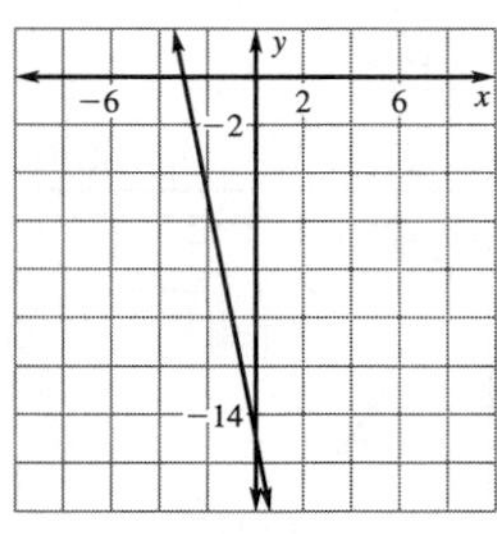

27.

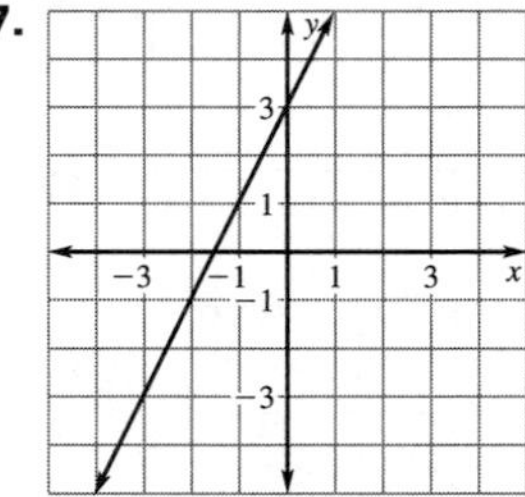

35.

Distance traveled, x, (in miles)	0	1	2	3	4	5	6
Total fare, y, (in dollars)	1.25	3.75	6.25	8.75	11.25	13.75	16.25

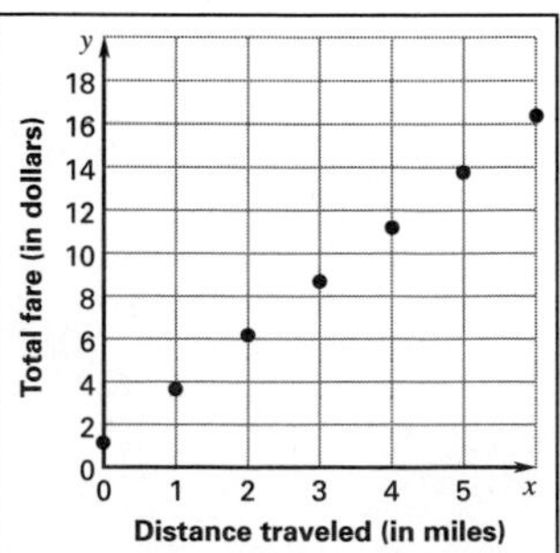

ADDITIONAL ANSWERS

11.7 Practice and Problem Solving (pp. 596–597)

8.

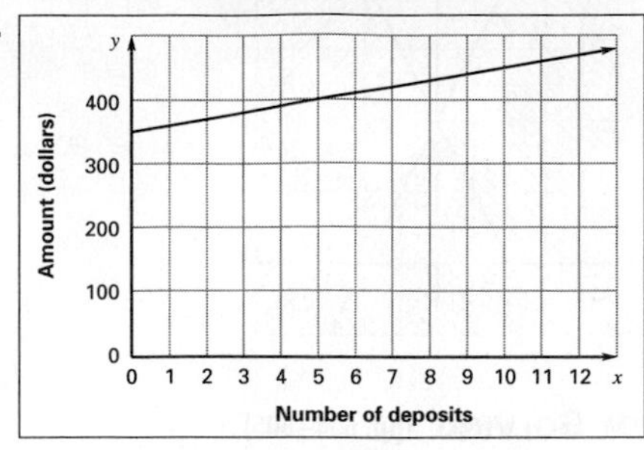

10.

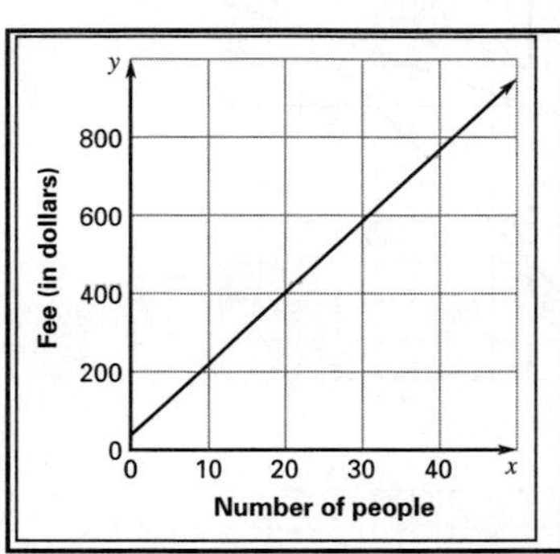

20.

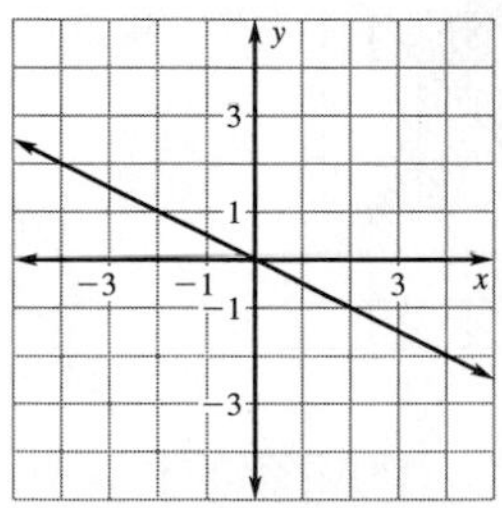

21.

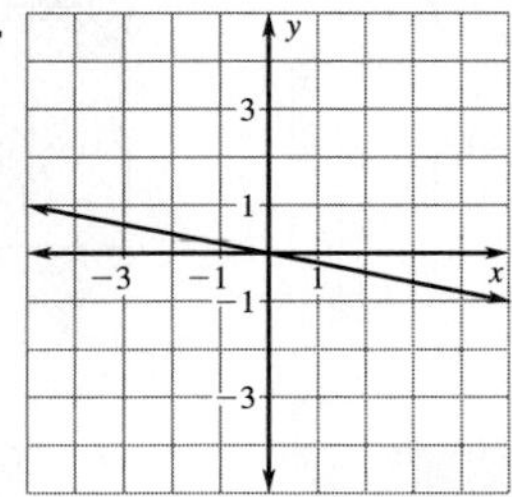

22.

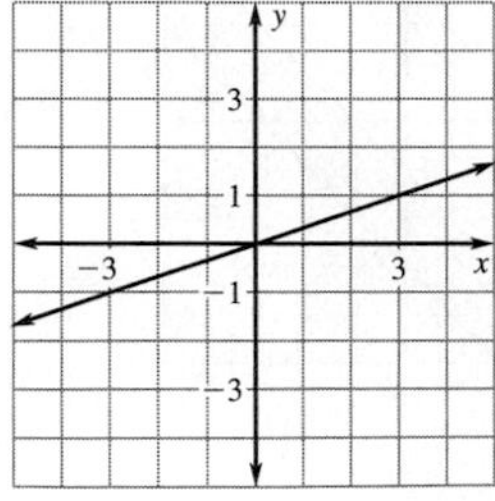

26.

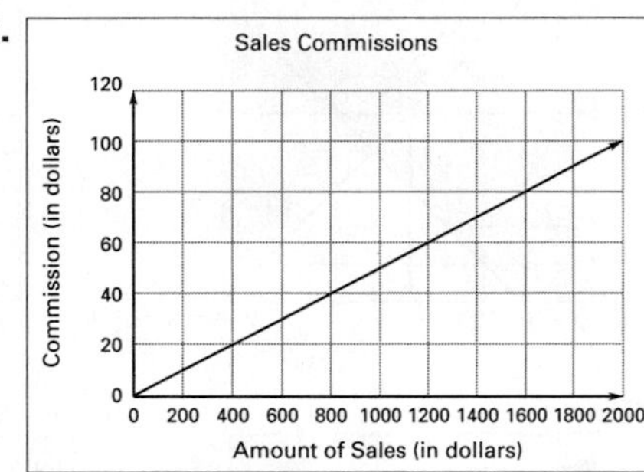

27.

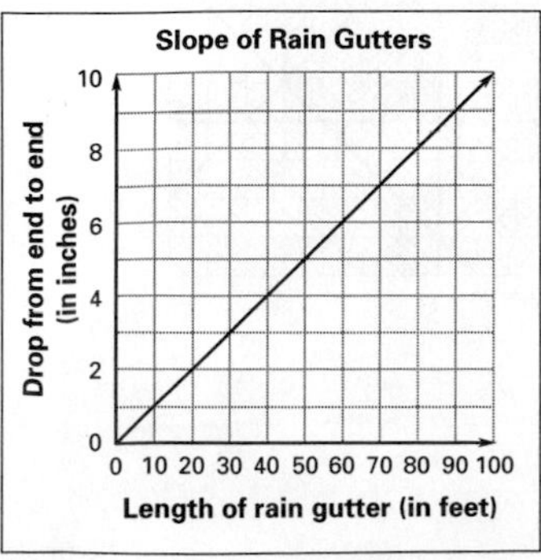

11.8 Guided Practice (p. 600)

13.

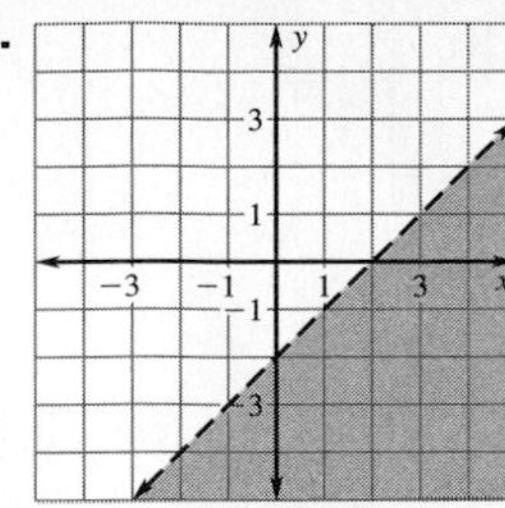

14.

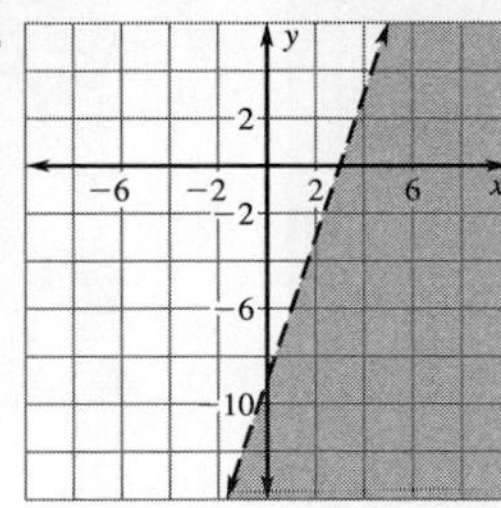

15.

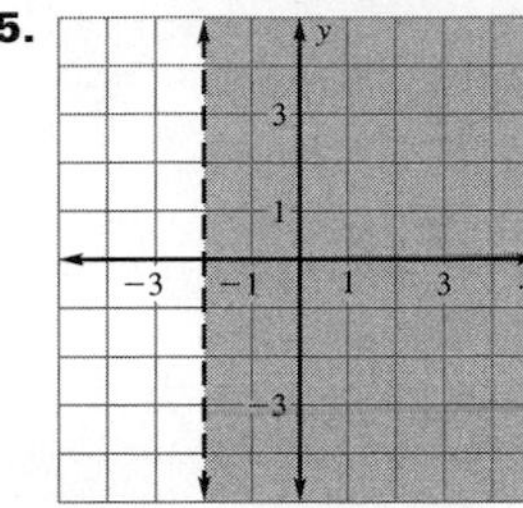

11.8 Practice and Problem Solving (pp. 600–601)

23.

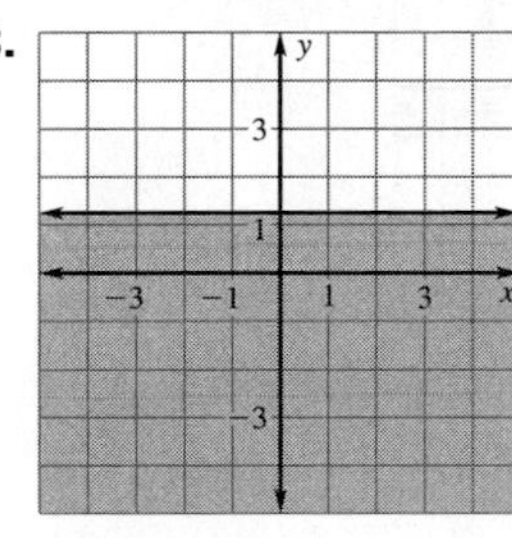

24.

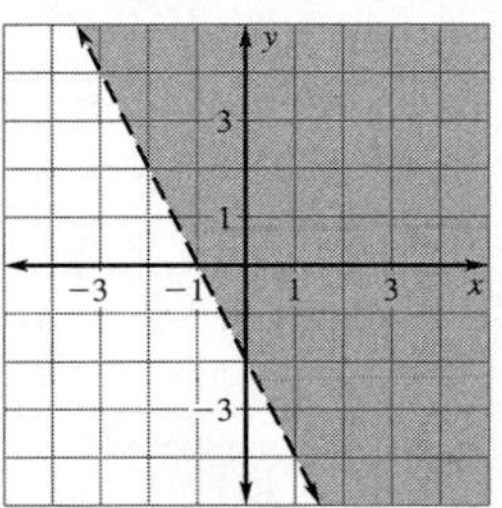

25.

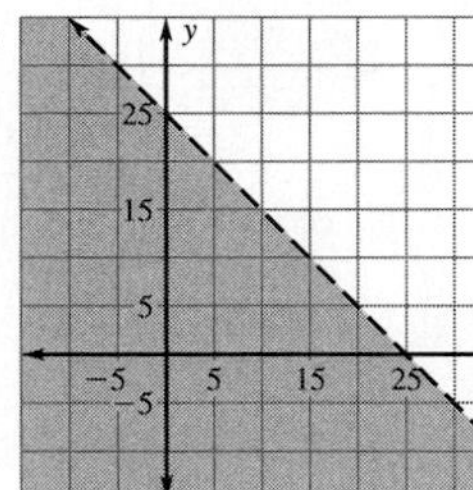

26.

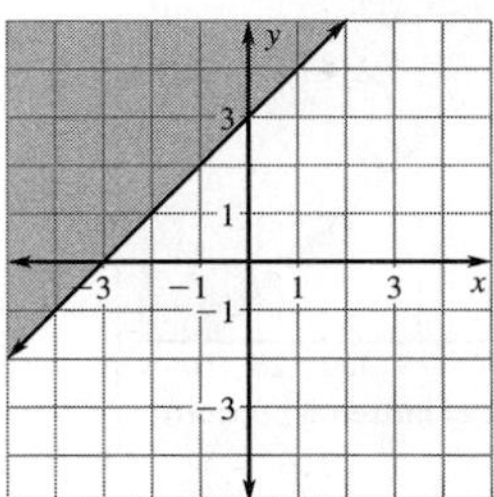

27.

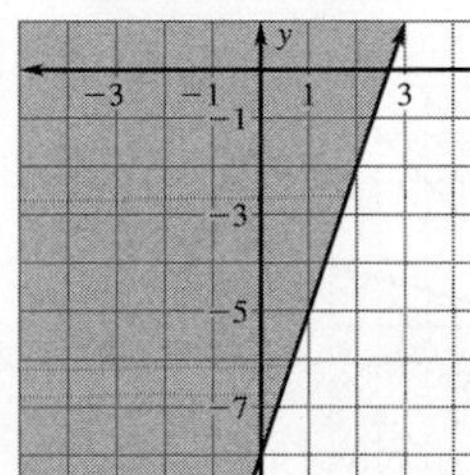

28.

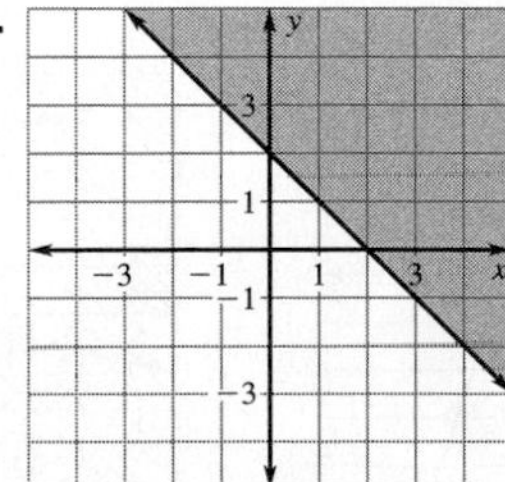

29.

30.

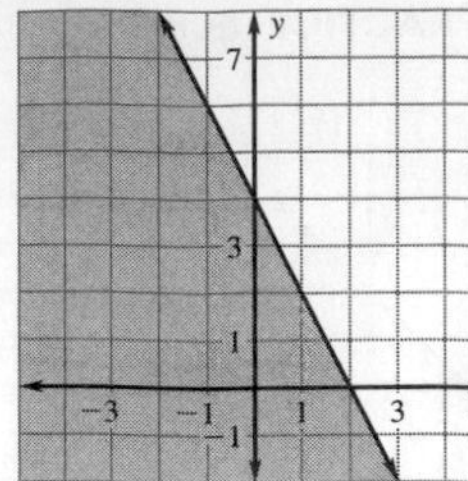

31.

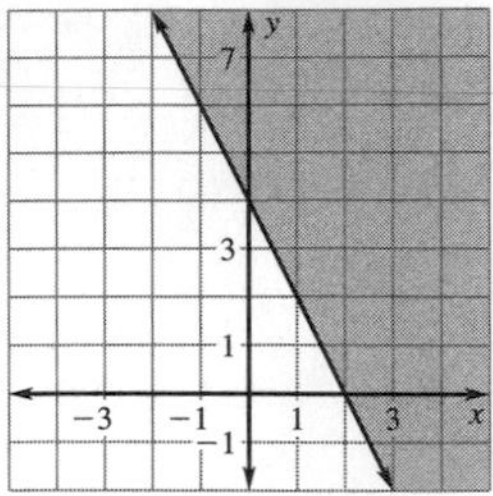

37.

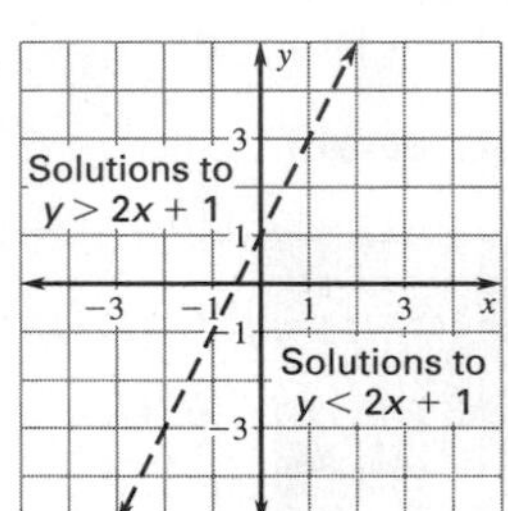

Solutions to $y > -3x + 4$

Solutions to $y < -3x + 4$

39.

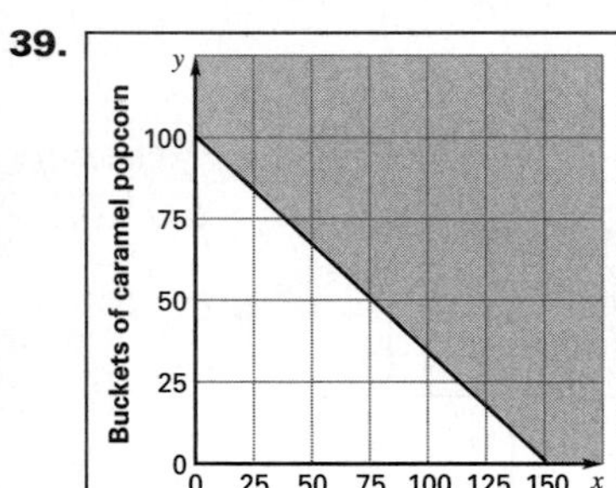

11.9 Guided Practice (p. 604)

5.

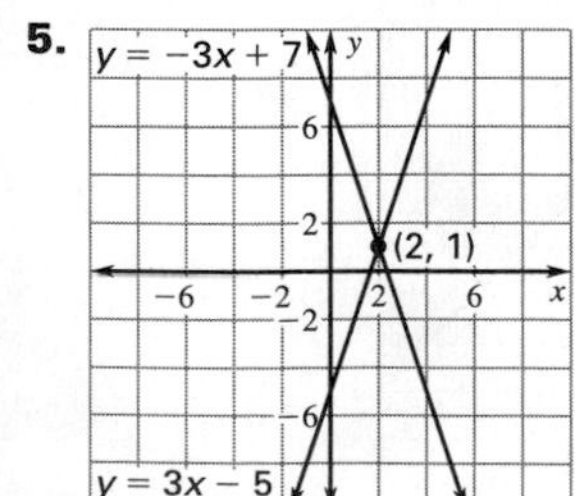

6.

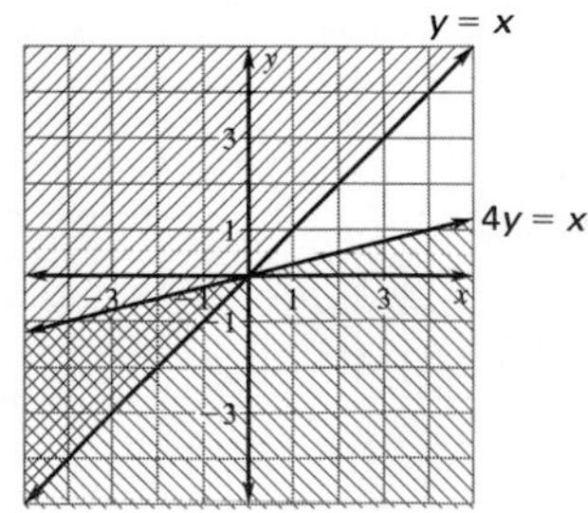

7.

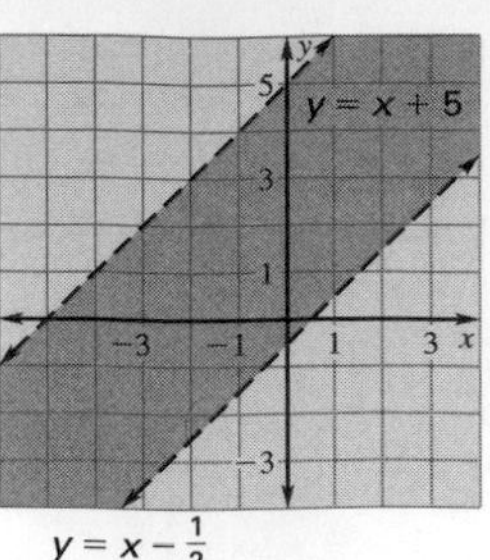

8.

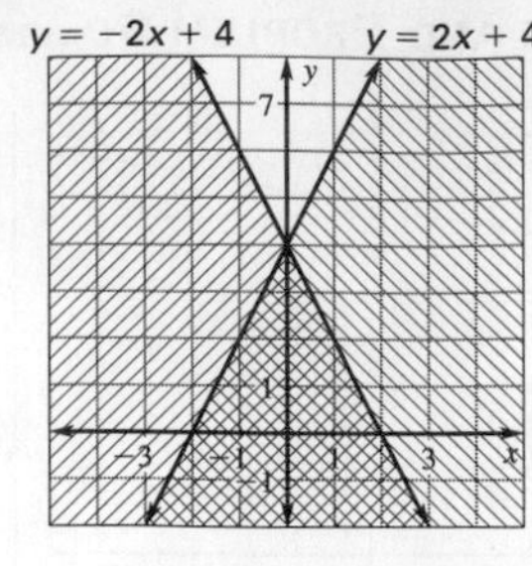

11.9 Practice and Problem Solving (pp. 604–605)

11.

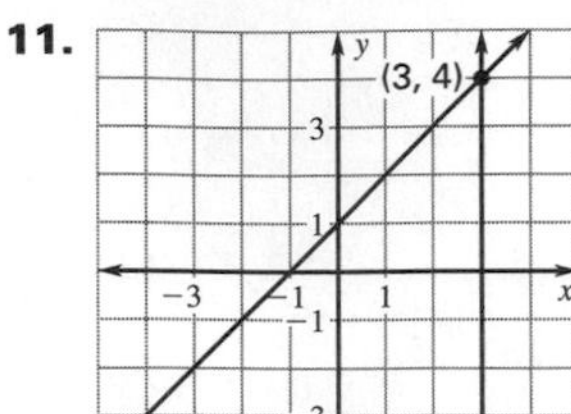

12.

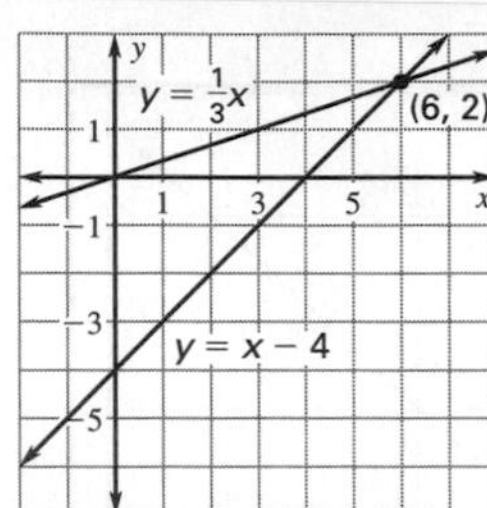

13.

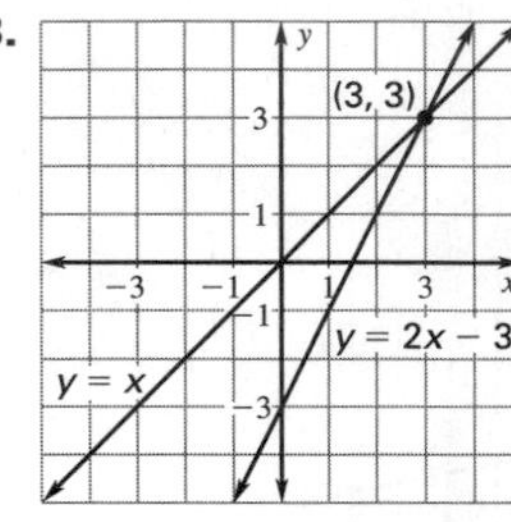

16.

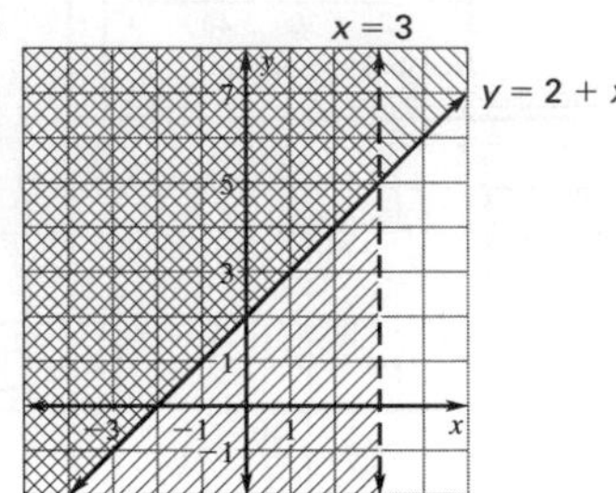

17.

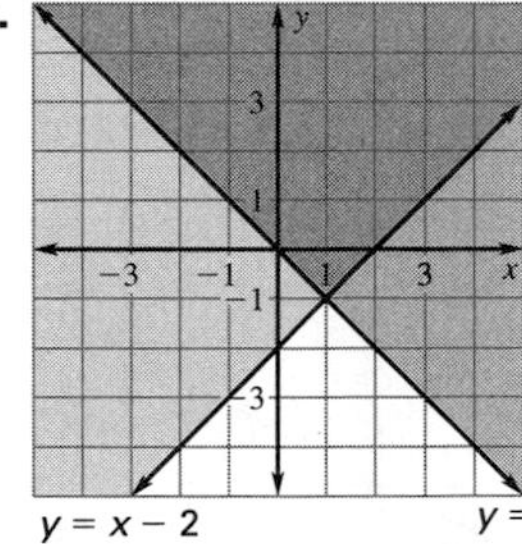

18.

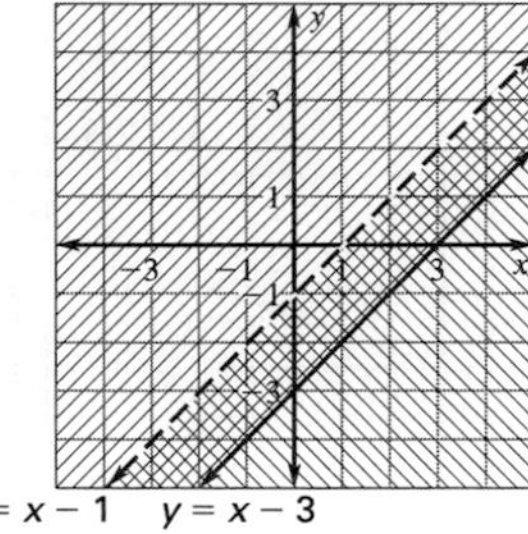

19.

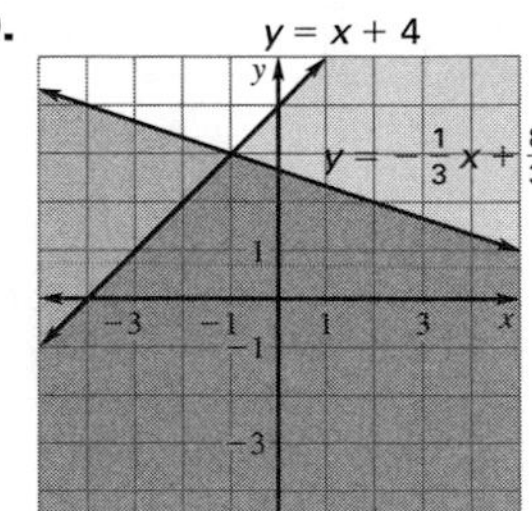

20.

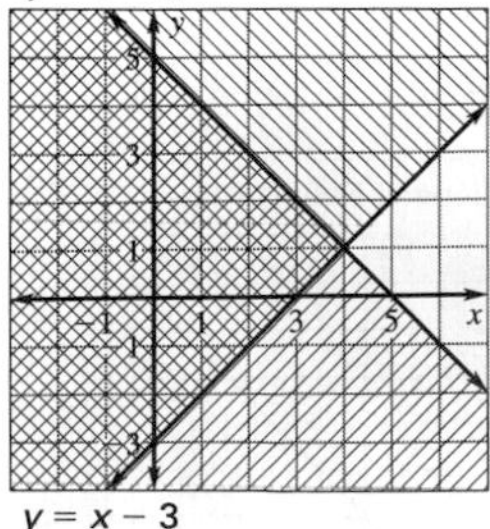

21.

$y = x + 3$

$y = 9 - x$

24.

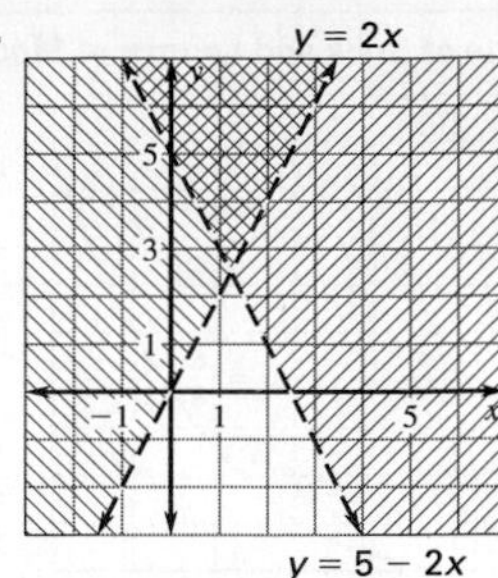

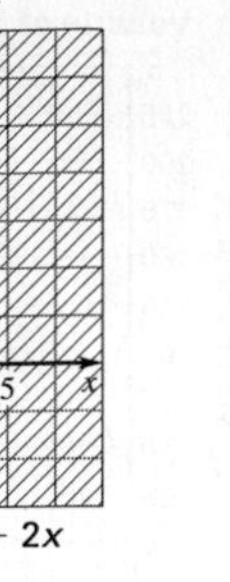

32.

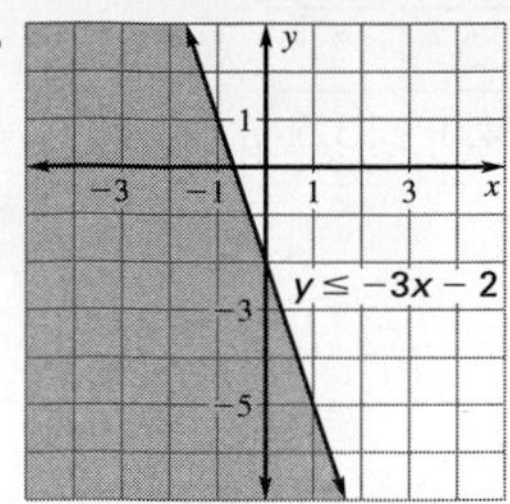

33.

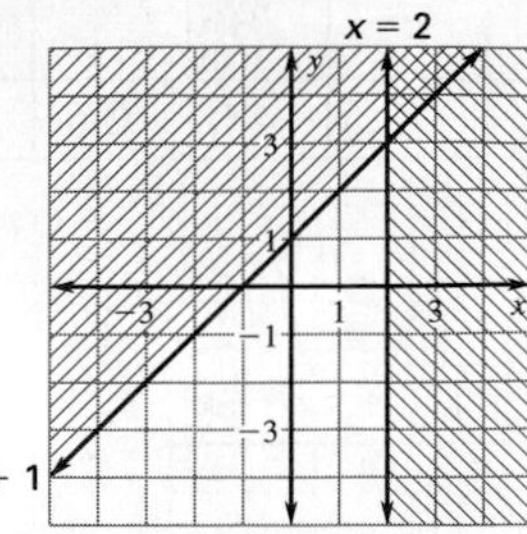

25.

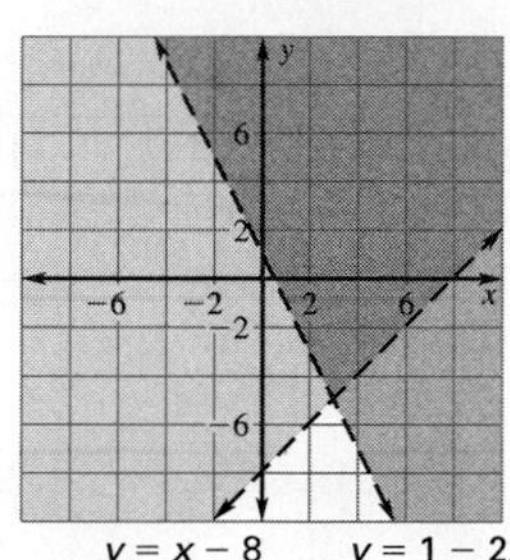

26.

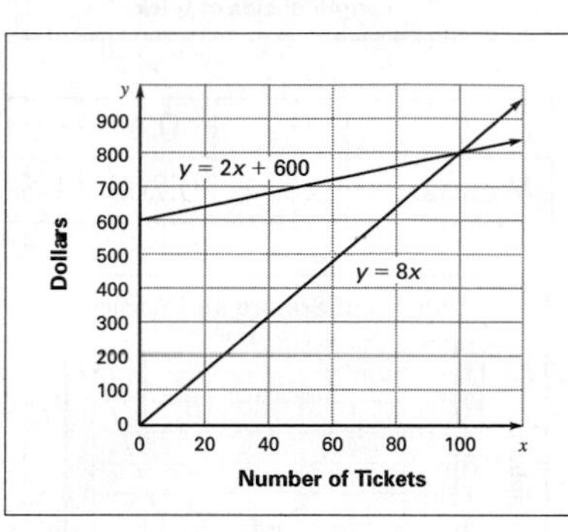

34.

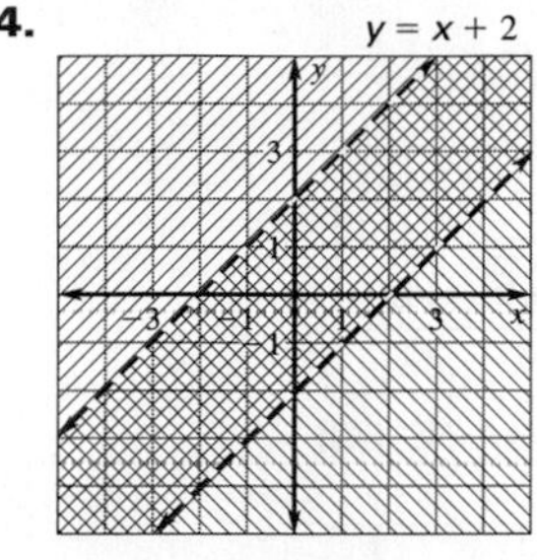

35.

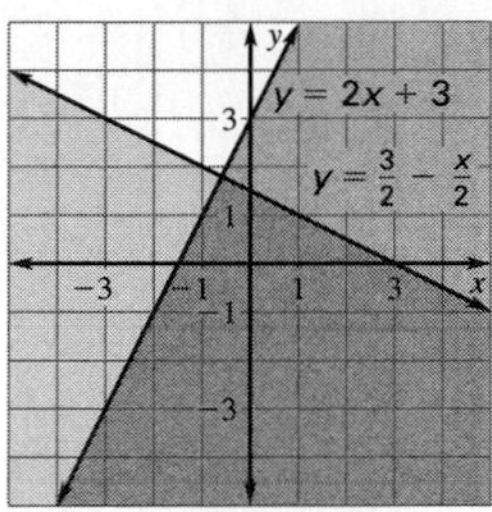

Chapter Summary and Review (pp. 606–609)

15. $2, -10$

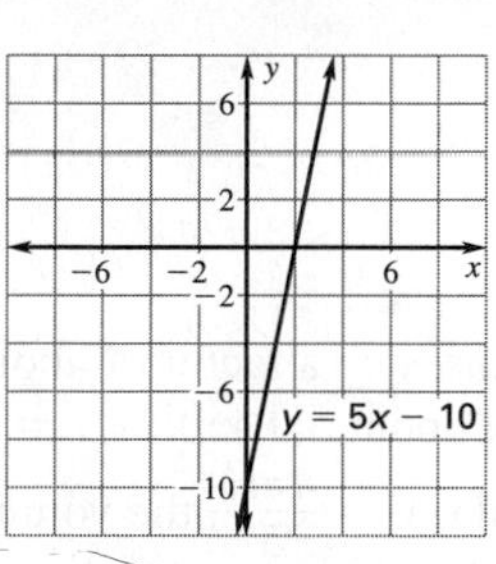

16. $\frac{1}{4}, 2$

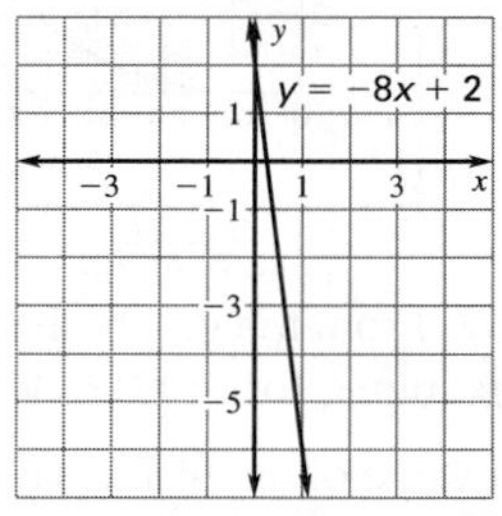

17. $-\frac{4}{3}, 4$

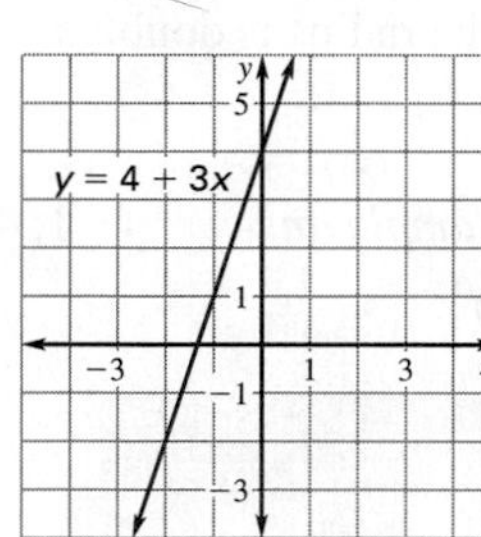

18. $\frac{7}{6}, 7$

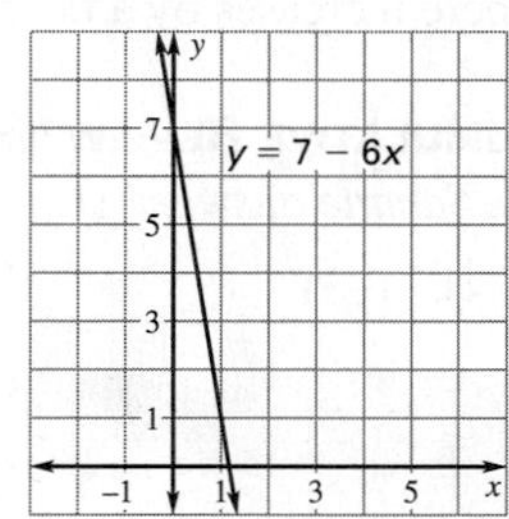

24.

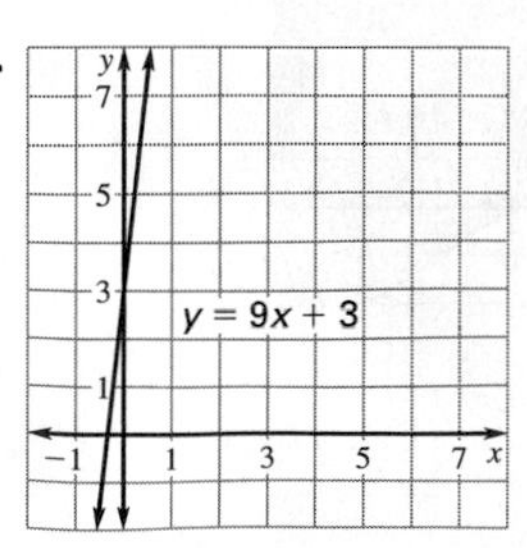

25.

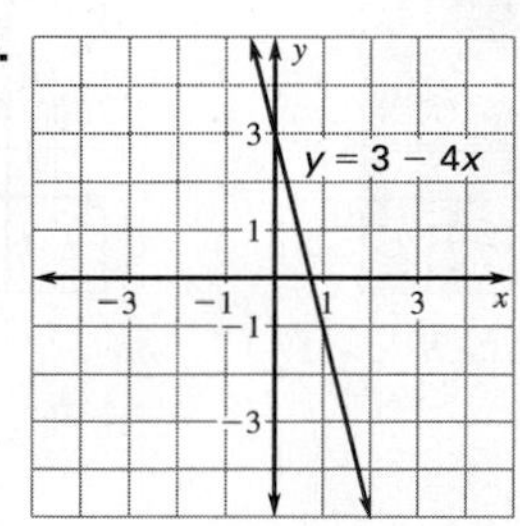

Chapter Test (p. 610)

23.

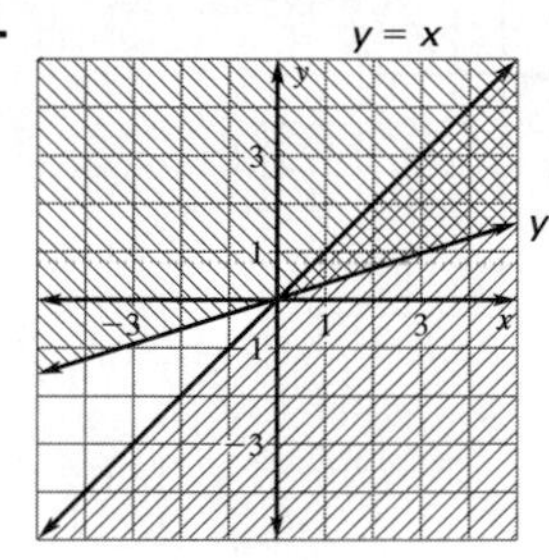

24.

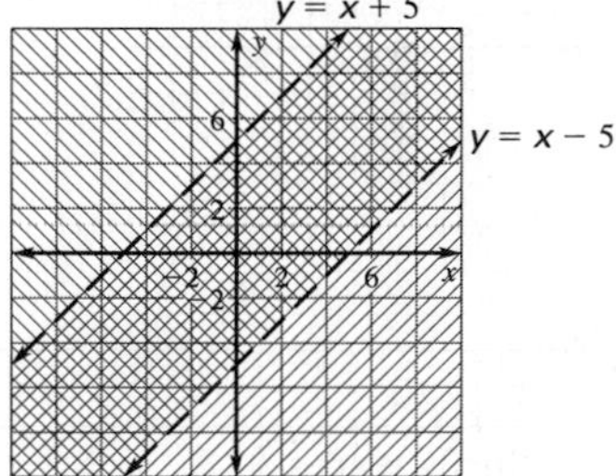

Chapter 12

12.6 Guided Practice (p. 645)

1.

x	−3	−2	−1	0	1	2	3
y	4.5	2.0	0.5	0	0.5	2.0	4.5

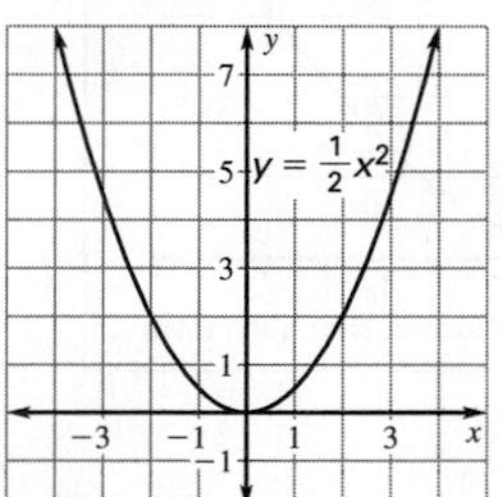

2.

x	-3	-2	-1	0	1	2	3
y	-13.5	-4.0	-0.5	0	0.5	4.0	13.5

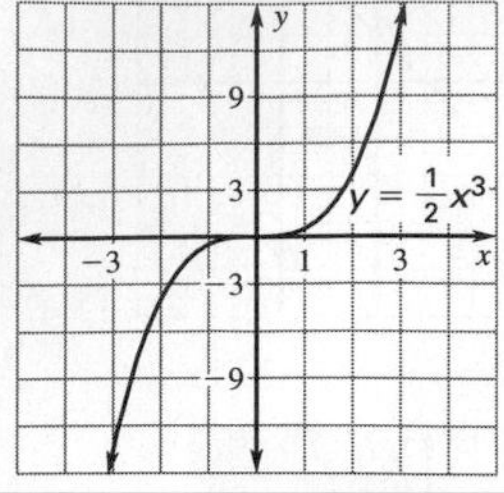

4.

x	0	0.5	1.0	1.5	2.0	2.5	3.0
V	0	$0.\overline{6}$	$2.\overline{6}$	6	$10.\overline{6}$	$16.\overline{6}$	24.0

12.6 Practice and Problem Solving (pp. 645–647)

16.

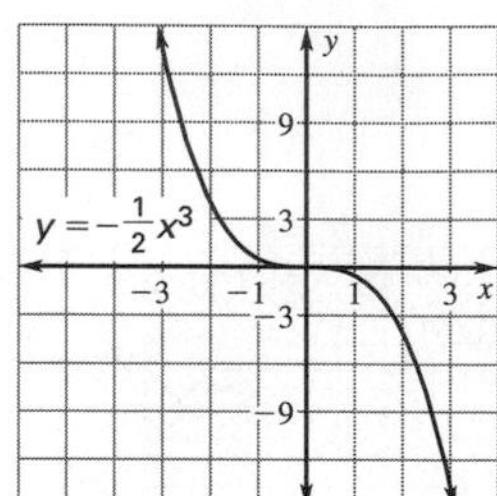

17.

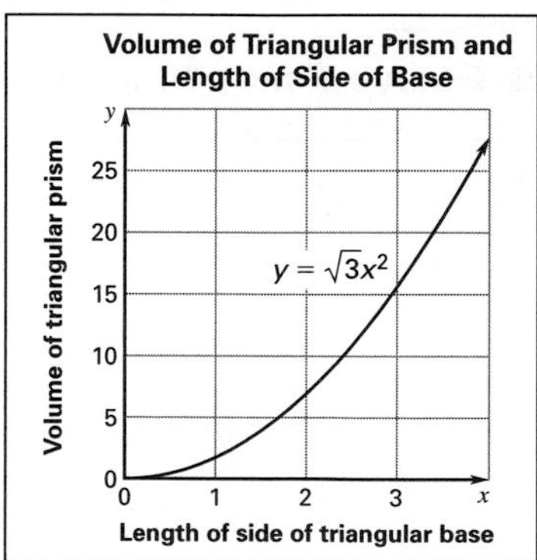

19.

x	1	2	3	4
Surface area	6	24	54	96

20.

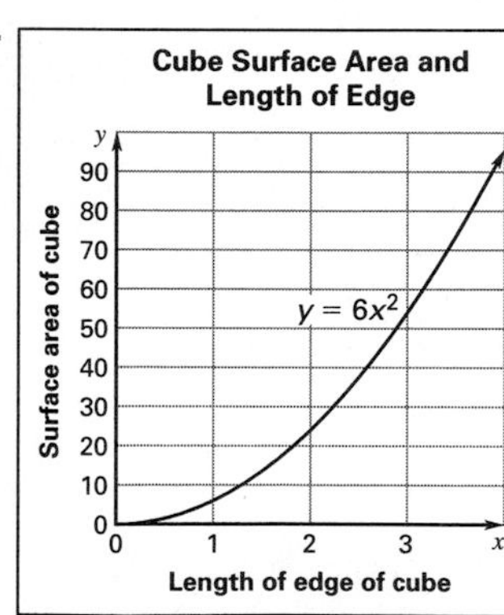

22. *Sample answer:* (1, 1.7), (2, 6.9), (3, 15.6), (4, 27.7)

24.

x (in.)	4	6	8	10	12
Volume (in.^{3})	8	27	64	125	216

25.

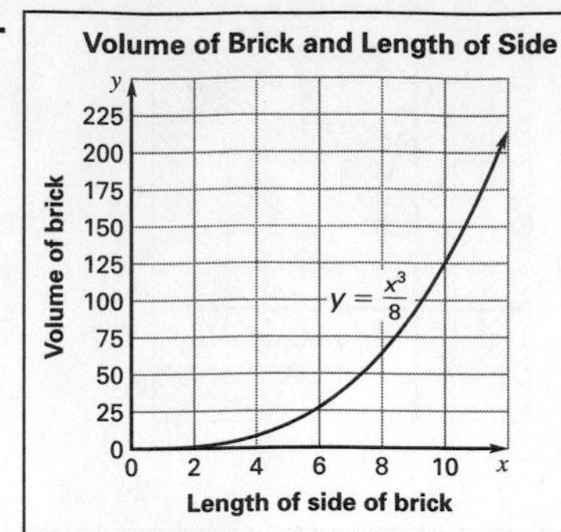

30.

r	0.2	0.4	0.6	0.8	1.0	1.2	1.4
Volume	0.034	0.268	0.905	2.145	4.189	7.238	11.494

31.

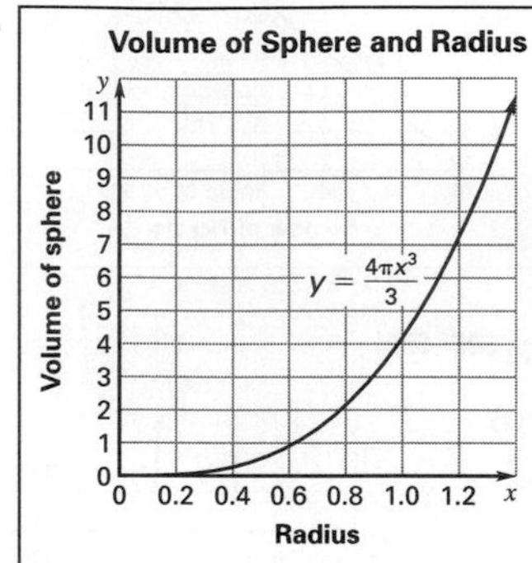

32. From the graph, the volume increases by a factor of about 8. For example, for $r = 0.6$, V has a value of about 0.9 and for $r = 1.2$, V has a value of about 7.2. Using the formula, $V = \frac{4\pi r^3}{3}$, the volume of the sphere increases by a factor of 8 when the radius is doubled.

Cumulative Review (pp. 662–663)

58. *Sample answer:* $(-1, 5)$, (0, 4), (1, 3)

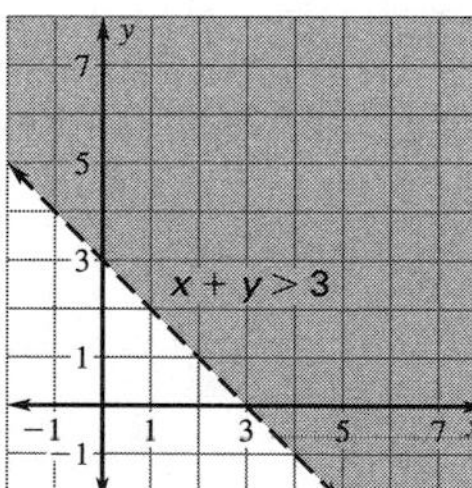

59. *Sample answer:* $(-1, 4)$, (0, 3), $\left(\frac{9}{2}, 0\right)$

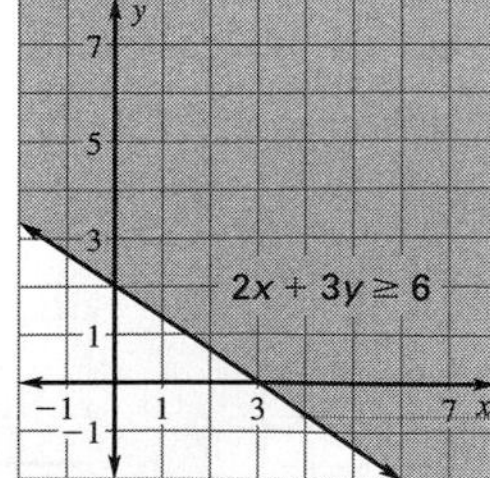

Extra Practice

CHAPTER 2 (pp. 692–693)

81.

Number of questions	$\cdot$	Number of minutes per question	$=$	Total number of minutes

Number of questions = 48, Number of minutes per question = x;
Total number of minutes = 120; divide 120 by 48.

82.

Number of miles hiked	$+$	Number of miles left	$=$	Total number of miles

Number of miles hiked = 1.9, Number of miles left = x;
Total number of miles = 2.7; subtract 1.9 from 2.7.

83.

Amount saved per week	$\cdot$	Number of weeks	$=$	Total amount saved

Amount saved per week = 15 dollars, Number of weeks = x,
Total amount saved = 135 dollars; divide 135 by 15.

CHAPTER 3 (pp. 694–695)

104.

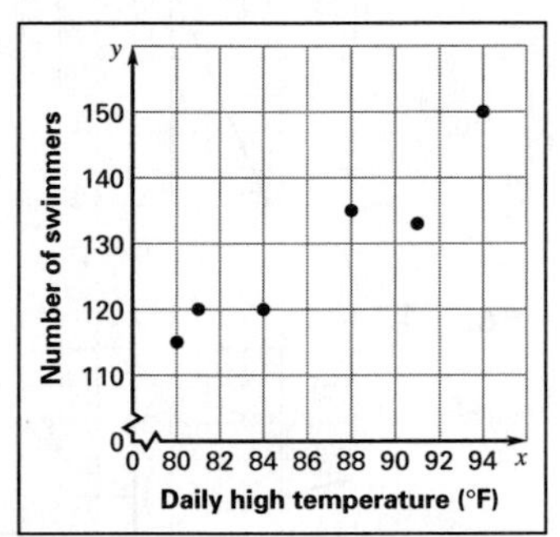

105.

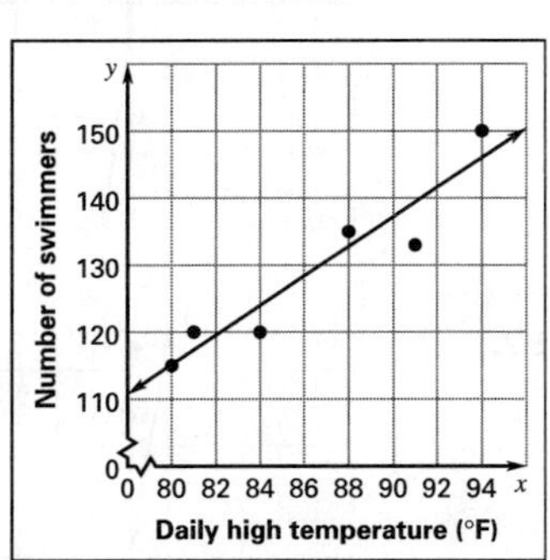

CHAPTER 4 (pp. 696–697)

21.

Cost of admission	$\cdot$	Number of members	$+$	Cost of lunch	$\cdot$
Number of members	$+$	Cost of bus	$=$	Total cost	;

Cost of admission = 5, Number of members = x, Cost of lunch = 3,
Cost of bus = 225, Total cost = 465;
$5x + 3x + 225 = 465$; 30 members

CHAPTER 9 (pp. 706–707)

89.

90.

91.

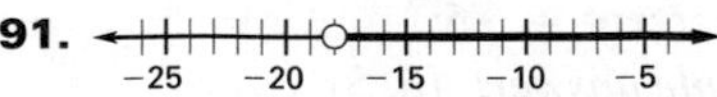

92.

93.

94.

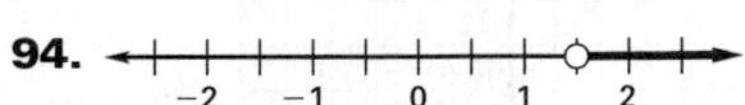

103.

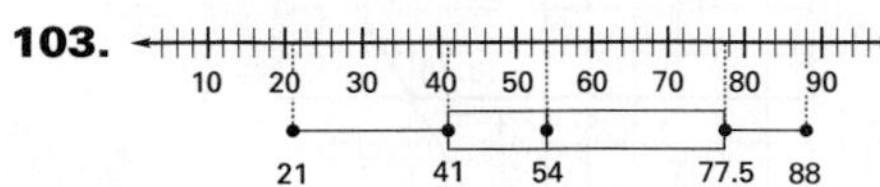

The range is 67 and the interquartile range is 36.5.

104.

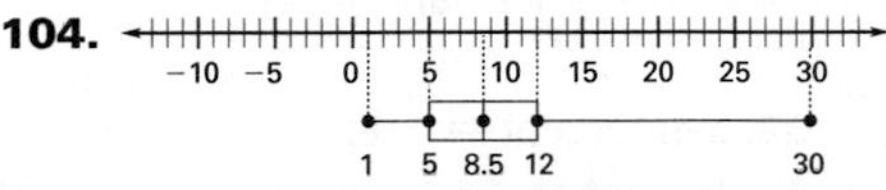

The range is 29 and the interquartile range is 7.

CHAPTER 11 (pp. 710–711)

19.

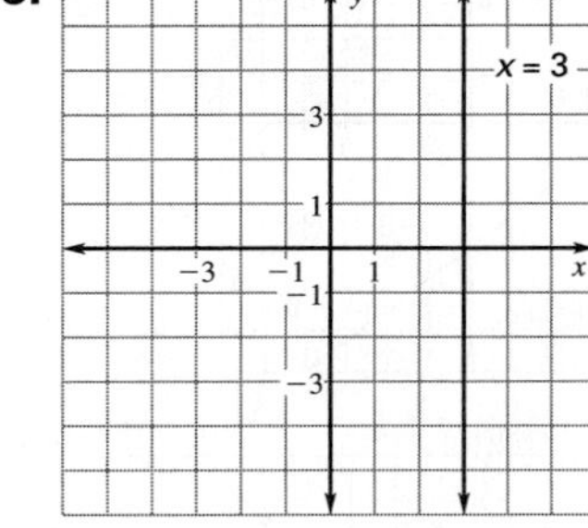

20.

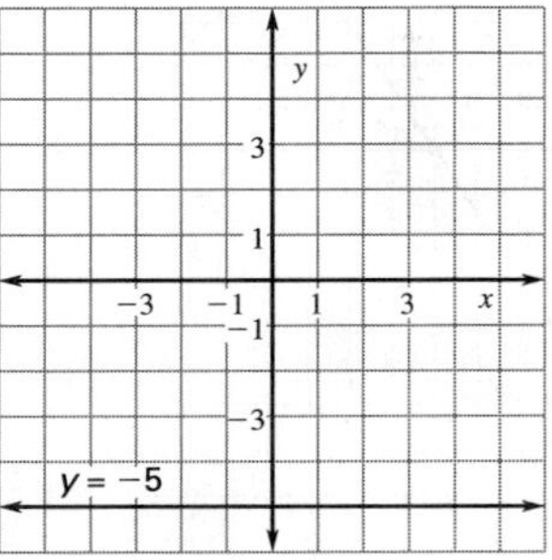

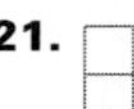

21.

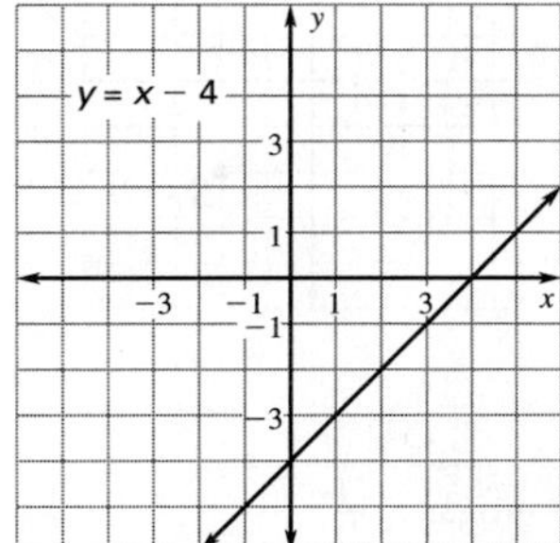

22.

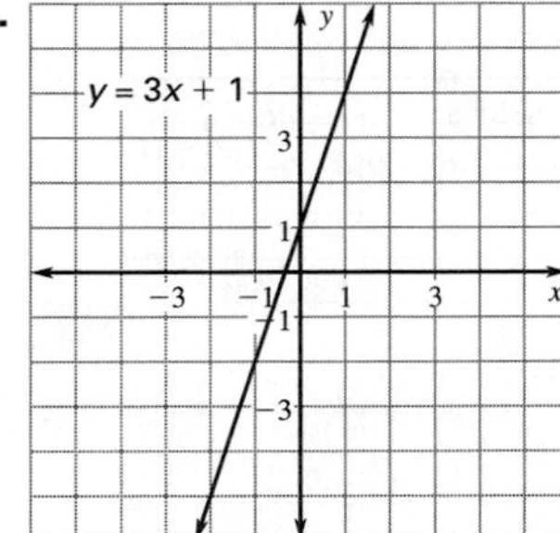

24.

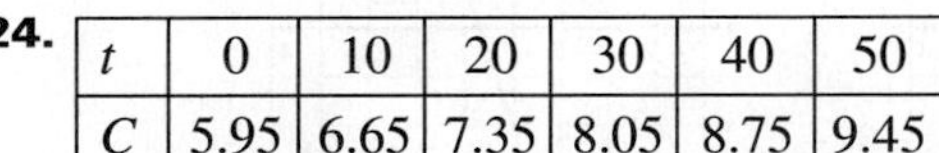

t	0	10	20	30	40	50
C	5.95	6.65	7.35	8.05	8.75	9.45

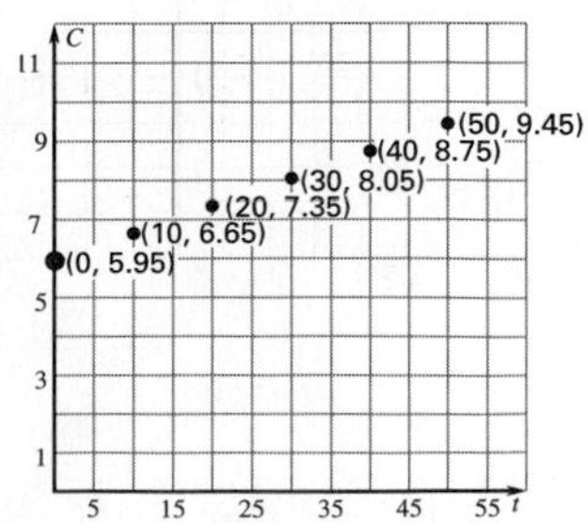

ADDITIONAL ANSWERS

25. x-intercept $= -1$; y-intercept $= 2$
26. x-intercept $= 5$; y-intercept $= 3$
27. x-intercept $= 7$; y-intercept $= -4$
28. x-intercept $= 3.5$; y-intercept $= 3$
29. x-intercept $= 4$;
y-intercept $= 4$;
Sample answer: (1, 3)

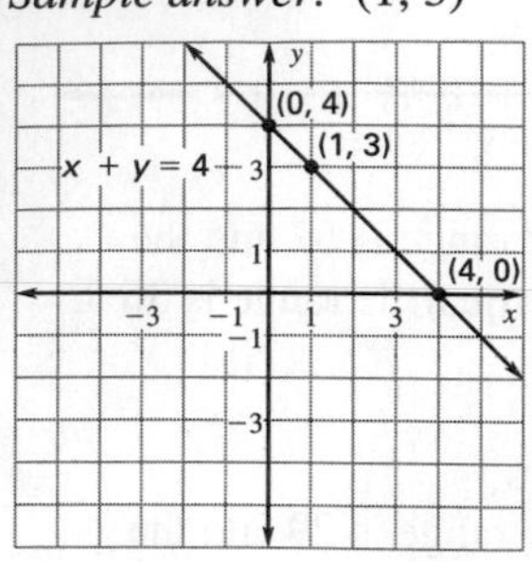

30. x-intercept $= 3$;
y-intercept $= -5$;
Sample answer: (6, 5)

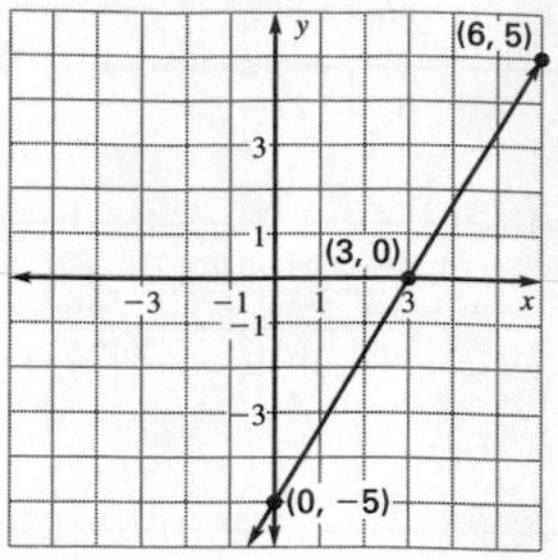

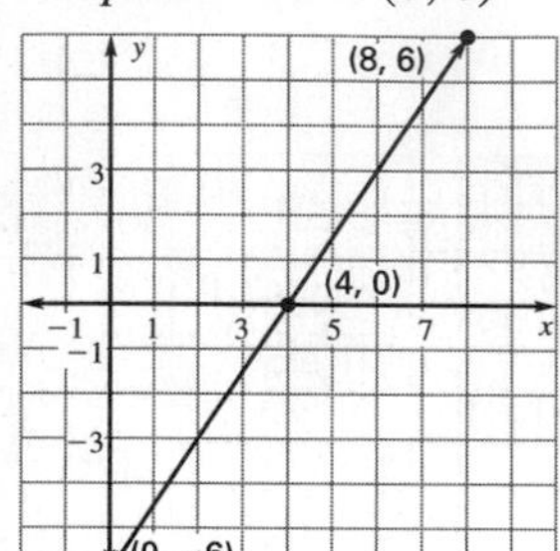

31. x-intercept $= 4$;
y-intercept $= -6$;
Sample answer: (8, 6)

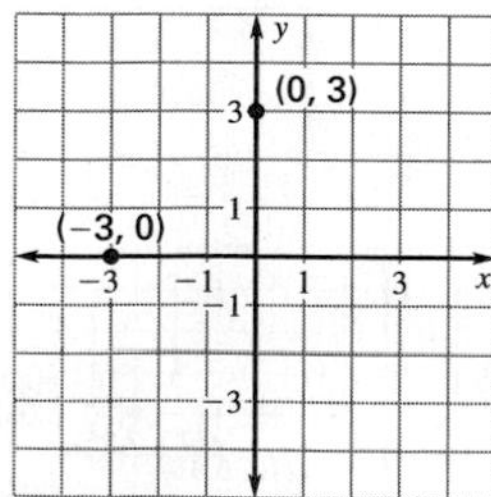

32. x-intercept $= -8$;
y-intercept $= -6$;
Sample answer: (4, −9)

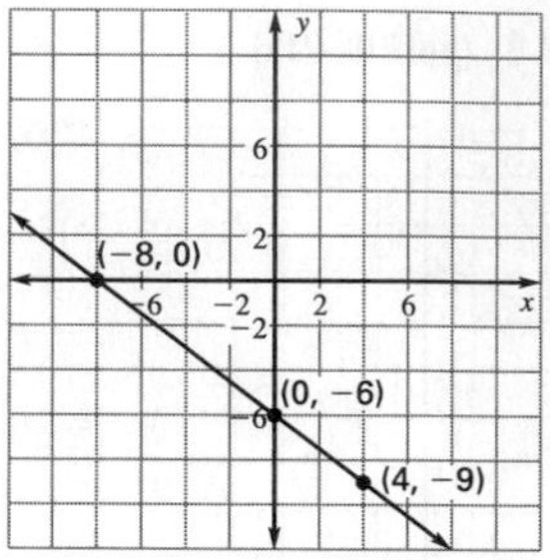

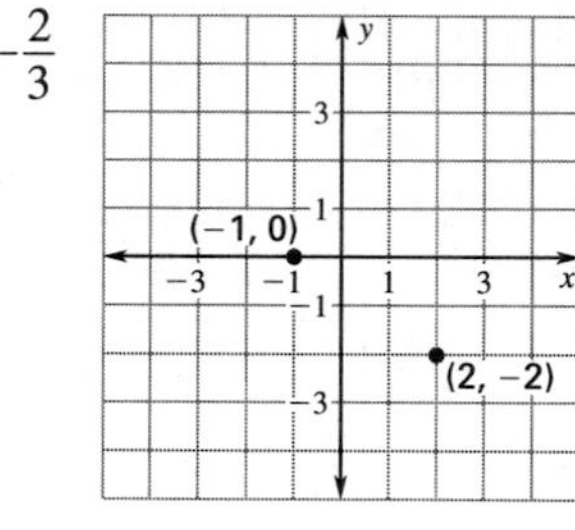

38. $\frac{1}{3}$

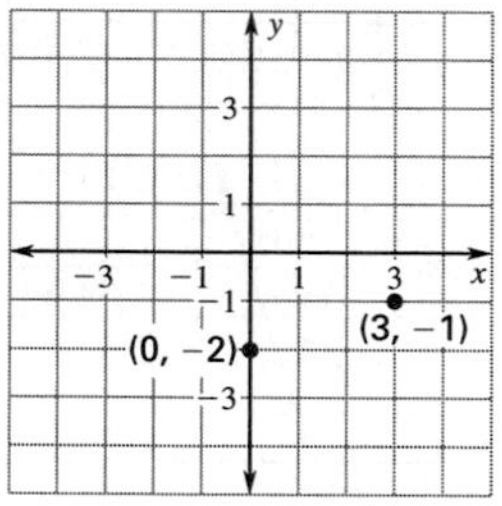

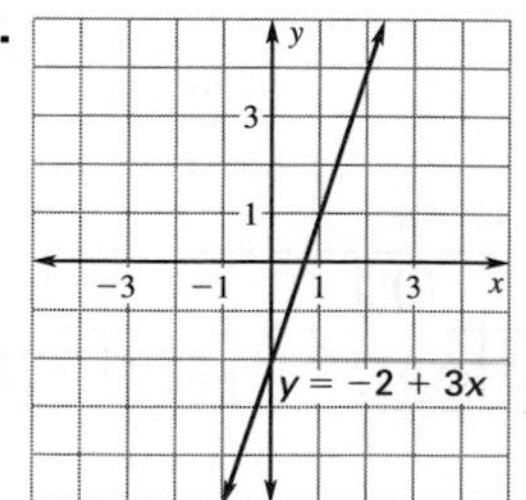

39. $-\frac{2}{3}$

40. 1

50.

51.

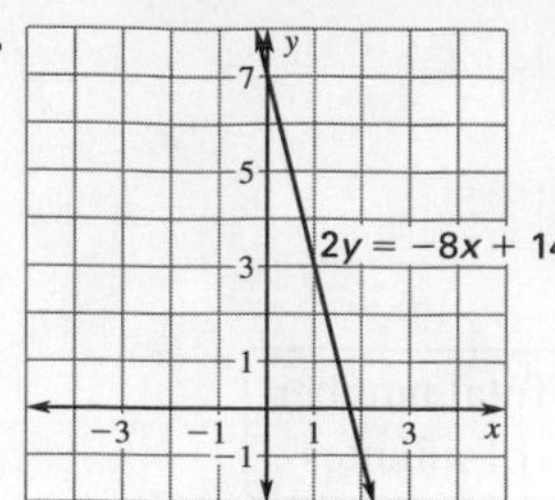

52.

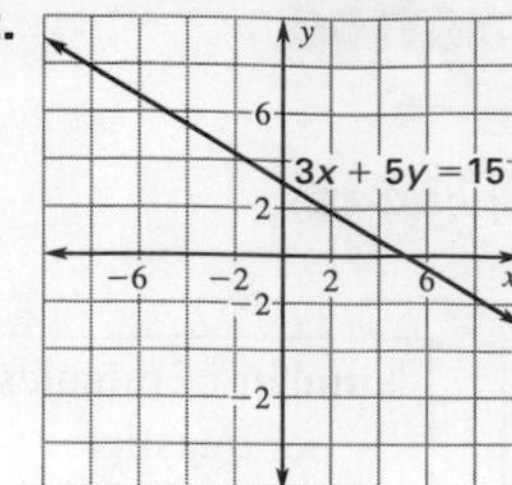

53.

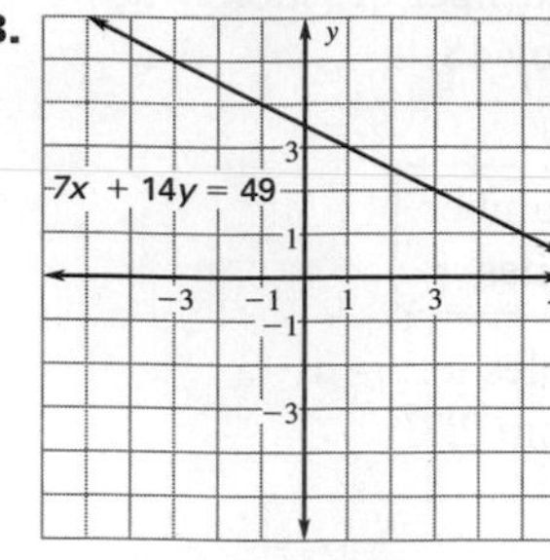

54. \$80

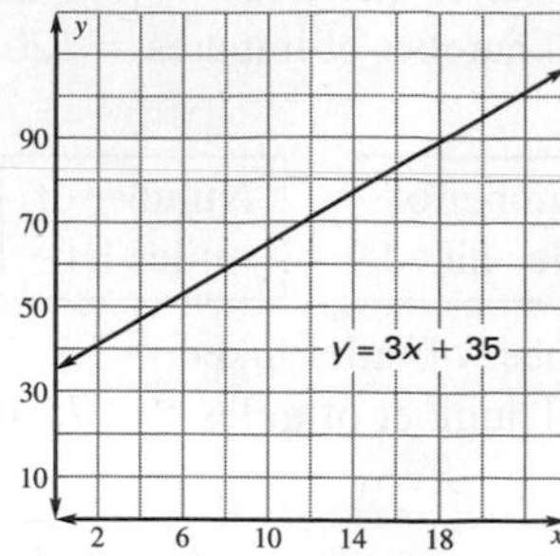

55. −32

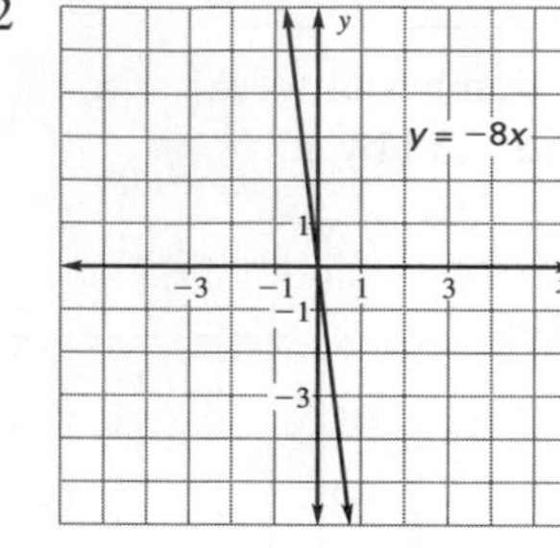

56. 9

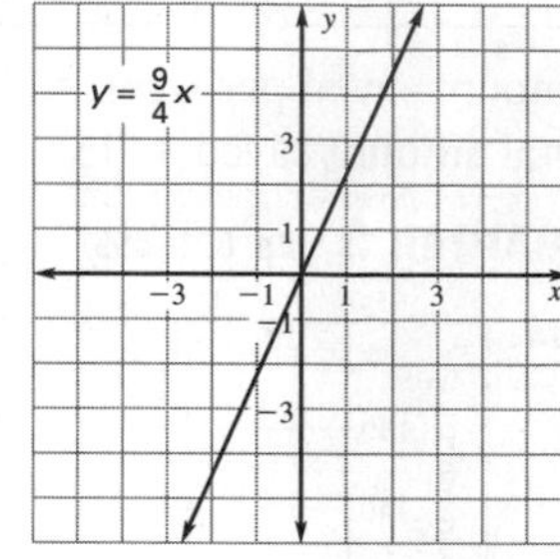

57. −24

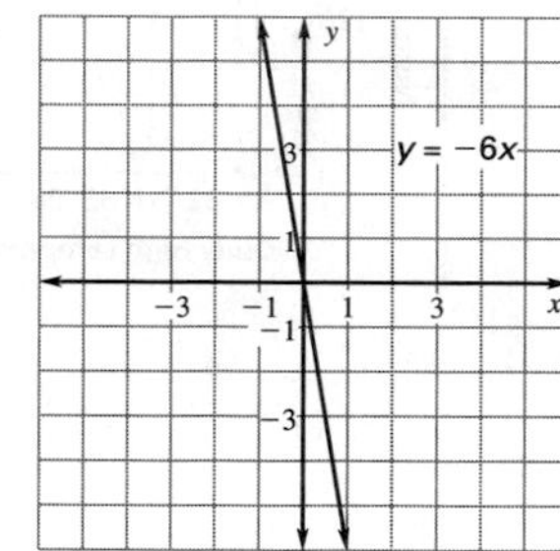

58. −1

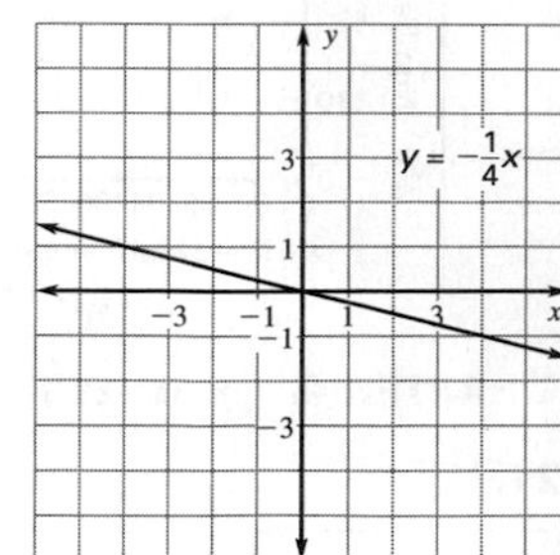

63. *Sample answer:*
(0, 0), (3, 0), (0, 3)

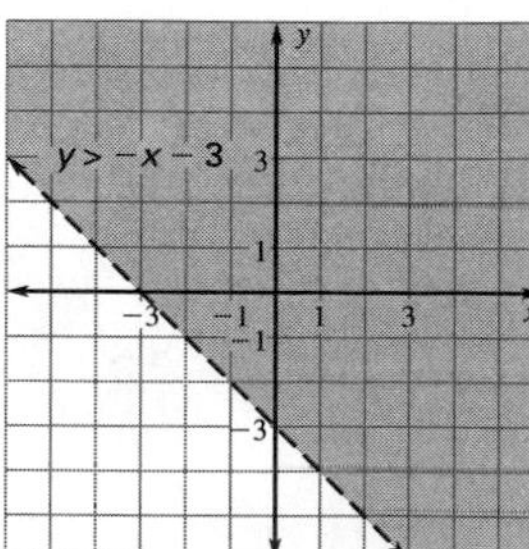

64. *Sample answer:*
(3, 3), (3, 0), (3, −3)

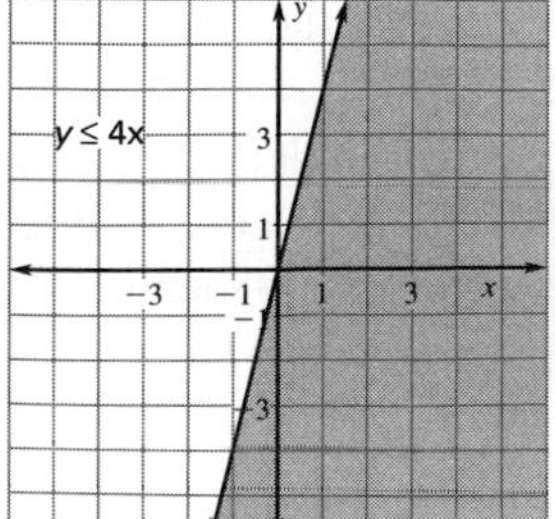

65. *Sample answer:*
(0, 0), (6, 6), (6, −6)

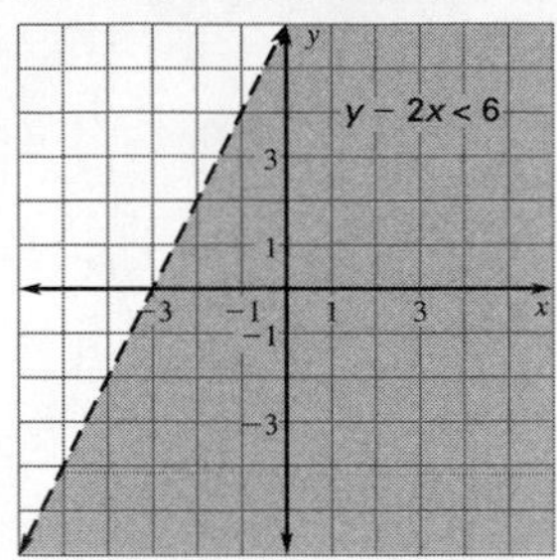

66. *Sample answer:*
(−5, −20), (15, −15), (20, 5)

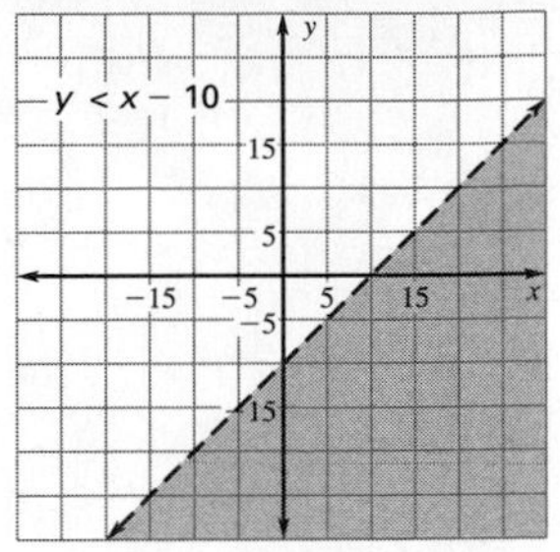

69.

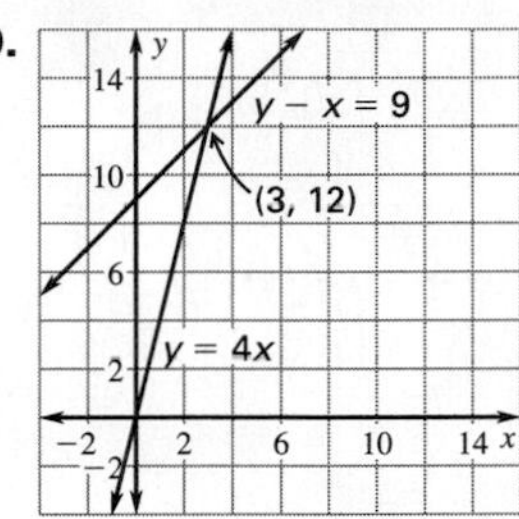

70.

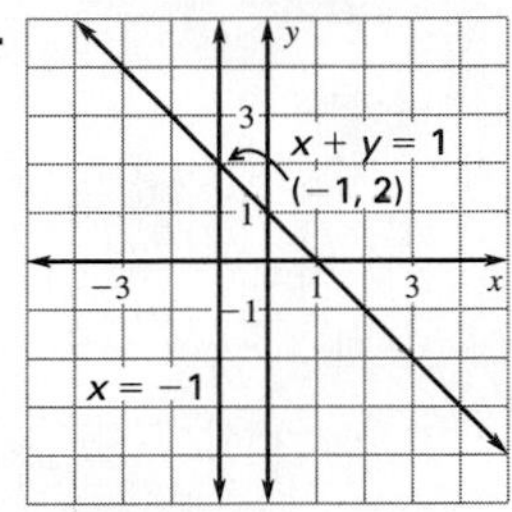

71.

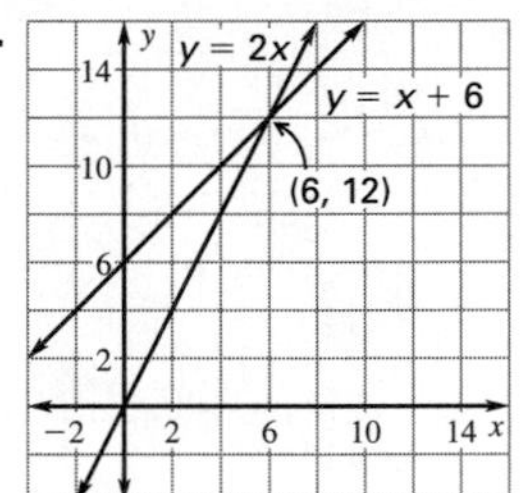

72.

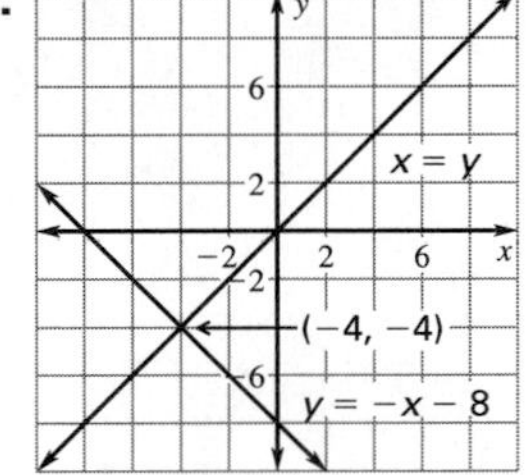

73. *Sample answer:*
(−4, 4), (−3, 4), (−2, 4)

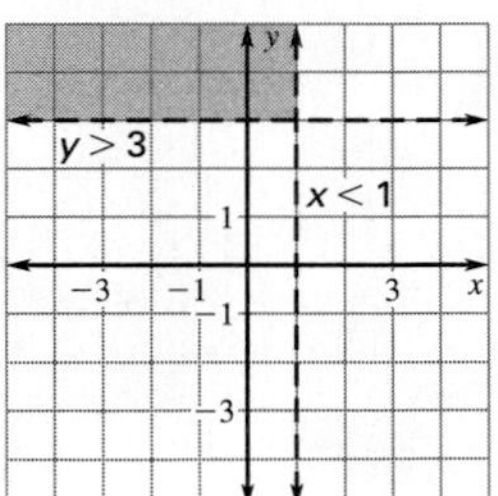

74. *Sample answer:*
(4, 2), (4, 0), (4, −2)

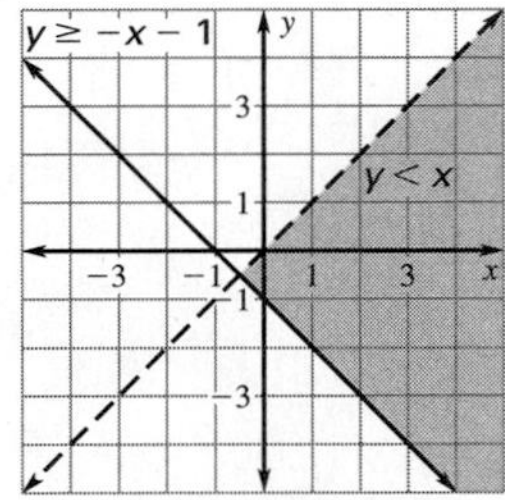

75. *Sample answer:*
(3, 1), (4, 0), (4, −1)

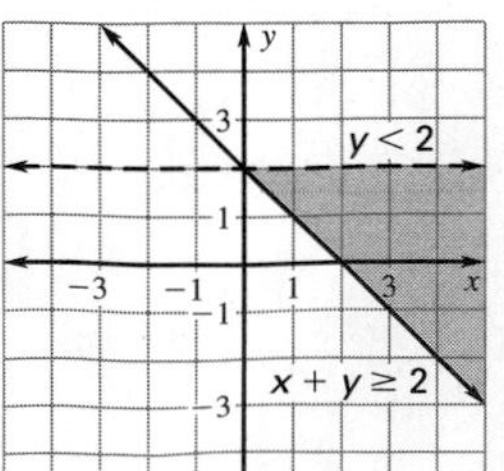

76. *Sample answer:*
(4, 2), (3, 0), (3, −3)

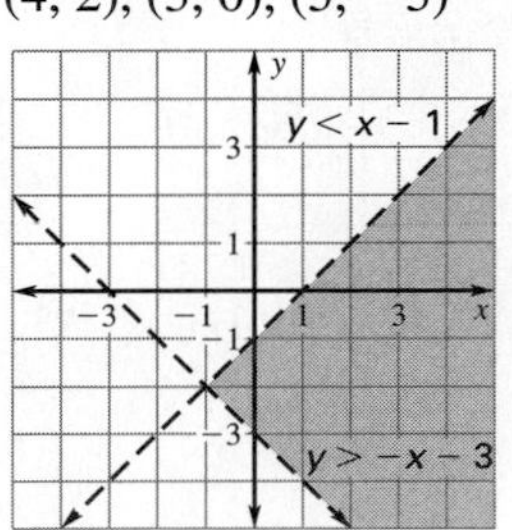

CHAPTER 12 (pp. 712–713)

81. *Sample answer:*

x	−2	−1	0	1	2
y	5	1.25	0	1.25	5

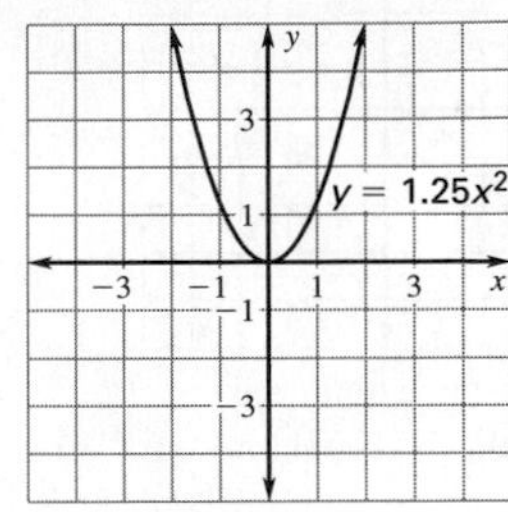

82. *Sample answer:*

x	−2	−1	0	1	2
y	6	$\frac{3}{2}$	0	$\frac{3}{2}$	6

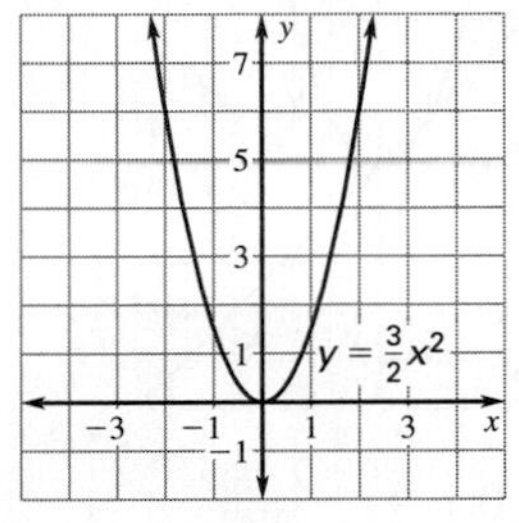

83. *Sample answer:*

x	−2	−1	0	1	2
y	−12	−1.5	0	1.5	12

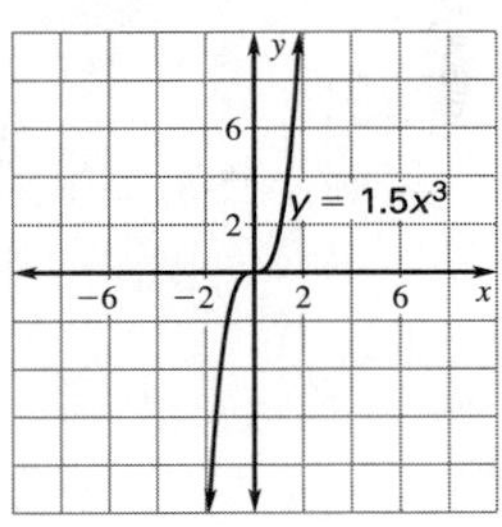

84. *Sample answer:*

x	−2	−1	0	1	2
y	16	2	0	−2	−16

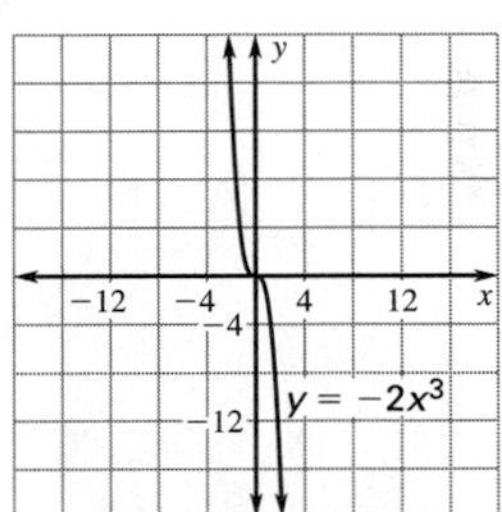

99.

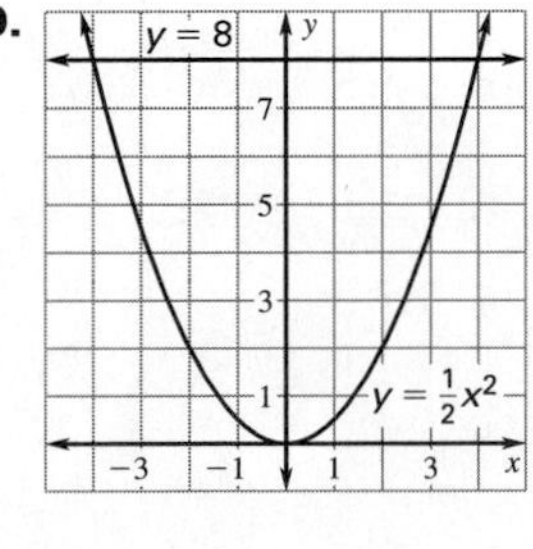

−4, 4

100.

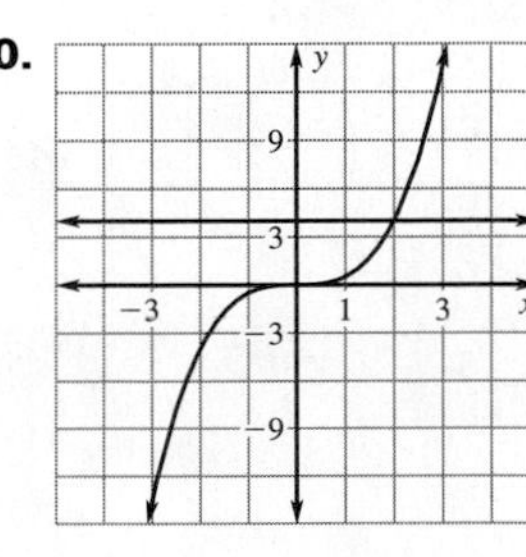

2

ADDITIONAL ANSWERS

101.

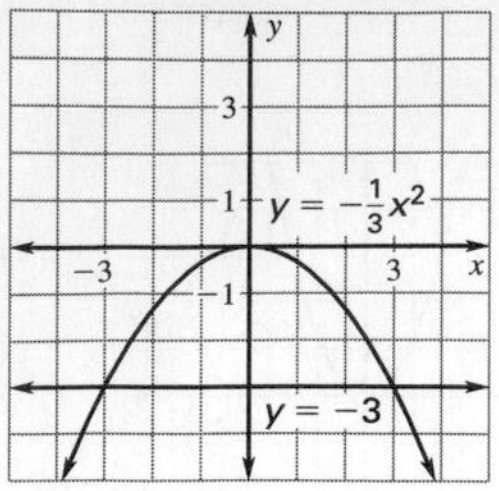

$y = -\frac{1}{3}x^2$

$y = -3$

$-3, 3$

102.

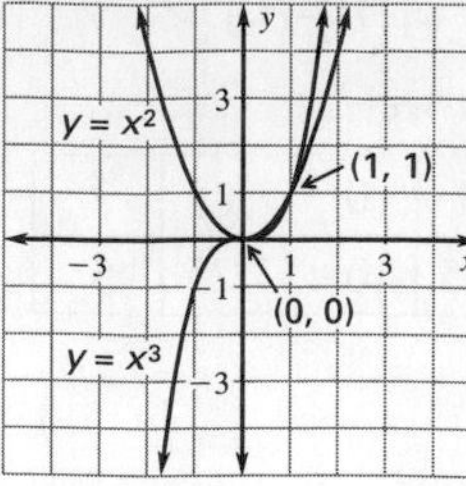

$0, 1$

103.

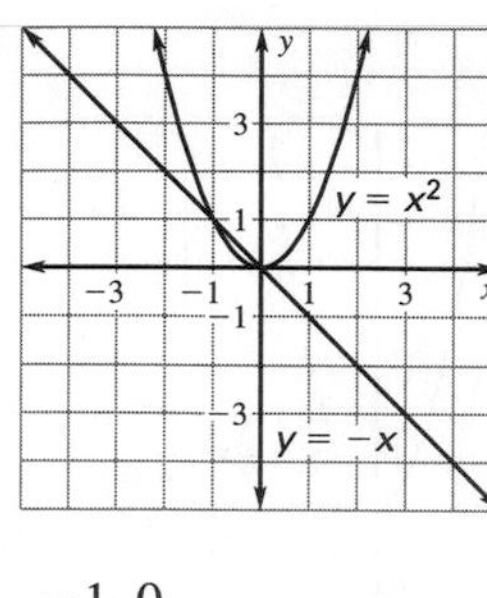

$-1, 0$

104.

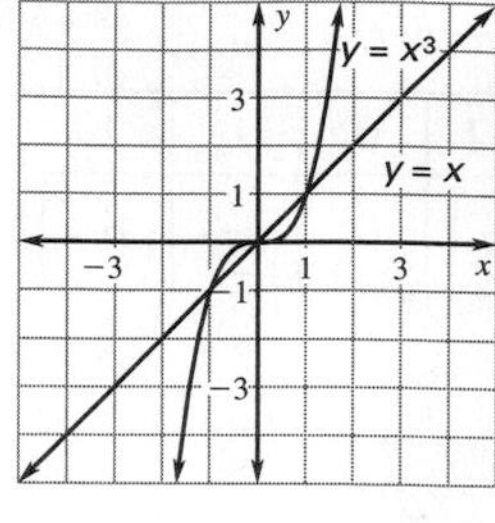

$-1, 0, 1$